CD-ROM with all content from 2009 *Fundamentals* inside back cover

2007 HVAC APPLICATIONS

COMFORT APPLICATIONS

INDUSTRIAL APPLICATIONS

ENERGY-RELATED APPLICATIONS

BUILDING OPERATIONS AND MANAGEMENT

GENERAL APPLICATIONS

2006 REFRIGERATION

REFRIGERATION SYSTEM PRACTICES

FOOD STORAGE AND EQUIPMENT

FOOD REFRIGERATION

DISTRIBUTION OF CHILLED AND FROZEN FOOD

INDUSTRIAL APPLICATIONS

LOW-TEMPERATURE APPLICATIONS

REFRIGERATION EQUIPMENT

UNITARY REFRIGERATION EQU

GENERAL

LICENSE AGREEMENT

2009 *ASHRAE Handbook—Fundamentals* CD-ROM

2009 ASHRAE® HANDBOOK

FUNDAMENTALS

SI Edition

American Society of Heating, Refrigerating and Air-Conditioning Engineers, Inc.

1791 Tullie Circle, N.E., Atlanta, GA 30329

(404) 636-8400 http://www.ashrae.org

DEDICATED TO THE ADVANCEMENT OF

THE PROFESSION AND ITS ALLIED INDUSTRIES

Volunteer members of ASHRAE Technical Committees and others compiled the information in this handbook, and it is generally reviewed and updated every four years. Comments, criticisms, and suggestions regarding the subject matter are invited. Any errors or omissions in the data should be brought to the attention of the Editor. Additions and corrections to Handbook volumes in print will be published in the Handbook published the year following their verification and, as soon as verified, on the ASHRAE Internet Web site.

DISCLAIMER

ASHRAE has compiled this publication with care, but ASHRAE has not investigated, and ASHRAE expressly disclaims any duty to investigate, any product, service, process, procedure, design, or the like that may be described herein. The appearance of any technical data or editorial material in this publication does not constitute endorsement, warranty, or guaranty by ASHRAE of any product, service, process, procedure, design, or the like. ASHRAE does not warrant that the information in this publication is free of errors. The entire risk of the use of any information in this publication is assumed by the user.

ISBN 978-1-933742-55-7
ISSN 1523-722282

The paper for this book is both acid- and elemental-chlorine-free and was manufactured with pulp obtained from sources using sustainable forestry practices. The printing used soy-based inks.

CONTENTS

CONTRIBUTORS

In addition to the Technical Committees, the following individuals contributed significantly to this volume. The appropriate chapter numbers follow each contributor's name.

Donald P. Gatley (1)
Gatley & Associates, Inc.

Jose A. Perez-Galindo (1)
Instituto Tecnologico de Durango

Rick J. Couvillion (3, 4, 5, 6)
University of Arkansas

Michael M. Ohadi (4, 6)
Petroleum Institute

Timothy A. Shedd (5)
University of Wisconsin–Madison

James Coogan (7)
Siemens Building Technologies

Larry Felker (7)
Belimo Aircontrols

Alfred Garza (7)
TekSys Dynamics

David Kahn (7)
RMH Group

Ken Kolkebeck (7)
Facility Diagnostics, Inc.

Karl Peterman (8)
Vibro-Acoustics

Bill Rockwood (8)
Trane Company

Jon Weinstein (8)
Industrial Acoustics Company

Steve Wise (8)
Wise Associates

Eric W. Adams (9)
Carrier Corporation

Larry G. Berglund (9)
U.S. Army Research Institute of Environmental Medicine

Hal Levin (9)
Building Ecology Research Group

Olli Seppänen (9)
Helsinki University of Technology

Constantinos A. Balaras (10)
GRoup Energy Conservation (GREC), Institute for Environmental Research and Sustainable Development (IERSD), and National Observatory of Athens (NOA)

William F. McCoy (10)
Phigenics, LLC

R. Mark Nunnelly (10)
Nunnelly & Associates

Steven Emmerich (10, 16)
National Institute of Standards and Technology

Matthew Middlebrooks (11)
Filtration Group, Inc.

Gemma Kerr (11, 12)

Douglas W. VanOsdell (11, 12)

Neal Lott (14)
NOAA National Climatic Data Center

Robert Morris (14)
Environment Canada

Didier Thevenard (14)
Numerical Logics, Inc.

Charles S. Barnaby (14, 17)
Wrightsoft Corporation

Michael Collins (15)
University of Waterloo

John Hogan (15)
Seattle Department of Planning and Development

Nathan Kotey (15)
University of Waterloo

Andrew K. Persily (16)
National Institute of Standards and Technology

Brian A. Rock (16)
University of Kansas

Steven F. Bruning (18)
Newcomb & Boyd

David John (20)
METALAIRE

Andrey Livchak (20)
Halton Group Americas

Fred Lorch (20)
Phoenix Controls Corporation

Herman F. Behls (21)

Scott Miller (23)
Knauf Insulation

Bert Blocken (24)
Eindhoven University of Technology

Patrick Saathoff (24)
Rowan Williams Davies & Irwin, Inc.

Ted Stathopoulos (24)
Concordia University

Hugo Hens (25)
Catholic University–Leuven

Achilles Karagiozis (25)
Oak Ridge National Laboratory

Hartwig Kuenzel (25)
Fraunhofer Institut für Bauphysik

Paul Shipp (25)
USG Corporation

Alex McGowan (26)
Levelton Consultants Ltd.

Anton TenWolde (26)
Forest Products Laboratory

William B. Rose (26, 27)
University of Illinois at Urbana–Champaign

Garth Hall (27)
Raths, Raths & Johnson, Inc.

Hall Virgil (28)

Cory Weiss (28)
Effikal, LLC

Van D. Baxter (29)
Oak Ridge National Laboratory

James G. Crawford (29)
Trane Company

Cynthia Gage (29)
U.S. Environmental Protection Agency

Barbara Minor (29)
DuPont Fluorochemicals

Mark O. McLinden (30)
National Institute of Standards and Technology

Kevin Connor (31)
The Dow Chemical Company, Larkin Lab

Don Brundage (34, 35)
Southern Company Services

William J. Coad (35)
Coad Engineering Consulting

David Grumman (35)
Grumman/Butkus Associates

Tom Lawrence (35)
University of Georgia

Stephen Turner (35)
Constructive Technologies Group, Inc.

B. Terry Beck (36)
Kansas State University

Leonard A. Damiano (36)
EBTRON

Charles C. Wright (36)
TSI, Inc.

David P. Yuill (36)
Building Solutions, Inc.

Bruce Billedeaux (37)
Maverick Technologies

David E. Bornside (37)
Siemens Building Technologies

Jaap J. Hogeling (37)
ISSO

Birol I. Kilkis (37)
Watts Radiant, Inc.

Roger W. Lautz (37)
Henneman Engineering

Suzanne LeViseur (37)
Haddad Engineering, Inc.

ASHRAE HANDBOOK COMMITTEE

Walter T. Grondzik, Chair

2009 Fundamentals Volume Subcommittee: **Dennis L. O'Neal**, Chair

Hassan M. Bagheri **Pradeep Kumar Bansal** **William J. Coad** **Kenneth M. Fulk**
Douglas C. Hittle **John W. Wells, III** **David P. Yuill**

ASHRAE HANDBOOK STAFF

W. Stephen Comstock, Publisher
Director of Publications and Education

Mark S. Owen, Editor

Heather E. Kennedy, Associate Editor

Nancy F. Thysell, Typographer/Page Designer

David Soltis, Manager and **Jayne E. Jackson**, Publications Traffic Administrator
Publishing Services

ASHRAE TECHNICAL COMMITTEES, TASK GROUPS, AND TECHNICAL RESOURCE GROUPS

SECTION 1.0—FUNDAMENTALS AND GENERAL

1.1 Thermodynamics and Psychrometrics
1.2 Instruments and Measurements
1.3 Heat Transfer and Fluid Flow
1.4 Control Theory and Application
1.5 Computer Applications
1.6 Terminology
1.7 Business, Management, and General Legal Education
1.8 Mechanical Systems Insulation
1.9 Electrical Systems
1.10 Cogeneration Systems
1.11 Electric Motors and Motor Control
1.12 Moisture Management in Buildings
TG1 Exergy Analysis for Sustainable Buildings (EXER)
TG1 Optimization (OPT)

SECTION 2.0—ENVIRONMENTAL QUALITY

2.1 Physiology and Human Environment
2.2 Plant and Animal Environment
2.3 Gaseous Air Contaminants and Gas Contaminant Removal Equipment
2.4 Particulate Air Contaminants and Particulate Contaminant Removal Equipment
2.5 Global Climate Change
2.6 Sound and Vibration Control
2.7 Seismic and Wind Restraint Design
2.8 Building Environmental Impacts and Sustainability
2.9 Ultraviolet Air and Surface Treatment
TG2 Heating, Ventilation, and Air-Conditioning Security (HVAC)

SECTION 3.0—MATERIALS AND PROCESSES

3.1 Refrigerants and Secondary Coolants
3.2 Refrigerant System Chemistry
3.3 Refrigerant Contaminant Control
3.4 Lubrication
3.6 Water Treatment
3.8 Refrigerant Containment
TG3 HVAC&R Contractors and Design-Build Firms (CDBF)

SECTION 4.0—LOAD CALCULATIONS AND ENERGY REQUIREMENTS

4.1 Load Calculation Data and Procedures
4.2 Climatic Information
4.3 Ventilation Requirements and Infiltration
4.4 Building Materials and Building Envelope Performance
4.5 Fenestration
4.7 Energy Calculations
4.10 Indoor Environmental Modeling
TRG4 Sustainable Building Guidance and Metrics (SBGM)

SECTION 5.0—VENTILATION AND AIR DISTRIBUTION

5.1 Fans
5.2 Duct Design
5.3 Room Air Distribution
5.4 Industrial Process Air Cleaning (Air Pollution Control)
5.5 Air-to-Air Energy Recovery
5.6 Control of Fire and Smoke
5.7 Evaporative Cooling
5.8 Industrial Ventilation Systems
5.9 Enclosed Vehicular Facilities
5.10 Kitchen Ventilation
5.11 Humidifying Equipment

SECTION 6.0—HEATING EQUIPMENT, HEATING AND COOLING SYSTEMS AND APPLICATIONS

6.1 Hydronic and Steam Equipment and Systems
6.2 District Energy
6.3 Central Forced-Air Heating and Cooling Systems
6.5 Radiant Heating and Cooling
6.6 Service Water Heating Systems
6.7 Solar Energy Utilization
6.8 Geothermal Energy Utilization
6.9 Thermal Storage
6.10 Fuels and Combustion

SECTION 7.0—BUILDING PERFORMANCE

7.1 Integrated Building Design
7.3 Operation and Maintenance Management
7.4 Building Operation Dynamics
7.5 Smart Building Systems
7.6 Systems Energy Utilization
7.7 Testing and Balancing
7.8 Owning and Operating Costs
7.9 Building Commissioning
TRG7 Tools for Sustainable Building Operations, Maintenance, and Cost Analysis (SBOMC)
TRG7 Underfloor Air Distribution (UFAD)

SECTION 8.0—AIR-CONDITIONING AND REFRIGERATION SYSTEM COMPONENTS

8.1 Positive Displacement Compressors
8.2 Centrifugal Machines
8.3 Absorption and Heat-Operated Machines
8.4 Air-to-Refrigerant Heat Transfer Equipment
8.5 Liquid-to-Refrigerant Heat Exchangers
8.6 Cooling Towers and Evaporative Condensers
8.8 Refrigerant System Controls and Accessories
8.9 Residential Refrigerators and Food Freezers
8.10 Mechanical Dehumidification Equipment and Heat Pipes
8.11 Unitary and Room Air Conditioners and Heat Pumps
8.12 Desiccant Dehumidification Equipment and Components
TG8 Variable Refrigerant Flow (VRF)

SECTION 9.0—BUILDING APPLICATIONS

9.1 Large-Building Air-Conditioning Systems
9.2 Industrial Air Conditioning
9.3 Transportation Air Conditioning
9.4 Applied Heat Pump/Heat Recovery Systems
9.5 Residential and Small-Building Applications
9.6 Healthcare Facilities
9.7 Educational Facilities
9.8 Large-Building Air-Conditioning Applications
9.9 Mission-Critical Facilities, Technology Spaces, and Electronic Equipment
9.10 Laboratory Systems
9.11 Clean Spaces
9.12 Tall Buildings
TG9 Justice Facilities (JF)

SECTION 10.0—REFRIGERATION SYSTEMS

10.1 Custom-Engineered Refrigeration Systems
10.2 Automatic Icemaking Plants and Skating Rinks
10.3 Refrigerant Piping
10.4 Ultralow-Temperature Systems and Cryogenics
10.5 Refrigerated Distribution and Storage Facilities
10.6 Transport Refrigeration
10.7 Commercial Food and Beverage Cooling Display and Storage
10.8 Refrigeration Load Calculations
10.9 Refrigeration Application for Foods and Beverages
10.10 Management of Lubricant in Circulation

ASHRAE Research: Improving the Quality of Life

The American Society of Heating, Refrigerating and Air-Conditioning Engineers is the world's foremost technical society in the fields of heating, ventilation, air conditioning, and refrigeration. Its members worldwide are individuals who share ideas, identify needs, support research, and write the industry's standards for testing and practice. The result is that engineers are better able to keep indoor environments safe and productive while protecting and preserving the outdoors for generations to come.

One of the ways that ASHRAE supports its members' and industry's need for information is through ASHRAE Research. Thousands of individuals and companies support ASHRAE Research annually, enabling ASHRAE to report new data about material properties and building physics and to promote the application of innovative technologies.

Chapters in the ASHRAE Handbook are updated through the experience of members of ASHRAE Technical Committees and through results of ASHRAE Research reported at ASHRAE meetings and published in ASHRAE special publications and in *ASHRAE Transactions*.

For information about ASHRAE Research or to become a member, contact ASHRAE, 1791 Tullie Circle, Atlanta, GA 30329; telephone: 404-636-8400; www.ashrae.org.

Preface

The 2009 *ASHRAE Handbook—Fundamentals* covers basic principles and data used in the HVAC&R industry. The ASHRAE Technical Committees that prepare these chapters strive not only to provide new information, but also to clarify existing information, delete obsolete materials, and reorganize chapters to make the Handbook more understandable and easier to use. An accompanying CD-ROM contains all the volume's chapters in both I-P and SI units.

This edition includes a new chapter (35), Sustainability, which defines this concept for HVAC&R and describes the principles, design considerations, and detailed evaluations needed in designing sustainable HVAC&R systems.

Also new for this volume, chapter order and groupings have been revised for more logical flow and use. Some of the other revisions and additions to the volume are as follows:

- Chapter 1, Psychrometrics, has new information on the composition of dry air, and revised table data for thermodynamic properties of water and moist air.
- Chapter 6, Mass Transfer, has added examples on evaluating diffusion coefficients, and on heat transfer and moisture removal rates.
- Chapter 7, Fundamentals of Control, includes new content on dampers, adaptive control, direct digital control (DDC) system architecture and specifications, and wireless control.
- Chapter 9, Thermal Comfort, has a new section on thermal comfort and task performance, based on multiple new studies done in laboratory and office environments.
- Chapter 10, Indoor Environmental Health, was reorganized to describe hazard sources, health effects, exposure standards, and exposure controls. New and updated topics include mold, legionella, indoor air chemistry, thermal impacts, and water quality standards.
- Chapter 14, Climatic Design Information, has new climate data for 5564 stations (an increase of 1142 new stations compared to 2005 *Fundamentals*) on the CD-ROM accompanying this book. A subset of data for selected stations is also included in the printed chapter for convenient access.
- Chapter 15, Fenestration, has been revised to include new examples of solar heat gain coefficient (SHGC) calculations, and new research results on shading calculations and U-factors for various specialized door types.
- Chapter 16, Ventilation and Infiltration, has new, detailed examples, updates from ASHRAE *Standards* 62.1 and 62.2, discussion of relevant LEED® aspects, and new information on airtightness and ventilation rates for commercial buildings.
- Chapter 18, Nonresidential Cooling and Heating Load Calculations, has been updated to reflect new ASHRAE research results on climate data and on heat gains from office equipment, lighting, and commercial cooking appliances.
- Chapter 20, Space Air Diffusion, has been completely rewritten to harmonize with related chapters in other volumes, with major sections on fully mixed, partially mixed, stratified, and task/ambient systems and the principles behind their design and operation.
- Chapter 21, Duct Design, has new data for round and rectangular fittings in agreement with the ASHRAE Duct Fitting Database, as well as new content on duct leakage requirements, spiral duct roughness, and flexible duct pressure loss correction.
- Chapter 23, Insulation for Mechanical Systems, has added tables from ASHRAE *Standard* 90.1-2007, and a new section on writing specifications.
- Chapter 24, Airflow Around Buildings, has added a detailed discussion on computational evaluation of airflow, plus new references including updated versions of design standards and manuals of practice.
- Chapters 25, 26, and 27 carry new titles, reorganized as chapters on Heat, Air, and Moisture Control Fundamentals, Material Properties, and Examples, respectively, with updated content throughout.
- Chapter 29, Refrigerants, has new content on stratospheric ozone depletion, global climate change, and global environmental characteristics of refrigerants.
- Chapter 30, Thermophysical Properties of Refrigerants, has updated data for R-125, R-245fa, R-170, R-290, R-600, and R-600a.
- Chapter 36, Measurement and Instruments, has revised content on measurement of air velocity, infiltration, airtightness, and outdoor air ventilation, plus new information on particle image velocimetry (PIV) and data acquisition and recording.

This volume is published, both as a bound print volume and in electronic format on a CD-ROM, in two editions: one using inch-pound (I-P) units of measurement, the other using the International System of Units (SI).

Corrections to the 2006, 2007, and 2008 Handbook volumes can be found on the ASHRAE Web site at http://www.ashrae.org and in the Additions and Corrections section of this volume. Corrections for this volume will be listed in subsequent volumes and on the ASHRAE Web site.

Reader comments are enthusiastically invited. To suggest improvements for a chapter, **please comment using the form on the ASHRAE Web site** or, using the cutout page(s) at the end of this volume's index, write to Handbook Editor, ASHRAE, 1791 Tullie Circle, Atlanta, GA 30329, or fax 678-539-2187, or e-mail mowen@ashrae.org.

Mark S. Owen
Editor

CHAPTER 1

PSYCHROMETRICS

PSYCHROMETRICS uses thermodynamic properties to analyze conditions and processes involving moist air. This chapter discusses perfect gas relations and their use in common heating, cooling, and humidity control problems. Formulas developed by Herrmann et al. (2009) may be used where greater precision is required.

Hyland and Wexler (1983a, 1983b), Nelson and Sauer (2002), and Herrmann et al. (2009) developed formulas for thermodynamic properties of moist air and water modeled as real gases. However, perfect gas relations can be substituted in most air-conditioning problems. Kuehn et al. (1998) showed that errors are less than 0.7% in calculating humidity ratio, enthalpy, and specific volume of saturated air at standard atmospheric pressure for a temperature range of −50 to 50°C. Furthermore, these errors decrease with decreasing pressure.

COMPOSITION OF DRY AND MOIST AIR

Atmospheric air contains many gaseous components as well as water vapor and miscellaneous contaminants (e.g., smoke, pollen, and gaseous pollutants not normally present in free air far from pollution sources).

Dry air is atmospheric air with all water vapor and contaminants removed. Its composition is relatively constant, but small variations in the amounts of individual components occur with time, geographic location, and altitude. Harrison (1965) lists the approximate percentage composition of dry air by volume as: nitrogen, 78.084; oxygen, 20.9476; argon, 0.934; neon, 0.001818; helium, 0.000524; methane, 0.00015; sulfur dioxide, 0 to 0.0001; hydrogen, 0.00005; and minor components such as krypton, xenon, and ozone, 0.0002. Harrison (1965) and Hyland and Wexler (1983a) used a value 0.0314 (circa 1955) for carbon dioxide. Carbon dioxide reached 0.0379 in 2005, is currently increasing by 0.00019 percent per year and is projected to reach 0.0438 in 2036 (Gatley et al. 2008; Keeling and Whorf 2005a, 2005b). Increases in carbon dioxide are offset by decreases in oxygen; consequently, the oxygen percentage in 2036 is projected to be 20.9352. Using the projected changes, the relative molecular mass for dry air for at least the first half of the 21st century is 28.966, based on the carbon-12 scale. The gas constant for dry air using the current Mohr and Taylor (2005) value for the universal gas constant is

$$R_{da} = 8314.472/28.966 = 287.042 \text{ J/(kg}_{da}\cdot\text{K)} \quad (1)$$

Moist air is a binary (two-component) mixture of dry air and water vapor. The amount of water vapor varies from zero (dry air) to a maximum that depends on temperature and pressure. **Saturation** is a state of neutral equilibrium between moist air and the condensed water phase (liquid or solid); unless otherwise stated, it assumes a flat interface surface between moist air and the condensed phase. Saturation conditions change when the interface radius is very small (e.g., with ultrafine water droplets). The relative molecular mass of water is 18.015 268 on the carbon-12 scale. The gas constant for water vapor is

$$R_w = 8314.472/18.015\,268 = 461.524 \text{ J/(kg}_w\cdot\text{K)} \quad (2)$$

U.S. STANDARD ATMOSPHERE

The temperature and barometric pressure of atmospheric air vary considerably with altitude as well as with local geographic and weather conditions. The standard atmosphere gives a standard of reference for estimating properties at various altitudes. At sea level, standard temperature is 15°C; standard barometric pressure is 101.325 kPa. Temperature is assumed to decrease linearly with increasing altitude throughout the troposphere (lower atmosphere), and to be constant in the lower reaches of the stratosphere. The lower atmosphere is assumed to consist of dry air that behaves as a perfect gas. Gravity is also assumed constant at the standard value, 9.806 65 m/s². Table 1 summarizes property data for altitudes to 10 000 m.

Pressure values in Table 1 may be calculated from

$$p = 101.325(1 - 2.25577 \times 10^{-5}Z)^{5.2559} \quad (3)$$

The equation for temperature as a function of altitude is

Table 1 Standard Atmospheric Data for Altitudes to 10 000 m

Altitude, m	Temperature, °C	Pressure, kPa
−500	18.2	107.478
0	15.0	101.325
500	11.8	95.461
1 000	8.5	89.875
1 500	5.2	84.556
2 000	2.0	79.495
2 500	−1.2	74.682
3 000	−4.5	70.108
4 000	−11.0	61.640
5 000	−17.5	54.020
6 000	−24.0	47.181
7 000	−30.5	41.061
8 000	−37.0	35.600
9 000	−43.5	30.742
10 000	−50	26.436

The preparation of this chapter is assigned to TC 1.1, Thermodynamics and Psychrometrics.

$$t = 15 - 0.0065Z \quad (4)$$

where

Z = altitude, m
p = barometric pressure, kPa
t = temperature, °C

Equations (3) and (4) are accurate from –5000 m to 11 000 m. For higher altitudes, comprehensive tables of barometric pressure and other physical properties of the standard atmosphere, in both SI and I-P units, can be found in NASA (1976).

THERMODYNAMIC PROPERTIES OF MOIST AIR

Table 2, developed from formulas by Herrmann et al. (2009), shows values of thermodynamic properties of moist air based on the International Temperature Scale of 1990 (ITS-90). This ideal scale differs slightly from practical temperature scales used for physical measurements. For example, the standard boiling point for water (at 101.325 kPa) occurs at 99.97°C on this scale rather than at the traditional 100°C. Most measurements are currently based on the International Temperature Scale of 1990 (ITS-90) (Preston-Thomas 1990).

The following properties are shown in Table 2:

t = Celsius temperature, based on the International Temperature Scale of 1990 (ITS-90) and expressed relative to absolute temperature T in kelvins (K) by the following relation:

$$T = t + 273.15$$

W_s = humidity ratio at saturation; gaseous phase (moist air) exists in equilibrium with condensed phase (liquid or solid) at given temperature and pressure (standard atmospheric pressure). At given values of temperature and pressure, humidity ratio W can have any value from zero to W_s.
v_{da} = specific volume of dry air, m^3/kg_{da}.
v_{as} = $v_s - v_{da}$, difference between specific volume of moist air at saturation and that of dry air, m^3/kg_{da}, at same pressure and temperature.
v_s = specific volume of moist air at saturation, m^3/kg_{da}.
h_{da} = specific enthalpy of dry air, kJ/kg_{da}. In Table 2, h_{da} has been assigned a value of 0 at 0°C and standard atmospheric pressure.
h_{as} = $h_s - h_{da}$, difference between specific enthalpy of moist air at saturation and that of dry air, kJ/kg_{da}, at same pressure and temperature.
h_s = specific enthalpy of moist air at saturation, kJ/kg_{da}.
s_{da} = specific entropy of dry air, $kJ/(kg_{da}\cdot K)$. In Table 2, s_{da} is assigned a value of 0 at °C and standard atmospheric pressure.
s_s = specific entropy of moist air at saturation $kJ/(kg_{da}\cdot K)$.

THERMODYNAMIC PROPERTIES OF WATER AT SATURATION

Table 3 shows thermodynamic properties of water at saturation for temperatures from –60 to 160°C, calculated by the formulations described by IAPWS (2007). Symbols in the table follow standard steam table nomenclature. These properties are based on the International Temperature Scale of 1990 (ITS-90). The internal energy and entropy of saturated liquid water are both assigned the value zero at the triple point, 0.01 °C. Between the triple-point and critical-point temperatures of water, two states (**saturated liquid** and **saturated vapor**) may coexist in equilibrium.

The **water vapor saturation pressure** is required to determine a number of moist air properties, principally the saturation humidity ratio. Values may be obtained from Table 3 or calculated from the following formulas (Hyland and Wexler 1983b). The 1983 formulas are within 300 ppm of the latest IAPWS formulations. For higher accuracy, developers of software and others are referred to IAPWS (2007) and (2008).

The saturation pressure over **ice** for the temperature range of −100 to 0°C is given by

$$\ln p_{ws} = C_1/T + C_2 + C_3T + C_4T^2 + C_5T^3 + C_6T^4 + C_7 \ln T \quad (5)$$

where

C_1 = −5.674 535 9 E+03
C_2 = 6.392 524 7 E+00
C_3 = −9.677 843 0 E–03
C_4 = 6.221 570 1 E–07
C_5 = 2.074 782 5 E–09
C_6 = −9.484 024 0 E–13
C_7 = 4.163 501 9 E+00

The saturation pressure over **liquid water** for the temperature range of 0 to 200°C is given by

$$\ln p_{ws} = C_8/T + C_9 + C_{10}T + C_{11}T^2 + C_{12}T^3 + C_{13} \ln T \quad (6)$$

where

C_8 = −5.800 220 6 E+03
C_9 = 1.391 499 3 E+00
C_{10} = −4.864 023 9 E–02
C_{11} = 4.176 476 8 E–05
C_{12} = −1.445 209 3 E–08
C_{13} = 6.545 967 3 E+00

In both Equations (5) and (6),

p_{ws} = saturation pressure, Pa
T = absolute temperature, K = °C + 273.15

The coefficients of Equations (5) and (6) were derived from the Hyland-Wexler equations. Because of rounding errors in the derivations and in some computers' calculating precision, results from Equations (5) and (6) may not agree precisely with Table 3 values.

The vapor pressure p_s of water in saturated moist air differs negligibly from the saturation vapor pressure p_{ws} of pure water at the same temperature. Consequently, p_s can be used in equations in place of p_{ws} with very little error:

$$p_s = x_{ws}p$$

where x_{ws} is the mole fraction of water vapor in saturated moist air at temperature t and pressure p, and p is the total barometric pressure of moist air.

HUMIDITY PARAMETERS

Basic Parameters

Humidity ratio W (alternatively, the moisture content or mixing ratio) of a given moist air sample is defined as the ratio of the mass of water vapor to the mass of dry air in the sample:

$$W = M_w/M_{da} \quad (7)$$

W equals the mole fraction ratio x_w/x_{da} multiplied by the ratio of molecular masses (18.015 268/28.966 = 0.621 945):

$$W = 0.621\ 945x_w/x_{da} \quad (8)$$

Specific humidity γ is the ratio of the mass of water vapor to total mass of the moist air sample:

$$\gamma = M_w/(M_w + M_{da}) \quad (9a)$$

In terms of the humidity ratio,

$$\gamma = W/(1 + W) \quad (9b)$$

Absolute humidity (alternatively, water vapor density) d_v is the ratio of the mass of water vapor to total volume of the sample:

$$d_v = M_w/V \quad (10)$$

Table 2 Thermodynamic Properties of Moist Air at Standard Atmospheric Pressure, 101.325 kPa

Temp., °C	Humidity Ratio	Specific Volume, m^3/kg_{da}			Specific Enthalpy, kJ/kg_{da}			Specific Entropy, $kJ/(kg_{da} \cdot K)$		Temp., °C
t	W_s, kg_w/kg_{da}	v_{da}	v_{as}	v_s	h_{da}	h_{as}	h_s	s_{da}	s_s	t
–60	0.0000067	0.6027	0.0000	0.6027	–60.341	0.016	–60.325	–0.2494	–0.2494	–60
–59	0.0000076	0.6055	0.0000	0.6055	–59.335	0.018	–59.317	–0.2447	–0.2446	–59
–58	0.0000087	0.6084	0.0000	0.6084	–58.329	0.021	–58.308	–0.2400	–0.2399	–58
–57	0.0000100	0.6112	0.0000	0.6112	–57.323	0.024	–57.299	–0.2354	–0.2353	–57
–56	0.0000114	0.6141	0.0000	0.6141	–56.317	0.027	–56.289	–0.2307	–0.2306	–56
–55	0.0000129	0.6169	0.0000	0.6169	–55.311	0.031	–55.280	–0.2261	–0.2260	–55
–54	0.0000147	0.6198	0.0000	0.6198	–54.305	0.035	–54.269	–0.2215	–0.2213	–54
–53	0.0000167	0.6226	0.0000	0.6226	–53.299	0.040	–53.258	–0.2169	–0.2167	–53
–52	0.0000190	0.6255	0.0000	0.6255	–52.293	0.046	–52.247	–0.2124	–0.2121	–52
–51	0.0000215	0.6283	0.0000	0.6283	–51.287	0.052	–51.235	–0.2078	–0.2076	–51
–50	0.0000243	0.6312	0.0000	0.6312	–50.281	0.059	–50.222	–0.2033	–0.2030	–50
–49	0.0000275	0.6340	0.0000	0.6340	–49.275	0.066	–49.209	–0.1988	–0.1985	–49
–48	0.0000311	0.6369	0.0000	0.6369	–48.269	0.075	–48.194	–0.1943	–0.1940	–48
–47	0.0000350	0.6397	0.0000	0.6397	–47.263	0.085	–47.179	–0.1899	–0.1895	–47
–46	0.0000395	0.6425	0.0000	0.6426	–46.257	0.095	–46.162	–0.1854	–0.1850	–46
–45	0.0000445	0.6454	0.0000	0.6454	–45.252	0.107	–45.144	–0.1810	–0.1805	–45
–44	0.0000500	0.6482	0.0001	0.6483	–44.246	0.121	–44.125	–0.1766	–0.1761	–44
–43	0.0000562	0.6511	0.0001	0.6511	–43.240	0.136	–43.104	–0.1722	–0.1716	–43
–42	0.0000631	0.6539	0.0001	0.6540	–42.234	0.153	–42.081	–0.1679	–0.1672	–42
–41	0.0000708	0.6568	0.0001	0.6568	–41.229	0.172	–41.057	–0.1635	–0.1628	–41
–40	0.0000793	0.6596	0.0001	0.6597	–40.223	0.192	–40.031	–0.1592	–0.1583	–40
–39	0.0000887	0.6625	0.0001	0.6626	–39.217	0.215	–39.002	–0.1549	–0.1539	–39
–38	0.0000992	0.6653	0.0001	0.6654	–38.212	0.241	–37.970	–0.1506	–0.1495	–38
–37	0.0001108	0.6682	0.0001	0.6683	–37.206	0.269	–36.936	–0.1464	–0.1451	–37
–36	0.0001237	0.6710	0.0001	0.6711	–36.200	0.301	–35.899	–0.1421	–0.1408	–36
–35	0.0001379	0.6738	0.0001	0.6740	–35.195	0.336	–34.859	–0.1379	–0.1364	–35
–34	0.0001536	0.6767	0.0002	0.6769	–34.189	0.374	–33.815	–0.1337	–0.1320	–34
–33	0.0001710	0.6795	0.0002	0.6797	–33.183	0.417	–32.766	–0.1295	–0.1276	–33
–32	0.0001902	0.6824	0.0002	0.6826	–32.178	0.464	–31.714	–0.1253	–0.1232	–32
–31	0.0002113	0.6852	0.0002	0.6855	–31.172	0.516	–30.656	–0.1211	–0.1189	–31
–30	0.0002345	0.6881	0.0003	0.6883	–30.167	0.573	–29.593	–0.1170	–0.1145	–30
–29	0.0002602	0.6909	0.0003	0.6912	–29.161	0.636	–28.525	–0.1129	–0.1101	–29
–28	0.0002883	0.6938	0.0003	0.6941	–28.156	0.706	–27.450	–0.1088	–0.1057	–28
–27	0.0003193	0.6966	0.0004	0.6970	–27.150	0.782	–26.368	–0.1047	–0.1013	–27
–26	0.0003532	0.6994	0.0004	0.6998	–26.144	0.866	–25.278	–0.1006	–0.0969	–26
–25	0.0003905	0.7023	0.0004	0.7027	–25.139	0.958	–24.181	–0.0965	–0.0924	–25
–24	0.0004314	0.7051	0.0005	0.7056	–24.133	1.059	–23.074	–0.0925	–0.0880	–24
–23	0.0004761	0.7080	0.0005	0.7085	–23.128	1.170	–21.958	–0.0884	–0.0835	–23
–22	0.0005251	0.7108	0.0006	0.7114	–22.122	1.291	–20.831	–0.0844	–0.0790	–22
–21	0.0005787	0.7137	0.0007	0.7143	–21.117	1.424	–19.693	–0.0804	–0.0745	–21
–20	0.0006373	0.7165	0.0007	0.7172	–20.111	1.570	–18.542	–0.0765	–0.0699	–20
–19	0.0007013	0.7193	0.0008	0.7201	–19.106	1.728	–17.377	–0.0725	–0.0653	–19
–18	0.0007711	0.7222	0.0009	0.7231	–18.100	1.902	–16.198	–0.0685	–0.0607	–18
–17	0.0008473	0.7250	0.0010	0.7260	–17.095	2.091	–15.003	–0.0646	–0.0560	–17
–16	0.0009303	0.7279	0.0011	0.7290	–16.089	2.298	–13.791	–0.0607	–0.0513	–16
–15	0.0010207	0.7307	0.0012	0.7319	–15.084	2.523	–12.560	–0.0568	–0.0465	–15
–14	0.0011191	0.7336	0.0013	0.7349	–14.078	2.769	–11.310	–0.0529	–0.0416	–14
–13	0.0012261	0.7364	0.0014	0.7378	–13.073	3.036	–10.037	–0.0490	–0.0367	–13
–12	0.0013425	0.7392	0.0016	0.7408	–12.067	3.326	–8.741	–0.0452	–0.0317	–12
–11	0.0014689	0.7421	0.0017	0.7438	–11.062	3.642	–7.419	–0.0413	–0.0267	–11
–10	0.0016062	0.7449	0.0019	0.7468	–10.056	3.986	–6.070	–0.0375	–0.0215	–10
–9	0.0017551	0.7478	0.0021	0.7499	–9.050	4.358	–4.692	–0.0337	–0.0163	–9
–8	0.0019166	0.7506	0.0023	0.7529	–8.045	4.763	–3.282	–0.0299	–0.0110	–8
–7	0.0020916	0.7534	0.0025	0.7560	–7.039	5.202	–1.838	–0.0261	–0.0055	–7
–6	0.0022812	0.7563	0.0028	0.7591	–6.034	5.677	–0.356	–0.0223	0.0000	–6
–5	0.0024863	0.7591	0.0030	0.7622	–5.028	6.193	1.164	–0.0186	0.0057	–5
–4	0.0027083	0.7620	0.0033	0.7653	–4.023	6.750	2.728	–0.0148	0.0115	–4
–3	0.0029482	0.7648	0.0036	0.7684	–3.017	7.354	4.337	–0.0111	0.0175	–3
–2	0.0032076	0.7677	0.0039	0.7716	–2.011	8.007	5.995	–0.0074	0.0236	–2
–1	0.0034877	0.7705	0.0043	0.7748	–1.006	8.712	7.707	–0.0037	0.0299	–1
0	0.0037900	0.7733	0.0047	0.7780	0.000	9.475	9.475	0.0000	0.0364	0
1	0.004076	0.7762	0.0051	0.7813	1.006	10.198	11.203	0.0037	0.0427	1
2	0.004382	0.7790	0.0055	0.7845	2.011	10.970	12.981	0.0073	0.0492	2
3	0.004708	0.7819	0.0059	0.7878	3.017	11.794	14.811	0.0110	0.0559	3
4	0.005055	0.7847	0.0064	0.7911	4.023	12.673	16.696	0.0146	0.0627	4
5	0.005425	0.7875	0.0068	0.7944	5.029	13.611	18.639	0.0182	0.0697	5
6	0.005819	0.7904	0.0074	0.7978	6.034	14.610	20.644	0.0219	0.0769	6
7	0.006238	0.7932	0.0079	0.8012	7.040	15.674	22.714	0.0254	0.0843	7
8	0.006684	0.7961	0.0085	0.8046	8.046	16.807	24.853	0.0290	0.0919	8
9	0.007158	0.7989	0.0092	0.8081	9.052	18.013	27.065	0.0326	0.0997	9
10	0.007663	0.8017	0.0098	0.8116	10.058	19.297	29.354	0.0362	0.1078	10
11	0.008199	0.8046	0.0106	0.8152	11.063	20.661	31.724	0.0397	0.1162	11
12	0.008768	0.8074	0.0113	0.8188	12.069	22.111	34.181	0.0432	0.1248	12
13	0.009372	0.8103	0.0122	0.8224	13.075	23.653	36.728	0.0468	0.1337	13
14	0.010013	0.8131	0.0131	0.8262	14.081	25.290	39.371	0.0503	0.1430	14

Table 2 Thermodynamic Properties of Moist Air at Standard Atmospheric Pressure, 101.325 kPa (*Concluded*)

Temp., °C	Humidity Ratio	Specific Volume, m^3/kg_{da}			Specific Enthalpy, kJ/kg_{da}			Specific Entropy, $kJ/(kg_{da}\cdot K)$		Temp., °C
t	W_s, kg_w/kg_{da}	v_{da}	v_{as}	v_s	h_{da}	h_{as}	h_s	s_{da}	s_s	t
15	0.010694	0.8159	0.0140	0.8299	15.087	27.028	42.115	0.0538	0.1525	15
16	0.011415	0.8188	0.0150	0.8338	16.093	28.873	44.966	0.0573	0.1624	16
17	0.012181	0.8216	0.0160	0.8377	17.099	30.830	47.929	0.0607	0.1726	17
18	0.012991	0.8245	0.0172	0.8416	18.105	32.906	51.011	0.0642	0.1832	18
19	0.013851	0.8273	0.0184	0.8457	19.111	35.107	54.219	0.0676	0.1942	19
20	0.014761	0.8301	0.0196	0.8498	20.117	37.441	57.558	0.0711	0.2057	20
21	0.015724	0.8330	0.0210	0.8540	21.124	39.914	61.037	0.0745	0.2175	21
22	0.016744	0.8358	0.0224	0.8583	22.130	42.533	64.663	0.0779	0.2298	22
23	0.017823	0.8387	0.0240	0.8626	23.136	45.308	68.444	0.0813	0.2426	23
24	0.018965	0.8415	0.0256	0.8671	24.142	48.245	72.388	0.0847	0.2560	24
25	0.020173	0.8443	0.0273	0.8716	25.148	51.355	76.503	0.0881	0.2698	25
26	0.021451	0.8472	0.0291	0.8763	26.155	54.646	80.801	0.0915	0.2842	26
27	0.022802	0.8500	0.0311	0.8811	27.161	58.128	85.289	0.0948	0.2992	27
28	0.024229	0.8529	0.0331	0.8860	28.167	61.812	89.979	0.0982	0.3148	28
29	0.025738	0.8557	0.0353	0.8910	29.174	65.708	94.882	0.1015	0.3311	29
30	0.027333	0.8585	0.0376	0.8961	30.180	69.829	100.009	0.1048	0.3481	30
31	0.029018	0.8614	0.0400	0.9014	31.187	74.185	105.372	0.1081	0.3658	31
32	0.030797	0.8642	0.0426	0.9069	32.193	78.791	110.985	0.1115	0.3843	32
33	0.032677	0.8671	0.0454	0.9124	33.200	83.660	116.860	0.1147	0.4035	33
34	0.034663	0.8699	0.0483	0.9182	34.207	88.806	123.013	0.1180	0.4236	34
35	0.036760	0.8727	0.0514	0.9241	35.213	94.245	129.458	0.1213	0.4447	35
36	0.038975	0.8756	0.0547	0.9302	36.220	99.993	136.213	0.1246	0.4666	36
37	0.041313	0.8784	0.0581	0.9365	37.227	106.068	143.294	0.1278	0.4895	37
38	0.043783	0.8813	0.0618	0.9430	38.233	112.487	150.720	0.1311	0.5135	38
39	0.046391	0.8841	0.0657	0.9498	39.240	119.270	158.510	0.1343	0.5386	39
40	0.049145	0.8869	0.0698	0.9567	40.247	126.438	166.685	0.1375	0.5649	40
41	0.052053	0.8898	0.0741	0.9639	41.254	134.014	175.268	0.1407	0.5923	41
42	0.055124	0.8926	0.0788	0.9714	42.261	142.021	184.282	0.1439	0.6211	42
43	0.058368	0.8955	0.0837	0.9791	43.268	150.483	193.751	0.1471	0.6512	43
44	0.061795	0.8983	0.0888	0.9871	44.275	159.429	203.704	0.1503	0.6828	44
45	0.065416	0.9011	0.0943	0.9955	45.282	168.887	214.169	0.1535	0.7159	45
46	0.069242	0.9040	0.1002	1.0041	46.289	178.889	225.178	0.1566	0.7507	46
47	0.073286	0.9068	0.1063	1.0131	47.297	189.466	236.763	0.1598	0.7871	47
48	0.077561	0.9096	0.1129	1.0225	48.304	200.656	248.960	0.1629	0.8254	48
49	0.082081	0.9125	0.1198	1.0323	49.311	212.497	261.808	0.1660	0.8655	49
50	0.086863	0.9153	0.1272	1.0425	50.319	225.030	275.349	0.1692	0.9078	50
51	0.091922	0.9182	0.1350	1.0531	51.326	238.300	289.627	0.1723	0.9522	51
52	0.097278	0.9210	0.1433	1.0643	52.334	252.357	304.690	0.1754	0.9989	52
53	0.102949	0.9238	0.1521	1.0759	53.341	267.251	320.592	0.1785	1.0481	53
54	0.108958	0.9267	0.1614	1.0881	54.349	283.041	337.389	0.1816	1.0999	54
55	0.115326	0.9295	0.1714	1.1009	55.356	299.788	355.144	0.1846	1.1545	55
56	0.122080	0.9324	0.1819	1.1143	56.364	317.560	373.924	0.1877	1.2121	56
57	0.129248	0.9352	0.1932	1.1284	57.372	336.431	393.803	0.1908	1.2729	57
58	0.136858	0.9380	0.2051	1.1432	58.380	356.482	414.862	0.1938	1.3371	58
59	0.144945	0.9409	0.2179	1.1587	59.388	377.800	437.188	0.1968	1.4050	59
60	0.153545	0.9437	0.2315	1.1752	60.396	400.484	460.880	0.1999	1.4769	60
61	0.162697	0.9465	0.2460	1.1925	61.404	424.641	486.044	0.2029	1.5530	61
62	0.172446	0.9494	0.2615	1.2108	62.412	450.388	512.799	0.2059	1.6337	62
63	0.182842	0.9522	0.2780	1.2302	63.420	477.856	541.276	0.2089	1.7194	63
64	0.193937	0.9551	0.2957	1.2508	64.428	507.192	571.620	0.2119	1.8105	64
65	0.205794	0.9579	0.3147	1.2726	65.436	538.557	603.993	0.2149	1.9074	65
66	0.218478	0.9607	0.3350	1.2957	66.445	572.131	638.576	0.2179	2.0107	66
67	0.232067	0.9636	0.3568	1.3204	67.453	608.118	675.572	0.2208	2.1209	67
68	0.246645	0.9664	0.3803	1.3467	68.462	646.746	715.208	0.2238	2.2386	68
69	0.262309	0.9692	0.4056	1.3748	69.470	688.271	757.741	0.2268	2.3646	69
70	0.279167	0.9721	0.4328	1.4049	70.479	732.985	803.464	0.2297	2.4997	70
71	0.297343	0.9749	0.4622	1.4372	71.488	781.220	852.707	0.2326	2.6449	71
72	0.316979	0.9778	0.4941	1.4719	72.496	833.353	905.850	0.2356	2.8011	72
73	0.338237	0.9806	0.5287	1.5093	73.505	889.821	963.326	0.2385	2.9697	73
74	0.361304	0.9834	0.5663	1.5497	74.514	951.124	1025.638	0.2414	3.1520	74
75	0.386399	0.9863	0.6072	1.5935	75.523	1017.843	1093.367	0.2443	3.3496	75
76	0.413774	0.9891	0.6520	1.6411	76.532	1090.659	1167.191	0.2472	3.5645	76
77	0.443727	0.9919	0.7010	1.6930	77.542	1170.366	1247.907	0.2501	3.7989	77
78	0.476610	0.9948	0.7550	1.7497	78.551	1257.907	1336.458	0.2529	4.0553	78
79	0.512842	0.9976	0.8145	1.8121	79.560	1354.402	1433.962	0.2558	4.3371	79
80	0.552926	1.0005	0.8805	1.8809	80.569	1461.196	1541.765	0.2587	4.6478	80
81	0.597470	1.0033	0.9539	1.9572	81.579	1579.917	1661.496	0.2615	4.9920	81
82	0.647218	1.0061	1.0360	2.0421	82.589	1712.556	1795.145	0.2644	5.3754	82
83	0.703089	1.0090	1.1283	2.1373	83.598	1861.573	1945.171	0.2672	5.8047	83
84	0.766233	1.0118	1.2328	2.2446	84.608	2030.041	2114.649	0.2701	6.2885	84
85	0.838105	1.0146	1.3519	2.3665	85.618	2221.858	2307.476	0.2729	6.8376	85
86	0.920580	1.0175	1.4887	2.5062	86.628	2442.035	2528.662	0.2757	7.4660	86
87	1.016105	1.0203	1.6473	2.6676	87.638	2697.127	2784.764	0.2785	8.1919	87
88	1.127952	1.0232	1.8332	2.8564	88.648	2995.880	3084.528	0.2813	9.0396	88
89	1.260579	1.0260	2.0539	3.0799	89.658	3350.228	3439.885	0.2841	10.0421	89
90	1.420235	1.0288	2.3198	3.3487	90.668	3776.888	3867.556	0.2869	11.2458	90

Table 3 Thermodynamic Properties of Water at Saturation

Temp., °C	Absolute Pressure	Specific Volume, m³/kg$_w$			Specific Enthalpy, kJ/kg$_w$			Specific Entropy, kJ/(kg$_w$·K)			Temp., °C
		Sat. Solid	Evap.	Sat. Vapor	Sat. Solid	Evap.	Sat. Vapor	Sat. Solid	Evap.	Sat. Vapor	
t	p_{ws}, kPa	v_i/v_f	v_{ig}/v_{fg}	v_g	h_i/h_f	h_{ig}/h_{fg}	h_g	s_i/s_f	s_{ig}/s_{fg}	s_g	t
–60	0.00108	0.001081	90971.58	90971.58	–446.12	2836.27	2390.14	–1.6842	13.3064	11.6222	–60
–59	0.00124	0.001082	79885.31	79885.31	–444.46	2836.45	2391.99	–1.6764	13.2452	11.5687	–59
–58	0.00141	0.001082	70235.77	70235.78	–442.79	2836.63	2393.85	–1.6687	13.1845	11.5158	–58
–57	0.00161	0.001082	61826.23	61826.24	–441.11	2836.81	2395.70	–1.6609	13.1243	11.4634	–57
–56	0.00184	0.001082	54488.28	54488.28	–439.42	2836.97	2397.55	–1.6531	13.0646	11.4115	–56
–55	0.00209	0.001082	48077.54	48077.54	–437.73	2837.13	2399.40	–1.6453	13.0054	11.3601	–55
–54	0.00238	0.001082	42470.11	42470.11	–436.03	2837.28	2401.25	–1.6375	12.9468	11.3092	–54
–53	0.00271	0.001082	37559.49	37559.50	–434.32	2837.42	2403.10	–1.6298	12.8886	11.2589	–53
–52	0.00307	0.001083	33254.07	33254.07	–432.61	2837.56	2404.95	–1.6220	12.8310	11.2090	–52
–51	0.00348	0.001083	29474.87	29474.87	–430.88	2837.69	2406.81	–1.6142	12.7738	11.1596	–51
–50	0.00394	0.001083	26153.80	26153.80	–429.16	2837.81	2408.66	–1.6065	12.7171	11.1106	–50
–49	0.00445	0.001083	23232.03	23232.04	–427.42	2837.93	2410.51	–1.5987	12.6609	11.0622	–49
–48	0.00503	0.001083	20658.70	20658.70	–425.68	2838.04	2412.36	–1.5909	12.6051	11.0142	–48
–47	0.00568	0.001083	18389.75	18389.75	–423.93	2838.14	2414.21	–1.5832	12.5498	10.9666	–47
–46	0.00640	0.001083	16387.03	16387.03	–422.17	2838.23	2416.06	–1.5754	12.4950	10.9196	–46
–45	0.00720	0.001084	14617.39	14617.39	–420.40	2838.32	2417.91	–1.5677	12.4406	10.8729	–45
–44	0.00810	0.001084	13052.07	13052.07	–418.63	2838.39	2419.76	–1.5599	12.3867	10.8267	–44
–43	0.00910	0.001084	11666.02	11666.02	–416.85	2838.47	2421.62	–1.5522	12.3331	10.7810	–43
–42	0.01022	0.001084	10437.46	10437.46	–415.06	2838.53	2423.47	–1.5444	12.2801	10.7356	–42
–41	0.01146	0.001084	9347.38	9347.38	–413.27	2838.59	2425.32	–1.5367	12.2274	10.6907	–41
–40	0.01284	0.001084	8379.20	8379.20	–411.47	2838.64	2427.17	–1.5289	12.1752	10.6462	–40
–39	0.01437	0.001085	7518.44	7518.44	–409.66	2838.68	2429.02	–1.5212	12.1234	10.6022	–39
–38	0.01607	0.001085	6752.43	6752.43	–407.85	2838.72	2430.87	–1.5135	12.0720	10.5585	–38
–37	0.01795	0.001085	6070.08	6070.08	–406.02	2838.74	2432.72	–1.5057	12.0210	10.5152	–37
–36	0.02004	0.001085	5461.68	5461.68	–404.19	2838.76	2434.57	–1.4980	11.9704	10.4724	–36
–35	0.02234	0.001085	4918.69	4918.69	–402.36	2838.78	2436.42	–1.4903	11.9202	10.4299	–35
–34	0.02489	0.001085	4433.64	4433.64	–400.51	2838.78	2438.27	–1.4825	11.8703	10.3878	–34
–33	0.02771	0.001085	3999.95	3999.95	–398.66	2838.78	2440.12	–1.4748	11.8209	10.3461	–33
–32	0.03081	0.001086	3611.82	3611.82	–396.80	2838.77	2441.97	–1.4671	11.7718	10.3047	–32
–31	0.03423	0.001086	3264.15	3264.16	–394.94	2838.75	2443.82	–1.4594	11.7231	10.2638	–31
–30	0.03801	0.001086	2952.46	2952.46	–393.06	2838.73	2445.67	–1.4516	11.6748	10.2232	–30
–29	0.04215	0.001086	2672.77	2672.77	–391.18	2838.70	2447.51	–1.4439	11.6269	10.1830	–29
–28	0.04672	0.001086	2421.58	2421.58	–389.29	2838.66	2449.36	–1.4362	11.5793	10.1431	–28
–27	0.05173	0.001086	2195.80	2195.80	–387.40	2838.61	2451.21	–1.4285	11.5321	10.1036	–27
–26	0.05724	0.001087	1992.68	1992.68	–385.50	2838.56	2453.06	–1.4208	11.4852	10.0644	–26
–25	0.06327	0.001087	1809.79	1809.79	–383.59	2838.49	2454.91	–1.4131	11.4386	10.0256	–25
–24	0.06989	0.001087	1644.99	1644.99	–381.67	2838.42	2456.75	–1.4054	11.3925	9.9871	–24
–23	0.07714	0.001087	1496.36	1496.36	–379.75	2838.35	2458.60	–1.3977	11.3466	9.9489	–23
–22	0.08508	0.001087	1362.21	1362.21	–377.81	2838.26	2460.45	–1.3899	11.3011	9.9111	–22
–21	0.09376	0.001087	1241.03	1241.03	–375.88	2838.17	2462.29	–1.3822	11.2559	9.8736	–21
–20	0.10324	0.001087	1131.49	1131.49	–373.93	2838.07	2464.14	–1.3745	11.2110	9.8365	–20
–19	0.11360	0.001088	1032.38	1032.38	–371.98	2837.96	2465.98	–1.3668	11.1665	9.7996	–19
–18	0.12490	0.001088	942.64	942.65	–370.01	2837.84	2467.83	–1.3591	11.1223	9.7631	–18
–17	0.13722	0.001088	861.34	861.34	–368.05	2837.72	2469.67	–1.3514	11.0784	9.7269	–17
–16	0.15065	0.001088	787.61	787.61	–366.07	2837.59	2471.51	–1.3437	11.0348	9.6910	–16
–15	0.16527	0.001088	720.70	720.70	–364.09	2837.45	2473.36	–1.3360	10.9915	9.6554	–15
–14	0.18119	0.001088	659.94	659.94	–362.10	2837.30	2475.20	–1.3284	10.9485	9.6201	–14
–13	0.19849	0.001089	604.72	604.73	–360.10	2837.14	2477.04	–1.3207	10.9058	9.5851	–13
–12	0.21729	0.001089	554.51	554.51	–358.10	2836.98	2478.88	–1.3130	10.8634	9.5504	–12
–11	0.23771	0.001089	508.81	508.81	–356.08	2836.80	2480.72	–1.3053	10.8213	9.5160	–11
–10	0.25987	0.001089	467.19	467.19	–354.06	2836.62	2482.56	–1.2976	10.7795	9.4819	–10
–9	0.28391	0.001089	429.25	429.26	–352.04	2836.44	2484.40	–1.2899	10.7380	9.4481	–9
–8	0.30995	0.001089	394.66	394.66	–350.00	2836.24	2486.23	–1.2822	10.6967	9.4145	–8
–7	0.33817	0.001090	363.09	363.09	–347.96	2836.03	2488.07	–1.2745	10.6558	9.3812	–7
–6	0.36871	0.001090	334.26	334.26	–345.91	2835.82	2489.91	–1.2668	10.6151	9.3482	–6
–5	0.40174	0.001090	307.92	307.92	–343.86	2835.60	2491.74	–1.2592	10.5747	9.3155	–5
–4	0.43745	0.001090	283.82	283.83	–341.79	2835.37	2493.57	–1.2515	10.5345	9.2830	–4
–3	0.47604	0.001090	261.78	261.78	–339.72	2835.13	2495.41	–1.2438	10.4946	9.2508	–3
–2	0.51770	0.001091	241.60	241.60	–337.64	2834.88	2497.24	–1.2361	10.4550	9.2189	–2
–1	0.56266	0.001091	223.10	223.11	–335.56	2834.63	2499.07	–1.2284	10.4157	9.1872	–1
0	0.61115	0.001091	206.15	206.15	–333.47	2834.36	2500.90	–1.2208	10.3766	9.1558	0

Table 3 Thermodynamic Properties of Water at Saturation (*Continued*)

Temp., °C t	Absolute Pressure p_{ws}, kPa	Specific Volume, m³/kg$_w$ Sat. Solid v_i/v_f	Evap. v_{ig}/v_{fg}	Sat. Vapor v_g	Specific Enthalpy, kJ/kg$_w$ Sat. Solid h_i/h_f	Evap. h_{ig}/h_{fg}	Sat. Vapor h_g	Specific Entropy, kJ/(kg$_w$·K) Sat. Solid s_i/s_f	Evap. s_{ig}/s_{fg}	Sat. Vapor s_g	Temp., °C t
0	0.6112	0.001000	206.139	206.140	−0.04	2500.93	2500.89	−0.0002	9.1559	9.1558	0
1	0.6571	0.001000	192.444	192.445	4.18	2498.55	2502.73	0.0153	9.1138	9.1291	1
2	0.7060	0.001000	179.763	179.764	8.39	2496.17	2504.57	0.0306	9.0721	9.1027	2
3	0.7581	0.001000	168.013	168.014	12.60	2493.80	2506.40	0.0459	9.0306	9.0765	3
4	0.8135	0.001000	157.120	157.121	16.81	2491.42	2508.24	0.0611	8.9895	9.0506	4
5	0.8726	0.001000	147.016	147.017	21.02	2489.05	2510.07	0.0763	8.9486	9.0249	5
6	0.9354	0.001000	137.637	137.638	25.22	2486.68	2511.91	0.0913	8.9081	8.9994	6
7	1.0021	0.001000	128.927	128.928	29.43	2484.31	2513.74	0.1064	8.8678	8.9742	7
8	1.0730	0.001000	120.833	120.834	33.63	2481.94	2515.57	0.1213	8.8278	8.9492	8
9	1.1483	0.001000	113.308	113.309	37.82	2479.58	2517.40	0.1362	8.7882	8.9244	9
10	1.2282	0.001000	106.308	106.309	42.02	2477.21	2519.23	0.1511	8.7488	8.8998	10
11	1.3129	0.001000	99.792	99.793	46.22	2474.84	2521.06	0.1659	8.7096	8.8755	11
12	1.4028	0.001001	93.723	93.724	50.41	2472.48	2522.89	0.1806	8.6708	8.8514	12
13	1.4981	0.001001	88.069	88.070	54.60	2470.11	2524.71	0.1953	8.6322	8.8275	13
14	1.5989	0.001001	82.797	82.798	58.79	2467.75	2526.54	0.2099	8.5939	8.8038	14
15	1.7057	0.001001	77.880	77.881	62.98	2465.38	2528.36	0.2245	8.5559	8.7804	15
16	1.8188	0.001001	73.290	73.291	67.17	2463.01	2530.19	0.2390	8.5181	8.7571	16
17	1.9383	0.001001	69.005	69.006	71.36	2460.65	2532.01	0.2534	8.4806	8.7341	17
18	2.0647	0.001001	65.002	65.003	75.55	2458.28	2533.83	0.2678	8.4434	8.7112	18
19	2.1982	0.001002	61.260	61.261	79.73	2455.92	2535.65	0.2822	8.4064	8.6886	19
20	2.3392	0.001002	57.760	57.761	83.92	2453.55	2537.47	0.2965	8.3696	8.6661	20
21	2.4881	0.001002	54.486	54.487	88.10	2451.18	2539.29	0.3108	8.3331	8.6439	21
22	2.6452	0.001002	51.421	51.422	92.29	2448.81	2541.10	0.3250	8.2969	8.6218	22
23	2.8109	0.001003	48.551	48.552	96.47	2446.45	2542.92	0.3391	8.2609	8.6000	23
24	2.9856	0.001003	45.862	45.863	100.66	2444.08	2544.73	0.3532	8.2251	8.5783	24
25	3.1697	0.001003	43.340	43.341	104.84	2441.71	2546.54	0.3673	8.1895	8.5568	25
26	3.3637	0.001003	40.976	40.977	109.02	2439.33	2548.35	0.3813	8.1542	8.5355	26
27	3.5679	0.001004	38.757	38.758	113.20	2436.96	2550.16	0.3952	8.1192	8.5144	27
28	3.7828	0.001004	36.674	36.675	117.38	2434.59	2551.97	0.4091	8.0843	8.4934	28
29	4.0089	0.001004	34.718	34.719	121.56	2432.21	2553.78	0.4230	8.0497	8.4727	29
30	4.2467	0.001004	32.881	32.882	125.75	2429.84	2555.58	0.4368	8.0153	8.4521	30
31	4.4966	0.001005	31.153	31.154	129.93	2427.46	2557.39	0.4506	7.9812	8.4317	31
32	4.7592	0.001005	29.528	29.529	134.11	2425.08	2559.19	0.4643	7.9472	8.4115	32
33	5.0351	0.001005	28.000	28.001	138.29	2422.70	2560.99	0.4780	7.9135	8.3914	33
34	5.3247	0.001006	26.561	26.562	142.47	2420.32	2562.79	0.4916	7.8800	8.3715	34
35	5.6286	0.001006	25.207	25.208	146.64	2417.94	2564.58	0.5052	7.8467	8.3518	35
36	5.9475	0.001006	23.931	23.932	150.82	2415.56	2566.38	0.5187	7.8136	8.3323	36
37	6.2818	0.001007	22.728	22.729	155.00	2413.17	2568.17	0.5322	7.7807	8.3129	37
38	6.6324	0.001007	21.594	21.595	159.18	2410.78	2569.96	0.5457	7.7480	8.2936	38
39	6.9997	0.001007	20.525	20.526	163.36	2408.39	2571.75	0.5591	7.7155	8.2746	39
40	7.3844	0.001008	19.516	19.517	167.54	2406.00	2573.54	0.5724	7.6832	8.2557	40
41	7.7873	0.001008	18.564	18.565	171.72	2403.61	2575.33	0.5858	7.6512	8.2369	41
42	8.2090	0.001009	17.664	17.665	175.90	2401.21	2577.11	0.5990	7.6193	8.2183	42
43	8.6503	0.001009	16.815	16.816	180.08	2398.82	2578.89	0.6123	7.5876	8.1999	43
44	9.1118	0.001009	16.012	16.013	184.26	2396.42	2580.67	0.6255	7.5561	8.1816	44
45	9.5944	0.001010	15.252	15.253	188.44	2394.02	2582.45	0.6386	7.5248	8.1634	45
46	10.0988	0.001010	14.534	14.535	192.62	2391.61	2584.23	0.6517	7.4937	8.1454	46
47	10.6259	0.001011	13.855	13.856	196.80	2389.21	2586.00	0.6648	7.4628	8.1276	47
48	11.1764	0.001011	13.212	13.213	200.98	2386.80	2587.77	0.6778	7.4320	8.1099	48
49	11.7512	0.001012	12.603	12.604	205.16	2384.39	2589.54	0.6908	7.4015	8.0923	49
50	12.3513	0.001012	12.027	12.028	209.34	2381.97	2591.31	0.7038	7.3711	8.0749	50
51	12.9774	0.001013	11.481	11.482	213.52	2379.56	2593.08	0.7167	7.3409	8.0576	51
52	13.6305	0.001013	10.963	10.964	217.70	2377.14	2594.84	0.7296	7.3109	8.0405	52
53	14.3116	0.001014	10.472	10.473	221.88	2374.72	2596.60	0.7424	7.2811	8.0235	53
54	15.0215	0.001014	10.006	10.007	226.06	2372.30	2598.35	0.7552	7.2514	8.0066	54
55	15.7614	0.001015	9.5639	9.5649	230.24	2369.87	2600.11	0.7680	7.2219	7.9899	55
56	16.5322	0.001015	9.1444	9.1454	234.42	2367.44	2601.86	0.7807	7.1926	7.9733	56
57	17.3350	0.001016	8.7461	8.7471	238.61	2365.01	2603.61	0.7934	7.1634	7.9568	57
58	18.1708	0.001016	8.3678	8.3688	242.79	2362.57	2605.36	0.8060	7.1344	7.9405	58
59	19.0407	0.001017	8.0083	8.0093	246.97	2360.13	2607.10	0.8186	7.1056	7.9243	59
60	19.9458	0.001017	7.6666	7.6677	251.15	2357.69	2608.85	0.8312	7.0770	7.9082	60
61	20.8873	0.001018	7.3418	7.3428	255.34	2355.25	2610.58	0.8438	7.0485	7.8922	61
62	21.8664	0.001018	7.0328	7.0338	259.52	2352.80	2612.32	0.8563	7.0201	7.8764	62
63	22.8842	0.001019	6.7389	6.7399	263.71	2350.35	2614.05	0.8687	6.9919	7.8607	63
64	23.9421	0.001019	6.4591	6.4601	267.89	2347.89	2615.78	0.8811	6.9639	7.8451	64
65	25.0411	0.001020	6.1928	6.1938	272.08	2345.43	2617.51	0.8935	6.9361	7.8296	65
66	26.1827	0.001020	5.9392	5.9402	276.27	2342.97	2619.23	0.9059	6.9083	7.8142	66
67	27.3680	0.001021	5.6976	5.6986	280.45	2340.50	2620.96	0.9182	6.8808	7.7990	67
68	28.5986	0.001022	5.4674	5.4684	284.64	2338.03	2622.67	0.9305	6.8534	7.7839	68
69	29.8756	0.001022	5.2479	5.2490	288.83	2335.56	2624.39	0.9428	6.8261	7.7689	69

Table 3 Thermodynamic Properties of Water at Saturation (*Concluded*)

Temp., °C t	Absolute Pressure p_{ws}, kPa	Specific Volume, m³/kg$_w$ Sat. Solid v_i/v_f	Evap. v_{ig}/v_{fg}	Sat. Vapor v_g	Specific Enthalpy, kJ/kg$_w$ Sat. Solid h_i/h_f	Evap. h_{ig}/h_{fg}	Sat. Vapor h_g	Specific Entropy, kJ/(kg$_w$·K) Sat. Solid s_i/s_f	Evap. s_{ig}/s_{fg}	Sat. Vapor s_g	Temp., °C t
70	31.2006	0.001023	5.0387	5.0397	293.02	2333.08	2626.10	0.9550	6.7990	7.7540	70
71	32.5750	0.001023	4.8392	4.8402	297.21	2330.60	2627.81	0.9672	6.7720	7.7392	71
72	34.0001	0.001024	4.6488	4.6498	301.40	2328.11	2629.51	0.9793	6.7452	7.7245	72
73	35.4775	0.001025	4.4671	4.4681	305.59	2325.62	2631.21	0.9915	6.7185	7.7100	73
74	37.0088	0.001025	4.2937	4.2947	309.78	2323.13	2632.91	1.0035	6.6920	7.6955	74
75	38.5954	0.001026	4.1281	4.1291	313.97	2320.63	2634.60	1.0156	6.6656	7.6812	75
76	40.2389	0.001026	3.9699	3.9709	318.17	2318.13	2636.29	1.0276	6.6393	7.6669	76
77	41.9409	0.001027	3.8188	3.8198	322.36	2315.62	2637.98	1.0396	6.6132	7.6528	77
78	43.7031	0.001028	3.6743	3.6754	326.56	2313.11	2639.66	1.0516	6.5872	7.6388	78
79	45.5271	0.001028	3.5363	3.5373	330.75	2310.59	2641.34	1.0635	6.5613	7.6248	79
80	47.4147	0.001029	3.4042	3.4053	334.95	2308.07	2643.01	1.0754	6.5356	7.6110	80
81	49.3676	0.001030	3.2780	3.2790	339.15	2305.54	2644.68	1.0873	6.5100	7.5973	81
82	51.3875	0.001030	3.1572	3.1582	343.34	2303.01	2646.35	1.0991	6.4846	7.5837	82
83	53.4762	0.001031	3.0415	3.0426	347.54	2300.47	2648.01	1.1109	6.4592	7.5701	83
84	55.6355	0.001032	2.9309	2.9319	351.74	2297.93	2649.67	1.1227	6.4340	7.5567	84
85	57.8675	0.001032	2.8249	2.8259	355.95	2295.38	2651.33	1.1344	6.4090	7.5434	85
86	60.1738	0.001033	2.7234	2.7244	360.15	2292.83	2652.98	1.1461	6.3840	7.5301	86
87	62.5565	0.001034	2.6262	2.6272	364.35	2290.27	2654.62	1.1578	6.3592	7.5170	87
88	65.0174	0.001035	2.5330	2.5341	368.56	2287.70	2656.26	1.1694	6.3345	7.5039	88
89	67.5587	0.001035	2.4437	2.4448	372.76	2285.14	2657.90	1.1811	6.3099	7.4909	89
90	70.1824	0.001036	2.3581	2.3591	376.97	2282.56	2659.53	1.1927	6.2854	7.4781	90
91	72.8904	0.001037	2.2760	2.2771	381.18	2279.98	2661.16	1.2042	6.2611	7.4653	91
92	75.6849	0.001037	2.1973	2.1983	385.38	2277.39	2662.78	1.2158	6.2368	7.4526	92
93	78.5681	0.001038	2.1217	2.1228	389.59	2274.80	2664.39	1.2273	6.2127	7.4400	93
94	81.5420	0.001039	2.0492	2.0502	393.81	2272.20	2666.01	1.2387	6.1887	7.4275	94
95	84.6089	0.001040	1.9796	1.9806	398.02	2269.60	2667.61	1.2502	6.1648	7.4150	95
96	87.7711	0.001040	1.9128	1.9138	402.23	2266.98	2669.22	1.2616	6.1411	7.4027	96
97	91.0308	0.001041	1.8486	1.8497	406.45	2264.37	2670.81	1.2730	6.1174	7.3904	97
98	94.3902	0.001042	1.7870	1.7880	410.66	2261.74	2672.40	1.2844	6.0938	7.3782	98
99	97.8518	0.001043	1.7277	1.7288	414.88	2259.11	2673.99	1.2957	6.0704	7.3661	99
100	101.4180	0.001043	1.6708	1.6719	419.10	2256.47	2675.57	1.3070	6.0471	7.3541	100
101	105.0910	0.001044	1.6161	1.6171	423.32	2253.83	2677.15	1.3183	6.0238	7.3421	101
102	108.8735	0.001045	1.5635	1.5645	427.54	2251.18	2678.72	1.3296	6.0007	7.3303	102
103	112.7678	0.001046	1.5129	1.5140	431.76	2248.52	2680.28	1.3408	5.9777	7.3185	103
104	116.7765	0.001047	1.4642	1.4653	435.99	2245.85	2681.84	1.3520	5.9548	7.3068	104
105	120.9021	0.001047	1.4174	1.4185	440.21	2243.18	2683.39	1.3632	5.9320	7.2951	105
106	125.1472	0.001048	1.3724	1.3734	444.44	2240.50	2684.94	1.3743	5.9092	7.2836	106
107	129.5145	0.001049	1.3290	1.3301	448.67	2237.81	2686.48	1.3854	5.8866	7.2721	107
108	134.0065	0.001050	1.2873	1.2883	452.90	2235.12	2688.02	1.3965	5.8641	7.2607	108
109	138.6261	0.001051	1.2471	1.2481	457.13	2232.41	2689.55	1.4076	5.8417	7.2493	109
110	143.3760	0.001052	1.2083	1.2094	461.36	2229.70	2691.07	1.4187	5.8194	7.2380	110
111	148.2588	0.001052	1.1710	1.1721	465.60	2226.99	2692.58	1.4297	5.7972	7.2268	111
112	153.2775	0.001053	1.1351	1.1362	469.83	2224.26	2694.09	1.4407	5.7750	7.2157	112
113	158.4348	0.001054	1.1005	1.1015	474.07	2221.53	2695.60	1.4517	5.7530	7.2047	113
114	163.7337	0.001055	1.0671	1.0681	478.31	2218.78	2697.09	1.4626	5.7310	7.1937	114
115	169.1770	0.001056	1.0349	1.0359	482.55	2216.03	2698.58	1.4735	5.7092	7.1827	115
116	174.7678	0.001057	1.0038	1.0049	486.80	2213.27	2700.07	1.4844	5.6874	7.1719	116
117	180.5090	0.001058	0.9739	0.9750	491.04	2210.51	2701.55	1.4953	5.6658	7.1611	117
118	186.4036	0.001059	0.9450	0.9461	495.29	2207.73	2703.02	1.5062	5.6442	7.1504	118
119	192.4547	0.001059	0.9171	0.9182	499.53	2204.94	2704.48	1.5170	5.6227	7.1397	119
120	198.6654	0.001060	0.8902	0.8913	503.78	2202.15	2705.93	1.5278	5.6013	7.1291	120
122	211.5782	0.001062	0.8392	0.8403	512.29	2196.53	2708.82	1.5494	5.5587	7.1081	122
124	225.1676	0.001064	0.7916	0.7927	520.80	2190.88	2711.69	1.5708	5.5165	7.0873	124
126	239.4597	0.001066	0.7472	0.7483	529.32	2185.19	2714.52	1.5922	5.4746	7.0668	126
128	254.4813	0.001068	0.7058	0.7068	537.85	2179.47	2717.32	1.6134	5.4330	7.0465	128
130	270.2596	0.001070	0.6670	0.6681	546.39	2173.70	2720.09	1.6346	5.3918	7.0264	130
132	286.8226	0.001072	0.6308	0.6318	554.93	2167.89	2722.83	1.6557	5.3508	7.0066	132
134	304.1989	0.001074	0.5969	0.5979	563.49	2162.04	2725.53	1.6767	5.3102	6.9869	134
136	322.4175	0.001076	0.5651	0.5662	572.05	2156.15	2728.20	1.6977	5.2698	6.9675	136
138	341.5081	0.001078	0.5353	0.5364	580.62	2150.22	2730.84	1.7185	5.2298	6.9483	138
140	361.5010	0.001080	0.5074	0.5085	589.20	2144.24	2733.44	1.7393	5.1900	6.9293	140
142	382.4271	0.001082	0.4813	0.4823	597.79	2138.22	2736.01	1.7600	5.1505	6.9105	142
144	404.3178	0.001084	0.4567	0.4577	606.39	2132.15	2738.54	1.7806	5.1112	6.8918	144
146	427.2053	0.001086	0.4336	0.4346	615.00	2126.04	2741.04	1.8011	5.0723	6.8734	146
148	451.1220	0.001088	0.4118	0.4129	623.62	2119.88	2743.50	1.8216	5.0335	6.8551	148
150	476.1014	0.001091	0.3914	0.3925	632.25	2113.67	2745.92	1.8420	4.9951	6.8370	150
152	502.1771	0.001093	0.3722	0.3733	640.89	2107.41	2748.30	1.8623	4.9569	6.8191	152
154	529.3834	0.001095	0.3541	0.3552	649.55	2101.10	2750.64	1.8825	4.9189	6.8014	154
156	557.7555	0.001097	0.3370	0.3381	658.21	2094.74	2752.95	1.9027	4.8811	6.7838	156
158	587.3287	0.001100	0.3209	0.3220	666.89	2088.32	2755.21	1.9228	4.8436	6.7664	158
160	618.1392	0.001102	0.3057	0.3068	675.57	2081.86	2757.43	1.9428	4.8063	6.7491	160

Density ρ of a moist air mixture is the ratio of total mass to total volume:

$$\rho = (M_{da} + M_w)/V = (1/v)(1 + W) \quad (11)$$

where v is the moist air specific volume, m^3/kg_{da}, as defined by Equation (26).

Humidity Parameters Involving Saturation

The following definitions of humidity parameters involve the concept of moist air saturation:

Saturation humidity ratio $W_s(t, p)$ is the humidity ratio of moist air saturated with respect to water (or ice) at the same temperature t and pressure p.

Degree of saturation μ is the ratio of air humidity ratio W to humidity ratio W_s of saturated moist air at the same temperature and pressure:

$$\mu = \left.\frac{W}{W_s}\right|_{t,p} \quad (12)$$

Relative humidity ϕ is the ratio of the mole fraction of water vapor x_w in a given moist air sample to the mole fraction x_{ws} in an air sample saturated at the same temperature and pressure:

$$\phi = \left.\frac{x_w}{x_{ws}}\right|_{t,p} \quad (13)$$

Combining Equations (8), (12), and (13)

$$\mu = \frac{\phi}{1 + (1 - \phi)W_s/(0.621\,945)} \quad (14)$$

Dew-point temperature t_d is the temperature of moist air saturated at pressure p, with the same humidity ratio W as that of the given sample of moist air. It is defined as the solution $t_d(p, W)$ of the following equation:

$$W_s(p, t_d) = W \quad (15)$$

Thermodynamic wet-bulb temperature t^* is the temperature at which water (liquid or solid), by evaporating into moist air at dry-bulb temperature t and humidity ratio W, can bring air to saturation adiabatically at the same temperature t^* while total pressure p is constant. This parameter is considered separately in the section on Thermodynamic Wet-Bulb and Dew-Point Temperature.

PERFECT GAS RELATIONSHIPS FOR DRY AND MOIST AIR

When moist air is considered a mixture of independent perfect gases (i.e., dry air and water vapor), each is assumed to obey the perfect gas equation of state as follows:

Dry air: $$p_{da}V = n_{da}RT \quad (16)$$

Water vapor: $$p_wV = n_wRT \quad (17)$$

where

p_{da} = partial pressure of dry air
p_w = partial pressure of water vapor
V = total mixture volume
n_{da} = number of moles of dry air
n_w = number of moles of water vapor
R = universal gas constant, 8314.472 J/(kmol·K)
T = absolute temperature, K

The mixture also obeys the perfect gas equation:

$$pV = nRT \quad (18)$$

or

$$(p_{da} + p_w)V = (n_{da} + n_w)RT \quad (19)$$

where $p = p_{da} + p_w$ is the total mixture pressure and $n = n_{da} + n_w$ is the total number of moles in the mixture. From Equations (16) to (19), the mole fractions of dry air and water vapor are, respectively,

$$x_{da} = p_{da}/(p_{da} + p_w) = p_{da}/p \quad (20)$$

and

$$x_w = p_w/(p_{da} + p_w) = p_w/p \quad (21)$$

From Equations (8), (20), and (21), the **humidity ratio** W is

$$W = 0.621\,945\frac{p_w}{p - p_w} \quad (22)$$

The degree of saturation μ is defined in Equation (12), where

$$W_s = 0.621\,945\frac{p_{ws}}{p - p_{ws}} \quad (23)$$

The term p_{ws} represents the saturation pressure of water vapor in the absence of air at the given temperature t. This pressure p_{ws} is a function only of temperature and differs slightly from the vapor pressure of water in saturated moist air.

The **relative humidity** ϕ is defined in Equation (13). Substituting Equation (21) for x_w and x_{ws},

$$\phi = \left.\frac{p_w}{p_{ws}}\right|_{t,p} \quad (24)$$

Substituting Equation (23) for W_s into Equation (14),

$$\phi = \frac{\mu}{1 - (1 - \mu)(p_w/p)} \quad (25)$$

Both ϕ and μ are zero for dry air and unity for saturated moist air. At intermediate states, their values differ, substantially so at higher temperatures.

The **specific volume** v of a moist air mixture is expressed in terms of a unit mass of dry air:

$$v = V/M_{da} = V/(28.966n_{da}) \quad (26)$$

where V is the total volume of the mixture, M_{da} is the total mass of dry air, and n_{da} is the number of moles of dry air. By Equations (16) and (26), with the relation $p = p_{da} + p_w$,

$$v = \frac{RT}{28.966(p - p_w)} = \frac{R_{da}T}{p - p_w} \quad (27)$$

Using Equation (22),

$$v = \frac{RT(1 + (1.607\,858)W)}{28.966p} = \frac{R_{da}T(1 + (1.607\,858)W)}{p} \quad (28)$$

In Equations (27) and (28), v is specific volume, T is absolute temperature, p is total pressure, p_w is partial pressure of water vapor, and W is humidity ratio.

In specific units, Equation (28) may be expressed as

$$v = 0.287\,042(t + 273.15)(1 + 1.607\,858W)/p$$

where

v = specific volume, m^3/kg_{da}

t = dry-bulb temperature, °C
W = humidity ratio, kg_w/kg_{da}
p = total pressure, kPa

The **enthalpy** of a mixture of perfect gases equals the sum of the individual partial enthalpies of the components. Therefore, the specific enthalpy of moist air can be written as follows:

$$h = h_{da} + Wh_g \tag{29}$$

where h_{da} is the specific enthalpy for dry air in kJ/kg_{da} and h_g is the specific enthalpy for saturated water vapor in kJ/kg_w at the temperature of the mixture. As an approximation,

$$h_{da} \approx 1.006t \tag{30}$$

$$h_g \approx 2501 + 1.86t \tag{31}$$

where t is the dry-bulb temperature in °C. The moist air specific enthalpy in kJ/kg_{da} then becomes

$$h = 1.006t + W(2501 + 1.86t) \tag{32}$$

THERMODYNAMIC WET-BULB AND DEW-POINT TEMPERATURE

For any state of moist air, a temperature t^* exists at which liquid (or solid) water evaporates into the air to bring it to saturation at exactly this same temperature and total pressure (Harrison 1965). During adiabatic saturation, saturated air is expelled at a temperature equal to that of the injected water. In this constant-pressure process,

- Humidity ratio increases from initial value W to W_s^*, corresponding to saturation at temperature t^*
- Enthalpy increases from initial value h to h_s^*, corresponding to saturation at temperature t^*
- Mass of water added per unit mass of dry air is $(W_s^* - W)$, which adds energy to the moist air of amount $(W_s^* - W)h_w^*$, where h_w^* denotes specific enthalpy in kJ/kg_w of water added at temperature t^*

Therefore, if the process is strictly adiabatic, conservation of enthalpy at constant total pressure requires that

$$h + (W_s^* - W)h_w^* = h_s^* \tag{33}$$

W_s^*, h_w^*, and h_s^* are functions only of temperature t^* for a fixed value of pressure. The value of t^* that satisfies Equation (33) for given values of h, W, and p is the **thermodynamic wet-bulb temperature**.

A **psychrometer** consists of two thermometers; one thermometer's bulb is covered by a wick that has been thoroughly wetted with water. When the wet bulb is placed in an airstream, water evaporates from the wick, eventually reaching an equilibrium temperature called the **wet-bulb temperature**. This process is not one of adiabatic saturation, which defines the thermodynamic wet-bulb temperature, but one of simultaneous heat and mass transfer from the wet bulb. The fundamental mechanism of this process is described by the Lewis relation [Equation (38) in Chapter 5]. Fortunately, only small corrections must be applied to wet-bulb thermometer readings to obtain the thermodynamic wet-bulb temperature.

As defined, thermodynamic wet-bulb temperature is a unique property of a given moist air sample independent of measurement techniques.

Equation (33) is exact because it defines the thermodynamic wet-bulb temperature t^*. Substituting the approximate perfect gas relation [Equation (32)] for h, the corresponding expression for h_s^*, and the approximate relation for saturated liquid water

$$h_w^* \approx 4.186t^* \tag{34}$$

into Equation (33), and solving for the humidity ratio,

$$W = \frac{(2501 - 2.326t^*)W_s^* - 1.006(t - t^*)}{2501 + 1.86t - 4.186t^*} \tag{35}$$

where t and t^* are in °C. Below freezing, the corresponding equations are

$$h_w^* \approx -333.4 + 2.1t^* \tag{36}$$

$$W = \frac{(2830 - 0.24t^*)W_s^* - 1.006(t - t^*)}{2830 + 1.86t - 2.1t^*} \tag{37}$$

A wet/ice-bulb thermometer is imprecise when determining moisture content at 0°C.

The **dew-point temperature t_d** of moist air with humidity ratio W and pressure p was defined as the solution $t_d(p, w)$ of $W_s(p, t_d)$. For perfect gases, this reduces to

$$p_{ws}(t_d) = p_w = (pW)/(0.621\,945 + W) \tag{38}$$

where p_w is the water vapor partial pressure for the moist air sample and $p_{ws}(t_d)$ is the saturation vapor pressure at temperature t_d. The saturation vapor pressure is obtained from Table 3 or by using Equation (5) or (6). Alternatively, the dew-point temperature can be calculated directly by one of the following equations (Peppers 1988):

Between dew points of 0 and 93°C,

$$td = C_{14} + C_{15}\alpha + C_{16}\alpha^2 + C_{17}\alpha^3 + C_{18}(p_w)^{0.1984} \tag{39}$$

Below 0°C,

$$t_d = 6.09 + 12.608\alpha + 0.4959\alpha^2 \tag{40}$$

where

t_d = dew-point temperature, °C
α = ln p_w
p_w = water vapor partial pressure, kPa
C_{14} = 6.54
C_{15} = 14.526
C_{16} = 0.7389
C_{17} = 0.09486
C_{18} = 0.4569

NUMERICAL CALCULATION OF MOIST AIR PROPERTIES

The following are outlines, citing equations and tables already presented, for calculating moist air properties using perfect gas relations. These relations are accurate enough for most engineering calculations in air-conditioning practice, and are readily adapted to either hand or computer calculating methods. For more details, refer to Tables 15 through 18 in Chapter 1 of Olivieri (1996). Graphical procedures are discussed in the section on Psychrometric Charts.

SITUATION 1.

Given: Dry-bulb temperature t, Wet-bulb temperature t^*, Pressure p

To Obtain	Use	Comments
$p_{ws}(t^*)$	Table 3 or Equation (5) or (6)	Sat. press. for temp. t^*
W_s^*	Equation (23)	Using $p_{ws}(t^*)$
W	Equation (35) or (37)	
$p_{ws}(t)$	Table 3 or Equation (5) or (6)	Sat. press. for temp. t
W_s	Equation (23)	Using $p_{ws}(t)$
μ	Equation (12)	Using W_s
ϕ	Equation (25)	Using $p_{ws}(t)$
v	Equation (28)	
h	Equation (32)	
p_w	Equation (38)	
t_d	Table 3 with Equation (38), (39), or (40)	

SITUATION 2.

Given: Dry-bulb temperature t, Dew-point temperature t_d, Pressure p

To Obtain	Use	Comments
$p_w = p_{ws}(t_d)$	Table 3 or Equation (5) or (6)	Sat. press. for temp. t_d
W	Equation (22)	
$p_{ws}(t)$	Table 3 or Equation (5) or (6)	Sat. press. for temp. t_d
W_s	Equation (23)	Using $p_{ws}(t)$
μ	Equation (12)	Using W_s
ϕ	Equation (25)	Using $p_{ws}(t)$
v	Equation (28)	
h	Equation (32)	
t^*	Equation (23) and (35) or (37) with Table 3 or with Equation (5) or (6)	Requires trial-and-error or numerical solution method

SITUATION 3.

Given: Dry-bulb temperature t, Relative humidity ϕ, Pressure p

To Obtain	Use	Comments
$p_{ws}(t)$	Table 3 or Equation (5) or (6)	Sat. press. for temp. t
p_w	Equation (24)	
W	Equation (22)	
W_s	Equation (23)	Using $p_{ws}(t)$
μ	Equation (12)	Using W_s
v	Equation (28)	
h	Equation (32)	
t_d	Table 3 with Equation (38), (39), or (40)	
t^*	Equation (23) and (35) or (37) with Table 3 or with Equation (5) or (6)	Requires trial-and-error or numerical solution method

Moist Air Property Tables for Standard Pressure

Table 2 shows thermodynamic properties for standard atmospheric pressure at temperatures from –60 to 90°C. Properties of intermediate moist air states can be calculated using the degree of saturation μ:

$$\text{Volume} \quad v = v_{da} + \mu v_{as} \tag{41}$$

$$\text{Enthalpy} \quad h = h_{da} + \mu h_{as} \tag{42}$$

These equations are accurate to about 70°C. At higher temperatures, errors can be significant. Hyland and Wexler (1983a) include charts that can be used to estimate errors for v and h for standard barometric pressure. Nelson and Sauer (2002) provide psychrometric tables and charts up to 320°C and 1.0 kg_w/kg_{da}.

PSYCHROMETRIC CHARTS

A psychrometric chart graphically represents the thermodynamic properties of moist air.

The choice of coordinates for a psychrometric chart is arbitrary. A chart with coordinates of enthalpy and humidity ratio provides convenient graphical solutions of many moist air problems with a minimum of thermodynamic approximations. ASHRAE developed five such psychrometric charts. Chart No. 1 is shown as Figure 1; the others may be obtained through ASHRAE.

Charts 1, 2, 3 and 4 are for sea-level pressure (101.325 kPa). Chart 5 is for 750 m altitude (92.634 kPa), Chart 6 is for 1500 m altitude (84.54 kPa), and Chart 7 is for 2250 m altitude (77.058 kPa). All charts use oblique-angle coordinates of enthalpy and humidity ratio, and are consistent with the data of Table 2 and the properties computation methods of Goff (1949) and Goff and Gratch (1945), as well as Hyland and Wexler (1983a). Palmatier (1963) describes the geometry of chart construction applying specifically to Charts 1 and 4.

The dry-bulb temperature ranges covered by the charts are

Charts 1, 5, 6, 7	Normal temperature	0 to 50°C
Chart 2	Low temperature	–40 to 10°C
Chart 3	High temperature	10 to 120°C
Chart 4	Very high temperature	100 to 200°C

Charts 8 to 16 are for 200 to 320°C and cover the same pressures as 1, 5, 6, and 7 plus the additional pressures of 0.2, 0.5,1.0, 2.0, and 5.0 MPa. They were produced by Nelson (2002) and are available on the CD-ROM included with Gatley (2005).

Psychrometric properties or charts for other barometric pressures can be derived by interpolation. Sufficiently exact values for most purposes can be derived by methods described in the section on Perfect Gas Relationships for Dry and Moist Air. Constructing charts for altitude conditions has been discussed by Haines (1961), Karig (1946), and Rohsenow (1946).

Comparison of Charts 1 and 4 by overlay reveals the following:

- The dry-bulb lines coincide.
- Wet-bulb lines for a given temperature originate at the intersections of the corresponding dry-bulb line and the two saturation curves, and they have the same slope.
- Humidity ratio and enthalpy for a given dry- and wet-bulb temperature increase with altitude, but there is little change in relative humidity.
- Volume changes rapidly; for a given dry-bulb and humidity ratio, it is practically inversely proportional to barometric pressure.

The following table compares properties at sea level (Chart 1) and 1500 m (Chart 6):

Chart No.	db	wb	h	W	rh	v
1	40	30	99.5	23.0	49	0.920
6	40	30	114.1	28.6	50	1.111

Figure 1 shows humidity ratio lines (horizontal) for the range from 0 (dry air) to 30 grams moisture per kilogram dry air. Enthalpy lines are oblique lines across the chart precisely parallel to each other.

Dry-bulb temperature lines are straight, not precisely parallel to each other, and inclined slightly from the vertical position. Thermodynamic wet-bulb temperature lines are oblique and in a slightly different direction from enthalpy lines. They are straight but are not precisely parallel to each other.

Relative humidity lines are shown in intervals of 10%. The saturation curve is the line of 100% rh, whereas the horizontal line for W = 0 (dry air) is the line for 0% rh.

Specific volume lines are straight but are not precisely parallel to each other.

A narrow region above the saturation curve has been developed for fog conditions of moist air. This two-phase region represents a mechanical mixture of saturated moist air and liquid water, with the two components in thermal equilibrium. Isothermal lines in the fog region coincide with extensions of thermodynamic wet-bulb temperature lines. If required, the fog region can be further expanded by extending humidity ratio, enthalpy, and thermodynamic wet-bulb temperature lines.

The protractor to the left of the chart shows two scales: one for sensible/total heat ratio, and one for the ratio of enthalpy difference to humidity ratio difference. The protractor is used to establish the direction of a condition line on the psychrometric chart.

Example 1 illustrates use of the ASHRAE Psychrometric Chart to determine moist air properties.

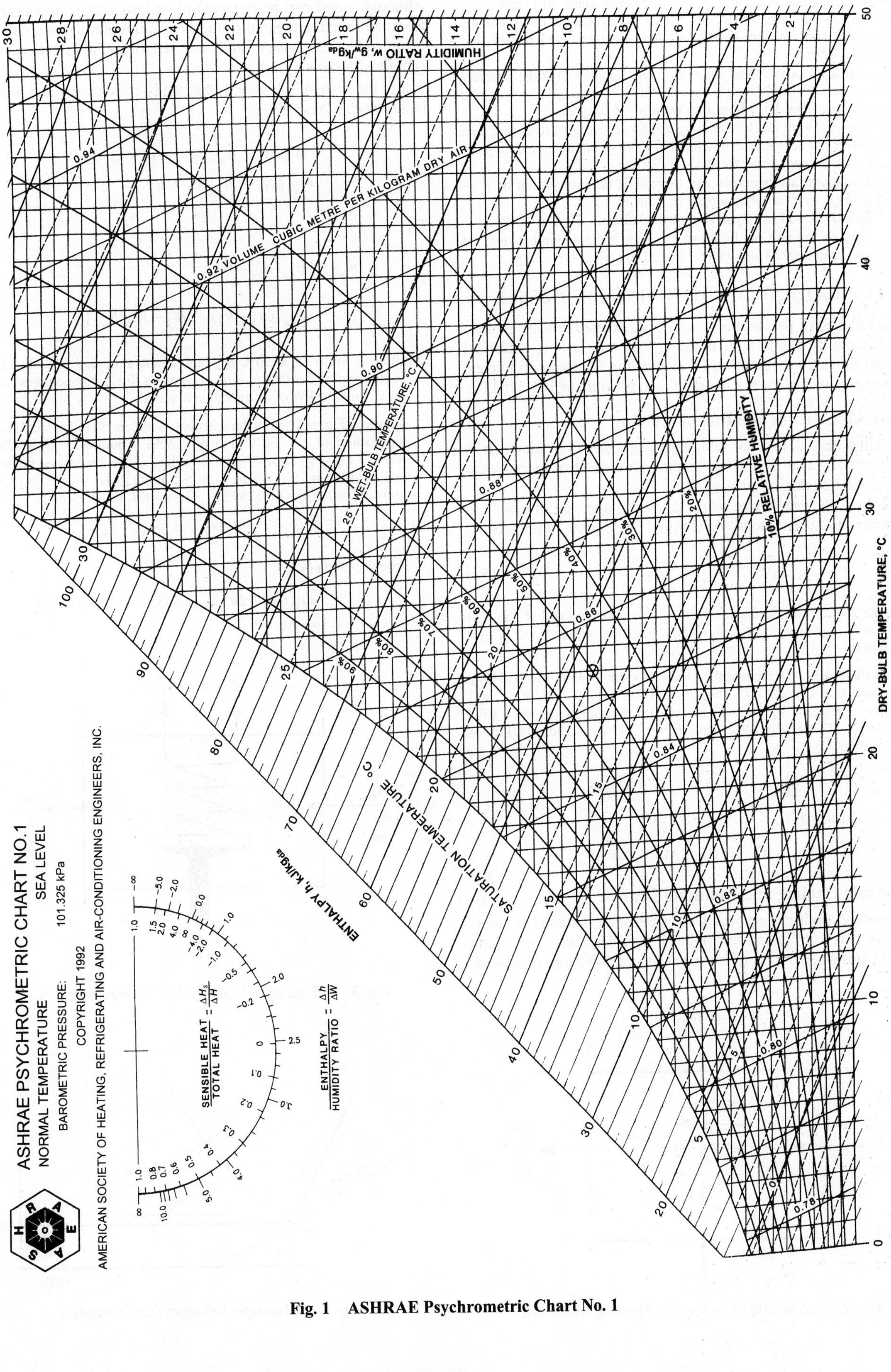

Fig. 1 ASHRAE Psychrometric Chart No. 1

Example 1. Moist air exists at 40°C dry-bulb temperature, 20°C thermodynamic wet-bulb temperature, and 101.325 kPa pressure. Determine the humidity ratio, enthalpy, dew-point temperature, relative humidity, and specific volume.

Solution: Locate state point on Chart 1 (Figure 1) at the intersection of 40°C dry-bulb temperature and 20°C thermodynamic wet-bulb temperature lines. Read **humidity ratio** $W = 6.5$ g_w/kg_{da}.

The **enthalpy** can be found by using two triangles to draw a line parallel to the nearest enthalpy line (60 kJ/kg_{da}) through the state point to the nearest edge scale. Read $h = 56.7$ kJ/kg_{da}.

Dew-point temperature can be read at the intersection of $W = 6.5$ g_w/kg_{da} with the saturation curve. Thus, $t_d = 7$°C.

Relative humidity ϕ can be estimated directly. Thus, $\phi = 14\%$.

Specific volume can be found by linear interpolation between the volume lines for 0.88 and 0.90 m^3/kg_{da}. Thus, $v = 0.896$ m^3/kg_{da}.

TYPICAL AIR-CONDITIONING PROCESSES

The ASHRAE psychrometric chart can be used to solve numerous process problems with moist air. Its use is best explained through illustrative examples. In each of the following examples, the process takes place at a constant total pressure of 101.325 kPa.

Moist Air Sensible Heating or Cooling

Adding heat alone to or removing heat alone from moist air is represented by a horizontal line on the ASHRAE chart, because the humidity ratio remains unchanged.

Figure 2 shows a device that adds heat to a stream of moist air. For steady-flow conditions, the required rate of heat addition is

$$_1q_2 = \dot{m}_{da}(h_2 - h_1) \tag{43}$$

Example 2. Moist air, saturated at 2°C, enters a heating coil at a rate of 10 m^3/s. Air leaves the coil at 40°C. Find the required rate of heat addition.

Solution: Figure 3 schematically shows the solution. State 1 is located on the saturation curve at 2°C. Thus, $h_1 = 13.0$ kJ/kg_{da}, $W_1 = 4.38$ g_w/kg_{da}, and $v_1 = 0.785$ m^3/kg_{da}. State 2 is located at the intersection of $t = 40$°C and $W_2 = W_1 = 4.38$ g_w/kg_{da}. Thus, $h_2 = 51.5$ kJ/kg_{da}. The mass flow of dry air is:

$$\dot{m}_{da} = 10/0.785 = 12.74 \text{ kg}_{da}/\text{s}$$

From Equation (43),

$$_1q_2 = 12.74(51.5 - 13.0) = 490 \text{ kW}$$

Moist Air Cooling and Dehumidification

Moisture condensation occurs when moist air is cooled to a temperature below its initial dew point. Figure 4 shows a schematic cooling coil where moist air is assumed to be uniformly processed.

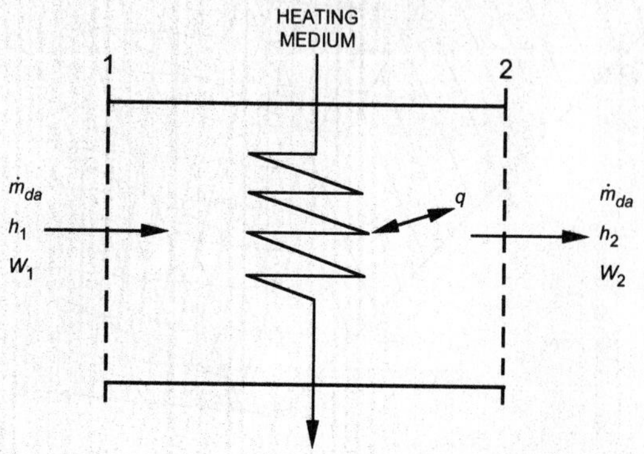

Fig. 2 Schematic of Device for Heating Moist Air

Although water can be removed at various temperatures ranging from the initial dew point to the final saturation temperature, it is assumed that condensed water is cooled to the final air temperature t_2 before it drains from the system.

For the system in Figure 4, the steady-flow energy and material balance equations are

$$\dot{m}_{da}h_1 = \dot{m}_{da}h_2 + {_1q_2} + \dot{m}_w h_{w2}$$

$$\dot{m}_{da}W_1 = \dot{m}_{da}W_2 + \dot{m}_w$$

Thus,

$$\dot{m}_w = \dot{m}_{da}(W_1 - W_2) \tag{44}$$

$$_1q_2 = \dot{m}_{da}[(h_1 - h_2) - (W_1 - W_2)h_{w2}] \tag{45}$$

Example 3. Moist air at 30°C dry-bulb temperature and 50% rh enters a cooling coil at 5 m^3/s and is processed to a final saturation condition at 10°C. Find the kW of refrigeration required.

Solution: Figure 5 shows the schematic solution. State 1 is located at the intersection of $t = 30$°C and $\phi = 50\%$. Thus, $h_1 = 64.3$ kJ/kg_{da}, $W_1 = 13.3$ g_w/kg_{da}, and $v_1 = 0.877$ m^3/kg_{da}. State 2 is located on the saturation curve at 10°C. Thus, $h_2 = 29.5$ kJ/kg_{da} and $W_2 = 7.66$ g_w/kg_{da}. From Table 2, $h_{w2} = 42.02$ kJ/kg_w. The mass flow of dry air is:

$$\dot{m}_{da} = 5/0.877 = 5.70 \text{ kg}_{da}/\text{s}$$

From Equation (45),

$$_1q_2 = 5.70[(64.3 - 29.5) - (0.0133 - 0.00766)42.02]$$
$$= 197 \text{ kW}$$

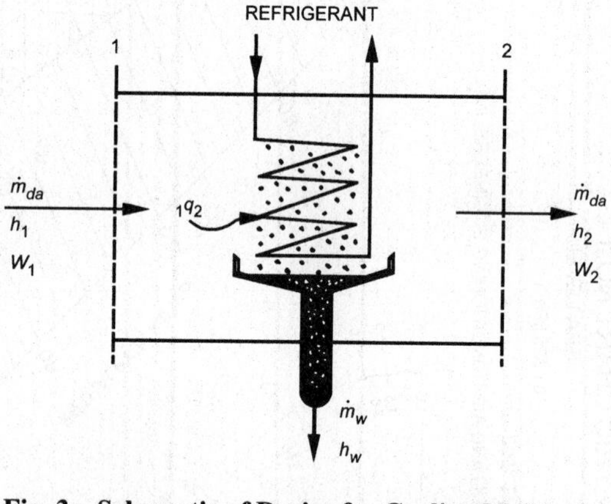

Fig. 3 Schematic of Device for Cooling Moist Air

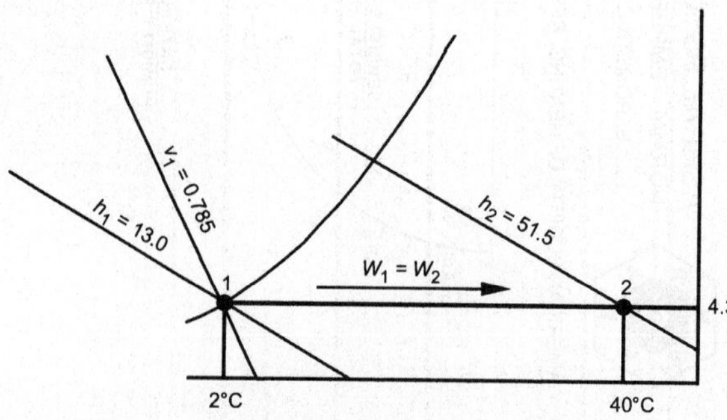

Fig. 4 Schematic Solution for Example 2

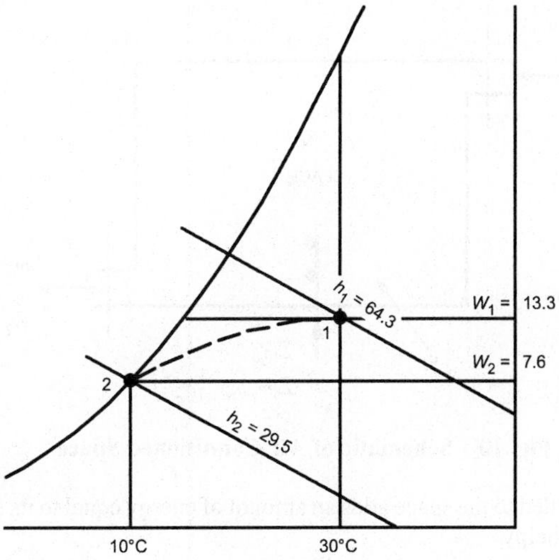

Fig. 5 Schematic Solution for Example 3

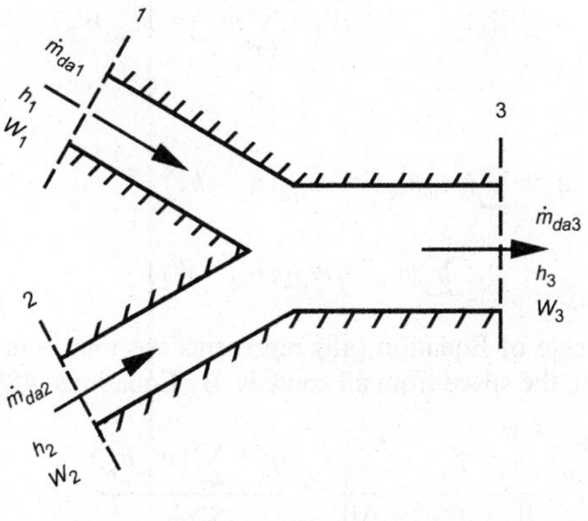

Fig. 6 Adiabatic Mixing of Two Moist Airstreams

Adiabatic Mixing of Two Moist Airstreams

A common process in air-conditioning systems is the adiabatic mixing of two moist airstreams. Figure 6 schematically shows the problem. Adiabatic mixing is governed by three equations:

$$\dot{m}_{da1}h_1 + \dot{m}_{da2}h_2 = \dot{m}_{da3}h_3$$
$$\dot{m}_{da1} + \dot{m}_{da2} = \dot{m}_{da3}$$
$$\dot{m}_{da1}W_1 + \dot{m}_{da2}W_2 = \dot{m}_{da3}W_3$$

Eliminating $\dot{m}_{da3}$ gives

$$\frac{h_2 - h_3}{h_3 - h_1} = \frac{W_2 - W_3}{W_3 - W_1} = \frac{\dot{m}_{da1}}{\dot{m}_{da2}} \quad (46)$$

according to which, on the ASHRAE chart, the state point of the resulting mixture lies on the straight line connecting the state points of the two streams being mixed, and divides the line into two segments, in the same ratio as the masses of dry air in the two streams.

Example 4. A stream of 2 m³/s of outdoor air at 4°C dry-bulb temperature and 2°C thermodynamic wet-bulb temperature is adiabatically mixed with 6.25 m³/s of recirculated air at 25°C dry-bulb temperature and 50% rh. Find the dry-bulb temperature and thermodynamic wet-bulb temperature of the resulting mixture.

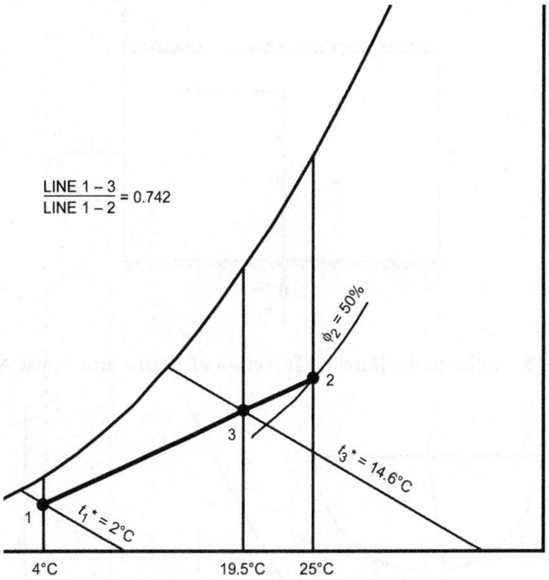

Fig. 7 Schematic Solution for Example 4

Solution: Figure 7 shows the schematic solution. States 1 and 2 are located on the ASHRAE chart: v_1 = 0.789 m³/kg$_{da}$, and v_2 = 0.858 m³/kg$_{da}$. Therefore,

$$\dot{m}_{da1} = 2 \S 0.789 = 2.535 \text{ kg}_{da}/\text{s}$$
$$\dot{m}_{da2} = 6.25 \S 0.858 = 7.284 \text{ kg}_{da}/\text{s}$$

According to Equation (46),

$$\frac{\text{Line 3–2}}{\text{Line 1–3}} = \frac{\dot{m}_{da1}}{\dot{m}_{da2}} \text{ or } \frac{\text{Line 1–3}}{\text{Line 1–2}} = \frac{\dot{m}_{da2}}{\dot{m}_{da3}} = \frac{7.284}{9.819} = 0.742$$

Consequently, the length of line segment 1–3 is 0.742 times the length of entire line 1–2. Using a ruler, State 3 is located, and the values t_3 = 19.5°C and t_3^* = 14.6°C found.

Adiabatic Mixing of Water Injected into Moist Air

Steam or liquid water can be injected into a moist airstream to raise its humidity, as shown in Figure 8. If mixing is adiabatic, the following equations apply:

$$\dot{m}_{da}h_1 + \dot{m}_w h_w = \dot{m}_{da}h_2$$
$$\dot{m}_{da}W_1 + \dot{m}_w = \dot{m}_{da}W_2$$

Therefore,

$$\frac{h_2 - h_1}{W_2 - W_1} = \frac{\Delta h}{\Delta W} = h_w \quad (47)$$

according to which, on the ASHRAE chart, the final state point of the moist air lies on a straight line in the direction fixed by the specific enthalpy of the injected water, drawn through the initial state point of the moist air.

Example 5. Moist air at 20°C dry-bulb and 8°C thermodynamic wet-bulb temperature is to be processed to a final dew-point temperature of 13°C by adiabatic injection of saturated steam at 110°C. The rate of dry airflow is 2 kg$_{da}$/s. Find the final dry-bulb temperature of the moist air and the rate of steam flow.

Solution: Figure 9 shows the schematic solution. By Table 3, the enthalpy of the steam h_g = 2691.07 kJ/kg$_w$. Therefore, according to Equation (47), the condition line on the ASHRAE chart connecting States 1 and 2 must have a direction:

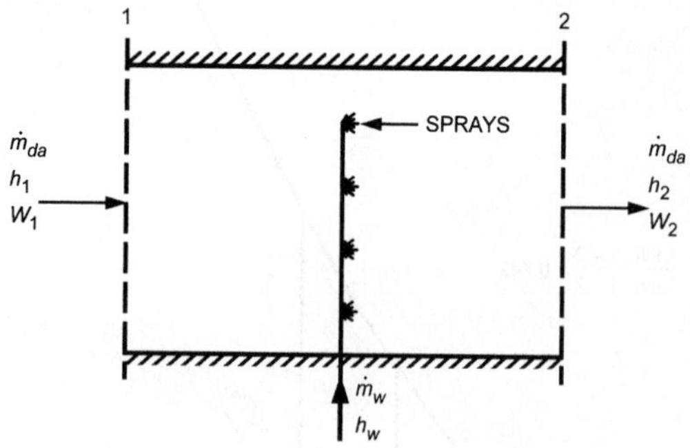

Fig. 8 Schematic Showing Injection of Water into Moist Air

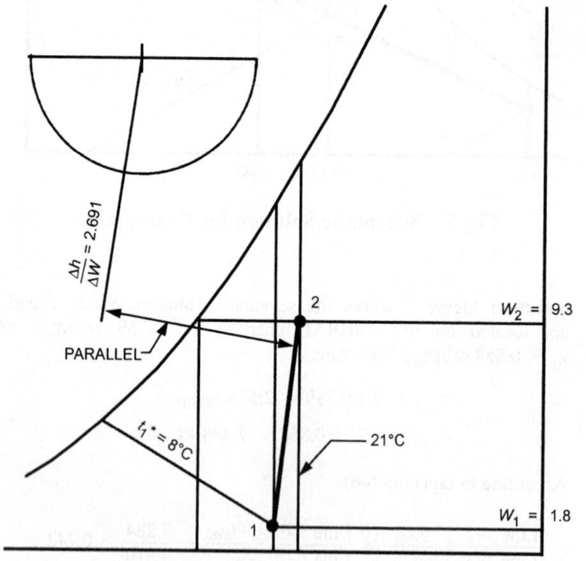

Fig. 9 Schematic Solution for Example 5

$$\Delta h/\Delta W = 2.691 \text{ kJ/g}_w$$

The condition line can be drawn with the $\Delta h/\Delta W$ protractor. First, establish the reference line on the protractor by connecting the origin with the value $\Delta h/\Delta W = 2.691$ kJ/g_w. Draw a second line parallel to the reference line and through the initial state point of the moist air. This second line is the condition line. State 2 is established at the intersection of the condition line with the horizontal line extended from the saturation curve at 13°C (t_{d2} = 13°C). Thus, t_2 = 21°C.

Values of W_2 and W_1 can be read from the chart. The required steam flow is,

$$\dot{m}_w = \dot{m}_{da}(W_2 - W_1) = 2 \times 1000(0.0093 - 0.0018)$$
$$= 15.0 \text{ kg}_w/\text{s}$$

Space Heat Absorption and Moist Air Moisture Gains

Air conditioning required for a space is usually determined by (1) the quantity of moist air to be supplied, and (2) the supply air condition necessary to remove given amounts of energy and water from the space at the exhaust condition specified.

Figure 10 shows a space with incident rates of energy and moisture gains. The quantity q_s denotes the net sum of all rates of heat gain in the space, arising from transfers through boundaries and from sources within the space. This heat gain involves energy addition alone and does not include energy contributions from water (or water vapor) addition. It is usually called the **sensible heat gain**. The quantity $\Sigma\dot{m}_w$ denotes the net sum of all rates of moisture gain on the space arising from transfers through boundaries and from sources within the space. Each kilogram of water

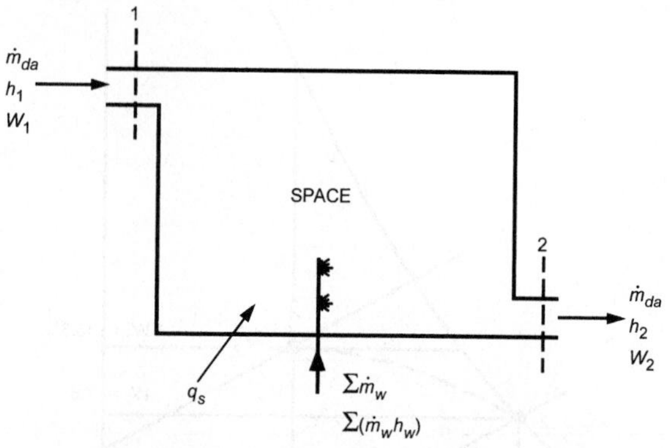

Fig. 10 Schematic of Air Conditioned Space

vapor added to the space adds an amount of energy equal to its specific enthalpy.

Assuming steady-state conditions, governing equations are

$$\dot{m}_{da}h_1 + q_s + \sum(\dot{m}_w h_w) = \dot{m}_{da}h_2$$

$$\dot{m}_{da}W_1 + \sum\dot{m}_w = \dot{m}_{da}W_2$$

or

$$q_s + \sum(\dot{m}_w h_w) = \dot{m}_{da}(h_2 - h_1) \quad (48)$$

$$\sum\dot{m}_w = \dot{m}_{da}(W_2 - W_1) \quad (49)$$

The left side of Equation (48) represents the total rate of energy addition to the space from all sources. By Equations (48) and (49),

$$\frac{h_2 - h_1}{W_2 - W_1} = \frac{\Delta h}{\Delta W} = \frac{q_s + \sum(\dot{m}_w h_w)}{\sum\dot{m}_w} \quad (50)$$

according to which, on the ASHRAE chart and for a given state of withdrawn air, all possible states (conditions) for supply air must lie on a straight line drawn through the state point of withdrawn air, with its direction specified by the numerical value of $[q_s + \Sigma(\dot{m}_w h_w)]/\Sigma\dot{m}_w$. This line is the condition line for the given problem.

Example 6. Moist air is withdrawn from a room at 25°C dry-bulb temperature and 19°C thermodynamic wet-bulb temperature. The sensible rate of heat gain for the space is 9 kW. A rate of moisture gain of 0.0015 kg_w/s occurs from the space occupants. This moisture is assumed as saturated water vapor at 30°C. Moist air is introduced into the room at a dry-bulb temperature of 15°C. Find the required thermodynamic wet-bulb temperature and volume flow rate of the supply air.

Solution: Figure 11 shows the schematic solution. State 2 is located on the ASHRAE chart. From Table 3, the specific enthalpy of the added water vapor is h_g = 2555.58 kJ/kg_w. From Equation (50),

$$\frac{\Delta h}{\Delta W} = \frac{9 + (0.0015 \times 2555.58)}{0.0015} = 8555 \text{ kJ/kg}_w$$

With the $\Delta h/\Delta W$ protractor, establish a reference line of direction $\Delta h/\Delta W$ = 8.555 kJ/g_w. Parallel to this reference line, draw a straight line on the chart through State 2. The intersection of this line with the 15°C dry-bulb temperature line is State 1. Thus, t_1^* = 14.0°C.

An alternative (and approximately correct) procedure in establishing the condition line is to use the protractor's sensible/total heat ratio scale instead of the $\Delta h/\Delta W$ scale. The quantity $\Delta H_s/\Delta H_t$ is the ratio of rate of sensible heat gain for the space to rate of total energy gain for the space. Therefore,

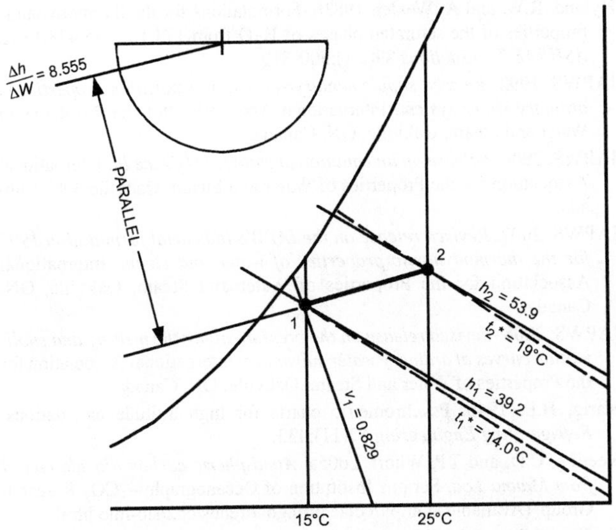

Fig. 11 Schematic Solution for Example 6

Table 4 Calculated Diffusion Coefficients for Water–Air at 101.325 kPa

Temp., °C	mm²/s	Temp., °C	mm²/s	Temp., °C	mm²/s
–70	13.2	0	22.2	50	29.5
–50	15.6	5	22.9	55	30.3
–40	16.9	10	23.6	60	31.1
–35	17.5	15	24.3	70	32.7
–30	18.2	20	25.1	100	37.6
–25	18.8	25	25.8	130	42.8
–20	19.5	30	26.5	160	48.3
–15	20.2	35	27.3	190	54.0
–10	20.8	40	28.0	220	60.0
–5	21.5	45	28.8	250	66.3

$$\frac{\Delta H_s}{\Delta H_t} = \frac{q_s}{q_s + \Sigma(\dot{m}_w h_w)} = \frac{9}{9 + (0.0015 \times 2555.58)} = 0.701$$

Note that $\Delta H_s/\Delta H_t = 0.701$ on the protractor coincides closely with $\Delta h/\Delta W = 8.555$ kJ/g$_w$.

The flow of dry air can be calculated from either Equation (48) or (49). From Equation (48),

$$\dot{m}_{da} = \frac{q_s + \Sigma(\dot{m}_w h_w)}{h_2 - h_1} = \frac{9 + (0.0015 \times 2555.58)}{53.9 - 39.2}$$

$$= 0.873 \text{ kg}_w/\text{s}$$

At State 1, $v_1 = 0.829 \text{ m}^3/\text{kg}_w$

Therefore, supply volume = $\dot{m}_{da} v_1 = 0.873 \times 0.829 = 0.724 \text{ m}^3/\text{s}$

TRANSPORT PROPERTIES OF MOIST AIR

For certain scientific and experimental work, particularly in the heat transfer field, many other moist air properties are important. Generally classified as transport properties, these include diffusion coefficient, viscosity, thermal conductivity, and thermal diffusion factor. Mason and Monchick (1965) derive these properties by calculation. Table 4 and Figures 12 and 13 summarize the authors' results on the first three properties listed. Note that, within the boundaries of ASHRAE Psychrometric Charts 1, 2, and 3, viscosity varies little from that of dry air at normal atmospheric pressure, and thermal conductivity is essentially independent of moisture content.

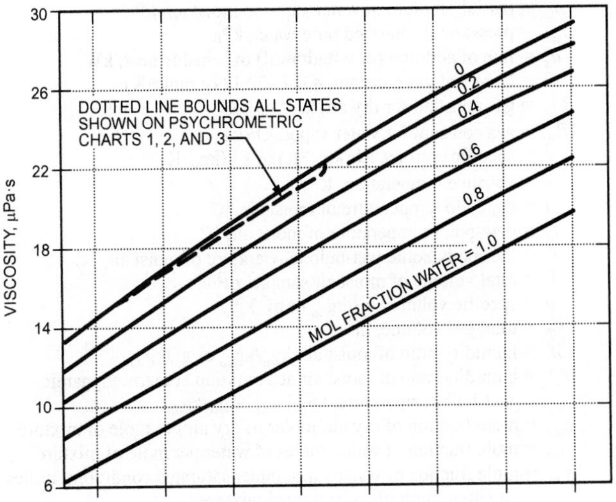

Fig. 12 Viscosity of Moist Air

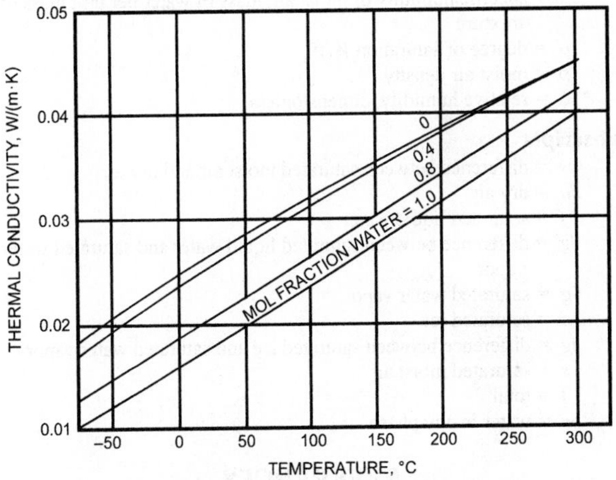

Fig. 13 Thermal Conductivity of Moist Air

SYMBOLS

C_1 to C_{18} = constants in Equations (5), (6), and (39)
d_v = absolute humidity of moist air, mass of water per unit volume of mixture, kg$_w$/m³
h = specific enthalpy of moist air, kJ/kg$_{da}$
H_s = rate of sensible heat gain for space, kW
h_s^* = specific enthalpy of saturated moist air at thermodynamic wet-bulb temperature, kJ/kg$_{da}$
H_t = rate of total energy gain for space, kW
h_w^* = specific enthalpy of condensed water (liquid or solid) at thermodynamic wet-bulb temperature and a pressure of 101.325 kPa, kJ/kg$_w$
M_{da} = mass of dry air in moist air sample, kg$_{da}$
$\dot{m}_{da}$ = mass flow of dry air, per unit time, kg$_{da}$/s
M_w = mass of water vapor in moist air sample, kg$_w$
$\dot{m}_w$ = mass flow of water (any phase), per unit time, kg$_w$/s
n = $n_{da} + n_w$, total number of moles in moist air sample
n_{da} = moles of dry air
n_w = moles of water vapor
p = total pressure of moist air, kPa
p_{da} = partial pressure of dry air, kPa
p_s = vapor pressure of water in moist air at saturation, kPa. Differs slightly from saturation pressure of pure water because of presence of air.

p_w = partial pressure of water vapor in moist air, kPa
p_{ws} = pressure of saturated pure water, kPa
q_s = rate of addition (or withdrawal) of sensible heat, kW
R = universal gas constant, 8314.472 J/(kg mole·K)
R_{da} = gas constant for dry air, kJ/(kg_{da}·K)
R_w = gas constant for water vapor, kJ/(kg_w·K)
s = specific entropy, kJ/(kg_{da}·K) or kJ/(kg_w·K)
T = absolute temperature, K
t = dry-bulb temperature of moist air, °C
t_d = dew-point temperature of moist air, °C
t^* = thermodynamic wet-bulb temperature of moist air, °C
V = total volume of moist air sample, m^3
v = specific volume, m^3/kg_{da} or m^3/kg_w
v_T = total gas volume, m^3
W = humidity ratio of moist air, kg_w/kg_{da} or g_w/kg_{da}
W_s^* = humidity ratio of moist air at saturation at thermodynamic wet-bulb temperature, kg_w/kg_{da} or g_w/kg_{da}
x_{da} = mole fraction of dry air, moles of dry air per mole of mixture
x_w = mole fraction of water, moles of water per mole of mixture
x_{ws} = mole fraction of water vapor under saturated conditions, moles of vapor per mole of saturated mixture
Z = altitude, m

Greek

α = $\ln(p_w)$, parameter used in Equations (39) and (40)
γ = specific humidity of moist air, mass of water per unit mass of mixture
μ = degree of saturation W/W_s
ρ = moist air density
ϕ = relative humidity, dimensionless

Subscripts

as = difference between saturated moist air and dry air
da = dry air
f = saturated liquid water
fg = difference between saturated liquid water and saturated water vapor
g = saturated water vapor
i = saturated ice
ig = difference between saturated ice and saturated water vapor
s = saturated moist air
t = total
w = water in any phase

REFERENCES

Gatley, D.P. 2005. *Understanding psychrometrics*, 2nd ed. ASHRAE.

Gatley, D.P. S. Herrmann, and H.J. Kretzschmar. 2008. A twenty-first century molar mass for dry air. *HVAC&R Research* 14:655-662.

Goff, J.A. 1949. Standardization of thermodynamic properties of moist air. *Heating, Piping, and Air Conditioning* 21(11):118-128.

Goff, J.A. and S. Gratch. 1945. Thermodynamic properties of moist air. *ASHVE Transactions* 51:125.

Haines, R.W. 1961. How to construct high altitude psychrometric charts. *Heating, Piping, and Air Conditioning* 33(10):144.

Harrison, L.P. 1965. Fundamental concepts and definitions relating to humidity. In *Humidity and moisture measurement and control in science and industry*, vol. 3. A. Wexler and W.A. Wildhack, eds. Reinhold, New York.

Herrmann, S., H.J. Kretzschmar, and D.P. Gatley. 2009. Thermodynamic properties of real moist air, dry air, steam, water, and ice. *HVAC&R Research* (forthcoming).

Hyland, R.W. and A. Wexler. 1983a. Formulations for the thermodynamic properties of dry air from 173.15 K to 473.15 K, and of saturated moist air from 173.15 K to 372.15 K, at pressures to 5 MPa. *ASHRAE Transactions* 89(2A):520-535.

Hyland, R.W. and A. Wexler. 1983b. Formulations for the thermodynamic properties of the saturated phases of H_2O from 173.15 K to 473.15 K. *ASHRAE Transactions* 89(2A):500-519.

IAPWS. 1992. *Revised supplementary release on saturation properties of ordinary water system.* International Association for the Properties of Water and Steam, Oakville, ON, Canada.

IAPWS. 2006. *Release on an equation of state for H_2O ice Ih.* International Association for the Properties of Water and Steam, Oakville, ON, Canada.

IAPWS. 2007. *Revised release on the IAPWS industrial formulation 1997 for the thermodynamic properties of water and steam.* International Association for the Properties of Water and Steam, Oakville, ON, Canada.

IAPWS. 2008. *Revised release on the pressure along the melting and sublimation curves of ordinary water substance.* International Association for the Properties of Water and Steam, Oakville, ON, Canada.

Karig, H.E. 1946. Psychrometric charts for high altitude calculations. *Refrigerating Engineering* 52(11):433.

Keeling, C.D. and T.P. Whorf. 2005a. *Atmospheric carbon dioxide record from Mauna Loa.* Scripps Institution of Oceanography—CO_2 Research Group. (Available at http://cdiac.ornl.gov/trends/co2/sio-mlo.html)

Keeling, C.D. and T.P. Whorf. 2005b. Atmospheric CO_2 records from sites in the SIO air sampling network. *Trends: A compendium of data on global change.* Carbon Dioxide Information Analysis Center, Oak Ridge National Laboratory.

Kuehn, T.H., J.W. Ramsey, and J.L. Threlkeld. 1998. *Thermal environmental engineering*, 3rd ed. Prentice-Hall, Upper Saddle River, NJ.

Lemmon, E.W., R.T. Jacobsen, S.G. Penoncello, and D.G. Friend. 2000. Thermodynamic properties of air and mixture of nitrogen, argon, and oxygen from 60 to 2000 K at pressures to 2000 MPa. *Journal of Physical and Chemical Reference Data* 29:331-385.

Mason, E.A. and L. Monchick. 1965. Survey of the equation of state and transport properties of moist gases. In *Humidity and moisture measurement and control in science and industry*, vol. 3. A. Wexler and W.A. Wildhack, eds. Reinhold, New York.

Mohr, P.J. and P.N. Taylor. 2005. CODATA recommended values of the fundamental physical constants: 2002. *Reviews of Modern Physics* 77:1-107.

NASA. 1976. U.S. Standard atmosphere, 1976. National Oceanic and Atmospheric Administration, National Aeronautics and Space Administration, and the United States Air Force. Available from National Geophysical Data Center, Boulder, CO.

Nelson, H.F. and H.J. Sauer, Jr. 2002. Formulation of high-temperature properties for moist air. *International Journal of HVAC&R Research* 8(3):311-334.

NIST. 1990. Guidelines for realizing the international temperature scale of 1990 (ITS-90). NIST *Technical Note* 1265. National Institute of Technology and Standards, Gaithersburg, MD.

Olivieri, J. 1996. *Psychrometrics—Theory and practice.* ASHRAE.

Palmatier, E.P. 1963. Construction of the normal temperature. ASHRAE psychrometric chart. *ASHRAE Journal* 5:55.

Peppers, V.W. 1988. *A new psychrometric relation for the dewpoint temperature.* Unpublished. Available from ASHRAE.

Preston-Thomas, H. 1990. The international temperature scale of 1990 (ITS-90). *Metrologia* 27(1):3-10.

Rohsenow, W.M. 1946. Psychrometric determination of absolute humidity at elevated pressures. *Refrigerating Engineering* 51(5):423.

BIBLIOGRAPHY

Kusuda, T. 1970. Algorithms for psychrometric calculations. NBS *Publication* BSS21 (January) for sale by Superintendent of Documents, U.S. Government Printing Office, Washington, D.C.

CHAPTER 2

THERMODYNAMICS AND REFRIGERATION CYCLES

THERMODYNAMICS is the study of energy, its transformations, and its relation to states of matter. This chapter covers the application of thermodynamics to refrigeration cycles. The first part reviews the first and second laws of thermodynamics and presents methods for calculating thermodynamic properties. The second and third parts address compression and absorption refrigeration cycles, two common methods of thermal energy transfer.

THERMODYNAMICS

A **thermodynamic system** is a region in space or a quantity of matter bounded by a closed surface. The surroundings include everything external to the system, and the system is separated from the surroundings by the system boundaries. These boundaries can be movable or fixed, real or imaginary.

Entropy and energy are important in any thermodynamic system. **Entropy** measures the molecular disorder of a system. The more mixed a system, the greater its entropy; an orderly or unmixed configuration is one of low entropy. **Energy** has the capacity for producing an effect and can be categorized into either stored or transient forms.

STORED ENERGY

Thermal (internal) energy is caused by the motion of molecules and/or intermolecular forces.

Potential energy (PE) is caused by attractive forces existing between molecules, or the elevation of the system.

$$\text{PE} = mgz \quad (1)$$

where

m = mass
g = local acceleration of gravity
z = elevation above horizontal reference plane

Kinetic energy (KE) is the energy caused by the velocity of molecules and is expressed as

$$\text{KE} = mV^2/2 \quad (2)$$

where V is the velocity of a fluid stream crossing the system boundary.

Chemical energy is caused by the arrangement of atoms composing the molecules.

Nuclear (atomic) energy derives from the cohesive forces holding protons and neutrons together as the atom's nucleus.

ENERGY IN TRANSITION

Heat Q is the mechanism that transfers energy across the boundaries of systems with differing temperatures, always toward the lower temperature. Heat is positive when energy is added to the system (see Figure 1).

Work is the mechanism that transfers energy across the boundaries of systems with differing pressures (or force of any kind), always toward the lower pressure. If the total effect produced in the system can be reduced to the raising of a weight, then nothing but work has crossed the boundary. Work is positive when energy is removed from the system (see Figure 1).

Mechanical or **shaft work** W is the energy delivered or absorbed by a mechanism, such as a turbine, air compressor, or internal combustion engine.

Flow work is energy carried into or transmitted across the system boundary because a pumping process occurs somewhere outside the system, causing fluid to enter the system. It can be more easily understood as the work done by the fluid just outside the system on the adjacent fluid entering the system to force or push it into the system. Flow work also occurs as fluid leaves the system.

$$\text{Flow work (per unit mass)} = pv \quad (3)$$

where p is the pressure and v is the specific volume, or the volume displaced per unit mass evaluated at the inlet or exit.

A **property** of a system is any observable characteristic of the system. The **state** of a system is defined by specifying the minimum

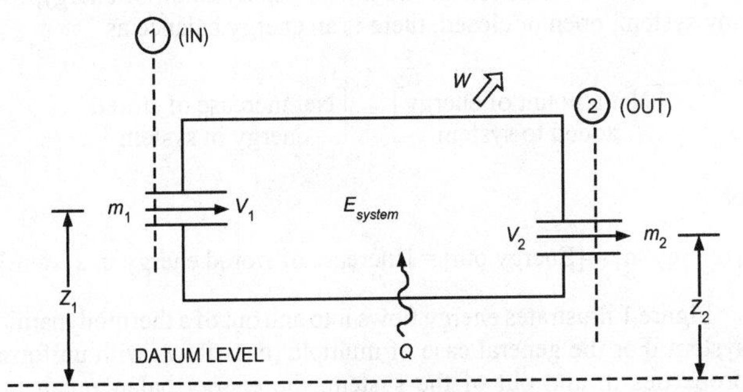

Fig. 1 Energy Flows in General Thermodynamic System

The preparation of the first and second parts of this chapter is assigned to TC 1.1, Thermodynamics and Psychrometrics. The third part is assigned to TC 8.3, Absorption and Heat-Operated Machines.

set of independent properties. The most common thermodynamic properties are temperature T, pressure p, and specific volume v or density ρ. Additional thermodynamic properties include entropy, stored forms of energy, and enthalpy.

Frequently, thermodynamic properties combine to form other properties. **Enthalpy h** is an important property that includes internal energy and flow work and is defined as

$$h \equiv u + pv \tag{4}$$

where u is the internal energy per unit mass.

Each property in a given state has only one definite value, and any property always has the same value for a given state, regardless of how the substance arrived at that state.

A **process** is a change in state that can be defined as any change in the properties of a system. A process is described by specifying the initial and final equilibrium states, the path (if identifiable), and the interactions that take place across system boundaries during the process.

A **cycle** is a process or a series of processes wherein the initial and final states of the system are identical. Therefore, at the conclusion of a cycle, all the properties have the same value they had at the beginning. Refrigerant circulating in a closed system undergoes a cycle.

A **pure substance** has a homogeneous and invariable chemical composition. It can exist in more than one phase, but the chemical composition is the same in all phases.

If a substance is liquid at the saturation temperature and pressure, it is called a **saturated liquid**. If the temperature of the liquid is lower than the saturation temperature for the existing pressure, it is called either a **subcooled liquid** (the temperature is lower than the saturation temperature for the given pressure) or a **compressed liquid** (the pressure is greater than the saturation pressure for the given temperature).

When a substance exists as part liquid and part vapor at the saturation temperature, its **quality** is defined as the ratio of the mass of vapor to the total mass. Quality has meaning only when the substance is saturated (i.e., at saturation pressure and temperature). Pressure and temperature of saturated substances are not independent properties.

If a substance exists as a vapor at saturation temperature and pressure, it is called a **saturated vapor**. (Sometimes the term **dry saturated vapor** is used to emphasize that the quality is 100%.) When the vapor is at a temperature greater than the saturation temperature, it is a **superheated vapor**. Pressure and temperature of a superheated vapor are independent properties, because the temperature can increase while pressure remains constant. Gases such as air at room temperature and pressure are highly superheated vapors.

FIRST LAW OF THERMODYNAMICS

The first law of thermodynamics is often called the **law of conservation of energy**. The following form of the first-law equation is valid only in the absence of a nuclear or chemical reaction.

Based on the first law or the law of conservation of energy, for any system, open or closed, there is an energy balance as

$$\begin{bmatrix}\text{Net amount of energy}\\ \text{added to system}\end{bmatrix} = \begin{bmatrix}\text{Net increase of stored}\\ \text{energy in system}\end{bmatrix}$$

or

[Energy in] – [Energy out] = [Increase of stored energy in system]

Figure 1 illustrates energy flows into and out of a thermodynamic system. For the general case of multiple mass flows with uniform properties in and out of the system, the energy balance can be written

$$\sum m_{in}\left(u + pv + \frac{V^2}{2} + gz\right)_{in} - \sum m_{out}\left(u + pv + \frac{V^2}{2} + gz\right)_{out} + Q - W = \left[m_f\left(u + \frac{V^2}{2} + gz\right)_f - m_i\left(u + \frac{V^2}{2} + gz\right)_i\right]_{system} \tag{5}$$

where subscripts i and f refer to the initial and final states, respectively.

Nearly all important engineering processes are commonly modeled as steady-flow processes. Steady flow signifies that all quantities associated with the system do not vary with time. Consequently,

$$\sum_{\substack{\text{all streams}\\ \text{entering}}} \dot{m}\left(h + \frac{V^2}{2} + gz\right) - \sum_{\substack{\text{all streams}\\ \text{leaving}}} \dot{m}\left(h + \frac{V^2}{2} + gz\right) + \dot{Q} - \dot{W} = 0 \tag{6}$$

where $h = u + pv$ as described in Equation (4).

A second common application is the closed stationary system for which the first law equation reduces to

$$Q - W = [m(u_f - u_i)]_{system} \tag{7}$$

SECOND LAW OF THERMODYNAMICS

The second law of thermodynamics differentiates and quantifies processes that only proceed in a certain direction (irreversible) from those that are reversible. The second law may be described in several ways. One method uses the concept of entropy flow in an open system and the irreversibility associated with the process. The concept of irreversibility provides added insight into the operation of cycles. For example, the larger the irreversibility in a refrigeration cycle operating with a given refrigeration load between two fixed temperature levels, the larger the amount of work required to operate the cycle. Irreversibilities include pressure drops in lines and heat exchangers, heat transfer between fluids of different temperature, and mechanical friction. Reducing total irreversibility in a cycle improves cycle performance. In the limit of no irreversibilities, a cycle attains its maximum ideal efficiency.

In an open system, the second law of thermodynamics can be described in terms of entropy as

$$dS_{system} = \frac{\delta Q}{T} + \delta m_i s_i - \delta m_e s_e + dI \tag{8}$$

where

dS_{system} = total change within system in time dt during process
$\delta m_i s_i$ = entropy increase caused by mass entering (incoming)
$\delta m_e s_e$ = entropy decrease caused by mass leaving (exiting)
$\delta Q/T$ = entropy change caused by reversible heat transfer between system and surroundings at temperature T
dI = entropy caused by irreversibilities (always positive)

Equation (8) accounts for all entropy changes in the system. Rearranged, this equation becomes

$$\delta Q = T[(\delta m_e s_e - \delta m_i s_i) + dS_{sys} - dI] \tag{9}$$

In integrated form, if inlet and outlet properties, mass flow, and interactions with the surroundings do not vary with time, the general equation for the second law is

$$(S_f - S_i)_{system} = \int_{rev} \frac{\delta Q}{T} + \sum (ms)_{in} - \sum (ms)_{out} + I \tag{10}$$

In many applications, the process can be considered to operate steadily with no change in time. The change in entropy of the system is therefore zero. The **irreversibility rate**, which is the rate of entropy production caused by irreversibilities in the process, can be determined by rearranging Equation (10):

$$\dot{I} = \sum(\dot{m}s)_{out} - \sum(\dot{m}s)_{in} - \sum\frac{\dot{Q}}{T_{surr}} \tag{11}$$

Equation (6) can be used to replace the heat transfer quantity. Note that the absolute temperature of the surroundings with which the system is exchanging heat is used in the last term. If the temperature of the surroundings is equal to the system temperature, heat is transferred reversibly and the last term in Equation (11) equals zero.

Equation (11) is commonly applied to a system with one mass flow in, the same mass flow out, no work, and negligible kinetic or potential energy flows. Combining Equations (6) and (11) yields

$$\dot{I} = \dot{m}\left[(s_{out} - s_{in}) - \frac{h_{out} - h_{in}}{T_{surr}}\right] \tag{12}$$

In a cycle, the reduction of work produced by a power cycle (or the increase in work required by a refrigeration cycle) equals the absolute ambient temperature multiplied by the sum of irreversibilities in all processes in the cycle. Thus, the difference in reversible and actual work for any refrigeration cycle, theoretical or real, operating under the same conditions, becomes

$$\dot{W}_{actual} = \dot{W}_{reversible} + T_0\sum\dot{I} \tag{13}$$

THERMODYNAMIC ANALYSIS OF REFRIGERATION CYCLES

Refrigeration cycles transfer thermal energy from a region of low temperature T_R to one of higher temperature. Usually the higher-temperature heat sink is the ambient air or cooling water, at temperature T_0, the temperature of the surroundings.

The first and second laws of thermodynamics can be applied to individual components to determine mass and energy balances and the irreversibility of the components. This procedure is illustrated in later sections in this chapter.

Performance of a refrigeration cycle is usually described by a **coefficient of performance (COP)**, defined as the benefit of the cycle (amount of heat removed) divided by the required energy input to operate the cycle:

$$\text{COP} \equiv \frac{\text{Useful refrigerating effect}}{\text{Net energy supplied from external sources}} \tag{14}$$

For a mechanical vapor compression system, the net energy supplied is usually in the form of work, mechanical or electrical, and may include work to the compressor and fans or pumps. Thus,

$$\text{COP} = \frac{Q_{evap}}{W_{net}} \tag{15}$$

In an absorption refrigeration cycle, the net energy supplied is usually in the form of heat into the generator and work into the pumps and fans, or

$$\text{COP} = \frac{Q_{evap}}{Q_{gen} + W_{net}} \tag{16}$$

In many cases, work supplied to an absorption system is very small compared to the amount of heat supplied to the generator, so the work term is often neglected.

Applying the second law to an entire refrigeration cycle shows that a completely reversible cycle operating under the same conditions has the maximum possible COP. Departure of the actual cycle from an ideal reversible cycle is given by the **refrigerating efficiency**:

$$\eta_R = \frac{\text{COP}}{(\text{COP})_{rev}} \tag{17}$$

The Carnot cycle usually serves as the ideal reversible refrigeration cycle. For multistage cycles, each stage is described by a reversible cycle.

EQUATIONS OF STATE

The equation of state of a pure substance is a mathematical relation between pressure, specific volume, and temperature. When the system is in thermodynamic equilibrium,

$$f(p,v,T) = 0 \tag{18}$$

The principles of statistical mechanics are used to (1) explore the fundamental properties of matter, (2) predict an equation of state based on the statistical nature of a particular system, or (3) propose a functional form for an equation of state with unknown parameters that are determined by measuring thermodynamic properties of a substance. A fundamental equation with this basis is the **virial equation**, which is expressed as an expansion in pressure p or in reciprocal values of volume per unit mass v as

$$\frac{pv}{RT} = 1 + B'p + C'p^2 + D'p^3 + \cdots \tag{19}$$

$$\frac{pv}{RT} = 1 + (B/v) + (C/v^2) + (D/v^3) + \cdots \tag{20}$$

where coefficients B', C', D', etc., and B, C, D, etc., are the virial coefficients. B' and B are the second virial coefficients; C' and C are the third virial coefficients, etc. The virial coefficients are functions of temperature only, and values of the respective coefficients in Equations (19) and (20) are related. For example, $B' = B/RT$ and $C' = (C - B^2)/(RT)^2$.

The universal gas constant $\bar{R}$ is defined as

$$\bar{R} = \lim_{p \to 0} \frac{(p\bar{v})_T}{T} \tag{21}$$

where $(p\bar{v})_T$ is the product of the pressure and the molar specific volume along an isotherm with absolute temperature T. The current best value of $\bar{R}$ is 8314.41 J/(kg mol·K). The gas constant R is equal to the universal gas constant $\bar{R}$ divided by the molecular mass M of the gas or gas mixture.

The quantity pv/RT is also called the **compressibility factor *Z***, or

$$Z = 1 + (B/v) + (C/v^2) + (D/v^3) + \cdots \tag{22}$$

An advantage of the virial form is that statistical mechanics can be used to predict the lower-order coefficients and provide physical significance to the virial coefficients. For example, in Equation (22), the term B/v is a function of interactions between two molecules, C/v^2 between three molecules, etc. Because lower-order interactions are common, contributions of the higher-order terms are successively less. Thermodynamicists use the partition or distribution function to determine virial coefficients; however, experimental values of the second and third coefficients are preferred. For dense fluids, many higher-order terms are necessary that can neither be satisfactorily predicted from theory nor determined from experimental measurements. In general, a truncated virial expansion of four terms is valid for densities of less than one-half the value at the critical point. For higher densities, additional terms can be used and determined empirically.

Computers allow the use of very complex equations of state in calculating p-v-T values, even to high densities. The Benedict-Webb-Rubin (B-W-R) equation of state (Benedict et al. 1940) and Martin-Hou equation (1955) have had considerable use, but should generally be limited to densities less than the critical value. Strobridge (1962) suggested a modified Benedict-Webb-Rubin relation that gives excellent results at higher densities and can be used for a p-v-T surface that extends into the liquid phase.

The B-W-R equation has been used extensively for hydrocarbons (Cooper and Goldfrank 1967):

$$P = (RT/v) + (B_oRT - A_o - C_o/T^2)/v^2 + (bRT - a)/v^3$$
$$+ (a\alpha)/v^6 + [c(1 + \gamma/v^2)e^{(-\gamma/v^2)}]/v^3T^2 \quad (23)$$

where the constant coefficients are A_o, B_o, C_o, a, b, c, α, and γ.

The Martin-Hou equation, developed for fluorinated hydrocarbon properties, has been used to calculate the thermodynamic property tables in Chapter 30 and in *ASHRAE Thermodynamic Properties of Refrigerants* (Stewart et al. 1986). The Martin-Hou equation is

$$p = \frac{RT}{v-b} + \frac{A_2 + B_2T + C_2e^{(-kT/T_c)}}{(v-b)^2} + \frac{A_3 + B_3T + C_3e^{(-kT/T_c)}}{(v-b)^3}$$
$$+ \frac{A_4 + B_4T}{(v-b)^4} + \frac{A_5 + B_5T + C_5e^{(-kT/T_c)}}{(v-b)^5} + (A_6 + B_6T)e^{av} \quad (24)$$

where the constant coefficients are A_i, B_i, C_i, k, b, and a.

Strobridge (1962) suggested an equation of state that was developed for nitrogen properties and used for most cryogenic fluids. This equation combines the B-W-R equation of state with an equation for high-density nitrogen suggested by Benedict (1937). These equations have been used successfully for liquid and vapor phases, extending in the liquid phase to the triple-point temperature and the freezing line, and in the vapor phase from 10 to 1000 K, with pressures to 1 GPa. The Strobridge equation is accurate within the uncertainty of the measured p-v-T data:

$$p = RT\rho + \left[Rn_1T + n_2 + \frac{n_3}{T} + \frac{n_4}{T^2} + \frac{n_5}{T^4}\right]\rho^2$$
$$+ (Rn_6T + n_7)\rho^3 + n_8T\rho^4$$
$$+ \rho^3\left[\frac{n_9}{T^2} + \frac{n_{10}}{T^3} + \frac{n_{11}}{T^4}\right]\exp(-n_{16}\rho^2)$$
$$+ \rho^5\left[\frac{n_{12}}{T^2} + \frac{n_{13}}{T^3} + \frac{n_{14}}{T^4}\right]\exp(-n_{16}\rho^2) + n_{15}\rho^6 \quad (25)$$

The 15 coefficients of this equation's linear terms are determined by a least-square fit to experimental data. Hust and McCarty (1967) and Hust and Stewart (1966) give further information on methods and techniques for determining equations of state.

In the absence of experimental data, Van der Waals' principle of corresponding states can predict fluid properties. This principle relates properties of similar substances by suitable reducing factors (i.e., the p-v-T surfaces of similar fluids in a given region are assumed to be of similar shape). The critical point can be used to define reducing parameters to scale the surface of one fluid to the dimensions of another. Modifications of this principle, as suggested by Kamerlingh Onnes, a Dutch cryogenic researcher, have been used to improve correspondence at low pressures. The principle of corresponding states provides useful approximations, and numerous modifications have been reported. More complex treatments for predicting properties, which recognize similarity of fluid properties, are by generalized equations of state. These equations ordinarily allow adjustment of the p-v-T surface by introducing parameters. One example (Hirschfelder et al. 1958) allows for departures from the principle of corresponding states by adding two correlating parameters.

CALCULATING THERMODYNAMIC PROPERTIES

Although equations of state provide p-v-T relations, thermodynamic analysis usually requires values for internal energy, enthalpy, and entropy. These properties have been tabulated for many substances, including refrigerants (see Chapters 1, 30, and 33), and can be extracted from such tables by interpolating manually or with a suitable computer program. This approach is appropriate for hand calculations and for relatively simple computer models; however, for many computer simulations, the overhead in memory or input and output required to use tabulated data can make this approach unacceptable. For large thermal system simulations or complex analyses, it may be more efficient to determine internal energy, enthalpy, and entropy using fundamental thermodynamic relations or curves fit to experimental data. Some of these relations are discussed in the following sections. Also, the thermodynamic relations discussed in those sections are the basis for constructing tables of thermodynamic property data. Further information on the topic may be found in references covering system modeling and thermodynamics (Howell and Buckius 1992; Stoecker 1989).

At least two intensive properties (properties independent of the quantity of substance, such as temperature, pressure, specific volume, and specific enthalpy) must be known to determine the remaining properties. If two known properties are either p, v, or T (these are relatively easy to measure and are commonly used in simulations), the third can be determined throughout the range of interest using an equation of state. Furthermore, if the specific heats at zero pressure are known, specific heat can be accurately determined from spectroscopic measurements using statistical mechanics (NASA 1971). Entropy may be considered a function of T and p, and from calculus an infinitesimal change in entropy can be written as

$$ds = \left(\frac{\partial s}{\partial T}\right)_p dT + \left(\frac{\partial s}{\partial p}\right)_T dp \quad (26)$$

Likewise, a change in enthalpy can be written as

$$dh = \left(\frac{\partial h}{\partial T}\right)_p dT + \left(\frac{\partial h}{\partial p}\right)_T dp \quad (27)$$

Using the Gibbs relation $Tds = dh - vdp$ and the definition of specific heat at constant pressure, $c_p \equiv (\partial h/\partial T)_p$, Equation (27) can be rearranged to yield

$$ds = \frac{c_p}{T}dT + \left[\left(\frac{\partial h}{\partial p}\right)_T - v\right]\frac{dp}{T} \quad (28)$$

Equations (26) and (28) combine to yield $(\partial s/\partial T)_p = c_p/T$. Then, using the Maxwell relation $(\partial s/\partial p)_T = -(\partial v/\partial T)_p$, Equation (26) may be rewritten as

$$ds = \frac{c_p}{T}dT - \left(\frac{\partial v}{\partial T}\right)_p dp \quad (29)$$

This is an expression for an exact derivative, so it follows that

$$\left(\frac{\partial c_p}{\partial p}\right)_T = -T\left(\frac{\partial^2 v}{\partial T^2}\right)_p \quad (30)$$

Integrating this expression at a fixed temperature yields

$$c_p = c_{p0} - \int_0^p T\left(\frac{\partial^2 v}{\partial T^2}\right) dp_T \quad (31)$$

where c_{p0} is the known zero-pressure specific heat, and dp_T is used to indicate that integration is performed at a fixed temperature. The second partial derivative of specific volume with respect to temperature can be determined from the equation of state. Thus, Equation (31) can be used to determine the specific heat at any pressure.

Using $Tds = dh - vdp$, Equation (29) can be written as

$$dh = c_p dT + \left[v - T\left(\frac{\partial v}{\partial T}\right)_p\right] dp \quad (32)$$

Equations (28) and (32) may be integrated at constant pressure to obtain

$$s(T_1, p_0) = s(T_0, p_0) + \int_{T_0}^{T_1} \frac{c_p}{T} dT_p \quad (33)$$

and

$$h(T_1, p_0) = h(T_0, p_0) + \int_{T_0}^{T_1} c_p dT \quad (34)$$

Integrating the Maxwell relation $(\partial s/\partial p)_T = -(\partial v/\partial T)_p$ gives an equation for entropy changes at a constant temperature as

$$s(T_0, p_1) = s(T_0, p_0) - \int_{p_0}^{p_1} \left(\frac{\partial v}{\partial T}\right)_p dp_T \quad (35)$$

Likewise, integrating Equation (32) along an isotherm yields the following equation for enthalpy changes at a constant temperature:

$$h(T_0, p_1) = h(T_0, p_0) + \int_{p_0}^{p_1} \left[v - T\left(\frac{\partial v}{\partial T}\right)_p\right] dp \quad (36)$$

Internal energy can be calculated from $u = h - pv$. When entropy or enthalpy are known at a reference temperature T_0 and pressure p_0, values at any temperature and pressure may be obtained by combining Equations (33) and (35) or Equations (34) and (36).

Combinations (or variations) of Equations (33) through (36) can be incorporated directly into computer subroutines to calculate properties with improved accuracy and efficiency. However, these equations are restricted to situations where the equation of state is valid and the properties vary continuously. These restrictions are violated by a change of phase such as evaporation and condensation, which are essential processes in air-conditioning and refrigerating devices. Therefore, the Clapeyron equation is of particular value; for evaporation or condensation, it gives

$$\left(\frac{dp}{dT}\right)_{sat} = \frac{s_{fg}}{v_{fg}} = \frac{h_{fg}}{Tv_{fg}} \quad (37)$$

where

s_{fg} = entropy of vaporization
h_{fg} = enthalpy of vaporization
v_{fg} = specific volume difference between vapor and liquid phases

If vapor pressure and liquid and vapor density data (all relatively easy measurements to obtain) are known at saturation, then changes in enthalpy and entropy can be calculated using Equation (37).

Phase Equilibria for Multicomponent Systems

To understand phase equilibria, consider a container full of a liquid made of two components; the more volatile component is designated *i* and the less volatile component *j* (Figure 2A). This mixture is all liquid because the temperature is low (but not so low that a solid appears). Heat added at a constant pressure raises the mixture's temperature, and a sufficient increase causes vapor to form, as shown in Figure 2B. If heat at constant pressure continues to be added, eventually the temperature becomes so high that only vapor remains in the container (Figure 2C). A temperature-concentration (T-x) diagram is useful for exploring details of this situation.

Figure 3 is a typical T-x diagram valid at a fixed pressure. The case shown in Figure 2A, a container full of liquid mixture with mole fraction $x_{i,0}$ at temperature T_0, is point 0 on the T-x diagram. When heat is added, the temperature of the mixture increases. The point at which vapor begins to form is the **bubble point**. Starting at point 0, the first bubble forms at temperature T_1 (point 1 on the diagram). The locus of bubble points is the **bubble-point curve**, which provides bubble points for various liquid mole fractions x_i.

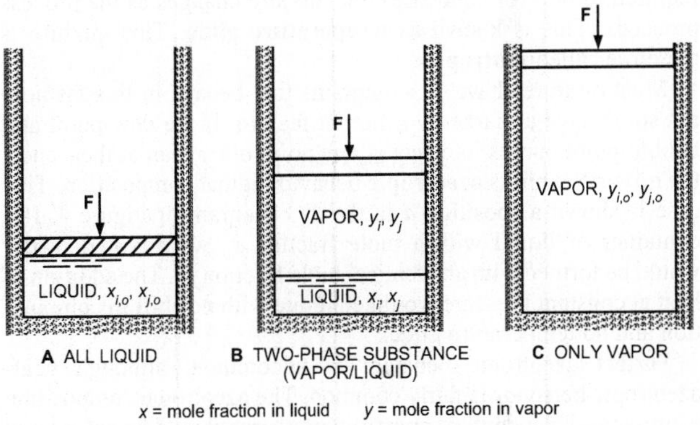

Fig. 2 Mixture of *i* and *j* Components in Constant-Pressure Container

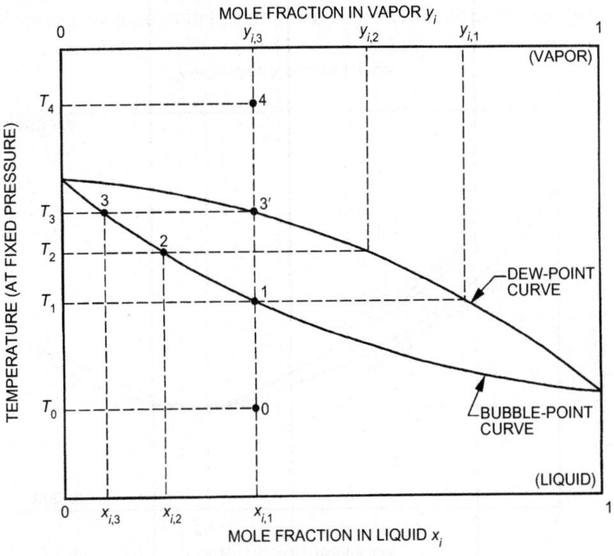

Fig. 3 Temperature-Concentration (*T*-*x*) Diagram for Zeotropic Mixture

When the first bubble begins to form, the vapor in the bubble may not have the same mole fraction as the liquid mixture. Rather, the mole fraction of the more volatile species is higher in the vapor than in the liquid. Boiling prefers the more volatile species, and the T-x diagram shows this behavior. At T_1, the vapor-forming bubbles have an i mole fraction of $y_{i,1}$. If heat continues to be added, this preferential boiling depletes the liquid of species i and the temperature required to continue the process increases. Again, the T-x diagram reflects this fact; at point 2 the i mole fraction in the liquid is reduced to $x_{i,2}$ and the vapor has a mole fraction of $y_{i,2}$. The temperature required to boil the mixture is increased to T_2. Position 2 on the T-x diagram could correspond to the physical situation shown in Figure 2B.

If constant-pressure heating continues, all the liquid eventually becomes vapor at temperature T_3. The vapor at this point is shown as position 3′ in Figure 3. At this point the i mole fraction in the vapor $y_{i,3}$ equals the starting mole fraction in the all-liquid mixture $x_{i,1}$. This equality is required for mass and species conservation. Further addition of heat simply raises the vapor temperature. The final position 4 corresponds to the physical situation shown in Figure 2C.

Starting at position 4 in Figure 3, heat removal leads to initial liquid formation when position 3′ (the **dew point**) is reached.The locus of dew points is called the **dew-point curve**. Heat removal causes the liquid phase of the mixture to reverse through points 3, 2, 1, and to starting point 0. Because the composition shifts, the temperature required to boil (or condense) this mixture changes as the process proceeds. This is known as **temperature glide**. This mixture is therefore called **zeotropic**.

Most mixtures have T-x diagrams that behave in this fashion, but some have a markedly different feature. If the dew-point and bubble-point curves intersect at any point other than at their ends, the mixture exhibits **azeotropic** behavior at that composition. This case is shown as position a in the T-x diagram of Figure 4. If a container of liquid with a mole fraction x_a were boiled, vapor would be formed with an identical mole fraction y_a. The addition of heat at constant pressure would continue with no shift in composition and no temperature glide.

Perfect azeotropic behavior is uncommon, although near-azeotropic behavior is fairly common. The azeotropic composition is pressure-dependent, so operating pressures should be considered for their effect on mixture behavior. Azeotropic and near-azeotropic refrigerant mixtures are widely used. The properties of an azeotropic mixture are such that they may be conveniently treated as pure substance properties. Phase equilibria for zeotropic mixtures, however, require special treatment, using an equation-of-state approach with appropriate mixing rules or using the fugacities with the standard state method (Tassios 1993). Refrigerant and lubricant blends are a zeotropic mixture and can be treated by these methods (Martz et al. 1996a, 1996b; Thome 1995).

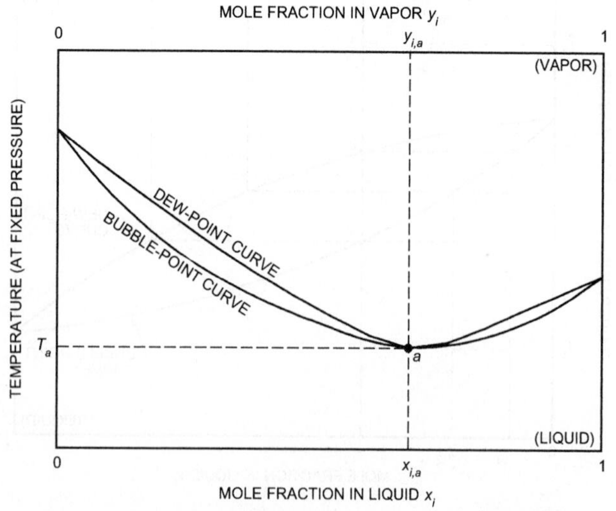

Fig. 4 Azeotropic Behavior Shown on T-x Diagram

COMPRESSION REFRIGERATION CYCLES

CARNOT CYCLE

The Carnot cycle, which is completely reversible, is a perfect model for a refrigeration cycle operating between two fixed temperatures, or between two fluids at different temperatures and each with infinite heat capacity. Reversible cycles have two important properties: (1) no refrigerating cycle may have a coefficient of performance higher than that for a reversible cycle operated between the same temperature limits, and (2) all reversible cycles, when operated between the same temperature limits, have the same coefficient of performance. Proof of both statements may be found in almost any textbook on elementary engineering thermodynamics.

Figure 5 shows the Carnot cycle on temperature-entropy coordinates. Heat is withdrawn at constant temperature T_R from the region to be refrigerated. Heat is rejected at constant ambient temperature T_0. The cycle is completed by an isentropic expansion and an isentropic compression. The energy transfers are given by

$$Q_0 = T_0(S_2 - S_3)$$

$$Q_i = T_R(S_1 - S_4) = T_R(S_2 - S_3)$$

$$W_{net} = Q_o - Q_i$$

Thus, by Equation (15),

$$\text{COP} = \frac{T_R}{T_0 - T_R} \qquad (38)$$

Example 1. Determine entropy change, work, and COP for the cycle shown in Figure 6. Temperature of the refrigerated space T_R is 250 K, and that of the atmosphere T_0 is 300 K. Refrigeration load is 125 kJ.

Solution:

$$\Delta S = S_1 - S_4 = Q_i/T_R = 125/250 = 0.5 \text{ kJ/K}$$

$$W = \Delta S(T_0 - T_R) = 0.5(300 - 250) = 25 \text{ kJ}$$

$$\text{COP} = Q_i/(Q_o - Q_i) = Q_i/W = 125/25 = 5$$

Flow of energy and its area representation in Figure 6 are

Energy	kJ	Area
Q_i	125	b
Q_o	150	$a + b$
W	25	a

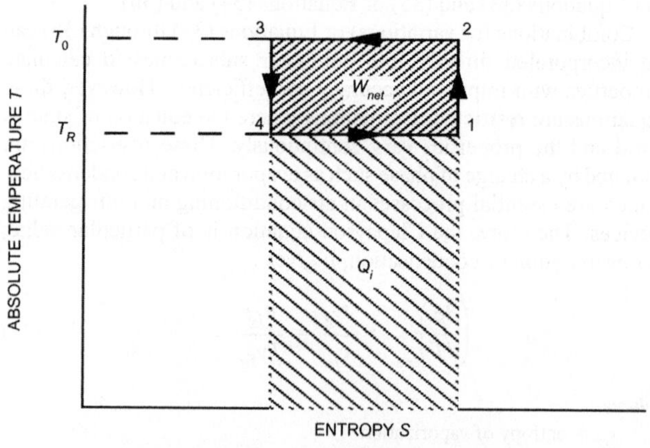

Fig. 5 Carnot Refrigeration Cycle

The net change of entropy of any refrigerant in any cycle is always zero. In Example 1, the change in entropy of the refrigerated space is $\Delta S_R = -125/250 = -0.5$ kJ/K and that of the atmosphere is $\Delta S_o = 125/250 = 0.5$ kJ/K. The net change in entropy of the isolated system is $\Delta S_{total} = \Delta S_R + \Delta S_o = 0$.

The Carnot cycle in Figure 7 shows a process in which heat is added and rejected at constant pressure in the two-phase region of a refrigerant. Saturated liquid at state 3 expands isentropically to the low temperature and pressure of the cycle at state d. Heat is added isothermally and isobarically by evaporating the liquid-phase refrigerant from state d to state 1. The cold saturated vapor at state 1 is compressed isentropically to the high temperature in the cycle at state b. However, the pressure at state b is below the saturation pressure corresponding to the high temperature in the cycle. The compression process is completed by an isothermal compression process from state b to state c. The cycle is completed by an isothermal and isobaric heat rejection or condensing process from state c to state 3.

Applying the energy equation for a mass of refrigerant m yields (all work and heat transfer are positive)

$$ {}_3W_d = m(h_3 - h_d) $$

$$ {}_1W_b = m(h_b - h_1) $$

$$ {}_bW_c = T_0(S_b - S_c) - m(h_b - h_c) $$

$$ {}_dQ_1 = m(h_1 - h_d) = \text{Area defld} $$

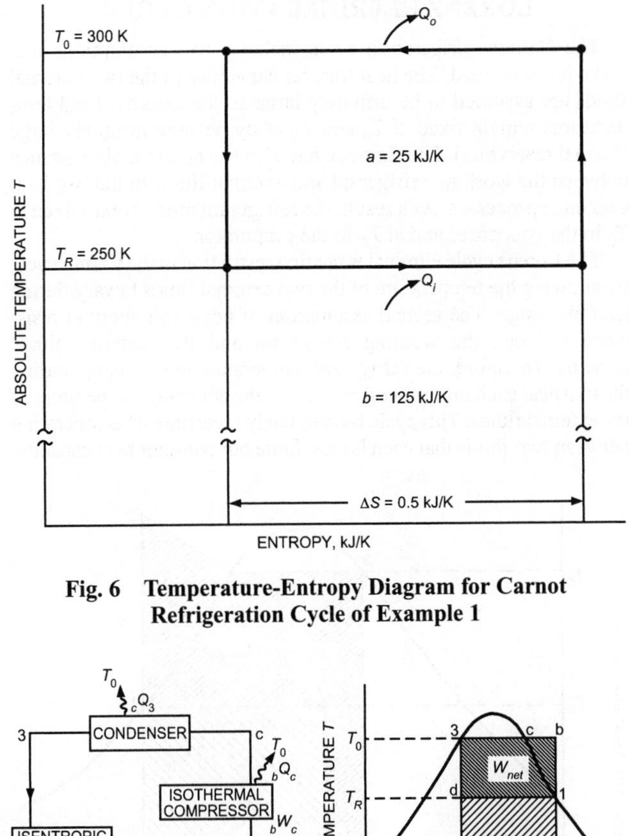

Fig. 6 Temperature-Entropy Diagram for Carnot Refrigeration Cycle of Example 1

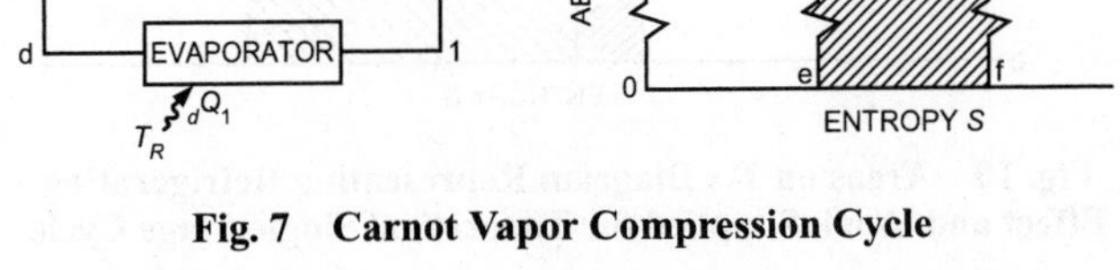

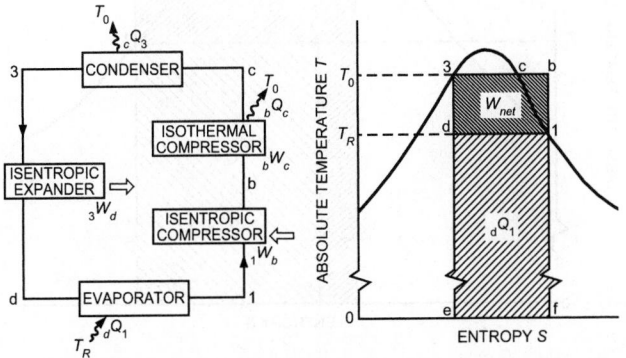

Fig. 7 Carnot Vapor Compression Cycle

The net work for the cycle is

$$ W_{net} = {}_1W_b + {}_bW_c - {}_3W_d = \text{Area d1bc3d} $$

and

$$ \text{COP} = \frac{{}_dQ_1}{W_{net}} = \frac{T_R}{T_0 - T_R} $$

THEORETICAL SINGLE-STAGE CYCLE USING A PURE REFRIGERANT OR AZEOTROPIC MIXTURE

A system designed to approach the ideal model shown in Figure 7 is desirable. A pure refrigerant or azeotropic mixture can be used to maintain constant temperature during phase changes by maintaining constant pressure. Because of concerns such as high initial cost and increased maintenance requirements, a practical machine has one compressor instead of two and the expander (engine or turbine) is replaced by a simple expansion valve, which throttles refrigerant from high to low pressure. Figure 8 shows the theoretical single-stage cycle used as a model for actual systems.

Applying the energy equation for a mass m of refrigerant yields

$$ {}_4Q_1 = m(h_1 - h_4) \tag{39a} $$

$$ {}_1W_2 = m(h_2 - h_1) \tag{39b} $$

$$ {}_2Q_3 = m(h_2 - h_3) \tag{39c} $$

$$ h_3 = h_4 \tag{39d} $$

Constant-enthalpy throttling assumes no heat transfer or change in potential or kinetic energy through the expansion valve.

The coefficient of performance is

$$ \text{COP} = \frac{{}_4Q_1}{{}_1W_2} = \frac{h_1 - h_4}{h_2 - h_1} \tag{40} $$

The theoretical compressor displacement CD (at 100% volumetric efficiency) is

$$ \text{CD} = \dot{m}v_1 \tag{41} $$

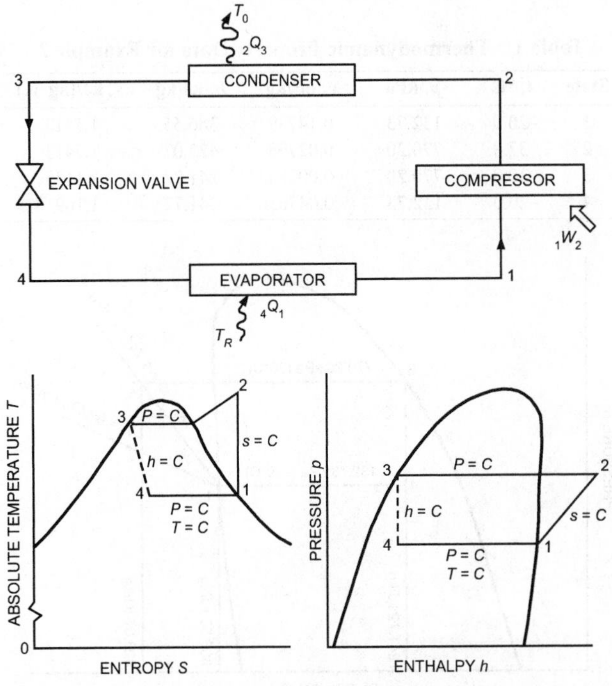

Fig. 8 Theoretical Single-Stage Vapor Compression Refrigeration Cycle

which is a measure of the physical size or speed of the compressor required to handle the prescribed refrigeration load.

Example 2. A theoretical single-stage cycle using R-134a as the refrigerant operates with a condensing temperature of 30°C and an evaporating temperature of −20°C. The system produces 50 kW of refrigeration. Determine the (a) thermodynamic property values at the four main state points of the cycle, (b) COP, (c) cycle refrigerating efficiency, and (d) rate of refrigerant flow.

Solution:

(a) Figure 9 shows a schematic *p-h* diagram for the problem with numerical property data. Saturated vapor and saturated liquid properties for states 1 and 3 are obtained from the saturation table for R-134a in Chapter 30. Properties for superheated vapor at state 2 are obtained by linear interpolation of the superheat tables for R-134a in Chapter 30. Specific volume and specific entropy values for state 4 are obtained by determining the quality of the liquid-vapor mixture from the enthalpy.

$$x_4 = \frac{h_4 - h_f}{h_g - h_f} = \frac{241.72 - 173.64}{386.55 - 173.64} = 0.3198$$

$$v_4 = v_f + x_4(v_g - v_f) = 0.0007362 + 0.3198(0.14739 - 0.0007362)$$
$$= 0.04764 \text{ m}^3/\text{kg}$$

$$s_4 = s_f + x_4(s_g - s_f) = 0.9002 + 0.3198(1.7413 - 0.9002)$$
$$= 1.16918 \text{ kJ/(kg·K)}$$

The property data are tabulated in Table 1.

(b) By Equation (40),

$$\text{COP} = \frac{386.55 - 241.71}{423.07 - 386.55} = 3.97$$

(c) By Equations (17) and (38),

$$\eta_R = \frac{\text{COP}(T_3 - T_1)}{T_1} = \frac{(3.97)(50)}{253.15} = 0.78 \text{ or } 78\%$$

(d) The mass flow of refrigerant is obtained from an energy balance on the evaporator. Thus,

$$\dot{m}(h_1 - h_4) = \dot{Q}_i = 50 \text{ kW}$$

Table 1 Thermodynamic Property Data for Example 2

State	t, °C	p, kPa	v, m³/kg	h, kJ/kg	s, kJ/(kg·K)
1	−20.0	132.73	0.14739	386.55	1.7413
2	37.8	770.20	0.02798	423.07	1.7413
3	30.0	770.20	0.000842	241.72	1.1435
4	−20.0	132.73	0.047636	241.72	1.16918

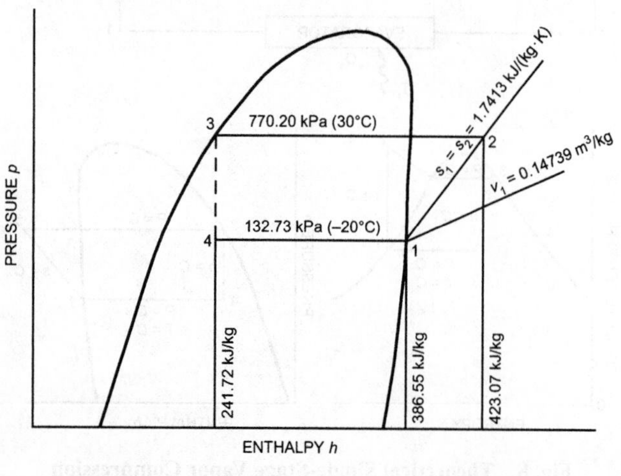

Fig. 9 Schematic *p-h* Diagram for Example 2

and

$$\dot{m} = \frac{\dot{Q}_i}{(h_1 - h_4)} = \frac{50}{(386.55 - 241.72)} = 0.345 \text{ kg/s}$$

The saturation temperatures of the single-stage cycle strongly influence the magnitude of the coefficient of performance. This influence may be readily appreciated by an area analysis on a temperature-entropy (*T-s*) diagram. The area under a reversible process line on a *T-s* diagram is directly proportional to the thermal energy added or removed from the working fluid. This observation follows directly from the definition of entropy [see Equation (8)].

In Figure 10, the area representing Q_o is the total area under the constant-pressure curve between states 2 and 3. The area representing the refrigerating capacity Q_i is the area under the constant pressure line connecting states 4 and 1. The net work required W_{net} equals the difference $(Q_o - Q_i)$, which is represented by the shaded area shown on Figure 10.

Because COP = Q_i/W_{net}, the effect on the COP of changes in evaporating temperature and condensing temperature may be observed. For example, a decrease in evaporating temperature T_E significantly increases W_{net} and slightly decreases Q_i. An increase in condensing temperature T_C produces the same results but with less effect on W_{net}. Therefore, for maximum coefficient of performance, the cycle should operate at the lowest possible condensing temperature and maximum possible evaporating temperature.

LORENZ REFRIGERATION CYCLE

The Carnot refrigeration cycle includes two assumptions that make it impractical. The heat transfer capacities of the two external fluids are assumed to be infinitely large so the external fluid temperatures remain fixed at T_0 and T_R (they become infinitely large thermal reservoirs). The Carnot cycle also has no thermal resistance between the working refrigerant and external fluids in the two heat exchange processes. As a result, the refrigerant must remain fixed at T_0 in the condenser and at T_R in the evaporator.

The Lorenz cycle eliminates the first restriction in the Carnot cycle by allowing the temperature of the two external fluids to vary during heat exchange. The second assumption of negligible thermal resistance between the working refrigerant and two external fluids remains. Therefore, the refrigerant temperature must change during the two heat exchange processes to equal the changing temperature of the external fluids. This cycle is completely reversible when operating between two fluids that each have a finite but constant heat capacity.

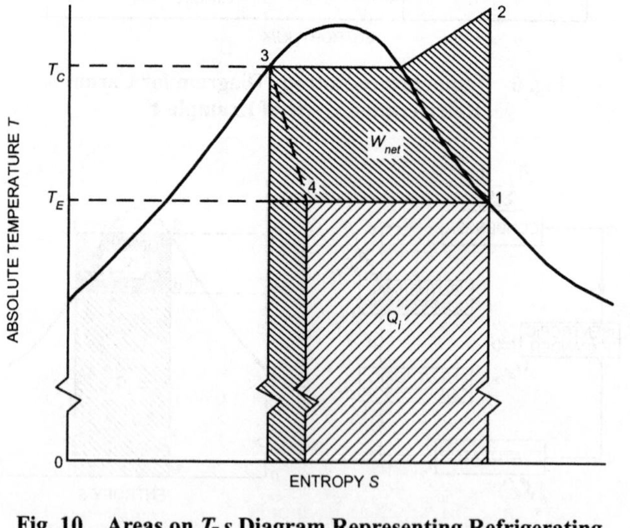

Fig. 10 Areas on *T-s* Diagram Representing Refrigerating Effect and Work Supplied for Theoretical Single-Stage Cycle

Figure 11 is a schematic of a Lorenz cycle. Note that this cycle does not operate between two fixed temperature limits. Heat is added to the refrigerant from state 4 to state 1. This process is assumed to be linear on *T-s* coordinates, which represents a fluid with constant heat capacity. The refrigerant temperature is increased in isentropic compression from state 1 to state 2. Process 2-3 is a heat rejection process in which the refrigerant temperature decreases linearly with heat transfer. The cycle ends with isentropic expansion between states 3 and 4.

The heat addition and heat rejection processes are parallel so the entire cycle is drawn as a parallelogram on *T-s* coordinates. A Carnot refrigeration cycle operating between T_0 and T_R would lie between states 1, a, 3, and b; the Lorenz cycle has a smaller refrigerating effect and requires more work, but this cycle is a more practical reference when a refrigeration system operates between two single-phase fluids such as air or water.

The energy transfers in a Lorenz refrigeration cycle are as follows, where ΔT is the temperature change of the refrigerant during each of the two heat exchange processes.

$$Q_o = (T_0 + \Delta T/2)(S_2 - S_3)$$

$$Q_i = (T_R - \Delta T/2)(S_1 - S_4) = (T_R - \Delta T/2)(S_2 - S_3)$$

$$W_{net} = Q_o - Q_R$$

Thus by Equation (15),

$$\text{COP} = \frac{T_R - (\Delta T/2)}{T_0 - T_R + \Delta T} \quad (42)$$

Example 3. Determine the entropy change, work required, and COP for the Lorenz cycle shown in Figure 11 when the temperature of the refrigerated space is T_R = 250 K, ambient temperature is T_0 = 300 K, ΔT of the refrigerant is 5 K, and refrigeration load is 125 kJ.

Solution:

$$\Delta S = \int_4^1 \frac{\delta Q_i}{T} = \frac{Q_i}{T_R - (\Delta T/2)} = \frac{125}{247.5} = 0.5051 \text{ kJ/K}$$

$$Q_o = [T_0 + (\Delta T/2)]\Delta S = (300 + 2.5)0.5051 = 152.78 \text{ kJ}$$

$$W_{net} = Q_o - Q_R = 152.78 - 125 = 27.78 \text{ kJ}$$

$$\text{COP} = \frac{T_R - (\Delta T/2)}{T_0 - T_R + \Delta T} = \frac{250 - (5/2)}{300 - 250 + 5} = \frac{247.5}{55} = 4.50$$

Note that the entropy change for the Lorenz cycle is larger than for the Carnot cycle when both operate between the same two temperature reservoirs and have the same capacity (see Example 1). That is, both the heat rejection and work requirement are larger for the Lorenz cycle. This difference is caused by the finite temperature difference between the working fluid in the cycle compared to the bounding temperature reservoirs. However, as discussed previously, the assumption of constant-temperature heat reservoirs is not necessarily a good representation of an actual refrigeration system because of the temperature changes that occur in the heat exchangers.

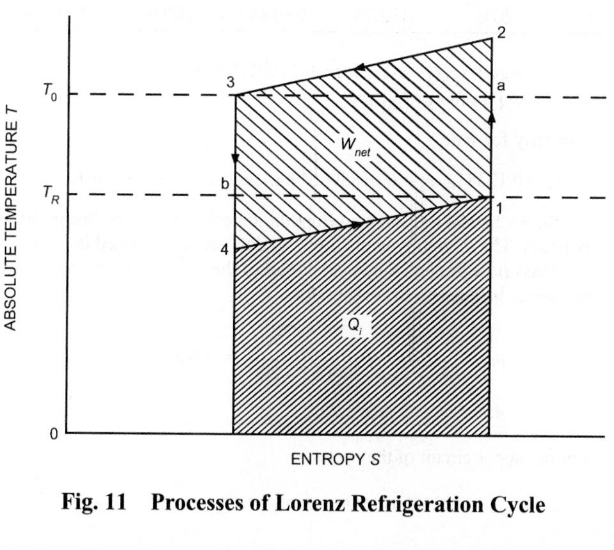

Fig. 11 Processes of Lorenz Refrigeration Cycle

THEORETICAL SINGLE-STAGE CYCLE USING ZEOTROPIC REFRIGERANT MIXTURE

A practical method to approximate the Lorenz refrigeration cycle is to use a fluid mixture as the refrigerant and the four system components shown in Figure 8. When the mixture is not azeotropic and the phase change occurs at constant pressure, the temperatures change during evaporation and condensation and the theoretical single-stage cycle can be shown on *T-s* coordinates as in Figure 12. In comparison, Figure 10 shows the system operating with a pure simple substance or an azeotropic mixture as the refrigerant. Equations (14), (15), (39), (40), and (41) apply to this cycle and to conventional cycles with constant phase change temperatures. Equation (42) should be used as the reversible cycle COP in Equation (17).

For zeotropic mixtures, the concept of constant saturation temperatures does not exist. For example, in the evaporator, the refrigerant enters at T_4 and exits at a higher temperature T_1. The temperature of saturated liquid at a given pressure is the **bubble point** and the temperature of saturated vapor at a given pressure is called the **dew point**. The temperature T_3 in Figure 12 is at the bubble point at the condensing pressure and T_1 is at the dew point at the evaporating pressure.

Areas on a *T-s* diagram representing additional work and reduced refrigerating effect from a Lorenz cycle operating between the same two temperatures T_1 and T_3 with the same value for ΔT can be analyzed. The cycle matches the Lorenz cycle most closely when counterflow heat exchangers are used for both the condenser and evaporator.

In a cycle that has heat exchangers with finite thermal resistances and finite external fluid capacity rates, Kuehn and Gronseth (1986) showed that a cycle using a refrigerant mixture has a higher coefficient of performance than one using a simple pure substance as a refrigerant. However, the improvement in COP is usually small. Performance of a mixture can be improved further by reducing the heat exchangers' thermal resistance and passing fluids through them in a counterflow arrangement.

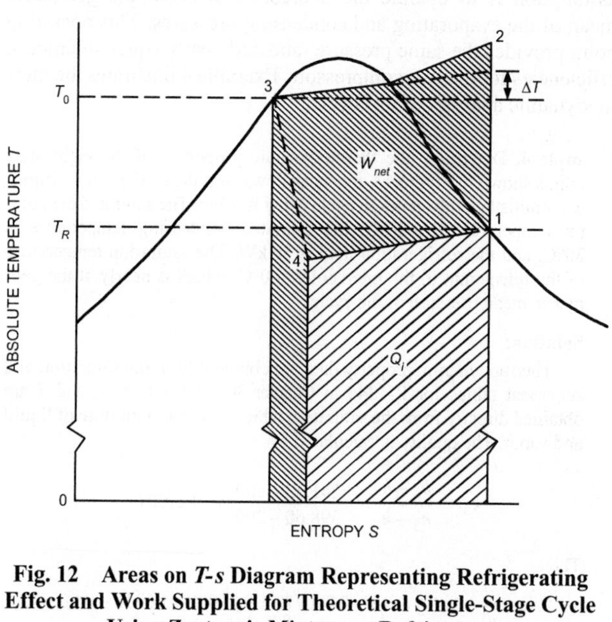

Fig. 12 Areas on *T-s* Diagram Representing Refrigerating Effect and Work Supplied for Theoretical Single-Stage Cycle Using Zeotropic Mixture as Refrigerant

MULTISTAGE VAPOR COMPRESSION REFRIGERATION CYCLES

Multistage or multipressure vapor compression refrigeration is used when several evaporators are needed at various temperatures, such as in a supermarket, or when evaporator temperature becomes very low. Low evaporator temperature indicates low evaporator pressure and low refrigerant density into the compressor. Two small compressors in series have a smaller displacement and usually operate more efficiently than one large compressor that covers the entire pressure range from the evaporator to the condenser. This is especially true in ammonia refrigeration systems because of the large amount of superheating that occurs during the compression process.

Thermodynamic analysis of multistage cycles is similar to analysis of single-stage cycles, except that mass flow differs through various components of the system. A careful mass balance and energy balance on individual components or groups of components ensures correct application of the first law of thermodynamics. Care must also be used when performing second-law calculations. Often, the refrigerating load is comprised of more than one evaporator, so the total system capacity is the sum of the loads from all evaporators. Likewise, the total energy input is the sum of the work into all compressors. For multistage cycles, the expression for the coefficient of performance given in Equation (15) should be written as

$$\text{COP} = \sum Q_i / W_{net} \tag{43}$$

When compressors are connected in series, the vapor between stages should be cooled to bring the vapor to saturated conditions before proceeding to the next stage of compression. Intercooling usually minimizes the displacement of the compressors, reduces the work requirement, and increases the COP of the cycle. If the refrigerant temperature between stages is above ambient, a simple intercooler that removes heat from the refrigerant can be used. If the temperature is below ambient, which is the usual case, the refrigerant itself must be used to cool the vapor. This is accomplished with a flash intercooler. Figure 13 shows a cycle with a flash intercooler installed.

The superheated vapor from compressor I is bubbled through saturated liquid refrigerant at the intermediate pressure of the cycle. Some of this liquid is evaporated when heat is added from the superheated refrigerant. The result is that only saturated vapor at the intermediate pressure is fed to compressor II. A common assumption is to operate the intercooler at about the geometric mean of the evaporating and condensing pressures. This operating point provides the same pressure ratio and nearly equal volumetric efficiencies for the two compressors. Example 4 illustrates the thermodynamic analysis of this cycle.

Example 4. Determine the thermodynamic properties of the eight state points shown in Figure 13, the mass flows, and the COP of this theoretical multistage refrigeration cycle using R-134a. The saturated evaporator temperature is −20°C, the saturated condensing temperature is 30°C, and the refrigeration load is 50 kW. The saturation temperature of the refrigerant in the intercooler is 0°C, which is nearly at the geometric mean pressure of the cycle.

Solution:

Thermodynamic property data are obtained from the saturation and superheat tables for R-134a in Chapter 30. States 1, 3, 5, and 7 are obtained directly from the saturation table. State 6 is a mixture of liquid and vapor. The quality is calculated by

$$x_6 = \frac{h_6 - h_7}{h_3 - h_7} = \frac{241.72 - 200}{398.60 - 200} = 0.21007$$

Then,

$$v_6 = v_7 + x_6(v_3 - v_7) = 0.000772 + 0.21007(0.06931 - 0.000772)$$
$$= 0.01517 \text{ m}^3/\text{kg}$$

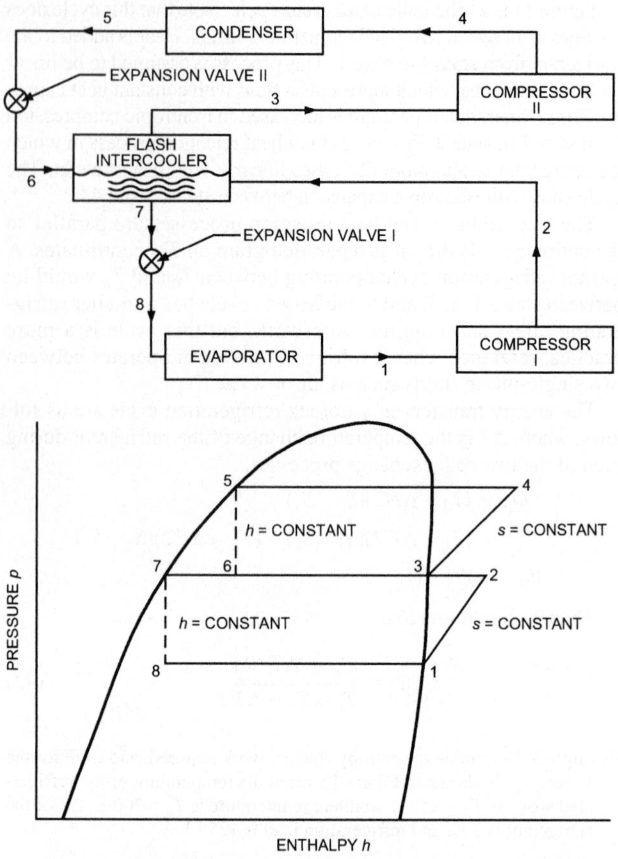

Fig. 13 Schematic and Pressure-Enthalpy Diagram for Dual-Compression, Dual-Expansion Cycle of Example 4

Table 2 Thermodynamic Property Values for Example 4

State	Temperature, °C	Pressure, kPa	Specific Volume, m³/kg	Specific Enthalpy, kJ/kg	Specific Entropy, kJ/(kg·K)
1	−20.0	132.73	0.14739	386.55	1.7413
2	2.8	292.80	0.07097	401.51	1.7413
3	0.0	292.80	0.06931	398.60	1.7282
4	33.6	770.20	0.02726	418.68	1.7282
5	30.0	770.20	0.00084	241.72	1.1435
6	0.0	292.80	0.01517	241.72	1.15297
7	0.0	292.80	0.000772	200.00	1.0000
8	−20.0	132.73	0.01889	200.00	1.00434

$$s_6 = s_7 + x_6(s_3 - s_7) = 1.0 + 0.21007(1.7282 - 1.0)$$
$$= 1.15297 \text{ kJ/(kg·K)}$$

Similarly for state 8,

$$x_8 = 0.12381,\quad v_8 = 0.01889 \text{ m}^3/\text{kg},\quad s_8 = 1.00434 \text{ kJ/(kg·K)}$$

States 2 and 4 are obtained from the superheat tables by linear interpolation. The thermodynamic property data are summarized in Table 2.

Mass flow through the lower circuit of the cycle is determined from an energy balance on the evaporator.

$$\dot{m}_1 = \frac{\dot{Q}_i}{h_1 - h_8} = \frac{50}{386.55 - 200} = 0.2680 \text{ kg/s}$$

$$\dot{m}_1 = \dot{m}_2 = \dot{m}_7 = \dot{m}_8$$

For the upper circuit of the cycle,

$$\dot{m}_3 = \dot{m}_4 = \dot{m}_5 = \dot{m}_6$$

Assuming the intercooler has perfect external insulation, an energy balance on it is used to compute $\dot{m}_3$.

$$\dot{m}_6 h_6 + \dot{m}_2 h_2 = \dot{m}_7 h_7 + \dot{m}_3 h_3$$

Rearranging and solving for $\dot{m}_3$,

$$\dot{m}_3 = \dot{m}_2 \frac{h_7 - h_2}{h_6 - h_3} = 0.2680 \frac{200 - 401.51}{241.72 - 398.60} = 0.3442 \text{ kg/s}$$

$$\dot{W}_I = \dot{m}_1(h_2 - h_1) = 0.2680(401.51 - 386.55)$$

$$= 4.009 \text{ kW}$$

$$\dot{W}_{II} = \dot{m}_3(h_4 - h_3) = 0.3442(418.68 - 398.60)$$

$$= 6.912 \text{ kW}$$

$$\text{COP} = \frac{\dot{Q}_i}{\dot{W}_I + \dot{W}_{II}} = \frac{50}{4.009 + 6.912} = 4.58$$

Examples 2 and 4 have the same refrigeration load and operate with the same evaporating and condensing temperatures. The two-stage cycle in Example 4 has a higher COP and less work input than the single-stage cycle. Also, the highest refrigerant temperature leaving the compressor is about 34°C for the two-stage cycle versus about 38°C for the single-stage cycle. These differences are more pronounced for cycles operating at larger pressure ratios.

ACTUAL REFRIGERATION SYSTEMS

Actual systems operating steadily differ from the ideal cycles considered in the previous sections in many respects. Pressure drops occur everywhere in the system except in the compression process. Heat transfers between the refrigerant and its environment in all components. The actual compression process differs substantially from isentropic compression. The working fluid is not a pure substance but a mixture of refrigerant and oil. All of these deviations from a theoretical cycle cause irreversibilities within the system. Each irreversibility requires additional power into the compressor. It is useful to understand how these irreversibilities are distributed throughout a real system; this insight can be useful when design changes are contemplated or operating conditions are modified. Example 5 illustrates how the irreversibilities can be computed in a real system and how they require additional compressor power to overcome. Input data have been rounded off for ease of computation.

Example 5. An air-cooled, direct-expansion, single-stage mechanical vapor-compression refrigerator uses R-22 and operates under steady conditions. A schematic of this system is shown in Figure 14. Pressure drops occur in all piping, and heat gains or losses occur as indicated. Power input includes compressor power and the power required to operate both fans. The following performance data are obtained:

Ambient air temperature	t_0	= 30°C
Refrigerated space temperature	t_R	= −10°C
Refrigeration load	$\dot{Q}_{evap}$	= 7.0 kW
Compressor power input	$\dot{W}_{comp}$	= 2.5 kW
Condenser fan input	$\dot{W}_{CF}$	= 0.15 kW
Evaporator fan input	$\dot{W}_{EF}$	= 0.11 kW

Refrigerant pressures and temperatures are measured at the seven locations shown in Figure 14. Table 3 lists the measured and computed thermodynamic properties of the refrigerant, neglecting the dissolved oil. A pressure-enthalpy diagram of this cycle is shown in Figure 15 and is compared with a theoretical single-stage cycle operating between the air temperatures t_R and t_0.

Compute the energy transfers to the refrigerant in each component of the system and determine the second-law irreversibility rate in each component. Show that the total irreversibility rate multiplied by the absolute ambient temperature is equal to the difference between the actual power input and the power required by a Carnot cycle operating between t_R and t_0 with the same refrigerating load.

Solution: The mass flow of refrigerant is the same through all components, so it is only computed once through the evaporator. Each component in the system is analyzed sequentially, beginning with the evaporator. Equation (6) is used to perform a first-law energy balance on each component, and Equations (11) and (13) are used for the second-law analysis. Note that the temperature used in the second-law analysis is the absolute temperature.

Table 3 Measured and Computed Thermodynamic Properties of R-22 for Example 5

	Measured		Computed		
State	Pressure, kPa	Temperature, °C	Specific Enthalpy, kJ/kg	Specific Entropy, kJ/(kg·K)	Specific Volume, m³/kg
1	310.0	−10.0	402.08	1.7810	0.07558
2	304.0	-4.0	406.25	1.7984	0.07946
3	1450.0	82.0	454.20	1.8165	0.02057
4	1435.0	70.0	444.31	1.7891	0.01970
5	1410.0	34.0	241.40	1.1400	0.00086
6	1405.0	33.0	240.13	1.1359	0.00086
7	320.0	−12.8	240.13	1.1561	0.01910

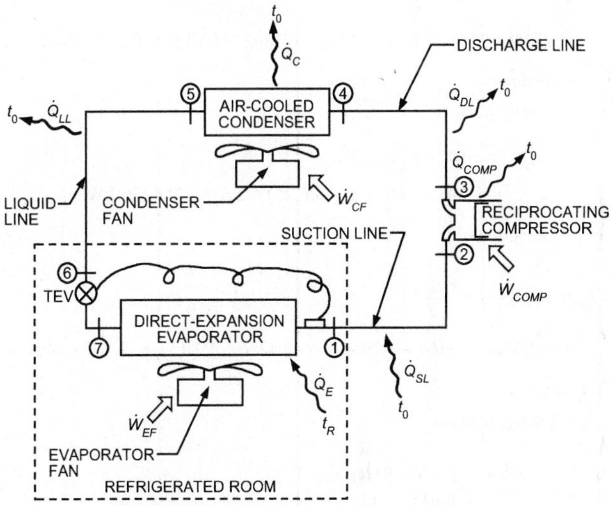

Fig. 14 Schematic of Real, Direct-Expansion, Single-Stage Mechanical Vapor-Compression Refrigeration System

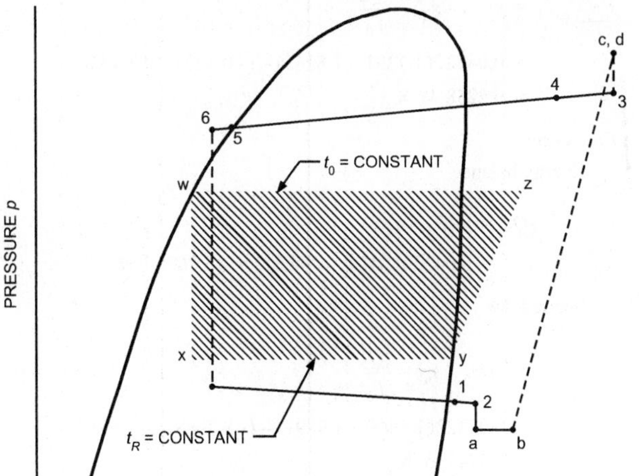

Fig. 15 Pressure-Enthalpy Diagram of Actual System and Theoretical Single-Stage System Operating Between Same Inlet Air Temperatures t_R and t_0

Evaporator:

Energy balance

$${}_7\dot{Q}_1 = \dot{m}(h_1 - h_7) = 7.0\text{ kW}$$

$$\dot{m} = \frac{7.0}{(402.08 - 240.13)} = 0.04322\text{ kg/s}$$

Second law

$${}_7\dot{I}_1 = \dot{m}(s_1 - s_7) - \frac{{}_7\dot{Q}_1}{T_R}$$

$$= 0.04322(1.7810 - 1.1561) - \frac{7.0}{263.15} = 0.4074\text{ W/K}$$

Suction Line:

Energy balance

$${}_1\dot{Q}_2 = \dot{m}(h_2 - h_1)$$

$$= 0.04322(406.25 - 402.08) = 0.1802\text{ kW}$$

Second law

$${}_1\dot{I}_2 = \dot{m}(s_2 - s_1) - \frac{{}_1\dot{Q}_2}{T_0}$$

$$= 0.04322(1.7984 - 1.7810) - 0.1802/303.15 = 0.1575\text{ W/K}$$

Compressor:

Energy balance

$${}_2\dot{Q}_3 = \dot{m}(h_3 - h_2) + {}_2\dot{W}_3$$

$$= 0.04322(454.20 - 406.25) - 2.5 = -0.4276\text{ kW}$$

Second law

$${}_2\dot{I}_3 = \dot{m}(s_3 - s_2) - \frac{{}_2\dot{Q}_3}{T_0}$$

$$= 0.04322(1.8165 - 1.7984) - (-0.4276/303.15) = 2.1928\text{ W/K}$$

Discharge Line:

Energy balance

$${}_3\dot{Q}_4 = \dot{m}(h_4 - h_3)$$

$$= 0.04322(444.31 - 454.20) = -0.4274\text{ kW}$$

Second law

$${}_3\dot{I}_4 = \dot{m}(s_4 - s_3) - \frac{{}_3\dot{Q}_4}{T_0}$$

$$= 0.04322(1.7891 - 1.8165) - (-0.4274/303.15)$$

$$= 0.2258\text{ W/K}$$

Condenser:

Energy balance

$${}_4\dot{Q}_5 = \dot{m}(h_5 - h_4)$$

$$= 0.04322(241.4 - 444.31) = -8.7698\text{ kW}$$

Second law

$${}_4\dot{I}_5 = \dot{m}(s_5 - s_4) - \frac{{}_4\dot{Q}_5}{T_0}$$

$$= 0.04322(1.1400 - 1.7891) - (-8.7698/303.15)$$

$$= 0.8747\text{ W/K}$$

Liquid Line:

Energy balance

$${}_5\dot{Q}_6 = \dot{m}(h_6 - h_5)$$

$$= 0.04322(240.13 - 241.40) = -0.0549\text{ kW}$$

Table 4 Energy Transfers and Irreversibility Rates for Refrigeration System in Example 5

Component	q, kW	$\dot{W}$, kW	$\dot{I}$, W/K	$\dot{I}/\dot{I}_{total}$, %
Evaporator	7.0000	0	0.4074	9
Suction line	0.1802	0	0.1575	3
Compressor	–0.4276	2.5	2.1928	46
Discharge line	–0.4274	0	0.2258	5
Condenser	–8.7698	0	0.8747	18
Liquid line	–0.0549	0	0.0039	≈0
Expansion device	0	0	0.8730	18
Totals	–2.4995	2.5	4.7351	

Second law

$${}_5\dot{I}_6 = \dot{m}(s_6 - s_5) - \frac{{}_5\dot{Q}_6}{T_0}$$

$$= 0.04322(1.1359 - 1.1400) - (-0.0549/303.15) = 0.0039\text{ W/K}$$

Expansion Device:

Energy balance

$${}_6\dot{Q}_7 = \dot{m}(h_7 - h_6) = 0$$

Second law

$${}_6\dot{I}_7 = \dot{m}(s_7 - s_6)$$

$$= 0.04322(1.1561 - 1.1359) = 0.8730\text{ W/K}$$

These results are summarized in Table 4. For the Carnot cycle,

$$\text{COP}_{Carnot} = \frac{T_R}{T_0 - T_R} = \frac{263.15}{40} = 6.579$$

The Carnot power requirement for the 7 kW load is

$$\dot{W}_{Carnot} = \frac{\dot{Q}_e}{\text{COP}_{Carnot}} = \frac{7.0}{6.579} = 1.064\text{ kW}$$

The actual power requirement for the compressor is

$$\dot{W}_{comp} = \dot{W}_{Carnot} + \dot{I}_{total}T_0$$

$$= 1.064 + \frac{4.7351(303.15)}{1000} = 2.4994\text{ kW}$$

This result is within computational error of the measured power input to the compressor of 2.5 kW.

The analysis demonstrated in Example 5 can be applied to any actual vapor compression refrigeration system. The only required information for second-law analysis is the refrigerant thermodynamic state points and mass flow rates and the temperatures in which the system is exchanging heat. In this example, the extra compressor power required to overcome the irreversibility in each component is determined. The component with the largest loss is the compressor. This loss is due to motor inefficiency, friction losses, and irreversibilities caused by pressure drops, mixing, and heat transfer between the compressor and the surroundings. The unrestrained expansion in the expansion device is also a large, but could be reduced by using an expander rather than a throttling process. An expander may be economical on large machines.

All heat transfer irreversibilities on both the refrigerant side and the air side of the condenser and evaporator are included in the analysis. Refrigerant pressure drop is also included. Air-side pressure drop irreversibilities of the two heat exchangers are not included, but these are equal to the fan power requirements because all the fan power is dissipated as heat.

An overall second-law analysis, such as in Example 5, shows the designer components with the most losses, and helps determine which components should be replaced or redesigned to improve performance. However, it does not identify the nature of the losses;

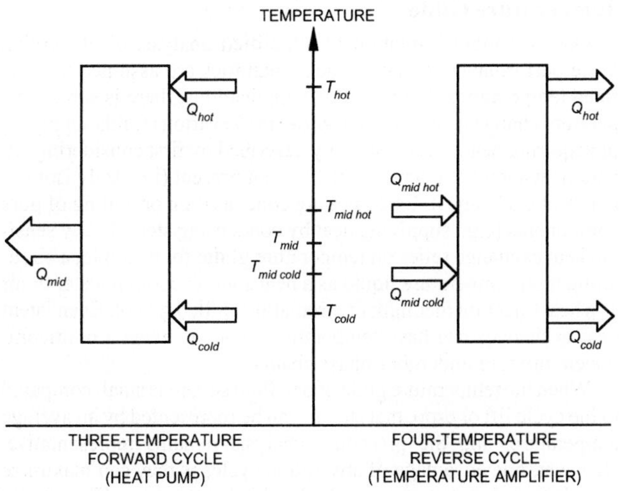

Fig. 16 Thermal Cycles

this requires a more detailed second-law analysis of the actual processes in terms of fluid flow and heat transfer (Liang and Kuehn 1991). A detailed analysis shows that most irreversibilities associated with heat exchangers are due to heat transfer, whereas air-side pressure drop causes a very small loss and refrigerant pressure drop causes a negligible loss. This finding indicates that promoting refrigerant heat transfer at the expense of increasing the pressure drop often improves performance. Using a thermoeconomic technique is required to determine the cost/benefits associated with reducing component irreversibilities.

ABSORPTION REFRIGERATION CYCLES

An absorption cycle is a heat-activated thermal cycle. It exchanges only thermal energy with its surroundings; no appreciable mechanical energy is exchanged. Furthermore, no appreciable conversion of heat to work or work to heat occurs in the cycle.

Absorption cycles are used in applications where one or more of the exchanges of heat with the surroundings is the useful product (e.g., refrigeration, air conditioning, and heat pumping). The two great advantages of this type of cycle in comparison to other cycles with similar product are

- No large, rotating mechanical equipment is required
- Any source of heat can be used, including low-temperature sources (e.g., waste heat)

IDEAL THERMAL CYCLE

All absorption cycles include at least three thermal energy exchanges with their surroundings (i.e., energy exchange at three different temperatures). The highest- and lowest-temperature heat flows are in one direction, and the mid-temperature one (or two) is in the opposite direction. In the **forward cycle**, the extreme (hottest and coldest) heat flows are into the cycle. This cycle is also called the heat amplifier, heat pump, conventional cycle, or Type I cycle. When the extreme-temperature heat flows are out of the cycle, it is called a **reverse cycle**, heat transformer, temperature amplifier, temperature booster, or Type II cycle. Figure 16 illustrates both types of thermal cycles.

This fundamental constraint of heat flow into or out of the cycle at three or more different temperatures establishes the first limitation on cycle performance. By the first law of thermodynamics (at steady state),

$$Q_{hot} + Q_{cold} = -Q_{mid} \tag{44}$$

(positive heat quantities are into the cycle)

The second law requires that

$$\frac{Q_{hot}}{T_{hot}} + \frac{Q_{cold}}{T_{cold}} + \frac{Q_{mid}}{T_{mid}} \geq 0 \tag{45}$$

with equality holding in the ideal case.

From these two laws alone (i.e., without invoking any further assumptions) it follows that, for the ideal forward cycle,

$$\text{COP}_{ideal} = \frac{Q_{cold}}{Q_{hot}} = \frac{T_{hot} - T_{mid}}{T_{hot}} \times \frac{T_{cold}}{T_{mid} - T_{cold}} \tag{46}$$

The heat ratio Q_{cold}/Q_{hot} is commonly called the **coefficient of performance (COP)**, which is the cooling realized divided by the driving heat supplied.

Heat rejected to ambient may be at two different temperatures, creating a **four-temperature cycle**. The ideal COP of the four-temperature cycle is also expressed by Equation (46), with T_{mid} signifying the entropic mean heat rejection temperature. In that case, T_{mid} is calculated as follows:

$$T_{mid} = \frac{Q_{mid\ hot} + Q_{mid\ cold}}{\dfrac{Q_{mid\ hot}}{T_{mid\ hot}} + \dfrac{Q_{mid\ cold}}{T_{mid\ cold}}} \tag{47}$$

This expression results from assigning all the entropy flow to the single temperature T_{mid}.

The ideal COP for the four-temperature cycle requires additional assumptions, such as the relationship between the various heat quantities. Under the assumptions that $Q_{cold} = Q_{mid\ cold}$ and $Q_{hot} = Q_{mid\ hot}$, the following expression results:

$$\text{COP}_{ideal} = \frac{T_{hot} - T_{mid\ hot}}{T_{hot}} \times \frac{T_{cold}}{T_{mid\ cold}} \times \frac{T_{cold}}{T_{mid\ hot}} \tag{48}$$

WORKING FLUID PHASE CHANGE CONSTRAINTS

Absorption cycles require at least two working substances: a sorbent and a fluid refrigerant; these substances undergo phase changes. Given this constraint, many combinations are not achievable. The first result of invoking the phase change constraints is that the various heat flows assume known identities. As illustrated in Figure 17, the refrigerant phase changes occur in an evaporator and a condenser, and the sorbent phase changes in an absorber and a desorber (generator). For the **forward absorption cycle**, the highest-temperature heat is always supplied to the generator,

$$Q_{hot} \equiv Q_{gen} \tag{49}$$

and the coldest heat is supplied to the evaporator:

$$Q_{cold} \equiv Q_{evap} \tag{50}$$

For the **reverse absorption cycle**, the highest-temperature heat is rejected from the absorber, and the lowest-temperature heat is rejected from the condenser.

The second result of the phase change constraint is that, for all known refrigerants and sorbents over pressure ranges of interest,

$$Q_{evap} \approx Q_{cond} \tag{51}$$

and

$$Q_{gen} \approx Q_{abs} \tag{52}$$

These two relations are true because the latent heat of phase change (vapor ↔ condensed phase) is relatively constant when far removed from the critical point. Thus, each heat input cannot be independently adjusted.

The ideal single-effect forward-cycle COP expression is

$$COP_{ideal} \le \frac{T_{gen} - T_{abs}}{T_{gen}} \times \frac{T_{evap}}{T_{cond} - T_{evap}} \times \frac{T_{cond}}{T_{abs}} \quad (53)$$

Equality holds only if the heat quantities at each temperature may be adjusted to specific values, which is not possible, as shown the following discussion.

The third result of invoking the phase change constraint is that only three of the four temperatures T_{evap}, T_{cond}, T_{gen}, and T_{abs} may be independently selected.

Practical liquid absorbents for absorption cycles have a significant negative deviation from behavior predicted by Raoult's law. This has the beneficial effect of reducing the required amount of absorbent recirculation, at the expense of reduced **lift** ($T_{cond} - T_{evap}$) and increased sorption duty. In practical terms, for most absorbents,

$$Q_{abs}/Q_{cond} \approx 1.2 \text{ to } 1.3 \quad (54)$$

and

$$T_{gen} - T_{abs} \approx 1.2(T_{cond} - T_{evap}) \quad (55)$$

The net result of applying these approximations and constraints to the ideal-cycle COP for the single-effect forward cycle is

$$COP_{ideal} \approx 1.2 \frac{T_{evap} T_{cond}}{T_{gen} T_{abs}} \approx \frac{Q_{cond}}{Q_{abs}} \approx 0.8 \quad (56)$$

In practical terms, the temperature constraint reduces the ideal COP to about 0.9, and the heat quantity constraint further reduces it to about 0.8.

Another useful result is

$$T_{gen\ min} = T_{cond} + T_{abs} - T_{evap} \quad (57)$$

where $T_{gen\ min}$ is the minimum generator temperature necessary to achieve a given evaporator temperature.

Alternative approaches are available that lead to nearly the same upper limit on ideal-cycle COP. For example, one approach equates the exergy production from a "driving" portion of the cycle to the exergy consumption in a "cooling" portion of the cycle (Tozer and James 1997). This leads to the expression

$$COP_{ideal} \le \frac{T_{evap}}{T_{abs}} = \frac{T_{cond}}{T_{gen}} \quad (58)$$

Another approach derives the idealized relationship between the two temperature differences that define the cycle: the cycle lift, defined previously, and **drop** ($T_{gen} - T_{abs}$).

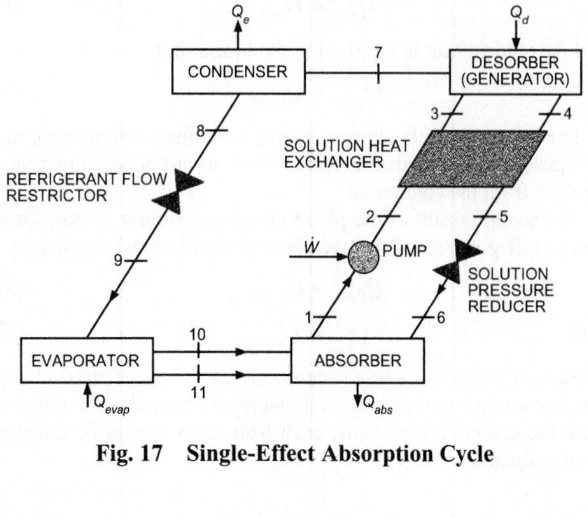

Fig. 17 Single-Effect Absorption Cycle

Temperature Glide

One important limitation of simplified analysis of absorption cycle performance is that the heat quantities are assumed to be at fixed temperatures. In most actual applications, there is some temperature change (**temperature glide**) in the various fluids supplying or acquiring heat. It is most easily described by first considering situations wherein temperature glide is not present (i.e., truly isothermal heat exchanges). Examples are condensation or boiling of pure components (e.g., supplying heat by condensing steam). Any sensible heat exchange relies on temperature glide: for example, a circulating high-temperature liquid as a heat source; cooling water or air as a heat rejection medium; or circulating chilled glycol. Even latent heat exchanges can have temperature glide, as when a multicomponent mixture undergoes phase change.

When the temperature glide of one fluid stream is small compared to the cycle lift or drop, that stream can be represented by an average temperature, and the preceding analysis remains representative. However, one advantage of absorption cycles is they can maximize benefit from low-temperature, high-glide heat sources. That ability derives from the fact that the desorption process inherently embodies temperature glide, and hence can be tailored to match the heat source glide. Similarly, absorption also embodies glide, which can be made to match the glide of the heat rejection medium.

Implications of temperature glide have been analyzed for power cycles (Ibrahim and Klein 1998), but not yet for absorption cycles.

WORKING FLUIDS

Working fluids for absorption cycles fall into four categories, each requiring a different approach to cycle modeling and thermodynamic analysis. Liquid absorbents can be **nonvolatile** (i.e., vapor phase is always pure refrigerant, neglecting condensables) or **volatile** (i.e., vapor concentration varies, so cycle and component modeling must track both vapor and liquid concentration). Solid sorbents can be grouped by whether they are **physisorbents** (also known as *adsorbents*), for which, as for liquid absorbents, sorbent temperature depends on both pressure and refrigerant loading (bivariance); or **chemisorbents**, for which sorbent temperature does not vary with loading, at least over small ranges.

Beyond these distinctions, various other characteristics are either necessary or desirable for suitable liquid absorbent/refrigerant pairs, as follows:

Absence of Solid Phase (Solubility Field). The refrigerant/absorbent pair should not solidify over the expected range of composition and temperature. If a solid forms, it will stop flow and shut down equipment. Controls must prevent operation beyond the acceptable solubility range.

Relative Volatility. The refrigerant should be much more volatile than the absorbent so the two can be separated easily. Otherwise, cost and heat requirements may be excessive. Many absorbents are effectively nonvolatile.

Affinity. The absorbent should have a strong affinity for the refrigerant under conditions in which absorption takes place. Affinity means a negative deviation from Raoult's law and results in an activity coefficient of less than unity for the refrigerant. Strong affinity allows less absorbent to be circulated for the same refrigeration effect, reducing sensible heat losses, and allows a smaller liquid heat exchanger to transfer heat from the absorbent to the pressurized refrigerant/absorption solution. On the other hand, as affinity increases, extra heat is required in the generators to separate refrigerant from the absorbent, and the COP suffers.

Pressure. Operating pressures, established by the refrigerant's thermodynamic properties, should be moderate. High pressure requires heavy-walled equipment, and significant electrical power may be needed to pump fluids from the low-pressure side to the high-pressure side. Vacuum requires large-volume equipment and special means of reducing pressure drop in the refrigerant vapor paths.

Stability. High chemical stability is required because fluids are subjected to severe conditions over many years of service. Instability can cause undesirable formation of gases, solids, or corrosive substances. Purity of all components charged into the system is critical for high performance and corrosion prevention.

Corrosion. Most absorption fluids corrode materials used in construction. Therefore, corrosion inhibitors are used.

Safety. Precautions as dictated by code are followed when fluids are toxic, inflammable, or at high pressure. Codes vary according to country and region.

Transport Properties. Viscosity, surface tension, thermal diffusivity, and mass diffusivity are important characteristics of the refrigerant/absorbent pair. For example, low viscosity promotes heat and mass transfer and reduces pumping power.

Latent Heat. The refrigerant latent heat should be high, so the circulation rate of the refrigerant and absorbent can be minimized.

Environmental Soundness. The two parameters of greatest concern are the global warming potential (GWP) and the ozone depletion potential (ODP). For more information on GWP and ODP, see Chapter 5 of the 2006 *ASHRAE Handbook—Refrigeration.*

No refrigerant/absorbent pair meets all requirements, and many requirements work at cross-purposes. For example, a greater solubility field goes hand in hand with reduced relative volatility. Thus, selecting a working pair is inherently a compromise.

Water/lithium bromide and ammonia/water offer the best compromises of thermodynamic performance and have no known detrimental environmental effect (zero ODP and zero GWP).

Ammonia/water meets most requirements, but its volatility ratio is low and it requires high operating pressures. Ammonia is also a Safety Code Group B2 fluid (ASHRAE *Standard* 34), which restricts its use indoors.

Advantages of water/lithium bromide include high (1) safety, (2) volatility ratio, (3) affinity, (4) stability, and (5) latent heat. However, this pair tends to form solids and operates at deep vacuum. Because the refrigerant turns to ice at 0°C, it cannot be used for low-temperature refrigeration. Lithium bromide (LiBr) crystallizes at moderate concentrations, as would be encountered in air-cooled chillers, which ordinarily limits the pair to applications where the absorber is water-cooled and the concentrations are lower. However, using a combination of salts as the absorbent can reduce this crystallization tendency enough to allow air cooling (Macriss 1968). Other disadvantages include low operating pressures and high viscosity. This is particularly detrimental to the absorption step; however, alcohols with a high relative molecular mass enhance LiBr absorption. Proper equipment design and additives can overcome these disadvantages.

Other refrigerant/absorbent pairs are listed in Table 5 (Macriss and Zawacki 1989). Several appear suitable for certain cycles and may solve some problems associated with traditional pairs. However, information on properties, stability, and corrosion is limited. Also, some of the fluids are somewhat hazardous.

ABSORPTION CYCLE REPRESENTATIONS

The quantities of interest to absorption cycle designers are temperature, concentration, pressure, and enthalpy. The most useful plots use linear scales and plot the key properties as straight lines. Some of the following plots are used:

- **Absorption plots** embody the vapor-liquid equilibrium of both the refrigerant and the sorbent. Plots on linear pressure-temperature coordinates have a logarithmic shape and hence are little used.
- In the **van't Hoff plot** ($\ln P$ versus $-1/T$), the constant concentration contours plot as nearly straight lines. Thus, it is more readily constructed (e.g., from sparse data) in spite of the awkward coordinates.

Table 5 Refrigerant/Absorbent Pairs

Refrigerant	Absorbents
H_2O	Salts
	Alkali halides
	LiBr
	$LiClO_3$
	$CaCl_2$
	$ZnCl_2$
	ZnBr
	Alkali nitrates
	Alkali thiocyanates
	Bases
	Alkali hydroxides
	Acids
	H_2SO_4
	H_3PO_4
NH_3	H_2O
	Alkali thiocyanates
TFE	NMP
(Organic)	E181
	DMF
	Pyrrolidone
SO_2	Organic solvents

- The **Dühring diagram** (solution temperature versus reference temperature) retains the linearity of the van't Hoff plot but eliminates the complexity of nonlinear coordinates. Thus, it is used extensively (see Figure 20). The primary drawback is the need for a reference substance.
- The **Gibbs plot** (solution temperature versus $T \ln P$) retains most of the advantages of the Dühring plot (linear temperature coordinates, concentration contours are straight lines) but eliminates the need for a reference substance.
- The **Merkel plot** (enthalpy versus concentration) is used to assist thermodynamic calculations and to solve the distillation problems that arise with volatile absorbents. It has also been used for basic cycle analysis.
- **Temperature-entropy coordinates** are occasionally used to relate absorption cycles to their mechanical vapor compression counterparts.

CONCEPTUALIZING THE CYCLE

The basic absorption cycle shown in Figure 17 must be altered in many cases to take advantage of the available energy. Examples include the following: (1) the driving heat is much hotter than the minimum required $T_{gen\ min}$: a multistage cycle boosts the COP; and (2) the driving heat temperature is below $T_{gen\ min}$: a different multistage cycle (half-effect cycle) can reduce the $T_{gen\ min}$.

Multistage cycles have one or more of the four basic exchangers (generator, absorber, condenser, evaporator) present at two or more places in the cycle at different pressures or concentrations. A **multi-effect** cycle is a special case of multistaging, signifying the number of times the driving heat is used in the cycle. Thus, there are several types of two-stage cycles: double-effect, half-effect, and two-stage, triple-effect.

Two or more single-effect absorption cycles, such as shown in Figure 17, can be combined to form a multistage cycle by coupling any of the components. **Coupling** implies either (1) sharing component(s) between the cycles to form an integrated single hermetic cycle or (2) exchanging heat between components belonging to two hermetically separate cycles that operate at (nearly) the same temperature level.

Figure 18 shows a **double-effect absorption cycle** formed by coupling the absorbers and evaporators of two single-effect cycles

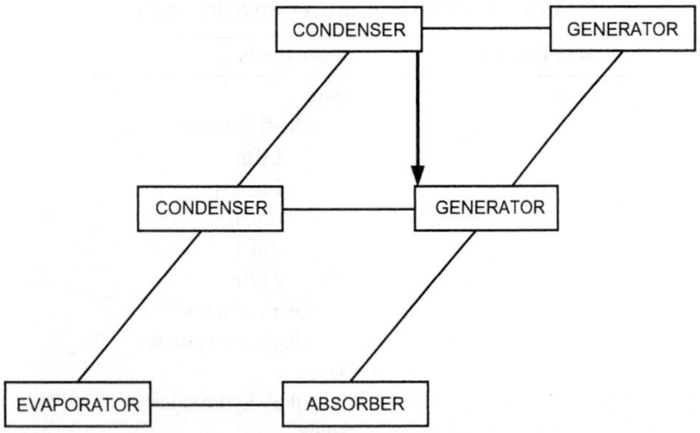

Fig. 18 Double-Effect Absorption Cycle

into an integrated, single hermetic cycle. Heat is transferred between the high-pressure condenser and intermediate-pressure generator. The heat of condensation of the refrigerant (generated in the high-temperature generator) generates additional refrigerant in the lower-temperature generator. Thus, the prime energy provided to the high-temperature generator is **cascaded** (used) twice in the cycle, making it a double-effect cycle. With the generation of additional refrigerant from a given heat input, the cycle COP increases. Commercial water/lithium bromide chillers normally use this cycle. The cycle COP can be further increased by coupling additional components and by increasing the number of cycles that are combined. This way, several different multieffect cycles can be combined by pressure-staging and/or concentration-staging. The double-effect cycle, for example, is formed by pressure-staging two single-effect cycles.

Figure 19 shows twelve generic triple-effect cycles identified by Alefeld and Radermacher (1994). Cycle 5 is a pressure-staged cycle, and Cycle 10 is a concentration-staged cycle. All other cycles are pressure- and concentration-staged. Cycle 1, which is called a dual-loop cycle, is the only cycle consisting of two loops that does not circulate absorbent in the low-temperature portion of the cycle.

Each of the cycles shown in Figure 19 can be made with one, two, or sometimes three separate **hermetic loops**. Dividing a cycle into separate hermetic loops allows the use of a different working fluid in each loop. Thus, a corrosive and/or high-lift absorbent can be restricted to the loop where it is required, and a conventional additive-enhanced absorbent can be used in other loops to reduce system cost significantly. As many as 78 hermetic loop configurations can be synthesized from the twelve triple-effect cycles shown in Figure 19. For each hermetic loop configuration, further variations are possible according to the absorbent flow pattern (e.g., series or parallel), the absorption working pairs selected, and various other hardware details. Thus, literally thousands of distinct variations of the triple-effect cycle are possible.

The ideal analysis can be extended to these multistage cycles (Alefeld and Radermacher 1994). A similar range of cycle variants is possible for situations calling for the half-effect cycle, in which the available heat source temperature is below $t_{gen\ min}$.

ABSORPTION CYCLE MODELING

Analysis and Performance Simulation

A physical-mathematical model of an absorption cycle consists of four types of thermodynamic equations: mass balances, energy balances, relations describing heat and mass transfer, and equations for thermophysical properties of the working fluids.

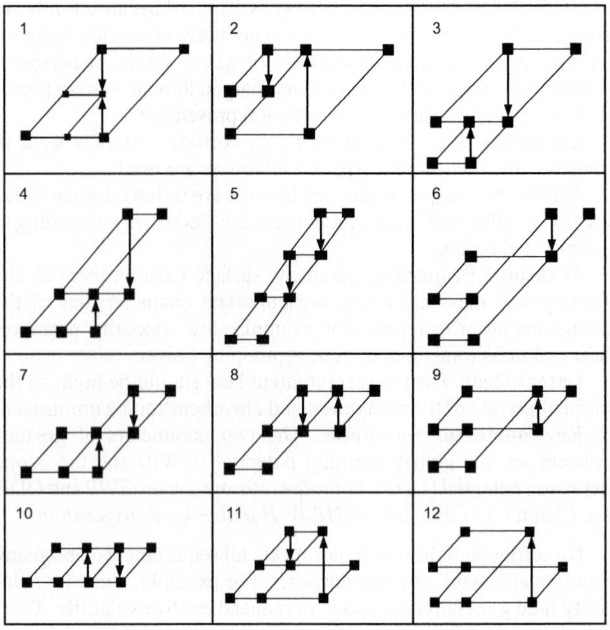

Fig. 19 Generic Triple-Effect Cycles

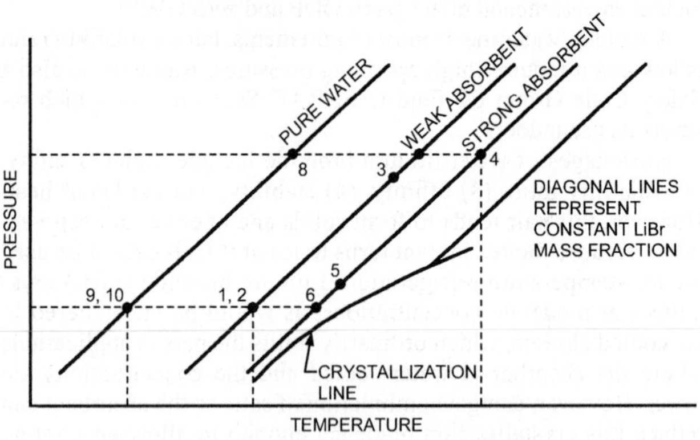

Fig. 20 Single-Effect Water/Lithium Bromide Absorption Cycle Dühring Plot

As an example of simulation, Figure 20 shows a Dühring plot of a single-effect water/lithium bromide absorption chiller. The chiller is hot-water-driven, rejects waste heat from the absorber and the condenser to a stream of cooling water, and produces chilled water. A simulation of this chiller starts by specifying the assumptions (Table 6) and the design parameters and operating conditions at the design point (Table 7). Design parameters are the specified *UA* values and the flow regime (co/counter/crosscurrent, pool, or film) of all heat exchangers (evaporator, condenser, generator, absorber, solution heat exchanger) and the flow rate of weak solution through the solution pump.

One complete set of input operating parameters could be the design point values of the chilled-water and cooling water temperatures $t_{chill\ in}$, $t_{chill\ out}$, $t_{cool\ in}$, $t_{cool\ out}$, hot-water flow rate $\dot{m}_{hot}$, and total cooling capacity Q_e. With this information, a cycle simulation calculates the required hot-water temperatures; cooling-water flow rate; and temperatures, pressures, and concentrations at all internal state points. Some additional assumptions are made that reduce the number of unknown parameters.

With these assumptions and the design parameters and operating conditions as specified in Table 7, the cycle simulation can be conducted by solving the following set of equations:

Table 6 Assumptions for Single-Effect Water/Lithium Bromide Model (Figure 20)

Assumptions
• Generator and condenser as well as evaporator and absorber are under same pressure
• Refrigerant vapor leaving the evaporator is saturated pure water
• Liquid refrigerant leaving the condenser is saturated
• Strong solution leaving the generator is boiling
• Refrigerant vapor leaving the generator has the equilibrium temperature of the weak solution at generator pressure
• Weak solution leaving the absorber is saturated
• No liquid carryover from evaporator
• Flow restrictors are adiabatic
• Pump is isentropic
• No jacket heat losses
• The LMTD (log mean temperature difference) expression adequately estimates the latent changes

Mass Balances

$$\dot{m}_{refr} + \dot{m}_{strong} = \dot{m}_{weak} \tag{59}$$

$$\dot{m}_{strong}\xi_{strong} = \dot{m}_{weak}\xi_{weak} \tag{60}$$

Energy Balances

$$\dot{Q}_{evap} = \dot{m}_{refr}(h_{vapor,\,evap} - h_{liq,\,cond}) = \dot{m}_{chill}(h_{chill\ in} - h_{chill\ out}) \tag{61}$$

$$\dot{Q}_{cond} = \dot{m}_{refr}(h_{vapor,\,gen} - h_{liq,\,cond}) = \dot{m}_{cool}(h_{cool\ out} - h_{cool\ mean}) \tag{62}$$

$$\dot{Q}_{abs} = \dot{m}_{refr}h_{vapor,\,evap} + \dot{m}_{strong}h_{strong,\,gen} - \dot{m}_{weak}h_{weak,\,abs} - \dot{Q}_{sol} = \dot{m}_{cool}(h_{cool\ mean} - h_{cool\ in}) \tag{63}$$

$$\dot{Q}_{gen} = \dot{m}_{refr}h_{vapor,\,gen} + \dot{m}_{strong}h_{strong,\,gen} - \dot{m}_{weak}h_{weak,\,abs} - \dot{Q}_{sol} = \dot{m}_{hot}(h_{hot\ in} - h_{hot\ out}) \tag{64}$$

$$\dot{Q}_{sol} = \dot{m}_{strong}(h_{strong,\,gen} - h_{strong,\,sol}) = \dot{m}_{weak}(h_{weak,\,sol} - h_{weak,\,abs}) \tag{65}$$

Heat Transfer Equations

$$\dot{Q}_{evap} = UA_{evap}\frac{t_{chill\ in} - t_{chill\ out}}{\ln\left(\dfrac{t_{chill\ in} - t_{vapor,\,evap}}{t_{chill\ out} - t_{vapor,\,evap}}\right)} \tag{66}$$

$$\dot{Q}_{cond} = UA_{cond}\frac{t_{cool\ out} - t_{cool\ mean}}{\ln\left(\dfrac{t_{liq,\,cond} - t_{cool\ mean}}{t_{liq,\,cond} - t_{cool\ out}}\right)} \tag{67}$$

$$\dot{Q}_{abs} = UA_{abs}\frac{(t_{strong,\,abs} - t_{cool\ mean}) - (t_{weak,\,abs} - t_{cool\ in})}{\ln\left(\dfrac{t_{strong,\,abs} - t_{cool\ mean}}{t_{weak,\,abs} - t_{cool\ in}}\right)} \tag{68}$$

Table 7 Design Parameters and Operating Conditions for Single-Effect Water/Lithium Bromide Absorption Chiller

	Design Parameters	Operating Conditions
Evaporator	UA_{evap} = 319.2 kW/K, countercurrent film	$t_{chill\ in}$ = 12°C $t_{chill\ out}$ = 6°C
Condenser	UA_{cond} = 180.6 kW/K, countercurrent film	$t_{cool\ out}$ = 35°C
Absorber	UA_{abs} = 186.9 kW/K, countercurrent film-absorber	$t_{cool\ in}$ = 27°C
Generator	UA_{gen} = 143.4 kW/K, pool-generator	$\dot{m}_{hot}$ = 74.4 kg/s
Solution	UA_{sol} = 33.8 kW/K, countercurrent	
General	$\dot{m}_{weak}$ = 12 kg/s	$\dot{Q}_{evap}$ = 2148 kW

Table 8 Simulation Results for Single-Effect Water/Lithium Bromide Absorption Chiller

	Internal Parameters	Performance Parameters
Evaporator	$t_{vapor,evap}$ = 1.8°C $p_{sat,evap}$ = 0.697 kPa	$\dot{Q}_{evap}$ = 2148 kW $\dot{m}_{chill}$ = 85.3 kg/s
Condenser	$T_{liq,cond}$ = 46.2°C $p_{sat,cond}$ = 10.2 kPa	$\dot{Q}_{cond}$ = 2322 kW $\dot{m}_{cool}$ = 158.7 kg/s
Absorber	ξ_{weak} = 59.6% t_{weak} = 40.7°C $t_{strong,abs}$ = 49.9°C	$\dot{Q}_{abs}$ = 2984 kW $t_{cool,mean}$ = 31.5°C
Generator	ξ_{strong} = 64.6% $t_{strong,gen}$ = 103.5°C $t_{weak,gen}$ = 92.4°C $t_{weak,sol}$ = 76.1°C	$\dot{Q}_{gen}$ = 3158 kW $t_{hot\ in}$ = 125°C $t_{hot\ out}$ = 115°C
Solution	$t_{strong,sol}$ = 62.4°C $t_{weak,sol}$ = 76.1°C	$\dot{Q}_{sol}$ = 825 kW ε = 65.4%
General	$\dot{m}_{vapor}$ = 0.93 kg/s $\dot{m}_{strong}$ = 11.06 kg/s	COP = 0.68

$$\dot{Q}_{gen} = UA_{gen}\frac{(t_{hot\ in} - t_{strong,\,gen}) - (t_{hot\ out} - t_{weak,\,gen})}{\ln\left(\dfrac{t_{hot\ in} - t_{strong,\,gen}}{t_{hot\ out} - t_{weak,\,gen}}\right)} \tag{69}$$

$$\dot{Q}_{sol} = UA_{sol}\frac{(t_{strong,\,gen} - t_{weak,\,sol}) - (t_{strong,\,sol} - t_{weak,\,abs})}{\ln\left(\dfrac{t_{strong,\,gen} - t_{weak,\,sol}}{t_{strong,\,sol} - t_{weak,\,abs}}\right)} \tag{70}$$

Fluid Property Equations at each state point

Thermal Equations of State: $h_{water}(t,p)$, $h_{sol}(t,p,\xi)$
Two-Phase Equilibrium: $t_{water,sat}(p)$, $t_{sol,sat}(p,\xi)$

The results are listed in Table 8.

A baseline correlation for the thermodynamic data of the H_2O/LiBr absorption working pair is presented in Hellman and Grossman (1996). Thermophysical property measurements at higher temperatures are reported by Feuerecker et al. (1993). Additional high-temperature measurements of vapor pressure and specific heat appear in Langeliers et al. (2003), including correlations of the data.

Double-Effect Cycle

Double-effect cycle calculations can be performed in a manner similar to that for the single-effect cycle. Mass and energy balances

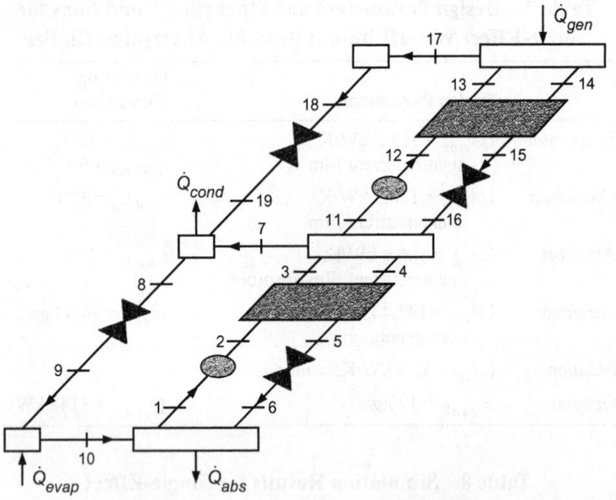

Fig. 21 Double-Effect Water/Lithium Bromide Absorption Cycle with State Points

of the model shown in Figure 21 were calculated using the inputs and assumptions listed in Table 9. The results are shown in Table 10. The COP is quite sensitive to several inputs and assumptions. In particular, the effectiveness of the solution heat exchangers and the driving temperature difference between the high-temperature condenser and the low-temperature generator influence the COP strongly.

AMMONIA/WATER ABSORPTION CYCLES

Ammonia/water absorption cycles are similar to water/lithium bromide cycles, but with some important differences because of ammonia's lower latent heat compared to water, the volatility of the absorbent, and the different pressure and solubility ranges. The latent heat of ammonia is only about half that of water, so, for the same duty, the refrigerant and absorbent mass circulation rates are roughly double that of water/lithium bromide. As a result, the sensible heat loss associated with heat exchanger approaches is greater. Accordingly, ammonia/water cycles incorporate more techniques to reclaim sensible heat, described in Hanna et al. (1995). The refrigerant heat exchanger (RHX), also known as refrigerant subcooler, which improves COP by about 8%, is the most important (Holldorff 1979). Next is the absorber heat exchanger (AHX), accompanied by a generator heat exchanger (GHX) (Phillips 1976). These either replace or supplement the traditional solution heat exchanger (SHX). These components would also benefit the water/lithium bromide cycle, except that the deep vacuum in that cycle makes them impractical there.

The volatility of the water absorbent is also key. It makes the distinction between crosscurrent, cocurrent, and countercurrent mass exchange more important in all of the latent heat exchangers (Briggs 1971). It also requires a distillation column on the high-pressure side. When improperly implemented, this column can impose both cost and COP penalties. Those penalties are avoided by refluxing the column from an internal diabatic section (e.g., solution-cooled rectifier [SCR]) rather than with an external reflux pump.

The high-pressure operating regime makes it impractical to achieve multieffect performance via pressure-staging. On the other hand, the exceptionally wide solubility field facilitates concentration staging. The generator-absorber heat exchange (GAX) cycle is an especially advantageous embodiment of concentration staging (Modahl and Hayes 1988).

Ammonia/water cycles can equal the performance of water/lithium bromide cycles. The single-effect or basic GAX cycle yields the same performance as a single-effect water/lithium bromide cycle; the branched GAX cycle (Herold et al. 1991) yields the same performance as a water/lithium bromide double-effect cycle; and the VX GAX cycle (Erickson and Rane 1994) yields the same performance as a water/lithium bromide triple-effect cycle. Additional

Table 9 Inputs and Assumptions for Double-Effect Water-Lithium Bromide Model (Figure 21)

Inputs		
Capacity	$\dot{Q}_{evap}$	1760 kW
Evaporator temperature	t_{10}	5.1°C
Desorber solution exit temperature	t_{14}	170.7°C
Condenser/absorber low temperature	t_1, t_8	42.4°C
Solution heat exchanger effectiveness	ε	0.6

Assumptions

- Steady state
- Refrigerant is pure water
- No pressure changes except through flow restrictors and pump
- State points at 1, 4, 8, 11, 14, and 18 are saturated liquid
- State point 10 is saturated vapor
- Temperature difference between high-temperature condenser and low-temperature generator is 5 K
- Parallel flow
- Both solution heat exchangers have same effectiveness
- Upper loop solution flow rate is selected such that upper condenser heat exactly matches lower generator heat requirement
- Flow restrictors are adiabatic
- Pumps are isentropic
- No jacket heat losses
- No liquid carryover from evaporator to absorber
- Vapor leaving both generators is at equilibrium temperature of entering solution stream

Table 10 State Point Data for Double-Effect Lithium Bromide/Water Cycle of Figure 21

Point	*h* kJ/kg	*m* kg/s	*p* kPa	*Q* Fraction	*t* °C	*x* % LiBr
1	117.7	9.551	0.88	0.0	42.4	59.5
2	117.7	9.551	8.36		42.4	59.5
3	182.3	9.551	8.36		75.6	59.5
4	247.3	8.797	8.36	0.0	97.8	64.6
5	177.2	8.797	8.36		58.8	64.6
6	177.2	8.797	0.88	0.004	53.2	64.6
7	2661.1	0.320	8.36		85.6	0.0
8	177.4	0.754	8.36	0.0	42.4	0.0
9	177.4	0.754	0.88	0.063	5.0	0.0
10	2510.8	0.754	0.88	1.0	5.0	0.0
11	201.8	5.498	8.36	0.0	85.6	59.5
12	201.8	5.498	111.8		85.6	59.5
13	301.2	5.498	111.8		136.7	59.5
14	378.8	5.064	111.8	0.00	170.7	64.6
15	270.9	5.064	111.8		110.9	64.6
16	270.9	5.064	8.36	0.008	99.1	64.6
17	2787.3	0.434	111.8		155.7	0.0
18	430.6	0.434	111.8	0.0	102.8	0.0
19	430.6	0.434	8.36	0.105	42.4	0.0

COP = 1.195	$\dot{Q}_{evap}$ = 1760 kW
Δt = 5 K	$\dot{Q}_{gen}$ = 1472 kW
ε = 0.600	$\dot{Q}_{shx1}$ = 617 kW
$\dot{Q}_{abs}$ = 2328 kW	$\dot{Q}_{shx2}$ = 546 kW
$\dot{Q}_{gen}$ = 1023 kW	$\dot{W}_{p1}$ = 0.043 kW
$\dot{Q}_{cond}$ = 905 kW	$\dot{W}_{p2}$ = 0.346 kW

Table 11 Inputs and Assumptions for Single-Effect Ammonia/Water Cycle (Figure 22)

Inputs		
Capacity	$\dot{Q}_{evap}$	1760 kW
High-side pressure	p_{high}	1461 kPa
Low-side pressure	p_{low}	515 kPa
Absorber exit temperature	t_1	40.6°C
Generator exit temperature	t_4	95°C
Rectifier vapor exit temperature	t_7	55°C
Solution heat exchanger effectiveness	ε_{shx}	0.692
Refrigerant heat exchanger effectiveness	ε_{rhx}	0.629

Assumptions

- Steady state
- No pressure changes except through flow restrictors and pump
- States at points 1, 4, 8, 11, and 14 are saturated liquid
- States at point 12 and 13 are saturated vapor
- Flow restrictors are adiabatic
- Pump is isentropic
- No jacket heat losses
- No liquid carryover from evaporator to absorber
- Vapor leaving generator is at equilibrium temperature of entering solution stream

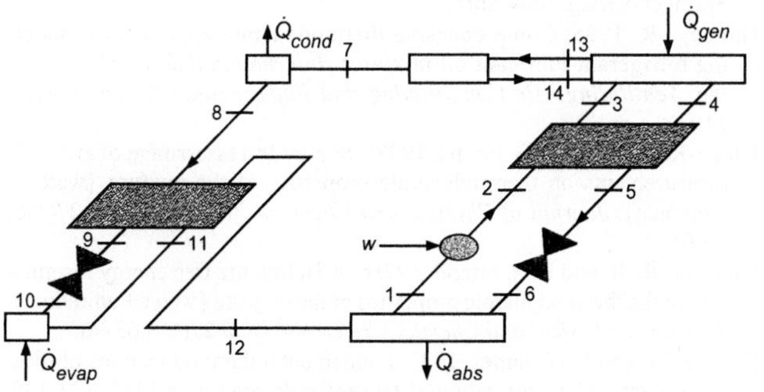

Fig. 22 Single-Effect Ammonia/Water Absorption Cycle

advantages of the ammonia/water cycle include refrigeration capability, air-cooling capability, all mild steel construction, extreme compactness, and capability of direct integration into industrial processes. Between heat-activated refrigerators, gas-fired residential air conditioners, and large industrial refrigeration plants, this technology has accounted for the vast majority of absorption activity over the past century.

Figure 22 shows the diagram of a typical single-effect ammonia-water absorption cycle. The inputs and assumptions in Table 11 are used to calculate a single-cycle solution, which is summarized in Table 12.

Comprehensive correlations of the thermodynamic properties of the ammonia/water absorption working pair are found in Ibrahim and Klein (1993) and Tillner-Roth and Friend (1998a, 1998b), both of which are available as commercial software. Figure 29 in Chapter 30 of this volume was prepared using the Ibrahim and Klein correlation, which is also incorporated in REFPROP7 (National Institute of Standards and Technology). Transport properties for ammonia/water mixtures are available in IIR (1994) and in Melinder (1998).

Table 12 State Point Data for Single-Effect Ammonia/Water Cycle of Figure 23

Point	h, kJ/kg	m, kg/s	p, kPa	Q, Fraction	t, °C	x, Fraction NH_3
1	–57.2	10.65	515.0	0.0	40.56	0.50094
2	–56.0	10.65	1461		40.84	0.50094
3	89.6	10.65	1461		78.21	0.50094
4	195.1	9.09	1461	0.0	95.00	0.41612
5	24.6	9.09	1461		57.52	0.41612
6	24.6	9.09	515.0	0.006	55.55	0.41612
7	1349	1.55	1461	1.000	55.00	0.99809
8	178.3	1.55	1461	0.0	37.82	0.99809
9	82.1	1.55	1461		17.80	0.99809
10	82.1	1.55	515.0	0.049	5.06	0.99809
11	1216	1.55	515.0	0.953	6.00	0.99809
12	1313	1.55	515.0	1.000	30.57	0.99809
13	1429	1.59	1461	1.000	79.15	0.99809
14	120.4	0.04	1461	0.0	79.15	0.50094

COP = 0.571	$\dot{Q}_{evap}$ = 1760 kW
Δt_{rhx} = 7.24 K	$\dot{Q}_{gen}$ = 3083 kW
Δt_{shx} = 16.68 K	$\dot{Q}_{rhx}$ = 149 kW
ε_{rhx} = 0.629	$\dot{Q}_r$ = 170 kW
ε_{rhx} = 0.692	$\dot{Q}_{shw}$ = 1550 kW
$\dot{Q}_{abs}$ = 2869 kW	$\dot{W}$ = 12.4 kW
$\dot{Q}_{cond}$ = 1862.2 kW	

SYMBOLS

c_p = specific heat at constant pressure, kJ/(kg·K)
COP = coefficient of performance
g = local acceleration of gravity, m/s²
h = enthalpy, kJ/kg
I = irreversibility, kJ/K
$\dot{I}$ = irreversibility rate, kW/K
m = mass, kg
$\dot{m}$ = mass flow, kg/s
p = pressure, kPa
Q = heat energy, kJ
$\dot{Q}$ = rate of heat flow, kJ/s
R = ideal gas constant, kPa·m³/(kg·K)
s = specific entropy, kJ/(kg·K)
S = total entropy, kJ/K
t = temperature, °C
T = absolute temperature, K
u = internal energy, kJ/kg
v = specific volume, m³/kg
V = velocity of fluid, m/s
W = mechanical or shaft work, kJ
$\dot{W}$ = rate of work, power, kW
x = mass fraction (of either lithium bromide or ammonia)
x = vapor quality (fraction)
z = elevation above horizontal reference plane, m
Z = compressibility factor
ε = heat exchanger effectiveness
η = efficiency
ρ = density, kg/m³

Subscripts

abs = absorber
cg = condenser to generator
cond = condenser or cooling mode
evap = evaporator
fg = fluid to vapor
gen = generator
gh = high-temperature generator
o, 0 = reference conditions, usually ambient
p = pump
R = refrigerating or evaporator conditions
rhx = refrigerant heat exchanger
shx = solution heat exchanger
sol = solution

REFERENCES

Alefeld, G. and R. Radermacher. 1994. *Heat conversion systems*. CRC Press, Boca Raton.

Benedict, M. 1937. Pressure, volume, temperature properties of nitrogen at high density, I and II. *Journal of American Chemists Society* 59(11): 2224-2233 and 2233-2242.

Benedict, M., G.B. Webb, and L.C. Rubin. 1940. An empirical equation for thermodynamic properties of light hydrocarbons and their mixtures. *Journal of Chemistry and Physics* 4:334.

Briggs, S.W. 1971. Concurrent, crosscurrent, and countercurrent absorption in ammonia-water absorption refrigeration. *ASHRAE Transactions* 77(1):171.

Cooper, H.W. and J.C. Goldfrank. 1967. B-W-R constants and new correlations. *Hydrocarbon Processing* 46(12):141.

Erickson, D.C. and M. Rane. 1994. Advanced absorption cycle: Vapor exchange GAX. *Proceedings of the International Absorption Heat Pump Conference*, Chicago.

Feuerecker, G., J. Scharfe, I. Greiter, C. Frank, and G. Alefeld. 1993. Measurement of thermophysical properties of aqueous LiBr solutions at high temperatures and concentrations. *Proceedings of the International Absorption Heat Pump Conference,* New Orleans, AES-30, pp. 493-499. American Society of Mechanical Engineers, New York.

Hanna, W.T., et al. 1995. Pinch-point analysis: An aid to understanding the GAX absorption cycle. *ASHRAE Technical Data Bulletin* 11(2).

Hellman, H.-M. and G. Grossman. 1996. Improved property data correlations of absorption fluids for computer simulation of heat pump cycles. *ASHRAE Transactions* 102(1):980-997.

Herold, K.E., et al. 1991. The branched GAX absorption heat pump cycle. *Proceedings of Absorption Heat Pump Conference,* Tokyo.

Hirschfelder, J.O., et al. 1958. Generalized equation of state for gases and liquids. *Industrial and Engineering Chemistry* 50:375.

Holldorff, G. 1979. Revisions up absorption refrigeration efficiency. *Hydrocarbon Processing* 58(7):149.

Howell, J.R. and R.O. Buckius. 1992. *Fundamentals of engineering thermodynamics*, 2nd ed. McGraw-Hill, New York.

Hust, J.G. and R.D. McCarty. 1967. Curve-fitting techniques and applications to thermodynamics. *Cryogenics* 8:200.

Hust, J.G. and R.B. Stewart. 1966. Thermodynamic property computations for system analysis. *ASHRAE Journal* 2:64.

Ibrahim, O.M. and S.A. Klein. 1993. Thermodynamic properties of ammonia-water mixtures. *ASHRAE Transactions* 99(1):1495-1502.

Ibrahim, O.M. and S.A. Klein. 1998. The maximum power cycle: A model for new cycles and new working fluids. *Proceedings of the ASME Advanced Energy Systems Division,* AES vol. 117. American Society of Mechanical Engineers. New York.

IIR. 1994. *R123—Thermodynamic and physical properties.* NH_3–H_2O. International Institute of Refrigeration, Paris.

Kuehn, T.H. and R.E. Gronseth. 1986. The effect of a nonazeotropic binary refrigerant mixture on the performance of a single stage refrigeration cycle. *Proceedings of the International Institute of Refrigeration Conference,* Purdue University, p. 119.

Langeliers, J., P. Sarkisian, and U. Rockenfeller. 2003. Vapor pressure and specific heat of Li-Br H_2O at high temperature. *ASHRAE Transactions* 109(1):423-427.

Liang, H. and T.H. Kuehn. 1991. Irreversibility analysis of a water to water mechanical compression heat pump. *Energy* 16(6):883.

Macriss, R.A. 1968. Physical properties of modified LiBr solutions. AGA Symposium on Absorption Air-Conditioning Systems, February.

Macriss, R.A. and T.S. Zawacki. 1989. Absorption fluid data survey: 1989 update. Oak Ridge National Laboratories *Report* ORNL/Sub84-47989/4.

Martin, J.J. and Y. Hou. 1955. Development of an equation of state for gases. *AIChE Journal* 1:142.

Martz, W.L., C.M. Burton, and A.M. Jacobi. 1996a. Liquid-vapor equilibria for R-22, R-134a, R-125, and R-32/125 with a polyol ester lubricant: Measurements and departure from ideality. *ASHRAE Transactions* 102(1):367-374.

Martz, W.L., C.M. Burton, and A.M. Jacobi. 1996b. Local composition modeling of the thermodynamic properties of refrigerant and oil mixtures. *International Journal of Refrigeration* 19(1):25-33.

Melinder, A. 1998. *Thermophysical properties of liquid secondary refrigerants.* Engineering Licentiate Thesis, Department of Energy Technology, The Royal Institute of Technology, Stockholm.

Modahl, R.J. and F.C. Hayes. 1988. Evaluation of commercial advanced absorption heat pump. *Proceedings of the 2nd DOE/ORNL Heat Pump Conference,* Washington, D.C.

NASA. 1971. Computer program for calculation of complex chemical equilibrium composition, rocket performance, incident and reflected shocks and Chapman-Jouguet detonations. SP-273. U.S. Government Printing Office, Washington, D.C.

Phillips, B. 1976. Absorption cycles for air-cooled solar air conditioning. *ASHRAE Transactions* 82(1):966. Dallas.

Stewart, R.B., R.T. Jacobsen, and S.G. Penoncello. 1986. *ASHRAE thermodynamic properties of refrigerants.*

Strobridge, T.R. 1962. The thermodynamic properties of nitrogen from 64 to 300 K, between 0.1 and 200 atmospheres. National Bureau of Standards *Technical Note* 129.

Stoecker, W.F. and J.W. Jones. 1982. *Refrigeration and air conditioning*, 2nd ed. McGraw-Hill, New York.

Tassios, D.P. 1993. *Applied chemical engineering thermodynamics.* Springer-Verlag, New York.

Thome, J.R. 1995. Comprehensive thermodynamic approach to modeling refrigerant-lubricant oil mixtures. *International Journal of Heating, Ventilating, Air Conditioning and Refrigeration Research* 1(2): 110.

Tillner-Roth, R. and D.G. Friend. 1998a. Survey and assessment of available measurements on thermodynamic properties of the mixture {water + ammonia}. *Journal of Physical and Chemical Reference Data* 27(1)S: 45-61.

Tillner-Roth, R. and D.G. Friend. 1998b. A Helmholtz free energy formulation of the thermodynamic properties of the mixture {water + ammonia}. *Journal of Physical and Chemical Reference Data* 27(1)S:63-96.

Tozer, R.M. and R.W. James. 1997. Fundamental thermodynamics of ideal absorption cycles. *International Journal of Refrigeration* 20 (2):123-135.

BIBLIOGRAPHY

Bogart, M. 1981. *Ammonia absorption refrigeration in industrial processes.* Gulf Publishing Co., Houston.

Herold, K.E., R. Radermacher, and S.A. Klein. 1996. *Absorption chillers and heat pumps.* CRC Press, Boca Raton.

Jain, P.C. and G.K. Gable. 1971. Equilibrium property data for aqua-ammonia mixture. *ASHRAE Transactions* 77(1):149.

Moran, M.J. and H. Shapiro. 1995. *Fundamentals of engineering thermodynamics*, 3rd ed. John Wiley & Sons, New York.

Pátek, J. and J. Klomfar. 1995. Simple functions for fast calculations of selected thermodynamic properties of the ammonia-water system. *International Journal of Refrigeration* 18(4):228-234.

Stoecker, W.F. 1989. *Design of thermal systems*, 3rd ed. McGraw-Hill, New York.

Van Wylen, C.J. and R.E. Sonntag. 1985. *Fundamentals of classical thermodynamics*, 3rd ed. John Wiley & Sons, New York.

Zawacki, T.S. 1999. Effect of ammonia-water mixture database on cycle calculations. *Proceedings of the International Sorption Heat Pump Conference,* Munich.

CHAPTER 3

FLUID FLOW

FLOWING fluids in HVAC&R systems can transfer heat, mass, and momentum. This chapter introduces the basics of fluid mechanics related to HVAC processes, reviews pertinent flow processes, and presents a general discussion of single-phase fluid flow analysis.

FLUID PROPERTIES

Solids and fluids react differently to shear stress: solids deform only a finite amount, whereas fluids deform continuously until the stress is removed. Both liquids and gases are fluids, although the natures of their molecular interactions differ strongly in both degree of compressibility and formation of a free surface (interface) in liquid. In general, liquids are considered incompressible fluids; gases may range from **compressible** to nearly **incompressible**. Liquids have unbalanced molecular cohesive forces at or near the surface (interface), so the liquid surface tends to contract and has properties similar to a stretched elastic membrane. A liquid surface, therefore, is under tension (**surface tension**).

Fluid motion can be described by several simplified models. The simplest is the **ideal-fluid** model, which assumes that the fluid has no resistance to shearing. Ideal fluid flow analysis is well developed (e.g., Schlichting 1979), and may be valid for a wide range of applications.

Viscosity is a measure of a fluid's resistance to shear. Viscous effects are taken into account by categorizing a fluid as either Newtonian or non-Newtonian. In **Newtonian fluids**, the rate of deformation is directly proportional to the shearing stress; most fluids in the HVAC industry (e.g., water, air, most refrigerants) can be treated as Newtonian. In **non-Newtonian fluids**, the relationship between the rate of deformation and shear stress is more complicated.

Density

The density ρ of a fluid is its mass per unit volume. The densities of air and water (Fox et al. 2004) at standard indoor conditions of 20°C and 101.325 kPa (sea-level atmospheric pressure) are

$$\rho_{water} = 998 \text{ kg/m}^3$$

$$\rho_{air} = 1.21 \text{ kg/m}^3$$

Viscosity

Viscosity is the resistance of adjacent fluid layers to shear. A classic example of shear is shown in Figure 1, where a fluid is between two parallel plates, each of area A separated by distance Y. The bottom plate is fixed and the top plate is moving, which induces a shearing force in the fluid. For a Newtonian fluid, the tangential force F per unit area required to slide one plate with velocity V parallel to the other is proportional to V/Y:

$$F/A = \mu(V/Y) \tag{1}$$

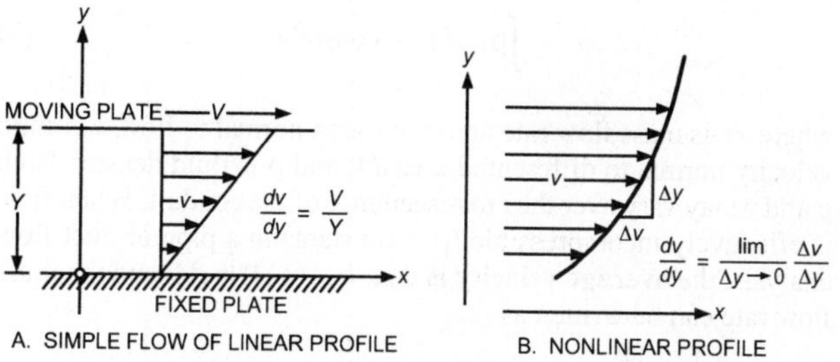

Fig. 1 Velocity Profiles and Gradients in Shear Flows

where the proportionality factor μ is the **absolute** or **dynamic viscosity** of the fluid. The ratio of F to A is the **shearing stress** τ, and V/Y is the **lateral velocity gradient** (Figure 1A). In complex flows, velocity and shear stress may vary across the flow field; this is expressed by

$$\tau = \mu \frac{dv}{dy} \tag{2}$$

The velocity gradient associated with viscous shear for a simple case involving flow velocity in the x direction but of varying magnitude in the y direction is illustrated in Figure 1B.

Absolute viscosity μ depends primarily on temperature. For gases (except near the critical point), viscosity increases with the square root of the absolute temperature, as predicted by the kinetic theory of gases. In contrast, a liquid's viscosity decreases as temperature increases. Absolute viscosities of various fluids are given in Chapter 33.

Absolute viscosity has dimensions of force × time/length². At standard indoor conditions, the absolute viscosities of water and dry air (Fox et al. 2004) are

$$\mu_{water} = 1.01 \text{ (mN·s)/m}^2$$

$$\mu_{air} = 18.1 \text{ (μN·s)/m}^2$$

Another common unit of viscosity is the **centipoise** (1 centipoise = 1 g/(s·m) = 1 mPa·s). At standard conditions, water has a viscosity close to 1.0 centipoise.

In fluid dynamics, **kinematic viscosity** ν is sometimes used in lieu of absolute or dynamic viscosity. Kinematic viscosity is the ratio of absolute viscosity to density:

$$\nu = \mu/\rho$$

At standard indoor conditions, the kinematic viscosities of water and dry air (Fox et al. 2004) are

$$\nu_{water} = 1.01 \text{ mm}^2\text{/s}$$

$$\nu_{air} = 15.0 \text{ mm}^2\text{/s}$$

The preparation of this chapter is assigned to TC 1.3, Heat Transfer and Fluid Flow.

The **stoke** (1 cm²/s) and **centistoke** (1 mm²/s) are common units for kinematic viscosity.

BASIC RELATIONS OF FLUID DYNAMICS

This section discusses fundamental principles of fluid flow for constant-property, homogeneous, incompressible fluids and introduces fluid dynamic considerations used in most analyses.

Continuity in a Pipe or Duct

Conservation of mass applied to fluid flow in a conduit requires that mass not be created or destroyed. Specifically, the mass flow rate into a section of pipe must equal the mass flow rate out of that section of pipe if no mass is accumulated or lost (e.g., from leakage). This requires that

$$\dot{m} = \int \rho v \, dA = \text{constant} \tag{3}$$

where $\dot{m}$ is mass flow rate across the area normal to flow, v is fluid velocity normal to differential area dA, and ρ is fluid density. Both ρ and v may vary over the cross section A of the conduit. When flow is effectively incompressible (ρ = constant) in a pipe or duct flow analysis, the **average velocity** is then $V = (1/A)\int v\,dA$, and the mass flow rate can be written as

$$\dot{m} = \rho V A \tag{4}$$

or

$$Q = \dot{m}/\rho = AV \tag{5}$$

where Q is **volumetric flow rate.**

Bernoulli Equation and Pressure Variation in Flow Direction

The **Bernoulli equation** is a fundamental principle of fluid flow analysis. It involves the conservation of momentum and energy along a streamline; it is not generally applicable across streamlines. Development is fairly straightforward. The first law of thermodynamics can apply to both mechanical flow energies (**kinetic** and **potential energy**) and thermal energies.

The change in energy content ΔE per unit mass of flowing fluid is a result of the work per unit mass w done on the system plus the heat per unit mass q absorbed or rejected:

$$\Delta E = w + q \tag{6}$$

Fluid energy is composed of kinetic, potential (because of elevation z), and internal (u) energies. Per unit mass of fluid, the energy change relation between two sections of the system is

$$\Delta\left(\frac{v^2}{2} + gz + u\right) = E_M - \Delta\left(\frac{p}{\rho}\right) + q \tag{7}$$

where the work terms are (1) external work E_M from a fluid machine (E_M is positive for a pump or blower) and (2) flow work p/ρ (where p = pressure), and g is the gravitational constant. Rearranging, the energy equation can be written as the **generalized Bernoulli equation**:

$$\Delta\left(\frac{v^2}{2} + gz + u + \frac{p}{\rho}\right) = E_M + q \tag{8}$$

The expression in parentheses in Equation (8) is the sum of the kinetic energy, potential energy, internal energy, and flow work per unit mass flow rate. In cases with no work interaction, no heat transfer, and no viscous frictional forces that convert mechanical energy into internal energy, this expression is constant and is known as the **Bernoulli constant *B***:

$$\frac{v^2}{2} + gz + \left(\frac{p}{\rho}\right) = B \tag{9}$$

Alternative forms of this relation are obtained through multiplication by ρ or division by g:

$$p + \frac{\rho v^2}{2} + \rho g z = \rho B \tag{10}$$

$$\frac{p}{\gamma} + \rho\frac{v^2}{2g} + z = \frac{B}{g} \tag{11}$$

where $\gamma = \rho g$ is the **specific mass** or **density**. Note that Equations (9) to (11) assume no frictional losses.

The units in the first form of the Bernoulli equation [Equation (9)] are energy per unit mass; in Equation (10), energy per unit volume; in Equation (11), energy per unit weight, usually called **head**. Note that the units for head reduce to just length [i.e., (N·m)/N to m]. In gas flow analysis, Equation (10) is often used, and ρgz is negligible. Equation (10) should be used when density variations occur. For liquid flows, Equation (11) is commonly used. Identical results are obtained with the three forms if the units are consistent and fluids are homogeneous.

Many systems of pipes, ducts, pumps, and blowers can be considered as one-dimensional flow along a streamline (i.e., variation in velocity across the pipe or duct is ignored, and local velocity v = average velocity V). When v varies significantly across the cross section, the kinetic energy term in the Bernoulli constant B is expressed as $\alpha V^2/2$, where the **kinetic energy factor** ($\alpha > 1$) expresses the ratio of the true kinetic energy of the velocity profile to that of the average velocity. For laminar flow in a wide rectangular channel, $\alpha = 1.54$, and in a pipe, $\alpha = 2.0$. For turbulent flow in a duct, $\alpha \approx 1$.

Heat transfer q may often be ignored. Conversion of mechanical energy to internal energy Δu may be expressed as a loss E_L. The change in the Bernoulli constant ($\Delta B = B_2 - B_1$) between stations 1 and 2 along the conduit can be expressed as

$$\left(\frac{p}{\rho} + \alpha\frac{V^2}{2} + gz\right)_1 + E_M - E_L = \left(\frac{p}{\rho} + \alpha\frac{V^2}{2} + gz\right)_2 \tag{12}$$

or, by dividing by g, in the form

$$\left(\frac{p}{\gamma} + \alpha\frac{V^2}{2g} + z\right)_1 + H_M - H_L = \left(\frac{p}{\gamma} + \alpha\frac{V^2}{2g} + z\right)_2 \tag{13}$$

Note that Equation (12) has units of energy per mass, whereas each term in Equation (13) has units of energy per weight, or head. The terms E_M and E_L are defined as positive, where $gH_M = E_M$ represents energy added to the conduit flow by pumps or blowers. A turbine or fluid motor thus has a negative H_M or E_M. The terms E_M and H_M (= E_M/g) are defined as positive, and represent energy added to the fluid by pumps or blowers. *The simplicity of Equation (13) should be noted*; the total head at station 1 (pressure head plus velocity head plus elevation head) plus the head added by a pump (H_M) minus the head lost through friction (H_L) is the total head at station 2.

Laminar Flow

When real-fluid effects of viscosity or turbulence are included, the continuity relation in Equation (5) is not changed, but V must be evaluated from the integral of the velocity profile, using local velocities. In fluid flow past fixed boundaries, velocity at the boundary is zero, velocity gradients exist, and shear stresses are produced. The equations of motion then become complex, and exact solutions are difficult to find except in simple cases for laminar flow between flat plates, between rotating cylinders, or within a pipe or tube.

For steady, fully developed laminar flow between two parallel plates (Figure 2), shear stress τ varies linearly with distance y from the centerline (transverse to the flow; $y = 0$ in the center of the channel). For a wide rectangular channel $2b$ tall, τ can be written as

$$\tau = \left(\frac{y}{b}\right)\tau_w = \mu\frac{dv}{dy} \tag{14}$$

where τ_w is wall shear stress $[b(dp/ds)]$, and s is flow direction. Because velocity is zero at the wall ($y = b$), Equation (14) can be integrated to yield

$$v = \left(\frac{b^2 - y^2}{2\mu}\right)\frac{dp}{ds} \tag{15}$$

The resulting parabolic velocity profile in a wide rectangular channel is commonly called **Poiseuille flow**. Maximum velocity occurs at the centerline ($y = 0$), and the average velocity V is 2/3 of the maximum velocity. From this, the longitudinal pressure drop in terms of V can be written as

$$\frac{dp}{ds} = -\left(\frac{3\mu V}{b^2}\right) \tag{16}$$

A parabolic velocity profile can also be derived for a pipe of radius R. V is 1/2 of the maximum velocity, and the pressure drop can be written as

$$\frac{dp}{ds} = -\left(\frac{8\mu V}{R^2}\right) \tag{17}$$

Turbulence

Fluid flows are generally turbulent, involving random perturbations or fluctuations of the flow (velocity and pressure), characterized by an extensive hierarchy of scales or frequencies (Robertson 1963). Flow disturbances that are not chaotic but have some degree of periodicity (e.g., the oscillating vortex trail behind bodies) have been erroneously identified as turbulence. Only flows involving random perturbations without any order or periodicity are turbulent; velocity in such a flow varies with time or locale of measurement (Figure 3).

Turbulence can be quantified statistically. The velocity most often used is the time-averaged velocity. The strength of turbulence is characterized by the root mean square (RMS) of the instantaneous variation in velocity about this mean. Turbulence causes the fluid to transfer momentum, heat, and mass very rapidly across the flow.

Laminar and turbulent flows can be differentiated using the **Reynolds number Re**, which is a dimensionless relative ratio of inertial forces to viscous forces:

$$Re_L = VL/\nu \tag{18}$$

where L is the characteristic length scale and ν is the kinematic viscosity of the fluid. In flow through pipes, tubes, and ducts, the characteristic length scale is the **hydraulic diameter D_h**, given by

$$D_h = 4A/P_w \tag{19}$$

where A is the cross-sectional area of the pipe, duct, or tube, and P_w is the wetted perimeter.

For a round pipe, D_h equals the pipe diameter. In general, **laminar flow** in pipes or ducts exists when the Reynolds number (based on D_h) is less than 2300. Fully **turbulent flow** exists when Re_{D_h} > 10 000. For 2300 < Re_{D_h} < 10 000, transitional flow exists, and predictions are unreliable.

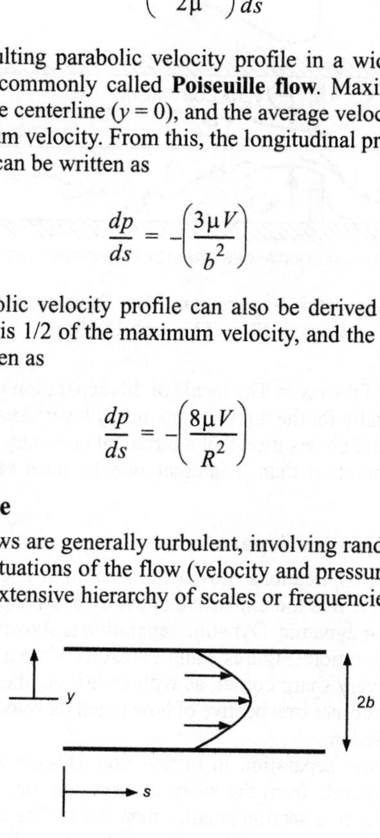

Fig. 2 Dimensions for Steady, Fully Developed Laminar Flow Equations

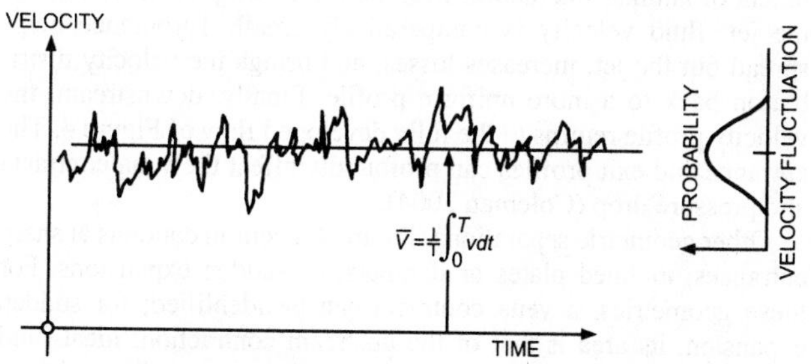

Fig. 3 Velocity Fluctuation at Point in Turbulent Flow

BASIC FLOW PROCESSES

Wall Friction

At the boundary of real-fluid flow, the relative tangential velocity at the fluid surface is zero. Sometimes in turbulent flow studies, velocity at the wall may appear finite and nonzero, implying a **fluid slip** at the wall. However, this is not the case; the conflict results from difficulty in velocity measurements near the wall (Goldstein 1938). Zero wall velocity leads to high shear stress near the wall boundary, which slows adjacent fluid layers. Thus, a velocity profile develops near a wall, with velocity increasing from zero at the wall to an exterior value within a finite lateral distance.

Laminar and turbulent flow differ significantly in their velocity profiles. Turbulent flow profiles are flat and laminar profiles are more pointed (Figure 4). As discussed, fluid velocities of the turbulent profile near the wall must drop to zero more rapidly than those of the laminar profile, so shear stress and friction are much greater in turbulent flow. Fully developed conduit flow may be characterized by the **pipe factor**, which is the ratio of average to maximum (centerline) velocity. Viscous velocity profiles result in pipe factors of 0.667 and 0.50 for wide rectangular and axisymmetric conduits. Figure 5 indicates much higher values for rectangular and circular conduits for turbulent flow. Because of the flat velocity profiles, the

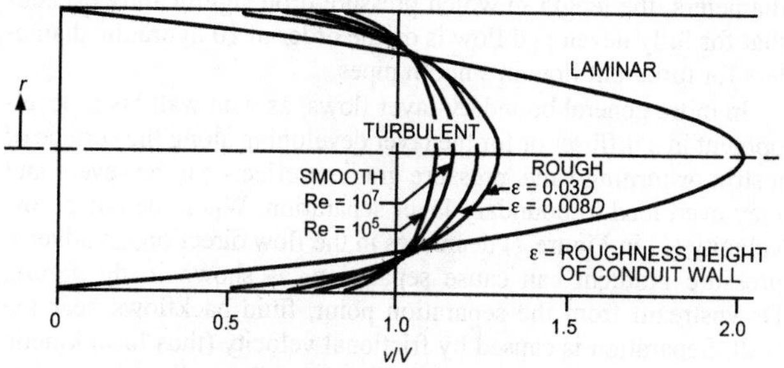

Fig. 4 Velocity Profiles of Flow in Pipes

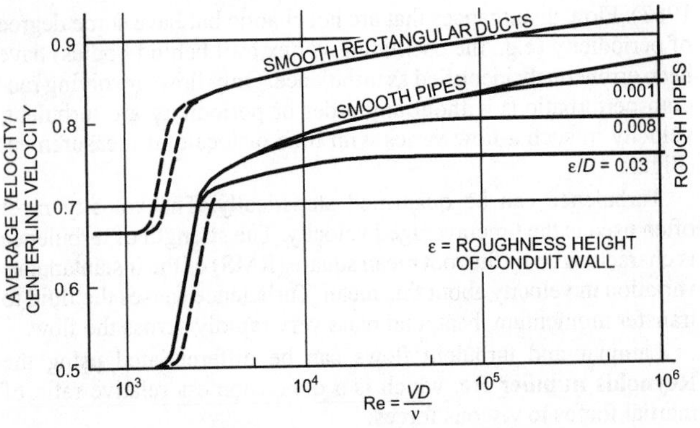

Fig. 5 Pipe Factor for Flow in Conduits

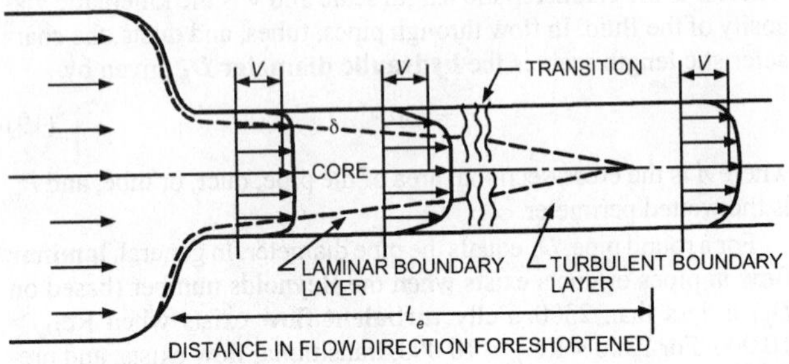

Fig. 6 Flow in Conduit Entrance Region

kinetic energy factor α in Equations (12) and (13) ranges from 1.01 to 1.10 for fully developed turbulent pipe flow.

Boundary Layer

The boundary layer is the region close to the wall where wall friction affects flow. Boundary layer thickness (usually denoted by δ) is thin compared to downstream flow distance. For external flow over a body, fluid velocity varies from zero at the wall to a maximum at distance δ from the wall. Boundary layers are generally laminar near the start of their formation but may become turbulent downstream.

A significant boundary-layer occurrence exists in a pipeline or conduit following a well-rounded entrance (Figure 6). Layers grow from the walls until they meet at the center of the pipe. Near the start of the straight conduit, the layer is very thin and most likely laminar, so the uniform velocity core outside has a velocity only slightly greater than the average velocity. As the layer grows in thickness, the slower velocity near the wall requires a velocity increase in the uniform core to satisfy continuity. As flow proceeds, the wall layers grow (and centerline velocity increases) until they join, after an **entrance length L_e**. Applying the Bernoulli relation of Equation (10) to core flow indicates a decrease in pressure along the layer. Ross (1956) shows that, although the entrance length L_e is many diameters, the length in which pressure drop significantly exceeds that for fully developed flow is on the order of 10 hydraulic diameters for turbulent flow in smooth pipes.

In more general boundary-layer flows, as with wall layer development in a diffuser or for the layer developing along the surface of a strut or turning vane, pressure gradient effects can be severe and may even lead to boundary layer separation. When the outer flow velocity (v_1 in Figure 7) decreases in the flow direction, an adverse pressure gradient can cause separation, as shown in the figure. Downstream from the separation point, fluid backflows near the wall. Separation is caused by frictional velocity (thus local kinetic energy) reduction near the wall. Flow near the wall no longer has energy to move into the higher pressure imposed by the decrease in

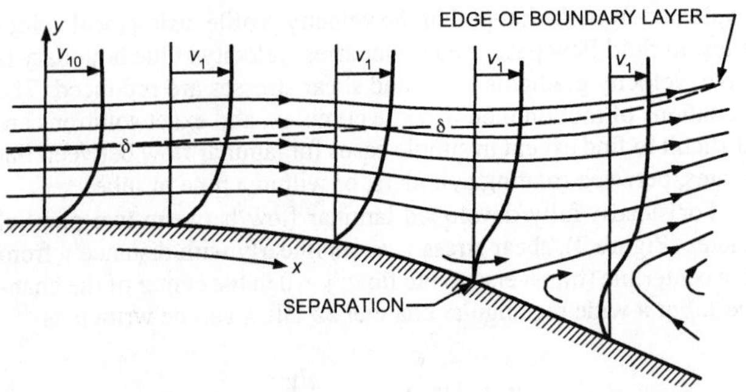

Fig. 7 Boundary Layer Flow to Separation

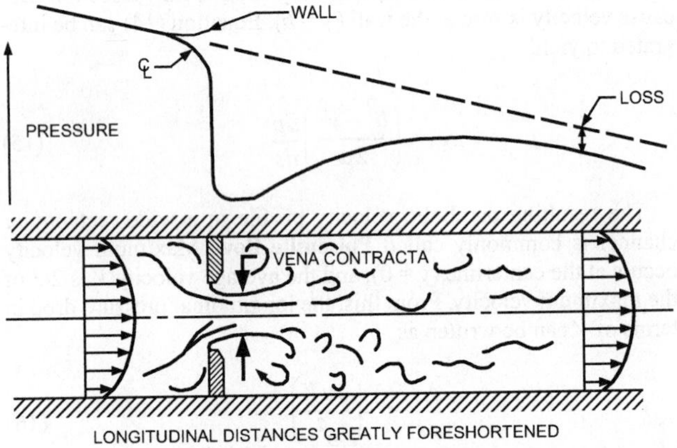

Fig. 8 Geometric Separation, Flow Development, and Loss in Flow Through Orifice

v_1 at the edge of the layer. The locale of this separation is difficult to predict, especially for the turbulent boundary layer. Analyses verify the experimental observation that a turbulent boundary layer is less subject to separation than a laminar one because of its greater kinetic energy.

Flow Patterns with Separation

In technical applications, flow with separation is common and often accepted if it is too expensive to avoid. Flow separation may be geometric or dynamic. Dynamic separation is shown in Figure 7. Geometric separation (Figures 8 and 9) results when a fluid stream passes over a very sharp corner, as with an orifice; the fluid generally leaves the corner irrespective of how much its velocity has been reduced by friction.

For geometric separation in orifice flow (Figure 8), the outer streamlines separate from the sharp corners and, because of fluid inertia, contract to a section smaller than the orifice opening. The smallest section is known as the **vena contracta** and generally has a limiting area of about six-tenths of the orifice opening. After the vena contracta, the fluid stream expands rather slowly through turbulent or laminar interaction with the fluid along its sides. Outside the jet, fluid velocity is comparatively small. Turbulence helps spread out the jet, increases losses, and brings the velocity distribution back to a more uniform profile. Finally, downstream, the velocity profile returns to the fully developed flow of Figure 4. The entrance and exit profiles can profoundly affect the vena contracta and pressure drop (Coleman 2004).

Other geometric separations (Figure 9) occur in conduits at sharp entrances, inclined plates or dampers, or sudden expansions. For these geometries, a vena contracta can be identified; for sudden expansion, its area is that of the upstream contraction. Ideal-fluid theory, using free streamlines, provides insight and predicts contraction coefficients for valves, orifices, and vanes (Robertson 1965).

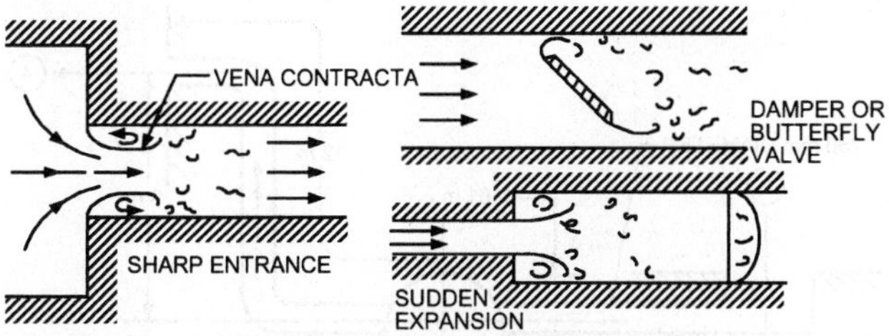

Fig. 9 Examples of Geometric Separation Encountered in Flows in Conduits

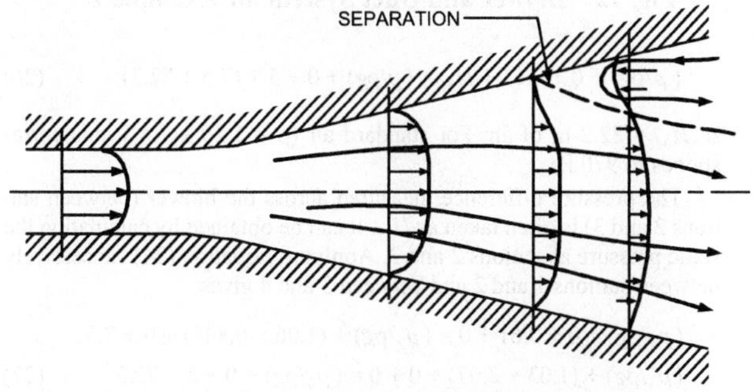

Fig. 10 Separation in Flow in Diffuser

These geometric flow separations produce large losses. To expand a flow efficiently or to have an entrance with minimum losses, design the device with gradual contours, a diffuser, or a rounded entrance.

Flow devices with gradual contours are subject to separation that is more difficult to predict, because it involves the dynamics of boundary-layer growth under an adverse pressure gradient rather than flow over a sharp corner. A diffuser is used to reduce the loss in expansion; it is possible to expand the fluid some distance at a gentle angle without difficulty, particularly if the boundary layer is turbulent. Eventually, separation may occur (Figure 10), which is frequently asymmetrical because of irregularities. Downstream flow involves flow reversal (backflow) and excess losses. Such separation is commonly called **stall** (Kline 1959). Larger expansions may use splitters that divide the diffuser into smaller sections that are less likely to have separations (Moore and Kline 1958). Another technique for controlling separation is to bleed some low-velocity fluid near the wall (Furuya et al. 1976). Alternatively, Heskested (1970) shows that suction at the corner of a sudden expansion has a strong positive effect on geometric separation.

Drag Forces on Bodies or Struts

Bodies in moving fluid streams are subjected to appreciable fluid forces or **drag**. Conventionally, the drag force F_D on a body can be expressed in terms of a **drag coefficient** C_D:

$$F_D = C_D \rho A \left(\frac{V^2}{2}\right) \tag{20}$$

where A is the projected (normal to flow) area of the body. The drag coefficient C_D is a strong function of the body's shape and angularity, and the Reynolds number of the relative flow in terms of the body's characteristic dimension.

For Reynolds numbers of 10^3 to 10^5, the C_D of most bodies is constant because of flow separation, but above 10^5, the C_D of rounded bodies drops suddenly as the surface boundary layer undergoes transition to turbulence. Typical C_D values are given in Table 1; Hoerner (1965) gives expanded values.

Table 1 Drag Coefficients

Body Shape	$10^3 < \text{Re} < 2 \times 10^5$	$\text{Re} > 3 \times 10^5$
Sphere	0.36 to 0.47	~0.1
Disk	1.12	1.12
Streamlined strut	0.1 to 0.3	< 0.1
Circular cylinder	1.0 to 1.1	0.35
Elongated rectangular strut	1.0 to 1.2	1.0 to 1.2
Square strut	~2.0	~2.0

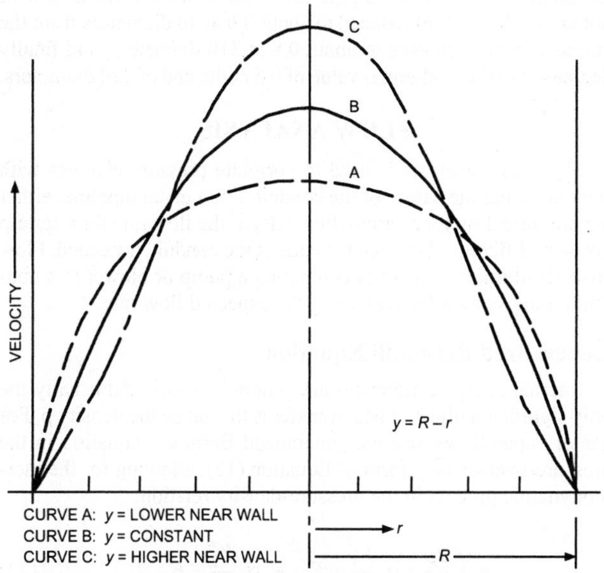

Fig. 11 Effect of Viscosity Variation on Velocity Profile of Laminar Flow in Pipe

Nonisothermal Effects

When appreciable temperature variations exist, the primary fluid properties (density and viscosity) may no longer assumed to be constant, but vary across or along the flow. The Bernoulli equation [Equations (9) to (11)] must be used, because volumetric flow is not constant. With gas flows, the thermodynamic process involved must be considered. In general, this is assessed using Equation (9), written as

$$\int \frac{dp}{\rho} + \frac{V^2}{2} + gz = B \tag{21}$$

Effects of viscosity variations also appear. In nonisothermal laminar flow, the parabolic velocity profile (see Figure 4) is no longer valid. In general, for gases, viscosity increases with the square root of absolute temperature; for liquids, viscosity decreases with increasing temperature. This results in opposite effects.

For fully developed pipe flow, the linear variation in shear stress from the wall value τ_w to zero at the centerline is independent of the temperature gradient. In the section on Laminar Flow, τ is defined as $\tau = (y/b)\,\tau_w$, where y is the distance from the centerline and $2b$ is the wall spacing. For pipe radius $R = D/2$ and distance from the wall $y = R - r$ (see Figure 11), then $\tau = \tau_w(R - y)/R$. Then, solving Equation (2) for the change in velocity yields

$$dv = \left[\frac{\tau_w(R-y)}{R\mu}\right] dy = -\left(\frac{\tau_w}{R\mu}\right) r\, dr \tag{22}$$

When fluid viscosity is lower near the wall than at the center (because of external heating of liquid or cooling of gas by heat transfer through the pipe wall), the velocity gradient is steeper near the wall and flatter near the center, so the profile is generally flattened. When liquid is cooled or gas is heated, the velocity profile is more pointed for laminar flow (Figure 11). Calculations for such flows of gases and liquid metals in pipes are in Deissler (1951). Occurrences in turbulent flow are less apparent than in laminar flow. If enough heating is applied to gaseous flows, the viscosity increase can cause reversion to laminar flow.

Buoyancy effects and the gradual approach of the fluid temperature to equilibrium with that outside the pipe can cause considerable variation in the velocity profile along the conduit. Colborne and Drobitch (1966) found the pipe factor for upward vertical flow of hot air at a Re < 2000 reduced to about 0.6 at 40 diameters from the entrance, then increased to about 0.8 at 210 diameters, and finally decreased to the isothermal value of 0.5 at the end of 320 diameters.

FLOW ANALYSIS

Fluid flow analysis is used to correlate pressure changes with flow rates and the nature of the conduit. For a given pipeline, either the pressure drop for a certain flow rate, or the flow rate for a certain pressure difference between the ends of the conduit, is needed. Flow analysis ultimately involves comparing a pump or blower to a conduit piping system for evaluating the expected flow rate.

Generalized Bernoulli Equation

Internal energy differences are generally small, and usually the only significant effect of heat transfer is to change the density ρ. For gas or vapor flows, use the generalized Bernoulli equation in the pressure-over-density form of Equation (12), allowing for the thermodynamic process in the pressure-density relation:

$$-\int_1^2 \frac{dp}{\rho} + \alpha_1 \frac{V_1^2}{2} + E_M = \alpha_2 \frac{V_2^2}{2} + E_L \quad (23)$$

Elevation changes involving z are often negligible and are dropped. The pressure form of Equation (10) is generally unacceptable when appreciable density variations occur, because the volumetric flow rate differs at the two stations. This is particularly serious in friction-loss evaluations where the density usually varies over considerable lengths of conduit (Benedict and Carlucci 1966). When the flow is essentially incompressible, Equation (20) is satisfactory.

Example 1. Specify a blower to produce isothermal airflow of 200 L/s through a ducting system (Figure 12). Accounting for intake and fitting losses, equivalent conduit lengths are 18 and 50 m, and flow is isothermal. Pressure at the inlet (station 1) and following the discharge (station 4), where velocity is zero, is the same. Frictional losses H_L are evaluated as 7.5 m of air between stations 1 and 2, and 72.3 m between stations 3 and 4.

Solution: The following form of the generalized Bernoulli relation is used in place of Equation (12), which also could be used:

$$(p_1/\rho_1 g) + \alpha_1(V_1^2/2g) + z_1 + H_M = (p_2/\rho_2 g) + \alpha_2(V_2^2/2g) + z_2 + H_L \quad (24)$$

The term $V_1^2/2g$ can be calculated as follows:

$$A_1 = \pi\left(\frac{D}{2}\right)^2 = \pi\left(\frac{0.250}{2}\right)^2 = 0.0491 \text{ m}^2$$

$$V_1 = Q/A_1 = \frac{0.200}{0.0491} = 4.07 \text{ m/s} \quad (25)$$

$$V_1^2/2g = (4.07)^2/2(9.8) = 0.846 \text{ m}$$

The term $V_2^2/2g$ can be calculated in a similar manner.

In Equation (24), H_M is evaluated by applying the relation between any two points on opposite sides of the blower. Because conditions at stations 1 and 4 are known, they are used, and the location-specifying subscripts on the right side of Equation (24) are changed to 4. Note that $p_1 = p_4 = p$, $\rho_1 = \rho_4 = \rho$, and $V_1 = V_4 = 0$. Thus,

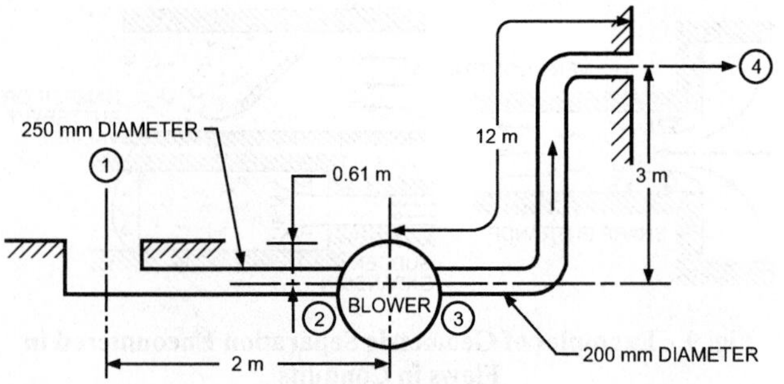

Fig. 12 Blower and Duct System for Example 1

$$(p/\rho g) + 0 + 0.61 + H_M = (p/\rho g) + 0 + 3 + (7.5 + 72.3) \quad (26)$$

so $H_M = 82.2$ m of air. For standard air ($\rho = 1.20$ kg/m^3), this corresponds to 970 Pa.

The pressure difference measured across the blower (between stations 2 and 3) is often taken as H_M. It can be obtained by calculating the static pressure at stations 2 and 3. Applying Equation (24) successively between stations 1 and 2 and between 3 and 4 gives

$$(p_1/\rho g) + 0 + 0.61 + 0 = (p_2/\rho g) + (1.06 \times 0.846) + 0 + 7.5$$
$$(p_3/\rho g) + (1.03 \times 2.07) + 0 + 0 = (p_4/\rho g) + 0 + 3 + 72.3 \quad (27)$$

where α just ahead of the blower is taken as 1.06, and just after the blower as 1.03; the latter value is uncertain because of possible uneven discharge from the blower. Static pressures p_1 and p_4 may be taken as zero gage. Thus,

$$p_2/\rho g = -7.8 \text{ m of air}$$
$$p_3/\rho g = 73.2 \text{ m of air} \quad (28)$$

The difference between these two numbers is 81 m, which is not the H_M calculated after Equation (24) as 82.2 m. The apparent discrepancy results from ignoring the velocity at stations 2 and 3. Actually, H_M is

$$H_M = (p_3/\rho g) + \alpha_3(V_3^2/2g) - [(p_2/\rho g) + \alpha_2(V_2^2/2g)]$$
$$= 73.2 + (1.03 \times 2.07) - [-7.8 + (1.06 \times 0.846)]$$
$$= 75.3 - (-6.9) = 82.2 \text{ m} \quad (29)$$

The required blower energy is the same, no matter how it is evaluated. It is the specific energy added to the system by the machine. Only when the conduit size and velocity profiles on both sides of the machine are the same is E_M or H_M simply found from $\Delta p = p_3 - p_2$.

Conduit Friction

The loss term E_L or H_L of Equation (12) or (13) accounts for friction caused by conduit-wall shearing stresses and losses from conduit-section changes. H_L is the head loss (i.e., loss of energy per unit weight).

In real-fluid flow, a frictional shear occurs at bounding walls, gradually influencing flow further away from the boundary. A lateral velocity profile is produced and flow energy is converted into heat (fluid internal energy), which is generally unrecoverable (a loss). This loss in fully developed conduit flow is evaluated using the **Darcy-Weisbach equation**:

$$H_{Lf} = f\left(\frac{L}{D}\right)\left(\frac{V^2}{2g}\right) \quad (30)$$

where L is the length of conduit of diameter D and f is the **Darcy-Weisbach friction factor**. Sometimes a numerically different relation is used with the **Fanning friction factor** (1/4 of the Darcy friction factor f). The value of f is nearly constant for turbulent flow, varying only from about 0.01 to 0.05.

For fully developed laminar-viscous flow in a pipe, loss is evaluated from Equation (17) as follows:

$$H_{Lf} = \frac{L}{\rho g}\left(\frac{8\mu V}{R^2}\right) = \frac{32 L \nu V}{D^2 g} = \frac{64}{VD/\nu}\left(\frac{L}{D}\right)\left(\frac{V^2}{2g}\right) \qquad (31)$$

where Re = VD/ν and f = 64/Re. Thus, for laminar flow, the friction factor varies inversely with the Reynolds number. The value of 64/Re varies with channel shape. A good summary of shape factors is provided by Incropera and DeWitt (2002).

With turbulent flow, friction loss depends not only on flow conditions, as characterized by the Reynolds number, but also on the **roughness height** ε of the conduit wall surface. The variation is complex and is expressed in diagram form (Moody 1944), as shown in Figure 13. Historically, the Moody diagram has been used to determine friction factors, but empirical relations suitable for use in modeling programs have been developed. Most are applicable to limited ranges of Reynolds number and relative roughness. Churchill (1977) developed a relationship that is valid for all ranges of Reynolds numbers, and is more accurate than reading the Moody diagram:

$$f = 8\left[\left(\frac{8}{\mathrm{Re}_{D_h}}\right)^{12} + \frac{1}{(A+B)^{1.5}}\right]^{1/12} \qquad (32a)$$

$$A = \left[2.457 \ln\left(\frac{1}{\left(7/\mathrm{Re}_{D_h}\right)^{0.9} + \left(0.27\varepsilon/D_h\right)}\right)\right]^{16} \qquad (32b)$$

$$B = \left(\frac{37\,530}{\mathrm{Re}_{D_h}}\right)^{16} \qquad (32c)$$

Inspection of the Moody diagram indicates that, for high Reynolds numbers and relative roughness, the friction factor becomes independent of the Reynolds number in a fully rough flow or fully turbulent regime. A **transition region** from laminar to turbulent flow occurs when 2000 < Re < 10 000. Roughness height ε, which may increase with conduit use, fouling, or aging, is usually tabulated for different types of pipes as shown in Table 2.

Table 2 Effective Roughness of Conduit Surfaces

Material	ε, µm
Commercially smooth brass, lead, copper, or plastic pipe	1.52
Steel and wrought iron	46
Galvanized iron or steel	152
Cast iron	259

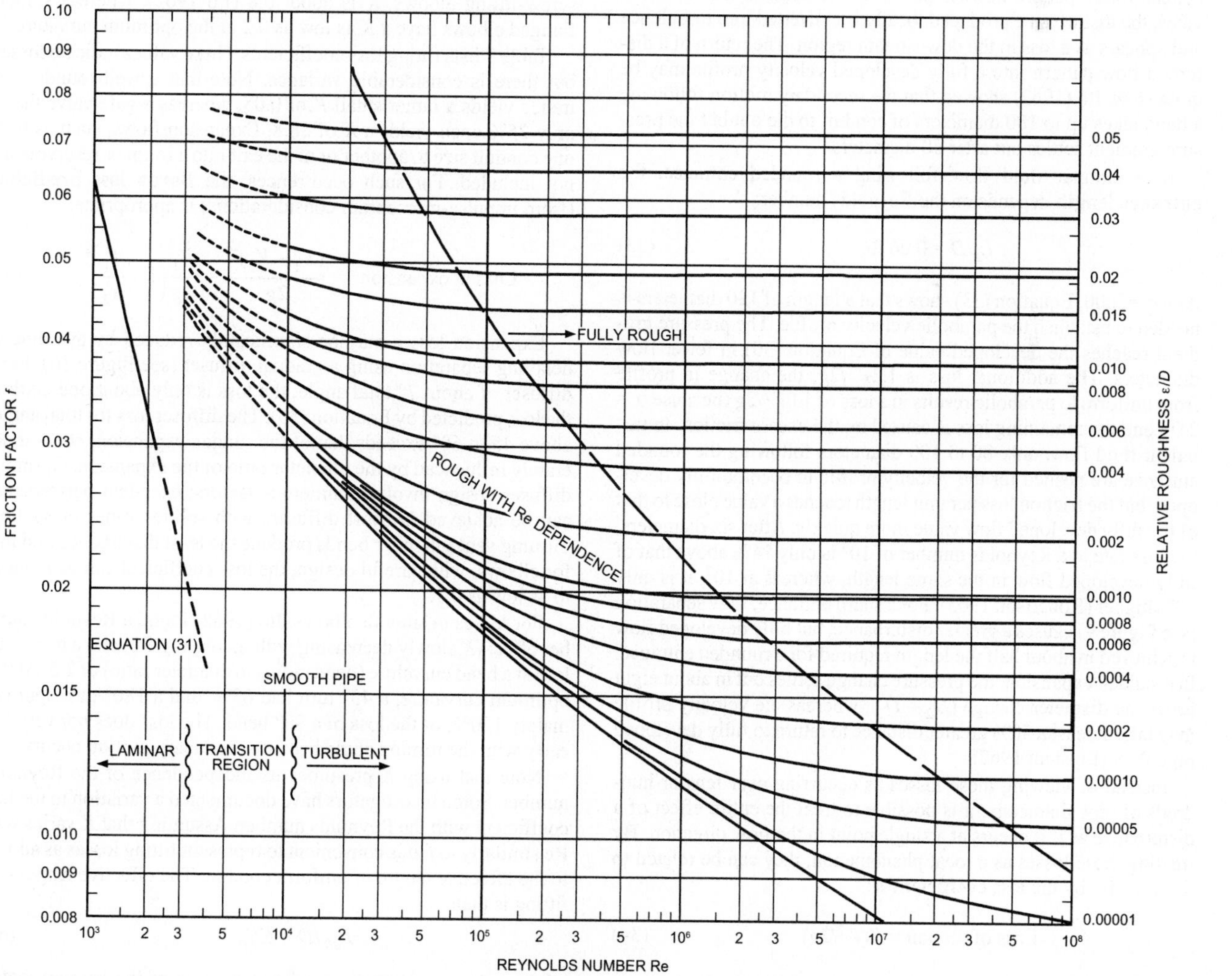

Fig. 13 Relation Between Friction Factor and Reynolds Number
(Moody 1944)

Noncircular Conduits. Air ducts are often rectangular in cross section. The equivalent circular conduit corresponding to the noncircular conduit must be found before the friction factor can be determined.

For turbulent flow, **hydraulic diameter D_h** is substituted for D in Equation (30) and in the Reynolds number. Noncircular duct friction can be evaluated to within 5% for all except very extreme cross sections (e.g., tubes with deep grooves or ridges). A more refined method for finding the equivalent circular duct diameter is given in Chapter 13. With laminar flow, the loss predictions may be off by a factor as large as two.

Valve, Fitting, and Transition Losses

Valve and section changes (contractions, expansions and diffusers, elbows, bends, or tees), as well as entrances and exits, distort the fully developed velocity profiles (see Figure 4) and introduce extra flow losses that may dissipate as heat into pipelines or duct systems. Valves, for example, produce such extra losses to control the fluid flow rate. In contractions and expansions, flow separation as shown in Figures 9 and 10 causes the extra loss. The loss at rounded entrances develops as flow accelerates to higher velocities; this higher velocity near the wall leads to wall shear stresses greater than those of fully developed flow (see Figure 6). In flow around bends, the velocity increases along the inner wall near the start of the bend. This increased velocity creates a secondary fluid motion in a double helical vortex pattern downstream from the bend. In all these devices, the disturbance produced locally is converted into turbulence and appears as a loss in the downstream region. The return of a disturbed flow pattern into a fully developed velocity profile may be quite slow. Ito (1962) showed that the secondary motion following a bend takes up to 100 diameters of conduit to die out but the pressure gradient settles out after 50 diameters.

In a laminar fluid flow following a rounded entrance, the **entrance length** depends on the Reynolds number:

$$L_e/D = 0.06\ \text{Re} \tag{33}$$

At Re = 2000, Equation (33) shows that a length of 120 diameters is needed to establish the parabolic velocity profile. The pressure gradient reaches the developed value of Equation (30) in fewer flow diameters. The additional loss is $1.2V^2/2g$; the change in profile from uniform to parabolic results in a loss of $1.0V^2/2g$ (because α = 2.0), and the remaining loss is caused by the excess friction. In turbulent fluid flow, only 80 to 100 diameters following the rounded entrance are needed for the velocity profile to become fully developed, but the friction loss per unit length reaches a value close to that of the fully developed flow value more quickly. After six diameters, the loss rate at a Reynolds number of 10^5 is only 14% above that of fully developed flow in the same length, whereas at 10^7, it is only 10% higher (Robertson 1963). For a sharp entrance, flow separation (see Figure 9) causes a greater disturbance, but fully developed flow is achieved in about half the length required for a rounded entrance. In a sudden expansion, the pressure change settles out in about eight times the diameter change ($D_2 - D_1$), whereas the velocity profile may take at least a 50% greater distance to return to fully developed pipe flow (Lipstein 1962).

Instead of viewing these losses as occurring over tens or hundreds of pipe diameters, it is possible to treat the entire effect of a disturbance as if it occurs at a single point in the flow direction. By treating these losses as a local phenomenon, they can be related to the velocity by the **loss coefficient *K***:

$$\text{Loss of section} = K(V^2/2g) \tag{34}$$

Chapter 22 and the *Pipe Friction Manual* (Hydraulic Institute 1961) have information for pipe applications. Chapter 21 gives information for airflow. The same type of fitting in pipes and ducts may yield a different loss, because flow disturbances are controlled by the detailed geometry of the fitting. The elbow of a small threaded pipe fitting differs from a bend in a circular duct. For 90° screw-fitting elbows, K is about 0.8 (Ito 1962), whereas smooth flanged elbows have a K as low as 0.2 at the optimum curvature.

Table 3 Fitting Loss Coefficients of Turbulent Flow

Fitting	Geometry	$K = \dfrac{\Delta P/\rho g}{V^2/2g}$
Entrance	Sharp	0.5
	Well-rounded	0.05
Contraction	Sharp (D_2/D_1 = 0.5)	0.38
90° Elbow	Miter	1.3
	Short radius	0.90
	Long radius	0.60
	Miter with turning vanes	0.2
Globe valve	Open	10
Angle valve	Open	5
Gate valve	Open	0.19 to 0.22
	75% open	1.10
	50% open	3.6
	25% open	28.8
Any valve	Closed	∞
Tee	Straight-through flow	0.5
	Flow through branch	1.8

Table 3 lists fitting loss coefficients. These values indicate losses, but there is considerable variance. Note that a well-rounded entrance yields a rather small K of 0.05, whereas a gate valve that is only 25% open yields a K of 28.8. Expansion flows, such as from one conduit size to another or at the exit into a room or reservoir, are not included. For such occurrences, the **Borda loss prediction** (from impulse-momentum considerations) is appropriate:

$$\text{Loss at expansion} = \frac{(V_1 - V_2)^2}{2g} = \frac{V_1^2}{2g}\left(1 - \frac{A_1}{A_2}\right)^2 \tag{35}$$

Expansion losses may be significantly reduced by avoiding or delaying separation using a gradual diffuser (see Figure 10). For a diffuser of about 7° total angle, the loss is only about one-sixth of the loss predicted by Equation (35). The diffuser loss for total angles above 45 to 60° exceeds that of the sudden expansion, but is moderately influenced by the diameter ratio of the expansion. Optimum diffuser design involves numerous factors; excellent performance can be achieved in short diffusers with splitter vanes or suction. Turning vanes in miter bends produce the least disturbance and loss for elbows; with careful design, the loss coefficient can be reduced to as low as 0.1.

For losses in smooth elbows, Ito (1962) found a Reynolds number effect (K slowly decreasing with increasing Re) and a minimum loss at a bend curvature (bend radius to diameter ratio) of 2.5. At this optimum curvature, a 45° turn had 63%, and a 180° turn approximately 120%, of the loss of a 90° bend. The loss does not vary linearly with the turning angle because secondary motion occurs.

Note that using K presumes its independence of the Reynolds number. Some investigators have documented a variation in the loss coefficient with the Reynolds number. Assuming that K varies with Re similarly to f, it is convenient to represent fitting losses as adding to the effective length of uniform conduit. The effective length of a fitting is then

$$L_{eff}/D = K/f_{ref} \tag{36}$$

where f_{ref} is an appropriate reference value of the friction factor. Deissler (1951) uses 0.028, and the air duct values in Chapter 21 are based on an f_{ref} of about 0.02. For rough conduits, appreciable

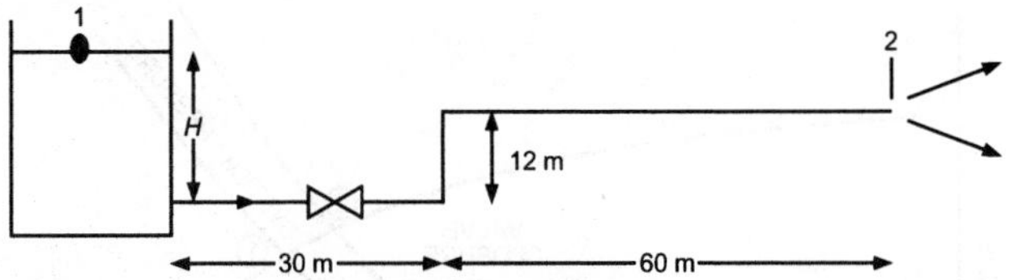

Fig. 14 Diagram for Example 2

errors can occur if the relative roughness does not correspond to that used when f_{ref} was fixed. It is unlikely that fitting losses involving separation are affected by pipe roughness. The effective length method for fitting loss evaluation is still useful.

When a conduit contains a number of section changes or fittings, the values of K are added to the fL/D friction loss, or the L_{eff}/D of the fittings are added to the conduit length L/D for evaluating the total loss H_L. This assumes that each fitting loss is fully developed and its disturbance fully smoothed out before the next section change. Such an assumption is frequently wrong, and the total loss can be overestimated. For elbow flows, the total loss of adjacent bends may be over- or underestimated. The secondary flow pattern after an elbow is such that when one follows another, perhaps in a different plane, the secondary flow of the second elbow may reinforce or partially cancel that of the first. Moving the second elbow a few diameters can reduce the total loss (from more than twice the amount) to less than the loss from one elbow. Screens or perforated plates can be used for smoothing velocity profiles (Wile 1947) and flow spreading. Their effectiveness and loss coefficients depend on their amount of open area (Baines and Peterson 1951).

Example 2. Water at 20°C flows through the piping system shown in Figure 14. Each ell has a very long radius and a loss coefficient of $K = 0.31$; the entrance at the tank is square-edged with $K = 0.5$, and the valve is a fully open globe valve with $K = 10$. The pipe roughness is 250 μm. The density $\rho = 1000$ kg/m³ and kinematic viscosity $\nu = 1.01$ mm²/s.

a. If pipe diameter $D = 150$ mm, what is the elevation H in the tank required to produce a flow of $Q = 60$ L/s?

Solution: Apply Equation (13) between stations 1 and 2 in the figure. Note that $p_1 = p_2$, $V_1 \approx 0$. Assume $\alpha \approx 1$. The result is

$$z_1 - z_2 = H - 12\text{ m} = H_L + V_2^2/2g$$

From Equations (30) and (34), total head loss is

$$H_L = \left(\frac{fL}{D} + \sum K\right)\frac{8Q^2}{\pi^2 g D^4}$$

where $L = 102$ m, $\sum K = 0.5 + (2 \times 0.31) + 10 = 11.1$, and $V^2/2g = V_2^2/2g = 8Q^2/\pi^2 gD^4$. Then, substituting into Equation (13),

$$H = 12\text{ m} + \left(1 + \frac{fL}{D} + \sum K\right)\frac{8Q^2}{\pi^2 g D^4}$$

To calculate the friction factor, first calculate Reynolds number and relative roughness:

$$\text{Re} = VD/\nu = 4Q/(\pi D\nu) = 495\ 150$$
$$\varepsilon/D = 0.0017$$

From the Moody diagram or Equation (32), $f = 0.023$. Then $H_L = 15.7$ m and $H = 27.7$ m.

b. For $H = 22$ m and $D = 150$ mm, what is the flow?

Solution: Applying Equation (13) again and inserting the expression for head loss gives

$$z_1 - z_2 = 10\text{ m} + \left(\frac{fL}{D} + \sum K + 1\right)\frac{8Q^2}{\pi^2 g D^4}$$

Because f depends on Q (unless flow is fully turbulent), iteration is required. The usual procedure is as follows:

1. Assume a value of f, usually the fully rough value for the given values of ε and D.
2. Use this value of f in the energy calculation and solve for Q.

$$Q = \sqrt{\frac{\pi^2 g D^4 (z_1 - z_2)}{8\left(\frac{fL}{D} + \sum K + 1\right)}}$$

3. Use this value of Q to recalculate Re and get a new value of f.
4. Repeat until the new and old values of f agree to two significant figures.

Iteration	f	Q, m/s	Re	f
0	0.0223	0.04737	3.98 E + 05	0.0230
1	0.0230	0.04699	3.95 E + 05	0.0230

As shown in the table, the result after two iterations is $Q \approx 0.047$ m³/s = 47 L/s.

If the resulting flow is in the fully rough zone and the fully rough value of f is used as first guess, only one iteration is required.

c. For $H = 22$ m, what diameter pipe is needed to allow $Q = 55$ L/s?

Solution: The energy equation in part (b) must now be solved for D with Q known. This is difficult because the energy equation cannot be solved for D, even with an assumed value of f. If Churchill's expression for f is stored as a function in a calculator, program, or spreadsheet with an iterative equation solver, a solution can be generated. In this case, $D \approx 0.166$ m = 166 mm. Use the smallest available pipe size greater than 166 mm and adjust the valve as required to achieve the desired flow.

Alternatively, (1) guess an available pipe size, and (2) calculate Re, f, and H for $Q = 55$ L/s. If the resulting value of H is greater than the given value of $H = 22$ m, a larger pipe is required. If the calculated H is less than 22 m, repeat using a smaller available pipe size.

Control Valve Characterization for Liquids

Control valves are characterized by a **discharge coefficient** C_d. As long as the Reynolds number is greater than 250, the orifice equation holds for liquids:

$$Q = C_d A_o \sqrt{2\Delta p/\rho} \tag{37}$$

where A_o is the area of the orifice opening and Δp is the pressure drop across the valve. The discharge coefficient is about 0.63 for sharp-edged configurations and 0.8 to 0.9 for chamfered or rounded configurations.

Incompressible Flow in Systems

Flow devices must be evaluated in terms of their interaction with other elements of the system [e.g., the action of valves in modifying flow rate and in matching the flow-producing device (pump or blower) with the system loss]. Analysis is by the general Bernoulli equation and the loss evaluations noted previously.

A valve regulates or stops the flow of fluid by throttling. The change in flow is not proportional to the change in area of the valve opening. Figures 15 and 16 indicate the nonlinear action of valves in controlling flow. Figure 15 shows flow in a pipe discharging water from a tank that is controlled by a gate valve. The fitting loss coefficient K values are from Table 3; the friction factor f is 0.027. The degree of control also depends on the conduit L/D ratio. For a relatively long conduit, the valve must be nearly closed before its high K value becomes a significant portion of the loss. Figure 16 shows a control damper (essentially a butterfly valve) in a duct discharging

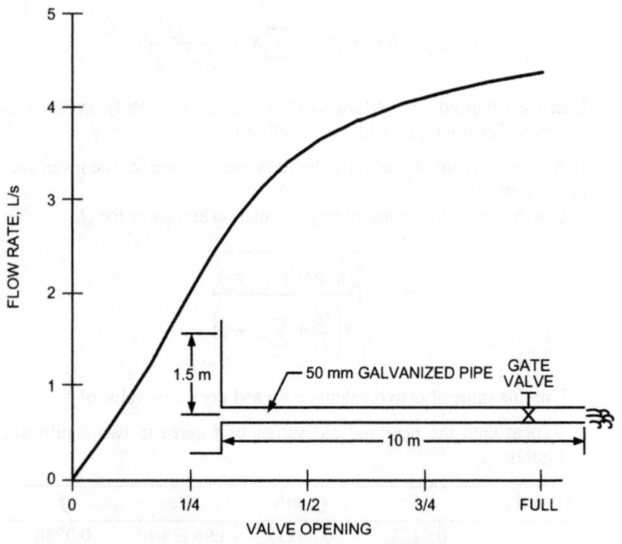

Fig. 15 Valve Action in Pipeline

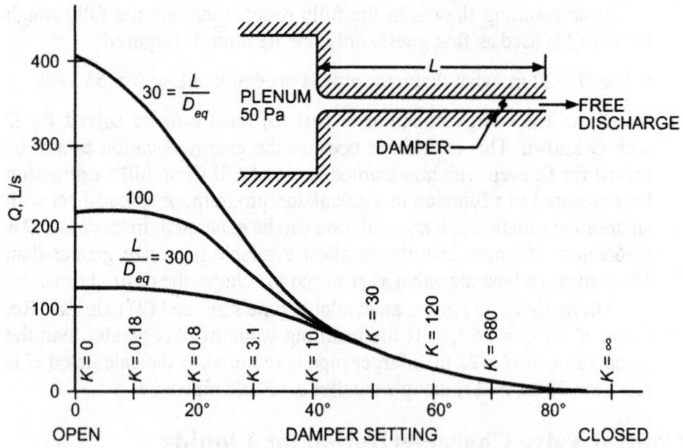

Fig. 16 Effect of Duct Length on Damper Action

air from a plenum held at constant pressure. With a long duct, the damper does not affect the flow rate until it is about one-quarter closed. Duct length has little effect when the damper is more than half closed. The damper closes the duct totally at the 90° position ($K = \infty$).

Flow in a system (pump or blower and conduit with fittings) involves interaction between the characteristics of the flow-producing device (pump or blower) and the loss characteristics of the pipeline or duct system. Often the devices are centrifugal, in which case the pressure produced decreases as flow increases, except for the lowest flow rates. System pressure required to overcome losses increases roughly as the square of the flow rate. The flow rate of a given system is that where the two curves of pressure versus flow rate intersect (point 1 in Figure 17). When a control valve (or damper) is partially closed, it increases losses and reduces flow (point 2 in Figure 17). For cases of constant pressure, the flow decrease caused by valving is not as great as that indicated in Figures 15 and 16.

Flow Measurement

The general principles noted (the continuity and Bernoulli equations) are basic to most fluid-metering devices. Chapter 36 has further details.

The pressure difference between the stagnation point (total pressure) and the ambient fluid stream (static pressure) is used to give a

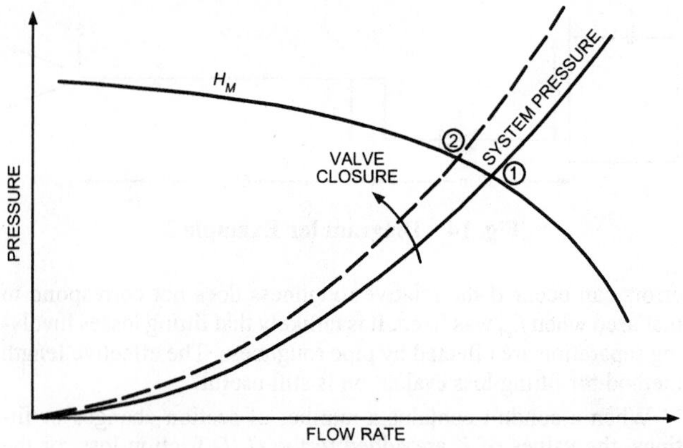

Fig. 17 Matching of Pump or Blower to System Characteristics

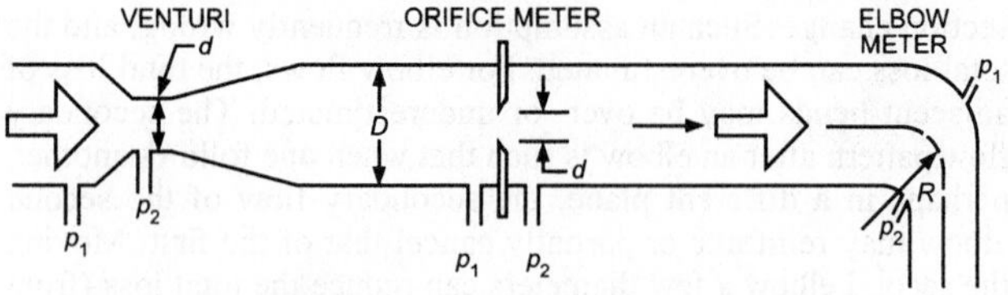

Fig. 18 Differential Pressure Flowmeters

point velocity measurement. Flow rate in a conduit is measured by placing a pitot device at various locations in the cross section and spatially integrating over the velocity found. A single-point measurement may be used for approximate flow rate evaluation. When flow is fully developed, the pipe-factor information of Figure 5 can be used to estimate the flow rate from a centerline measurement. Measurements can be made in one of two modes. With the pitot-static tube, the ambient (static) pressure is found from pressure taps along the side of the forward-facing portion of the tube. When this portion is not long and slender, static pressure indication will be low and velocity indication high; as a result, a tube coefficient less than unity must be used. For parallel conduit flow, wall piezometers (taps) may take the ambient pressure, and the pitot tube indicates the impact (total pressure).

The venturi meter, flow nozzle, and orifice meter are flow-rate-metering devices based on the pressure change associated with relatively sudden changes in conduit section area (Figure 18). The elbow meter (also shown in Figure 18) is another differential pressure flowmeter. The flow nozzle is similar to the venturi in action, but does not have the downstream diffuser. For all these, the flow rate is proportional to the square root of the pressure difference resulting from fluid flow. With area-change devices (venturi, flow nozzle, and orifice meter), a theoretical flow rate relation is found by applying the Bernoulli and continuity equations in Equations (12) and (3) between stations 1 and 2:

$$Q = C_d A_o \sqrt{2g\Delta h} \quad (38)$$

where $\Delta h = h_1 - h_2 = (p_1 - p_2)/\rho g$ (h = static pressure).

The actual flow rate through the device can differ because the approach flow kinetic energy factor α deviates from unity and because of small losses. More significantly, jet contraction of orifice flow is neglected in deriving Equation (38), to the extent that it can reduce the effective flow area by a factor of 0.6. The effect of all these factors can be combined into the discharge coefficient C_d:

$$Q_{theoretical} = \frac{\pi d^2}{4}\sqrt{\frac{2g\Delta h}{1-\beta^4}} \quad (39)$$

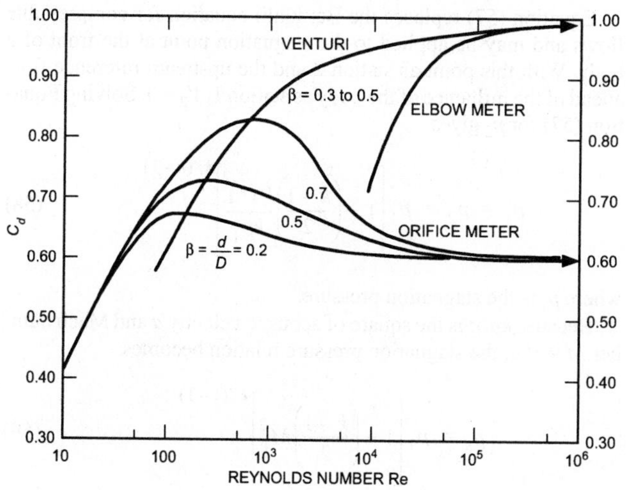

Fig. 19 Flowmeter Coefficients

where $\beta = d/D$ = ratio of throat (or orifice) diameter to conduit diameter. Sometimes the following alternative coefficient is used:

$$\frac{C_d}{\sqrt{1-\beta^4}} \tag{40}$$

The general mode of variation in C_d for orifices and venturis is indicated in Figure 19 as a function of Reynolds number and, to a lesser extent, diameter ratio β. For Reynolds numbers less than 10, the coefficient varies as $\sqrt{Re}$.

The elbow meter uses the pressure difference inside and outside the bend as the metering signal (Murdock et al. 1964). Momentum analysis gives the flow rate as

$$Q_{theoretical} = \frac{\pi d^2}{4}\sqrt{\frac{R}{2D}(2g\Delta h)} \tag{41}$$

where R is the radius of curvature of the bend. Again, a discharge coefficient C_d is needed; as in Figure 19, this drops off for lower Reynolds numbers (below 10^5). These devices are calibrated in pipes with fully developed velocity profiles, so they must be located far enough downstream of sections that modify the approach velocity.

Unsteady Flow

Conduit flows are not always steady. In a compressible fluid, acoustic velocity is usually high and conduit length is rather short, so the time of signal travel is negligibly small. Even in the incompressible approximation, system response is not instantaneous. If a pressure difference Δp is applied between the conduit ends, the fluid mass must be accelerated and wall friction overcome, so a finite time passes before the steady flow rate corresponding to the pressure drop is achieved.

The time it takes for an incompressible fluid in a horizontal, constant-area conduit of length L to achieve steady flow may be estimated by using the unsteady flow equation of motion with wall friction effects included. On the quasi-steady assumption, friction loss is given by Equation (30); also by continuity, V is constant along the conduit. The occurrences are characterized by the relation

$$\frac{dV}{d\theta} + \left(\frac{1}{\rho}\right)\frac{dp}{ds} + \frac{fV^2}{2D} = 0 \tag{42}$$

where θ is the time and s is the distance in flow direction. Because a certain Δp is applied over conduit length L,

$$\frac{dV}{d\theta} = \frac{\Delta p}{\rho L} - \frac{fV^2}{2D} \tag{43}$$

For laminar flow, f is given by Equation (31):

$$\frac{dV}{d\theta} = \frac{\Delta p}{\rho L} - \frac{32\mu V}{\rho D^2} = A - BV \tag{44}$$

Equation (44) can be rearranged and integrated to yield the time to reach a certain velocity:

$$\theta = \int d\theta = \int \frac{dV}{A - BV} = -\frac{1}{B}\ln(A - BV) \tag{45}$$

and

$$V = \frac{\Delta p}{L}\left(\frac{D^2}{32\mu}\right)\left[1 - \frac{\rho L}{\Delta p}\exp\left(\frac{-32\nu\theta}{D^2}\right)\right] \tag{46}$$

For long times ($\theta \to \infty$), the steady velocity is

$$V_\infty = \frac{\Delta p}{L}\left(\frac{D^2}{32\mu}\right) = \frac{\Delta p}{L}\left(\frac{R^2}{8\mu}\right) \tag{47}$$

as given by Equation (17). Then, Equation (47) becomes

$$V = V_\infty\left[1 - \frac{\rho L}{\Delta p}\exp\left(\frac{-f_\infty V_\infty \theta}{2D}\right)\right] \tag{48}$$

where

$$f_\infty = \frac{64\nu}{V_\infty D} \tag{49}$$

The general nature of velocity development for start-up flow is derived by more complex techniques; however, the temporal variation is as given here. For shutdown flow (steady flow with $\Delta p = 0$ at $\theta > 0$), flow decays exponentially as $e^{-\theta}$.

Turbulent flow analysis of Equation (42) also must be based on the quasi-steady approximation, with less justification. Daily et al. (1956) indicate that frictional resistance is slightly greater than the steady-state result for accelerating flows, but appreciably less for decelerating flows. If the friction factor is approximated as constant,

$$\frac{dV}{d\theta} = \frac{\Delta p}{\rho L} - \frac{fV^2}{2D} = A - BV^2 \tag{50}$$

and for the accelerating flow,

$$\theta = \frac{1}{\sqrt{AB}}\tanh^{-1}\left(V\sqrt{\frac{B}{A}}\right) \tag{51}$$

or

$$V = \sqrt{A/B}\,\tanh(\theta\sqrt{AB}) \tag{52}$$

Because the hyperbolic tangent is zero when the independent variable is zero and unity when the variable is infinity, the initial ($V = 0$ at $\theta = 0$) and final conditions are verified. Thus, for long times ($\theta \to \infty$),

$$V_\infty = \sqrt{A/B} = \sqrt{\frac{\Delta p/\rho L}{f_\infty/2D}} = \sqrt{\frac{\Delta p}{\rho L}\left(\frac{2D}{f_\infty}\right)} \tag{53}$$

which is in accord with Equation (30) when f is constant (the flow regime is the fully rough one of Figure 13). The temporal velocity variation is then

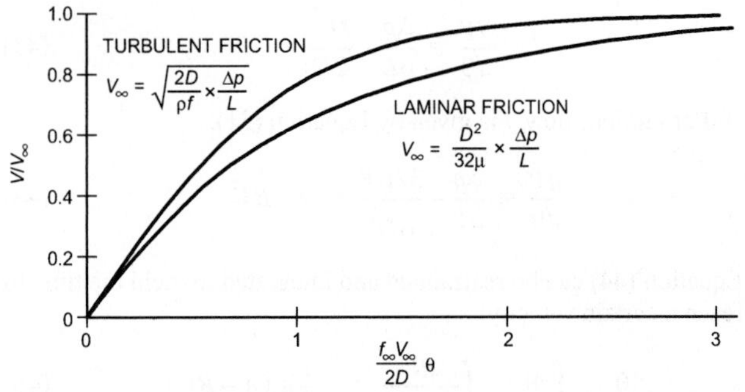

Fig. 20 Temporal Increase in Velocity Following Sudden Application of Pressure

$$V = V_\infty \tanh(f_\infty V_\infty \theta / 2D) \tag{54}$$

In Figure 20, the turbulent velocity start-up result is compared with the laminar one, where initially the turbulent is steeper but of the same general form, increasing rapidly at the start but reaching V_∞ asymptotically.

Compressibility

All fluids are compressible to some degree; their density depends somewhat on the pressure. Steady liquid flow may ordinarily be treated as incompressible, and incompressible flow analysis is satisfactory for gases and vapors at velocities below about 20 to 40 m/s, except in long conduits.

For liquids in pipelines, a severe pressure surge or water hammer may be produced if flow is suddenly stopped. This pressure surge travels along the pipe at the speed of sound in the liquid, alternately compressing and decompressing the liquid. For steady gas flows in long conduits, pressure decrease along the conduit can reduce gas density significantly enough to increase velocity. If the conduit is long enough, velocities approaching the speed of sound are possible at the discharge end, and the Mach number (ratio of flow velocity to speed of sound) must be considered.

Some compressible flows occur without heat gain or loss (adiabatically). If there is no friction (conversion of flow mechanical energy into internal energy), the process is reversible (isentropic), as well, and follows the relationship

$$p/\rho^k = \text{constant}$$
$$k = c_p/c_v$$

where k, the ratio of specific heats at constant pressure and volume, has a value of 1.4 for air and diatomic gases.

The Bernoulli equation of steady flow, Equation (21), as an integral of the ideal-fluid equation of motion along a streamline, then becomes

$$\int \frac{dp}{\rho} + \frac{V^2}{2} = \text{constant} \tag{55}$$

where, as in most compressible flow analyses, the elevation terms involving z are insignificant and are dropped.

For a frictionless adiabatic process, the pressure term has the form

$$\int_1^2 \frac{dp}{\rho} = \frac{k}{k-1}\left(\frac{p_2}{\rho_2} - \frac{p_1}{\rho_1}\right) \tag{56}$$

Then, between stations 1 and 2 for the isentropic process,

$$\frac{p_1}{\rho_1}\left(\frac{k}{k-1}\right)\left[\left(\frac{p_2}{p_1}\right)^{(k-1)/k} - 1\right] + \frac{V_2^2 - V_1^2}{2} = 0 \tag{57}$$

Equation (57) replaces the Bernoulli equation for compressible flows and may be applied to the stagnation point at the front of a body. With this point as station 2 and the upstream reference flow ahead of the influence of the body as station 1, $V_2 = 0$. Solving Equation (57) for p_2 gives

$$p_s = p_2 = p_1\left[1 + \left(\frac{k-1}{2}\right)\frac{\rho_1 V_1^2}{kp_1}\right]^{k/(k-1)} \tag{58}$$

where p_s is the stagnation pressure.

Because kp/ρ is the square of acoustic velocity a and Mach number $M = V/a$, the stagnation pressure relation becomes

$$p_s = p_1\left[1 + \left(\frac{k-1}{2}\right)M_1^2\right]^{k/(k-1)} \tag{59}$$

For Mach numbers less than one,

$$p_s = p_1 + \frac{\rho_1 V_1^2}{2}\left[1 + \frac{M_1^2}{4} + \left(\frac{2-k}{24}\right)M_1^4 + \cdots\right] \tag{60}$$

When $M = 0$, Equation (60) reduces to the incompressible flow result obtained from Equation (9). Appreciable differences appear when the Mach number of approaching flow exceeds 0.2. Thus, a pitot tube in air is influenced by compressibility at velocities over about 66 m/s.

Flows through a converging conduit, as in a flow nozzle, venturi, or orifice meter, also may be considered isentropic. Velocity at the upstream station 1 is negligible. From Equation (57), velocity at the downstream station is

$$V_2 = \sqrt{\frac{2k}{k-1}\left(\frac{p_1}{\rho_1}\right)\left[1 - \left(\frac{p_2}{p_1}\right)^{(k-1)/k}\right]} \tag{61}$$

The mass flow rate is

$$\dot{m} = V_2 A_2 \rho_2$$
$$= A_2\sqrt{\frac{2k}{k-1}(p_1\rho_1)\left[\left(\frac{p_2}{p_1}\right)^{2/k} - \left(\frac{p_2}{p_1}\right)^{(k+1)/k}\right]} \tag{62}$$

The corresponding incompressible flow relation is

$$\dot{m}_{in} = A_2\rho\sqrt{2\Delta p/\rho} = A_2\sqrt{2\rho(p_1 - p_2)} \tag{63}$$

The compressibility effect is often accounted for in the **expansion factor** $\boldsymbol{Y}$:

$$\dot{m} = Y\dot{m}_{in} = A_2 Y\sqrt{2\rho(p_1 - p_2)} \tag{64}$$

Y is 1.00 for the incompressible case. For air (k = 1.4), a Y value of 0.95 is reached with orifices at $p_2/p_1 = 0.83$ and with venturis at about 0.90, when these devices are of relatively small diameter ($D_2/D_1 > 0.5$).

As p_2/p_1 decreases, flow rate increases, but more slowly than for the incompressible case because of the nearly linear decrease in Y. However, downstream velocity reaches the local acoustic value and discharge levels off at a value fixed by upstream pressure and density at the critical ratio:

$$\left.\frac{p_2}{p_1}\right|_c = \left(\frac{2}{k+1}\right)^{k/(k-1)} = 0.53 \text{ for air} \tag{65}$$

At higher pressure ratios than critical, **choking** (no increase in flow with decrease in downstream pressure) occurs and is used in some flow control devices to avoid flow dependence on downstream conditions.

For compressible fluid metering, the expansion factor Y must be included, and the mass flow rate is

$$\dot{m} = C_d Y \frac{\pi d^2}{4} \sqrt{\frac{2\rho\Delta p}{1-\beta^4}} \tag{66}$$

Compressible Conduit Flow

When friction loss is included, as it must be except for a very short conduit, incompressible flow analysis applies until pressure drop exceeds about 10% of the initial pressure. The possibility of sonic velocities at the end of relatively long conduits limits the amount of pressure reduction achieved. For an inlet Mach number of 0.2, discharge pressure can be reduced to about 0.2 of the initial pressure; for inflow at $M = 0.5$, discharge pressure cannot be less than about $0.45p_1$ (adiabatic) or about $0.6p_1$ (isothermal).

Analysis must treat density change, as evaluated from the continuity relation in Equation (3), with frictional occurrences evaluated from wall roughness and Reynolds number correlations of incompressible flow (Binder 1944). In evaluating valve and fitting losses, consider the reduction in K caused by compressibility (Benedict and Carlucci 1966). Although the analysis differs significantly, isothermal and adiabatic flows involve essentially the same pressure variation along the conduit, up to the limiting conditions.

Cavitation

Liquid flow with gas- or vapor-filled pockets can occur if the absolute pressure is reduced to vapor pressure or less. In this case, one or more cavities form, because liquids are rarely pure enough to withstand any tensile stressing or pressures less than vapor pressure for any length of time (John and Haberman 1980; Knapp et al. 1970; Robertson and Wislicenus 1969). Robertson and Wislicenus (1969) indicate significant occurrences in various technical fields, chiefly in hydraulic equipment and turbomachines.

Initial evidence of cavitation is the collapse noise of many small bubbles that appear initially as they are carried by the flow into higher-pressure regions. The noise is not deleterious and serves as a warning of the occurrence. As flow velocity further increases or pressure decreases, the severity of cavitation increases. More bubbles appear and may join to form large fixed cavities. The space they occupy becomes large enough to modify the flow pattern and alter performance of the flow device. Collapse of cavities on or near solid boundaries becomes so frequent that, in time, the cumulative impact causes cavitational erosion of the surface or excessive vibration. As a result, pumps can lose efficiency or their parts may erode locally. Control valves may be noisy or seriously damaged by cavitation.

Cavitation in orifice and valve flow is illustrated in Figure 21. With high upstream pressure and a low flow rate, no cavitation occurs. As pressure is reduced or flow rate increased, the minimum pressure in the flow (in the shear layer leaving the edge of the orifice) eventually approaches vapor pressure. Turbulence in this layer causes fluctuating pressures below the mean (as in vortex cores) and small bubble-like cavities. These are carried downstream into the region of pressure regain where they collapse, either in the fluid or on the wall (Figure 21A). As pressure reduces, more vapor- or gas-filled bubbles result and coalesce into larger ones. Eventually, a single large cavity results that collapses further downstream (Figure 21B). The region of wall damage is then as many as 20 diameters downstream from the valve or orifice plate.

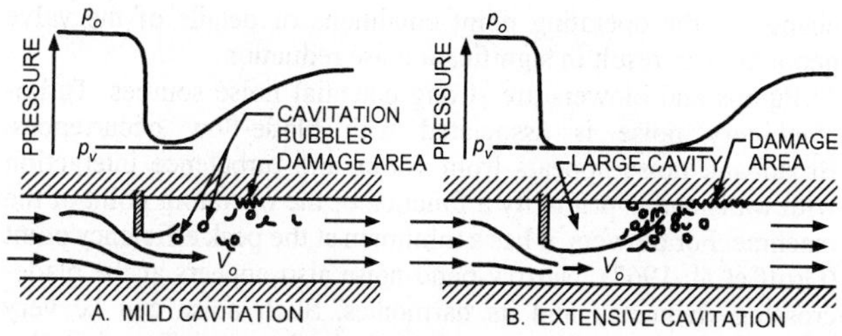

Fig. 21 Cavitation in Flows in Orifice or Valve

Sensitivity of a device to cavitation is measured by the **cavitation index** or **cavitation number**, which is the ratio of the available pressure above vapor pressure to the dynamic pressure of the reference flow:

$$\sigma = \frac{2(p_o - p_v)}{\rho V_o^2} \tag{67}$$

where p_v is vapor pressure, and the subscript o refers to appropriate reference conditions. Valve analyses use such an index to determine when cavitation will affect the discharge coefficient (Ball 1957). With flow-metering devices such as orifices, venturis, and flow nozzles, there is little cavitation, because it occurs mostly downstream of the flow regions involved in establishing the metering action.

The detrimental effects of cavitation can be avoided by operating the liquid-flow device at high enough pressures. When this is not possible, the flow must be changed or the device must be built to withstand cavitation effects. Some materials or surface coatings are more resistant to cavitation erosion than others, but none is immune. Surface contours can be designed to delay the onset of cavitation.

NOISE IN FLUID FLOW

Noise in flowing fluids results from unsteady flow fields and can be at discrete frequencies or broadly distributed over the audible range. With liquid flow, cavitation results in noise through the collapse of vapor bubbles. Noise in pumps or fittings (e.g., valves) can be a rattling or sharp hissing sound, which is easily eliminated by raising the system pressure. With severe cavitation, the resulting unsteady flow can produce indirect noise from induced vibration of adjacent parts. See Chapter 47 of the 2007 *ASHRAE Handbook—HVAC Applications* for more information on sound control.

The disturbed laminar flow behind cylinders can be an oscillating motion. The shedding frequency f of these vortexes is characterized by a **Strouhal number** $\text{St} = fd/V$ of about 0.21 for a circular cylinder of diameter d, over a considerable range of Reynolds numbers. This oscillating flow can be a powerful noise source, particularly when f is close to the natural frequency of the cylinder or some nearby structural member so that resonance occurs. With cylinders of another shape, such as impeller blades of a pump or blower, the characterizing Strouhal number involves the trailing-edge thickness of the member. The strength of the vortex wake, with its resulting vibrations and noise potential, can be reduced by breaking up flow with downstream splitter plates or boundary-layer trip devices (wires) on the cylinder surface.

Noises produced in pipes and ducts, especially from valves and fittings, are associated with the loss through such elements. The sound pressure of noise in water pipe flow increases linearly with pressure loss; broadband noise increases, but only in the lower-frequency range. Fitting-produced noise levels also increase with fitting loss (even without cavitation) and significantly exceed noise levels of the pipe flow. The relation between noise and loss is not surprising because both involve excessive flow perturbations. A valve's pressure-flow characteristics and structural elasticity may be such that for some operating point it oscillates, perhaps in resonance with part of the piping system, to produce excessive noise. A change in the operating point conditions or details of the valve geometry can result in significant noise reduction.

Pumps and blowers are strong potential noise sources. Turbomachinery noise is associated with blade-flow occurrences. Broadband noise appears from vortex and turbulence interaction with walls and is primarily a function of the operating point of the machine. For blowers, it has a minimum at the peak efficiency point (Groff et al. 1967). Narrow-band noise also appears at the blade-crossing frequency and its harmonics. Such noise can be very annoying because it stands out from the background. To reduce this noise, increase clearances between impeller and housing, and space impeller blades unevenly around the circumference.

SYMBOLS

A = area, m^2
A_o = area of orifice opening
B = Bernoulli constant
C_D = drag coefficient
C_d = discharge coefficient
D_h = hydraulic diameter
E_L = loss during conversion of energy from mechanical to internal
E_M = external work from fluid machine
F = tangential force per unit area required to slide one of two parallel plates
f = Darcy-Weisbach friction factor, or shedding frequency
F_D = drag force
f_{ref} = reference value of friction factor
g = gravitational acceleration, m/s^2
g_c = gravitational constant = 1 (kg·m)/(N·s^2)
H_L = head lost through friction
H_M = head added by pump
K = loss coefficient
k = ratio of specific heats at constant pressure and volume
L = length
L_e = entrance length
L_{eff} = effective length
$\dot{m}$ = mass flow rate
p = pressure
P_w = wetted perimeter
Q = volumetric flow rate
q = heat per unit mass absorbed or rejected
R = pipe radius
Re = Reynolds number
s = flow direction
St = Strouhal number
u = internal energy
V = velocity
v = fluid velocity normal to differential area dA
w = work per unit mass
y = distance from centerline
Y = distance between two parallel plates, m, or expansion factor
z = elevation

Greek

α = kinetic energy factor
β = d/D = ratio of throat (or orifice) diameter to conduit diameter
γ = specific mass or density
δ = boundary layer thickness
ΔE = change in energy content per unit mass of flowing fluid
Δp = pressure drop across valve
Δu = conversion of energy from mechanical to internal
ε = roughness height
θ = time
μ = proportionality factor for absolute or dynamic viscosity of fluid, (mN·s)/m^2
ν = kinematic viscosity, mm^2/s
ρ = density, kg/m^3
σ = cavitation index or number
τ = shear stress, Pa
τ_w = wall shear stress

REFERENCES

Baines, W.D. and E.G. Peterson. 1951. An investigation of flow through screens. *ASME Transactions* 73:467.

Ball, J.W. 1957. Cavitation characteristics of gate valves and globe values used as flow regulators under heads up to about 125 ft. *ASME Transactions* 79:1275.

Benedict, R.P. and N.A. Carlucci. 1966. *Handbook of specific losses in flow systems.* Plenum Press Data Division, New York.

Binder, R.C. 1944. Limiting isothermal flow in pipes. *ASME Transactions* 66:221.

Churchill, S.W. 1977. Friction-factor equation spans all fluid flow regimes. *Chemical Engineering* 84(24):91-92.

Colborne, W.G. and A.J. Drobitch. 1966. An experimental study of non-isothermal flow in a vertical circular tube. *ASHRAE Transactions* 72(4):5.

Coleman, J.W. 2004. An experimentally validated model for two-phase sudden contraction pressure drop in microchannel tube header. *Heat Transfer Engineering* 25(3):69-77.

Daily, J.W., W.L. Hankey, R.W. Olive, and J.M. Jordan. 1956. Resistance coefficients for accelerated and decelerated flows through smooth tubes and orifices. *ASME Transactions* 78:1071-1077.

Deissler, R.G. 1951. Laminar flow in tubes with heat transfer. *National Advisory Technical Note* 2410, Committee for Aeronautics.

Fox, R.W., A.T. McDonald, and P.J. Pritchard. 2004. *Introduction to fluid mechanics.* Wiley, New York.

Furuya, Y., T. Sate, and T. Kushida. 1976. The loss of flow in the conical with suction at the entrance. *Bulletin of the Japan Society of Mechanical Engineers* 19:131.

Goldstein, S., ed. 1938. *Modern developments in fluid mechanics.* Oxford University Press, London. Reprinted by Dover Publications, New York.

Groff, G.C., J.R. Schreiner, and C.E. Bullock. 1967. Centrifugal fan sound power level prediction. *ASHRAE Transactions* 73(II):V.4.1.

Heskested, G. 1970. Further experiments with suction at a sudden enlargement. *Journal of Basic Engineering, ASME Transactions* 92D:437.

Hoerner, S.F. 1965. *Fluid dynamic drag*, 3rd ed. Hoerner Fluid Dynamics, Vancouver, WA.

Hydraulic Institute. 1990. *Engineering data book*, 2nd ed. Parsippany, NJ.

Incropera, F.P. and D.P. DdeWitt. 2002. *Fundamentals of heat and mass transfer*, 5th ed. Wiley, New York.

Ito, H. 1962. Pressure losses in smooth pipe bends. *Journal of Basic Engineering, ASME Transactions* 4(7):43.

John, J.E.A. and W.L. Haberman. 1980. *Introduction to fluid mechanics*, 2nd ed. Prentice Hall, Englewood Cliffs, NJ.

Kline, S.J. 1959. On the nature of stall. *Journal of Basic Engineering, ASME Transactions* 81D:305.

Knapp, R.T., J.W. Daily, and F.G. Hammitt. 1970. *Cavitation.* McGraw-Hill, New York.

Lipstein, N.J. 1962. Low velocity sudden expansion pipe flow. *ASHRAE Journal* 4(7):43.

Moody, L.F. 1944. Friction factors for pipe flow. *ASME Transactions* 66:672.

Moore, C.A. and S.J. Kline. 1958. Some effects of vanes and turbulence in two-dimensional wide-angle subsonic diffusers. National Advisory Committee for Aeronautics, *Technical Memo* 4080.

Murdock, J.W., C.J. Foltz, and C. Gregory. 1964. Performance characteristics of elbow flow meters. *Journal of Basic Engineering, ASME Transactions* 86D:498.

Robertson, J.M. 1963. A turbulence primer. University of Illinois–Urbana, *Engineering Experiment Station Circular* 79.

Robertson, J.M. 1965. *Hydrodynamics in theory and application.* Prentice-Hall, Englewood Cliffs, NJ.

Robertson, J.M. and G.F. Wislicenus, eds. 1969 (discussion 1970). *Cavitation state of knowledge.* American Society of Mechanical Engineers, New York.

Ross, D. 1956. Turbulent flow in the entrance region of a pipe. *ASME Transactions* 78:915.

Schlichting, H. 1979. *Boundary layer theory*, 7th ed. McGraw-Hill, New York.

Wile, D.D. 1947. Air flow measurement in the laboratory. *Refrigerating Engineering*: 515.

BIBLIOGRAPHY

Olson, R.M. 1980. *Essentials of engineering fluid mechanics*, 4th ed. Harper and Row, New York.

CHAPTER 4

HEAT TRANSFER

HEAT transfer is energy transferred because of a temperature difference. Energy moves from a higher-temperature region to a lower-temperature region by one or more of three modes: **conduction, radiation**, and **convection**. This chapter presents elementary principles of single-phase heat transfer, with emphasis on HVAC applications. Boiling and condensation are discussed in Chapter 5. More specific information on heat transfer to or from buildings or refrigerated spaces can be found in Chapters 14 to 19, 23, and 27 of this volume and in Chapter 13 of the 2006 *ASHRAE Handbook—Refrigeration*. Physical properties of substances can be found in Chapters 26, 28, 32, and 33 of this volume and in Chapter 9 of the 2006 *ASHRAE Handbook—Refrigeration*. Heat transfer equipment, including evaporators, condensers, heating and cooling coils, furnaces, and radiators, is covered in the 2008 *ASHRAE Handbook—HVAC Systems and Equipment*. For further information on heat transfer, see the Bibliography.

HEAT TRANSFER PROCESSES

Conduction

Consider a wall that is 10 m long, 3 m tall, and 100 mm thick (Figure 1A). One side of the wall is maintained at t_{s1} = 25°C, and the other is kept at t_{s2} = 20°C. Heat transfer occurs at rate q through the wall from the warmer side to the cooler. The heat transfer mode is conduction (the only way energy can be transferred through a solid).

- If t_{s1} is raised from 25 to 30°C while everything else remains the same, q doubles because $t_{s1} - t_{s2}$ doubles.
- If the wall is twice as tall, thus doubling the area A_c of the wall, q doubles.
- If the wall is twice as thick, q is halved.

From these relationships,

$$q \propto \frac{(t_{s1} - t_{s2})A_c}{L}$$

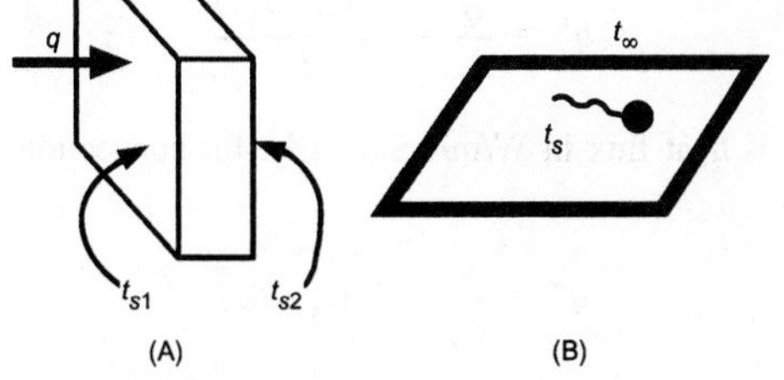

Fig. 1 (A) Conduction and (B) Convection

where ∝ means "proportional to" and L = wall thickness. However, this relation does not take wall material into account: if the wall is foam instead of concrete, q would clearly be less. The constant of proportionality is a material property, **thermal conductivity** k. Thus,

$$q = k\frac{(t_{s1} - t_{s2})A_c}{L} = \frac{(t_{s1} - t_{s2})}{L/(kA_c)} \tag{1}$$

where k has units of W/(m·K). The denominator $L/(kA_c)$ can be considered the **conduction resistance** associated with the driving potential $(t_{s1} - t_{s2})$. This is analogous to current flow through an electrical resistance, $I = (V_1 - V_2)/R$, where $(V_1 - V_2)$ is driving potential, R is electrical resistance, and current I is rate of flow of charge instead of rate of heat transfer q.

Thermal resistance has units K/W. A wall with a resistance of 5 K/W requires $(t_{s1} - t_{s2})$ = 5 K for heat transfer q of 1 W. The thermal/electrical resistance analogy allows tools used to solve electrical circuits to be used for heat transfer problems.

Convection

Consider a surface at temperature t_s in contact with a fluid at t_∞ (Figure 1B). **Newton's law of cooling** expresses the rate of heat transfer from the surface of area A_s as

$$q = h_c A_s(t_s - t_\infty) = \frac{(t_s - t_\infty)}{1/(h_c A_s)} \tag{2}$$

where h_c is the **heat transfer coefficient** (Table 1) and has units of W/(m²·K). The **convection resistance** $1/(h_c A_s)$ has units of K/W.

If $t_\infty > t_s$, heat transfers from the fluid to the surface, and q is written as just $q = h_c A_s(t_\infty - t_s)$. Resistance is the same, but the sign of the temperature difference is reversed.

For heat transfer to be considered convection, fluid in contact with the surface must be in motion; if not, the mode of heat transfer is conduction. If fluid motion is caused by an external force (e.g., fan, pump, wind), it is **forced convection**. If fluid motion results from buoyant forces caused by the surface being warmer or cooler than the fluid, it is **free** (or **natural**) **convection**.

Table 1 Heat Transfer Coefficients by Convection Type

Convection Type	h_c, W/(m²·K)
Free, gases	2 to 25
Free, liquids	10 to 1000
Forced, gases	25 to 250
Forced, liquids	50 to 20 000
Boiling, condensation	2500 to 100 000

The preparation of this chapter is assigned to TC 1.3, Heat Transfer and Fluid Flow.

Radiation

Matter emits thermal radiation at its surface when its temperature is above absolute zero. This radiation is in the form of photons of varying frequency. These photons leaving the surface need no medium to transport them, unlike conduction and convection (in which heat transfer occurs through matter). The rate of thermal radiant energy emitted by a surface depends on its absolute temperature and its surface characteristics. A surface that absorbs all radiation incident upon it is called a **black surface**, and emits energy at the maximum possible rate at a given temperature. The heat emission from a black surface is given by the **Stefan-Boltzmann law:**

$$q_{emitted,\,black} = A_s \sigma T_s^4$$

where $E_b = \sigma T_s^4$ is the **blackbody emissive power** in W/m²; T_s is absolute surface temperature, K; and $\sigma = 5.67 \times 10^{-8}$ W/(m²·K⁴) is the Stefan-Boltzmann constant. If a surface is not black, the emission per unit time per unit area is

$$E = \varepsilon \sigma T_s^4$$

where E is emissive power, and ε is emissivity, where $0 \le \varepsilon \le 1$. For a black surface, $\varepsilon = 1$.

Nonblack surfaces do not absorb all incident radiation. The absorbed radiation is

$$q_{absorbed} = \alpha A_s G$$

where **absorptivity** α is the fraction of incident radiation absorbed, and **irradiation** G is the rate of radiant energy incident on a surface per unit area of the receiving surface due to emission and reflection from surrounding surfaces. For a black surface, $\alpha = 1$.

A surface's emissivity and absorptivity are often both functions of the wavelength distribution of photons emitted and absorbed, respectively, by the surface. However, in many cases, it is reasonable to assume that both α and ε are independent of wavelength. If so, $\alpha = \varepsilon$ (a **gray surface**).

Two surfaces at different temperatures that can "see" each other can exchange energy through radiation. The net exchange rate depends on the surfaces' (1) relative size, (2) relative orientation and shape, (3) temperatures, and (4) emissivity and absorptivity. However, for a small area A_s in a large enclosure at constant temperature t_{surr}, the irradiation on A_s from the surroundings is the blackbody emissive power of the surroundings $E_{b,surr}$. So, if $t_s > t_{surr}$, net heat loss from gray surface A_s in the radiation exchange with the surroundings at T_{surr} is

$$q_{net} = q_{emitted} - q_{absorbed} = \varepsilon A_s E_{bs} - \alpha A_s E_{b,surr} = \varepsilon A_s \sigma (t_s^4 - t_{sum}^4) \quad (3)$$

where $\alpha = \varepsilon$ for the gray surface. If $t_s < t_{surr}$, the expression for q_{net} is the same with the sign reversed, and q_{net} is the net gain by A_s.

Note that q_{net} can be written as

$$q_{net} = \frac{E_{bs} - E_{b,surr}}{1/(\varepsilon A_s)}$$

In this form, $E_{bs} - E_{b,surr}$ is analogous to the driving potential in an electric circuit, and $1/(\varepsilon A_s)$ is analogous to electrical resistance. This is a convenient analogy when only radiation is being considered, but if convection and radiation both occur at a surface, convection is described by a driving potential based on the difference in the first power of the temperatures, whereas radiation is described by the difference in the fourth power of the temperatures. In cases like this, it is often useful to express net radiation as

$$q_{net} = h_r A_s (t_s - t_{surr}) = (t_s - t_{surr})/(1/h_r A_s) \quad (4)$$

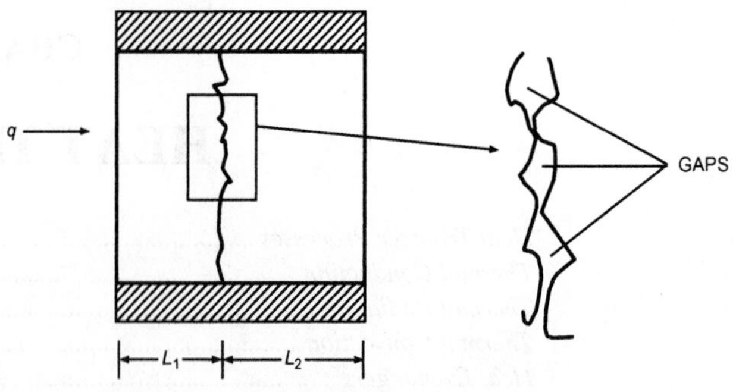

Fig. 2 Interface Resistance Across Two Layers

where $h_r = \sigma\varepsilon(t_s^2 + t_{surr}^2)(t_s + t_{surr})$ is often called a **radiation heat transfer coefficient**. The disadvantage of this form is that h_r depends on t_s, which is often the desired result of the calculation.

Combined Radiation and Convection

When $t_{surr} = t_\infty$ in Equation (4), the total heat transfer from a surface by convection and radiation combined is then

$$q = q_{rad} + q_{conv} = (t_s - t_\infty) A_s (h_r + h_c)$$

The temperature difference $t_s - t_\infty$ is in either kelvins or °C; the difference is the same. Either can be used; however, absolute temperatures *must* be used to calculate h_r. (Absolute temperatures are K = °C + 273.15.) Note that h_c and h_r are always positive, and that the direction of q is determined by the sign of $(t_s - t_\infty)$.

Contact or Interface Resistance

Heat flow through two layers encounters two conduction resistances L_1/k_1A and L_2/k_2A (Figure 2). At the interface between two layers are gaps across which heat is transferred by a combination of conduction at contact points and convection and radiation across gaps. This multimode heat transfer process is usually characterized using a contact resistance coefficient R''_{cont} or contact conductance h_{cont}.

$$q = \frac{\Delta T}{R''_{cont}/A} = h_{cont} A \Delta t$$

where Δt is the temperature drop across the interface. R''_{cont} is in (m²·K)/W, and h_{cont} is in W/(m²·K). The contact or interface resistance is $R_{cont} = R''_{cont}/A = 1/h_{cont}A$, and the resistance of the two layers combined is the sum of the resistances of the two layers and the contact resistance.

Contact resistance can be reduced by lowering surface roughnesses, increasing contact pressure, or using a conductive grease or paste to fill the gaps.

Heat Flux

The conduction heat transfer can be written as

$$q'' = \frac{q}{A_c} = \frac{k(t_{s1} - t_{s2})}{L}$$

where q'' is heat flux in W/m². Similarly, for convection the heat flux is

$$q'' = \frac{q}{A_s} = h_c (t_s - t_\infty)$$

and net heat flux from radiation at the surface is

$$q''_{net} = \frac{q_{net}}{A_s} = \varepsilon\sigma(t_s^4 - t_{surr}^4)$$

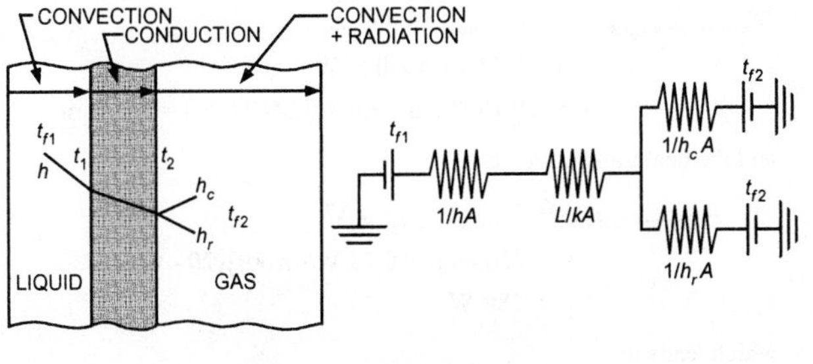

Fig. 3 Thermal Circuit

Overall Resistance and Heat Transfer Coefficient

In Equation (1) for conduction in a slab, Equation (4) for radiative heat transfer rate between two surfaces, and Equation (2) for convective heat transfer rate from a surface, the heat transfer rate is expressed as a temperature difference divided by a thermal resistance. Using the electrical resistance analogy, with temperature difference and heat transfer rate instead of potential difference and current, respectively, tools for solving series electrical resistance circuits can also be applied to heat transfer circuits. For example, consider the heat transfer rate from a liquid to the surrounding gas separated by a constant cross-sectional area solid, as shown in Figure 3. The heat transfer rate from the fluid to the adjacent surface is by convection, then across the solid body by conduction, and finally from the solid surface to the surroundings by both convection and radiation. A circuit using the equations for resistances in each mode is also shown. From the circuit, the heat transfer rate is

$$q = \frac{(t_{f1} - t_{f2})}{R_1 + R_2 + R_3}$$

where

$$R_1 = 1/hA \qquad R_2 = L/kA \qquad R_3 = \frac{(1/h_cA)(1/h_rA)}{(1/h_cA) + (1/h_rA)}$$

Resistance R_3 is the parallel combination of the convection and radiation resistances on the right-hand surface, $1/h_cA$ and $1/h_rA$. Equivalently, $R_3 = 1/h_{rc}A$, where h_{rc} on the air side is the sum of the convection and radiation heat transfer coefficients (i.e., $h_{rc} = h_c + h_r$).

The heat transfer rate can also be written as

$$q = UA(t_{f1} - t_{f2})$$

where U is the overall heat transfer coefficient that accounts for all the resistances involved. Note that

$$\frac{t_{f1} - t_{f2}}{q} = \frac{1}{UA} = R_1 + R_2 + R_3$$

The product UA is overall conductance, the reciprocal of overall resistance. The surface area A on which U is based is not always constant as in this example, and should always be specified when referring to U.

Heat transfer rates are equal from the warm liquid to the solid surface, through the solid, and then to the cool gas. Temperature drops across each part of the heat flow path are related to the resistances (as voltage drops are in an electric circuit), so that

$$t_{f1} - t_1 = qR_1 \qquad t_1 - t_2 = qR_2 \qquad t_2 - t_{f2} = qR_3$$

THERMAL CONDUCTION

One-Dimensional Steady-State Conduction

Steady-state heat transfer rates and resistances for (1) a slab of constant cross-sectional area, (2) a hollow cylinder with radial heat transfer, and (3) a hollow sphere are given in Table 2.

Table 2 One-Dimensional Conduction Shape Factors

Configuration		Heat Transfer Rate	Thermal Resistance
Constant cross-sectional area slab	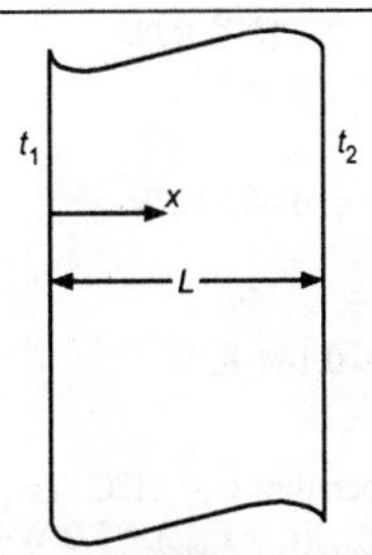	$q_x = kA_x \frac{t_1 - t_2}{L}$	$\frac{L}{kA_x}$
Hollow cylinder of length L with negligible heat transfer from end surfaces	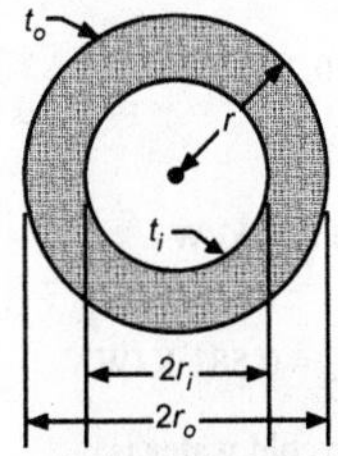	$q_r = \frac{2\pi kL(t_i - t_o)}{\ln\left(\frac{r_o}{r_i}\right)}$	$R = \frac{\ln(r_o/r_i)}{2\pi kL}$
Hollow sphere	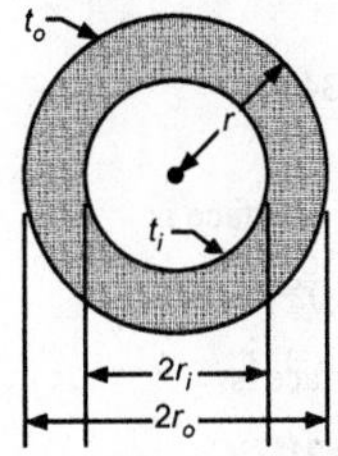	$q_r = \frac{4\pi k(t_i - t_o)}{\frac{1}{r_i} + \frac{1}{r_o}}$	$R = \frac{1/r_i - 1/r_o}{4\pi k}$

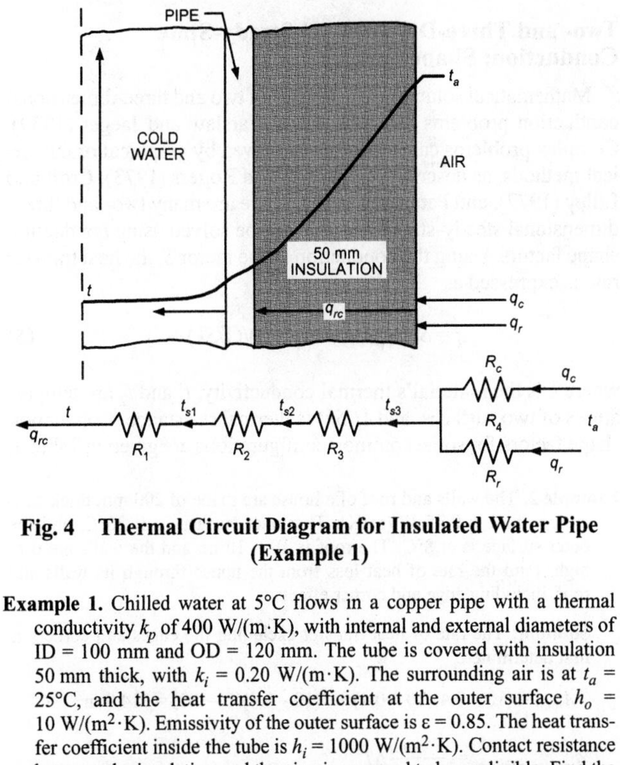

Fig. 4 Thermal Circuit Diagram for Insulated Water Pipe (Example 1)

Example 1. Chilled water at 5°C flows in a copper pipe with a thermal conductivity k_p of 400 W/(m·K), with internal and external diameters of ID = 100 mm and OD = 120 mm. The tube is covered with insulation 50 mm thick, with k_i = 0.20 W/(m·K). The surrounding air is at t_a = 25°C, and the heat transfer coefficient at the outer surface h_o = 10 W/(m²·K). Emissivity of the outer surface is ε = 0.85. The heat transfer coefficient inside the tube is h_i = 1000 W/(m²·K). Contact resistance between the insulation and the pipe is assumed to be negligible. Find the rate of heat gain per unit length of pipe and the temperature at the pipe-insulation interface.

Solution: The outer diameter of the insulation is D_{ins} = 120 + 2(50) = 220 mm. For L = 1 m,

$$R_1 = \frac{1}{h_i \pi \text{ID} L} = 3.2 \times 10^{-3} \text{ K/W}$$

$$R_2 = \frac{\ln(\text{OD}/\text{ID})}{2\pi k_p L} = 7 \times 10^{-5} \text{ K/W}$$

$$R_3 = \frac{\ln(D_{ins}/\text{OD})}{2\pi k_i L} = 0.482 \text{ K/W}$$

$$R_c = \frac{1}{h_o \pi D_{ins} L} = 0.144 \text{ K/W}$$

Assuming insulation surface temperature $t_s = 21°C$ (i.e., 294 K) and $t_{surr} = t_a = 298.15$ K, $h_r = \varepsilon\sigma(t_s^2 + t_{surr}^2)(t_s + t_{surr}) = 5.0$ W/(m²·K).

$$R_r = \frac{1}{h_r \pi D_{ins} L} = 0.288 \text{ K/W}$$

$$R_4 = \frac{R_r R_c}{R_r + R_c} = 0.096 \text{ K/W}$$

$$R_{tot} = R_1 + R_2 + R_3 + R_4 = 0.581 \text{ K/W}$$

Finally, the rate of heat gain by the cold water is

$$q_{rc} = \frac{t_a - t}{R_{tot}} = 34.4 \text{ W}$$

Temperature at the pipe/insulation interface is

$$t_{s2} = t + q_{rc}(R_1 + R_2) = 5.1°\text{C}$$

Temperature at the insulation's surface is

$$t_{s3} = t_a - q_{rc} R_4 = 21.7°\text{C}$$

which is very close to the assumed value of 22°C.

Two- and Three-Dimensional Steady-State Conduction: Shape Factors

Mathematical solutions to a number of two and three-dimensional conduction problems are available in Carslaw and Jaeger (1959). Complex problems can also often be solved by graphical or numerical methods, as described by Adams and Rogers (1973), Croft and Lilley (1977), and Patankar (1980). There are many two- and three-dimensional steady-state cases that can be solved using conduction shape factors. Using the conduction shape factor S, the heat transfer rate is expressed as

$$q = Sk(t_1 - t_2) = (t_1 - t_2)/(1/Sk) \tag{5}$$

where k is the material's thermal conductivity, t_1 and t_2 are temperatures of two surfaces, and $1/(Sk)$ is thermal resistance. Conduction shape factors for some common configurations are given in Table 3.

Example 2. The walls and roof of a house are made of 200 mm thick concrete with $k = 0.75$ W/(m·K). The inner surface is at 20°C, and the outer surface is at 8°C. The roof is 10 × 10 m, and the walls are 6 m high. Find the rate of heat loss from the house through its walls and roof, including edge and corner effects.

Solution: The rate of heat transfer excluding the edges and corners is first determined:

$$A_{total} = (10 - 0.4)(10 - 0.4) + 4(10 - 0.4)(6 - 0.2) = 314.9 \text{ m}^2$$

$$q_{walls+ceiling} = \frac{kA_{total}}{L}\Delta T$$

$$= \frac{[0.75 \text{ W/(m·K)}](314.9 \text{ m}^2)}{0.2 \text{ m}}(20 - 8)°\text{C} = 14\,170 \text{ W}$$

The shape factors for the corners and edges are in Table 2:

$$S_{corners+edges} = 4 \times S_{corner} + 4 \times S_{edge}$$
$$= 4 \times 0.15L + 4 \times 0.54W$$
$$= 4 \times 0.15(0.2 \text{ m}) + 4 \times 0.54(9.6 \text{ m}) = 20.86 \text{ m}$$

and the heat transfer rate is

$$q_{corners+edges} = S_{corners+edges} k\Delta T$$
$$= (20.86 \text{ m})[0.75 \text{ W/(m·K)}](20 - 8)°\text{C}$$
$$= 188 \text{ W}$$

which leads to

$$q_{total} = 14\,170 \text{ W} + 188 \text{ W} = 14\,358 \text{ W} = 14.4 \text{ kW}$$

Note that the edges and corners are 1.3% of the total.

Extended Surfaces

Heat transfer from a surface can be increased by attaching fins or extended surfaces to increase the area available for heat transfer. A few common fin geometries are shown in Figures 5 to 8. Fins provide a large surface area in a low volume, thus lowering material costs for a given performance. To achieve optimum design, fins are generally located on the side of the heat exchanger with lower heat transfer coefficients (e.g., the air side of an air-to-water coil). Equipment with extended surfaces includes natural- and forced-convection coils and shell-and-tube evaporators and condensers. Fins are also used inside tubes in condensers and dry expansion evaporators.

Fin Efficiency. As heat flows from the root of a fin to its tip, temperature drops because of the fin material's thermal resistance. The temperature difference between the fin and surrounding fluid is therefore greater at the root than at the tip, causing a corresponding variation in heat flux. Therefore, increases in fin length result in proportionately less additional heat transfer. To account for this effect, **fin efficiency** ϕ is defined as the ratio of the actual heat transferred from the fin to the heat that would be transferred if the entire fin were at its root or base temperature:

$$\phi = \frac{q}{hA_s(t_r - t_e)} \tag{6}$$

where q is heat transfer rate into/out of the fin's root, t_e is temperature of the surrounding environment, t_r is temperature at fin root, and A_s is surface area of the fin. Fin efficiency is low for long or thin fins, or fins made of low-thermal-conductivity material. Fin efficiency decreases as the heat transfer coefficient increases because of increased heat flow. For natural convection in air-cooled condensers and evaporators, where the air-side h is low, fins can be fairly large and fabricated from low-conductivity materials such as steel instead of from copper or aluminum. For condensing and boiling, where large heat transfer coefficients are involved, fins must be very short for optimum use of material. Fin efficiencies for a few geometries are shown in Figures 5 to 8. Temperature distribution and fin efficiencies for various fin shapes are derived in most heat transfer texts.

Constant-Area Fins and Spines. Fins or spines with constant cross-sectional area [e.g., straight fins (option A in Figure 7), cylindrical spines (option D in Figure 8)], the efficiency can be calculated as

$$\phi = \frac{\tanh(mW_c)}{mW_c} \tag{7}$$

where

$m = \sqrt{hP/kA_c}$
P = fin perimeter
A_c = fin cross-sectional area
W_c = corrected fin/spine length = $W + A_c/P$
A_c/P = $d/4$ for a cylindrical spine with diameter d
= $a/4$ for an $a \times a$ square spine
= $y_b = \delta/2$ for a straight fin with thickness δ

Table 3 Multidimensional Conduction Shape Factors

Configuration	Shape Factor *S*, m	Restriction	
Edge of two adjoining walls	$0.54W$	$W > L/5$	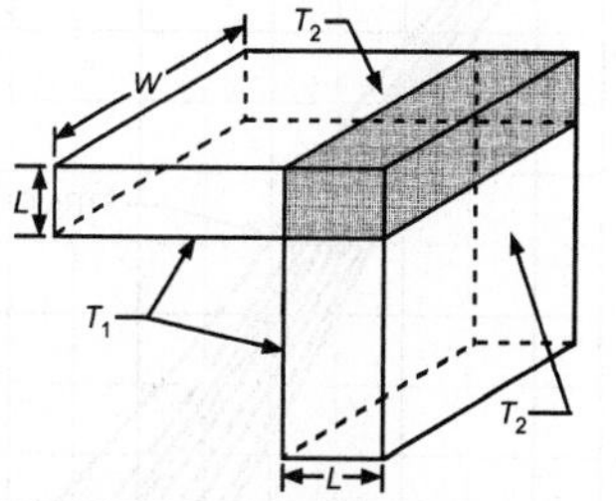
Corner of three adjoining walls (inner surface at T_1 and outer surface at T_2)	$0.15L$	$L \ll$ length and width of wall	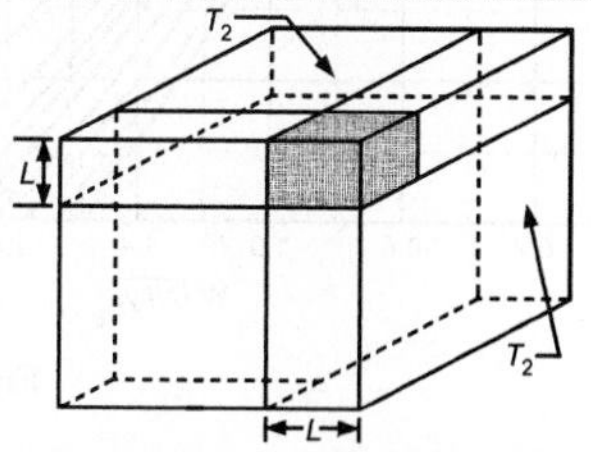
Isothermal rectangular block embedded in semi-infinite body with one face of block parallel to surface of body	$\dfrac{2.756L}{\left[\ln\left(1+\dfrac{d}{W}\right)\right]^{0.59}}\left(\dfrac{H}{d}\right)^{0.078}$	$L > W$ $L \gg d, W, H$	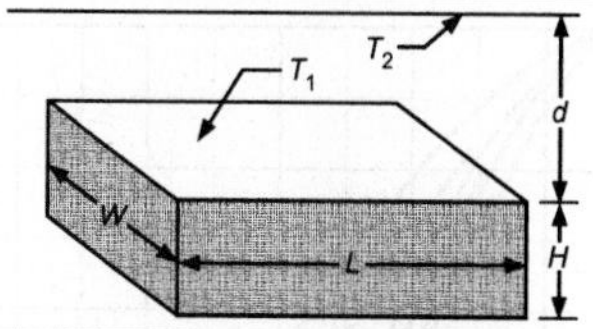
Thin isothermal rectangular plate buried in semi-infinite medium	$\dfrac{\pi W}{\ln(4W/L)}$	$d = 0, W > L$	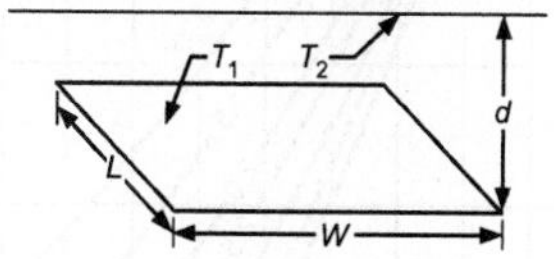
	$\dfrac{2\pi W}{\ln(4W/L)}$	$d \gg W$ $W > L$	
	$\dfrac{2\pi W}{\ln(2\pi d/L)}$	$d > 2W$ $W \gg L$	
Cylinder centered inside square of length L	$\dfrac{2\pi L}{\ln(0.54W/R)}$	$L \gg W$ $W > 2R$	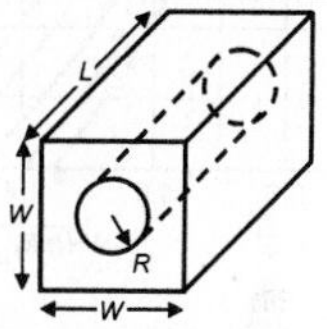
Isothermal cylinder buried in semi-infinite medium	$\dfrac{2\pi L}{\cosh^{-1}(d/R)}$	$L \gg R$	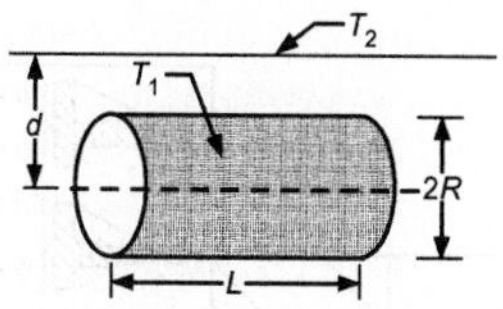
	$\dfrac{2\pi L}{\ln(2d/R)}$	$L \gg R$ $d > 3R$	
	$\dfrac{2\pi L}{\ln\dfrac{L}{R}\left[1-\dfrac{\ln(L/2d)}{\ln(L/R)}\right]}$	$d \gg R$ $L \gg d$	
Horizontal cylinder of length L midway between two infinite, parallel, isothermal surfaces	$\dfrac{2\pi L}{\ln\left(\dfrac{4d}{R}\right)}$	$L \gg d$	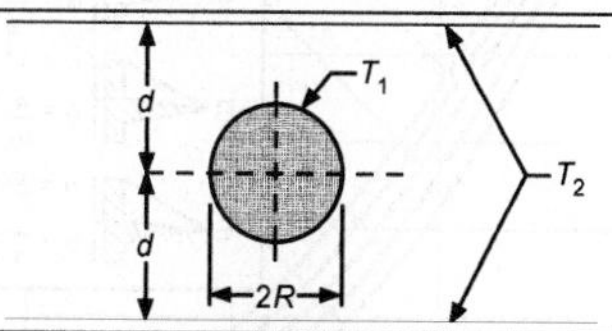
Isothermal sphere in semi-infinite medium	$\dfrac{4\pi R}{1-(R/2d)}$		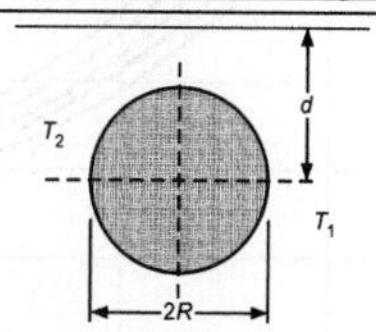
Isothermal sphere in infinite medium	$4\pi R$		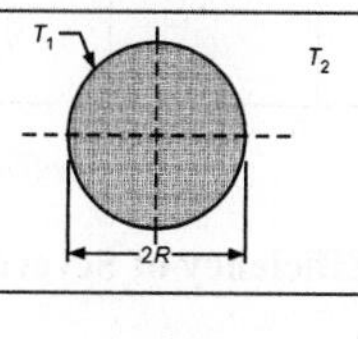

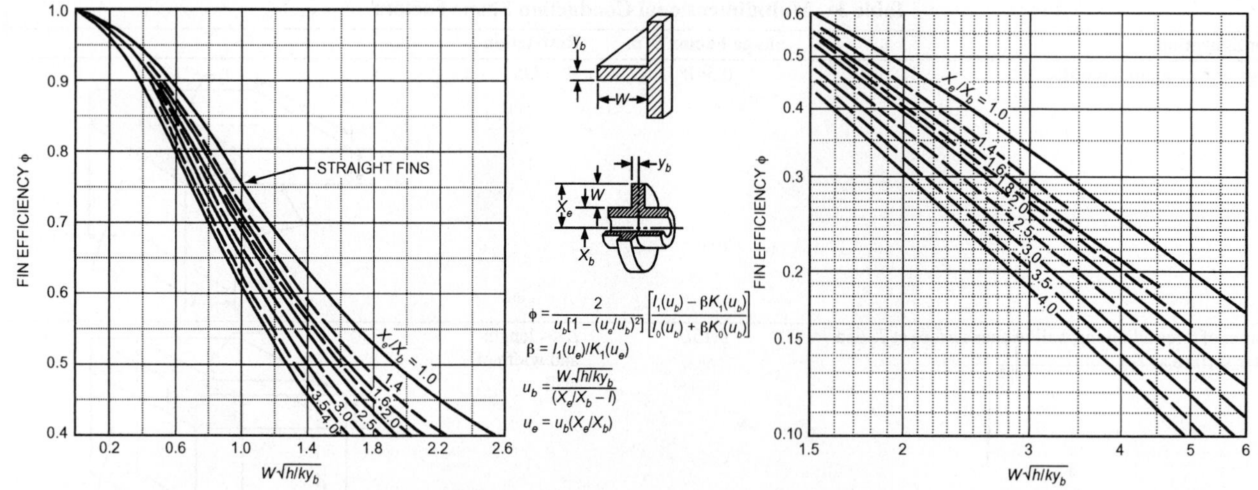

Fig. 5 Efficiency of Annular Fins of Constant Thickness

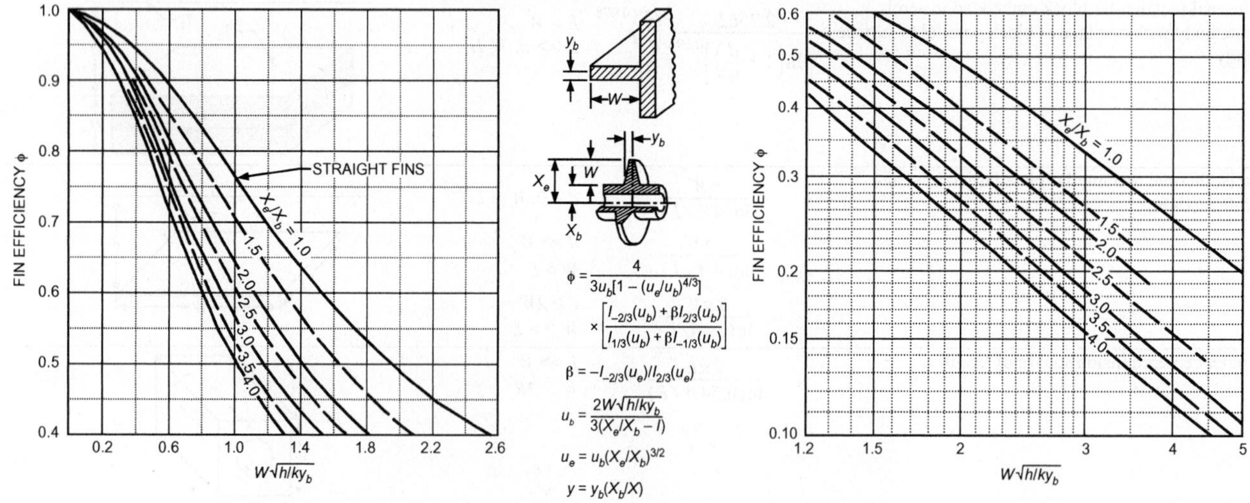

Fig. 6 Efficiency of Annular Fins with Constant Metal Area for Heat Flow

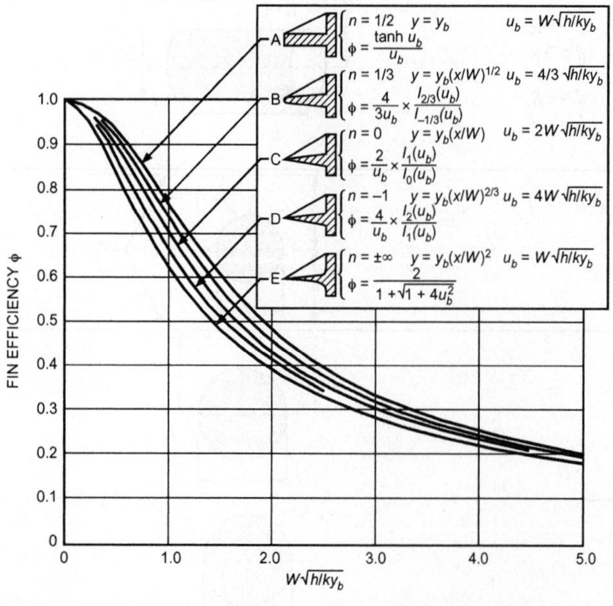

Fig. 7 Efficiency of Several Types of Straight Fins

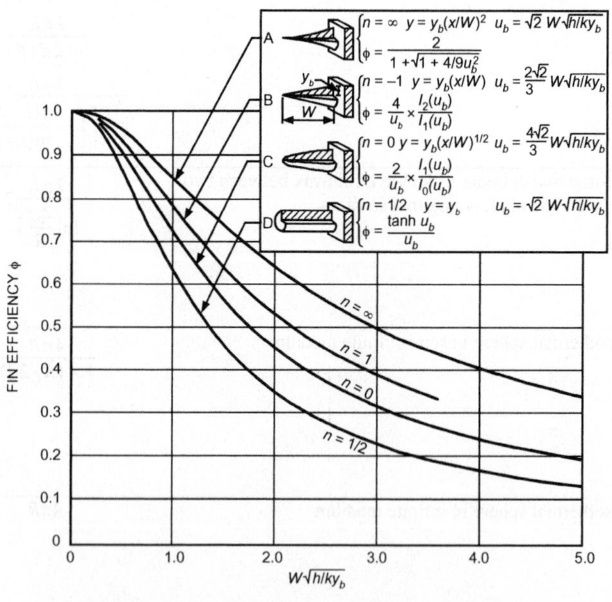

Fig. 8 Efficiency of Four Types of Spines

Empirical Expressions for Fins on Tubes. Schmidt (1949) presents approximate, but reasonably accurate, analytical expressions (for computer use) for the fin efficiency of circular, rectangular, and hexagonal arrays of fins on round tubes, as shown in Figures 5, 9, and 10, respectively. Rectangular fin arrays are used for an in-line tube arrangement in finned-tube heat exchangers, and hexagonal arrays are used for staggered tubes. Schmidt's empirical solution is given by

$$\phi = \frac{\tanh(mr_bZ)}{mr_bZ} \tag{8}$$

where r_b is tube radius, $m = \sqrt{2h/k\delta}$, δ = fin thickness, and Z is given by

$$Z = [(r_e/r_b) - 1][1 + 0.35 \ln(r_e/r_b)]$$

where r_e is the actual or equivalent fin tip radius. For **circular fins**, r_e/r_b is the actual ratio of fin tip radius to tube radius. For rectangular fins (Figure 9),

$$r_e/r_b = 1.28\Psi\sqrt{\beta - 0.2} \qquad \Psi = M/r_b \qquad \beta = L/M \geq 1$$

where M and L are defined by Figure 9 as $a/2$ or $b/2$, depending on which is greater. For hexagonal fins (Figure 10),

$$r_e/r_b = 1.27\Psi\sqrt{\beta - 0.3}$$

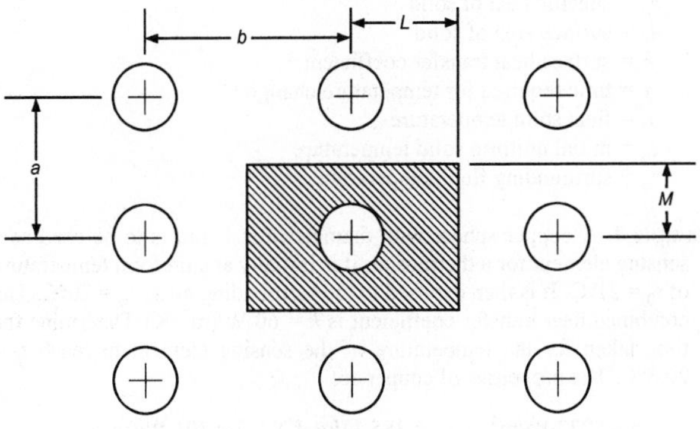

Fig. 9 Rectangular Tube Array

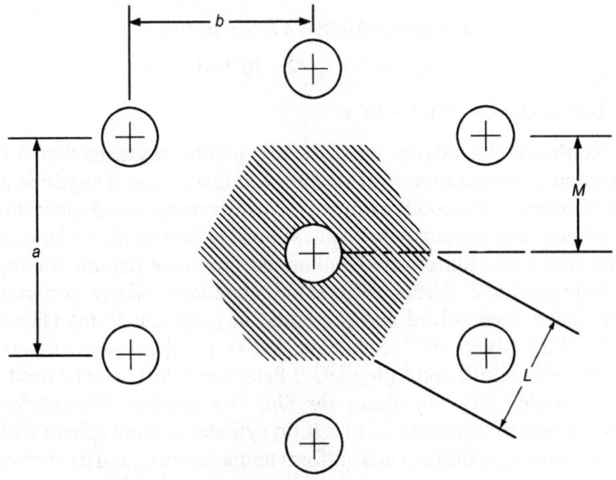

Fig. 10 Hexagonal Tube Array

where Ψ and β are defined as previously, and M and L are defined by Figure 10 as $a/2$ or b (whichever is less) and $0.5\sqrt{(a/2)^2 + b^2}$, respectively.

For constant-thickness square fins on a round tube ($L = M$ in Figure 9), the efficiency of a constant-thickness annular fin of the same area can be used. For more accuracy, particularly with rectangular fins of large aspect ratio, divide the fin into circular sectors as described by Rich (1966).

Other sources of information on finned surfaces are listed in the References and Bibliography.

Surface Efficiency. Heat transfer from a finned surface (e.g., a tube) that includes both fin area A_s and unfinned or prime area A_p is given by

$$q = (h_pA_p + \phi h_sA_s)(t_r - t_e) \tag{9}$$

Assuming the heat transfer coefficients for the fin and prime surfaces are equal, a **surface efficiency** ϕ_s can be derived as

$$\phi_s = \frac{A_p + \phi A_s}{A} \tag{10}$$

where $A = A_s + A_p$ is the total surface area, the sum of the fin and prime areas. The heat transfer in Equation (8) can then be written as

$$q = \phi_s hA(t_r - t_e) = \frac{t_r - t_e}{1/(\phi_s hA)} \tag{11}$$

where $1/(\phi_s hA)$ is the finned surface resistance.

Example 3. An aluminum tube with k = 186 W/(m·K), ID = 45 mm, and OD = 50 mm has circular aluminum fins δ = 1 mm thick with an outer diameter of D_{fin} = 100 mm. There are N' = 250 fins per metre of tube length. Steam condenses inside the tube at t_i = 200°C with a large heat transfer coefficient on the inner tube surface. Air at t_∞ = 25°C is heated by the steam. The heat transfer coefficient outside the tube is 40 W/(m²·K). Find the rate of heat transfer per metre of tube length.

Solution: From Figure 5's efficiency curve, the efficiency of these circular fins is

$$\left.\begin{aligned} &W = (D_{fin} - \text{OD})/2 = (0.10 - 0.05)/2 = 0.025 \text{ m} \\ &X_e/X_b = 0.10/0.05 = 2.0 \\ &W\sqrt{\frac{h}{k(\delta/2)}} = 0.025\sqrt{\frac{40 \text{ W/(m}^2\cdot\text{K)}}{[186 \text{ W/(m}\cdot\text{K)}](0.0005 \text{ m})}} = 0.52 \end{aligned}\right\} \phi = 0.89$$

The fin area for L = 1 m is

$$A_s = 250 \times 2\pi(D_{fin}^2 - \text{OD}^2)/4 = 2.945 \text{ m}^2$$

The unfinned area for L = 1 m is

$$A_p = \pi \times \text{OD} \times L(1 - N'\delta) = \pi(0.05 \text{ m})(1 \text{ m})(1 - 250 \times 0.001) = 0.118 \text{ m}^2$$

and the total area $A = A_s + A_p = 3.063$ m². Surface efficiency is

$$\phi_s = \frac{\phi A_f + A_s}{A} = 0.894$$

and resistance of the finned surface is

$$R_s = \frac{1}{\phi_s hA} = 9.13 \times 10^{-3} \text{ K/W}$$

Tube wall resistance is

$$R_{wall} = \frac{\ln(\text{OD/ID})}{2\pi L k_{tube}} = \frac{\ln(5/4.5)}{2\pi(1 \text{ m})[186 \text{ W/(m}\cdot\text{K)}]} = 9.02 \times 10^{-5} \text{ K/W}$$

The rate of heat transfer is then

$$q = \frac{t_i - t_\infty}{R_s + R_{wall}} = 18\ 981\ \text{W}$$

Had Schmidt's approach been used for fin efficiency,

$$m = \sqrt{2h/k\delta} = 20.74\ \text{m}^{-1} \qquad r_b = \text{OD}/2 = 0.025\ \text{m}$$

$$Z = [(D_{fin}/\text{OD}) - 1]\ [1 + 0.35\ \ln(D_{fin}/\text{OD})] = 1.243$$

$$\phi = \frac{\tanh(mr_bZ)}{mr_bZ} = 0.88$$

the same ϕ as given by Figure 5.

Contact Resistance. Fins can be extruded from the prime surface (e.g., short fins on tubes in flooded evaporators or water-cooled condensers) or can be fabricated separately, sometimes of a different material, and bonded to the prime surface. Metallurgical bonds are achieved by furnace-brazing, dip-brazing, or soldering; nonmetallic bonding materials, such as epoxy resin, are also used. Mechanical bonds are obtained by tension-winding fins around tubes (spiral fins) or expanding the tubes into the fins (plate fins). Metallurgical bonding, properly done, leaves negligible thermal resistance at the joint but is not always economical. Contact resistance of a mechanical bond may or may not be negligible, depending on the application, quality of manufacture, materials, and temperatures involved. Tests of plate-fin coils with expanded tubes indicate that substantial losses in performance can occur with fins that have cracked collars, but negligible contact resistance was found in coils with continuous collars and properly expanded tubes (Dart 1959).

Contact resistance at an interface between two solids is largely a function of the surface properties and characteristics of the solids, contact pressure, and fluid in the interface, if any. Eckels (1977) modeled the influence of fin density, fin thickness, and tube diameter on contact pressure and compared it to data for wet and dry coils. Shlykov (1964) showed that the range of attainable contact resistances is large. Sonokama (1964) presented data on the effects of contact pressure, surface roughness, hardness, void material, and the pressure of the gas in the voids. Lewis and Sauer (1965) showed the resistance of adhesive bonds, and Clausing (1964) and Kaspareck (1964) gave data on the contact resistance in a vacuum environment.

Transient Conduction

Often, heat transfer and temperature distribution under transient (i.e., varying with time) conditions must be known. Examples are (1) cold-storage temperature variations on starting or stopping a refrigeration unit, (2) variation of external air temperature and solar irradiation affecting the heat load of a cold-storage room or wall temperatures, (3) the time required to freeze a given material under certain conditions in a storage room, (4) quick-freezing objects by direct immersion in brines, and (5) sudden heating or cooling of fluids and solids from one temperature to another.

Lumped Mass Analysis. Often, the temperature within a mass of material can be assumed to vary with time but be uniform within the mass. Examples include a well-stirred fluid in a thin-walled container, or a thin metal plate with high thermal conductivity. In both cases, if the mass is heated or cooled at its surface, the temperature can be assumed to be a function of time only and not location within the body. Such an approximation is valid if

$$\text{Bi} = \frac{h(V/A_s)}{k} \le 0.1$$

where

- Bi = Biot number
- h = surface heat transfer coefficient
- V = material's volume
- A_s = surface area exposed to convective and/or radiative heat transfer
- k = material's thermal conductivity

The temperature is given by

$$Mc_p\frac{dt}{d\tau} = q_{net} + q_{gen} \qquad (12)$$

where

- M = body mass
- c_p = specific heat
- q_{gen} = internal heat generation
- q_{net} = net heat transfer rate to substance (into substance is positive, and out of substance is negative)

Equation (12) applies to liquids and solids. If the material is a gas being heated or cooled at constant volume, replace c_p with the constant-volume specific heat c_v. The term q_{net} may include heat transfer by conduction, convection, or radiation and is the difference between the heat transfer rates into and out of the body. The term q_{gen} may include a chemical reaction (e.g., curing concrete) or heat generation from a current passing through a metal.

For a lumped mass M initially at a uniform temperature t_0 that is suddenly exposed to an environment at a different temperature t_∞, the time taken for the temperature of the mass to change to t_f is given by the solution of Equation (12) as

$$\ln\frac{t_f - t_\infty}{t_0 - t_\infty} = -\frac{hA_s\tau}{Mc_p} \qquad (13)$$

where

- M = mass of solid
- c_p = specific heat of solid
- A_s = surface area of solid
- h = surface heat transfer coefficient
- τ = time required for temperature change
- t_f = final solid temperature
- t_0 = initial uniform solid temperature
- t_∞ = surrounding fluid temperature

Example 4. A copper sphere with diameter d = 1 mm is to be used as a sensing element for a thermostat. It is initially at a uniform temperature of t_0 = 21°C. It is then exposed to the surrounding air at t_∞ = 20°C. The combined heat transfer coefficient is h = 60 W/(m²·K). Determine the time taken for the temperature of the sensing element to reach t_f = 20.5°C. The properties of copper are

$$\rho = 8933\ \text{kg/m}^3 \quad c_p = 385\ \text{J/(kg·K)} \quad k = 401\ \text{W/(m·K)}$$

Solution: Bi = $h(d/2)/k$ = 60.35(0.001/2)/401 = 7.5 × 10⁻⁵, which is much less than 1. Therefore, lumped analysis is valid.

$$M = \rho[4\pi(d/2)^3/3] = 4.677 \times 10^{-6}\ \text{kg}$$

$$A_s = \pi d^2 = 3.142 \times 10^{-6}\ \text{m}^2$$

Using Equation (13), τ = 6.6 s.

Nonlumped Analysis. When the Biot number is greater than 0.1, variation of temperature with location within the mass is significant. One example is the cooling time of meats in a refrigerated space: the meat's size and conductivity do not allow it to be treated as a lumped mass that cools uniformly. Nonlumped problems require solving multidimensional partial differential equations. Many common cases have been solved and presented in graphical forms (Jakob 1949, 1957; Myers 1971; Schneider 1964). In other cases, numerical methods (Croft and Lilley 1977; Patankar 1980) must be used.

Estimating Cooling Times for One-Dimensional Geometries. When a slab of thickness $2L$ or a solid cylinder or solid sphere with outer radius r_m is initially at a uniform temperature t_1, and its surface is suddenly heated or cooled by convection with a fluid at t_∞, a mathematical solution is available for the temperature t as a function of

Table 4 Values of c_1 and μ_1 in Equations (14) to (17)

	Slab		Solid Cylinder		Solid Sphere	
Bi	c_1	μ_1	c_1	μ_1	c_1	μ_1
0.5	1.0701	0.6533	1.1143	0.9408	1.1441	1.1656
1.0	1.1191	0.8603	1.2071	1.2558	1.2732	1.5708
2.0	1.1785	1.0769	1.3384	1.5995	1.4793	2.0288
4.0	1.2287	1.2646	1.4698	1.9081	1.7202	2.4556
6.0	1.2479	1.3496	1.5253	2.0490	1.8338	2.6537
8.0	1.2570	1.3978	1.5526	2.1286	1.8920	2.7654
10.0	1.2620	1.4289	1.5677	2.1795	1.9249	2.8363
30.0	1.2717	1.5202	1.5973	2.3261	1.9898	3.0372
50.0	1.2727	1.5400	1.6002	2.3572	1.9962	3.0788

location and time τ. The solution is an infinite series. However, after a short time, the temperature is very well approximated by the first term of the series. The single-term approximations for the three cases are of the form

$$Y = Y_0 f(\mu_1 n) \tag{14}$$

where

$$Y = \frac{t - t_\infty}{t_1 - t_\infty}$$

$$Y_0 = \frac{t_0 - t_\infty}{t_1 - t_\infty} = c_1 \exp(-\mu_1^2 \text{Fo})$$

t_0 = temperature at center of slab, cylinder, or sphere
Fo = $\alpha\tau/L_c^2$ = Fourier number
α = thermal diffusivity of solid = $k/\rho c_p$
L_c = L for slab, r_o for cylinder, sphere
n = x/L for slab, r/r_m for cylinder
c_1, μ_1 = coefficients that are functions of Bi
Bi = Biot number = hL_c/k
$f(\mu_1 n)$ = function of $\mu_1 n$, different for each geometry
x = distance from midplane of slab of thickness $2L$ cooled on both sides
ρ = density of solid
c_p = constant pressure specific heat of solid
k = thermal conductivity of solid

The single term solution is valid for Fo > 0.2. Values of c_1 and μ_1 are given in Table 4 for a few values of Bi, and Couvillion (2004) provides a procedure for calculating them. Expressions for c_1 for each case, along with the function $f(\mu_1 n)$, are as follows:

Slab

$$f(\mu_1 n) = \cos(\mu_1 n) \qquad c_1 = \frac{4\sin(\mu_1)}{2\mu_1 + \sin(2\mu_1)} \tag{15}$$

Long solid cylinder

$$f(\mu_1 n) = J_0(\mu_1 n) \qquad c_1 = \frac{2}{\mu_1} \times \frac{J_1(\mu_1)}{J_0^2(\mu_1) + J_1^2(\mu_1)} \tag{16}$$

where J_0 is the Bessel function of the first kind, order zero. It is available in math tables, spreadsheets, and software packages. $J_0(0) = 1$.

Solid sphere

$$f(\mu_1 n) = \frac{\sin(\mu_1 n)}{\mu_1 n} \qquad c_1 = \frac{4[\sin(\mu_1) - \mu_1 \cos(\mu_1)]}{2\mu_1 - \sin(2\mu_1)} \tag{17}$$

These solutions are presented graphically (McAdams 1954) by Gurnie-Lurie charts (Figures 11 to 13). The charts are also valid for Fo < 0.2.

Example 5. Apples, approximated as 0.60 mm diameter solid spheres and initially at 30°C, are loaded into a chamber maintained at 0°C. If the surface heat transfer coefficient h = 14 W/(m²·K), estimate the time required for the center temperature to reach t = 1°C.

Properties of apples are

$$\rho = 830 \text{ kg/m}^3 \qquad k = 0.42 \text{ W/(m}^2\cdot\text{K)}$$

$$c_p = 3600 \text{ J/(kg·K)} \qquad r_m = d/2 = 30 \text{ mm} = 0.03 \text{ m}$$

Solution: Assuming that it will take a long time for the center temperature to reach 1°C, use the one-term approximation Equation (14). From the values given,

$$Y = \frac{t_\infty - t}{t_\infty - t_1} = \frac{0-1}{0-30} = \frac{1}{30}$$

$$n = \frac{r}{r_m} = \frac{0}{0.03} = 0 \qquad \text{Bi} = \frac{hr_m}{k} = \frac{14 \times 0.03}{0.42} = 1$$

$$\alpha = \frac{k}{\rho c_p} = \frac{0.42}{830 \times 3600} = 1.406 \times 10^{-7} \text{ m}^2/\text{s}$$

From Equations (14) and (17) with lim(sin 0/0) = 1, $Y = Y_0 = c_1 \exp(-\mu_1^2\text{Fo})$. For Bi = 1, from Table 4, c_1 = 1.2732 and μ_1 = 1.5708. Thus,

$$\text{Fo} = -\frac{1}{\mu_1^2}\ln\frac{Y}{c_1} = -\frac{1}{1.5708^2}\ln 0.0333 = 1.476 = \frac{\alpha\tau}{r_m^2} = \frac{0.00545\tau}{(0.1967/2)^2}$$

$$\tau = 2.62 \text{ h}$$

Note that Fo = 0.2 corresponds to an actual time of 1280 s.

Multidimensional Cooling Times. One-dimensional transient temperature solutions can be used to find the temperatures with two- and three-dimensional temperatures of solids. For example, consider a solid cylinder of length $2L$ and radius r_m exposed to a fluid at t_c on all sides with constant surface heat transfer coefficients h_1 on the end surfaces and h_2 on the cylindrical surface, as shown in Figure 14.

The two-dimensional, dimensionless temperature $Y(x_1,r_1,\tau)$ can be expressed as the product of two one-dimensional temperatures $Y_1(x_1,\tau) \times Y_2(r_1,\tau)$, where

Y_1 = dimensionless temperature of constant cross-sectional area slab at (x_1,τ), with surface heat transfer coefficient h_1 associated with two parallel surfaces
Y_2 = dimensionless temperature of solid cylinder at (r_1,τ) with surface heat transfer coefficient h_2 associated with cylindrical surface

From Figures 11 and 12 or Equations (14) to (16), determine Y_1 at $(x_1/L, \alpha\tau/L^2, h_1L/k)$ and Y_2 at $(r_1/r_m, \alpha\tau/r_m^2, h_2r_m/k)$.

Example 6. A 70 mm diameter by 125 mm high soda can, initially at t_1 = 30°C, is cooled in a chamber where the air is at t_∞ = 0°C. The heat transfer coefficient on all surfaces is h = 20 W/(m²·K). Determine the maximum temperature in the can τ = 1 h after starting the cooling. Assume the properties of the soda are those of water, and that the soda inside the can behaves as a solid body.

Solution: Because the cylinder is short, the temperature of the soda is affected by the heat transfer rate from the cylindrical surface and end surfaces. The slowest change in temperature, and therefore the maximum temperature, is at the center of the cylinder. Denoting the dimensionless temperature by Y,

$$Y = Y_{cyl} \times Y_{pl}$$

where Y_{cyl} is the dimensionless temperature of an infinitely long 70 mm diameter cylinder, and Y_{pl} is the dimensionless temperature of a

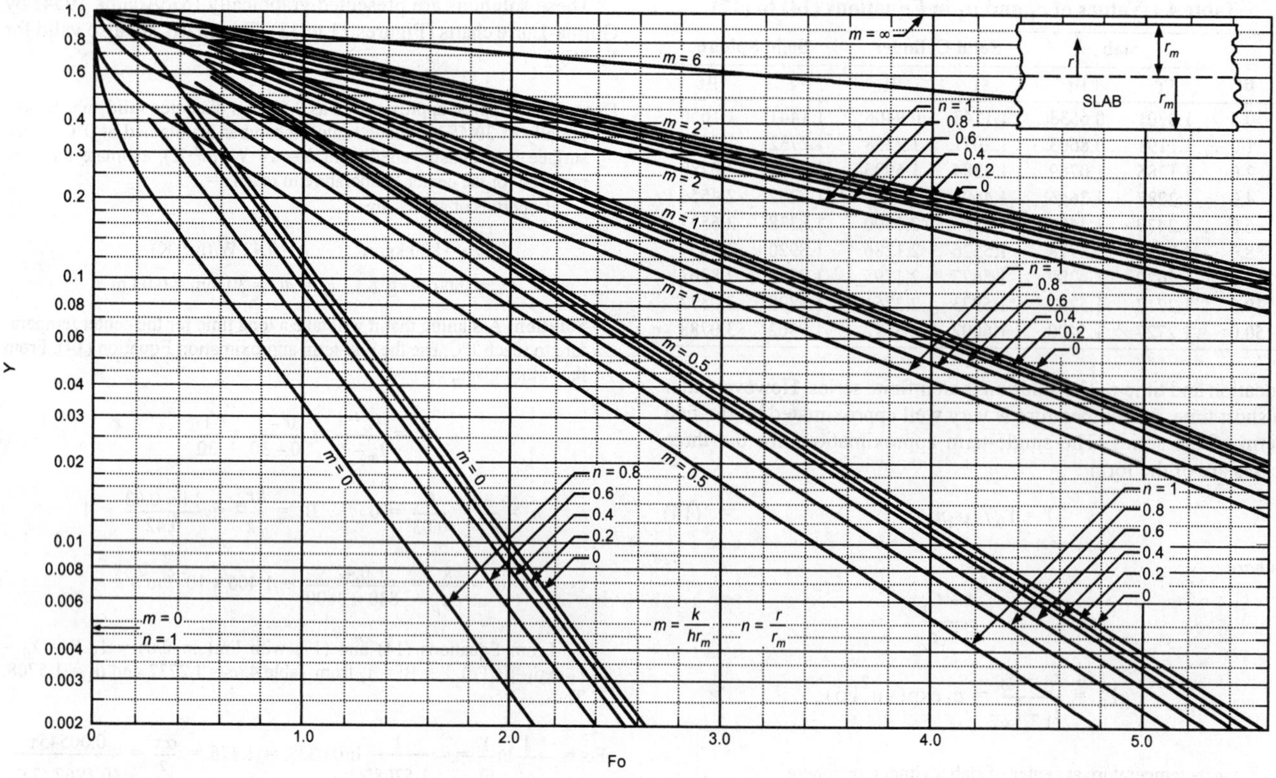

Fig. 11 Transient Temperatures for Infinite Slab, m = 1/Bi

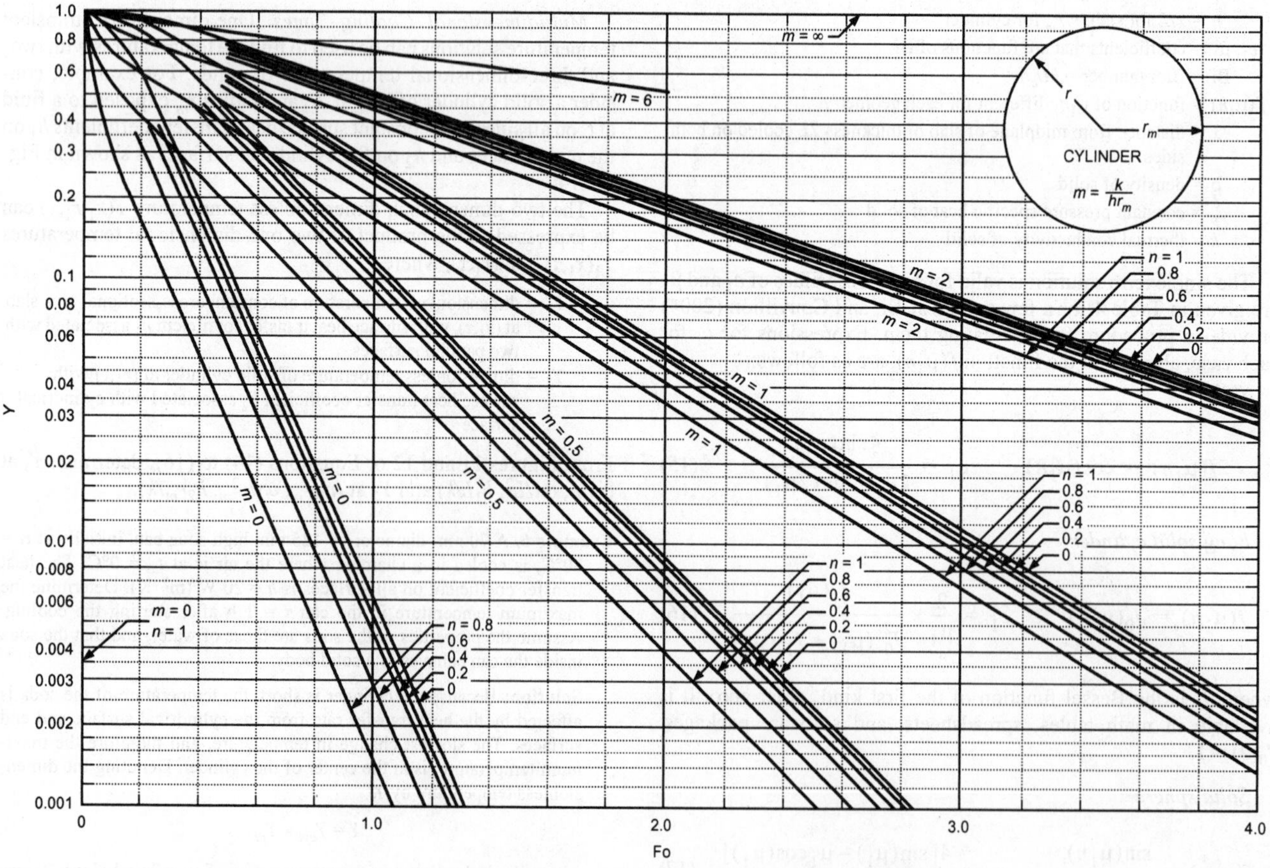

Fig. 12 Transient Temperatures for Infinite Cylinder, m = 1/Bi

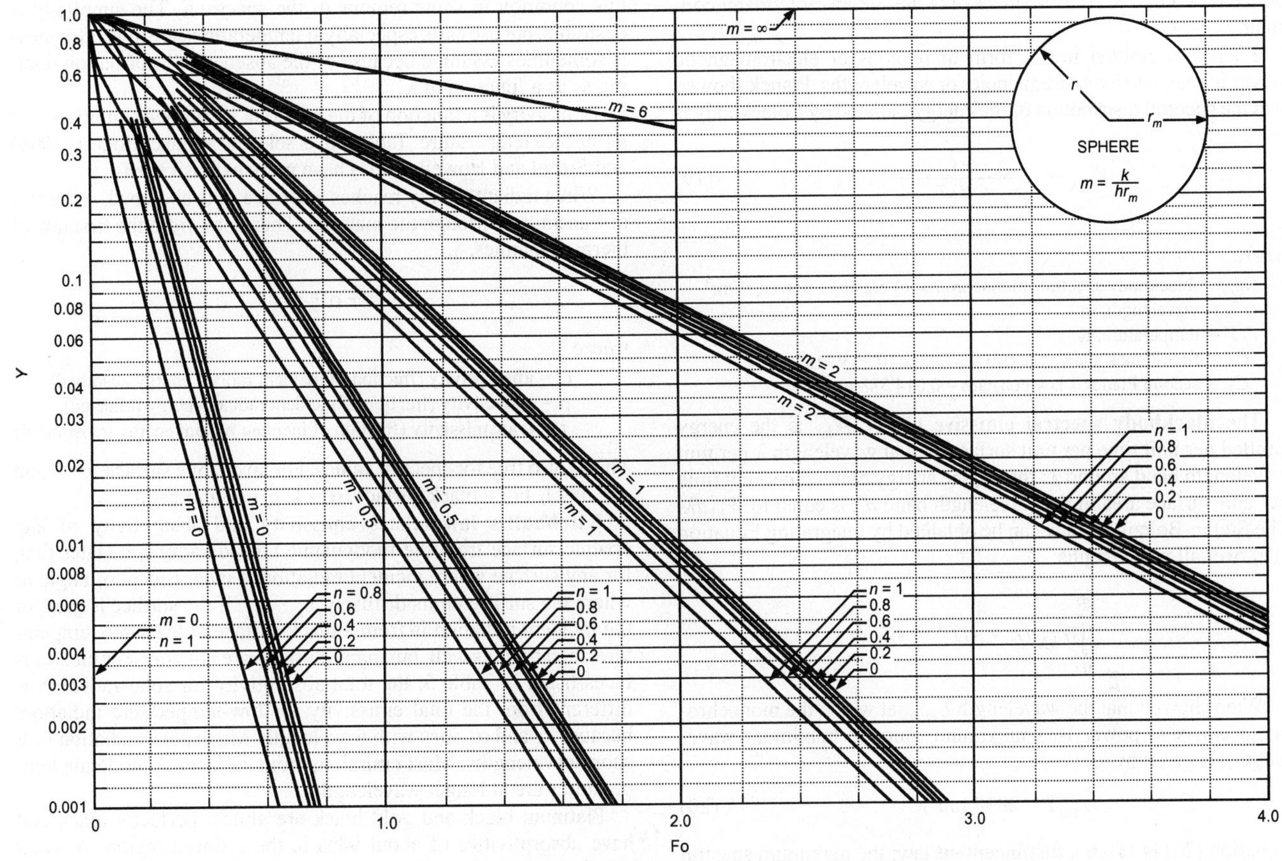

Fig. 13 Transient Temperatures for Sphere, $m = 1/\mathrm{Bi}$

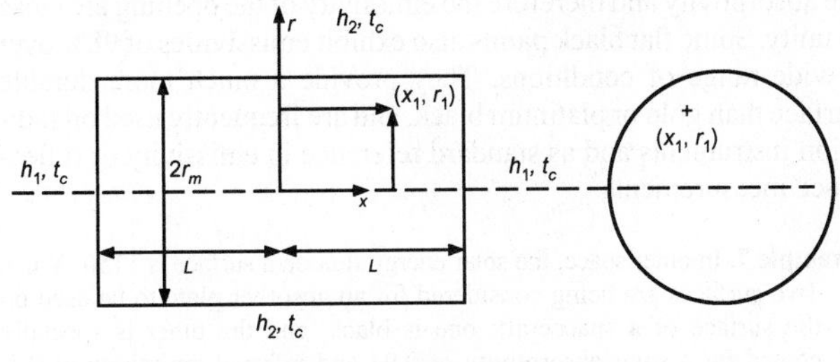

Fig. 14 Solid Cylinder Exposed to Fluid

125 mm thick slab. Each of them is found from the appropriate Biot and Fourier number. For evaluating the properties of water, choose a temperature of 15°C and a pressure of 101.35 kPa. The properties of water are

$$\rho = 999.1\ \mathrm{kg/m^3} \qquad k = 0.5894\ \mathrm{W/(m\cdot K)} \qquad c_p = 4184\ \mathrm{J/(kg\cdot K)}$$

$$\alpha = k/\rho = 1.41 \times 10^{-7}\ \mathrm{m^2/s} \qquad \tau = 3600\ \mathrm{s}$$

1. Determine Y_{cyl} at $n = 0$.

$$\mathrm{Bi}_{cyl} = hr_m/k = 20 \times 0.035/0.5894 = 1.188$$

$$\mathrm{Fo}_{cyl} = \alpha\tau/r_m{}^2 = (1.41 \times 10^{-7}) \times 3600/0.035^2 = 0.4144$$

$\mathrm{Fo}_{cyl} > 0.2$, so use the one-term approximation with Equations (14) and (16).

$$Y_{cyl} = c_1 \exp(-\mu^2{}_1\mathrm{Fo}_{cyl})J_0(0)$$

Interpolating in Table 4 for $\mathrm{Bi}_{cyl} = 1.188$, $\mu_{cyl} = 1.3042$, $J_0(0) = 1$, $c_{cyl} = 1.237$, $Y_{cyl} = 0.572$.

2. Determine Y_{pl} at $n = 0$.

$$\mathrm{Bi}_{pl} = hL/k = 20 \times 0.0625/0.5894 = 2.121$$

$$\mathrm{Fo}_{pl} = 1.41 \times 10^{-7} \times 3600/0.0625^2 = 0.1299$$

$\mathrm{Fo}_{pl} < 0.2$, so the one-term approximation is not valid. Using Figure 11, $Y_{pl} = 0.9705$. Thus,

$$Y = 0.572 \times 0.9705 = 0.5551 = (t - t_\infty)/(t_1 - t_\infty) \Rightarrow t = 16.7°\mathrm{C}$$

Note: The solution may not be exact because convective motion of the soda during heat transfer has been neglected. The example illustrates the use of the technique. For well-stirred soda, with uniform temperature within the can, the lumped mass solution should be used.

THERMAL RADIATION

Radiation, unlike conduction and convection, does not need a solid or fluid to transport energy from a high-temperature surface to a lower-temperature one. (Radiation is in fact impeded by such a material.) The rate of radiant energy emission and its characteristics from a surface depend on the underlying material's nature, microscopic arrangement, and absolute temperature. The rate of emission from a surface is independent of the surfaces surrounding it, but the rate and characteristics of radiation incident on a surface do depend on the temperatures and spatial relationships of the surrounding surfaces.

Blackbody Radiation

The total energy emitted per unit time per unit area of a black surface is called the **blackbody emissive power W_b** and is given by the **Stefan-Boltzmann law**:

$$W_b = \sigma T^4 \qquad (18)$$

where $\sigma = 5.670 \times 10^{-8}$ W/(m²·K⁴) is the Stefan-Boltzmann constant.

Energy is emitted in the form of photons or electromagnetic waves of many different frequencies or wavelengths. Planck showed that the spectral distribution of the energy radiated by a blackbody is

$$W_{b\lambda} = \frac{C_1}{\lambda^5 (e^{C_2/\lambda T} - 1)} \tag{19}$$

where

$W_{b\lambda}$ = blackbody spectral (monochromatic) emissive power, W/m³
λ = wavelength, m
T = temperature, K
C_1 = first Planck's law constant = 3.742×10^{-16} W·m²
C_2 = second Planck's law constant = 0.014 388 m·K

The **blackbody spectral emissive power $W_{b\lambda}$** is the energy emitted per unit time per unit surface area at wavelength λ per unit wavelength band around λ; that is, the energy emitted per unit time per unit surface area in the wavelength band $d\lambda$ is equal to $W_{b\lambda} d\lambda$. The Stefan-Boltzmann law can be obtained by integrating Equation (19) over all wavelengths:

$$\int_0^\infty W_{b\lambda} d\lambda = \sigma T^4 = W_b$$

Wien showed that the wavelength λ_{max}, at which the monochromatic emissive power is a maximum (not the maximum wavelength), is given by

$$\lambda_{max} T = 2898 \ \mu\text{m·K} \tag{20}$$

Equation (20) is **Wien's displacement** law; the maximum spectral emissive power shifts to shorter wavelengths as temperature increases, such that, at very high temperatures, significant emission eventually occurs over the entire visible spectrum as shorter wavelengths become more prominent. For additional details, see Incropera et al. (2007).

Actual Radiation

The blackbody emissive power W_b and blackbody spectral emissive power $W_{b\lambda}$ are the maxima at a given surface temperature. Actual surfaces emit less and are called **nonblack**. The **emissive power W** of a nonblack surface at temperature T radiating to the hemispherical region above it is given by

$$W = \varepsilon \sigma T^4 \tag{21}$$

where ε is the **total emissivity**. The **spectral emissive power W_λ** of a nonblack surface is given by

$$W_\lambda = \varepsilon_\lambda W_{b\lambda} \tag{22}$$

where ε_λ is the **spectral emissivity**, and $W_{b\lambda}$ is given by Equation (19). The relationship between ε and ε_λ is given by

$$W = \varepsilon \sigma T^4 = \int_0^\infty W_\lambda d\lambda = \int_0^\infty \varepsilon_\lambda W_{b\lambda} d\lambda$$

or

$$\varepsilon = \frac{1}{\sigma T^4} \int_0^\infty \varepsilon_\lambda W_{b\lambda} d\lambda \tag{23}$$

If ε_λ does not depend on λ, then, from Equation (23), $\varepsilon = \varepsilon_\lambda$, and the surface is called **gray**. Gray surface characteristics are often assumed in calculations. Several classes of surfaces approximate this condition in some regions of the spectrum. The simplicity is desirable, but use care, especially if temperatures are high. Grayness is sometimes assumed because of the absence of information relating ε_λ as a function of λ.

Emissivity is a function of the material, its surface condition, and its surface temperature. Table 5 lists selected values; Modest (2003) and Siegel and Howell (2002) have more extensive lists.

When radiant energy reaches a surface, it is absorbed, reflected, or transmitted through the material. Therefore, from the first law of thermodynamics,

$$\alpha + \rho + \tau = 1$$

where

α = **absorptivity** (fraction of incident radiant energy absorbed)
ρ = **reflectivity** (fraction of incident radiant energy reflected)
τ = **transmissivity** (fraction of incident radiant energy transmitted)

This is also true for spectral values. For an opaque surface, $\tau = 0$ and $\rho + \alpha = 1$. For a black surface, $\alpha = 1$, $\rho = 0$, and $\tau = 0$.

Kirchhoff's law relates emissivity and absorptivity of any opaque surface from thermodynamic considerations; it states that, for any surface where incident radiation is independent of angle or where the surface emits diffusely, $\varepsilon_\lambda = \alpha_\lambda$. If the surface is gray, or the incident radiation is from a black surface at the same temperature, then $\varepsilon = \alpha$ as well, but many surfaces are not gray. For most surfaces listed in Table 5, the total absorptivity for solar radiation is different from the total emissivity for low-temperature radiation, because ε_λ and α_λ vary with wavelength. Much solar radiation is at short wavelengths. Most emissions from surfaces at moderate temperatures are at longer wavelengths.

Platinum black and gold black are almost perfectly black and have absorptivities of about 98% in the infrared region. A small opening in a large cavity approaches blackbody behavior because most of the incident energy entering the cavity is absorbed by repeated reflection within it, and very little escapes the cavity. Thus, the absorptivity and therefore the emissivity of the opening are close to unity. Some flat black paints also exhibit emissivities of 98% over a wide range of conditions. They provide a much more durable surface than gold or platinum black, and are frequently used on radiation instruments and as standard reference in emissivity or reflectance measurements.

Example 7. In outer space, the solar energy flux on a surface is 1150 W/m². Two surfaces are being considered for an absorber plate to be used on the surface of a spacecraft: one is black, and the other is specially coated for a solar absorptivity of 0.94 and infrared emissivity of 0.1. Coolant flowing through the tubes attached to the plate maintains the plate at 340 K. The plate surface is normal to the solar beam. For each surface, determine the (1) heat transfer rate to the coolant per unit area of the plate, and (2) temperature of the surface when there is no coolant flow.

Solution: For the black surface,

$$\varepsilon = \alpha = 1, \rho = 0$$

Absorbed energy flux = 1150 W/m²

At T_s = 340 K, emitted energy flux = $W_b = 5.67 \times 10^{-8} \times 340^4$ = 757.7 W/m².

In space, there is no convection, so an energy balance on the surface gives

Heat flux to coolant = Absorbed energy flux – Emitted energy flux = 1150 – 757.7 = 392.3 W/m²

For the special surface, use solar absorptivity to determine the absorbed energy flux, and infrared emissivity to calculate the emitted energy flux.

Absorbed energy flux = 0.94 × 1150 = 1081 W/m²
Emitted energy flux = 0.1 × 757.7 = 75.8 W/m²
Heat flux to coolant = 1081 – 75.8 = 1005 W/m²

Table 5 Emissivities and Absorptivities of Some Surfaces

Surface	Total Hemispherical Emissivity	Solar Absorptivity*
Aluminum		
Foil, bright dipped	0.03	0.10
Alloy: 6061	0.04	0.37
Roofing	0.24	
Asphalt	0.88	
Brass		
Oxidized	0.60	
Polished	0.04	
Brick	0.90	
Concrete, rough	0.91	0.60
Copper		
Electroplated	0.03	0.47
Black oxidized in Ebanol C	0.16	0.91
Plate, oxidized	0.76	
Glass		
Polished	0.87 to 0.92	
Pyrex	0.80	
Smooth	0.91	
Granite	0.44	
Gravel	0.30	
Ice	0.96 to 0.97	
Limestone	0.92	
Marble		
Polished or white	0.89 to 0.92	
Smooth	0.56	
Mortar, lime	0.90	
Nickel		
Electroplated	0.03	0.22
Solar absorber, electro-oxidized on copper	0.05 to 0.11	0.85
Paints		
Black		
Parsons optical, silicone high heat, epoxy	0.87 to 0.92	0.94 to 0.97
Gloss	0.90	
Enamel, heated 1000 h at 650 K	0.80	
Silver chromatone	0.24	0.20
White		
Acrylic resin	0.90	0.26
Gloss	0.85	
Epoxy	0.85	0.25
Paper, roofing or white	0.88 to 0.86	
Plaster, rough	0.89	
Refractory	0.90 to 0.94	
Sand	0.75	
Sandstone, red	0.59	
Silver, polished	0.02	
Snow, fresh	0.82	0.13
Soil	0.94	
Water	0.90	0.98
White potassium zirconium silicate	0.87	0.13

Source: Mills (1999)
*Values are for extraterrestrial conditions, except for concrete, snow, and water.

Without coolant flow, heat flux to the coolant is zero. Therefore, absorbed energy flux = emitted energy flux. For the black surface,

$$1150 = 5.67 \times 10^{-8} \times T_s^4 \Rightarrow T_s = 377.1 \text{ K}$$

For the special surface,

$$0.94 \times 1150 = 0.1 \times 5.67 \times 10^{-8} \times T_s^4 \Rightarrow T_s = 660.8 \text{ K}$$

Angle Factor

The foregoing discussion addressed emission from a surface and absorption of radiation leaving surrounding surfaces. Before radiation exchange among a number of surfaces can be addressed, the amount of radiation leaving one surface that is incident on another must be determined.

The fraction of all radiant energy leaving a surface i that is directly incident on surface k is the **angle factor F_{ik}** (also known as **view factor**, **shape factor**, and **configuration factor**). The angle factor from area A_k to area A_j, F_{ki}, is similarly defined, merely by interchanging the roles of i and k. The following relations assume

- All surfaces are gray or black
- Emission and reflection are diffuse (i.e., not a function of direction)
- Properties are uniform over the surfaces
- Absorptivity equals emissivity and is independent of temperature of source of incident radiation
- Material located between radiating surfaces neither emits nor absorbs radiation

These assumptions greatly simplify problems, and give good approximate results in many cases. Some of the relations for the angle factor are given below.

Reciprocity relation.

$$F_{ik} A_i = F_{ki} A_k \qquad (24a)$$

Decomposition relation. For three surfaces i, j, and k, with A_{ij} indicating one surface with two parts denoted by A_i and A_j,

$$A_k F_{k\text{-}ij} = A_k F_{k\text{-}i} + A_k F_{k\text{-}j} \qquad (24b)$$

$$A_{ij} F_{ij\text{-}k} = A_i F_{i\text{-}k} + A_j F_{j\text{-}k} \qquad (24c)$$

Law of corresponding corners. This law is discussed by Love (1968) and Suryanarayana (1995). Its use is shown in Example 8.

Summation rule. For an enclosure with n surfaces, some of which may be inside the enclosure,

$$\sum_{k=1}^{n} F_{ik} = 1 \qquad (24d)$$

Note that a concave surface may "see itself," and $F_{ii} \neq 0$ for such a surface.

Numerical values of the angle factor for common geometries are given in Figure 15. For equations to compute angle factors for many configurations, refer to Siegel and Howell (2002).

Example 8. A picture window, 3 m long and 1.8 m high, is installed in a wall as shown in Figure 16. The bottom edge of the window is on the floor, which is 6 by 10 m. Denoting the window by 1 and the floor by 234, find $F_{234\text{-}1}$.

Solution: From decomposition rule,

$$A_{234} F_{234\text{-}1} = A_2 F_{2\text{-}1} + A_3 F_{3\text{-}1} + A_4 F_{4\text{-}1}$$

By symmetry, $A_2 F_{2\text{-}1} = A_4 F_{4\text{-}1}$ and $A_{234\text{-}1} = A_3 F_{3\text{-}1} + 2A_2 F_{2\text{-}1}$.

$$A_{23} F_{23\text{-}15} = A_2 F_{2\text{-}1} + A_2 F_{2\text{-}5} + A_3 F_{3\text{-}1} + A_3 F_{3\text{-}5}$$

From the law of corresponding corners, $A_2 F_{2\text{-}1} = A_3 F_{3\text{-}5}$, so therefore $A_{23} F_{23\text{-}5} = A_2 F_{2\text{-}5} + A_3 F_{3\text{-}1} + 2A_2 F_{2\text{-}1}$. Thus,

$$A_{234} F_{234\text{-}1} = A_3 F_{3\text{-}1} + A_{23} F_{23\text{-}15} - A_2 F_{2\text{-}5} - A_3 F_{3\text{-}1} = A_{23} F_{23\text{-}15} - A_2 F_{2\text{-}5}$$

$$A_{234} = 60 \text{ m}^2 \qquad A_{23} = 45 \text{ m}^2 \qquad A_2 = 15 \text{ m}^2$$

From Figure 15A with $Y/X = 10/6 = 1.67$ and $Z/X = 1.8/4.5 = 0.4$, $F_{2315} = 0.061$. With $Y/X = 10/1.5 = 6.66$ and $Z/X = 1.8/1.5 = 1.2$, $F_{25} = 0.041$. Substituting the values, $F_{234\text{-}1} = 1/60(45 \times 0.061 - 15 \times 0.041) = 0.036$.

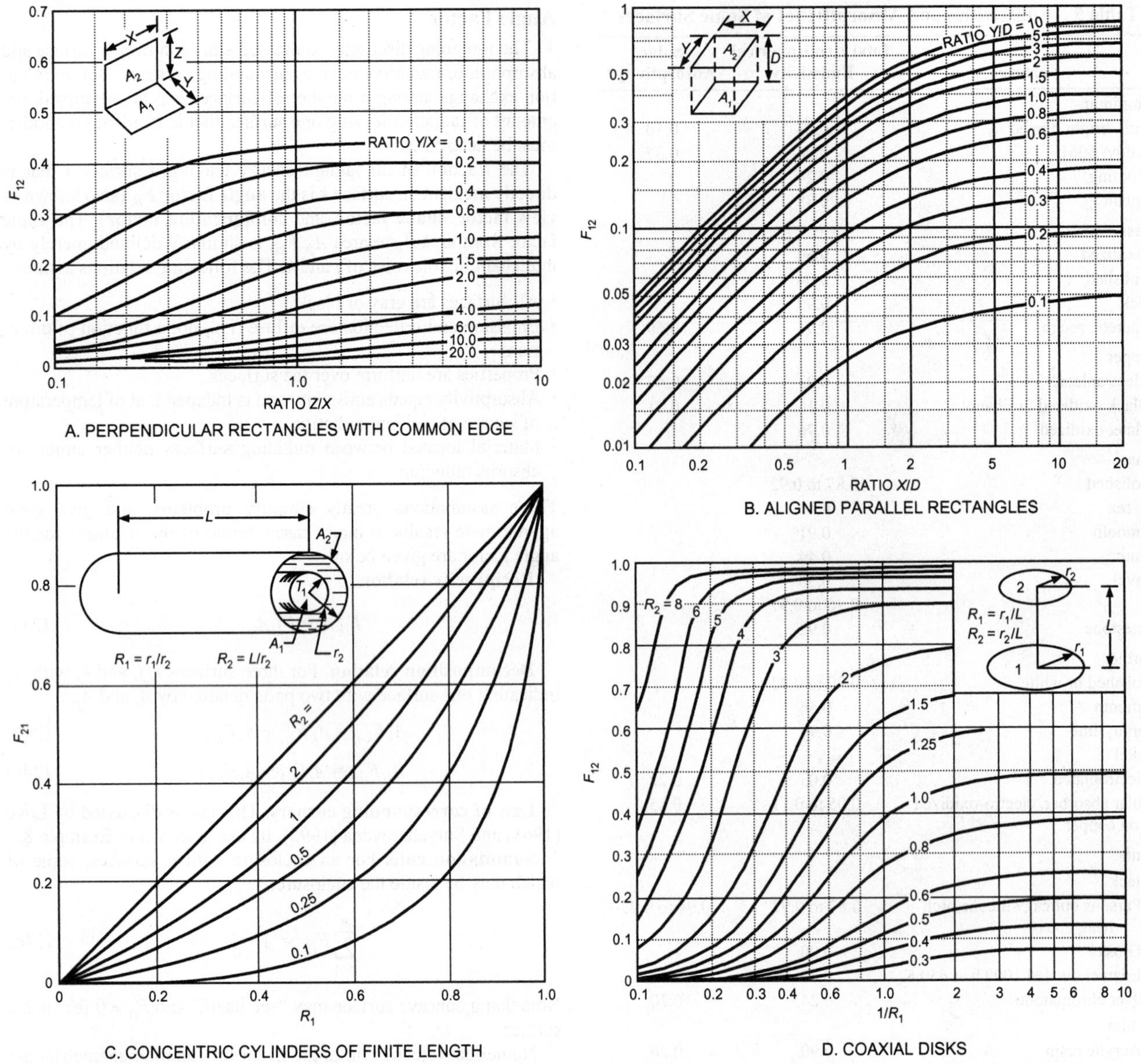

Fig. 15 Radiation Angle Factors for Various Geometries

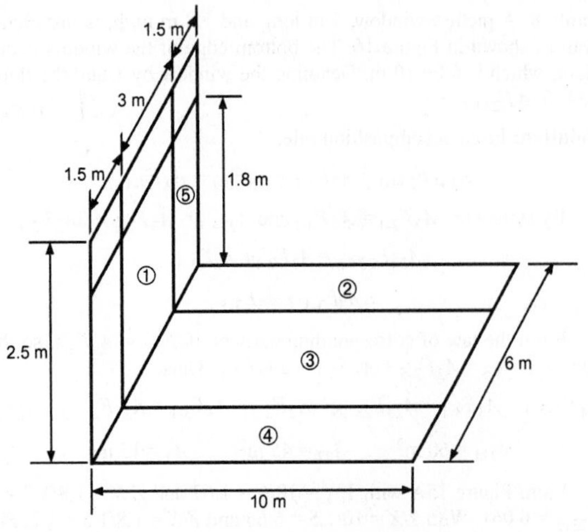

Fig. 16 Diagram for Example 8

Radiant Exchange Between Opaque Surfaces

A surface A_i radiates energy at a rate independent of its surroundings. It absorbs and reflects incident radiation from surrounding surfaces at a rate dependent on its absorptivity. The net heat transfer rate q_i is the difference between the rate radiant energy leaves the surface and the rate of incident radiant energy; it is the rate at which energy must be supplied from an external source to maintain the surface at a constant temperature. The net radiant heat flux from a surface A_i is denoted by q''_i.

Several methods have been developed to solve specific radiant exchange problems. The radiosity method and thermal circuit method are presented here.

Consider the heat transfer rate from a surface of an n-surface enclosure with an intervening medium that does not participate in radiation. All surfaces are assumed gray and opaque. The **radiosity** $\boldsymbol{J_i}$ is the total rate of radiant energy leaving surface i per unit area (i.e., the sum of energy flux emitted and energy flux reflected):

$$J_i = \varepsilon_i W_b + \rho_i G_i \qquad (25)$$

where G_i is the total rate of radiant energy incident on surface *i* per unit area. For opaque gray surfaces, the reflectivity is

$$\rho_i = 1 - \alpha_i = 1 - \varepsilon_i$$

Thus,

$$J_i = \varepsilon_i W_b + (1 - \varepsilon_i) G_i \tag{26}$$

Note that for a black surface, $\varepsilon = 1$, $\rho = 0$, and $J = W_b$.

The net radiant energy transfer q_i is the difference between the total energy leaving the surface and the total incident energy:

$$q_i = A_i (J_i - G_i) \tag{27}$$

Eliminating G_i between Equations (26) and (27),

$$q_i = \frac{W_{bi} - J_i}{(1 - \varepsilon_i)/\varepsilon_i A_i} \tag{28}$$

Radiosity Method. Consider an enclosure of *n* isothermal surfaces with areas of $A_1, A_2, \ldots, A_n$, and emissivities of $\varepsilon_1, \varepsilon_2, \ldots, \varepsilon_n$, respectively. Some may be at uniform but different known temperatures, and the remaining surfaces have uniform but different and known heat fluxes. The radiant energy flux incident on a surface G_i is the sum of the radiant energy reaching it from each of the *n* surfaces:

$$G_i A_i = \sum_{k=1}^{n} F_{ki} J_k A_k = \sum_{k=1}^{n} F_{ik} J_k A_i \quad \text{or} \quad G_i = \sum_{k=1}^{n} F_{ik} J_k \tag{29}$$

Substituting Equation (29) into Equation (26),

$$J_i = \varepsilon_i W_{bi} + (1 - \varepsilon_i) \sum_{k=1}^{n} F_{ik} J_k \tag{30}$$

Combining Equations (30) and (28),

$$J_i = \frac{q_i}{A_i} + \sum_{k=1}^{n} F_{ik} J_k \tag{31}$$

Note that in Equations (30) and (31), the summation includes surface *i*.

Equation (30) is for surfaces with known temperatures, and Equation (31) for those with known heat fluxes. An opening in the enclosure is treated as a black surface at the temperature of the surroundings. The resulting set of simultaneous, linear equations can be solved for the unknown J_is.

Once the radiosities (J_is) are known, the net radiant energy transfer to or from each surface or the emissive power, whichever is unknown is determined.

For surfaces where E_{bi} is known and q_i is to be determined, use Equation (28) for a nonblack surface. For a black surface, $J_i = W_{bi}$ and Equation (31) can be rearranged to give

$$\frac{q_i}{A_i} = W_{bi} - \sum_{k=1}^{n} F_{ik} J_k \tag{32}$$

At surfaces where q_i is known and E_{bi} is to be determined, rearrange Equation (28):

$$E_{bi} = J_i + q_i \left(\frac{1 - \varepsilon_i}{A_i \varepsilon_i} \right) \tag{33}$$

The temperature of the surface is then

$$T_i = \left(\frac{W_{bi}}{\sigma} \right)^{1/4} \tag{34}$$

A surface in radiant balance is one for which radiant emission is balanced by radiant absorption (i.e., heat is neither removed from nor supplied to the surface). These are called **reradiating, insulated**, or **refractory surfaces**. For these surfaces, $q_i = 0$ in Equation (31). After solving for the radiosities, W_{bi} can be found by noting that $q_i = 0$ in Equation (33) gives $W_{bi} = J_i$.

Thermal Circuit Method. Another method to determine the heat transfer rate is using thermal circuits for radiative heat transfer rates. Heat transfer rates from surface *i* to surface *k* and surface *k* to surface *i*, respectively, are given by

$$q_{i\text{-}k} = A_i F_{i\text{-}k} (J_i - J_k) \quad \text{and} \quad q_{k\text{-}i} = A_k F_{ik\text{-}i} (J_k - J_i)$$

Using the reciprocity relation $A_i F_{i\text{-}k} = A_k F_{k\text{-}i}$, the net heat transfer rate from surface *i* to surface *k* is

$$q_{ik} = q_{i\text{-}k} - q_{k\text{-}i} = A_i F_{i\text{-}k} (J_i - J_k) = \frac{J_i - J_k}{1/A_i F_{i\text{-}k}} \tag{35}$$

Equations (28) and (35) are analogous to the current in a resistance, with the numerators representing a potential difference and the denominator representing a thermal resistance. This analogy can be used to solve radiative heat transfer rates among surfaces, as illustrated in Example 9.

Using angle factors and radiation properties as defined assumes that the surfaces are diffuse radiators, which is a good assumption for most nonmetals in the infrared region, but poor for highly polished metals. Subdividing the surfaces and considering the variation of radiation properties with angle of incidence improves the approximation but increases the work required for a solution. Also note that radiation properties, such as absorptivity, have significant uncertainties, for which the final solutions should account.

Example 9. Consider a 4 m wide, 5 m long, 2.5 m high room as shown in Figure 17. Heating pipes, embedded in the ceiling (1), keep its temperature at 40°C. The floor (2) is at 30°C, and the side walls (3) are at 18°C. The emissivity of each surface is 0.8. Determine the net radiative heat transfer rate to/from each surface.

Solution: Consider the room as a three-surface enclosure. The corresponding thermal circuit is also shown. The heat transfer rates are found after finding the radiosity of each surface by solving the thermal circuit.

From Figure 15A,

$$F_{1\text{-}2} = F_{2\text{-}1} = 0.376$$

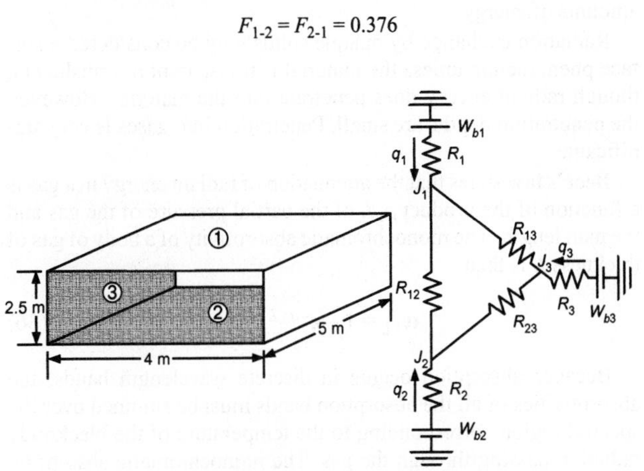

Fig. 17 Diagrams for Example 9

From the summation rule, $F_{1\text{-}1} + F_{1\text{-}2} + F_{1\text{-}3} = 1$. With $F_{1\text{-}1} = 0$,

$$F_{1\text{-}3} = 1 - F_{1\text{-}2} = 0.624 = F_{2\text{-}3}$$

$$R_1 = \frac{1-\varepsilon_1}{A_1\varepsilon_1} = \frac{1-0.8}{20 \times 0.8} = 0.0125 \text{ m}^{-2} = R_2$$

$$R_3 = \frac{1-\varepsilon_3}{A_3\varepsilon_3} = \frac{1-0.8}{45 \times 0.8} = 0.005\,556 \text{ m}^{-2}$$

$$R_{12} = \frac{1}{A_1F_{1\text{-}2}} = \frac{1}{20 \times 0.376} = 0.133 \text{ m}^{-2}$$

$$R_{13} = \frac{1}{A_1F_{1\text{-}3}} = \frac{1}{20 \times 0.624} = 0.080\,13 \text{ m}^{-2} = R_{23}$$

Performing a balance on each of the three J_i nodes gives

$$\text{Surface 1:} \quad \frac{W_{b1}-J_1}{R_1} + \frac{J_2-J_1}{R_{12}} + \frac{J_3-J_1}{R_{13}} = 0$$

$$\text{Surface 2:} \quad \frac{W_{b2}-J_2}{R_2} + \frac{J_1-J_2}{R_{12}} + \frac{J_3-J_2}{R_{23}} = 0$$

$$\text{Surface 3:} \quad \frac{W_{b3}-J_3}{R_3} + \frac{J_1-J_3}{R_{13}} + \frac{J_2-J_3}{R_{23}} = 0$$

$$W_{b1} = 5.67 \times 10^{-8} \times 313.2^4 = 545.6 \text{ W/m}^2$$

$$W_{b2} = 479.2 \text{ W/m}^2 \qquad W_{b3} = 407.7 \text{ W/m}^2$$

Substituting the values and solving for J_1, J_2, and J_3,

$$J_1 = 524.5 \text{ W/m}^2 \quad J_2 = 475.1 \text{ W/m}^2 \quad J_3 = 418.9 \text{ W/m}^2$$

$$q_1 = \frac{W_{b1}-J_1}{R_1} = \frac{545.6-524.5}{0.0125} = 1688 \text{ W}$$

$$q_2 = 328 \text{ W} \qquad q_3 = -2016 \text{ W}$$

Radiation in Gases

Monatomic and diatomic gases such as oxygen, nitrogen, hydrogen, and helium are essentially transparent to thermal radiation. Their absorption and emission bands are confined mainly to the ultraviolet region of the spectrum. The gaseous vapors of most compounds, however, have absorption bands in the infrared region. Carbon monoxide, carbon dioxide, water vapor, sulfur dioxide, ammonia, acid vapors, and organic vapors absorb and emit significant amounts of energy.

Radiation exchange by opaque solids may be considered a surface phenomenon unless the material is transparent or translucent, though radiant energy does penetrate into the material. However, the penetration depths are small. Penetration into gases is very significant.

Beer's law states that the attenuation of radiant energy in a gas is a function of the product p_gL of the partial pressure of the gas and the path length. The monochromatic absorptivity of a body of gas of thickness L is then

$$\alpha_{\lambda L} = 1 - e^{-\alpha_\lambda L} \tag{36}$$

Because absorption occurs in discrete wavelength bands, the absorptivities of all the absorption bands must be summed over the spectral region corresponding to the temperature of the blackbody radiation passing through the gas. The monochromatic absorption coefficient α_λ is also a function of temperature and pressure of the gas; therefore, detailed treatment of gas radiation is quite complex.

Table 6 Emissivity of CO_2 and Water Vapor in Air at 24°C

Path Length, m	CO_2, % by Volume 0.1	0.3	Relative Humidity, % 1.0	10	50	100
3	0.03	0.06	0.09	0.06	0.17	0.22
30	0.09	0.12	0.16	0.22	0.39	0.47
300	0.16	0.19	0.23	0.47	0.64	0.70

Table 7 Emissivity of Moist Air and CO_2 in Typical Room

Relative Humidity, %	ε_g
10	0.10
50	0.19
75	0.22

Estimated emissivity for carbon dioxide and water vapor in air at 24°C is a function of concentration and path length (Table 6). Values are for an isothermal hemispherically shaped body of gas radiating at its surface. Among others, Hottel and Sarofim (1967), Modest (2003), and Siegel and Howell (2002) describe geometrical calculations in their texts on radiation heat transfer. Generally, at low values of p_gL, the mean path length L (or equivalent hemispherical radius for a gas body radiating to its surrounding surfaces) is four times the mean hydraulic radius of the enclosure. A room with a dimensional ratio of 1:1:4 has a mean path length of 0.89 times the shortest dimension when considering radiation to all walls. For a room with a dimensional ratio of 1:2:6, the mean path length for the gas radiating to all surfaces is 1.2 times the shortest dimension. The mean path length for radiation to the 2 by 6 face is 1.18 times the shortest dimension. These values are for cases where the partial pressure of the gas times the mean path length approaches zero ($p_gL \approx 0$). The factor decreases with increasing values of p_gL. For average rooms with approximately 2.4 m ceilings and relative humidity ranging from 10 to 75% at 24°C, the effective path length for carbon dioxide radiation is about 85% of the ceiling height, or 2 m. The effective path length for water vapor is about 93% of the ceiling height, or 2.3 m. The effective emissivity of the water vapor and carbon dioxide radiating to the walls, ceiling, and floor of a room 4.9 by 14.6 m with 2.4 m ceilings is in Table 7.

Radiation heat transfer from the gas to the walls is then

$$q = \sigma A_w \varepsilon_g (T_g^4 - T_w^4) \tag{37}$$

The preceding discussion indicates the importance of gas radiation in environmental heat transfer problems. In large furnaces, gas radiation is the dominant mode of heat transfer, and many additional factors must be considered. Increased pressure broadens the spectral bands, and interaction of different radiating species prohibits simple summation of emissivity factors for the individual species. Nonblackbody conditions require separate calculations of emissivity and absorptivity. Hottel and Sarofim (1967) and McAdams (1954) discuss gas radiation more fully.

THERMAL CONVECTION

Convective heat transfer coefficients introduced previously can be estimated using correlations presented in this section.

Forced Convection

Forced-air coolers and heaters, forced-air- or water-cooled condensers and evaporators, and liquid suction heat exchangers are examples of equipment that transfer heat primarily by forced convection. Although some generalized heat transfer coefficient correlations have been mathematically derived from fundamentals, they are usually obtained from correlations of experimental data. Most correlations for forced convection are of the form

$$\text{Nu} = \frac{hL_c}{k} = f(\text{Re}_{Lc}, \text{Pr})$$

where

Nu = Nusselt number
h = convection heat transfer coefficient
L_c = characteristic length
$\text{Re}_{Lc} = \rho V L_c/\mu = VL_c/\nu$
V = fluid velocity
Pr = Prandtl number = $c_p\mu/k$
c_p = fluid specific heat
μ = fluid dynamic viscosity
ρ = fluid density
ν = kinematic viscosity = μ/ρ
k = fluid conductivity

Fluid velocity and characteristic length depend on the geometry.

External Flow. When fluid flows over a flat plate, a **boundary layer** forms adjacent to the plate. The velocity of fluid at the plate surface is zero and increases to its maximum free-stream value at the edge of the boundary layer (Figure 18). Boundary layer formation is important because the temperature change from plate to fluid occurs across this layer. Where the boundary layer is thick, thermal resistance is great and the heat transfer coefficient is small. Flow within the boundary layer immediately downstream from the leading edge is laminar. As flow proceeds along the plate, the laminar boundary layer increases in thickness to a critical value. Then, turbulent eddies develop in the boundary layer, except in a thin laminar sublayer adjacent to the plate.

The boundary layer beyond this point is turbulent. The region between the breakdown of the laminar boundary layer and establishment of the turbulent boundary layer is the **transition region**. Because turbulent eddies greatly enhance heat transport into the main stream, the heat transfer coefficient begins to increase rapidly through the transition region. For a flat plate with a smooth leading edge, the turbulent boundary layer starts at distance x_c from the leading edge where the Reynolds number $\text{Re} = Vx_c/\nu$ is in the range 300 000 to 500 000 (in some cases, higher). In a plate with a blunt front edge or other irregularities, it can start at much smaller Reynolds numbers.

Internal Flow. For tubes, channels, or ducts of small diameter at sufficiently low velocity, the laminar boundary layers on each wall grow until they meet. This happens when the Reynolds number based on tube diameter, $\text{Re} = V_{avg}D/\nu$, is less than 2000 to 2300. Beyond this point, the velocity distribution does not change, and no transition to turbulent flow takes place. This is called **fully developed laminar flow**. When the Reynolds number is greater than 10 000, the boundary layers become turbulent before they meet, and fully developed turbulent flow is established (Figure 19). If flow is turbulent, three different flow regions exist. Immediately next to the wall is a **laminar sublayer**, where heat transfer occurs by thermal conduction; next is a transition region called the **buffer layer**, where both eddy mixing and conduction effects are significant; the final layer, extending to the pipe's axis, is the **turbulent region**, where the dominant mechanism of transfer is eddy mixing.

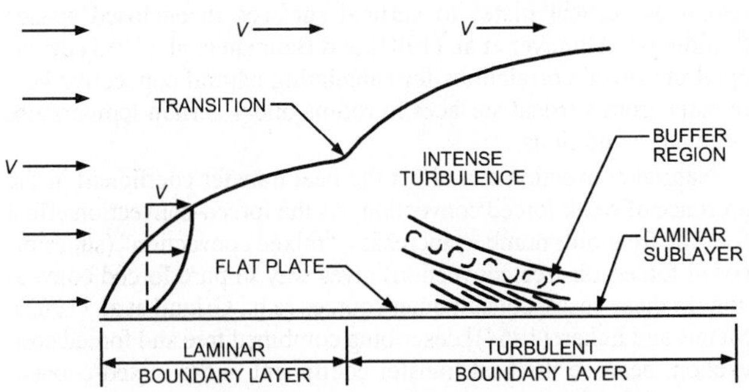

Fig. 18 External Flow Boundary Layer Build-up (Vertical Scale Magnified)

In most equipment, flow is turbulent. For low-velocity flow in small tubes, or highly viscous liquids such as glycol, the flow may be laminar.

The characteristic length for internal flow in pipes and tubes is the inside diameter. For noncircular tubes or ducts, the **hydraulic diameter D_h** is used to compute the Reynolds and Nusselt numbers. It is defined as

$$D_h = 4 \times \frac{\text{Cross-sectional area for flow}}{\text{Total wetted perimeter}} \tag{38}$$

Inserting expressions for cross-sectional area and wetted perimeter of common cross sections shows that the hydraulic diameter is equal to

- The diameter of a round pipe
- Twice the gap between two parallel plates
- The difference in diameters for an annulus
- The length of the side for square tubes or ducts

Table 8 lists various forced-convection correlations. In general, the Nusselt number is determined by the flow geometry, Reynolds number, and Prandtl number. One often useful form for internal flow is known as **Colburn's analogy**:

$$j = \frac{\text{Nu}}{\text{RePr}^{1/3}} = \frac{f_F}{2}$$

where f_F is the Fanning friction factor and j is the Colburn j-factor. It is related to the friction factor by the interrelationship of the transport of momentum and energy in turbulent flow. These factors are plotted in Figure 20.

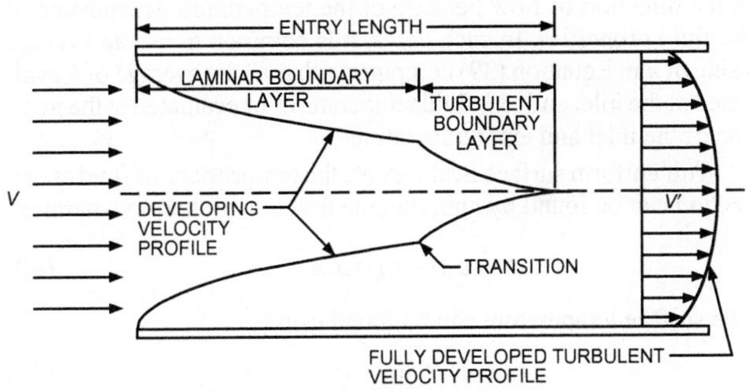

Fig. 19 Boundary Layer Build-up in Entrance Region of Tube or Channel

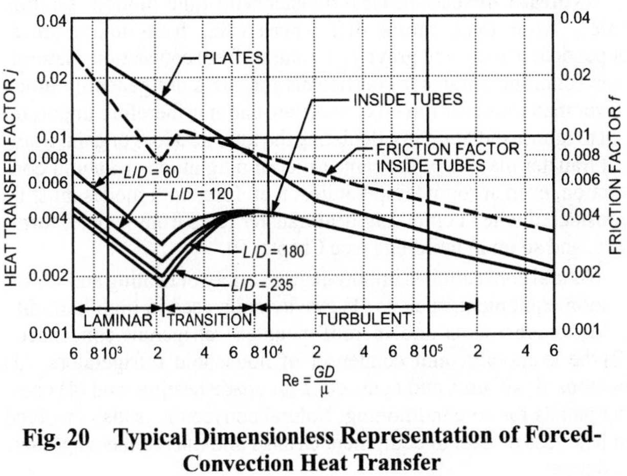

Fig. 20 Typical Dimensionless Representation of Forced-Convection Heat Transfer

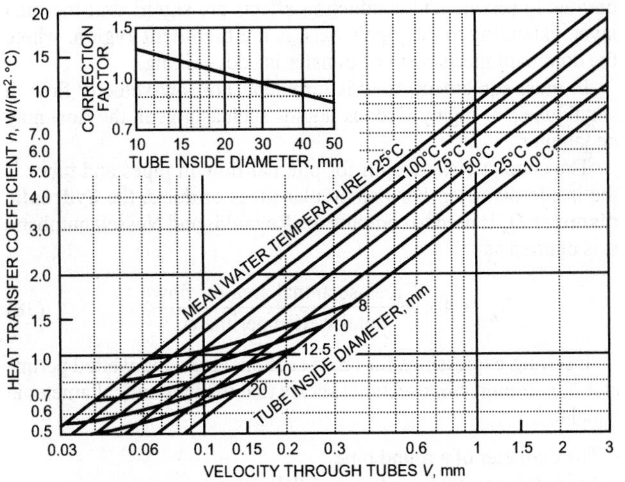

Re = 2100 at velocity where diameter curve crosses mean water temperature lines.

Fig. 21 Heat Transfer Coefficient for Turbulent Flow of Water Inside Tubes

Simplified correlations for atmospheric air are also given in Table 8. Figure 21 gives graphical solutions for water.

With a uniform tube surface temperature and heat transfer coefficient, the exit temperature can be calculated using

$$\ln\frac{t_s - t_e}{t_s - t_i} = -\frac{hA}{\dot{m}c_p} \qquad (39)$$

where t_i and t_e are the inlet and exit bulk temperatures of the fluid, t_s is the pipe/duct surface temperature, and A is the surface area inside the pipe/duct. The convective heat transfer coefficient varies in the direction of flow because of the temperature dependence of the fluid properties. In such cases, it is common to use an average value of h in Equation (39) computed either as the average of h evaluated at the inlet and exit fluid temperatures or evaluated at the average of the inlet and exit temperatures.

With uniform surface heat flux q'', the temperature of fluid at any section can be found by applying the first law of thermodynamics:

$$\dot{m}\,c_p(t - t_i) = q''A \qquad (40)$$

The surface temperature can be found using

$$q'' = h(t_s - t) \qquad (41)$$

With uniform surface heat flux, surface temperature increases in the direction of flow along with the fluid.

Natural Convection. Heat transfer with fluid motion resulting solely from temperature differences (i.e., from temperature-dependent density and gravity) is natural (free) convection. Natural-convection heat transfer coefficients for gases are generally much lower than those for forced convection, and it is therefore important not to ignore radiation in calculating the total heat loss or gain. Radiant transfer may be of the same order of magnitude as natural convection, even at room temperatures; therefore, both modes must be considered when computing heat transfer rates from people, furniture, and so on in buildings (see Chapter 9).

Natural convection is important in a variety of heating and refrigeration equipment, such as (1) gravity coils used in high-humidity cold-storage rooms and in roof-mounted refrigerant condensers, (2) the evaporator and condenser of household refrigerators, (3) baseboard radiators and convectors for space heating, and (4) cooling panels for air conditioning. Natural convection is also involved in heat loss or gain to equipment casings and interconnecting ducts and pipes.

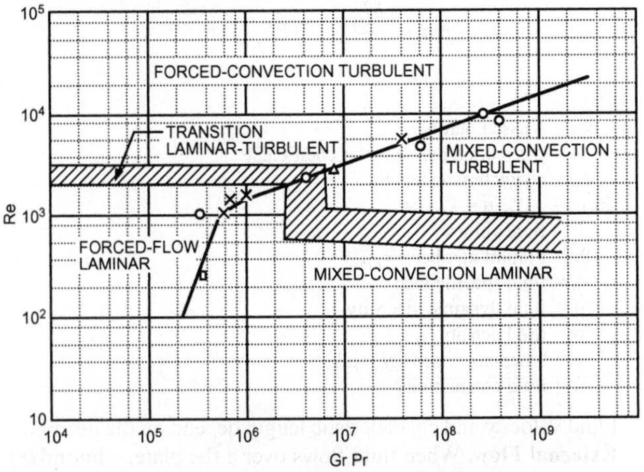

Fig. 22 Regimes of Free, Forced, and Mixed Convection—Flow in Horizontal Tubes

Consider heat transfer by natural convection between a cold fluid and a hot vertical surface. Fluid in immediate contact with the surface is heated by conduction, becomes lighter, and rises because of the difference in density of the adjacent fluid. The fluid's viscosity resists this motion. The heat transfer rate is influenced by fluid properties, temperature difference between the surface at t_s and environment at t_∞, and characteristic dimension L_c. Some generalized heat transfer coefficient correlations have been mathematically derived from fundamentals, but they are usually obtained from correlations of experimental data. Most correlations for natural convection are of the form

$$\text{Nu} = \frac{hL_c}{k} = f(\text{Ra}_{Lc}, \text{Pr})$$

where

Nu = Nusselt number
H = convection heat transfer coefficient
L_c = characteristic length
K = fluid thermal conductivity
Ra_{Lc} = Rayleigh number = $g\beta\,\Delta t L_c^3/\nu\alpha$
Δt = $|t_s - t_\infty|$
g = gravitational acceleration
β = coefficient of thermal expansion
ν = fluid kinematic viscosity = μ/ρ
α = fluid thermal diffusivity = $k/\rho c_p$
Pr = Prandtl number = ν/α

Correlations for a number of geometries are given in Table 9. Other information on natural convection is available in the Bibliography under Heat Transfer, General.

Comparison of experimental and numerical results with existing correlations for natural convective heat transfer coefficients indicates that caution should be used when applying coefficients for (isolated) vertical plates to vertical surfaces in enclosed spaces (buildings). Altmayer et al. (1983) and Bauman et al. (1983) developed improved correlations for calculating natural convective heat transfer from vertical surfaces in rooms under certain temperature boundary conditions.

Natural convection can affect the heat transfer coefficient in the presence of weak forced convection. As the forced-convection effect (i.e., the Reynolds number) increases, "mixed convection" (superimposed forced-on-free convection) gives way to pure forced convection. In these cases, consult other sources [e.g., Grigull et al. (1982); Metais and Eckert (1964)] describing combined free and forced convection, because the heat transfer coefficient in the mixed-convection region is often larger than that calculated based on the natural- or forced-convection calculation alone. Metais and Eckert (1964) summarize natural-, mixed-, and forced-convection regimes for vertical

Table 8 Forced-Convection Correlations

I. General Correlation $Nu = f(Re, Pr)$

II. Internal Flows for Pipes and Ducts: Characteristic length = D, pipe diameter, or D_h, hydraulic diameter.

$$Re = \frac{\rho V_{avg} D_h}{\mu} = \frac{\dot{m} D_h}{A_c \mu} = \frac{Q D_h}{A_c \nu} = \frac{4\dot{m}}{\mu P_{wet}} = \frac{4Q}{\nu P_{wet}}$$

where $\dot{m}$ = mass flow rate, Q = volume flow rate, P_{wet} = wetted perimeter, A_c = cross-sectional area, and ν = kinematic viscosity (μ/ρ).

	$\frac{Nu}{Re\,Pr^{1/3}} = \frac{f}{2}$	Colburn's analogy	(T8.1)
Laminar: Re < 2300	$Nu = 1.86\left(\frac{Re\,Pr}{L/D}\right)^{1/3}\left(\frac{\mu}{\mu_s}\right)^{0.14}$	$\frac{L}{D} < \frac{Re\,Pr}{8}\left(\frac{\mu}{\mu_s}\right)^{0.42}$	(T8.2)[a]
Developing	$Nu = 3.66 + \frac{0.065(D/L)Re\,Pr}{1 + 0.04[(D/L)Re\,Pr]^{2/3}}$		(T8.3)
Fully developed, round	$Nu = 3.66$	Uniform surface temperature	(T8.4a)
	$Nu = 4.36$	Uniform heat flux	(T8.4b)
Turbulent:	$Nu = 0.023\,Re^{4/5}Pr^{0.4}$	Heating fluid, $Re \geq 10\,000$	(T8.5a)[b]
Fully developed	$Nu = 0.023\,Re^{4/5}Pr^{0.3}$	Cooling fluid, $Re \geq 10\,000$	(T8.5b)[b]
Evaluate properties at bulk temperature t_b except μ_s and t_s at surface temperature	$Nu = \frac{(f_s/2)(Re - 1000)Pr}{1 + 12.7(f_s/2)^{1/2}(Pr^{2/3} - 1)}\left[1 + \left(\frac{D}{L}\right)^{2/3}\right]$ For fully developed flows, set $D/L = 0$.	$f_s = \frac{1}{(1.58 \ln Re - 3.28)^2}$ Multiply Nu by $(T/T_s)^{0.45}$ for gases and by $(Pr/Pr_s)^{0.11}$ for liquids	(T8.6)[c]
	$Nu = 0.027\,Re^{4/5}Pr^{1/3}\left(\frac{\mu}{\mu_s}\right)^{0.14}$	For viscous fluids	(T8.7)[a]

For noncircular tubes, use hydraulic mean diameter D_h in the equations for Nu for an approximate value of h.

III. External Flows for Flat Plate: Characteristic length = L = length of plate. $Re = VL/\nu$.
All properties at arithmetic mean of surface and fluid temperatures.

Laminar boundary layer: $Re < 5 \times 10^5$	$Nu = 0.332\,Re^{1/2}Pr^{1/3}$	Local value of h	(T8.8)
	$Nu = 0.664\,Re^{1/2}Pr^{1/3}$	Average value of h	(T8.9)
Turbulent boundary layer: $Re > 5 \times 10^5$	$Nu = 0.0296\,Re^{4/5}Pr^{1/3}$	Local value of h	(T8.10)
Turbulent boundary layer beginning at leading edge: All Re	$Nu = 0.037\,Re^{4/5}Pr^{1/3}$	Average value of h	(T8.11)
Laminar-turbulent boundary layer: $Re > 5 \times 10^5$	$Nu = (0.37\,Re^{4/5} - 871)Pr^{1/3}$	Average value $Re_c = 5 \times 10^5$	(T8.12)

IV. External Flows for Cross Flow over Cylinder: Characteristic length = D = diameter. $Re = VD/\nu$.
All properties at arithmetic mean of surface and fluid temperatures.

$$Nu = 0.3 + \frac{0.62\,Re^{1/2}Pr^{1/3}}{[1 + (0.4/Pr)^{2/3}]^{1/4}}\left[1 + \left(\frac{Re}{282\,000}\right)^{5/8}\right]^{4/5}$$

Average value of h (T8.14)[d]

V. Simplified Approximate Equations: h is in W/(m²·K), V is in m/s, D is in m, and t is in °C.

Flows in pipes, Re > 10 000

Atmospheric air (0 to 200°C):	$h = (3.76 - 0.00497t)V^{0.8}/D^{0.2}$		(T8.15a)[e]
Water (3 to 200°C):	$h = (1206 + 23.9t)V^{0.8}/D^{0.2}$		(T8.15b)[e]
Water (4 to 104°C):	$h = (1431 + 20.9t)V^{0.8}/D^{0.2}$ (McAdams 1954)		(T8.15c)[g]
			(T8.15a)

Flow over cylinders

Atmospheric air: 0°C < t < 200°C, where t = arithmetic mean of air and surface temperature.

$h = 2.755V^{0.471}/D^{0.529}$	$35 < Re < 5000$	(T8.16a)
$h = (4.22 - 0.002\,57t)V^{0.633}/D^{0.367}$	$5000 < Re < 50\,000$	(T8.16b)

Water: 5°C < t < 90°C, where t = arithmetic mean of water and surface temperature.

$h = (461.8 + 2.01t)V^{0.471}/D^{0.529}$	$35 < Re < 5000$	(T8.17a)
$h = (1012 + 9.19t)V^{0.633}/D^{0.367}$	$5000 < Re < 50\,000$	(T8.17b)[f]

Sources: [a]Sieder and Tate (1936), [b]Dittus and Boelter (1930), [c]Gnielinski (1990), [d]Churchill and Bernstein (1977), [e]Based on $Nu = 0.023\,Re^{4/5}Pr^{1/3}$, [f]Based on Morgan (1975). [g]McAdams (1954).

Table 9 Natural Convection Correlations

I. General relationships	$Nu = f(Ra, Pr)$ or $f(Ra)$		(T9.1)
Characteristic length depends on geometry	$Ra = Gr\,Pr \quad Gr = \dfrac{g\beta\rho^2\lvert\Delta T\rvert L^3}{\mu^2}$	$Pr = \dfrac{c_p\mu}{k} \quad \Delta t = t_s - t_\infty$	
II. Vertical plate			
t_s = constant	$Nu = 0.68 + \dfrac{0.67Ra^{1/4}}{[1 + (0.492/Pr)^{9/16}]^{4/9}}$	$10^{-1} < Ra < 10^9$	(T9.2)[a]
Characteristic dimension: L = height Properties at $(t_s + t_\infty)/2$ except β at t_∞	$Nu = \left\{0.825 + \dfrac{0.387Ra^{1/6}}{[1 + (0.492/Pr)^{9/16}]^{8/27}}\right\}^2$	$10^9 < Ra < 10^{12}$	(T9.3)[a]
q''_s = constant Characteristic dimension: L = height Properties at $t_{s,L/2} - t_\infty$ except β at t_∞	$Nu = \left\{0.825 + \dfrac{0.387Ra^{1/6}}{[1 + (0.437/Pr)^{9/16}]^{8/27}}\right\}^2$	$10^{-1} < Ra < 10^{12}$	(T9.4)[a]
Equations (T9.2) and (T9.3) can be used for vertical cylinders if $D/L > 35/Gr^{1/4}$ where D is diameter and L is axial length of cylinder			
III. Horizontal plate			
Characteristic dimension = $L = A/P$, where A is plate area and P is perimeter			
Properties of fluid at $(t_s + t_\infty)/2$			
Downward-facing cooled plate and upward-facing heated plate	$Nu = 0.96\,Ra^{1/6}$	$1 < Ra < 200$	(T9.5)[b]
	$Nu = 0.59\,Ra^{1/4}$	$200 < Ra < 10^4$	(T9.6)[b]
	$Nu = 0.54\,Ra^{1/4}$	$2.2 \times 10^4 < Ra < 8 \times 10^6$	(T9.7)[b]
	$Nu = 0.15\,Ra^{1/3}$	$8 \times 10^6 < Ra < 1.5 \times 10^9$	(T9.8)[b]
Downward-facing heated plate and upward-facing cooled plate	$Nu = 0.27\,Ra^{1/4}$	$10^5 < Ra < 10^{10}$	(T9.9)[b]
IV. Horizontal cylinder			
Characteristic length = d = diameter Properties of fluid at $(t_s + t_\infty)/2$ except β at t_∞	$Nu = \left\{0.6 + \dfrac{0.387\,Ra^{1/6}}{[1 + (0.559/Pr)^{9/16}]^{8/27}}\right\}^2$	$10^9 < Ra < 10^{13}$	(T9.10)[c]
V. Sphere			
Characteristic length = D = diameter Properties at $(t_s + t_\infty)/2$ except β at t_∞	$Nu = 2 + \dfrac{0.589\,Ra^{1/4}}{[1 + (0.469/Pr)^{9/16}]^{4/9}}$	$Ra < 10^{11}$	(T9.11)[d]
VI. Horizontal wire			
Characteristic dimension = D = diameter Properties at $(t_s + t_\infty)/2$	$\dfrac{2}{Nu} = \ln\left(1 + \dfrac{3.3}{cRa^n}\right)$	$10^{-8} < Ra < 10^6$	(T9.12)[e]
VII. Vertical wire			
Characteristic dimension = D = diameter; L = length of wire	$Nu = c(Ra\,D/L)^{0.25} + 0.763\,c^{(1/6)}(Ra\,D/L)^{(1/24)}$	$c(Ra\,D/L)^{0.25} > 2 \times 10^{-3}$	(T9.13)[e]
Properties at $(t_s + t_\infty)/2$	In both Equations (T9.12) and (T9.13), $c = \dfrac{0.671}{[1 + (0.492/Pr)^{(9/16)}]^{(4/9)}}$ and $n = 0.25 + \dfrac{1}{10 + 5(Ra)^{0.175}}$		
VIII. Simplified equations with air at mean temperature of 21°C: h is in W/(m²·K), L and D are in m, and Δt is in °C.			
Vertical surface	$h = 1.33\left(\dfrac{\Delta t}{L}\right)^{1/4}$	$10^5 < Ra < 10^9$	(T9.14)
	$h = 1.26(\Delta t)^{1/3}$	$Ra > 10^9$	(T9.15)
Horizontal cylinder	$h = 1.04\left(\dfrac{\Delta T}{D}\right)^{1/4}$	$10^5 < Ra < 10^9$	(T9.16)
	$h = 1.23(\Delta t)^{1/3}$	$Ra > 10^9$	(T9.17)

Sources: [a]Churchill and Chu (1975a), [b]Lloyd and Moran (1974), Goldstein et al. (1973), [c]Churchill and Chu (1975b), [d]Churchill (1990), [e]Fujii et al. (1986).

and horizontal tubes. Figure 22 shows the approximate limits for horizontal tubes. Other studies are described by Grigull et al. (1982).

Example 10. Chilled water at 5°C flows inside a freely suspended 20 mm OD pipe at a velocity of 2.5 m/s. Surrounding air is at 30°C, 70% rh. The pipe is to be insulated with cellular glass having a thermal conductivity of 0.045 W/(m·K). Determine the radial thickness of the insulation to prevent condensation of water on the outer surface.

Solution: In Figure 23,

t_{fi} = 5°C $\quad t_{fo}$ = 30°C $\quad d_i$ = OD of tube = 0.02 m

k_i = thermal conductivity of insulation material = 0.045 W/(m·K)

From the problem statement, the outer surface temperature t_o of the insulation should not be less than the dew-point temperature of air. The dew-point temperature of air at 30°C, 70% rh = 23.93°C. To determine the outer diameter of the insulation, equate the heat transfer rate per unit length of pipe (from the outer surface of the pipe to the water) to the heat transfer rate per unit length from the air to the outer surface:

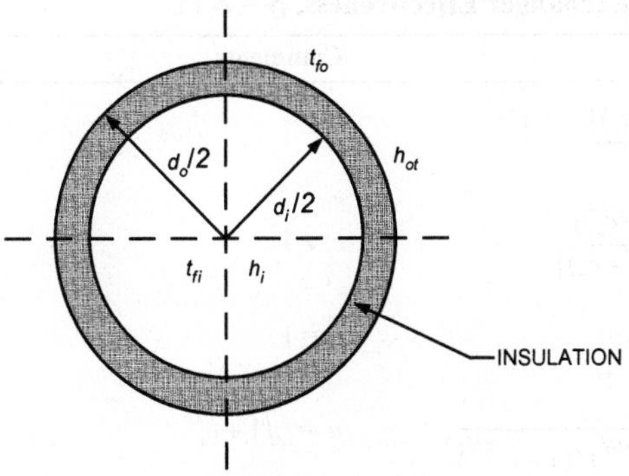

Fig. 23 Diagram for Example 10

$$\frac{t_o - t_{fi}}{\frac{1}{h_i d_i} + \frac{1}{2k_i}\ln\frac{d_o}{d_i}} = \frac{t_{fo} - t_o}{\frac{1}{h_{ot} d_o}} \tag{42}$$

Heat transfer from the outer surface is by natural convection to air, so the surface heat transfer coefficient h_{ot} is the sum of the convective heat transfer coefficient h_o and the radiative heat transfer coefficient h_r. With an assumed emissivity of 0.7 and using Equation (4), h_r = 4.3 W/(m²·K). To determine the value of d_o, the values of the heat transfer coefficients associated with the inner and outer surfaces (h_i and h_o, respectively) are needed. Compute the value of h_i using Equation (T8.6). Properties of water at an assumed temperature of 5°C are

$$\rho_w = 1000 \text{ kg/m}^3 \quad \mu_w = 0.001\,518 \text{ (N·s)/m}^2 \quad c_{pw} = 4197 \text{ W/(m·K)}$$
$$k_w = 0.5708 \text{ W/(m·K)} \quad \text{Pr}_w = 11.16 \quad \text{Re}_d = \frac{\rho v d}{\mu} = 32\,944$$
$$f_s = 0.023\,11 \quad \text{Nu}_d = 205.6 \quad h_i = 5869 \text{ W/(m}^2\text{·K)}$$

To compute h_o using Equation (T9.10), the outer diameter of the insulation material must be found. Determine it by iteration by assuming a value of d_o, computing the value of h_o, and determining the value of d_o from Equation (42). If the assumed and computed values of d_o are close to each other, the correct solution has been obtained. Otherwise, recompute h_o using the newly computed value of d_o and repeat the process.

Assume d_o = 0.05 m. Properties of air at t_f = 27°C and 101.325 kPa are

$$\rho = 1.176 \text{ kg/m}^3 \quad k = 0.025\,66 \text{ W/(m·K)} \quad \mu = 1.858 \times 10^{-5} \text{ (N·s)/m}^2$$
$$\text{Pr} = 0.729 \quad \beta = 0.003\,299 \text{ (at } 273.15 + 30 = 293.15 \text{ K)}$$
$$\text{Ra} = 71\,745 \quad \text{Nu} = 7.157 \quad h_o = 3.67 \text{ W/(m}^2\text{·K)}$$
$$h_{ot} = 3.67 + 4.3 = 7.97 \text{ W/(m}^2\text{·K)}$$

From Equation (42), d_o = 0.044 28 m. Now, using the new value of 0.044 28 m for the outer diameter, the new values of h_o and h_{ot} are 3.78 W/(m²·K) and 8.07 W/(m²·K), respectively. The updated value of d_o is 0.044 03 m. Repeating the process, the final value of d_o = 0.044 01 m. Thus, an outer diameter of 0.045 m (corresponding to an insulation radial thickness of 12.5 mm) keeps the outer surface temperature at 24.1°C, higher than the dew point. (Another method to find the outer diameter is to iterate on the outer surface temperature for different values of d_o.)

HEAT EXCHANGERS

Mean Temperature Difference Analysis

With heat transfer from one fluid to another (separated by a solid surface) flowing through a heat exchanger, the local temperature difference Δt varies along the flow path. Heat transfer rate may be calculated using

$$q = UA\,\Delta t_m \tag{43}$$

where U is the overall uniform heat transfer coefficient, A is the area associated with the coefficient U, and Δt_m is the appropriate mean temperature difference.

For a parallel or counterflow heat exchanger, the mean temperature difference is given by

$$\Delta t_m = \Delta t_1 - \Delta t_2/\ln(\Delta t_1/\Delta t_2) \tag{44}$$

where Δt_1 and Δt_2 are temperature differences between the fluids at each end of the heat exchanger; Δt_m is the **logarithmic mean temperature difference (LMTD)**. For the special case of $\Delta t_1 = \Delta t_2$ (possible only with a counterflow heat exchanger with equal capacities), which leads to an indeterminate form of Equation (44), $\Delta t_m = t_1 = \Delta t_2$.

Equation (44) for Δt_m is true only if the overall coefficient and the specific heat of the fluids are constant through the heat exchanger, and no heat losses occur (often well-approximated in practice). Parker et al. (1969) give a procedure for cases with variable overall coefficient U. For heat exchangers other than parallel and counterflow, a correction factor [see Incropera et al. (2007)] is needed for Equation (44) to obtain the correct mean temperature difference.

NTU-Effectiveness (ε) Analysis

Calculations using Equations (43) and (44) for Δt_m are convenient when inlet and outlet temperatures are known for both fluids. Often, however, the temperatures of fluids leaving the exchanger are unknown. To avoid trial-and-error calculations, the **NTU-ε method** uses three dimensionless parameters: effectiveness ε, number of transfer units (NTU), and capacity rate ratio c_r; the mean temperature difference in Equation (44) is not needed.

Heat exchanger effectiveness ε is the ratio of actual heat transfer rate to maximum possible heat transfer rate in a counterflow heat exchanger of infinite surface area with the same mass flow rates and inlet temperatures. The maximum possible heat transfer rate for hot fluid entering at t_{hi} and cold fluid entering at t_{ci} is

$$q_{max} = C_{min}(t_{hi} - t_{ci}) \tag{45}$$

where C_{min} is the smaller of the hot $[C_h = ((\dot{m}c_p)_h]$ and cold $[C_c = (\dot{m}c_p)_c]$ fluid capacity rates, W/K; C_{max} is the larger. The actual heat transfer rate is

$$q = \varepsilon q_{max} \tag{46}$$

or a given exchanger type, heat transfer effectiveness can generally be expressed as a function of the **number of transfer units (NTU)** and the **capacity rate ratio** c_r:

$$\varepsilon = f(\text{NTU}, c_r, \text{Flow arrangement}) \tag{47}$$

where

$\text{NTU} = UA/C_{min}$
$c_r = C_{min}/C_{max}$

Effectiveness is independent of exchanger inlet temperatures. For any exchanger in which c_r is zero (where one fluid undergoing a phase change, as in a condenser or evaporator, has an effective $c_p = \infty$), the effectiveness is

$$\varepsilon = 1 - \exp(-\text{NTU}) \tag{48}$$

The mean temperature difference in Equation (44) is then given by

$$\Delta t_m = \frac{(t_{hi} - t_{ci})\varepsilon}{\text{NTU}} \tag{49}$$

After finding the heat transfer rate q, exit temperatures for constant-density fluids are found from

Table 10 Equations for Computing Heat Exchanger Effectiveness, N = NTU

Flow Configuration	Effectiveness ε	Comments	
Parallel flow	$\dfrac{1-\exp[-N(1-c_r)]}{1+c_r}$		(T10.1)
Counterflow	$\dfrac{1-\exp[-N(1-c_r)]}{1-c_r\exp[-N(1-c_r)]}$	$c_r \neq 1$	(T10.2)
	$\dfrac{N}{1+N}$	$c_r = 1$	(T10.3)
Shell-and-tube (one-shell pass, 2, 4, etc. tube passes)	$\dfrac{2}{1+c_r+a(1+e^{-aN})/(1-e^{-aN})}$	$a = \sqrt{1+c_r^2}$	(T10.4)
Shell-and-tube (n-shell pass, $2n$, $4n$, etc. tube passes)	$\left[\left(\dfrac{1-\varepsilon_1 c_r}{1-\varepsilon_1}\right)^n-1\right]\left[\left(\dfrac{1-\varepsilon_1 c_r}{1-\varepsilon_1}\right)^n-c_r\right]^{-1}$	ε_1 = effectiveness of one-shell pass shell-and-tube heat exchanger	(T10.5)
Cross-flow (single phase)			
Both fluids unmixed	$1-\exp\left(\dfrac{\gamma N^{0.22}}{c_r}\right)$	$\gamma = \exp(-c_r N^{0.78}) - 1$	(T10.6)
C_{max} (mixed), C_{min} (unmixed)	$\dfrac{1-\exp(c_r\gamma)}{c_r}$	$\gamma = 1-\exp(-N)$	(T10.7)
C_{max} (unmixed), C_{min} (mixed)	$1-\exp(-\gamma/c_r)$	$\gamma = 1-\exp(-Nc_r)$	(T10.8)
Both fluids mixed	$\dfrac{N}{N/(1-e^{-N})+c_r N/(1-e^{-Nc_r})-1}$		(T10.9)
All exchangers with $c_r = 0$	$1-\exp(-N)$		(T10.10)

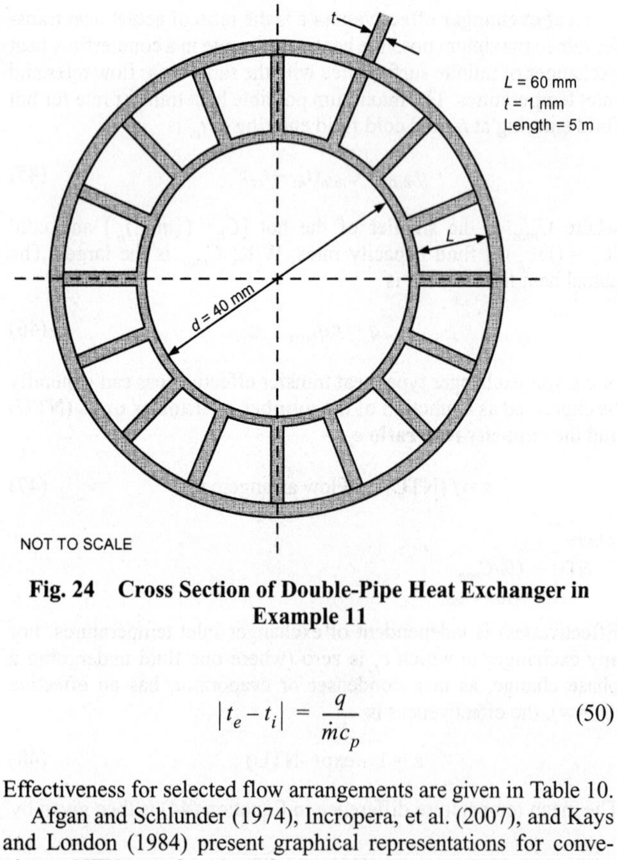

Fig. 24 Cross Section of Double-Pipe Heat Exchanger in Example 11

$$|t_e - t_i| = \frac{q}{\dot{m}c_p} \quad (50)$$

Effectiveness for selected flow arrangements are given in Table 10.

Afgan and Schlunder (1974), Incropera, et al. (2007), and Kays and London (1984) present graphical representations for convenience. NTUs as a function of ε expressions are available in Incropera et al. (2007).

Example 11. Flue gases from a gas-fired furnace are used to heat water in a 5 m long counterflow, double-pipe heat exchanger. Water enters the inner, thin-walled 40 mm diameter pipe at 40°C with a velocity of 0.5 m/s. Flue gases enter the annular space with a mass flow rate of 0.12 kg/s at 200°C. To increase the heat transfer rate to the gases, 16 rectangular axial copper fins are attached to the outer surface of the inner pipe. Each fin is 60 mm high (radial height) and 1 mm thick, as shown in Figure 24. The gas-side surface heat transfer coefficient is 115 W/(m²·K). Find the heat transfer rate and the exit temperatures of the gases and water.

The heat exchanger has the following properties:

Water in the pipe	t_{ci} = 40°C	v_c = 0.5 m/s
Gases	t_{hi} = 200°C	$\dot{m}_h$ = 0.12 kg/s

Length of heat exchanger L_{tube} = 5 m d = 0.04 m L = 0.06 m

t = 0.001 m N = number of fins = 16

Solution: The heat transfer rate is computed using Equations (45) and (46), and exit temperatures from Equation (50). To find the heat transfer rates, UA and ε are needed.

$$\frac{1}{UA} = \frac{1}{(\phi_s hA)_o} + \frac{1}{(hA)_i}$$

where

h_i = convective heat transfer coefficient on water side
h_o = gas-side heat transfer coefficient
ϕ_s = surface effectiveness = $(A_{uf} + A_f\phi)/A_o$
ϕ = fin efficiency
A_{uf} = surface area of unfinned surface = $L_{tube}(\pi d - Nt)$ = 0.548 m²
A_f = fin surface area = $2LNL_{tube}$ = 9.6 m²
$A_o = A_{uf} + A_f$ = 10.15 m²
$A_i = \pi dL_{tube}$ = 0.628 m²

Step 1. Find h_i using Equation (T8.6). Properties of water at an assumed mean temperature of 45°C are

ρ = 990.4 kg/m³ c_{pc} = 4181 J/(kg·K) μ = 5.964 × 10⁻⁴ (N·s)/m²

k = 0.6376 W/(m·K) Pr = 3.91

$$\text{Re} = \frac{\rho v_c d}{\mu} = \frac{990.4 \times 0.5 \times 0.04}{5.964 \times 10^{-4}} = 33\ 213$$

$f_s/2 = [1.58 \ln(\text{Re}) - 3.28]^{-2}/2 = (1.58 \ln 33\,213 - 3.28)^{-2}/2 = 0.002\,88$

$$\text{Nu}_d = \frac{0.002\,88 \times (33\,213 - 1000) \times 3.91}{1 + 12.7 \times (0.002\,88)^{1/2} \times (3.91^{2/3} - 1)} = 180.4$$

$$h_i = \frac{180.4 \times 0.6376}{0.04} = 2876 \text{ W/(m}^2\cdot\text{K)}$$

Step 2. Compute fin efficiency ϕ and surface effectiveness ϕ_s. For a rectangular fin with the end of the fin not exposed,

$$\phi = \frac{\tanh(mL)}{mL}$$

For copper, $k = 401$ W/(m·K).

$$mL = (2h_o/kt)^{1/2}L = [(2 \times 115)/(401 \times 0.001)]^{1/2}(0.06) = 1.44$$

$$\phi = \frac{\tanh 1.44}{1.44} = 0.62$$

$$\phi_s = (A_{uf} + \phi A_f)/A_0 = (0.548 + 0.62 \times 9.6)/10.15 = 0.64$$

Step 3. Find heat exchanger effectiveness. For air at an assumed mean temperature of 175°C, $c_{ph} = 1018$ J/(kg·K).

$$C_h = \dot{m}_h c_{ph} = 0.12 \times 1018 = 122.2 \text{ W/K}$$

$$\dot{m}_c = \rho v_c \pi d^2/4 = (990.4 \times 0.5 \times \pi \times 0.04^2)/4 = 0.6223 \text{ kg/s}$$

$$C_c = \dot{m}_c c_{pc} = 0.6223 \times 4181 = 2602 \text{ W/K}$$

$$c_r = C_{min}/C_{max} = 122.2/2602 = 0.04696$$

$$UA = [1/(0.64 \times 115 \times 10.15) + 1/(2876 \times 0.628)]^{-1} = 528.5 \text{ W/K}$$

$$\text{NTU} = UA/C_{min} = 528.5/122.2 = 4.32$$

From Equation (T10.2),

$$\varepsilon = \frac{1 - \exp[-N(1 - c_r)]}{1 - c_r \exp[-N(1 - c_r)]}$$

$$= \frac{1 - \exp[-4.24 \times (1 - 0.046\,96)]}{1 - 0.046\,96 \times \exp[-4.24 \times (1 - 0.046\,96)]} = 0.983$$

Step 4. Find heat transfer rate:

$$q_{max} = C_{min} \times (t_{hi} - t_{ci}) = 122.2 \times (200 - 40) = 19\,552 \text{ W}$$

$$q = \varepsilon q_{max} = 0.985 \times 19\,552 = 19\,255 \text{ W}$$

Step 5. Find exit temperatures:

$$t_{he} = t_{hi} - \frac{q}{C_h} = 200 - \frac{19\,255}{122.2} = 42.4\text{°C}$$

$$t_{ce} = t_{ci} + \frac{q}{C_c} = 40 + \frac{19\,255}{2602} = 47.4\text{°C}$$

The mean temperature of water now is 43.7°C. The properties of water at this temperature are not very different from those at the assumed value of 45°C. The only property of air that needs to be updated is the specific heat, which at the updated mean temperature of 121°C is 1011 J/(kg·K), which is not very different from the assumed value of 1018 J/(kg·K). Therefore, no further iteration is necessary.

Plate Heat Exchangers

Plate heat exchangers (PHEs) are used regularly in HVAC&R. The three main types of plate exchangers are plate-and-frame (gasket or semi-welded), compact brazed (CBE), and shell-and-plate. The basic plate geometry is shown in Figure 25.

Plate Geometry. Different geometric parameters of a plate are defined as follows (Figure 25):

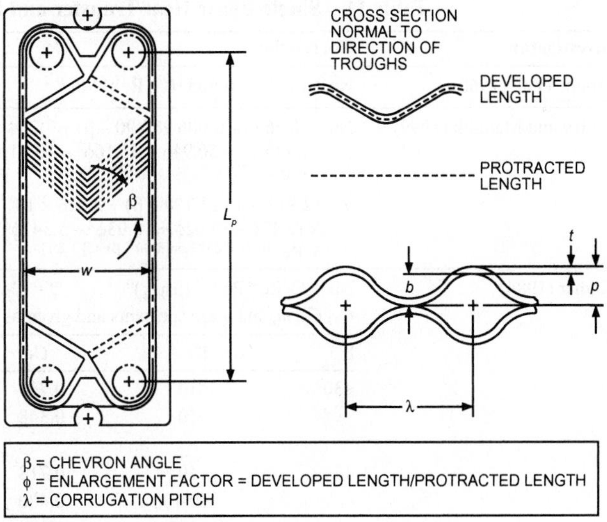

Fig. 25 Plate Parameters

- **Chevron angle** β varies between 22 and 65°. This angle also defines the thermal hydraulic softness (low thermal efficiency and pressure drop) and hardness (high thermal efficiency and pressure drop).
- **Enlargement factor** ϕ is the ratio of developed length to protracted length.
- **Mean flow channel gap** b is the actual gap available for the flow: $b = p - t$.
- **Channel flow area** A_x is the actual flow area: $A_x = bw$.
- **Channel equivalent diameter** d_e is defined as $d_e = 4A_x/P$, where $P = 2(b + \phi w) = 2\phi w$, because $b << w$; therefore, $d_e = 2b/\phi$.

Heat Transfer and Pressure Drop. Table 11 (Ayub 2003) shows correlations for single-phase flow. For quick calculations, the correlations by Kumar (1984) are recommended. For more elaborate calculations, Heavner et al. (1993), Muley and Manglik (1999), and Wanniarachchi et al. (1995) are appropriate.

Heat Exchanger Transients

Determining the transient behavior of heat exchangers is increasingly important in evaluating the dynamic behavior of heating and air-conditioning systems. Many studies of counterflow and parallel flow heat exchangers have been conducted; some are listed in the Bibliography.

HEAT TRANSFER AUGMENTATION

As discussed by Bergles (1998, 2001), techniques applied to augment (enhance) heat transfer can be classified as passive (requiring no direct application of external power) or active (requiring external power). Passive techniques include rough surfaces, extended surfaces, displaced promoters, and vortex flow devices. Active techniques include mechanical aids, surface or fluid vibration, and electrostatic fields. The effectiveness of a given augmentation technique depends largely on the mode of heat transfer or type of heat exchanger to which it is applied.

When augmentation is used, the dominant thermal resistances in the circuit should be considered. Do not invest in reducing an already low thermal resistance or increasing an already high heat transfer coefficient. Also, heat exchangers with a high NTU [number of heat exchanger transfer units; see Equation (47)] benefit little from augmentation. Finally, the increased friction factor that usually accompanies heat transfer augmentation must also be considered.

Table 11 Single-Phase Heat Transfer and Pressure Drop Correlations for Plate Exchangers

Investigator	Correlation	Comments
Troupe et al. (1960)	$Nu = (0.383 - 0.505\ ^{Lp/b})\ Re^{0.65}\ Pr^{0.4}$	$Re > Re_{cr}$, $10 < Re_{cr} < 400$, water.
Muley and Manglik (1999)	$Nu = [0.2668 - 0.006\,967(90 - \beta) + 7.244 \times 10^{-5}(90 - \beta)^2] \times (20.78 - 50.94\phi + 41.16\phi^2 - 10.51\phi^3) \times Re^{\{0.728 + 0.0543 \sin[\pi(90 - \beta)/45] + 3.7\}}\ Pr^{1/3}\ (\mu/\mu_w)^{0.14}$ $f = [2.917 - 0.1277(90 - \beta) + 2.016 \times 10^{-3}(90 - \beta)^2] \times (5.474 - 19.02\phi + 18.93\phi^2 - 5.341\phi^3) \times Re^{-\{0.2 + 0.0577 \sin[\pi(90 - \beta)/45] + 2.1\}}$	$Re \ge 10^3$, $30 \le \beta \le 60$, $1 \le \phi \le 1.5$.
Kumar (1984)	$Nu = C_1\ Re^m\ Pr^{0.33}\ (\mu/\mu_w)^{0.17}$ $f = C_2/(Re)^p$ C_1, C_2, m, and p are constants and given as	Water, herringbone plates, $\phi = 1.17$.

β	Re	C_1	m	Re	C_2	p
≤30	≤10	0.718	0.349	<10	50.0	1.0
	>10	0.348	0.663	10-100	19.40	0.589
				>100	2.990	0.183
45	<10	0.718	0.349	<15	47.0	1.0
	10-100	0.400	0.598	15-300	18.29	0.652
	>100	0.300	0.663	>300	1.441	0.206
50	<20	0.630	0.333	<20	34.0	1.0
	20-300	0.291	0.591	20-300	11.25	0.631
	>300	0.130	0.732	>300	0.772	0.161
60	<20	0.562	0.326	<40	24.0	1.0
	20-400	0.306	0.529	40-400	3.24	0.457
	>400	0.108	0.703	>400	0.760	0.215
≥65	<20	0.562	0.326	<50	24.0	1.0
	20-500	0.331	0.503	50-500	2.80	0.451
	>500	0.087	0.718	>500	0.639	0.213

Investigator	Correlation	Comments
Heavner et al. (1993)	$Nu = C_1(\phi)^{1-m}\ Re^m\ Pr^{0.5}(\mu/\mu_w)^{0.17}$ $f = C_2(\phi)^{p+1}\ Re^{-p}$ C_1, C_2, m, and p are constants and given as	$400 < Re < 10\,000$, $3.3 < Pr < 5.9$, water chevron plate ($0° \le \beta \le 67°$).

β	β_{avg}	C_1	m	C_2	p
67/67	67	0.089	0.718	0.490	0.1814
67/45	56	0.118	0.720	0.545	0.1555
67/0	33.5	0.308	0.667	1.441	0.1353
45/45	45	0.195	0.692	0.687	0.1405
45/0	22.5	0.278	0.683	1.458	0.0838

Investigator	Correlation	Comments
Wanniarachchi et al. (1995)	$Nu = (Nu_l^3 + Nu_t^3)^{1/3}\ Pr^{1/3}(\mu/\mu_w)^{0.17}$ $Nu_l = 3.65(\beta)^{-0.455}(\phi)^{0.661}\ Re^{0.339}$ $Nu_t = 12.6(\beta)^{-1.142}(\phi)^{1-m}\ Re^m$ $m = 0.646 + 0.0011(\beta)$ $f = (f_l^3 + f_t^3)^{1/3}$ $f_l = 1774(\beta)^{-1.026}(\phi)^2\ Re^{-1}$ $f_t = 46.6(\beta)^{-1.08}(\phi)^{1+p}\ Re^{-p}$ $p = 0.004\,23(\beta) + 0.000\,022\,3(\beta)^2$	$1 \le Re \le 10^4$, herringbone plates ($20° \le \beta \le 62$, $\beta > 62° = 62°$).

Source: Ayub (2003).

Passive Techniques

Finned-Tube Coils. Heat transfer coefficients for finned coils follow the basic equations of convection, condensation, and evaporation. The fin arrangement affects the values of constants and exponential powers in the equations. It is generally necessary to refer to test data for the exact coefficients.

For natural-convection finned coils (gravity coils), approximate coefficients can be obtained by considering the coil to be made of tubular and vertical fin surfaces at different temperatures and then applying the natural-convection equations to each. This is difficult because the natural-convection coefficient depends on the temperature difference, which varies at different points on the fin.

Fin efficiency should be high (80 to 90%) for optimum natural-convection heat transfer. A low fin efficiency reduces temperatures near the tip. This reduces Δt near the tip and also the coefficient h, which in natural convection depends on Δt. The coefficient of heat transfer also decreases as fin spacing decreases because of interfering convection currents from adjacent fins and reduced free-flow passage; 50 to 100 mm spacing is common. Generally, high coefficients result from large temperature differences and small flow restriction.

Edwards and Chaddock (1963) give coefficients for several circular fin-on-tube arrangements, using fin spacing δ as the characteristic length and in the form $Nu = f(Ra_\delta, \delta/D_o)$, where D_o is the fin diameter.

Forced-convection finned coils are used extensively in a wide variety of equipment. Fin efficiency for optimum performance is smaller than that for gravity coils because the forced-convection coefficient is almost independent of the temperature difference between surface and fluid. Very low fin efficiencies should be avoided because an inefficient surface gives a high (uneconomical) pressure drop. An efficiency of 70 to 90% is often used.

As fin spacing is decreased to obtain a large surface area for heat transfer, the coefficient generally increases because of higher air velocity between fins at the same face velocity and reduced equivalent diameter. The limit is reached when the boundary layer formed on one fin surface (see Figure 19) begins to interfere with the boundary layer formed on the adjacent fin surface, resulting in a decrease of the heat transfer coefficient, which may offset the advantage of larger surface area.

Selection of fin spacing for forced-convection finned coils usually depends on economic and practical considerations, such as fouling, frost formation, condensate drainage, cost, weight, and volume. Fins for conventional coils generally are spaced 1.8 to 4.2 mm apart, except where factors such as frost formation necessitate wider spacing.

There are several ways to obtain higher coefficients with a given air velocity and surface, usually by creating air turbulence, generally with a higher pressure drop: (1) staggered tubes instead of in-line tubes for multiple-row coils; (2) artificial additional tubes, or collars or fingers made by forming the fin materials; (3) corrugated fins instead of plane fins; and (4) louvered or interrupted fins.

Figure 26 shows data for one-row coils. Thermal resistances plotted include the temperature drop through the fins, based on one square metre of total external surface area.

Internal Enhancement. Several examples of tubes with internal roughness or fins are shown in Figure 27. Rough surfaces of the spiral repeated rib variety are widely used to improve in-tube heat transfer with water, as in flooded chillers. Roughness may be produced by spirally indenting the outer wall, forming the inner wall, or inserting coils. Longitudinal or spiral internal fins in tubes can be produced by extrusion or forming and substantially increase surface area. Efficiency of extruded fins can usually be taken as unity (see the section on Fin Efficiency). Twisted strips (vortex flow devices) can be inserted as original equipment or as a retrofit (Manglik and Bergles 2002). From a practical point of view, the twisted tape width should be such that the tape can be easily inserted or removed. Ayub and Al-Fahed (1993) discuss clearance between the twisted tape and tube inside dimension.

Microfin tubes (internally finned tubes with about 60 short fins around the circumference) are widely used in refrigerant evaporation and condensers. Because gas entering the condenser in vapor-compression refrigeration is superheated, a portion of the condenser that desuperheats the flow is single phase. Some data on single-phase performance of microfin tubes, showing considerably higher heat transfer coefficients than for plain tubes, are available [e.g., Al-Fahed et al. (1993); Khanpara et al. (1986)], but the upper Reynolds numbers of about 10 000 are lower than those found in practice. ASHRAE research [e.g., Eckels (2003)] is addressing this deficiency.

The increased friction factor in microfin tubes may not require increased pumping power if the flow rate can be adjusted or the length of the heat exchanger reduced. Nelson and Bergles (1986) discuss performance evaluation criteria, especially for HVAC applications.

In chilled-water systems, fouling may, in some cases, seriously reduce the overall heat transfer coefficient U. In general, fouled enhanced tubes perform better than fouled plain tubes, as shown in studies of scaling caused by cooling tower water (Knudsen and Roy 1983) and particulate fouling (Somerscales et al. 1991). A comprehensive review of fouling with enhanced surfaces is presented by Somerscales and Bergles (1997).

Fire-tube boilers are frequently fitted with turbulators to improve the turbulent convective heat transfer coefficient (addressing the dominant thermal resistance). Also, because of high gas temperatures, radiation from the convectively heated insert to the tube wall can represent as much as 50% of the total heat transfer. (Note, however, that the magnitude of convective contribution decreases as the radiative contribution increases because of the reduced temperature difference.) Two commercial bent-strip inserts, a twisted-strip insert, and a simple bent-tab insert are depicted in Figure 28. Design equations for convection only are included in Table 12. Beckermann and Goldschmidt (1986) present procedures to include radiation,

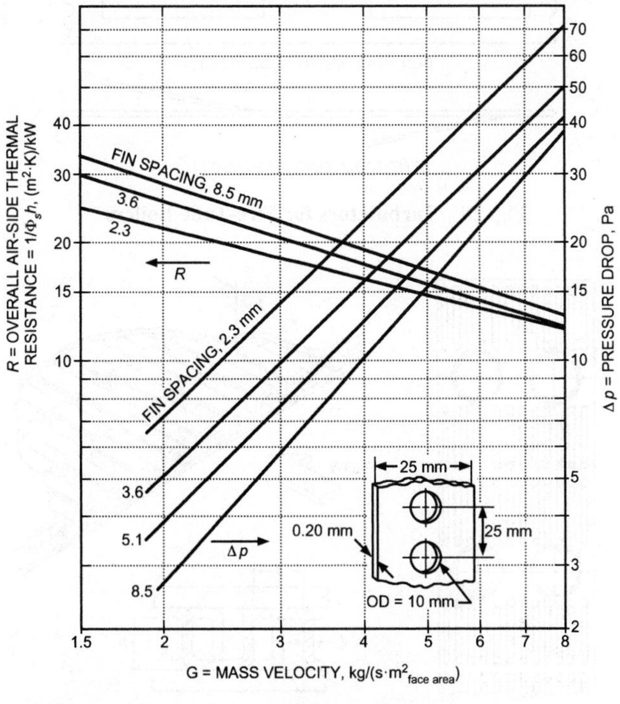

Fig. 26 Overall Air-Side Thermal Resistance and Pressure Drop for One-Row Coils
(Shepherd 1946)

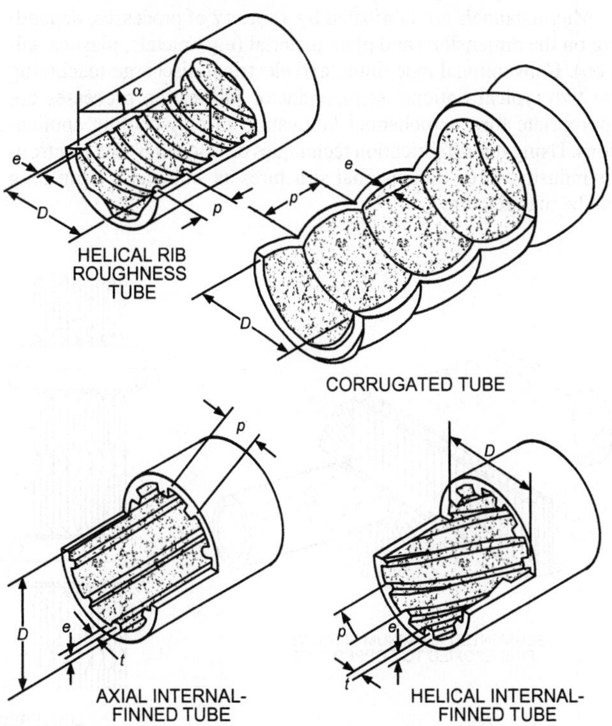

Fig. 27 Typical Tube-Side Enhancements

and Junkhan et al. (1985, 1988) give friction factor data and performance evaluations.

Enhanced Surfaces for Gases. Several such surfaces are depicted in Figure 29. The offset strip fin is an example of an interrupted fin that is often found in compact plate fin heat exchangers used for heat recovery from exhaust air. Design equations in Table 12 apply to laminar and transitional flow as well as to turbulent flow, which is a necessary feature because the small hydraulic diameter of these surfaces drives the Reynolds number down. Data for other surfaces (wavy, spine, louvered, etc.) are available in the References.

Microchannel Heat Exchangers. Microchannels for heat transfer enhancement are widely used, particularly for compact heat exchangers in automotive, aerospace, fuel cell, and high-flux electronic cooling applications. Bergles (1964) demonstrated the potential of narrow passages for heat transfer enhancement; more recent experimental and numerical work includes Adams et al. (1998), Costa et al. (1985), Kandlikar (2002), Ohadi et al. (2008), Pei et al. (2001), and Rin et al. (2006).

Compared with channels of normal size, microchannels have many advantages. Because microchannels have an increased heat transfer surface area per unit volume and a large surface-to-volume ratio, they provide much higher heat transfer rates. This feature allows heat exchangers to be compact and lightweight. Despite their thin walls, microchannels can withstand high operating pressures: for example, a microchannel with a hydraulic diameter of 0.8 mm and a wall thickness of 0.3 mm can easily withstand operating pressures of up to 14 MPa. This feature makes microchannels particularly suitable for use with high-pressure refrigerants such as carbon dioxide (CO_2). For high-flux electronics (with heat flux at 1 kW/cm^2 or higher), microchannels can provide cooling with small temperature gradients (Ohadi et al. 2008). Microchannels have been used for both single-phase and phase-change heat transfer applications.

Drawbacks of microchannels include large pressure drop, high cost of manufacture, dirt clogging, and flow maldistribution, especially for two-phase flows. Most of these weaknesses, however, may be solved by optimizing design of the surface and the heat exchanger manifold and feed system.

Microchannels are fabricated by a variety of processes, depending on the dimensions and plate material (e.g., metals, plastics, silicon). Conventional machining and electrical discharge machining are two typical options; semiconductor fabrication processes are appropriate for microchannel fabrication in chip-cooling applications. Using microfabrication techniques developed by the electronics industry, three-dimensional structures as small as 0.1 μm long can be manufactured.

Fluid flow and heat transfer in microchannels may be substantially different from those encountered in the conventional tubes. Early research indicates that deviations might be particularly important for microchannels with hydraulic diameters less than 100 μm.

Recent Progress. The automotive, aerospace, and cryogenic industries have made major progress in compact evaporator development. Thermal duty and energy efficiency have substantially increased, and space constraints have become more important, encouraging greater heat transfer rates per unit volume. The hot side of the evaporators in these applications is generally air, gas, or a condensing vapor. Air-side fin geometry improvements derive from increased heat transfer coefficients and greater surface area densities. To decrease the air-side heat transfer resistance, more aggressive fin designs have been used on the evaporating side, resulting in narrower flow passages. The narrow refrigerant channels with large aspect ratios are brazed in small cross-ribbed sections to improve

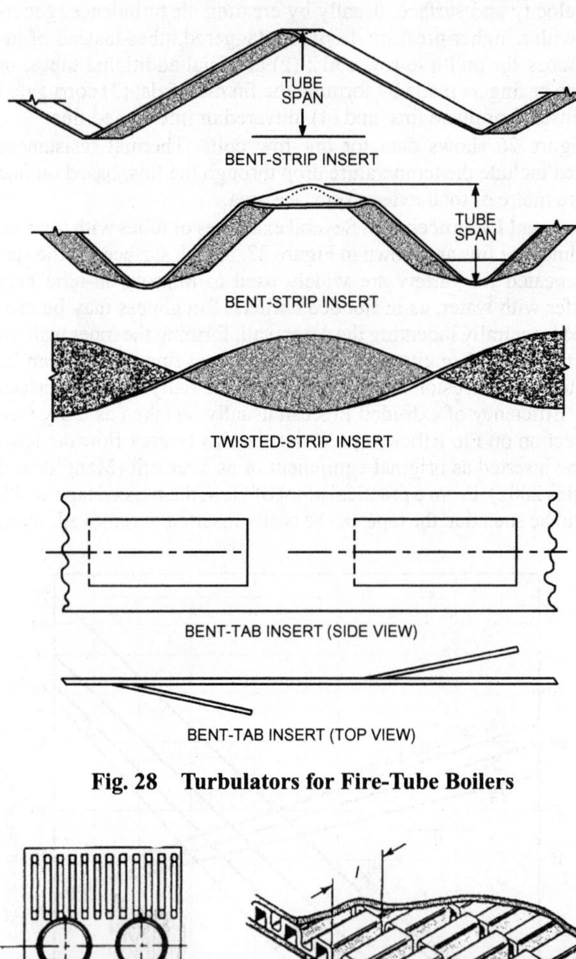

Fig. 28 Turbulators for Fire-Tube Boilers

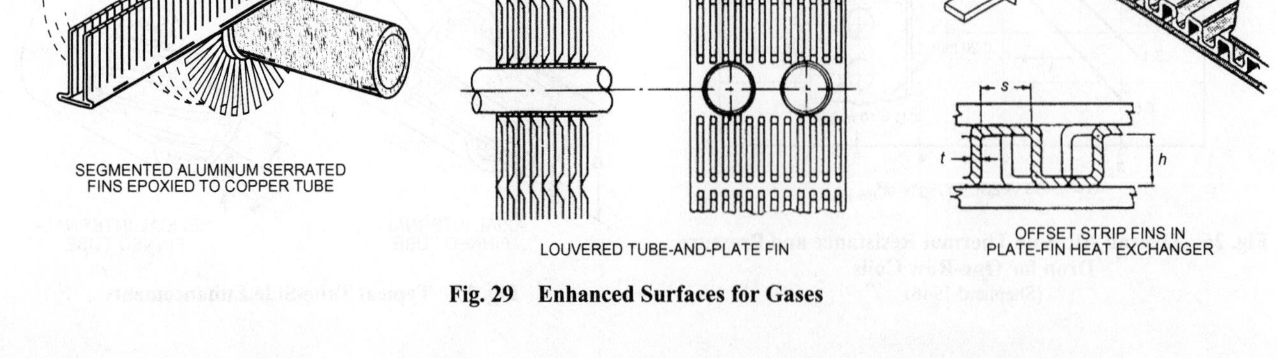

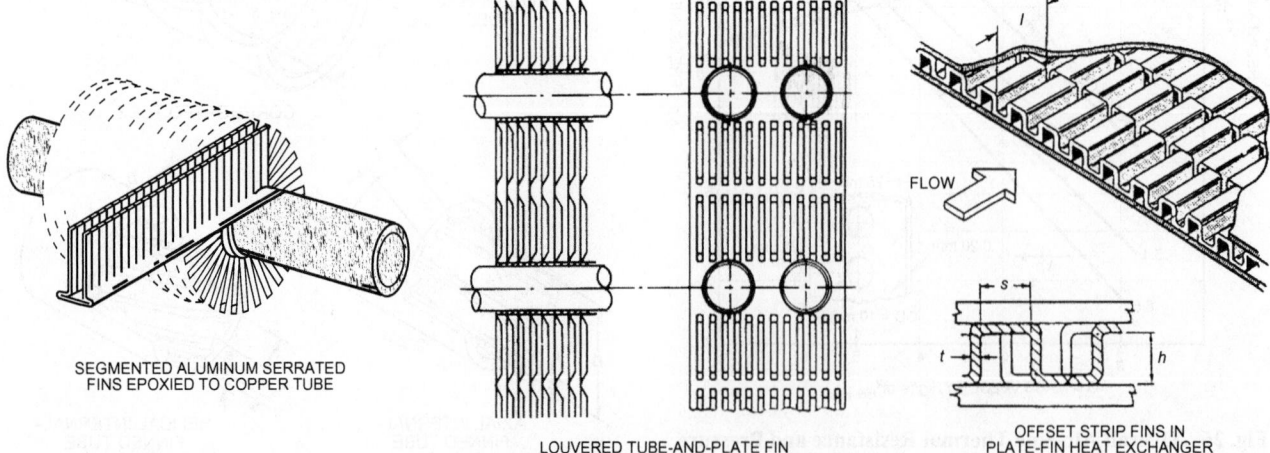

Fig. 29 Enhanced Surfaces for Gases

flow distribution along the width of the channels. Major recent changes in designs involve individual, small-hydraulic-diameter flow passages, arranged in multichannel configuration for the evaporating fluid. Figure 30 shows a plate-fin evaporator geometry widely used in compact refrigerant evaporators.

The refrigerant-side passages are made from two plates brazed together, and air-side fins are placed between two refrigerant microchannel flow passages. Figure 31 depicts two representative microchannel geometries widely used in the compact heat exchanger industry, with corresponding approximate nominal dimensions provided in Table 13 (Zhao 1997).

Plastic heat exchangers have been suggested for HVAC applications (Pescod 1980) and are being manufactured for refrigerated sea water (RSW) applications. They can be made of materials impervious to corrosion [e.g., by acidic condensate when cooling a gaseous stream (flue gas heat recovery)], and are easily manufactured with enhanced surfaces. Several companies now offer heat exchangers in plastic, including various enhancements.

Active Techniques

Unlike passive techniques, active techniques require external power to sustain the enhancement mechanism.

Table 14 lists the more common active heat transfer augmentation techniques and the corresponding heat transfer mode believed most applicable to the particular technique. Various active techniques and their world-wide status are listed in Table 15. Except for mechanical aids, which are universally used for selected applications, most other active techniques have found limited commercial applications and are still in development. However, with increasing demand for smart and miniaturized thermal management systems, actively controlled heat transfer augmentation techniques will soon become necessary for some advanced thermal management systems. All-electric ships, airplanes, and cars use electronics for propulsion, auxiliary systems, sensors, countermeasures, and other system needs. Advances in power electronics and control systems will allow optimized and tactical allocation of total installed power among system components. This in turn will require smart (online/on-demand), compact heat exchangers and thermal management systems that can communicate and respond to transient system needs. This section briefly overviews active techniques and recent progress; for additional details, see Ohadi et al (1996).

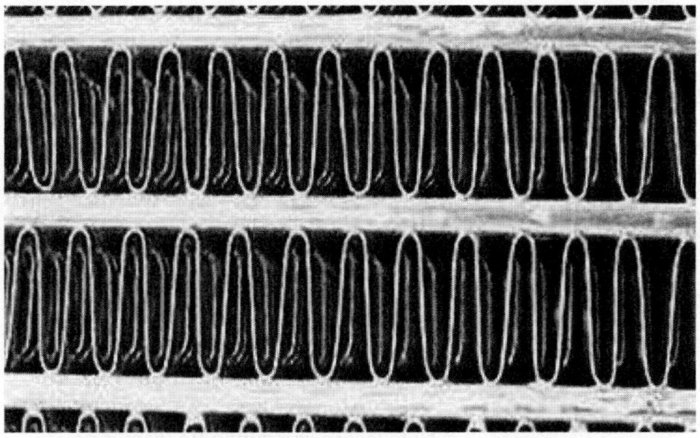

Fig. 30 Typical Refrigerant and Air-Side Flow Passages in Compact Automotive Microchannel Heat Exchanger

Mechanical Aids. Augmentation by mechanical aids involves stirring the fluid mechanically. Heat exchangers that use mechanical enhancements are often called **mechanically assisted heat exchangers**. Stirrers and mixers that scrape the surface are extensively used in chemical processing of highly viscous fluids, such as blending a flow of highly viscous plastic with air. Surface scraping can also be applied to duct flow of gases. Hagge and Junkhan (1974) reported tenfold improvement in the heat transfer coefficient for laminar airflow over a flat plate. Table 16 lists selected works on mechanical aids, suction, and injection.

Injection. This method involves supplying a gas to a flowing liquid through a porous heat transfer surface or injecting a fluid of a similar type upstream of the heat transfer test section. Injected bubbles produce an agitation similar to that of nucleate boiling. Gose et al. (1957) bubbled gas through sintered or drilled heated surfaces and found that the heat transfer coefficient increased 500% in laminar flow and about 50% in turbulent flow. Tauscher et al. (1970) demonstrated up to a fivefold increase in local heat transfer coefficients by injecting a similar fluid into a turbulent tube flow, but the effect dies out at a length-to-diameter ratio of 10. Practical application of injection appears to be rather limited because of difficulty in cost-effectively supplying and removing the injection fluid.

Suction. The suction method involves removing fluid through a porous heated surface, thus reducing heat/mass transfer resistance at the surface. Kinney (1968) and Kinney and Sparrow (1970) reported that applying suction at the surface increased heat transfer coefficients for laminar film and turbulent flows, respectively. Jeng et al. (1995) conducted experiments on a vertical parallel channel with asymmetric, isothermal walls. A porous wall segment was embedded in a segment of the test section wall, and enhancement occurred as hot air was sucked from the channel. The local heat transfer coefficient increased with increasing porosity. The maximum heat transfer enhancement obtained was 140%.

Fluid or Surface Vibration. Fluid or surface vibrations occur naturally in most heat exchangers; however, naturally occurring vibration is rarely factored into thermal design. Vibration equipment

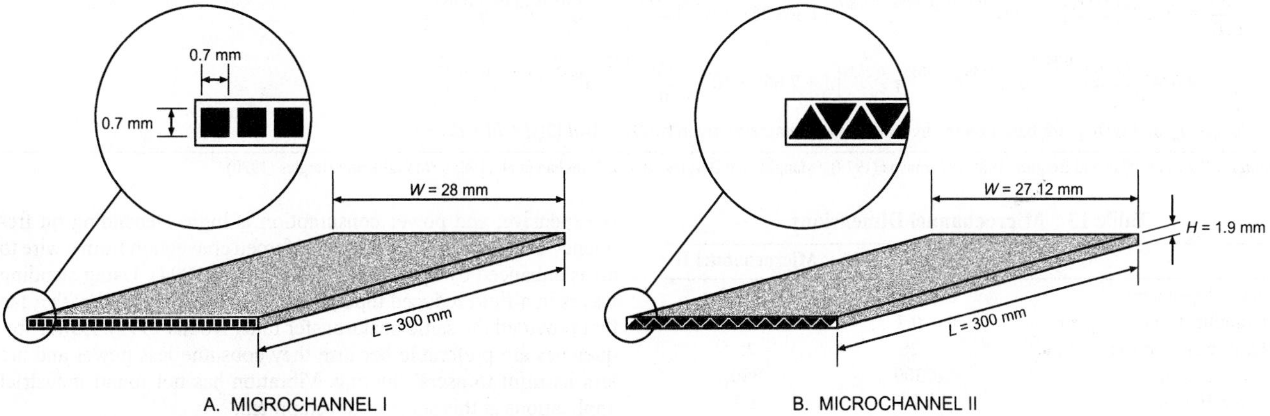

Fig. 31 Microchannel Dimensions

Table 12 Equations for Augmented Forced Convection (Single Phase)

Description	Equation	Comments
I. Turbulent in-tube flow of liquids		
Spiral repeated rib[a]	$\frac{h_a}{h_s} = \left\{\left[1 + 2.64\,\text{Re}^{0.036}\left(\frac{e}{d}\right)^{0.212}\left(\frac{p}{d}\right)^{-0.21}\left(\frac{\alpha}{90}\right)^{0.29}\text{Pr}^{-0.024}\right]^7\right\}^{1/7}$	$\text{Re} = GD/\mu$
	$\frac{f_a}{f_s} = \left\{1 + 29.1\left[\text{Re}^w\left(\frac{e}{d}\right)^x\left(\frac{p}{d}\right)^y\left(\frac{\alpha}{90}\right)^z\left(1 + \frac{2.94}{n}\right)\sin\beta\right]^{15/16}\right\}^{16/15}$	
	$w = 0.67 - 0.06(p/d) - 0.49(\alpha/90)$	
	$x = 1.37 - 0.157(p/d)$	
	$y = -1.66 \times 10^{-6}\,\text{Re} - 0.33\alpha/90$	
	$z = 4.59 + 4.11 \times 10^{-6}\,\text{Re} - 0.15(p/d)$	
	$h_s = \frac{(k/D)(f_s/2)\text{Re Pr}}{1 + 12.7(f_s/2)^{1/2}(\text{Pr}^{2/3} - 1)}$	
	$f_s = (1.58 \ln \text{Re} - 3.28)^{-2}$	
Fins[b]	$\frac{hD_h}{k} = 0.023\,\text{Pr}^{0.4}\left(\frac{GD_h}{\mu}\right)^{0.8}\left(\frac{A_F}{AF_i}\right)^{0.1}\left(\frac{A_i}{A}\right)^{0.5}(\sec\alpha)^3$	Note that in computing Re for fins and twisted-strip inserts there is allowance for reduced cross-sectional area.
	$f_h = 0.046\left(\frac{GD_h}{\mu}\right)^{-0.2}\left(\frac{A_F}{AF_i}\right)^{0.5}(\sec\alpha)^{0.75}$	
Twisted-strip inserts[c]	$\frac{(hd/k)}{(hd/k)_{y\to\infty}} = 1 + 0.769/y$	
	$\left(\frac{hd}{k}\right)_{y\to\infty} = 0.023\left(\frac{GD}{\mu}\right)^{0.8}\text{Pr}^{0.4}\left(\frac{\pi}{\pi - 4\delta/d}\right)^{0.8}\left(\frac{\pi + 2 - 2\delta/d}{\pi - 4\delta/d}\right)^{0.2}\phi$	
	$\phi = (\mu_b/\mu_w)^n$	
	$n = 0.18$ for liquid heating, 0.30 for liquid cooling	
	$f = \frac{0.0791}{(GD/\mu)^{0.25}}\left(\frac{\pi}{\pi - 4\delta/d}\right)^{1.75}\left(\frac{\pi + 2 - 2\delta/d}{\pi - 4\delta/d}\right)^{1.25}\left(1 + \frac{2.752}{y^{1.29}}\right)$	
II. Turbulent in-tube flow of gases		
Bent-strip inserts[d]	$\frac{hD}{k}\left(\frac{T_w}{T_b}\right)^{0.45} = 0.258\left(\frac{GD}{\mu}\right)^{0.6}$ or $\frac{hD}{k}\left(\frac{T_w}{T_b}\right)^{0.45} = 0.208\left(\frac{GD}{\mu}\right)^{0.63}$	Respectively, for configurations shown in Figure 28.
Twisted-strip inserts[d]	$\frac{hD}{k}\left(\frac{T_w}{T_b}\right)^{0.45} = 0.122\left(\frac{GD}{\mu}\right)^{0.65}$	
Bent-tab inserts[d]	$\frac{hD}{k}\left(\frac{T_w}{T_b}\right)^{0.45} = 0.406\left(\frac{GD}{\mu}\right)^{0.54}$	Note that in computing Re there is no allowance for flow blockage of the insert.
III. Offset strip fins for plate-fin heat exchangers[e]		
	$\frac{h}{c_pG} = 0.6522\left(\frac{GD_h}{\mu}\right)^{-0.5403}\alpha^{-0.1541}\delta^{0.1499}\gamma^{-0.0678}\left[1 + 5.269 \times 10^{-5}\left(\frac{GD_h}{\mu}\right)^{1.340}\alpha^{0.504}\delta^{0.456}\gamma^{-1.055}\right]^{0.1}$	
	$f_h = 9.6243\left(\frac{GD_h}{\mu}\right)^{-0.7422}\alpha^{-0.1856}\delta^{-0.3053}\gamma^{-0.2659}\left[1 + 7.669 \times 10^{-8}\left(\frac{GD_h}{\mu}\right)^{4.429}\alpha^{0.920}\delta^{3.767}\gamma^{0.236}\right]^{0.1}$	
	h/c_pG, f_h, and GD_h/μ are based on the hydraulic mean diameter given by $D_h = 4shl/[2(sl + hl + th) + ts]$	

Sources: [a]Ravigururajan and Bergles (1985), [b]Carnavos (1979), [c]Manglik and Bergles (1993), [d]Junkhan et al. (1985), [e]Manglik and Bergles (1990).

Table 13 Microchannel Dimensions

	Microchannel I	Microchannel II
Channel geometry	Rectangular	Triangular
Hydraulic diameter D_h, mm	0.7	0.86
Number of channels	28	25
Length L, mm	300	300
Height H, mm	1.5	1.9
Width W, mm	28	27.12
Wall thickness, mm	0.4	0.3

is expensive, and power consumption is high. Depending on frequency and amplitude of vibration, forced convection from a wire to air is enhanced by up to 300% (Nesis et al. 1994). Using standing waves in a fluid reduced input power by 75% compared with a fan that provided the same heat transfer rate (Woods 1992). Lower frequencies are preferable because they consume less power and are less harmful to users' hearing. Vibration has not found industrial applications at this stage of development.

Rotation. Rotation heat transfer enhancement occurs naturally in rotating electrical machinery, gas turbine blades, and some

Table 14 Active Heat Transfer Augmentation Techniques and Most Relevant Heat Transfer Modes

	Heat Transfer Mode					
	Forced Convection					
Technique	(Gases)	(Liquids)	Boil-ing	Evapo-ration	Conden-sation	Mass Transfer
Mechanical aids	NA	**	*	*	NA	**
Surface vibration	**	**	**	**	**	***
Fluid vibration	**	**	**	**	—	**
Electrostatic/electro-hydrodynamic	**	**	***	***	***	***
Suction/injection	*	**	NA	NA	**	**
Jet impingement	**	**	NA	**	NA	*
Rotation	*	*	***	***	***	***
Induced flow	**	**	NA	NA	NA	*

*** = Highly significant ** = Significant * = Somewhat significant
— = Not significant NA = Not believed to be applicable

Table 15 Worldwide Status of Active Techniques

Technique	Country or Countries
Mechanical aids	Universally used in selected applications (e.g., fluid mixers, liquid injection jets)
Surface vibration	Most recent work in United States; not significant
Fluid vibration	Sweden; mostly used for sonic cleaning
Electrostatic/electro-hydrodynamic	Japan, United States, United Kingdom; successful prototypes demonstrated
Other electrical methods	United Kingdom, France, United States
Suction/injection	No recent significant developments
Jet impingement	France, United States; high-temperature units and aerospace applications
Rotation	United States (industry), United Kingdom (R&D)
Induced flow	United States; particularly combustion

Table 16 Selected Studies on Mechanical Aids, Suction, and Injection

Source	Process	Heat Transfer Surface	Fluid	α_{max}
Valencia et al. (1996)	Natural convection	Finned tube	Air	0.5
Jeng et al. (1995)	Natural convection/suction	Asymmetric isothermal wall	Air	1.4
Inagaki and Komori (1993)	Turbulent natural convection/suction	Vertical plate	Air	1.8
Dhir et al. (1992)	Forced convection/injection	Tube	Air	1.45
Duignan et al. (1993)	Forced convection/film boiling	Horizontal plate	Air	2.0
Son and Dhir (1993)	Forced convection/injection	Annuli	Air	1.85
Malhotra and Majumdar (1991)	Water to bed/stirring	Granular bed	Air	3.0
Aksan and Borak (1987)	Pool of water/stirring	Tube coils	Water	1.7
Hagge and Junkhan (1974)	Forced convection/scraping	Cylindrical wall	Air	11.0
Hu and Shen (1996)	Turbulent natural convection	Converging ribbed tube	Air	1.0

α = Enhancement factor (ratio of enhanced to unenhanced heat transfer coefficient)

other equipment. The rotating evaporator, rotating heat pipe, high-performance distillation column, and Rotex absorption cycle heat pump are typical examples of previous work in this area. In rotating evaporators, the rotation effectively distributes liquid on the outer part of the rotating surface. Rotating the heat transfer surface also seems promising for effectively removing condensate and decreasing liquid film thickness. Heat transfer coefficients have been substantially increased by using centrifugal force, which may be several times greater than the gravity force.

As shown in Table 17, heat transfer enhancement varies from slight improvement up to 450%, depending on the system and rotation speed. The rotation technique is of particular interest for use in two-phase flows, particularly in boiling and condensation. This technique is not effective in the gas-to-gas heat recovery mode in laminar flow, but its application is more likely in turbulent flow. High power consumption, sealing and vibration problems, moving parts, and the expensive equipment required for rotation are some of this technique's drawbacks.

Electrohydrodynamics. Electrohydrodynamic (EHD) enhancement of single-phase heat transfer refers to coupling an electric field with the fluid field in a dielectric fluid medium. The net effect is production of secondary motions that destabilize the thermal boundary layer near the heat transfer surface, leading to heat transfer coefficients that are often an order of magnitude higher than those achievable by most conventional enhancement techniques. EHD heat transfer enhancement has applicability to both single-phase and phase-change heat transfer processes, although only enhancement of single-phase flows is discussed here.

Selected work in EHD enhancement of single-phase flow is shown in Table 18. High enhancement magnitudes have been found for single-phase air and liquid flows. However, high enhancement magnitude is not enough to warrant practical implementation. EHD electrodes must be compatible with cost-effective, mass-production technologies, and power consumption must be kept low, to minimize the required power supply cost and complexity.

The following brief overview discusses recent work on EHD enhancement of air-side heat transfer; additional details are in Ohadi et al. (2001).

EHD Air-Side Heat Transfer Augmentation. In a typical liquid-to-air heat exchanger, air-side thermal resistance is often the limiting factor to improving the overall heat transfer coefficient. Electrohydrodynamic enhancement of air-side heat transfer involves ionizing air molecules under a high-voltage, low-current electric field, leading to generation of secondary motions that are known as **corona** or **ionic wind**, generated between the charged electrode and receiving (ground) electrode. Typical wind velocities of 1 to 3 m/s have been verified experimentally. Studies of this enhancement method include Ohadi et al. (1991), who studied laminar and turbulent forced-convection heat transfer of air in tube flow, and Owsenek and Seyed-Yagoobi (1995), who investigated heat transfer augmentation of natural convection with the corona wind effect. Other studies are documented in Ohadi et al. (2001). The general finding has been that corona wind is effective for Reynolds numbers up to transitional values, 2300 or less, and becomes less effective as Re increases. At high Reynolds numbers, turbulence-induced effects overwhelm the corona wind effect.

Most studies addressed EHD air-side enhancement in classical geometries, but recent work has focused on issues of practical significance. These include (1) EHD applicability in highly compact heat exchangers, (2) electrode designs to minimize power consumptions to avoid joule heating and costly power supply requirements, and (3) cost-effective mass production of EHD-enhanced surfaces.

Lawler et al. (2002) examined air-side enhancement of an air-to-air heat exchanger with 4.2 to 6.4 mm fin spacing. Unlike previous studies, this study investigated placing electrodes on the heat transfer surface itself, integrated into the surface as an embedded wire, thus avoiding suspended wires in the flow field. This arrangement could

Table 17 Selected Studies on Rotation

Source	Process	Heat Transfer Surface	Fluid	Rotational Speed, rpm	α_{max}
Prakash and Zerle (1995)	Natural convection	Ribbed duct	Air	Given as a function	1.3
Mochizuki et al. (1994)	Natural convection	Serpentine duct	Air	Given as a function	3.0
Lan (1991)	Solidification	Vertical tube	Water	400	NA
McElhiney and Preckshot (1977)	External condensation	Horizontal tube	Steam	40	1.7
Nichol and Gacesa (1970)	External condensation	Vertical cylinder	Steam	2700	4.5
Astaf'ev and Baklastov (1970)	External condensation	Circular disk	Steam	2500	3.4
Tang and McDonald (1971)	Nucleate boiling	Horizontal heated circular cylinder	R-113	1400	<1.2
Marto and Gray (1971)	In-tube boiling	Vertical heated circular cylinder	Water	2660	1.6

α = Enhancement factor (ratio of enhanced to unenhanced heat transfer coefficient)

Table 18 Selected Previous Work with EHD Enhancement of Single-Phase Heat Transfer

Source	Process	Heat Transfer Surface/ Electrode	Fluid	P/Q, %	α_{max}
Poulter and Allen (1986)	Internal flow	Tube/wire	Aviation fuel-hexane	NA	20
Fernandez and Poulter (1987)	Internal flow	Tube/wire	Transformer oil	NA	23
Ohadi et al. (1995)	Internal flow	Smooth surface/rod	PAO	1.2	3.2
Ohadi et al. (1991)	Internal flow	Tube/wire	Air	15	3.2

NA = Not available
P = EHD power consumption
Q = Heat exchange rate in the heat exchanger
α = Enhancement factor (ratio of enhanced to unenhanced heat transfer coefficient)

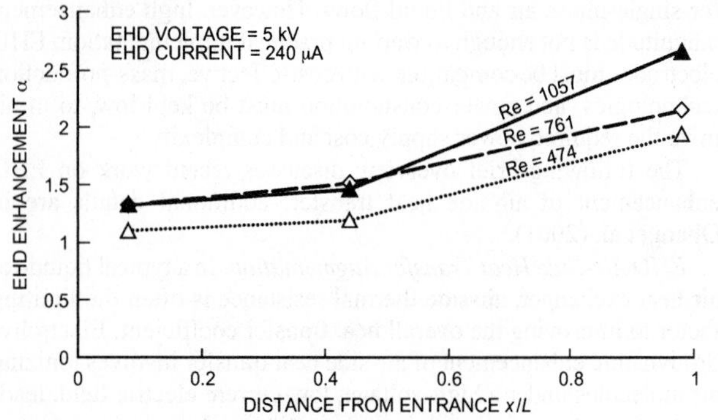

Fig. 32 Ratio of Heat Transfer Coefficient with EHD to Coefficient Without EHD as Function of Distance from Front of Module

greatly simplify manufacturing/fabrication for EHD-enhanced embedded electrodes. Insulating materials (in this case, polyimide tape) were placed between the heat transfer surface and electrodes. The height of the channel (8 mm) represented typical heights used in passive metallic designs and prevented sparking between the electrodes and upper and lower channel walls.

Figure 32 shows the ratio of heat transfer coefficients (EHD/non-EHD) as a function of position in the module for three different Reynolds numbers. For nonentry regions of the duct, enhancement is 100 to 150% for Reynolds numbers above 400. Near the module entrance, EHD enhancement is reduced, probably because of the higher heat transfer coefficient in the entry region, before viscous and thermal boundary layers have been established.

Tests for a finned heat exchanger with 6 mm fin spacing obtained comparable enhancements for Reynolds numbers up to 4000. The results are shown in Figure 33. At higher Re, the effect of EHD enhancement diminishes, as turbulence-induced enhancements predominate.

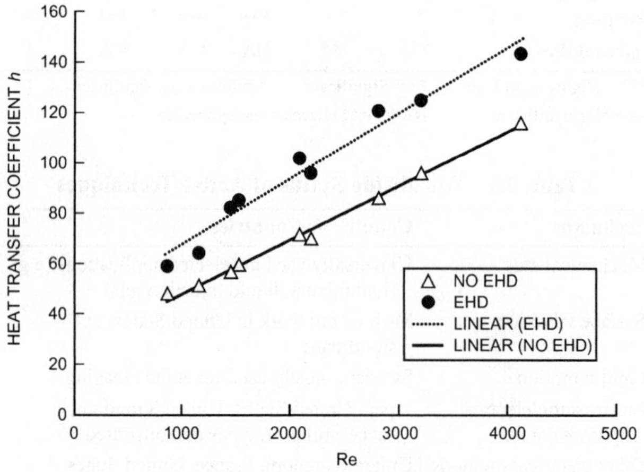

Fig. 33 Heat Transfer Coefficients (With and Without EHD) as Functions of Reynolds Number

EHD can also be used for other process control applications, including frost control, enhancing liquid/vapor separation for flow maldistribution control in heat exchangers, and oil separation in heat exchanger equipment. ASHRAE has recently sponsored three EHD research projects: (1) EHD-enhanced boiling of refrigerants (Seyed-Yagoobi 1997), (2) EHD frost control in HVAC&R equipment (Ohadi 2002), and (3) EHD flow maldistribution control in heat exchangers (Seyed-Yagoobi and Feng 2005). Reports for these projects are available through ASHRAE headquarters.

SYMBOLS

A = surface area for heat transfer
A_F, A_x = cross-sectional flow area
b = flow channel gap
Bi = Biot number (hL/k)
C = conductance; fluid capacity rate
c = coefficient; constant
C_1, C_2 = Planck's law constants [see Equation (19)]
c_p = specific heat at constant pressure
c_r = capacity ratio
c_v = specific heat at constant volume
D = tube (inside) or rod diameter; diameter of vessel
d = diameter; prefix meaning differential
E = electric field
e = protuberance height
f = Fanning friction factor for single-phase flow; electric body force
F_{ij} = angle factor
Fo = Fourier number
G = mass velocity; irradiation
g = gravitational acceleration
Gr = Grashof number
Gz = Graetz number
H = height
h = heat transfer coefficient; offset strip fin height

I = modified Bessel function
J = radiosity
J_0 = Bessel function of the first kind, order zero
j = Colburn heat transfer factor
k = thermal conductivity
L = length; height of liquid film
l = length; length of one module of offset strip fins; liquid
M = mass; molecular mass
m = general exponent; inverse of Biot number
$\dot{m}$ = mass rate of flow
n = general number; ratio r/r_m (dimensionless distance); number of blades
NTU = number of exchanger heat transfer units
Nu = Nusselt number
P = perimeter
p = pressure; fin pitch; repeated rib pitch
Pr = Prandtl number
Q = volume flow rate
q = heat transfer rate
q'' = heat flux
R = thermal resistance; radius
r = radius
Ra = Rayleigh number (Gr Pr)
Re = pipe Reynolds number (GD/μ); film Reynolds number ($4\Gamma/h$)
Re* = rotary Reynolds number (D^2Np/h)
S = conduction shape factor
s = lateral spacing of offset fin strips
T = absolute temperature
t = temperature; fin thickness at base; plate thickness
U = overall heat transfer coefficient
V = linear velocity; volume
W = work; emissive power; fin dimension
w = wall; effective plate width
W_b = blackbody emissive power
W_λ = monochromatic emissive power
x, y, z = lengths along principal coordinate axes
Y = temperature ratio
y = one-half diametrical pitch of a twisted tape: length of 180° revolution/tube diameter

Greek

α = thermal diffusivity = $k/\rho c_p$; absorptivity; spiral angle for helical fins; aspect ratio of offset strip fins, s/h; enhancement factor: ratio of enhanced to unenhanced heat transfer coefficient (conditions remaining the same)
β = coefficient of thermal expansion; contact angle of rib profile; chevron angle, °
Γ = mass flow of liquid per unit length
γ = ratio, t/s
δ = distance between fins; ratio t/l; thickness of twisted tape
ε = hemispherical emissivity; exchanger heat transfer effectiveness; dielectric constant
λ = wavelength; corrugation pitch
μ = absolute viscosity
ν = kinematic viscosity (μ/ρ), m^2/s
ϖ = eigenvalue
ρ = density; reflectance
σ = Stefan-Boltzmann constant, 5.67×10^{-8} $W/(m^2 \cdot K^4)$
τ = time; transmissivity
Φ = dimensionless fin resistance; Φ_{max} is maximum limiting value of Φ
ϕ = fin efficiency; angle; temperature correction factor; ratio of developed length to protracted length

Subscripts

a = augmented
b = blackbody; based on bulk fluid temperature
c = convection; critical; cold (fluid); cross section
cr = critical
e = equivalent; environment; exit
f = film; fin; final
g = gas
gen = internal generation
h = horizontal; hot (fluid); hydraulic
i = inlet; inside; particular surface (radiation); based on maximum inside (envelope) diameter
if = interface
iso = isothermal conditions
j = particular surface (radiation)
k = particular surface (radiation)
L = thickness
l = liquid
m = mean
n = counter variable
o = outside; outlet; overall; at base of fin
p = prime heat transfer surface; plate
r = radiation; root (fin); reduced
s = surface; secondary heat transfer surface; straight or plain; accounting for flow blockage of twisted tape
st = static (pressure)
t = temperature; terminal temperature; tip (fin)
uf = unfinned
v = vapor; vertical
W = width
wet = wetted
w = wall; or wafer
λ = monochromatic

REFERENCES

Adams, J.A. and D.F. Rogers. 1973. *Computer aided heat transfer analysis*. McGraw-Hill, New York.

Adams, T.M., S.I. Abdel-Khalik, S.M. Jeter, and Z.H. Qureshi. 1998. An experimental investigation of single-phase forced convection in microchannels. *International Journal of Heat and Mass Transfer* 41(6):851-857.

Afgan, N.H. and E.U. Schlunder. 1974. *Heat exchangers: Design and theory sourcebook*. McGraw-Hill, New York.

Aksan, D. and F. Borak. 1987. Heat transfer coefficients in coiled stirred tank systems. *Canadian Journal of Chemical Engineering* 65:1013-1014.

Al-Fahed, S.F., Z.H. Ayub, A.M. Al-Marafie, and B.M. Soliman. 1993. Heat transfer and pressure drop in a tube with internal microfins under turbulent water flow conditions. *Experimental Thermal and Fluid Science* 7:249-253.

Altmayer, E.F., A.J. Gadgil, F.S. Bauman, and R.C. Kammerud. 1983. Correlations for convective heat transfer from room surfaces. *ASHRAE Transactions* 89(2A):61-77.

Astaf'ev, B.F. and A.M. Baklastov. 1970. Condensation of steam on a horizontal rotating disc. *Teploenergetika* 17:55-57.

Ayub, Z.H. 2003. Plate heat exchanger literature survey and new heat transfer and pressure drop correlations for refrigerant evaporators. *Heat Transfer Engineering* 24(5):3-16.

Ayub, Z.H. and S.F. Al-Fahed. 1993. The effect of gap width between horizontal tube and twisted tape on the pressure drop in turbulent water flow. *International Journal of Heat and Fluid Flow* 14(1):64-67.

Bauman, F., A. Gadgil, R. Kammerud, E. Altmayer, and M. Nansteel. 1983. Convective heat transfer in buildings. *ASHRAE Transactions* 89(1A): 215-233.

Beckermann, C. and V. Goldschmidt. 1986. Heat transfer augmentation in the flueway of a water heater. *ASHRAE Transactions* 92(2B):485-495.

Bergles, A.E. 1964. Burnout in tubes of small diameter. ASME *Paper* 63-WA-182.

Bergles, A.E. 1998. Techniques to enhance heat transfer. In *Handbook of heat transfer*, 3rd ed., pp. 11.1-11.76. McGraw-Hill, New York.

Bergles, A.E. 2001. The implications and challenges of enhanced heat transfer for the chemical process industries. *Chemical Engineering Research and Design* 79:437-434.

Carnavos, T.C. 1979. Heat transfer performance of internally finned tubes in turbulent flow. In *Advances in enhanced heat transfer*, pp. 61-67. American Society of Mechanical Engineers, New York.

Carslaw, H.S. and J.C. Jaeger. 1959. *Conduction of heat in solids*. Oxford University Press, UK.

Churchill, S.W. 1990. Free convection around immersed bodies. In *Handbook of heat exchanger design*, G.F. Hewitt, ed. Hemisphere, New York.

Churchill, S.W. and M. Bernstein. 1977. A correlating equation for forced convection from gases and liquids to a circular cylinder in cross flow. *Journal of Heat Transfer* 99:300.

Churchill, S.W. and H.H.S. Chu. 1975a. Correlating equations for laminar and turbulent free convection from a vertical plate. *International Journal of Heat and Mass Transfer* 18(11):1323-1329.

Churchill, S.W. and H.H.S. Chu. 1975b. Correlating equations for laminar and turbulent free convection from a horizontal cylinder. *International Journal of Heat and Mass Transfer* 18(9):1049-1053.

Clausing, A.M. 1964. Thermal contact resistance in a vacuum environment. ASME *Paper* 64-HT-16, Seventh National Heat Transfer Conference.

Costa, R., R. Muller, and C. Tobias. 1985. Transport processes in narrow (capillary) channels. *AIChE Journal* 31:473-482.

Couvillion, R.J. 2004. Curve fits for Heisler chart eigenvalues. *Computers in Education Journal*. July-September.

Croft, D.R. and D.G. Lilley. 1977. *Heat transfer calculations using finite difference equations*. Applied Science, London.

Dart, D.M. 1959. Effect of fin bond on heat transfer. *ASHRAE Journal* 5:67.

Dhir, V.K., F. Chang, and G. Son. 1992. Enhancement of single-phase forced convection heat transfer in tubes and ducts using tangential flow injection. *Annual Report*. Contract 5087-260135. Gas Research Institute.

Dittus, F.W. and L.M.K. Boelter. 1930. Heat transfer in automobile radiators of the tubular type. *University of California Engineering Publication* 13:443.

Duignan, M., G. Greene, and T. Irvine. 1993. The effect of surface gas injection on film boiling heat transfer. *Journal of Heat Transfer* 115:986-992.

Eckels, P.W. 1977. Contact conductance of mechanically expanded plate finned tube heat exchangers. AIChE-ASME Heat Transfer Conference, Salt Lake City.

Eckels, S.J. 2003. Single-phase refrigerant heat transfer and pressure drop characterization of high Reynolds number flow for internally finned tubes including the effects of miscible oils (RP-1067). ASHRAE Research Project, *Final Report*.

Edwards, J.A. and J.B. Chaddock. 1963. An experimental investigation of the radiation and free-convection heat transfer from a cylindrical disk extended surface. *ASHRAE Transactions* 69:313.

Fernandez, J. and R. Poulter. 1987. Radial mass flow in electrohydrodynamically-enhanced forced heat transfer in tubes. *International Journal of Heat and Mass Transfer* 80:2125-2136.

Fujii, T., S. Koyama, and M. Fujii. 1986. Experimental study of free convection heat transfer from an inclined fine wire to air. *Proceedings of the VIII International Heat Transfer Conference*, San Francisco, vol. 3.

Gnielinski, V. 1990. Forced convection in ducts. In *Handbook of heat exchanger design*, G.F. Hewitt, ed. Hemisphere, New York.

Goldstein, R.J., E.M. Sparrow, and D.C. Jones. 1973. Natural convection mass transfer adjacent to horizontal plates. *International Journal of Heat and Mass Transfer* 16:1025.

Gose, E.E., E.E. Peterson, and A. Acrivos. 1957. On the rate of heat transfer in liquids with gas injection through the boundary layer. *Journal of Applied Physics* 28:1509.

Grigull, U., I. Straub, E. Hahne, and K. Stephan. 1982. Heat transfer. *Proceedings of the Seventh International Heat Transfer Conference*, Munich, vol. 3.

Hagge, J.K. and G.H. Junkhan. 1974. Experimental study of a method of mechanical augmentation of convective heat transfer in air. *Report* HTL3, ISU-ERI-Ames-74158, Nov. 1975. Iowa State University, Ames.

Heavner, R.L., H. Kumar, and A.S. Wanniarachchi. 1993. Performance of an industrial heat exchanger: Effect of chevron angle. *AIChE Symposium Series* 295(89):262-267.

Hottel, H.C. and A.F. Sarofim. 1967. *Radiation transfer.* McGraw-Hill, New York.

Hu, Z. and J. Shen. 1996. Heat transfer enhancement in a converging passage with discrete ribs. *International Journal of Heat and Mass Transfer* 39(8):1719-1727.

Inagaki, T. and I. Komori. 1993. Experimental study of heat transfer enhancement in turbulent natural convection along a vertical flat plate, Part 1: The effect of injection and suction. *Heat Transactions—Japanese Research* 22:387.

Incropera, F.P., D.P. DeWitt, T.L. Bergman, and A.S. Lavine. 2007. *Fundamentals of heat and mass transfer*, 6th ed. John Wiley & Sons, New York.

Jakob, M. 1949, 1957. *Heat transfer*, vols. I and II. John Wiley & Sons, New York.

Jeng, Y., J. Chen, and W. Aung. 1995. Heat transfer enhancement in a vertical channel with asymmetric isothermal walls by local blowing or suction. *International Journal of Heat and Fluid Flow* 16:25.

Junkhan, G.H., A.E. Bergles, V. Nirmalan, and T. Ravigururajan. 1985. Investigation of turbulators for fire tube boilers. *Journal of Heat Transfer* 107:354-360.

Junkhan, G.H., A.E. Bergles, V. Nirmalan, and W. Hanno. 1988. Performance evaluation of the effects of a group of turbulator inserts on heat transfer from gases in tubes. *ASHRAE Transactions* 94(2):1195-1212.

Kandlikar, S.G. 2002. Fundamental issues related to flow boiling in mini channels and microchannels. *Experimental Thermal and Fluid Science* 26:389-407.

Kaspareck, W.E. 1964. Measurement of thermal contact conductance between dissimilar metals in a vacuum. ASME *Paper* 64-HT-38, Seventh National Heat Transfer Conference.

Kays, W.M. and A.L. London. 1984. *Compact heat exchangers*, 3rd ed. McGraw-Hill, New York.

Khanpara, J.C., A.E. Bergles, and M.B. Pate. 1986. Augmentation of R-113 in-tube condensation with micro-fin tubes. *Proceedings of the ASME Heat Transfer Division*, HTD 65, pp. 21-32.

Kinney, R.B. 1968. Fully developed frictional and heat transfer characteristics of laminar flow in porous tubes. *International Journal of Heat and Mass Transfer* 11:1393-1401.

Kinney, R.B. and E.M. Sparrow. 1970. Turbulent flow: Heat transfer and mass transfer in a tube with surface suction. *Journal of Heat Transfer* 92:117-125.

Knudsen, J.G. and B.V. Roy. 1983. Studies on scaling of cooling tower water. In *Fouling of heat enhancement surfaces*, pp. 517-530. Engineering Foundation, New York.

Kumar, H. 1984. The plate heat exchanger: Construction and design. *Institute of Chemical Engineering Symposium Series* 86:1275-1288.

Lan, C.W. 1991. Effects of rotation on heat transfer fluid flow and interface in normal gravity floating zone crystal growth. *Journal of Crystal Growth* 114:517.

Lawler, J., et al. 2002. EHD enhanced liquid-air heat exchangers. *Final Report*, Contract M67854-00-C-0015. Advanced Thermal and Environmental Concepts, College Park, MD.

Lewis, D.M. and H.J. Sauer, Jr. 1965. The thermal resistance of adhesive bonds. *ASME Journal of Heat Transfer* 5:310.

Lloyd, J.R. and W.R. Moran. 1974. Natural convection adjacent to horizontal surfaces of various plan forms. *Journal of Heat Transfer* 96:443

Love, T.J. 1968. *Radiative heat transfer.* Merrill, Columbus, OH.

Malhotra, K. and A.S. Mujumdar. 1991. Wall to bed contact heat transfer rates in mechanically stirred granular beds. *International Journal of Heat and Mass Transfer* 34:724-735.

Manglik, R.M. and A.E. Bergles. 1990. The thermal-hydraulic design of the rectangular offset-strip-fin-compact heat exchanger. In *Compact heat exchangers*, pp. 123-149. Hemisphere, New York.

Manglik, R.M. and A.E. Bergles. 1993. Heat transfer and pressure drop correlation for twisted-tape insert in isothermal tubes: Part II —Transition and turbulent flows. *Journal of Heat Transfer* 115:890-896.

Manglik, R.M. and A.E. Bergles. 2002. Swirl flow heat transfer and pressure drop with twisted-tape inserts. *Advances in Heat Transfer* 36:183.

Marto, P.J. and V.H. Gray. 1971. Effects of high accelerations and heat fluxes on nucleate boiling of water in an axisymmetric rotating boiler. NASA *Technical Note* TN. D-6307. Washington, D.C.

McAdams, W.H. 1954. *Heat transmission*, 3rd ed. McGraw-Hill, New York.

McElhiney, J.E. and G.W. Preckshot. 1977. Heat transfer in the entrance length of a horizontal rotating tube. *International Journal of Heat and Mass Transfer* 20:847-854.

Metais, B. and E.R.G. Eckert. 1964. Forced, mixed and free convection regimes. *ASME Journal of Heat Transfer* 86(C2)(5):295.

Mills, A.F. 1999. *Basic heat & mass transfer*. Prentice Hall, Saddle River, NJ.

Mochizuki, S., J. Takamura, and S. Yamawaki. 1994. Heat transfer in serpentine flow passages with rotation. *Journal of Turbomachinery* 116:133.

Modest, M.F. 2003. *Radiative heat transfer*, 2nd ed. Academic Press, Oxford, U.K.

Morgan, V.T. 1975. The overall convective heat transfer from smooth circular cylinders. In *Advances in heat transfer*, vol. 11, T.F. Irvine and J.P. Hartnett, eds. Academic Press, New York.

Muley, A. and R.M. Manglik. 1999. Experimental study of turbulent flow heat transfer and pressure drop in a plate heat exchanger with chevron plates. *Journal of Heat Transfer* 121(1):110-117.

Myers, G.E. 1971. Analytical methods in conduction heat transfer. McGraw-Hill, New York.

Nelson, R.M. and A.E. Bergles. 1986. Performance evaluation for tubeside heat transfer enhancement of a flooded evaporative water chiller. *ASHRAE Transactions* 92(1B):739-755.

Nesis, E.I., A.F. Shatalov, and N.P. Karmatskii. 1994. Dependence of the heat transfer coefficient on the vibration amplitude and frequency of a vertical thin heater. *Journal of Engineering Physics and Thermophysics* 67(1-2).

Nichol, A.A. and M. Gacesa. 1970. Condensation of steam on a rotating vertical cylinder. *Journal of Heat Transfer* 144-152.

Ohadi, M.M. 2002. Control of frost accumulation in refrigeration equipment using the electrohydrodynamic (EHD) technique (RP-1100). ASHRAE Research Project, *Final Report.*

Ohadi, M. and J. Qi. (In press). *Thermal management of the next generation high flux electronics*. Springer, Norwell, MA.

Ohadi, M.M., N. Sharaf, and D.A. Nelson. 1991. Electrohydrodynamic enhancement of heat transfer in a shell-and-tube heat exchanger. *Enhanced Heat Transfer* 4(1):19-39.

Ohadi, M.M., S. Dessiatoun, A. Singh, K. Cheung, and M. Salehi. 1995. EHD-enhancement of boiling/condensation heat transfer of alternate refrigerants. *Progress Report* 6. Presented to U.S. Department of Energy and the EHD Consortium Members, under DOE Grant DE-FG02-93CE23803.A000, Chicago, January.

Ohadi, M.M., S.V. Dessiatoun, J. Darabi, and M. Salehi. 1996. Active augmentation of single-phase and phase-change heat transfer—An overview. In *Process, enhanced, and multiphase heat transfer: A festschrift for A.E. Bergles*, pp. 277-286, R.M. Manglik and A.D. Kraus, eds. Begell House, New York.

Ohadi, M.M., J. Darabi, and B. Roget. 2001. Electrode design, fabrication, and materials science for EHD-enhanced heat and mass transfer. In *Annual review of heat transfer*, vol. 22, pp. 563-623.

Owsenek, B. and J. Seyed-Yagoobi. 1995. Experimental investigation of corona wind heat transfer enhancement with a heated horizontal flat plate. *Journal of Heat Transfer* 117:309.

Parker, J.D., J.H. Boggs, and E.F. Blick. 1969. *Introduction to fluid mechanics and heat transfer.* Addison Wesley, Reading, MA.

Patankar, S.V. 1980. *Numerical heat transfer and fluid flow.* McGraw-Hill, New York.

Pei, X.J., H.F. Ming, S.S. Guang, and P.R. Ze. 2001. Thermal–hydraulic performance of small scale micro-channel and porous-media heat-exchangers. *International Journal of Heat and Mass Transfer* 44(5): 1039-1051.

Pescod, D. 1980. An advance in plate heat exchanger geometry giving increased heat transfer. *Proceedings of the ASME Heat Transfer Division*, HTD 10, pp. 73-77.

Poulter, R. and P.H.G. Allen. 1986. Electrohydrodynamincally augmented heat and mass transfer in the shell tube heat exchanger. *Proceedings of the Eighth International Heat Transfer Conference* 6:2963-2968.

Prakash, C. and R. Zerle. 1995. Prediction of turbulent flow and heat transfer in a ribbed rectangular duct with and without rotation. *Journal of Turbomachinery* 117:255.

Ravigururajan, T.S. and A.E. Bergles. 1985. General correlations for pressure drop and heat transfer for single-phase turbulent flow in internally ribbed tubes. *Augmentation of Heat Transfer in Energy Systems*, HTD 52, pp. 9-20. American Society of Mechanical Engineers, New York.

Rich, D.G. 1966. The efficiency and thermal resistance of annular and rectangular fins. *Proceedings of the Third International Heat Transfer Conference, AIChE* 111:281-289.

Rin, Y., H.H. Jae, and K. Yongchan. 2006. Evaporative heat transfer and pressure drop of R410A in micro channels. *International Journal of Refrigeration* 29(1):92-100.

Schmidt, T.E. 1949. Heat transfer calculations for extended surfaces. *Refrigerating Engineering* 4:351-57.

Schneider, P.J. 1964. *Temperature response charts.* John Wiley & Sons, New York.

Seyed-Yagoobi, J. 1997. The applicability, design aspects, and long-term effects of EHD-enhanced heat transfer of alternate refrigerants/refrigerant mixtures for HVAC applications (RP-857). ASHRAE Research Project, *Final Report.*

Seyed-Yagoobi, J.S. and Y. Feng. 2005. Refrigerant flow mal-distribution control in evaporators using electrohydrodynamics technique (RP-1213). ASHRAE Research Project, *Final Report.*

Shepherd, D.G. 1946. Performance of one-row tube coils with thin plate fins, low velocity forced convection. *Heating, Piping, and Air Conditioning* (April).

Shlykov, Y.P. 1964. Thermal resistance of metallic contacts. *International Journal of Heat and Mass Transfer* 7(8):921.

Sieder, E.N., and C.E. Tate. 1936. Heat transfer and pressure drop of liquids in tubes. *Industrial & Engineering Chemistry Research* 28:1429.

Siegel, R. and J.R. Howell. 2002. *Thermal radiation heat transfer*, 4th ed. Taylor & Francis, New York.

Somerscales, E.F.C. and A.E. Bergles. 1997. Enhancement of heat transfer and fouling mitigation. *Advances in Heat Transfer* 30:197-253.

Somerscales, E.F.C., A.F. Pontedure, and A.E. Bergles. 1991. Particulate fouling of heat transfer tubes enhanced on their inner surface. *Fouling and enhancement interactions: Proceedings of the ASME Heat Transfer Division*, HTD 164, pp. 17-28.

Son, G. and V.K. Dhir. 1993. Enhancement of heat transfer in annulus using tangential flow injection. *Proceedings of the ASME Heat Transfer Division*, HTD 246.

Sonokama, K. 1964. Contact thermal resistance. *Journal of the Japan Society of Mechanical Engineers* 63(505):240. English translation in RSIC-215, AD-443429.

Suryanarayana, N.V. 1995. *Engineering heat transfer.* West Publishing, St. Paul, MN.

Tang, S. and T.W. McDonald. 1971. A study of boiling heat transfer from a rotating horizontal cylinder. *International Journal of Heat and Mass Transfer* 14:1643-1657.

Tauscher, W.A., E.M. Sparrow, and J.R. Lloyd. 1970. Amplification of heat transfer by local injection of fluid into a turbulent tube flow. *International Journal of Heat and Mass Transfer* 13:681-688.

Troupe, R.A., J.C. Morgan, and J. Prifiti. 1960. The plate heater versatile chemical engineering tool. *Chemical Engineering Progress* 56 (1):124-128.

Valencia, A., M. Fiebig, and V.K. Mitra. 1996. Heat transfer enhancement by longitudinal vortices in a fin tube heat exchanger. *Journal of Heat Transfer* 118:209.

Wanniarachchi, A.S., U. Ratnam, B.E. Tilton, and K. Dutta-Roy. 1995. Approximate correlations for chevron-type plate heat exchangers. *30th National Heat Transfer Conference*, ASME HTD 314, pp. 145-151.

Woods, B.G. 1992. Sonically enhanced heat transfer from a cylinder in cross flow and its impact on process power consumption. *International Journal of Heat and Mass Transfer* 35:2367-2376.

BIBLIOGRAPHY

Fins

General

Gardner, K.A. 1945. Efficiency of extended surface. *ASME Transactions* 67:621.

Gunter, A.Y. and A.W. Shaw. 1945. A general correlation of friction factors for various types of surfaces in cross flow. *ASME Transactions* 11:643.

Shah, R.K. and R.L. Webb. 1981. *Compact and enhanced heat exchangers, heat exchangers, theory and practice*, pp. 425-468. J. Taborek, G.F. Hewitt, and N. Afgan, eds. Hemisphere, New York.

Webb, R.L. 1980. Air-side heat transfer in finned tube heat exchangers. *Heat Transfer Engineering* 1(3):33-49.

Smooth

Clarke, L. and R.E. Winston. 1955. Calculation of finside coefficients in longitudinal finned heat exchangers. *Chemical Engineering Progress* 3:147.

Elmahdy, A.H. and R.C. Biggs. 1979. Finned tube heat exchanger: Correlation of dry surface heat transfer data. *ASHRAE Transactions* 85:2.

Ghai, M.L. 1951. Heat transfer in straight fins. General discussion on heat transfer. London Conference, September.

Gray, D.L. and R.L. Webb. 1986. Heat transfer and friction correlations for plate finned-tube heat exchangers having plain fins. *Proceedings of Eighth International Heat Transfer Conference*, San Francisco.

Wavy

Beecher, D.T. and T.J. Fagan. 1987. Fin patternization effects in plate finned tube heat exchangers. *ASHRAE Transactions* 93:2.

Yashu, T. 1972. Transient testing technique for heat exchanger fin. *Reito* 47(531):23-29.

Spines

Abbott, R.W., R.H. Norris, and W.A. Spofford. 1980. Compact heat exchangers for General Electric products—Sixty years of advances in design and manufacturing technologies. In *Compact heat exchangers—History, technological advancement and mechanical design problems*, ASME HTD 10, pp. 37-55. R.K. Shah, C.F. McDonald, and C.P. Howard, eds.

Moore, F.K. 1975. Analysis of large dry cooling towers with spine-fin heat exchanger elements. ASME *Paper* 75-WA/HT-46.

Rabas, T.J. and P.W. Eckels. 1975. Heat transfer and pressure drop performance of segmented surface tube bundles. ASME *Paper* 75-HT-45.

Weierman, C. 1976. Correlations ease the selection of finned tubes. *Oil and Gas Journal* 9:94-100.

Louvered

Hosoda, T., H. Uzuhashi, and N. Kobayashi. 1977. Louver fin type heat exchangers. *Heat Transfer—Japanese Research* 6(2):69-77.

Mahaymam, W. and L.P. Xu. 1983. Enhanced fins for air-cooled heat exchangers—Heat transfer and friction factor correlations. Y. Mori and W. Yang, eds. *Proceedings of the ASME-JSME Thermal Engineering Joint Conference*, Hawaii.

Senshu, T., T. Hatada, and K. Ishibane. 1979. Surface heat transfer coefficient of fins used in air-cooled heat exchangers. *Heat Transfer—Japanese Research* 8(4):16-26.

Circular

Jameson, S.L. 1945. Tube spacing in finned tube banks. *ASME Transactions* 11:633.

Katz, D.L. 1954-55. Finned tubes in heat exchangers; Cooling liquids with finned coils; Condensing vapors on finned coils; and Boiling outside finned tubes. Bulletin reprinted from *Petroleum Refiner*.

Heat Exchangers

Amooie-Foomeny, M.M. 1977. *Flow distribution in plate heat exchanger*. Ph.D. dissertation, University of Bradford, Bradford, U.K.

Buonopane, R.A., R.A. Troupe, and J.C. Morgan. 1963. Heat transfer design methods for plate heat exchangers. *Chemical Engineering Progress* 59(7):57-61.

Changal Vaie, A.A. 1975. *The performance of plate heat exchanger*. Ph.D. dissertation, University of Bradford, Bradford, U.K.

Chisholm, D. and A.S. Wanniarachchi. 1992. Maldistribution in single-pass mixed-channel plate heat exchangers. *Proceedings of the ASME Heat Transfer Division: Compact Heat Exchangers for Power and Process Industries*, HTD 201, pp. 95-99.

Clark, D.F. 1974. Plate heat exchanger design and recent developments. *The Chemical Engineer* 285:275-279.

Cooper, A. 1974. Recover more heat with plate heat exchangers. *The Chemical Engineer* 285:280-285.

Crozier, R.D., J.R. Booth, and J.E. Stewart. 1964. Heat transfer in plate and frame heat exchangers. *Chemical Engineering Progress* 60(8):43-45.

Edwards, M.F., A.A. Changal Vaie, and D.L. Parrott. 1974. Heat transfer and pressure drop characteristics of a plate heat exchanger using non-Newtonian liquids. *The Chemical Engineer* 285:286-288.

Focke, W.W., J. Zacharides, and I. Oliver. 1985. The effect of the corrugation inclination angle on the thermohydraulic performance of plate heat exchangers. *International Journal of Heat and Mass Transfer* 28(8):1469-1479.

Jackson, B.W. and R.A. Troupe. 1964. Laminar flow in a plate heat exchanger. *Chemical Engineering Progress* 60(7):65-67.

Gartner, J.R. and H.L. Harrison. 1963. Frequency response transfer functions for a tube in crossflow. *ASHRAE Transactions* 69:323.

Gartner, J.R. and H.L. Harrison. 1965. Dynamic characteristics of water-to-air crossflow heat exchangers. *ASHRAE Transactions* 71:212.

Kovalenko, L.M. and A.M. Maslov. 1970. Soviet plate heat exchangers. *Konservnaya I Ovoshchesushil Naya Promyshlennost* 7:15-17. (In Russian.)

Leuliet, J.C., J.F. Mangonnat, and M. Lalande. 1987. Etude de la perte de charge dans des echangeurs de chaleur a plaques traitant des produits non-Newtoniens. *Revue Generale de Thermique* 26 (308-309):445-450. (In French.)

Leuliet, J.C., J.F. Mangonnat, and M. Laiande. 1990. Flow and heat transfer in plate heat exchangers treating viscous Newtonian and pseudoplastic products, Part 1: Modeling the variations of the hydraulic diameter, *Canadian Journal of Chemical Engineering* 68(2):220-229.

Marriott, J. 1971. Where and how to use plate heat exchangers. *Chemical Engineering* 78:127-134.

Marriott, J. 1977. Performance of an Alfaflex plate heat exchanger. *Chemical Engineering Progress* 73(2):73-78.

Maslov, A. and L. Kovalenko. 1972. Hydraulic resistance and heat transfer in plate heat exchangers. *Molochnaya Promyshlennost* 10:20-22. (In Russian.)

McQuiston, F.C. 1981. Finned tube heat exchangers: State of the art for the air side. *ASHRAE Transactions* 87:1.

Moghaddam, S., K.T. Kiger, and M. Ohadi. 2006. Measurement of corona wind velocity and calculation of energy conversion efficiency for air side heat transfer enhancement in compact heat exchangers. *HVAC&R Research* 12(1):57-68.

Myers, G.E., J.W. Mitchell, and R. Nagaoka. 1965. A method of estimating crossflow heat exchanger transients. *ASHRAE Transactions* 71:225.

Okada, K., M. Ono, T. Tomimura, T. Okuma, H. Konno, and S. Ohtani. 1972. Design and heat transfer characteristics of a new plate heat exchanger. *Heat Transfer Japanese Research* 1(1):90-95.

Rene, F., J.C. Leuliet, and M. Lanlande. 1991. Heat transfer to Newtonian and non-Newtonian food fluids in plate heat exchangers: Experimental and numerical approaches. *Food and Bioproducts Processing: Transaction of the IChE*, Part C 69(3):115-126.

Roetzel W., S.K. Das, and X. Luo. 1994. Measurement of the heat transfer coefficient in plate heat exchangers using a temperature oscillation technique. *International Journal of Heat and Mass Transfer* 37(1):325-331.

Rosenblad, G. and A. Kullendroff. 1975. Estimating heat transfer from mass transfer studies on plate heat exchanger surfaces, *Warme- und Stoffubertragung* 8(3):187-191.

Savostin, A.F. and A.M. Tikhonov. 1970. Investigation of the characteristics of plate type heating surfaces. *Thermal Engineering* 17:113-117.

Stermole, F.J. and M.H. Carson. 1964. Dynamics of forced flow distributed parameter heat exchangers. *AIChE Journal* 10(5):9.

Talik, A.C., L.S. Fletcher, N.K. Anand, and L.W. Swanson. 1995. Heat transfer and pressure drop characteristics of a plate heat exchanger. *Proceedings of the ASME/JSME Thermal Engineering Conference*, vol. 4, pp. 321-329.

Thomasson, R.K. 1964. Frequency response of linear counterflow heat exchangers. *Journal of Mechanical Engineering Science* 6(1):3.

Wyngaard, J.C. and F.W. Schmidt. Comparison of methods for determining transient response of shell and tube heat exchangers. ASME *Paper* 64-WA/HT-20.

Yang, W.J. Frequency response of multipass shell and tube heat exchangers to timewise variant flow perturbance. ASME *Paper* 64-HT-18.

Heat Transfer, General

Bennet, C.O. and J.E. Myers. 1984. *Momentum, heat and mass transfer*, 3rd ed. McGraw-Hill, New York.

Brown, A.I. and S.M. Marco. 1958. *Introduction to heat transfer*, 3rd ed. McGraw-Hill, New York.

Burmeister, L.C. 1983. *Convective heat transfer*. John Wiley & Sons, New York.

Chapman, A.J. 1981. *Heat transfer*, 4th ed. Macmillan, New York.

Hausen, H. 1943. Dastellung des Warmeuberganges in Rohren durch verallgemeinerte Potenzbeziehungen. *VDI Zeitung*, Supplement 4: *Verfahrenstechnik*. Quoted in R.K. Shah and M.S. Bhatti, in *Handbook of single-phase convective heat transfer*, John Wiley & Sons, New York, 1987.

Holman, J.D. 1981. *Heat transfer*, 5th ed. McGraw-Hill, New York.

Kays, W.M. and M.E. Crawford. 1993. *Convective heat and mass transfer*, 3rd ed. McGraw-Hill, New York.

Kern, D.Q. and A.D. Kraus. 1972. *Extended surface heat transfer*. McGraw-Hill, New York.

Kreith, F. and W.Z. Black. 1980. *Basic heat transfer*. Harper and Row, New York.

Lienhard, J.H. 1981. *A heat transfer textbook*. Prentice Hall, Englewood Cliffs, NJ.

McQuiston, F.C. and J.D. Parker. 1988. *Heating, ventilating and air-conditioning, analysis and design*, 4th ed. John Wiley & Sons, New York.

Rohsenow, W.M. and J.P. Hartnett, eds. 1973. *Handbook of heat transfer*. McGraw-Hill, New York.

Sissom, L.E. and D.R. Pitts. 1972. *Elements of transport phenomena*. McGraw-Hill, New York.

Smith, E.M. 1997. *Thermal design of heat exchangers*. John Wiley & Sons, Chichester, UK.

Todd, J.P. and H.B. Ellis. 1982. *Applied heat transfer*. Harper and Row, New York.

Webb, R.L. and A.E. Bergles. 1983. Heat transfer enhancement, second generation technology. *Mechanical Engineering* 6:60-67.

Welty, J.R. 1974. *Engineering heat transfer*. John Wiley & Sons, New York.

Welty, J.R., C.E. Wicks, and R.E. Wilson. 1972. *Fundamentals of momentum, heat and mass transfer*. John Wiley & Sons, New York.

Wolf, H. 1983. *Heat transfer*. Harper and Row, New York.

CHAPTER 5

TWO-PHASE FLOW

TWO-phase flow is encountered extensively in the HVAC&R industries. A combination of liquid and vapor refrigerant exists in flooded coolers, direct-expansion coolers, thermosiphon coolers, brazed and gasketed plate evaporators and condensers, and tube-in-tube evaporators and condensers, as well as in air-cooled evaporators and condensers. In heating system pipes, steam and liquid water may both be present. Because the hydrodynamic and heat transfer aspects of two-phase flow are not as well understood as those of single-phase flow, no comprehensive model has yet been created to predict pressure drops or heat transfer rates. Instead, the correlations are for specific thermal and hydrodynamic operating conditions.

This chapter introduces two-phase flow and heat transfer processes of pure substances and refrigerant mixtures. Thus, some multiphase processes that are important to HVAC&R applications are not discussed here. The 2008 *ASHRAE Handbook—HVAC Systems and Equipment* provides information on several such applications, including humidification (Chapter 21), particulate contaminants (Chapter 28), cooling towers (Chapter 39), and evaporative air cooling (Chapter 40). See Chapter 41 of the 2006 *ASHRAE Handbook—Refrigeration* for information on absorption processes.

BOILING

Two-phase heat and mass transport are characterized by various flow and thermal regimes, whether vaporization occurs under natural convection or in forced flow. Unlike single-phase flow systems, the heat transfer coefficient for a two-phase mixture depends on the flow regime, thermodynamic and transport properties of both vapor and liquid, roughness of heating surface, wetting characteristics of the surface/liquid pair, and other parameters. Therefore, it is necessary to consider each flow and boiling regime separately to determine the heat transfer coefficient.

Accurate data defining regime limits and determining the effects of various parameters are not available. The accuracy of correlations in predicting the heat transfer coefficient for two-phase flow is generally not known beyond the range of the test data.

Boiling and Pool Boiling in Natural Convection Systems

Regimes of Boiling. The different regimes of pool boiling described by Farber and Scorah (1948) verified those suggested by Nukiyama (1934). The regimes are illustrated in Figure 1. When the temperature of the heating surface is near the fluid saturation temperature, heat is transferred by convection currents to the free surface, where evaporation occurs (region I). Transition to nucleate boiling occurs when the surface temperature exceeds saturation by a few degrees (region II).

In **nucleate boiling** (region III), a thin layer of superheated liquid forms adjacent to the heating surface. In this layer, bubbles nucleate and grow from spots on the surface. The thermal resistance of the superheated liquid film is greatly reduced by bubble-induced agitation and vaporization. Increased wall temperature increases bubble population, causing a large increase in heat flux.

As heat flux or temperature difference increases further and as more vapor forms, liquid flow toward the surface is interrupted, and a vapor blanket forms. This gives the **maximum heat flux**, which is

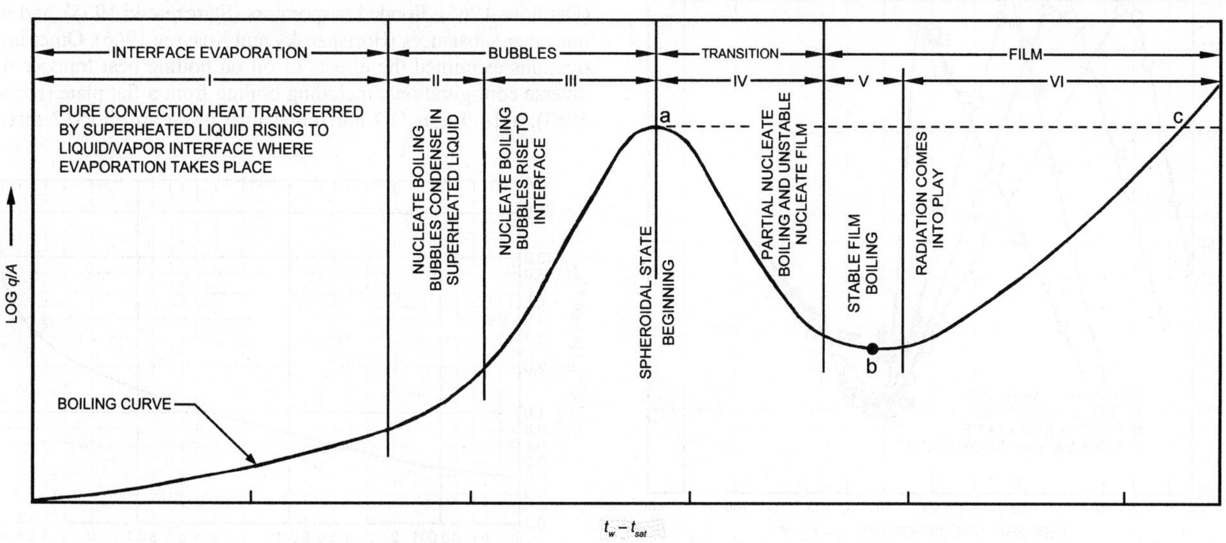

Fig. 1 Characteristic Pool Boiling Curve

The preparation of this chapter is assigned to TC 1.3, Heat Transfer and Fluid Flow.

at the **departure from nucleate boiling (DNB)** at point a in Figure 1. This flux is often called the **burnout heat flux** or **boiling crisis** because, for constant power-generating systems, an increase of heat flux beyond this point results in a jump of the heater temperature (to point c), often beyond the melting point of a metal heating surface.

In systems with controllable surface temperature, an increase beyond the temperature for DNB causes a decrease of heat flux density. This is the **transition boiling regime** (region IV); liquid alternately falls onto the surface and is repulsed by an explosive burst of vapor.

At sufficiently high surface temperatures, a stable vapor film forms at the heater surface; this is the **film boiling regime** (regions V and VI). Because heat transfer is by conduction (and some radiation) across the vapor film, the heater temperature is much higher than for comparable heat flux densities in the nucleate boiling regime. The **minimum film boiling (MFB)** heat flux (point b) is the lower end of the film boiling curve.

Free Surface Evaporation. In region I, where surface temperature exceeds liquid saturation temperature by less than a few degrees, no bubbles form. Evaporation occurs at the free surface by convection of superheated liquid from the heated surface. Correlations of heat transfer coefficients for this region are similar to those for fluids under ordinary natural convection [Equations (T1.1) to (T1.4)].

Nucleate Boiling. Much information is available on boiling heat transfer coefficients, but no universally reliable method is available for correlating the data. In the nucleate boiling regime, heat flux density is not a single valued function of the temperature but depends also on the nucleating characteristics of the surface, as illustrated by Figure 2 (Berenson 1962).

The equations proposed for correlating nucleate boiling data can be put in a form that relates heat transfer coefficient h to temperature difference $(t_s - t_{sat})$:

$$h = \text{constant}(t_s - t_{sat})^a \qquad (1)$$

Exponent a is normally about 3 for a plain, smooth surface; its value depends on the thermodynamic and transport properties of the vapor and liquid. Nucleating characteristics of the surface, including the size distribution of surface cavities and wetting characteristics of the surface/liquid pair, affect the value of the multiplying constant and the value of a in Equation (1).

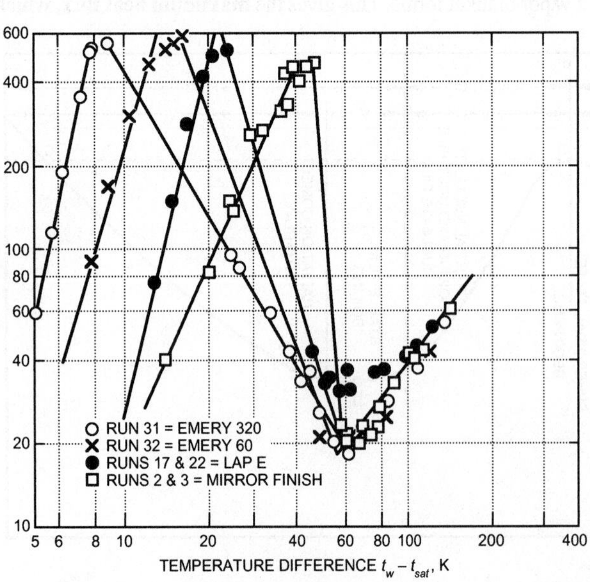

Fig. 2 Effect of Surface Roughness on Temperature in Pool Boiling of Pentane
(Berenson 1962)

A generalized correlation cannot be expected without considering the nucleating characteristics of the heating surface. Statistical analysis of data for 25 liquids by Hughmark (1962) shows that, in a correlation not considering surface condition, deviations of more than 100% are common.

In the following sections, correlations and nomographs for predicting nucleate and flow boiling of various refrigerants are given. For most cases, these correlations have been tested for refrigerants (e.g., R-11, R-12, R-113, and R-114) that are now identified as environmentally harmful and are no longer used in new equipment. Thermal and fluid characteristics of alternative refrigerants/refrigerant mixtures have recently been extensively researched, and some correlations have been suggested.

Stephan and Abdelsalam (1980) developed a statistical approach for estimating heat transfer during nucleate boiling. The correlation [Equation (T1.5)] should be used with a fixed contact angle θ regardless of the fluid. Cooper (1984) proposed a dimensional correlation for nucleate boiling [Equation (T1.6)]. The dimensions required are listed in Table 1. This correlation is recommended for fluids with poorly defined physical properties.

Gorenflo (1993) proposed a nucleate boiling correlation based on a set of reference conditions and a base heat transfer coefficient [Equation (T1.7)]. The correlation was developed for a reduced pressure p_r of 0.1 and the reference conditions given in Table 1. Base heat transfer coefficients are given for three fluids in Table 1; consult Gorenflo (1993) for additional fluids.

In addition to correlations dependent on thermodynamic and transport properties of the vapor and liquid, Borishansky et al. (1962), Lienhard and Schrock (1963) and Stephan (1992) documented a correlating method based on the law of corresponding states. The properties can be expressed in terms of fundamental molecular parameters, leading to scaling criteria based on reduced pressure $p_r = p/p_c$, where p_c is the critical thermodynamic pressure for the coolant. An example of this method of correlation is shown in Figure 3. Reference pressure p^* was chosen as $p^* = 0.029p_c$. This is a simple method for scaling the effect of pressure if data are available for one pressure level. It also is advantageous if the thermodynamic and particularly the transport properties used in several equations in Table 1 are not accurately known. In its present form, this correlation gives a value of $a = 2.33$ for the exponent in Equation (1) and consequently should apply for typical aged metal surfaces.

There are explicit heat transfer coefficient correlations based on the law of corresponding states for halogenated refrigerants (Danilova 1965), flooded evaporators (Starczewski 1965), and various other substances (Borishansky and Kosyrev 1966). Other investigations examined the effects of oil on boiling heat transfer from diverse configurations, including boiling from a flat plate (Stephan 1963), a 14.0 mm OD horizontal tube using an oil/R-12 mixture

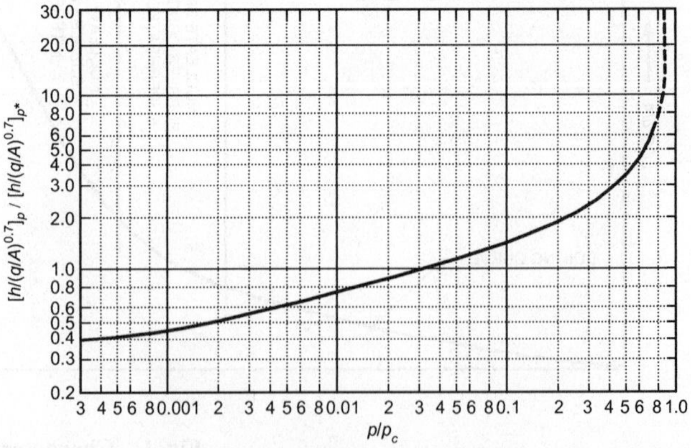

Fig. 3 Correlation of Pool Boiling Data in Terms of Reduced Pressure

Table 1 Equations for Boiling Heat Transfer

Description	References	Equations	
Free convection	Jakob (1949, 1957)	$Nu = C(Gr)^m(Pr)^n$	(T1.1)
Free convection boiling, or boiling without bubbles for low Δt and Gr Pr < 10^8. All properties based on liquid state.		Characteristic length scale for vertical surfaces is vertical height of plate or cylinder. For horizontal surfaces, $L_c = A_s/P$, where A_s is plate surface area and P is plate perimeter, is recommended. $Gr = \frac{g\beta(t_s - t_{sat})L_c^3}{\nu^2}$	
Vertical submerged surface		$Nu = 0.61(Gr)^{0.25}(Pr)^{0.25}$	(T1.2)
Horizontal submerged surface		$Nu = 0.16(Gr)^{1/3}(Pr)^{1/3}$	(T1.3)
Simplified equation for water		$h \sim 80(\Delta t)^{1/3}$, where h is in Btu/h·ft²·°F, Δt in °F	(T1.4)
Nucleate boiling	Stephan and Abdelsalam (1980)	$\frac{hD_d}{k_l} = 0.0546\left[\left(\frac{\rho_v}{\rho_l}\right)^{0.5}\left(\frac{qD_d}{Ak_lt_{sat}}\right)\right]^{0.67}\left(\frac{h_{fg}D_d^2}{\alpha_l^2}\right)^{0.248}\left(\frac{\rho_l-\rho_v}{\rho_l}\right)^{-4.33}$ where $D_d = 0.0208\theta\left[\frac{\sigma}{g(\rho_l-\rho_v)}\right]^{0.5}$ with $\theta = 35°$.	(T1.5)
	Cooper (1984)	$h = 55p_r^{0.12-0.4343\ln(R_p)}(-0.4343\ln p_r)^{-0.55}M^{-0.5}\left(\frac{q}{A}\right)^{0.67}$ where h is in W/(m²·K), q/A is in W/m², and R_p is surface roughness in μm (if unknown, use 1 μm). Multiply h by 1.7 for copper surfaces.	(T1.6)
	Gorenflo (1993)	$h = h_oF_{PF}\left(\frac{q/A}{(q/A)_o}\right)^{nf}\left(\frac{R_p}{R_{po}}\right)^{0.133}$ where reference conditions for water are $(q/A)_o$ = 20 000 W/m², and R_{po} = 0.4 μm $F_{PF} = 1.2p_r^{0.27} + 2.5p_r + \frac{p_r}{1-p_r}$ $nf = 0.9 - 0.3p_r^{0.15}$ For all fluids except water and helium. **Fluid** — **h_o, W/(m²·K)** R-134a — 4500 R-22 — 3900 Ammonia — 7000	(T1.7)
Critical heat flux	Kutateladze (1951)	$\frac{q/A}{\rho_v h_{fg}}\left[\frac{\rho_l^2}{\sigma g(\rho_l-\rho_v)}\right]^{0.25} = K_D$	(T1.8)
	Zuber et al. (1962)	For many liquids, K_D varies from 0.12 to 0.16; an average value of 0.13 is recommended.	
Minimum heat flux in film boiling from horizontal plate	Zuber (1959)	$\frac{q}{A} = 0.09\rho_v h_{fg}\left[\frac{\sigma g(\rho_l-\rho_v)}{(\rho_l+\rho_v)^2}\right]^{1/4}$	(T1.9)
Minimum heat flux in film boiling from horizontal cylinders	Lienhard and Wong (1964)	$q/A = 0.633\left\{\frac{4B^2}{1+B/2}\right\}^{0.25}\left\{0.09\rho_v h_{fg}\left[\frac{g\sigma(\rho_l-\rho_v)}{(\rho_l+\rho_v)^2}\right]^{0.25}\right\}$ where $B = (2L_b/D)^2$ and $L_b = \left[\frac{\sigma}{g(\rho_l-\rho_v)}\right]^{0.5}$	(T1.10)
Minimum temperature difference for film boiling from horizontal plate	Berenson (1961)	$(t_s - t_{sat}) = 0.127L_b\left(\frac{\rho_v h_{fg}}{k_v}\right)\left[\frac{g(\rho_l-\rho_v)}{\rho_l+\rho_v}\right]^{2/3}\left[\frac{\mu_v}{g(\rho_l-\rho_v)}\right]^{1/3}$	(T1.11)
Film boiling from horizontal plate	Berenson (1961)	$h = 0.425\left[\frac{k_v^3\rho_v h_{fg}g(\rho_l-\rho_v)}{\mu_v(t_s-t_{sat})L_b}\right]^{0.25}$	(T1.12)
Film boiling from horizontal cylinders	Bromley (1950)	$h = 0.62\left[\frac{k_v^3\rho_v h_{fg}g(\rho_l-\rho_v)}{\mu_v(t_s-t_{sat})D}\right]^{0.25}$	(T1.13)
Effect of radiation	Anderson et al. (1966)	Substitute $h'_{fg} = h_{fg}\left(1+0.4c_p\frac{t_w-t_b}{h_{fg}}\right)$	
Quenching spheres	Frederking and Clark (1962)	$Nu = 0.15(Ra)^{1/3}$ for $Ra > 5 \times 10^7$ $Ra = \left[\frac{D^3g(\rho_l-\rho_v)}{\nu_v^2\rho_v}Pr_v\left(\frac{h_{fg}}{c_{p,v}(t_s-t_{sat})}+0.4\right)\frac{a}{g}\right]^{1/3}$ where a = local acceleration	(T1.14)

(Tschernobyiski and Ratiani 1955), inside horizontal tubes using an oil/R-12 mixture (Breber et al. 1980; Green and Furse 1963; Worsoe-Schmidt 1959), and commercial copper tubing using R-11 and R-113 with oil content to 10% (Dougherty and Sauer 1974). Additionally, Furse (1965) examined R-11 and R-12 boiling over a flat horizontal copper surface.

Maximum Heat Flux and Film Boiling

Maximum, or critical, heat flux and the film boiling region are not as strongly affected by conditions of the heating surface as heat flux in the nucleate boiling region, making analysis of DNB and of film boiling more tractable.

Several mechanisms have been proposed for the onset of DNB [see Carey (1992) for a summary]. Each model is based on the scenario that a vapor blanket exists on portions of the heat transfer surface, greatly increasing thermal resistance. Zuber (1959) proposed that these blankets may result from Helmholtz instabilities in columns of vapor rising from the heated surface; another prominent theory supposes a macrolayer beneath the mushroom-shaped bubbles (Haramura and Katto 1983). In this case, DNB occurs when the liquid beneath the bubbles is consumed before the bubbles depart and allow surrounding liquid to re-wet the surface. Dhir and Liaw (1989) used a concept of bubble crowding proposed by Rohsenow and Griffith (1956) to produce a model that incorporates the effect of contact angle. Sefiane (2001) suggested that instabilities near the triple contact lines cause DNB. Fortunately, though significant disagreement remains about the mechanism of DNB, models using these differing conceptual approaches tend to lead to predictions within a factor of 2.

When DNB (point a in Figure 1) is assumed to be a hydrodynamic instability phenomenon, a simple relation [Equation (T1.8)] can be derived to predict this flux for pure, wetting liquids (Kutateladze 1951; Zuber et al. 1962). The dimensionless constant K varies from approximately 0.12 to 0.16 for a large variety of liquids. Kandlikar (2001) created a model for maximum heat flux explicitly incorporating the effects of contact angle and orientation. Equation (T1.8) compares favorably to Kandlikar's, and, because it is simpler, it is still recommended for general use. Carey (1992) provides correlations to calculate the maximum heat flux for a variety of geometries based on this equation. For orientations other than upward-facing, consult Brusstar and Merte (1997) and Howard and Mudawar (1999).

Van Stralen (1959) found that, for liquid mixtures, DNB is a function of concentration. As discussed by Stephan (1992), the maximum heat flux always lies between the values of the pure components. Unfortunately, the relationship of DNB to concentration is not simple, and several hypotheses [e.g., McGillis and Carey (1996); Reddy and Lienhard (1989); Van Stralen and Cole (1979)] have been put forward to explain the experimental data. For a more detailed overview of mixture boiling, refer to Thome and Shock (1984).

Hall and Mudawar (2000a, 2000b) presented an extensive review of critical heat flux data and correlations for flow boiling in tubes.

The minimum heat flux density (point b in Figure 1) in film boiling from a horizontal surface and a horizontal cylinder can be predicted by Equation (T1.9). The factor 0.09 was adjusted to fit experimental data; values predicted by the analysis were approximately 30% higher. The accuracy of Equation (T1.9) falls off rapidly with increasing p_r (Rohsenow et al. 1998). Berenson's (1961) Equations (T1.11) and (T1.12) predict the temperature difference at minimum heat flux and heat transfer coefficient for film boiling on a flat plate. The minimum heat flux for film boiling on a horizontal cylinder can be predicted by Equation (T1.10). As in Equation (T1.9), the factor 0.633 was adjusted to fit experimental data.

The heat transfer coefficient in film boiling from a horizontal surface can be predicted by Equation (T1.12), and from a horizontal cylinder by Equation (T1.13) (Bromley 1950).

Frederking and Clark (1962) found that, for turbulent film boiling, Equation (T1.14) agrees with data from experiments at reduced gravity (Jakob 1949, 1957; Kutateladze 1963; Rohsenow 1963; Westwater 1963).

Flooded Evaporators

Equations in Table 1 merely approximate heat transfer rates in flooded evaporators. One reason is that vapor entering the evaporator combined with vapor generated within the evaporator can produce significant forced convection effects superimposed on those caused by nucleation. Nonuniform distribution of two-phase, vapor/liquid flow in the tube bundle of shell-and-tube evaporators or tubes of vertical-tube flooded evaporators is also important.

Bundle data and design methods for plain, low-fin, and enhanced tubes were reviewed in Collier and Thome (1996) and Thome (1990).

Typical performance of vertical-tube natural circulation evaporators, based on data for water, is shown in Figure 4 (Perry 1950). Low coefficients are at low liquid levels because insufficient liquid covers the heating surface. The lower coefficient at high levels results from an adverse effect of hydrostatic head on temperature difference and circulation rate. Perry (1950) noted similar effects in horizontal shell-and-tube evaporators.

Forced-Convection Evaporation in Tubes

Flow Mechanics. When a mixture of liquid and vapor flows inside a tube, the flow pattern that develops depends on the mass fraction of liquid, fluid properties of each phase, and flow rate. In an evaporator tube, the mass fraction of liquid decreases along the circuit length, resulting in a series of changing vapor/liquid flow patterns. If the fluid enters as a subcooled liquid, the first indications of vapor generation are bubbles forming at the heated tube wall (nucleation). Subsequently, bubble, plug, churn (or semiannular), annular, spray annular, and mist flows can occur as vapor content increases for two-phase flows in horizontal tubes. Idealized flow patterns are illustrated in Figure 5A for a horizontal tube evaporator. Note that there is currently no general agreement on the names of two-phase flow patterns, and the same name may mean different patterns in vertical, horizontal and small tube flow. For detailed delineation of flow patterns, see Barnea and Taitel (1986) or Spedding and Spence (1993) for tubes and pipes between 3 and 75 mm in diameter, Coleman and Garimella (1999) for tubes less than 3 mm in diameter, and Thome (2001) for flow regime definitions useful in modeling heat transfer.

Increased computing power has allowed greater emphasis on flow-pattern-specific heat transfer and pressure drop models (although there is not uniform agreement among researchers and practitioners that this is always appropriate). Virtually all of the over 1000 articles on two-phase flow patterns and transitions have studied air/water or air/oil flows. Dobson and Chato (1998) found that

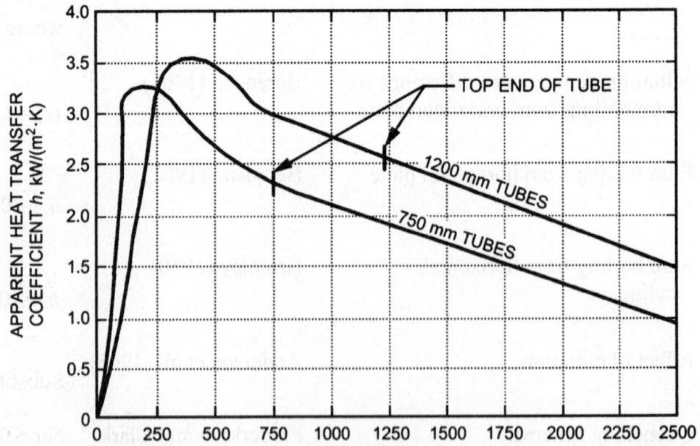

Fig. 4 Boiling Heat Transfer Coefficients for Flooded Evaporator
(Perry 1950)

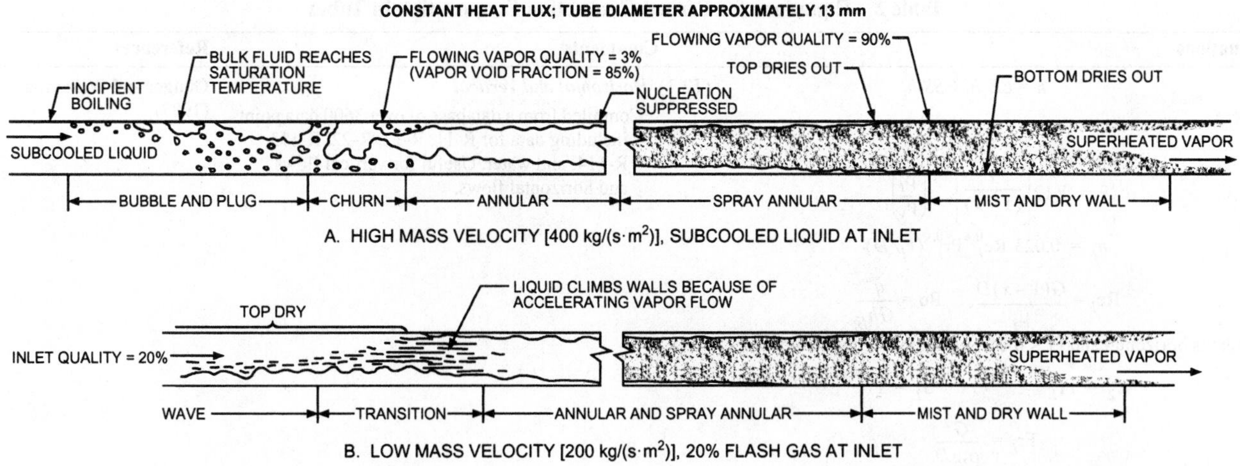

Fig. 5 Flow Regimes in Typical Smooth Horizontal Tube Evaporator

the Mandhane et al. (1974) flow map, adjusted for the properties of refrigerants, produced satisfactory agreement with their observations in horizontal condensation. Thome (2003) summarized recent efforts to generate diabatic flow pattern maps in both evaporation and condensation for a number of refrigerants.

The concepts of vapor quality and void fraction are frequently used in two-phase flow models. **Vapor quality** x is the ratio of mass (or mass flow rate) of vapor to total mass (or mass flow rate) of the mixture. The usual flowing vapor quality or vapor fraction is referred to throughout this discussion. Static vapor quality is smaller because vapor in the core flows at a higher average velocity than liquid at the walls. In addition, it is very important to recognize that vapor quality as defined here is frequently not equal to the thermodynamic equilibrium quality, because of significant temperature and velocity gradients in a diabatic flowing vapor/liquid mixture. Some models use the thermodynamic equilibrium quality, and, as a result, require negative values in the subcooled boiling region and values greater than unity in the post-dryout or mist flow region. This is discussed further in Hetsroni (1986) and Kandlikar (1999).

The **area void fraction**, or just **void fraction**, ε_v is the ratio of the tube cross section filled with vapor to the total cross-sectional area. Vapor quality and area void fraction are related by definition:

$$\frac{x}{1-x} = \frac{\rho_v}{\rho_l} \times \frac{V_v}{V_l} \times \frac{\varepsilon_v}{1-\varepsilon_v} \tag{2}$$

The ratio of velocities V_v/V_l in Equation (2) is called the **slip ratio**. Note that the static void fraction and the flowing void fraction at a given vapor quality differ by a factor equal to the slip ratio.

Because nucleation occurs at the heated surface in a thin sublayer of superheated liquid, boiling in forced convection may begin while the bulk of the liquid is subcooled. Depending on the nature of the fluid and amount of subcooling, bubbles can either collapse or continue to grow and coalesce (Figure 5A), as Gouse and Coumou (1965) observed for R-113. Bergles and Rohsenow (1964) developed a method to determine the point of incipient surface boiling.

After nucleation begins, bubbles quickly agglomerate to form vapor plugs at the center of a vertical tube, or, as shown in Figure 5A, along the top surface of a horizontal tube. At the point where the bulk of the fluid reaches saturation temperature, which corresponds to local static pressure, there will be up to 1% vapor quality (and a negative thermodynamic equilibrium quality) because of the preceding surface boiling (Guerrieri and Talty 1956).

Further coalescence of vapor bubbles and plugs results in churn, or semiannular flow. If fluid velocity is high enough, a continuous vapor core surrounded by a liquid annulus at the tube wall soon forms. This occurs when the void fraction is approximately 85%; with common refrigerants, this equals a vapor quality of about 10 to 30%.

If two-phase mass velocity is high [greater than 200 kg/(s·m²) for a 12 mm tube], annular flow with small drops of entrained liquid in the vapor core (spray) can persist over a vapor quality range from about 10% to more than 90%. Refrigerant evaporators are fed from an expansion device at vapor qualities of approximately 20%, so that annular and spray annular flow predominates in most tube lengths. In a vertical tube, the liquid annulus is distributed uniformly over the periphery, but it is somewhat asymmetric in a horizontal tube (Figure 5A). As vapor quality reaches about 80% (the actual quality varies from about 70 to 90%, depending on tube diameter, mass velocity, refrigerant, and wall enhancement), portions of the surface dry out. Chaddock and Noerager (1966) found that, in a horizontal tube, dryout occurs first at the top of the tube and progresses toward the bottom with increasing vapor quality (Figure 5A). Kattan et al. (1998a, 1998b) indicated a very sharp decrease in the local heat transfer coefficient as well as the pressure drop at this point.

If two-phase mass velocity is low [less than 200 kg/(s·m²) for a 12 mm horizontal tube], liquid occupies only the lower cross section of the tube. This causes a wavy type of flow at vapor qualities above about 5%. As the vapor accelerates with increasing evaporation, the interface is disturbed sufficiently to develop annular flow (Figure 5B). Liquid slugging can be superimposed on the flow configurations illustrated; the liquid forms a continuous, or nearly continuous, sheet over the tube cross section, and the slugs move rapidly and at irregular intervals. Kattan et al. (1998a) presented a general method for predicting flow pattern transitions (i.e., a flow pattern map) based on observations for R-134a, R-125, R-502, R-402A, R-404A, R-407C, and ammonia.

Heat Transfer. It is difficult to develop a single relation to describe heat transfer performance for evaporation in a tube over the full quality range. For refrigerant evaporators with several percentage points of flash gas at entrance, it is less difficult because annular flow occurs in most of the tube length. However, the reported data are accurate only within the geometry, flow, and refrigerant conditions tested, so numerous methods for calculating heat transfer coefficients for evaporation in tubes are presented in Table 2 (also see Figure 6).

Figure 6 gives heat transfer data for R-22 evaporating in a 19.6 mm tube (Gouse and Coumou 1965). At low mass velocities [below 200 kg/(s·m²)], the wavy flow regime shown in Figure 5B probably exists, and the heat transfer coefficient is nearly constant along the tube length, dropping at the exit as complete vaporization occurs. At higher mass velocities, flow is usually annular, and the

Table 2 Equations for Forced Convection Evaporation in Tubes

Equations	Comments	References

$$h = EE_2h_f + SS_2h_f \quad \text{(T2.1)}$$

where

$$E = 1 + 3000\,\text{Bo}^{0.86}$$

$$S = 1.12\left[\frac{x}{(1-x)}\right]^{0.75}\left(\frac{\rho_l}{\rho_v}\right)^{0.41}$$

$$h_f = 0.023\,\text{Re}_l^{0.8}\,\text{Pr}_l^{0.4}(k_l/D)$$

$$\text{Re}_l = \frac{G(1-x)D}{\mu_l}, \qquad \text{Bo} = \frac{q''}{Gh_{fg}}$$

If tube is horizontal and Fr < 0.05, use the following multipliers:

$$E_2 = \text{Fr}_l^{(0.1-2\,\text{Fr}_l)} \qquad S_2 = \text{Fr}_l^{1/2}$$

$$\text{Fr}_l = \frac{G^2}{\rho_l g D}$$

Otherwise, $E_2 = S_2 = 1$.

Horizontal and Vertical

Compiled from a database of over 3600 data points, including data for R-11, R-12, R-22, R-113, R-114, and water. Useful for vertical flows and horizontal flows.

Gungor and Winterton (1987)

Boiling heat transfer coefficient h is the largest of that given by the following expressions:

Nucleate-boiling-dominated (T2.2a)

$$\frac{h}{h_f} = 0.6683\left(\frac{\rho_l}{\rho_v}\right)^{0.1} x^{0.16}(1-x)^{0.64} f_2(\text{Fr}_l) + 1058\,\text{Bo}^{0.7}(1-x)^{0.8}F_{fl}$$

Convective-boiling-dominated (T2.2b)

$$\frac{h}{h_f} = 1.136\left(\frac{\rho_l}{\rho_v}\right)^{0.45} x^{0.72}(1-x)^{0.08} f_2(\text{Fr}_l) + 667.2\,\text{Bo}^{0.7}(1-x)^{0.8}F_{fl}$$

For $0.5 \le \text{Pr}_l \le 2000$ and $10^4 \le \text{Re}_l \le 5 \times 10^6$,

$$h_f = \frac{\text{Re}_l\text{Pr}_l(f/2)(k_l/D)}{1.07 + 12.7(\text{Pr}_l^{2/3} - 1)(f/2)^{0.5}}$$

For $0.5 \le \text{Pr}_l \le 2000$ and $2300 \le \text{Re}_l \le 10^4$,

$$h_f = \frac{(\text{Re}_l - 1000)\text{Pr}_l(f/2)(k_l/D)}{1 + 12.7(\text{Pr}_l^{2/3} - 1)(f/2)^{0.5}}$$

where

$$f = [1.58\ln(\text{Re}_l) - 3.28]^{-2}$$

For $\text{Fr}_l < 0.04$ in horizontal tubes,

$$f_2(\text{Fr}_l) = (25\,\text{Fr}_l)^{0.3}$$

For all other cases,

$$f_2 = 1$$

Horizontal and Vertical

Compiled from a database of 5246 data points, including data for R-11, R-12, R-22, R-113, R-114, R-152a, nitrogen, neon, and water. Tube sizes ranged from 6 to 31 mm.

Fluid-specific F_{fl} values are as follows (commercial copper tubes unless otherwise specified):

Water	1.00
R-11	1.30
R-12	1.50
R-13B1	1.31
R-22	2.20
R-113	1.30
R-114	1.24
R-134a	1.63
R-152a	1.10
R-32/R-132 (60 to 40% wt.)	3.30
Kerosene	0.488
All fluids with stainless steel	1.0

Kandlikar (1999)

Boiling heat transfer coefficient h is the largest of that given by the following equations:

$$h = 230\,\text{Bo}^{0.5}h_f \quad \text{(T2.3a)}$$

$$h = 1.8\,[\text{Co}(0.38\,\text{Fr}_l^{-0.3})^n]^{-0.8}h_f \quad \text{(T2.3b)}$$

$$h = F\exp\{2.47[\text{Co}(0.38\,\text{Fr}_l^{-0.3})^n]^{-0.15}\}h_f \quad \text{(T2.3c)}$$

$$h = F\exp\{2.74[\text{Co}(0.38\,\text{Fr}_l^{-0.3})^n]^{-0.1}\}h_f \quad \text{(T2.3d)}$$

where h_f is calculated as for the Kandlikar correlation, and

$$F = 14.7\,\text{Bo}^{0.5} \text{ if Bo} > 0.0011$$

$$F = 15.4\,\text{Bo}^{0.5} \text{ if Bo} < 0.0011$$

Vertical:

$$n = 0$$

Horizontal:

$$n = 0 \text{ if } \text{Fr}_l > 0.04$$

$$n = 1 \text{ for } \text{Fr}_l < 0.04$$

$$\text{Co} = \left(\frac{1-x}{x}\right)^{0.8}\left(\frac{\rho_v}{\rho_l}\right)^{0.5}$$

Horizontal and Vertical

Applicable to all fluids.

Shah (1982)

Table 2 Equations for Forced Convection Evaporation in Tubes (*Continued*)

Equations	Comments	References
$h = h_{mac} + h_{mic}$ (T2.4) where $h_{mac} = h_f E$ $h_{mic} = h_{pb} S$ $E = \left(1 + X_{tt}^{-0.5}\right)^{1.78} [(\mathrm{Pr}_l + 1)/2]^{0.444}$ $x_{tt} = \left(\frac{1-x}{x}\right)^{0.9} \left(\frac{\rho_v}{\rho_l}\right)^{0.5} \left(\frac{\mu_l}{\mu_v}\right)^{0.1}$ $S = 0.9622 - \tan^{-1}\left(\frac{\mathrm{Re}_l E^{1.25}}{6.18 \times 10^4}\right)$ $h_f = 0.023 \mathrm{Re}_l^{0.8} \mathrm{Pr}_l^{0.4} (k_l/D)$ $h_{pb} = \frac{0.00122 k_l^{0.79} c_{p,l}^{0.45} \rho_l^{0.49}}{\sigma^{0.5} \mu_l^{0.29} h_{fg}^{0.24} \rho_v^{0.24}} \Delta t_{sat}^{0.24} \Delta p_{sat}^{0.75}$ $\Delta t_{sat} = t_s - t_{sat};\ \Delta p_{sat} = p_{sat}(t_s) - p_{sat}(t_{sat})$	*Vertical* This correlation is based on the idea that nucleation transfer mechanism h_{mic} and convective transfer mechanism h_{mac} are additive. Found to work well for low-pressure steam and some hydrocarbons.	Bennett and Chen (1980); Chen (1963)

Note: Except for dimensionless equations, inch-pound units (lb_m, h, ft, °F, and Btu) must be used.

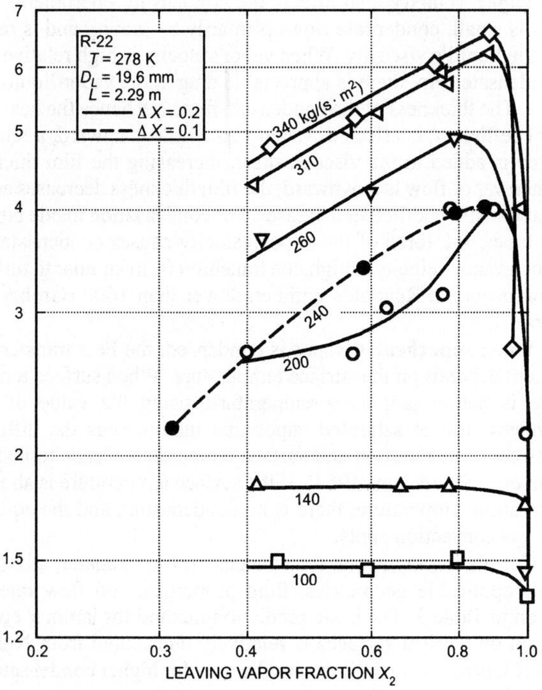

Fig. 6 Heat Transfer Coefficient Versus Vapor Fraction for Partial Evaporation

coefficient increases as the vapor accelerates. As the surface dries and flow reaches between 70 and 90% vapor quality, the coefficient drops sharply.

Table 2 also gives methods to estimate local heat transfer coefficients during evaporation [e.g., Gungor and Winterton (1986); Kandlikar (1999)]. The Shah (1982) model [Equations (T2.3a) to (T2.3d)] is also recommended for estimating local heat transfer coefficients during annular flow. These local models have been found accurate for a wide range of refrigerants, but do not include ways to model dryout. The flow-pattern-based model described by Thome (2001) includes specific models for each flow pattern type and has been tested with newer refrigerants such as R-134a and R-407C.

Heat transfer coefficients during flow in vertical tubes can be estimated with the Chen (1963) correlation [Equation (T2.4)]. It includes terms for velocity effect (convection) and heat flux (nucleation) and produces local heat transfer coefficients as a function of local vapor quality. The Chen correlation is relatively simple and provides a good first estimate for vertical convective boiling, particularly for low-pressure steam. Although much more complex, the method developed by Steiner and Taborek (1992) includes an asymptotic model for the convection and nucleation component of heat transfer, and is recommended for most situations. This method requires fluid-specific constants, so is not presented in detail here; see Collier and Thome (1996) for more information.

The effect of lubricant on evaporation heat transfer coefficients has been studied by a number of authors. Eckels et al. (1994) and Schlager et al. (1987) showed that the average heat transfer coefficients during evaporation of R-22 and R-134a in smooth and enhanced tubes are decreased by the presence of lubricant (up to a 20% reduction at 5% lubricant concentration by mass). Slight enhancements at lubricant concentrations under 3% are observed with some refrigerant lubricant mixtures. Zeurcher et al. (1998) studied local heat transfer coefficients of refrigerant/lubricant mixtures in the dry wall region of the evaporator (see Figure 5) and proposed prediction methods. The effect of lubricant concentration on local heat transfer coefficients was shown to depend on mass flux and vapor quality. At low mass fluxes [less than about 200 kg/(m²·s)], oil sharply decreased performance, whereas at higher mass fluxes [greater than 200 kg/(m²·s)], enhancements at vapor qualities in the range of 0.35 to 0.7 were seen.

Boiling in Plate Heat Exchangers

For a description of plate heat exchanger geometry, see the Plate Heat Exchangers section of Chapter 4.

Little information is available on two-phase flow in plate exchangers; for brief discussions, see Hesselgreaves (1990), Jonsson (1985), Kumar (1984), Panchal (1985, 1990), Panchal and Hillis (1984), Panchal et al. (1983), Syed (1990), Thonon (1995), Thonon et al. (1995), and Young (1994).

General correlations for evaporators and condensers should be similar to those for circular and noncircular conduits, with specific constants or variables defining plate geometry. Correlations for flooded evaporators differ somewhat from those for a typical flooded shell-and-tube, where the bulk of heat transfer results mainly from pool boiling. Because of the narrow, complex passages in the PHE flooded evaporator, it is possible that the majority of heat transfer occurs through convective boiling rather than localized nucleate boiling, which probably affects mainly the lower section of a plate in a flooded system. This aspect could be enhanced by modifying the surface structure of the lower third of the plates in contact with the refrigerant. It is also possible that the contact points (nodes) between two adjacent plates of opposite chevron enhance nucleate boiling. Each nodal contact point could create a favorable site for a re-entrant cavity.

The same applies to thermosiphon and direct-expansion evaporators. The simplest approach would be to formulate a correlation of the type proposed by Pierre (1964) for varying quality, as suggested by Baskin (1991). A positive feature about a PHE evaporator is that flow is vertical, against gravity, as opposed to horizontal flow in a shell-and-tube evaporator. Therefore, the flow regime does not get too complicated and phase separation is not a severe issue, even at low mass fluxes along the flow path, which has always been a problem in ammonia shell-and-tube direct-expansion (DX) evaporators. Generally, the profile is flat, except at the end plates. For more complete analysis, correlations could be developed that involve the local bubble point temperature concept for evaluation of wall superheat and local Froude number and boiling number Bo.

Yan and Lin's (1999) experimental study of a compact brazed exchanger (CBE) with R-134a as a refrigerant revealed some interesting features about flow evaporation in plate exchangers. Heat transfer coefficients were higher compared to circular tubes, especially at high-vapor-quality convective regimes. Mass flux played a significant role, whereas heat flux had very little effect on overall performance.

Ayub (2003) presented simple correlations based on design and field data collected over a decade on ammonia and R-22 direct-expansion and flooded evaporators in North America. The goal was to formulate equations that could be readily used by a design and field engineer without referral to complicated two-phase models. The correlations take into account the effect of chevron angle of the mating plates, making it a universal correlation applied to any chevron angle plate. The correlation has a statistical error of ±8%. The expression for heat transfer coefficient is

$$h = C(k_l/d_e)(\mathrm{Re}_l{}^2 h_{fg}/L_p)^{0.4124}(p_r)^{0.12}(65/\beta)^{0.35} \quad (3)$$

where $C = 0.1121$ for flooded and thermosiphons and $C = 0.0675$ for DX. This is a dimensional correlation where the values of k_l, d_e, h_{fg}, and L_p are in I-P units of Btu/h·ft·°F, ft, Btu/lb, and ft, respectively. Chevron angle β is in degrees.

CONDENSING

In most applications, condensation is initiated by removing heat at a solid/vapor interface, either through the walls of the vessel containing the saturated vapor or through the solid surface of a cooling mechanism placed within the saturated vapor. If sufficient energy is removed, the local temperature of vapor near the interface drops below its equilibrium saturation temperature. Because heat removal creates a temperature gradient, with the lowest temperature near the interface, droplets most likely form at this location. This defines one type of heterogeneous nucleation that can result in either dropwise or film condensation, depending on the physical characteristics of the solid surface and the working fluid.

Dropwise condensation occurs on the cooling solid surface when its surface free energy is relatively low compared to that of the liquid. Examples include highly polished or fatty-acid-impregnated surfaces in contact with steam. **Film condensation** occurs when a cooling surface with relatively high surface free energy contacts a fluid with lower surface free energy [see Chen (2003) and Isrealachvili (1991)]; this type of condensation occurs in most systems.

For smooth film flow, the rate of heat transport depends on the condensate film thickness, which depends on the rates of vapor condensation and condensate removal. At high reduced pressures (p_r), heat transfer coefficients for dropwise condensation are higher than those for film condensation at the same surface loading. At low reduced pressures, the reverse is true. For example, there is a reduction of 6 to 1 in the dropwise condensation coefficient of steam when saturation pressure is decreased from 91 to 16 kPa. One method for correlating the dropwise condensation heat transfer coefficient uses nondimensional parameters, including the effect of surface tension gradient, temperature difference, and fluid properties [see, e.g., Rose (1998)].

When condensation occurs on horizontal tubes and short vertical plates, condensate film motion is laminar. On vertical tubes and long vertical plates, film motion can become turbulent. Grober et al. (1961) suggest using a Reynolds number (Re) of 1600 as the critical point at which the flow pattern changes from laminar to turbulent. This Reynolds number is based on condensate flow rate divided by the breadth of the condensing surface. For the outside of a vertical tube, the breadth is the circumference of the tube; for the outside of a horizontal tube, the breadth is twice the length of the tube. Re = $4\Gamma/\mu_l$, where Γ is the mass flow of condensate per unit of breadth, and μ_l is the absolute (dynamic) viscosity of the condensate at film temperature t_f. In practice, condensation is usually laminar in shell-and-tube condensers with the vapor outside horizontal tubes.

Vapor velocity also affects the condensing coefficient. When this is small, condensate flows primarily by gravity and is resisted by the liquid's viscosity. When vapor velocity is high relative to the condensate film, there is appreciable drag at the vapor/liquid interface. The thickness of the condensate film, and hence the heat transfer coefficient, is affected. When vapor flow is upward, a retarding force is added to the viscous shear, increasing the film thickness. When vapor flow is downward, the film thickness decreases and the heat transfer coefficient increases. For condensation inside horizontal tubes, the force of the vapor velocity causes condensate flow. When vapor velocity is high, the transition from laminar to turbulent flow occurs at Reynolds numbers lower than 1600 (Grober et al. 1961).

When **superheated** vapor is condensed, the heat transfer coefficient depends on the surface temperature. When surface temperature is below saturation temperature, using the value of h for condensation of saturated vapor that incorporates the difference between the saturation and surface temperatures leads to insignificant error (McAdams 1954). If the surface temperature is above the saturation temperature, there is no condensation and the equations for gas convection apply.

Correlation equations for condensing heat transfer, along with their applicable geometries, fluid properties, and flow rates, are given in Table 3. The basic prediction method for laminar condensation on vertical surfaces is relatively unchanged from Nusselt's (1916). Empirical relations must be used for higher condensate flow rates, however.

For condensation on the outside surface of horizontal finned tubes, use Equation (T3.5) for liquids that drain readily from the surface (Beatty and Katz 1948). For condensing steam outside finned tubes, where liquid is retained in spaces between tubes, coefficients substantially lower than those given by this equation were reported, because of the high surface tension of water relative to other liquids. For additional data on condensation on the outside of finned tubes, please refer to Webb (1994).

Condensation on Inside Surface of Horizontal Tubes

A significant amount of work has been performed on internal flow condensation in recent years [see Cavallini et al. (2002) for a thorough overview]. Table 3 summarizes recommended correlations, along with the ranges of variables where the authors consider the correlations to be accurate. Note that the annular flow correlations assume uniform liquid film on the inside tube wall, which theoretically allows them to be applied to both vertical and horizontal

Table 3 Heat Transfer Coefficients for Film-Type Condensation

Description	References	Equations
Vertical Surfaces, Height L		
Laminar, non-wavy liquid film* $Re = 4\Gamma/\mu_l < 1800$ $\Gamma = \dot{m}_l/b$ = mass flow rate of liquid condensate per unit breadth of surface	Based on Nusselt (1916)	$h = 0.943\left[\frac{\rho_l g(\rho_l - \rho_v)h_{fg}k_l}{\mu_l L^3(t_{sat} - t_s)}\right]^{1/4}$ (T3.1)
Turbulent flow $Re = 4\Gamma/\mu_f > 1800$	McAdams (1954)	$h = 0.0077\left[\frac{k_l^3\rho_l(\rho_l - \rho_v)g}{\mu_l^2}\right]^{1/3} Re^{0.4}$ (T3.2)
Horizontal Tubes		
Single tube*	Dhir and Lienhard (1971)	$h = 0.729\left[\frac{k_l^3\rho_l(\rho_l - \rho_v)gh_{fg}}{\mu_l^2(t_{sat} - t_s)D}\right]^{1/4}$ (T3.3)
N tubes, vertically aligned	Incropera and DeWitt (2002)	$h = h_D N^{-1/4}$ (T3.4) where h_D is the heat transfer coefficient for one tube calculated from Dhir and Lienhard (1971).
Finned tubes This correlation is acceptable for low-surface-tension fluids and low-fin-density tubes. It overpredicts in cases where space between tubes floods with liquid (as when either surface tension becomes relatively large or fin spacing relatively small).	Beatty and Katz (1948)	$h = 0.689\left[\frac{\rho_l^2 k_l^3 g h_{fg}}{\mu_l(t_{sat} - t_s)D_e}\right]^{1/4}$ (T3.5) $\frac{1}{D_e^{1/4}} = 1.30\frac{A_s\phi}{A_{eff}L_{mf}^{1/4}} + \frac{A_p}{A_{eff}D^{1/4}}$ $A_{eff} = A_s\phi + A_p$, $L_{mf} = \pi(D_o^2 - D_r^2)/D_o$ ϕ = fin efficiency D_o = outside tube diameter (including fins) D_r = diameter at fin root (i.e., smooth tube outer diameter) A_s = fin surface area A_p = surface area of tube between fins
Internal Flow in Round Tubes		
Annular flow with uniform film distribution (horizontal or vertical) $0.002 < p_r < 0.44$, $0 < x < 1$ $10.8\ kg/(m^2\cdot s) < G < 1599\ kg/(m^2\cdot s)$ $Re_l > 350$ $Pr_l > 0.5$	Shah (1979)	$Nu = Nu_{lo}\left[(1-x)^{0.8} + \frac{3.8x^{0.76}(1-x)^{0.04}}{p_r^{0.38}}\right]$ $p_r = \frac{p}{p_c}$ (T3.6) $Nu_{lo} = 0.023\ Re_l^{0.8}Pr_l^{0.4}$ $Re_l = \frac{GD}{\mu_l}$
$10 < \rho_l/\rho_v < 2000$ $0.01 < \mu_v/\mu_l < 1$ $5000 < Re < 500\ 000$ $Re = \frac{GD}{\mu_l}$ $0.8 < Pr_l < 20$ $0.1 < x < 0.9$	Cavallini and Zecchin (1974)	$Nu = 0.0344\ Re_l^{0.83}\left[1 + x\left(\sqrt{\frac{\rho_l}{\rho_v}} - 1\right)\right]^{0.82} Pr_l^{0.35}$ (T3.7)
	Fujii (1995)	$Nu = 0.018\left(Re_l\sqrt{\frac{\rho_l}{\rho_v}}\right)^{0.9}\left(\frac{x}{1-x}\right)^{(0.1x+0.8)} Pr_l^{1/3}(1 + AH/Pr_l)$ (T3.8) $H = \frac{c_{p,l}(t_{sat} - t_s)}{h_{fg}}$ $A = 0.071\ Re_l^{0.1}\left(\frac{\rho_l}{\rho_v}\right)^{0.55}\left(\frac{x}{1-x}\right)^{(0.2-1x)} Pr_l^{1/3}$
Horizontal stratified wavy flow $G < 500\ kg/(m^2\cdot s)$ $Fr_m < 20$	Dobson and Chato (1998)	$Nu = Nu_{film} + \left(1 - \frac{\theta}{\pi}\right)Nu_{forced}$ (T3.9) $\left(1 - \frac{\theta}{\pi}\right) \approx \frac{\cos^{-1}(2\varepsilon_v - 1)}{\pi}$ $Nu_{film} = \frac{0.23\ Re_v^{0.12}}{1 + 1.11X_{tt}^{0.58}}\left\{\frac{Ga\ Pr_l}{H}\right\}^{1/4}$

(continued)

Table 3 Heat Transfer Coefficients for Film-Type Condensation (*Continued*)

Description	References	Equations
		$\mathrm{Re}_v = \dfrac{GD}{\mu_v}$
$\mathrm{Fr}_m = a\left\{\dfrac{\mathrm{Re}_l^b}{\mathrm{Ga}^{0.5}}\right\}\left\{\dfrac{1+1.09X_{tt}^{0.039}}{X_{tt}}\right\}^{1.5}$		$H = \dfrac{c_{p,l}(t_{sat}-t_s)}{h_{fg}}$
$X_{tt} = \left(\dfrac{1-x}{x}\right)^{0.9}\left(\dfrac{\rho_v}{\rho_l}\right)^{0.5}\left(\dfrac{\mu_l}{\mu_v}\right)^{0.1}$		$\mathrm{Nu}_{forced} = 0.0195\,\mathrm{Re}_l^{0.8}\,\mathrm{Pr}_l^{0.4}\sqrt{1.376+\dfrac{a}{X_{tt}^b}}$
$\mathrm{Ga} = \dfrac{\rho_l(\rho_l-\rho_g)gD^3}{\mu_l^2}$		For $\mathrm{Fr}_l < 0.7$,
$a = 0.025$ and $b = 1.59$ if $\mathrm{Re}_l < 1250$		$a = 4.72 + 5.48\,\mathrm{Fr}_l - \mathrm{Fr}_l^2$
$a = 1.26$ and $b = 1.04$ if $\mathrm{Re}_l > 1250$		$b = 1.773 - 0.169\,\mathrm{Fr}_l$
		For $\mathrm{Fr}_l > 0.7$,
		$a = 7.242$, $b = 1.655$
		$\mathrm{Fr}_l = \dfrac{(G/\rho_l)^2}{gD}$

Note: Properties in Equation (T3.1) evaluated at $t_f = (t_{sat} + t_s)/2$; h_{fg} evaluated at t_{sat}.

*For increased accuracy use $h'_{fg} = h_{fg} + 0.80c_{p,v}(t_{sat} - t_s)$ in place of h_{fg}.

flows. The Shah (1979) model has been verified for both orientations by several research groups; the Cavallini and Zecchin (1974) and Fujii (1995) models have been shown effective for horizontal flow.

Outside the annular flow regime, care must be taken to account for asymmetry in the liquid film in horizontal flow. The Dobson and Chato (1998) model adapts previous work and captures the effects of gravity fairly well. Condensation in vertical tubes becomes very complex if the vapor and liquid are in counterflow (i.e., vapor flows upward against gravity), although there are applications (e.g., reflux condensers) where this mode is an intentional part of the design. See Palen and Yang (2001) for more information on reflux condenser design.

As with convective evaporation, progress is being made in implementing flow-regime-based models for convective internal flow condensation. Models for flow regime transitions during condensation of pure components in a horizontal tube are presented in Breber et al. (1980) and El Hajal et al. (2003); Dobson and Chato (1998) and Thome et al. (2003) describe prediction methods for flow-regime-based heat transfer coefficients.

Noncondensable Gases

Condensation heat transfer rates reduce drastically if one or more noncondensable gases are present in the condensing vapor/gas mixture. In mixtures, the condensable component is called *vapor* and the noncondensable component is called *gas*. As the mass fraction of gas increases, the heat transfer coefficient decreases in an approximately linear manner. In a steam chest with 2.89% air by volume, Othmer (1929) found that the heat transfer coefficient dropped from about 11.4 to about 3.4 kW/(m^2·K).

Consider a surface cooled to temperature t_s below the saturation temperature of the vapor (Figure 7). In this system, accumulated condensate falls or is driven across the condenser surface. At a finite heat transfer rate, the temperature profile across the condensate can be estimated from Table 3; the interface of the condensate is at a temperature $t_{if} > t_s$. In the absence of gas, the interface temperature is the vapor saturation temperature at the pressure of the condenser.

The presence of noncondensable gas lowers the vapor partial pressure and hence the saturation temperature of the vapor in equilibrium with the condensate. Further, vapor movement toward the cooled surface implies similar bulk motion of the gas. At the condensing interface, vapor condenses at temperature t_{if} and is then swept out of the system as a liquid. The gas concentration rises to

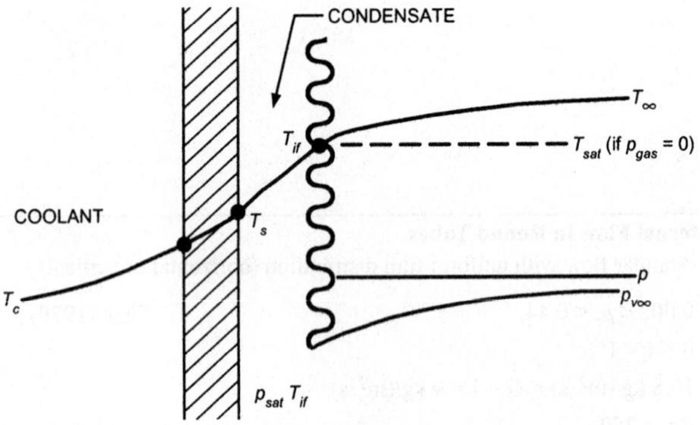

Fig. 7 Origin of Noncondensable Resistance

ultimately diffuse away from the cooled surface at the same rate as it is convected toward the surface (Figure 7). If gas (mole fraction) concentration is Y_g and total pressure of the system is p, the partial pressure of the bulk gas is

$$p_{g\infty} = Y_{g\infty}p \tag{4}$$

The partial pressure of the bulk vapor is

$$p_{v\infty} = (1 - Y_{g\infty})p = Y_{g\infty}p \tag{5}$$

As opposing fluxes of convection and diffusion of the gas increase, the partial pressure of gas at the condensing interface is $p_{gif} > p_{g\infty}$. By Dalton's law, assuming isobaric condition,

$$p_{gif} + p_{vif} = p \tag{6}$$

Hence, $p_{vif} < p_{v\infty}$.

Sparrow et al. (1967) noted that thermodynamic equilibrium exists at the interface, except in the case of very low pressures or liquid metal condensation, so that

$$p_{vif} = p_{sat}(t_{if}) \tag{7}$$

where $p_{sat}(t)$ is the saturation pressure of vapor at temperature t. The available Δt for condensation across the condensate film is reduced from $(t_\infty - t_s)$ to $(t_{if} - t_s)$, where t_∞ is the bulk temperature of the condensing vapor/gas mixture, caused by the additional noncondensable resistance.

The equations in Table 3 are still valid for condensate resistance, but interface temperature t_{if} must be found. The noncondensable resistance, which accounts for the temperature difference $(t_\infty - t_{if})$, depends on the heat flux (through the convecting flow to the interface) and the diffusion of gas away from the interface.

In simple cases, Rose (1969), Sparrow and Lin (1964), and Sparrow et al. (1967) found solutions to the combined energy, diffusion, and momentum problem of noncondensables, but they are cumbersome.

A general method given by Colburn and Hougen (1934) can be used over a wide range if correct expressions are provided for the rate equations; add the contributions of sensible heat transport through the noncondensable gas film and latent heat transport via condensation:

$$h_g(t_\infty - t_{if}) + K_D M_v h_{fg}(p_{v\infty} - p_{vif}) = h(t_{if} - t_s) = U(t_{if} - t_c) \quad (8)$$

where h is from the appropriate equation in Table 3.

The value of the heat transfer coefficient for stagnant gas depends on the geometry and flow conditions. For flow parallel to a condenser tube, for example,

$$j = \left[\frac{h_g}{(c_p)_g G}\right]\left[\frac{(c_p)_g \mu_{gv}}{K_{Dg}}\right]^{2/3} \quad (9)$$

where j is a known function of $Re = GD/\mu_{gv}$. The mass transfer coefficient K_D is

$$\frac{K_D}{M_m}\left[\frac{p_{g\infty} - p_{gif}}{\ln(p_{g\infty}/p_{gif})}\right]\left(\frac{\mu_{gv}}{\rho_g D}\right)^{2/3} = j \quad (10)$$

The calculation method requires substitution of Equation (10) into Equation (8). For a given flow condition, G, Re, j, M_m, $\rho_{g\infty}$, h_g, and h (or U) are known. Assume values of t_{if}; calculate $p_{sat}(t_{if}) = p_{vif}$ and hence p_{gif}. If t_s is not known, use the overall coefficient U to the coolant and t_c in place of h and t_s in Equation (8). For either case, at each location in the condenser, iterate Equation (8) until it balances, giving the condensing interface temperature and, hence, the thermal load to that point (Colburn 1951; Colburn and Hougen 1934). For more detail, refer to Chapter 10 in Collier and Thome (1996).

Other Impurities

Vapor entering the condenser often contains a small percentage of impurities such as oil. Oil forms a film on the condensing surfaces, creating additional resistance to heat transfer. Some allowance should be made for this, especially in the absence of an oil separator or when the discharge line from the compressor to the condenser is short.

PRESSURE DROP

Total pressure drop for two-phase flow in tubes consists of friction, change in momentum, and gravitational components:

$$\left(\frac{dp}{dz}\right)_{total} = \left(\frac{dp}{dz}\right)_{static} + \left(\frac{dp}{dz}\right)_{mom} + \left(\frac{dp}{dz}\right)_{fric} \quad (11a)$$

The momentum pressure gradient accounts for the acceleration of the flow, usually caused by evaporation of liquid or condensation of vapor. In this case,

$$\left(\frac{dp}{dz}\right)_{mom} = G^3\left\{\left[\frac{(1-x)^2}{\rho_l(1-\varepsilon_v)} + \frac{x^2}{\rho_v\varepsilon_v}\right]_2 - \left[\frac{(1-x)^2}{\rho_l(1-\varepsilon_v)} + \frac{x^2}{\rho_v\varepsilon_v}\right]_1\right\} \quad (11b)$$

where G is total mass velocity, and subscripts 1 and 2 represent two different locations along the flow. An empirical model for the void fraction with good accuracy is presented by Steiner (1993), based on the (dimensional) correlation of Rouhani and Axelsson (1970).

$$\varepsilon_v = \frac{x}{\rho_v}\left\{[1 + 0.12(1-x)]\left(\frac{x}{\rho_v} + \frac{1-x}{\rho_l}\right) + \left[\frac{1.18(1-x)[g\sigma(\rho_l - \rho_v)]^{0.25}}{G^2\rho_l^{0.5}}\right]\right\}^{-1} \quad (11c)$$

A generalized expression for ε_v was suggested by Butterworth (1975):

$$\varepsilon_v = \left[1 + A_l\left(\frac{1-x}{x}\right)^{q_l}\left(\frac{\rho_v}{\rho_l}\right)^{r_l}\left(\frac{\mu_l}{\mu_v}\right)^{S_l}\right]^{-1} \quad (11d)$$

This generalized form represents the models of several researchers; constants and exponents needed for each model are given in Table 4.

The homogeneous model provides a simple method for computing the acceleration and gravitational components of pressure drop. It assumes that flow can be characterized by average fluid properties and that the velocities of liquid and vapor phases are equal (Collier and Thome 1996; Wallis 1969). The following discussion of several empirical correlations for computing frictional pressure drop in two-phase internal flow is based on Ould Didi et al. (2002).

Friedel Correlation

A common strategy in both two-phase heat transfer and pressure drop modeling is to begin with a single-phase model and determine an appropriate **two-phase multiplier** to correct for the enhanced energy and momentum transfer in two-phase flow. The Friedel (1979) correlation follows this strategy:

$$\frac{dp}{dz} = \left(\frac{dp}{dz}\right)_l \Phi_{lo}^2 \quad (12a)$$

In this case,

$$\left(\frac{dp}{dz}\right)_l = 4f_l\frac{[G_{tot}(1-x)]^2}{2\rho_l D} \quad (12b)$$

with

$$f = \frac{0.079}{Re^{0.25}} \quad (12c)$$

Table 4 Constants in Equation (11d) for Different Void Fraction Correlations

Model	A_l	q_l	r_l	S_l
Homogeneous (Collier 1972)	1.0	1.0	1.0	0
Lockhart and Martinelli (1949)	0.28	0.64	0.36	0.07
Baroczy (1963)	1.0	0.74	0.65	0.13
Thom (1964)	1.0	1.0	0.89	0.18
Zivi (1964)	1.0	1.0	0.67	0
Turner and Wallis (1965)	1.0	0.72	0.40	0.08

and

$$\mathrm{Re} = \frac{G_{tot} D}{\mu} \tag{12d}$$

with $\mu = \mu_l$ used to calculate f_l for use in Equation (12b). The two-phase multiplier Φ_{lo}^2 is determined by

$$\Phi_{lo}^2 = E + \frac{3.24FH}{\mathrm{Fr}_h^{0.045}\,\mathrm{We}_l^{0.035}} \tag{12e}$$

where

$$\mathrm{Fr}_h = \frac{G_{tot}^2}{gD\rho_h^2} \tag{12f}$$

$$E = (1-x)^2 + x^2\left(\frac{\rho_l}{\rho_v}\right)\left(\frac{f_v}{f_l}\right) \tag{12g}$$

$$F = x^{0.78}(1-x)^{0.224} \tag{12h}$$

$$H = \left(\frac{\rho_l}{\rho_v}\right)^{0.91}\left(\frac{\mu_v}{\mu_l}\right)^{0.19}\left(1-\frac{\mu_v}{\mu_l}\right)^{0.7} \tag{12i}$$

$$\mathrm{We}_l = \frac{G_{tot}^2 D}{\sigma_l \rho_h} \tag{12j}$$

Note that friction factors in Equation (12g) are calculated from Equations (12c) and (12d) using the vapor and liquid fluid properties, respectively. The homogeneous density ρ_h is given by

$$\rho_h = \left(\frac{x}{\rho_v} + \frac{1-x}{\rho_l}\right)^{-1} \tag{12k}$$

This method is generally recommended when the viscosity ratio μ_l/μ_v is less than 1000.

Lockhart and Martinelli Correlation

One of the earliest two-phase pressure drop correlations was proposed by Martinelli and Nelson (1948) and rendered more useful by Lockhart and Martinelli (1949). A relatively straightforward implementation of this model requires that Re_l be calculated first, based on Equation (12d) and liquid properties. If $\mathrm{Re}_l > 4000$,

$$\frac{dp}{dz} = \Phi_{ltt}^2\left(\frac{dp}{dz}\right)_l \tag{13a}$$

where

$$\Phi_{ltt}^2 = 1 + \frac{C}{X_{tt}} + \frac{1}{X_{tt}^2} \tag{13b}$$

and $(dp/dz)_l$ is calculated using Equation (12b).

If $\mathrm{Re}_l < 4000$,

$$\frac{dp}{dz} = \Phi_{Vtt}^2\left(\frac{dp}{dz}\right)_v \tag{13c}$$

where

$$\Phi_{Vtt}^2 = 1 + CX_{tt} + X_{tt}^2 \tag{13d}$$

In both cases,

$$X_{tt} = \left(\frac{1-x}{x}\right)^{0.9}\left(\frac{\rho_v}{\rho_l}\right)^{0.5}\left(\frac{\mu_l}{\mu_v}\right)^{0.1} \tag{13e}$$

and $C = 20$ for most cases of interest in internal flow in HVAC&R systems.

Grönnerud Correlation

Much of the two-phase pressure drop modeling has been based on adiabatic air/water data. To address this, Grönnerud (1979) developed a correlation based on refrigerant flow data, also using a two-phase multiplier:

$$\frac{dp}{dz} = \Phi_{gd}\left(\frac{dp}{dz}\right)_l \tag{14a}$$

with

$$\Phi_{gd} = 1 + \left(\frac{dp}{dz}\right)_{\mathrm{Fr}}\left[\frac{(\rho_l/\rho_v)}{(\mu_l/\mu_v)^{0.25}} - 1\right] \tag{14b}$$

The liquid-only pressure gradient in Equation (14a) is calculated as before, using Equation (12b) with $x = 0$ and

$$\left(\frac{dp}{dz}\right)_{\mathrm{Fr}} = f_{\mathrm{Fr}}\left[x + 4\left(x^{1.8} - x^{10} f_{\mathrm{Fr}}^{0.5}\right)\right] \tag{14c}$$

The friction factor f_{Fr} in this method depends on the liquid Froude number, defined by

$$\mathrm{Fr}_l = \frac{G_{tot}^2}{gD\rho_l^2} \tag{14d}$$

If Fr_l is greater than or equal to 1, $f_{\mathrm{Fr}} = 1.0$. If $\mathrm{Fr}_l < 1$,

$$f_{\mathrm{Fr}} = \mathrm{Fr}_l^{0.3} + 0.0055\left[\ln\left(\frac{1}{\mathrm{Fr}_l}\right)\right]^2 \tag{14e}$$

Müller-Steinhagen and Heck Correlation

A simple, purely empirical correlation was proposed by Müller-Steinhagen and Heck (1986):

$$\frac{dp}{dz} = \Lambda(1-x)^{1/3} + \left(\frac{dp}{dz}\right)_{vo} x^3 \tag{15a}$$

where

$$\Lambda = \left(\frac{dp}{dz}\right)_{lo} + 2\left[\left(\frac{dp}{dz}\right)_{vo} - \left(\frac{dp}{dz}\right)_{lo}\right]x \tag{15b}$$

and

$$\left(\frac{dp}{dz}\right)_{lo} = f_l\frac{2G_{tot}^2}{D\rho_l} \tag{15c}$$

$$\left(\frac{dp}{dz}\right)_{vo} = f_v\frac{2G_{tot}^2}{D\rho_v} \tag{15d}$$

where friction factors in Equations (15c) and (15d) are again calculated from Equations (12c) and (12d) using the liquid and vapor properties, respectively.

The general nature of annular vapor/liquid flow in vertical pipes is indicated in Figure 8 (Wallis 1970), which plots the effective vapor friction factor versus the liquid fraction $(1 - \varepsilon_v)$, where ε_v is the vapor void fraction as defined by Equations (11c) or (11d).

The effective vapor friction factor in Figure 8 is defined as

$$f_{eff} = \left[\frac{\varepsilon_v^{2.5} D}{2\rho_v\left(\frac{4Q_v}{\pi D^2}\right)^2}\right]\left(\frac{dp}{dz}\right) \quad (16a)$$

where D is the pipe diameter, ρ_v is gas density, and Q_v is volumetric flow rate. The friction factor of vapor flowing by itself in the pipe (presumed smooth) is denoted by f_v. Wallis' analysis of the flow occurrences is based on interfacial friction between the gas and liquid. The wavy film corresponds to a conduit with roughness height of about four times the liquid film thickness. Thus, the pressure drop relation for vertical flow is

$$\frac{dp}{dz} = 0.01\left(\frac{\rho_v}{D^5}\right)\left(\frac{4Q_v}{\pi}\right)^2\left(\frac{1+75(1-\varepsilon_v)}{\varepsilon_v^{2.5}}\right) \quad (16b)$$

This corresponds to the Martinelli-type analysis with

$$f_{two\text{-}phase} = \Phi_v^2 f_v \quad (16c)$$

when

$$\Phi_v^2 = \frac{1+75(1-\varepsilon_v)}{\varepsilon_v} \quad (16d)$$

The friction factor f_v (of the vapor alone) is taken as 0.02, an appropriate turbulent flow value. This calculation can be modified for more detailed consideration of factors such as Reynolds number variation in friction, gas compressibility, and entrainment (Wallis 1970).

Recommendations

Although many references recommend the Lockhart and Martinelli (1949) correlation, recent reviews of pressure drop correlations found other methods to be more accurate. Tribbe and Müller-Steinhagen (2000) found that the Müller-Steinhagen and Heck (1986) correlation worked quite well for a database of horizontal flows that included air/water, air/oil, steam, and several refrigerants. Ould Didi et al. (2002) also found that this method offered accuracies nearly as good or better than several other models; the Friedel (1979) and Grönnerud (1979) correlations also performed favorably. Note, however, that mean deviations of as much as 30% are common using these correlations; calculations for individual flow conditions can easily deviate 50% or more from measured pressure drops, so use these models as approximations only.

Evaporators and condensers often have valves, tees, bends, and other fittings that contribute to the overall pressure drop of the heat exchanger. Collier and Thome (1996) summarize methods predicting the two-phase pressure drop in these fittings.

Pressure Drop in Plate Heat Exchangers

For a description of plate heat exchanger geometry, see the Plate Heat Exchangers section of Chapter 4.

Ayub (2003) presented simple correlations for Fanning friction factor based on design and field data collected over a decade on ammonia and R-22 direct-expansion and flooded evaporators in North America. The goal was to formulate equations that could be readily used by a design and field engineer without reference to complicated two-phase models. Correlations within the plates are formulated as if the entire flow were saturated vapor. The correlation is accordingly adjusted for the chevron angle, and thus generalized for application to any type of commercially available plate, with a statistical error of ±10%:

$$f = (n/\text{Re}^m)(-1.89 + 6.56R - 3.69R^2) \quad (17)$$

for $30 \le \beta \le 65$ where $R = (30/\beta)$, and β is the chevron angle in degrees. The values of m and n depend on Re.

m	*n*	Re
0.137	2.99	<4000
0.172	2.99	4000 < Re < 8000
0.161	3.15	8000 < Re < 16 000
0.195	2.99	>16 000

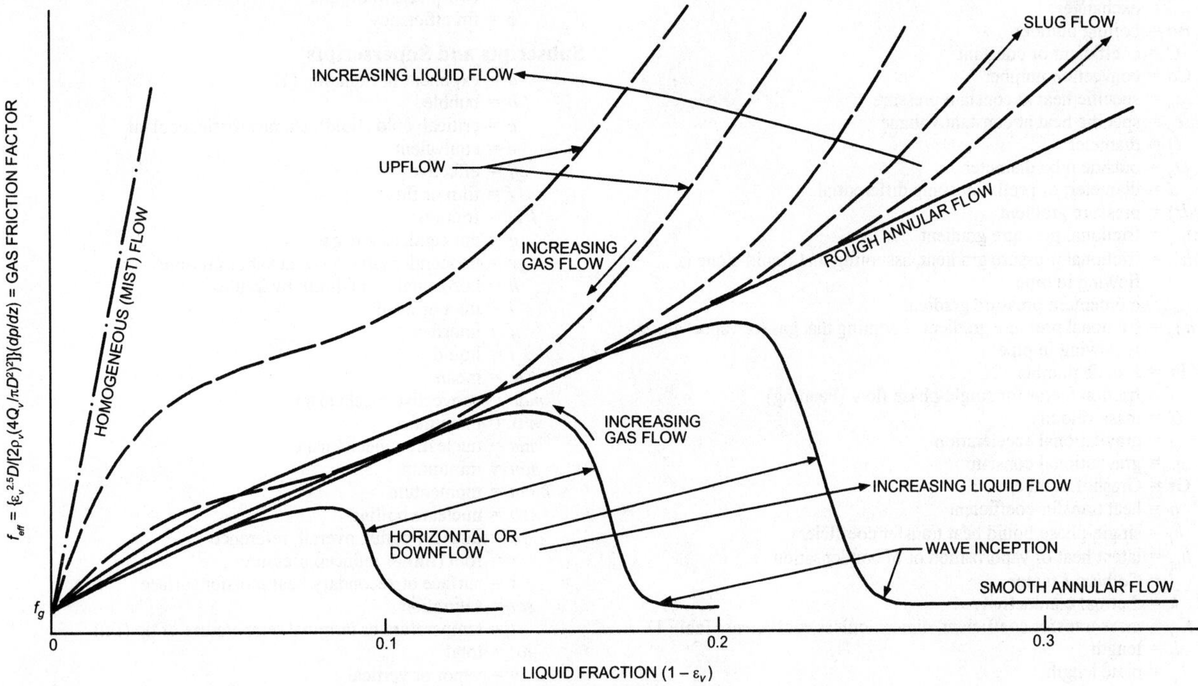

Fig. 8 Qualitative Pressure Drop Characteristics of Two-Phase Flow Regime
(Wallis 1970)

Pressure drop within the port holes is correlated as follows, treating the entire flow as saturated vapor:

$$\Delta p_{port} = 0.0076\rho V^2/2g \quad (18)$$

This equation accounts for pressure drop in both inlet and outlet refrigerant ports and gives the pressure drop in I-P units of lb/in^2 with input for ρ in lb/ft^3, V in ft/s, and g in ft/s^2.

ENHANCED SURFACES

Enhanced heat transfer surfaces are used in heat exchangers to improve performance and decrease cost. Condensing heat transfer is often enhanced with circular fins attached to the external surfaces of tubes to increase the heat transfer area. Other enhancement methods (e.g., porous coatings, integral fins, reentrant cavities) are used to augment boiling heat transfer on external surfaces of evaporator tubes. Webb (1981) surveyed external boiling surfaces and compared performances of several enhanced surfaces with performance of smooth tubes. For heat exchangers, the heat transfer coefficient for the refrigerant side is often smaller than the coefficient for the water side. Thus, enhancing the refrigerant-side surface can reduce the size of the heat exchanger and improve its performance.

Internal fins increase the heat transfer coefficients during evaporation or condensation in tubes. However, internal fins increase refrigerant pressure drop and reduce the heat transfer rate by decreasing the available temperature difference between hot and cold fluids. Designers should carefully determine the number of parallel refrigerant passes that give optimum loading for best overall heat transfer. For a review of internal enhancements for two-phase heat transfer, including the effects of oil, see Newell and Shah (2001).

For additional information on enhancement methods in two-phase flow, consult Bergles (1976, 1985), Thome (1990), and Webb (1994).

SYMBOLS

A = area, effective plate area
a = local acceleration
b = breadth of condensing surface. For vertical tube, $b = \pi d$; for horizontal tube, $b = 2L$; flow channel gap in flat plate heat exchanger.
Bo = boiling number
C = coefficient or constant
Co = convection number
c_p = specific heat at constant pressure
c_v = specific heat at constant volume
D = diameter
D_o = outside tube diameter
d = diameter; or prefix meaning differential
(dp/dz) = pressure gradient
$(dp/dz)_{fric}$ = frictional pressure gradient
$(dp/dz)_l$ = frictional pressure gradient, assuming that liquid alone is flowing in pipe
$(dp/dz)_{mom}$ = momentum pressure gradient
$(dp/dz)_v$ = frictional pressure gradient, assuming that gas (or vapor) alone is flowing in pipe
Fr = Froude number
f = friction factor for single-phase flow (Fanning)
G = mass velocity
g = gravitational acceleration
g_c = gravitational constant
Gr = Grashof number
h = heat transfer coefficient
h_f = single-phase liquid heat transfer coefficient
h_{fg} = latent heat of vaporization or of condensation
j = Colburn j-factor
k = thermal conductivity
K_D = mass transfer coefficient, dimensionless coefficient (Table 1)
L = length
L_p = plate length
M = mass; or molecular weight
m = general exponent
$\dot{m}$ = mass flow rate
M_m = mean molecular weight of vapor/gas mixture
M_v = molecular weight of condensing vapor
N = number of tubes in vertical tier
n = general exponent
Nu = Nusselt number
P = plate perimeter
p = pressure
p_c = critical thermodynamic pressure for coolant
p_g = partial pressure of noncondensable gas
Pr = Prandtl number
p_r = reduced pressure = p/p_c
p_v = partial pressure of vapor
Q_v = volumetric flow rate
q = heat transfer rate
r = radius
Ra = Rayleigh number
Re = Reynolds number
R_p = surface roughness, μm
t = temperature
U = overall heat transfer coefficient
V = linear velocity
We = Weber number
x = quality (i.e., mass fraction of vapor); or distance in dt/dx
X_{tt} = Martinelli parameter
x, y, z = lengths along principal coordinate axes
Y_g = mole fraction of noncondensable gas
Y_v = mole fraction of vapor

Greek

α = thermal diffusivity = $k/\rho c_p$
β = coefficient of thermal expansion, chevron angle
Γ = mass rate of flow of condensate per unit of breadth (see section on Condensing)
Δ = difference between values
ε = roughness of interface
ε_v = vapor void fraction
θ = contact angle
μ = absolute (dynamic) viscosity
μ_l = dynamic viscosity of saturated liquid
μ_v = dynamic viscosity of saturated vapor
ν = kinematic viscosity
ρ = density
ρ_l = density of saturated liquid
ρ_v = density of saturated vapor phase
σ = surface tension
Φ = two-phase multiplier
ϕ = fin efficiency

Subscripts and Superscripts

a = exponent in Equation (1)
b = bubble
c = critical, cold (fluid), characteristic, coolant
e = equivalent
eff = effective
f = film or fin
$fric$ = friction
g = noncondensable gas
gv = noncondensable gas and vapor mixture
h = horizontal, hot (fluid), hydraulic
i = inlet or inside
if = interface
l = liquid
m = mean
mac = convective mechanism
max = maximum
mic = nucleation mechanism
min = minimum
mom = momentum
ncb = nucleate boiling
o = outside, outlet, overall, reference
r = root (fin) or reduced pressure
s = surface or secondary heat transfer surface
sat = saturation
t = temperature or terminal temperature of tip (fin)
tot = total
v = vapor or vertical
w = wall
∞ = bulk or far-field
* = reference

REFERENCES

Anderson, W., D.G. Rich, and D.F. Geary. 1966. Evaporation of Refrigerant 22 in a horizontal 3/4-in. OD tube. *ASHRAE Transactions* 72(1):28.

Ayub, Z.H. 2003. Plate heat exchanger literature survey and new heat transfer and pressure drop correlations for refrigerant evaporators. *Heat Transfer Engineering* 24(5):3-16.

Barnea, D. and Y. Taitel. 1986. Flow pattern transition in two-phase gas-liquid flows. In *Encyclopedia of Fluid Mechanics*, vol. 3. Gulf Publishing, Houston.

Baroczy, C.J. 1963. Correlation of liquid fraction in two-phase flow with application to liquid metals. North American Aviation *Report* SR-8171, El Segundo, CA.

Baskin, E. 1991. Applicability of plate heat exchangers in heat pumps. *ASHRAE Transactions* 97(2):305-308.

Beatty, K.O. and D.L. Katz. 1948. Condensation of vapors on outside of finned tubes. *Chemical Engineering Progress* 44(1):55.

Bennett, D.L. and J.C. Chen. 1980. Forced convective boiling in vertical tubes for saturated pure components and binary mixtures. *AIChE Journal* 26(3):454-461.

Berenson, P.J. 1961. Film boiling heat transfer from a horizontal surface. *ASME Journal of Heat Transfer* 85:351.

Berenson, P.J. 1962. Experiments on pool boiling heat transfer. *International Journal of Heat and Mass Transfer* 5:985.

Bergles, A.E. 1976. Survey and augmentation of two-phase heat transfer. *ASHRAE Transactions* 82(1):891-905.

Bergles, A.E. 1985. Techniques to augment heat transfer. In *Handbook of heat transfer application*, 2nd ed. McGraw-Hill, New York.

Bergles, A.E. and W.M. Rohsenow. 1964. The determination of forced convection surface-boiling heat transfer. *ASME Journal of Heat Transfer*, Series C, 86(August):365.

Borishansky, W. and A. Kosyrev. 1966. Generalization of experimental data for the heat transfer coefficient in nucleate boiling. *ASHRAE Journal* (May):74.

Borishansky, V.M., I.I. Novikov, and S.S. Kutateladze. 1962. Use of thermodynamic similarity in generalizing experimental data on heat transfer. *Proceedings of the International Heat Transfer Conference*.

Breber, G., J.W. Palen, and J. Taborek. 1980. Prediction of the horizontal tubeside condensation of pure components using flow regime criteria. *ASME Journal of Heat Transfer* 102(3):471-476.

Bromley, L.A. 1950. Heat transfer in stable film boiling. *Chemical Engineering Progress* (46):221.

Brusstar, M.J. and H. Merte, Jr. 1997. Effects of heater surface orientation on the critical heat flux—II. A model for pool and forced convection subcooled boiling. *International Journal of Heat and Mass Transfer* 40(17):4021-4030.

Butterworth, D. 1975. A comparison of some void-fraction relationships for co-current gas-liquid flow. *International Journal of Multiphase Flow* 1:845-850.

Carey, V.P. 1992. *Liquid-vapor phase change phenomena: An introduction to the thermophysics of vaporization and condensation processes in heat transfer equipment*. Hemisphere Publishing, Washington, D.C.

Cavallini, A. and R. Zecchin, 1974. A dimensionless correlation for heat transfer in forced convection condensation. *Proceedings of the 5th International Heat Transfer Conference* 3:309-313.

Cavallini, A., G. Censi, D. Del Col, L. Doretti, G.A. Longo, and L. Rosetto. 2002. In-tube condensation of halogenated refrigerants. *ASHRAE Transactions* 108(1):146-161.

Chaddock, J.B. and J.A. Noerager. 1966. Evaporation of Refrigerant 12 in a horizontal tube with constant wall heat flux. *ASHRAE Transactions* 72(1):90.

Chen, J.C. 1963. A correlation for boiling heat transfer to saturated fluids on convective flow. ASME *Paper* 63-HT-34. American Society of Mechanical Engineers, New York.

Chen, J.C. 2003. Surface contact—Its significance for multiphase heat transfer: Diverse examples. *Journal of Heat Transfer* 125:549-566.

Colburn, A.P. 1951. Problems in design and research on condensers of vapours and vapour mixtures. *Proceedings of the Institute of Mechanical Engineers*, London, vol. 164, p. 448.

Colburn, A.P. and O.A. Hougen. 1934. Design of cooler condensers for mixtures of vapors with noncondensing gases. *Industrial and Engineering Chemistry* 26 (November):1178.

Coleman, J.W. and S. Garimella. 1999. Characterization of two-phase flow patterns in small-diameter round and rectangular tubes. *International Journal of Heat and Mass Transfer* 42:2869-2881.

Collier, J.G. 1972. *Convective boiling and condensation*. McGraw-Hill.

Collier, J.G. and J.R. Thome. 1996. *Convective boiling and condensation*, 3rd ed. Oxford University Press.

Cooper, M.G. 1984. Heat flow rates in saturated nucleate pool boiling—A wide-ranging examination using reduced properties. *Advances in Heat Transfer* 16:157-239.

Danilova, G. 1965. Influence of pressure and temperature on heat exchange in the boiling of halogenated hydrocarbons. *Kholodilnaya Teknika* 2. English abstract, *Modern Refrigeration* (December).

Dhir, V.K. and S.P. Liaw. 1989. Framework for a unified model for nucleate and transition pool boiling. *Journal of Heat Transfer* 111:739-745.

Dhir, V. K. and J. Lienhard. 1971. Laminar film condensation on plan and axisymmetric bodies in non-uniform gravity. *Journal of Heat Transfer* 91:97-100.

Dobson, M.K. and J.C. Chato. 1998. Condensation in smooth horizontal tubes. *Journal of Heat Transfer* 120:193-213.

Dougherty, R.L. and H.J. Sauer, Jr. 1974. Nucleate pool boiling of refrigerant-oil mixtures from tubes. *ASHRAE Transactions* 80(2):175.

Eckels, S.J., T.M. Doer, and M.B. Pate. 1994. In-tube heat transfer and pressure drop of R-134a and ester lubricant mixtures in a smooth tube and a micro-fin tube, part 1: Evaporation. *ASHRAE Transactions* 100(2): 265-282.

El Hajal, J., J.R. Thome, and A. Cavallini. 2003. Condensation in horizontal tubes, part 1: Two-phase flow pattern map. *International Journal of Heat and Mass Transfer* 46(18):3349-3363.

Farber, E.A. and R.L. Scorah. 1948. Heat transfer to water boiling under pressure. *ASME Transactions* (May):373.

Frederking, T.H.K. and J.A. Clark. 1962. Natural convection film boiling on a sphere. In *Advances in cryogenic engineering*, K.D. Timmerhouse, ed. Plenum Press, New York.

Friedel, L. 1979. Improved friction pressure drop correlations for horizontal and vertical two-phase pipe flow. European Two-Phase Flow Group Meeting, Paper E2, Ispra, Italy.

Fujii, T. 1995. Enhancement to condensing heat transfer—New developments. *Journal of Enhanced Heat Transfer* 2:127-138.

Furse, F.G. 1965. Heat transfer to Refrigerants 11 and 12 boiling over a horizontal copper surface. *ASHRAE Transactions* 71(1):231.

Gorenflo, D. 1993. *Pool boiling*. VDI-Heat Atlas. VDI-Verlag, Düsseldorf.

Gouse, S.W., Jr. and K.G. Coumou. 1965. Heat transfer and fluid flow inside a horizontal tube evaporator, phase I. *ASHRAE Transactions* 71(2):152.

Green, G.H. and F.G. Furse. 1963. Effect of oil on heat transfer from a horizontal tube to boiling Refrigerant 12-oil mixtures. *ASHRAE Journal* (October):63.

Grober, H., S. Erk, and U. Grigull. 1961. *Fundamentals of heat transfer*. McGraw-Hill, New York.

Grönnerud, R. 1979. Investigation of liquid hold-up, flow resistance and heat transfer in circulation type evaporators, part IV: Two-phase flow resistance in boiling refrigerants. Annexe 1972-1, *Bulletin de l'Institut du Froid*.

Guerrieri, S.A. and R.D. Talty. 1956. A study of heat transfer to organic liquids in single tube boilers. *Chemical Engineering Progress Symposium Series* 52(18):69.

Gungor, K.E. and R.H.S. Winterton. 1986. A general correlation for flow boiling in tubes and annuli. *International Journal of Heat and Mass Transfer* 29:351-358.

Gungor, K.E. and R.H.S. Winterton. 1987. Simplified general correlation for saturated flow boiling and comparison of correlations with data. *Chemical Engineering Research and Design* 65:148-156.

Hall, D.D. and I. Mudawar. 2000a. Critical heat flux (CHF) for water flow in tubes—I. Compilation and assessment of world CHF data. *International Journal of Heat and Mass Transfer* 43(14):2573-2604.

Hall, D.D. and I. Mudawar. 2000b. Critical heat flux (CHF) for water flow in tubes—II: Subcooled CHF correlations. *International Journal of Heat and Mass Transfer* 43(14):2605-2640.

Haramura, Y. and Y. Katto. 1983. A new hydrodynamic model of critical heat flux, applicable widely to both pool and forced convection boiling on submerged bodies in saturated liquids. *International Journal of Heat and Mass Transfer* 26:389-399.

Hesselgreaves, J.E. 1990. The impact of compact heat exchangers on refrigeration technology and CFC replacement. *Proceedings of the 1990 USNC/IIR-Purdue Refrigeration Conference*, ASHRAE/Purdue CFC Conference, pp. 492-500.

Hetsroni, G., ed. 1986. *Handbook of multiphase systems*. Hemisphere Publishing, Washington D.C.

Howard, A.H. and I. Mudawar. 1999. Orientation effects on pool boiling critical heat flux (CHF) and modeling of CHF for near-vertical surfaces. *International Journal of Heat and Mass Transfer* 42:1665-1688.

Hughmark, G.A. 1962. A statistical analysis of nucleate pool boiling data. *International Journal of Heat and Mass Transfer* 5:667.

Incropera, F.P. and D.P. DeWitt. 2002. *Fundamentals of heat and mass transfer*, 5th ed. John Wiley & Sons, New York.

Isrealachvili, J.N. 1991. *Intermolecular surface forces*. Academic Press, New York.

Jakob, M. 1949, 1957. *Heat transfer*, vols. I and II. John Wiley & Sons, New York.

Jonsson, I. 1985. Plate heat exchangers as evaporators and condensers for refrigerants. *Australian Refrigeration, Air Conditioning and Heating* 39(9):30-31, 33-35.

Kandlikar, S.G., ed. 1999. *Handbook of phase change: Boiling and condensation*. Taylor and Francis, Philadelphia.

Kandlikar, S.G. 2001. A theoretical model to predict pool boiling CHF incorporating effects of contact angle and orientation. *Journal of Heat Transfer* 123:1071-1079.

Kattan, N., J.R. Thome, and D. Favrat. 1998a. Flow boiling in horizontal tubes, part 1: Development of diabatic two-phase flow pattern map. *Journal of Heat Transfer* 120(1):140-147.

Kattan, N., J.R. Thome, and D. Favrat. 1998b. Flow boiling in horizontal tubes, part 3: Development of new heat transfer model based on flow patterns. *Journal of Heat Transfer* 120(1):156-165.

Kumar, H. 1984. The plate heat exchanger: Construction and design. *Institute of Chemical Engineering Symposium Series* 86:1275-1288.

Kutateladze, S.S. 1951. A hydrodynamic theory of changes in the boiling process under free convection. Izvestia Akademii Nauk, USSR, *Otdelenie Tekhnicheski Nauk* 4:529.

Kutateladze, S.S. 1963. *Fundamentals of heat transfer*. E. Arnold Press, London.

Lienhard, J.H. and V.E. Schrock. 1963. The effect of pressure, geometry and the equation of state upon peak and minimum boiling heat flux. *ASME Journal of Heat Transfer* 85:261.

Lienhard, J.H. and P.T.Y. Wong. 1964. The dominant unstable wavelength and minimum heat flux during film boiling on a horizontal cylinder. *Journal of Heat Transfer* 86:220-226.

Lockhart, R.W. and R.C. Martinelli. 1949. Proposed correlation of data for isothermal two-phase, two-component flow in pipes. *Chemical Engineering Progress* 45(1):39-48.

Mandhane, J.M., G.A. Gregory, and K. Aziz. 1974. A flow pattern map for gas-liquid flow in horizontal pipes. *International Journal of Multiphase Flow* 1:537-553.

Martinelli, R.C. and D.B. Nelson. 1948. Prediction of pressure drops during forced circulation boiling of water. *ASME Transactions* 70:695.

McAdams, W.H. 1954. *Heat transmission*, 3rd ed. McGraw-Hill, New York.

McGillis, W.R. and V.P. Carey. 1996. On the role of the Marangoni effects on the critical heat flux for pool boiling of binary mixture. *Journal of Heat Transfer* 118(1):103-109.

Müller-Steinhagen, H. and K. Heck. 1986. A simple friction pressure drop correlation for two-phase flow in pipes. *Chemical Engineering Progress* 20:297-308.

Newell, T.A. and R.K. Shah. 2001. An assessment of refrigerant heat transfer, pressure drop, and void fraction effects in microfin tubes. *International Journal of HVAC&R Research* 7(2):125-153.

Nukiyama, S. 1934. The maximum and minimum values of heat transmitted from metal to boiling water under atmospheric pressure. *Journal of the Japanese Society of Mechanical Engineers* 37:367.

Nusselt, W. 1916. Die Oberflächenkondensation des Wasserdampfes. *Zeitung Verein Deutscher Ingenieure* 60:541.

Othmer, D.F. 1929. The condensation of steam. *Industrial and Engineering Chemistry* 21(June):576.

Ould Didi, M.B., N. Kattan and J.R. Thome. 2002. Prediction of two-phase pressure gradients of refrigerants in horizontal tubes. *International Journal of Refrigeration* 25:935-947.

Palen, J. and Z.H. Yang. 2001. Reflux condensation flooding prediction: A review of current status. *Transactions of the Institute of Chemical Engineers* 79(A):463-469.

Panchal, C.B. 1985. Condensation heat transfer in plate heat exchangers. *Two-Phase Heat Exchanger Symposium*, HTD vol. 44, pp. 45-52. American Society of Mechanical Engineers, New York.

Panchal, C.B. 1990. Experimental investigation of condensation of steam in the presence of noncondensable gases using plate heat exchangers. Argonne National Laboratory *Report* CONF-900339-1.

Panchal, C.B. and D.L. Hillis. 1984. OTEC Performance tests of the Alfa-Laval plate heat exchanger as an ammonia evaporator. Argonne National Laboratory *Report* ANL-OTEC-PS-13.

Panchal, C.B., D.L. Hillis, and A. Thomas. 1983. Convective boiling of ammonia and Freon 22 in plate heat exchangers. Argonne National Laboratory *Report* CONF-830301-13.

Perry, J.H. 1950. *Chemical engineers handbook*, 3rd ed. McGraw-Hill, New York.

Pierre, B. 1964. Flow resistance with boiling refrigerant. *ASHRAE Journal* (September/October).

Reddy, R.P. and J.H. Lienhard. 1989. The peak heat flux in saturated ethanol-water mixtures. *Journal of Heat Transfer* 111:480-486.

Rohsenow, W.M. 1963. Boiling heat transfer. In *Modern developments in heat transfer*, W. Ibele, ed. Academic Press, New York.

Rohsenow, W.M. and P. Griffith. 1956. Correlation of maximum heat flux data for boiling of saturated liquids. *Chemical Engineering Progress Symposium Series* 52:47-49.

Rohsenow, W.M., J.P. Hartnett, and Y.I. Cho. 1998. *Handbook of heat transfer*, 3rd ed., pp. 1570-1571. McGraw-Hill.

Rose, J.W. 1969. Condensation of a vapour in the presence of a noncondensable gas. *International Journal of Heat and Mass Transfer* 12:233.

Rose, J.W. 1998. Condensation heat transfer fundamentals. *Transactions of the Institution of Chemical Engineers* 76(A):143-152.

Rouhani, Z. and E. Axelsson. 1970. Calculation of void volume fraction in the subcooled and quality boiling regions. *International Journal of Heat and Mass Transfer* 13:383-393.

Schlager, L.M., M.B. Pate, and A.E. Bergles. 1987. Evaporation and condensation of refrigerant-oil mixtures in a smooth tube and micro-fin tube. *ASHRAE Transactions* 93:293-316.

Sefiane, K. 2001. A new approach in the modeling of the critical heat flux and enhancement techniques. *AIChE Journal* 47(11):2402-2412.

Shah, M.M. 1979. A general correlation for heat transfer during film condensation inside pipes. *International Journal of Heat and Mass Transfer* 22:547-556.

Shah, M.M. 1982. A new correlation for saturated boiling heat transfer: Equations and further study. *ASHRAE Transactions* 88(1):185-196.

Sparrow, E.M. and S.H. Lin. 1964. Condensation in the presence of a noncondensable gas. *ASME Transactions, Journal of Heat Transfer* 86C: 430.

Sparrow, E.M., W.J. Minkowycz, and M. Saddy. 1967. Forced convection condensation in the presence of noncondensables and interfacial resistance. *International Journal of Heat and Mass Transfer* 10:1829.

Spedding, P.L. and D.R. Spence. 1993. Flow regimes in two-phase gas-liquid flow. *International Journal of Multiphase Flow* 19(2):245-280.

Starczewski, J. 1965. Generalized design of evaporation heat transfer to nucleate boiling liquids. *British Chemical Engineering* (August).

Steiner, D. 1993. *VDI-Wärmeatlas (VDI Heat Atlas)*. Verein Deutscher Ingenieure, VDI-Gesellschaft Verfahrenstechnik und Chemieingenieurwesen (GCV), Düsseldorf, Chapter Hbb.

Steiner, D. and J. Taborek. 1992. Flow boiling heat transfer in vertical tubes correlated by an asymptotic model. *Heat Transfer Engineering* 13(2): 43-69.

Stephan, K. 1963. Influence of oil on heat transfer of boiling Freon-12 and Freon-22. Eleventh International Congress of Refrigeration, IIR *Bulletin* 3.

Stephan, K. 1992. *Heat transfer in condensation and boiling*. Springer-Verlag, Berlin.

Stephan, K. and M. Abdelsalam. 1980. Heat transfer correlations for natural convection boiling. *International Journal of Heat and Mass Transfer* 23:73-87.

Syed, A. 1990. The use of plate heat exchangers as evaporators and condensers in process refrigeration. Symposium on Advanced Heat Exchanger Design. Institute of Chemical Engineers, Leeds, U.K.

Thom, J.R.S. 1964. Prediction of pressure drop during forced circulation boiling water. *International Journal of Heat and Mass Transfer* 7: 709-724.

Thome, J.R. 1990. *Enhanced boiling heat transfer*. Hemisphere (Taylor and Francis), New York.

Thome, J.R. 2001. Flow regime based modeling of two-phase heat transfer. *Multiphase Science and Technology* 13(3-4):131-160.

Thome, J.R. 2003. Update on the Kattan-Thome-Favrat flow boiling model and flow pattern map. Fifth International Conference on Boiling Heat Transfer, Montego Bay, Jamaica.

Thome, J.R. and A.W. Shock. 1984. Boiling of multicomponent liquid mixtures. In *Advances in heat transfer*, vol. 16, pp. 59-156. Academic Press, New York.

Thome, J.R., J. El Hajal, and A. Cavallini. 2003. Condensation in horizontal tubes, Part 2: New heat transfer model based on flow regimes. *International Journal of Heat and Mass Transfer* 46(18):3365-3387.

Thonon, B. 1995. Design method for plate evaporators and condensers. *1st International Conference on Process Intensification for the Chemical Industry, BHR Group Conference Series Publication* 18, pp. 37-47.

Thonon, B., R. Vidil, and C. Marvillet. 1995. Recent research and developments in plate heat exchangers. *Journal of Enhanced Heat Transfer* 2(12):149-155.

Tribbe, C. and H. Müller-Steinhagen. 2000. An evaluation of the performance of phenomenological models for predicting pressure gradient during gas-liquid flow in horizontal pipelines. *International Journal of Multiphase Flow* 26:1019-1036.

Tschernobyiski, I. and G. Ratiani. 1955. *Kholodilnaya Teknika* 32.

Turner, J.M. and G.B. Wallis. 1965. The separate-cylinders model of two-phase flow. *Report* NYO-3114-6. Thayer's School of Engineering, Dartmouth College, Hanover, NH.

Van Stralen, S.J. 1959. Heat transfer to boiling binary liquid mixtures. *British Chemical Engineering* 4(January):78.

Van Stralen, S.J. and R. Cole. 1979. *Boiling phenomena*, vol. 1. Hemisphere Publishing, Washington, D.C.

Wallis, G.B. 1969. *One-dimensional two-phase flow.* McGraw-Hill, New York.

Wallis, G.C. 1970. Annular two-phase flow, part I: A simple theory, part II: Additional effect. *ASME Transactions, Journal of Basic Engineering* 92D:59 and 73.

Webb, R.L. 1981. The evolution of enhanced surface geometrics for nucleate boiling. *Heat Transfer Engineering* 2(3-4):46-69.

Webb, J.R. 1994. *Enhanced boiling heat transfer.* John Wiley & Sons, New York.

Westwater, J.W. 1963. Things we don't know about boiling. In *Research in Heat Transfer*, J. Clark, ed. Pergamon Press, New York.

Worsoe-Schmidt, P. 1959. Some characteristics of flow-pattern and heat transfer of Freon-12 evaporating in horizontal tubes. *Ingenieren*, International edition, 3(3).

Yan, Y.-Y. and T.-F. Lin. 1999. Evaporation heat transfer and pressure drop of refrigerant R-134a in a plate heat exchanger. *Journal of Heat Transfer* 121(1):118-127.

Young, M. 1994. Plate heat exchangers as liquid cooling evaporators in ammonia refrigeration systems. *Proceedings of the IIAR 16th Annual Meeting*, St. Louis.

Zeurcher O., J.R. Thome, and D. Favrat. 1998. In-tube flow boiling of R-407C and R-407C/oil mixtures, part II: Plain tube results and predictions. *International Journal of HVAC&R Research* 4(4):373-399.

Zivi, S.M. 1964. Estimation of steady-state steam void-fraction by means of the principle of minimum entropy production. *Journal of Heat Transfer* 86:247-252.

Zuber, N. 1959. Hydrodynamic aspects of boiling heat transfer. U.S. Atomic Energy Commission, Technical Information Service, *Report* AECU 4439. Oak Ridge, TN.

Zuber, N., M. Tribus, and J.W. Westwater. 1962. The hydrodynamic crisis in pool boiling of saturated and subcooled liquids. *Proceedings of the International Heat Transfer Conference* 2:230, and discussion of the papers, vol. 6.

CHAPTER 6

MASS TRANSFER

MASS transfer by either molecular diffusion or convection is the transport of one component of a mixture relative to the motion of the mixture and is the result of a **concentration gradient**. Mass transfer can occur in liquids and solids as well as gases. For example, water on the wetted slats of a cooling tower evaporates into air in a cooling tower (liquid to gas mass transfer), and water vapor from a food product transfers to the dry air as it dries. A piece of solid CO_2 (dry ice) also gets smaller and smaller over time as the CO_2 molecules diffuse into air (solid to gas mass transfer). A piece of sugar added to a cup of coffee eventually dissolves and diffuses into the solution, sweetening the coffee, although the sugar molecules are much heavier than the water molecules (solid to liquid mass transfer). Air freshener does not just smell where sprayed, but rather the smell spreads throughout the room. The air freshener (matter) moves from an area of high concentration where sprayed to an area of low concentration far away. In an absorption chiller, low-pressure, low-temperature refrigerant vapor from the evaporator enters the thermal compressor in the absorber section, where the refrigerant vapor is absorbed by the strong absorbent (concentrated solution) and dilutes the solution.

In air conditioning, water vapor is added or removed from the air by simultaneous transfer of heat and mass (water vapor) between the airstream and a wetted surface. The wetted surface can be water droplets in an air washer, condensate on the surface of a dehumidifying coil, a spray of liquid absorbent, or wetted surfaces of an evaporative condenser. Equipment performance with these phenomena must be calculated carefully because of simultaneous heat and mass transfer.

This chapter addresses mass transfer principles and provides methods of solving a simultaneous heat and mass transfer problem involving air and water vapor, emphasizing air-conditioning processes. The formulations presented can help analyze performance of specific equipment. For discussion of performance of cooling coils, evaporative condensers, cooling towers, and air washers, see Chapters 22, 38, 39, and 40, respectively, of the 2008 *ASHRAE Handbook—HVAC Systems and Equipment.*

MOLECULAR DIFFUSION

Most mass transfer problems can be analyzed by considering diffusion of a gas into a second gas, a liquid, or a solid. In this chapter, the diffusing or dilute component is designated as component B, and the other component as component A. For example, when water vapor diffuses into air, the water vapor is component B and dry air is component A. Properties with subscripts *A* or *B* are local properties of that component. Properties without subscripts are local properties of the mixture.

The primary mechanism of mass diffusion at ordinary temperature and pressure conditions is **molecular diffusion**, a result of density gradient. In a binary gas mixture, the presence of a concentration gradient causes transport of matter by molecular diffusion; that is, because of random molecular motion, gas B diffuses through the mixture of gases A and B in a direction that reduces the concentration gradient.

Fick's Law

The basic equation for molecular diffusion is Fick's law. Expressing the concentration of component B of a binary mixture of components A and B in terms of the mass fraction ρ_B/ρ or mole fraction C_B/C, Fick's law is

$$J_B = -\rho D_v \frac{d(\rho_B/\rho)}{dy} = -J_A \tag{1a}$$

$$J_B^* = -CD_v \frac{d(C_B/C)}{dy} = -J_A^* \tag{1b}$$

where $\rho = \rho_A + \rho_B$ and $C = C_A + C_B$.

The minus sign indicates that the concentration gradient is negative in the direction of diffusion. The proportionality factor D_v is the **mass diffusivity** or the **diffusion coefficient**. The total mass flux $\dot{m}_B''$ and molar flux $\dot{m}_B''^*$ are due to the average velocity of the mixture plus the diffusive flux:

$$\dot{m}_B'' = \rho_B v - \rho D_v \frac{d(\rho_B/\rho)}{dy} \tag{2a}$$

$$\dot{m}_B''^* = C_B v^* - CD_v \frac{d(C_B/C)}{dy} \tag{2b}$$

where v is the mixture's mass average velocity and v^* is the molar average velocity.

Bird et al. (1960) present an analysis of Equations (1a) and (1b). Equations (1a) and (1b) are equivalent forms of Fick's law. The equation used depends on the problem and individual preference. This chapter emphasizes mass analysis rather than molar analysis. However, all results can be converted to the molar form using the relation $C_B \equiv \rho_B / M_B$.

Fick's Law for Dilute Mixtures

In many mass diffusion problems, component B is dilute, with a density much smaller than the mixture's. In this case, Equation (1a) can be written as

$$J_B = -D_v \frac{d\rho_B}{dy} \tag{3}$$

when $\rho_B << \rho$ and $\rho_A \approx \rho$.

Equation (3) can be used without significant error for water vapor diffusing through air at atmospheric pressure and a temperature less than 27°C. In this case, $\rho_B < 0.02\rho$, where ρ_B is the density of water vapor and ρ is the density of moist air (air and water vapor mixture). The error in J_B caused by replacing $\rho[d(\rho_B/\rho)/dy]$ with $d\rho_B/dy$ is less than 2%. At temperatures below 60°C where $\rho_B < 0.10\rho$, Equation (3) can still be used if errors in J_B as great as 10% are tolerable.

The preparation of this chapter is assigned to TC 1.3, Heat Transfer and Fluid Flow.

Fick's Law for Mass Diffusion Through Solids or Stagnant Fluids (Stationary Media)

Fick's law can be simplified for cases of dilute mass diffusion in solids, stagnant liquids, or stagnant gases. In these cases, $\rho_B << \rho$ and $v \approx 0$, which yields the following approximate result:

$$\dot{m}''_B = J_B = -D_v \frac{d\rho_B}{dy} \qquad (4)$$

Fick's Law for Ideal Gases with Negligible Temperature Gradient

For dilute mass diffusion, Fick's law can be written in terms of partial pressure gradient instead of concentration gradient. When gas B can be approximated as ideal,

$$p_B = \frac{\rho_B R_u T}{M_B} = C_B R_u T \qquad (5)$$

and when the gradient in T is small, Equation (3) can be written as

$$J_B = -\left(\frac{M_B D_v}{R_u T}\right)\frac{dp_B}{dy} \qquad (6a)$$

or

$$J_B^* = -\left(\frac{D_v}{R_u T}\right)\frac{dp_B}{dy} \qquad (6b)$$

If $v \approx 0$, Equation (4) may be written as

$$\dot{m}''_B = J_B = -\left(\frac{M_B D_v}{R_u T}\right)\frac{dp_B}{dy} \qquad (7a)$$

or

$$\dot{m}''^*_B = J_B^* = -\left(\frac{D_v}{R_u T}\right)\frac{dp_B}{dy} \qquad (7b)$$

The partial pressure gradient formulation for mass transfer analysis has been used extensively; this is unfortunate because the pressure formulation [Equations (6) and (7)] applies only when one component is dilute, the fluid closely approximates an ideal gas, and the temperature gradient has a negligible effect. The density (or concentration) gradient formulation expressed in Equations (1) to (4) is more general and can be applied to a wider range of mass transfer problems, including cases where neither component is dilute [Equation (1)]. The gases need not be ideal, nor the temperature gradient negligible. Consequently, this chapter emphasizes the density formulation.

Diffusion Coefficient

For a binary mixture, the diffusion coefficient D_v is a function of temperature, pressure, and composition. Experimental measurements of D_v for most binary mixtures are limited in range and accuracy. Table 1 gives a few experimental values for diffusion of some gases in air. For more detailed tables, see the Bibliography.

Table 1 Mass Diffusivities for Gases in Air*

Gas	D_v, mm²/s
Ammonia	27.9
Benzene	8.8
Carbon dioxide	16.5
Ethanol	11.9
Hydrogen	41.3
Oxygen	20.6
Water vapor	25.5

*Gases at 25°C and 101.325 kPa.

In the absence of data, use equations developed from (1) theory or (2) theory with constants adjusted from limited experimental data. For binary gas mixtures at low pressure, D_v is inversely proportional to pressure, increases with increasing temperature, and is almost independent of composition for a given gas pair. Bird et al. (1960) present the following equation, developed from kinetic theory and corresponding states arguments, for estimating D_v at pressures less than $0.1p_{c\,min}$:

$$D_v = a\left(\frac{T}{\sqrt{T_{cA}T_{cB}}}\right)^b \sqrt{\frac{1}{M_A}+\frac{1}{M_B}} \times \frac{(p_{cA}p_{cB})^{1/3}(T_{cA}T_{cB})^{5/12}}{p} \qquad (8)$$

where

D_v = diffusion coefficient, mm²/s
a = constant, dimensionless
b = constant, dimensionless
T = absolute temperature, K
p = pressure, kPa
M = relative molecular mass, kg/kg mol

Subscripts cA and cB refer to the critical states of the two gases. Analysis of experimental data gives the following values of the constants a and b:

For nonpolar gas pairs

$$a = 0.1280 \quad \text{and} \quad b = 1.823$$

For water vapor with a nonpolar gas

$$a = 0.1697 \quad \text{and} \quad b = 2.334$$

In **nonpolar gas**, intermolecular forces are independent of the relative orientation of molecules, depending only on the separation distance from each other. Air, composed almost entirely of nonpolar gases O_2 and N_2, is nonpolar.

Equation (8) is stated to agree with experimental data at atmospheric pressure to within about 8% (Bird et al. 1960).

Mass diffusivity D_v for binary mixtures at low pressure is predictable within about 10% by kinetic theory (Reid et al. 1987).

$$D_v = 0.1881\frac{T^{1.5}}{p(\sigma_{AB})^2\Omega_{D,AB}}\sqrt{\frac{1}{M_A}+\frac{1}{M_B}} \qquad (9)$$

where

σ_{AB} = characteristic molecular diameter, nm
$\Omega_{D,AB}$ = temperature function, dimensionless

D_v is in mm²/s, p in kPa, and T in kelvins. If the gas molecules of A and B are considered rigid spheres having diameters σ_A and σ_B [and $\sigma_{AB} = (\sigma_A/2) + (\sigma_B/2)$], all expressed in nanometres, the dimensionless function $\Omega_{D,AB}$ equals unity. More realistic models for molecules having intermolecular forces of attraction and repulsion lead to values that are functions of temperature. Bird et al. (1960) and Reid et al. (1987) present tabulations of $\Omega_{D,AB}$. These results show that D_v increases as the 2.0 power of T at low temperatures and as the 1.65 power of T at very high temperatures.

The diffusion coefficient of moist air has been calculated for Equation (8) using a simplified intermolecular potential field function for water vapor and air (Mason and Monchick 1965). The following empirical equation is for mass diffusivity of water vapor in air up to 1100°C (Sherwood and Pigford 1952):

$$D_v = \frac{0.926}{p}\left(\frac{T^{2.5}}{T+245}\right) \qquad (10)$$

Example 1. Evaluate the diffusion coefficient of CO_2 in air at 293 K and atmospheric pressure (101.325 kPa) using Equation (9).

Solution: In Equation (9), D_v is in mm²/s, $\sigma_{AB} = (\sigma_A/2) + (\sigma_B/2)$, and the Lennard-Jones energy parameter $\varepsilon_{AB}/k = \sqrt{(\varepsilon_A/k)(\varepsilon_B/k)}$. Values of σ and ε for each gas are as follows:

	σ, nm	ε/k, K
CO_2	0.3996	190
Air	0.3617	97

The combined values for use in Equation (9) are

$$\sigma_{AB} = 0.3996/2 + 0.3617/2 = 0.3806 \text{ nm}$$

$$\varepsilon_{AB}/k = \sqrt{(190)(97)} = 136 \text{ at } P = 101.325 \text{ kPa and } T = 293 \text{ K}$$

$$\frac{\varepsilon_{AB}}{kT} = \frac{136}{293} = 0.463 \qquad \frac{kT}{\varepsilon_{AB}} = \frac{1}{0.463} = 2.16$$

From tables for $\Omega_{D,AB}$ at $kT/\varepsilon_{AB} = 2.16$ (Bird et al. 1960; Reid et al. 1987), the collision integral $\Omega_{D,AB} = 1.047$. The relative molecular masses of CO_2 and air are 44 and 29, respectively. Substituting these values gives

$$D_v = 0.1881[293^{1.5}/(101.325 \times 0.3806^2 \times 1.047)](1/44 + 1/29)^{0.5}$$
$$= 14.68 \text{ mm}^2/\text{s}$$

Diffusion of One Gas Through a Second Stagnant Gas

Figure 1 shows diffusion of one gas through a second, stagnant gas. Water vapor diffuses from the liquid surface into surrounding stationary air. It is assumed that local equilibrium exists through the gas mixture, that the gases are ideal, and that the Gibbs-Dalton law is valid, which implies that temperature gradient has a negligible effect. Water vapor diffuses because of concentration gradient, as given by Equation (6a). There is a continuous gas phase, so the mixture pressure p is constant, and the Gibbs-Dalton law yields

$$p_A + p_B = p = \text{constant} \tag{11a}$$

or

$$\frac{\rho_A}{M_A} + \frac{\rho_B}{M_B} = \frac{p}{R_u T} = \text{constant} \tag{11b}$$

The partial pressure gradient of the water vapor causes a partial pressure gradient of the air such that

$$\frac{dp_A}{dy} = -\frac{dp_B}{dy} \tag{11c}$$

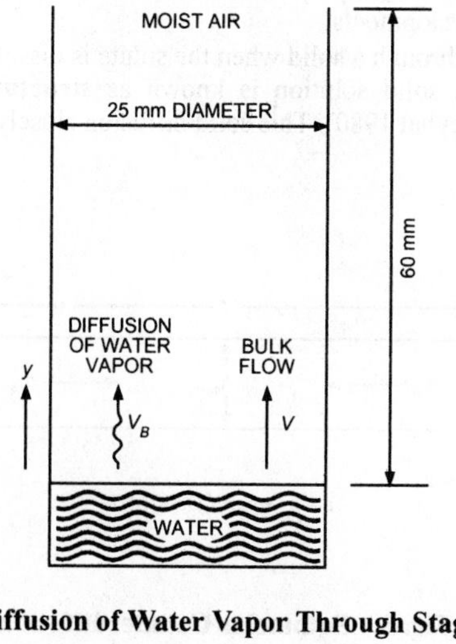

Fig. 1 Diffusion of Water Vapor Through Stagnant Air

or

$$\left(\frac{1}{M_A}\right)\frac{d\rho_A}{dy} = -\left(\frac{1}{M_B}\right)\frac{d\rho_B}{dy} \tag{12}$$

Air, then, diffuses toward the liquid water interface. Because it cannot be absorbed there, a bulk velocity v of the gas mixture is established in a direction away from the liquid surface, so that the net transport of air is zero (i.e., the air is stagnant):

$$\dot{m}''_A = -D_v \frac{d\rho_A}{dy} + \rho_A v = 0 \tag{13}$$

The bulk velocity v transports not only air but also water vapor away from the interface. Therefore, the total rate of water vapor diffusion is

$$\dot{m}''_B = -D_v \frac{d\rho_B}{dy} + \rho_B v \tag{14}$$

Substituting for the velocity v from Equation (13) and using Equations (11b) and (12) gives

$$\dot{m}''_B = \left(\frac{D_v M_B p}{\rho_A R_u T}\right)\frac{d\rho_A}{dy} \tag{15}$$

Integration yields

$$\dot{m}''_B = \frac{D_v M_B p}{R_u T}\left[\frac{\ln(\rho_{AL}/\rho_{A0})}{y_L - y_0}\right] \tag{16a}$$

or

$$\dot{m}''_B = -D_v P_{Am}\left(\frac{\rho_{BL} - \rho_{B0}}{y_L - y_0}\right) \tag{16b}$$

where

$$P_{Am} \equiv \frac{p}{p_{AL}}\rho_{AL}\left[\frac{\ln(\rho_{AL}/\rho_{A0})}{\rho_{AL} - \rho_{A0}}\right] \tag{17}$$

P_{Am} is the logarithmic mean density factor of the stagnant air. The pressure distribution for this type of diffusion is illustrated in Figure 2. **Stagnant** refers to the net behavior of the air; it does not move because bulk flow exactly offsets diffusion. The term P_{Am} in Equation (16b) approximately equals unity for dilute mixtures such as water vapor in air at near-atmospheric conditions. This condition makes it possible to simplify Equations (16) and implies that, for dilute mixtures, the partial pressure distribution curves in Figure 2 are straight lines.

Example 2. A vertical tube of 25 mm diameter is partially filled with water so that the distance from the water surface to the open end of the tube is 60 mm, as shown in Figure 1. Perfectly dried air is blown over the open tube end, and the complete system is at a constant temperature of 15°C. In 200 h of steady operation, 2.15 g of water evaporates from the tube. The total pressure of the system is 101.325 kPa. Using these data, (1) calculate the mass diffusivity of water vapor in air, and (2) compare this experimental result with that from Equation (10).

Solution:

(1) The mass diffusion flux of water vapor from the water surface is

$$\dot{m}_B = 2.15/200 = 0.01075 \text{ g/h}$$

The cross-sectional area of a 25 mm diameter tube is $\pi(12.5)^2$ = 491 mm². Therefore, $\dot{m}''_B$ = 0.00608 g/(m²·s). The partial densities are determined from psychrometric tables.

$$\rho_{BL} = 0; \ \rho_{B0} = 12.8 \text{ g/m}^3$$

$$\rho_{AL} = 1.225 \text{ kg/m}^3; \ \rho_{A0} = 1.204 \text{ kg/m}^3$$

Because $p = p_{AL} = 101.325$ kPa, the logarithmic mean density factor [Equation (17)] is

$$P_{Am} = 1.225\left[\frac{\ln(1.225/1.204)}{1.225 - 1.204}\right] = 1.009$$

The mass diffusivity is now computed from Equation (16b) as

$$D_v = \frac{-\dot{m}_B''(y_L - y_0)}{P_{Am}(\rho_{BL} - \rho_{B0})} = \frac{-(0.00608)(0.060)(10^6)}{(1.009)(0 - 12.8)}$$

$$= 28.2 \text{ mm}^2/\text{s}$$

(2) By Equation (10), with $p = 101.325$ kPa and $T = 15 + 273 = 288$ K,

$$D_v = \frac{0.926}{101.325}\left(\frac{288^{2.5}}{288 + 245}\right) = 24.1 \text{ mm}^2/\text{s}$$

Neglecting the correction factor P_{Am} for this example gives a difference of less than 1% between the calculated experimental and empirically predicted values of D_v.

Equimolar Counterdiffusion

Figure 3 shows two large chambers, both containing an ideal gas mixture of two components A and B (e.g., air and water vapor) at the same total pressure p and temperature T. The two chambers are connected by a duct of length L and cross-sectional area A_{cs}. Partial pressure p_B is higher in the left chamber, and partial pressure p_A is higher in the right chamber. The partial pressure differences cause component B to migrate to the right and component A to migrate to the left.

At steady state, the molar flows of A and B must be equal but opposite:

$$\dot{m}_A''^* + \dot{m}_B''^* = 0 \quad (18)$$

because the total molar concentration C must stay the same in both chambers if p and T remain constant. Because molar fluxes are the same in both directions, the molar average velocity $v^* = 0$. Thus, Equation (7b) can be used to calculate the molar flux of B (or A):

$$\dot{m}_B''^* = \frac{-D_v}{R_u T}\frac{dp_B}{dy} \quad (19)$$

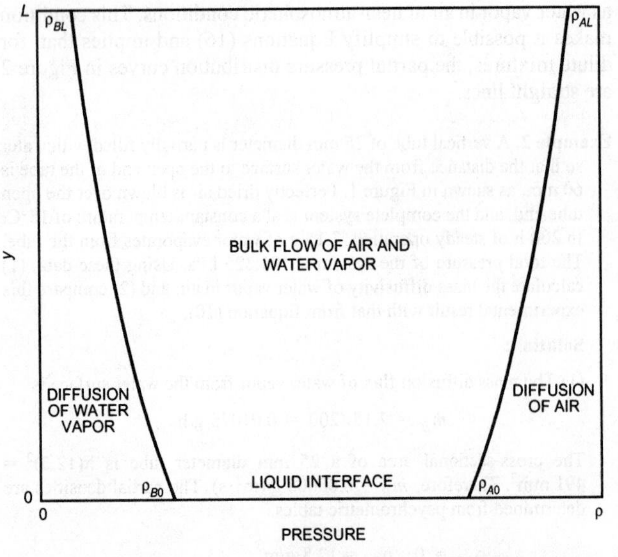

Fig. 2 Pressure Profiles for Diffusion of Water Vapor Through Stagnant Air

or

$$\dot{m}_B^* = \frac{A_{cs}D_v}{R_u T}\left(\frac{p_{B0} - p_{BL}}{L}\right) \quad (20)$$

or

$$\dot{m}_B = \frac{M_B A_{cs} D_v}{R_u T}\left(\frac{p_{B0} - p_{BL}}{L}\right) \quad (21)$$

Example 3. One large room is maintained at 22°C (295 K), 101.3 kPa, 80% rh. A 20 m long duct with cross-sectional area of 0.15 m² connects the room to another large room at 22°C, 101.3 kPa, 10% rh. What is the rate of water vapor diffusion between the two rooms?

Solution: Let air be component A and water vapor be component B. Equation (21) can be used to calculate the mass flow of water vapor B. Equation (10) can be used to calculate the diffusivity.

$$D_v = \frac{0.926}{101.3}\left(\frac{295^{2.5}}{295 + 245}\right) = 25.3 \text{ mm}^2/\text{h}$$

From a psychrometric table (Table 3, Chapter 1), the saturated vapor pressure at 22°C is 2.645 kPa. The vapor pressure difference $p_{B0} - p_{BL}$ is

$$p_{B0} - p_{BL} = (0.8 - 0.1)2.645 \text{ kPa} = 1.85 \text{ kPa}$$

Then, Equation (21) gives

$$\dot{m}_b = \frac{18 \times 0.15(25.3/10^6)}{8.314 \times 295}\frac{1.85}{20} = 2.58 \times 10^{-9} \text{ kg/s}$$

Molecular Diffusion in Liquids and Solids

Because of the greater density, diffusion is slower in liquids than in gases. No satisfactory molecular theories have been developed for calculating diffusion coefficients. The limited measured values of D_v show that, unlike for gas mixtures at low pressures, the diffusion coefficient for liquids varies appreciably with concentration.

Reasoning largely from analogy to the case of one-dimensional diffusion in gases and using Fick's law as expressed by Equation (4) gives

$$\dot{m}_B'' = D_v\left(\frac{\rho_{B1} - \rho_{B2}}{y_2 - y_1}\right) \quad (22)$$

Equation (22) expresses steady-state diffusion of solute B through solvent A in terms of the molal concentration difference of the solute at two locations separated by the distance $\Delta y = y_2 - y_1$. Bird et al. (1960), Eckert and Drake (1972), Hirschfelder et al. (1954), Reid and Sherwood (1966), Sherwood and Pigford (1952), and Treybal (1980) provide equations and tables for evaluating D_v. Hirschfelder et al. (1954) provide comprehensive treatment of the molecular developments.

Diffusion through a solid when the solute is dissolved to form a homogeneous solid solution is known as **structure-insensitive diffusion** (Treybal 1980). This solid diffusion closely parallels dif-

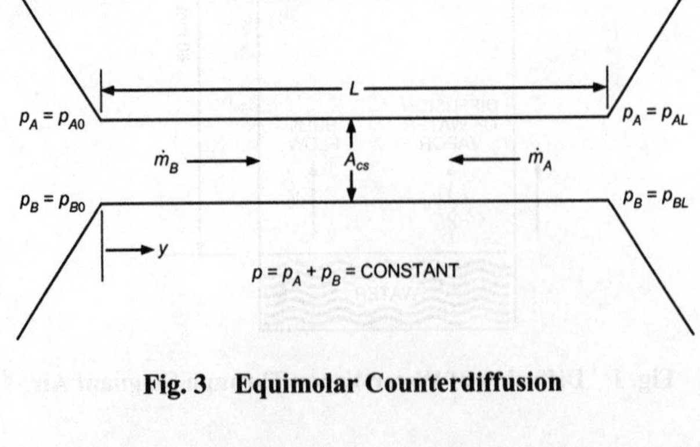

Fig. 3 Equimolar Counterdiffusion

fusion through fluids, and Equation (22) can be applied to one-dimensional steady-state problems. Values of mass diffusivity are generally lower than they are for liquids and vary with temperature.

Diffusion of a gas mixture through a porous medium is common (e.g., diffusion of an air/vapor mixture through porous insulation). Vapor diffuses through the air along the tortuous narrow passages within the porous medium. Mass flux is a function of the vapor pressure gradient and diffusivity, as indicated in Equation (7a). It is also a function of the structure of the pathways within the porous medium and is therefore called **structure-sensitive diffusion**. All these factors are taken into account in the following version of Equation (7a):

$$\dot{m}_B'' = -\bar{\mu}\frac{dp_B}{dy} \tag{23}$$

where $\bar{\mu}$ is called the permeability of the porous medium. Chapter 25 presents this topic in more depth.

CONVECTION OF MASS

Convection of mass involves the mass transfer mechanisms of molecular diffusion and bulk fluid motion. Fluid motion in the region adjacent to a mass transfer surface may be laminar or turbulent, depending on geometry and flow conditions.

Mass Transfer Coefficient

Convective mass transfer is analogous to convective heat transfer where geometry and boundary conditions are similar. The analogy holds for both laminar and turbulent flows and applies to both external and internal flow problems.

Mass Transfer Coefficients for External Flows. Most external convective mass transfer problems can be solved with an appropriate formulation that relates the mass transfer flux (to or from an interfacial surface) to the concentration difference across the boundary layer illustrated in Figure 4. This formulation gives rise to the convective mass transfer coefficient, defined as

$$h_M \equiv \frac{\dot{m}_B''}{\rho_{Bi} - \rho_{B\infty}} \tag{24}$$

where

h_M = local external mass transfer coefficient, m/s
$\dot{m}_B''$ = mass flux of gas B from surface, kg/(m²·s)
ρ_{Bi} = density of gas B at interface (saturation density), kg/m³
$\rho_{B\infty}$ = density of component B outside boundary layer, kg/m³

If ρ_{Bi} and $\rho_{B\infty}$ are constant over the entire interfacial surface, the mass transfer rate from the surface can be expressed as

$$\dot{m}_B'' = \bar{h}_M(\rho_{Bi} - \rho_{B\infty}) \tag{25}$$

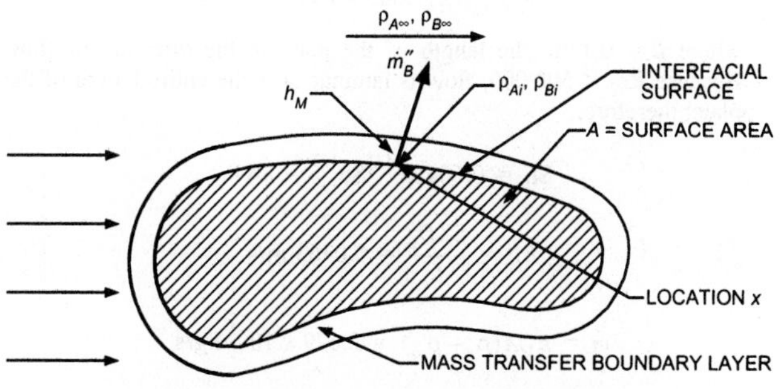

Fig. 4 Nomenclature for Convective Mass Transfer from External Surface at Location *x* Where Surface Is Impermeable to Gas A

where $\bar{h}_M$ is the average mass transfer coefficient, defined as

$$\bar{h}_M \equiv \frac{1}{A}\int_A h_m\, dA \tag{26}$$

Mass Transfer Coefficients for Internal Flows. Most internal convective mass transfer problems, such as those that occur in channels or in the cores of dehumidification coils, can be solved if an appropriate expression is available to relate the mass transfer flux (to or from the interfacial surface) to the difference between the concentration at the surface and the bulk concentration in the channel, as shown in Figure 5. This formulation leads to the definition of the mass transfer coefficient for internal flows:

$$h_M \equiv \frac{\dot{m}_B''}{\rho_{Bi} - \rho_{Bb}} \tag{27}$$

where

h_M = internal mass transfer coefficient, m/s
$\dot{m}_B''$ = mass flux of gas B at interfacial surface, kg/(m²·s)
ρ_{Bi} = density of gas B at interfacial surface, kg/m³
$\rho_{Bb} \equiv (1/\bar{u}_B A_{cs})\int_{A_{cs}} u_B \rho_B\, dA_{cs}$ = bulk density of gas B at location x
$\bar{u}_B \equiv (1/A_{cs})\int_A u_B\, dA_{cs}$ = average velocity of gas B at location x, m/s
A_{cs} = cross-sectional area of channel at station x, m²
u_B = velocity of component B in x direction, m/s
ρ_B = density distribution of component B at station x, kg/m³

Often, it is easier to obtain the bulk density of gas B from

$$\rho_{Bb} = \frac{\dot{m}_{Bo} + \int_A \dot{m}_B'' dA}{\bar{u}_B A_{cs}} \tag{28}$$

where

$\dot{m}_{Bo}$ = mass flow rate of component B at station $x = 0$, kg/s
A = interfacial area of channel between station $x = 0$ and station $x = x$, m²

Equation (28) can be derived from the preceding definitions. The major problem is the determination of $\bar{u}_B$. If, however, analysis is restricted to cases where B is dilute and concentration gradients of B in the x direction are negligibly small, $\bar{u}_B \approx \bar{u}$. Component B is swept along in the x direction with an average velocity equal to the average velocity of the dilute mixture.

Analogy Between Convective Heat and Mass Transfer

Most expressions for the convective mass transfer coefficient h_M are determined from expressions for the convective heat transfer coefficient h.

For problems in internal and external flow where mass transfer occurs at the convective surface and where component B is dilute,

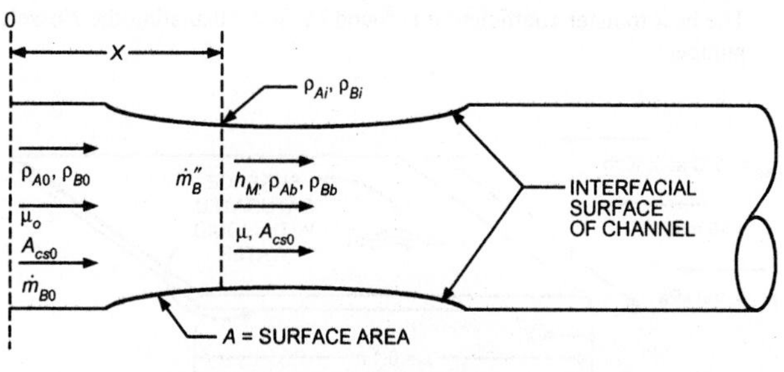

Fig. 5 Nomenclature for Convective Mass Transfer from Internal Surface Impermeable to Gas A

Bird et al. (1960) and Incropera and DeWitt (1996) found that the Nusselt and Sherwood numbers are defined as follows:

$$\mathrm{Nu} = f(X, Y, Z, \mathrm{Pr}, \mathrm{Re}) \quad (29)$$

$$\mathrm{Sh} = f(X, Y, Z, \mathrm{Sc}, \mathrm{Re}) \quad (30)$$

and

$$\overline{\mathrm{Nu}} = g(\mathrm{Pr}, \mathrm{Re}) \quad (31)$$

$$\overline{\mathrm{Sh}} = g(\mathrm{Sc}, \mathrm{Re}) \quad (32)$$

where f in Equations (29) and (30) indicates a functional relationship among the dimensionless groups shown. The function f is the same in both equations. Similarly, g indicates a functional relationship that is the same in Equations (31) and (32). Pr and Sc are dimensionless Prandtl and Schmidt numbers, respectively, as defined in the Symbols section. The primary restrictions on the analogy are that the surface shapes are the same and that the temperature boundary conditions are analogous to the density distribution boundary conditions for component B when cast in dimensionless form. Several primary factors prevent the analogy from being perfect. In some cases, the Nusselt number was derived for smooth surfaces. Many mass transfer problems involve wavy, droplet-like, or roughened surfaces. Many Nusselt number relations are obtained for constant-temperature surfaces. Sometimes ρ_{Bi} is not constant over the entire surface because of varying saturation conditions and the possibility of surface dryout.

In all mass transfer problems, there is some blowing or suction at the surface because of condensation, evaporation, or transpiration of component B. In most cases, this blowing/suction has little effect on the Sherwood number, but the analogy should be examined closely if $v_i/u_\infty > 0.01$ or $v_i/\bar{u} > 0.01$, especially if the Reynolds number is large.

Example 4. Air at 25°C, 100 kPa, and 60% rh flows at 10 m/s, as shown in Figure 6. Find the rate of evaporation, rate of heat transfer to the water, and water surface temperature.

Solution: Heat transfer to water from air supplies the energy required to evaporate the water.

$$q = hA(t_\infty - t_s) = \dot{m}h_{fg} = h_M A(\rho_s - \rho_\infty)h_{fg}$$

where

h = convective heat transfer coefficient
h_M = convective mass transfer coefficient
$A = 0.1 \times 1.5 \times 2 = 0.3$ m² = surface area (both sides)
$\dot{m}$ = evaporation rate
t_s, ρ_s = temperature and vapor density at water surface
t_∞, ρ_∞ = temperature and vapor density of airstream

This energy balance can be rearranged to give

$$\rho_s - \rho_\infty = \frac{h}{h_M}\left[\frac{(t_\infty - t_s)}{h_{fg}}\right]$$

The heat transfer coefficient h is found by first calculating the Nusselt number:

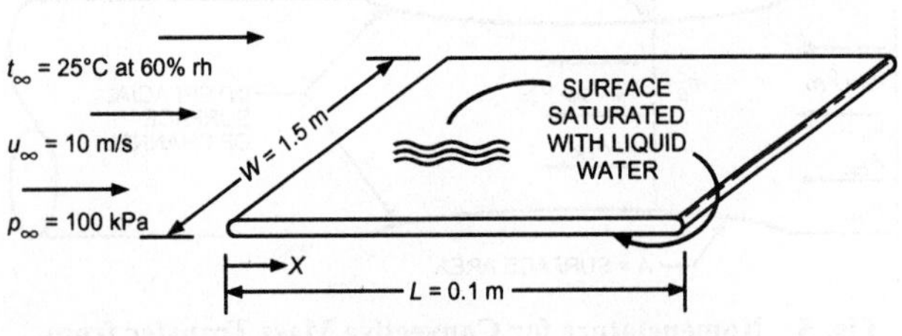

Fig. 6 Water-Saturated Flat Plate in Flowing Airstream

$$\mathrm{Nu} = 0.664\mathrm{Re}^{1/2}\mathrm{Pr}^{1/3} \quad \text{for laminar flow}$$

$$\mathrm{Nu} = 0.037\mathrm{Re}^{4/5}\mathrm{Pr}^{1/3} \quad \text{for turbulent flow}$$

The mass transfer coefficient h_M requires calculation of Sherwood number Sh, obtained using the analogy expressed in Equations (31) and (32):

$$\mathrm{Sh} = 0.664\mathrm{Re}^{1/2}\mathrm{Sc}^{1/3} \quad \text{for laminar flow}$$

$$\mathrm{Sh} = 0.037\mathrm{Re}^{4/5}\mathrm{Sc}^{1/3} \quad \text{for turbulent flow}$$

With Nu and Sh known,

$$h_M = \frac{\mathrm{Sh}\,D_v}{L} \qquad h = \frac{\mathrm{Nu}\,k}{L}$$

or

$$\frac{h}{h_M} = \frac{\mathrm{Nu}\,k}{\mathrm{Sh}\,D_v} = \left(\frac{\mathrm{Pr}}{\mathrm{Sc}}\right)^{1/3}\frac{k}{D_v}$$

This result is valid for both laminar and turbulent flow. Using this result in the preceding energy balance gives

$$\rho_s - \rho_\infty = \left(\frac{\mathrm{Pr}}{\mathrm{Sc}}\right)^{1/3}\frac{k}{D_v}\left[\frac{(t_\infty - t_s)}{h_{fg}}\right]$$

This equation must be solved for ρ_s. Then, water surface temperature t_s is the saturation temperature corresponding to ρ_s. Air properties Sc, Pr, D_v, and k are evaluated at film temperature $t_f = (t_\infty + t_s)/2$, and h_{fg} is evaluated at t_s. Because t_s appears in the right side and all the air properties also vary somewhat with t_s, iteration is required. Start by guessing t_s = 14°C (the dew point of the airstream), giving t_f = 19.5°C. At these temperatures, values on the right side are found in property tables or calculated as

k = 0.0257 W/(m·K)
Pr = 0.709
$D_v = 2.521 \times 10^{-5}$ m²/s [from Equation (10)]
ρ = 1.191 kg/m³
$\mu = 1.809 \times 10^{-5}$ kg/(m·s)
Sc = $\mu/\rho D_v$ = 0.6025
$h_{fg} = 2.455 \times 10^6$ J/kg (at 14°C)
ρ_∞ = 0.01417 kg/m³ (from psychrometric chart at 25°C, 60% rh)
t_s = 14°C (initial guess)

Solving yields ρ_s = 0.01896 kg/m³. The corresponding value of t_s = 21.6°C. Repeat the process using t_s = 21.6°C as the initial guess. The result is ρ_s = 0.01565 kg/m³ and t_s = 18.3°C. Continue iterations until ρ_s converges to 0.01663 kg/m³ and t_s = 19.4°C.

To solve for the rates of evaporation and heat transfer, first calculate the Reynolds number using air properties at t_f = (25 + 19.4)/2 = 22.2°C.

$$\mathrm{Re}_L = \frac{\rho u_\infty L}{\mu} = \frac{(1.191)(10)(0.1)}{1.809 \times 10^{-5}} = 65\,837$$

where L = 0.1 m, the length of the plate in the direction of flow. Because Re_L < 500 000, flow is laminar over the entire length of the plate; therefore,

$$\mathrm{Sh} = 0.664\mathrm{Re}^{1/2}\mathrm{Sc}^{1/3} = 144$$

$$h_M = \frac{\mathrm{Sh}D_v}{L} = 0.0363 \text{ m/s}$$

$$\dot{m} = h_M A(\rho_s - \rho_\infty) = 2.679 \times 10^{-5} \text{ kg/s}$$

$$q = \dot{m}h_{fg} = 65.8 \text{ W}$$

The same value for q would be obtained by calculating the Nusselt number and heat transfer coefficient h and setting $q = hA(t_\infty - t_s)$.

The kind of similarity between heat and mass transfer that results in Equations (29) to (32) can also be shown to exist between heat and momentum transfer. Chilton and Colburn (1934) used this similarity to relate Nusselt number to friction factor by the analogy

$$j_H = \frac{\mathrm{Nu}}{\mathrm{Re}\,\mathrm{Pr}^{(1-n)}} = \mathrm{St}\,\mathrm{Pr}^n = \frac{f}{2} \qquad (33)$$

where $n = 2/3$, $\mathrm{St} = \mathrm{Nu}/(\mathrm{Re\,Pr})$ is the Stanton number, and j_H is the Chilton-Colburn *j*-factor for heat transfer. Substituting Sh for Nu and Sc for Pr in Equations (31) and (32) gives the Chilton-Colburn *j*-factor for mass transfer, j_D:

$$j_D = \frac{\mathrm{Sh}}{\mathrm{Re}\,\mathrm{Sc}^{(1-n)}} = \mathrm{St}_m\mathrm{Sc}^n = \frac{f}{2} \qquad (34)$$

where $\mathrm{St}_m = \mathrm{Sh}P_{Am}/(\mathrm{Re\,Sc})$ is the Stanton number for mass transfer. Equations (33) and (34) are called the **Chilton-Colburn *j*-factor analogy**.

The power of the Chilton-Colburn *j*-factor analogy is represented in Figures 7 to 10. Figure 7 plots various experimental values of j_D from a flat plate with flow parallel to the plate surface. The solid line, which represents the data to near perfection, is actually $f/2$ from Blasius' solution of laminar flow on a flat plate (left-hand portion of the solid line) and Goldstein's solution for a turbulent boundary layer (right-hand portion). The right-hand part also represents McAdams' (1954) correlation of turbulent flow heat transfer coefficient for a flat plate.

A **wetted-wall column** is a vertical tube in which a thin liquid film adheres to the tube surface and exchanges mass by evaporation or absorption with a gas flowing through the tube. Figure 8 illustrates typical data on vaporization in wetted-wall columns, plotted as j_D versus Re. The point spread with variation in $\mu/\rho D_v$ results from Gilliland's finding of an exponent of 0.56, not 2/3, representing the effect of the Schmidt number. Gilliland's equation can be written as follows:

$$j_D = 0.023\mathrm{Re}^{-0.17}\left(\frac{\mu}{\rho D_v}\right)^{-0.56} \qquad (35)$$

Similarly, McAdams' (1954) equation for heat transfer in pipes can be expressed as

$$j_H = 0.023\mathrm{Re}^{-0.20}\left(\frac{c_p\mu}{k}\right)^{-0.7} \qquad (36)$$

This is represented by the dash-dot curve in Figure 8, which falls below the mass transfer data. The curve $f/2$, representing friction in smooth tubes, is the upper, solid curve.

Data for liquid evaporation from single cylinders into gas streams flowing transversely to the cylinders' axes are shown in Figure 9. Although the dash-dot line in Figure 9 represents the data, it is actually taken from McAdams (1954) as representative of a large collection of data on heat transfer to single cylinders placed transverse to airstreams. To compare these data with friction, it is necessary to distinguish between total drag and skin friction. Because the analogies are based on skin friction, normal pressure drag must be subtracted from the measured total drag. At Re = 1000, skin friction is 12.6% of the total drag; at Re = 31 600, it is only 1.9%. Consequently, values of $f/2$ at a high Reynolds number, obtained by the difference, are subject to considerable error.

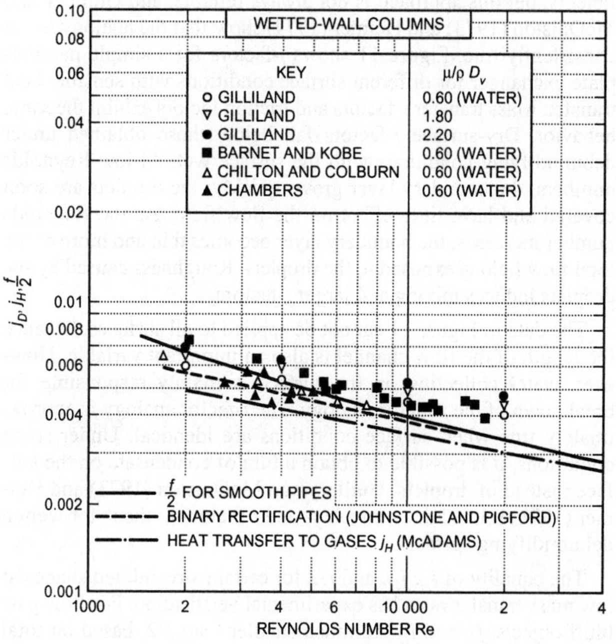

Fig. 8 Vaporization and Absorption in Wetted-Wall Column

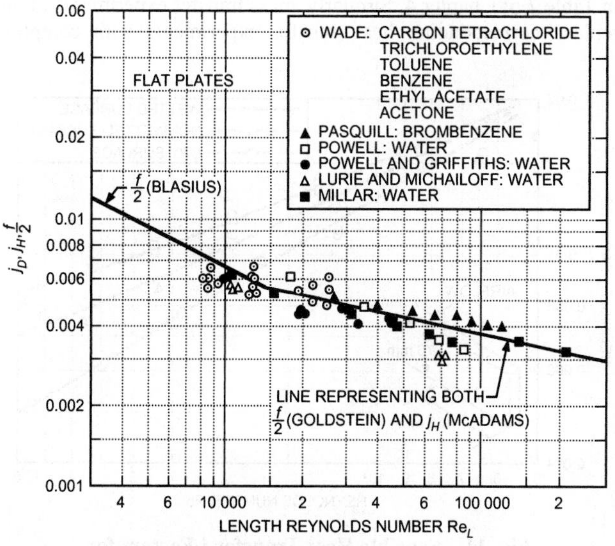

Fig. 7 Mass Transfer from Flat Plate

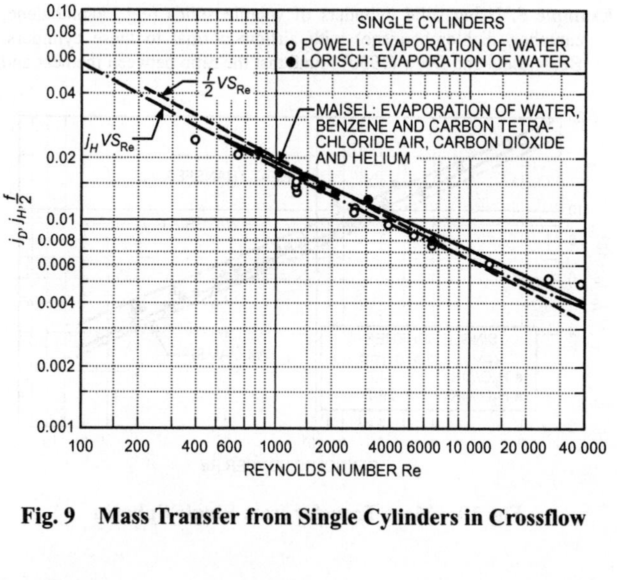

Fig. 9 Mass Transfer from Single Cylinders in Crossflow

In Figure 10, data on evaporation of water into air for single spheres are presented. The solid line, which best represents these data, agrees with the dashed line representing McAdams' correlation for heat transfer to spheres. These results cannot be compared with friction or momentum transfer because total drag has not been allocated to skin friction and normal pressure drag. Application of these data to air/water-contacting devices such as air washers and spray cooling towers is well substantiated.

When the temperature of the heat exchanger surface in contact with moist air is below the air's dew-point temperature, vapor condensation occurs. Typically, air dry-bulb temperature and humidity ratio both decrease as air flows through the exchanger. Therefore, sensible and latent heat transfer occur simultaneously. This process is similar to one that occurs in a spray dehumidifier and can be analyzed using the same procedure; however, this is not generally done.

Cooling coil analysis and design are complicated by the problem of determining transport coefficients h, h_M, and f. It would be convenient if heat transfer and friction data for dry heating coils could be used with the Colburn analogy to obtain the mass transfer coefficients, but this approach is not always reliable, and Guillory and McQuiston (1973) and Helmer (1974) show that the analogy is not consistently true. Figure 11 shows j-factors for a simple parallel-plate exchanger for different surface conditions with sensible heat transfer. Mass transfer j-factors and friction factors exhibit the same behavior. Dry-surface j-factors fall below those obtained under dehumidifying conditions with the surface wet. At low Reynolds numbers, the boundary layer grows quickly; the droplets are soon covered and have little effect on the flow field. As the Reynolds number increases, the boundary layer becomes thin and more of the total flow field is exposed to the droplets. Roughness caused by the droplets induces mixing and larger j-factors.

The data in Figure 11 cannot be applied to all surfaces, because the length of the flow channel is also an important variable. However, water collecting on the surface is mainly responsible for breakdown of the j-factor analogy. The j-factor analogy is approximately true when surface conditions are identical. Under some conditions, it is possible to obtain a film of condensate on the surface instead of droplets. Guillory and McQuiston (1973) and Helmer (1974) related dry sensible j- and f-factors to those for wetted dehumidifying surfaces.

The equality of j_H, j_D, and $f/2$ for certain streamlined shapes at low mass transfer rates has experimental verification. For flow past bluff objects, j_H and j_D are much smaller than $f/2$, based on total pressure drag. The heat and mass transfer, however, still relate in a useful way by equating j_H and j_D.

Example 5. Using solid cylinders of volatile solids (e.g., naphthalene, camphor, dichlorobenzene) with airflow normal to these cylinders, Bedingfield and Drew (1950) found that the ratio between the heat and mass transfer coefficients could be closely correlated by the following relation:

$$\frac{h}{\rho h_M} = [1230\ \mathrm{J/(kg\cdot K)}]\left(\frac{\mu}{\rho D_v}\right)^{0.56}$$

For completely dry air at 21°C flowing at a velocity of 9.5 m/s over a wet-bulb thermometer of diameter d = 7.5 mm, determine the heat and mass transfer coefficients from Figure 9 and compare their ratio with the Bedingfield-Drew relation.

Solution: For dry air at 21°C and standard pressure, ρ = 1.198 kg/m³, μ = 1.82 × 10^{-5} kg/(s·m), k = 0.02581 W/(m·K), and c_p = 1.006 kJ/(kg·K). From Equation (10), D_v = 25.13 mm²/s. Therefore,

$$Re_{da} = \rho u_\infty d/\mu = 1.198 \times 9.5 \times 7.5/(1000 \times 1.82 \times 10^{-5}) = 4690$$

$$Pr = c_p\mu/k = 1.006 \times 1.82 \times 10^{-5} \times 1000/0.02581 = 0.709$$

$$Sc = \mu/\rho D_v = 1.82 \times 10^{-5} \times 10^6/(1.198 \times 25.13) = 0.605$$

From Figure 9 at Re_{da} = 4700, read j_H = 0.0089, and j_D = 0.010. From Equations (33) and (34),

$$h = j_H \rho c_p u_\infty/(Pr)^{2/3}$$
$$= 0.0089 \times 1.198 \times 1.006 \times 9.5 \times 1000/(0.709)^{2/3}$$
$$= 128\ \mathrm{W/(m^2\cdot K)}$$
$$h_M = j_D u_\infty/(Sc)^{2/3} = 0.010 \times 9.5/(0.605)^{2/3}$$
$$= 0.133\ \mathrm{m/s}$$
$$h/\rho h_M = 128/(1.198 \times 0.133) = 803\ \mathrm{J/(kg\cdot K)}$$

From the Bedingfield-Drew relation,

$$h/\rho h_M = 1230(0.605)^{0.56} = 928\ \mathrm{J/(kg\cdot K)}$$

Equations (34) and (35) are called the Reynolds analogy when Pr = Sc = 1. This suggests that $h/\rho h_M = c_p$ = 1006 J/(kg·K). This close agreement is because the ratio Sc/Pr is 0.605/0.709 or 0.85, so that the exponent of these numbers has little effect on the ratio of the transfer coefficients.

The extensive developments for calculating heat transfer coefficients can be applied to calculate mass transfer coefficients under similar geometrical and flow conditions using the j-factor analogy. For example, Table 7 of Chapter 4 lists equations for calculating heat transfer coefficients for flow inside and normal to pipes. Each equation can be used for mass transfer coefficient calculations by equating j_H and j_D and imposing the same restriction to each stated in Table 7 of Chapter 4. Similarly, mass transfer experiments often replace corresponding heat transfer experiments with complex

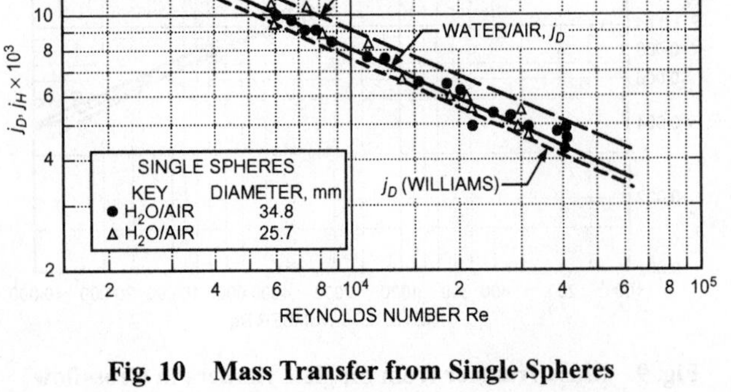

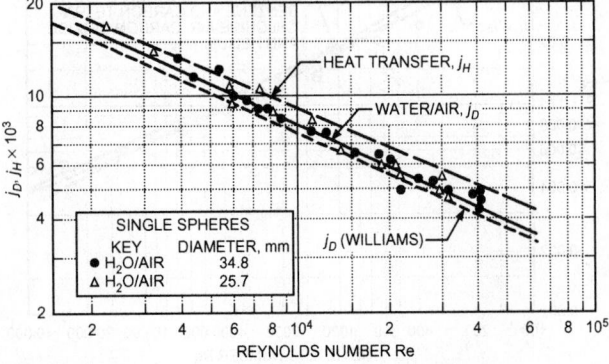

Fig. 10 Mass Transfer from Single Spheres

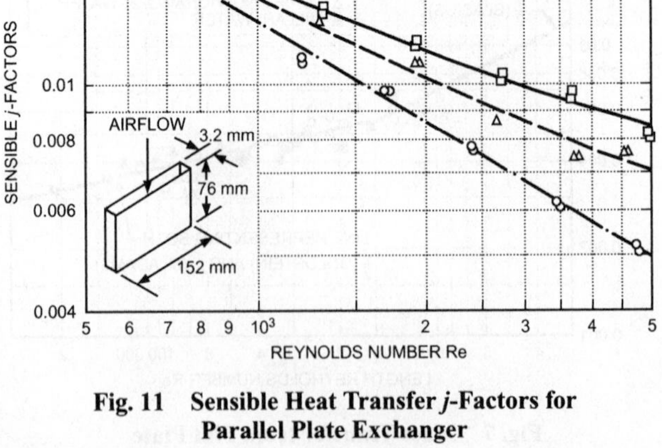

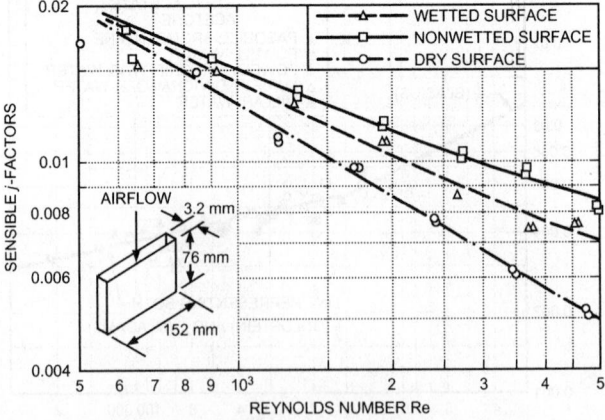

Fig. 11 Sensible Heat Transfer *j*-Factors for Parallel Plate Exchanger

geometries where exact boundary conditions are difficult to model (Sparrow and Ohadi 1987a, 1987b).

The *j*-factor analogy is useful only at low mass transfer rates. As the rate increases, the movement of matter normal to the transfer surface increases the convective velocity. For example, if a gas is blown from many small holes in a flat plate placed parallel to an airstream, the boundary layer thickens, and resistance to both mass and heat transfer increases with increasing blowing rate. Heat transfer data are usually collected at zero or, at least, insignificant mass transfer rates. Therefore, if such data are to be valid for a mass transfer process, the mass transfer rate (i.e., the blowing) must be low.

The *j*-factor relationship $j_H = j_D$ can still be valid at high mass transfer rates, but neither j_H nor j_D can be represented by data at zero mass transfer conditions. Chapter 24 of Bird et al. (1960) and Eckert and Drake (1972) have detailed information on high mass transfer rates.

Lewis Relation

Heat and mass transfer coefficients are satisfactorily related at the same Reynolds number by equating the Chilton-Colburn *j*-factors. Comparing Equations (33) and (34) gives

$$\text{St}\,\text{Pr}^n = f/2 = \text{St}_m \text{Sc}^n$$

Inserting the definitions of St, Pr, St_m, and Sc gives

$$\frac{h}{\rho c_p \bar{u}}\left(\frac{c_p \mu}{k}\right)^{2/3} = \frac{h_M P_{Am}}{\bar{u}}\left(\frac{\mu}{\rho D_v}\right)^{2/3}$$

or

$$\frac{h}{h_M \rho c_p} = P_{Am}\left[\frac{(\mu/\rho D_v)}{(c_p \mu/k)}\right]^{2/3} = P_{Am}(\alpha/D_v)^{2/3} \quad (37)$$

The quantity α/D_v is the **Lewis number Le**. Its magnitude expresses relative rates of propagation of energy and mass within a system. It is fairly insensitive to temperature variation. For air and water vapor mixtures, the ratio is (0.60/0.71) or 0.845, and $(0.845)^{2/3}$ is 0.894. At low diffusion rates, where the heat/mass transfer analogy is valid, P_{Am} is essentially unity. Therefore, for air and water vapor mixtures,

$$h/h_M \rho c_p \approx 1 \quad (38)$$

The ratio of the heat transfer coefficient to the mass transfer coefficient equals the specific heat per unit volume of the mixture at constant pressure. This relation [Equation (38)] is usually called the Lewis relation and is nearly true for air and water vapor at low mass transfer rates. It is generally not true for other gas mixtures because the ratio Le of thermal to vapor diffusivity can differ from unity. Agreement between wet-bulb temperature and adiabatic saturation temperature is a direct result of the nearness of the Lewis number to unity for air and water vapor.

The Lewis relation is valid in turbulent flow whether or not α/D_v equals 1 because eddy diffusion in turbulent flow involves the same mixing action for heat exchange as for mass exchange, and this action overwhelms any molecular diffusion. Deviations from the Lewis relation are, therefore, due to a laminar boundary layer or a laminar sublayer and buffer zone where molecular transport phenomena are the controlling factors.

SIMULTANEOUS HEAT AND MASS TRANSFER BETWEEN WATER-WETTED SURFACES AND AIR

A simplified method used to solve simultaneous heat and mass transfer problems was developed using the Lewis relation, and it gives satisfactory results for most air-conditioning processes. Extrapolation to very high mass transfer rates, where the simple heat-mass transfer analogy is not valid, leads to erroneous results.

Enthalpy Potential

The water vapor concentration in the air is the humidity ratio *W*, defined as

$$W \equiv \frac{\rho_B}{\rho_A} \quad (39)$$

A mass transfer coefficient is defined using *W* as the driving potential:

$$\dot{m}_B'' = K_M(W_i - W_\infty) \quad (40)$$

where the coefficient K_M is in kg/(s·m²). For dilute mixtures, $\rho_{Ai} \cong \rho_{A\infty}$; that is, the partial mass density of dry air changes by only a small percentage between interface and free stream conditions. Therefore,

$$\dot{m}_B'' = \frac{K_M}{\rho_{Am}}(\rho_{Bi} - \rho_\infty) \quad (41)$$

where ρ_{Am} = mean density of dry air, kg/m³. Comparing Equation (41) with Equation (24) shows that

$$h_M = \frac{K_M}{\rho_{Am}} \quad (42)$$

The **humid specific heat c_{pm}** of the airstream is, by definition (Mason and Monchick 1965),

$$c_{pm} = (1 + W_\infty)c_p \quad (43a)$$

or

$$c_{pm} = (\rho/\rho_{A\infty})c_p \quad (43b)$$

where c_{pm} is in kJ/(kg$_{da}$·K).

Substituting from Equations (42) and (43b) into Equation (38) gives

$$\frac{h\rho_{Am}}{K_M \rho_{A\infty} c_{pm}} = 1 \approx \frac{h}{K_M c_{pm}} \quad (44)$$

because $\rho_{Am} \cong \rho_{A\infty}$ because of the small change in dry-air density. Using a mass transfer coefficient with the humidity ratio as the driving force, the Lewis relation becomes ratio of heat to mass transfer coefficient equals humid specific heat.

For the plate humidifier illustrated in Figure 6, the total heat transfer from liquid to interface is

$$q'' = q_A'' + \dot{m}_B'' h_{fg} \quad (45)$$

Using the definitions of the heat and mass transfer coefficients gives

$$q'' = h(t_i - t_\infty) + K_M(W_i - W_\infty)h_{fg} \quad (46)$$

Assuming Equation (44) is valid gives

$$q'' = K_M[c_{pm}(t_i - t_\infty) + (W_i - W_\infty)h_{fg}] \quad (47)$$

The enthalpy of the air is approximately

$$h = c_{pa}t + Wh_s \quad (48)$$

The enthalpy h_s of the water vapor can be expressed by the ideal gas law as

$$h_s = c_{ps}(t - t_o) + h_{fgo} \tag{49}$$

where the base of enthalpy is taken as saturated water at temperature t_o. Choosing t_o = 0°C to correspond with the base of the dry-air enthalpy gives

$$h = (c_{pa} + Wc_{ps})t + Wh_{fgo} = c_{pm}t + Wh_{fgo} \tag{50}$$

If small changes in the latent heat of vaporization of water with temperature are neglected when comparing Equations (48) and (50), the total heat transfer can be written as

$$q'' = K_M(h_i - h_\infty) \tag{51}$$

Where the driving potential for heat transfer is temperature difference and the driving potential for mass transfer is mass concentration or partial pressure, the driving potential for simultaneous transfer of heat and mass in an air water/vapor mixture is, to a close approximation, enthalpy.

Basic Equations for Direct-Contact Equipment

Air-conditioning equipment can be classified by whether the air and water used as a cooling or heating fluid are (1) in direct contact or (2) separated by a solid wall. Examples of the former are air washers and cooling towers; an example of the latter is a direct-expansion refrigerant (or water) cooling and dehumidifying coil. In both cases, the airstream is in contact with a water surface. Direct contact implies contact directly with the cooling (or heating) fluid. In the dehumidifying coil, contact is direct with condensate removed from the airstream, but is indirect with refrigerant flowing inside the coil tubes. These two cases are treated separately because the surface areas of direct-contact equipment cannot be evaluated.

For the direct-contact spray chamber air washer of cross-sectional area A_{cs} and length l (Figure 12), the steady mass flow rate of dry air per unit cross-sectional area is

$$\dot{m}_a / A_{cs} = G_a \tag{52}$$

and the corresponding mass flux of water flowing parallel with the air is

$$\dot{m}_L / A_{cs} = G_L \tag{53}$$

where

$\dot{m}_a$ = mass flow rate of air, kg/s
G_a = mass flux or flow rate per unit cross-sectional area for air, kg/(s·m²)
$\dot{m}_L$ = mass flow rate of liquid, kg/s
G_L = mass flux or flow rate per unit cross-sectional area for liquid, kg/(s·m²)

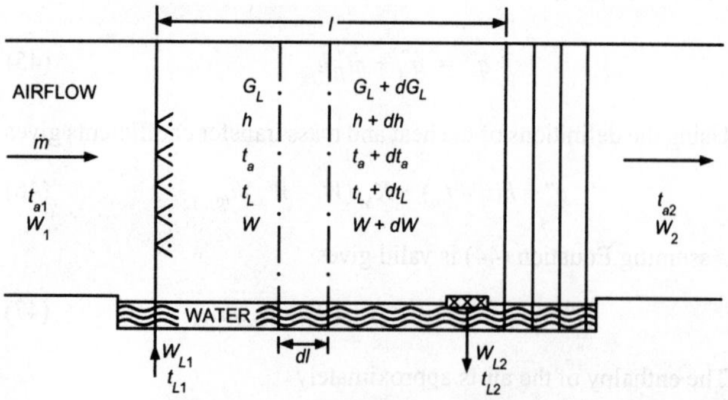

Fig. 12 Air Washer Spray Chamber

Because water is evaporating or condensing, G_L changes by an amount dG_L in a differential length dl of the chamber. Similar changes occur in temperature, humidity ratio, enthalpy, and other properties.

Because evaluating the true surface area in direct-contact equipment is difficult, it is common to work on a unit volume basis. If a_H and a_M are the areas of heat transfer and mass transfer surface per unit of chamber volume, respectively, the total surface areas for heat and mass transfer are

$$A_H = a_H A_{cs} l \quad \text{and} \quad A_M = a_M A_{cs} l \tag{54}$$

The basic equations for the process occurring in the differential length dl can be written for

Mass transfer

$$-dG_L = G_a dW = K_M a_M (W_i - W) dl \tag{55}$$

That is, the water evaporation rate, air moisture content increase, and mass transfer rate are all equal.

Heat transfer to air

$$G_a c_{pm} dt_a = h_a a_H (t_i - t_a) dl \tag{56}$$

Total energy transfer to air

$$G_a(c_{pm} dt_a + h_{fgo} dW) = [K_M a_M (W_i - W) h_{fg} + h_a a_H (t_i - t_a)] dl \tag{57}$$

Assuming $a_H = a_M$ and Le = 1, and neglecting small variations in h_{fg}, Equation (57) reduces to

$$G_a dh = K_M a_M (h_i - h) dl \tag{58}$$

The heat and mass transfer areas of spray chambers are assumed to be identical ($a_H = a_M$). Where packing materials, such as wood slats or Raschig rings, are used, the two areas may be considerably different because the packing may not be wet uniformly. The validity of the Lewis relation was discussed previously. It is not necessary to account for small changes in latent heat h_{fg} after making the two previous assumptions.

Energy balance

$$G_a dh = \pm G_L c_L dt_L \tag{59}$$

A minus sign refers to parallel flow of air and water; a plus refers to counterflow (water flow in the opposite direction from airflow).

The water flow rate changes between inlet and outlet as a result of the mass transfer. For exact energy balance, the term ($c_L t_L dG_L$) should be added to the right side of Equation (59). The percentage change in G_L is quite small in usual applications of air-conditioning equipment and, therefore, can be ignored.

Heat transfer to water

$$\pm G_L c_L dt_L = h_L a_H (t_L - t_i) dl \tag{60}$$

Equations (55) to (60) are the basic relations for solution of simultaneous heat and mass transfer processes in direct-contact air-conditioning equipment.

To facilitate use of these relations in equipment design or performance, three other equations can be extracted from the above set. Combining Equations (58), (59), and (60) gives

$$\frac{h - h_i}{t_L - t_i} = -\frac{h_L a_H}{K_M a_M} = -\frac{h_L}{K_M} \tag{61}$$

Equation (61) relates the enthalpy potential for total heat transfer through the gas film to the temperature potential for this same transfer through the liquid film. Physical reasoning leads to the conclusion that this ratio is proportional to the ratio of gas film resistance ($1/K_M$) to liquid film resistance ($1/h_L$). Combining Equations (56), (58), and (44) gives

$$\frac{dh}{dt_a} = \frac{h - h_i}{t_a - t_i} \tag{62}$$

Similarly, combining Equations (55), (56), and (44) gives

$$\frac{dW}{dt_a} = \frac{W - W_i}{t_a - t_i} \tag{63}$$

Equation (63) indicates that, at any cross section in the spray chamber, the instantaneous slope of the air path dW/dt_a on a psychrometric chart is determined by a straight line connecting the air state with the interface saturation state at that cross section. In Figure 13, state 1 represents the state of the air entering the parallel-flow air washer chamber of Figure 12. The washer is operating as a heating and humidifying apparatus, so the interface saturation state of the water at air inlet is the state designated 1_i. Therefore, the initial slope of the air path is along a line directed from state 1 to state 1_i. As the air is heated, the water cools and the interface temperature drops. Corresponding air states and interface saturation states are indicated by the letters *a*, *b*, *c*, and *d* in Figure 13. In each instance, the air path is directed toward the associated interface state. The interface states are derived from Equations (59) and (61). Equation (59) describes how air enthalpy changes with water temperature; Equation (61) describes how the interface saturation state changes to accommodate this change in air and water conditions. The solution for the interface state on the normal psychrometric chart of Figure 13 can be determined either by trial and error from Equations (59) and (61) or by a complex graphical procedure (Kusuda 1957).

Air Washers

Air washers are direct-contact apparatus used to (1) simultaneously change the temperature and humidity content of air passing through the chamber and (2) remove air contaminants such as dust and odors. Adiabatic spray washers, which have no external heating or chilling source, are used to cool and humidify air. Chilled-spray air washers have an external chiller to cool and dehumidify air. Heated-spray air washers, with an external heating source that provides additional energy for water evaporation, are used to humidify and possibly heat air.

Example 6. A parallel-flow air washer with the following design conditions is to be designed (see Figure 12).

Water temperature at inlet t_{L1} = 35°C

Water temperature at outlet t_{L2} = 23.9°C

Air temperature at inlet t_{a1} = 18.3°C

Air wet-bulb at inlet t'_{a1} = 7.2°C

Air mass flow rate per unit area G_a = 1.628 kg/(s·m²)

Spray ratio G_L/G_a = 0.70

Air heat transfer coefficient per cubic metre of chamber volume $h_a a_H$ = 1.34 kW/(m³·K)

Liquid heat transfer coefficient per cubic metre of chamber volume $h_L a_H$ = 16.77 kW/(m³·K)

Air volumetric flow rate Q = 3.07 m³/s

Solution: The air mass flow rate $\dot{m}_a$ = 3.07 × 1.20 = 3.68 kg/s; the required spray chamber cross-sectional area is then $A_{cs} = \dot{m}_a/G_a$ = 3.68/1.628 = 2.26 m². The mass transfer coefficient is given by the Lewis relation [Equation (44)] as

$$K_M a_M = (h_a a_H)/c_{pm} = 1.34/1.005 = 1.33 \text{ kg/(m}^3\cdot\text{s)}$$

Figure 14 shows the enthalpy/temperature psychrometric chart with the graphical solution for the interface states and the air path through the washer spray chamber.

1. Enter bottom of chart with t'_{a1} of 7.2°C, and follow up to saturation curve to establish air enthalpy h_1 of 41.1 kJ/kg. Extend this enthalpy line to intersect initial air temperature t_{a1} of 18.3°C (state 1 of air) and initial water temperature t_{L1} of 35°C at point A. (Note that the temperature scale is used for both air and water temperatures.)
2. Through point A, construct the *energy balance* line A-B with a slope of

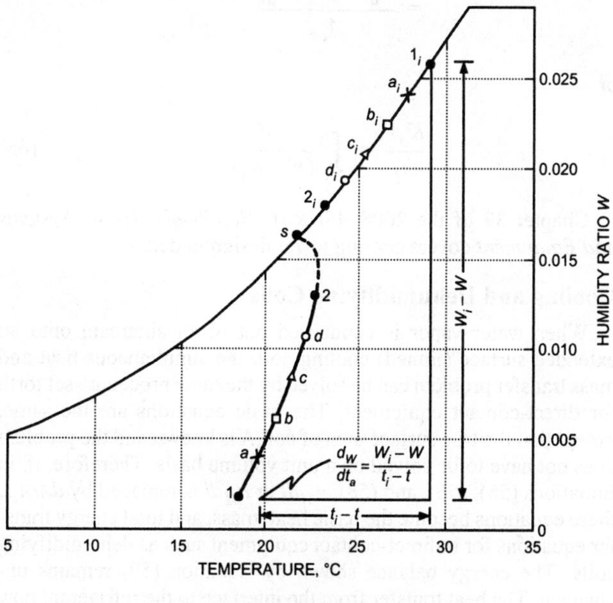

Fig. 13 Air Washer Humidification Process on Psychrometric Chart

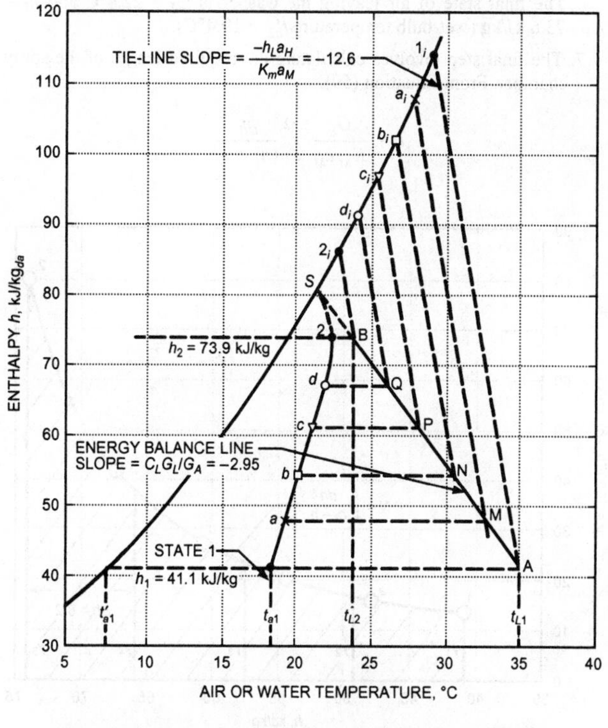

Fig. 14 Graphical Solution for Air-State Path in Parallel Flow Air Washer

$$\frac{dh}{dt_L} = -\frac{c_L G_L}{G_a} = -2.95$$

Point B is determined by intersection with the leaving water temperature t_{L2} = 23.9°C. The negative slope here is a consequence of the parallel flow, which results in the air/water mixture's approaching, but not reaching, the common saturation state *s*. (Line A-B has no physical significance in representing any *air state* on the psychrometric chart. It is merely a construction line in the graphical solution.)

3. Through point A, construct the *tie-line* A-1_i having a slope of

$$\frac{h - h_i}{t_L - t_i} = -\frac{h_L a_H}{K_M a_M} = -\frac{16.77}{1.33} = -12.6$$

The intersection of this line with the saturation curve gives the initial interface state 1_i at the chamber inlet. [Note how the energy balance line and tie-line, representing Equations (59) and (61), combine for a simple graphical solution on Figure 14 for the interface state.]

4. The initial slope of the air path can now be constructed, according to Equation (62), drawing line 1-*a* toward the initial interface state 1_i. (The length of line 1-*a* depends on the degree of accuracy required in the solution and the rate at which the slope of the air path changes.)
5. Construct the horizontal line *a*-M, locating point M on the energy-balance line. Draw a new tie-line (slope of −12.6 as before) from M to a_i locating interface state a_i. Continue the air path from *a* to *b* by directing it toward the new interface state a_i. (Note that the change in slope of the air path from 1-*a* to *a*-*b* is quite small, justifying the path incremental lengths used.)
6. Continue in the manner of step 5 until point 2, the final state of air leaving the chamber, is reached. In this example, six steps are used in the graphical construction, with the following results:

State	1	*a*	*b*	*c*	*d*	2
t_L	35	32.8	30.6	28.3	26.1	23.9
h	41.1	47.7	54.3	60.8	67.4	73.9
t_i	29.2	27.9	26.7	25.4	24.2	22.9
h_i	114.4	108.0	102.3	96.9	91.3	86.4
t_a	18.3	19.3	20.3	21.1	21.9	22.4

The final state of air leaving the washer is t_{a2} = 22.4°C and h_2 = 73.6 kJ/kg (wet-bulb temperature t'_{a2} = 19.4°C).

7. The final step involves calculating the required length of the spray chamber. From Equation (59),

$$l = \frac{G_a}{K_M a_M} \int_1^2 \frac{dh}{(h_i - h)}$$

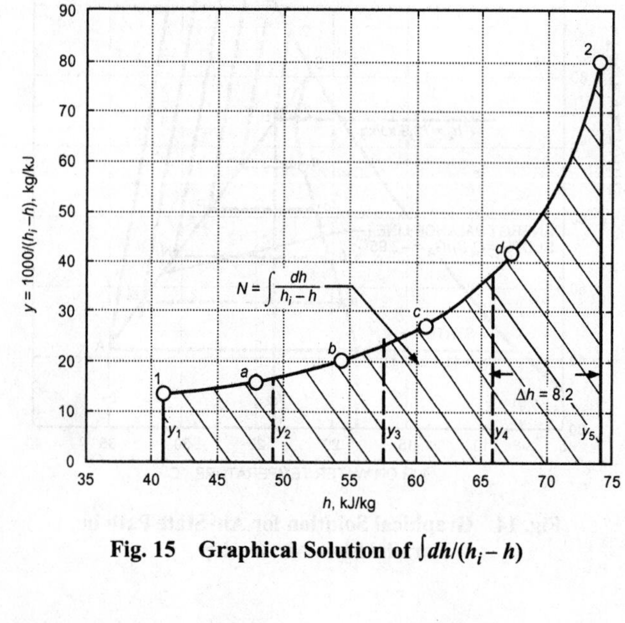

Fig. 15 Graphical Solution of $\int dh/(h_i - h)$

The integral is evaluated graphically by plotting $1/(h_i - h)$ versus h, as shown in Figure 15. Any satisfactory graphical method can be used to evaluate the area under the curve. Simpson's rule with four equal increments of Δh equal to 8.2 gives

$$N = \int_1^2 \frac{dh}{(h_i - h)} \approx (\Delta h/3)(y_1 + 4y_2 + 2y_3 + 4y_4 + y_5)$$

$$N = (8.2/3)[0.0136 + (4 \times 0.0167) + (2 \times 0.0238) + (4 \times 0.0372) + 0.0800] = 0.975$$

Therefore, the design length is l = (1.628/1.33)(0.975) = 1.19 m.

This method can also be used to predict performance of existing direct-contact equipment and to determine transfer coefficients when performance data from test runs are available. By knowing the water and air temperatures entering and leaving the chamber and the spray ratio, it is possible, by trial and error, to determine the proper slope of the tie-line necessary to achieve the measured final air state. The tie-line slope gives the ratio $h_L a_H / K_M a_M$; $K_M a_M$ is found from the integral relationship in Example 6 from the known chamber length l.

Additional descriptions of air spray washers and general performance criteria are given in Chapter 40 of the 2008 *ASHRAE Handbook—HVAC Systems and Equipment*.

Cooling Towers

A cooling tower is a direct-contact heat exchanger in which waste heat picked up by the cooling water from a refrigerator, air conditioner, or industrial process is transferred to atmospheric air by cooling the water. Cooling is achieved by breaking up the water flow to provide a large water surface for air, moving by natural or forced convection through the tower, to contact the water. Cooling towers may be counterflow, crossflow, or a combination of both.

The temperature of water leaving the tower and the packing depth needed to achieve the desired leaving water temperature are of primary interest for design. Therefore, the mass and energy balance equations are based on an overall coefficient K, which is based on (1) the enthalpy driving force from h at the bulk water temperature and (2) neglecting the film resistance. Combining Equations (58) and (59) and using the parameters described previously yields

$$G_L c_L dt = K_M a_M (h_i - h) dl = G_a dh = \frac{K_a dV (h' - h_a)}{A_{cs}} \qquad (64)$$

or

$$\frac{K_a V}{\dot{m}_L} = \int_{t_1}^{t_2} \frac{c_L dt}{(h' - h_a)} \qquad (65)$$

Chapter 39 of the 2008 *ASHRAE Handbook—HVAC Systems and Equipment* covers cooling tower design in detail.

Cooling and Dehumidifying Coils

When water vapor is condensed out of an airstream onto an extended-surface (finned) cooling coil, the simultaneous heat and mass transfer problem can be solved by the same procedure set forth for direct-contact equipment. The basic equations are the same, except that the true surface area of coil A is known and the problem does not have to be solved on a unit volume basis. Therefore, if, in Equations (55), (56), and (58), $a_M dl$ or $a_H dl$ is replaced by dA/A_{cs}, these equations become the basic heat, mass, and total energy transfer equations for indirect-contact equipment such as dehumidifying coils. The energy balance shown by Equation (59) remains unchanged. The heat transfer from the interface to the refrigerant now encounters the combined resistances of the condensate film ($R_L = 1/h_L$); the metal wall and fins, if any (R_m); and the refrigerant film

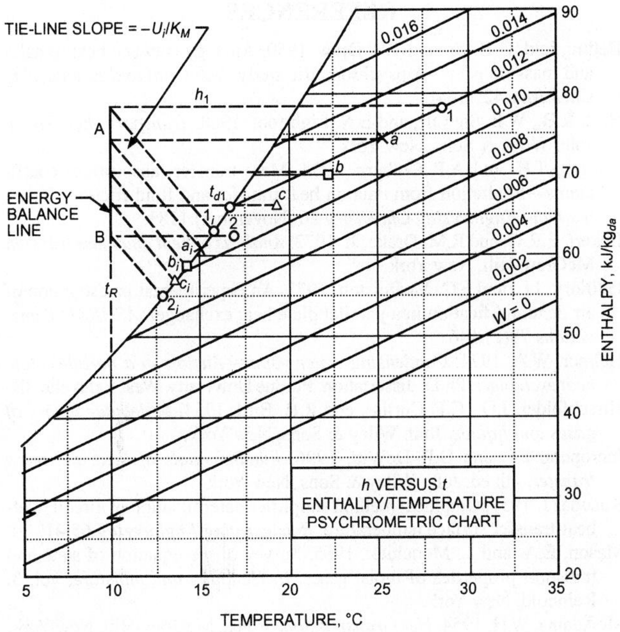

Fig. 16 Graphical Solution for Air-State Path in Dehumidifying Coil with Constant Refrigerant Temperature

($R_r = A/h_r A_r$). If this combined resistance is designated as $R_i = R_L + R_m + R_r = 1/U_i$, Equation (60) becomes, for a coil dehumidifier,

$$\pm \dot{m}_L c_L dt_L = U_i(t_L - t_i)dA \tag{66}$$

(plus sign for counterflow, minus sign for parallel flow).

The tie-line slope is then

$$\frac{h - h_i}{t_L - t_i} = \pm \frac{U_i}{K_M} \tag{67}$$

Figure 16 illustrates the graphical solution on a psychrometric chart for the air path through a dehumidifying coil with a constant refrigerant temperature. Because the tie-line slope is infinite in this case, the energy balance line is vertical. The corresponding interface states and air states are denoted by the same letter symbols, and the solution follows the same procedure as in Example 6.

If the problem is to determine the required coil surface area for a given performance, the area is computed by the following relation:

$$A = \frac{\dot{m}_a}{K_M} \int_1^2 \frac{dh}{(h_i - h)} \tag{68}$$

This graphical solution on the psychrometric chart automatically determines whether any part of the coil is dry. Thus, in the example illustrated in Figure 16, entering air at state 1 initially encounters an interface saturation state 1_i, clearly below its dew-point temperature t_{d1}, so the coil immediately becomes wet. Had the graphical technique resulted in an initial interface state above the dew-point temperature of the entering air, the coil would be initially dry. The air would then follow a constant humidity ratio line (the sloping W = constant lines on the chart) until the interface state reached the air dew-point temperature.

Mizushina et al. (1959) developed this method not only for water vapor and air, but also for other vapor/gas mixtures. Chapter 22 of the 2008 *ASHRAE Handbook—HVAC Systems and Equipment* shows another related method, based on ARI *Standard* 410, of determining air-cooling and dehumidifying coil performance.

Example 7. Air enters an air conditioner at 101.325 kPa, 30°C, and 85% rh at a rate of 0.2 m³/s and leaves as saturated air at 14°C. Condensed moisture is also removed at 14°C. Calculate the heat transfer and moisture removal rate from the air.

Solution: Water mass flow is

$$\dot{m}_w = \dot{m}_a(W_1 - W_2)$$

and energy or heat transfer rate is

$$\dot{q}_{out} = \dot{m}_a(h_1 - h_2) - \dot{m}_w h_w$$

Properties of air both at inlet and exit states can be determined from the psychrometric chart as follows:

$$h_1 = 89.0 \text{ kJ/kg}_{da}, \quad W_1 = 0.023 \text{ kg}_{H_2O}/\text{kg}_{da}$$

$$\text{specific volume} = 0.89 \text{ m}^3/\text{kg}_{da}$$

$$h_2 = 39.3 \text{ kJ/kg}_{da}, \quad W_2 = 0.010 \text{ kg}_{H_2O}/\text{kg}_{da}$$

Enthalpy of the condensate from saturated-water temperature table is

$$h_w = h_f \text{ at } 14°\text{C} = 58.81 \text{ kJ/kg}$$

Then,

$$\dot{m}_a = 0.2/0.89 = 0.225 \text{ kg/s}$$

$$\dot{m}_w = (0.225)(0.023 - 0.010) = 0.002925 \text{ kg/s}$$

$$\dot{q}_{out} = (0.225)(89.0 - 39.3) - (0.002925)(58.81) = 11.0 \text{ kJ/s}$$

So, the air conditioner's heat transfer and moisture removal rates are 10.5 kJ/s and 0.002925 kg/s, respectively.

SYMBOLS

A = surface area, m²
a = constant, dimensionless; or surface area per unit volume, m²/m³
A_{cs} = cross-sectional area, m²
b = exponent or constant, dimensionless
C = molal concentration of solute in solvent, mol/m³
c_L = specific heat of liquid, kJ/(kg·K)
c_p = specific heat at constant pressure, kJ/(kg·K)
c_{pm} = specific heat of moist air at constant pressure, kJ/(kg$_{da}$·K)
d = diameter, m
D_v = diffusion coefficient (mass diffusivity), mm²/s
f = Fanning friction factor, dimensionless
G = mass flux, flow rate per unit of cross-sectional area, kg/(s·m²)
h = enthalpy, kJ/kg; or heat transfer coefficient, W/(m²·K)
h_{fg} = enthalpy of vaporization, kJ/kg
h_M = mass transfer coefficient, m/s
J = diffusive mass flux, kg/(s·m²)
J^* = diffusive molar flux, mol/(s·m²)
j_D = Colburn mass transfer group = Sh/(ReSc$^{1/3}$), dimensionless
j_H = Colburn heat transfer group = Nu/(RePr$^{1/3}$), dimensionless
k = thermal conductivity, W/(m·K)
K_M = mass transfer coefficient, kg/(s·m²)
L = characteristic length, m
l = length, m
Le = Lewis number = α/D_v, dimensionless
M = relative molecular mass, kg/kg mol
$\dot{m}$ = rate of mass transfer, kg/s
$\dot{m}''$ = mass flux, kg/(s·m²)
$\dot{m}''^*$ = molar flux, mol/(s·m²)
Nu = Nusselt number = hL/k, dimensionless
p = pressure, kPa
P_{Am} = logarithmic mean density factor
Pr = Prandtl number = $c_p\mu/k$, dimensionless
Q = volumetric flow rate, m³/s
q = rate of heat transfer, W
q'' = heat flux per unit area, W/m²
Re = Reynolds number = $\rho uL/\mu$, dimensionless
R_i = combined thermal resistance, (m²·K)/W
R_L = thermal resistance of condensate film, (m²·K)/W

R_m = thermal resistance across metal wall and fins, $(m^2 \cdot K)/W$
R_r = thermal resistance of refrigerant film, $(m^2 \cdot K)/W$
R_u = universal gas constant = 8.314 kJ/(mol·K)
Sc = Schmidt number = $\mu/\rho D_v$, dimensionless
Sh = Sherwood number = $h_M L/D_v$, dimensionless
St = Stanton number = $h/\rho c_p \bar{u}$, dimensionless
St_m = mass transfer Stanton number = $h_M P_{Am}/\bar{u}$, dimensionless
T = absolute temperature, K
t = temperature, °C
u = velocity in x direction, m/s
U_i = overall conductance from refrigerant to air-water interface for dehumidifying coil, $W/(m^2 \cdot K)$
V = fluid stream velocity, m/s
v = velocity in y direction, m/s
v_i = velocity normal to mass transfer surface for component i, m/s
W = humidity ratio, kg_w/kg_{da}
X,Y,Z = coordinate direction, dimensionless
x,y,z = coordinate direction, m

Greek

α = thermal diffusivity = $k/\rho c_p$, m^2/s
ε = Lennard-Jones energy parameter
ε_D = eddy mass diffusivity, m^2/s
θ = time parameter, dimensionless
μ = absolute (dynamic) viscosity, kg/(m·s)
$\bar{\mu}$ = permeability, mg/(s·m·Pa)
ν = kinematic viscosity, m^2/s
ρ = mass density or concentration, kg/m^3
σ = characteristic molecular diameter, nm
τ = time
τ_i = shear stress in the x-y coordinate plane, N/m^2
ω = mass fraction, kg/kg
$\Omega_{D,AB}$ = temperature function in Equation (9)

Subscripts

A = gas component of binary mixture
a = air property
Am = logarithmic mean
B = more dilute gas component of binary mixture
c = critical state
da = dry-air property or air-side transfer quantity
H = heat transfer quantity
i = air/water interface value
L = liquid
M = mass transfer quantity
m = mean value or metal
min = minimum
o = property evaluated at 0°C
s = water vapor property or transport quantity
w = water vapor
∞ = property of main fluid stream

Superscripts

* = on molar basis
– = average value
′ = wet bulb

REFERENCES

Bedingfield, G.H., Jr. and T.B. Drew. 1950. Analogy between heat transfer and mass transfer—A psychrometric study. *Industrial and Engineering Chemistry* 42:1164.

Bird, R.B., W.E. Stewart, and E.N. Lightfoot. 1960. *Transport phenomena.* John Wiley & Sons, New York.

Chilton, T.H. and A.P. Colburn. 1934. Mass transfer (absorption) coefficients—Prediction from data on heat transfer and fluid friction. *Industrial and Engineering Chemistry* 26 (November):1183.

Eckert, E.R.G. and R.M. Drake, Jr. 1972. *Analysis of heat and mass transfer.* McGraw-Hill, New York.

Guillory, J.L. and F.C. McQuiston. 1973. An experimental investigation of air dehumidification in a parallel plate heat exchanger. *ASHRAE Transactions* 79(2):146.

Helmer, W.A. 1974. *Condensing water vapor—Airflow in a parallel plate heat exchanger.* Ph.D. dissertation, Purdue University, West Lafayette, IN.

Hirschfelder, J.O., C.F. Curtiss, and R.B. Bird. 1954. *Molecular theory of gases and liquids.* John Wiley & Sons, New York.

Incropera, F.P. and D.P. DeWitt. 1996. *Fundamentals of heat and mass transfer*, 4th ed. John Wiley & Sons, New York.

Kusuda, T. 1957. Graphical method simplifies determination of aircoil, wet-heat-transfer surface temperature. *Refrigerating Engineering* 65:41.

Mason, E.A. and L. Monchick. 1965. Survey of the equation of state and transport properties of moist gases. In *Humidity and moisture*, vol. 3. Reinhold, New York.

McAdams, W.H. 1954. *Heat transmission*, 3rd ed. McGraw-Hill, New York.

Mizushina, T., N. Hashimoto, and M. Nakajima. 1959. Design of cooler condensers for gas-vapour mixtures. *Chemical Engineering Science* 9:195.

Reid, R.C. and T.K. Sherwood. 1966. *The properties of gases and liquids: Their estimation and correlation*, 2nd ed. McGraw-Hill, New York.

Reid, R.C., J.M. Prausnitz, and B.E. Poling. 1987. *The properties of gases and liquids*, 4th ed. McGraw-Hill, New York.

Sherwood, T.K. and R.L. Pigford. 1952. *Absorption and extraction.* McGraw-Hill, New York.

Sparrow, E.M. and M.M. Ohadi. 1987a. Comparison of turbulent thermal entrance regions for pipe flows with developed velocity and velocity developing from a sharp-edged inlet. *ASME Transactions, Journal of Heat Transfer* 109:1028-1030.

Sparrow, E.M. and M.M. Ohadi. 1987b. Numerical and experimental studies of turbulent flow in a tube. *Numerical Heat Transfer* 11:461-476.

Treybal, R.E. 1980. *Mass transfer operations*, 3rd ed. McGraw-Hill, New York.

BIBLIOGRAPHY

Bennett, C.O. and J.E. Myers. 1982. *Momentum, heat and mass transfer*, 3rd ed. McGraw-Hill, New York.

DeWitt, D.P. and E.L. Cussler. 1984. *Diffusion, mass transfer in fluid systems.* Cambridge University Press, U.K.

Geankopolis, C.J. 1993. *Transport processes and unit operations*, 3rd ed. Prentice Hall, Englewood Cliffs, NJ.

Kays, W.M. and M.E. Crawford. 1993. *Convective heat and mass transfer.* McGraw-Hill, New York.

Mikielviez, J. and A.M.A. Rageb. 1995. Simple theoretical approach to direct-contact condensation on subcooled liquid film. *International Journal of Heat and Mass Transfer* 38(3):557.

Ohadi, M.M. and E.M. Sparrow. 1989. Heat transfer in a straight tube situated downstream of a bend. *International Journal of Heat and Mass Transfer* 32(2):201-212.

CHAPTER 7

FUNDAMENTALS OF CONTROL

AUTOMATIC HVAC control systems are designed to maintain temperature, humidity, pressure, energy use, power, lighting levels, and safe levels of indoor contaminants. Automatic control primarily modulates actuators; stages modes of action; or sequences the mechanical and electrical equipment on and off to satisfy load requirements, provide safe equipment operation, and maintain safe building contaminant levels. Automatic control systems can use digital, pneumatic, mechanical, electrical, and electronic control devices. Human intervention often involves scheduling equipment operation and adjusting control set points; but also includes tracking trends and programming control logic algorithms to fulfill building needs.

This chapter focuses on the fundamental concepts and devices normally used by a control system designer. It covers (1) control fundamentals, including terminology; (2) types of control components; (3) methods of connecting components to form various individual control loops, subsystems, or networks; and (4) commissioning and operation. Chapter 46 of the 2007 *ASHRAE Handbook—HVAC Applications* discusses the design of controls for specific HVAC applications.

TERMINOLOGY

A **closed loop** or **feedback** control measures actual changes in the controlled variable and actuates the controlled device to bring about a change. The corrective action may continue until the variable is brought to a desired value within the design limitations of the controller. This arrangement of having the controller respond to the value of the controlled variable is known as feedback. Figure 1 shows an example of feedback control.

An **open-loop** control does not have a direct link between the value of the controlled variable and the controller. An open-loop control anticipates the effect of an external variable on the system and adjusts the set point to avoid excessive offset. An example is an outdoor thermostat arranged to control heat to a building in proportion to the calculated load caused by changes in outdoor temperature. In essence, the designer presumes a fixed relationship between outside air temperature and the building's heat requirement, and specifies control action based on the outdoor air temperature. The actual space temperature has no effect on this controller. Because there is no feedback on the controlled variable (space temperature), the control is an open loop.

Every **closed loop** must contain a sensor, a controller, and a controlled device. Figure 1 illustrates the components of the typical control loop. The **sensor** measures the controlled variable and transmits to the controller a signal (pneumatic, electric, or electronic)

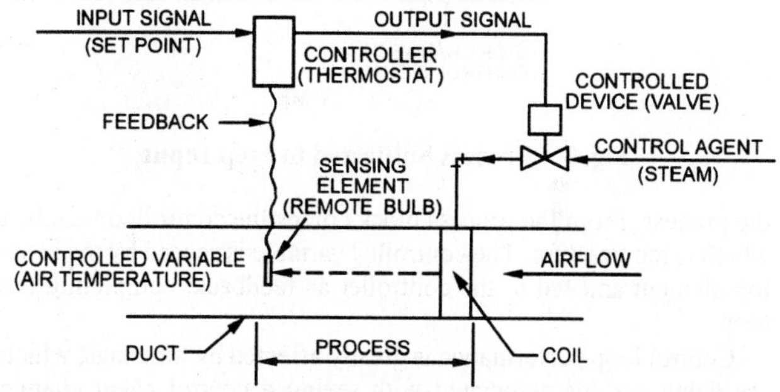

Fig. 1 Example of Feedback Control: Discharge Air Temperature Control

having a pressure, voltage, or current value related by a known function to the value of the variable being measured. The **controller** compares this value with the set point and signals to the controlled device for corrective action. A controller can be hardware or software. A hardware controller is an analog device (e.g., thermostat, humidistat, pressure control) that continuously receives and acts on data. A software controller is a digital device (e.g., digital algorithm) that receives and acts on data on a sample-rate basis. The **controlled device** is typically a valve, damper, heating element, or variable-speed drive.

The **set point** is the desired value of the controlled variable. The controller seeks to maintain this set point. The controlled device reacts to signals from the controller to vary the control agent.

The **control agent** is the medium manipulated by the controlled device. It may be air or gas flowing through a damper; gas, steam, or water flowing through a valve; or an electric current.

The **process** is the HVAC apparatus being controlled, such as a coil, fan, or humidifier. It reacts to the control agent's output and effects the change in the controlled variable.

The **controlled variable** is the temperature, humidity, pressure, or other condition being controlled.

A control loop can be represented in the form of a **block diagram**, in which each component is modeled and represented in its own block. Figure 2 is a block diagram of the control loop shown in Figure 1. Information flow from one component to the next is shown by lines between the blocks. The figure shows the set point being compared to the controlled variable. The difference is the **error**. If the error persists, it may be called offset drift, deviation, droop, or steady-state error. The error is fed into the controller, which sends a control signal to the controlled device (in this case, a valve that can change the amount of steam flow through the coil of Figure 1). The amount of steam flow is the input to the next block, which represents

The preparation of this chapter is assigned to TC 1.4, Control Theory and Application.

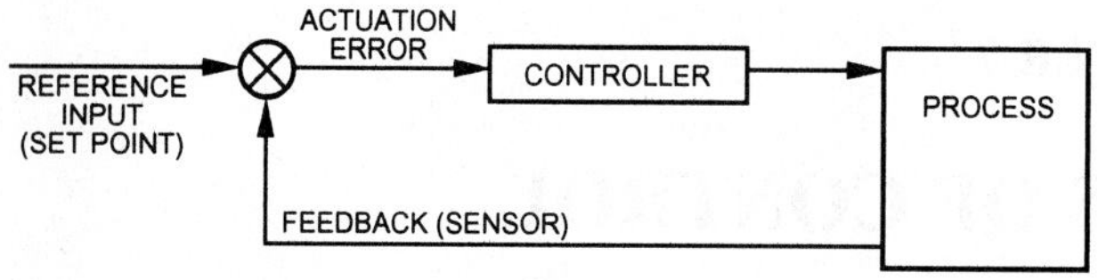

Fig. 2 Block Diagram of Discharge Air Temperature Control

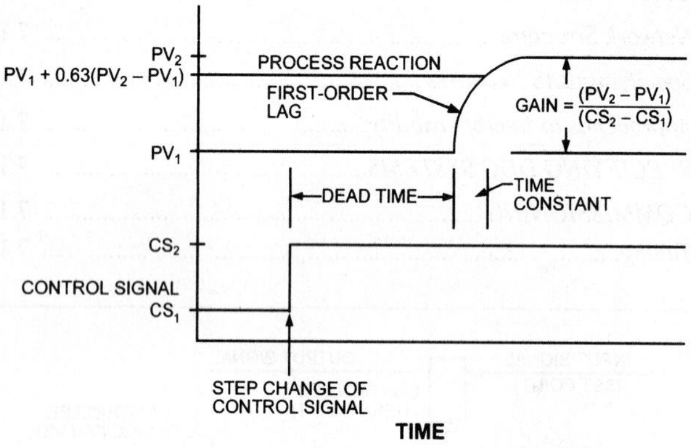

Fig. 3 Process Subjected to Step Input

the process. From the process block comes the controlled variable, which is temperature. The controlled variable is sensed by the sensing element and fed to the controller as feedback, completing the loop.

Control loop performance is greatly affected by time lags, which are delay periods associated with seeing a control agent change reflected in the desired end-point condition. Time lags can cause control and modeling problems and should be understood and evaluated carefully. There are two types of time lags: first-order lags and dead time.

First-order lags involve the time it takes for the change to be absorbed by the system. If heat is supplied to a cold room, the room heats up gradually, even though heat may be applied at the maximum rate. The **time constant** is the unit of measure used to describe first-order lags and it is defined as the time it takes for the controlled variable of a first-order, linear system to reach 63.2% of its final value when a step change in the input occurs. Components with small time constants alter their output rapidly to reflect changes in the input; components with a larger time constant are sluggish in responding to input changes.

Dead time (or time lag) is the time from when a change in the controller output is made to when the controlled variable exhibits a measurable response. Dead time can occur in the control loop of Figure 1 because of the transportation time of the air from the coil to the space. After a coil temperature changes, there is dead time while the supply air travels the distribution system and finally reaches the sensor in the space. The mass of air in the space further delays the coil temperature change's effect on the controlled variable (space temperature). Dead time can also be caused by a slow sensor or a time lag in the signal from the controller when it first begins to affect the output of the process. Dead time is most often associated with the time it takes to transport the media changed by the control agent from one place to another. Dead time may also be inadvertently added to a control loop by a controller with an excessive scan time. If the dead time is small, it may be ignored in the control system model; if it is significant, it must be considered.

Figure 1 depicts the mechanisms that create both first-order and dead-time lags, and Figure 3 shows the effect related to time. Dead time is the time it takes warmer air resulting from a higher set point to reach the space, followed by the first-order lag created by the wall on which the thermostat is mounted, and that of the temperature

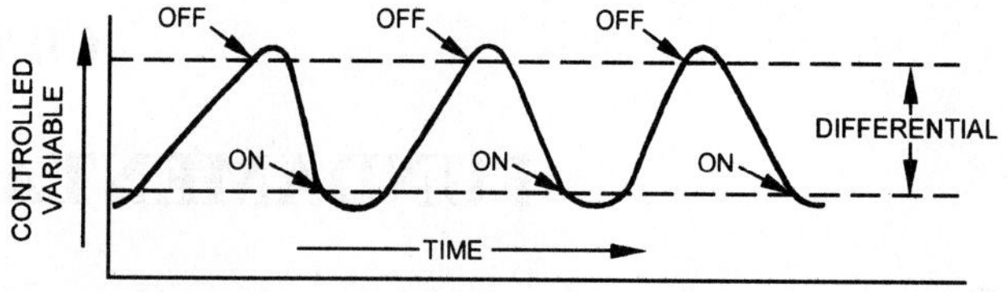

Fig. 4 Two-Position Control

sensor (all of which warm gradually rather than all at once). The control loop must be tuned to account for the combined effect of each time lag. Note that, in most HVAC systems, the first-order lag element predominates.

The **gain** of a transfer function is the amount the output of the component changes for a given change of input under steady-state conditions. If the element (valve, damper, and/or temperature/pressure differential) is linear, its gain remains constant. However, many control components are nonlinear and have gains that depend on the operating conditions. Figure 3 shows the response of the first-order-plus-dead-time process to a step change of the input signal. Note that the process shows no reaction during dead time, followed by a response that resembles a first-order exponential.

TYPES OF CONTROL ACTION

Control loops can be classified by the adjustability of the controlled device. A **two-position** controlled device has two operating states (e.g., open and closed), whereas a **modulating** controlled device has a continuous range of operating states (e.g., 0 to 100% open).

Two-Position Action

The control device shown in Figure 4 can be positioned only to a maximum or minimum state (i.e., on or off). Because two-position control is simple and inexpensive, it is used extensively for both industrial and commercial control. A typical home thermostat that starts and stops a furnace is an example.

Controller differential, as it applies to two-position control action, is the difference between a setting at which the controller operates to one position and a setting at which it operates to the other. Thermostat ratings usually refer to the differential (in degrees) that becomes apparent by raising and lowering the dial setting. This differential is known as the **manual differential** of the thermostat. When the same thermostat is applied to an operating system, the total change in temperature that occurs between a "turn-on" state and a "turn-off" state is usually different from the mechanical differential. The **operating differential** may be greater because of thermostat lag or hysteresis, or less because of heating or cooling anticipators built into the thermostat.

Anticipation Applied to Two-Position Action. This common variation of strictly two-position action is often used on room thermostats to reduce the operating differential. In heating thermostats, a heater element in the thermostat is energized during *on* periods, thus shortening the *on* time because the heater warms the thermostat (**heat anticipation**). The same anticipation action can be obtained in cooling thermostats by energizing a heater thermostat at *off* periods. In both cases, the percentage of *on* time is varied in proportion to the load, and the total cycle time remains relatively constant.

Modulating Control

With modulating control, the controller's output of the controller can vary over its entire range. The following terms are used to describe this type of control:

- **Throttling range** is the amount of change in the controlled variable required to cause the controller to move the controlled device from one extreme to the other. It can be adjusted to meet job requirements. The throttling range is inversely proportional to proportional gain.

- **Control point** is the actual value of the controlled variable at which the instrument is controlling. It varies within the controller's throttling range and changes with changing load on the system and other variables.
- **Offset**, or error signal, is the difference between the set point and actual control point under stable conditions. This is sometimes called drift, deviation, droop, or steady-state error.

In each of the following examples of modulating control, there is a set of parameters that quantifies the controller's response. The values of these parameters affect the control loop's speed, stability, and accuracy. In every case, control loop performance depends on matching (or **tuning**) the parameter values to the characteristics of the system under control.

Proportional Control. In proportional control, the controlled device is positioned proportionally in response to changes in the controlled variable (Figure 5). A proportional controller can be described mathematically by

$$V_p = K_p e + V_o \quad (1)$$

where

V_p = controller output
K_p = proportional gain parameter (inversely proportional to throttling range)
e = error signal or offset
V_o = offset adjustment parameter

The controller output is proportional to the difference between the sensed value, the controlled variable, and its set point. The controlled device is normally adjusted to be in the middle of its control range at set point by using an offset adjustment. This control is similar to that shown in Figure 5.

Proportional plus Integral (PI) Control. PI control improves on simple proportional control by adding another component to the control action that eliminates the offset typical of proportional control (Figure 6). Reset action may be described by

$$V_p = K_p e + K_i \int e \, d\theta + V_o \quad (2)$$

where

K_i = integral gain parameter
θ = time

The second term in Equation (2) implies that the longer error *e* exists, the more the controller output changes in attempting to eliminate the error. Proper selection of proportional and integral gain constants increases stability and eliminates offset, giving greater control accuracy. PI control can also improve energy efficiency in applications such as VAV fan control, chiller control, and hot- and cold-deck control of an air handler because it reduces steady-state error.

Proportional-Integral-Derivative (PID) Control. This is PI control with a derivative term added to the controller. It varies with the value of the derivative of the error. The equation for PID control is

$$V_p = K_p e + K_i \int e \, d\theta + K_d \frac{de}{d\theta} + V_o \quad (3)$$

where

K_d = derivative gain parameter of controller
$de/d\theta$ = time derivative of error

Adding the derivative term gives some anticipatory action to the controller, which results in a faster response and greater stability. However, the derivative term also makes the controller more sensitive to noisy signals and harder to tune than a PI controller. Most HVAC control loops perform satisfactorily with PI control alone.

Adaptive Control. An adaptive controller adjusts the parameters that define its response as the dynamic characteristics of the process change. If the controller is PID-based, then it adjusts feedback gains. An adaptive controller may be based on other feedback rules. The key is that it adjusts its parameters to match the characteristics of the process. When the process changes, the tuning parameters change to match it. Adaptive control is applied in HVAC systems because normal variations in the operating conditions affect the characteristics relevant to tuning. For instance, the extent to which zone dampers are open or closed in a VAV system affects the way duct pressure responds to fan speed, and entering fluid temperatures at a coil affect the way the leaving temperature responds to the valve position.

Fuzzy Logic. This type of control offers an alternative to traditional control algorithms. A fuzzy logic controller uses a series of "if-then" rules that emulates the way a human operator might control the process. Examples of fuzzy logic might include

- IF room temperature is high AND temperature is decreasing, THEN increase cooling a little.
- IF room temperature is high AND temperature is increasing, THEN increase cooling a lot.

The designer of a fuzzy logic controller must first define the rules and then define terms such as *high, increasing, decreasing, a lot,* and *a little*. Room temperature, for instance, might be mapped into a series of functions that include *very low, low, OK, high,* and *very high*. The "fuzzy" element is introduced when the functions overlap and the room temperature is, for example, 70% high and 30% OK. In this case, multiple rules are combined to determine the appropriate control action.

Combinations of Two-Position and Modulating

Some control loops include two-position components in a system that exhibits nearly modulating response.

Timed Two-Position Control. This cycles a two-position heating or cooling element on and off quickly enough that the effect on the controlled temperature approximates a modulating device. In this case, a controller may adjust the duty cycle ("on-time" as a percentage of "cycle-time") as a modulating control variable. For example, an element may be turned on for two minutes and off

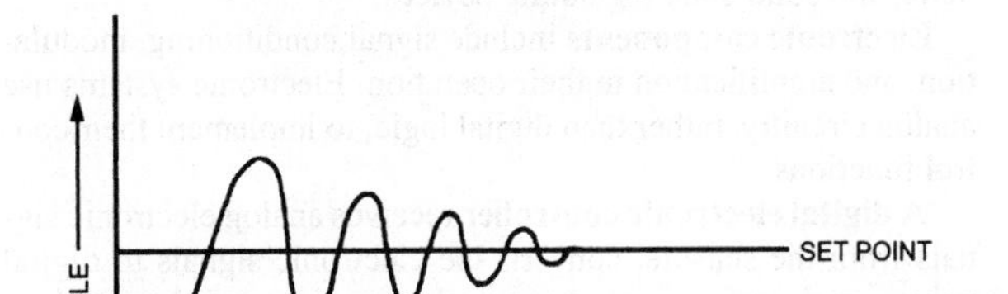

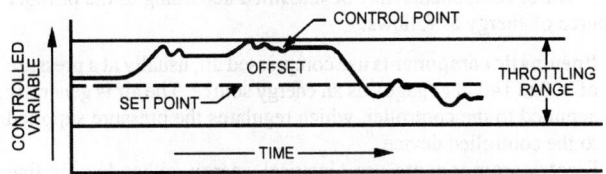

Fig. 5 Proportional Control Showing Variations in Controlled Variable as Load Changes

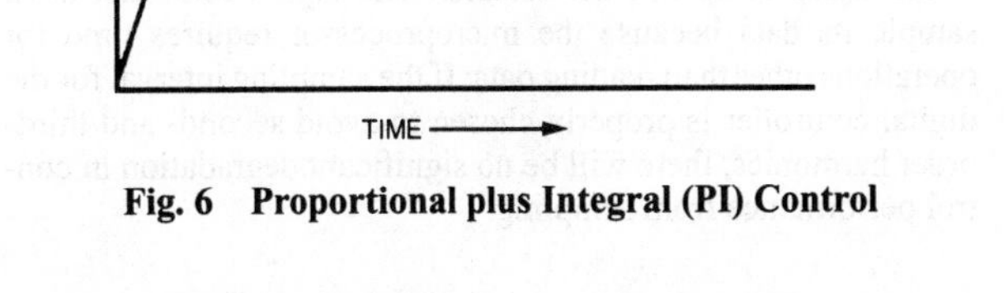

Fig. 6 Proportional plus Integral (PI) Control

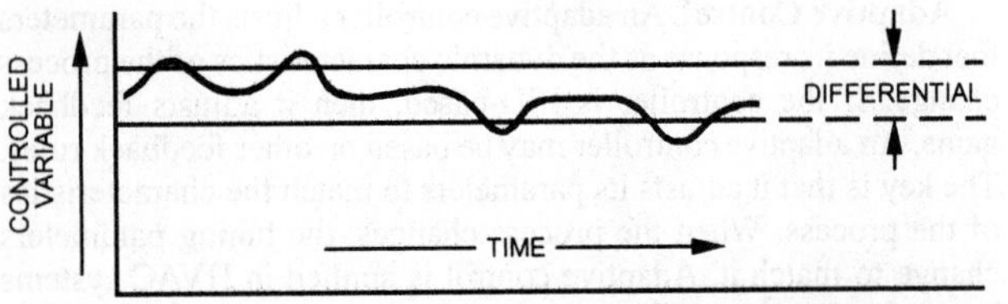

Fig. 7 Floating Control Showing Variations in Controlled Variable as Load Changes

for one minute when the deviation from set point is 2 K. Timed two-position action combines a modulating controller with a two-position controlled device.

Floating Control. This combines a modulating controlled device with a pair of two-position outputs. The controlled device has a continuous operating range, but the actuators that move it only turn on and off. The controller selects one of three operations: moving the controlled device toward its open position, moving it toward its closed position, or leaving the device in its current position. Control is accomplished by applying a pair of two-position contacts with a selected gap between their set points (Figure 7). Generally, a neutral zone between the two positions allows the controlled device to stop at any position when the controlled variable is within the differential of the controller. When the controlled variable falls outside the differential of the controller, the controller moves the controlled device in the proper direction. To function properly, the sensing element must react faster than the actuator drive time. If not, the control functions the same as a two-position control. When applied with a digital controller, floating-point control is also referred to as **tri-state control**.

Incremental Control. This variation of floating control varies the pulse action to open or close an actuator, depending on how close the controlled variable is to the set point. As the controlled variable comes close to the set point, the pulses become shorter. This allows closer control using floating motor actuators. When applied with a digital controller, incremental control is also referred to as **pulse-width-modulation (PWM) control**.

CLASSIFICATION BY ENERGY SOURCE

Control components may be classified according to the primary source of energy as follows:

- **Pneumatic components** use compressed air, usually at a pressure of 100 to 140 kPa (gage), as an energy source. The air is generally supplied to the controller, which regulates the pressure supplied to the controlled device.
- **Electric components** use electrical energy, either low or line voltage, as the energy source. The controller regulates electrical energy supplied to the controlled device. Controlled devices in this category include relays and electromechanical, electromagnetic, and solid-state regulating devices.

  Electronic components include signal conditioning, modulation, and amplification in their operation. Electronic systems use analog circuitry, rather than digital logic, to implement their control functions.

  A **digital electronic controller** receives analog electronic signals from the sensors, converts the electronic signals to digital values, and performs mathematical operations on these values inside a microprocessor. Output from the digital controller takes the form of a digital value, which is then converted to an electronic signal to operate the actuator. The digital controller must sample its data because the microprocessor requires time for operations other than reading data. If the sampling interval for the digital controller is properly chosen to avoid second- and third-order harmonics, there will be no significant degradation in control performance from sampling.
- **Self-powered components** apply the power of the measured system to induce the necessary corrective action. The measuring system derives its energy from the process under control, without any auxiliary source of energy. Temperature changes at the sensor result in pressure or volume changes of the enclosed media that are transmitted directly to the operating device of the valve or damper. A component using a thermopile in a pilot flame to generate electrical energy is also self-powered.

This method of classification can be extended to individual control loops and to complete control systems. For example, the room temperature control for a particular room that includes a pneumatic room thermostat and a pneumatically actuated reheat coil would be referred to as a pneumatic control loop. Many control systems use a combination of control components and are called **hybrid** systems.

Computers for Automatic Control

Computers perform the control functions in direct digital control (DDC) systems. Uses range from personal computers used as operator interfaces for DDC systems to embedded program microprocessors used to control variable air volume boxes, fan-coil units, heat pumps, and other terminal HVAC equipment. Other uses include primary HVAC equipment programmable controllers, distributed network controllers, and servers used to store DDC system trend data. Chapter 39 of the 2007 *ASHRAE Handbook—HVAC Applications* covers computer components and HVAC computer applications more extensively.

CONTROL COMPONENTS

CONTROLLED DEVICES

A control device is the component of a control loop used to vary the input (controlled variable). Both **valves** and **dampers** perform essentially the same function and must be properly sized and selected for the particular application. The control link to the valve or damper is called an **actuator** or **operator**, and uses electricity, compressed air, hydraulic fluid, or some other means to power the motion of the valve stem or damper linkage through its operating range. For additional information, see Chapter 36.

Valves

An automatic valve is designed to control the flow of steam, water, gas, or other fluids. It can be considered a variable orifice positioned by an actuator in response to impulses or signals from the controller. It may be equipped with either a throttling plug, V-port, or rotating ball specially designed to provide a desired flow characteristic.

Types of automatic valves include the following:

A **single-seated valve** (Figure 8A) is designed for tight shutoff. Appropriate disk materials for various pressures and media are used.

A **double-seated** or **balanced valve** (Figure 8B) is designed so that the media pressure acting against the valve disk is essentially balanced, reducing the actuator force required. It is widely used where fluid pressure is too high to allow a single-seated valve to close or to modulate properly. It is not usually used where tight shutoff is required.

A **three-way mixing valve** (Figure 9A) has two inlet connections and one outlet connection and a double-faced disk operating between two seats. It is used to mix two fluids entering through the two inlet connections and leaving through the common outlet, according to the position of the valve stem and disk.

A **three-way diverting valve** (Figure 9B) has one inlet connection and two outlet connections, and two separate disks and seats. It is used to divert flow to either of the outlets or to proportion the flow

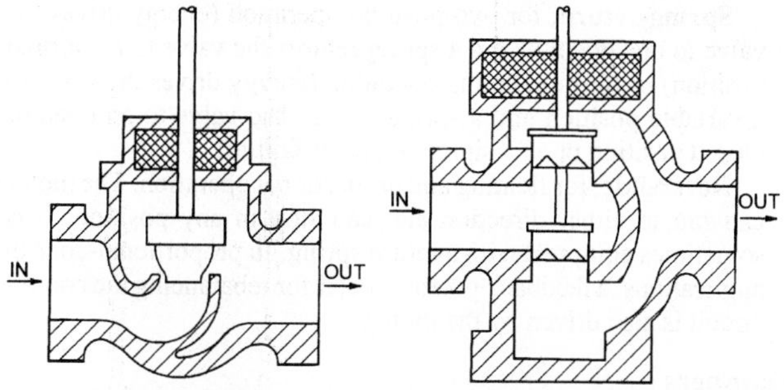

Fig. 8 Typical Single- and Double-Seated Two-Way Valves

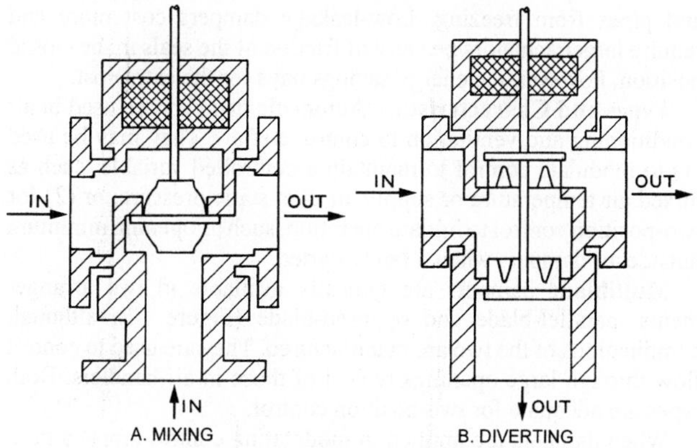

Fig. 9 Typical Three-Way Mixing and Diverting Valves

to both outlets. Three-way diverting valves are more expensive and have more complex applications, and generally are not used in typical HVAC systems.

A **butterfly valve** consists of a heavy ring enclosing a disk that rotates on an axis at or near its center and is similar to a round single-blade damper. In principle, the disk seats against a ring machined within the body or a resilient liner in the body. Two butterfly valves can be used together to act like a three-way valve for mixing or diverting. Butterfly valves are designed for two-position action. In condenser water applications with pipe sizes 100 mm and above, butterfly valves are often used in modulating positions because they are less expensive than globe-style valves (see Chapter 46 of the 2008 *ASHRAE Handbook—HVAC Systems and Equipment* for information on globe valves).

A **ball valve** consists of a ball with a hole drilled through it, rotating in a valve body. Ball valves are increasingly popular because of their low cost and high close-off ratings. Features that provide flow characteristics similar to globe valves are available.

Pressure-independent valves are control valves with integral pressure regulators. This allows the valve to respond in a more linear way, because pressure is constant.

Flow Characteristics. Valve performance is expressed in terms of its flow characteristics as it operates through its stroke, based on a constant pressure drop. Three common characteristics are shown in Figure 10 and are defined as follows:

- **Quick opening.** Maximum flow is approached rapidly as the device begins to open.
- **Linear.** Opening and flow are related in direct proportion.
- **Equal percentage.** Each equal increment of opening increases flow by an equal percentage over the previous value.

Because pressure drop across a valve seldom remains constant as its opening changes, actual performance usually deviates from the published characteristic curve. The magnitude of deviation is determined by the overall design. For example, in a system arranged so that control valves or dampers can shut off all flow, pressure drop across a controlled device increases from a minimum at design conditions to total pressure drop at no flow. Figure 11 shows the extent of resulting deviations for a valve or damper designed with a linear characteristic, when selection is based on various percentages of total system pressure drop. To allow for adequate control by valve or damper, design pressure drop should be a reasonably large percentage of total system pressure drop, or the system should be designed and controlled so that pressure drop remains relatively constant.

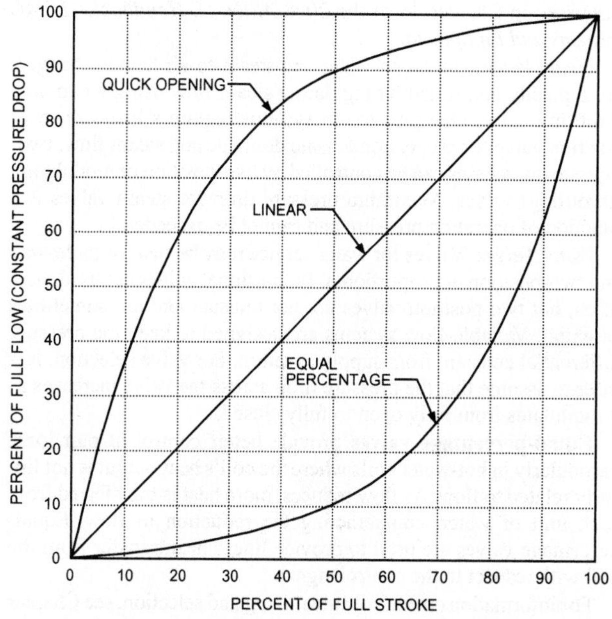

Fig. 10 Typical Flow Characteristics of Valves

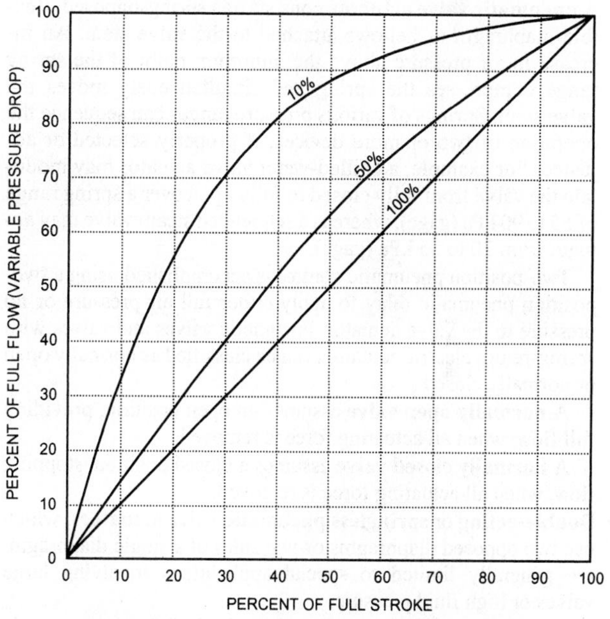

Fig. 11 Typical Performance Curves for Linear Devices at Various Percentages of Total System Pressure Drop

Selection and Sizing. Higher pressure drops for controlled devices are obtained by using smaller sizes, with a possible increase in size of other equipment in the system. Sizing control valves is discussed in Chapter 46 of the 2008 *ASHRAE Handbook—HVAC Systems and Equipment.*

Steam Valves. Steam-to-water and steam-to-air heat exchangers are typically controlled by regulating steam flow using a two-way throttling valve. One-pipe steam systems require a line-size, two-position valve for proper condensate drainage and steam flow; two-pipe steam systems can be controlled by two-position or modulating (throttling) valves. Maximum pressure drop for steam valves is a function of operating pressure and cannot be exceeded.

Water Valves. Valves for water service may be two- or three-way and two-position or proportional. Proportional valves are used most often, but two-position valves are not unusual and are sometimes essential. Variable-flow systems are designed to keep the pressure differential constant from supply to return. For valve selection, it is safer to assume that the pressure drop across the valve increases as it modulates from fully open to fully closed.

Equal-percentage valves provide better control at part load, particularly in hot-water coils where the coil's heat output is not linearly related to flow. As flow reduces, more heat is transferred from each unit of water, counteracting the reduction in flow. Equal-percentage valves are used to provide linear heat transfer from the coil with respect to the control signal.

For information on control valve sizing and selection, see Chapter 46 of the 2008 *ASHRAE Handbook—HVAC Systems and Equipment.*

Actuators. Valve actuators include the following general types:

- A **pneumatic valve actuator** consists of a spring-opposed, flexible diaphragm or bellows attached to the valve stem. An increase in air pressure above the minimum point of the spring range compresses the spring and simultaneously moves the valve stem. Springs of various pressure ranges can sequence the operation of two or more devices, if properly selected or adjusted. For example, a chilled-water valve actuator may modulate the valve from fully closed to fully open over a spring range of 55 to 90 kPa (gage), whereas a sequenced steam valve may actuate from 20 to 55 kPa (gage).

  Two-position pneumatic control is accomplished using a two-position pneumatic relay to apply either full air pressure or no pressure to the valve actuator. Pneumatic valves and valves with spring-return electric actuators can be classified as normally open or normally closed.

  A **normally open valve** assumes an open position, providing full flow, when all actuating force is removed.

  A **normally closed valve** assumes a closed position, stopping flow, when all actuating force is removed.
- **Double-acting** or **springless pneumatic valve actuators**, which use two opposed diaphragms or two sides of a single diaphragm, are generally limited to special applications involving large valves or high fluid pressure.
- An **electric-hydraulic valve actuator** is similar to a pneumatic one, except that it uses an incompressible fluid circulated by an internal electric pump.
- A **solenoid** consists of a magnetic coil operating a movable plunger. Most are for two-position operation, but modulating solenoid valves are available with a pressure equalization bellows or piston to achieve modulation. Solenoid valves are generally limited to relatively small sizes (up to 100 mm).
- An **electric motor** actuates the valve stem through a gear train and linkage. Electric motor actuators are classified in the following three types:

  Unidirectional, for two-position operation. The valve opens during one half-revolution of the output shaft and closes during the other half-revolution. Once started, it continues until the half-revolution is completed, regardless of subsequent action by the controller. Limit switches in the actuator stop the motor at the end of each stroke. If the controller has been satisfied during this interval, the actuator continues to the other position.

  Spring-return, for two-position operation (energy drives the valve to one position and a spring returns the valve to its normal position) or for modulating operation (energy drives the valve to a variable position and a spring returns the valve to an open or closed position upon a signal or power failure).

  Reversible, for floating and proportional operation. The motor can run in either direction and can stop in any position. It is sometimes equipped with a return spring. In proportional-control applications, a feedback potentiometer for rebalancing the control circuit is also driven by the motor.

Dampers

Damper leakage is a concern, particularly where tight shutoff is necessary to significantly reduce energy consumption. Also, outdoor air dampers in cold climates must close tightly to prevent coils and pipes from freezing. Low-leakage dampers cost more and require larger actuators because of friction of the seals in the closed position; however, the energy savings pays for the extra cost.

Types and Characteristics. Automatic dampers are used in air conditioning and ventilation to control airflow. They may be used (1) to modulate control to maintain a controlled variable, such as mixed air temperature or supply air duct static pressure; or (2) for two-position control to initiate operation, such as opening minimum outside air dampers when a fan is started.

Multiblade dampers are typically available in two arrangements: parallel-blade and opposed-blade (Figure 12), although combinations of the two are manufactured. They are used to control flow through large openings typical of those in air handlers. Both types are adequate for two-position control.

When dampers are applied in modulating control loops, a nonlinear relationship between flow and stroke can lead to difficulties in tuning a control loop for performance. Nonlinearity is expressed as variation in the slope of the flow versus stroke curve. Perfect linearity is not required: if slope varies throughout the range of required flow by less than a factor of 2 from the slope at the point where the loop is tuned, nonlinearity is not likely to disrupt performance.

Parallel blades are used for modulating control when the pressure drop of the damper is about 25% or more of the pressure in a subsystem (Figure 13A). **Opposed-blade dampers** are preferable for modulating control when the damper is about 15% or less of the pressure drop in a subsystem (Figure 13B). A subsystem is defined as a portion of the duct system between two relatively constant pressure points (e.g., the return air section between the mixed air and

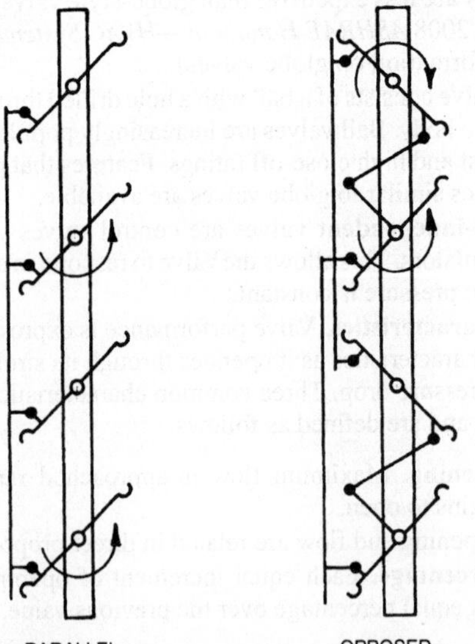

Fig. 12 Typical Multiblade Dampers

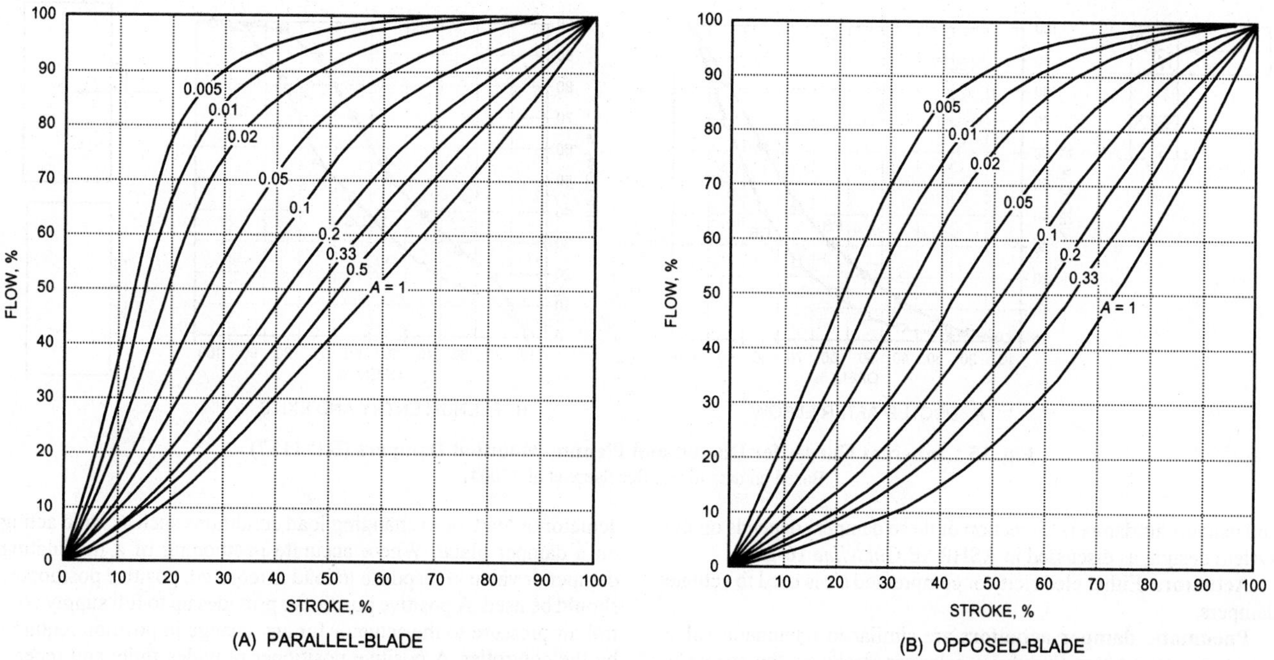

Fig. 13 Characteristic Curves of Installed Dampers in an AMCA 5.3 Geometry

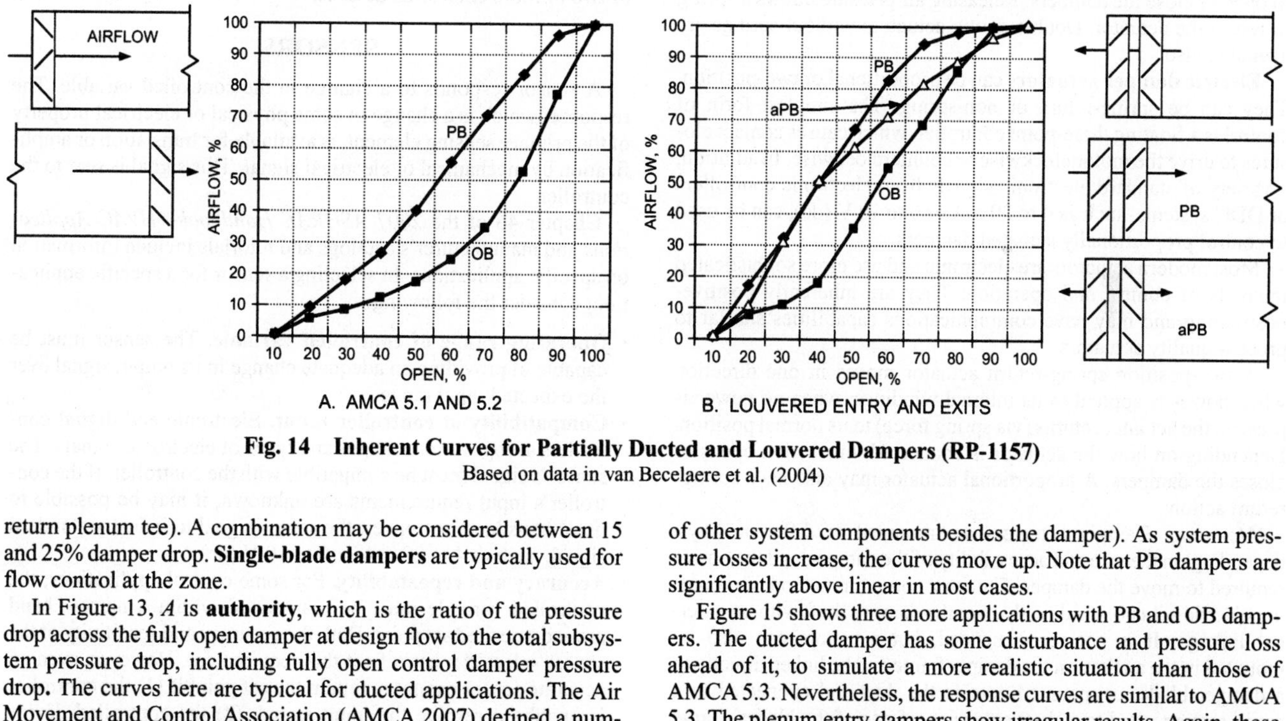

Fig. 14 Inherent Curves for Partially Ducted and Louvered Dampers (RP-1157)

Based on data in van Becelaere et al. (2004)

return plenum tee). A combination may be considered between 15 and 25% damper drop. **Single-blade dampers** are typically used for flow control at the zone.

In Figure 13, *A* is **authority**, which is the ratio of the pressure drop across the fully open damper at design flow to the total subsystem pressure drop, including fully open control damper pressure drop. The curves here are typical for ducted applications. The Air Movement and Control Association (AMCA 2007) defined a number of geometric arrangements of dampers for testing pressure losses. The curves in Figure 13 are those of an AMCA 5.3 geometry, which is a fully ducted arrangement with long sections of duct before and after a damper. Other geometric applications, such as plenum or wall-mounted dampers, exhibit different response curves (van Becelaere et al. 2004).

Figure 14 shows four applications with parallel-blade (PB) and opposed-blade (OB) as well as an "anti-PB" arrangement. The response curves are not like those of the AMCA 5.3 ducted application. These are "inherent" curves, where pressure drop across a damper is held constant as the damper rotates (so it has 100% authority). In real applications, the authority is lower (higher losses of other system components besides the damper). As system pressure losses increase, the curves move up. Note that PB dampers are significantly above linear in most cases.

Figure 15 shows three more applications with PB and OB dampers. The ducted damper has some disturbance and pressure loss ahead of it, to simulate a more realistic situation than those of AMCA 5.3. Nevertheless, the response curves are similar to AMCA 5.3. The plenum entry dampers show irregular results. Again, these are inherent curves, and lower authority causes the curves to move up toward more flow at smaller angles.

The curves shown here are typical, but do not represent every scenario. Thousands of installation variations exist, and slight variations in response always occur. For additional application examples and greater detail, see ASHRAE research project RP-1157 (van Becelaere et al. 2004).

Application. Dampers require engineering to achieve defined goals. A common application is a flow control damper, which modulates airflow. The curves in Figure 13 can be used to pick a damper with a pressure drop and authority that provides near-linear response. Another common application is economizer outdoor air, return air,

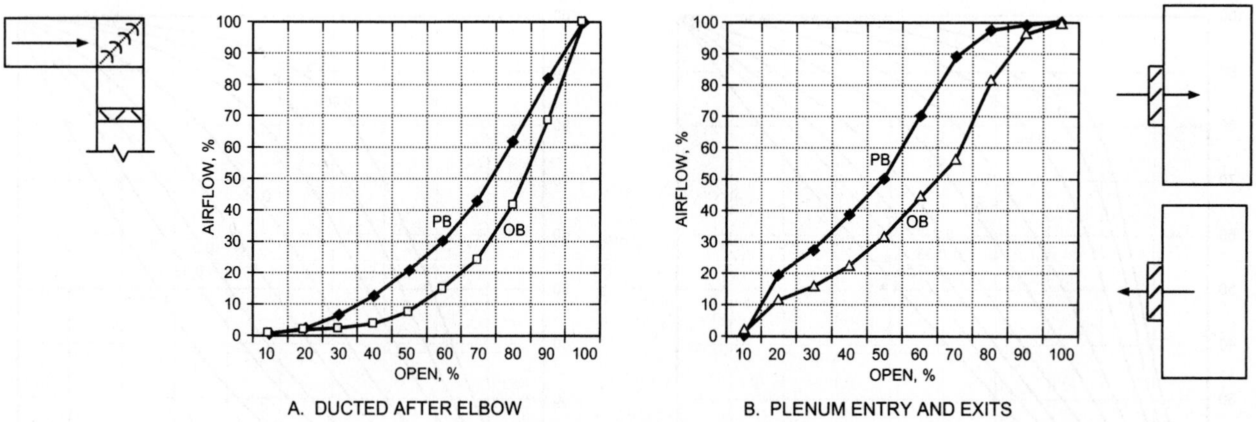

Fig. 15 Inherent Curves for Ducted and Plenum-Mounted Dampers (RP-1157)
Based on data in van Becelaere et al. (2004)

and exhaust air dampers. Selection of these dampers depends on the system design, as discussed in ASHRAE *Guideline* 16-2003.

Actuators. Either electricity or compressed air is used to actuate dampers.

Pneumatic damper actuators are similar to pneumatic valve actuators, except that they have a longer stroke or the stroke is increased by a multiplying lever. Increasing air pressure produces a linear shaft motion, which, through a linkage, moves the crank arm to open or close the dampers. Releasing air pressure allows a spring to return the actuator. Double-acting actuators without springs are available also.

Electric damper actuators can be proportional or two-position. They can be spring-return or non-spring. The simplest form of control is a floating three-point controller, which causes contact closures to drive the motor clockwise or counterclockwise. In addition, a variety of standard electronic signals from electronic controllers or DDC systems, such as 4 to 20 mA or 0 to 10 V (dc), can be used to control proportionally actuated dampers.

Most modern actuators are electronic and use more sophisticated methods of control and operation. They are inherently positive-positioning and may have communications capabilities similar to process quality actuators.

A two-position spring-return actuator moves in one direction when power is applied to its internal windings; when no power is present, the actuator returns (via spring force) to its normal position. Depending on how the actuator is connected, this action opens or closes the dampers. A proportional actuator may also have spring-return action.

Mounting. Damper actuators are mounted in different ways, depending on the size and accessibility of the damper, and the power required to move the damper. The most common method of mounting electric actuators is directly over the damper shaft with no external linkage. It is not recommended, but actuators can also be mounted in the airflow on the damper frame and be linked directly to a damper blade, or mounted outside the duct and connected to a crank arm attached to a shaft extension of one of the blades. Large dampers may require two or more actuators, which are usually mounted at separate points on the damper. An alternative is to install the damper in two or more sections, each section being controlled by a single damper actuator; however, proper flow control is easier with a single proportional damper. Positive positioners may be required for proper sequencing. A small damper with a two-position spring-return actuator may be used for minimum outside flow, with a large damper being independently controlled for economy-cycle cooling.

Positive (Pilot) Positioners

A pneumatic actuator may not respond quickly or accurately enough to small changes in control pressure caused by friction in the actuator or load, or to changing load conditions such as wind acting on a damper blade. Where accurate positioning of a modulating damper or valve in response to load is required, positive positioners should be used. A positive positioner provides up to full supply control air pressure to the actuator for any change in position required by the controller. A positive positioner provides finite and repeatable positioning change and allows adjustment of the control range (spring range of the actuator) to provide a proper sequencing control of two or more controlled devices.

SENSORS

A sensor responds to a change in the controlled variable. The response, which is a change in some physical or electrical property of the primary sensing element, is available for translation or amplification by mechanical or electrical signal. This signal is sent to the controller.

Chapter 46 of the 2007 *ASHRAE Handbook—HVAC Applications* and manufacturer's catalogs and tutorials include information on specific applications. In selecting a sensor for a specific application, consider the following:

- **Operating range of controlled variable.** The sensor must be capable of providing an adequate change in its output signal over the expected input range.
- **Compatibility of controller input.** Electronic and digital controllers accept various ranges and types of electronic signals. The sensor's signal must be compatible with the controller. If the controller's input requirements are unknown, it may be possible to use a transducer to convert the sensor signal to industry standard signal, such as 4 to 20 mA or 0 to 10 V (dc).
- **Accuracy and repeatability.** For some control applications, the controlled variable must be maintained within a narrow band around a desired set point. Both the accuracy and sensitivity of the sensor selected must reflect this requirement. However, even an accurate sensor cannot maintain the set point if (1) the controller is unable to resolve the input signal, (2) the controlled device cannot be positioned accurately, (3) the controlled device exhibits excessive hysteresis, or (4) disturbances drive its system faster than the controls can regulate it.
- **Sensor response time.** Associated with a sensor/transducer arrangement is a response curve, which describes the response of the sensor output to change in the controlled variable. If the time constant of the process being controlled is short and stable and accurate control is important, then the sensor selected must have a fast response time.
- **Control agent properties and characteristics.** The control agent is the medium to which the sensor is exposed, or with which it comes in contact, for measuring a controlled variable such as

temperature or pressure. If the agent corrodes the sensor or otherwise degrades its performance, a different sensor should be selected, or the sensor must be isolated or protected from direct contact with the control agent.

- **Ambient environment characteristics.** Even when the sensor's components are isolated from direct contact with the control agent, the ambient environment must be considered. The temperature and humidity range of the ambient environment must not reduce the sensor's accuracy. Likewise, the presence of certain gases, chemicals, and electromagnetic interference (EMI) can cause component degradation. In such cases, a special sensor or transducer housing can be used to protect the element, ensuring a true indication of the controlled variable.

Temperature Sensors

Temperature-sensing elements generally detect changes in either (1) relative dimension (caused by differences in thermal expansion), (2) the state of a vapor or liquid, or (3) some electrical property. Within each category, there are a variety of sensing elements to measure room, duct, water, and surface temperatures. Temperature-sensing technologies commonly used in HVAC applications are as follows:

- A **bimetal element** is composed of two thin strips of dissimilar metals fused together. Because the two metals have different coefficients of thermal expansion, the element bends and changes position as the temperature varies. Depending on the space available and the movement required, it may be straight, U-shaped, or wound into a spiral. This element is commonly used in room, insertion, and immersion thermostats.
- A **rod-and-tube element** consists of a high-expansion metal tube containing a low-expansion rod. One end of the rod is attached to the rear of the tube. The tube changes length with changes in temperature, causing the free end of the rod to move. This element is commonly used in certain insertion and immersion thermostats.
- A **sealed bellows element** is either vapor-, gas-, or liquid-filled. Temperature changes vary the pressure and volume of the gas or liquid, resulting in a change in force or a movement.
- A **remote bulb element** is a bulb or capsule connected to a sealed bellows or diaphragm by a capillary tube; the entire system is filled with vapor, gas, or liquid. Temperature changes at the bulb cause volume or pressure changes that are conveyed to the bellows or diaphragm through the capillary tube. This element is useful where the temperature-measuring point is remote from the desired thermostat location.
- A **thermistor** is a semiconductor that changes electrical resistance with temperature. It has a negative temperature coefficient (i.e., resistance decreases as temperature increases). Its characteristic curve of temperature versus resistance is nonlinear over a wide range. Several techniques are used to convert its response to a linear change over a particular temperature range. With digital control, one technique is to store a computer look-up table that maps the temperature corresponding to the measured resistance. The table breaks the curve into small segments, and each segment is assumed to be linear over its range. Thermistors are used because of their relatively low cost and the large change in resistance possible for a small change in temperature.
- A **resistance temperature device (RTD)** also changes resistance with temperature. Most metallic materials increase in resistance with increasing temperature; over limited ranges, this variation is linear for certain metals (e.g., platinum, copper, tungsten, nickel/iron alloys). Platinum, for example, is linear within ±0.3% from –18 to 150°C. The RTD sensing element is available in several forms for surface or immersion mounting. Flat grid windings are used for measurements of surface temperatures. For direct measurement of fluid temperatures, the windings are encased in a stainless steel bulb to protect them from corrosion.

Humidity Sensors

Humidity sensors, or **hygrometers**, measure relative humidity, dew point, or absolute humidity of ambient or moving air. Two types that detect relative humidity are mechanical hygrometers and electronic hygrometers.

A **mechanical hygrometer** operates on the principle that a hygroscopic material, usually a moisture-sensitive nylon or bulk polymer material, retains moisture and expands when exposed to water vapor. The change in size or form is detected by a mechanical linkage and converted to a pneumatic or electronic signal. Mechanical sensors using hair, wood, paper, or cotton are not widely used anymore because they are less accurate.

Electronic hygrometers can use either resistance or capacitance sensing elements. The resistance element is a conductive grid coated with a hygroscopic (water-absorbent) substance. The grid's conductivity varies with the water retained; thus, resistance varies with relative humidity. The conductive element is arranged in an ac-excited Wheatstone bridge and responds rapidly to humidity changes.

The capacitance element is a stretched membrane of nonconductive film, coated on both sides with metal electrodes and mounted in a perforated plastic capsule. The response of the sensor's capacity to rising relative humidity is nonlinear. The signal is linearized and temperature is compensated in the amplifier circuit to provide an output signal as relative humidity changes from 0 to 100%.

The **chilled-mirror humidity sensor** determines dew point rather than relative humidity. Air flows across a small mirror in the sensor. A thermoelectric cooler lowers the surface temperature of the mirror until it reaches the dew point of the air. Condensation on the surface reduces the amount of light reflected from the mirror compared to a reference light level.

Dispersive infrared (DIR) technology can be used to sense absolute humidity or dew point. It is similar to technology used to sense carbon dioxide or other gases. Infrared water vapor sensors are optical sensors that detect the amount of water vapor in air based on the infrared light absorption characteristics of water molecules. Light absorption is proportional to the number of molecules present. An **infrared hygrometer** typically provides a value of absolute humidity or dew point, and can operate in diffusion or flow-through sample mode. This type of humidity sensor is unique in that the sensing element (a light detector and an infrared filter) is behind a transparent window and is never exposed directly to the sample environment. As a result, this sensor has excellent long-term stability and life and fast response time, is not subject to saturation, and operates equally well in very high or low humidity. Previously used solely for high-end applications, infrared hygrometers are now commonly used in HVAC applications because they cost about the same as mid-range-accuracy (1 to 3%) humidity sensors.

Pressure Transmitters and Transducers

A pneumatic pressure transmitter converts a change in absolute, gage, or differential pressure to a mechanical motion using a bellows, diaphragm, or Bourdon tube mechanism. When corrected through appropriate links, this mechanical motion produces a change in air pressure to a controller. In some instances, sensing and control functions are combined in a single component, a pressure controller.

An electronic pressure transducer may use mechanical actuation of a diaphragm or Bourdon tube to operate a potentiometer or differential transformer. Another type uses a strain gage bonded to a diaphragm. The strain gage detects displacement resulting from the force applied to the diaphragm. Capacitance transducers are most often used for measurements below 250 Pa because of their high sensitivity and repeatability. Electronic circuits provide temperature compensation and amplification to produce a standard output signal.

Flow Rate Sensors

Orifice plate, pitot-static tube, venturi, turbine, magnetic flow, thermal dispersion, vortex shedding, and Doppler effect meters are some of the technologies used to sense fluid flow. In general, pressure differential devices (orifice plates, venturi, and pitot tubes) are less expensive and simpler to use, but have limited range; thus, their accuracy depends on how they are applied and where in a system they are located.

More sophisticated flow devices, such as turbine, magnetic, and vortex shedding meters, usually have better range and are more accurate over a wide range. If an existing piping system is being considered for retrofit with a flow device, the expense of shutting down the system and cutting into a pipe must be considered. In this case, a noninvasive meter, such as a Doppler effect meter, can be cost-effective.

For air velocity metering, pitot-static tubes provide a naturally larger signal change at high velocities, with limitations on their application below 2.5 to 3 m/s. Vortex shedding for airflow applications has similar low velocity limitations. Thermal dispersion sensors provide a naturally larger signal change at lower velocities without appreciable losses through velocities common in most ventilation systems, which makes them more suitable for applications below 5 m/s.

Indoor Air Quality Sensors

Indoor air quality control can be divided into two categories: ventilation control and contamination protection. In spaces with dense populations and intermittent or highly variable occupancy, ventilation can be more efficiently applied by detecting changes in population or ventilation requirements (**demand-controlled ventilation**). This involves using time schedules and population counters and measuring the indoor/outdoor differential levels of carbon dioxide (CO_2) or other contaminants in a space; the amount of outdoor air introduced into the occupied space is then controlled. Demand control helps maintain proper ventilation rates at all levels of occupancy. Control set-point levels for carbon dioxide are determined by the specific relationships between differential CO_2, rate of CO_2 production by occupants, the variable airflow rate required by the changing population, and a fixed amount of ventilation required to dilute building-generated contaminants unrelated to CO_2 production. ASHRAE *Standard* 62.1 and its user's manual (ASHRAE 2007) provide further information on ventilation for acceptable indoor air quality.

Contamination protection sensors monitor levels of hazardous or toxic substances and issue warning signals and/or initiate corrective actions through the building automation system (BAS). Sensors are available for many different gases. The carbon monoxide (CO) sensor is one of the most common, and is often used in buildings wherever combustion occurs (e.g., parking garages). Refrigerant-specific sensors are used to measure, alarm, and initiate ventilation purging in enclosed spaces that house refrigeration equipment, to prevent occupant suffocation upon a refrigeration leak (see ASHRAE *Standard* 15 for more information). The application of these sensors determines the type selected, the substances monitored, and the action taken in an alarm condition.

Lighting Level Sensors

Analog lighting level transmitters packaged in various configurations allow control of ambient lighting levels using building automation strategies for energy conservation. Examples include ceiling-mounted indoor light sensors used to measure room lighting levels; outdoor ambient lighting sensors used to control parking, general exterior, security, and sign lighting; and interior skylight sensors used to monitor and control light levels in skylight wells and other atrium spaces.

Power Sensing and Transmission

Passive electronic devices that sense the magnetic field around a conductor carrying current allow low-cost instrumentation of power circuits. A wire in the sensor forms an inductive coupling that powers the internal function and senses the level of the power signal. These devices can provide an analog output signal to monitor current flow or operate a switch at a user-set level to turn on an alarm or other device.

CONTROLLERS

A controller compares the sensor's signal with a desired set point and regulates an output signal to a controlled device. Digital controllers perform the control function using a microprocessor and control algorithm. The sensor and controller can be combined in a single instrument, such as a room thermostat, or they may be two separate devices.

Digital Controllers

Digital controls use microprocessors to execute software programs that are customized for use in commercial buildings. Controllers use sensors to measure values such as temperature and humidity, perform control routines in software programs, and perform control using output signals to actuators such as valves and electric or pneumatic actuators connected to dampers. The operator may enter parameters such as set points, proportional or integral gains, minimum on and off times, or high and low limits, but the control algorithms make the control decisions. The computer scans input devices, executes control algorithms, and then positions the output device(s), in a stepwise scheme. The controller calculates proper control signals digitally rather than using an analog circuit or mechanical change, as in electric/electronic and pneumatic controllers. Use of digital controls in building automation is referred to as direct digital control (DDC).

Digital controls can be used as stand-alones or can be integrated into building management systems though network communications. Simple controls may have a single control loop that can perform a single control function (e.g., temperature control of a unit ventilator), or larger versions can control a larger number of loops.

Advantages of digital controls include the following:

- Sequences or equipment can be modified by changing software, which reduces the cost and diversity of hardware necessary to achieve control.
- Features such as demand setback, reset, data logging, diagnostics, and time-clock integration can be added to the controller with small incremental cost.
- Precise, accurate control can be implemented, limited by the resolution of sensor and analog-to-digital (A/D) and digital-to-analog (D/A) conversion processes. PID and other control algorithms can be implemented mathematically and can adjust performance based on multiple sequences or inputs.
- Controls can communicate with each other using open or proprietary networking (e.g., Ethernet or Internet) standards.

Digital controls can operate at the system level, which includes applications that span multiple HVAC applications or single-zone controllers.

A single control that is fixed in functionality with flexibility to change set points and small configurations is called an **application-specific controller**. Many manufacturers include application-specific controls with their HVAC equipment, such as air-handling units and chillers.

Firmware and Software. Preprogrammed control routines, known as firmware, are sometimes stored in permanent memory such as programmable read-only memory (PROM) or electrically programmable read-only memory (EPROM), and the application or set points are stored in changeable memory such as electrically erasable programmable read-only memory (EEPROM). The operator can modify parameters such as set points, limits, and minimum *off* times within the control routines, but the primary program logic cannot be changed without replacing the memory chips.

User-programmable controllers allow the algorithms to be changed by the user. The programming language provided with the controller can vary from a derivation of a standard language to custom language developed by the controller's manufacturer, to graphically based programming. Preprogrammed routines for proportional, proportional plus integral, Boolean logic, timers, etc., are typically included in the language. Standard energy management routines may also be preprogrammed and may interact with other control loops where appropriate.

Digital controllers can have both preprogrammed firmware and user-programmed routines. These routines can automatically modify the firmware's parameters according to user-defined conditions to accomplish the control sequence designed by the control engineer.

Operator Interface. Some digital controllers (e.g., a programmable room thermostat) are designed for dedicated purposes and are adjustable only through manual switches and potentiometers mounted on the controller. This type of controller cannot be networked with other controllers. A **direct digital controller** can have manually adjustable features, but it is more typically adjusted through a built-in LED or LCD display, a hand-held device, or a terminal or computer. The direct digital controller's digital communication allows remote connection to other controllers and to higher-level computing devices and host operating stations.

A **terminal** allows the user to communicate with the controller and, where applicable, to modify the program in the controller. Terminals can range from hand-held units with an LCD display and several buttons to a full-sized console with a video monitor and keyboard. The terminal can be limited in function to allow only display of sensor and parameter values, or powerful enough to allow changing or reprogramming the control strategies. In some instances, a terminal can communicate remotely with one or more controllers, thus allowing central displays, alarms, and commands. Usually, hand-held terminals are used by technicians for troubleshooting, and full-sized, fully functional terminals are used at a fixed location to monitor the entire digital control system. Standard Internet browsers can be used to access system information.

Electric/Electronic Controllers

For **two-position control**, the controller output may be a simple electrical contact that starts a fan or pump, or one that actuates a spring-return valve or damper actuator. **Single-pole, double-throw (SPDT)** switching circuits control a three-wire unidirectional motor actuator. SPDT circuits are also used for heating and cooling applications. Both single-pole, single-throw (SPST) and SPDT circuits can be modified for timed two-position action.

Output for **floating control** is a SPDT switching circuit with a neutral zone where neither contact is made. This control is used with reversible motors; it has a slow response and a wide throttling range.

Pulse modulation control is an improvement over floating control. It provides closer control by varying the duration of the contact closure. As the actual condition moves closer to the set point, the pulse duration shortens for closer control. As the actual condition moves farther from the set point, the pulse duration lengthens.

Proportional control gives continuous or incremental changes in output signal to position an electrical actuator or controlled device.

Pneumatic Receiver-Controllers

Pneumatic receiver-controllers are normally combined with pneumatic elements that use a mechanical force or position reaction to the sensed variable to obtain a variable-output air pressure. Control is usually proportional, but other modes (e.g., proportional-plus-integral) can be used. These controllers are generally classified as nonrelay or relay, and as direct-acting or reverse-acting.

The nonrelay pneumatic controller uses low-volume output. A relay pneumatic controller actuates a relay device that amplifies the air volume available for control. The relay provides quicker response to a variable change.

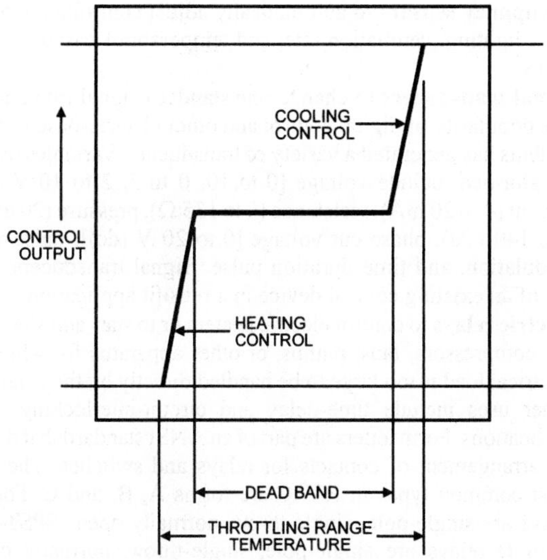

Fig. 16 Dead-Band Thermostat

Direct-acting controllers increase the output signal as the controlled variable increases. Reverse-acting controllers increase the output signal as the controlled variable decreases. A reverse-acting thermostat increases output pressure when the temperature drops.

Thermostats

Thermostats combine sensing and control functions in a single device. Microprocessor-based thermostats have many of the following features.

- An **occupied/unoccupied** or **dual-temperature room thermostat** controls at an offset temperature at night. It may be indexed (changed from occupied to unoccupied) individually or in a group by a manual switch or time switch from a remote point. Some electric units have an individual clock and switch built into the thermostat.
- A **pneumatic day/night thermostat** uses a two-pressure air supply system [often 90 and 120 kPa (gage), or 100 and 140 kPa (gage)]. Changing pressure at a central point from one value to the other actuates switching devices in the thermostat that index it from occupied to unoccupied or vice versa.
- A **heating/cooling** or **summer/winter thermostat** can have its action reversed and its set point changed by indexing. It is used to actuate controlled devices, such as valves or dampers, that regulate a heating source at one time and a cooling source at another.
- A **multistage thermostat** operates two or more successive steps in sequence.
- A **submaster thermostat** has its set point raised or lowered over a predetermined range in accordance with variations in output from a master controller. The master controller can be a thermostat, manual switch, pressure controller, or similar device.
- A **dead-band thermostat** has a wide differential over which the thermostat remains neutral, requiring neither heating nor cooling. This differential may be adjustable up to 5 K. The thermostat then controls to maximum or minimum output over a small differential at the end of each dead band (Figure 16).

AUXILIARY CONTROL DEVICES

Auxiliary control devices for electric systems include

- **Transformers** to provide current at the required voltage.

- **Occupancy sensors** to automatically adjust controlled variables (e.g., lighting, ventilation rate, and temperature) based on occupancy.
- **Signal transducers** to change one standard signal into another. The popularity of digital control and other electric-based control systems has generated a variety of transducers. Variables usually transformed include voltage [0 to 10, 0 to 5, 2 to 10 V (dc)], current (4 to 20 mA), resistance (0 to 135 Ω), pressure (20 to 100, 0 to 140 kPa), phase cut voltage [0 to 20 V (dc)], pulse-width modulation, and time duration pulse. Signal transducers allow use of an existing control device in a retrofit application.
- **Electric relays** to control electric heaters or to start and stop burners, compressors, fans, pumps, or other apparatus for which the electrical load is too large to be handled directly by the controller. Other uses include time-delay and circuit-interlocking safety applications. Form letters are part of an ANSI standard that defines the arrangement of contacts for relays and switches. The three most common types in HVAC are forms A, B, and C. Form A relays are single-pole, single-throw, normally open (SPST-NO). Form B relays are single-pole, single-throw, normally closed (SPST-NC). Form C relays are single-pole, double-throw (SPDT) and can be either normally open or normally closed, so control panels can be built using all form C (SPDT) relays. In small sizes, the added cost of the second contact is insignificant. As current ratings go up, forms A and B become more cost-effective.
- **Control relay sockets** are used with control relays to terminate wires from the device being switched or controlled. They may have either blade- or pin-type terminals.
- **Relays** are available prewired in a field-mounted housing using a 13 mm knockout in a panel or motor starter. The coil requires a low current to operate the relay, which can control either ac or dc power loads. The device typically has an LED indicator and may have an optional hand-off-auto switch.
- **Time-delay relays**, similar to control relays, include an adjustable time delay that is set using dipswitches and an external knob. The device is either a delay-on-make (*on* delay) or delay-on-break (*off* delay). The time delay is either in seconds to minutes or minutes to hours.
- **Power relays** handle high-power switching of electrical loads in motor control centers and lighting control applications. They may be of open-frame construction or may be encased by a clear polycarbonate cover. They may be either single- or multiple-pole devices that are field- or panel-mounted.
- **Solid-state relays** are photo-isolated and optically isolated relays used to switch voltages up to 600 V with high amperage loads using a form-A, normally open contact. They have a high surge dielectric strength, and reverse voltage protection. They operate using an input voltage of 4 to 32 V dc. Operation of this device is easily affected by high temperatures and induced currents.
- **Potentiometers** are used for manual positioning of proportional control devices, for remote set-point adjustment of electronic controllers, and for feedback.
- **Manual switches**, either two-position or multiple-position with single or multiple poles, are used to switch equipment from one state to another.
- **Auxiliary switches** on valve and damper actuators are used to select a sequence of operation.
- **Smoke detectors** provide early detection of both smoke and other combustion products in air moving through HVAC ducts. Sampling tubes, selected based on duct size, test air moving in the duct. Based on the application, either a photoelectric or ionization head is installed in the device. The device typically has two alarm contacts, used to shut down the associated equipment and provide remote indication, and a trouble contact, which monitors incoming power and removal of the detector head. Where a fire alarm system is installed, the smoke detectors must be listed for use with the fire alarm system. Addressable fire alarm systems may use a programmable relay for fan shutdown rather than a hard-wired connection to the detector.
- **Transient voltage surge suppressors (TVSSs)**, formerly called **lightning arrestors**, protect communication lines and critical power lines between buildings or at building entrance vaults against high-voltage transients caused by variable-frequency drives, motors, transmitters, and lightning. To be effective, they must be grounded to a grounding rod in compliance with the National Electric Code and the manufacturer's recommendations.
- **Analog time switches** are set manually to control an electrical load. They are spring-wound and have either normally open or normally closed contacts. Timing is either in minutes or hours and may have an override hold feature to keep the load on or off continuously.
- **Digital time switches** are set manually to control an electrical load and have either normally open or normally closed contacts. The timing function is either in minutes or hours, and may have an override hold feature to keep the load on or off continuously, a flash option, or a beeper option to notify the operator that the load will be turning off shortly.
- **Time clocks** (mechanical or electronic) turn electrical loads on and off, based on a 24 h/7 day or 24 h/365 day schedule.
- **Regulated dc power supply** devices convert ac voltage into a regulated dc voltage between 12 and 24 V dc. They may be used to power temperature and humidity transmitters.
- **Fuses** are safety devices with a specific amp rating, used with power supplies, circuit boards, control transformers, and transducers. They may be rated for either high or low inrush currents, and are available in slow-blow or fast-acting models.
- **Strobes** are lights that use a high-intensity xenon flash tube to generate a high-intensity light that is visible in all directions. If this device is used in a safety application such as refrigeration monitoring, it must comply with UL *Standard* 1971.
- **Horns** provide an audible tone with a specified loudness rated in decibels (dB), and are mounted in a panel or junction box. Its tone may be continuous, warbled, short beeps, or long beeps. The tone should be at least 10 dB above the ambient noise level in the area that the device is mounted. The operating voltage may be either dc or ac.

Auxiliary control devices for pneumatic systems include

- **Air compressors** and accessories, including driers, filters, and pressure regulators, provide a source of clean, dry air at the required pressure.
- **Electropneumatic relays** are electrically actuated air valves that operate pneumatic equipment according to variations in electrical input to the relay.
- **Pneumatic-electric switches**, driven by pressure from a controller, allow a controller actuating a proportional device to also actuate one or more two-position devices.
- **Pneumatic transducers**, which reverse the action of a proportional controller, select the higher or lower of two or more pressures, average two or more pressures, respond to the difference between two pressures, add or subtract pressures, and amplify or retard pressure changes.
- **Positive-positioning relays** ensure accurate positioning of a valve or damper actuator in response to changes in pressure from a controller.
- **Switching relays** are pneumatically operated air valves used to divert air from one circuit to another or to open and close air circuits.
- Manually operated **pneumatic switches** divert air from one circuit to another or open and close air circuits. They can be two-position or multiple-position.
- **Gradual switches** are proportional devices used to manually vary air pressure in a circuit.

Auxiliary control devices common to both electric and pneumatic systems include the following:

- **Step controllers** operate several switches in sequence using a proportional electric or pneumatic actuator. They are commonly used to control several steps of refrigeration capacity. They may be arranged to prevent simultaneous starting of compressors and to alternate the sequence to equalize wear. These controllers may also be used for sequenced operation of electric heating elements and other equipment.
- **Power controllers** control electric power input to resistance heating elements. They are available with various ratings for single- or three-phase heater loads and are usually arranged to regulate power input to the heater in response to the demands of the proportional electronic or pneumatic controllers. A **silicon controlled rectifier (SCR)** is the most common form of power controller used for electric heat. Solid-state controllers may also be used in two-position control modes because they do not use contacts, which can arc when power is applied or removed.
- **Clocks** or **timers** turn apparatus on and off at predetermined times, switch control systems from day to night operation, and regulate other time-sequence functions.
- **High-temperature limits** are safety devices, typically set at 50 to 65°C, that shut down equipment when the temperature exceeds its set point. A manual reset reactivates the device once the condition has cleared. These devices are typically used when airflow is less than 100 L/s. **Low-temperature limits** typically have a 6 m long vapor-charged sensing element, set at 2°C, that shuts down equipment when the temperature in a 300 or 450 mm section falls below its set point. The limit may be manually or automatically reset. The device must be mounted parallel to the tubes with capillary mounting clips for proper measurement. The device may be either SPST or double-pole, double-throw (DPDT). A typical use is to protect chilled-water coils from freezing.
- **Transducers**, which consist of combinations of electric and pneumatic control devices, convert electric signals to pneumatic output or vice versa. Transducers may convert proportional input to either proportional or two-position output.

The **electronic-to-pneumatic transducer (EPT)** is used in many applications. It converts a proportional electronic output signal into a proportional pneumatic signal (Figure 17) and can be used to combine electronic and pneumatic control components to form a control loop (Figure 18). Electronic components are used for sensing and signal conditioning, whereas pneumatic components are used for actuation. The electronic controller can be either analog or digital.

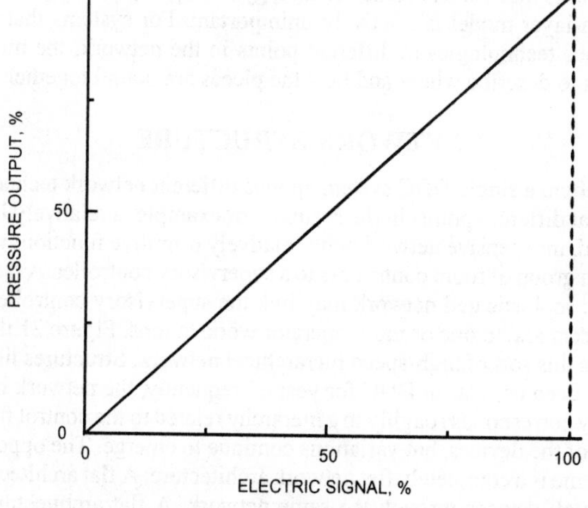

Fig. 17 Response of Electronic-to-Pneumatic Transducer (EPT)

The EPT presents a special option for retrofit applications. An existing HVAC system with pneumatic controls can be retrofitted with electronic sensors and controllers while retaining the existing pneumatic actuators (Figure 19).

- **Thermostat guards** are plastic or metal covers that protect switches, thermostat controllers, and sensors from damage, tampering, and unauthorized adjustment.
- **Enclosures** may be used indoors or outdoors to protect equipment and people. Enclosures are rated by the National Electrical Manufacturers Association (NEMA *Standard* 250) and Electrical and Electronic Manufacturer Association of Canada (EEMAC).
- **Pilot lights** are replaceable incandescent or light-emitting diode (LED) lights that indicate modes of operation of mechanical and electrical equipment. They are panel-mounted, and may be round or flat, of various colors, and powered using either ac or dc power. They are typically installed in an enclosure rated for the application under National Electrical Manufacturers Association (NEMA) *Standard* 250.
- **Three-** and **five-valve manifolds** protect water differential pressure sensors from overpressurization during installation, start-up, shutdown, system testing, and maintenance. Three-valve manifolds are comprised of two isolation valves and a bypass valve. A five-valve manifold includes two additional valves to allow online calibration. Depending on the application, snubbers may be required, as well.

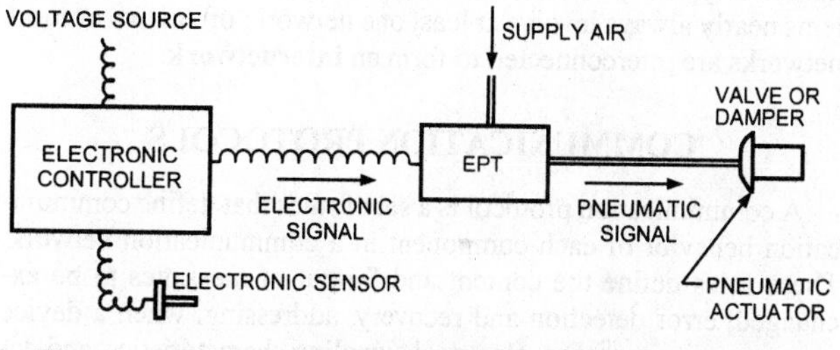

Fig. 18 Electronic and Pneumatic Control Components Combined with Electronic-to-Pneumatic Transducer (EPT)

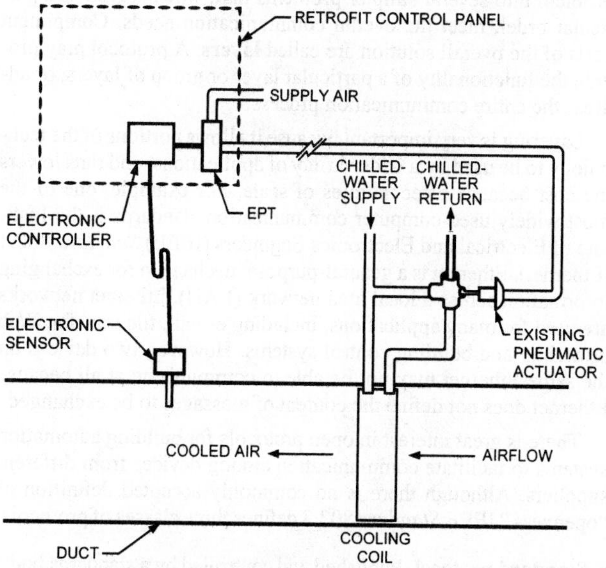

Fig. 19 Retrofit of Existing Pneumatic Control with Electronic Sensors and Controllers

- **Snubbers**, made of brass or stainless steel, stop shocks and pulsations caused by fluid hammering and system surges. Two types of pressure snubbers are used in HVAC applications: porous and piston. A porous snubber has no moving parts and uses a porous material to stop device damage. A piston snubber uses a moving piston inside a tube that moves up and down to stop device damage and push away any sediment or scale that may clog the system's monitoring devices. Depending on the application, the type of piston to be used may need to be specified.
- **Steam pigtail siphons** protect pressure transmitters from the high temperature of steam. They are typically made from steel or stainless steel of a specific length with a loop. The temperature of the medium being monitored determines the length and material. Most pressure devices have an operating temperature range of –18 to 95°C.

COMMUNICATION NETWORKS FOR BUILDING AUTOMATION SYSTEMS

A **building automation system (BAS)** is a centralized control and/or monitoring system for many or all building systems (e.g., HVAC, electrical, life safety, security). A BAS may link information from control systems actuated by different technologies.

One important characteristic of direct digital control (DDC) is the ability to share information. Information is transferred between (1) controllers to coordinate their action, (2) controllers and building operator interfaces to monitor and command systems, and (3) controllers and other computers for off-line calculation. This information is typically shared over communication networks. DDC systems nearly always involve at least one network; often, two or more networks are interconnected to form an **internetwork**.

COMMUNICATION PROTOCOLS

A communication protocol is a set of rules that define communication behavior of each component in a communication network. These rules define the content and format of messages to be exchanged, error detection and recovery, addressing, when a device may transmit a message, electrical signaling characteristics, and details of the communication medium such as wire type and pin connections. Protocols are often defined by dividing the complex problem into several simpler problems that, when solved in a particular order, meet the overall communication needs. Component parts of the overall solution are called **layers**. A protocol may provide the functionality of a particular layer or group of layers, or address the entire communication process.

Layering is very important because it allows portions of the technology to be used by a wide variety of applications, and thus lowers the cost because of economies of scale. For example, one of the most widely used computer communication standards is the Institute of Electrical and Electronics Engineers (IEEE) *Standard* 802.3 (Ethernet). Ethernet is a general-purpose mechanism for exchanging information across a local area network (LAN). Ethernet networks are used for many applications, including e-mail, file transfer, Web browsing, and building control systems. However, two devices on the same Ethernet may not be able to communicate at all because Ethernet does not define the content of messages to be exchanged.

There is great interest in open protocols for building automation systems to facilitate communication among devices from different suppliers. Although there is no commonly accepted definition of "openness," IEEE *Standard* 802.3 defines three classes of protocols:

- **Standard protocol.** Published and controlled by a standards body.
- **Public protocol.** Published but controlled by a private organization.

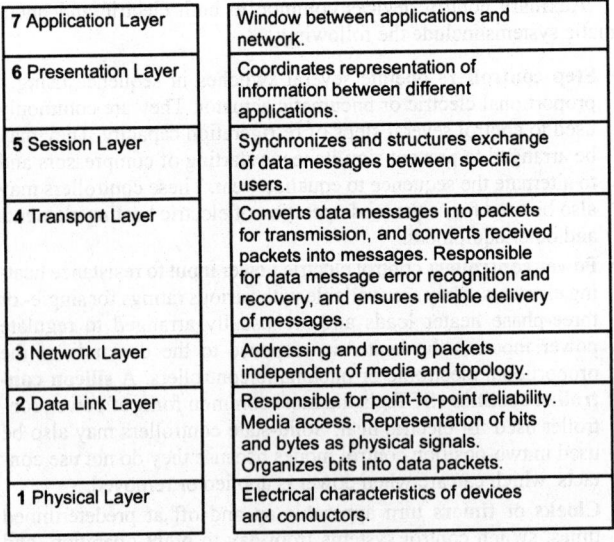

7 Application Layer	Window between applications and network.
6 Presentation Layer	Coordinates representation of information between different applications.
5 Session Layer	Synchronizes and structures exchange of data messages between specific users.
4 Transport Layer	Converts data messages into packets for transmission, and converts received packets into messages. Responsible for data message error recognition and recovery, and ensures reliable delivery of messages.
3 Network Layer	Addressing and routing packets independent of media and topology.
2 Data Link Layer	Responsible for point-to-point reliability. Media access. Representation of bits and bytes as physical signals. Organizes bits into data packets.
1 Physical Layer	Electrical characteristics of devices and conductors.

Fig. 20 OSI Reference Model

- **Private protocol.** Unpublished; use and specification controlled by a private organization. Examples include the proprietary communications used by many building automation devices.

Multivendor communication is possible with any of these three classes, but the challenges vary. Specifying a standard or widely used public protocol can improve the chances for a competitive bidding process and provide economic options for future expansions. However, specifying a common protocol does not ensure that the requirement for interoperability is met. It is also necessary to specify the desired interaction between devices.

OSI NETWORK MODEL

ISO *Standard* 7498-1 presents a seven-layer model of information exchange called the Open Systems Interconnection (OSI) Reference Model (Figure 20). Most descriptions of computer networks, especially open networks, are based on this reference model. The layers can be thought of as steps in the translation of a message from something with meaning at the application layer, to something measurable at the physical layer, and back to meaningful information at the application layer.

The full seven-layer model does not apply to every network, but it is still used to describe the aspects that fit. When describing DDC networks that use the same technology throughout the system, the seven-layer model is relatively unimportant. For systems that use various technologies at different points in the network, the model helps to describe where and how the pieces are bound together.

NETWORK STRUCTURE

Often, a single DDC system applies different network technologies at different points in the system. For example, a relatively low-speed, inexpensive network with relatively primitive functions may link a group of room controllers to a supervisory controller. A faster, more sophisticated network may link the supervisory controller to its peers and to one or more operator workstations. Figure 21 illustrates this sort of high-speed hierarchical network. Structures like it have been popular in DDC for years. Frequently, the network hierarchy corresponds roughly to a hierarchy related to the control function of the devices, but variations continue to emerge. The opposite extreme is a completely flat network architecture. A flat architecture links all devices through the same network. A flat architecture is more viable in small systems than in large ones, because economic constraints typically dictate that low-cost (and therefore low-speed)

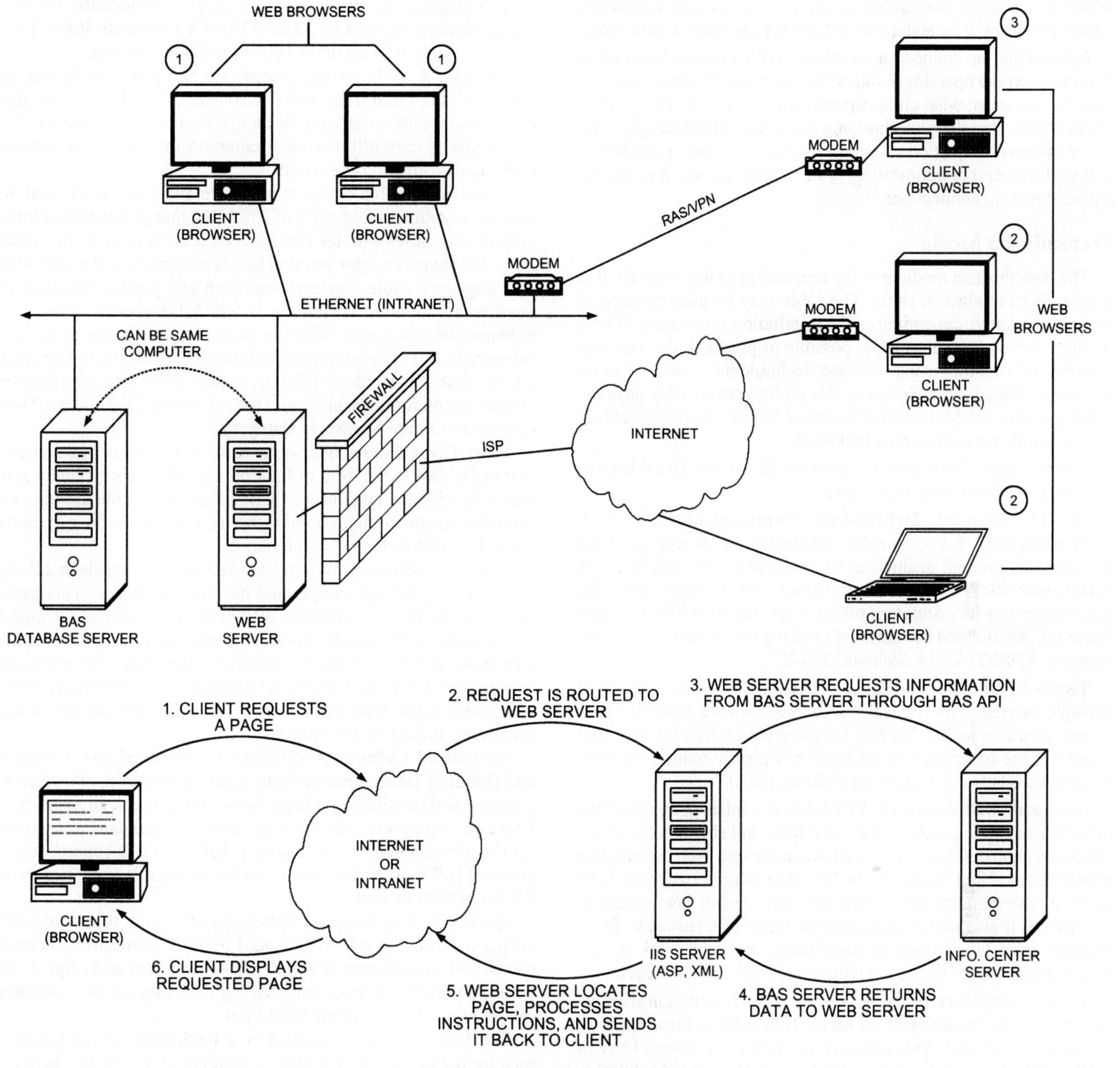

Fig. 21 Hierarchical Network

networks be used to connect field-level controllers. Because of their performance limitations, these networks do not scale well to large numbers of devices. As the cost of electronics for communication drops, the flatter networks become more feasible.

Network structure can affect

- Opportunities for expansion of a BAS.
- Reliability and failure modes. It may be appropriate to separate sections of a network to isolate failures.
- How devices load the information-carrying capacity of the network. It can isolate one busy branch from the rest of the system, or isolate branches from the high-speed backbone.
- How and where information is displayed to operating personnel; Web servers accessible through the Internet make BAS information available to anyone, anywhere, who has a standard Web browser and access rights to view the server pages.
- System cost, because it determines the mix of low- and high-speed devices.
- System data security and access control.

The relative merits of one structure versus another depend on the communication functions required, hardware and software available for the task, and cost. For a given job, there is probably more than one suitable structure. Product capabilities change quickly. Engineers who choose to specify network structure must be aware of new technologies to take advantage of the most cost-effective solutions.

Connections Between BAS Networks and Other Computer Networks

Some BAS networks use other networks to connect segments of the BAS. This occurs

- Within a building, using the information technology network
- Between buildings, using an intranet or the Internet
- Between buildings, using telephone lines

In each case, the link between BAS segments must be considered part of the BAS network when evaluating function, security, and performance. The link also raises new issues. The connecting segment is likely to be outside the control of the owner of the BAS, which could affect availability of service. Traffic and bandwidth issues may have to be addressed outside the facilities department.

Using a dial-up connection to interact with a remote building or to serve a remote operator requires consideration of which segment may dial the other, what circumstances trigger the call, and security implications. Handling interbuilding communication through intranet or Internet connections, with the operator interface provided by a Web browser communicating with a Web server, has largely replaced dial-up connections.

Transmission Media

The transmission medium is the foundation of the network. It is usually, but not always, cable. The cable may be plenum-rated or non-plenum-rated, depending on the installation application. Where physical cable connection is not possible or practical, devices may transfer information using wireless technologies, such as radio waves or infrared light. However, this section covers only physical cabling media. ANSI/TIA/EIA *Standard* 568-B.1 provides cabling specifications for commercial buildings.

Cable length. The maximum cable length varies with cable type, transmission speed, and the protocol.

100 Ω Balanced Twisted-Pair Communications Outlet/ Connector. Each four-pair cable terminates on an eight-position modular jack, and all unshielded twisted-pair (UTP) and screened twisted-pair (ScTP) telecommunications outlets must meet the requirements of IEC *Standard* 60603-7, as well as ANSI/TIA/EIA *Standard* 568-B.2 and the terminal marking and mounting requirements of ANSI/TIA/EIA *Standard* 570-B.

Twisted-Pair Copper Cable. A twisted-pair cable consists of multiple twisted pairs (typically 24 AWG) of wire covered by an overall sheath or jacket. Varying the number of twists for each pair relative to the other pairs in the cable can greatly reduce crosstalk (interference between signals on different pairs).

Screened twisted-pair (ScTP) cable is similar in construction to UTP data cabling, except that ScTP has a foil shield between the conductors and outer jacket, as well as a drain wire used to minimize interference-related problems. ScTP cable is preferred over UTP cable in environments where high immunity and/or low emissions are critical. It also allows less crosstalk than UTP. However, ScTP requires more labor-intensive installation, and any break or improper grounding of the shield reduces its overall effectiveness.

Category 3 cable connects hardware and patch cords that are rated to a maximum frequency of 16 MHz. This cable is rated up to 16 megabits per second. This category is usually the lowest level of cable installed and is used mainly for voice and low-speed networks.

Category 5 cable connects hardware and patch cords that are rated to a maximum frequency of 100 MHz. The actual data transmission rate varies with the compression scheme used. Category 5 was defined in ANSI/TIA/EIA *Standard* 568-A, but is no longer recognized in the new ANSI/TIA/EIA *Standard* 568-B.1.

Category 5e cable connects hardware and patch cords that are rated to a maximum frequency of 100 MHz. The actual data transmission rate varies with the compression or encoding scheme used. Category 5e, the lowest category recommended for data installations, is defined by ANSI/TIA/EIA *Standards* 568-B.1 and B.2. This cable is rated up to 100 megabits per second.

Table 1 Comparison of Fiber Optic Technology

	Multimode Fiber	Single-Mode Fiber
Light source	LED	Laser
Cable designation (core/cladding diameter)	62.6/125	8.3/125
Transmission distance	2000 m	3000 m
Data rate	>10 gigabit/s and increasing	Even higher
Relative cost	Less per connection, more per data rate	More per connection, less per data rate

Category 6 cable connects hardware and patch cords that are rated to a maximum frequency of 250 MHz, though the actual data transmission rate varies with the compression scheme used. UTP or STP cable is currently the most common medium. This cable is rated up to 1 gigabit per second.

Category 6e cable connects hardware and patch cords that are rated to a maximum frequency of 250 MHz, though actual data transmission rate varies with the compression scheme used. With all Category 6 systems, an eight-position jack is mandatory in the work area.

Category 7 cable connects hardware and patch cords that are rated to a maximum frequency of 600 MHz, though actual data transmission rate varies with the compression scheme used. This category is still in development and uses a braided shield surrounding all four foil shielded pairs to reduce noise and interference. Depending on future technological developments, the current RJ-45 connector will not be used in Category 7.

Fiber-Optic Cable. Fiber-optic cable uses glass or plastic fibers to transfer data in the form of light pulses, which are typically generated by either a laser or an LED. Fiber-optic cable systems are classified as either single-mode fiber or multimode fiber systems. Table 1 compares their characteristics.

Light in a fiber-optic system loses less energy than electrical signals traveling through copper and has no capacitance. This translates into greater transmission distances and dramatically higher data transfer rates, which impose no limits on a BAS. Fiber optics also have exceptional noise immunity. However, the necessary conversions between light-based signaling and electricity-based computing make fiber optics more expensive per device, which sometimes offsets its advantages.

Structured Cabling. ANSI/TIA/EIA *Standard* 568, Commercial Building Telecommunications Cabling Standard, allows cable planning and installation to begin before the network engineering is finalized. It supports both voice and data. The standard was written for the telecommunications industry, but cabling is gaining recognition as building infrastructure, and the standard is being applied to BAS networks as well.

ANSI/TIA/EIA *Standard* 568-B specifies **star topology** (each device individually cabled to a hub) because connectivity is more robust and management is simpler than for busses and rings. If the wires in a leg are shorted, only that leg fails, making fault isolation easier; with a bus, all drops would fail.

The basic structure specified is a **backbone**, which typically runs from floor to floor within a building and possibly between buildings. **Horizontal cabling** runs between the distribution frames on each floor and the information outlets in the work areas.

Wireless Sensors and Controls. The rapid maturity of everyday wireless technologies, now widely used for mobile phones, Internet access, and even barcode replacement, has tremendously increased the ability to collect information from the physical world. Wireless technologies offer significant opportunities in sensors and controls for building operation, especially in reducing the cost of installing data acquisition and control devices. Installation costs typically represent 20 to 80% of the total cost of a sensor and control point in any HVAC system, so reducing or eliminating the cost of installation has a dramatic effect on the overall installed system cost. Low-cost wireless sensors and control systems also make it economical to use more sensors, thereby establishing highly energy-efficient building operations and demand responsiveness that enhance the electric grid reliability.

Wireless sensors and control networks consist of sensor and control devices that are connected to a network using radio-frequency (RF) or optical (infrared) signals. Devices can communicate bidirectionally (i.e., transmitting and receiving) or one way (transmitting only). Most RF products transmit in the industrial, scientific, or medical frequency bands, which are set aside by the Federal Communication Commission (FCC) for use without an FCC license. Wireless sensor networks have different requirements than computer networks and, thus, different network topologies, and separate communication protocols have evolved for them. The simplest is the **point-to-point topology**, in which two nodes communicate directly with each other. The **point-to-multipoint** or **star topology** is an extension of the point-to-point configuration in which many nodes communicate with a central receiving or gateway node. In either topology, sensor nodes might have pure transmitters, which provide one-way communication only, or transceivers, which enable two-way communication and verification of the receipt of messages. Gateways provide a means to convert and pass data between protocols (e.g., from a wireless sensor network protocol to the wired Ethernet protocol).

The communication range of the point-to-point and star topologies is limited by the maximum communication range between the sensor node (from which the measured data originates) and the receiver node. This range can be extended by using repeaters, which receive transmissions from sensor nodes and then retransmit them, usually at higher power than the original transmissions. In the **mesh network topology**, each sensor node includes a transceiver that can communicate directly with any other node within its communication range. These networks connect many devices to many other devices, thus forming a mesh of nodes in which signals are transmitted between distant points via multiple hops. This approach decreases the distance over which each node must communicate and reduces each node's power use substantially, making them more compatible with onboard power sources such as batteries (Capehardt 2005).

SPECIFYING BAS NETWORKS

Specifying a DDC system includes specifying a network. The many network technologies available deliver many performance levels at many different prices. Rational selection requires assessing the requirements (i.e., what information will pass between devices and at what rates). In some cases, new equipment must interface with existing devices, which may limit networking options.

Specification Method

As with other aspects of an HVAC system, an engineer must choose a method of specification. There are four basic types of specifications for BAS networks:

- **Descriptive.** Calls out the exact properties of the products. Properties could include communication protocols and data transfer rates.
- **Performance.** Tells what result is required and the criteria by which performance will be verified. Allows bidders to propose products to meet the need.
- **Reference standard.** Requires products to conform to an established standard. Does not oblige contractor to meet end user's needs not addressed in the standard.
- **Proprietary.** Calls out brand names. May be necessary in expansion of existing systems.

Writing a descriptive network specification requires knowledge of the details of network technology. To succeed with any specification, the designer must articulate the end user's needs. Typically, performance-based specification is the best value for the customer (Ehrlich and Pittel 1999).

Communication Tasks

Determining network performance requirements means identifying and quantifying the communication functions required. Ehrlich and Pittel (1999) identified the following five basic communication tasks necessary to establish network requirements.

Data Exchange. What data passes between which devices? What control and optimization data passes between controllers? What update rates are required? What data does an operator need to reach? How much delay is acceptable in retrieving values? What update rates are required on "live" data displays? (Within one system, answers may vary according to data use.) Which set points and control parameters do operators need to adjust over the network?

Alarms and Events. Where do alarms originate? Where are they logged and displayed? How much delay is acceptable? Where are they acknowledged? What information must be delivered along with the alarm? (Depending on system design, alarm messages may be passed over the network along with the alarms.) Where are alarm summary reports required? How and where do operators need to adjust alarm limits, etc.?

Schedules. For HVAC equipment that runs on schedules, where can the schedules be read? Where can they be modified?

Trends. Where does trend data originate? Where is it stored? How much will be transmitted? Where is it displayed and processed? Which user interfaces can set and modify trend collection parameters?

Network Management. What network diagnostic and maintenance functions are required at which user interfaces? Data access and security functions may be handled as network management functions.

Bushby et al. (1999) refer to the same five communication tasks as **interoperability areas** and list many more specific considerations in each area. ASHRAE *Guideline* 13 also provides more detailed information that is helpful.

APPROACHES TO INTEROPERABILITY

Many approaches to interoperability have been proposed and applied, each with varying degrees of success under various circumstances. The field changes quickly as product lines emerge and standards develop and gain acceptance. The building automation world continues to evaluate options project by project.

Typically, an interoperable system uses one of two approaches: standard protocols or special-purpose gateways. With a standard, the supplier is responsible for compliance with the standard; the system specifier or integrator is responsible for interoperation. With a gateway, the supplier takes responsibility for interoperation. Where the job requires interoperation with existing equipment, gateways may be the only solution available. Bushby (1998) addressed this issue and some of the limitations associated with gateways. To date, interoperability by any method requires solid field engineering and capable system integration; the issues extend well beyond the selection of a communication protocol.

Standard Protocols

Table 2 lists some applicable standard protocols that have been used in BAS. Their different characteristics make some more suited to particular tasks than others. PROFIBUS (www.profibus.com) and MODBUS (www.modbus.org) were designed for low-cost industrial process control and automated manufacturing applications, but they have been applied to BAS. LonTalk defines a LAN

Table 2 Some Standard Communication Protocols Applicable to BAS

Protocol	Definition
BACnet®	ANSI/ASHRAE *Standard* 135-2004, EN/ISO *Standard* 16484-5:2003
LonTalk	ANSI/CEA *Standard* 709.1
PROFIBUS FMS	EN 50170:1996 Volume 2
Konnex	EN 50090
MODBUS	Modbus Application Protocol Specification V1.1

technology but not messages that are to be exchanged for BAS applications. BACnet® or implementers' agreements, such as those made by members of LonMark International, are necessary to achieve interoperability with LonTalk devices. Konnex evolved from the European Installation Bus (EIB) and several other European protocols developed for residential applications, including multifamily housing.

BACnet is the only standard protocol developed specifically for commercial BAS applications. BACnet has been adopted as a national standard in the United States, Korea, and Japan, as a European standard, and as a world standard (EN/ISO *Standard* 16484-5). BACnet was designed to be used with a variety of LAN technologies and also defines a way to connect BACnet devices with Konnex devices.

Gateways and Interfaces

Rather than conforming to a published standard, a supplier can design a specific device to exchange data with another specific device. This typically requires cooperation between two manufacturers. In some cases, it can be simpler and more cost-effective than for both manufacturers to conform to an agreed-upon standard. The device can be either custom-designed or off the shelf. In either case, the communication tasks must be carefully specified to ensure that the gateway performs as needed.

Choosing a system that supports a variety of gateways may be a way to maintain a flexible position as products and standards continue to develop.

SPECIFYING DDC SYSTEMS

Successful DDC installation depends in part on a clear description (specification) of what is required to meet the customer's needs. The specification should include descriptions of the products desired, or of the performance and features expected. Needed points or data objects should be listed. A control schematic shows the layout of each system to be controlled, including instrumentation and input/output objects and any hard-wired interlocks. A sequence of operation should be provided for each system. Additional information on specifying DDC controls can be found in ASHRAE *Guideline* 13. ASHRAE (2005) provides sample sequences of control for air-handling systems.

COMMISSIONING

A successful control system requires a proper start-up and testing, not merely the adjustment of a few parameters (set points and throttling ranges) and a few quick checks. With the services of an experienced control professional, the typical DDC system can be used effectively in the commissioning process to test and document HVAC system performance. In general, increased use of VAV systems and digital controls has increased the importance of and need for commissioning.

Design and construction specifications should include specific commissioning procedures. In addition, commissioning should be coordinated with testing, adjusting, and balancing (TAB) because each affects the other. The commissioning procedure begins by checking each control device to ensure that it is installed and connected according to approved drawings. Each electrical and pneumatic connection is verified, and all interlocks to fan and pump motors and primary heating and cooling equipment are checked. Chapter 42 of the 2007 *ASHRAE Handbook—HVAC Applications* and ASHRAE *Guideline* 1 explain how commissioning starts with project conception and continues for the life of the building.

TUNING

Systematic tuning of controllers improves performance of all controls and is particularly important for digital control. First, the controlled process should be controlled manually between various set points to evaluate the following questions:

- Is the process noisy (rapid fluctuations in controlled variable)?
- Is there appreciable hysteresis (backlash) in the actuator?
- How easy (or difficult) is it to maintain and change set point?
- In which operating region is the process most sensitive (highest gain)?

If the process cannot be controlled manually, the reason should be identified and corrected before the controller is tuned.

Tuning optimizes control parameters that determine steady-state and transient characteristics of the control system. HVAC processes are nonlinear, and characteristics change seasonally. Controllers tuned under one operating condition may become unstable as conditions change. A well-tuned controller (1) minimizes steady-state error for set point, (2) responds quickly to disturbances, and (3) remains stable under all operating conditions. Tuning proportional controllers is a compromise between minimizing steady-state error and maintaining margins of stability. Proportional plus integral (PI) control minimizes this compromise because the integral action reduces steady-state error, and the proportional term determines the controller's response to disturbances.

Tuning Proportional, PI, and PID Controllers

Popular methods of determining proportional, PI, and PID controller tuning parameters include closed- and open-loop process identification methods and trial-and-error methods. Two of the most widely used techniques for tuning these controllers are ultimate oscillation and first-order-plus-dead-time. There are many optimization calculations for these two techniques. The Ziegler-Nichols, which is given here, is well established.

Ultimate Oscillation (Closed-Loop) Method. The closed-loop method increases controller gain in proportional-only mode until the equipment continuously cycles after a set-point change (Figure 22, where K_p = 40). Proportional and integral terms are then computed from the cycle's period of oscillation and the K_p value that caused cycling. The ultimate oscillation method is as follows:

1. Adjust control parameters so that all are essentially off. This corresponds to a proportion band (gain) at its maximum (minimum), the integral time (repeats per minute) or integral gain to maximum (minimum), and derivative to its minimum.
2. Adjust manual output of the controller to give a measurement as close to midscale as possible.
3. Put controller in automatic.
4. Gradually increase proportional feedback (this corresponds to reducing the proportional band or increasing the proportional gain) until observed oscillations neither grow nor diminish in amplitude. If response saturates at either extreme, start over at Step 2 to obtain a stable response. If no oscillations are observed, change the set point and try again.
5. Record the proportional band as PB_u and the period of oscillations as T_u.
6. Use the recorded proportional band and oscillation period to calculate controller settings as follows:

Proportional only:

$$PB = 1.8(PB_u) \text{ percent} \tag{4}$$

Proportional plus integral (PI):

$$PB = 2.22(PB_u) \text{ percent} \tag{5}$$

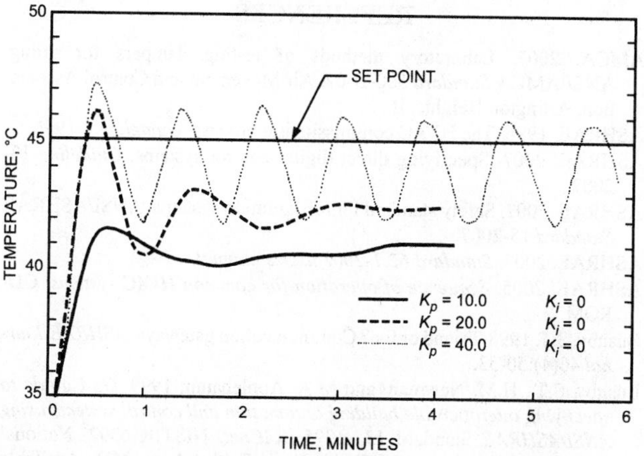

Fig. 22 Response of Discharge Air Temperature to Step Change in Set Points at Various Proportional Constants with No Integral Action

$$T_i = 0.83T_u \quad \text{minute per repeat} \tag{6}$$

Proportional plus integral plus derivative (PID):

$$PB = 1.67(PB_u) \text{ percent} \tag{7}$$

$$T_i = 0.50T_u \quad \text{minute per repeat} \tag{8}$$

$$T_d = 0.125T_u \quad \text{minute} \tag{9}$$

First-Order-plus-Dead-Time (Open-Loop) Method. The open-loop method introduces a step change in input into the opened control loop. A graphical technique is used to estimate the process transfer function parameters. Proportional and integral terms are calculated from the estimated process parameters using a series of equations.

The value of the process variable must be recorded over time, and the dead time and time constant must be determined from it. This can be accomplished graphically as seen in Figure 23. The first-order-plus-dead-time method is as follows:

1. Adjust controller manual output to give a midscale measurement.
2. Arrange to record the process variable over time.
3. Move the manual output of the controller by 10% as rapidly as possible to approximate a step change.
4. Record the value of the process variable over time until it reaches a new steady-state value.
5. Determine dead time and time constant.
6. Use dead time (TD) and time constant (TC) values to calculate PID values as follows:

$$\text{Gain} = \frac{\text{\% change in controlled variable}}{\text{\% change in control signal}} \tag{10}$$

Proportional only:

$$PB = \text{Gain}/(TC/TD) \tag{11}$$

Proportional plus integral (PI):

$$PB = 0.9(\text{Gain})/(TC/TD) \tag{12}$$

$$T_i = 3.33(TD) \tag{13}$$

Proportional-integral-derivative (PID):

$$PB = 1.2(\text{Gain})/(TC/TD) \tag{14}$$

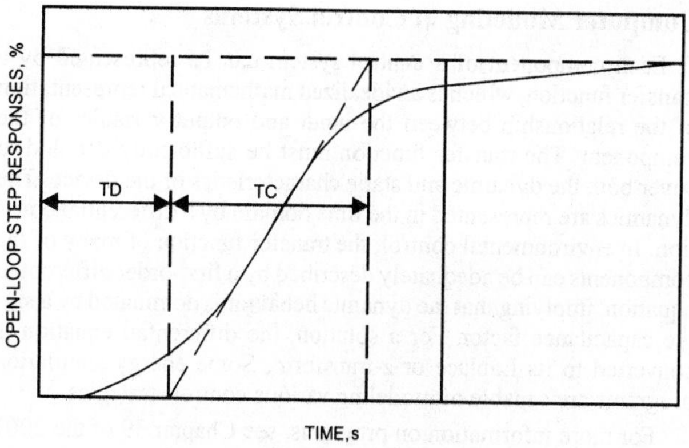

Fig. 23 Open-Loop Step Response Versus Time

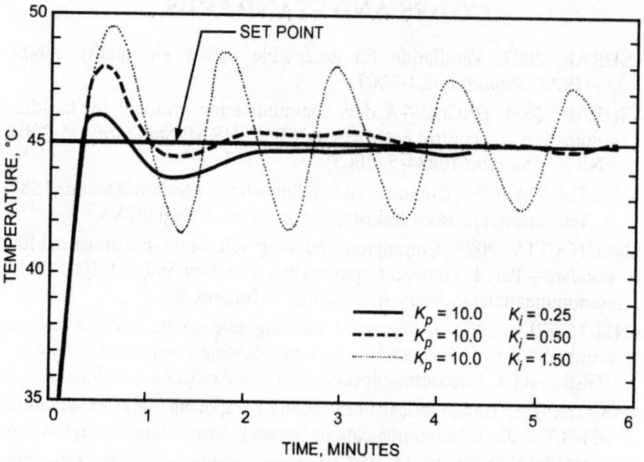

Fig. 24 Response of Discharge Air Temperature to Step Change in Set Points at Various Integral Constants with Fixed Proportional Constant

$$T_i = 2(TD) \tag{15}$$

$$T_d = 0.5(TD) \tag{16}$$

Trial and Error. This method involves adjusting the gain of the proportion-only controller until the desired response to a set point is observed. Conservative tuning dictates that this response should have a small initial overshoot and quickly damp to steady-state conditions. Set-point changes should be made in the range where controller saturation, or output limit, is avoided. The integral term is then increased until changes in set point produce the same dynamic response as the controller under proportional control, but with the response now centered about the set point (Figure 24).

Tuning Digital Controllers

In tuning digital controllers, additional parameters may need to be specified. The digital controller sampling interval is critical because it can introduce harmonic distortion if not selected properly. This sampling interval is usually set at the factory and may not be adjustable. A controller sampling interval of about one-tenth of the controlled-process time constant usually provides adequate control. Many digital control algorithms include an error dead band to eliminate unnecessary control actions when the process is near set point. Hysteresis compensation is possible with digital controllers, but it must be carefully applied because overcompensation can cause continuous cycling of the control loop.

Computer Modeling of Control Systems

Each component of a control system can be represented by a transfer function, which is an idealized mathematical representation of the relationship between the input and output variables of the component. The transfer function must be sufficiently detailed to cover both the dynamic and static characteristics of the device. The dynamics are represented in the time domain by a differential equation. In environmental control, the transfer function of many of the components can be adequately described by a first-order differential equation, implying that the dynamic behavior is dominated by a single capacitance factor. For a solution, the differential equation is converted to its Laplace or *z*-transform. Some energy simulation programs are capable of modeling various control strategies.

For more information on programs, see Chapter 39 of the 2007 *ASHRAE Handbook—HVAC Applications*.

CODES AND STANDARDS

ASHRAE. 2007. Ventilation for acceptable indoor air quality. ANSI/ASHRAE *Standard* 62.1-2007.

ASHRAE. 2004. BACnet—A data communication protocol for building automation and control networks. ANSI/ASHRAE *Standard* 135-2004, EN/ISO *Standard* 16484-5 (2003).

ANSI/TIA/EIA. 1995. Commercial building wiring standard. *Standard* 568-A. Telecommunications Industry Association, Arlington, VA.

ANSI/TIA/EIA. 2003. Commercial building telecommunications cabling standard—Part 1: General requirements. *Standard* 568-B.1-2003. Telecommunications Industry Association, Arlington, VA.

ANSI/TIA/EIA. 2003. Commercial building telecommunications cabling standard—Part 2: Balanced twisted pair cabling components. *Standard* 568-B.2-2003. Telecommunications Industry Association, Arlington, VA.

ANSI/TIA/EIA. 2002. Optical fiber cabling component standard. *Standard* 568-B.3-2002. Telecommunications Industry Association, Arlington, VA.

ANSI/TIA/EIA. 2004. Residential telecommunications infrastructure standard. *Standard* 570-B. Telecommunications Industry Association, Arlington, VA.

ANSI/CEA. 2002. Control network protocol specification. ANSI/CEA *Standard* 709.1-B-2002. Consumer Electronics Association, Arlington, VA.

ANSI/CEA. 1999. Free-topology twisted-pair channel specification. ANSI/CEA *Standard* 709.3-1999. Consumer Electronics Association, Arlington, VA.

ANSI/CEA. 2004. Tunneling component network protocols over Internet protocol channels. ANSI/CEA *Standard* 852-A-2004. Consumer Electronics Association, Arlington, VA.

CENELEC. 2004. Home and building electronic systems. EN *Standard* 50090 (various parts).

EIA. 2003. Electrical characteristics of generators and receivers for use in balanced digital multipoint systems. TIA/EIA *Standard* 485-2003.

IEC. 2008. Connectors for electronic equipment—Part 7: Detail specification for 8-way, unshielded, free and fixed connectors. *Standard* 60603-7 ed. 3. International Electrotechnical Commission, Geneva.

IEEE. 2005. Information technology—Telecommunications and information exchange between systems—Local and metropolitan area network—Specific requirements—Part 3: Carrier sense multiple access with collision detection (CSMA/CD) access method and physical layer specifications. *Standard* 802.3-2005. Institute of Electrical and Electronics Engineers, Piscataway, NJ.

ISO. 1994. Information processing systems—Open systems interconnection—Basic reference model: The basic model. ISO/IEC *Standard* 7498-1:1994. International Organization for Standardization, Geneva.

NEMA. 2003. Enclosures for electrical equipment (1000 volts maximum). *Standard* 250. National Electrical Manufacturers Association, Rosslyn, VA.

UL. 2002. Signaling devices for the hearing impaired. ANSI/UL *Standard* 1971. Underwriters Laboratories, Northbrook, IL.

REFERENCES

AMCA. 2007. Laboratory methods of testing dampers for rating. ANSI/AMCA *Standard* 500-D-07. Air Movement and Control Association, Arlington Heights, IL.

ASHRAE. 1996. The HVAC commissioning process. *Guideline* 1-1996.

ASHRAE. 2007. Specifying direct digital control systems. *Guideline* 13-2007.

ASHRAE. 2007. Safety standard for refrigeration systems. ANSI/ASHRAE *Standard* 15-2007.

ASHRAE. 2007. *Standard 62.1-2007 user's manual.*

ASHRAE. 2005. *Sequence of operation for common HVAC systems*. CD-ROM.

Bushby, S.T. 1998. Friend or foe? Communication gateways. *ASHRAE Journal* 40(4):50-53.

Bushby, S.T., H.M. Newman, and M.A. Applebaum. 1999. *GSA guide to specifying interoperable building automation and control systems using ANSI/ASHRAE* Standard *135-1995, BACnet*. NISTIR 6392. National Institute of Standards and Technology, Gaithersburg, MD. Available from National Technical Information Service, Springfield, VA.

Capehardt, B. and L. Capehardt. 2005. *Web based energy information and control system: Case studies and applications*, Chapter 27, Wireless Sensor Applications for Building Operation and Management. Fairmont Press and CRC, Boca Raton, FL.

Ehrlich, P. and O. Pittel. 1999. Specifying interoperability. *ASHRAE Journal* 41(4):25-29.

van Becelaere, R., H.J. Sauer, and F. Finaish. 2004. Flow resistance and modulating characteristics of control dampers. ASHRAE Research Project RP-1157, *Final Report*.

BIBLIOGRAPHY

ASHRAE. 2003. Selecting outdoor, return, and relief dampers for air-side economizer systems. *Guideline* 16-2003.

Avery, G. 1989. Updating the VAV outside air economizer controls. *ASHRAE Journal* (April).

Avery, G. 1992. The instability of VAV systems. *Heating, Piping and Air Conditioning* (February).

BICSI. 1999. *LAN and internetworking design manual*, 3rd ed. Building Industry Consulting Service International, Tampa.

CEN. 1999. *Building control systems, Part 1: Overview and definitions*. prEN ISO16484-1. CEN, the European Committee for Standardization.

Haines, R.W. and D.C. Hittle. 2003. *Control systems for heating, ventilating and air conditioning*, 6th ed. Springer.

Hartman, T.B. 1993. *Direct digital controls for HVAC systems*. McGraw-Hill, New York.

Kettler, J.P. 1998. Controlling minimum ventilation volume in VAV systems. *ASHRAE Journal* (May).

Levenhagen, J.I. and D.H. Spethmann. 1993. *HVAC controls and systems*. McGraw-Hill, New York.

Lizardos, E. and K. Elovitz. 2000. Damper sizing using damper authority. *ASHRAE Journal* (April).

LonMark. 1998. *LonMark application layer interoperability guidelines*. LonMark Interoperability Association, Sunnyvale, CA.

LonMark. 1999. *LonMark functional profile: Space comfort controller*. 8500-10. LonMark Interoperability Association.

Newman, H.M. 1994. *Direct digital control for building systems: Theory and practice*. John Wiley & Sons, New York.

OPC Foundation. 1998. *OPC overview*. OPC Foundation, Boca Raton, FL. Available from http://www.opcfoundation.org/Archive/c9cf0fff-65fa-4362-bc93-aa7d0ab58016/General/OPC Overview 1.00.pdf.

Rose, M.T. 1990. *The open book: A practical perspective on OSI*. Prentice-Hall, Englewood Cliffs, NJ.

Seem, J.E., J.M. House, and R.H. Monroe. 1999. On-line monitoring and fault detection. *ASHRAE Journal* (July).

Starr, R. 1999. Pneumatic controls in a digital age. *Heating, Piping and Air Conditioning* (November).

Tillack, L. and J.B. Rishel. 1998. Proper control of HVAC variable speed pumps. *ASHRAE Journal* (November).

CHAPTER 8

SOUND AND VIBRATION

IF FUNDAMENTAL principles of sound and vibration control are applied in the design, installation, and use of HVAC and refrigeration systems, suitable levels of noise and vibration can be achieved with a high probability of user acceptance. This chapter introduces these fundamental principles, including characteristics of sound, basic definitions and terminology, human response to sound, acoustic design goals, and vibration isolation fundamentals. Chapter 47 of the 2007 *ASHRAE Handbook—HVAC Applications* and the references at the end of this chapter contain technical discussions, tables, and design examples helpful to HVAC designers.

ACOUSTICAL DESIGN OBJECTIVE

The primary objective for acoustical design of HVAC systems and equipment is to ensure that the acoustical environment in a given space is not unacceptably affected by HVAC system-related noise or vibration. Sound and vibration are created by a **source**, are transmitted along one or more **paths**, and reach a **receiver**. Treatments and modifications can be applied to any or all of these elements to reduce unwanted noise and vibration, although it is usually most effective and least expensive to reduce noise at the source.

CHARACTERISTICS OF SOUND

Sound is a propagating disturbance in a fluid (gas or liquid) or in a solid. In fluid media, the disturbance travels as a longitudinal compression wave. Sound in air is called *airborne sound* or just *sound*. It is generated by a vibrating surface or turbulent fluid stream. In solids, sound can travel as bending, compressional, torsional, shear, or other waves, which, in turn, are sources of airborne sound. Sound in solids is generally called *structureborne sound*. In HVAC system design, both airborne and structureborne sound propagation are important.

Levels

Magnitude of sound and vibration physical properties are almost always expressed in *levels*. As shown in the following equations, the level L is based on the common (base 10) logarithm of a ratio of the magnitude of a physical property of power, intensity, or energy to a reference magnitude of the same type of property:

$$L = 10 \log\left(\frac{A}{A_{ref}}\right) \tag{1}$$

where A is the magnitude of the physical property of interest and A_{ref} is the reference value. Note that the ratio is dimensionless. In this equation, a factor of 10 is included to convert bels to decibels (dB).

The preparation of this chapter is assigned to TC 2.6, Sound and Vibration Control.

Sound Pressure and Sound Pressure Level

Sound waves in air are variations in pressure above and below atmospheric pressure. **Sound pressure** is measured in pascals (Pa). The human ear responds across a broad range of sound pressures; the threshold of hearing to the threshold of pain covers a range of approximately 10^{14}:1. Table 1 gives approximate values of sound pressure by various sources at specified distances from the source.

The range of sound pressure in Table 1 is so large that it is more convenient to use a scale proportional to the logarithm of this quantity. Therefore, the **decibel** (dB) scale is the preferred method of presenting quantities in acoustics, not only because it collapses a large range of pressures to a more manageable range, but also because its levels correlate better with human responses to the magnitude of sound than do sound pressures. Equation (1) describes levels of power, intensity, and energy, which are proportional to the square of other physical properties, such as sound pressure and vibration acceleration. Thus, the **sound pressure level L_p** corresponding to a sound pressure is given by

$$L_p = 10 \log\left(\frac{p}{p_{ref}}\right)^2 = 20 \log\left(\frac{p}{p_{ref}}\right) \tag{2}$$

where p is the root mean square (RMS) value of acoustic pressure in pascals. The root mean square is the square root of the time average

Table 1 Typical Sound Pressures and Sound Pressure Levels

Source	Sound Pressure, Pa	Sound Pressure Level, dB re 20 μPa	Subjective Reaction
Military jet takeoff at 30 m	200	140	Extreme danger
Artillery fire at 3 m	63.2	130	
Passenger jet takeoff at 15 m	20	120	Threshold of pain
Loud rock band	6.3	110	Threshold of discomfort
Automobile horn at 3 m	2	100	
Unmuffled large diesel engine at 40 m	0.6	90	Very loud
Accelerating diesel truck at 15 m	0.2	80	
Freight train at 30 m	0.06	70	Loud
Conversational speech at 1 m	0.02	60	
Window air conditioner at 3 m	0.006	50	Moderate
Quiet residential area	0.002	40	Quiet
Whispered conversation at 2 m	0.0006	30	
Buzzing insect at 1 m	0.0002	20	Perceptible
Threshold of good hearing	0.00006	10	Faint
Threshold of excellent youthful hearing	0.00002	0	Threshold of hearing

of the square of the pressure ratio. The ratio p/p_{ref} is squared to give quantities proportional to intensity or energy. A reference quantity is needed so the term in parentheses is nondimensional. For sound pressure levels in air, the reference pressure p_{ref} is 20 μPa, which corresponds to the approximate threshold of hearing for a young person with good hearing exposed to a pure tone with a frequency of 1000 Hz.

The decibel scale is used for many different descriptors relating to sound: source strength, sound level at a specified location, and attenuation along propagation paths; each has a different reference quantity. For this reason, it is important to be aware of the context in which the term *decibel* or *level* is used. For most acoustical quantities, there is an internationally accepted reference value. A reference quantity is always implied even if it does not appear.

Sound pressure level is relatively easy to measure and thus is used by most noise codes and criteria. (The human ear and microphones are pressure-sensitive.) Sound pressure levels for the corresponding sound pressures are also given in Table 1.

Frequency

Frequency is the number of oscillations (or cycles) completed per second by a vibrating object. The international unit for frequency is hertz (Hz) with dimension s^{-1}. When the motion of vibrating air particles is simple harmonic, the sound is said to be a **pure tone** and the sound pressure p as a function of time and frequency can be described by

$$p(t,f) = p_0 \sin(2\pi ft) \tag{3}$$

where f is frequency in hertz, p_0 is the maximum amplitude of oscillating (or acoustic) pressure, and t is time in seconds.

The **audible frequency range** for humans with unimpaired hearing extends from about 20 Hz to 20 kHz. In some cases, infrasound (<20 Hz) or ultrasound (>20 kHz) are important, but methods and instrumentation for these frequency regions are specialized and are not considered here.

Speed

The speed of a longitudinal wave in a fluid is a function of the fluid's density and bulk modulus of elasticity. In air, at room temperature, the speed of sound is about 340 m/s; in water, about 1500 m/s. In solids, there are several different types of waves, each with a different speed. The speeds of **compressional**, **torsional**, and **shear waves** do not vary with frequency, and are often greater than the speed of sound in air. However, these types of waves are not the primary source of radiated noise because resultant displacements at the surface are small compared to the internal displacements. **Bending waves**, however, are significant sources of radiation, and their speed changes with frequency. At lower frequencies, bending waves are slower than sound in air, but can exceed this value at higher frequencies (e.g., above approximately 1000 Hz).

Wavelength

The wavelength of sound in a medium is the distance between successive maxima or minima of a simple harmonic disturbance propagating in that medium at a single instant in time. Wavelength, speed, and frequency are related by

$$\lambda = c/f \tag{4}$$

where

λ = wavelength, m
c = speed of sound, m/s
f = frequency, Hz

Table 2 Typical Sound Power Outputs and Sound Power Levels

Source	Sound Power, W	Sound Power Level, dB re 10^{-12} W
Space shuttle launch	10^8	200
Jet aircraft at takeoff	10^4	160
Large pipe organ	10	130
Small aircraft engine	1	120
Large HVAC fan	0.1	110
Heavy truck at highway speed	0.01	100
Voice, shouting	0.001	90
Garbage disposal unit	10^{-4}	80
Voice, conversation level	10^{-5}	70
Electronic equipment ventilation fan	10^{-6}	60
Office air diffuser	10^{-7}	50
Small electric clock	10^{-8}	40
Voice, soft whisper	10^{-9}	30
Rustling leaves	10^{-10}	20
Human breath	10^{-11}	10

Sound Power and Sound Power Level

The **sound power** of a source is its rate of emission of acoustical energy and is expressed in watts. Sound power depends on the operating conditions but not the distance of the observation location from the source or surrounding environment. Approximate sound power outputs for common sources are shown in Table 2 with the corresponding sound power levels. For **sound power level L_w**, the power reference is 10^{-12} W or 1 picowatt. The definition of sound power level is therefore

$$L_w = 10 \log(w/10^{-12}) \tag{5}$$

where w is the sound power emitted by the source in watts. (Sound power emitted by a source is not the same as the power consumed by the source. Only a small fraction of the consumed power is converted into sound. For example, a loudspeaker rated at 100 W may be only 1 to 5% efficient, generating only 1 to 5 watts of sound power.) Note that the sound power level is 10 times the logarithm of the ratio of the power to the reference power, and the sound pressure is 20 times the logarithm of the ratio of the pressure to the reference pressure.

Most mechanical equipment is rated in terms of sound power levels so that comparisons can be made using a common reference independent of distance and acoustical conditions in the room. AMCA *Publication* 303-79 provides guidelines for using sound power level ratings. Also, AMCA *Standards* 301-06 and 311-05 provide methods for developing fan sound ratings from laboratory test data.

Sound Intensity and Sound Intensity Level

The **sound intensity** I at a point in a specified direction is the rate of flow of sound energy (i.e., power) through unit area at that point. The unit area is perpendicular to the specified direction, and the units of intensity are watts per square metre. **Sound intensity level L_I** is expressed in dB with a reference quantity of 10^{-12} W/m², thus

$$L_I = 10 \log(I/10^{-12}) \tag{6}$$

The instantaneous intensity I is the product of the pressure and velocity of air motion (e.g., particle velocity), as shown here.

$$I = pv \tag{7}$$

Both pressure and particle velocity are oscillating, with a magnitude and time variation. Usually, the time-averaged intensity I_{ave} (i.e., the net power flow through a surface area, often simply called "the intensity") is of interest.

Taking the time average of Equation (7) over one period yields

$$I_{ave} = \text{Re}\{pv\} \tag{8}$$

where Re is the real part of the complex (with amplitude and phase) quantity. At locations far from the source and reflecting surfaces,

$$I_{ave} \approx p^2/\rho_0 c \tag{9}$$

where p is the RMS sound pressure, ρ_0 is the density of air (1.2 kg/m^3), and c is the acoustic phase speed in air (335 m/s). Equation (11) implies that the relationship between sound intensity and sound pressure varies with air temperature and density. Conveniently, the sound intensity level differs from the sound pressure level by less than 0.5 dB for temperature and densities normally experienced in HVAC environments. Therefore, sound pressure level is a good measure of the intensity level at locations far from sources and reflecting surfaces. Note that all equations in this chapter that relate sound power level to sound pressure level are based on the assumption that sound pressure level is equal to sound intensity level.

Combining Sound Levels

To estimate the levels from multiple sources from the levels from each source, the intensities (not the levels) must be added. Thus, the levels must first be converted to find intensities, the intensities summed, and then converted to a level again, so the combination of two levels L_1 and L_2 produces a level L_{sum} given by

$$L_{sum} = 10 \log(10^{L_1/10} + 10^{L_2/10}) \tag{10}$$

where for sound pressure level (L_p), $10^{L_i/10}$ is p_i^2/p_{ref}^2.

This process may be extended to combine as many levels as needed using the following equation:

$$L_{sum} = 10 \log\left(\sum_i 10^{L_i/10}\right) \tag{11}$$

where L_i is the sound level for the ith source. A simpler and slightly less accurate method is outlined in Table 3. This method, although not exact, results in errors of 1 dB or less. The process with a series of levels may be shortened by combining the largest with the next largest, then combining this sum with the third largest, then the fourth largest, and so on until the combination of the remaining levels is 10 dB lower than the combined level. The process may then be stopped.

The procedures in Table 3 and Equations (10) and (11) are valid if the individual sound levels are not highly correlated, which is true for most (but not all) sounds encountered in HVAC systems. One notable exception is the pure tone. If two or more sound signals contain pure tones at the same frequency, the pressures (amplitude and phase) should be added and the level (20 log) taken of the sum to find the sound pressure level of the two combined tones. The combined sound level is a function of not only the level of each tone (i.e., amplitude of the pressure), but also the phase difference between the tones. Combined sound levels from two tones of equal amplitude and frequency can range from zero (if the tones are 180° out of phase) up to 6 dB greater than the level of either tone (if the tones are exactly in phase). When two tones of similar amplitude are very close in frequency but not exactly the same, the combined sound level oscillates as the tones move in and out of phase. This effect creates an audible "beating" with a period equal to the inverse of the difference in frequency between the two tones.

Table 3 Combining Two Sound Levels

Difference between levels to be combined, dB	0 to 1	2 to 4	5 to 9	10 and More
Number of decibels to add to highest level to obtain combined level	3	2	1	0

Measurements of sound levels generated by individual sources are made in the presence of background noise (i.e., noise from sources other than the ones of interest). Thus, the measurement includes noise from the source and background noise. To remove background noise, the levels are unlogged and the square of the background sound pressure subtracted from the square of the sound pressure for the combination of the source and background noise:

$$L_p(\text{source}) = 10 \log\left(10^{L(\text{comb})/10} - 10^{L(\text{bkgd})/10}\right) \tag{12}$$

where L(bkgd) is the sound pressure level of the background noise, measured with the source of interest turned off. If the difference between the levels with the source on and off is greater than 10 dB, then background noise levels are low enough that the effect of background noise on the levels measured with the source on can be ignored.

Resonances

Acoustic resonances occur in enclosures, such as a room or HVAC plenum, and mechanical resonances occur in structures, such as the natural frequency of vibration of a duct wall. Resonances occur at discrete frequencies, similar to the frequencies of radiation from musical instruments. System response to excitation at frequencies of resonance is high. To prevent this, the frequencies at which resonances occur must be known and avoided, particularly by sources of discrete-frequency tones. Avoid aligning the frequency of tonal noise with any frequencies of resonance of the space into which the noise is radiated.

At resonance, multiple reflections inside the space form a standing wave pattern (called a **mode shape**) with nodes at minimum pressure and antinodes at maximum pressure. Spacing between nodes (minimum acoustic pressure) and antinodes (maximum acoustic pressure) is one-quarter of an acoustic wavelength for the frequency of resonance.

Absorption and Reflection of Sound

Sound incident on a surface, such as a ceiling, is either absorbed, reflected, or transmitted. **Absorbed sound** is the part of incident sound that is transmitted through the surface and either dissipated (as in acoustic tiles) or transmitted into the adjoining space (as through an intervening partition). The fraction of acoustic intensity incident on the surface that is absorbed is called the **absorption coefficient** α, as defined by the following equation:

$$\alpha = I_{abs}/I_{inc} \tag{13}$$

where I_{abs} is the intensity of absorbed sound and I_{inc} is the intensity of sound incident on the surface.

The absorption coefficient depends on the frequency and angle of incident sound. In frequency bands, the absorption coefficient of nearly randomly incident sound is measured in large reverberant rooms. The difference in the rates at which sound decays after the source is turned off is measured before and after the sample is placed in the reverberant room. The rate at which sound decays is related to the total absorption in the room via the Sabine equation:

$$T_{60} = 0.161(V/A) \tag{14}$$

where

T_{60} = reverberation time (time required for average sound pressure level in room to decay by 60 dB), s
V = volume of room, m^3
A = total absorption in room, given by

$$A = \sum_i S_i \alpha_i$$

S_i = surface area for ith surface, m²
α_i = absorption coefficient for ith surface

Just as for absorption coefficients, reverberation time varies with frequency.

For sound to be incident on surfaces from all directions during absorption measurement, the room must be reverberant so that most of the sound incident on surfaces is reflected and bounced around the room in all directions. In a **diffuse sound field**, sound is incident on the absorbing sample equally from all directions. The Sabine equation applies only in a diffuse field.

Reflected sound superimposes on the incident sound, which increases the level of sound at and near the surfaces (i.e., the sound level near a surface is higher than those away from the surface in the free field). Because the energy in the room is related to the free-field sound pressure levels (see the section on Determining Sound Power for a discussion of free fields), and is often used to relate the sound power emitted into the room and the room's total absorption, it is important that sound pressure level measurements not be made close to reflecting surfaces, where the levels will be higher than in the free field. Measurements should be made at least one-quarter of a wavelength from the nearest reflecting surface (i.e., at a distance of $d \approx \lambda/4 \approx 85/f$, where d is in metres and f is frequency in Hz).

Room Acoustics

Because surfaces in a room either absorb, reflect, or transmit sound, room surfaces change the characteristics of sound radiated into the room. The changes of primary concern are the increase in sound levels from those that would exist without the room (i.e., in the open) and the reverberation. Lower absorption leads to higher sound pressure levels away from the sources of noise (see the section on Sound Transmission Paths). Also, the lower the absorption, the longer the reverberation times. Reverberation can affect the perception of music (e.g., in a concert hall) and speech intelligibility (e.g., in a lecture hall). Thus, when adding absorption to reduce a room's background HVAC-generated noise levels, it is important to be aware of the added absorption's effect on reverberation in the room.

Acoustic Impedance

Acoustic impedance z_a is the ratio of acoustic pressure p to particle velocity v:

$$z_a = p/v \tag{15}$$

For a wave propagating in free space far (more than ~1 m) from a source, the acoustic impedance is

$$z_a \approx \rho_0 c \tag{16}$$

where ρ_0 is the density of air (1.2 kg/m³) and c is the sound speed in air (335 m/s).

Where acoustic impedance changes abruptly, some of the sound incident at the location of the impedance change is reflected. For example, inside an HVAC duct, the acoustic impedance is different from the free field acoustic impedance, so at the duct termination there is an abrupt change in the acoustic impedance from inside the duct to outside into the room, particularly at low frequencies. Thus, some sound inside the duct is reflected back into the duct (**end reflection**). Losses from end reflection are discussed in Chapter 47 of the 2007 *ASHRAE Handbook—HVAC Applications*.

MEASURING SOUND

Instrumentation

The basic instrument for measuring sound is a **sound level meter**, which comprises a microphone, electronic circuitry, and a display device. The microphone converts sound pressure at a point to an electronic signal, which is then processed and the sound pressure level displayed using analog or digital circuitry. Sound level meters are usually battery-operated, lightweight, handheld units with outputs that vary in complexity depending on cost and level of technology.

Time Averaging

Most sounds are not constant; pressure fluctuates from moment to moment and the level can vary quickly or slowly. Sound level meters can show time fluctuations of the sound pressure level using specified time constants (slow, fast, impulse), or can hold the maximum or minimum level recorded during some specified interval. All sound level meters perform some kind of time averaging. Some integrating sound level meters take an average of the sound pressure level over a user-definable time, then hold and display the result. The advantage of an integrating meter is that it is easier to read and more repeatable (especially if the measurement period is long). The quantity measured by the integrating sound level meter is the **equivalent continuous sound pressure level L_{eq}**, which is the level of the time average of the squared pressure:

$$L_{eq} = 10 \log\left[\frac{1}{T}\int_0^T \frac{p^2(t)}{p_{ref}^2} dt\right] \tag{17}$$

where $1/T \int_0^T dt$ is the time average (i.e., the sum $\int_0^T dt$ divided by the time over which the sum is taken).

Spectra and Analysis Bandwidths

Real sounds are much more complex than simple pure tones, where all the energy is at a single frequency. A tone, such as generated by a musical instrument, contains harmonically related pure tones. **Broadband sound** contains energy at many different frequencies, usually covering most of the audible frequency range but not harmonically related. All sounds, however, can be represented as levels as a function of frequency using **frequency** or **spectral analysis**, which is similar to spectral analysis in optics.

A **constant-bandwidth analysis** expresses a sound's energy content as a spectrum where each data point represents the same spectral width in frequency (e.g., 1 Hz). This is useful when an objectionable sound contains strong tones and the tones' frequencies must be accurately identified before remedial action is taken. A constant-bandwidth spectrum usually contains too much information for typical noise control work or for specifications of acceptable noise levels.

Measurements for most HVAC noise control work are usually made with filters that extract the energy in either **octave** or **one-third octave bands.** An octave band is a frequency band with an upper frequency limit twice that of its lower frequency limit. Octave and 1/3 octave bands are identified by their respective center frequencies, which are the geometric means of the upper and lower band limits: $f_c = \sqrt{f_{upper} f_{lower}}$ (ANSI *Standards* S1.6, S1.11). Three 1/3 octave bands make up an octave band. Table 4 lists the upper, lower, and center frequencies for the preferred series of octave and 1/3 octave bands. For most HVAC sound measurements, filters for the range 20 to 5000 Hz are usually adequate.

Although octave band analysis is usually acceptable for rating acoustical environments in rooms, 1/3 octave band analysis is often useful in product development, in assessing transmission losses through partitions, and for remedial investigations.

Some sound level meters have octave or 1/3 octave filters for determining frequency content, usually using standard broadband filters that simulate the frequency response to sound of the average human ear. The **A-weighting** filter, which simulates the response of the human ear to low levels of sound, is the most common (Figure 1 and Table 5). It deemphasizes the low-frequency portions of a sound spectrum, automatically compensating for the lower sensitivity of the human ear to low-frequency sounds.

The **C-weighting** filter weights the sound less as a function of frequency than the A-weighting, as shown in Figure 1. Because sound levels at low frequencies are attenuated by A-weighting but

Table 4 Midband and Approximate Upper and Lower Cutoff Frequencies for Octave and 1/3 Octave Band Filters

Octave Bands, Hz			1/3 Octave Bands, Hz		
Lower	Midband	Upper	Lower	Midband	Upper
			11.2	12.5	14
11.2	16	22.4	14	16	18
			18	20	22.4
			22.4	25	28
22.4	31.5	45	28	31.5	35.5
			35.5	40	45
			45	50	56
45	63	90	56	63	71
			71	80	90
			90	100	112
90	125	180	112	125	140
			140	160	180
			180	200	224
180	250	355	224	250	280
			280	315	355
			355	400	450
355	500	710	450	500	560
			560	630	710
			710	800	900
710	1 000	1 400	900	1 000	1 120
			1 120	1 250	1 400
			1 400	1 600	1 800
1 400	2 000	2 800	1 800	2 000	2 240
			2 240	2 500	2 800
			2 800	3 150	3 550
2 800	4 000	5 600	3 550	4 000	4 500
			4 500	5 000	5 600
			5 600	6 300	7 100
5 600	8 000	11 200	7 100	8 000	9 000
			9 000	10 000	11 200
			11 200	12 500	14 000
11 200	16 000	22 400	14 000	16 000	18 000
			18 000	20 000	22 400

not by C-weighting, these weightings can be used to estimate whether a particular sound has excessive low-frequency energy when a spectrum analyzer is not available. If the difference between C- and A-weighted levels for the sound exceeds about 20 dB, then the sound is likely to be annoying because of excessive low-frequency noise. Note that C-weighting provides some attenuation at very low and very high frequencies: C-weighting is not the same as no weighting (i.e., flat weighting).

Sound level meters are available in several accuracy grades specified by ANSI *Standard* S1.4. A Type 1 meter has an accuracy of about ±1.0 dB from 50 to 4000 Hz. The general-purpose Type 2 meter, which is less expensive, has a tolerance of about ±1.5 dB from 100 to 1000 Hz, and is adequate for most HVAC sound measurements.

Manually selecting filters sequentially to cover the frequency range from 20 to 5000 Hz is time-consuming. An instrument that gives all filtered levels simultaneously is called a **real-time analyzer (RTA)**. It speeds up measurement significantly, and most models can save information to an internal or external digital storage device.

The process described in Equation (11) for adding a series of levels can be applied to a set of octave or 1/3 octave bands to calculate the overall broadband level (see Table 6 for an example). The A-weighted sound level may be estimated using octave or 1/3 octave band levels by adding A-weightings given in Table 5 to octave or 1/3 octave band levels before combining the levels.

Sound Measurement Basics

The sound pressure level in an occupied space can be measured directly with a sound level meter, or estimated from published sound

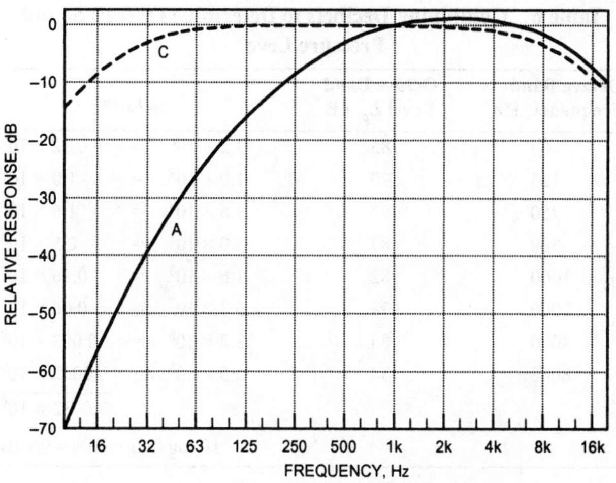

Fig. 1 Curves Showing A- and C-Weighting Responses for Sound Level Meters

Table 5 A-Weighting for 1/3 Octave and Octave Bands

1/3 Octave Band Center Frequency, Hz	A-Weighting, dB	Octave Band Center Frequency, Hz	A-Weighting, dB
16	−56.7	16	−56.7
20	−50.5		
25	−44.7		
31.5	−39.4	31.5	−39.4
40	−34.6		
50	−30.2		
63	−26.2	63	−26.2
80	−22.5		
100	−19.1		
125	−16.1	125	−16.1
160	−13.4		
200	−10.9		
250	−8.6	250	−8.6
315	−6.6		
400	−4.8		
500	−3.2	500	−3.2
630	−1.9		
800	−0.8		
1000	0	1000	0
1250	+0.6		
1600	+1.0		
2000	+1.2	2000	+1.2
2500	+1.3		
3150	+1.2		
4000	+1.0	4000	+1.0
5000	+0.5		
6300	−0.1		
8000	−1.1	8000	−1.1
10,000	−2.5		

source, and other acoustical factors (see the section on Sound Transmission Paths). Sound level meters measure sound pressure at the microphone location. Estimation techniques calculate sound pressure at a specified point in an occupied space. Measured or estimated sound pressure levels in frequency bands can then be plotted, analyzed, and compared with established criteria for acceptance.

Measurements of HVAC sound must be done carefully to ensure repeatable and accurate results. Sound levels may not be steady, particularly at low frequencies (250 Hz and lower), and can vary significantly with time. In these cases, both peak and average levels should be recorded.

Table 6 Combining Decibels to Determine Overall Sound Pressure Level

Octave Band Frequency, Hz	Octave Band Level L_p, dB	$10^{L_p/10}$		
63	85	3.2×10^8	=	0.32×10^9
125	90	1.0×10^9	=	1.0×10^9
250	92	1.6×10^9	=	1.6×10^9
500	87	5.0×10^8	=	0.5×10^9
1000	82	1.6×10^8	=	0.16×10^9
2000	78	6.3×10^7	=	0.06×10^9
4000	65	3.2×10^6	=	0.003×10^9
8000	54	2.5×10^5	=	0.0002×10^9
				3.6432×10^9
				$10 \log (3.6 \times 10^9) = 96$ dB

Sophisticated sound measurements and their procedures should be carried out by individuals experienced in acoustic measurements. At present, there are only a few noise standards that can be used to measure interior sound levels from mechanical equipment (e.g., ASTM *Standards* E1573 and E1574). Most manuals for sound level meters include sections on how to measure sound, but basic methods that can help obtain acceptable measurements are included here.

Determining the sound spectrum in a room or investigating a noise complaint usually requires measuring sound pressure levels in the octave bands from 16 to 8000 Hz. In cases where tonal noise or rumble is the complaint, narrow-band or 1/3 octave band measurements are recommended because of their greater frequency resolution. Whatever the measurement method, remember that sound pressure levels can vary significantly from point to point in a room. In a room, each measurement point often provides a different value for sound pressure level, so the actual location of measurement is very important and must be detailed in the report. A survey could record the location and level of the loudest position, or could establish a few representative locations where occupants are normally situated. In general, the most appropriate height is 1.2 to 1.8 m above the floor. The exact geometric center of the room should be avoided, as should any location within 1 m of a wall, floor, or ceiling. Wherever the location, it must be defined and recorded. If the meter has an integrating-averaging function, one can use a rotating boom to sample a large area, or slowly walk around the room, and the meter will determine the average sound pressure level for that path. However, care must be taken that no extraneous sounds are generated by microphone movement or by walking; using a windscreen reduces extraneous noise generated by airflow over the moving microphone. Also, locations where sound levels are notably higher than average should be recorded. See the section on Measurement of Room Sound Pressure Level for more details.

When measuring HVAC noise, **background noise** from other sources (occupants, wind, nearby traffic, elevators, etc.) must be determined. Sometimes the sound from a particular piece of HVAC equipment must be measured in the presence of background sound from sources that cannot be turned off, such as automobile traffic or certain office equipment. Determining the sound level of just the selected equipment requires making two sets of measurements: one with both the HVAC equipment sound and background sound, and another with only the background sound (with HVAC equipment turned off). This situation might also occur, for example, when determining whether noise exposure at the property line from a cooling tower meets a local noise ordinance. The guidelines in Table 7 help determine the sound level of a particular machine in the presence of background sound. Equation (12) in the section on Combining Sound Levels may be used.

The uncertainty associated with correcting for background sound depends on the uncertainty of the measuring instrument and the

Table 7 Guidelines for Determining Equipment Sound Levels in the Presence of Contaminating Background Sound

Measurement A minus Measurement B	Correction to Measurement A to Obtain Equipment Sound Level
10 dB or more	0 dB
6 to 9 dB	−1 dB
4 to 5 dB	−2 dB
Less than 4 dB	Equipment sound level is more than 2 dB below Measurement A

Measurement A = Tested equipment plus background sound
Measurement B = Background sound alone

steadiness of the sounds being measured. In favorable circumstances, it might be possible to extend Table 7. In particularly unfavorable circumstances, even values obtained from the table could be substantially in error.

Measuring sound emissions from a particular piece of equipment or group of equipment requires a measurement plan specific to the situation. The Air-Conditioning and Refrigeration Institute (ARI), Air Movement and Control Association International (AMCA), American Society of Testing and Materials (ASTM), American National Standards Institute (ANSI), and Acoustical Society of America (ASA) all publish sound level measurement procedures for various laboratory and field sound measurement situations.

Outdoor measurements are somewhat easier to make than indoor because there are typically few or no boundary surfaces to affect sound build-up or absorption. Nevertheless, important issues such as the effect of large, nearby sound-reflecting surfaces and weather conditions such as wind, temperature, and precipitation must be addressed. Where measurements are made close to extended surfaces (i.e., flat or nearly flat surfaces with dimensions more than four times the wavelength of the sound of interest), sound pressure levels can be significantly increased. These effects can be estimated through guidelines in many sources such as Harris (1991).

Measurement of Room Sound Pressure Level

In commissioning building HVAC systems, often a specified room noise criterion must demonstratively be met. Measurement procedures for obtaining the data to demonstrate compliance are often not specified, which can lead to confusion when different parties make measurements using different procedures, because the results often do not agree. The problem is that most rooms exhibit significant point-to-point variation in sound pressure level.

When a noise has no audible tonal components, differences in measured sound pressure level at several locations in a room may be as high as 3 to 5 dB. However, when audible tonal components are present, especially at low frequencies, variations caused by standing waves that occur at frequencies of resonance may exceed 10 dB. These are generally noticeable to the average listener when moving through the room.

Although commissioning procedures usually set precise limits for demonstrating compliance, the outcome can unfortunately be controversial unless the measurement procedure has been specified in detail. At the time of writing, there was no general agreement in the industry on an acoustical measurement procedure for commissioning HVAC systems. However, ARI *Standard* 885 incorporates a "suggested procedure for field verification of NC/RC levels."

Measurement of Acoustic Intensity

Equation (8) for the time-averaged intensity (often called simply *intensity*) requires both the pressure and particle velocity. Pressure is easily measured with a microphone, but there is no simple transducer that converts particle velocity to a measurable electronic signal. Fortunately, particle velocity can be estimated from sound pressures measured at closely spaced (less than ~1/10 of an acoustic wavelength) locations, using Euler's equation:

$$v = -\frac{1}{i2\pi f\rho_0} \times \frac{\partial p}{\partial x} \approx -\frac{1}{i2\pi f\rho_0} \times \frac{p_2 - p_1}{x_2 - x_1} \tag{18}$$

where x_2 and x_1 are the locations of measurements of pressures p_2 and p_1, f is frequency in Hz, and ρ_0 is density of air. The spatial derivative of pressure $(\partial p/\partial x)$ is approximated with $(\Delta p/\Delta x) = [(p_2 - p_1)/(x_2 - x_1)]$. Thus, intensity probes contain two closely spaced microphones that have nearly identical responses (i.e., are phase-matched). Because intensity is a vector, it shows the direction of sound propagation along the line between the microphones, in addition to the magnitude of the sound. Also, because intensity is power/area, it is not sensitive to the acoustic nearfield (see the section on Typical Sources of Sound) or to standing waves where the intensity is zero. Therefore, unlike pressure measurement, intensity measurements can be made in the acoustic nearfield of a source or in the reverberant field in a room to determine the power radiated from the source. However, intensity measurements cannot be used in a diffuse field to determine the acoustic energy in the field, such as used for determining sound power using the reverberation room method.

DETERMINING SOUND POWER

The sound power of a source cannot be measured directly. Rather, it is calculated from several measurements of sound pressure or sound intensity created by a source in one of several test environments. The following four methods are commonly used.

Free-Field Method

A **free field** is a sound field where the effects of any boundaries are negligible over the frequency range of interest. In ideal conditions, there are no boundaries. Free-field conditions can be approximated in rooms with highly sound-absorbing walls, floor, and ceiling (**anechoic rooms**). In a free field, the sound power of a sound source can be determined from measurements of sound pressure level on an imaginary spherical surface centered on and surrounding the source. This method is based on the fact that, because sound absorption in air can be practically neglected at small distances from the sound source, all of the sound power generated by a source must flow through an imagined sphere with the source at its center. The intensity I of the sound (conventionally expressed in W/m^2) is estimated from measured sound pressure levels using the following equation:

$$I = (1 \times 10^{-12})10^{L_p/10} \tag{19}$$

where L_p is sound pressure level. The intensity at each point around the source is multiplied by that portion of the area of the imagined sphere associated with the measuring points. Total sound power W is the sum of these products for each point.

$$W = \sum_i I_i A_i \tag{20}$$

where A_i is the surface area (in m^2) associated with the ith measurement location.

ANSI *Standard* S12.55 describes various methods used to calculate sound power level under free-field conditions. Measurement accuracy is limited at lower frequencies by the difficulty of obtaining room surface treatments with high sound absorption coefficients at low frequencies. For example, a glass fiber wedge structure that gives significant absorption at 70 Hz must be at least 1.2 m long.

The relationship between sound power level L_w and sound pressure level L_p for a nondirectional sound source in a free field at distance r in m can be written as

$$L_w = L_p + 20 \log r + 11 \tag{21}$$

For directional sources, use Equation (20) to compute sound power.

Often, a completely free field is not available, and measurements must be made in a free field over a reflecting plane. This means that the sound source is placed on a hard floor (in an otherwise sound-absorbing room) or on smooth, flat pavement outdoors. Because the sound is then radiated into a hemisphere rather than a full sphere, the relationship for L_w and L_p for a nondirectional sound source becomes

$$L_w = L_p + 20 \log r + 8 \tag{22}$$

A sound source may radiate different amounts of sound power in different directions. A directivity pattern can be established by measuring sound pressure under free-field conditions, either in an anechoic room or over a reflecting plane in a hemianechoic space at several points around the source. The directivity factor Q is the ratio of the squared sound pressure at a given angle from the sound source to the squared sound pressure that would be produced by the same source radiating uniformly in all directions. Q is a function of frequency and direction. The section on Typical Sources of Sound in this chapter and Chapter 47 of the 2007 *ASHRAE Handbook—HVAC Applications* provide more detailed information on sound source directivity.

Reverberation Room Method

Another method to determine sound power places the sound source in a reverberation room. ANSI *Standard* S12.51 gives standardized methods for determining the sound power of HVAC equipment in reverberation rooms when the sound source contains mostly broadband sound or when tonal sound is prominent. Use AMCA *Standard* 300 for testing fans.

Some sound sources that can be measured by these methods are room air conditioners, refrigeration compressors, components of central HVAC systems, and air terminal devices. AMCA *Standard* 300, ANSI/ASHRAE *Standard* 130, and ARI *Standard* 880 establish special measuring procedures for some of these units. Two measurement methods may be used in reverberation rooms: direct and substitution.

In **direct reverberation room measurement**, the sound pressure level is measured with the source in the reverberation room at several locations at a distance of at least 1 m from the source and at least one-quarter of a wavelength from the surfaces of the room. The sound power level is calculated from the average of the sound pressure levels, using the reverberation time and the volume of the reverberation room.

The relationship between sound power level and sound pressure level in a reverberation room is given by

$$L_w = L_p + 10 \log V - 10 \log T_{60} - 14 \tag{23}$$

where

L_p = sound pressure level averaged over room, dB re 20 μPa
V = volume of room, m^3
T_{60} = room reverberation time (time required for a 60 dB decay), s

The **substitution** procedure is used by most ASHRAE, ARI, and AMCA test standards where a calibrated reference sound source (RSS) is used. The sound power levels of noise radiated by an RSS are known by calibration using the free-field method. The most common RSS is a small, direct-drive fan impeller that has no volute housing or scroll. The forward-curved impeller has a choke plate on its inlet face, causing the fan to operate in a rotating-stall condition that is very noisy. The reference source is designed to have a stable sound power level output from 63 to 8000 Hz and a relatively uniform frequency spectrum in each octave band.

Sound pressure level measurements are first made in the reverberant field (far from the RSS or source in question) with only the reference sound source operating in the test room. Then the reference source is turned off and the measurements are repeated with the given source in operation. Because the acoustical environment and measurement locations are the same for both sources, the differences in sound pressure levels measured represent differences in sound power level between the two sources.

Using this method, the relationship between sound power level and sound pressure level for the two sources is given by

$$L_w = L_p + (L_w - L_p)_{ref} \qquad (24)$$

where

L_p = sound pressure level averaged over room, dB re 20 μPa
$(L_w - L_p)_{ref}$ = difference between sound power level and sound pressure level of reference sound source

Progressive Wave (In-Duct) Method

By attaching a fan to one end of a duct, sound energy is confined to a progressive wave field in the duct. Fan sound power can then be determined by measuring the sound pressure level inside the duct. Intensity is then estimated from the sound pressure levels (see the section on the Free-Field Method) and multiplied by the cross-sectional area of the duct to find the sound power. The method is described in detail in ASHRAE *Standard* 68 (AMCA *Standard* 330) for in-duct testing of fans. This method is not commonly used because of difficulties in constructing the required duct termination and in discriminating between fan noise and flow noise caused by the presence of the microphone in the duct.

Sound Intensity Method

The average sound power radiated by the source can be determined by measuring the sound intensity over the sphere or hemisphere surrounding a sound source (see the sections on Measurement of Acoustic Intensity and on the Free-Field Method). One advantage of this method is that, with certain limitations, sound intensity (and therefore sound power) measurements can be made in the presence of steady background noise in semireverberant environments and in the acoustic nearfield of sources. Another advantage is that by measuring sound intensity over surfaces that enclose a sound source, sound directivity can be determined. Also, for large sources, areas of radiation can be localized using intensity measurements. This procedure can be particularly useful in diagnosing sources of noise during product development.

International and U.S. standards that prescribe methods for making sound power measurements with sound intensity probes consisting of two closely spaced microphones include ISO *Standards* 9614-1 and 9614-2, and ANSI *Standard* S12.12. In some situations, the sound fields may be so complex that measurements become impractical. A particular concern is that small test rooms or those with somewhat flexible boundaries (e.g., sheet metal or thin drywall) can increase the radiation impedance for the source, which could affect the source's sound power output.

Measurement Bandwidths for Sound Power

Sound power is normally determined in octave or 1/3 octave bands. Occasionally, more detailed determination of the sound source spectrum is required: **narrow-band analysis**, using either constant fractional bandwidth (1/12 or 1/24 octave) or constant absolute bandwidth (e.g., 1 Hz). The most frequently used analyzer types are digital filter analyzers for constant-percent bandwidth measurements and fast Fourier transform (FFT) analyzers for constant-bandwidth measurements. Narrow-band analyses are used to determine the frequencies of pure tones and their harmonics in a sound spectrum.

CONVERTING FROM SOUND POWER TO SOUND PRESSURE

Designers are often required to use sound power level information of a source to predict the sound pressure level at a given location. Sound pressure at a given location in a room from a source of known sound power level depends on (1) room volume, (2) room furnishings and surface treatments, (3) magnitude of sound source(s), (4) distance from sound source(s) to point of observation, and (5) directivity of source.

The classic relationship between source sound power level and room sound pressure level at some frequency is

$$L_p = L_w + 10\log(Q/4\pi r^2 + 4/R) \qquad (25)$$

where

L_p = sound pressure level, dB re 20 μPa
L_w = sound power level, dB re 10^{-12} W
Q = directivity of sound source (dimensionless)
r = distance from source, m
R = room constant, $S\bar{\alpha}/(1 - \bar{\alpha})$
S = sum of all surface areas, m²
$\bar{\alpha}$ = average absorption coefficient of room surfaces at given frequency, given by

$$\sum_i S_i\alpha_i / \sum_i S_i$$

where S_i is area of ith surface and α_i is absorption coefficient for ith surface.

If the source is outside, far from reflecting surfaces, this relationship simplifies to

$$L_p = L_w + 10\log(Q/4\pi r^2) \qquad (26)$$

This relationship does not account for atmospheric absorption, weather effects, and barriers. Note that r^2 is present because the sound pressure in a free field decreases with $1/r^2$ (the inverse-square law; see the section on Sound Transmission Paths). Each time the distance from the source is doubled, the sound pressure level decreases by 6 dB.

For a simple source centered in a large, flat, reflecting surface, Q may be taken as 2. At the junction of two large flat surfaces, Q is 4; in a corner, Q is 8.

In most typical rooms, the presence of acoustically absorbent surfaces and sound-scattering elements (e.g., furniture) creates a relationship between sound power and sound pressure level that is difficult to predict. For example, hospital rooms, which have only a small amount of absorption, and executive offices, which have substantial absorption, are similar when the comparison is based on the same room volume and distance between the source and point of observation.

Using a series of measurements taken in typical rooms, Equation (27) was developed to estimate the sound pressure level at a chosen observation point in a normally furnished room. The estimate is accurate to ±2 dB (Schultz 1985).

$$L_p = L_w - 5\log V - 3\log f - 10\log r + 12 \qquad (27)$$

Equation (27) applies to a single sound source in the room itself, not to sources above the ceiling. With more than one source, total sound pressure level at the observation point is obtained by adding the contribution from each source in energy or power-like units, not decibels, and then converting back to sound pressure level [see Equation (11)]. Studies (Warnock 1997, 1998a, 1998b) indicate that sound sources above ceilings may not act as a point sources, and Equation (27) may not apply (ARI *Standard* 885).

SOUND TRANSMISSION PATHS

Sound from a source is transmitted along one or more paths to a receiver. Airborne and structureborne transmission paths are both of concern for the HVAC system designer. Sound transmission between rooms occurs along both airborne and structureborne transmission paths. Chapter 47 of the 2007 *ASHRAE Handbook—HVAC Applications* has additional information on transmission paths.

Spreading Losses

In a free field, the intensity I of sound radiated from a single source with dimensions that are not large compared to an acoustic wavelength is equal to the power W radiated by the source divided by the surface area A (expressed in m^2) over which the power is spread:

$$I = W/A \tag{28}$$

In the absence of reflection, the spherical area over which power spreads is $A = 4\pi r^2$, so that the intensity is

$$I = W/4\pi r^2 \tag{29}$$

where r is the distance from the source in metres. Taking the level of the intensity (i.e., 10 log) and using Equation (21) to relate intensity to sound pressure levels leads to

$$L_p = L_w - 10\log(4\pi r^2) \tag{30}$$

which becomes

$$L_p = L_w - 20\log r - 11 = L_w - 10\log(r^2) - 11 \tag{31}$$

Thus, the sound pressure level decreases as 10 log(r^2), or 6 dB per doubling of distance. This reduction in sound pressure level of sound radiated into the free field from a single source is called **spherical spreading loss.**

Direct Versus Reverberant Fields

Equation (25) relates the sound pressure level L_p in a room at distance r from a source to the sound power level L_w of the source. The first term in the brackets ($Q/4\pi r^2$) represents sound radiated directly from the source to the receiver, and includes the source's directivity Q and the spreading loss $1/4\pi r^2$ from the source to the observation location. The second term in the brackets, $4/R$, represents the reverberant field created by multiple reflections from room surfaces. The room constant is

$$R = \frac{\sum_i S_i \alpha_i}{1 - \bar{\alpha}} \tag{32}$$

where $\bar{\alpha}$ is the spatial average absorption coefficient,

$$\bar{\alpha} = \frac{\sum_i S_i \alpha_i}{\sum_i S_i} \tag{33}$$

At distances close enough to the source that $Q/4\pi r^2$ is larger than $4/R$, the direct field is dominant and Equation (25) can be approximated by

$$L_p = L_w + 10\log\left(\frac{Q}{4\pi r^2}\right) \tag{34}$$

Equation (34) is independent of room absorption R, which indicates that adding absorption to the room will not change the sound pressure level. At distances far enough from the source that $Q/4\pi r^2$ is less than $4/R$, Equation (25) can be approximated by

$$L_p = L_w + 10\log\left(\frac{4}{R}\right) = L_w - 10\log R + 6 \tag{35}$$

Adding absorption to the room increases the room constant and thereby reduces the sound pressure level. The reduction in reverberant sound pressure levels associated with adding absorption in the room is approximated by

$$\text{Reduction} \approx 10\log\left(\frac{R_2}{R_1}\right) \tag{36}$$

where R_2 is the room constant for the room with added absorption and R_1 is the room constant for the room before absorption is added. The distance from the source where the reverberant field first becomes dominant such that adding absorption to the room is effective is the critical distance r_c, obtained by setting $Q/4\pi r^2 = 4/R$. This leads to

$$r_c \approx 0.14\sqrt{QR} \tag{37}$$

where R is in m^2 and r_c is in m.

Airborne Transmission

Sound transmits readily through air, both indoors and outdoors. Indoor sound transmission paths include the direct line of sight between the source and receiver, as well as reflected paths introduced by the room's walls, floor, ceiling, and furnishings, which cause multiple sound reflection paths.

Outdoors, the effects of the reflections are small, unless the source is located near large reflecting surfaces. However, wind and temperature gradients can cause sound outdoors to refract (bend) and change propagation direction. Without strong wind and temperature gradients and at small distances, sound propagation outdoors follows the inverse square law. Therefore, Equations (21) and (22) can generally be used to calculate the relationship between sound power level and sound pressure level for fully free-field and hemispherical free-field conditions, respectively.

Ductborne Transmission

Ductwork can provide an effective sound transmission path because the sound is primarily contained within the boundaries of the ductwork and thus suffers only small spreading losses. Sound can transmit both upstream and downstream from the source. A special case of ductborne transmission is **crosstalk**, where sound is transmitted from one room to another via the duct path. Where duct geometry changes abruptly (e.g., at elbows, branches, and terminations), the resulting change in the acoustic impedance reflects sound, which increases propagation losses. Chapter 47 of the 2007 *ASHRAE Handbook—HVAC Applications* has additional information on losses for airborne sound propagation in ducts.

Room-to-Room Transmission

Room-to-room sound transmission generally involves both airborne and structureborne sound paths. The sound power incident on a room surface element undergoes three processes: (1) some sound energy is reflected from the surface element back into the source room, (2) a portion of the energy is lost through energy transfer into the material comprising the surface element, and (3) the remainder is transmitted through the surface element to the other room. Airborne sound is radiated as the surface element vibrates in the receiving room, and structureborne sound can be transmitted via the studs of a partition or the floor and ceiling surfaces.

Structureborne Transmission

Solid structures are efficient transmission paths for sound, which frequently originates as a vibration imposed on the transmitting structure. Typically, only a small amount of the input energy is radiated by the structure as airborne sound. With the same force excitation, a lightweight structure with little inherent damping radiates more sound than a massive structure with greater damping.

Flanking Transmission

Sound from the source room can bypass the primary separating element and get into the receiving room along other paths, called **flanking paths**. Common sound flanking paths include return air plenums, doors, and windows. Less obvious paths are those along floor and adjoining wall structures. Such flanking paths can reduce sound isolation between rooms. Flanking can explain poor sound isolation between spaces when the partition between them is known to provide very good sound insulation, and how sound can be heard in a location far from the source in a building. Determining whether flanking sound transmission is important and what paths are involved can be difficult. Experience with actual situations and the theoretical aspects of flanking transmission is very helpful. Sound intensity methods may be useful in determining flanking paths.

TYPICAL SOURCES OF SOUND

Whenever mechanical power is generated or transmitted, a fraction of the power is converted into sound power and radiated into the air. Therefore, virtually any major component of an HVAC system could be considered a sound source (e.g., fans, pumps, ductwork, piping, motors). The component's sound source characteristics depend on its construction, form of mechanical power, and integration with associated system components. The most important source characteristics include total sound power output L_w, frequency distribution, and radiation directivity Q. In addition, a vibrating HVAC system may be relatively quiet but transmit noise to connecting components, such as the unit casing, which may be serious sources of radiated noise. All of these characteristics vary with frequency.

Source Strength

For airborne noise, source strength should be expressed in terms of sound power levels. For structureborne noise (i.e., vibration), source strengths should be expressed in terms of free vibration levels (measured with the source free from any attachments). Because it is difficult to free a source from all attachments, measurements made with the source on soft mounts, with small mechanical impedances compared to the impedance of the source, can be used to obtain good approximations to free vibration levels.

Directivity of Sources

Noise radiation from sources can be directional. The larger the source, relative to an acoustic wavelength, the greater the potential of the source to be directional. Small sources tend to be nondirectional. The directivity of a source is expressed by the directivity factor Q as

$$Q = \frac{p^2(\theta)}{p^2_{ave}} \tag{38}$$

where $p^2(\theta)$ is the squared pressure observed in direction θ and p^2_{ave} is the energy average of the squared pressures measured over all directions.

Acoustic Nearfield

Not all unsteady pressures produced by the vibrating surfaces of a source or directly by disturbances in flow result in radiated sound. Some unsteady pressures "cling" to the surface. Their magnitude decreases rapidly with distance from the source, whereas the magnitude of radiating pressures decreases far less rapidly. The region close to the source where nonradiating unsteady pressures are significant is called the **acoustic nearfield**. Sound pressure level measurements should not be made in the acoustic nearfield because it is difficult to relate sound pressure levels measured in the nearfield to radiated levels. In general, the nearfield for most sources extends no more than 1 m from the source. However, at lower frequencies and for large sources, sound pressure level measurements should be made more than 1 m from the source when possible.

Sound and vibration sources in HVAC systems are so numerous that it is impractical to provide a complete listing here. Typical sources include

- Rotating and reciprocating equipment such as fans, motors, pumps, and chillers.
- There are several sources of fan noise, which is common in HVAC systems. Noise generated by vortices shed at the trailing edges of fan blades can be tonal. The levels of vortex shedding noise increase with the velocity of flow v_b over the blade as 50 to 60 log(v_b). Turbulence generated upstream of the fan and ingested into the fan is the source of broadband noise, with levels that increase as 60 to 80 log(v_0), where v_0 is the free stream velocity of flow into the fan. Turbulence in the boundary layer on the surface of fan blades also causes broadband noise that increases as 60 to 80 log(v_b). Flow that separates from blade surfaces can cause low-frequency noise. Nonuniform inflow to fans, created by obstructions, can produce tonal noise at frequencies of blade passage ($f_b = Nf_r$, where N is the number of blades and f_r is the rotation speed in rev/s) and integer multiples. Fan imbalance produces vibration at frequencies of shaft rotation and multiples. These low-frequency vibrations can couple to the structures to which the fan is attached, which can transmit the vibration over long distances and radiate low-frequency noise into rooms.
- Air and fluid sounds, such as those associated with flow through ductwork, piping systems, grilles, diffusers, terminal boxes, manifolds, and pressure-reducing stations.
- Flow inside ducts is often turbulent, which is a source of broadband noise. Levels increase at 60 to 80 log(v_0). Sharp corners of elbows and branches can separate flow from duct walls, producing low-frequency noise.
- Excitation of surfaces (e.g., friction); movement of mechanical linkages; turbulent flow impacts on ducts, plenum panels, and pipes; and impacts within equipment, such as cams and valve slap. Broadband flow noise increases rapidly with flow velocity v [60 to 80 log(v)], so reducing flow velocities can be very effective in reducing broadband noise.
- Magnetostriction (transformer hum), which becomes significant in motor laminations, transformers, switchgear, lighting ballasts, and dimmers. A characteristic of magnetostrictive oscillations is that their fundamental frequency is twice the electrical line frequency (120 Hz in a 60 Hz electrical distribution system.)

CONTROLLING SOUND

Terminology

The following noninterchangeable terms are used to describe the acoustical performance of many system components. ASTM *Standard* C634 defines additional terms.

Sound attenuation is a general term describing the reduction of the level of sound as it travels from a source to a receiver.

Insertion loss (IL) of a silencer or other sound-attenuating element, expressed in dB, is the decrease in sound pressure level or sound intensity level, measured at a fixed receiver location, when the sound-attenuating element is inserted into the path between the source and receiver. For example, if a straight, unlined piece of ductwork were replaced with a duct silencer, the sound level difference at a fixed location would be considered the silencer's insertion loss. Measurements are typically in either octave or 1/3 octave bands.

Sound transmission loss (TL) of a partition or other building element is equal to 10 times the logarithm of the ratio of the airborne sound power incident on the partition to the sound power transmitted by the partition and radiated on the other side, in decibels. Measurements are typically in octave or 1/3 octave bands. Chapter 47 of the 2007 *ASHRAE Handbook—HVAC Applications* defines the special case of breakout transmission loss through duct walls.

Noise reduction (NR) is the difference between the space-average sound pressure levels produced in two enclosed spaces or rooms (a receiving room and a source room) by one or more sound sources in the source room. An alternative, non-ASTM definition of NR is the difference in sound pressure levels measured upstream and downstream of a duct silencer or sound-attenuating element. Measurements are typically in octave or 1/3 octave bands. For partitions, NR is related to the transmission loss TL as follows:

$$NR = TL - 10\log\left(\frac{S}{R}\right) \tag{39}$$

where S is the partition's surface area and R is the room constant for the receiving room. Note that sound pressure levels measured close to the partition on the receiving side may be higher and should not be included in the space average used to compute the noise reduction.

Random-incidence sound absorption coefficient α is the fraction of incident sound energy absorbed by a surface exposed to randomly incident sound. It is measured in a reverberation room using 1/3 octave bands of broadband sound (ASTM *Standard* C423). The sound absorption coefficient of a material in a specific 1/3 octave band depends on the material's thickness, airflow resistivity, stiffness, and method of attachment to the supporting structure.

Scattering is the change in direction of sound propagation caused by an obstacle or inhomogeneity in the transmission medium. It results in the incident sound energy being dispersed in many directions.

Enclosures and Barriers

Enclosing a sound source is a common means of controlling airborne radiation from a source. Enclosure performance is expressed in terms of insertion loss. The mass of the enclosure panels combines with the stiffness (provided by compression) of the air trapped between the source and enclosure panel to produce a resonance. At resonance, the insertion loss may be negative, indicating that radiated noise levels are higher with the enclosure than without it. Therefore, the enclosure design should avoid aligning the enclosure resonance with frequencies commonly radiated from the source at high levels. At low frequencies, insertion loss of enclosures is more sensitive to stiffness of the enclosure panels than to the surface mass density of the panels. At high frequencies, the opposite is true.

The insertion loss of an enclosure may be severely compromised by openings or leaks. When designing penetrations through an enclosure, ensure that all penetrations are sealed. Also, at higher frequencies, adding an enclosure creates a reverberant space between the outer surfaces of the source and the inside surfaces of the enclosure. To avoid build-up of reverberant noise, and thereby noise transmitted through the enclosure, add absorption inside the enclosure.

A barrier is a solid element that blocks line-of-sight transmission but does not totally enclose the source or receiver. Properly designed barriers can effectively block sound that propagates directly from the source to the receiver. Barrier performance is expressed in terms of insertion loss: in general, the greater the increase in the path over or around the barrier relative to the direct path between the source and receiver without the barrier, the greater the barrier's insertion losses. Thus, placing the barrier close to the source or receiver is better than midway between the two. The barrier must break the line of sight between the source and receiver to be effective. The greater the height of the barrier, the higher the insertion loss. Barriers are only effective in reducing levels for sound propagated directly from the source to the receiver; they do not reduce levels of sound reflected from surfaces in rooms that bypass the barrier. Therefore, barriers are less effective in reverberant spaces than in nonreverberant spaces.

Partitions

Partitions are typically either single- or double-leaf. **Single-leaf partitions** are solid homogeneous panels with both faces rigidly connected. Examples are gypsum board, plywood, concrete block, brick, and poured concrete. The transmission loss of a single-leaf partition depends mainly on its surface mass (mass per unit area): the heavier the partition, the less it vibrates in response to sound waves and the less sound it radiates on the side opposite the sound source. Surface mass can be increased by increasing the partition's thickness or its density.

The **mass law** is a semiempirical expression that can predict transmission loss for randomly incident sound for thin, homogeneous single-leaf panels below the critical frequency (discussed later in this section) for the panel. It is written as

$$TL = 20\log(w_s f) - 47 \tag{40}$$

where

TL = transmission loss
w_s = surface mass of panel, kg/m²
f = frequency, Hz

The mass law predicts that transmission loss increases by 6 dB for each doubling of surface mass or frequency. If sound is incident only perpendicularly on the panel (rarely found in real-world applications), TL is about 5 dB greater than that predicted by Equation (40).

Transmission loss also depends on stiffness and internal damping. The transmission losses of three single-leaf walls are illustrated in Figure 2. For 16 mm gypsum board, TL depends mainly on the surface mass of the wall at frequencies below about 1 kHz; agreement with the mass law is good. At higher frequencies, there is a dip in the TL curve called the **coincidence dip** because it occurs at the frequency where the wavelength of flexural vibrations in the wall coincides with the wavelength of sound on the panel surface. The lowest frequency where coincidence between the flexural and surface pressure waves can occur is called the **critical frequency** f_c:

$$f_c = \frac{c^2}{2\pi}\left(\frac{12\rho}{Eh^2}\right)^{1/2} \tag{41}$$

where

ρ = density of panel material, kg/m³
E = Young's modulus of panel material, N/m²
h = thickness of outer panel of partition, m
c = sound speed in air, m/s

This equation indicates that increasing the material's stiffness and/or thickness reduces the critical frequency, and that increasing the material's density increases the critical frequency. For example, the 150 mm concrete slab has a mass of about 370 kg/m² and has a coincidence frequency at 125 Hz. Thus, over most of the frequency range shown in Figure 2, the transmission loss for the 150 mm concrete slab is well below that predicted by mass law. The coincidence dip for the 25 gage (0.531 mm thick) steel sheet occurs at high frequencies not shown in the figure.

The **sound transmission class (STC) rating** of a partition or assembly is a single number rating often used to classify sound isolation for speech (ASTM *Standards* E90 and E413). To determine a partition's STC rating, compare transmission losses measured in 1/3 octave bands with center frequencies from 125 to

4000 Hz to the STC contour shown in Figure 3. This contour is moved up until either

- The sum of differences between TL values below the contour and the corresponding value on the contour is no more than 32, or
- One of the differences between the contour and a TL value is no greater than 8.

The STC is then the value on the contour at 500 Hz. As shown in Figure 3, the STC contour deemphasizes transmission losses at low frequencies, so the STC rating should not be used as an indicator of an assembly's ability to control sound that is rich in low frequencies. Most fan sound spectra have dominant low-frequency sound; therefore, to control fan sound, walls and slabs should be selected only on the basis of 1/3 octave or octave band sound transmission loss values, particularly at low frequencies.

Note also that sound transmission loss values for ceiling tile are inappropriate for estimating sound reduction between a sound source located in a ceiling plenum and the room below. See ARI *Standard* 885 for guidance.

Walls with identical STC ratings may not provide identical sound insulation at all frequencies. Most single-number rating systems have limited frequency ranges, so designers should select partitions

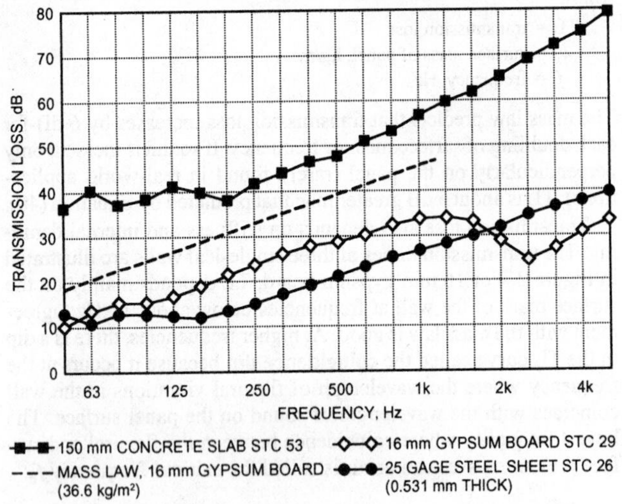

Fig. 2 Sound Transmission Loss Spectra for Single Layers of Some Common Materials

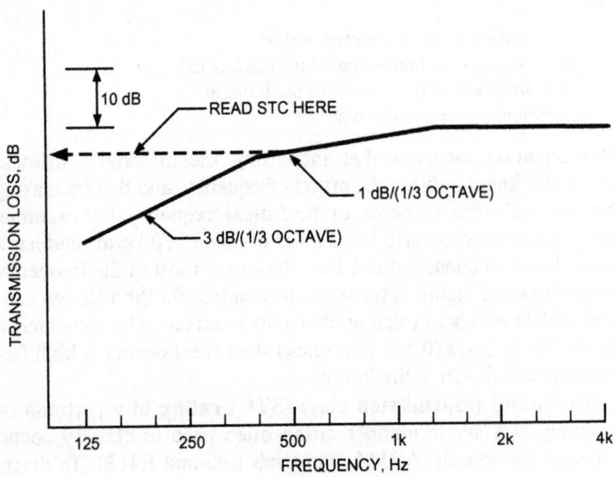

Fig. 3 Contour for Determining Partition's STC

and floors based on their 1/3 octave or octave band sound transmission loss values instead, especially when frequencies below 125 Hz are important.

For a given total mass in a wall or floor, much higher values of TL can be obtained by forming a **double-leaf** construction where each layer is independently or resiliently supported so vibration transmission between them is minimized. As well as mass, TL for such walls depends on cavity depth. Mechanical decoupling of leaves reduces sound transmission through the panel, relative to the transmission that would occur with the leaves structurally connected. However, transmission losses for a double-leaf panel are less than the sum of the transmission losses for each leaf. Air in the cavity couples the two mechanically decoupled leaves. Also, resonances occur inside the cavity between the leaves, thus increasing transmission (decreasing transmission loss) through the partition. Negative effects at resonances can be reduced by adding sound-absorbing material inside the cavity. For further information, see Chapter 47 of the 2007 *ASHRAE Handbook—HVAC Applications*.

Transmission losses of an enclosure may be severely compromised by openings or leaks in the partition. Ducts that lead into or through a noisy space can carry sound to many areas of a building. Designers need to consider this factor when designing duct, piping, and electrical systems.

When a partition contains two different constructions (e.g., a partition with a door), the transmission loss TL_c of the composite partition may be estimated using the following equation:

$$TL_c = 10 \log\left[\frac{S_1 + S_2}{S_1\tau_1 + S_2\tau_2}\right] \tag{42}$$

where S_1 and S_2 are the surface areas of the two types of constructions, and τ_1 and τ_2 are the transmissibilities, where $\tau = 10^{-TL/10}$. For leaks, $\tau = 1$. For a partition with a transmission of 40 dB, a hole that covers only 1% of the surface area results in a composite transmission loss of 20 dB, a 20 dB reduction in the transmission loss without the hole. This illustrates the importance of sealing penetrations through partitions to maintain design transmission losses.

Sound Attenuation in Ducts and Plenums

Most ductwork, even a sheet metal duct without acoustical lining or silencers, attenuates sound to some degree. The natural attenuation of unlined ductwork is minimal, but can, especially for long runs of rectangular ductwork, significantly reduce ductborne sound. Acoustic lining of ductwork can greatly attenuate sound propagation through ducts, particularly at middle to high frequencies. Chapter 47 of the 2007 *ASHRAE Handbook—HVAC Applications* has a detailed discussion of lined and unlined ductwork attenuation.

If analysis shows that lined ductwork will not reduce sound propagation adequately, commercially available sound attenuators (also known as **sound traps** or **duct silencers**) can be used. There are three types: dissipative, reactive, and active. The first two are commonly known as **passive attenuators.**

- **Dissipative silencers** use absorptive media such as glass or rock fiber as the principal sound-absorption mechanism. Thick, perforated sheet metal baffles filled with low-density fiber insulation restrict the air passage width within the attenuator housing. The fiber is sometimes protected from the airstream by cloths or films. This type of attenuator is most effective in reducing mid- and high-frequency sound energy.
- **Reactive silencers** (sometimes called **mufflers**) rely on changes in impedance to reflect energy back toward the source and away from the receiver. This attenuator type is typically used in HVAC systems serving hospitals, laboratories, or other areas with strict air quality standards. They are constructed only of metal, both solid and perforated. Chambers of specially designed shapes and sizes behind the perforated metal are tuned as

resonators or expansion chambers to react with and reduce sound power at selected frequencies. When designed for a broad frequency range, they are usually not as effective as dissipative attenuators of the same length. However, they can be highly effective and compact if designed for a limited frequency range (e.g., for a pure tone).

- **Active silencer systems** use microphones, loudspeakers, and appropriate electronics to reduce in-duct sound by generating sound 180° out of phase that destructively interferes with the incident sound energy. Microphones sample the sound field in the duct and loudspeakers generate signals with phase opposite to the original noise. Controlled laboratory experiments have shown that active attenuators reduce both broadband and tonal sound, but are typically only effective in the 31.5 through 250 Hz octave bands. Active silencers are more effective for tonal than for broadband noise. Insertion losses of as much as 30 dB have been achieved under controlled conditions. Because the system's microphones and loudspeakers are mounted flush with the duct wall, there is no obstruction to airflow and therefore negligible pressure drop. Because active silencers are not effective in excessively turbulent airflow, their use is limited to relatively long, straight duct sections with an air velocity less than about 7.5 m/s.

Silencers are available for fans, cooling towers, air-cooled condensers, compressors, gas turbines, and many other pieces of commercial and industrial equipment. HVAC silencers are normally installed on the intake or discharge side (or both) of a fan or air-handling unit. They may also be used on the receiver side of other noise generators such as terminal boxes, valves, and dampers.

Self-noise (i.e., noise generated by airflow through the silencer), can limit an attenuator's effective insertion loss for air velocities over about 10 m/s. Sound power at the silencer outlet is a combination of the power of the noise attenuated by the silencer and the noise generated inside the silencer by flow. Thus, output power W_M is related to input power W_0 as follows:

$$W_M = W_0 10^{-\mathrm{IL}/10} + W_{SG} \quad (43)$$

where IL is the insertion loss and W_{SG} is the power of the self-noise. It is also important to determine the dynamic insertion loss at design airflow velocity through the silencer, because a silencer's insertion loss varies with flow velocity.

End reflection losses caused by abrupt area changes in duct cross section are sometimes useful in controlling propagation at low frequencies. Low-frequency noise reduction is inversely proportional to the cross-sectional dimension of the duct, with the end reflection effect maximized in smaller cross sections and when the duct length of the smaller cross section is several duct diameters. Note, however, that abrupt area changes can increase flow velocities, which increase broadband high-frequency noise.

Where space is available, a **lined plenum** can provide excellent attenuation across a broad frequency range, especially effective at low frequencies. The combination of end reflections at the plenum's entrance and exit, a large offset between the entrance and exit, and sound-absorbing lining on the plenum walls can result in an effective sound-attenuating device.

Chapter 47 of the 2007 *ASHRAE Handbook—HVAC Applications* has additional information on sound control.

Standards for Testing Duct Silencers

Attenuators and duct liner materials are tested according to ASTM *Standard* E477 in North America and ISO *Standard* 7235 elsewhere. These define acoustic and aerodynamic performance in terms of dynamic insertion loss, self-noise, and airflow pressure drop. Many similarities exist, but the ASTM and ISO standards produce differing results because of variations in loudspeaker location, orientation, duct termination conditions, and computation methods. Currently, no standard test methods are available to measure attenuation by active silencers, although it is easy to measure the effectiveness simply by turning the active silencer control system on and off.

Dynamic insertion loss is measured in the presence of both forward and reverse flows. Forward flow occurs when air and sound move in the same direction, as in a supply air or fan discharge system; reverse flow occurs when air and sound travel in opposite directions, as in a return air or fan intake system.

SYSTEM EFFECTS

The way the HVAC components are assembled into a system affects the sound level generated by the system. Many engineers believe that satisfactory noise levels in occupied spaces can be achieved solely by using a manufacturer's sound ratings as a design tool, without considering the system influence.

However, most manufacturers' sound data are obtained under standardized (ideal) laboratory test conditions. In the field, different configurations of connected ductwork, and interactions with other components of the installation, often significantly change the operating noise level. For example, uniform flow into or out of a fan is rare in typical field applications. Nonuniform flow conditions usually increase the noise generated by fans, and are difficult to predict. However, the increases can be large (e.g., approaching 10 dB), so it is desirable to design systems to provide uniform inlet conditions. One method is to avoid locating duct turns near the inlet or discharge of a fan. Furthermore, components such as dampers and silencers installed close to fan equipment can produce nonuniformities in the velocity profile at the entrance to the silencer, which results in a significantly higher-than-anticipated pressure drop across that component. The combination of these two system effects changes the operating point on the fan curve. As a result, airflow is reduced and must be compensated for by increasing fan speed, which may increase noise. Conversely, a well-designed damper or silencer can actually improve flow conditions, which may reduce noise levels.

HUMAN RESPONSE TO SOUND

Noise

Noise may be defined as any unwanted sound. Sound becomes noise when it

- Is too loud: the sound is uncomfortable or makes speech difficult to understand
- Is unexpected (e.g., the sound of breaking glass)
- Is uncontrolled (e.g., a neighbor's lawn mower)
- Happens at the wrong time (e.g., a door slamming in the middle of the night)
- Contains unwanted pure tones (e.g., a whine, whistle, or hum)
- Contains unwanted information or is distracting (e.g., an adjacent telephone conversation or undesirable music)
- Is unpleasant (e.g., a dripping faucet)
- Connotes unpleasant experiences (e.g., a mosquito buzz or a siren wail)
- Is any combination of the previous examples

To be noise, sound does not have to be loud, just unwanted. In addition to being annoying, loud noise can cause hearing loss, and, depending on other factors, can affect stress level, sleep patterns, and heart rate.

To increase privacy, broadband sound may be radiated into a room by an electronic sound-masking system that has a random noise generator, amplifier, and multiple loudspeakers. Noise from such a system can mask low-level intrusive sounds from adjacent spaces. This controlled sound may be referred to as *noise*, but not in the context of unwanted sound; rather, it is a broadband, neutral sound that is frequently unobtrusive. It is difficult to design air-conditioning systems to produce noise that effectively masks low-level intrusive sound from adjacent spaces without also being a source of annoyance.

Random noise is an oscillation, the instantaneous magnitude of which cannot be specified for any given instant. The instantaneous magnitudes of a random noise are specified only by probability distributions, giving the fraction of the total time that the magnitude, or some sequence of magnitudes, lies within a specified range (ANSI *Standard* S1.1). There are three types of random noise: white, pink, and red.

- **White noise** has a continuous frequency spectrum with equal energy per hertz over a specified frequency range. Because octave bands double in width for each successive band, for white noise the energy also doubles in each successive octave band. Thus white noise displayed on a 1/3 octave or octave band chart increases in level by 3 dB per octave.
- **Pink noise** has a continuous frequency spectrum with equal energy per constant-percentage bandwidth, such as per octave or 1/3 octave band. Thus pink noise appears on a 1/3 octave or octave band chart as a horizontal line.
- **Red noise** has a continuous frequency spectrum with octave band levels that decrease at a rate of 4 to 5 dB per octave with increasing frequency. Red noise is typical of noise from well-designed HVAC systems.

Predicting Human Response to Sound

Predicting the response of people to any given sound is, at best, only a statistical concept, and, at worst, very inaccurate. This is because response to sound is not only physiological but psychological and depends on the varying attitude of the listener. Hence, the effect of sound is often unpredictable. However, people respond adversely if the sound is considered too loud for the situation or if it sounds "wrong." Therefore, criteria are based on descriptors that account for level and spectrum shape.

Sound Quality

To determine the acoustic acceptability of a space to occupants, sound pressure levels in the space must be known. This, however, is often not sufficient; sound quality is important, too. Factors influencing sound quality include (1) loudness, (2) tone perception, (3) frequency balance, (4) harshness, (5) time and frequency fluctuation, and (6) vibration.

People often perceive sounds with tones (such as a whine or hum) as particularly annoying. A tone can cause a relatively low-level sound to be perceived as noise.

Loudness

The primary method for determining subjective estimations of loudness is to present sounds to a sample of listeners under controlled conditions. Listeners compare an unknown sound with a standard sound. (The accepted standard sound is a pure tone of 1000 Hz or a narrow band of random noise centered on 1000 Hz.) Loudness level is expressed in **phons**, and the loudness level of any sound in phons is equal to the sound pressure level in decibels of a standard sound deemed to be equally loud. Thus, a sound that is judged as loud as a 40 dB, 1000 Hz tone has a loudness level of 40 phons.

Average reactions of humans to tones are shown in Figure 4 (Robinson and Dadson 1956). The reaction changes when the sound is a band of random noise (Pollack 1952), rather than a pure tone (Figure 5). The figures indicate that people are most sensitive in the midfrequency range. The contours in Figure 4 are closer together at low frequencies, showing that at lower frequencies, people are less sensitive to sound level, but are more sensitive to *changes* in level.

Under carefully controlled experimental conditions, humans can detect small changes in sound level. However, for humans to describe a sound as being half or twice as loud requires changes in the overall sound pressure level of about 10 dB. For many people, a 3 dB change is the minimum perceptible difference. This means that halving the power output of the source causes a barely noticeable change in sound pressure level, and power output must be reduced by a factor of 10 before humans determine that loudness has been halved. Table 8 summarizes the effect of changes in sound levels for simple sounds in the frequency range of 250 Hz and higher.

The phon scale covers the large dynamic range of the ear, but does not fit a subjective linear loudness scale. Over most of the audible range, a doubling of loudness corresponds to a change of approximately 10 phons. To obtain a quantity proportional to the loudness sensation, use a loudness scale based on the **sone**. One sone equals the loudness level of 40 phons. A rating of two sones corresponds to 50 phons, and so on. In HVAC, only the ventilation fan industry (e.g., bathroom exhaust and sidewall propeller fans) uses loudness ratings.

Standard objective methods for calculating loudness have been developed. ANSI *Standard* S3.4 calculates loudness or loudness level using 1/3 octave band sound pressure level data as a starting

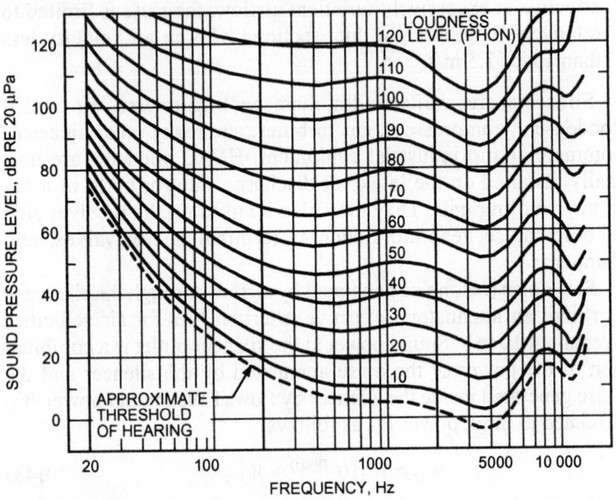

Fig. 4 Free-Field Equal Loudness Contours for Pure Tones
(Robinson and Dadson 1956)

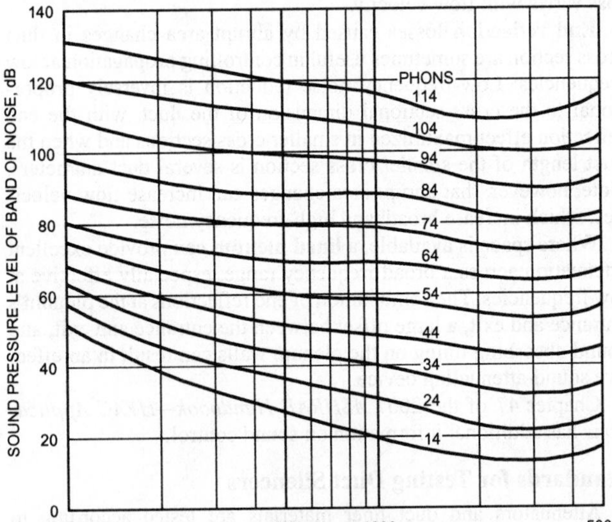

Fig. 5 Equal Loudness Contours for Relatively Narrow Bands of Random Noise
(Pollack 1952)

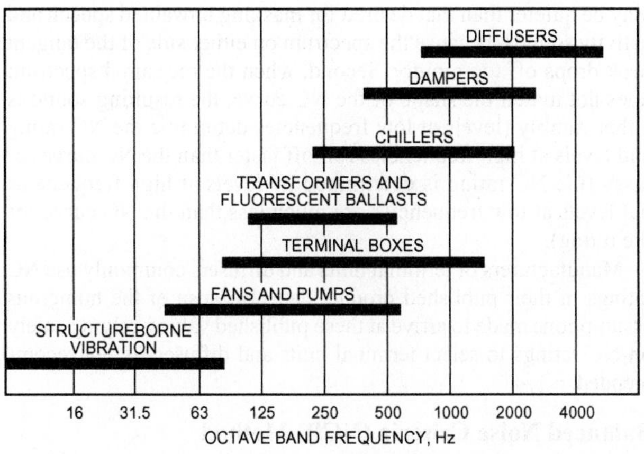

Fig. 6 Frequencies at Which Various Types of Mechanical and Electrical Equipment Generally Control Sound Spectra

Table 8 Subjective Effect of Changes in Sound Pressure Level, Broadband Sounds (Frequency 250 ≥ Hz)

Subjective Change	Objective Change in Sound Level (Approximate)
Much louder	More than +10 dB
Twice as loud	+10 dB
Louder	+5 dB
Just perceptibly louder	+3 dB
Just perceptibly quieter	−3 dB
Quieter	−5 dB
Half as loud	−10 dB
Much quieter	Less than −10 dB

point. The loudness index for each 1/3 octave band is obtained from a graph or by calculation. Total loudness is then calculated by combining the loudnesses for each band according to a formula given in the standard. A graphic method using 1/3 octave band sound pressure levels to predict loudness of sound spectra containing tones is presented in Zwicker (ISO *Standard* 532) and German *Standard* DIN 45631. Because of its complexity, loudness has not been widely used in engineering practice in the past.

Acceptable Frequency Spectrum

The most acceptable frequency spectrum for HVAC sound is a balanced or neutral spectrum in which octave band levels decrease at a rate of 4 to 5 dB per octave with increasing frequency. This means that it is not too hissy (excessive high frequency content) or too rumbly (excessive low frequency content). Unfortunately, achieving a balanced sound spectrum is not always easy: there may be numerous sound sources to consider. As a design guide, Figure 6 shows the more common mechanical and electrical sound sources and frequency regions that control the indoor sound spectrum. Chapter 47 of the 2007 *ASHRAE Handbook—HVAC Applications* provides more detailed information on treating some of these sound sources.

SOUND RATING SYSTEMS AND ACOUSTICAL DESIGN GOALS

This section presents information to help the design engineer decide which of the several background sound rating methods is most appropriate for a specific project. Current methods include the A-weighted sound pressure level (dBA), noise criteria (NC), room criterion (RC), balanced noise criterion (NCB), and RC Mark II. Each sound rating method was developed from data for specific applications; not all methods are equally suitable for rating HVAC-related sound in the variety of applications encountered.

It is also important to determine the purpose for which the rating system will be used, because each system has strengths and weaknesses. Tangency methods are typically best for design criteria, whereas some of the more complicated sound rating systems are useful for diagnosing the nature and magnitude of particular problems. The simplest sound rating systems may be appropriate for commissioning work, depending on project sensitivity to noise levels or annoyance.

The degree of occupant satisfaction achieved with a given level of background sound is determined by many factors, including sound perception and acoustical privacy. **Sound perception** of desired sounds (e.g., speech, music) makes low background noise levels desirable. For **privacy**, higher background noise levels are desired to mask intruding sound, such as in open-plan offices where a certain amount of speech and activity masking is essential. Large conference rooms, auditoriums, and recording studios, in comparison, can tolerate only a low level of background sound. Therefore, the system sound control goal varies depending on the required use of the space.

To be unobtrusive, HVAC-related background sound should have the following properties:

- Balanced distribution of sound energy over a broad frequency range
- No audible tonal or other characteristics such as whine, whistle, hum, or rumble
- No noticeable time-varying levels from beats or other system-induced aerodynamic instability
- No fluctuations in level such as a throbbing or pulsing

Unfortunately, there is no acceptable process to easily characterize the effects of audible tones and level fluctuations, so currently available rating methods do not adequately address these issues.

Some sound rating methods comprise two distinct parts: a single number related to the overall magnitude of the noise, and a procedure for determining the quality of the noise (i.e., the degree of frequency balance, which is based on a family of criterion curves specifying sound levels by octave bands).

A-Weighted Sound Level (dBA)

The A-weighted sound level L_A is an easy-to-determine, single-number rating widely used to state acoustical design goals. However, its usefulness is limited because it gives no information on spectrum content. The rating is expressed as a number followed by dBA (e.g., 40 dBA). See the section on Measuring Sound for the definition and method for determining dBA levels.

A-weighted sound levels correlate well with human judgments of relative loudness, but do not indicate degree of spectral balance. Thus, they do not necessarily correlate well with the annoyance caused by the noise. Many different-sounding spectra can have the same numeric rating but quite different subjective qualities. A-weighted comparisons are best used with sounds that sound alike but differ in level. They should not be used to compare sounds with distinctly different spectral characteristics; two sounds at the same sound level but with different spectral content are likely to be judged differently by the listener in terms of acceptability as a background sound. One of the sounds might be completely acceptable; the other could be objectionable because its spectrum shape was rumbly, hissy, or tonal in character.

A-weighted sound levels are used extensively in outdoor environmental noise standards and for estimating the risk of damage to hearing for long-term exposures to noise, such as in industrial environments and other workplaces. In outdoor environmental noise standards, the principle sources of noise are vehicular traffic and aircraft, for which A-weighted criteria of acceptability have been developed empirically.

Outdoor HVAC equipment can create significant sound levels that affect nearby properties and buildings. Local noise ordinances often limit property line A-weighted sound levels and typically are more restrictive during nighttime hours.

Noise Criteria (NC) Method

The NC method remains the predominant design criterion used by HVAC engineers. This single-number rating is somewhat sensitive to the relative loudness and speech interference properties of a given sound spectrum. Its wide use derives in part from its ease of use and its publication in HVAC design textbooks. The method consists of a family of criterion curves extending from 63 to 8000 Hz, and a tangency rating procedure (Beranek 1957). The criterion curves define the limits of octave band spectra that must not be exceeded to meet acceptance in certain spaces. The NC curves shown in Figure 7 are in steps of 5 dB. To obtain an NC rating to the nearest decibel, interpolate between the curves in Figure 7.

The rating is expressed as NC followed by a number. For example, the spectrum shown is rated NC 43 because this is the lowest rating curve that falls entirely above the measured data. An NC 35 design goal is common for private offices. The background sound level meets this goal if no portion of its spectrum lies above the designated NC 35 curve.

The NC method is sensitive to level but has the disadvantage as a design criterion method that it does not require the sound spectrum to approximate the shape of the NC curves. Thus, many different sounds can have the same numeric rating, but rank differently on the basis of subjective sound quality. In many HVAC systems that do not produce excessive low-frequency sound, the NC rating correlates relatively well with occupant satisfaction if sound quality is not a significant concern or if the octave band levels have a shape similar to the nearest NC curves.

Two problems occur in using the NC procedure as a diagnostic tool. First, when the NC level is determined by a prominent peak in the spectrum, the actual level of resulting background sound may be quieter than that desired for masking unwanted speech and activity sounds, because the spectrum on either side of the tangent peak drops off too rapidly. Second, when the measured spectrum does not match the shape of the NC curve, the resulting sound is either rumbly (levels at low frequencies determine the NC rating and levels at high frequencies roll off faster than the NC curve) or hissy (the NC rating is determined by levels at high frequencies but levels at low frequencies are much less than the NC curve for the rating).

Manufacturers of terminal units and diffusers commonly use NC ratings in their published product data. Because of the numerous assumptions made to arrive at these published values, relying solely on NC ratings to select terminal units and diffusers is not recommended.

Balanced Noise Criteria (NCB) Method

The balanced noise criteria (NCB) method (Beranek 1989) is intended to specify or evaluate room sound, including noise caused by occupant activities. Compared with the NC method, the NCB criteria curves (Figure 8) include both the addition of two low-frequency octave bands (16 and 31.5 Hz) and lower permissible sound levels in the high-frequency octave bands (4000 and 8000 Hz). The NCB rating procedure is based on the speech interference level (SIL; the average of sound pressure levels in the four octave bands centered at 500, 1000, 2000, and 4000 Hz) with additional tests for rumble and hiss compliance. The rating is expressed as NCB followed by a number (e.g., NCB 40).

As a diagnostic tool, the NCB method helps to determine whether a sound spectrum has an unbalanced shape that may require corrective action. Also, it addresses the issue of low-frequency sound. If any sound pressure levels in the 16, 31.5, or 63 Hz octave bands fall within the lightly shaded area, it indicates that low-frequency vibration may be a problem. Any octave band levels above the lightly

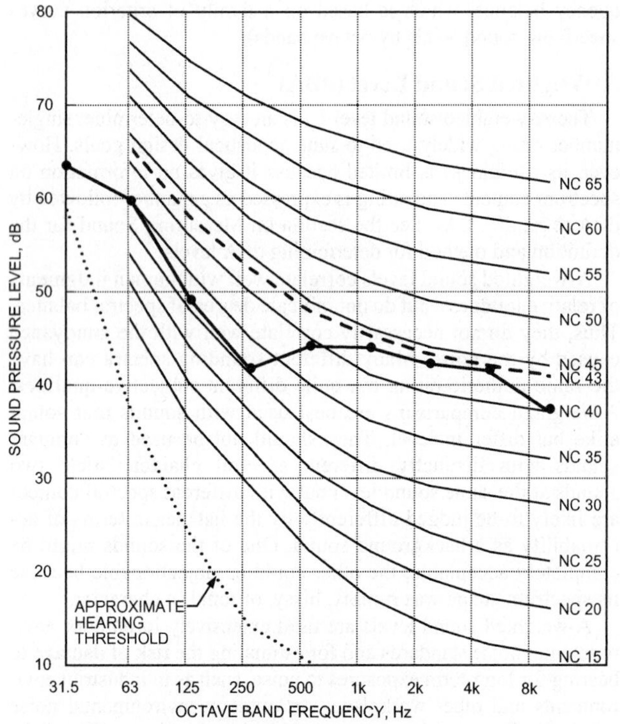

Fig. 7 NC (Noise Criteria) Curves and Sample Spectrum (Curve with Symbols)

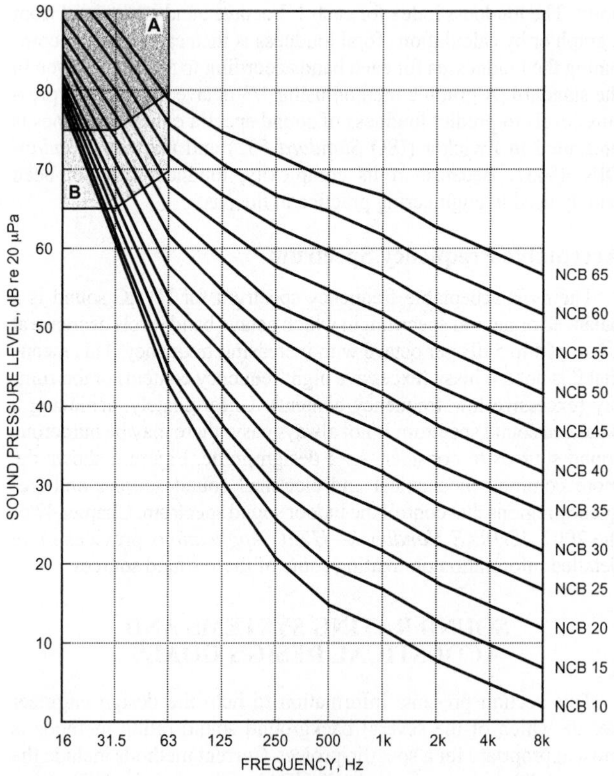

Fig. 8 NCB (Noise Criteria Balanced) Curves Drawn from ANSI *Standard* S12.2

shaded area indicate that low-frequency vibration is a likely problem. The existence of low-frequency rumble or high-frequency hissy imbalances are determined as follows:

- Rumble imbalance exists if any of the octave band levels with center frequencies below 1000 Hz are above the curve that is 3 dB above the NCB rating curve
- Hissy imbalance exists if any of the octave band levels with center frequencies above 1000 Hz are above the NCB rating curve that is the best fit to the levels in the 125, 250, and 500 octave bands.

Room Criterion (RC) Method

The room criterion (RC) method (ANSI *Standard* S12.2; Blazier 1981a, 1981b) is based on measured levels of HVAC noise in spaces and is used primarily as a diagnostic tool.The RC method consists of a family of criteria curves and a rating procedure. The shape of these curves differs from the NC curves to approximate a well-balanced, neutral-sounding spectrum; two additional octave bands (16 and 31.5 Hz) are added to deal with low-frequency sound and the 8000 Hz octave band is dropped. This rating procedure assesses background sound in spaces based on its effect on speech communication, and on estimates of subjective sound quality. The rating is expressed as RC followed by a number to show the level of the sound and a letter to indicate the quality [e.g., RC 35(N), where N denotes neutral].

RC curves are the same as the RC-II curves shown in Figure 9, except the RC-II are flat from 16 to 31.5 Hz, whereas the RC curves continue on the same slope. The RC rating value is the average of the levels in the 500, 1000, and 2000 Hz octave bands. The A and B regions are identical to those shown in Figure 8 for NCB, with the same interpretation. Rumble imbalance exists if any levels in octave bands with center frequencies from 31.5 to 250 Hz are more than 5 dB above the RC rating curve, and a hissy imbalance exists if any of the levels in the octave bands with center frequencies from 1000 to 4000 Hz are above the RC rating curve by more than 3 dB.

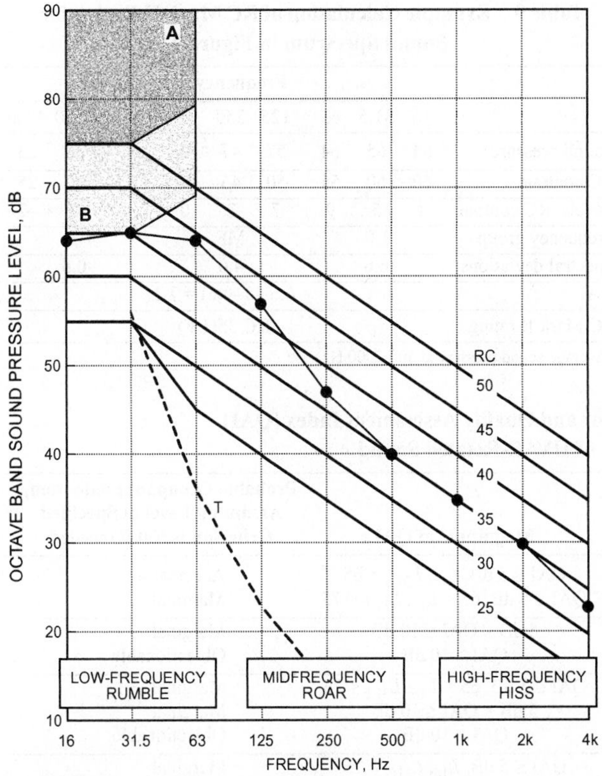

Sound levels in Region B may generate perceptible vibration in light wall and ceiling construction. Rattles in light fixtures, doors, windows, etc., are a slight possibility. Sound levels in Region A have a high probability of generating easily perceptible sound-induced vibration in light wall and ceiling construction. Audible rattling in light fixtures, doors, windows, etc., may be anticipated. The solid dots are octave band sound pressure levels for the example in the text.

Fig. 9 Room Criteria Curves, Mark II

Room Criteria (RC) Mark II Method

The RC method was revised to the RC Mark II method (Blazier 1997) to add additional parameters that further describe a measured sound.

Like its predecessor, the RC Mark II method is intended for rating sound performance of an HVAC system as a whole. The method is primarily used as a diagnostic tool for analyzing sound problems in the field. Because the RC Mark II method is somewhat complicated to use, it is discussed in some detail below.

The RC Mark II method of rating HVAC system sound comprises three parts:

- Family of criterion curves (Figure 9)
- Procedure for determining the RC numerical rating and the sound spectral balance (quality)
- Procedure for estimating occupant satisfaction when the spectrum does not have the shape of an RC curve (Quality Assessment Index)

The rating is expressed as RC followed by a number and a letter [e.g., RC 45(N)]. The number is the arithmetic average rounded to the nearest integer of the sound pressure levels in the 500, 1000, and 2000 Hz octave bands (the principal speech frequency region). The letter is a qualitative descriptor that identifies the perceived character of the sound: (N) for neutral, (LF) for low-frequency rumble, (MF) for mid-frequency roar, and (HF) for high-frequency hiss. There are also two subcategories of the low-frequency descriptor: (LF_B), denoting a moderate but perceptible degree of sound-induced ceiling/wall vibration, and (LF_A), denoting a noticeable degree of sound-induced vibration.

Each reference curve in Figure 9 identifies the shape of a neutral-sounding spectrum, indexed to a curve number corresponding to the sound level in the 1000 Hz octave band. The shape of these curves is based on research (Blazier 1981a, 1981b) and modified at 16 Hz following recommendations of Broner (1994). Regions A and B denote levels at which sound can induce vibration in lightweight wall and ceiling constructions that can potentially cause rattles in light fixtures, furniture, etc. Curve T is the octave-band threshold of hearing as defined by ANSI *Standard* 12.2.

Procedure for Determining the RC Mark II Rating for a System

Step 1. Determine the appropriate RC reference curve. This is done by obtaining the arithmetic average of the sound levels in the principal speech frequency range represented by the levels in the 500, 1000, and 2000 Hz octave bands. [This is the **preferred speech interference level (PSIL)**, which should not be confused with the ANSI-defined **speech interference level (SIL)**, a four-band average obtained by including the 4000 Hz octave band level.] The RC reference curve is chosen to have the same value at 1000 Hz as the calculated average value (rounded to the nearest integer).

Step 2. Assign a subjective quality by calculating the **quality assessment index (QAI)** (Blazier 1995). This is a measure of the degree the shape of the spectrum under evaluation deviates from the shape of the RC reference curve. The procedure requires calculation of the energy-average spectral deviations from the RC reference curve in each of three frequency groups: low (LF; 16-63 Hz), medium (MF; 125-500 Hz), and high (HF; 1000-4000 Hz). However, when evaluating typical HVAC-related sounds, a simple arithmetic average of these deviations is often adequate if the range of values does not exceed 3 dB. The procedure for the LF region is given by

Equation (44) and is repeated in the MF and HF regions by substituting the corresponding values at each frequency.

$$\Delta LF = 10 \log[(10^{0.1\Delta L_{16}} + 10^{0.1\Delta L_{31.5}} + 10^{0.1\Delta L_{63}})/3] \quad (44)$$

where the ΔL terms are the differences between the spectrum being evaluated and the RC reference curve in each frequency band. In this way, three specific spectral deviation factors (ΔLF, ΔMF, and ΔHF), expressed in dB with either positive or negative values, are associated with the spectrum being rated. QAI is the range in decibels between the highest and lowest values of the spectral deviation factors.

If QAI ≤ 5 dB, the spectrum is assigned a neutral (N) rating. If QAI exceeds 5 dB, the sound quality descriptor of the RC rating is the letter designation of the frequency region of the deviation factor having the highest positive value. As an example, the spectrum plotted in Figure 9 is processed in Table 9.

The arithmetic average of the sound levels in the 500, 1000, and 2000 Hz octave bands is 35 dB, so the RC 35 curve is selected as the reference for spectrum quality evaluation.

The spectral deviation factors in the LF, MF, and HF regions are 6.6, 4.0 and –0.6, respectively, giving a QAI of 7.2. The maximum positive deviation factor occurs in the LF region, and the QAI exceeds 5, resulting in a rating of RC 35(LF). An average room occupant would perceive this spectrum as marginally rumbly (see Table 10).

Estimating Occupant Satisfaction Using QAI

The quality assessment index (QAI) is useful in estimating an occupant's probable reaction when the system design does not produce optimum sound quality. The basis for the procedure outlined here is that changes in sound level of less than 5 dB do not cause subjects to change their ranking of sounds of similar spectral content, whereas changes greater than 5 dB do. A QAI of 5 dB or less corresponds to a generally acceptable condition, provided that the perceived level of the sound is in a range consistent with the given type of space occupancy. A QAI between 5 and 10 dB represents a marginal situation in which acceptance by an occupant is questionable. However, a QAI greater than 10 dB will likely be objectionable to the average occupant. Table 10 lists sound quality descriptors and QAI values and relates them to probable occupant reaction to the sound. However, when sound pressure levels in the 16 or 31.5 Hz octave bands exceed 65 dB, vibration in lightweight office construction is possible (and likely if levels exceed 75 dB).

Even at moderate levels, if the dominant portion of the background sound occurs in the very low-frequency region, some people experience a sense of oppressiveness or depression in the environment (Persson-Waye et al. 1997). In such situations, the basis for complaint may result from exposure to that environment for several hours, and thus may not be noticeable during short exposures.

Criteria Selection Guidelines

In general, these basic guidelines are important:

- Sound levels below NC, NCB, or RC 35 are not detrimental to good speech intelligibility. Sound levels at or above these levels may interfere with or mask speech.
- Even if the occupancy sound is significantly higher than the anticipated background sound level generated by mechanical equipment, the sound design goal should not necessarily be raised to levels approaching the occupancy sound. This avoids occupants having to raise their voices uncomfortably to be heard over the noise.

For recommended background sound level criteria for different spaces, see Chapter 47 of the 2007 *ASHRAE Handbook—HVAC Applications*.

FUNDAMENTALS OF VIBRATION

A rigidly mounted machine transmits its internal vibratory forces directly to the supporting structure. However, by inserting resilient mountings (**vibration isolators**) between the machine and supporting structure, the magnitude of transmitted force can be dramatically reduced. Vibration isolators can also be used to protect sensitive equipment from floor vibration.

Table 9 Example Calculation of RC Mark II Rating for Sound Spectrum in Figure 9

	Frequency, Hz								
	16	31.5	63	125	250	500	1000	2000	4000
Sound pressure*	64	65	64	57	47	40	35	30	23
RC contour	60	60	55	50	45	40	35	30	25
Levels: RC contour	4	5	9	7	2	0	0	0	–2
Frequency group		LF			MF			HF	
Spectral deviations		6.6			4.0			–0.6	
QAI					6.6 – (–0.6) = 7.2				
RC Mark II rating					RC 35(LF)				

*Average sound pressure at 500-2000 Hz = 35

Table 10 Definition of Sound Quality Descriptor and Quality Assessment Index (QAI) to Interpret RC Mark II Ratings of HVAC-Related Sound

Sound Quality Descriptor	Description of Subjective Perception	Magnitude of QAI	Probable Occupant Evaluation, Assuming Level of Specified Criterion is Not Exceeded
(N) Neutral (Bland)	Balanced sound spectrum, no single frequency range dominant	QAI ≤ 5 dB, L_{16}, $L_{31.5}$ ≤ 65 QAI ≤ 5 dB, 65 < L_{16}, $L_{31.5}$ < 75	Acceptable Marginal
(LF) Rumble	Low-frequency range dominant (16-63 Hz)	5 dB < QAI ≤ 10 dB QAI > 10 dB	Marginal Objectionable
(LFV_B) Rumble, with moderately perceptible room surface vibration	Low-frequency range dominant (16-63 Hz)	QAI ≤ 5 dB, 65 < L_{16}, $L_{31.5}$ < 75 5 dB < QAI ≤ 10 dB QAI > 10 dB	Marginal Marginal Objectionable
(LFV_A) Rumble, with clearly perceptible room surface vibration	Low-frequency range dominant (16-63 Hz)	QAI ≤ 5 dB, L_{16}, $L_{31.5}$ > 75 5 dB < QAI ≤ 10 dB QAI > 10 dB	Marginal Marginal Objectionable
(MF) Roar	Midfrequency range dominant (125-500 Hz)	5 dB < QAI ≤ 10 dB QAI > 10 dB	Marginal Objectionable
(HF) Hiss	High-frequency range dominant (1000-4000 Hz)	5 dB < QAI ≤ 10 dB QAI > 10 dB	Marginal Objectionable

Single-Degree-of-Freedom Model

The simplest representation of a vibration isolation system is the single-degree-of-freedom model, illustrated in Figure 10. Only motion along the vertical axis is considered. The isolated system is represented by a mass and the isolator is represented by a spring, which is considered fixed to ground. Excitation (i.e., the vibratory forces generated by the isolated equipment, such as shaft imbalance in rotating machinery) is applied to the mass. This simple model is the basis for catalog information provided by most manufacturers of vibration isolation hardware.

Mechanical Impedance

Mechanical impedance Z_m is a structural property useful in understanding the performance of vibration isolators in a given installation. Z_m is the ratio of the force F applied to the structure divided by the velocity v of the structure's vibration response at the point of excitation:

$$Z_m = F/v \tag{45}$$

At low frequencies, the mechanical impedance of a vibration isolator is approximately equal to $k/2\pi f$, where k is the stiffness of the isolator (force per unit deflection) and f is frequency in Hz (cycles/second). Note that the impedance of the isolator is inversely proportional to frequency. This characteristic is the basis for an isolator's ability to block vibration from the supported structure. In the simple single-degree-of-freedom model, impedance of the isolated mass is proportional to frequency. Thus, as frequency increases, the isolator increasingly provides an impedance mismatch between the isolated structure and ground. This mismatch attenuates the forces imposed on the ground. However, at the system's particular natural frequency (discussed in the following section), the effects of the isolator are decidedly detrimental.

Natural Frequency

Using the single-degree-of-freedom model, the frequency at which the magnitude of the spring and mass impedances are equal is the **natural frequency f_n**. At this frequency, the mass's vibration response to the applied excitation is a maximum, and the isolator actually amplifies the force transmitted to ground. The natural frequency of the system (also called the **isolation system resonance**) is given approximately by

$$f_n = \frac{1}{2\pi}\sqrt{\frac{k}{M}} \tag{46}$$

where M is the mass of the equipment supported by the isolator. The stiffness k is expressed as N/m, and M as kg.

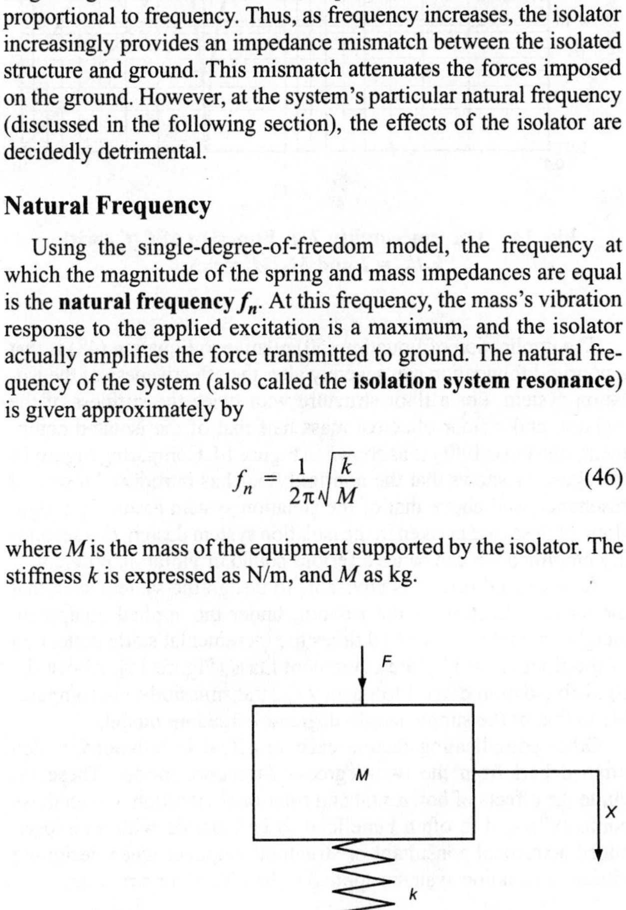

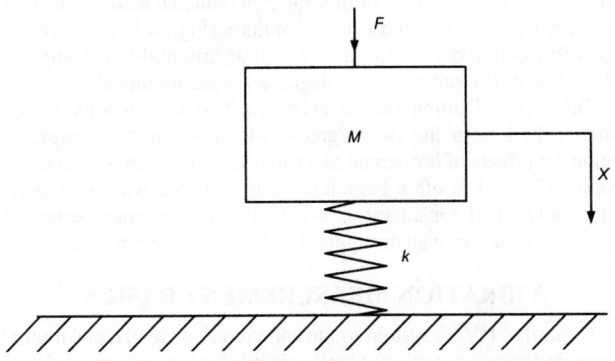

Fig. 10 Single-Degree-of-Freedom System

This equation simplifies to

$$f_n = \frac{15.8}{\sqrt{\delta_{st}}} \tag{47}$$

where δ_{st} is the **isolator static deflection** (the incremental distance the isolator spring compresses under the weight of the supported equipment) in millimetres. Thus, to achieve the appropriate system natural frequency for a given application, it is customary to specify the corresponding isolator static deflection and the load to be supported at each of the mounting points.

The **transmissibility T** of this system is the ratio of the amplitudes of the force transmitted to the building structure to the exciting force produced inside the vibrating equipment. For disturbing frequency f_d, T is given by

$$T = \left|\frac{1}{1-(f_d/f_n)^2}\right| \tag{48}$$

The transmissibility equation is plotted in Figure 11.

It is important to note that T is inversely proportional to the square of the ratio of the disturbing frequency f_d to the system natural frequency f_n. At $f_d = f_n$, resonance occurs: the denominator of Equation (48) equals zero and transmission of vibration is theoretically infinite. In practice, transmissibility at resonance is limited by damping in the system, which is always present to some degree. Thus, the magnitude of vibration amplification at resonance always has a finite, though often dramatically high, value.

Note that vibration isolation (attenuation of force applied to ground) does not occur until the ratio of the disturbing frequency f_d to the system natural frequency f_n is greater than 1.4. Above this ratio, vibration transmissibility decreases (attenuation increases) with the square of frequency.

In designing isolators, it is customary to specify a frequency ratio of at least 3.5, which corresponds to an isolation efficiency of about 90%, or 10% transmissibility. Higher ratios may be specified, but in practice this often does not greatly increase isolation efficiency, especially at frequencies above about 10 times the natural frequency. The reason is that wave effects and other nonlinear characteristics in real isolators cause a deviation from the theoretical curve that limits performance at higher frequencies.

To obtain the design objective of $f_d/f_n \approx 3.5$, the lowest frequency of excitation f_d is determined first. This is usually the shaft rotation rate in Hz (cycles/second). Because it is usually not possible to change the mass of the isolated equipment, the combined stiffness of the isolators is then selected such that

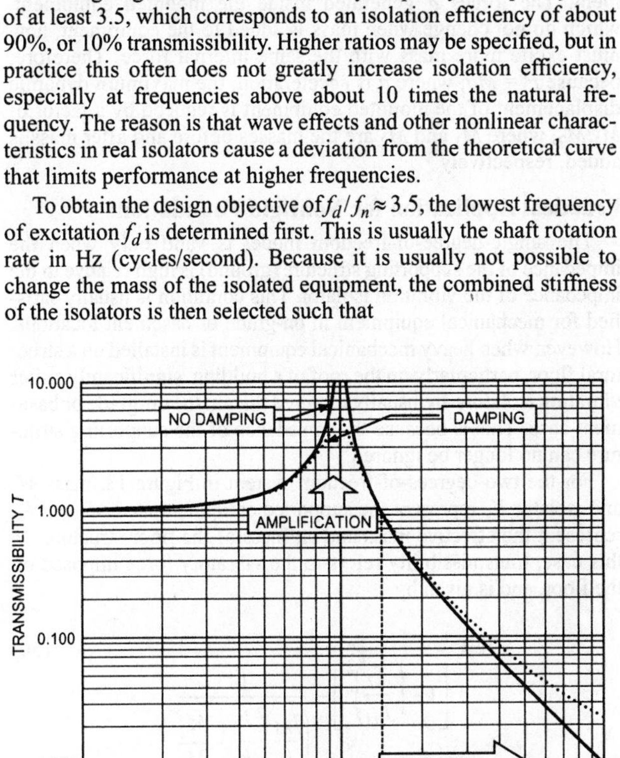

Fig. 11 Vibration Transmissibility T as Function of f_d/f_n

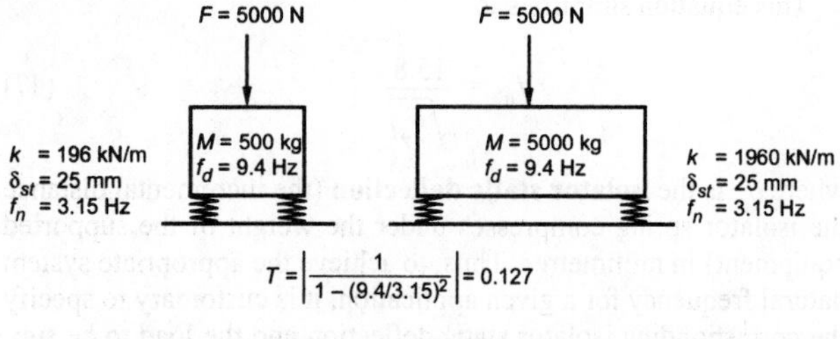

Fig. 12 Effect of Mass on Transmissibility

$$k = (2\pi f_d/3.5)^2 M \tag{49}$$

where M is the mass of the mounted equipment in kg, and k is in N/m. With four mounts, the stiffness of each mount is $k/4$.

For a given set of isolators, as shown by Equations (46) and (48), if the equipment mass is increased, the resonance frequency decreases and isolation increases. In practice, the load-carrying capacity of isolators usually requires that their stiffness or their number be increased. Consequently, the static deflection and transmissibility may remain unchanged.

For example, as shown in Figure 12, a 500 kg piece of equipment installed on isolators with stiffness k of 196 kN/m results in a 25 mm deflection and a system resonance frequency f_n of 3.15 Hz. If the equipment operates at 564 rpm (9.4 Hz) and develops an internal force of 5000 N, 635 N is transmitted to the structure. If the total mass is increased to 5000 kg by placing the equipment on a concrete inertia base and the stiffness of the springs is increased to 1960 kN/m, the deflection is still 25 mm, the resonance frequency of the system is maintained at 3.15 Hz, and the force transmitted to the structure remains at 635 N.

The increased mass, however, reduces equipment displacement. The forces F generated inside the mounted equipment, which do not change when mass is added to the equipment, now must excite more mass with the same internal force. Therefore, because $F = Ma$, where a is acceleration, the maximum dynamic displacement of the mounted equipment is reduced by a factor of M_1/M_2, where M_1 and M_2 are the masses before and after mass is added, respectively.

Practical Application for Nonrigid Foundations

The single-degree-of-freedom model is valid only when the impedance of the supporting structure (ground) is high relative to the impedance of the vibration isolator. This condition is usually satisfied for mechanical equipment in on-grade or basement locations. However, when heavy mechanical equipment is installed on a structural floor, particularly on the roof of a building, significantly softer vibration isolators are usually required than in the on-grade or basement case. This is because the impedance of the supporting structure can no longer be ignored.

For the two-degrees-of-freedom system in Figure 13, mass M_1 and isolator K_1 represent the supported equipment, and M_2 and K_2 represent the effective mass and stiffness of the floor structure. In this case, transmissibility refers to the vibratory force imposed on the floor, and is given by

$$T = \frac{1}{\left[1 - \left(\frac{f_d}{f_{n1}}\right)^2\right] - \frac{1}{\left(\frac{f_{n1}}{f_d}\right)^2 \frac{k_2}{k_1} - \frac{M_2}{M_1}}} \tag{50}$$

As in Equation (48), f_d is the forcing frequency. Frequency f_{n1} is the natural frequency of the isolated equipment with a rigid foundation [Equation (46)].

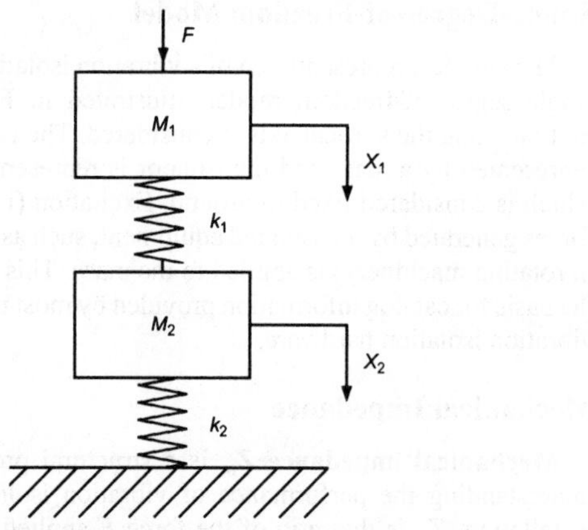

Fig. 13 Two-Degrees-of-Freedom System

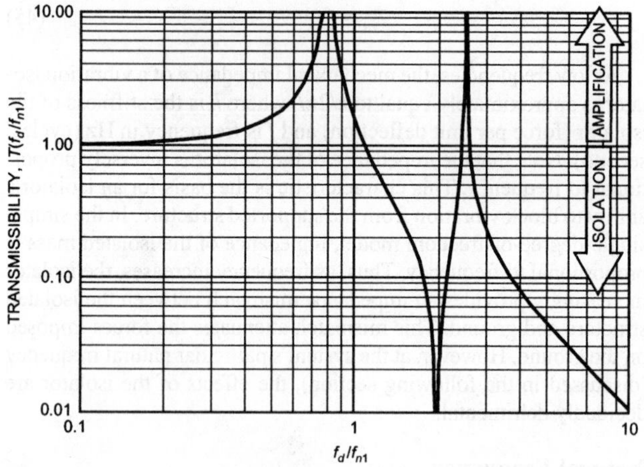

Fig. 14 Transmissibility T as Function of f_d/f_{n1} with $k_2/k_1 = 2$ and $M_2/M_1 = 0.5$

The implication of Equation (50) relative to Equation (48) is that a nonrigid foundation can severely alter the effectiveness of the isolation system. For a floor structure with twice the stiffness of the isolator, and a floor effective mass half that of the isolated equipment, transmissibility is as shown in Figure 14. Comparing Figure 14 to Figure 11 shows that the nonrigid floor has introduced a second resonance well above that of the isolation system assuming a rigid floor. Unless care is taken in the isolation system design, this secondary amplification can cause a serious sound or vibration problem.

As a general rule, it is advisable to design the system such that the static deflection of the isolator, under the applied equipment weight, is on the order of 10 times the incremental static deflection of the floor caused by the equipment mass (Figure 15). Above the rigid-foundation natural frequency f_{n1}, transmissibility is comparable to that of the simple single-degree-of-freedom model.

Other complicating factors exist in actual installations, which often depart from the two-degrees-of-freedom model. These include the effects of horizontal and rotational vibration. Given these complexities, it is often beneficial to collaborate with an experienced acoustical consultant or structural engineer when designing vibration isolation systems applied to flexible floor structures.

VIBRATION MEASUREMENT BASICS

Control of HVAC system sound and vibration are of equal importance, but measurement of vibration is often not necessary to determine sources or transmission paths of disturbing sound.

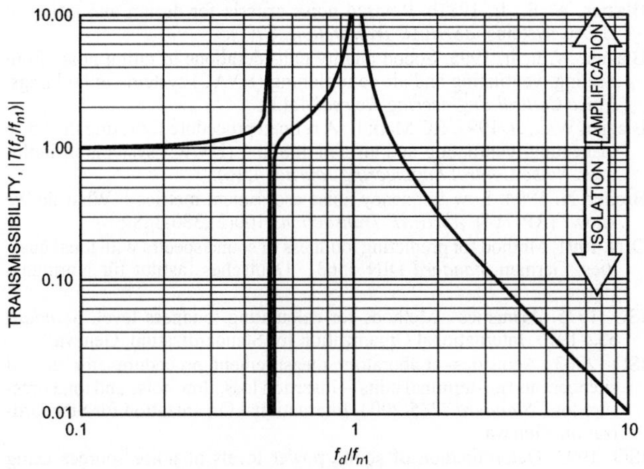

Fig. 15 Transmissibility T as Function of f_d/f_{n1} with $k_2/k_1 = 10$ and $M_2/M_1 = 40$

The typical vibrations measured are periodic motions of a surface. This surface displacement oscillates at one or more frequencies produced by mechanical equipment (e.g., rotating shafts or gears), thermal processes (e.g., combustion), or fluid-dynamic means (e.g., airflow through a duct or fan interactions with air).

A **transducer** detects displacement, velocity, or acceleration of a surface and converts the motion to electrical signals. Displacement transducers are often most appropriate for low-frequency measurements. For most HVAC applications, the transducer of choice is an **accelerometer**, which is rugged and compact. The accelerometer attaches to an amplifier, which connects to a meter, much like the microphone on a sound level meter. Readouts may be in acceleration level or decibels. The measurement also specifies whether the amplitude of the acceleration sinusoid is defined by its peak, peak-to-peak, or RMS level.

For steady-state (continuous) vibration, simple relationships exist between displacement, velocity, and acceleration; output can be specified as any of these, regardless of which transducer type is used. For a given frequency f,

$$a = (2\pi f)^2 d = (2\pi f)v \tag{51}$$

where a is acceleration, v is velocity, and d is displacement.

The simplest measure is the overall signal level as a function of time. This is analogous to the unfiltered sound pressure level. If a detailed frequency analysis is needed, there is a choice of filters similar to those available for sound measurements: octave band, 1/3 octave band, or 1/12 octave band. In addition, there are narrow-band analyzers that use the fast Fourier transform (FFT) to analyze and filter a signal. Though widely used, they should only be used by a specialist for accurate results.

The most important issues in vibration measurement include (1) choosing a transducer with a frequency range appropriate to the measurement, (2) properly mounting the transducer to ensure that the frequency response claimed is achieved, and (3) properly calibrating the vibration measurement system for the frequency range of interest.

For more thorough descriptions of specialized vibration measurement and analysis methods, designers should consult other sources [e.g., Harris (1991)].

SYMBOLS

a = acceleration, m/s^2
A = magnitude of physical property [Equation (1)]
A = surface area, m^2
c = speed of sound in air, 335 m/s
d = distance of measurement from nearest reflecting surface, or displacement, m
d_f = deflection of foundation
d_I = deflection of mounts
E = Young's modulus, N/m^2
F = force applied to structure, N
f = frequency, Hz
f_c = critical frequency, Hz
f_d = disturbing frequency, Hz
f_n = system natural frequency, Hz
f_r = rotation speed of fan blades, rev/s
h = thickness of outer panel of partition, mm
I = sound intensity, dB
I_{ave} = time-averaged sound intensity
k = stiffness of vibration isolator, N/m
L = level of magnitude of sound or vibration
L_{eq} = equivalent continuous sound pressure level
L_I = level of sound intensity
L_p = sound pressure level, dB
L_w = sound power level
M = mass of equipment supported by isolator, kg
M_1 = mass of equipment before additional mass added, kg
M_2 = mass of equipment after additional mass added, kg
N = number of fan blades
p = acoustic pressure
Q = directivity factor, dimensionless
r = distance between site of measurement and nondirectional sound source, m
R = room constant
Re = real part of complex quantity
S = surface area, m^2
t or T = time, s
T = system transmissibility
T_{60} = reverberation time
v = velocity
v_b = velocity of flow over fan blade, m/s
v_0 = free stream velocity of flow into fan, m/s
V = volume of room, m^3
w = sound power of source, W
W = total sound power
W_M = output power
W_0 = input power
W_{SG} = power of self-noise
w_s = surface mass of panel, kg/m^2
x = location of measurement of pressure p, Equation (18)
z_a = acoustic impedance, kg/(m^2·s) or N·s/m^3
Z_f = impedance of foundation where isolator attached, (N·s)/m
Z_I = isolator impedance, (N·s)/m
Z_m = mechanical impedance of structure, (N·s)/m

Greek

α = absorption coefficient
$\bar{\alpha}$ = average absorption coefficient of room surface at given frequency
δ_{st} = isolator static deflection, mm
θ = direction
λ = wavelength, m
ρ = density, kg/m^3

Subscripts

0 = maximum amplitude
abs = absorbed
ave = average
i = value for *i*th source
inc = incident
ref = reference magnitude of physical property [Equation (1)]
w = sound power

REFERENCES

AMCA. 2005. Reverberant room method for sound testing of fans. *Standard* 300-05. Air Movement and Control Association International, Inc., Arlington Heights, IL.

AMCA. 2006. Methods for calculating fan sound ratings from laboratory test data. *Standard* 301-06. Air Movement and Control Association International, Inc., Arlington Heights, IL.

AMCA. 2005. Certified ratings program—Product rating manual for fan sound performance. *Standard* 311-05. Air Movement and Control Association International, Inc., Arlington Heights, IL.

AMCA. 1997. Laboratory method of testing to determine the sound power in a duct. *Standard* 330-97 (ASHRAE *Standard* 68-1997). Air Movement and Control Association International, Inc., Arlington Heights, IL.

AMCA. 1979. Application of sound power level ratings for fans. *Publication* 303-79. Air Movement and Control Association International, Inc., Arlington Heights, IL.

ANSI. 2006. Specification for sound level meters. *Standard* S1.4-1983 (R2006). American National Standards Institute, New York.

ANSI. 2006. Preferred frequencies, frequency levels, and band numbers for acoustical measurements. *Standard* S1.6-1984 (R2006). American National Standards Institute, New York.

ANSI. 2004. Specifications for octave-band and fractional octave-band analog and digital filters. *Standard* S1.11-2004. American National Standards Institute, New York.

ANSI. 2007. Procedure for the computation of loudness of steady sound. *Standard* S3.4-2007. American National Standards Institute, New York.

ANSI. 1999. Criteria for evaluating room noise. *Standard* S12.2-1995 (R1999). American National Standards Institute, New York.

ANSI. 2007. Engineering method for determination of sound power level of noise sources using sound intensity. *Standard* S12.12-1992 (R2007). American National Standards Institute, New York.

ANSI. 2007. Determination of sound power levels of noise sources using sound pressure—Precision methods for reverberation rooms. *Standard* S12.51-2002 (R2007). American National Standards Institute, New York.

ANSI. 2006. Determination of sound power levels of noise sources using sound pressure—Precision methods for anechoic and hemi-anechoic rooms. *Standard* S12.55-2006. American National Standards Institute, New York.

ANSI. 2002. Acoustical performance criteria, sound requirements, and guidelines for schools. *Standard* 12.60-2002. American National Standards Institute, New York.

ARI. 1998. Air terminals. *Standard* 880-98. Air-Conditioning and Refrigeration Institute, Arlington, VA.

ARI. 1998. Procedure for estimating occupied space sound levels in the application of air terminals and air outlets. *Standard* 885-98 (addendum 2002). Air-Conditioning and Refrigeration Institute, Arlington, VA.

ASHRAE. 2007. Ventilation for acceptable indoor air quality. *Standard* 62.1-2007.

ASHRAE. 2007. Ventilation and acceptable indoor air quality in low-rise residential buildings. *Standard* 62.2-2007.

ASHRAE. 1997. Laboratory method of testing to determine the sound power in a duct. *Standard* 68-1997 (AMCA *Standard* 330-92).

ASHRAE. 2008. Methods of testing air terminal units. ANSI/ASHRAE *Standard* 130.

ASTM. 2004. Test method for laboratory measurement of airborne sound transmission loss of building partitions and elements. *Standard* E90-04. American Society for Testing and Materials, West Conshohocken, PA.

ASTM. 2004. Classification for rating sound insulation. *Standard* E413-04. American Society for Testing and Materials, West Conshohocken, PA.

ASTM. 2006. Test method for measuring acoustical and airflow performance of duct liner materials and prefabricated silencers. *Standard* E477-06a. American Society for Testing and Materials, West Conshohocken, PA.

ASTM. 2002. Test method for evaluating masking sound in open offices using A-weighted and one-third octave band sound pressure levels. *Standard* E1573-02. American Society for Testing and Materials, West Conshohocken, PA.

ASTM. 2006. Test method for measurement of sound in residential spaces. *Standard* E1574-98 (2006). American Society for Testing and Materials, West Conshohocken, PA.

ASTM. 2008. Test method for sound absorption and sound absorption coefficients by the reverberation room method. *Standard* C423-08. American Society for Testing and Materials, West Conshohocken, PA.

ASTM. 2008. Terminology relating to building and environmental acoustics. *Standard* C634-08. American Society for Testing and Materials, West Conshohocken, PA.

Beranek, L.L. 1957. Revised criteria for noise in buildings. *Noise Control* 1:19.

Beranek, L.L. 1989. Balanced noise criterion (NCB) curves. *Journal of the Acoustic Society of America* (86):650-654.

Blazier, W.E., Jr. 1981a. Revised noise criteria for application in the acoustical design and rating of HVAC systems. *Noise Control Engineering Journal* 16(2):64-73.

Blazier, W. E., Jr. 1981b. Revised noise criteria for design and rating of HVAC systems. *ASHRAE Transactions* 87(1).

Blazier, W.E., Jr. 1995. Sound quality considerations in rating noise from heating, ventilating and air-conditioning (HVAC) systems in buildings. *Noise Control Engineering Journal* 43(3).

Blazier, W.E., Jr. 1997. RC Mark II: A refined procedure for rating the noise of heating, ventilating and air-conditioning (HVAC) systems in buildings. *Noise Control Engineering Journal* 45(6).

Broner, N. 1994. Low-frequency noise assessment metrics—What do we know? (RP-714). *ASHRAE Transactions* 100(2):380-388.

DIN. 1991. Method for predicting loudness of sound spectra with tonal qualities. German *Standard* DIN 45631. Deutsches Institut für Normung, Berlin.

ISO. 1975. Acoustics—Methods for calculating loudness level. *Standard* 532-1975. International Organization for Standardization, Geneva.

ISO. 2003. Acoustics—Laboratory measurement procedures for ducted silencers and air-terminal units—Insertion loss, flow noise and total pressure loss. *Standard* 7235-2003. International Organization for Standardization, Geneva.

ISO. 1993. Determination of sound power levels of noise sources using sound intensity—Part 1: Measurements at discrete points. *Standard* 9614-1. International Organization for Standardization, Geneva.

ISO. 1996. Acoustics—Determination of sound power levels of noise sources using sound intensity—Part 2: Measurement by scanning. *Standard* 9614-2. International Organization for Standardization, Geneva.

ISO. 2002. Acoustics—Determination of sound power levels of noise sources using sound intensity—Part 3: Precision method for measurement by scanning. *Standard* 9614-3. International Organization for Standardization, Geneva.

Persson-Waye, K., R. Rylander, S. Benton, and H.G. Leventhall. 1997. Effects on performance and work quality due to low-frequency ventilation noise. *Journal of Sound and Vibration* 205(4):467-474.

Pollack, I. 1952. The loudness of bands of noise. *Journal of the Acoustical Society of America* 24(9):533.

Robinson, D.W. and R.S. Dadson. 1956. A redetermination of the equal loudness relations for pure tones. *British Journal of Applied Physics* 7(5):166.

Schultz, T.J. 1985. Relationship between sound power level and sound pressure level in dwellings and offices. *ASHRAE Transactions* 91(1):124-153.

Warnock, A.C.C. 1997. Sound transmission through ceilings from air terminal devices in the plenum. ASHRAE Research Project RP-755, *Final Report*.

Warnock, A.C.C. 1998a. Sound pressure level versus distance from sources in rooms. *ASHRAE Transactions* 104(1):643-649.

Warnock, A.C.C. 1998b. Transmission of sound from air terminal devices through ceiling systems. *ASHRAE Transactions* 104(1):650-657.

BIBLIOGRAPHY

AMCA. 2008. Application of sone ratings for non-ducted air moving devices. *Publication* 302-73 (R2008). Air Movement and Control Association International, Inc., Arlington Heights, IL.

Beranek, L.L. 1988. *Noise and vibration control*, rev. ed. Institute of Noise Control Engineering, Washington, D.C.

Beranek, L.L. 1986. *Acoustics*, rev. ed. American Institute of Physics, Acoustical Society of America, New York.

Beranek, L.L. and I.L. Ver. 2005. *Noise and vibration control engineering: Principles and applications*, 2nd ed. John Wiley & Sons, New York.

Bies, D.A. and C.H. Hansen. 1996. *Engineering noise control: Theory and practice*, 2nd ed. E&F Spon, New York.

Crede, C.E. 1951. *Vibration and shock isolation*. John Wiley & Sons, New York.

Ebbing, C.E. and W. Blazier, eds. 1998. *Application of manufacturers' sound data*. ASHRAE.

Harris, C.M. 1991. *Handbook of acoustical measurements and noise control*, 3rd ed. Acoustical Society of America, Melville, NY.

Harris, C.M. and C.E. Crede. 2001. *Shock and vibration handbook*, 5th ed. McGraw-Hill, New York.

Peterson, A.P.G. and E.E. Gross, Jr. 1974. *Handbook of noise measurement*. GenRad, Inc., Concord, MA.

Plunkett, R. 1958. Interaction between a vibratory machine and its foundation. *Noise Control* 4(1).

Schaffer, M.E. 1991. *A practical guide to noise and vibration control for HVAC systems*. ASHRAE.

CHAPTER 9

THERMAL COMFORT

A principal purpose of HVAC is to provide conditions for human thermal comfort, "that condition of mind that expresses satisfaction with the thermal environment" (ASHRAE *Standard* 55). This definition leaves open what is meant by "condition of mind" or "satisfaction," but it correctly emphasizes that judgment of comfort is a cognitive process involving many inputs influenced by physical, physiological, psychological, and other processes. This chapter summarizes the fundamentals of human thermoregulation and comfort in terms useful to the engineer for operating systems and designing for the comfort and health of building occupants.

The conscious mind appears to reach conclusions about thermal comfort and discomfort from direct temperature and moisture sensations from the skin, deep body temperatures, and the efforts necessary to regulate body temperatures (Berglund 1995; Gagge 1937; Hardy et al. 1971; Hensel 1973, 1981). In general, comfort occurs when body temperatures are held within narrow ranges, skin moisture is low, and the physiological effort of regulation is minimized.

Comfort also depends on behaviors that are initiated consciously or unconsciously and guided by thermal and moisture sensations to reduce discomfort. Some examples are altering clothing, altering activity, changing posture or location, changing the thermostat setting, opening a window, complaining, or leaving the space.

Surprisingly, although climates, living conditions, and cultures differ widely throughout the world, the temperature that people choose for comfort under similar conditions of clothing, activity, humidity, and air movement has been found to be very similar (Busch 1992; de Dear et al. 1991; Fanger 1972).

HUMAN THERMOREGULATION

Metabolic activities of the body result almost completely in heat that must be continuously dissipated and regulated to maintain normal body temperatures. Insufficient heat loss leads to overheating (**hyperthermia**), and excessive heat loss results in body cooling (**hypothermia**). Skin temperature greater than 45°C or less than 18°C causes pain (Hardy et al. 1952). Skin temperatures associated with comfort at sedentary activities are 33 to 34°C and decrease with increasing activity (Fanger 1967). In contrast, internal temperatures rise with activity. The temperature regulatory center in the brain is about 36.8°C at rest in comfort and increases to about 37.4°C when walking and 37.9°C when jogging. An internal temperature less than about 28°C can lead to serious cardiac arrhythmia and death, and a temperature greater than 46°C can cause irreversible brain damage. Therefore, careful regulation of body temperature is critical to comfort and health.

A resting adult produces about 100 W of heat. Because most of this is transferred to the environment through the skin, it is often convenient to characterize metabolic activity in terms of heat production per unit area of skin. For a resting person, this is about 58 W/m^2 and is called 1 **met**. This is based on the average male European, with a skin surface area of about 1.8 m^2. For comparison, female Europeans have an average surface area of 1.6 m^2. Systematic differences in this parameter may occur between ethnic and geographical groups. Higher metabolic rates are often described in terms of the resting rate. Thus, a person working at metabolic rate five times the resting rate would have a metabolic rate of 5 met.

The **hypothalamus**, located in the brain, is the central control organ for body temperature. It has hot and cold temperature sensors and is bathed by arterial blood. Because the recirculation rate of blood is rapid and returning blood is mixed together in the heart before returning to the body, arterial blood is indicative of the average internal body temperature. The hypothalamus also receives thermal information from temperature sensors in the skin and perhaps other locations as well (e.g., spinal cord, gut), as summarized by Hensel (1981).

The hypothalamus controls various physiological processes to regulate body temperature. Its control behavior is primarily proportional to deviations from set-point temperatures with some integral and derivative response aspects. The most important and often-used physiological process is regulating blood flow to the skin: when internal temperatures rise above a set point, more blood is directed to the skin. This **vasodilation** of skin blood vessels can increase skin blood flow by 15 times [from 1.7 mL/(s·m^2) at resting comfort to 25 mL/(s·m^2)] in extreme heat to carry internal heat to the skin for transfer to the environment. When body temperatures fall below the set point, skin blood flow is reduced (**vasoconstricted**) to conserve heat. The effect of maximum vasoconstriction is equivalent to the insulating effect of a heavy sweater. At temperatures less than the set point, muscle tension increases to generate additional heat; where muscle groups are opposed, this may increase to visible shivering, which can increase resting heat production to 4.5 met.

At elevated internal temperatures, sweating occurs. This defense mechanism is a powerful way to cool the skin and increase heat loss from the core. The sweating function of the skin and its control is more advanced in humans than in other animals and is increasingly necessary for comfort at metabolic rates above resting level (Fanger 1967). Sweat glands pump perspiration onto the skin surface for evaporation. If conditions are good for evaporation, the skin can remain relatively dry even at high sweat rates with little perception of sweating. At skin conditions less favorable for evaporation, the sweat must spread on the skin around the sweat gland until the sweat-covered area is sufficient to evaporate the sweat coming to the surface. The fraction of the skin that is covered with water to account for the observed total evaporation rate is termed **skin wettedness** (Gagge 1937).

Humans are quite good at sensing skin moisture from perspiration (Berglund 1994; Berglund and Cunningham 1986), and skin moisture correlates well with warm discomfort and unpleasantness (Winslow et al. 1937). It is rare for a sedentary or slightly active person to be comfortable with a skin wettedness greater than 25%. In addition to the perception of skin moisture, skin wettedness

The preparation of this chapter is assigned to TC 2.1, Physiology and Human Environment.

increases the friction between skin and fabrics, making clothing feel less pleasant and fabrics feel more coarse (Gwosdow et al. 1986). This also occurs with architectural materials and surfaces, particularly smooth, nonhygroscopic surfaces.

With repeated intermittent heat exposure, the set point for the onset of sweating decreases and the proportional gain or temperature sensitivity of the sweating system increases (Gonzalez et al. 1978; Hensel 1981). However, under long-term exposure to hot conditions, the set point increases, perhaps to reduce the physiological effort of sweating. Perspiration as secreted has a lower salt concentration than interstitial body fluid or blood plasma. After prolonged heat exposure, sweat glands further reduce the salt concentration of sweat to conserve salt.

At the surface, the water in sweat evaporates while the dissolved salt and other constituents remain and accumulate. Because salt lowers the vapor pressure of water and thereby impedes its evaporation, the accumulating salt results in increased skin wettedness. Some of the relief and pleasure of washing after a warm day is related to the restoration of a hypotonic sweat film and decreased skin wettedness. Other adaptations to heat are increased blood flow and sweating in peripheral regions where heat transfer is better. Such adaptations are examples of **integral control**.

Role of Thermoregulatory Effort in Comfort. Chatonnet and Cabanac (1965) compared the sensation of placing a subject's hand in relatively hot or cold water (30 to 38°C) for 30 s with the subject at different thermal states. When the person was overheated (hyperthermic), the cold water was pleasant and the hot water was very unpleasant, but when the subject was cold (hypothermic), the hand felt pleasant in hot water and unpleasant in cold water. Kuno (1995) describes similar observations during transient whole-body exposures to hot and cold environment. When a subject is in a state of thermal discomfort, any move away from the thermal stress of the uncomfortable environment is perceived as pleasant during the transition.

ENERGY BALANCE

Figure 1 shows the thermal interaction of the human body with its environment. The total metabolic rate M within the body is the metabolic rate required for the person's activity M_{act} plus the metabolic level required for shivering M_{shiv} (should shivering occur). A portion of the body's energy production may be expended as external work W; the net heat production $M - W$ is transferred to the environment through the skin surface (q_{sk}) and respiratory tract (q_{res}) with any surplus or deficit stored (S), causing the body's temperature to rise or fall.

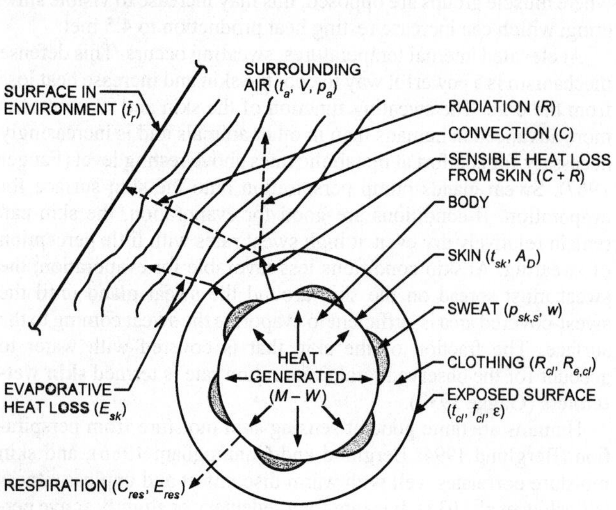

Fig. 1 Thermal Interaction of Human Body and Environment

$$M - W = q_{sk} + q_{res} + S$$
$$= (C + R + E_{sk}) + (C_{res} + E_{res}) + (S_{sk} + S_{cr}) \quad (1)$$

where

M = rate of metabolic heat production, W/m²
W = rate of mechanical work accomplished, W/m²
q_{sk} = total rate of heat loss from skin, W/m²
q_{res} = total rate of heat loss through respiration, W/m²
$C + R$ = sensible heat loss from skin, W/m²
E_{sk} = total rate of evaporative heat loss from skin, W/m²
C_{res} = rate of convective heat loss from respiration, W/m²
E_{res} = rate of evaporative heat loss from respiration, W/m²
S_{sk} = rate of heat storage in skin compartment, W/m²
S_{cr} = rate of heat storage in core compartment, W/m²

Heat dissipates from the body to the immediate surroundings by several modes of heat exchange: sensible heat flow $C + R$ from the skin; latent heat flow from sweat evaporation E_{rsw} and from evaporation of moisture diffused through the skin E_{dif}; sensible heat flow during respiration C_{res}; and latent heat flow from evaporation of moisture during respiration E_{res}. Sensible heat flow from the skin may be a complex mixture of conduction, convection, and radiation for a clothed person; however, it is equal to the sum of the convection C and radiation R heat transfer at the outer clothing surface (or exposed skin).

Sensible and latent heat losses from the skin are typically expressed in terms of environmental factors, skin temperature t_{sk}, and skin wettedness w. Factors also account for the thermal insulation and moisture permeability of clothing. The independent environmental variables can be summarized as air temperature t_a, mean radiant temperature $\bar{t}_r$, relative air velocity V, and ambient water vapor pressure p_a. The independent personal variables that influence thermal comfort are activity and clothing.

The rate of heat storage in the body equals the rate of increase in internal energy. The body can be considered as two thermal compartments: the skin and the core (see the section on Two-Node Model under Prediction of Thermal Comfort). The storage rate can be written separately for each compartment in terms of thermal capacity and time rate of change of temperature in each compartment:

$$S_{cr} = \frac{(1 - \alpha_{sk}) m c_{p,b}}{A_D} \times \frac{dt_{cr}}{d\theta} \quad (2)$$

$$S_{sk} = \frac{\alpha_{sk} m c_{p,b}}{A_D} \times \frac{dt_{sk}}{d\theta} \quad (3)$$

where

α_{sk} = fraction of body mass concentrated in skin compartment
m = body mass, kg
$c_{p,b}$ = specific heat capacity of body = 3490 J/(kg·K)
A_D = DuBois surface area, m²
t_{cr} = temperature of core compartment, °C
t_{sk} = temperature of skin compartment, °C
θ = time, s

The fractional skin mass α_{sk} depends on the rate $\dot{m}_{bl}$ of blood flowing to the skin surface.

THERMAL EXCHANGES WITH THE ENVIRONMENT

Fanger (1967, 1970), Gagge and Hardy (1967), Hardy (1949), and Rapp and Gagge (1967) give quantitative information on calculating heat exchange between people and the environment. This section summarizes the mathematical statements for various terms of heat exchange used in the heat balance equations (C, R, E_{sk}, C_{res}, E_{res}). Terms describing the heat exchanges associated with the thermoregulatory control mechanisms ($q_{cr,sk}$, M_{shiv}, E_{rsw}), values for the coefficients, and appropriate equations for M_{act} and A_D are presented in later sections.

Mathematical description of the energy balance of the human body combines rational and empirical approaches to describing thermal exchanges with the environment. Fundamental heat transfer theory is used to describe the various mechanisms of sensible and latent heat exchange, and empirical expressions are used to determine the values of coefficients describing these rates of heat exchange. Empirical equations are also used to describe the thermophysiological control mechanisms as a function of skin and core temperatures in the body.

Body Surface Area

The terms in Equation (1) have units of power per unit area and refer to the surface area of the nude body. The most useful measure of nude body surface area, originally proposed by DuBois and DuBois (1916), is described by

$$A_D = 0.202m^{0.425}l^{0.725} \tag{4}$$

where

A_D = DuBois surface area, m²
m = mass, kg
l = height, m

A correction factor $f_{cl} = A_{cl}/A_D$ must be applied to the heat transfer terms from the skin (C, R, and E_{sk}) to account for the actual surface area A_{cl} of the clothed body. Table 7 presents f_{cl} values for various clothing ensembles. For a 1.73 m tall, 70 kg man, $A_D = 1.8$ m². All terms in the basic heat balance equations are expressed per unit DuBois surface area.

Sensible Heat Loss from Skin

Sensible heat exchange from the skin must pass through clothing to the surrounding environment. These paths are treated in series and can be described in terms of heat transfer (1) from the skin surface, through the clothing insulation, to the outer clothing surface, and (2) from the outer clothing surface to the environment.

Both convective C and radiative R heat losses from the outer surface of a clothed body can be expressed in terms of a heat transfer coefficient and the difference between the mean temperature t_{cl} of the outer surface of the clothed body and the appropriate environmental temperature:

$$C = f_{cl}h_c(t_{cl} - t_a) \tag{5}$$

$$R = f_{cl}h_r(t_{cl} - \bar{t}_r) \tag{6}$$

where

h_c = convective heat transfer coefficient, W/(m²·K)
h_r = linear radiative heat transfer coefficient, W/(m²·K)
f_{cl} = clothing area factor A_{cl}/A_D, dimensionless

The coefficients h_c and h_r are both evaluated at the clothing surface. Equations (5) and (6) are commonly combined to describe the total sensible heat exchange by these two mechanisms in terms of an operative temperature t_o and a combined heat transfer coefficient h:

$$C + R = f_{cl}h(t_{cl} - t_o) \tag{7}$$

where

$$t_o = \frac{h_r\bar{t}_r + h_c t_a}{h_r + h_c} \tag{8}$$

$$h = h_r + h_c \tag{9}$$

Based on Equation (8), operative temperature t_o can be defined as the average of the mean radiant and ambient air temperatures, weighted by their respective heat transfer coefficients.

The actual transport of sensible heat through clothing involves conduction, convection, and radiation. It is usually most convenient to combine these into a single thermal resistance value R_{cl}, defined by

$$C + R = (t_{sk} - t_{cl})/R_{cl} \tag{10}$$

where R_{cl} is the thermal resistance of clothing in (m²·K)/W.

Because it is often inconvenient to include the clothing surface temperature in calculations, Equations (7) and (10) can be combined to eliminate t_{cl}:

$$C + R = \frac{t_{sk} - t_o}{R_{cl} + 1/(f_{cl}h)} \tag{11}$$

where t_o is defined in Equation (8).

Evaporative Heat Loss from Skin

Evaporative heat loss E_{sk} from skin depends on the amount of moisture on the skin and the difference between the water vapor pressure at the skin and in the ambient environment:

$$E_{sk} = \frac{w(p_{sk,s} - p_a)}{R_{e,cl} + 1/(f_{cl}h_e)} \tag{12}$$

where

w = skin wettedness, dimensionless
$p_{sk,s}$ = water vapor pressure at skin, normally assumed to be that of saturated water vapor at t_{sk}, kPa
p_a = water vapor pressure in ambient air, kPa
$R_{e,cl}$ = evaporative heat transfer resistance of clothing layer (analogous to R_{cl}), (m²·kPa)/W
h_e = evaporative heat transfer coefficient (analogous to h_c), W/(m²·kPa)

Procedures for calculating $R_{e,cl}$ and h_e are given in the section on Engineering Data and Measurements. Skin wettedness is the ratio of the actual evaporative heat loss to the maximum possible evaporative heat loss E_{max} with the same conditions and a completely wet skin ($w = 1$). Skin wettedness is important in determining evaporative heat loss. Maximum evaporative potential E_{max} occurs when $w = 1$.

Evaporative heat loss from the skin is a combination of the evaporation of sweat secreted because of thermoregulatory control mechanisms E_{rsw} and the natural diffusion of water through the skin E_{dif}:

$$E_{sk} = E_{rsw} + E_{dif} \tag{13}$$

Evaporative heat loss by regulatory sweating is directly proportional to the rate of regulatory sweat generation:

$$E_{rsw} = \dot{m}_{rsw}h_{fg} \tag{14}$$

where

h_{fg} = heat of vaporization of water = 2.43 × 10⁶ J/kg at 30°C
$\dot{m}_{rsw}$ = rate at which regulatory sweat is generated, kg/(s·m²)

The portion w_{rsw} of a body that must be wetted to evaporate the regulatory sweat is

$$w_{rsw} = E_{rsw}/E_{max} \tag{15}$$

With no regulatory sweating, skin wettedness caused by diffusion is approximately 0.06 for normal conditions. For large values of E_{max} or long exposures to low humidities, the value may drop to as low as

0.02, because dehydration of the outer skin layers alters its diffusive characteristics. With regulatory sweating, the 0.06 value applies only to the portion of skin not covered with sweat $(1 - w_{rsw})$; the diffusion evaporative heat loss is

$$E_{dif} = (1 - w_{rsw})0.06E_{max} \tag{16}$$

These equations can be solved for w, given the maximum evaporative potential E_{max} and the regulatory sweat generation E_{rsw}:

$$w = w_{rsw} + 0.06(1 - w_{rsw}) = 0.06 + 0.94E_{rsw}/E_{max} \tag{17}$$

Once skin wettedness is determined, evaporative heat loss from the skin is calculated from Equation (12), or by

$$E_{sk} = wE_{max} \tag{18}$$

To summarize, the following calculations determine w and E_{sk}:

E_{max}	Equation (12), with $w = 1.0$
E_{rsw}	Equation (14)
w	Equation (17)
E_{sk}	Equation (18) or (12)

Although evaporation from the skin E_{sk} as described in Equation (12) depends on w, the body does not directly regulate skin wettedness but, rather, regulates sweat rate $\dot{m}_{rsw}$ [Equation (14)]. Skin wettedness is then an indirect result of the relative activity of the sweat glands and the evaporative potential of the environment. Skin wettedness of 1.0 is the upper theoretical limit. If the aforementioned calculations yield a wettedness of more than 1.0, then Equation (14) is no longer valid because not all the sweat is evaporated. In this case, $E_{sk} = E_{max}$.

Skin wettedness is strongly correlated with warm discomfort and is also a good measure of thermal stress. Theoretically, skin wettedness can approach 1.0 while the body still maintains thermoregulatory control. In most situations, it is difficult to exceed 0.8 (Berglund and Gonzalez 1977). Azer (1982) recommends 0.5 as a practical upper limit for sustained activity for a healthy, acclimatized person.

Respiratory Losses

During respiration, the body loses both sensible and latent heat by convection and evaporation of heat and water vapor from the respiratory tract to the inhaled air. A significant amount of heat can be associated with respiration because air is inspired at ambient conditions and expired nearly saturated at a temperature only slightly cooler than t_{cr}.

The total heat and moisture losses through respiration are

$$q_{res} = C_{res} + E_{res} = \frac{\dot{m}_{res}(h_{ex} - h_a)}{A_D} \tag{19}$$

$$\dot{m}_{w,res} = \frac{\dot{m}_{res}(W_{ex} - W_a)}{A_D} \tag{20}$$

where

$\dot{m}_{res}$ = pulmonary ventilation rate, kg/s
h_{ex} = enthalpy of exhaled air, J/kg (dry air)
h_a = enthalpy of inspired (ambient) air, J/kg (dry air)
$\dot{m}_{w,res}$ = pulmonary water loss rate, kg/s
W_{ex} = humidity ratio of exhaled air, kg (water vapor)/kg (dry air)
W_a = humidity ratio of inspired (ambient) air, kg (water vapor)/kg (dry air)

Under normal circumstances, pulmonary ventilation rate is primarily a function of metabolic rate (Fanger 1970):

$$\dot{m}_{res} = K_{res}MA_D \tag{21}$$

where

M = metabolic rate, W/m^2
K_{res} = proportionality constant (1.43×10^{-6} kg/J)

For typical indoor environments (McCutchan and Taylor 1951), the exhaled temperature and humidity ratio are given in terms of ambient conditions:

$$t_{ex} = 32.6 + 0.066t_a + 32W_a \tag{22}$$

$$W_{ex} = 0.0277 + 0.000065t_a + 0.2W_a \tag{23}$$

where ambient t_a and exhaled t_{ex} air temperatures are in °C. For extreme conditions, such as outdoor winter environments, different relationships may be required (Holmer 1984).

The humidity ratio of ambient air can be expressed in terms of total or barometric pressure p_t and ambient water vapor pressure p_a:

$$W_a = \frac{0.622p_a}{p_t - p_a} \tag{24}$$

Respiratory heat loss is often expressed in terms of sensible C_{res} and latent E_{res} heat losses. Two approximations are commonly used to simplify Equations (22) and (23) for that purpose. First, because dry respiratory heat loss is relatively small compared to the other terms in the heat balance, an average value for t_{ex} is determined by evaluating Equation (22) at standard conditions of 20°C, 50% rh, sea level. Second, noting in Equation (23) that there is only a weak dependence on t_a, the second term in Equation (23) and the denominator in Equation (24) are evaluated at standard conditions. Using these approximations and substituting latent heat h_{fg} and specific heat of air $c_{p,a}$ at standard conditions, C_{res} and E_{res} can be determined by

$$C_{res} = 0.0014M(34 - t_a) \tag{25}$$

$$E_{res} = 0.0173M(5.87 - p_a) \tag{26}$$

where p_a is expressed in kPa and t_a is in °C.

Alternative Formulations

Equations (11) and (12) describe heat loss from skin for clothed people in terms of clothing parameters R_{cl}, $R_{e,cl}$, and f_{cl}; parameters h and h_e describe outer surface resistances. Other parameters and definitions are also used. Although these alternative parameters and definitions may be confusing, note that information presented in one form can be converted to another form. Table 1 presents common parameters and their qualitative descriptions. Table 2 presents equations showing their relationship to each other. Generally, parameters related to dry or evaporative heat flows are not independent because they both rely, in part, on the same physical processes. The **Lewis relation** describes the relationship between convective heat transfer and mass transfer coefficients for a surface [see Equation (39) in Chapter 6]. The Lewis relation can be used to relate convective and evaporative heat transfer coefficients defined in Equations (5) and (12) according to

$$\text{LR} = h_e/h_c \tag{27}$$

where LR is the **Lewis ratio** and, at typical indoor conditions, equals approximately 16.5 K/kPa. The Lewis relation applies to surface convection coefficients. Heat transfer coefficients that include the effects of insulation layers and/or radiation are still coupled, but the relationship may deviate significantly from that for a surface. The i terms in Tables 1 and 2 describe how the actual ratios of these

Table 1 Parameters Used to Describe Clothing

Sensible Heat Flow

R_{cl} = intrinsic clothing insulation: thermal resistance of a uniform layer of insulation covering entire body that has same effect on sensible heat flow as actual clothing.

R_t = total insulation: total equivalent uniform thermal resistance between body and environment: clothing and boundary resistance.

R_{cle} = effective clothing insulation: increased body insulation due to clothing as compared to nude state.

R_a = boundary insulation: thermal resistance at skin boundary for nude body.

$R_{a,cl}$ = outer boundary insulation: thermal resistance at outer boundary (skin or clothing).

R_{te} = total effective insulation.

h' = overall sensible heat transfer coefficient: overall equivalent uniform conductance between body (including clothing) and environment.

h'_{cl} = clothing conductance: thermal conductance of uniform layer of insulation covering entire body that has same effect on sensible heat flow as actual clothing.

F_{cle} = effective clothing thermal efficiency: ratio of actual sensible heat loss to that of nude body at same conditions.

F_{cl} = intrinsic clothing thermal efficiency: ratio of actual sensible heat loss to that of nude body at same conditions including adjustment for increase in surface area due to clothing.

Evaporative Heat Flow

$R_{e,cl}$ = evaporative heat transfer resistance of clothing: impedance to transport of water vapor of uniform layer of insulation covering entire body that has same effect on evaporative heat flow as actual clothing.

$R_{e,t}$ = total evaporative resistance: total equivalent uniform impedance to transport of water vapor from skin to environment.

F_{pcl} = permeation efficiency: ratio of actual evaporative heat loss to that of nude body at same conditions, including adjustment for increase in surface area due to clothing.

Parameters Relating Sensible and Evaporative Heat Flows

i_{cl} = clothing vapor permeation efficiency: ratio of actual evaporative heat flow capability through clothing to sensible heat flow capability as compared to Lewis ratio.

i_m = total vapor permeation efficiency: ratio of actual evaporative heat flow capability between skin and environment to sensible heat flow capability as compared to Lewis ratio.

i_a = air layer vapor permeation efficiency: ratio of actual evaporative heat flow capability through outer air layer to sensible heat flow capability as compared to Lewis ratio.

Table 2 Relationships Between Clothing Parameters

Sensible Heat Flow

$$R_t = R_{cl} + 1/(hf_{cl}) = R_{cl} + R_a/f_{cl}$$
$$R_{te} = R_{cle} + 1/h = R_{cle} + R_a$$
$$h'_{cl} = 1/R_{cl}$$
$$h' = 1/R_t$$
$$h = 1/R_a$$
$$R_{a,cl} = R_a/f_{cl}$$
$$F_{cl} = h'/(hf_{cl}) = 1/(1 + f_{cl}hR_{cl})$$
$$F_{cle} = h'/h = f_{cl}/(1 + f_{cl}hR_{cl}) = f_{cl}F_{cl}$$

Evaporative Heat Flow

$$R_{e,t} = R_{e,cl} + 1/(h_e f_{cl}) = R_{e,cl} + R_{e,a}/f_{cl}$$
$$h_e = 1/R_{e,a}$$
$$h'_{e,cl} = 1/R_{e,cl}$$
$$h'_e = 1/R_{e,t} = f_{cl}F_{pcl}h_e$$
$$F_{pcl} = 1/(1 + f_{cl}h_e R_{e,cl})$$

Parameters Relating Sensible and Evaporative Heat Flows

$$i_{cl}\mathrm{LR} = h'_{e,cl}/h'_{cl} = R_{cl}/R_{e,cl}$$
$$i_m\mathrm{LR} = h'_e/h' = R_t/R_{e,t}$$
$$i_m = (R_{cl} + R_{a,cl})/[(R_{cl}/i_{cl}) + (R_{a,cl}/i_a)]$$
$$i_a\mathrm{LR} = h_e/h$$
$$i_a = h_c/(h_c + h_r)$$

Table 3 Skin Heat Loss Equations

Sensible Heat Loss

$$C + R = (t_{sk} - t_o)/[R_{cl} + 1/(f_{cl}h)]$$
$$C + R = (t_{sk} - t_o)/R_t$$
$$C + R = F_{cle}h(t_{sk} - t_o)$$
$$C + R = F_{cl}f_{cl}h(t_{sk} - t_o)$$
$$C + R = h'(t_{sk} - t_o)$$

Evaporative Heat Loss

$$E_{sk} = w(p_{sk,s} - p_a)/[R_{e,cl} + 1/(f_{cl}h_e)]$$
$$E_{sk} = w(p_{sk,s} - p_a)/R_{e,t}$$
$$E_{sk} = wF_{pcl}f_{cl}h_e(p_{sk,s} - p_a)$$
$$E_{sk} = h'_e w(p_{sk,s} - p_a)$$
$$E_{sk} = h'wi_m\mathrm{LR}(p_{sk,s} - p_a)$$

parameters deviate from the ideal Lewis ratio (Oohori et al. 1984; Woodcock 1962).

Depending on the combination of parameters used, heat transfer from the skin can be calculated using several different formulations (see Tables 2 and 3). If the parameters are used correctly, the end result will be the same regardless of the formulation used.

Total Skin Heat Loss

Total skin heat loss (sensible heat plus evaporative heat) can be calculated from any combination of the equations presented in Table 3. Total skin heat loss is used as a measure of the thermal environment; two combinations of parameters that yield the same total heat loss for a given set of body conditions (t_{sk} and w) are considered to be approximately equivalent. The fully expanded skin heat loss equation, showing each parameter that must be known or specified, is as follows:

$$q_{sk} = \frac{t_{sk} - t_o}{R_{cl} + R_{a,cl}} + \frac{w(p_{sk,s} - p_a)}{R_{e,cl} + 1/(\mathrm{LR}h_c f_{cl})} \quad (28)$$

where t_o is the operative temperature and represents the temperature of a uniform environment ($t_a - \bar{t}_r$) that transfers dry heat at the same rate as in the actual environment [$t_o = (\bar{t}_r h_r + t_a h_c)/(h_c + h_r)$]. After rearranging, Equation (28) becomes

$$q_{sk} = F_{cl}f_{cl}h(t_{sk} - t_o) + w\mathrm{LR}F_{pcl}h_c(p_{sk,s} - p_a) \quad (29)$$

This equation allows the tradeoff between any two or more parameters to be evaluated under given conditions. If the tradeoff between two specific variables (e.g., between operative temperature and humidity) is to be examined, then a simplified form of the equation suffices (Fobelets and Gagge 1988):

$$q_{sk} = h'[(t_{sk} + wi_m\mathrm{LR}p_{sk,s}) - (t_o + wi_m\mathrm{LR}p_a)] \quad (30)$$

Equation (30) can be used to define a combined temperature t_{com}, which reflects the combined effect of operative temperature and humidity for an actual environment:

$$t_{com} + wi_m\mathrm{LR}p_{t_{com}} - t_o + wi_m\mathrm{LR}p_a$$

or

$$t_{com} = t_o + wi_m\mathrm{LR}p_a - wi_m\mathrm{LR}p_{t_{com}} \quad (31)$$

where $p_{t_{com}}$ is a vapor pressure related in some fixed way to t_{com} and is analogous to $p_{wb,s}$ for t_{wb}. The term $wi_m\mathrm{LR}p_{t_{com}}$ is constant to the extent that i_m is constant, and any combination of t_o and p_a that gives the same t_{com} results in the same total heat loss.

Two important environmental indices, the humid operative temperature t_{oh} and the effective temperature ET*, can be represented in terms of Equation (31). The humid operative temperature is that temperature which at 100% rh yields the same total heat loss as for the actual environment:

$$t_{oh} = t_o + wi_m LR(p_a - p_{oh,s}) \quad (32)$$

where $p_{oh,s}$ is saturated vapor pressure, in kPa, at t_{oh}.

The effective temperature is the temperature at 50% rh that yields the same total heat loss from the skin as for the actual environment:

$$ET^* = t_o + wi_m LR(p_a - 0.5p_{ET^*,s}) \quad (33)$$

where $p_{ET^*,s}$ is saturated vapor pressure, in kPa, at ET*.

The psychrometric chart in Figure 2 shows a constant total heat loss line and the relationship between these indices. This line represents only one specific skin wettedness and permeation efficiency index. The relationship between indices depends on these two parameters (see the section on Environmental Indices).

ENGINEERING DATA AND MEASUREMENTS

Applying basic equations to practical problems of the thermal environment requires quantitative estimates of the body's surface area, metabolic requirements for a given activity and the mechanical efficiency for the work accomplished, evaluation of heat transfer coefficients h_r and h_c, and the general nature of clothing insulation used. This section provides the necessary data and describes how to measure the parameters of the heat balance equation.

Metabolic Rate and Mechanical Efficiency

Maximum Capacity. In choosing optimal conditions for comfort and health, the rate of work done during routine physical activities must be known, because metabolic power increases in proportion to exercise intensity. Metabolic rate varies over a wide range, depending on the activity, person, and conditions under which the activity is performed. Table 4 lists typical metabolic rates for an average adult (A_D = 1.8 m²) for activities performed continuously. The highest power a person can maintain for any continuous period is approximately 50% of the maximal capacity to use oxygen (maximum energy capacity).

A unit used to express the metabolic rate per unit DuBois area is the **met**, defined as the metabolic rate of a sedentary person (seated, quiet): 1 met = 58.1 W/m² = 50 kcal/(h·m²). A normal, healthy man at age 20 has a maximum capacity of approximately M_{act} = 12 met, which drops to 7 met at age 70. Maximum rates for women are about 30% lower. Long-distance runners and trained athletes have maximum rates as high as 20 met. An average 35-year-old who does not exercise has a maximum rate of about 10 met, and activities with M_{act} > 5 met are likely to prove exhausting.

Intermittent Activity. Often, people's activity consists of a mixture of activities or a combination of work/rest periods. A weighted average metabolic rate is generally satisfactory, provided that activities alternate frequently (several times per hour). For example, a person whose activities consist of typing 50% of the time, filing while seated 25% of the time, and walking about 25%

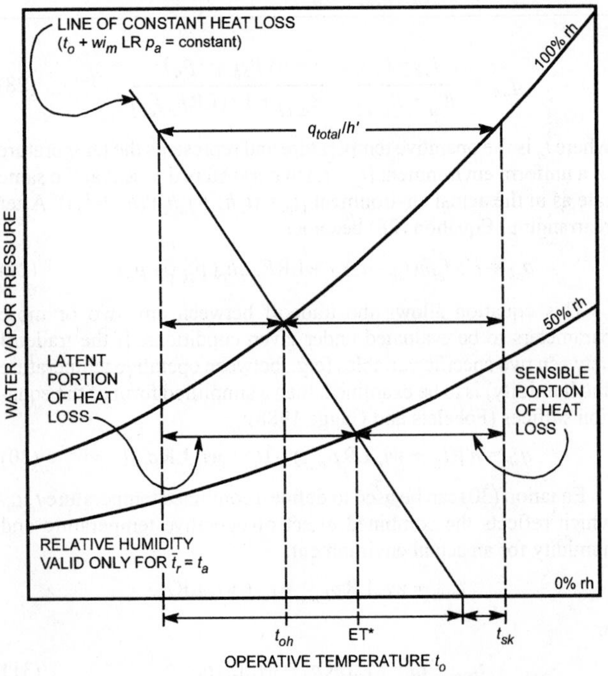

Fig. 2 Constant Skin Heat Loss Line and Its Relationship to t_{oh} and ET*

Table 4 Typical Metabolic Heat Generation for Various Activities

	W/m²	met*
Resting		
Sleeping	40	0.7
Reclining	45	0.8
Seated, quiet	60	1.0
Standing, relaxed	70	1.2
Walking (on level surface)		
3.2 km/h (0.9 m/s)	115	2.0
4.3 km/h (1.2 m/s)	150	2.6
6.4 km/h (1.8 m/s)	220	3.8
Office Activities		
Reading, seated	55	1.0
Writing	60	1.0
Typing	65	1.1
Filing, seated	70	1.2
Filing, standing	80	1.4
Walking about	100	1.7
Lifting/packing	120	2.1
Driving/Flying		
Car	60 to 115	1.0 to 2.0
Aircraft, routine	70	1.2
Aircraft, instrument landing	105	1.8
Aircraft, combat	140	2.4
Heavy vehicle	185	3.2
Miscellaneous Occupational Activities		
Cooking	95 to 115	1.6 to 2.0
Housecleaning	115 to 200	2.0 to 3.4
Seated, heavy limb movement	130	2.2
Machine work		
sawing (table saw)	105	1.8
light (electrical industry)	115 to 140	2.0 to 2.4
heavy	235	4.0
Handling 50 kg bags	235	4.0
Pick and shovel work	235 to 280	4.0 to 4.8
Miscellaneous Leisure Activities		
Dancing, social	140 to 255	2.4 to 4.4
Calisthenics/exercise	175 to 235	3.0 to 4.0
Tennis, singles	210 to 270	3.6 to 4.0
Basketball	290 to 440	5.0 to 7.6
Wrestling, competitive	410 to 505	7.0 to 8.7

Sources: Compiled from various sources. For additional information, see Buskirk (1960), Passmore and Durnin (1967), and Webb (1964).
*1 met = 58.1 W/m²

of the time would have an average metabolic rate of 0.50 × 65 + 0.25 × 70 + 0.25 × 100 = 75 W/m² (see Table 4).

Accuracy. Estimating metabolic rates is difficult. The values given in Table 4 indicate metabolic rates only for the specific activities listed. Some entries give a range and some a single value, depending on the data source. The level of accuracy depends on the value of M_{act} and how well the activity can be defined. For well-defined activities with M_{act} < 1.5 met (e.g., reading), Table 4 is sufficiently accurate for most engineering purposes. For values of M_{act} > 3, where a task is poorly defined or where there are various ways of performing a task (e.g., heavy machine work), the values may be in error by as much as ±50% for a given application. Engineering calculations should thus allow for potential variations.

Measurement. When metabolic rates must be determined more accurately than is possible with tabulated data, physiological measurements with human subjects may be necessary. The rate of metabolic heat produced by the body is most accurately measured by the rate of respiratory oxygen consumption and carbon dioxide production. An empirical equation for metabolic rate is given by Nishi (1981):

$$M = \frac{21(0.23RQ + 0.77)Q_{O_2}}{A_D} \tag{34}$$

where

M = metabolic rate, W/m²
RQ = respiratory quotient; molar ratio of Q_{CO_2} exhaled to Q_{O_2} inhaled, dimensionless
Q_{O_2} = volumetric rate of oxygen consumption at conditions (STPD) of 0°C, 101.325 kPa, mL/s

The exact value of the respiratory quotient RQ depends on a person's activity, diet, and physical condition. It can be determined by measuring both carbon dioxide and oxygen in the respiratory airflows, or it can be estimated with reasonable accuracy. A good estimate for the average adult is RQ = 0.83 for light or sedentary activities (M < 1.5 met), increasing proportionately to RQ = 1.0 for extremely heavy exertion (M = 5.0 met). Estimating RQ is generally sufficient for all except precision laboratory measurements because it does not strongly affect the value of the metabolic rate: a 10% error in estimating RQ results in an error of less than 3% in the metabolic rate.

A second, much less accurate, method of estimating metabolic rate physiologically is to measure the heart rate. Table 5 shows the relationship between heart rate and oxygen consumption at different levels of physical exertion for a typical person. Once oxygen consumption is estimated from heart rate information, Equation (34) can be used to estimate the metabolic rate. Other factors that affect heart rate include physical condition, heat, emotional factors, and muscles used. Astrand and Rodahl (1977) show that heart rate is only a very approximate measure of metabolic rate and should not be the only source of information where accuracy is required.

Mechanical Efficiency. In the heat balance equation, the rate W of work accomplished must be in the same units as metabolism M

Table 5 Heart Rate and Oxygen Consumption at Different Activity Levels

Level of Exertion	Heart Rate, bpm	Oxygen Consumed, mL/s
Light work	<90	<8
Moderate work	90 to 110	8 to 16
Heavy work	110 to 130	16 to 24
Very heavy work	130 to 150	24 to 32
Extremely heavy work	150 to 170	>32

Source: Astrand and Rodahl (1977).

and expressed in terms of A_D in W/m². The mechanical work done by the muscles for a given task is often expressed in terms of the body's mechanical efficiency $\mu = W/M$. It is unusual for μ to be more than 0.05 to 0.10; for most activities, it is close to zero. The maximum value under optimal conditions (e.g., bicycle ergometer) is μ = 0.20 to 0.24 (Nishi 1981). It is common to assume that mechanical work is zero for several reasons: (1) mechanical work produced is small compared to metabolic rate, especially for office activities; (2) estimates for metabolic rates are often inaccurate; and (3) this assumption gives a more conservative estimate when designing air-conditioning equipment for upper comfort and health limits. More accurate calculation of heat generation may require estimating mechanical work produced for activities where it is significant (walking on a grade, climbing a ladder, bicycling, lifting, etc.). In some cases, it is possible to either estimate or measure the mechanical work. For example, a 90 kg person walking up a 5% grade at 1.0 m/s would be lifting an 882 N (90 kg × 9.8 N/kg) weight over a height of 0.05 m every second, for a work rate of 44 (N·m)/s = 44 W. This rate of mechanical work would then be subtracted from M to determine the net heat generated.

Heat Transfer Coefficients

Values for the linearized radiative heat transfer coefficient, convective heat transfer coefficient, and evaporative heat transfer coefficient are required to solve the equations describing heat transfer from the body.

Radiative Heat Transfer Coefficient. The linearized radiative heat transfer coefficient can be calculated by

$$h_r = 4\varepsilon\sigma\frac{A_r}{A_D}\left(273.2 + \frac{t_{cl} + \bar{t}_r}{2}\right)^3 \tag{35}$$

where

h_r = radiative heat transfer coefficient, W/(m²·K)
ε = average emissivity of clothing or body surface, dimensionless
σ = Stefan-Boltzmann constant, 5.67 × 10^{-8} W/(m²·K⁴)
A_r = effective radiation area of body, m²

The ratio A_r/A_D is 0.70 for a sitting person and 0.73 for a standing person (Fanger 1967). Emissivity ε is close to unity (typically 0.95), unless special reflective materials are used or high-temperature sources are involved. It is not always possible to solve Equation (35) explicitly for h_r, because t_{cl} may also be unknown. Some form of iteration may be necessary if a precise solution is required. Fortunately, h_r is nearly constant for typical indoor temperatures, and a value of 4.7 W/(m²·K) suffices for most calculations. If emissivity is significantly less than unity, adjust the value by

$$h_r = 4.7\varepsilon \tag{36}$$

where ε represents the area-weighted average emissivity for the clothing/body surface.

Convective Heat Transfer Coefficient. Heat transfer by convection is usually caused by air movement within the living space or by body movements. Equations for estimating h_c under various conditions are presented in Table 6. Where two conditions apply (e.g., walking in moving air), a reasonable estimate can be obtained by taking the larger of the two values for h_c. Limits have been given to all equations. If no limits were given in the source, reasonable limits have been estimated. Be careful using these values for seated and reclining persons. The heat transfer coefficients may be accurate, but the effective heat transfer area may be substantially reduced through body contact with a padded chair or bed.

Quantitative values of h_c are important, not only in estimating convection loss, but in evaluating (1) operative temperature t_o, (2) clothing parameters I_t and i_m, and (3) rational effective temperatures t_{oh} and ET*. All heat transfer coefficients in Table 6 were

Table 6 Equations for Convection Heat Transfer Coefficients

Equation	Limits	Condition	Remarks/Sources
$h_c = 8.3V^{0.6}$ $h_c = 3.1$	$0.2 < V < 4.0$ $0 < V < 0.2$	Seated with moving air	Mitchell (1974)
$h_c = 2.7 + 8.7V^{0.67}$ $h_c = 5.1$	$0.15 < V < 1.5$ $0 < V < 0.15$	Reclining with moving air	Colin and Houdas (1967)
$h_c = 8.6V^{0.53}$	$0.5 < V < 2.0$	Walking in still air	V is walking speed (Nishi and Gagge 1970)
$h_c = 5.7(M - 0.8)^{0.39}$	$1.1 < M < 3.0$	Active in still air	Gagge et al. (1976)
$h_c = 6.5V^{0.39}$	$0.5 < V < 2.0$	Walking on treadmill in still air	V is treadmill speed (Nishi and Gagge 1970)
$h_c = 14.8V^{0.69}$ $h_c = 4.0$	$0.15 < V < 1.5$ $0 < V < 0.15$	Standing person in moving air	Developed from data presented by Seppänen et al. (1972)

Note: h_c in W/(m²·K), V in m/s, and M in mets, where 1 met = 58.1 W/m².

evaluated at or near 101.33 kPa. These coefficients should be corrected as follows for atmospheric pressure:

$$h_{cc} = h_c(p_t/101.33)^{0.55} \tag{37}$$

where

h_{cc} = corrected convective heat transfer coefficient, W/(m²·K)
p_t = local atmospheric pressure, kPa

The combined coefficient h is the sum of h_r and h_c, described in Equation (35) and Table 6, respectively. The coefficient h governs exchange by radiation and convection from the exposed body surface to the surrounding environment.

Evaporative Heat Transfer Coefficient. The evaporative heat transfer coefficient h_e for the outer air layer of a nude or clothed person can be estimated from the convective heat transfer coefficient using the Lewis relation given in Equation (27). If the atmospheric pressure is significantly different from the reference value (101.33 kPa), the correction to the value obtained from Equation (27) is

$$h_{ec} = h_e(101.33/p_t)^{0.45} \tag{38}$$

where h_{ec} is the corrected evaporative heat transfer coefficient in W/(m²·kPa).

Clothing Insulation and Permeation Efficiency

Thermal Insulation. The most accurate ways to determine clothing insulation are (1) measurements on heated mannequins (McCullough and Jones 1984; Olesen and Nielsen 1983) and (2) measurements on active subjects (Nishi et al. 1975). For most routine engineering work, estimates based on tables and equations in this section are sufficient. Thermal mannequins can measure the sensible heat loss from "skin" ($C + R$) in a given environment. Equation (11) can then be used to evaluate R_{cl} if environmental conditions are well defined and f_{cl} is measured. Evaluation of clothing insulation on subjects requires measurement of t_{sk}, t_{cl}, and t_o. Clothing thermal efficiency is calculated by

$$F_{cl} = \frac{t_{cl} - t_o}{t_{sk} - t_o} \tag{39}$$

The intrinsic clothing insulation can then be calculated from mannequin measurements, provided f_{cl} is measured and conditions are sufficiently well defined to determine h accurately:

Table 7 Typical Insulation and Permeability Values for Clothing Ensembles

Ensemble Description[a]	I_{cl}, clo	I_t,[b] clo	f_{cl}	i_{cl}	i_m[b]
Walking shorts, short-sleeved shirt	0.36	1.02	1.10	0.34	0.42
Trousers, short-sleeved shirt	0.57	1.20	1.15	0.36	0.43
Trousers, long-sleeved shirt	0.61	1.21	1.20	0.41	0.45
Same as above, plus suit jacket	0.96	1.54	1.23		
Same as above, plus vest and T-shirt	1.14	1.69	1.32	0.32	0.37
Trousers, long-sleeved shirt, long-sleeved sweater, T-shirt	1.01	1.56	1.28		
Same as above, plus suit jacket and long underwear bottoms	1.30	1.83	1.33		
Sweat pants, sweat shirt	0.74	1.35	1.19	0.41	0.45
Long-sleeved pajama top, long pajama trousers, short 3/4 sleeved robe, slippers (no socks)	0.96	1.50	1.32	0.37	0.41
Knee-length skirt, short-sleeved shirt, panty hose, sandals	0.54	1.10	1.26		
Knee-length skirt, long-sleeved shirt, full slip, panty hose	0.67	1.22	1.29		
Knee-length skirt, long-sleeved shirt, half slip, panty hose, long-sleeved sweater	1.10	1.59	1.46		
Same as above, replace sweater with suit jacket	1.04	1.60	1.30	0.35	0.40
Ankle-length skirt, long-sleeved shirt, suit jacket, panty hose	1.10	1.59	1.46		
Long-sleeved coveralls, T-shirt	0.72	1.30	1.23		
Overalls, long-sleeved shirt, T-shirt	0.89	1.46	1.27	0.35	0.40
Insulated coveralls, long-sleeved thermal underwear, long underwear bottoms	1.37	1.94	1.26	0.35	0.39

Source: From McCullough and Jones (1984) and McCullough et al. (1989).
[a]All ensembles include shoes and briefs or panties. All ensembles except those with panty hose include socks unless otherwise noted.
[b]For $t_r = t_a$ and air velocity less than 0.2 m/s (I_a = 0.72 clo and i_m = 0.48 when nude). 1 clo = 0.155 (m²·K)/W.

$$R_{cl} = \frac{t_{sk} - t_o}{q} - \frac{1}{hf_{cl}} \tag{40}$$

where q is heat loss from the mannequin in W/m².

Clothing insulation value may be expressed in clo units. To avoid confusion, the symbol I is used with the clo unit instead of the symbol R. The relationship between the two is

$$R = 0.155I \tag{41}$$

or 1.0 clo is equivalent to 0.155 (m²·K)/W.

Because clothing insulation cannot be measured for most routine engineering applications, tables of measured values for various clothing ensembles can be used to select an ensemble comparable to the one(s) in question. Table 7 gives values for typical indoor clothing ensembles. More detailed tables are presented by McCullough and Jones (1984) and Olesen and Nielsen (1983). Accuracies for I_{cl} on the order of ±20% are typical if good matches between ensembles are found.

When a premeasured ensemble cannot be found to match the one in question, estimate the ensemble insulation from the insulation of individual garments. Table 8 gives a list of individual garments commonly worn. The insulation of an ensemble is estimated from the individual values using a summation formula (McCullough and Jones 1984):

$$I_{cl} = 0.835\sum_i I_{clu,i} + 0.161 \tag{42}$$

where $I_{clu,i}$ is the effective insulation of garment i, and I_{cl}, as before, is the insulation for the entire ensemble. A simpler and nearly as accurate summation formula is (Olesen 1985)

$$I_{cl} = \sum_i I_{clu,i} \tag{43}$$

Either Equation (42) or (43) gives acceptable accuracy for typical indoor clothing. The main source of inaccuracy is in determining the appropriate values for individual garments. Overall accuracies are on the order of ±25% if the tables are used carefully. If it is important to include a specific garment not included in Table 8, its insulation can be estimated by (McCullough and Jones 1984)

$$I_{clu,i} = (0.534 + 135x_f)(A_G/A_D) - 0.0549 \tag{44}$$

where

x_f = fabric thickness, mm
A_G = body surface area covered by garment, m²

Values in Table 7 may be adjusted by information in Table 8 and a summation formula. Using this method, values of $I_{clu,i}$ for the selected items in Table 8 are then added to or subtracted from the ensemble value of I_{cl} in Table 7.

When a person is sitting, the chair generally has the effect of increasing clothing insulation by up to 0.15 clo, depending on the contact area A_{ch} between the chair and body (McCullough et al. 1994). A string webbed or beach chair has little or no contact area, and the insulation actually decreases by about 0.1 clo, likely because of compression of the clothing in the contact area. In contrast, a cushioned executive chair has a large contact area that can increase the intrinsic clothing insulation by 0.15 clo. For other chairs, the increase in intrinsic insulation ΔI_{cl} can be estimated from

$$\Delta I_{cl} = 0.748A_{ch} - 0.1 \tag{45}$$

where A_{ch} is in m².

For example, a desk chair with a body contact area of 0.27 m² has a ΔI_{cl} of 0.1 clo. This amount should be added to the intrinsic insulation of the standing clothing ensemble to obtain the insulation of the ensemble when sitting in the desk chair.

Although sitting increases clothing insulation, walking decreases it (McCullough and Hong 1994). The change in clothing insulation ΔI_{cl} can be estimated from the standing intrinsic insulation I_{cl} of the ensemble and the walking speed (Walkspeed) in steps per minute:

$$\Delta I_{cl} = -0.504I_{cl} - 0.00281(\text{Walkspeed}) + 0.24 \tag{46}$$

For example, the clothing insulation of a person wearing a winter business suit with a standing intrinsic insulation of 1 clo would decrease by 0.52 clo when the person walks at 90 steps per minute (about 3.7 km/h). Thus, when the person is walking, the intrinsic insulation of the ensemble would be 0.48 clo.

Permeation Efficiency. Permeation efficiency data for some clothing ensembles are presented in terms of i_{cl} and i_m in Table 7. The values of i_m can be used to calculate $R_{e,t}$ using the relationships in Table 2. Ensembles worn indoors generally fall in the range $0.3 < i_m < 0.5$. Assuming $i_m = 0.4$ is reasonably accurate (McCullough et al. 1989) and may be used if a good match to ensembles in Table 7 cannot be made. The value of i_m or $R_{e,t}$ may be substituted directly into equations for body heat loss calculations (see Table 3). However, i_m for a given clothing ensemble is a function of the environment as well as the clothing properties. Unless i_m is evaluated at conditions very similar to the intended application, it is more rigorous to use i_{cl} to describe the permeation efficiency of the clothing. The value of i_{cl} is not as sensitive to environmental conditions; thus, given data are more accurate over a wider range of air velocity and radiant and air temperature combinations for i_{cl} than for i_m. The relationships in Table 2 can be used to determine $R_{e,cl}$ from i_{cl}, and $R_{e,cl}$ can then be used for body heat loss calculations (see Table 3). McCullough et al. (1989) found an average value of $i_{cl} = 0.34$ for common indoor clothing; this value can be used when other data are not available.

Measuring i_m or i_{cl} may be necessary if unusual clothing (e.g., impermeable or metallized) and/or extreme environments (e.g., high radiant temperatures, high air velocities) are to be addressed. There are three different methods for measuring the permeation efficiency of clothing: (1) using a wet mannequin to measure the effect of sweat evaporation on heat loss (McCullough 1986), (2) using permeation efficiency measurements on component fabrics as well as dry mannequin measurements (Umbach 1980), and (3) using measurements from sweating subjects (Holmer 1984; Nishi et al. 1975).

Table 8 Garment Insulation Values

Garment Description[a]	$I_{clu,i}$, clo[b]	Garment Description[a]	$I_{clu,i}$, clo[b]	Garment Description[a]	$I_{clu,i}$, clo[b]
Underwear		Long-sleeved, flannel shirt	0.34	Long-sleeved (thin)	0.25
Men's briefs	0.04	Short-sleeved, knit sport shirt	0.17	Long-sleeved (thick)	0.36
Panties	0.03	Long-sleeved, sweat shirt	0.34	**Dresses and skirts**[c]	
Bra	0.01	**Trousers and Coveralls**		Skirt (thin)	0.14
T-shirt	0.08	Short shorts	0.06	Skirt (thick)	0.23
Full slip	0.16	Walking shorts	0.08	Long-sleeved shirtdress (thin)	0.33
Half slip	0.14	Straight trousers (thin)	0.15	Long-sleeved shirtdress (thick)	0.47
Long underwear top	0.20	Straight trousers (thick)	0.24	Short-sleeved shirtdress (thin)	0.29
Long underwear bottoms	0.15	Sweatpants	0.28	Sleeveless, scoop neck (thin)	0.23
Footwear		Overalls	0.30	Sleeveless, scoop neck (thick)	0.27
Ankle-length athletic socks	0.02	Coveralls	0.49	**Sleepwear and Robes**	
Calf-length socks	0.03	**Suit jackets and vests (lined)**		Sleeveless, short gown (thin)	0.18
Knee socks (thick)	0.06	Single-breasted (thin)	0.36	Sleeveless, long gown (thin)	0.20
Panty hose	0.02	Single-breasted (thick)	0.44	Short-sleeved hospital gown	0.31
Sandals/thongs	0.02	Double-breasted (thin)	0.42	Long-sleeved, long gown (thick)	0.46
Slippers (quilted, pile-lined)	0.03	Double-breasted (thick)	0.48	Long-sleeved pajamas (thick)	0.57
Boots	0.10	Sleeveless vest (thin)	0.10	Short-sleeved pajamas (thin)	0.42
Shirts and Blouses		Sleeveless vest (thick)	0.17	Long-sleeved, long wrap robe (thick)	0.69
Sleeveless, scoop-neck blouse	0.12	**Sweaters**		Long-sleeved, short wrap robe (thick)	0.48
Short-sleeved, dress shirt	0.19	Sleeveless vest (thin)	0.13	Short-sleeved, short robe (thin)	0.34
Long-sleeved, dress shirt	0.25	Sleeveless vest (thick)	0.22		

[a]"Thin" garments are summerweight; "thick" garments are winterweight. [b]1 clo = 0.155 (m²·K)/W [c]Knee-length

Clothing Surface Area. Many clothing heat transfer calculations require that clothing area factor f_{cl} be known. The most reliable approach is to measure it using photographic methods (Olesen et al. 1982). Other than actual measurements, the best method is to use previously tabulated data for similar clothing ensembles. Table 7 is adequate for most indoor clothing ensembles. No good method of estimating f_{cl} for an ensemble from other information is available, although a rough estimate can be made by (McCullough and Jones 1984)

$$f_{cl} = 1.0 + 0.3I_{cl} \tag{47}$$

Total Evaporative Heat Loss

The total evaporative heat loss (latent heat) from the body through both respiratory and skin losses, $E_{sk} + E_{res}$, can be measured directly from the body's rate of mass loss as observed by a sensitive scale:

$$E_{sk} + E_{res} = \frac{h_{fg}}{A_D} \times \frac{dm}{d\theta} \tag{48}$$

where

h_{fg} = latent heat of vaporization of water, J/kg
m = body mass, kg
θ = time, s

When using Equation (48), adjustments should be made for any food or drink consumed, body effluents (e.g., wastes), and metabolic mass losses. Metabolism contributes slightly to mass loss primarily because the oxygen absorbed during respiration is converted to heavier CO_2 and exhaled. It can be calculated by

$$\frac{dm_{ge}}{d\theta} = Q_{O_2}(1.977\text{RQ} - 1.429)/10^6 \tag{49}$$

where

$dm_{ge}/d\theta$ = rate of mass loss due to respiratory gas exchange, kg/s
Q_{O_2} = oxygen uptake at STPD, mL/s
RQ = respiratory quotient
1.977 = density of CO_2 at STPD, kg/m^3
1.429 = density of O_2 at STPD, kg/m^3
STPD = standard temperature and pressure of dry air at 0°C and 101.325 kPa

Environmental Parameters

Thermal environment parameters that must be measured or otherwise quantified to obtain accurate estimates of human thermal response are divided into two groups: those that can be measured directly and those calculated from other measurements.

Directly Measured Parameters. Seven psychrometric parameters used to describe the thermal environment are (1) air temperature t_a, (2) wet-bulb temperature t_{wb}, (3) dew-point temperature t_{dp}, (4) water vapor pressure p_a, (5) total atmospheric pressure p_t, (6) relative humidity (rh), and (7) humidity ratio W_a. These parameters are discussed in detail in Chapter 1, and methods for measuring them are discussed in Chapter 36. Two other important parameters include air velocity V and mean radiant temperature $\bar{t}_r$. Air velocity measurements are also discussed in Chapter 36. The radiant temperature is the temperature of an exposed surface in the environment. The temperatures of individual surfaces are usually combined into a mean radiant temperature $\bar{t}_r$. Finally, globe temperature t_g, which can also be measured directly, is a good approximation of the operative temperature t_o and is also used with other measurements to calculate the mean radiant temperature.

Calculated Parameters. The **mean radiant temperature** $\bar{t}_r$ is a key variable in thermal calculations for the human body. It is the uniform temperature of an imaginary enclosure in which radiant heat transfer from the human body equals the radiant heat transfer in the actual nonuniform enclosure. Measurements of the globe temperature, air temperature, and air velocity can be combined to estimate the mean radiant temperature (see Chapter 36). The accuracy of the mean radiant temperature determined this way varies considerably, depending on the type of environment and the accuracy of the individual measurements. Because the mean radiant temperature is defined with respect to the human body, the shape of the sensor is also a factor. The spherical shape of the globe thermometer gives a reasonable approximation of a seated person; an ellipsoid sensor gives a better approximation of the shape of a human, both upright and seated.

Mean radiant temperature can also be calculated from the measured temperature of surrounding walls and surfaces and their positions with respect to the person. Most building materials have a high emittance ε, so all surfaces in the room can be assumed to be black. The following equation is then used:

$$\bar{T}_r^4 = T_1^4 F_{p-1} + T_2^4 F_{p-2} + \cdots + T_N^4 F_{p-N} \tag{50}$$

where

$\bar{T}_r$ = mean radiant temperature, K
T_N = surface temperature of surface N, K
F_{p-N} = angle factor between a person and surface N

Because the sum of the angle factors is unity, the fourth power of mean radiant temperature equals the mean value of the surrounding surface temperatures to the fourth power, weighted by the respective angle factors. In general, angle factors are difficult to determine, although Figures 3A and 3B may be used to estimate them for rectangular surfaces. The angle factor normally depends on the position and orientation of the person (Fanger 1982).

If relatively small temperature differences exist between the surfaces of the enclosure, Equation (50) can be simplified to a linear form:

$$\bar{t}_r = t_1 F_{p-1} + t_2 F_{p-2} + \cdots + t_N F_{p-N} \tag{51}$$

Equation (51) always gives a slightly lower mean radiant temperature than Equation (50), but the difference is small. If, for example, half the surroundings ($F_{p-N} = 0.5$) has a temperature 5 K higher than the other half, the difference between the calculated mean radiant temperatures [according to Equations (50) and (51)] is only 0.2 K. If, however, this difference is 100 K, the mean radiant temperature calculated by Equation (51) is 10 K too low.

Mean radiant temperature may also be calculated from the plane radiant temperature t_{pr} in six directions (up, down, right, left, front, back) and for the projected area factors of a person in the same six directions. For a standing person, the mean radiant temperature may be estimated as

$$\begin{aligned}\bar{t}_r = \{&0.08[t_{pr}(\text{up}) + t_{pr}(\text{down})] + 0.23[t_{pr}(\text{right}) \\ &+ t_{pr}(\text{left})] + 0.35[t_{pr}(\text{front}) + t_{pr}(\text{back})]\} \\ &\div [2(0.08 + 0.23 + 0.35)]\end{aligned} \tag{52}$$

For a seated person,

$$\begin{aligned}\bar{t}_r = \{&0.18[t_{pr}(\text{up}) + t_{pr}(\text{down})] + 0.22[t_{pr}(\text{right}) \\ &+ t_{pr}(\text{left})] + 0.30[t_{pr}(\text{front}) + t_{pr}(\text{back})]\} \\ &\div [2(0.18 + 0.22 + 0.30)]\end{aligned} \tag{53}$$

The **plane radiant temperature** t_{pr}, introduced by Korsgaard (1949), is the uniform temperature of an enclosure in which the incident radiant flux on one side of a small plane element is the same as that in the actual environment. The plane radiant temperature describes thermal radiation in one direction, and its value thus

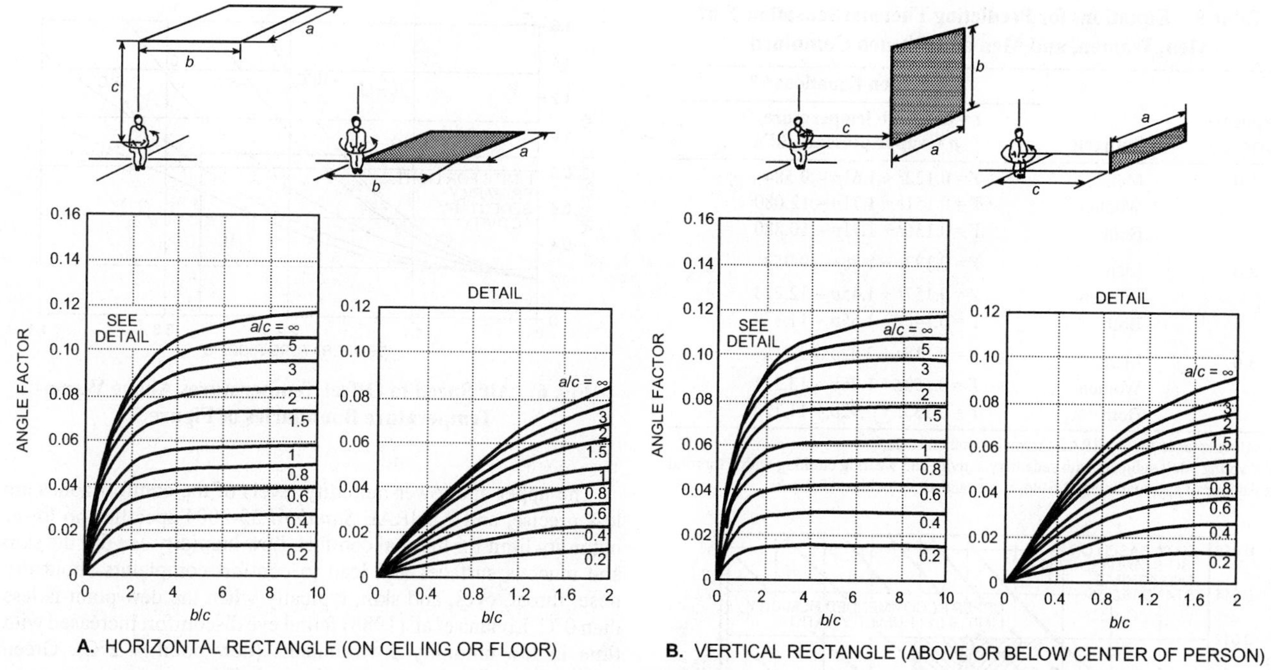

Fig. 3 Mean Value of Angle Factor Between Seated Person and Horizontal or Vertical Rectangle when Person is Rotated Around Vertical Axis
(Fanger 1982)

depends on the direction. In comparison, mean radiant temperature $\bar{t}_r$ describes the thermal radiation for the human body from all directions. The plane radiant temperature can be calculated using Equations (50) and (51) with the same limitations. Area factors are determined from Figure 4.

The **radiant temperature asymmetry** Δt_{pr} is the difference between the plane radiant temperature of the opposite sides of a small plane element. This parameter describes the asymmetry of the radiant environment and is especially important in comfort conditions. Because it is defined with respect to a plane element, its value depends on the plane's orientation, which may be specified in some situations (e.g., floor to ceiling asymmetry) and not in others. If direction is not specified, the radiant asymmetry should be for the orientation that gives the maximum value.

CONDITIONS FOR THERMAL COMFORT

In addition to the previously discussed independent environmental and personal variables influencing thermal response and comfort, other factors may also have some effect. These secondary factors include nonuniformity of the environment, visual stimuli, age, and outdoor climate. Studies by Rohles (1973) and Rohles and Nevins (1971) on 1600 college-age students revealed correlations between comfort level, temperature, humidity, sex, and length of exposure. Many of these correlations are given in Table 9. The thermal sensation scale developed for these studies is called the **ASHRAE thermal sensation scale**:

+3	hot
+2	warm
+1	slightly warm
0	neutral
−1	slightly cool
−2	cool
−3	cold

The equations in Table 9 indicate that women in this study were more sensitive to temperature and less sensitive to humidity than the

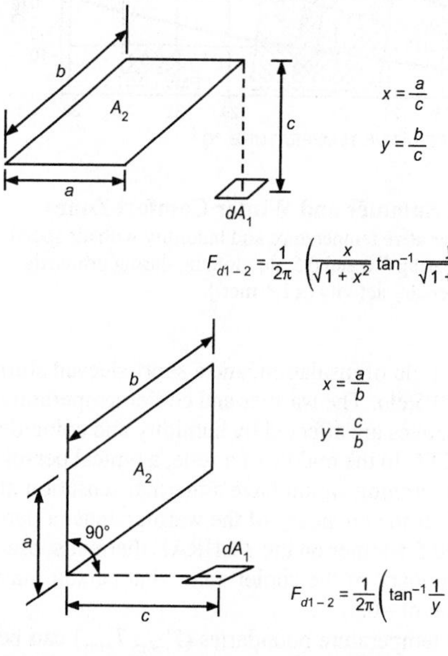

$$x = \frac{a}{c} \qquad y = \frac{b}{c}$$

$$F_{d1-2} = \frac{1}{2\pi}\left(\frac{x}{\sqrt{1+x^2}}\tan^{-1}\frac{y}{\sqrt{1+x^2}} + \frac{y}{\sqrt{1+y^2}}\tan^{-1}\frac{x}{\sqrt{1+y^2}}\right)$$

$$x = \frac{a}{b} \qquad y = \frac{c}{b}$$

$$F_{d1-2} = \frac{1}{2\pi}\left(\tan^{-1}\frac{1}{y} - \frac{y}{\sqrt{x^2+y^2}}\tan^{-1}\frac{1}{\sqrt{x^2+y^2}}\right)$$

Fig. 4 Analytical Formulas for Calculating Angle Factor for Small Plane Element

men, but in general about a 3 K change in temperature or a 3 kPa change in water vapor pressure is necessary to change a thermal sensation vote by one unit or temperature category.

Current and past studies are periodically reviewed to update ASHRAE *Standard* 55, which specifies conditions or comfort zones where 80% of sedentary or slightly active persons find the environment thermally acceptable.

Because people wear different levels of clothing depending on the situation and seasonal weather, ASHRAE *Standard* 55-2004 defines comfort zones for 0.5 and 1.0 clo [0.078 and 0.155 (m²·K)/W)] clothing levels (Figure 5). For reference, a winter

Table 9 Equations for Predicting Thermal Sensation *Y* of Men, Women, and Men and Women Combined

Exposure Period, h	Subjects	Regression Equations[a, b] t = dry-bulb temperature, °C p = vapor pressure, kPa
1.0	Men	$Y = 0.122t + 1.61p - 9.584$
	Women	$Y = 0.151t + 1.71p - 12.080$
	Both	$Y = 0.136t + 1.71p - 10.880$
2.0	Men	$Y = 0.123t + 1.86p - 9.953$
	Women	$Y = 0.157t + 1.45p - 12.725$
	Both	$Y = 0.140t + 1.65p - 11.339$
3.0	Men	$Y = 0.118t + 2.02p - 9.718$
	Women	$Y = 0.153t + 1.76p - 13.511$
	Both	$Y = 0.135t + 1.92p - 11.122$

[a] *Y* values refer to the ASHRAE thermal sensation scale.
[b] For young adult subjects with sedentary activity and wearing clothing with a thermal resistance of approximately 0.5 clo, $\bar{t}_r < \bar{t}_a$ and air velocities < 0.2 m/s.

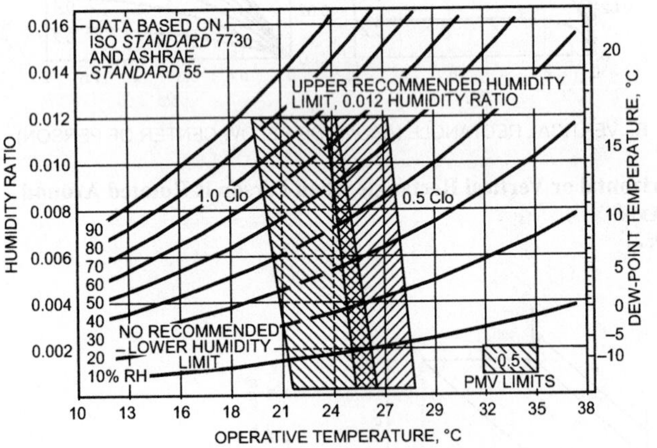

Fig. 5 ASHRAE Summer and Winter Comfort Zones
[Acceptable ranges of operative temperature and humidity with air speed ≤ 0.2 m/s for people wearing 1.0 and 0.5 clo clothing during primarily sedentary activity (≤1.1 met)].

business suit has about 1 clo of insulation, and a short-sleeved shirt and trousers has about 0.5 clo. The warmer and cooler temperature borders of the comfort zones are affected by humidity and coincide with lines of constant ET*. In the middle of a zone, a typical person wearing the prescribed clothing would have a thermal sensation at or very near neutral. Near the boundary of the warmer zone, a person would feel about +0.5 warmer on the ASHRAE thermal sensation scale; near the boundary of the cooler zone, that person may have a thermal sensation of –0.5.

The comfort zone's temperature boundaries (T_{min}, T_{max}) can be adjusted by interpolation for clothing insulation levels (I_{cl}) between those in Figure 5 by using the following equations:

$$T_{min,I_{cl}} = \frac{(I_{cl} - 0.5\text{ clo})T_{min,1.0\text{ clo}} + (1.0\text{ clo} - I_{cl})T_{min,0.5\text{ clo}}}{0.5\text{ clo}}$$

$$T_{max,I_{cl}} = \frac{(I_{cl} - 0.5\text{ clo})T_{max,1.0\text{ clo}} + (1.0\text{ clo} - I_{cl})T_{max,0.5\text{ clo}}}{0.5\text{ clo}}$$

In general, comfort temperatures for other clothing levels can be approximated by decreasing the temperature borders of the zone by 0.6 K for each 0.1 clo increase in clothing insulation and vice versa. Similarly, a zone's temperatures can be decreased by 1.4 K per met increase in activity above 1.2 met.

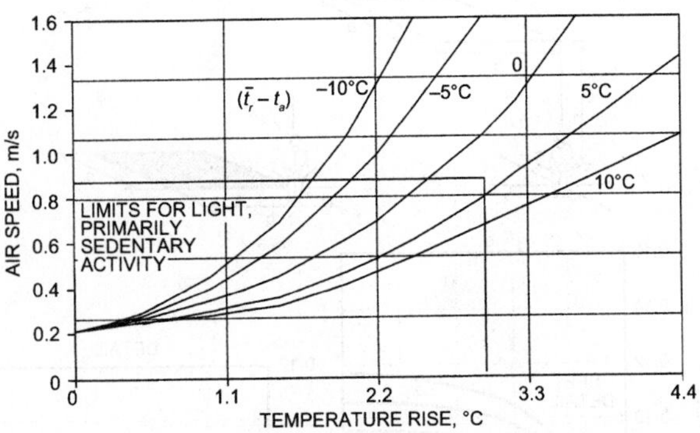

Fig. 6 Air Speed to Offset Temperatures Above Warm-Temperature Boundaries of Figure 5

The upper and lower humidity levels of the comfort zones are less precise, and ASHRAE *Standard* 55-2004 specifies no lower humidity limit for thermal comfort. Low humidity can dry the skin and mucous surfaces and lead to comfort complaints about dry nose, throat, eyes, and skin, typically when the dew point is less than 0°C. Liviana et al. (1988) found eye discomfort increased with time in low-humidity environments (dew point < 2°C). Green (1982) found that respiratory illness and absenteeism increase in winter with decreasing humidity and found that any increase in humidity from very low levels decreased absenteeism in winter. In compliance with these and other discomfort observations, ASHRAE *Standard* 55 recommends that the dew-point temperature of occupied spaces not be less than 2°C.

At high humidity, too much skin moisture tends to increase discomfort (Berglund and Cunningham 1986; Gagge 1937), particularly skin moisture of physiological origin (water diffusion and perspiration). At high humidity, thermal sensation alone is not a reliable predictor of thermal comfort (Tanabe et al. 1987). The discomfort appears to be due to the feeling of the moisture itself, increased friction between skin and clothing with skin moisture (Gwosdow et al. 1986), and other factors. To prevent warm discomfort, Nevins et al. (1975) recommended that, on the warm side of the comfort zone, the relative humidity not exceed 60%. ASHRAE *Standard* 55-2004 specifies an upper humidity ratio limit of 0.012 $kg_w/kg_{dry\ air}$, which corresponds to a dew point of 16.8°C at standard pressure.

The comfort zones of Figure 5 are for air speeds not to exceed 0.2 m/s. However, elevated air speeds can be used to improve comfort beyond the maximum temperature limit of this figure. The air speeds necessary to compensate for a temperature increase above the warm-temperature border are shown in Figure 6. The combination of air speed and temperature defined by the curves in this figure result in the same heat loss from the skin.

The amount of air speed increase is affected by the mean radiant temperature $\bar{t}_r$. The curves of Figure 6 are for different levels of $\bar{t}_r - t_a$. That is, when the mean radiant temperature is low and the air temperature is high, elevated air speed is less effective at increasing heat loss and a higher air speed is needed for a given temperature increase. Conversely, elevated air speed is more effective when the mean radiant temperature is high and air temperature is low; then, less of an air speed increase is needed. Figure 6 applies to lightly clothed individuals (clothing insulation between 0.5 and 0.7 clo) who are engaged in near-sedentary physical activity. The elevated air speed may be used to offset an increase in temperature by up to 3 K above the warm-temperature boundary of Figure 5.

Thermal Complaints

Unsolicited thermal complaints can increase a building's operation and maintenance (O&M) cost by requiring unscheduled maintenance to correct the problem.

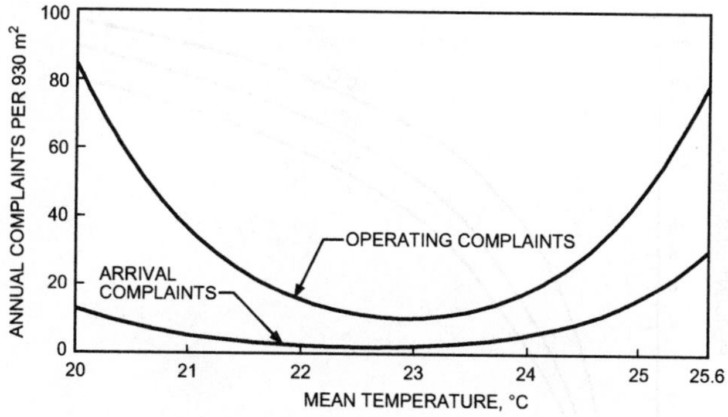

Fig. 7 Predicted Rate of Unsolicited Thermal Operating Complaints

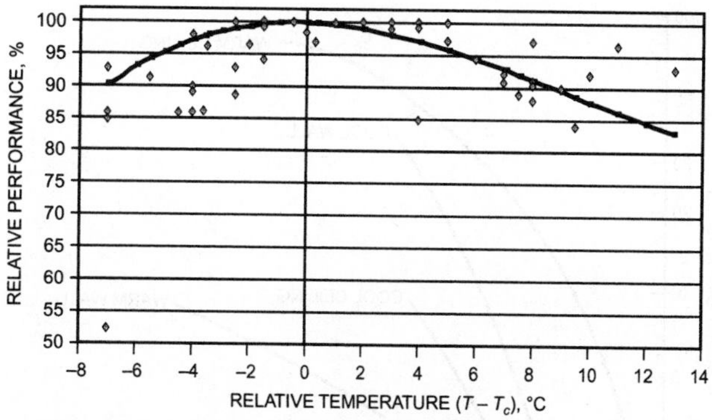

Fig. 8 Relative Performance of Office Work Performance versus Deviation from Optimal Comfort Temperature T_c

Table 10 Model Parameters

Zone, m²	μ_{T_H}, °C	σ_{T_H}, K	$\sigma_{\dot{T}_H}$, K/h	μ_{T_L}, °C	σ_{T_L}, K	$\sigma_{\dot{T}_L}$, K/h
430	32.8	2.81	0.63	10.24	3.41	2.27

Federspiel (1998) analyzed complaint data from 690 commercial buildings with a total of 23 500 occupants. The most common kind of unsolicited complaint was of temperature extremes. Complaints were rarely due to individual differences in preferred temperature, because 96.5% of the complaints occurred at temperatures less than 21°C or greater than 24°C; most complaints were caused by HVAC faults or poor control performance.

The hourly complaint rate per zone area of being too hot (ν_h) or too cold (ν_l) can be predicted from the HVAC system's operating parameters, specifically the mean space temperature (μ_T), standard deviation of the space temperature (σ_T), and the standard deviation of the rate of change in space temperature ($\sigma_{\dot{T}_H}$, $\sigma_{\dot{T}_L}$):

$$\nu_h = \frac{1}{2\pi}\left(\frac{\sigma_{\dot{T}_H}^2 + \sigma_{\dot{T}_B}^2}{\sigma_{T_H}^2 + \sigma_{T_B}^2}\right)^{1/2} \exp\left(-\frac{1}{2}\frac{(\mu_{T_B} - \mu_{T_H})^2}{(\sigma_{T_H}^2 + \sigma_{T_B}^2)}\right) \tag{54}$$

$$\nu_l = \frac{1}{2\pi}\left(\frac{\sigma_{\dot{T}_L}^2 + \sigma_{\dot{T}_B}^2}{\sigma_{T_L}^2 + \sigma_{T_B}^2}\right)^{1/2} \exp\left(-\frac{1}{2}\frac{(\mu_{T_B} - \mu_{T_L})^2}{(\sigma_{T_L}^2 + \sigma_{T_B}^2)}\right) \tag{55}$$

where the subscripts H, L, and B refer to too hot, too cold, and building (Federspiel 2001).

The building maintenance and space temperature records of six commercial buildings in Minneapolis, Seattle, and San Francisco were analyzed for the values of the H and L model parameters (Federspiel et al. 2003) of Table 10. Complaint rates predicted by the model for these building parameters are graphed in Figure 7. **Arrival complaints** occur when the temperature exceeds either the hot or cold complaint level when occupants arrive in the morning. **Operating complaints** occur during the occupied period when the temperature crosses above the hot complaint level or below the cold complaint level. Arriving occupants generally have a higher metabolic power because of recent activity (e.g., walking).

Complaint prediction models can be used to determine the minimum discomfort temperature (MDT) setting that minimizes the occurrences of thermal complaints for a building with known or measured HVAC system parameters σ_{T_B} and $\sigma_{\dot{T}_B}$. Similarly, complaint models can be used with building energy models and service call costs to determine the minimum cost temperature (MCT) where the operating costs are minimized. For example, the summer MDT and MCT in Sacramento, California, are 22.8 and 25°C for a commercial building at design conditions with σ_{T_B} = 0.3 K and $\sigma_{\dot{T}_B}$ = 0.6 K. For these conditions, temperatures below 22.8°C increase both cold complaints and energy costs, and those above 25°C increase hot complaints and costs. Thus, the economically logical acceptable temperature range for this building is 22.8 to 25°C for minimum operating cost and discomfort (Federspiel et al. 2003).

THERMAL COMFORT AND TASK PERFORMANCE

The generally held belief that improving indoor environmental quality enhances productivity often depends on indirect evidence, because direct evidence is difficult to obtain (Levin 1995). However, numerous studies have measured performance over a wide range of tasks and indoor environments [e.g., Berglund et al. (1990); Link and Pepler (1970); Niemelä et al. (2001); Pepler and Warner (1968); Roelofsen (2001); Seppänen et al. (2006); Wyon (1996)]. Task performance is generally highest at comfort conditions (Gonzalez 1975; Griffiths and McIntyre 1975), and a range of temperature at comfort conditions exists within which there is no significant further effect on performance (Federspiel 2001; Federspiel et al. 2002; McCartney and Humphreys 2002; Witterseh 2001).

Twenty-four studies were analyzed and normalized to quantify and generalize the effects of room temperature as a surrogate for thermal comfort on office task performance (Seppänen and Fisk 2006). Of these, 11 were field studies with data collected in working offices and 9 were conducted in controlled laboratory environments. Most of the office field studies were performed in call centers; in these studies, the speed of work (e.g., average time per call) was used as a measure of work performance. Laboratory studies typically assessed work performance by evaluating the speed and accuracy with which subjects performed tasks, such as text processing and simple calculations, simulating aspects of office work.

The percentage of performance change per degree increase in temperature was calculated for all studies, positive values indicating increases in performance with increasing temperature, and negative values indicating decreases in performance with increasing temperature. A weighted average of the measured performance changes per degree change results in the curve shown in Figure 8. In averaging the measurements, work done by subjects in office field studies was assumed more representative of overall real-world performance and was weighted higher than performance changes in simulated computerized tasks.

Data points from 11 of the studies are also shown in Figure 8. Note the large amount of scatter in the individual studies about the line, indicating a high level of uncertainty. However, as a first approximation, the performance versus temperature relationship in the graph may still be useful as a general representation of real-world office work performance for the tasks performed in the studies, and helpful as a guide in design, operation, and cost analysis.

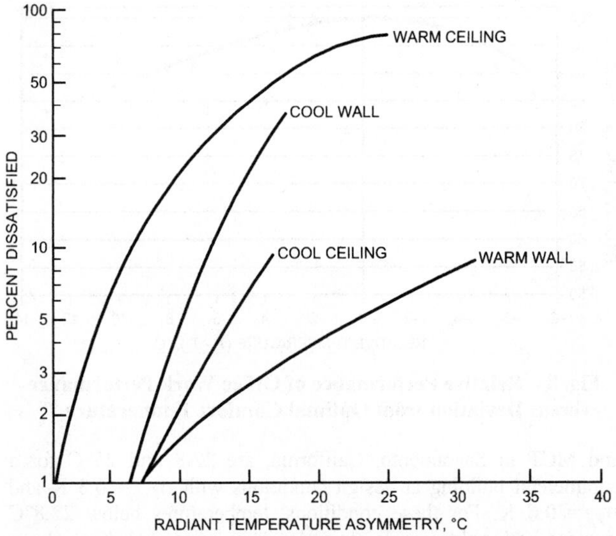

Fig. 9 Percentage of People Expressing Discomfort due to Asymmetric Radiation

The results show that performance decreases as temperature deviates above or below a thermal comfort temperature range. As shown in Figure 8, at a temperature 8 K higher than optimal, average office task performance decreased to about 91% of the value at optimum temperature.

THERMAL NONUNIFORM CONDITIONS AND LOCAL DISCOMFORT

A person may feel thermally neutral as a whole but still feel uncomfortable if one or more parts of the body are too warm or too cold. Nonuniformities may be due to a cold window, a hot surface, a draft, or a temporal variation of these. Even small variations in heat flow cause the thermal regulatory system to compensate, thus increasing the physiological effort of maintaining body temperatures. The boundaries of the comfort zones (Figure 5) of ASHRAE *Standard* 55 provide a thermal acceptability level of 90% if the environment is thermally uniform. Because the standard's objective is to specify conditions for 80% acceptability, the standard permits nonuniformities to decrease acceptability by 10%. Fortunately for the designer and user, the effect of common thermal nonuniformities on comfort is quantifiable and predictable, as discussed in the following sections. Furthermore, most humans are fairly insensitive to small nonuniformities.

Asymmetric Thermal Radiation

Asymmetric or nonuniform thermal radiation in a space may be caused by cold windows, uninsulated walls, cold products, cold or warm machinery, or improperly sized heating panels on the wall or ceiling. In residential buildings, offices, restaurants, etc., the most common causes are cold windows or improperly sized or installed ceiling heating panels. At industrial workplaces, the reasons include cold or warm products, cold or warm equipment, etc.

Recommendations in ISO *Standard* 7730 and ASHRAE *Standard* 55 are based primarily on studies reported by Fanger et al. (1980). These standards include guidelines regarding the radiant temperature asymmetry from an overhead warm surface (heated ceiling) and a vertical cold surface (cold window). Among the studies conducted on the influence of asymmetric thermal radiation are those by Fanger and Langkilde (1975), McIntyre (1974, 1976), McIntyre and Griffiths (1975), McNall and Biddison (1970), and Olesen et al. (1972). These studies all used seated subjects, who were always in thermal neutrality and exposed only to the discomfort resulting from excessive asymmetry.

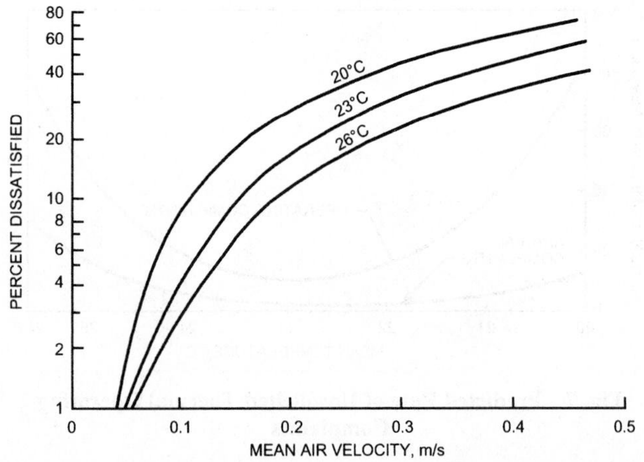

Fig. 10 Percentage of People Dissatisfied as Function of Mean Air Velocity

The subjects gave their reactions on their comfort sensation, and a relationship between the radiant temperature asymmetry and the number of subjects feeling dissatisfied was established (Figure 9). Radiant asymmetry, as defined in the section on Environmental Parameters, is the difference in radiant temperature of the environment on opposite sides of the person. More precisely, radiant asymmetry is the difference in radiant temperatures seen by a small flat element looking in opposite directions.

Figure 9 shows that people are more sensitive to asymmetry caused by an overhead warm surface than by a vertical cold surface. The influence of an overhead cold surface or a vertical warm surface is much less. These data are particularly important when using radiant panels to provide comfort in spaces with large cold surfaces or cold windows.

Other studies of clothed persons in neutral environments found thermal acceptability unaffected by radiant temperature asymmetries of 10 K or less (Berglund and Fobelets 1987) and comfort unaffected by asymmetries of 20 K or less (McIntyre and Griffiths 1975).

Draft

Draft is an undesired local cooling of the human body caused by air movement. This is a serious problem, not only in many ventilated buildings but also in automobiles, trains, and aircraft. Draft has been identified as one of the most annoying factors in offices. When people sense draft, they often demand higher air temperatures in the room or that ventilation systems be stopped.

Fanger and Christensen (1986) aimed to establish the percentage of the population feeling draft when exposed to a given mean velocity. Figure 10 shows the percentage of subjects who felt draft on the head region (the dissatisfied) as a function of mean air velocity at the neck. The head region comprises head, neck, shoulders, and back. Air temperature significantly influenced the percentage of dissatisfied. There was no significant difference between responses of men and women. The data in Figure 10 apply only to persons wearing normal indoor clothing and performing light, mainly sedentary work. Persons with higher activity levels are not as sensitive to draft (Jones et al. 1986).

A study of the effect of air velocity over the whole body found thermal acceptability unaffected in neutral environments by air speeds of 0.25 m/s or less (Berglund and Fobelets 1987). This study also found no interaction between air speed and radiant temperature asymmetry on subjective responses. Thus, acceptability changes and the percent dissatisfied because of draft and radiant asymmetry are independent and additive.

Fanger et al. (1989) investigated the effect of turbulence intensity on sensation of draft. Turbulence intensity significantly affects draft

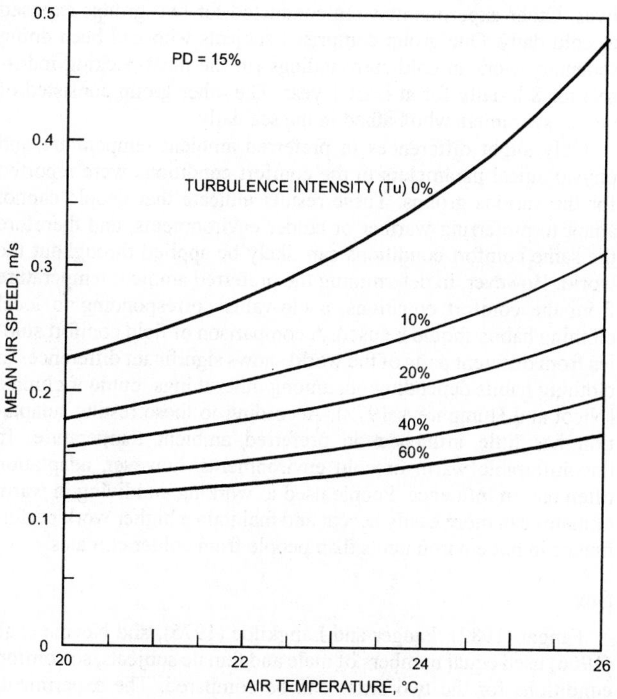

Fig. 11 Draft Conditions Dissatisfying 15% of Population (PD = 15%)

sensation, as predicted by the following model. This model can be used to quantify draft risk in spaces and to develop air distribution systems with a low draft risk.

$$PD = (34 - t_a)(V - 0.05)^{0.62}(0.37 V\text{Tu} + 3.14) \qquad (56)$$

where PD is percent dissatisfied and Tu is the turbulence intensity in % defined by

$$\text{Tu} = 100\,\frac{V_{sd}}{V} \qquad (57)$$

For $V < 0.05$ m/s, insert $V = 0.05$, and for PD > 100%, insert PD = 100%. V_{sd} is the standard deviation of the velocity measured with an omnidirectional anemometer having a 0.2 s time constant.

The model extends the Fanger and Christensen (1986) draft chart model to include turbulence intensity. In this study, Tu decreases when V increases. Thus, the effects of V for the experimental data to which the model is fitted are $20 < t_a < 26$°C, $0.05 < V < 0.5$ m/s, and $0 < \text{Tu} < 70\%$. Figure 11 gives more precisely the curves that result from intersections between planes of constant Tu and the surfaces of PD = 15%.

Vertical Air Temperature Difference

In most buildings, air temperature normally increases with height above the floor. If the gradient is sufficiently large, local warm discomfort can occur at the head and/or cold discomfort can occur at the feet, although the body as a whole is thermally neutral. Among the few studies of vertical air temperature differences and the influence of thermal comfort reported are Eriksson (1975), McNair (1973), McNair and Fishman (1974), and Olesen et al. (1979). Subjects were seated in a climatic chamber so they were individually exposed to different air temperature differences between head and ankles (Olesen et al. 1979). During the tests, the subjects were in thermal neutrality because they were allowed to change the temperature level in the test room whenever they desired; the vertical temperature difference, however, was kept

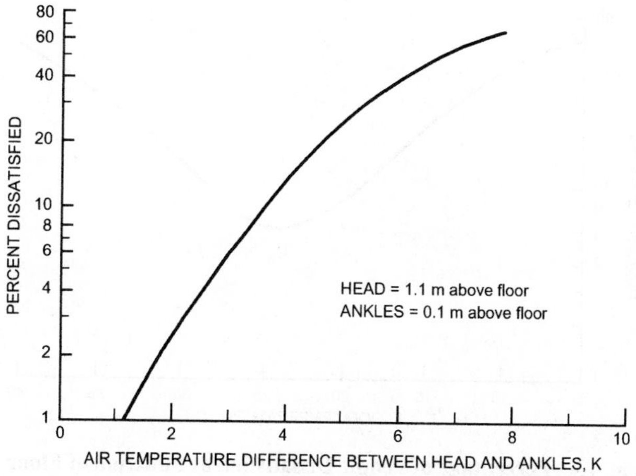

Fig. 12 Percentage of Seated People Dissatisfied as Function of Air Temperature Difference Between Head and Ankles

unchanged. Subjects gave subjective reactions to their thermal sensation; Figure 12 shows the percentage of dissatisfied as a function of the vertical air temperature difference between head (1.1 m above the floor) and ankles (0.1 m above the floor).

A head-level air temperature lower than that at ankle level is not as critical for occupants. Eriksson (1975) indicated that subjects could tolerate much greater differences if the head were cooler. This observation is verified in experiments with asymmetric thermal radiation from a cooled ceiling (Fanger et al. 1985).

Warm or Cold Floors

Because of direct contact between the feet and the floor, local discomfort of the feet can often be caused by a too-high or too-low floor temperature. Also, floor temperature significantly influences a room's mean radiant temperature. Floor temperature is greatly affected by building construction (e.g., insulation of the floor, above a basement, directly on the ground, above another room, use of floor heating, floors in radiant heated areas). If a floor is too cold and the occupants feel cold discomfort in their feet, a common reaction is to increase the temperature level in the room; in the heating season, this also increases energy consumption. A radiant system, which radiates heat from the floor, can also prevent discomfort from cold floors.

The most extensive studies of the influence of floor temperature on feet comfort were performed by Olesen (1977a, 1977b), who, based on his own experiments and reanalysis of the data from Nevins and Feyerherm (1967), Nevins and Flinner (1958), and Nevins et al. (1964), found that flooring material is important for people with bare feet (e.g., in swimming halls, gymnasiums, dressing rooms, bathrooms, bedrooms). Ranges for some typical floor materials are as follows:

Textiles (rugs)	21 to 28°C
Pine floor	22.5 to 28°C
Oak floor	24.5 to 28°C
Hard linoleum	24 to 28°C
Concrete	26 to 28.5°C

To save energy, flooring materials with a low contact coefficient (cork, wood, carpets), radiant heated floors, or floor heating systems can be used to eliminate the desire for higher ambient temperatures caused by cold feet. These recommendations should also be followed in schools, where children often play directly on the floor.

For people wearing normal indoor footwear, flooring material is insignificant. Olesen (1977b) found an optimal temperature of 25°C for sedentary and 23°C for standing or walking persons. At the optimal temperature, 6% of occupants felt warm or cold discomfort in the feet. Figure 13 shows the relationship between floor temperature and

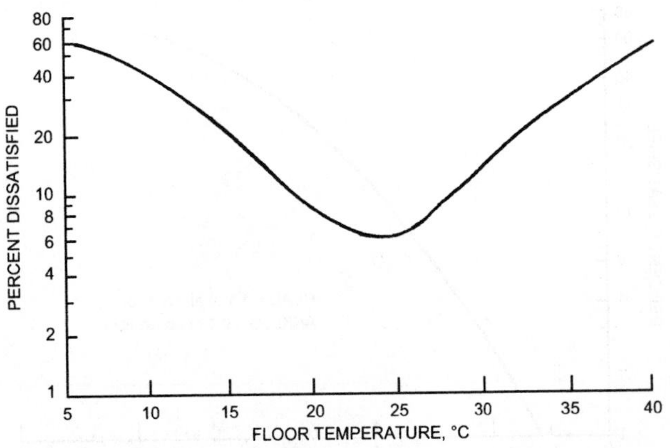

Fig. 13 Percentage of People Dissatisfied as Function of Floor Temperature

percent dissatisfied, combining data from experiments with seated and standing subjects. In all experiments, subjects were in thermal neutrality; thus, the percentage of dissatisfied is only related to discomfort caused by cold or warm feet. No significant difference in preferred floor temperature was found between females and males.

SECONDARY FACTORS AFFECTING COMFORT

Temperature, air speed, humidity, their variation, and personal parameters of metabolism and clothing insulation are primary factors that directly affect energy flow and thermal comfort. However, many secondary factors, some of which are discussed in this section, may more subtly influence comfort.

Day-to-Day Variations

Fanger (1973) determined the preferred ambient temperature for each of a group of subjects under identical conditions on four different days. Because the standard deviation was only 0.6 K, Fanger concluded that comfort conditions for an individual can be reproduced and vary only slightly from day to day.

Age

Because metabolism decreases slightly with age, many have stated that comfort conditions based on experiments with young and healthy subjects cannot be used for other age groups. Fanger (1982), Fanger and Langkilde (1975), Langkilde (1979), Nevins et al. (1966), and Rohles and Johnson (1972) conducted comfort studies in Denmark and the United States on different age groups (mean ages 21 to 84). The studies revealed that the thermal environments preferred by older people do not differ from those preferred by younger people. The lower metabolism in older people is compensated for by a lower evaporative loss. Collins and Hoinville (1980) confirmed these results.

The fact that young and old people prefer the same thermal environment does not necessarily mean that they are equally sensitive to cold or heat. In practice, the ambient temperature level in the homes of older people is often higher than that for younger people. This may be explained by the lower activity level of elderly people, who are normally sedentary for a greater part of the day.

Adaptation

Many believe that people can acclimatize themselves by exposure to hot or cold surroundings, so that they prefer other thermal environments. Fanger (1982) conducted experiments involving subjects from the United States, Denmark, and tropical countries. The latter group was tested in Copenhagen immediately after their arrival by plane from the tropics, where they had lived all their lives. Other experiments were conducted for two groups exposed to cold daily. One group comprised subjects who had been doing sedentary work in cold surroundings (in the meat-packing industry) for 8 h daily for at least 1 year. The other group consisted of winter swimmers who bathed in the sea daily.

Only slight differences in preferred ambient temperature and physiological parameters in the comfort conditions were reported for the various groups. These results indicate that people cannot adapt to preferring warmer or colder environments, and therefore the same comfort conditions can likely be applied throughout the world. However, in determining the preferred ambient temperature from the comfort equations, a clo-value corresponding to local clothing habits should be used. A comparison of field comfort studies from different parts of the world shows significant differences in clothing habits depending on, among other things, outdoor climate (Nicol and Humphreys 1972). According to these results, adaptation has little influence on preferred ambient temperature. In uncomfortable warm or cold environments, however, adaptation often has an influence. People used to working and living in warm climates can more easily accept and maintain a higher work performance in hot environments than people from colder climates.

Sex

Fanger (1982), Fanger and Langkilde (1975), and Nevins et al. (1966) used equal numbers of male and female subjects, so comfort conditions for the two sexes can be compared. The experiments show that men and women prefer almost the same thermal environments. Women's skin temperature and evaporative loss are slightly lower than those for men, and this balances the somewhat lower metabolism of women. The reason that women often prefer higher ambient temperatures than men may be partly explained by the lighter clothing normally worn by women.

Seasonal and Circadian Rhythms

Because people cannot adapt to prefer warmer or colder environments, it follows that there is no difference between comfort conditions in winter and in summer. McNall et al. (1968) confirmed this in an investigation where results of winter and summer experiments showed no difference. On the other hand, it is reasonable to expect comfort conditions to alter during the day because internal body temperature has a daily rhythm, with a maximum late in the afternoon, and a minimum early in the morning.

In determining the preferred ambient temperature for each of 16 subjects both in the morning and in the evening, Fanger et al. (1974) and Ostberg and McNicholl (1973) observed no difference. Furthermore, Fanger et al. (1973) found only small fluctuations in preferred ambient temperature during a simulated 8 h workday (sedentary work). There is a slight tendency to prefer somewhat warmer surroundings before lunch, but none of the fluctuations are significant.

PREDICTION OF THERMAL COMFORT

Thermal comfort and thermal sensation can be predicted several ways. One way is to use Figure 5 and Table 9 and adjust for clothing and activity levels that differ from those of the figure. More numerical and rigorous predictions are possible by using the PMV-PPD and two-node models described in this section.

Steady-State Energy Balance

Fanger (1982) related comfort data to physiological variables. At a given level of metabolic activity M, and when the body is not far from thermal neutrality, mean skin temperature t_{sk} and sweat rate E_{rsw} are the only physiological parameters influencing heat balance. However, heat balance alone is not sufficient to establish thermal comfort. In the wide range of environmental conditions where heat balance can be obtained, only a narrow range provides thermal comfort. The following linear regression equations, based on data from

Rohles and Nevins (1971), indicate values of t_{sk} and E_{rsw} that provide thermal comfort:

$$t_{sk,req} = 35.7 - 0.0275(M - W) \quad (58)$$

$$E_{rsw,req} = 0.42\,(M - W - 58.15) \quad (59)$$

At higher activity levels, sweat loss increases and mean skin temperature decreases, both of which increase heat loss from the body core to the environment. These two empirical relationships link the physiological and heat flow equations and thermal comfort perceptions. By substituting these values into Equation (11) for $C + R$, and into Equations (17) and (18) for E_{sk}, Equation (1) (the energy balance equation) can be used to determine combinations of the six environmental and personal parameters that optimize comfort for steady-state conditions.

Fanger (1982) reduced these relationships to a single equation, which assumed all sweat generated is evaporated, eliminating clothing permeation efficiency i_{cl} as a factor in the equation. This assumption is valid for normal indoor clothing worn in typical indoor environments with low or moderate activity levels. At higher activity levels ($M_{act} > 3$ met), where a significant amount of sweating occurs even at optimum comfort conditions, this assumption may limit accuracy. The reduced equation is slightly different from the heat transfer equations developed here. The radiant heat exchange is expressed in terms of the Stefan-Boltzmann law (instead of using h_r), and diffusion of water vapor through the skin is expressed as a diffusivity coefficient and a linear approximation for saturated vapor pressure evaluated at t_{sk}. The combination of environmental and personal variables that produces a neutral sensation may be expressed as follows:

$$\begin{aligned} M - W &= 3.96 \times 10^{-8} f_{cl}[(t_{cl} + 273)^4 - (\bar{t}_r + 273)^4] + f_{cl} h_c (t_{cl} - t_a) \\ &+ 3.05[5.73 - 0.007(M - W) - p_a] \\ &+ 0.42[(M - W) - 58.15] + 0.0173M(5.87 - p_a) \\ &+ 0.0014M(34 - t_a) \end{aligned} \quad (60)$$

where

$$\begin{aligned} t_{cl} &= 35.7 - 0.0275(M - W) - R_{cl}\{(M - W) \\ &- 3.05[5.73 - 0.007(M - W) - p_a] \\ &- 0.42[(M - W) - 58.15] - 0.0173M(5.87 - p_a) \\ &- 0.0014M(34 - t_a)\} \end{aligned} \quad (61)$$

The values of h_c and f_{cl} can be estimated from tables and equations given in the section on Engineering Data and Measurements. Fanger used the following relationships:

$$h_c = \begin{cases} 2.38(t_{cl} - t_a)^{0.25} & 2.38(t_{cl} - t_a)^{0.25} > 12.1\sqrt{V} \\ 12.1\sqrt{V} & 2.38(t_{cl} - t_a)^{0.25} < 12.1\sqrt{V} \end{cases} \quad (62)$$

$$f_{cl} = \begin{cases} 1.0 + 0.2I_{cl} & I_{cl} < 0.5 \text{ clo} \\ 1.05 + 0.1I_{cl} & I_{cl} > 0.5 \text{ clo} \end{cases} \quad (63)$$

Figures 14 and 15 show examples of how Equation (60) can be used.

Equation (60) is expanded to include a range of thermal sensations by using a **predicted mean vote (PMV) index**. The PMV index predicts the mean response of a large group of people according to the ASHRAE thermal sensation scale. Fanger (1970) related PMV to the imbalance between the actual heat flow from the body in a given environment and the heat flow required for optimum comfort at the specified activity by the following equation:

$$\text{PMV} = [0.303 \exp(-0.036M) + 0.028]L \quad (64)$$

where L is the thermal load on the body, defined as the difference between internal heat production and heat loss to the actual environment for a person hypothetically kept at comfort values of t_{sk} and E_{rsw} at the actual activity level. Thermal load L is then the difference between the left and right sides of Equation (58) calculated for the actual values of the environmental conditions. As part of this calculation, clothing temperature t_{cl} is found by iteration as

$$\begin{aligned} t_{cl} &= 35.7 - 0.028(M - W) \\ &- R_{cl}\{39.6 \times 10^{-9} f_{cl}[(t_{cl} + 273)^4 - (\bar{t}_r + 273)^4] \\ &+ f_{cl} h_c (t_{cl} - t_a)\} \end{aligned} \quad (65)$$

After estimating the PMV with Equation (64) or another method, the **predicted percent dissatisfied (PPD)** with a condition can also be estimated. Fanger (1982) related the PPD to the PMV as follows:

$$\text{PPD} = 100 - 95 \exp[-(0.03353\,\text{PMV}^4 + 0.2179\,\text{PMV}^2)] \quad (66)$$

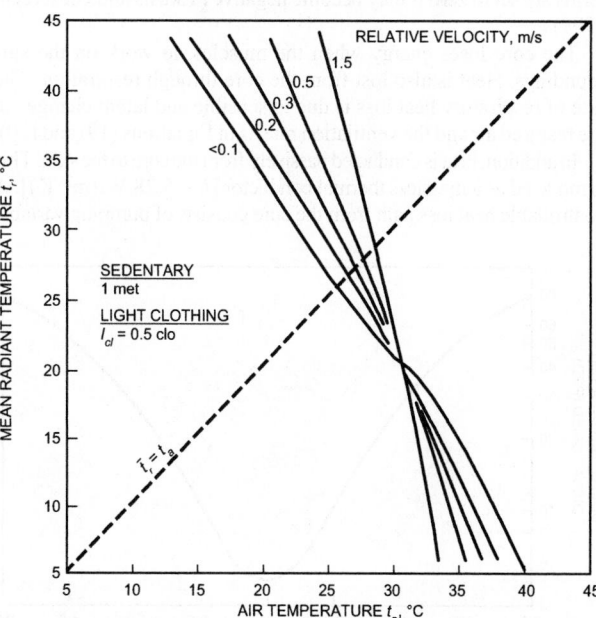

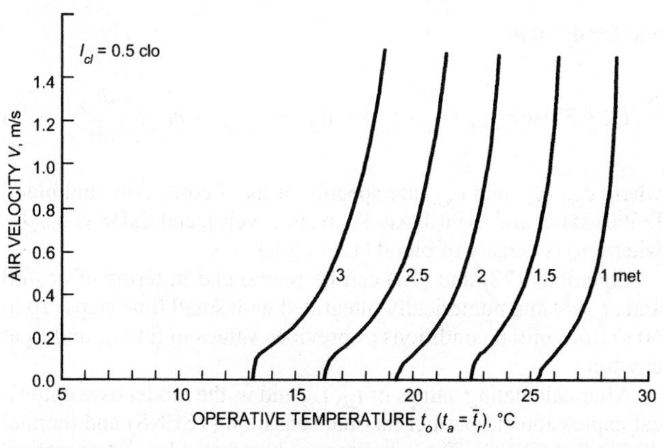

Fig. 14 Air Velocities and Operative Temperatures at 50% rh Necessary for Comfort (PMV = 0) of Persons in Summer Clothing at Various Levels of Activity

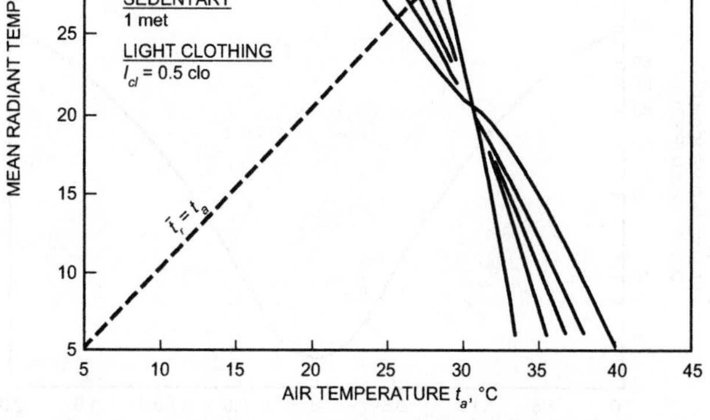

Fig. 15 Air Temperatures and Mean Radiant Temperatures Necessary for Comfort (PMV = 0) of Sedentary Persons in Summer Clothing at 50% rh

where dissatisfied is defined as anybody not voting −1, +1, or 0. This relationship is shown in Figure 16. A PPD of 10% corresponds to the PMV range of ±0.5, and even with PMV = 0, about 5% of the people are dissatisfied.

The **PMV-PPD model** is widely used and accepted for design and field assessment of comfort conditions. ISO *Standard* 7730 includes a short computer listing that facilitates computing PMV and PPD for a wide range of parameters.

Two-Node Model

The PMV model is useful only for predicting steady-state comfort responses. The two-node model can be used to predict physiological responses or responses to transient situations, at least for low and moderate activity levels in cool to very hot environments (Gagge et al. 1971a, 1986). This model is a simplification of thermoregulatory models developed by Stolwijk and Hardy (1966). The simple, lumped parameter model considers a human as two concentric thermal compartments that represent the skin and the core of the body.

The **skin compartment** simulates the epidermis and dermis and is about 1.6 mm thick. Its mass, which is about 10% of the total body, depends on the amount of blood flowing through it for thermoregulation. Compartment temperature is assumed to be uniform so that the only temperature gradients are between compartments. In a cold environment, blood flow to the extremities may be reduced to conserve the heat of vital organs, resulting in axial temperature gradients in the arms, legs, hands, and feet. Heavy exercise with certain muscle groups or asymmetric environmental conditions may also cause nonuniform compartment temperatures and limit the model's accuracy.

All the heat is assumed to be generated in the **core compartment**. In the cold, shivering and muscle tension may generate additional metabolic heat. This increase is related to skin and core temperature depressions from their set point values, or

$$M_{shiv} = [156(37 - t_c) + 47(33 - t_{sk}) - 1.57(33 - t_{sk})^2]/\mathrm{BF}^{0.5} \quad (67)$$

where BF is percentage body fat and the temperature difference terms are set to zero if they become negative (Tikusis and Giesbrecht 1999).

The core loses energy when the muscles do work on the surroundings. Heat is also lost from the core through respiration. The rate of respiratory heat loss is due to sensible and latent changes in the respired air and the ventilation rate as in Equations (19) and (20).

In addition, heat is conducted passively from the core to the skin. This is modeled as a massless thermal conductor [K = 5.28 W/(m²·K)]. A controllable heat loss path from the core consists of pumping variable

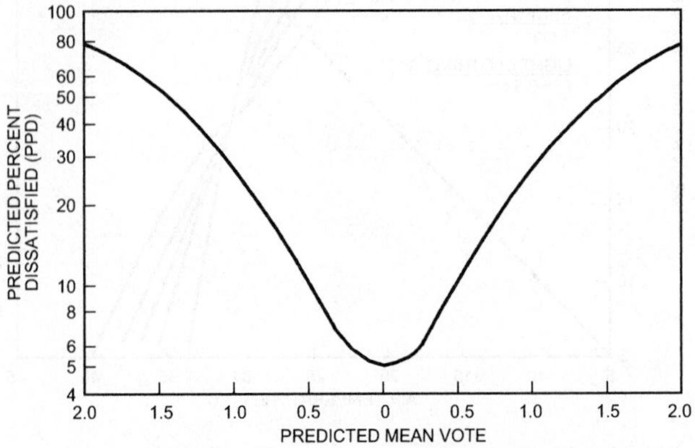

Fig. 16 Predicted Percentage of Dissatisfied (PPD) as Function of Predicted Mean Vote (PMV)

amounts of warm blood to the skin for cooling. This peripheral blood flow Q_{bl} in L/(h·m²) depends on skin and core temperature deviations from their respective set points:

$$Q_{bl} = \frac{\mathrm{BFN} + c_{dil}(t_{cr} - 37)}{1 + S_{tr}(34 - t_{sk})} \quad (68)$$

The temperature terms can only be > 0. If the deviation is negative, the term is set to zero. For average persons, the coefficients BFN, c_{dil}, and S_{tr} are 6.3, 50, and 0.5. Further, skin blood flow Q_{bl} is limited to a maximum of 90 L/(h·m²). A very fit and well-trained athlete could expect to have c_{dil} = 175.

Dry (sensible) heat loss q_{dry} from the skin flows through the clothing by conduction and then by parallel paths to the air and surrounding surfaces. Evaporative heat follows a similar path, flowing through the clothing and through the air boundary layer. Maximum evaporation E_{max} occurs if the skin is completely covered with sweat. The actual evaporation rate E_{sw} depends on the size w of the sweat film:

$$E_{sw} = wE_{max} \quad (69)$$

where w is E_{rsw}/E_{max}.

The rate of regulatory sweating E_{rsw} (rate at which water is brought to the surface of the skin in W/m) can be predicted by skin and core temperature deviations from their set points:

$$E_{rsw} = c_{sw}(t_b - t_{bset}) \exp[-(t_{sk} - 34)/10.7] \quad (70)$$

where $t_b = (1 - \alpha_{sk})t_{cr} + \alpha_{sk}t_{sk}$ and is the mean body temperature, and c_{sw} = 170 W/(m²·K). The temperature deviation terms are set to zero when negative. The fraction of the total body mass considered to be thermally in the skin compartment is α_{sk}:

$$\alpha_{sk} = 0.0418 + \frac{0.745}{\dot{Q}_{bl} - 0.585} \quad (71)$$

Regulatory sweating Q_{rsw} in the model is limited to 1 L/(h·m²) or 670 W/m². E_{rsw} evaporates from the skin, but if E_{rsw} is greater than E_{max}, the excess drips off.

An energy balance on the core yields

$$M + M_{shiv} = W + q_{res} + (K + \mathrm{SkBF}c_{p,bl})(t_{cr} - t_{sk}) + m_{cr}c_{cr}\frac{dt_{cr}}{d\theta} \quad (72)$$

and for the skin,

$$(K + \mathrm{SkBF}c_{p,bl})(t_{cr} - t_{sk}) = q_{dry} + q_{evap} + m_{sk}c_{sk}\frac{dt_{sk}}{d\theta} \quad (73)$$

where c_{cr}, c_{sk}, and $c_{p,bl}$ are specific heats of core, skin, and blood [3500, 3500, and 4190 J/(kg·K), respectively], and SkBF is $\rho_{bl}Q_{bl}$, where ρ_{bl} is density of blood (12.9 kg/L).

Equations (72) and (73) can be rearranged in terms of $dt_{sk}/d\theta$ and $dt_{cr}/d\theta$ and numerically integrated with small time steps (10 to 60 s) from initial conditions or previous values to find t_{cr} and t_{sk} at any time.

After calculating values of t_{sk}, t_{cr}, and w, the model uses empirical expressions to predict thermal sensation (TSENS) and thermal discomfort (DISC). These indices are based on 11-point numerical scales, where positive values represent the warm side of neutral sensation or comfort, and negative values represent the cool side. TSENS is based on the same scale as PMV, but with extra terms for

±4 (very hot/cold) and ±5 (intolerably hot/cold). Recognizing the same positive/negative convention for warm/cold discomfort, DISC is defined as

5 intolerable
4 limited tolerance
3 very uncomfortable
2 uncomfortable and unpleasant
1 slightly uncomfortable but acceptable
0 comfortable

TSENS is defined in terms of deviations of mean body temperature t_b from cold and hot set points representing the lower and upper limits for the zone of evaporative regulation: $t_{b,c}$ and $t_{b,h}$, respectively. The values of these set points depend on the net rate of internal heat production and are calculated by

$$t_{b,c} = \frac{0.194}{58.15}(M - W) + 36.301 \tag{74}$$

$$t_{b,h} = \frac{0.347}{58.15}(M - W) + 36.669 \tag{75}$$

TSENS is then determined by

$$\text{TSENS} = \begin{cases} 0.4685(t_b - t_{b,c}) & t_b < t_{b,c} \\ 4.7\eta_{ev}(t_b - t_{b,c})/(t_{b,h} - t_{b,c}) & t_{b,c} \le t_b \le t_{b,h} \\ 4.7\eta_{ev} + 0.4685(t_b - t_{b,h}) & t_{b,h} < t_b \end{cases} \tag{76}$$

where η_{ev} is the evaporative efficiency (assumed to be 0.85).

DISC is numerically equal to TSENS when t_b is below its cold set point $t_{b,c}$ and it is related to skin wettedness when body temperature is regulated by sweating:

$$\text{DISC} = \begin{cases} 0.4685(t_b - t_{b,c}) & t_b < t_{b,c} \\ \dfrac{4.7(E_{rsw} - E_{rsw,req})}{E_{max} - E_{rsw,req} - E_{dif}} & t_{b,c} \le t_b \end{cases} \tag{77}$$

where $E_{rsw,req}$ is calculated as in Fanger's model, using Equation (59).

Adaptive Models

Adaptive models do not actually predict comfort responses but rather the almost constant conditions under which people are likely to be comfortable in buildings. In general, people naturally adapt and may also make various adjustments to themselves and their surroundings to reduce discomfort and physiological strain. It has been observed that, through adaptive actions, an acceptable degree of comfort in residences and offices is possible over a range of air temperatures from about 17 to 31°C (Humphreys and Nicol 1998).

Adaptive adjustments are typically conscious actions such as altering clothing, posture, activity schedules or levels, rate of working, diet, ventilation, air movement, and local temperature. They may also include unconscious longer-term changes to physiological set points and gains for control of shivering, skin blood flow, and sweating, as well as adjustments to body fluid levels and salt loss. However, only limited documentation and information on such changes is available.

An important driving force behind the adaptive process is the pattern of outside weather conditions and exposure to them. This is the principal input to adaptive models, which predict likely comfort temperatures t_c or ranges of t_c from monthly mean outdoor temperatures t_{out}. Humphreys and Nicol's (1998) model is based on data from a wide range of buildings, climates, and cultures:

$$t_c = 24.2 + 0.43(t_{out} - 22)\exp - \left(\frac{t_{out} - 22}{24\sqrt{2}}\right)^2 \tag{78}$$

Adaptive models are useful to guide design and energy decisions, and to specify building temperature set points throughout the year. A recent ASHRAE-sponsored study (de Dear and Brager 1998) on adaptive models compiled an extensive database from field studies to study, develop, and test adaptive models. For climates and buildings where cooling and central heating are not required, the study suggests the following model:

$$t_{oc} = 18.9 + 0.255t_{out} \tag{79}$$

where t_{oc} is the operative comfort temperature. The adaptive model boundary temperatures for 90% thermal acceptability are approximately t_{oc}+ 2.5°C and t_{oc} − 2.2°C according to ASHRAE *Standard* 55-2004.

In general, the value of using an adaptive model to specify set points or guide temperature control strategies is likely to increase with the freedom that occupants are given to adapt (e.g., by having flexible working hours, locations, or dress codes).

Zones of Comfort and Discomfort

The section on Two-Node Model shows that comfort and thermal sensation are not necessarily the same variable, especially for a person in the zone of evaporative thermal regulation. Figures 17 and 18 show this difference for the standard combination of met-clo-air movement used in the standard effective temperature ET*. Figure 17 demonstrates that practically all basic physiological variables predicted by the two-node model are functions of ambient temperature and are relatively independent of vapor pressure. All exceptions occur at relative humidities above 80% and as the isotherms reach the ET* = 41.5°C line, where regulation by evaporation fails. Figure 18 shows that lines of constant ET* and wettedness are functions of both ambient temperature and vapor pressure. Thus, human thermal responses are divided into two classes: those in Figure 17, which respond only to heat stress from the environment, and those in Figure 18, which respond to both heat stress from the environment and the resultant heat strain (Stolwijk et al. 1968).

For warm environments, any index with isotherms parallel to skin temperature is a reliable index of thermal sensation alone, and not of discomfort caused by increased humidity. Indices with isotherms parallel to ET* are reliable indicators of discomfort or dissatisfaction with thermal environments. For a fixed exposure time to cold, lines of constant t_{sk}, ET*, and t_o are essentially identical, and cold sensation is no different from cold discomfort. For a state of comfort with

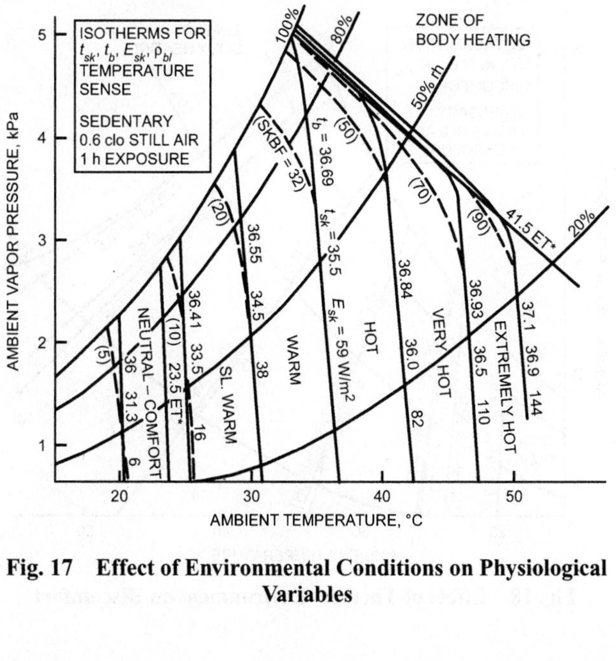

Fig. 17 Effect of Environmental Conditions on Physiological Variables

sedentary or light activity, lines of constant t_{sk} and ET* coincide. Thus, comfort and thermal sensations coincide in this region as well. The upper and lower temperature limits for comfort at these levels can be specified either by thermal sensation (Fanger 1982) or by ET*, as is done in ASHRAE *Standard* 55, because lines of constant comfort and lines of constant thermal sensation should be identical.

ENVIRONMENTAL INDICES

An environmental index combines two or more parameters (e.g., air temperature, mean radiant temperature, humidity, air velocity) into a single variable. Indices simplify description of the thermal environment and the stress it imposes. Environmental indices may be classified according to how they are developed. Rational indices are based on the theoretical concepts presented earlier. Empirical indices are based on measurements with subjects or on simplified relationships that do not necessarily follow theory. Indices may also be classified according to their application, generally either heat stress or cold stress.

Effective Temperature

Effective temperature ET* is probably the most common environmental index, and has the widest range of application. It combines temperature and humidity into a single index, so two environments with the same ET* should evoke the same thermal response even though they have different temperatures and humidities, as long as they have the same air velocities.

The original empirical effective temperature was developed by Houghten and Yaglou (1923). Gagge et al. (1971a, 1971b) defined a new effective temperature using a rational approach. Defined mathematically in Equation (33), this is the temperature of an environment at 50% rh that results in the same total heat loss E_{sk} from the skin as in the actual environment.

Because the index is defined in terms of operative temperature t_o, it combines the effects of three parameters ($\bar{t}_r$, t_a, and p_a) into a single index. Skin wettedness w and the permeability index i_m must be specified and are constant for a given ET* line for a particular situation. The two-node model is used to determine skin wettedness in the zone of evaporative regulation. At the upper limit of regulation, w approaches 1.0; at the lower limit, w approaches 0.06. Skin wettedness equals one of these values when the body is outside the zone of evaporative regulation. Because the slope of a constant ET* line depends on skin wettedness and clothing moisture permeability, effective temperature for a given temperature and humidity may depend on the person's clothing and activity. This difference is shown in Figure 19. At low skin wettedness, air humidity has little influence, and lines of constant ET* are nearly vertical. As skin wettedness increases due to activity and/or heat stress, the lines become more horizontal and the influence of humidity is much more pronounced. The ASHRAE comfort envelope shown in Figure 5 is described in terms of ET*.

Because ET* depends on clothing and activity, it is not possible to generate a universal ET* chart. A standard set of conditions representative of typical indoor applications is used to define a **standard effective temperature SET***, defined as the equivalent air temperature of an isothermal environment at 50% rh in which a subject, wearing clothing standardized for the activity concerned, has the same heat stress (skin temperature t_{sk}) and thermoregulatory strain (skin wettedness w) as in the actual environment.

Humid Operative Temperature

The **humid operative temperature t_{oh}** is the temperature of a uniform environment at 100% rh in which a person loses the same

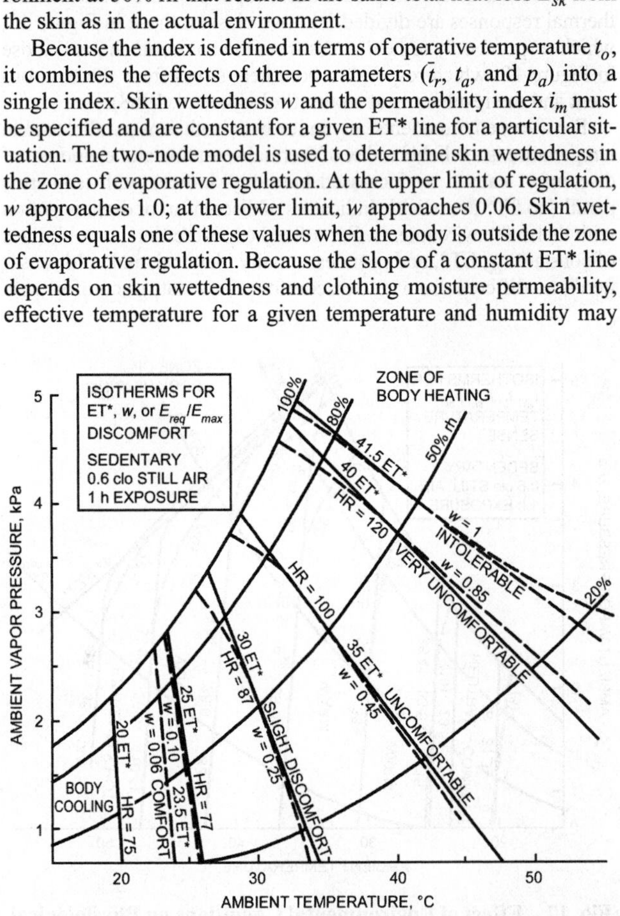

Fig. 18 Effect of Thermal Environment on Discomfort

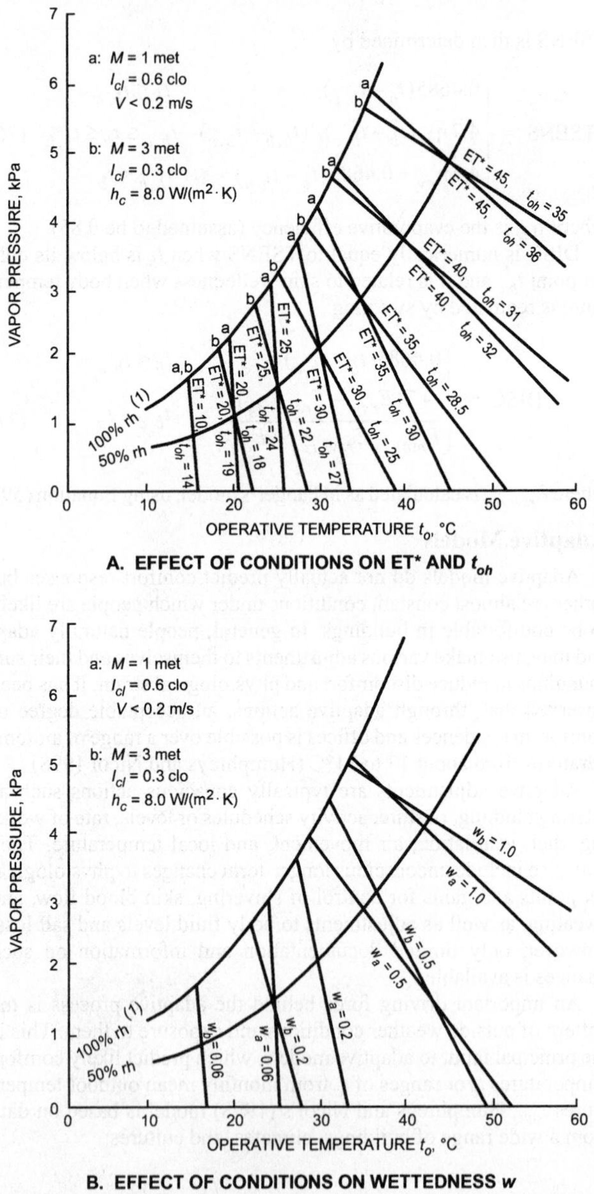

Fig. 19 Effective Temperature ET* and Skin Wettedness *w*
[Adapted from Gonzalez et al. (1978) and Nishi et al. (1975)]

Table 11 Evaluation of Heat Stress Index

Heat Stress Index	Physiological and Hygienic Implications of 8 h Exposures to Various Heat Stresses
0	*No* thermal strain.
10 20 30	*Mild to moderate* heat strain. If job involves higher intellectual functions, dexterity, or alertness, subtle to substantial decrements in performance may be expected. In performing heavy physical work, little decrement is expected, unless ability of individuals to perform such work under no thermal stress is marginal.
40 50 60	*Severe* heat strain involving a threat to health unless workers are physically fit. Break-in period required for men not previously acclimatized. Some decrement in performance of physical work is to be expected. Medical selection of personnel desirable, because these conditions are unsuitable for those with cardiovascular or respiratory impairment or with chronic dermatitis. These working conditions are also unsuitable for activities requiring sustained mental effort.
70 80 90	*Very severe* heat strain. Only a small percentage of the population may be expected to qualify for this work. Personnel should be selected (a) by medical examination, and (b) by trial on the job (after acclimatization). Special measures are needed to ensure adequate water and salt intake. Amelioration of working conditions by any feasible means is highly desirable, and may be expected to decrease the health hazard while increasing job efficiency. Slight "indisposition," which in most jobs would be insufficient to affect performance, may render workers unfit for this exposure.
100	The *maximum* strain tolerated daily by fit, acclimatized young men.

total amount of heat from the skin as in the actual environment. This index is defined mathematically in Equation (32). It is analogous to ET*, except that it is defined at 100% rh and 0% rh rather than at 50% rh. Figures 2 and 19 indicate that lines of constant ET* are also lines of constant t_{oh}. However, the values of these two indices differ for a given environment.

Heat Stress Index

Originally proposed by Belding and Hatch (1955), this rational index is the ratio of total evaporative heat loss E_{sk} required for thermal equilibrium (the sum of metabolism plus dry heat load) to maximum evaporative heat loss E_{max} possible for the environment, multiplied by 100, for steady-state conditions (S_{sk} and S_{cr} are zero) and with t_{sk} held constant at 35°C. The ratio E_{sk}/E_{max} equals skin wettedness w [Equation (18)]. When **heat stress index (HSI)** > 100, body heating occurs; when HSI < 0, body cooling occurs. Belding and Hatch (1955) limited E_{max} to 700 W/m², which corresponds to a sweat rate of approximately 280 mg/(s·m²). When t_{sk} is constant, loci of constant HSI coincide with lines of constant ET* on a psychrometric chart. Other indices based on wettedness have the same applications (Belding 1970; Gonzalez et al. 1978; ISO *Standard* 7933) but differ in their treatment of E_{max} and the effect of clothing. Table 11 describes physiological factors associated with HSI values.

Index of Skin Wettedness

Skin wettedness w is the ratio of observed skin sweating E_{sk} to the E_{max} of the environment as defined by t_{sk}, t_a, humidity, air movement, and clothing in Equation (12). Except for the factor of 100, it is essentially the same as HSI. Skin wettedness is more closely related to the sense of discomfort or unpleasantness than to temperature sensation (Gagge et al. 1969a, 1969b; Gonzalez et al. 1978).

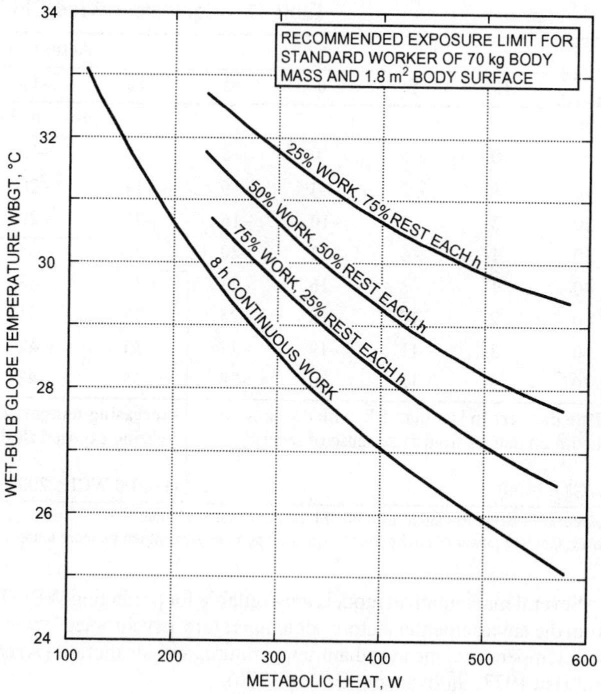

Fig. 20 Recommended Heat Stress Exposure Limits for Heat Acclimatized Workers
[Adapted from NIOSH (1986)]

Wet-Bulb Globe Temperature

The WBGT is an environmental heat stress index that combines dry-bulb temperature t_{db}, a **naturally ventilated** (not aspirated) wet-bulb temperature t_{nwb}, and black globe temperature t_g, according to the relation (Dukes-Dobos and Henschel 1971, 1973)

$$WBGT = 0.7t_{nwb} + 0.2t_g + 0.1t_a \quad (80)$$

This form of the equation is usually used where solar radiation is present. The naturally ventilated wet-bulb thermometer is left exposed to sunlight, but the air temperature t_a sensor is shaded. In enclosed environments, Equation (80) is simplified by dropping the t_a term and using a 0.3 weighting factor for t_g.

The black globe thermometer responds to air temperature, mean radiant temperature, and air movement, whereas the naturally ventilated wet-bulb thermometer responds to air humidity, air movement, radiant temperature, and air temperature. Thus, WBGT is a function of all four environmental factors affecting human environmental heat stress.

The WBGT index is widely used for estimating the heat stress potential of industrial environments (Davis 1976). In the United States, the National Institute of Occupational Safety and Health (NIOSH) developed criteria for a heat-stress-limiting standard (NIOSH 1986). ISO *Standard* 7243 also uses the WBGT. Figure 20 summarizes permissible heat exposure limits, expressed as working time per hour, for a fit individual, as specified for various WBGT levels. Values apply for normal permeable clothing (0.6 clo) and must be adjusted for heavy or partly vapor-permeable clothing. For example, the U.S. Air Force (USAF) recommended adjusting the measured WBGT upwards by 6 K for personnel wearing chemical protective clothing or body armor. This type of clothing increases resistance to sweat evaporation about threefold (higher if it is totally impermeable), requiring an adjustment in WBGT level to compensate for reduced evaporative cooling at the skin.

Table 12 Equivalent Wind Chill Temperatures of Cold Environments

Wind Speed, km/h	Actual Thermometer Reading, °C												
	10	5	0	−5	−10	−15	−20	−25	−30	−35	−40	−45	−50
	Equivalent Wind Chill Temperature, °C												
Calm	10	5	0	−5	−10	−15	−20	−25	−30	−35	−40	−45	−50
10	8	2	−3	−9	−14	−20	−25	−31	−37	−42	−48	−53	−59
20	3	−3	−10	−16	−23	−29	−35	−42	−48	−55	−61	−68	−74
30	1	−6	−13	−20	−27	−34	−42	−49	−56	−63	−70	−77	−84
40	−1	−8	−16	−23	−31	−38	−46	−53	−60	−68	−75	−83	−90
50	−2	−10	−18	−25	−33	−41	−48	−56	−64	−71	−79	−87	−94
60	−3	−11	−19	−27	−35	−42	−50	−58	−66	−74	−82	−90	−97
70	−4	−12	−20	−28	−35	−43	−51	−59	−67	−75	−83	−91	−99
Little danger: In less than 5 h, with dry skin. Maximum danger from false sense of security. (WCI < 1400)					**Increasing danger:** Danger of freezing exposed flesh within 1 min. (1400 ≤ WCI ≤ 2000)			**Great danger:** Flesh may freeze within 30 s. (WCI > 2000)					

Source: U.S. Army Research Institute of Environmental Medicine.
Notes: Cooling power of environment expressed as an equivalent temperature under calm conditions [Equation (83)].
Winds greater than 70 km/h have little added chilling effect.

Several mathematical models are available for predicting WBGT from the environmental factors: air temperature, psychrometric wet-bulb temperature, mean radiant temperature, and air motion (Azer and Hsu 1977; Sullivan and Gorton 1976).

Wet-Globe Temperature

The WGT, introduced by Botsford (1971), is a simpler approach to measuring environmental heat stress than the WBGT. The measurement is made with a wetted globe thermometer called a Botsball, which consists of a 65 mm black copper sphere covered with a fitted wet black mesh fabric, into which the sensor of a dial thermometer is inserted. A polished stem attached to the sphere supports the thermometer and contains a water reservoir for keeping the sphere covering wet. This instrument is suspended by the stem at the site to be measured.

Onkaram et al. (1980) showed that WBGT can be predicted with reasonable accuracy from WGT for temperate to warm environments with medium to high humidities. With air temperatures between 20 and 35°C, dew points from 7 to 25°C (relative humidities above 30%), and wind speeds of 7 m/s or less, the experimental regression equation (r = 0.98) in °C for an outdoor environment is

$$\mathrm{WBGT} = 1.044(\mathrm{WGT}) - 0.187 \quad (81)$$

This equation should not be used outside the experimental range given because data from hot/dry desert environments show differences between WBGT and WGT that are too large (6 K and above) to be adjusted by Equation (81) (Matthew et al. 1986). At very low humidity and high wind, WGT approaches the psychrometric wet-bulb temperature, which is greatly depressed below t_a. However, in the WBGT, t_{nwb} accounts for only 70% of the index value, with the remaining 30% at or above t_a.

Wind Chill Index

The wind chill index (WCI) is an empirical index developed from cooling measurements obtained in Antarctica on a cylindrical flask partly filled with water (Siple and Passel 1945). The index describes the rate of heat loss from the cylinder by radiation and convection for a surface temperature of 33°C, as a function of ambient temperature and wind velocity. As originally proposed,

$$\mathrm{WCI} = (10.45 + 10\sqrt{V} - V)(33 - t_a) \text{ in kcal/(h·m}^2) \quad (82)$$

where V and t_a are in m/s and °C, respectively. Multiply WCI by 0.8606 to convert to W/m². The 33°C surface temperature was chosen to be representative of the mean skin temperature of a resting human in comfortable surroundings.

Some valid objections have been raised about this formulation. Cooling rate data from which it was derived were measured on a 57 mm diameter plastic cylinder, making it unlikely that WCI would be an accurate measure of heat loss from exposed flesh, which has different characteristics from plastic (curvature, roughness, and radiation exchange properties) and is invariably below 33°C in a cold environment. Moreover, values given by the equation peak at 90 km/h, then decrease with increasing velocity.

Nevertheless, for velocities below 80 km/h, this index reliably expresses combined effects of temperature and wind on subjective discomfort. For example, if the calculated WCI is less than 1400 kcal/(h·m²) and actual air temperature is above −10°C, there is little risk of frostbite during brief exposures (1 h or less), even for bare skin. However, at a WCI of 2000 or more, the probability is high that exposed flesh will begin to freeze in 1 min or less unless measures are taken to shield exposed skin (such as a fur ruff to break up wind around the face).

Rather than using the WCI to express the severity of a cold environment, meteorologists use an index derived from the WCI called the **equivalent wind chill temperature** $t_{eq,wc}$. This is the ambient temperature that would produce, in a calm wind (defined for this application as 6.4 km/h), the same WCI as the actual combination of air temperature and wind velocity:

$$t_{eq,wc} = -0.0528(\mathrm{WCI}) + 33 \quad (83)$$

where $t_{eq,wc}$ is in °C (and frequently referred to as a **wind chill factor**), thus distinguishing it from WCI, which is given either as a cooling rate or as a plain number with no units. For velocities less than 6.4 km/h (1.8 m/s), Equation (83) does not apply, and the wind chill temperature is equal to the air temperature.

Equation (83) does not imply cooling to below ambient temperature, but recognizes that, because of wind, the cooling rate is increased as though it were occurring at the lower equivalent wind chill temperature. Wind accelerates the rate of heat loss, so that the skin surface cools more quickly toward the ambient temperature. Table 12 shows a typical wind chill chart, expressed in equivalent wind chill temperature.

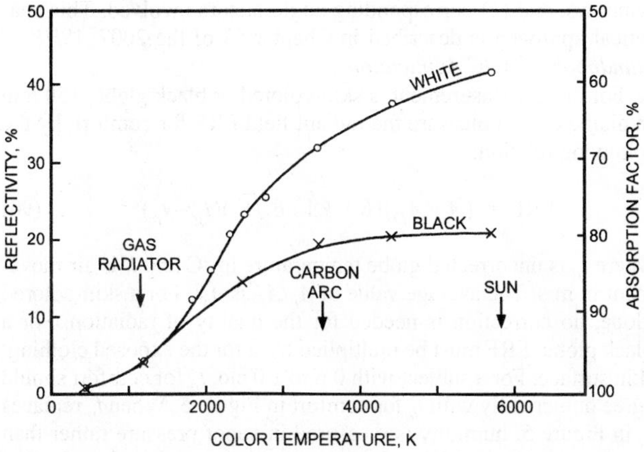

Fig. 21 Variation in Skin Reflection and Absorptivity for Blackbody Heat Sources

SPECIAL ENVIRONMENTS

Infrared Heating

Optical and thermal properties of skin must be considered in studies of the effects of infrared radiation in (1) producing changes in skin temperature and skin blood flow, and (2) evoking sensations of temperature and comfort (Hardy 1961). Although the body can be considered to have the properties of water, thermal sensation and heat transfer with the environment require a study of the skin and its interaction with visible and infrared radiation.

Figure 21 shows how skin reflectance and absorptance vary for a blackbody heat source at the temperature (in K) indicated. These curves show that darkly pigmented skin is heated more by direct radiation from a high-intensity heater at 2500 K than is lightly pigmented skin. With low-temperature, low-intensity heating equipment used for total area heating, there is minimal, if any, difference. Also, in practice, clothing minimizes differences.

Changes in skin temperature caused by high-intensity infrared radiation depend on the thermal conductivity, density, and specific heat of the living skin (Lipkin and Hardy 1954). Modeling skin heating with the heat transfer theory yields a parabolic relation between exposure time and skin temperature rise for nonpenetrating radiation:

$$t_{sf} - t_{si} = \Delta t = 2J\alpha\sqrt{\theta/(\pi k\rho c_p)} \qquad (84)$$

where

t_{sf} = final skin temperature, °C
t_{si} = initial skin temperature, °C
J = irradiance from source radiation temperatures, W/m²
α = skin absorptance at radiation temperatures, dimensionless
θ = time, h
k = specific thermal conductivity of tissue, W/(m·K)
ρ = density, kg/m³
c_p = specific heat, J/(kg·K)

Product $k\rho c_p$ is the physiologically important quantity that determines temperature elevation of skin or other tissue on exposure to nonpenetrating radiation. Fatty tissue, because of its relatively low specific heat, is heated more rapidly than moist skin or bone. Experimentally, $k\rho c_p$ values can be determined by plotting Δt^2 against $1.13J^2\theta$ (Figure 22). The relationship is linear, and the slopes are inversely proportional to the $k\rho c_p$ of the specimen. Comparing leather and water with body tissues suggests that thermal inertia values depend largely on tissue water content.

Living tissues do not conform strictly to this simple mathematical formula. Figure 23 compares excised skin with living skin with normal blood flow, and skin with blood flow occluded. For short

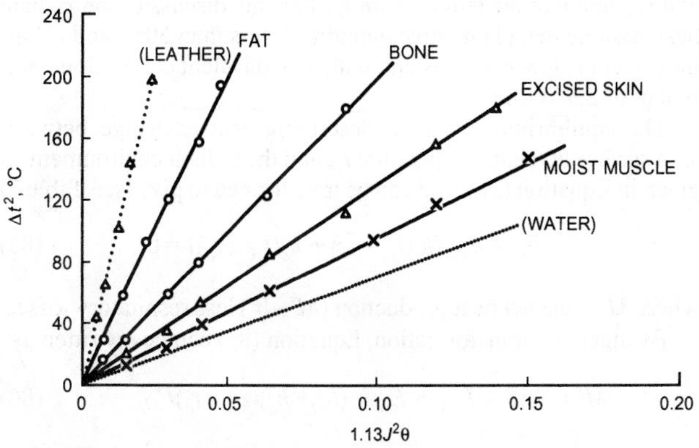

Fig. 22 Comparing Thermal Inertia of Fat, Bone, Moist Muscle, and Excised Skin to That of Leather and Water

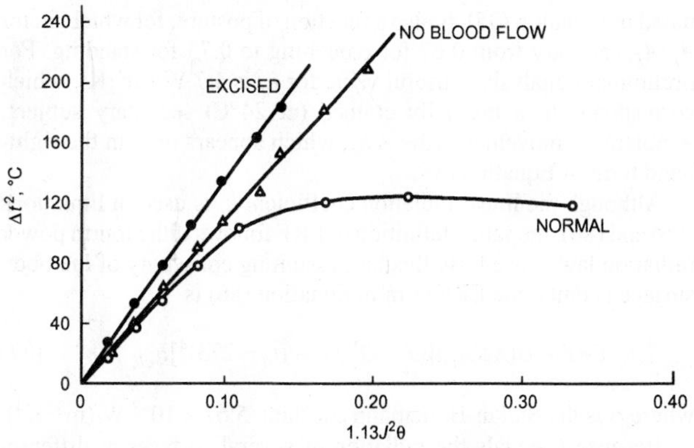

Fig. 23 Thermal Inertias of Excised, Bloodless, and Normal Living Skin

exposure times, the $k\rho c_p$ of normal skin is the same as that in which blood flow has been stopped; excised skin heats more rapidly because of unavoidable dehydration that occurs postmortem. However, with longer exposure to thermal radiation, vasodilation increases blood flow, cooling the skin. For the first 20 s of irradiation, skin with normally constricted blood vessels has a $k\rho c_p$ value one-fourth that for skin with fully dilated vessels.

Skin temperature is the best single index of thermal comfort. The most rapid changes in skin temperature occur during the first 60 s of exposure to infrared radiation. During this initial period, thermal sensation and the heating rate of the skin vary with the quality of infrared radiation (color temperature in K). Because radiant heat from a gas-fired heater is absorbed at the skin surface, the same unit level of absorbed radiation during the first 60 s of exposure can cause an even warmer initial sensation than penetrating solar radiation. Skin heating curves tend to level off after a 60 s exposure (Figure 23), which means that a relative balance is quickly created between heat absorbed, heat flow to the skin surface, and heat loss to the ambient environment. Therefore, the effects of radiant heating on thermal comfort should be examined for conditions approaching thermal equilibrium.

Stolwijk and Hardy (1966) described an unclothed subject's response for a 2 h exposure to temperatures of 5 to 35°C. Nevins et al. (1966) showed a relation between ambient temperatures and thermal comfort of clothed, resting subjects. For any given uniform environmental temperature, both initial physiological response and degree of comfort can be determined for a subject at rest.

Physiological implications for radiant heating can be defined by two environmental temperatures: (1) mean radiant temperature $\bar{t}_r$

and (2) ambient air temperature t_a. For this discussion on radiant heat, assume that (1) relative humidity is less than 50%, and (2) air movement is low and constant, with an equivalent convection coefficient of 2.9 W/(m²·K).

The equilibrium equation, describing heat exchange between skin surface at mean temperature t_{sk} and the radiant environment, is given in Equation (28), and can be transformed to give (see Table 2)

$$M' - E_{sk} - F_{cle}[h_r(t_{sk} - \bar{t}_r) + h_c(t_{sk} - t_o)] = 0 \quad (85)$$

where M' is the net heat production ($M - W$) less respiratory losses.

By algebraic transformation, Equation (85) can be rewritten as

$$M' + \text{ERF} \times F_{cle} = E_{sk} + (h_r + h_c)(t_{sk} - t_a)F_{cle} \quad (86)$$

where ERF $= h_r(\bar{t}_r - t_a)$ is the effective radiant field and represents the additional radiant exchange with the body when $\bar{t}_r \neq t_a$.

The last term in Equation (86) describes heat exchange with an environment uniformly heated to temperature t_a. The term h_r, evaluated in Equation (35), is also a function of posture, for which factor A_r/A_D can vary from 0.67 for crouching to 0.73 for standing. For preliminary analysis, a useful value for h_r is 4.7 W/(m²·K), which corresponds to a normally clothed (at 24°C) sedentary subject. Ambient air movement affects h_c, which appears only in the right-hand term of Equation (86).

Although the linear radiation coefficient h_r is used in Equations (85) and (86), the same definition of ERF follows if the fourth power radiation law is used. By this law, assuming emissivity of the body surface is unity, the ERF term in Equation (86) is

$$\text{ERF} = \sigma(A_r/A_D)[(\bar{t}_r - 273)^4 - (t_a + 273)^4]F_{cle} \quad (87)$$

where σ is the Stefan-Boltzmann constant, 5.67×10^{-8} W/(m²·K⁴).

Because $\bar{t}_r$ equals the radiation of several surfaces at different temperatures ($T_1, T_2, \ldots, T_j$),

$$\text{ERF} = (\text{ERF})_1 + (\text{ERF})_2 + \cdots + (\text{ERF})_j \quad (88)$$

where

$\text{ERF}_j = \sigma(A_r/A_D)\alpha_j F_{m-j}(T_j^4 - T_a^4)F_{cle}$

α_j = absorptance of skin or clothing surface for source radiating at temperature T_j

F_{m-j} = angle factor to subject m from source j

T_a = ambient air temperature, K

ERF is the sum of the fields caused by each surface T_j [e.g., T_1 may be an infrared beam heater; T_2, a heated floor; T_3, a warm ceiling; T_4, a cold plate glass window ($T_4 < T_a$); etc.]. Only surfaces with T_j differing from T_a contribute to the ERF.

Comfort Equations for Radiant Heating

The **comfort equation for radiant heat** (Gagge et al. 1967a, 1967b) follows from definition of ERF and Equation (8):

$$t_o \text{ (for comfort)} = t_a + \text{ERF (for comfort)}/h \quad (89)$$

Thus, operative temperature for comfort is the temperature of the ambient air plus a temperature increment ERF/h, a ratio that measures the effectiveness of the incident radiant heating on occupants. Higher air movement (which increases the value of h or h_c) reduces the effectiveness of radiant heating systems. Clothing lowers t_o for comfort and for thermal neutrality.

Values for ERF and h must be determined to apply the comfort equation for radiant heating. Table 3 may be used to estimate h. One method of determining ERF is to calculate it directly from radiometric data that give (1) radiation emission spectrum of the source, (2) concentration of the beam, (3) radiation from the floor, ceiling, and windows, and (4) corresponding angle factors involved. This analytical approach is described in Chapter 53 of the 2007 *ASHRAE Handbook—HVAC Applications*.

For direct measurement, a skin-colored or black globe, 150 mm in diameter, can measure the radiant field ERF for comfort, by the following relation:

$$\text{ERF} = (A_r/A_D)(6.1 + 13.6\sqrt{V})(t_g - t_a) \quad (90)$$

where t_g is uncorrected globe temperature in °C and V is air movement in m/s. The average value of A_r/A_D is 0.7. For a skin-colored globe, no correction is needed for the quality of radiation. For a black globe, ERF must be multiplied by α for the exposed clothing/skin surface. For a subject with 0.6 to 1.0 clo, t_o for comfort should agree numerically with t_a for comfort in Figure 5. When t_o replaces t_a in Figure 5, humidity is measured in vapor pressure rather than relative humidity, which refers only to air temperature.

Other methods may be used to measure ERF. The most accurate is by physiological means. In Equation (86), when M, $t_{sk} - t_a$, and the associated transfer coefficients are experimentally held constant,

$$\Delta E = \Delta\text{ERF} \quad (91)$$

The variation in evaporative heat loss E (rate of mass loss) caused by changing the wattage of two T-3 infrared lamps is a measure in absolute terms of the radiant heat received by the body.

A third method uses a directional radiometer to measure ERF directly. For example, radiation absorbed at the body surface (in W/m²) is

$$\text{ERF} = \alpha(A_i/A_D)J \quad (92)$$

where irradiance J can be measured by a directional (Hardy-type) radiometer, α is the surface absorptance effective for the source used, and A_i is the projection area of the body normal to the directional irradiance. Equation (92) can be used to calculate ERF only for the simplest geometrical arrangements. For a human subject lying supine and irradiated uniformly from above, A_i/A_D is 0.3. Figure 21 shows variance of α for human skin with blackbody temperature (in K) of the radiating source. When irradiance J is uneven and coming from many directions, as is usually the case, the previous physiological method can be used to obtain an effective A_i/A_D from the observed ΔE and Δ(αJ).

Hot and Humid Environments

Tolerance limits to high temperature vary with the ability to (1) sense temperature, (2) lose heat by regulatory sweating, and (3) move heat from the body core by blood flow to the skin surface, where cooling is the most effective. Many interrelating processes are involved in heat stress (Figure 24).

Skin surface temperatures of 46°C trigger pain receptors in the skin; direct contact with metal at this temperature is painful. However, because thermal insulation of the air layer around the skin is high, much higher dry-air temperatures can be tolerated (e.g., 185°F for brief periods in a sauna). For lightly clothed subjects at rest, tolerance times of nearly 50 min have been reported at 82°C db; 33 min at 93°C; 26 min at 104°C; and 24 min at 115°C. In each case, dew points were lower than 30°C. Short exposures to these extremely hot environments are tolerable because of cooling by sweat evaporation. However, when ambient vapor pressure approaches 6.0 kPa (36°C dp, typically found on sweating skin), tolerance is drastically reduced. Temperatures of 50°C can be intolerable if the dew-point temperature is greater than 25°C, and both deep body temperature and heart rate rise within minutes (Gonzalez et al. 1978).

The rate at which and length of time a body can sweat are limited. The maximum rate of sweating for an average man is about 0.5 g/s.

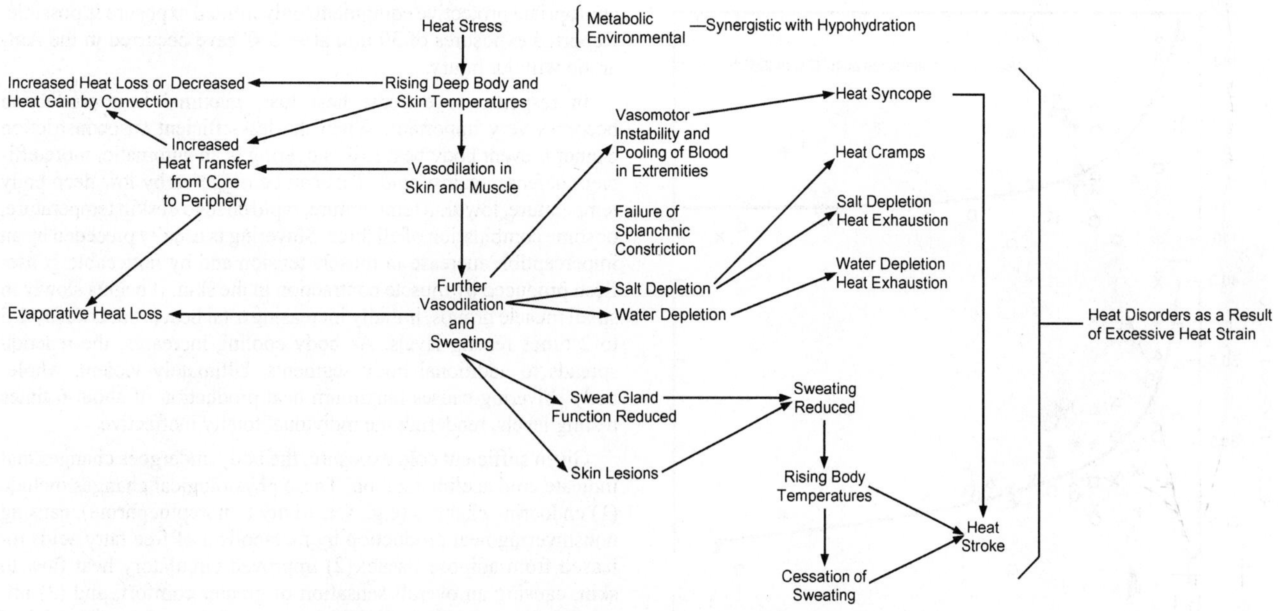

Fig. 24 Schematic Design of Heat Stress and Heat Disorders
[Modified by Buskirk (1960) from scale diagram by Belding (1967) and Leithead and Lind (1964)]

If all this sweat evaporates from the skin surface under conditions of low humidity and air movement, maximum cooling is about 675 W/m^2. However, because sweat rolls off the skin surface without evaporative cooling or is absorbed by or evaporated within clothing, a more typical cooling limit is 6 met (350 W/m^2), representing approximately 0.3 g/s (1 L/h) of sweating for the average man.

Thermal equilibrium is maintained by dissipation of resting heat production (1 met) plus any radiant and convective load. If the environment does not limit heat loss from the body during heavy activity, decreasing skin temperature compensates for the core temperature rise. Therefore, mean body temperature is maintained, although the gradient from core to skin is increased. Blood flow through the skin is reduced, but muscle blood flow necessary for exercise is preserved. The upper limit of skin blood flow is about 25 g/s (Burton and Bazett 1936).

Body heat storage of 335 kJ (or a rise in t_b of 1.4 K) for an average-sized man represents an average voluntary tolerance limit. Continuing work beyond this limit increases the risk of heat exhaustion. Collapse can occur at about 670 kJ of storage (2.8 K rise); few individuals can tolerate heat storage of 920 kJ (3.8 K above normal).

The cardiovascular system affects tolerance limits. In normal, healthy subjects exposed to extreme heat, heart rate and cardiac output increase in an attempt to maintain blood pressure and supply of blood to the brain. At a heart rate of about 180 bpm, the short time between contractions prevents adequate blood supply to the heart chambers. As heart rate continues to increase, cardiac output drops, causing inadequate convective blood exchange with the skin and, perhaps more important, inadequate blood supply to the brain. Victims of this heat exhaustion faint or black out. Accelerated heart rate can also result from inadequate venous return to the heart caused by blood pooling in the skin and lower extremities. In this case, cardiac output is limited because not enough blood is available to refill the heart between beats. This occurs most frequently when an overheated individual, having worked hard in the heat, suddenly stops working. The muscles no longer massage the blood back past the valves in the veins toward the heart. Dehydration compounds the problem by reducing fluid volume in the vascular system.

If core temperature t_{cr} increases above 41 °C, critical hypothalamic proteins can be damaged, resulting in inappropriate vasoconstriction, cessation of sweating, increased heat production by shivering, or some combination of these. Heat stroke damage is frequently irreversible and carries a high risk of death.

A final problem, hyperventilation, occurs mainly in hot/wet conditions, when too much CO_2 is washed from the blood. This can lead to tingling sensations, skin numbness, and vasoconstriction in the brain with occasional loss of consciousness.

Because a rise in heart rate or rectal temperature is essentially linear with ambient vapor pressure above a dew point of 25 °C, these two changes can measure severe heat stress. Although individual heart rate and rectal temperature responses to mild heat stress vary, severe heat stress saturates physiological regulating systems, producing uniform increases in heart rate and rectal temperature. In contrast, sweat production measures stress under milder conditions but becomes less useful under more severe stress. The maximal sweat rate compatible with body cooling varies with (1) degree of heat acclimatization, (2) duration of sweating, and (3) whether the sweat evaporates or merely saturates the skin and drips off. Total sweat rates over 2 L/h can occur in short exposures, but about 1 L/h is an average maximum sustainable level for an acclimatized man.

Figure 25 illustrates the decline in heart rate, rectal temperature, and skin temperature when exercising subjects are exposed to 40 °C over a period of days. Acclimatization can be achieved by working in the heat for 100 min each day: 30% improvement occurs after the first day, 50% after 3 days, and 95% after 6 or 7 days. Increased sweat secretion while working in the heat can be induced by rest. Although reducing salt intake during the first few days in the heat can conserve sodium, heat cramps may result. Working regularly in the heat improves cardiovascular efficiency, sweat secretion, and sodium conservation. Once induced, heat acclimatization can be maintained by as few as one workout a week in the heat; otherwise, it diminishes slowly over a 2- to 3-week period and disappears.

Extremely Cold Environments

Human performance in extreme cold ultimately depends on maintaining thermal balance. Subjective discomfort is reported by a 70 kg man with 1.8 m^2 of body surface area when a heat debt of about 104 kJ is incurred. A heat debt of about 630 kJ is acutely uncomfortable; this represents a drop of approximately 2.6 K (or about 7% of total heat content) in mean body temperature.

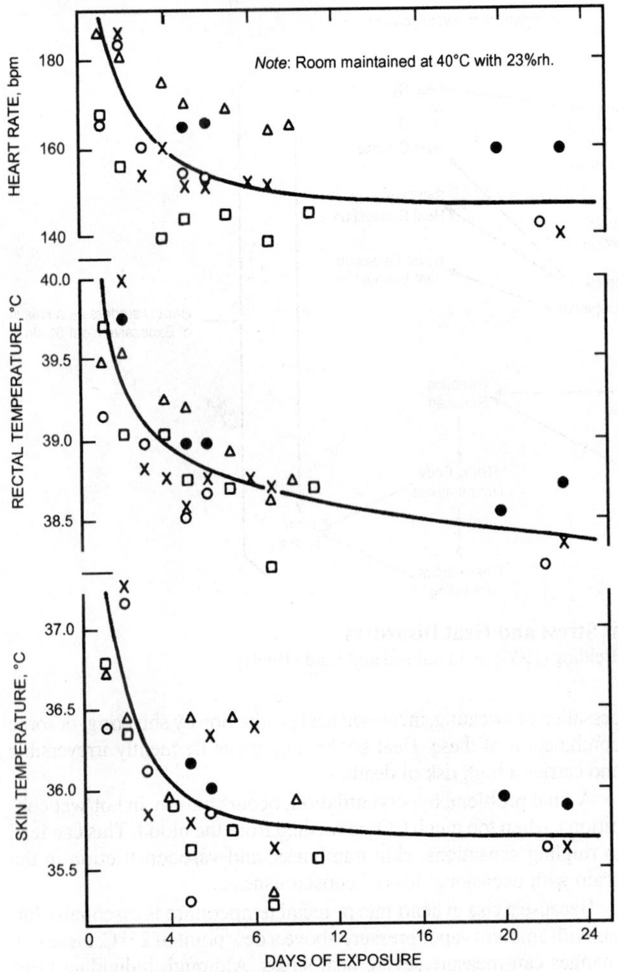

Fig. 25 Acclimatization to Heat Resulting from Daily Exposure of Five Subjects to Extremely Hot Room
(Robinson et al. 1943)

This loss can occur during 1 to 2 h of sedentary activity outdoors. A sleeping individual will wake after losing about 314 kJ, decreasing mean skin temperature by about 3 K and deep body temperature by about 0.5 K. A drop in deep body temperature (e.g., rectal temperature) below 35°C threatens a loss of body temperature regulation, and 28°C is considered critical for survival, despite recorded survival from a deep body temperature of 18°C.

Activity level also affects human performance. Subjective sensations reported by sedentary subjects at a mean skin temperature of 33.3°C are comfortable; at 31°C, uncomfortably cold; at 30°C, shivering cold; and at 29°C, extremely cold. The critical subjective tolerance limit (without numbing) for mean skin temperature appears to be about 25°C. However, during moderate to heavy activity, subjects reported the same skin temperatures as comfortable. Although mean skin temperature is significant, the temperature of the extremities is more frequently the critical factor for comfort in the cold. Consistent with this, one of the first responses to cold exposure is vasoconstriction, which reduces circulatory heat input to the hands and feet. A hand-skin temperature of 20°C causes a report of uncomfortably cold; 15°C, extremely cold; and 5°C, painful. Identical verbal responses for the foot surface occur at approximately 1.5 to 2 K warmer temperatures.

An ambient temperature of −35°C is the lower limit for useful outdoor activity, even with adequate insulative clothing. At −50°C, almost all outdoor effort becomes exceedingly difficult; even with appropriate protective equipment, only limited exposure is possible. Reported exposures of 30 min at −75°C have occurred in the Antarctic without injury.

In response to extreme heat loss, maximal heat production becomes very important. When the less-efficient vasoconstriction cannot prevent body heat loss, shivering is an automatic, more efficient defense against cold. This can be triggered by low deep body temperature, low skin temperature, rapid change of skin temperature, or some combination of all three. Shivering is usually preceded by an imperceptible increase in muscle tension and by noticeable gooseflesh produced by muscle contraction in the skin. It begins slowly in small muscle groups, initially increasing total heat production by 1.5 to 2 times resting levels. As body cooling increases, the reaction spreads to additional body segments. Ultimately violent, whole-body shivering causes maximum heat production of about 6 times resting levels, rendering the individual totally ineffective.

Given sufficient cold exposure, the body undergoes changes that indicate cold acclimatization. These physiological changes include (1) endocrine changes (e.g., sensitivity to norepinephrine), causing nonshivering heat production by metabolism of free fatty acids released from adipose tissue; (2) improved circulatory heat flow to skin, causing an overall sensation of greater comfort; and (3) improved circulatory heat flow to the extremities, reducing the risk of injury and allowing activities at what ordinarily would be severely uncomfortable temperatures in the extremities. Generally, these physiological changes are minor and are induced only by repeated extreme exposures. Nonphysiological factors, including training, experience, and selection of adequate protective clothing, are more useful and may be safer than dependence on physiological changes.

Food energy intake requirements for adequately clothed subjects in extreme cold are only slightly greater than those for subjects living and working in temperate climates. This greater requirement results from added work caused by (1) carrying the weight of heavy clothing (energy cost for heavy protective footwear may be six times that of an equivalent weight on the torso); and (2) the inefficiency of walking in snow, snowshoeing, or skiing, which can increase energy cost up to 300%.

To achieve proper protection in low temperatures, a person must either maintain high metabolic heat production by activity or reduce heat loss by controlling the body's microclimate with clothing. Other protective measures include spot radiant heating, showers of hot air for work at a fixed site, and warm-air-ventilated or electrically heated clothing. Extremities (e.g., fingers and toes) are at greater risk than the torso because, as thin cylinders, they are particularly susceptible to heat loss and difficult to insulate without increasing the surface for heat loss. Vasoconstriction can reduce circulatory heat input to extremities by over 90%.

Although there is no ideal insulating material for protective clothing, radiation-reflective materials are promising. Insulation is primarily a function of clothing thickness; the thickness of trapped air, rather than fibers used, determines insulation effectiveness.

Protection for the respiratory tract seems unnecessary in healthy individuals, even at −45°C. However, asthmatics or individuals with mild cardiovascular problems may benefit from a face mask that warms inspired air. Masks are unnecessary for protecting the face because heat to facial skin is not reduced by local vasoconstriction, as it is for hands. If wind chill is great, there is always a risk of cold injury caused by freezing of exposed skin. Using properly designed torso clothing, such as a parka with a fur-lined hood to minimize wind penetration to the face, and 10 W of auxiliary heat to each hand and foot, inactive people can tolerate −55°C with a 16 km/h wind for more than 6 h. As long as the skin temperature of fingers remains above 15°C, manual dexterity can be maintained and useful work performed without difficulty.

SYMBOLS

A = area, m^2
BFN = neutral skin blood flow, g/(m^2·s)
c = specific heat, J/(kg·K)
c_{dil} = specific heat (constant) for skin blood flow
c_{sw} = proportionality constant for sweat control, 170 W/(m^2·K)
C = convective heat loss, W/m^2
$C + R$ = total sensible heat loss from skin, W/m^2
DISC = thermal discomfort
E = evaporative heat loss, W/m^2
ERF = effective radiant field, W/m^2
ET* = effective temperature based on 50% rh, °C
f_{cl} = clothing area factor, A_{cl}/A_D, dimensionless
F = thermal efficiency, or angle factor
h = enthalpy, kJ/kg (dry air), or heat transfer coefficient, W/(m^2·K)
HSI = heat stress index
i = vapor permeation efficiency, dimensionless
I = thermal resistance in clo units, clo
J = irradiance, W/m^2
k = thermal conductivity of body tissue, W/(m·K)
K = effective conductance between core and skin, W/(m^2·K)
K_{res} = proportionality constant, 1.43 kg/kJ
l = height, m
L = thermal load on body, W/m^2
LR = Lewis ratio, K/kPa
m = mass, kg
$\dot{m}$ = mass flow, kg/(s·m^2)
M = metabolic heat production, W/m^2
p = water vapor pressure, kPa
PD = percent dissatisfied
PMV = predicted mean vote
PPD = predicted percent dissatisfied
q = heat flow, W/m^2
Q = volume rate, L/(h·m^2)
R = thermal resistance, (m^2·K)/W, or radiative heat loss from skin, W/m^2
RQ = respiratory quotient, dimensionless
S = heat storage, W/m^2
SET* = standard effective temperature, °C
SkBF = skin blood flow, g/(m^2·s)
t = temperature, °C
$\bar{t}_r$ = mean temperature, °C
T = absolute temperature, K
TSENS = thermal sensation
Tu = turbulence intensity, %
V = air velocity, m/s
V_{sd} = standard deviation of velocity measured with omnidirectional anemometer with 0.2 s time constant
w = skin wettedness, dimensionless
W = external work accomplished, W/m^2, or humidity ratio of air, kg (water vapor)/kg (dry air)
WBGT = wet-bulb globe temperature, °C
WCI = wind chill index, W/m^2
WGT = wet-globe temperature, °C
x_f = fabric thickness, mm

Greek

α = skin absorptance, dimensionless
ε = emissivity, dimensionless
η_{ev} = evaporative efficiency, dimensionless
θ = time, s
μ = mechanical efficiency of body = W/M, dimensionless
μ_T = mean space temperature, °C
ν = unsolicited thermal complaint rate, complaints/(h·zone area)
ρ = density, kg/m^3
ρ_{bl} = density of blood, 12.9 kg/L
σ = Stefan-Boltzmann constant = 5.67 × 10^{-8} W/(m^2·K^4)
σ_T = standard deviation of space temperature, K
$\sigma_{\dot{T}_H}, \sigma_{\dot{T}_L}$ = standard deviation of rate of change of high and low space temperature, K/h

Superscripts and Subscripts

$'$ = overall, net
a = ambient air
act = activity
b = of body tissue
B = building
b,c = lower limit for evaporative regulation zone
b,h = upper limit for evaporative regulation zone
bl = of blood
c = convection, or comfort
cc = corrected convection value
ch = between chair and body
cl = of clothed body or clothing
cle = of clothing, effective
clu,i = effective insulation of garment i
com = combined
cr = body core
cr,sk = from core to skin
D = DuBois value
db = dry bulb
dif = due to moisture diffusion through skin
dil = skin blood flow
dp = dew point
dry = sensible
e = evaporative, at surface
ec = at surface, corrected
eq,wc = equivalent wind chill
$evap$ = latent
ex = exhaled air
fg = vaporization of water
g = globe
G = covered by garment
ge = gas exchange
h = too hot
l = too cold
m = total
max = maximum
$m-j$ = from person to source j
N = of surface N
nwb = naturally ventilated wet bulb
o = operative
oc = operative comfort
oh = humid operation
out = monthly mean outside
p = at constant pressure
pcl = permeation
$p-N$ = between person and source N
pr = plane radiant
r = radiation, radiant
req = required
res = respiration
rsw = regulatory sweat
s = saturated
sf = final skin
$shiv$ = shivering
si = initial skin
sk = skin
sw = sweat
t = atmospheric, or total
tr = constriction constant for skin blood flow
wb = wet bulb
w,res = respiratory water loss

CODES AND STANDARDS

ASHRAE. 1992. Thermal environmental conditions for human occupancy. ANSI/ASHRAE *Standard* 55-1992.

ASHRAE. 1995. Addendum to thermal environmental conditions for human occupancy. ANSI/ASHRAE *Standard* 55a-1995.

ISO. 1989. Hot environments—Analytical determination and interpretation of thermal stress using calculation of required sweat rates. *Standard* 7933. International Organization for Standardization, Geneva.

ISO. 1989. Hot environments—Estimation of the heat stress on working man, based on the WBGT-index (wet bulb globe temperature). *Standard* 7243. International Organization for Standardization, Geneva.

ISO. 1994. Moderate thermal environments—Determination of the PMV and PPD indices and specification of the conditions for thermal comfort. *Standard* 7730. International Organization for Standardization, Geneva.

REFERENCES

Astrand, P. and K. Rodahl. 1977. *Textbook of work physiology: Physiological bases of exercise*. McGraw-Hill, New York.

Azer, N.Z. 1982. Design guidelines for spot cooling systems: Part I—Assessing the acceptability of the environment. *ASHRAE Transactions* 88:1.

Azer, N.Z. and S. Hsu. 1977. OSHA heat stress standards and the WBGT index. *ASHRAE Transactions* 83(2):30.

Belding, H.D. 1967. Heat stress. In *Thermobiology*, A.H. Rose, ed. Academic Press, New York.

Belding, H.S. 1970. The search for a universal heat stress index. In *Physiological and behavioral temperature regulation*, J.D. Hardy, A.P. Gagge, and J.A.J. Stolwijk, eds. Springfield, IL.

Belding, H.S. and T.F. Hatch. 1955. Index for evaluating heat stress in terms of resulting physiological strains. *Heating, Piping and Air Conditioning* 207:239.

Berglund, L.G. 1994. Common elements in the design and operation of thermal comfort and ventilation systems. *ASHRAE Transactions* 100(1): 776-781.

Berglund, L.G. 1995. Comfort criteria: Humidity and standards. *Proceedings of Pan Pacific Symposium on Building and Urban Environmental Conditioning in Asia* vol. 2, pp. 369-382. University of Nagoya, Japan.

Berglund, L.G. and D.J. Cunningham. 1986. Parameters of human discomfort in warm environments. *ASHRAE Transactions* 92(2):732-746.

Berglund, L.G. and A. Fobelets. 1987. A subjective human response to low level air currents and asymmetric radiation. *ASHRAE Transactions* 93(1):497-523.

Berglund, L.G. and R.R. Gonzalez. 1977. Evaporation of sweat from sedentary man in humid environments. *Journal of Applied Physiology* 42(5): 767-772.

Berglund, L., R. Gonzales, and A. Gagge. 1990. Predicted human performance decrement from thermal discomfort and ET*. *Proceedings of Indoor Air '90*, Toronto, vol. 1, pp. 215-220.

Botsford, J.H. 1971. A wet globe thermometer for environmental heat measurement. *American Industrial Hygiene Association Journal* 32:1-10.

Burton, A.C. and H.C. Bazett. 1936. A study of the average temperature of the tissues, the exchange of heat and vasomotor responses in man, by a bath calorimeter. *American Journal of Physiology* 117:36.

Busch, J.F. 1992. A tale of two populations: Thermal comfort in air-conditioned and naturally ventilated offices in Thailand. *Energy and Buildings* 18:235-249.

Buskirk, E.R. 1960. Problems related to the caloric cost of living. *Bulletin of the New York Academy of Medicine* 26:365.

Chatonnet, J. and M. Cabanac. 1965. The perception of thermal comfort. *International Journal of Biometeorology* 9:183-193.

Colin, J. and Y. Houdas. 1967. Experimental determination of coefficient of heat exchange by convection of the human body. *Journal of Applied Physiology* 22:31.

Collins, K.J. and E. Hoinville. 1980. Temperature requirements in old age. *Building Services Engineering Research and Technology* 1(4):165-172.

Davis, W.J. 1976. Typical WBGT indexes in various industrial environments. *ASHRAE Transactions* 82(2):303.

de Dear, R.J. and G.S. Brager. 1998. Developing an adaptive model of thermal comfort and preference. *ASHRAE Technical Data Bulletin* 14(1):27-49.

de Dear, R., K. Leow, and A. Ameen. 1991. Thermal comfort in the humid tropics—Part I. *ASHRAE Transactions* 97(1):874-879.

DuBois, D. and E.F. DuBois. 1916. A formula to estimate approximate surface area, if height and weight are known. *Archives of Internal Medicine* 17:863-871.

Dukes-Dobos, F. and A. Henschel. 1971. The modification of the WBGT index for establishing permissible heat exposure limits in occupational work. HEW/USPHE/NIOSH *Report* TR-69.

Dukes-Dobos, F. and A. Henschel. 1973. Development of permissible heat exposure limits for occupational work. *ASHRAE Journal* 9:57.

Eriksson, H.A. 1975. Heating and ventilating of tractor cabs. Presented at the 1975 Winter Meeting, American Society of Agricultural Engineers, Chicago.

Fanger, P.O. 1967. Calculation of thermal comfort: Introduction of a basic comfort equation. *ASHRAE Transactions* 73(2):III.4.1.

Fanger, P.O. 1970. *Thermal comfort analysis and applications in environmental engineering*. McGraw-Hill, New York.

Fanger, P.O. 1972. *Thermal comfort*. McGraw-Hill, New York.

Fanger, P.O. 1973. The variability of man's preferred ambient temperature from day to day. *Archives des Sciences Physiologiques* 27(4):A403.

Fanger, P.O. 1982. *Thermal comfort*. Robert E. Krieger, Malabar, FL.

Fanger, P.O. and N.K. Christensen. 1986. Perception of draught in ventilated spaces. *Ergonomics* 29(2):215-235.

Fanger, P.O. and G. Langkilde. 1975. Interindividual differences in ambient temperature preferred by seated persons. *ASHRAE Transactions* 81(2): 140-147.

Fanger, P.O., J. Hojbjerre, and J.O.B. Thomsen. 1973. Man's preferred ambient temperature during the day. *Archives des Sciences Physiologiques* 27(4): A395-A402.

Fanger, P.O., J. Hojbjerre, and J.O.B. Thomsen. 1974. Thermal comfort conditions in the morning and the evening. *International Journal of Biometeorology* 18(1):16.

Fanger, P.O., L. Banhidi, B.W. Olesen, and G. Langkilde. 1980. Comfort limits for heated ceilings. *ASHRAE Transactions* 86.

Fanger, P.O., B.M. Ipsen, G. Langkilde, B.W. Olesen, N.K. Christensen, and S. Tanabe. 1985. Comfort limits for asymmetric thermal radiation. *Energy and Buildings*.

Fanger, P.O., A.K. Melikov, H. Hanzawa, and J. Ring. 1989. Turbulence and draft. *ASHRAE Journal* 31(4):18-25.

Federspiel, C.C. 1998. Statistical analysis of unsolicited thermal sensation complaints in commercial buildings. *ASHRAE Transactions* 104(1): 912-923.

Federspiel, C.C. 2001. Estimating the frequency and cost of responding to building complaints. In *Indoor air quality handbook*, J. Spengler, J.M. Sammet, and J.F. McCarthy, eds. McGraw-Hill.

Federspiel, C., G. Liu, M. Lahiff, D. Faulkner, D. Dibartolomeo, W. Fisk, P. Price, and D. Sullivan. 2002. Worker performance and ventilation: Analysis of individual data for call-center workers. *Proceedings of Indoor Air 2002*, pp. 796-801.

Federspiel, C.C., R. Martin, and H. Yan. 2003. Thermal comfort models and "call-out" (complaint) frequencies. ASHRAE Research Project RP-1129, *Final Report*.

Fobelets, A.P.R. and A.P. Gagge. 1988. Rationalization of the ET* as a measure of the enthalpy of the human environment. *ASHRAE Transactions* 94:1.

Gagge, A.P. 1937. A new physiological variable associated with sensible and insensible perspiration. *American Journal of Physiology* 20(2):277-287.

Gagge, A.P. and J.D. Hardy. 1967. Thermal radiation exchange of the human by partitional calorimetry. *Journal of Applied Physiology* 23(2):248-258.

Gagge, A.P., G.M. Rapp, and J.D. Hardy. 1967a. The effective radiant field and operative temperature necessary for comfort with radiant heating. *ASHRAE Transactions* 73(1):I.2.1.

Gagge, A.P., G.M. Rapp, and J.D. Hardy. 1967b. The effective radiant field and operative temperature necessary for comfort with radiant heating. *ASHRAE Journal* 9(5):63.

Gagge, A.P., J.A.J. Stolwijk, and B. Saltin. 1969a. Comfort and thermal sensation and associated physiological responses during exercise at various ambient temperatures. *Environmental Research* 2:209.

Gagge, A.P., J.A.J. Stolwijk, and Y. Nishi. 1969b. The prediction of thermal comfort when thermal equilibrium is maintained by sweating. *ASHRAE Transactions* 75(2):108.

Gagge, A.P., J. Stolwijk, and Y. Nishi. 1971a. An effective temperature scale based on a simple model of human physiological regulatory response. *ASHRAE Transactions* 77(1):247-262.

Gagge, A.P., A.C. Burton, and H.D. Bazett. 1971b. A practical system of units for the description of heat exchange of man with his environment. *Science* 94:428-430.

Gagge, A.P., Y. Nishi, and R.G. Nevins. 1976. The role of clothing in meeting FEA energy conservation guidelines. *ASHRAE Transactions* 82(2):234.

Gagge, A.P., A.P. Fobelets, and L.G. Berglund. 1986. A standard predictive index of human response to the thermal environment. *ASHRAE Transactions* 92(2B).

Gonzalez, R.R. 1975. Effects of ambient temperature and humidity on human performance. *Special Technical Report* 4. John B. Pierce Foundation Laboratory, New Haven, CT.

Gonzalez, R.R., L.G. Berglund, and A.P. Gagge. 1978. Indices of thermoregulatory strain for moderate exercise in the heat. *Journal of Applied Physiology* 44(6):889-899.

Green, G.H. 1982. Positive and negative effects of building humidification. *ASHRAE Transactions* 88(1):1049-1061.

Griffiths, T. and D. McIntyre. 1975. The effect of mental effect on subjective assessments on warmth. *Ergonomics* 18(1):29-32.

Gwosdow, A.R., J.C. Stevens, L. Berglund, and J.A.J. Stolwijk. 1986. Skin friction and fabric sensations in neutral and warm environments. *Textile Research Journal* 56:574-580.

Hardy, J.D. 1949. Heat transfer. In *Physiology of heat regulation and science of clothing*, L.H. Newburgh, ed. W.B. Saunders, London.

Hardy, J.D. 1961. Physiological effects of high intensity infrared heating. *ASHRAE Journal* 4:11.

Hardy, J.D., H.G. Wolf, and H. Goodell. 1952. *Pain sensations and reactions*. Williams and Wilkins, Baltimore.

Hardy, J.D., J.A.J. Stolwijk, and A.P. Gagge. 1971. Man. In *Comparative physiology of thermoregulation*, Chapter 5. Charles C. Thomas, Springfield, IL.

Hensel, H. 1973. Temperature reception and thermal comfort. *Archives des Sciences Physiologiques* 27:A359-A370.

Hensel, H. 1981. *Thermoreception and temperature regulation*. Academic Press, London.

Holmer, I. 1984. Required clothing insulation (IREQ) as an analytical index of cold stress. *ASHRAE Transactions* 90(1B):1116-1128.

Houghten, F.C. and C.P. Yaglou. 1923. ASHVE *Research Report* 673. *ASHVE Transactions* 29:361.

Humphreys, M. and J.F. Nicol. 1998. Understanding the adaptive approach to thermal comfort. *ASHRAE Technical Data Bulletin* 14(1):1-14.

Jones, B.W., K. Hsieh, and M. Hashinaga. 1986. The effect of air velocity on thermal comfort at moderate activity levels. *ASHRAE Transactions* 92:2.

Korsgaard, V. 1949. Necessity of using a directional mean radiant temperature to describe thermal conditions in rooms. *Heating, Piping and Air Conditioning* 21(6):117-120.

Kuno, S. 1995. Comfort and pleasantness. In *Proceedings of Pan Pacific Symposium on Building and Urban Environmental Conditioning in Asia*, 2:383-392. University of Nagoya, Japan.

Langkilde, G. 1979. Thermal comfort for people of high age. In *Confort thermique: Aspects physiologiques et psychologiques*, INSERM, Paris 75:187-93.

Leithead, C.S. and A.R. Lind. 1964. *Heat stress and heat disorders*. Cassell & Co., London.

Levin, H. 1995. Preface. *Proceedings, Indoor Environment and Productivity Workshop*, Atlanta. H. Levin, ed. ASHRAE.

Link, J. and R. Pepler. 1970. Associated fluctuations in daily temperature, productivity and absenteeism (RP-57). *ASHRAE Transactions* 76(2): 326-337.

Lipkin, M. and J.D. Hardy 1954. Measurement of some thermal properties of human tissues. *Journal of Applied Physiology* 7:212.

Liviana, J.E., F.H. Rohles, and O.D. Bullock. 1988. Humidity, comfort and contact lenses. *ASHRAE Transactions* 94(1):3-11.

Matthew, W.H. et al. 1986. Botsball (WGT) performance characteristics and their impact on the implementation of existing military hot weather doctrine. U.S. Army Reserves Institute of Environmental Medicine *Technical Report* T 9/86, April.

McCartney, K.J. and M.A. Humphreys. 2002. Thermal comfort and productivity. *Proceedings of Indoor Air 2002*, pp. 822-827.

McCullough, E.A. 1986. An insulation data base for military clothing. Institute for Environmental Research *Report* 86-01, Kansas State University, Manhattan.

McCullough, E.A. and S. Hong. 1994. A data base for determining the decrease in clothing insulation due to body motion. *ASHRAE Transactions* 100(1):765.

McCullough, E.A. and B.W. Jones. 1984. A comprehensive data base for estimating clothing insulation. IER Technical *Report* 84-01, Institute for Environmental Research, Kansas State University, Manhattan. ASHRAE Research Project RP-411, *Final Report*.

McCullough, E.A., B.W. Jones, and T. Tamura. 1989. A data base for determining the evaporative resistance of clothing. *ASHRAE Transactions* 95(2).

McCullough, E.A., B.W. Olesen, and S.W. Hong. 1994. Thermal insulation provided by chairs. *ASHRAE Transactions* 100(1):795-802.

McCutchan, J.W. and C.L. Taylor. 1951. Respiratory heat exchange with varying temperature and humidity of inspired air. *Journal of Applied Physiology* 4:121-135.

McIntyre, D.A. 1974. The thermal radiation field. *Building Science* 9:247-262.

McIntyre, D.A. 1976. Overhead radiation and comfort. *The Building Services Engineer* 44:226-232.

McIntyre, D.A. and I.D. Griffiths. 1975. The effects of uniform and asymmetric thermal radiation on comfort. *CLIMA 2000, 6th International Congress of Climatritics*, Milan.

McNair, H.P. 1973. A preliminary study of the subjective effects of vertical air temperature gradients. British Gas Corporation *Report* WH/T/R&D/73/94, London.

McNair, H.P. and D.S. Fishman. 1974. A further study of the subjective effects of vertical air temperature gradients. British Gas Corporation *Report* WH/T/R&D/73/94, London.

McNall, P.E., Jr. and R.E. Biddison. 1970. Thermal and comfort sensations of sedentary persons exposed to asymmetric radiant fields. *ASHRAE Transactions* 76(1):123.

McNall, P.E., P.W. Ryan, and J. Jaax. 1968. Seasonal variation in comfort conditions for college-age persons in the Middle West. *ASHRAE Transactions* 74(1):IV.2.1-9.

Mitchell, D. 1974. Convective heat transfer in man and other animals. In *Heat loss from animals and man*, J.L. Monteith and L.E. Mount, eds. Butterworth Publishing, London.

Nevins, R.G. and A.M. Feyerherm. 1967. Effect of floor surface temperature on comfort: Part IV, Cold floors. *ASHRAE Transactions* 73(2):III.2.1.

Nevins, R.G. and A.O. Flinner. 1958. Effect of heated-floor temperatures on comfort. *ASHRAE Transactions* 64:175.

Nevins, R.G., K.B. Michaels, and A.M. Feyerherm. 1964. The effect of floor surface temperature on comfort: Part 1, College age males; Part II, College age females. *ASHRAE Transactions* 70:29.

Nevins, R.G., F.H. Rohles, Jr., W.E. Springer, and A.M. Feyerherm. 1966. Temperature-humidity chart for thermal comfort of seated persons. *ASHRAE Transactions* 72(1):283.

Nevins, R.G., R.R. Gonzalez, Y. Nishi, and A.P. Gagge. 1975. Effect of changes in ambient temperature and level of humidity on comfort and thermal sensations. *ASHRAE Transactions* 81(2).

Nicol, J.F. and M.A. Humphreys. 1972. Thermal comfort as part of a self-regulating system. *Proceedings of CIB Symposium on Thermal Comfort*, Building Research Station, London.

Niemelä, R., J. Railio, M. Hannula, S. Rautio, and K. Reijula. 2001. Assessing the effect of indoor environment on productivity. *Proceedings of Clima 2000 (CD-ROM)*, Napoli.

Niemelä, R., M. Hannula, S. Rautio, K. Reijula, and J. Railio. 2002. The effect of indoor air temperature on labour productivity in call centers—A case study. *Energy and Buildings* 34:759-764.

NIOSH. 1986. Criteria for a recommended standard—Occupational exposure to hot environments, revised criteria. U.S. Dept. of Health and Human Services, USDHHS (NIOSH) *Publication* 86-113. Available from www.cdc.gov/NIOSH/86-113.html.

Nishi, Y. 1981. Measurement of thermal balance of man. In *Bioengineering Thermal Physiology and Comfort*, K. Cena and J.A. Clark, eds. Elsevier New York.

Nishi, Y. and A.P. Gagge. 1970. Direct evaluation of convective heat transfer coefficient by naphthalene sublimation. *Journal of Applied Physiology* 29:830.

Nishi, Y., R.R. Gonzalez, and A.P. Gagge. 1975. Direct measurement of clothing heat transfer properties during sensible and insensible heat exchange with thermal environment. *ASHRAE Transactions* 81(2):183.

Olesen, B.W. 1977a. Thermal comfort requirements for floors. In *Proceedings of Commissions B1, B2, E1 of the IIR*, Belgrade, 337-43.

Olesen, B.W. 1977b. Thermal comfort requirements for floors occupied by people with bare feet. *ASHRAE Transactions* 83(2).

Olesen, B.W. 1985. A new and simpler method for estimating the thermal insulation of a clothing ensemble. *ASHRAE Transactions* 91(2).

Olesen, B.W. and R. Nielsen. 1983. *Thermal insulation of clothing measured on a moveable manikin and on human subjects*. Technical University of Denmark, Lyngby.

Olesen, S., J.J. Bassing, and P.O. Fanger. 1972. Physiological comfort conditions at sixteen combinations of activity, clothing, air velocity and ambient temperature. *ASHRAE Transactions* 78(2):199.

Olesen, B.W., M. Scholer, and P.O. Fanger. 1979. Vertical air temperature differences and comfort. In *Indoor climate,* P.O. Fanger and O. Valbjorn, eds. Danish Building Research Institute, Copenhagen.

Olesen, B.W., E. Sliwinska, T.L. Madsen, and P.O. Fanger. 1982. Effect of posture and activity on the thermal insulation of clothing. Measurement by a movable thermal manikin. *ASHRAE Transactions* 82(2):791-805.

Onkaram, B., L. Stroschein, and R.F. Goldman. 1980. Three instruments for assessment of WBGT and a comparison with WGT (Botsball). *American Industrial Hygiene Association* 41:634-641.

Oohori, T., L.G. Berglund, and A.P. Gagge. 1984. Comparison of current two-parameter indices of vapor permeation of clothing—As factors governing thermal equilibrium and human comfort. *ASHRAE Transactions* 90(2).

Ostberg, O. and A.G. McNicholl. 1973. The preferred thermal conditions for "morning" and "evening" types of subjects during day and night—Preliminary results. *Build International* 6(1):147-157.

Passmore, R. and J.V.G. Durnin. 1967. *Energy, work and leisure.* Heinemann Educational Books, London.

Pepler, R. and R. Warner. 1968. Temperature and learning: An experimental study. *ASHRAE Transactions* 74(2):211-219.

Rapp, G. and A.P. Gagge. 1967. Configuration factors and comfort design in radiant beam heating of man by high temperature infrared sources. *ASHRAE Transactions* 73(2):III.1.1.

REHVA. 2006. Indoor climate and productivity in offices. *REHVA Guidebook* 6, pp. 29-34. P. Wargocki, and O. Seppänen, eds. Federation of European Heating and Air-Conditioning Associations, Brussels.

Robinson, et al. 1943. *American Journal of Physiology* 140:168.

Roelofsen, P. 2001. The design of workplace as a strategy for productivity enhancement. *Proceedings of Clima 2000,* Napoli.

Rohles, F.H., Jr. 1973. The revised modal comfort envelope. *ASHRAE Transactions* 79(2):52.

Rohles, F.H., Jr. and M.A. Johnson. 1972. Thermal comfort in the elderly. *ASHRAE Transactions* 78(1):131.

Rohles, F.H., Jr. and R.G. Nevins. 1971. The nature of thermal comfort for sedentary man. *ASHRAE Transactions* 77(1):239.

Seppänen, O. and W.J. Fisk. 2006. Some quantitative relations between indoor environmental quality and work performance and health. *International Journal of HVAC&R Research* (now *HVAC&R Research)* 12(4): 957-973.

Seppänen, O., P.E. McNall, D.M. Munson, and C.H. Sprague. 1972. Thermal insulating values for typical indoor clothing ensembles. *ASHRAE Transactions* 78(1):120-30.

Seppänen, O., W.J. Fisk, and Q.H. Lei. 2006. Effect of temperature on task performance in office environment. *Report* LBNL-60946. http://eetd.lbl.gov/ied/pdf/LBNL-60946.pdf (29 Feb. 2008).

Siple, P.A. and C.F. Passel. 1945. Measurements of dry atmospheric cooling in subfreezing temperatures. *Proceedings of the American Philosophical Society* 89:177.

Stolwijk, J.A.J. and J.D. Hardy. 1966. Partitional calorimetric studies of response of man to thermal transients. *Journal of Applied Physiology* 21:967.

Stolwijk, J.A.J., A.P. Gagge, and B. Saltin. 1968. Physiological factors associated with sweating during exercise. *Journal of Aerospace Medicine* 39: 1101.

Sullivan, C.D. and R.L. Gorton. 1976. A method of calculating WBGT from environmental factors. *ASHRAE Transactions* 82(2):279.

Tanabe, S., K. Kimura, and T. Hara. 1987. Thermal comfort requirements during the summer season in Japan. *ASHRAE Transactions* 93(1):564-577.

Tikusis, P. and G.G. Giesbrecht. 1999. Prediction of shivering heat production from core and mean skin temperatures. *European Journal of Applied Physiology* 79:221-229.

Umbach, K.H. 1980. Measuring the physiological properties of textiles for clothing. *Melliand Textilberichte* (English edition) G1:543-548.

Webb, P. 1964. *Bioastronautics data base.* NASA.

Winslow, C.-E.A., L.P. Herrington, and A.P. Gagge. 1937. Relations between atmospheric conditions, physiological reactions and sensations of pleasantness. *American Journal of Hygiene* 26(1):103-115.

Witterseh, T. 2001. *Environmental perception, SBS symptoms and performance of office work under combined exposure to temperature, noise and air pollution.* Ph.D. dissertation. International Center for Indoor Environment and Energy, Department of Mechanical Engineering, Technical University of Denmark.

Woodcock, A.H. 1962. Moisture transfer in textile systems. *Textile Research Journal* 8:628-633.

Wyon, D.P. 1996. Individual microclimate control: Required range, probable benefits and current feasibility. *Proceedings of Indoor Air '96,* Nagoya, Japan, vol. 2, pp. 27-36.

BIBLIOGRAPHY

Fanger, P.O., A. Melikov, H. Hanzawa, and J. Ring. 1988. Air turbulence and sensation of draught. *Energy and Buildings* 12:21-39.

Witherspoon, J.M., R.F. Goldman, and J.R. Breckenridge. 1971. Heat transfer coefficients of humans in cold water. *Journal de Physiologie* 63:459.

Wyon, D., I. Wyon, and F. Norin. 1996. Effects of moderate heat stress on driver vigilance in a moving vehicle. *Ergonomics* 39(1):61-75.

CHAPTER 10

INDOOR ENVIRONMENTAL HEALTH

INDOOR environmental health comprises those aspects of human health and disease that are determined by factors in the indoor environment. It also refers to the theory and practice of assessing and controlling factors in the indoor environment that can potentially affect health. The practice of indoor environmental health requires consideration of chemical, biological, physical and ergonomic hazards.

It is essential for engineers to understand the fundamentals of indoor environmental health because the design, operation, and maintenance of buildings and their HVAC systems significantly affect the health of building occupants. In many cases, buildings and systems can be designed and operated to reduce the exposure of occupants to potential hazards. Unfortunately, neglecting to consider indoor environmental health can lead to conditions that create or worsen those hazards.

The first three sections of this chapter provide general background information, describe relevant health sciences, and introduce important concepts of hazard recognition, analysis and control. The remainder of the chapter is devoted to presenting information on specific hazards, and describes sources of exposure to each hazard, potential health effects, relevant exposure standards and guidelines, and methods to control exposure.

This chapter is introductory in nature, and indoor environmental health is a very broad and dynamic field. Thus, descriptions of potential hazards (and especially their controls) presented are not a comprehensive, state-of-the-art review. Additional detail is available on many important topics in other ASHRAE Handbook chapters, including

- Chapter 9, Thermal Comfort, of this volume
- Chapter 11, Air Contaminants, of this volume
- Chapter 12, Odors, of this volume
- Chapter 16, Ventilation and Infiltration, of this volume
- Chapter 28, Air Cleaners for Particulate Contaminants, of the 2008 *ASHRAE Handbook—HVAC Systems and Equipment*
- Chapter 29, Ventilation of the Industrial Environment, of the 2007 *ASHRAE Handbook—HVAC Applications*
- Chapter 45, Control of Gaseous Indoor Air Contaminants, of the 2007 *ASHRAE Handbook—HVAC Applications*

Other important sources of information from ASHRAE include the building ventilation and related requirements in *Standards* 62.1 and 62.2. Additional details are available from governmental and private sources, including the U.S. Center for Disease Control, U.S. Environmental Protection Agency, Occupational Safety and Health Administration, World Health Organization, American Conference of Governmental Industrial Hygienists, and National Institute for Occupational Safety and Health.

The preparation of this chapter is assigned to the Environmental Health Committee.

BACKGROUND

The most clearly defined area of indoor environmental health is occupational health, particularly as it pertains to workplace airborne contaminants. Evaluation of exposure incidents and laboratory studies with humans and animals have generated reasonable consensus on safe and unsafe workplace exposures for about 1000 chemicals and particles. Consequently, many countries regulate exposures of workers to these agents. However, chemical and dust contaminant concentrations that meet occupational health criteria usually exceed levels found acceptable to occupants in nonindustrial spaces such as offices, schools, and residences, where exposures often last longer and may involve mixtures of many contaminants and a less robust population (e.g., infants, the elderly, and the infirm) (NAS 1981).

Operational definitions of health, disease, and discomfort are controversial (Cain et al. 1995). However, the most generally accepted definition is that in the constitution of the World Health Organization (WHO): "Health is a state of complete physical, mental, and social well-being and not merely the absence of disease or infirmity."

Definitions of comfort also vary. Comfort encompasses perception of the environment (e.g., hot/cold, humid/dry, noisy/quiet, bright/dark) and a value rating of affective implications (e.g., too hot, too cold). Rohles et al. (1989) noted that acceptability may represent a more useful concept of evaluating occupant response, because it allows progression toward a concrete goal. Acceptability is the foundation of a number of standards covering thermal comfort and acoustics. Nevertheless, acceptability varies between climatic regions and cultures, and may change over time as expectations change.

Concern about the health effects associated with indoor air dates back several hundred years, and has increased dramatically in recent decades. This attention was partially the result of increased reporting by building occupants of complaints about poor health associated with exposure to indoor air. Since then, two types of diseases associated with exposure to indoor air have been identified: **sick building syndrome (SBS)** and **building-related illness (BRI)**.

SBS describes a number of adverse health symptoms related to occupancy in a "sick" building, including mucosal irritation, fatigue, headache, and, occasionally, lower respiratory symptoms and nausea. There is no widespread agreement on an operational definition of SBS. Some authors define it as acute discomfort (e.g., eye, nose, or throat irritation; sore throat; headache; fatigue; skin irritation; mild neurotoxic symptoms; nausea; building odors) that persists for more than two weeks at frequencies significantly greater than 20%; with a substantial percentage of complainants reporting almost immediate relief upon exiting the building.

The increased prevalence of health complaints among office workers is typical of sick building syndrome (Burge et al. 1987;

Table 1 Illnesses Related to Exposure in Buildings

Illness	Physical Examination	Laboratory Testing	Linkage	Causes/Exposures
Allergic rhinitis, Sinusitis	Stuffy/runny nose, post-nasal drip, pale or erythematous mucosa	Anterior and posterior rhinomanometry, acoustic rhinometry, nasal lavage, biopsy, rhinoscopy, RAST or skin prick testing	Immunologic skin prick or RAST testing, bracketed physiology	Mold, pollen, and dust mites are common examples
Building-related asthma	Coughing, wheezing, episodic dyspnea, wheezing on examination, chest tightness, temporal pattern at work	Spirometry before and after work at start of week, peak expiratory flow diary, methacholine challenge	Immunology testing: skin prick or RAST; physiology testing*	Pet dander, mold, environmental tobacco smoke, and dust mites are common examples
Organic dust toxic syndrome	Cough, dyspnea, chest tightness, feverishness	DLCO, TLC	Temporal pattern related to work	Gram-negative bacteria or endotoxin
Hypersensitivity pneumonitis	Cough, dyspnea, myalgia, weakness, rales, clubbing, feverishness	DLCO, FVC, TLC, CXR, lung biopsy	Immunology testing: IgG antibody to agents present, challenge testing, physiology testing (in acute forms): spirometry, DLCO	Causative agents include thermophilic actinomycetes; molds; mixed amoebae, fungi, and bacteria; avian proteins; certain metals and chemicals
Contact dermatitis	Dry skin, itching, scaling skin	Scaling, rash, eczema, biopsy	Patch testing; allergy testing	Range of microorganisms, chemicals
Urticaria (hives)	Multiple swollen raised itchy areas of skin	Inspection, biopsy	Provocation testing	Skin irritation, foods, heat/cold, direct pressure, sunlight, drugs
Eye irritation	Eye itching, irritation, dryness	Tear-film break-up time, conjunctival staining (fluorescein)	Temporal pattern	Low relative humidity, VOCs, and particulate matter are common examples
Nasal irritation	Stuffy, congested nose, rhinitis	Acoustic rhinometry, posterior and anterior rhinomanometry, nasal lavage, nasal biopsy	Temporal pattern	Low relative humidity, VOCs, and particulate matter are common examples
Central nervous system symptoms	Headache, fatigue, irritability, difficulty concentrating	Neuropsychological testing	Temporal pattern (epidemiology)	Organic compounds, noise, lighting, work stress, and carbon monoxide are common examples
Legionnaires' disease, Aspergillosis, *Pseudomonas* infection	Pneumonia, high fever, organ dysfunction	Environmental surveillance (water system monitoring), *Legionella pneumophila* identification from patient	Organism isolated from patient and source; immunology testing	*Legionella* (and other microorganism)-contaminated aerosols from water sources
Pontiac fever	Non-pneumonic flulike illness	Environmental surveillance (water system monitoring)		*Legionella*-contaminated aerosols from water sources

*(1) 10% decrement in FEV_1 across workday,
(2) peak flow changes suggestive of work relatedness
(3) methacholine reactivity resolving after six weeks away from exposure
RAST = radio allergen sorbent test
DLCO = single breath carbon monoxide diffusing capacity
FVC = forced vital capacity
TLC = total lung capacity
CXR = chest X-ray
IgG = class G immune globulins
FEV_1 = forced expiratory volume in the first second

Skov and Valbjorn 1987). Widespread occurrence of these symptoms has prompted the World Health Organization to classify SBS into several categories (Morey et al. 1984):

- Sensory irritation in the eyes, nose, or throat
- Skin irritation
- Neurotoxic symptoms
- Odor and taste complaints

Sick building syndrome is characterized by an absence of routine physical signs and clinical laboratory abnormalities. The term *nonspecific* is sometimes used to imply that the pattern of symptoms reported by afflicted building occupants is not consistent with that for a particular disease. Additional symptoms can include nosebleeds, chest tightness, and fever.

Some investigations have sought to correlate SBS symptoms with reduced neurological and physiological performance. In controlled studies, SBS symptoms can reduce performance in susceptible individuals (Mølhave et al. 1986).

Building-related illnesses, in contrast, have a known origin, may have a different set of symptoms, and are often accompanied by physical signs and abnormalities that can be clinically identified with laboratory measurements. For example, hypersensitivity illnesses, including hypersensitivity pneumonitis, humidifier fever, asthma, and allergic rhinitis, are caused by individual sensitization to bioaerosols.

Illnesses associated with exposure in indoor environments are listed in Table 1. Laboratory testing and development of linkages should be performed under direction of a qualified health care professional.

DESCRIPTIONS OF SELECTED HEALTH SCIENCES

The study of health effects in indoor environments includes a number of scientific disciplines. A few are briefly described here to further the engineer's understanding of which health sciences may be applicable to a given environmental health problem.

Epidemiology and Biostatistics

Epidemiology studies the cause, distribution, and control of disease in human and animal populations. It represents the application of quantitative methods to evaluate health-related events and effects. Epidemiology is traditionally subdivided into observational and analytical components; the focus may be descriptive, or may attempt to identify causal relationships. Some classical criteria for determining causal relationships in epidemiology are consistency, temporality, plausibility, specificity, strength of association, and dose/response.

Observational epidemiology studies are generally performed with a defined group of interest because of a specific exposure or risk factor. A control group is selected on the basis of similar criteria, but without the exposure or risk factor present. A prospective study (cohort study) consists of observations of a specific group.

Examples of epidemiological investigations are cross-sectional, experimental, and case-control studies. Observations conducted at one point in time are considered cross-sectional studies. In experimental studies, individuals are selectively exposed to a specific agent or condition. These studies are performed with the consent of the participants unless the condition is part of the usual working condition and it is known to be harmless. Control groups must be observed in parallel. Case-control studies are conducted by identifying individuals with the condition of interest and comparing factors of interest in individuals without that condition.

Industrial Hygiene

Industrial hygiene is the science of anticipating, recognizing, evaluating, and controlling workplace conditions that may cause worker illness or injury. Important aspects of industrial hygiene include identifying toxic exposures and physical stressors, determining methods for collecting and analyzing contaminant samples, evaluating measurement results, and developing control measures. Industrial hygienists also create regulatory standards for the work environment, prepare programs to comply with regulations, and collaborate with epidemiologists in studies to document exposures and potential exposures to help determine occupation-related illness.

Microbiology and Mycology

Microbiology studies microorganisms, including bacteria, viruses, fungi, and parasites; mycology is a subspecialty that focuses on fungi. Environmental microbiologists and mycologists investigate the growth, activity, and effect of microorganisms found in nature, many of which can colonize and grow in buildings and building systems. Important aspects of environmental microbiology and mycology are identification of populations of contaminant microorganisms in buildings; determination of methods of collection of air, water, and surface samples; and evaluation of results of microbiological measurements. Effective, practical, and safe disinfection practices are usually developed and validated by microbiologists and mycologists.

Aerobiology is the study of airborne microorganisms or other biologically produced particles, and the effects of these aerosols (bioaerosols) on other living organisms. The section on Bioaerosols has more information on these contaminants.

Toxicology

Toxicology studies the influence of chemicals on health. All chemical substances may function as toxins, but low concentrations prevent many of them from being harmful. Defining which component of the structure of a chemical predicts the harmful effect is of fundamental importance in toxicology. A second issue is defining the dose/response relationships of a chemical and the exposed population. Dose may refer to delivered dose (exposure presented to the target tissue) or absorbed dose (the dose actually absorbed by the body and available for metabolism). Measures of exposure may be quite distinct from measures of effect because of internal dose modifiers (e.g., delayed metabolism of some toxins because of a lack of enzymes to transform or deactivate them). In addition, the mathematical characteristics of a dose may vary, depending on whether a peak dose, a geometric or arithmetic mean dose, or an integral under the dose curve is used.

Because permission to conduct exposure of human subjects in experimental conditions is difficult to obtain, most toxicological literature is based on animal studies. Isolated animal systems (e.g., homogenized rat livers, purified enzyme systems, or other isolated living tissues) are used to study the effects of chemicals, but extrapolation between dose level effects from animals to humans is problematic.

HAZARD RECOGNITION, ANALYSIS, AND CONTROL

Hazard recognition and analysis are conducted to determine the presence of hazardous materials or conditions as sources of potential problems. Research, inspection, and analysis determine how a particular hazard affects occupant health. Exposure assessment, an element of hazard recognition, relies on qualitative, semiquantitative, or quantitative approaches. In many situations, air sampling can determine whether a hazardous material is present. An appropriate sampling strategy must be used to ensure validity of collected samples, determining worst-case (for compliance) or usual (average) exposures. Air sampling can be conducted to determine **time-weighted average (TWA)** exposures, which cover a defined period of time, or **short-term exposures**, which determine the magnitude of exposures to materials that are acutely hazardous. Samples may be collected for a single substance or a multicomponent mixture. Hazard analysis also characterizes the potential skin absorption or ingestion hazards of an indoor environment. Analyses of bulk material samples and surface wipe samples are also used to determine whether hazardous conditions exist. Physical agent characterization may require direct-reading sampling methods. After collection and analysis, the results must be interpreted and an appropriate control strategy developed to control, reduce, or eliminate the hazard.

Hazards are generally grouped into one of the following four classes of environmental stressors:

- **Chemical hazards.** Routes of exposure to airborne chemicals are inhalation (aspiration), dermal (skin) contact, dermal absorption, and ingestion. The degree of risk from exposure depends on the nature and potency of the toxic effects, susceptibility of the person exposed, and magnitude and duration of exposure. Airborne contaminants are very important because of their ease of dispersal from sources and the risk of exposure through the lungs when they are inhaled. Airborne chemical hazards can be gaseous (vapors or gases) or particulate (e.g., dusts, fumes, mists, aerosols, fibers). For more information, see Chapter 11.
- **Biological hazards.** Bacteria, viruses, fungi, and other living or nonliving organisms that can cause acute and chronic illness in workers and building occupants are classified as biological hazards in indoor environments. Routes of exposure are inhalation, dermal (skin) contact, and ingestion. The degree of risk from exposure depends on the nature and potency of the biological hazard, susceptibility of the person exposed, and magnitude and duration of exposure.
- **Physical hazards.** These include excessive levels of ionizing and nonionizing electromagnetic radiation, noise, vibration, illumination, temperature, and force.
- **Ergonomic hazards.** Tasks that involve repetitive motions, require excessive force, or must be carried out in awkward postures can damage muscles, nerves, and joints.

Hazard Control

Strategies for controlling exposures in indoor environment are substitution (removal of the hazardous substance), isolation, disinfection, ventilation, and air cleaning. Not all measures may be applicable to all types of hazards, but all hazards can be controlled by using one of them. Personal protective equipment and engineering, work practice, and administrative controls are used to apply these methods. Source removal or substitution, customarily the most effective measure, is not always feasible. Engineering controls (e.g., ventilation, air cleaning) may be effective for a range of hazards. Local exhaust ventilation is more effective for controlling point-source contaminants than is general dilution ventilation, such as with a building HVAC system.

Hazard Analysis and Control Processes. The goal of hazard analysis and control processes is to prevent harm to people from hazards associated with buildings. Quantitative hazard analysis and control processes are practical and cost-effective. Preventing disease from hazards requires facility managers and owners to answer three simple, site-specific questions:

- What is the hazard?
- How can it be prevented from harming people?
- How can it be verified that the hazard has been prevented from harming people?

Seven principles comprise effective hazard analysis and control:

- Use process flow diagrams to perform systematic hazard analysis
- Identify critical control points (process steps at which the hazard can be eliminated or prevented from harming people)
- Establish hazard control critical limits at each critical control point
- Establish a hazard control monitoring plan for critical limits at critical control points
- Establish hazard control corrective actions for each critical limit
- Establish procedures to document all activities and results
- Establish procedures to confirm that the plan (1) actually works under operating conditions (**validation**), (2) is being implemented properly (**verification**), and (3) is periodically reassessed

AIRBORNE CONTAMINANTS

Many of the same airborne contaminants cause problems in both industrial and nonindustrial indoor environments. These include nonbiological particles [e.g., synthetic vitreous fibers, asbestos, environmental tobacco smoke (ETS), combustion nuclei, nuisance dust], bioaerosols, and chemical gases and vapors. Airborne contaminants may be brought in from the outdoors or released indoors by industrial processes, building materials, furnishings, equipment, or occupant activities. In industrial environments, airborne contaminants are usually associated with the type of process that occurs in a specific setting, and exposures may be determined relatively easily by air sampling. Airborne contaminants in nonindustrial environments may result from emissions and/or shedding of building materials and systems; originate in outside air; or result from building operating and maintenance programs, procedures, or conditions. In general, compared to industrial settings, nonindustrial environments include many more contaminants that may contribute to health-related problems. These contaminants are usually present in lower concentrations and often are more difficult to identify. More information on contaminant types, characteristics, typical levels, and measurement methods is presented in Chapter 11.

PARTICLES

Particulate matter can be solid or liquid; typical examples include dust, smoke, fumes, and mists. Dusts are solid particles that range in size from 0.1 to 100 μm, whereas smoke particles are typically 0.25 μm and fumes are usually less than 0.1 μm in diameter (Zenz 1988). In contrast, mists are fine droplets of liquid in the air. Fibers are solid particles with length several times greater than their diameter, such as asbestos, manufactured mineral fibers, synthetic vitreous fibers, and refractory ceramic fibers. Bioaerosols of concern to human health range from 0.5 to 30 μm in diameter, but generally bacterial and fungal aerosols range from 2 to 8 μm in diameter because of agglomeration or rafting of cells or spores (Lighthart 1994).

Units of Measurement. The quantity of particles in the air is frequently reported as the mass or particle count in a given volume of air. Mass units are milligrams per cubic metre of air sampled (mg/m^3) or micrograms per cubic metre of air sampled ($\mu g/m^3$). For conversion, 1 mg/m^3 = 1000 $\mu g/m^3$. Mass units are widely used in industrial environments because these units are used to express occupational exposure limits.

Particle counts are usually expressed in volumes of 1 cubic foot, 1 litre, or 1 cubic metre and are specified for a given range of particle diameter. Particle count measurements are generally used in environments such as office buildings and industrial cleanrooms.

General Health Effects of Exposure. Health effects of airborne particulate matter depend on several factors, including particle dimension, durability, dose, and toxicity of materials in the particle. Respirable particles vary in size from <1 to 10 μm (Alpaugh and Hogan 1988). Methods for measuring airborne particles are discussed in Chapter 11. **Durability** (how long the particle can exist in the biological system before it dissolves or is transported from the system) and **dose** (amount of exposure encountered by the worker) both affect relative toxicity. In some instances, very low exposures can cause adverse health effects (hazardous exposures), and in others, seemingly high exposures may not cause any adverse health effects (nuisance exposures).

Safety and health professionals are primarily concerned with particles smaller than 2 μm. Particles larger than 8 to 10 μm in aerodynamic diameter are primarily separated and retained by the upper respiratory tract. Intermediate sizes are deposited mainly in the conducting airways of the lungs, from which they are rapidly cleared and swallowed or coughed out. About 50% or less of the particles in inhaled air settle in the respiratory tract. Submicron particles penetrate deeper into the lungs, but many do not deposit and are exhaled.

Industrial Environments

Exposures and Exposure Sources. In industrial environments, airborne particles are generated by work-related activities (e.g., adding batch ingredients for a manufacturing process, applying asphalt in a roofing operation, or drilling an ore deposit in preparation for blasting). The engineer must recognize sources of particle generation to appropriately address exposure concerns. Dusts are generated by handling, crushing, or grinding, and may become airborne during generation or during handling. Any industrial process that produces dust fine enough (about 10 μm) to remain in the air long enough to be inhaled or ingested should be regarded as potentially hazardous. In determining worker exposure, the nature of particles released by the activity, local air movement caused by makeup air and exhaust, and worker procedures should be assessed for a complete evaluation (Burton 2000).

Health Effects of Industrial Exposures. Pneumoconiosis is a fibrous hardening of the lungs caused by irritation from inhaling dust in industrial settings. The most commonly known pneumoconioses are asbestosis, silicosis, and coal worker's pneumoconiosis.

Asbestosis results from inhalation of asbestos fibers found in the work environment. The U.S. Department of Health and Human Services (ATSDR 2001) characterizes the toxicological and adverse health effects of asbestos and indicates that asbestos-induced respiratory disease can generally take 10 to 20 years to develop, although there is evidence that early cases of asbestosis can develop in five to six years when fiber concentrations are very high. Asbestos fibers cause fibrosis (scarring) of lung tissue, which clinically manifests itself as dyspnea (shortness of breath) and a nonproductive, irritating cough. Asbestos fiber is both dimensionally respirable and durable in the respiratory system.

Silicosis, probably the most common of all industrial occupational lung diseases, is caused by inhalation of silica dust. Workers with silicosis usually are asymptomatic, even in the early stages of massive fibrosis (Leathart 1972). It is not considered a problem in nonindustrial indoor environments.

Coal worker's pneumoconiosis (**CWP**, also known as "black lung") results from inhalation of dust generated in coal-mining operations. The dust is composed of a combination of carbon and varying percentages of silica (usually <10%) (Alpaugh and Hogan 1988). Because of the confined underground work environment, exposures can be very high at times, thus creating very high doses.

Table 2 OSHA Permissible Exposure Limits (PELs) for Particles (29CFR1910.1000, 29CFR1926.1101)

Substance	CAS* #	PEL
Cadmium	7440-43-9	0.05 mg/m³
Manganese fume	7439-96-5	1.0 mg/m³
Plaster of Paris	Nuisance	10.0 mg/m³
Emery	Nuisance	10.0 mg/m³
Grain dust	Nuisance	10.0 mg/m³
Crystalline silica (as quartz)	14808-60-7	0.1 mg/m³
Asbestos	1332-21-4	0.1 fibers/cm³
Total dust	Nuisance	15.0 mg/m³

*Chemical Abstract Survey

Data show that workers may develop CWP at exposures below the current dust standard of 1 mg/m^3).

Exposure Standards and Criteria. In the United States, the Occupational Safety and Health Administration (OSHA) has established permissible exposure limits (PELs) for many airborne particles. PELs are published in the Code of Federal Regulations (CFR 1989a, 1989b) under the authority of the Department of Labor. Table 2 lists PELs for several common workplace particles.

Exposure Control Strategies. Particulate or dust control strategies include source elimination or enclosure, local exhaust, general dilution ventilation, wetting, filtration, and use of personal protective devices such as respirators.

The most effective way to control exposures to particles is to totally eliminate them from the work environment. The best dust control method is total enclosure of the dust-producing process, with negative pressure maintained inside the entire enclosure by exhaust ventilation (Alpaugh and Hogan 1988).

Local exhaust ventilation as an exposure control strategy is most frequently used where particles are generated either in large volumes or with high velocities (e.g., lathe and grinding operations). High-velocity air movement captures the particles and removes them from the work environment.

General dilution ventilation in the work environment reduces particulate exposure. This type of ventilation is used when particulate sources are numerous and widely distributed over a large area. This strategy is often the least effective means of control, and may be very costly if conditioned (warm or cold) air is exhausted and unconditioned air is introduced without benefit of airside energy recovery. Ventilation and local exhaust for industrial environments are discussed more thoroughly in Chapters 29 and 30 of the 2007 *ASHRAE Handbook—HVAC Applications*.

Filtration can be an effective control strategy and may be less expensive than general ventilation, although increased pressure drop across a filter adds to fan power requirements, and maintenance adds to system operating cost.

Using personal protective equipment (e.g., a respirator) is appropriate as a primary control during intermittent maintenance or cleaning activities when other controls are not feasible. Respirators can also supplement good engineering and work practice controls to increase employee protection and comfort (Alpaugh and Hogan 1988). Consultation with an industrial hygienist or other qualified health professional is needed to ensure proper selection, fit, and use of respirators.

Synthetic Vitreous Fibers

Exposures and Exposure Sources. Fibers are defined as slender, elongated structures with substantially parallel sides (as distinguished from a dust, which is more spherical). Synthetic vitreous fibers (SVFs) are inorganic fibrous materials such as glass wool, mineral wool (also known as rock and slag wool), textile glass fibers, and refractory ceramic fibers. These fibers are used primarily in thermal and acoustical insulation products, but are also used for filtration, fireproofing, and other applications. Human exposure to SVFs occurs mostly during manufacture, fabrication and installation, and demolition of those products, because the installed products do not result in airborne fiber levels that could produce significant consumer exposure. Simultaneous exposure to other dusts (e.g., asbestos during manufacture, demolition products and bioaerosols during demolition) is also important.

Health Effects of Exposure. Possible effects of SVFs on health include the following.

Cancer. In October 2001, an international review by the International Agency for Research on Cancer (IARC) reevaluated the 1988 IARC assessment of SVFs and insulation glass wool and rock wool. This resulted in a downgrading of the classification of these fibers from Group 2B (possible carcinogen) to Group 3 (not classifiable as to the carcinogenicity in humans). IARC noted specifically that "Epidemiologic studies published during the 15 years since the previous IARC Monographs review of these fibers in 1988 provide no evidence of increased risks of lung cancer or mesothelioma (cancer of the lining of the body cavities) from occupational exposures during manufacture of these materials, and inadequate evidence of any overall cancer risk." IARC retained the Group 2B classification for special-purpose glass fibers and refractory ceramic fibers, but its review indicated that many of the previous studies need to be updated and reevaluated, because they did not include the National Toxicology Program's Report on Carcinogens and the State of California's listing of substances known to cause cancer.

Dermatitis. SVFs may cause an irritant contact dermatitis with dermal contact and embedding in the skin, or local inflammation of the conjunctiva when fibers contact the eye. Resin binders sometimes used to tie fibers together have, on rare occasions, been associated with allergic contact dermatitis.

Exposure Standards and Criteria. OSHA has not adopted specific occupational exposure standards for SVFs. A voluntary workplace health and safety program has been established with fibrous glass and rock and slag wool insulation industries under OSHA oversight. This Health and Safety Partnership Program established an 8 h, time-weighted average permissible exposure limit of 1 fiber per cubic centimetre for respirable SVFs.

Exposure Control Strategies. As with other particles, SVF exposure control strategies include engineering controls, work practices, and use of personal protective devices. Appropriate intervention strategies focus on source control.

Combustion Nuclei

Exposures and Sources. Combustion products include water vapor, carbon dioxide, heat, oxides of carbon and nitrogen, and combustion nuclei. Combustion nuclei, defined in this chapter as particulate products of combustion, can be hazardous in many situations. They may contain potential carcinogens such as polycyclic aromatic hydrocarbons (PAHs).

Polycyclic aromatic compounds (PACs) are the nitrogen-, sulfur-, and oxygen-heterocyclic analogs of PAHs and other related PAH derivatives. Depending on their relative molecular mass and vapor pressure, PACs are distributed between vapor and particle phases. In general, combustion particles are smaller than mechanically generated dusts.

Typical sources of combustion nuclei are tobacco smoke, fossil-fuel-based heating devices (e.g., unvented space heaters and gas ranges), and flue gas from improperly vented gas- or oil-fired furnaces and wood-burning fireplaces or stoves. Infiltration of outdoor combustion contaminants can also be a significant source of these contaminants in indoor air. Therefore, combustion nuclei are important in both industrial and nonindustrial settings.

Exposure Standards and Criteria. OSHA established exposure limits for several of the carcinogens categorized as combustion nuclei [i.e., benzo(a)pyrene, cadmium, nickel, benzene, *n*-nitrosodimethylamine]. These limits are established for industrial work environments and are not directly applicable to general indoor air situations. Underlying atherosclerotic heart disease may be exacerbated by carbon monoxide (CO) exposures.

Exposure Control Strategies. Exposure control strategies for combustion nuclei are similar in many ways to those for other particles. For combustion nuclei derived from space heating, air contamination can be avoided by proper installation and venting of equipment to ensure that these contaminants cannot enter the work or personal environment. Proper equipment maintenance is also essential to minimize exposures to combustion nuclei.

Particles in Nonindustrial Environments

Exposures and Sources. In the nonindustrial indoor environment, particle concentrations are greatly affected by the outdoor environment. Diesel engines emit large quantities of fine particulate matter. Indoor particle sources may include cleaning, resuspension of particles from carpets and other surfaces, construction and renovation debris, paper dust, deteriorated insulation, office equipment, and combustion processes (including cooking stoves, fires, and environmental tobacco smoke).

Although **asbestos** is commonly found in buildings constructed before the 1970s, it generally does not represent a respiratory hazard except to individuals who actively disturb it during maintenance and construction. School custodians, therefore, are recognized to be at risk for asbestos-related changes. Anderson et al. (1991) and Lilienfeld (1991) raise questions about risk to teachers.

An important source of particulates, **environmental tobacco smoke (ETS)** consists of exhaled mainstream smoke from the smoker and sidestream smoke emitted from the smoldering tobacco. Approximately 70 to 90% of ETS results from sidestream smoke, which has a chemical composition somewhat different from mainstream smoke. More than 4700 compounds have been identified in laboratory-based studies, including known human toxic and carcinogenic compounds such as carbon monoxide, ammonia, formaldehyde, nicotine, tobacco-specific nitrosamines, benzo(a)pyrene, benzene, cadmium, nickel, and aromatic amines. Many of these constituents are more concentrated in sidestream smoke than in mainstream smoke (Glantz and Parmley 1991). In studies conducted in residences and office buildings with tobacco smoking permitted, ETS was a substantial source of many gaseous and particulate PACs (Offermann et al. 1991).

Health Effects of Exposure. The health effects of exposure to combustion nuclei depend on many factors, including concentration, toxicity, and individual susceptibility or sensitivity to the particular substance. Combustion-generated PACs include many PAHs and nitro-PAHs that have been shown to be carcinogenic in animals (NAS 1983). Other PAHs are biologically active as tumor promoters and/or cocarcinogens. Mumford et al. (1987) reported high exposures to PAH and aza-arenes for a population in China with very high lung cancer rates.

According to the U.S. EPA (2005) fine particulate matter (particles less than 2.5 μm in diameter) is associated with lung disease, asthma, and other respiratory problems. Short-term exposure may cause shortness of breath, eye and lung irritation, nausea, lightheadedness, and possible allergy aggravations.

ETS has been shown to be causally associated with lung cancer in adults and respiratory infections, asthma exacerbations, middle ear effusion (DHHS 1986; NRC 1986), and low birth mass in children (Martin and Bracken 1986). The U.S. Environmental Protection Agency classifies ETS as a known human carcinogen (EPA 1992). Health effects can also include heart disease, headache, and irritation. ETS is also a cause of sensory irritation and annoyance (odors and eye irritation).

Exposure Standards. There are no established exposure guidelines for particles in nonindustrial indoor environments. The EPA National Ambient Air Quality standard (NAAQS) is 150 μg/m^3 for a 24 h average for particles smaller than 10 μm in diameter, and 35 μg/m^3 for a 24 h average for particles smaller than 2.5 μm in diameter.

Exposure Control Strategies. Particulate or dust control strategies for the nonindustrial environment include source elimination or reduction, good housekeeping, general dilution ventilation, and upgraded filtration. In general, source control is preferred. Combustion appliances must be properly vented and maintained. If a dust problem exists, identify the type of dust to develop an appropriate intervention strategy. Damp dusting and high-efficiency vacuum cleaners may be considered. Building spaces under construction or renovation should be properly isolated from occupied spaces to limit transport of dust and other contaminants. Minimizing idling of diesel-powered vehicles near buildings can reduce entry of fine particulate matter.

Control of ETS has been accomplished primarily through regulatory mandates on the practice of tobacco smoking indoors. Most U.S. states and E.U. member states have passed laws to control tobacco smoking in at least some public places, including public buildings, restaurants, and workplaces, and the FAA (2000) has prohibited smoking on all flights to and from the United States, as have many airlines throughout the world. Where tobacco smoking is permitted, appropriate local and general dilution ventilation can be used for control; however, the efficacy of ventilation is unproven (Repace 1984). Some studies indicate that extremely high ventilation rates may be needed to dilute secondhand smoke to minimal risk levels (Repace and Lowrey 1985, 1993). Although subsequently withdrawn (OSHA 2001), the Occupational Safety and Health Administration proposed (OSHA 1994) that tobacco smoke in indoor environments be controlled by using separately ventilated and exhausted smoking lounges, in which no work activities would occur concurrent with smoking. These lounges were to be kept under negative pressure relative to all adjacent and communicating indoor spaces, with smoking allowed only when the exhaust ventilation system was working properly.

Bioaerosols

Bioaerosols are airborne biological particles derived from viruses, bacteria, fungi, protozoa, algae, mites, plants, insects, and their by-products and cell mass components. Bioaerosols are present in both indoor and outdoor environments. For the indoor environment, locations that provide appropriate temperature and humidity conditions and a food source for biological growth may become problematic.

In microbiology, **reservoirs** allow microorganisms to survive, **amplifiers** allow them to proliferate, and **disseminators** effectively distribute bioaerosols. Building components and systems may have only one factor, or all three; for instance, a cooling tower is an ideal location for growth and dispersal of microbial contaminants and can be the reservoir, amplifier, and disseminator for *Legionella* (harboring microorganisms in scale, allowing them to proliferate, and generating an aerosol).

Both the physical and biological properties of bioaerosols need to be understood. For a microorganism to cause illness in building occupants, it must be transported in sufficient dose to a susceptible occupant. Airborne infectious particles behave physically in the same way as any other aerosol-containing particles with similar size, density, and electrostatic charge. The major difference is that bioaerosols may cause disease by several mechanisms (infection, allergic disease, toxicosis), depending on the organism, dose, and susceptibility of the exposed population. Although microorganisms exist normally in indoor environments, the presence of abundant moisture and nutrients in interior spaces results in the growth of fungi, bacteria, protozoa, algae, or even nematodes (Arnow et al. 1978; Morey and Jenkins 1989; Morey et al. 1986; Strindehag et al. 1988). Thus, humidifiers, water spray systems, and wet porous surfaces can be reservoirs and sites for growth. Excessive air moisture (Burge 1995) and floods (Hodgson et al. 1985) can also result in proliferation of these microorganisms indoors. Turbulence associated with the start-up of air-handling unit plenums may also elevate concentrations of bacteria and fungi in occupied spaces (Buttner and Stetzenbach 1999; Yoshizawa et al. 1987).

Building Surface and Material Sources. Floors and floor coverings can be reservoirs for organisms that are subsequently resuspended into the air. Routine activity, including walking and vacuuming (Buttner et al. 2002), may even promote resuspension (Cox 1987). Some viruses may persist up to eight weeks on nonporous surfaces (Mbithi et al. 1991).

Building Water System Sources. Although potable water is usually delivered to buildings free of biological hazards, once the water enters the facility it becomes the responsibility of facility managers and owners to ensure that its microbial and chemical quality does not degrade. In fact, biological hazards associated with processes in building water systems cause considerable disease. Most cases of legionellosis, for example, result from exposure to potable water in buildings (McCoy 2005; WHO 2007).

Nonpotable water is a well-known source of infective agents, even by aerosolization. Baylor et al. (1977) demonstrated the sequestering of small particles by foam and their subsequent dispersal through bubble bursting. This dispersal may take place in surf, river sprays, or artificial sources such as whirlpools.

Building Occupant Sources. People are an important source of bacteria and viruses in indoor air. Infected humans can release virulent agents from skin lesions or disperse them by coughing, sneezing, or talking. Other means for direct release include sprays of saliva and respiratory secretions during dental and respiratory therapy procedures. Blood sprays during dental and surgical procedures are of potential concern for aerosol transmission of bloodborne diseases, including HIV and hepatitis. Large droplets can transmit infectious particles to those close to the disseminator, and smaller particles can remain airborne for short or very long distances (Moser et al. 1979).

Health Effects. The presence of microorganisms in indoor environments may cause infective and/or allergic building-related illnesses (Burge 1989; Morey and Feeley 1988). Some microorganisms under certain conditions may produce volatile chemicals (Hyppel 1984) that are malodorous. Microorganisms must remain viable to cause infection, although nonviable particles may promote an allergic disease, which is an immunological response. An organism that does not remain virulent in the airborne state cannot cause infection, regardless of how many units of organisms are deposited in the human respiratory tract. Virulence depends on factors such as relative humidity, temperature, oxygen, pollutants, ozone, and ultraviolet light (Burge 1995), each of which can affect survival and virulence differently for different microorganisms. Harmful chemicals produced by microorganisms can also cause irritant responses or toxicosis.

A wide variety of bacteria, fungi, and protozoa are prevalent in health care building water systems and can cause disease by transmission through water and air. Clinically important microorganisms known to cause disease in health care facilities include the bacteria *Legionella*, *Pseudomonas*, and *Mycobacteria*; the fungi *Aspergillus* and *Fusarium*; and the protozoa *Cryptosporidium*, *Giardia*, and *Acanthamoeba*.

Fungal Pathogens. Exposure to airborne fungal spores, hyphal fragments, or metabolites can cause respiratory problems ranging from allergic diseases (e.g., allergic rhinitis, asthma, hypersensitivity pneumonitis) to infectious diseases such as histoplasmosis, blastomycosis, and aspergillosis. In addition, acute toxicosis and cancer have been ascribed to respiratory exposure to mycotoxins (Levetin 1995). A large body of literature supports an association between moisture indicators in the home and symptoms of coughing and wheezing (Miller and Day 1997; Spengler et al. 1992).

Many fungal genera are widely distributed in nature and are common in the soil and on decaying vegetation, dust, and other organic debris (Levetin 1995). Fungi that have a filamentous structure are called **molds**, and reproduce by spores. Mold spores are small (2 to 10 μm in diameter), readily dispersed by water splash and air currents, and may remain airborne for long periods of time (Lighthart and Stetzenbach 1994; Streifel et al. 1989). *Aspergillus fumigatus* is one of the few molds that can cause infections in humans, and is the most frequent cause of **aspergillosis**, a lung infection that has been extensively researched. Aspergillosis in hospital patients has been caused by environmental sources, especially during renovation or nearby construction activity. **Histoplasmosis** is an infection caused by *Histoplasma capsulatum*, which has been reported to cause building-related illness among workers removing bat or bird droppings in abandoned buildings (Bartlett et al. 1982) or cleaning chicken coops. Presumably, asexual spores from this fungus were inhaled by workers who removed the droppings without adequate respiratory protection.

When moisture problems result in mold growth, building occupants may begin to report odors and a variety of health problems, such as headaches, breathing difficulties, skin irritation, allergic diseases, and aggravation of asthma symptoms, all of which may be associated with mold exposure. All molds have the potential to cause health effects. Molds produce allergens, irritants, and, in some cases, toxins that may cause reactions in humans. The types and severity of the symptoms depend, in part, on the types of mold present, extent of an individual's exposure, ages of exposed individuals, and their existing sensitivities or allergies (EPA 2001).

Symptoms of irritant responses and toxigenic reactions from exposure to molds in indoor environments range from mild to severe. Irritant reactions, including conjunctivitis, vasomotor or irritant rhinitis, rhinosinusitis, and asthma exacerbation, are poorly understood but are thought to be a nonspecific reaction to bioaerosol particles rather than a specific allergic response to a particular protein. The specific toxigenic effects of mycotoxins remain controversial, but are under investigation. More than 300 toxins are produced by molds (mycotoxins); *Stachybotrys chartarum* is often cited as a toxigenic mold, but all fungal genera have the potential to produce chemicals that could be harmful to humans. Ingestion of contaminated grain is the most common route of exposure to mycotoxins, but inhalation and dermal contact have also resulted in toxicoses in building occupants and agricultural workers. Mycotoxins are associated with actively growing colonies and spores; they are not gaseous, unlike microbial volatile organic compounds (MVOCs). MVOCs are natural by-products of microbial metabolism produced by actively growing organisms, and they have been alleged to cause headache, nausea, and malaise in building occupants.

Bacterial Pathogens. Diseases produced by the bacterial genus ***Legionella*** are collectively called legionelloses. More than 45 species have been identified, with over 20 isolated from both environmental and clinical sources. Conditions favorable for *Legionellae* growth include water temperatures of 25 to 42°C; stagnant conditions; presence of scale, sediment, and biofilms; and the presence of amoebas (Geary 2000). Diseases produced by *Legionella pneumophila* include Legionnaires' disease (pneumonia form) and Pontiac fever (flulike form). *L. pneumophila* serogroup 1 is the most frequently isolated from nature and most frequently associated with disease, but characteristics of the exposed individual (e.g., tobacco smoking, excessive weight, age) and viability of the bacterium affect the virulence. Legionellosis is not rare, but it is rarely diagnosed, and is severely underreported, often lost among other causes of pneumonia. McCoy (2006) estimated that, every day in the United States, an average of about 11 people die from legionellosis, and another 57 are infected but recover, often with lifelong debilitation.

In a review of waterborne infections from building water systems, it was estimated that 1400 deaths occur each year in the United States from *Pseudomonas aeruginosa*, another waterborne bacteria commonly found in building water systems (Anaissie et al. 2002).

Viral Pathogens. Outbreaks of infection in indoor air may also be caused by **viruses**. Viruses are readily disseminated from infected individuals, but cannot reproduce outside a host cell. Therefore, they do not reproduce in building structures or air-handling components, but can be distributed throughout buildings through duct systems and on air currents. Human-to-human dispersal is common. In one example, most of the passengers in an airline cabin developed influenza following exposure to one acutely ill person (Moser et al. 1979). In this case, the plane had been parked on a runway for several hours with the ventilation system turned off. Severe acute respiratory syndrome (SARS), caused by a corona virus similar to the common cold, was assumed to result from large droplet transmission; however, in an outbreak in a high-rise apartment, airborne transmission was the primary mode of disease spread, likely through dissemination from a bathroom drain (Yu et al. 2004).

Infectious diseases are transmitted through three primary routes: (1) direct contact and fomites (i.e., inanimate objects that transport infectious organisms from one individual to another), (2) large droplets [generally with a mass median aerodynamic diameter (MMAD) > 10 μm], and (3) fine particles, sometimes called *droplet nuclei* (MMAD < 10 μm) (Mandell et al. 1999). Additional transmission routes, such as through blood transfusions, intravenous injections, or injuries, are not of concern here. Table 3 lists infections considered transmissible by air.

Nonviable Biological Substances. **Allergic reactions** are an immunological response to foreign protein. Allergies may develop after dermal contact or inhalation of particles containing microorganisms, microbial fragments or by-products, and other biological components (e.g., enzymes, mite and cockroach excreta, pet dander). Cases of allergic respiratory illness (e.g., humidifier fever, hypersensitivity pneumonitis) manifest acute symptoms such as malaise, fever, chills, shortness of breath, and coughing (Edwards 1980; Morey 1988). In buildings, these illnesses may occur as a response to microbiological contaminants from HVAC system components, such as humidifiers and water spray systems, or other mechanical components that have been damaged by chronic water exposure (Hodgson et al. 1985, 1987). The severity of immunological reactions to bioaerosols can vary dramatically, from discomfort (allergic rhinitis and sinusitis) to life-threatening asthma. Allergy testing may be helpful in identifying an offending agent, but often is not. In cases of more severe illness, it may be necessary to remove an affected individual from exposure, even after appropriate abatement and exposure control methods have been instituted within the building.

Crandall and Sieber (1996) demonstrated that 47 of 104 problem buildings evaluated had water damage in occupied areas. Other studies concluded that unusual populations and high concentrations of microorganisms in indoor air may increase occupants' health complaints (Brundage et al. 1988; Burge 1995; Burge et al. 1987).

Exposure Guidelines for Bioaerosols. At present, numerical guidelines for bioaerosol exposure in indoor environments are not available for the following reasons (Morey 1990):

- Incomplete data on background concentrations and types of microorganisms indoors, especially as affected by geographical, seasonal, and building parameters
- Incomplete understanding of and ability to measure routes of exposure, internal dose, and intermediate and ultimate clinical effects
- Absence of epidemiological data relating bioaerosol exposure indoors to illness
- Enormous variability in types of microbial particles, including viable cells, dead spores, toxins, antigens, MVOCs, and viruses
- Large variation in human susceptibility to microbial particles, making estimates of health risk difficult

However, even without numerical guidelines, bioaerosol sampling data can be interpreted based on factors such as

- Rank order assessment of the kinds (genera/species) of microorganisms present in complainant and control locations (ACGIH 1999)
- Medical or laboratory evidence that illness is caused by a microorganism (ACGIH 1999)
- Indoor/outdoor concentration ratios for various microbial agents (ACGIH 1999; Morey and Jenkins 1989)

Table 3 Diseases Spread by Droplet or Airborne Transmission

Disease	Organism	Clinical Manifestations
Adenovirus	Adenovirus	Rhinitis, pharyngitis, malaise, rash, cough
Influenza*	Influenza virus	Fever, chills, malaise, headache cough, coryza, myalgias
Measles (rubeola)*	Rubeola virus	Fever, rash, malaise, coryza, conjunctivitis, Koplik's spots, adenopathy, CNS complications
Meningococcal disease	*Neisseria meningitides*	Fever, headache, vomiting, confusion, convulsions, petechial rash, neck stiffness
Mumps*	Mumps virus	Painful/swollen salivary glands, orchitis, meningoencephalitis
Pertussis (whooping cough)	*Bordetella pertussis*	Malaise, cough, coryza, lymphocytosis
Parvovirus B19	Parvovirus B19	Rash, aplastic anemia, arthritis, myalgias
Respiratory syncytial virus	RSV	Often asymptomatic; respiratory symptoms
Rubella	Rubella virus	Fever, malaise, coryza, rash
Tuberculosis*	*Mycobacterium* species	Fever, weight loss, fatigue, night sweats, pulmonary disease, extra pulmonary involvement including lymphatic, genitourinary, bone, meningeal, peritoneal, miliary
Varicella	Human herpes virus 3	Chickenpox or zoster presentation

Source: Adapted from Russi et al. (2008).
*Airborne transmission is reasonably certain, although it may not be primary mode.

Exposure Control Strategies. Because of the wide variety of pathogens and sources, a range of bioaerosol exposure control strategies may be required. Typically, these strategies should focus on source control (including good housekeeping and proper HVAC system operation and maintenance), but dilution ventilation, local exhaust ventilation, disinfection procedures, space pressure control, and filtration may also be considered.

Moisture control is the key to mold control. Molds need both food and water to survive; because molds can digest most things, water is the key factor that limits mold growth. Molds often grow in damp or wet areas indoors, including bathroom tiles, basement walls, areas around windows where moisture condenses, and near leaky water fountains or sinks. Uncontrolled humidity can also be a source of moisture leading to mold growth, particularly in hot, humid climates. For this reason, manage indoor relative humidity to minimize dew-point conditions that can result in moisture accumulation in building materials and contents (EPA 2001). More detailed information may be found in Harriman et al. (2001) and ASHRAE's (2003) *Mold and Moisture Management in Buildings*.

ASHRAE *Guideline* 12 provides environmental and operational guidance for safe operation of building water systems to minimize the risk of Legionnaires' disease. It is in the process of being upgraded to a standard by ASHRAE special project committee SPC 188.

GASEOUS CONTAMINANTS

Gaseous contaminants include both true gases (which have boiling points less than room temperature) and vapors of liquids with boiling points above normal indoor temperatures. It also includes both volatile organic compounds and inorganic air contaminants.

Volatile organic compounds (VOCs) include 4- to 16-carbon alkanes, chlorinated hydrocarbons, alcohols, aldehydes, ketones, esters, terpenes, ethers, aromatic hydrocarbons (such as benzene and toluene), and heterocyclic hydrocarbons. Also included are chlorofluorocarbons (CFCs) and hydrochlorofluorocarbons (HCFCs), which are still commonly used as refrigerants in existing installations, although production and importation have been phased out for environmental protection (Calm and Domanski 2004). More information on classifications, characteristics, and measurement methods can be found in Chapter 11.

Inorganic gaseous air contaminants include ammonia, nitrogen oxides, ozone, sulfur dioxide, carbon monoxide, and carbon dioxide. Although the last two contain carbon, they are by tradition regarded as inorganic chemicals.

The most common units of measurement for gaseous contaminants are parts per million by volume (ppm) and milligrams per cubic metre (mg/m^3). For smaller quantities, parts per billion (ppb) and micrograms per cubic metre ($\mu g/m^3$) are used. The relationship between these units of measure is also described in Chapter 11.

Industrial Environments

Exposures and Sources. In the industrial environment, a wide variety of gaseous contaminants may be emitted as process by-products (e.g., paints, solvents, and welding fumes) or as accidental spills and releases.

Health Effects of Industrial Exposures. Given that tens of thousands of contaminants are regularly used by industry, possible health effects can range from mild skin or eye irritation and headaches, to failure of major organs or systems and death. Exposure standards and specific health effects for various industrial contaminants are discussed in the following section.

Exposure Standards. The U.S. Occupational Safety and Health Administration (OSHA) sets permissible exposure limits (PELs) for toxic and hazardous substances, which are enforceable workplace regulatory standards. These are published yearly in the *Code of Federal Regulations* (29CFR1910, Subpart Z) and intermittently in the *Federal Register*. Most of the regulatory levels were derived from those recommended by the American Conference of Governmental Industrial Hygienists (ACGIH) and American National Standards Institute (ANSI). The health effects on which these standards were based can be found in their publications. ACGIH reviews data on a regular basis and publishes annual revisions to their Threshold Limit Values (TLVs®).

The National Institute for Occupational Safety and Health (NIOSH), a research agency of the U.S. Department of Health and Human Service, conducts research and makes recommendations to prevent work-related illness and injury. NIOSH publishes the *Registry of Toxic Effects and Chemical Substances* (RTECS), as well as numerous criteria on recommended standards for occupational exposures. Some compounds not listed by OSHA are covered by NIOSH, and their recommended exposure limits (RELs) are sometimes lower than the legal requirements set by OSHA. The NIOSH *Pocket Guide to Chemical Hazards* (NIOSH 1997) condenses these references and is a convenient reference for engineering purposes.

The harmful effects of gaseous pollutants depend on both short-term peak concentrations and the time-integrated exposures received by the person. OSHA defined three periods for concentration averaging and assigned allowable levels that may exist in these categories in workplaces for over 490 compounds, mostly gaseous contaminants. Abbreviations for concentrations for the three averaging periods are

AMP = acceptable maximum peak (for a short exposure)

ACC = acceptable ceiling concentration (not to be exceeded during an 8 h shift, except for periods where an AMP applies)

TWA8 = time-weighted average (not to be exceeded in any 8 h shift of a 40 h week)

The respective levels are presented in Tables Z-1, Z-2 and Z-3 of 29CFR1910.1000, *Occupational safety and health standards: Air contaminants*.

In non-OSHA literature, the AMP is sometimes called a short-term exposure limit (STEL), and a TWA8 is sometimes called a threshold limit value (TLV). NIOSH (1997) also lists values for the toxic limit that is immediately dangerous to life and health (IDLH).

Standards differ for industrial and nonindustrial environments (EHD 1987). A Canadian National Task Force developed guideline criteria for residential indoor environments, and the World Health Organization (WHO) published indoor air quality guidelines for Europe (WHO 2000). Table 4 compares these guidelines with occupational criteria for selected contaminants.

The National Primary Drinking Water Standards (EPA 2003) are legally enforceable standards that apply to public water systems. Primary standards protect public health by limiting the levels of contaminants in drinking water.

Exposure Control Strategies. Gaseous contaminant control strategies include eliminating or reducing sources, local exhaust, general dilution ventilation, and using personal protective devices such as respirators. The most effective control strategy is source control. If source control is not possible, local exhaust ventilation can often be the most cost-effective method of controlling airborne contaminants. General dilution ventilation is often the least effective means of control. Ventilation and local exhaust for industrial environments are discussed more thoroughly in Chapters 29 and 30 of the 2007 *ASHRAE Handbook—HVAC Applications*.

Nonindustrial Environments

Gaseous contaminants of concern in nonindustrial environments include volatile organic compounds, refrigerants, and inorganic gases.

Volatile Organic Compounds.

Sources. Indoor sources of VOCs include building materials, furnishings, cleaning products, office and HVAC equipment, ETS, people and their personal care products, and outdoor air. The California Environmental Protection Agency's Office of Environmental Health Hazard Assessment (OEHHA 2008) maintains a list of VOCs and other chemicals known to the state to cause cancer or reproductive toxicity.

Health Effects. Potential adverse health effects of VOCs in nonindustrial indoor environments are not well understood, but may include (1) irritant effects, including perception of unpleasant odors, mucous membrane irritation, and exacerbation of asthma; (2) systemic effects, such as fatigue and difficulty concentrating; and (3) toxic, chronic effects, such as carcinogenicity (Girman 1989).

Chronic adverse health effects from VOC exposure are of concern because some VOCs commonly found in indoor air are human (benzene) or animal (chloroform, trichloroethylene, carbon tetrachloride, p-dichlorobenzene) carcinogens. Some other VOCs are also genotoxic. Theoretical risk assessment studies suggest that risk from chronic VOC exposures in residential indoor air is greater than that associated with exposure to VOCs in the outdoor air or in drinking water (McCann et al. 1987; Tancrede et al. 1987).

A biological model for acute human response to low levels of VOCs indoors is based on three mechanisms: sensory perception of the environment, weak inflammatory reactions, and environmental stress reaction (Mølhave 1991). A growing body of literature summarizes measurement techniques for the effects of VOCs on nasal (Koren 1990; Koren et al. 1992; Meggs 1994; Mølhave et al. 1993; Ohm et al. 1992) and ocular (Franck et al. 1993; Kjaergaard 1992; Kjaergaard et al. 1991) mucosa. It is not well known how different sensory receptions to VOCs are combined into perceived comfort and the sensation of air quality. This perception is apparently related

Table 4 Comparison of Indoor Environment Standards and Guidelines

	Canadian[c]	WHO/Europe	NAAQS/EPA[f]	NIOSH REL (TWA)[h]	OSHA (TWA)[h]	ACGIH (TWA)[h]	MAK[g] (TWA)[h]
Acrolein	0.02 ppm[a]			0.1 ppm 0.3 ppm (15 min)	0.1 ppm	C 0.1 ppm, A4	
Acetaldehyde	5.0 ppm			Ca: ALARA[b]	200 ppm	C 25 ppm	50 ppm 100 ppm (5 min)
Formaldehyde	0.1 ppm (1 h) 0.04 ppm (8 h)	0.081 ppm (30 min)		0.016 ppm 0.1 ppm (15 min) Ca	0.75 ppm 2 ppm (15 min) Ca	C 0.3 ppm, A2	0.3 ppm 1.0 ppm (5 min)
Carbon dioxide	3500 ppm			5000 ppm 30 000 ppm (15 min)	5000 ppm	5000 ppm 30 000 ppm (15 min)	5000 ppm 10 000 ppm (60 min)
Carbon monoxide	11 ppm (8 h) 25 ppm (1 h)	8.6 ppm (8 h) 25 ppm (1 h) 51 ppm (30 min) 86 ppm (15 min)	9 ppm (8 h) 35 ppm (1 h)	35 ppm C 200 ppm	50 ppm	25 ppm	30 ppm 60 ppm (30 min)
Nitrogen dioxide	0.05 ppm 0.25 ppm (1 h)	0.02 ppm (1 yr) 0.1 ppm (1 h)	0.053 ppm (1 yr)	1 ppm (15 min)	C 5 ppm	3 ppm 5 ppm (15 min), A4	5 ppm 10 ppm (5 min)
Ozone	0.12 ppm (1 h); Insufficient data for long-term level	0.06 ppm (8 h)	0.12 ppm (1 h) 0.085 ppm (8 h)	C 0.1 ppm	0.1 ppm	0.05 ppm, A4 (for heavy work) 0.2 ppm (2 h) (light, moderate, or heavy work)	
Particles <2.5 MMAD[d]	40 μg/m^3 (8 h) 100 μg/m^3 (1 h)		15 μg/m^3 (1 yr) 35 μg/m^3 (24 h)		5 mg/m^3 (respirable fraction)	3 mg/m^3 (8 h) (no asbestos, <1% crystalline silica, with median cut point of 4.0 μm)	1.5 mg/m^3 (for less than 4 μm)
Sulfur dioxide	0.019 ppm 0.38 ppm (5 min)	0.047 ppm (24 h) 0.019 ppm (1 yr)	0.03 ppm (1 yr) 0.14 ppm (24 h)	2 ppm (8 h) 5 ppm (15 min)	5 ppm	2 ppm 5 ppm (15 min)	0.5 ppm 1.0 ppm (5 min)
Radon	800 Bq/m^3 [e]		4 pCi/l				

( ) Numbers in parentheses represent averaging periods
C = ceiling limit
Ca = carcinogen
A4 = not classifiable as human carcinogen per ACGIH

[a]Parts per million (10^6)
[b]As low as reasonably achievable
[c]Health Canada *Exposure Guidelines for Residential Indoor Air Quality*
[d]Mass median aerodynamic diameter
[e]Mean in normal living areas
[f]U.S. EPA National Ambient Air Quality Standards
[g]German Maximale Arbeitsplatz Konzentrationen
[h]Value for 8-h TWA, unless otherwise noted
[i]WHO Air Quality Guidelines for Europe

to stimulation of the olfactory sense in the nasal cavity, the gustatory sense on the tongue, and the common chemical sense (Cain 1989; Mølhave 1991).

Cometto-Muñiz and Cain (1994a, 1994b) addressed the independent contribution of the trigeminal and olfactory nerves to the detection of airborne chemicals. Smell is experienced through olfactory nerve receptors in the nose. Nasal pungency, described as common chemical sensations such as prickling, irritation, tingling, freshness, stinging, and burning, is experienced through nonspecialized receptors of the trigeminal nerve in the face. Odor and pungency thresholds follow different patterns related to chemical concentration. Odor is often detected at much lower levels. A linear correlation between pungency thresholds of homologous series (of alcohols, acetates, ketones, and alkylbenzenes, all relatively nonreactive agents) suggests that nasal pungency relies on a physicochemical interaction with a susceptible biophase within the cell membrane. Through this nonspecific mechanism, low, subthreshold levels of a wide variety of VOCs, as found in many polluted indoor environments, may be additive in sensory impact to produce noticeable sensory irritation.

Exposure Standards. Few standards exist for exposure to VOCs in nonindustrial indoor environments. NIOSH, OSHA, and ACGIH have regulatory standards or recommended limits for industrial occupational exposures [ACGIH (annual); NIOSH 1992]. With few exceptions, concentrations observed in nonindustrial indoor environments fall well below (100 to 1000 times lower) published pollutant-specific occupational exposure limits. The California Office of Environmental Health Hazard Assessment (OEHHA 2007) established chronic reference exposure limits (cRELs) for inhalation exposure to 80 compounds, including many VOCs found in indoor air, which can be used as guidelines for establishing appropriate IAQ criteria regarding specific VOCs of interest.

Total VOC (TVOC) concentrations have been suggested as an indicator of the ability of combined VOC exposures to produce adverse health effects. This approach is no longer supported, because the irritant potential and toxicity of individual VOCs vary widely, and measured concentrations are highly dependent on the sampling and analytical methods used (Hodgson 1995). In controlled exposure experiments, odors become significant at roughly 3 mg/m^3. At 5 mg/m^3, objective effects were seen, in addition to subjective reports of irritation. Exposures for 50 min to 8 mg/m^3 of synthetic mixtures of 20 VOCs led to significant irritation of mucous membranes in the eyes, nose, and throat.

Exposure Control Strategies. VOC control strategies include source elimination or reduction, local exhaust, air cleaning, and general dilution ventilation. Ventilation requirements and other means of control of gaseous contaminants are discussed more thoroughly in Chapter 16 of this volume and Chapter 45 of the 2007 *ASHRAE Handbook—HVAC Applications*.

Refrigerants.

Sources. The primary sources of exposure to refrigerants are leaks from refrigeration and HVAC equipment and refrigerant storage containers. Exposure may also result from poor practice when servicing refrigeration equipment.

Health Effects. ASHRAE *Standard* 34 assigns refrigerants to one of two toxicity classes (A or B) based on allowable exposure.

Fatalities have been reported following acute exposure to fluorocarbon refrigerants. Chronic, low-level inhalation exposures to refrigerants can cause cardiotoxicity. Some are thought to be cardiac sensitizers to epinephrine and put occupants at risk for arrhythmias. Central nervous system (CNS) depression and asphyxia have been noted with exposures to very high concentrations. Hathaway et al. (1991) found that volunteers exposed to 200 000 ppm of R-12 experienced significant eye irritation and CNS effects. Chronic exposure to 1000 ppm for 8 h per day for up to 17 days caused no subjective symptoms or changes in pulmonary function.

A significant hazard exists when chlorinated hydrocarbons (R-11, for example) are used near open flame or heated surfaces. Phosgene gas (carbonyl chloride, an extreme irritant to the lungs) and halogen acids may be generated when chlorinated or fluorinated solvents or gases decompose in the presence of heat.

Exposure Standards. ASHRAE *Standard* 15 discusses safety for refrigeration systems, and *Standard* 34 classifies refrigerants by safety levels.

Exposure Control Strategies. Refrigerant-containing systems may only be serviced by certified technicians. Controls for preventing exposures include selection and use of appropriate fittings and valves, and ensuring that compressed gas cylinders are secured during use, transport, and storage. When repairs are made to leaking or defective HVAC equipment, adequate dilution ventilation should be provided to the work area. ASHRAE *Standard* 15 establishes specific requirements for designing, installing, operating, and servicing mechanical refrigeration equipment.

Inorganic Gases.

Sources. Inorganic gases in the nonindustrial environment may come from a combination of outdoor air and indoor sources, including occupants (e.g., respiration, toiletries), processes (e.g., combustion, office equipment), and indoor air chemistry (e.g., reaction between ozone and alkenes).

Health Effects. **Carbon monoxide** is a chemical asphyxiant. Inhalation of CO causes a throbbing headache because hemoglobin has a greater affinity for CO than for oxygen (about 240 times greater), and because of a detrimental shift in the oxygen dissociation curve. Carbon monoxide inhibits oxygen transport in the blood by forming carboxyhemoglobin and inhibiting cytochrome oxidase at the cellular level. Cobb and Etzel (1991) suggested that CO poisoning at home represented a major preventable disease. Moolenaar et al. (1995) had similar findings, and suggested that motor vehicles and home furnaces were primary causes of mortality. Girman et al. (1998) identified both fatal outcomes and "episodes." Respectively, 35.9% and 30.6% of fatal outcomes and episodes resulted from motor vehicles, 34.8% and 39.9% from appliance combustion, 4.5% and 5.2% from small appliances, 2.2% and 2.3% from camping equipment, 5.6% and 5.0% from fires, 13.4% and 13.3% from grills and hibachis, and the remainder were unknown. In a review of CO exposures in the United States from 2001 to 2003, the Centers for Disease Control (CDC 2005) found that nearly 500 people died and over 15 000 were treated in emergency departments each year after unintentional, non-fire-related CO exposures. Of cases with known sources, the most common source of CO was furnaces (18.5%), followed by motor vehicles (9.1%). Inappropriate use of portable generators, a growing problem, resulted in around 50 deaths per year from 2002 to 2005 (CPSC 2006).

Carbon dioxide can become dangerous not as a toxic agent but as a simple asphyxiant. When concentrations exceed 35 000 ppm, central breathing receptors are triggered and cause the sensation of shortness of breath. At progressively higher concentrations, central nervous system dysfunction begins because of simple displacement of oxygen. Concentrations of CO_2 in the nonindustrial environment are often measured in the range of 400 to 1200 ppm, depending on occupant density and ventilation quantity and effectiveness.

Inhalation of **nitric oxide (NO)** causes methemoglobin formation, which adversely affects the body by interfering with oxygen transport at the cellular level. NO exposures of 3 ppm have been compared to carbon monoxide exposures of 10 to 15 ppm (Case et al. 1979, in EPA 1991).

Nitrogen dioxide (NO_2) is a corrosive gas with a pungent odor, with a reported odor threshold between 0.11 and 0.22 ppm. NO_2 has low water solubility, and is therefore inhaled into the deep lung, where it causes a delayed inflammatory response. Increased airway resistance has been reported at 1.5 to 2 ppm (Bascom 1996). NO_2 is reported to be a potential carcinogen through free radical production (Burgess and Crutchfield 1995). At high concentrations, NO_2 causes lung damage directly by its oxidant properties, and may cause health effects indirectly by increasing host susceptibility to respiratory infections. Health effects from exposures to ambient outdoor concentrations or in residential situations are inconsistent, especially in studies relating to exposures from gas cooking stoves (Samet et al. 1987). Indoor concentrations of NO_2 often exceed ambient concentrations because of the presence of strong indoor sources and a trend toward more energy-efficient (tighter) homes. Acute toxicity is seldom seen from NO_2 produced by unvented indoor combustion, because insufficient quantities of NO_2 are produced. Chronic pulmonary effects from exposure to combinations of low-level combustion pollutants are possible, however (Bascom et al. 1996).

Sulfur dioxide (SO_2) is a colorless gas with a pungent odor detected at about 0.5 ppm (EPA 1991). Because SO_2 is quite soluble in water, it readily reacts with moisture in the respiratory tract to irritate the upper respiratory mucosa. Concomitant exposure to fine particles, an individual's depth and rate of breathing, and preexisting disease can influence the degree of response to SO_2 exposure.

Ozone (O_3) is a pulmonary irritant and alters human pulmonary function at concentrations of approximately 0.12 ppm (Bates 1989). Exposure to ozone at 60 to 80 ppb causes inflammation, bronchoconstriction, and increased airway responsiveness. The EPA's BASE study of over 100 randomly selected typical U.S. office buildings (Apte et al. 2007) found a clear statistical relationship between ambient ozone concentrations and building-related health symptoms, despite the fact that only one building had a workday average ambient ozone concentration greater than the 8 h national ambient air quality standards (NAAQS; EPA 2008a) level of 80 ppb.

Ozone reacts with many organic chemicals and airborne particulate matter commonly found indoors. Weschler (2006) summarizes current knowledge of these reactions and their products, which include both stable reaction products that may be more irritating than their chemical precursors (Mølhave et al. 2005; Tamas et al. 2006; Weschler and Shields 2000) and relatively short-lived products that are highly irritating and may also have chronic toxicity or carcinogenicity (Destaillats et al. 2006; Nazaroff et al. 2006; Weschler 2000; Wilkins et al. 2001; Wolkoff et al. 2000).

Inhalation exposures to gaseous oxides of nitrogen (NO_x), sulfur (SO_2), and ozone (O_3) occur in residential and commercial buildings. These air pollutants are of considerable concern because of the potential for acute and chronic respiratory tract health effects in exposed individuals, particularly individuals with preexisting pulmonary disease.

Exposure Standards and Guidelines. Currently, there are no specific U.S. government standards for nonindustrial occupational exposures to air contaminants. Occupational exposure criteria are health-based; that is, they consider only healthy workers, and not necessarily individuals who may be unusually responsive to the effects of chemical exposures. The U.S. EPA's (2008a) NAAQS are also health-based standards designed to protect the general public from the effects of hazardous airborne pollutants (see Chapter 11); however, there is debate as to whether these standards truly represent health-based thresholds, because two (ozone and carbon monoxide) of the six criteria involve toxicologically based research for standard development.

Table 5 Inorganic Gas Comparative Criteria

Contaminant	OSHA TWA[a]	U.S. EPA NAAQS[b]
Nitric oxide	25 ppm (30 mg/m^3)	None
Nitrogen dioxide	Ceiling[c] 5 ppm (9 mg/m^3)	0.053 ppm (100 μg/m^3)
Sulfur dioxide	5 ppm (13 mg/m^3)	0.03 ppm (80 μg/m^3) 24 h: 0.14 ppm (365 μg/m^3)[d]
Ozone	0.1 ppm (0.2 mg/m^3)	0.08 ppm (8 h in specified form)[e]

[a]TWA: 8 h time-weighted average
[b]Values are annual arithmetic mean unless otherwise specified
[c]Ceiling value, not to be exceeded during any part of working exposure
[d]Not to be exceeded more than once per year
[e]Per revision July 1997; see Final Rule at *Federal Register* 62(138):38856

Table 5 is not meant as a health-based guideline for evaluating indoor exposures to inorganic gases; rather, it is intended for comparison and consideration by investigators of the indoor environment. These criteria may not be completely protective for all workers.

Exposure Control Strategies. Inorganic gas contaminant control strategies include source elimination or reduction, local exhaust, space pressure control, and general dilution ventilation. Ventilation requirements and other means of control of gaseous contaminants are discussed more thoroughly in Chapter 16 of this volume and Chapter 45 of the 2007 *ASHRAE Handbook—HVAC Applications*.

The by-products of indoor air chemistry can be limited by using carbon-based filters in locations where outdoor ozone concentrations commonly approach or exceed the NAAQS.

PHYSICAL AGENTS

Physical factors in the indoor environment include thermal conditions (temperature, moisture, air velocity, and radiant energy); mechanical energy (noise and vibration); and electromagnetic radiation, including ionizing (radon) and nonionizing [light, radiofrequency, and extremely low frequency (ELF)] magnetic and electric fields. Physical agents can act directly on building occupants, interact with indoor air quality factors, or affect human responses to the indoor environment. Though not categorized as indoor air quality factors, physical agents often affect perceptions of indoor air quality.

THERMAL ENVIRONMENT

The thermal environment affects human health in that it affects body temperature regulation and heat exchange with the environment. A normal, healthy, resting adult's internal or core body temperatures are very stable, with variations seldom exceeding 0.5 K. The internal temperature of a resting adult, measured orally, averages about 37.0°C; measured rectally, it is about 0.5 K higher. Core temperature is carefully modulated by an elaborate physiological control system. In contrast, skin temperature is basically unregulated and can (depending on environmental temperature) vary from about 31 to 36°C in normal environments and activities. It also varies between different parts of the skin, with the greatest range of variation in the hands and feet.

Range of Healthy Living Conditions

Environmental conditions for good thermal comfort minimize effort of the physiological control system. The control system regulates internal body temperature by varying the amount of blood flowing to different skin areas, thus increasing or decreasing heat loss to the environment. Additional physiological response includes secreting sweat, which can evaporate from the skin in warm or hot environments, or increasing the body's rate of metabolic heat production by shivering in the cold. For a resting person wearing trousers and a long-sleeved shirt, thermal comfort in a steady state is experienced in

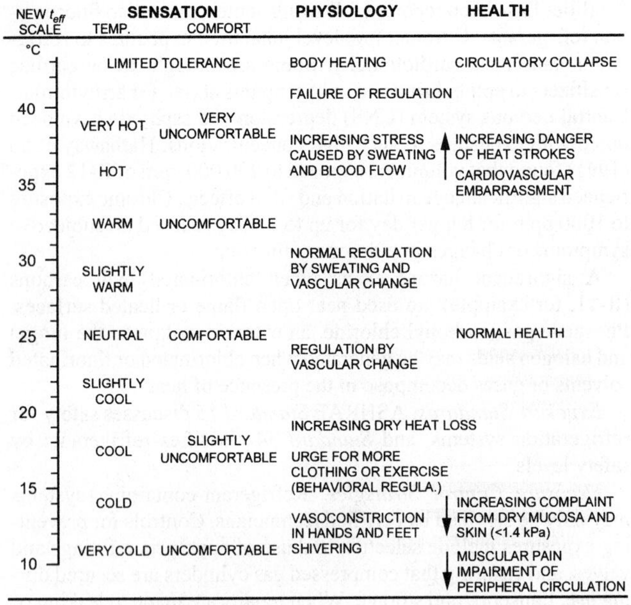

Fig. 1 Related Human Sensory, Physiological, and Health Responses for Prolonged Exposure

a still-air environment at 24°C. A zone of comfort extends about 1.5 K above and below this optimum level (Fanger 1970).

An individual can minimize the need for physiological (involuntary) responses to the thermal environment, which generally are perceived as uncomfortable, in various ways. In a cool or cold environment, these responses include increased clothing, increased activity, or seeking or creating an environment that is warmer. In a warm or hot environment, the amount of clothing or level of physical activity can be reduced, or an environment that is more conducive to increased heat loss can be created. Some human responses to the thermal environment are shown in Figure 1.

Cardiovascular and other diseases and aging can reduce the capacity or ability of physiological processes to maintain internal body temperature through balancing heat gains and losses. Thus, some persons are less able to deal with thermal challenges and deviations from comfortable conditions. Metabolic heat production tends to decrease with age, as a result of decreasing basal metabolism together with decreased physical activity. Metabolic heat production at age 80 is about 20% less than that at 20 years of age, for comparable size and mass. Persons in their eighties, therefore, may prefer an environmental temperature about 1.5 K warmer than persons in their twenties. Older people may have reduced capacity to secrete sweat and to increase their skin blood flow, and are therefore more likely to experience greater strain in warm and hot conditions, as well as in cool and cold conditions. However, the effect of age on metabolism and other factors related to thermal response varies considerably from person to person, and care should be exercised in applying these generalizations to specific individuals.

Hypothermia

Hypothermia is defined as a core body temperature of less than 35°C. Hypothermia can result from environmental cold exposure, but may also be induced by other conditions, such as metabolic disorders and drug use. Occupational hypothermia occurs in workers in a cold environment when heat balance cannot be met while maintaining work performance. Elderly persons sitting inactive in a cool room may become hypothermic, because they often fail to observe a slow fall in body temperature (Nordic Conference on Cold 1991).

Deleterious effects of cold on work performance derive from peripheral vasoconstriction and cooling, which slows down the rate of nerve conduction and muscle contraction, and increases stiffness in tendons and connective tissues. This induces clumsiness and increases risk for injury (e.g., in occupational settings). Direct effects of cold include injuries from frostbite (skin freezes at 0 to 2°C) and a condition called **immersion foot**, in which the feet are exposed to wetness and temperatures of 1 to 10°C for more than 12 h, and vasoconstriction and low oxygen supply lead to edema and tissue damage.

Hyperthermia

In hyperthermia, body temperatures are above normal. A deep-body temperature increase of 2 K above normal does not generally impair body function. For example, it is not unusual for runners to have rectal temperatures of 40°C after a long race. An elevated body temperature increases metabolism. However, when body temperature increases above normal for reasons other than exercise, heat illness may develop. Heat illness represents a number of disorders from mild to fatal, which do not depend only on the hyperthermia in itself. In heat stroke, the most severe condition, the heat balance regulation system collapses, resulting in a rapid rise in body temperature. Central nervous system function deteriorates at deep body temperatures above 41 to 42°C. Convulsions may occur above such temperatures, and cells may be damaged. This condition is particularly dangerous for the brain, because lost neurons are not replaced. Thermoregulatory functions of sweating and peripheral vasodilation cease at about 43°C, after which body temperatures tend to rise rapidly if external cooling is not imposed (Blatteis 1998; Hales et al. 1996).

Seasonal Patterns

Ordinary seasonal changes in temperate climates are temporally associated with illness. Many acute and several chronic diseases vary in frequency or severity with time of year, and some are present only in certain seasons. Most countries report increased mortality from cardiovascular disease during colder winter months. Minor respiratory infections, such as colds and sore throats, occur mainly in fall and winter. More serious infections, such as pneumonia, have a somewhat shorter season in winter. Intestinal infections, such as dysentery and typhoid fever, are more prevalent in summer. Diseases transmitted by insects, such as encephalitis and endemic typhus, are limited to summer, because insects are active in warm temperatures only.

Hryhorczuk et al. (1992), Martinez et al. (1989), and others describe a correlation between weather and seasonal illnesses, but correlations do not necessarily establish a causal relationship. Daily or weekly mortality and heat stress in heat waves have a strong physiological basis directly linked to outdoor temperature. In indoor environments, which are well controlled with respect to temperature and humidity, such temperature extremes and the possible adverse effects on health are strongly attenuated.

Increased Deaths in Heat Waves

The role of ambient temperature extremes produced by weather conditions in producing discomfort, incapacity, and death has been studied extensively (Katayama and Momiyana-Sakamoto 1970). Military personnel, deep-mine workers, and other workers occupationally exposed to extremes of high and low temperature have been studied, but the importance of thermal stress affecting both the sick and healthy general population is not sufficiently appreciated. Collins and Lehmann (1953) studied weekly deaths over many years in large U.S. cities and demonstrated the effect of heat waves in producing conspicuous periods of excess mortality. Excess mortality caused by heat waves was of the same amplitude as that from influenza epidemics, but tended to last one week instead of the 4 to 6 weeks of influenza epidemics.

Ellis (1972) reviewed heat wave-related excess mortality in the United States. Mortality increases of 30% over background are commonly seen, especially in heat waves early in the summer. Much of the increase occurs in the population over age 65, more of it in women than in men, and many deaths are from cardiovascular, cerebrovascular, or respiratory causes (often exacerbated preexisting conditions). Oeschli and Buechley (1970) studied heat-related deaths in Los Angeles heat waves of 1939, 1955, and 1963. Kilbourne et al. (1982) suggested that the same risk factors (i.e., age, low income, and African-American derivation) persist in more recent heat death epidemics. In Paris, about 3000 persons died during the heat wave in the summer of 2003.

Among the most notable lethal heat waves in Europe are Athens in 1987 and 1988 (Giles et al. 1990), Seville in 1988 (Diaz et al. 2002), Valencia in 1991 and 1993 (Ballester et al. 1997), London in 1995 (Hajat et al. 2002), the Netherlands between 1979 and 1991 (Kunst et al. 1993), and Paris in 2003 (Thirion et al. 2005).

The temperature/mortality relation varies greatly by latitude and climatic zone (McMichael et al. 2006). Occupants of hotter cities are more affected by colder temperatures, and occupants of colder cities are more affected by warmer temperatures. People living in urban environments are at greater risk than those in nonurban regions. Thermally inefficient housing and the so-called urban heat island effect amplify and extend the rise in temperatures (especially overnight).

Hardy (1971) showed the relationship of health data to comfort on a psychrometric diagram (Figure 2). The diagram contains ASHRAE effective temperature (ET*) lines and lines of constant skin moisture level or skin wettedness. Skin wettedness is defined as that fraction of the skin covered with water to account for the observed evaporation rate. The ET* lines are loci of constant physiological strain, and also correspond to constant levels of physiological discomfort (i.e., slightly uncomfortable, comfortable, and very comfortable) (Gonzalez et al. 1978). Skin wettedness, as an indicator of strain (Berglund and Cunningham 1986; Berglund and Gonzalez 1977) and the fraction of the skin wet with perspiration, is fairly constant along an ET* line. Numerically, ET* is the equivalent temperature at 50% rh that produces the strain and discomfort of the actual condition. The summer comfort range is between an ET* of 23 and 26°C. In this region, skin wettedness is less than 0.2. Heat strokes occur generally when ET* exceeds 34°C (Bridger and Helfand 1968). Thus, the ET* line of 35°C is generally considered dangerous. At this point, skin wettedness will be 0.4 or higher.

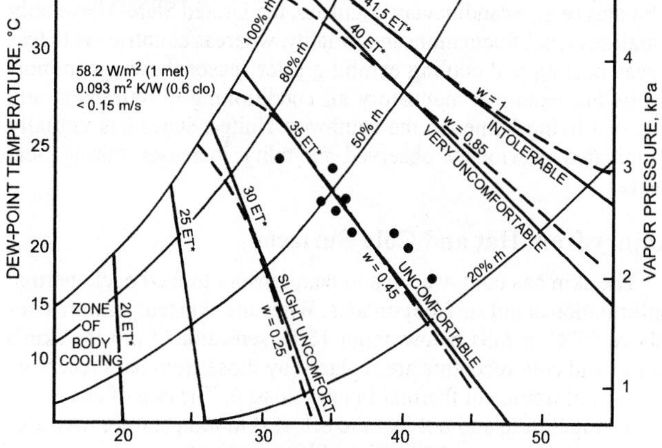

Fig. 2 Isotherms for Comfort, Discomfort, Physiological Strain, Effective Temperature (ET*), and Heat Stroke Danger Threshold

The black dots in Figure 2 correspond to heat stroke deaths of healthy male U.S. soldiers assigned to sedentary duties in midwestern army camp offices (Shickele 1947). Older people can be expected to respond less well to thermal challenges than do healthy soldiers. This was apparently the case in the Illinois heat wave study (Bridger and Helfand 1968), where the first wave with a 33% increase in death rate and an ET* of 29.5°C affected mainly the over-65-year-old group. The studies suggest that the "danger line" represents a threshold of significant risk for young healthy people, and that the danger tends to move to lower values of ET* with increasing age.

Effects of Thermal Environment on Specific Diseases

Cardiovascular diseases are largely responsible for excess mortality during heat waves. For example, Burch and DePasquale (1962) found that heart disease patients with decompensation (i.e., inadequate circulation) were extremely sensitive to high temperatures, and particularly to moist heat. However, both cold and hot temperature extremes have been associated with increased coronary heart disease deaths and anginal symptoms (Teng and Heyer 1955).

Both acute and chronic respiratory diseases often increase in frequency and severity during extreme cold weather. No increase in these diseases has been noted in extreme heat. Additional studies of hospital admissions for acute respiratory illness show a negative correlation with temperature after removal of seasonal trends (Holland 1961). Symptoms of chronic respiratory disease (bronchitis, emphysema) increase in cold weather, probably because reflex constriction of the bronchi adds to the obstruction already present. Greenberg (1964) found evidence of cold sensitivity in asthmatics: emergency room treatments for asthma increased abruptly in local hospitals with early and severe autumn cold spells. Later cold waves with even lower temperatures produced no such effects, and years without early extreme cold had no asthma epidemics of this type. Patients with cystic fibrosis are extremely sensitive to heat because their reduced sweat gland function greatly diminishes their ability to cope with increased temperature (Kessler and Anderson 1951).

Itching and chapping of the skin are influenced by (1) atmospheric factors, particularly cold and dry air; (2) frequent washing or wetting of skin; and (3) low indoor humidities. Although skin itching is usually a winter cold-climate illness in the general population, it can be caused by excessive summer air conditioning (Gaul and Underwood 1952; Susskind and Ishihara 1965).

People suffering from chronic illness (e.g., heart disease) or serious acute illnesses that require hospitalization often manage to avoid serious thermal stress. Katayama and Momiyana-Sakamoto (1970) found that countries with the most carefully regulated indoor climates (e.g., Scandinavian countries, the United States) have only small seasonal fluctuations in mortality, whereas countries with less space heating and cooling exhibit greater seasonal swings in mortality. For example, mandatory air conditioning in retirement and assisted living homes in the southwest United States has virtually eliminated previously observed mortality increases during heat waves.

Injury from Hot and Cold Surfaces

The skin has cold, warm, and pain sensors to feed back thermal information about surface contacts. When the skin temperature rises above 45°C or falls below about 15°C, sensations from the skin's warm and cold receptors are replaced by those from pain receptors to warn of imminent thermal injury to tissue. The rate of change of skin temperature and not just the actual skin temperature may also be important in pain perception. Skin temperature and its rate of change depend on the temperature of the contact surface, its conductivity, and contact time. Table 6 gives approximate temperature limits to avoid pain and injury when contacting three classes of conductors for various contact times (ISO 2006).

Table 6 Approximate Surface Temperature Limits to Avoid Pain and Injury

	Contact Time				
Material	**1 s**	**10 s**	**1 min**	**10 min**	**8 h**
Metal, water	65°C	56°C	51°C	48°C	43°C
Glass, concrete	80°C	66°C	54°C	48°C	43°C
Wood	120°C	88°C	60°C	48°C	43°C

Source: ISO *Standard* 13732-1:2006.

ELECTRICAL HAZARDS

Electrical current can cause burns, neural disturbances, and cardiac fibrillation (Billings 1975). The threshold of perception is about 5 mA for direct current, with a feeling of warmth at the contact site. The threshold is 1 mA for alternating current, which causes a tingling sensation.

Resistance of the current pathway through the body is a combination of core and skin resistance. The core is basically a saline volume conductor with very little resistance; therefore, the skin provides the largest component of the resistance. Skin resistance decreases with moisture. If the skin is moist, voltages as low as 2 V (ac) or 5 V (dc) are sufficient to be detected, and voltages as low as 20 V (ac) or 100 V (dc) can cause a 50% loss in muscular control.

The dangerous aspect of alternating electrical current is its ability to cause cardiac arrest by ventricular fibrillation. If a weak alternating current (100 mA for 2 s) passes through the heart (as it would in going from hand to foot), the current can force the heart muscle to fibrillate and lose the rhythmic contractions of the ventricles necessary to pump blood. Unconsciousness and death will soon follow if medical aid cannot rapidly restore normal rhythm.

MECHANICAL ENERGIES

Vibration

Vibration in a building originates from both outside and inside the building. Sources outside a building include blasting operations, road traffic, overhead aircraft, underground railways, earth movements, and weather conditions. Sources inside a building include doors closing, foot traffic, moving machinery, elevators, HVAC systems, and other building services. Vibration is an omnipresent, integral part of the built environment. The effects of vibration on building occupants depend on whether it is perceived by those persons and on factors related to the building, building location, activities of occupants in the building, and perceived source and magnitude of vibration. Factors influencing the acceptability of building vibration are presented in Figure 3.

The combination of hearing, seeing, or feeling vibration determines human response. Components concerned with hearing and seeing are part of the visual environment of a room and can be assessed as such. The perception of mechanical vibration by feeling is generally through the cutaneous and kinesthetic senses at high frequencies, and through the vestibular and visceral senses at low frequencies. Because of this and the nature of vibration sources and building responses, building vibration may be conveniently considered in two categories: low-frequency vibrations less than 1 Hz and high-frequency vibrations of 1 to 80 Hz.

Measurement and Assessment. Human response to vibration depends on vibration of the body. The main vibrational characteristics are vibration level, frequency, axis (and area of the body), and exposure time. A root-mean-square (RMS) averaging procedure (over the time of interest) is often used to represent vibration acceleration [$m/(s^2 \cdot RMS)$]. Vibration frequency is measured in cycles per second (Hz), and the vibration axis is usually considered in three orthogonal, human-centered translational directions (up-and-down, side-to-side, and fore-and-aft). Although the coordinate system is centered inside the body, in practice, vibration is measured at the

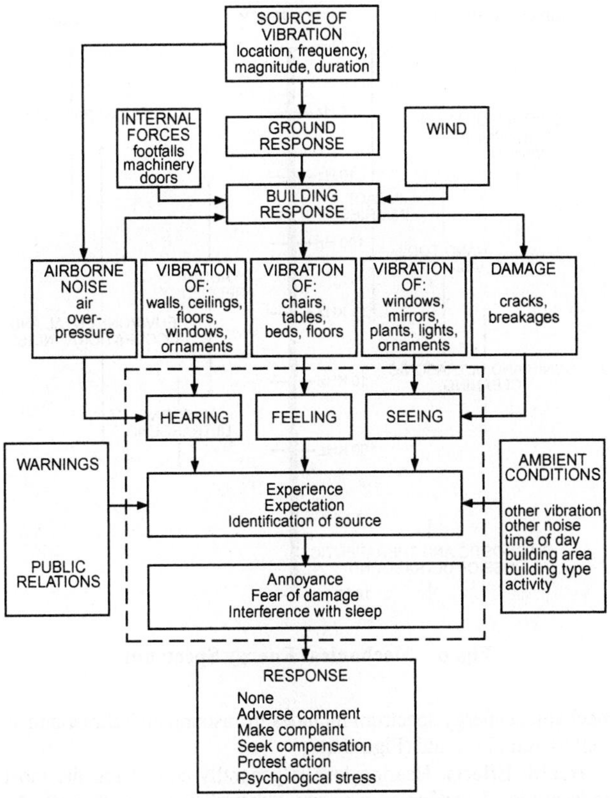

Fig. 3 Factors Affecting Acceptability of Building Vibration

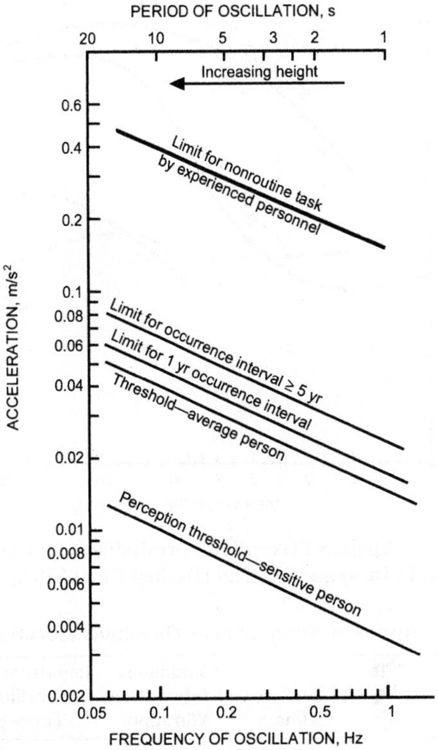

Fig. 4 Acceleration Perception Thresholds and Acceptability Limits for Horizontal Oscillations

human surface, and measurements are directly compared with relevant limit values or other data concerning human response.

Rotational motions of a building in roll, pitch, and yaw are usually about an axis of rotation some distance from the building occupants. For most purposes, these motions can be considered as the translational motions of the person. For example, a roll motion in a building about an axis of rotation some distance from a seated person has a similar effect as side-to-side translational motions of that person, etc.

Most methods assess building vibrations with RMS averaging and frequency analysis. However, human response is related to the time-varying characteristics of vibration as well. For example, many stimuli are transient, such as those caused by a train passing a building. The vibration event builds to a peak, followed by a decay in level over a total period of about 10 s. The nature of the time-varying event and the number of occasions it occurs during a day are important factors that might be overlooked if data are treated as steady-state and continuous.

Standard Limits

Low-Frequency Motion (1 Hz). The most commonly experienced form of slow vibration in buildings is building sway. This motion can be alarming to occupants if there is fear of building damage or injury. Whereas occupants of two-story wood frame houses accept occasional creaks and motion from wind storms or a passing heavy vehicle, such events are not as accepted by occupants of high-rise buildings. Detected motion in tall buildings can cause discomfort and alarm. The perception thresholds of normal, sensitive humans to low-frequency horizontal motion are given in Figure 4 (Chen and Robertson 1972; ISO 1984). The frequency range is from 0.06 to 1 Hz or, conversely, for oscillations with periods of 1 to 17 s. The natural frequency of sway of the Empire State Building in New York City, for example, has a period of 8.3 s (Davenport 1988). The thresholds are expressed in terms of relative acceleration, which is the actual acceleration divided by the standard acceleration of gravity g (9.8 m/s^2). The perception threshold to sway in terms of building accelerations decreases with increasing frequency and ranges from 50 to 20 mm/s^2.

For tall buildings, the highest horizontal accelerations generally occur near the top at the building's natural frequency of oscillation. Other parts of the building may have high accelerations at multiples of the natural frequency. Tall buildings always oscillate at their natural frequency, but the deflection is small and the motion undetectable. In general, short buildings have a higher natural frequency of vibration than taller ones. However, strong wind forces energize the oscillation and increase the horizontal deflection, speed, and accelerations of the structure.

ISO (1984) states that building motions should not produce alarm and adverse comment from more than 2% of the building's occupants. The level of alarm depends on the interval between events. If noticeable building sway occurs for at least 10 min at intervals of 5 years or more, the acceptable acceleration limit is higher than if this sway occurs annually (Figure 4). For annual intervals, the acceptable limit is only slightly above the normal person's threshold of perception. Motion at the 5-year limit level is estimated to cause 12% to complain if it occurred annually. The recommended limits are for purely horizontal motion; rotational oscillations, wind noise, and/or visual cues of the building's motion exaggerate the sensation of motion, and, for such factors, the acceleration limit is lower.

The upper line in Figure 4 is intended for offshore fixed structures such as oil drilling platforms. The line indicates the level of horizontal acceleration above which routine tasks by experienced personnel would be difficult to accomplish on the structure. Because they are routinely in motion in three dimensions, Figure 4 does not apply to transportation vehicles.

High-Frequency Motion (1 to 80 Hz). Higher-frequency vibrations in buildings are caused by machinery, elevators, foot traffic, fans, pumps, and HVAC equipment. Further, the steel structures of

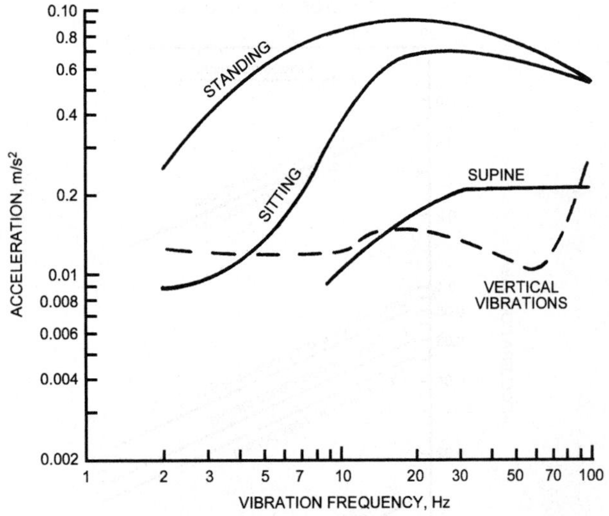

Fig. 5 Median Perception Thresholds to Horizontal (Solid Lines) and Vertical (Dashed Line) Vibrations

Table 7 Ratios of Acceptable to Threshold Vibration Levels

Place	Time	Continuous or Intermittent Vibration	Impulse or Transient Vibration Several Times per Day
Critical work areas	Day or night	1	1
Residential	Day/night	2 to 4/1.4	30 to 90/1.4 to 20
Office	Day or night	4	60 to 128
Workshop	Day or night	8	90 to 128

Note: Ratios for continuous or intermittent vibration and repeated impulse shock range from 0.7 to 1.0 for hospital operating theaters (room) and critical working areas. In other situations, impulse shock can generally be much higher than when vibration is more continuous.

modern buildings are good transmitters of high-frequency vibrations. The sensitivity to these higher frequency vibrations is indicated in Figure 5 (Parsons and Griffin 1988). Displayed are median perception thresholds to vertical and horizontal vibrations in the 2 to 100 Hz frequency range. The average perception threshold for vibrations of this type is from 10 to 90 mm/s^2, depending on frequency and on whether the person is standing, sitting, or lying down.

People detect horizontal vibrations at lower acceleration levels when lying down than when standing. However, a soft bed decouples and isolates a person fairly well from vibrations of the structure. The threshold to vertical vibrations is nearly constant at approximately 12 mm/s^2 for both sitting and standing positions from 2 to 100 Hz. This agrees with earlier observations by Reiher and Meister (1931).

Many building spaces with critical work areas (surgery, precision laboratory work) are considered unacceptable if vibration is perceived by the occupants. In other situations and activities, perceived vibration may be acceptable. Parsons and Griffin (1988) found that accelerations twice the threshold level were unacceptable to occupants in their homes. A method of assessing acceptability in buildings is to compare the vibration with perception threshold values (Table 7).

Sound and Noise

In general terms, sound transmitted through air consists of oscillations in pressure above and below ambient atmospheric pressure. A vibrating object causes high- and low-pressure areas to be formed; these areas propagate away from the source. The entire mechanical energy spectrum includes infrasound and ultrasound as well as audible sound (Figure 6).

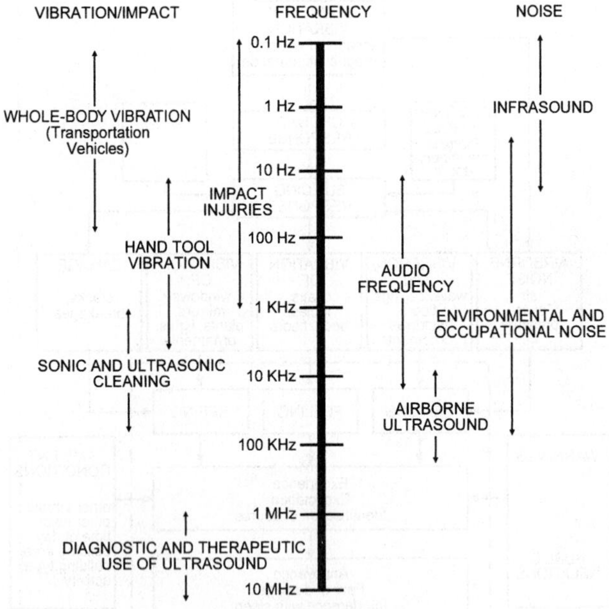

Fig. 6 Mechanical Energy Spectrum

Health Effects. Hearing loss is generally considered the most undesirable effect of noise exposure, although there are other effects. **Tinnitus**, a ringing in the ears, is really the hearing of sounds that do not exist. It often accompanies hearing loss. **Paracusis** is a disorder where a sound is heard incorrectly; that is, a tone is heard, but has an inappropriate pitch. **Speech misperception** occurs when an individual mistakenly hears one sound for another (e.g., when the sound for *t* is heard as a *p*).

Hearing loss can be categorized as conductive, sensory, or neural. **Conductive** hearing loss results from a general decrease in the amount of sound transmitted to the inner ear. Excessive ear wax, a ruptured eardrum, fluid in the middle ear, or missing elements of bone structures in the middle ear are all associated with conductive hearing loss. These are generally not occupationally related and are generally reversible by medical or surgical means. **Sensory** hearing losses are associated with irreversible damage to the inner ear. Sensory hearing loss is further classified as (1) presbycusis, loss caused as the result of aging; (2) noise-induced hearing loss (industrial hearing loss and sociacusis, which is caused by noise in everyday life); and (3) nosoacusis, losses attributed to all other causes. **Neural** deficits are related to damage to higher centers of the auditory system.

Noise-induced hearing loss is believed to occur in the most sensitive individuals among those exposed for 8 h per day over a working lifetime at levels of 75 dBA, and for most people similarly exposed to 85 dBA.

ELECTROMAGNETIC RADIATION

Radiation energy is emitted, transmitted, or absorbed in wave or particulate form. This energy consists of electric and magnetic forces, which, when disturbed in some manner, produce electromagnetic radiation. Electromagnetic radiation is grouped into a spectrum arranged by frequency and/or wavelength. The product of frequency and wavelength is the speed of light (3×10^8 m/s). The spectrum includes ionizing, ultraviolet, visible, infrared, microwave, radio, and extremely low frequency (ELF) (Figure 7). Table 8 presents these electromagnetic radiations by their range of energies, frequencies, and wavelengths. The regions are not sharply delineated from

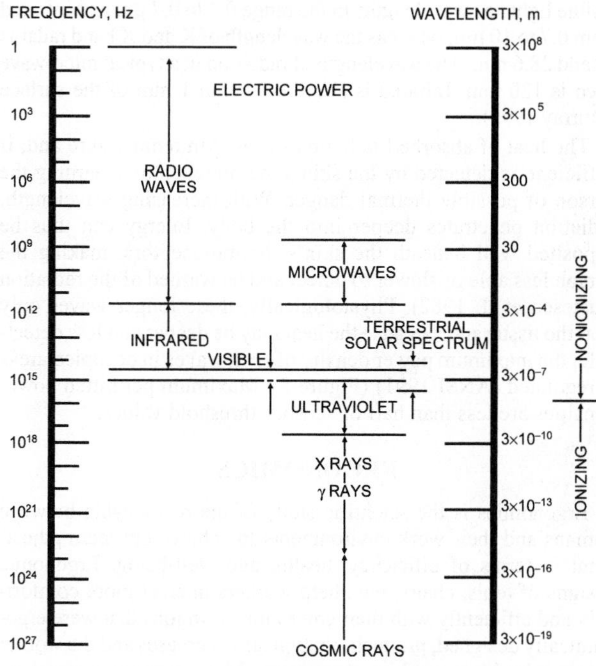

Fig. 7 Electromagnetic Spectrum

Table 8 Energy, Wavelength, and Frequency Ranges for Electromagnetic Radiation

Radiation Type	Energy Range	Wavelength Range	Frequency Range
Ionizing	>12.4 eV	<100 nm	>3.00 PHz
Ultraviolet (UV)	12.40 to 3.10 eV	100 to 400 nm	3.00 to 0.75 PHz
Visible	3.10 to 1.63 eV	400 to 760 nm	750 to 395 THz
Infrared (IR)	1.63 to 1.24 meV	760 nm to 1 mm	395 to 0.30 THz
Microwave (MW)	1.24 meV to 1.24 eV	1 mm to 1 m	300 GHz to 300 MHz
Radio-frequency (RF)	1.24 eV to 1.24 peV	1 m to 1 Mm	300 MHz to 300 Hz
Extremely low frequency (ELF)	<1.24 peV	>1 Mm	<300 Hz

each other and often overlap. It is convenient to divide these regions as listed in Table 8, because of the nature of the physical and biological effects.

Ionizing Radiation

Ionizing radiation is the part of the electromagnetic spectrum with very short wavelengths and high frequencies, and it has the ability to ionize matter. These ionizations tend to be very damaging to living matter. Background radiation that occurs naturally in the environment is from cosmic rays and naturally occurring radionuclides. It has not been established whether exposure at the low dose rate of average background levels is harmful to humans.

The basic standards for permissible air concentrations of radioactive materials are those of the National Committee on Radiation Protection, published by the National Bureau of Standards as *Handbook* No. 69. Industries operating under licenses from the U.S. Nuclear Regulatory Commission or state licensing agencies must meet requirements of the *Code of Federal Regulations*, Title 10, Part 20. Some states have additional requirements.

Table 9 Action Levels for Radon Concentration Indoors

Country/Agency	Action Level Bq/m³	pCi/L
Australia	200	5.4
Austria	400	10.8
Belgium	400	10.8
CEC	400	10.8
Canada	800	21.6
Czech Republic	400	10.8
P.R. China	200	5.4
Finland	400	10.8
Germany	250	6.7
ICRP	200	5.4
Ireland	200	5.4
Italy	400	10.8
Norway	400	10.8
Sweden	400	10.8
United Kingdom	200	5.4
United States	148	4.0
World Health Organization	200	5.4

Source: Tansey and Fliermans (1978).

An important naturally occurring radionuclide is radon (^{222}Rn), a decay product of uranium in the soil (^{238}U). Radon, denoted by the symbol Rn, is chemically inert. Details of units of measurement, typical radon levels, measurement methods and control strategies can be found in Chapter 11.

Health Effects of Radon. Radon is the leading cause of lung cancer among nonsmokers, according to EPA (2008b) estimates. Most information about radon's health risks comes from studies of workers in uranium and other underground mines. The radioactive decay of radon produces a series of radioactive isotopes of polonium, bismuth, and lead. Unlike their chemically inert radon parent, these progeny are chemically active and can attach to airborne particles that subsequently deposit in the lung, or deposit directly in the lung without attachment to particles. Some of these progeny, like radon, are alpha-particle emitters, which can cause cellular changes that may initiate lung cancer when they pass through lung cells (Samet 1989). Thus, adverse health effects associated with radon are caused by exposures to radon decay products, and the amount of risk is assumed to be directly related to the total exposure. Even though it is the radon progeny that present the possibility of adverse health risks, radon itself is usually measured and used as a surrogate for progeny measurements because of the expense involved in accurate measurements of radon progeny.

Exposure Standards. Many countries have established standards for exposure to radon. International action levels are listed in Table 9.

About 6% of U.S. homes (i.e., 5.8 million homes) have annual average radon concentrations exceeding 148 Bq/m³ (4 pCi/L), the action level set by the U.S. Environmental Protection Agency (Marcinowski et al. 1994). Because there is no known safe level of exposure to radon, the EPA (2008b) also recommends that all homes should be tested for radon, regardless of geographic location, and consideration should be given to remedial measures in homes with radon levels between 2 and 4 pCi/L.

Nonionizing Radiation

Ultraviolet radiation, visible light, and infrared radiation are components of sunlight and of all artificial light sources. Microwave and radio-frequency radiation are essential in a wide range of communication technologies and are also in widespread use for heating as in microwave ovens and heat sealers, and for heat treatments of various products. Power frequency fields are an essential and unavoidable consequence of the generation, transmission, distribution, and use of electrical power.

Optical Radiation. Ultraviolet (UV), visible, and infrared (IR) radiation compose the optical radiation region of the electromagnetic spectrum. The wavelengths range from 100 nm in the UV to 1 mm in the IR, with 100 nm generally considered to be the boundary between ionizing and nonionizing. The UV region wavelengths range from 100 to 400 nm, the visible region from 400 to 760 nm, and the IR from 760 nm to 1 mm.

Optical radiation can interact with a medium by reflection, absorption, or transmission. The skin and eyes are the organs at risk in humans. Optical radiation from any spectral region can cause acute and/or chronic biologic effects given appropriate energy characteristics and exposure. These effects include tanning, burning (erythema), premature "aging," and skin cancer; and dryness, irritation, cataracts, and blindness in the eyes.

The region of the electromagnetic spectrum visible to humans is known as light. There can be biological, behavioral, psychological, and health effects from exposure to light. Assessment of these effects depends on the purpose and application of the illumination. Individual susceptibility varies, with other environmental factors (air quality, noise, chemical exposures, and diet) acting as modifiers. It is difficult, therefore, to generalize potential hazards. **Light pollution** is the presence of unwanted light.

Light penetrating the retina not only allows the exterior world to be seen, but, like food and water, it is used in a variety of metabolic processes. Light stimulates the pineal gland to secrete melatonin, which regulates the human biological clock. This, in turn, influences reproductive cycles, sleeping, eating patterns, activity levels, and moods. The color of light affects the way the objects appear. Distortion of color rendition may result in disorientation, headache, dizziness, nausea, and fatigue.

As the daylight shortens, the human body may experience a gradual slowing down, loss of energy, and a need for more sleep. It becomes harder to get to work, and depression or even withdrawal may take place. This type of seasonal depression, brought on by changes in light duration and intensity, is called **seasonal affective disorder (SAD)**. Sufferers also complain of anxiety, irritability, headache, weight gain, and lack of concentration and motivation. Treatment of this problem is through manipulation of environmental lighting (exposure to full-spectrum lighting for extended periods, 12 h/day).

Radio-Frequency Radiation. Just as the body absorbs infrared and light energy, which can affect thermal balance, it can also absorb other longer wavelength electromagnetic radiation. For comparison, visible light has wavelengths in the range 0.4 to 0.7 μm and infrared from 0.7 to 10 μm, whereas the wavelength of K and X band radar is 12 and 28.6 mm. The wavelength of radiation in a typical microwave oven is 120 mm. Infrared is absorbed within 1 mm of the surface (Murray 1995).

The heat of absorbed radiation raises skin temperature and, if sufficient, is detected by the skin's thermoreceptors, warning the person of possible thermal danger. With increasing wavelength, radiation penetrates deeper into the body. Energy can thus be deposited well beneath the skin's thermoreceptors, making the person less able or slower to detect and be warned of the radiation (Justesen et al. 1982). Physiologically, these longer waves only heat the tissue and, because the heat may be deeper and less detectable, the maximum power density of such waves in occupied areas is regulated (ANSI 1991) (Figure 8). Maximum permitted power densities are less than half of sensory threshold values.

ERGONOMICS

Ergonomics is the scientific study of the relationship between humans and their work environments to achieve optimum adjustment in terms of efficiency, health, and well-being. Ergonomic designs of tools, chairs, etc., help workers interact more comfortably and efficiently with their environment. In jobs that were ergonomically designed, productivity typically increases and the worker enjoys a healthier working experience. More recently, researchers have distinguished intrinsic ergonomics from extrinsic, or traditional, ergonomics. Intrinsic ergonomics considers how the interface between an individual and the environment affects and relies on specific body parts (i.e., muscles, tendons, and bones) and work practices such as force of application, relaxation intervals, styles, and strength reserves that are not adequately considered in simple analyses of the physical environment.

The goals of ergonomic programs range from making work safe and humane, to increasing human efficiency, to creating human well-being. The successful application of ergonomic factors is measured by improved productivity, efficiency, safety, and acceptance of the resultant system design. The design engineer uses not only engineering skills, but also the principles of anatomy, orthopedics, physiology, medicine, psychology, and sociology to apply ergonomics to a design.

Implementing ergonomic principles in the workplace helps minimize on-the-job stress and strain, and prevents cumulative trauma

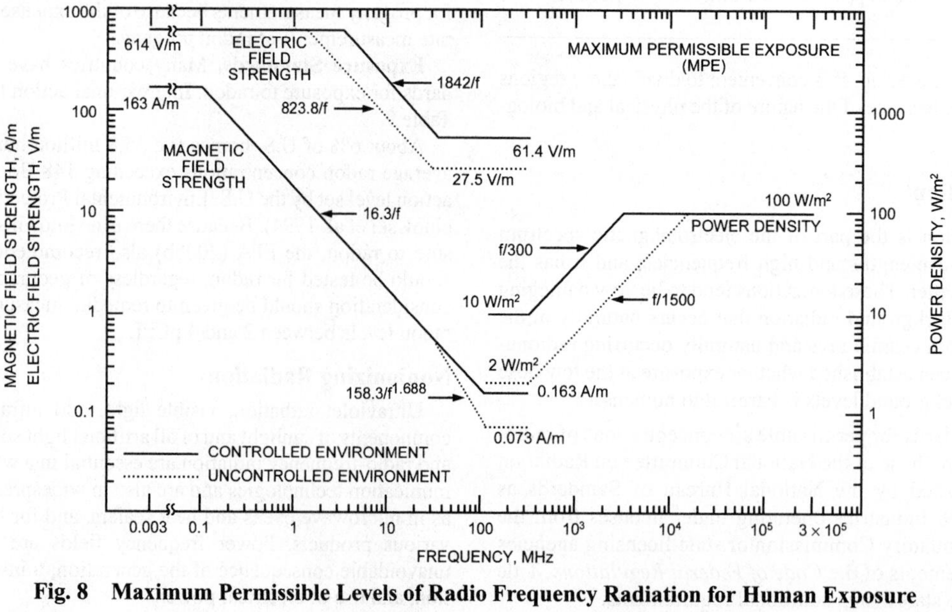

Fig. 8 Maximum Permissible Levels of Radio Frequency Radiation for Human Exposure

disorders (CTDs). These disorders are subtle injuries that can affect the muscles, tendons, and nerves at body joints, especially the hands, wrists, elbows, shoulders, neck, back, and knees. Carpal tunnel syndrome is an example of a CTD. CTDs most frequently occur as a result of strain from performing the same task on a continuous or repetitive basis. This strain can slowly build over time, until the worker experiences pain and difficulty using the injured part of the body. Higher risks of developing CTDs are encountered when the work task requires repetitive motions, excessive force, or awkward postures. The ergonomics engineer addresses these risk factors by analyzing the task thoroughly and minimizing the repetitive motion, excessive force, and awkward posture.

Poor space ergonomics (Hartkopf and Loftness 1999) and consequent occupant interventions may also directly affect indoor conditions. For example, inappropriate use of cabinets, closets, furniture, partitions, room equipment or other obstructions may block air supply or exhaust vents, reduce airflow rates and temperature or humidity regulation, and disturb airflow (Lee and Awbi 2004). These kinds of problems are usually attributed to poor space layout and ventilation design, but usually originate from lack of space availability, such as small room dimensions and high occupancies. Reduced ventilation rates deteriorate conditions for indoor environmental health, working, and comfort. They may be encountered in overstaffed offices (Mahdavi and Unzeitig 2005) or in demanding environments such as hospital operating theatres (Balaras et al. 2006).

REFERENCES

ACGIH. 1999. *Bioaerosols: Assessment and control*. American Conference of Government Industrial Hygienists, Cincinnati, OH.

ACGIH. Annual. *TLVs® and BEIs®*. American Conference of Government Industrial Hygienists, Cincinnati, OH.

ACSM. 1996. American College of Sports Medicine position stand on heat and cold illnesses during distance running. *Medicine & Science in Sports & Exercise* 28(12):1.

Alpaugh, E.L. and T.J. Hogan. 1988. *Fundamentals of industrial hygiene*, 3rd ed. National Safety Council, Itasca, IL.

Anaissie, E.J., S.R. Penzak, and M.C. Dignani. 2002. The hospital water supply as a source of nosocomial infections: A plea for action. *Archives of Internal Medicine* 162(13):1483-1492.

Anderson, H.A., D. Higgins, L.P. Hanrahan, P. Sarow, and J. Schirmer. 1991. Mesothelioma among employees with likely contact with in-place asbestos-containing building materials. *Annals of the New York Academy of Sciences* 643:550-572.

ANSI. 2005. Safety levels with respect to human exposure to radio frequency electromagnetic radiation, 3 kHz to 300 GHz. *Standard* C95.1-2005. American National Standards Institute, New York.

Apte, M.G., I.S.H. Buchanan, and M.J. Mendell. 2007. Outdoor ozone and building related symptoms in the BASE study. *Report* LBNL-62419. Lawrence Berkeley National Laboratory, Berkeley, CA.

Arnow, P.M., J.N. Fink, D.P. Schlueter, J.J. Barboriak, G. Mallison, S.I. Said, S. Martin, G.F. Unger, G.T. Scanlon, and V.P. Kurup. 1978. Early detection of hypersensitivity pneumonitis in office workers. *American Journal of Medicine* 64(2):237-242.

ASHRAE. 2000. Minimizing the risk of legionellosis associated with building water systems. *Guideline* 12-2000.

ASHRAE. 2003. M*old and moisture management in buildings*.

ASHRAE. 2004. Safety standard for refrigeration systems. *Standard* 15-2004.

ASHRAE. 2007. Designation and safety classification of refrigerants. ANSI/ASHRAE *Standard* 34-2007.

ATSDR. 2001. *Toxicological profile for asbestos*. Agency for Toxic Substances and Disease Registry, U.S. Department of Health and Human Services, Washington, D.C.

Balaras, C.A., E. Dascalaki, and A. Gaglia. 2006. HVAC and indoor thermal conditions in hospital operating rooms, *Energy and Buildings* 39(4): 454-470.

Ballester, F., D. Corella, S. Perez-Hoyos, M. Saez, and A. Hervas. 1997. Mortality as a function of temperature: A study in Valencia, Spain, 1991–1993. *International Journal of Epidemiology* 26(3):551-561.

Bartlett, P.C., L.A. Vonbehren, R.P. Tewari, R.J. Martin, L. Eagleton, M.J. Isaac, and P.S. Kulkarni. 1982. Bats in the belfry: An outbreak of histoplasmosis. *American Journal of Public Health* 72(12):1369-1372.

Bascom, R.A. 1996. Environmental factors and respiratory hypersensitivity: The Americas. *Toxicology Letters* 86:115-130.

Bascom, R., P. Bromberg, D.A. Costa, R. Devlin, D.W. Dockery, M.W. Frampton, W. Lambert, J.M. Samet, F.E. Speizer, and M. Utell. 1996. Health effects of outdoor pollution, parts I and II. *American Journal of Respiratory and Critical Care Medicine* 153:3-50, 477-489.

Bates, D.V. 1989. Ozone—Myth and reality. *Environmental Research* 50: 230-237.

Baylor, E.R., V. Peters, and M.B. Baylor. 1977. Water-to-air transfer of virus. *Science* 252:763.

Berglund, L.G. and D. Cunningham. 1986. Parameters of human discomfort in warm environments. *ASHRAE Transactions* 92(2).

Berglund, L.G. and R.R. Gonzalez. 1977. Evaporation of sweat from sedentary man in humid environments. *Journal of Applied Physiology, Respiratory, Environmental and Exercise Physiology* 42(5):767-772.

Billings, C.E. 1975. Electrical shock. In *Textbook of medicine*. Saunders, Philadelphia.

Blatteis, C.M., ed. 1998. *Physiology and pathophysiology of temperature regulation*. World Scientific, Singapore.

Bridger, C.A. and L.A. Helfand. 1968. Mortality from heat during July 1966 in Illinois. *International Journal of Biometeorology* 12:51.

Brundage, J.F., R.M. Scott, W.M. Lednar, D.W. Smith, and R.N. Miller. 1988. Building-associated risk of febrile acute respiratory diseases in Army trainees. *Journal of the American Medical Association* 259:2108.

Burch, G.E. and N.P. DePasquale. 1962. *Hot climates, man and his heart*. Charles C. Thomas, Springfield, IL.

Burge, H.A. 1989. In *Occupational medicine: State of the art reviews*, vol. 4, *Problem buildings: Building-associated illness and the sick building syndrome*, pp. 713-721. J.E. Cone and M.J. Hodgson, eds. Hanley and Belfus, Philadelphia.

Burge, H.A. 1995. *Bioaerosols*. Lewis, Chelsea, MI.

Burge, S., A. Hedge, S. Wilson, J.H. Bass, and A. Robertson. 1987. Sick building syndrome: A study of 4373 office workers. *Annals of Occupational Hygiene* 31:493-504.

Burgess, J.L. and C.D. Crutchfield. 1995. Quantitative respirator fit tests of Tucson fire fighters and measures of negative pressure excursions during exertion. *Applied Occupational and Environmental Hygiene* 10(1): 29-36.

Burton, D.J. 2000. *Industrial ventilation: A self-directed learning workbook*, 4th ed. Carr, North Bountiful, UT.

Buttner, M.P. and L.D. Stetzenbach. 1999. Dispersal of fungal spores from three types of air handling system duct material. *Aerobiologia* 15:1-8.

Buttner, M.P., P. Cruz-Perez, L.D. Stetzenbach, P.J. Garrett, and A.E. Luedtke. 2002. Measurement of airborne fungal spore dispersal from three types of flooring materials. *Aerobiologia* 18:1-11.

Cain, W.S. 1989. *Perceptual characteristics of nasal irritation*. National Danish Institute on Occupational Health, Copenhagen.

Cain, W.S., J.M. Samet, and M.J. Hodgson. 1995. The quest for negligible health risk from indoor air. *ASHRAE Journal* 37(7):38.

Calm, J.M. and P.A. Domanski. 2004. R-22 replacement status. *ASHRAE Journal* 46(8):29-39.

CDC. 2005. Unintentional non-fire-related carbon monoxide exposures—United States, 2001-2003. *Morbidity and Mortality Weekly Report* 54(2): 36-39.

CEN. *Surface temperatures of touchable parts, a draft proposal*. TC 114 N 122 D/E. European Standards Group.

CFR. 2001a. *Occupational safety and health standards: Air contaminants*. 29CFR1910.1000. U.S. Government Printing Office, Washington, D.C.

CFR. 2001b. *Occupational safety and health standards: Asbestos*. 29CFR1926.1101. U.S. Government Printing Office, Washington, D.C.

Chen, P.W. and L.E. Robertson. 1972. Human perception thresholds of horizontal motion. *ASCE Journal*, Structure Division, August.

Cobb, N. and R.A. Etzel. 1991. Unintentional carbon monoxide-related deaths in the United States, 1979 through 1988. *Journal of the American Medical Association* 266:659-663.

Collins, S.D. and J. Lehmann. 1953. Excess deaths from influenza and pneumonia and from important chronic diseases during epidemic periods, 1918-51. *Public Health Monograph* 20.10, U.S. Public Health Service *Publication* 213.

Cometto-Muñiz, J.E. and W.S. Cain. 1994a. Sensory reactions of nasal pungency and odor to volatile organic compounds: The alkylbenzenes. *American Industrial Hygiene Association Journal* 55(9):811-817.

Cometto-Muñiz, J.E. and W.S. Cain. 1994b. Perception of odor and nasal pungency from homologous series of volatile organic compounds. *Indoor Air* 4:140-145.

Cox, C.S. 1987. *The aerobiological pathway of microorganisms*. John Wiley & Sons, New York.

CPSC. 2006. *Portable generators: Legal memorandum and staff briefing package for ANPR*. Consumer Product Safety Commission, Washington, D.C.

Crandall, M.S. and W.K. Sieber. 1996. The NIOSH indoor environmental evaluation experience: Part one, building evaluations. *Applied Occupational and Environmental Hygiene*.

Davenport, A.G. 1988. The response of supertall buildings to wind. In *Second century of the skyscraper*, pp. 705-726. L. Beedle, ed. Van Nostrand Reinhold, New York.

Destaillats, H., M.M. Lunden, B.C. Singer, B.K. Coleman, A.T. Hodgson, C.J. Weschler, and W.W. Nazaroff. 2006. Indoor secondary pollutants from household product emissions in the presence of ozone: A bench-scale chamber study. *Environmental Science & Technology* 40:4421-4428.

DHHS. 1986. The health consequences of involuntary smoking. A report of the surgeon general. DHHS *Publication* (PHS) 87-8398. U.S. Department of Health and Human Services, Public Health Services, Office of the Assistant Secretary for Health, Office of Smoking and Health.

Diaz, J., R. Garcia, F. Velazquez de Castro, E. Hernandez, C. Lopez, and A. Otero. 2002. Effects of extremely hot days on people older than 65 years in Seville (Spain) from 1986 to 1997. *International Journal of Biometeorology* 46(3):145–149.

Edwards, J.H. 1980. Microbial and immunological investigations and remedial action after an outbreak of humidifier fever. *British Journal of Industrial Medicine* 37:55-62.

EHD. 1987. *Exposure guidelines for residential indoor air quality*. EHD-TR-156. Environmental Health Directorate, Health Protection Branch. Ottawa, ON.

Ellis, F.P. 1972. Mortality from heat illness and heat aggravated illness in the United States. *Environmental Research* 5.

EPA. 1991. Introduction to indoor air quality, a reference manual. *Report* EPA 400/3-91/003.

EPA. 1992. *Respiratory health effects of passive smoking: Lung cancer and other disorders, review draft*. EPA/600-6-90/006F. Office of Research and Development, Washington, D.C.

EPA. 2001. Mold remediation in schools and commercial buildings. *Report* 402-K-01-001. U.S. Environmental Protection Agency, Washington, D.C.

EPA. 2003. National primary drinking water standards. *Standard* 816-F-03-016. U.S. Environmental Protection Agency, Washington, D.C. Available at http://www.epa.gov/safewater/consumer/pdf/mcl.pdf.

EPA. 2005. IAQ tools for schools—IAQ reference guide. *Report* 402-K-95-001. U.S. Environmental Protection Agency, Washington, D.C.

EPA. 2008a. *National ambient air quality standards (NAAQS)*. U.S. Environmental Protection Agency, Washington, D.C. Available at http://www. epa.gov/air/criteria.html.

EPA. 2008b. *Radon: Health risks*. U.S. Environmental Protection Agency, Washington, D.C. Available at www.epa.gov/radon/healthrisks.html.

FAA. 2000. Prohibition of smoking on scheduled passenger flights: Final rules. 14CFR121, 129, and 135. *Federal Register* 65(112):36, 776-36, 780.

Fanger, P.O. 1970. *Thermal comfort*. Teknisk Forlag, Copenhagen.

Franck, C., P. Skov, and O. Bach. 1993. Prevalence of objective eye manifestations in people working in office buildings with different prevalences of the sick building syndrome compared with the general population. *International Archives of Occupational and Environmental Health* 65:65-69.

Gaul, L.E. and G.B. Underwood. 1952. Relation of dew point and barometric pressure to chapping of normal skin. *Journal of Investigative Dermatology* 19:9.

Geary, D.F. 2000. New guidelines on *Legionella*. *ASHRAE Journal* 44(9): 44-49.

Giles, B., C. Balafoutis, and P. Maheras. 1990. Too hot for comfort: The heatwaves in Greece in 1987 and 1988. *International Journal of Biometeorology* 34:98-104.

Girman, J.R. 1989. Volatile organic compounds and building bake-out. In *Occupational medicine: State of the art reviews*, vol. 4, *Problem buildings: Building-associated illness and the sick building syndrome*, pp. 695-712. J.E. Cone and M.J. Hodgson, eds. Hanley and Belfus, Philadelphia.

Girman, J., Y.-L. Chang, S.B. Hayward, and K.S. Liu. 1998. Causes of unintentional deaths from carbon monoxide poisonings in California. *Western Journal of Medicine* 168(3):158-165.

Glantz, S.A. and W.W. Parmley. 1991. Passive smoking and heart disease epidemiology, physiology, and biochemistry. *Circulation* 83:633-642.

Gonzalez, R.R., L.G. Berglund, and A.P. Gagge. 1978. Indices of thermoregulatory strain for moderate exercise. *Journal of Applied Physiology: Respiratory Environmental and Exercise Physiology* 44(6):889-899.

Greenberg, L. 1964. Asthma and temperature change. *Archives of Environmental Health* 8:642.

Hajat, S., R.S. Kovats, R.W. Atkinson, and A. Haines. 2002. Impact of hot temperatures on death in London: A time series approach. *Journal of Epidemiology and Community Health* 56(5):367-372.

Hales, J.B.S., R.W. Hubbard, and S.L. Graffin. 1996. Limits of heat tolerance. Chapter 15 in *Handbook of physiology*, sect. 4, *Environmental physiology*. M.J. Fregly and C.M. Blatteis, eds. *American Physiological. Society*, Bethesda, MD.

Hardy, J.D. 1971. Thermal comfort and health. *ASHRAE Journal* 13:43.

Hartkopf, V. and V. Loftness. 1999. Global relevance of total building performance. *Automation in Construction* 8(4):377-393.

Harriman, L., G. Brundrett, and R. Kittler. 2001. *Humidity control design guide for commercial and institutional buildings*. ASHRAE.

Hathaway, G.J., N.H. Proctor, J.P. Hughes, and M.L. Fischman, eds. 1991. *Proctor and Hughes' chemical hazards in the workplace*, 3rd ed. Van Nostrand Reinhold, New York.

HC. 2006. *Residential indoor air quality guideline: Formaldehyde*. Health Canada.

Hodgson, A.T. 1995. A review and a limited comparison of methods for measuring total volatile organic compounds in indoor air. *Indoor Air* 5(4):247.

Hodgson, M.J., P.R. Morey, M. Attfield, W. Sorenson, J.N. Fink, W.W. Rhodes, and G.S. Visvesvara. 1985. *Archives of Environmental Health* 40:96.

Hodgson, M.J., P.R. Morey, J.S. Simon, T.D. Waters, and J.N. Fink. 1987. An outbreak of recurrent acute and chronic hypersensitivity pneumonitis in office workers. *American Journal of Epidemiology* 125:631-638.

Holland, W.W. 1961. Influence of the weather on respiratory and heart disease. *Lancet* 2:338.

Hryhorczuk, D.O., L.J. Frateschi, J.W. Lipscomb, and R. Zhang. 1992. Use of the scan statistic to detect temporal clustering of poisonings. *Journal of Toxicology—Clinical Toxicology* 30:459-465.

Hyppel, A. 1984. Fingerprint of a mould odor. *Proceedings of the 3rd International Conference on Indoor Air Quality and Climate*, Stockholm, Sweden, vol. 3, pp. 443-447. B. Berglund, T. Lindvall, and J. Sundell, eds.

ISO. 1984. Guidelines for the evaluation of the response of occupants of fixed structures, especially buildings and off-shore structures, to low-frequency horizontal motion (0.063 to 1 Hz). ISO *Standard* 6897. International Organization for Standardization, Geneva.

ISO. 2006. Ergonomics of the thermal environment—Methods for the assessment of human responses to contact with surfaces—Part 1: Hot surfaces. *Standard* 13732-1:2006. International Organization for Standardization, Geneva.

Justesen, D.R., E.R. Adair, J.C. Stevens, and V. Bruce-Wolfe. 1982. A comparative study of human sensory thresholds: 2450 MHz microwaves vs. far-infrared radiation. *Bioelectromagnetics* 3:117-125.

Katayama, K. and M. Momiyana-Sakamoto. 1970. A biometeorological study of mortality from stroke and heart diseases. *Meteorological Geophysics* 21:127.

Kessler, W.R. and W.R. Anderson. 1951. Heat prostration in fibrocystic disease of pancreas and other conditions. *Pediatrics* 8:648.

Kilbourne, E.M., T.S. Jones, K. Choi, and S.B. Thacker. 1982. Risk factors for heatstroke: A case-control study. *Journal of the American Medical Association* 247(24):3332-3336.

Kjaergaard, S. 1992. Assessment methods and causes of eye irritation in humans in indoor environments. In *Chemical, microbiological, health, and comfort aspects of indoor air quality*, H. Knoeppel and P. Wolkoff, eds., pp. 115-127. Energy Cost Savings Council, European Economic Community, and European Atomic Energy Council, Brussels.

Kjaergaard, S., L. Molhave, and O.F. Pedersen. 1991. Human reactions to a mixture of indoor pollutants. *Atmospheric Environment* 25:1417-1426.

Koren, H. 1990. The inflammatory response of the human upper airways to volatile organic compounds. *Proceedings of Indoor Air '90*, vol. 1, pp. 325-330.

Koren, H., D.E. Graham, and R.B. Devlin. 1992. Exposure of humans to a volatile organic mixture III: Inflammatory response. *Archives of Environmental Health* 47:39-44.

Kunst, A.E., C.W. Looman, and J.P. Mackenbach. 1993. Outdoor air temperature and mortality in The Netherlands: A time-series analysis. *American Journal of Epidemiology* 137(3):331–341.

Leathart, G.L. 1972. Clinical aspects of respiratory disease due to mining. In *Medicine in the mining industry*, J.M. Rogan, ed. Heinemann Medical, London.

Lee, H., and H. B. Awbi. 2004. Effect of internal partitioning on indoor air quality of rooms with mixing ventilation—Basic study. *Building and Environment* 39(2):127-141.

Levetin, E. 1995. Fungi. In *Bioaerosols*, H.A. Burge, ed. CRC Press, Lewis Publishers, Boca Raton, FL.

Lighthart, B. 1994. Physics of bioaerosols. In *Atmospheric microbial aerosols: Theory and applications*, pp. 5-27. B. Lighthart and J. Mohr, eds. Chapman and Hall, New York.

Lighthart, B. and L.D. Stetzenbach. 1994. Distribution of microbial aerosol. In *Atmospheric microbial aerosols: Theory and applications*, pp. 68-98. B. Lighthart and J. Mohr, eds. Chapman and Hall, New York.

Lilienfeld, D.E. 1991. Asbestos-associated pleural mesothelioma in school teachers: A discussion of four cases. *Annals of the New York Academy of Sciences* 643:454-486.

Liu, K.S., J. Wesolowski, F.Y. Huang, K. Sexton, and S.B. Hayward. 1991. Irritant effects of formaldehyde exposure in mobile homes. *Environmental Health Perspectives* 94:91-94.

Mahdavi, A. and U. Unzeitig. 2005. Occupancy implications of spatial, indoor-environmental, and organizational features of office spaces. *Building and Environment* 40(1):113-123.

Mandell, G.L., J.E. Bennett, and R. Dolin, eds. 1999. *Principles and practice of infectious disease*. G. Churchill Livingstone, New York.

Marcinowski, F., R.M. Lucas, and W.M. Yeager. 1994. National and regional distributions of airborne radon concentrations in U.S. homes. *Health Physics* 66(6):699-706.

Martin, T.R. and M.B. Bracken. 1986. Association of low birth weight with passive smoke exposure in pregnancy. *American Journal of Epidemiology* 124(4):633-642.

Martinez, B.F., M.L. Kirk, J.L. Annest, K.J. Lui, E.M. Kilbourne, and S.M. Smith. 1989. Geographic distribution of heat-related deaths among elderly persons: Use of county-level dot maps for injury surveillance and epidemiologic research. *Journal of the American Medical Association* 262:2246-2250.

Mbithi, J.N., V.S. Springthorpe, and S.A. Sattar. 1991. Effect of relative humidity and air temperature on survival of hepatitis A virus on environmental surfaces. *Applied and Environmental Microbiology* 57(5):1394-1399.

McCann, J., L. Horn, J. Girman, and A.V. Nero. 1987. *Short-term bioassays in the analysis of complex mixtures V*, pp. 325-354. Plenum Press, New York.

McCoy, W.F. 2005. *Preventing legionellosis*. International Water Association Publishing, London.

McCoy, W.F. 2006. Legionellosis: Why the problem continues. *ASHRAE Journal* 45(1):24-27.

McMichael, A.J., R.E. Woodruff, and S. Hales. 2006. Climate change and human health: Present and future risks. *The Lancet* 367(9513):859-869.

Meggs, W.J. 1994. RADS and RUDS—The toxic induction of asthma and rhinitis. *Journal of Toxicology—Clinical Toxicology.* 32:487-501.

Miller, J.D. and J. Day. 1997. Indoor mold exposure: Epidemiology, consequences and immunotherapy. *Journal of the Canadian Society of Allergy and Clinical Immunology* 2(1):25-32.

Mølhave, L., R. Bach, and O.F. Pederson. 1986. Human reactions to low concentrations of volatile organic compounds. *Environment International* 12:167-175.

Mølhave, L. 1991. Volatile organic compounds, indoor air quality and health. *Indoor Air* 1(4):357-376.

Mølhave, L., Z. Liu, A.H. Jorgensen, O.F. Pederson, and S. Kjaergard. 1993. Sensory and physiologic effects on humans of combined exposures to air temperatures and volatile organic compounds. *Indoor Air* 3:155-169.

Mølhave, L., S.K. Kjaergaard, T. Sigsgaard, and M. Lebowitz. 2005. Interaction between ozone and airborne particulate matter in office air. *Indoor Air* 15:383-392.

Moolenaar, R.L., R.A. Etzel, and R.G. Parrish. 1995. Unintentional deaths from carbon monoxide poisoning in New Mexico, 1980 to 1988: A comparison of medical examiner and national mortality data. *Western Journal of Medicine* 163(5):431-434.

Morey, P.R. 1988. Experience on the contribution of structure to environmental pollution. In *Architectural design and indoor microbial pollution*, pp. 40-80. R.B. Kundsin, ed. Oxford University Press, New York.

Morey, P.R. 1990. The practitioner's approach to indoor air quality investigations. *Proceedings of the Indoor Air Quality International Symposium*, American Industrial Hygiene Association, Akron, OH.

Morey, P.R. and J.C. Feeley. 1988. *ASTM Standardization News* 16:54.

Morey, P.R. and B.A. Jenkins. 1989. What are typical concentrations of fungi, total volatile organic compounds, and nitrogen dioxide in an office environment? *Proceedings of IAQ '89, The Human Equation: Health and Comfort*, pp. 67-71.

Morey, P.R., M.J. Hodgson, W.G. Sorenson, G.J. Kullman, W.W. Rhodes, and G.S. Visvesvara. 1986. Environmental studies in moldy office buildings. *ASHRAE Transactions* 93(1B):399-419.

Moser, M.R., T.R. Bender, H.S. Margolis, G.R. Noble. A.P. Kendal, and D.G. Ritter. 1979. An outbreak of influenza aboard a commercial airliner. *American Journal of Epidemiology* 110:1-6.

Mumford, J.L., X.Z. He, R.S. Chapman, S.R. Cao, D.B. Harris, K.M. Li, Y.L. Xian, W.Z. Jiang, C.W. Xu, J.C. Chang, W.E. Wilson, and M. Cooke. 1987. Lung cancer and indoor air pollution in Xuan Wei, China. *Science* 235:217-220.

Murray, W. 1995. Nonionizing electromagnetic energies. Chapter 14 in *Patty's industrial hygiene and toxicology*, vol. 3B, pp. 623-727. R.L. Harris, L.J. Cralley, and L.V. Cralley, eds. John Wiley & Sons, Hoboken, NJ.

NAS. 1981. *Indoor pollutants*. National Research Council/National Academy of Sciences, Committee on Indoor Pollutants. National Academy of Sciences Press, Washington, D.C.

NAS. 1983. *Polycyclic aromatic hydrocarbons: Evaluation of sources and effects*. National Academy Press, Washington, D.C.

Nazaroff, W.W., B.K. Coleman, H. Destaillats, A. Hodgson, D.T.L. Liu, M.M. Lunden, B.C. Singer, and C.J. Weschler. 2006. Indoor air chemistry: Cleaning agents, ozone and toxic air contaminants. *Final Report*, ARB Contract 01-336. California Environmental Protection Agency, Air Resources Board, Sacramento.

NIOSH. 1992. NIOSH recommendations for occupational safety and health compendium of policy documents and statements. DHHS (NIOSH) *Publication* 92-100. U.S. Department of Health and Human Services, Public Health Service, Centers for Disease Control, National Institute for Occupational Safety and Health, Atlanta.

NIOSH. 2007. NIOSH pocket guide to chemical hazards. DHHS (NIOSH) *Publication* 2005-149. U.S. Department of Labor, Occupational Safety and Health Administration, Washington, D.C. Available at www.cdc.gov/niosh/npg/pdfs/2005-249.pdf.

NIOSH. *Annual registry of toxic effects of chemical substances*. U.S. Department of Health and Human Services, National Institute for Occupational Safety and Health, Washington, D.C.

Nordic Conference on Cold. 1991. Cold physiology and cold injuries. *Arctic Medical Research* (now *International Journal of Circumpolar Health*) 50(6).

NRC. 1986. *Environmental tobacco smoke: Measuring exposures and assessing health effects*. National Research Council. National Academy Press, Washington, D.C.

OEHHA. 2007. Air toxicology and epidemiology: All chronic reference exposure levels (cRELs). California Environmental Protection Agency, Office of Environmental Health Hazard Assessment, Sacramento. Available at http://www.oehha.ca.gov/air/chronic_rels/AllChrels.html.

OEHHA. 2008. *Chemicals known to the state to cause cancer or reproductive toxicity.* California Environmental Protection Agency, Office of Environmental Health Hazard Assessment, Sacramento. Available at http://www.oehha.ca.gov/prop65/prop65_list/files/032108list.pdf.

Oeschli, F.W. and R.W. Buechley. 1970. Excess mortality associated with three Los Angeles September hot spells. *Environmental Research* 3:277.

Ohm, M., J.E. Juto, and K. Andersson. 1992. Nasal hyper-reactivity and sick building syndrome. *IAQ '92: Environments for People*. ASHRAE.

Offermann, F.J., S.A. Loiselle, A.T. Hodgson, L.A. Gundel, and J.M. Daisey. 1991. A pilot study to measure indoor concentrations and emission rates of polycyclic aromatic hydrocarbons. *Indoor Air* 4:497-512.

OSHA. 1994. Proposed rulemaking: Indoor air quality. 29CFR1910, 1915, 1926, and 1928. *Federal Register* 59:15,968-16,039.

OSHA. 2001. Withdrawal of proposal: Indoor air quality. *Federal Register* 66(24).

Parsons, K.C. and M.J. Griffin. 1988. Whole-body vibration perception thresholds. *Journal of Sound and Vibration* 121(2):237-258.

Reiher, H. and F.J. Meister. 1931. The sensitivities of the human body to vibrations. *Forschung* VDI 2:381-386. 1946 translation of *Report* Fts616RE. Headquarters Air Material Command, Wright Field, Dayton, OH.

Repace, J.L. 1984. Effect of ventilation on passive smoking in a model workplace. *Proceedings of an Engineering Foundation Conference on Management of Atmospheres in Tightly Enclosed Spaces*, Santa Barbara.

Repace, J.L. and A.H. Lowrey. 1985. An indoor air quality standard for ambient tobacco smoke based on carcinogenic risk. *New York State Journal of Medicine* 85:381-383.

Repace, J.L. and A.H. Lowrey. 1993. An enforceable indoor air quality standard for environmental tobacco smoke in the workplace. *Risk Analysis* 13(4).

Rohles, F.H., J.A. Woods, and P.R. Morey. 1989. Indoor environmental acceptability: Development of a rating scale. *ASHRAE Transactions* 95(1):23-27.

Russi, M., W. Buchta, M. Swift, L. Budnick, M. Hodgson, D. Berube, and G. Kelefant. 2008. *Guidance for occupational health services in medical centers*. American College of Occupational and Environmental Medicine, Elk Grove Village, IL. Available at www.acoem.org/uploadedFiles/Policies_And_Position_Statements/Guidelines/Guidelines/MCOH Guidance.pdf.

Samet, J.M. 1989. Radon and lung cancer. *Journal of the National Cancer Institute* 81:145.

Samet, J.M., M.C. Marbury, and J.D. Spengler. 1987. Health effects and sources of indoor air pollution. *American Review of Respiratory Disease* 136:1486-1508.

Schulman, J.H. and E.M. Kilbourne. 1962. Airborne transmission of influenza virus infection in mice. *Nature* 195:1129.

Shickele, E. 1947. Environment and fatal heat stroke. *Military Surgeon* 100:235.

Skov, P. and O. Valbjorn. 1987. Danish indoor climate, study group: The sick building syndrome in the office environment: The Danish town hall study. *Environment International* 13:339-349.

Spengler, J.D., H.A. Burge, and H.J. Su. 1992. Biological agents and the home environment. *Bugs, Mold and Rot (I): Proceedings of the Moisture Control Workshop*, E. Bales and W.B. Rose, eds., pp. 11-18. Building Thermal Envelope Council, National Institute of Building Sciences, Washington, D.C.

Strindehag, O., I. Josefsson, and E. Hennington. 1988. *Healthy Buildings '88*, Stockholm, vol. 3, pp. 611-620.

Streifel, A.J., D. Vesley, F.S. Rhame, and B. Murray. 1989. Control of airborne fungal spores in a university hospital. *Environment International* 15:221.

Susskind, R.R. and M. Ishihara. 1965. The effects of wetting on cutaneous vulnerability. *Archives of Environmental Health* 11:529.

Tamas, G., C.J. Weschler, J. Toftum, and P.O. Fanger. 2006. Influence of ozone-limonene reactions on perceived air quality. *Indoor Air* 16: 168-178.

Tancrede, M., R. Wilson, L. Ziese, and E.A.C. Crouch. 1987. *Atmospheric Environment* 21:2187.

Tansey, M.R. and C.B. Fliermans. 1978. Pathogenic species of thermophilic and thermotolerant fungi in reactor effluents of the Savannah River Plant. *DOE Symposium Series CONF-77114: Energy and Environmental Stress in Aquatic Systems Symposium*, pp. 663-690. J.H. Thorpe and J.W. Gibbons, eds.

Teng, H.C. and H.E. Heyer, eds. 1955. The relationship between sudden changes in the weather and acute myocardial infarction. *American Heart Journal* 49:9.

Thirion, X., D. Debensason, J.C. Delaroziere, and J.L. San Marco. 2005. August 2003: Reflections on a French summer disaster. *Journal of Contingencies and Crisis Management* 13(4):153-158.

Weschler, C.J. 2000. Ozone in indoor environments: Concentration and chemistry. *Indoor Air* 10:269.

Weschler, C.J. 2006. Ozone's impact on public health: Contributions from indoor exposures to ozone and products of ozone-initiated chemistry. *Environmental Health Perspectives* 114:1489-1496.

Weschler, C.J. and H.C. Shields. 2000. The influence of ventilation on reactions among indoor pollutants: Modeling and experimental observations. *Indoor Air* 10:92-100.

WHO. 2000. Air quality guidelines for Europe, 2nd ed. *European Series* 91. World Health Organization, Copenhagen.

WHO. 2007. *Legionella and the prevention of Legionellosis.* World Health Organization, Geneva.

Wilkins, C.K., P.A. Clausen, P. Wolkoff, S.T. Larsen, M. Hammer, K. Larsen, V. Hansen, and G.D. Nielsen. 2001. Formation of strong airway irritants in mixtures of isoprene/ozone and isoprene/ozone/nitrogen dioxide. *Environmental Health Perspectives* 109:937-941.

Wolkoff, P., P.A. Clausen, C.K. Wilkins, and G.D. Nielsen. 2000. Formation of strong airway irritants in terpene/ozone mixtures. *Indoor Air* 10: 82-91.

Yoshizawa, S., F. Surgawa, S. Ozawo, Y. Kohsaka, and A. Matsumae. 1987. *Proceedings of the 4th International Conference on Indoor Air Quality and Climate*, Berlin, vol. 1, pp. 627-631.

Yu I.T., Y. Li, T.W. Wong, W. Tam, A.T. Chan, J.H. Lee, D.Y. Leung, and T. Ho. 2004. Evidence of airborne transmission of the severe acute respiratory syndrome virus. *New England Journal of Medicine* 350(17):1731-1739.

Zenz, C., ed. 1988. *Occupational safety in industry, occupational medicine, principles and practical applications*. Year Book Medical Publishers, Chicago.

CHAPTER 11

AIR CONTAMINANTS

AIR contamination is a concern for ventilation engineers when it causes problems for building occupants. Engineers need to understand the vocabulary used by the air sampling and building air cleaning industry. This chapter focuses on the types and levels of air contaminants that might enter ventilation systems or be found as indoor contaminants. Industrial contaminants are included only for special cases. Because it is not a building air concern, the effects of refrigerants on the atmosphere are not included in this chapter; see Chapter 29 for discussion of this topic.

Air is composed mainly of gases. The major gaseous components of clean, dry air near sea level are approximately 21% oxygen, 78% nitrogen, 1% argon, and 0.04% carbon dioxide. Normal outdoor air contains varying amounts of other materials (permanent atmospheric impurities) from natural processes such as wind erosion, sea spray evaporation, volcanic eruption, and metabolism or decay of organic matter. The concentration of permanent atmospheric impurities varies, but is usually lower than that of anthropogenic air contaminants.

Anthropogenic outdoor air contaminants are many and varied, originating from numerous types of human activity. Electric power generating plants, various modes of transportation, industrial processes, mining and smelting, construction, and agriculture generate large amounts of contaminants. These outdoor air contaminants can also be transmitted to the indoor environment. In addition, the indoor environment can exhibit a wide variety of local contaminants, both natural and anthropogenic.

Contaminants that present particular problems in the indoor environment include allergens (e.g., dust mite or cat antigen), tobacco smoke, radon, and formaldehyde.

Air composition may be changed accidentally or deliberately. In sewers, sewage treatment plants, agricultural silos, sealed storage vaults, tunnels, and mines, the oxygen content of air can become so low that people cannot remain conscious or survive. Concentrations of people in confined spaces (theaters, survival shelters, submarines) require that carbon dioxide given off by normal respiratory functions be removed and replaced with oxygen. Pilots of high-altitude aircraft, breathing at greatly reduced pressure, require systems that increase oxygen concentration. Conversely, for divers working at extreme depths, it is common to increase the percentage of helium in the atmosphere and reduce nitrogen and sometimes oxygen concentrations.

At atmospheric pressure, oxygen concentrations less than 12% or carbon dioxide concentrations greater than 5% are dangerous, even for short periods. Lesser deviations from normal composition can be hazardous under prolonged exposures. Chapter 10 further details environmental health issues.

The preparation of this chapter is assigned to TC 2.3, Gaseous Air Contaminants and Gas Contaminant Removal Equipment, in conjunction with TC 2.4, Particulate Air Contaminants and Particulate Contaminant Removal Equipment.

CLASSES OF AIR CONTAMINANTS

Air contaminants are generally classified as either particles or gases. (Particles dispersed in air are also known as **aerosols.** In common usage, the terms *aerosol*, *airborne particle*, and *particulate contaminant* are interchangeable.) The distinction between particles and gases is important when determining removal strategies and equipment. Although the motion of particles is described using the same equations used to describe gas movement, even the smallest of particles (approximately 3 nm) are much larger than individual gas molecules, and have a much greater mass and a much lower diffusion rate. Conversely, particles are typically present in much fewer numbers than even trace levels of contaminant gases.

The **particulate** class covers a vast range of particle sizes, from dust large enough to be visible to the eye (100 μm) to submicroscopic particles that elude most filters (a few nanometers). Particles may be liquid, solid, or have a solid core surrounded by liquid. They are present in the atmosphere at concentrations ranging from 100 particles/cm^3 (mass concentration of a few μg/m^3) in the cleanest environments to millions per cubic centimetre and several hundred μg/m^3 in polluted urban environments. The following traditional particulate contaminant classifications arise in various situations, and overlap. They are all still in common use.

- **Dusts**, **fumes**, and **smokes** are mostly solid particulate matter, although smoke often contains liquid particles.
- **Mists**, **fogs**, and **smogs** are mostly suspended liquid particles smaller than those in dusts, fumes, and smokes.
- **Bioaerosols** include primarily intact and fragmentary viruses, bacteria, fungal spores, and plant and animal allergens; their primary effect is related to their biological origin. Common indoor particulate allergens (dust mite allergen, cat dander, house dust, etc.) and endotoxins are included in the bioaerosol class.
- Particulate contaminants may be defined by their size, such as **coarse** or **fine**; **visible** or **invisible**; or **macroscopic**, **microscopic**, or **submicroscopic**.
- Particles may be described using terms that relate to their interaction with the human respiratory system, such as **inhalable** and **respirable**

The **gaseous** class covers chemical contaminants that can exist as free molecules or atoms in air. Molecules and atoms are smaller than particles and may behave differently as a result. This class covers two important subclasses:

- **Gases**, which are naturally gaseous under ambient indoor or outdoor conditions (i.e., their boiling point is less than ambient temperature at ambient pressure)
- **Vapors**, which are normally solid or liquid under ambient indoor or outdoor conditions (i.e., their boiling point is greater than ambient temperature at ambient pressure), but which evaporate readily

Through evaporation, liquids change into vapors and mix with the surrounding atmosphere. Like gases, they are formless fluids that expand to occupy the space or enclosure in which they are confined.

Air contaminants can also be classified according to their sources; properties; or the health, safety, and engineering issues faced by people exposed to them. Any of these can form a convenient classification system because they allow grouping of applicable standards, guidelines, and control strategies. Most such special classes include both particulate and gaseous contaminants.

This chapter also covers background information for selected special air contaminant classes (Chapter 10 deals with applicable indoor health and comfort regulations).

- Outdoor air contaminants
- Industrial air contaminants
- Nonindustrial indoor air contaminants and indoor air quality
- Flammable gases and vapors
- Combustible dusts
- Radioactive contaminants
- Soil gases

In the 2008 *ASHRAE Handbook—HVAC Systems and Equipment*, Chapter 28 discusses particulate air contaminant removal, and Chapter 29 covers industrial air cleaning. Chapter 45 in the 2007 *ASHRAE Handbook—HVAC Applications* deals with gaseous contaminant removal.

PARTICULATE CONTAMINANTS

PARTICULATE MATTER

Airborne particulate contamination ranges from dense clouds of desert dust storms to completely invisible and dilute cleanroom particles. It may be anthropogenic or completely natural. It is often a mixture of many different components from several different sources. A much more extensive discussion of particulate contamination by the EPA (2004) is available at http://cfpub2.epa.gov/ncea/cfm/recordisplay.cfm?deid=87903.

Particles occur in a variety of different shapes, including spherical, irregular, and fibers, which are defined as particles with aspect ratio (length-to-width ratio) greater than 3. In describing particle size ranges, *size* is the diameter of an assumed spherical particle.

Solid Particles

Dusts are solid particles projected into the air by natural forces such as wind, volcanic eruption, or earthquakes, or by mechanical processes such as crushing, grinding, demolition, blasting, drilling, shoveling, screening, and sweeping. Some of these forces produce dusts by reducing larger masses, whereas others disperse materials that have already been reduced. Particles are not considered to be dust unless they are smaller than about 100 μm. Dusts can be mineral, such as rock, metal, or clay; vegetable, such as grain, flour, wood, cotton, or pollen; or animal, including wool, hair, silk, feathers, and leather. *Dust* is also used as a catch-all term (house dust, for example) that can have broad meaning.

Fumes are solid particles formed by condensation of vapors of solid materials. Metallic fumes are generated from molten metals and usually occur as oxides because of the highly reactive nature of finely divided matter. Fumes can also be formed by sublimation, distillation, or chemical reaction. Such processes create submicrometre airborne primary particles that may agglomerate into larger particle (1 to 2 μm) clusters if aged at high concentration.

Bioaerosols are airborne biological materials, including viruses and intact and fragments of bacteria, pollen, fungi, and bacterial and fungal spores. Individual **viruses** range in size from 0.003 to 0.06 μm, although they usually occur as aggregates and are associated with sputum or saliva and therefore are generally much larger. Most individual **bacteria** range between 0.4 and 5 μm and may be found singly or as aggregates. Intact individual **fungal** and **bacterial** spores are usually 2 to 10 μm, whereas **pollen** grains are 10 to 100 μm, with many common varieties in the 20 to 40 μm range. The size range of **allergens** varies widely: the allergenic molecule is very small, but the source of the allergen (mite feces or cat dander) may be quite large.

Liquid Particles

Mists are aggregations of small airborne droplets of materials that are ordinarily liquid at normal temperatures and pressure. They can be formed by atomizing, spraying, mixing, violent chemical reactions, evolution of gas from liquid, or escape as a dissolved gas when pressure is released.

Fogs are clouds of fine airborne droplets, usually formed by condensation of vapor, which remain airborne longer than mists. Fog nozzles are named for their ability to produce extra-fine droplets, as compared with mists from ordinary spray devices. Many droplets in fogs or clouds are microscopic and submicroscopic and serve as a transition stage between larger mists and vapors. The volatile nature of most liquids reduces the size of their airborne droplets from the mist to the fog range and eventually to the vapor phase, until the air becomes saturated with that liquid. If solid material is suspended or dissolved in the liquid droplet, it remains in the air as particulate contamination. For example, sea spray evaporates fairly rapidly, generating a large number of fine salt particles that remain suspended in the atmosphere.

Complex Particles

Smokes are small solid and/or liquid particles produced by incomplete combustion of organic substances such as tobacco, wood, coal, oil, and other carbonaceous materials. The term *smoke* is applied to a mixture of solid, liquid, and gaseous products, although technical literature distinguishes between such components as soot or carbon particles, fly ash, cinders, tarry matter, unburned gases, and gaseous combustion products. Smoke particles vary in size, the smallest being much less than 1 μm in diameter. The average is often in the range of 0.1 to 0.3 μm.

Environmental tobacco smoke (ETS) consists of a suspension of 0.01 to 1.0 μm (mass median diameter of 0.3 μm) solid and liquid particles that form as the superheated vapors leaving burning tobacco condense, agglomerate into larger particles, and age. Numerous gaseous contaminants are also produced, including carbon monoxide.

Smog commonly refers to air pollution; it implies an airborne mixture of smoke particles, mists, and fog droplets of such concentration and composition as to impair visibility, in addition to being irritating or harmful. The composition varies among different locations and at different times. The term is often applied to haze caused by a sunlight-induced photochemical reaction involving materials in automobile exhausts. Smog is often associated with temperature inversions in the atmosphere that prevent normal dispersion of contaminants.

Sizes of Airborne Particles

Particle size can be defined in several different ways. These depend, for example, on the source or method of generation, visibility, effects, or measurement instrument. Ambient atmospheric particulate contamination is classified by aerosol scientists and the EPA by source mode, with common usage now recognizing two primary modes: coarse and fine.

Coarse-mode aerosol particles are largest, and are generally formed by mechanical breaking up of solids. They generally have a minimum size of 1 to 3 μm (EPA 2004). Coarse particles also include bioaerosols such as mold spores, pollen, animal dander, and dust mite particles that can affect the immune system. Coarse-mode particles are predominantly primary, natural, and chemically inert. Road dust is a good example. Chemically, coarse particles tend to contain crustal material components such as silicon compounds, iron, aluminum, sea salt, and vegetative particles.

Fine-mode particles are generally secondary particles formed from chemical reactions or condensing gases. They have a maximum size of about 1 to 3 μm. Fine particles are usually more chemically complex than coarse-mode particles and result from human activity. Smoke is a good example. Chemically, fine aerosols typically include sulfates, organics, ammonium, nitrates, carbon, lead, and some trace constituents. The modes overlap, and their definitions are not precise. In addition, some aerosol researchers recognize additional modes. Figure 1 shows a typical urban distribution, including the chemical species present in each mode.

Recently, there has been increased interest in even smaller particles, known as **ultrafine**-mode particles, or **nanoparticles**. Ultrafines have a maximum size of 0.1 μm (100 nm) (EPA 2004). The U.S. National Nanotechnology Initiative (NNI 2008) also uses this definition for nanoparticles.

The size of a particle determines where in the human respiratory system particles are deposited, and various samplers collect particles that penetrate more or less deeply into the lungs. Figure 2 illustrates the relative deposition efficiencies of various sizes of particles in the human nasal and respiratory systems. The **inhalable mass** is made up of particles that may deposit anywhere in the respiratory system, and is represented by a sample with a median cut point of 100 μm. Most of the inhalable mass is captured in the nasal passages. The **thoracic particle mass** is the fraction that can penetrate to the lung airways and is represented by a sample with a median cut point of 10 μm (PM_{10}). The **respirable particle mass** is the fraction that can penetrate to the gas-exchange region of the lungs, which ACGIH (1989) defines as having a median cut point of 4 μm. The EPA no longer uses the term *respirable*. Their current concern is with particles having a median cut point of 2.5 μm ($PM_{2.5}$), which they refer to as **fine particles**.

Particles differ in density, and may be irregular in shape. It is useful to characterize mixed aerosol size in terms of some standard particle. The **aerodynamic (equivalent) diameter** of a particle, defined as the diameter of a unit-density sphere having the same gravitational settling velocity as the particle in question (Willeke and Baron 1993), is commonly used as the standard particle size. Samplers that fractionate particles based on their inertial properties, such as impactors and cyclones, naturally produce results as functions of the aerodynamic diameters. Samplers that use other sizing principles, such as optical particle counters, must be calibrated to give aerodynamic diameter.

The tendency of particles to settle on surfaces is of interest. Figure 3 shows the sizes of typical indoor airborne solid and liquid particles. Particles smaller than 0.1 μm behave like gas molecules, exhibiting irregular motion from collisions with air molecules and having no measurable settling velocity. Particles in the range from 0.1 to 1 μm have calculable settling velocities, but they are so low that settling is usually negligible, because normal air currents counteract any settling. By number, over 99.9% of the particles in a typical atmosphere are below 1 μm (i.e., fewer than 1 particle in every 1000 is larger than 1 μm). Particles between 1 and 10 μm settle in still air at constant and appreciable velocity. However, normal air currents keep them in suspension for appreciable periods. Particles larger than 10 μm settle fairly rapidly and can be found suspended in air only near their source or under strong wind conditions. Exceptions are lint and other light, fibrous materials, such as portions of some weed seeds, which remain suspended longer because their aerodynamic behavior is similar to that of smaller particles (they have aerodynamic diameters smaller than their physical dimensions suggest.)

Table 1 shows settling times for various types of particles. Most individual particles 10 μm or larger are visible to the naked eye under favorable conditions of lighting and contrast. Smaller particles are visible only in high concentrations. Cigarette smoke (with an average particle size less than 0.5 μm) and clouds are common examples. Direct fallout in the vicinity of the dispersing stack or flue and other nuisance problems of air pollution involve larger particles. Smaller particles, as well as mists, fogs, and fumes, remain in suspension longer. In this size range, meteorology and topography are more important than physical characteristics of the particles. Because settling velocities are small, the atmosphere's ability to disperse these small particles depends largely on local weather conditions. Comparison is often made to screen sizes used for grading useful industrial dusts and granular materials. Table 2 illustrates the relationship of U.S. standard sieve mesh to particle size in micrometers. Particles above 40 μm are known as the screen sizes, and those below are known as the subscreen or microscopic sizes.

Table 1 Approximate Particle Sizes and Time to Settle 1 m

Type of Particle	Diameter, μm	Settling Time
Human hair	100 to 150	5 s
Skin flakes	20 to 40	
Observable dust in air	>10	
Common pollens	15 to 25	
Mite allergens	10 to 20	5 min
Common spores	2 to 10	
Bacteria	1 to 5	
Cat dander	1 to 5	10 h
Tobacco smoke	0.1 to 1	
Metal and organic fumes	<0.1 to 1	
Cell debris	0.01 to 1	
Viruses	<0.1	10 days

Note: Spores, bacteria, and virus sizes are for the typical complete unit. As entrained in the air, they may be smaller (fragments) or larger (attached to debris, enclosed in sputum, etc.)

Source: J.D. Spengler, Harvard School of Public Health.

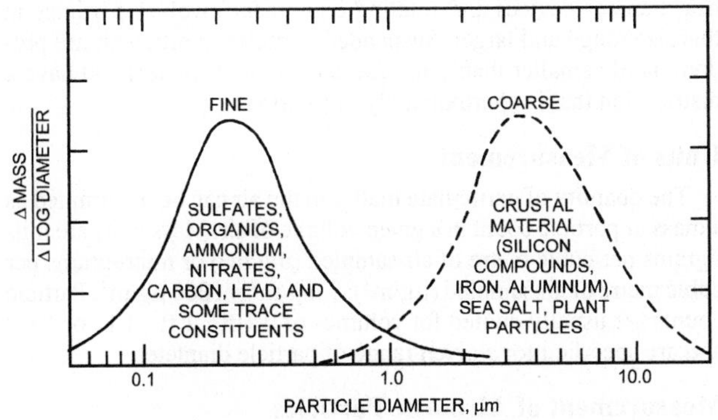

Fig. 1 Typical Urban Aerosol Composition by Particle Size Fraction
(EPA 1982; Willeke and Baron 1993)

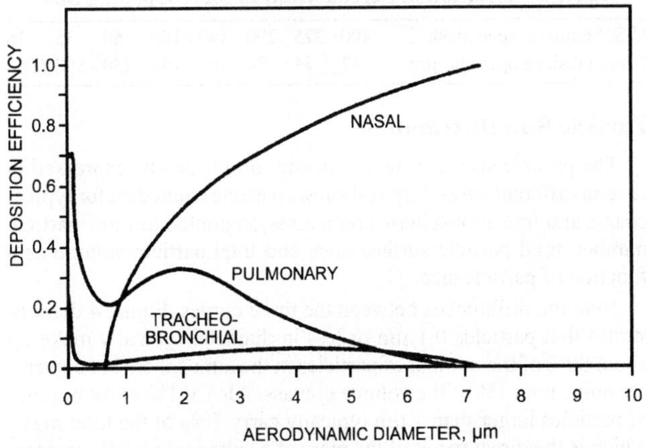

Fig. 2 Relative Deposition Efficiencies of Different-Sized Particles in the Three Main Regions of the Human Respiratory System, Calculated for Moderate Activity Level
(Task Group on Lung Dynamics 1966)

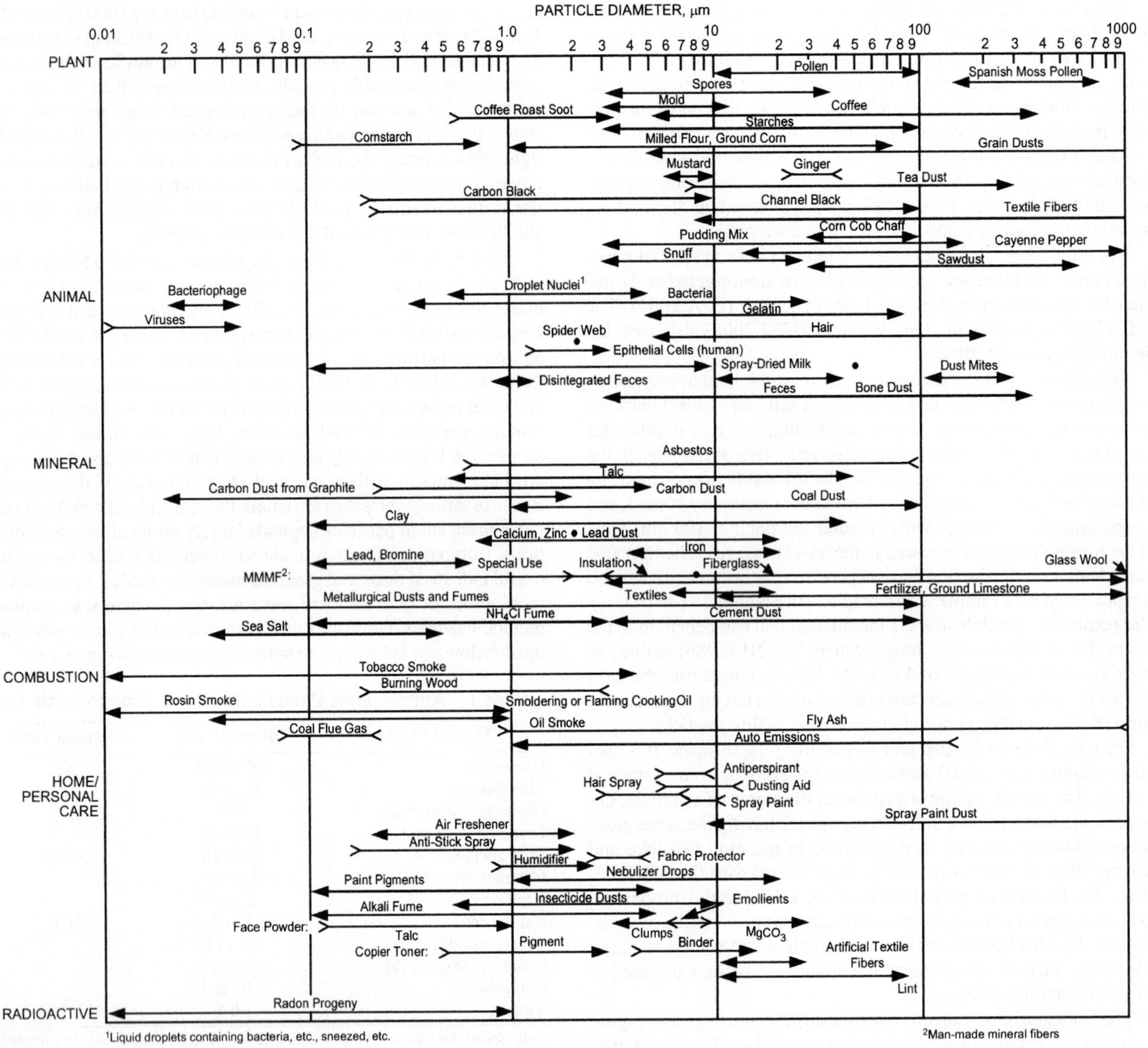

Fig. 3 Sizes of Indoor Particles
(Owen et al. 1992)

Table 2 Relation of Screen Mesh to Sieve Opening Size

U.S. Standard sieve mesh	400	325	200	140	100	60	35	18
Nominal sieve opening, µm	37	44	74	105	149	250	500	1000

Particle Size Distribution

The particle size distribution in any sample can be expressed in several different ways. Figure 4 shows particle count data for typical coarse and fine atmospheric contamination plotted to show particle number, total particle surface area, and total particle volume as a function of particle size.

Note the differences between the three curves. Figure 4 demonstrates that particles 0.1 µm or less in diameter typically make up about 80% of the number of particles in the atmosphere but contribute only about 1% of the volume or mass. Also, 0.1% of the number of particles larger than 1 µm typically carry 70% of the total mass, which is the direct result of the mass of a spherical particle increasing as the cube of its diameter. Although most of the mass is contributed by intermediate and larger particles, over 80% of the area (staining) contamination is supplied by particles less than 1 µm in diameter, which is in the center of the respirable particle size range and is the size most likely to remain in the lungs (see Figure 2 and Chapter 10). Of possible concern to the HVAC industry is the fact that most of the staining effect on ceilings, walls, windows, and light fixtures results from particles less than 1 µm in diameter. Fouling of heat transfer devices and rotating equipment involves particles in this size range and larger. Suspended particles in urban air are predominantly smaller than 1 µm (aerodynamic diameter) and have a distribution that is approximately log-normal.

Units of Measurement

The quantity of particulate matter in the air can be determined as a mass or particle count in a given volume of air. Mass units are milligrams per cubic metre of air sampled (mg/m^3) or micrograms per cubic metre of air sampled (µg/m^3); 1 mg/m^3 = 1000 µg/m^3. Particle counts are usually quoted for volumes of 0.1 ft^3, 1 ft^3, 1 L, or 1 m^3 and are specified for a given range of particle diameter.

Measurement of Airborne Particles

Suitable methods for determining the quantity of particulate matter in the air vary, depending on the amount present and on the size of particles involved. **Direct gravimetric measurement**, in which a

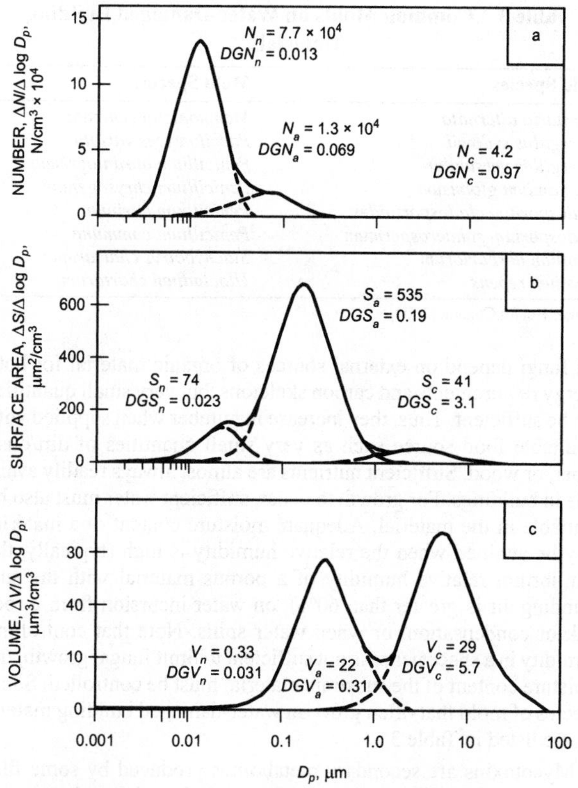

Data are plotted by particle number *N* (plot A), surface area *S* (plot B), and volume *V* (plot C). D_p is particle diameter in microns. Legends show geometric mean diameters (*DG*) for each distribution, and particle number, surface area, or volume in mode.

Fig. 4 Typical Urban Outdoor Distributions of Ultrafine or Nuclei (n) Particles, Fine or Accumulation (a) Particles, and Coarse (c) Particles (Whitby 1978)

dusty air sample is drawn through a preweighed filter, is a common technique in industrial workplaces that often contain significant numbers of large particles. If the total airstream is drawn through the test filter, the sample is known as the **total mass**; if a size-selective inlet is used on the filter, the sample is characterized by the inlet used ($PM_{2.5}$, PM_{10}, respirable, etc.). Gravimetric methods have the advantage of providing an integrated sample (over the sample duration) and of providing a direct measure of the mass concentration (mass/volume). In general, gravimetric methods are not real-time, although some innovative samplers use secondary methods (e.g., beta attenuation, crystal vibration frequency changes) to infer mass on a real-time basis. Further, gravimetric methods require increasing test effort (sample duration and balance quality) as the mass concentration drops toward office and indoor air levels.

Normal daily activities of individuals cause higher personal exposures to both particles and gas contaminants than would be expected from measurements of undisturbed air. Personal activities frequently bring individuals close to air contaminant sources, and also generate particles. Sampling near a person requires special care because the degree of exposure also depends on particle transport as air flows around the body because of convective forces, air turbulence, and obstructions nearby (Rodes and Thornburg 2004).

Optical particle counters (OPCs) are widely used and likely to become more so. They are very convenient and provide real-time, size-selective data. Individual aerosol particles are illuminated with a bright light as they singly pass through the OPC viewing volume. Each particle scatters light, which is collected to produce a voltage pulse in the detector. The pulse size is proportional to the particle size, and the electronics of the OPC assign counts to size ranges based on the pulse size. ASHRAE *Standard* 52.2 defines a laboratory method for assessing the performance of media filters using an OPC to measure particle counts up- and downstream of the filter in 12 size ranges between 0.3 and 10 µm. Filters are then given a **minimum efficiency reporting value (MERV)** rating based on the count data. It is important to sample isokinetically in fast-moving airstreams, such as found in air ducts. This involves sizing the OPC sampling inlet so that the speed of sampled air entering the device is the same as that of air moving past the OPC. If this is not done, the OPC samples inaccurately, capturing too few particles when sampling speed is greater than surrounding air speed, and too many when sampling speed is less than that of the surrounding air.

Counters are also used to test cleanrooms for compliance with the U.S. General Services Administration's (GSA) *Federal Standard* 209E and ISO *Standard* 14644-1. Cleanrooms are defined in terms of the number of particles in certain size ranges that they contain; for more information, see Chapter 16 of the 2007 *ASHRAE Handbook—HVAC Applications*.

Modern OPCs use laser light scattering to continuously count and size airborne particles and, depending on design, can detect particles down to 0.1 µm (ASTM *Standard* F50). Like all aerosol instruments, OPCs should be used with awareness of their limitations. They report particle size from a calibration curve that was developed from a particle having particular optical properties. Actual ambient aerosol particle size is usually close to that indicated by an OPC, but significant errors are possible. Further, many OPCs were developed for cleanroom applications and can become overloaded in other applications. In general, they do not inform the user when they are out of range.

A **condensation nucleus counter (CNC)** can count particles to below 0.01 µm. These particles, present in great numbers in the atmosphere, serve as nuclei for condensation of water vapor (Scala 1963). CNCs provide total particle numbers, and cannot directly provide particle sizing information.

Another indirect method measures the **optical density** of the collected dust, based on the projected area of the particles. Dust particles can be sized with graduated scales or optical comparisons using a standard microscope. The lower limit for sizing with the light-field microscope is approximately 0.9 µm, depending on the vision of the observer, dust color, and available contrast. This size can be reduced to about 0.4 µm by using oil-immersion objective techniques. Dark-field microscopic techniques reveal particles smaller than these, to a limit of approximately 0.1 µm. Smaller submicroscopic dusts can be sized and compared with the aid of an electron microscope.

Other sizing techniques may take into account velocity of samplings in calibrated devices and actual settlement measurements in laboratory equipment. The electron microscope and sampling instruments such as the cascade impactor have been successful in sizing particulates, including fogs and mists. Each method of measuring particle size distribution gives a different value for the same size particle, because different properties are actually measured. For example, a microscopic technique may measure longest dimension, whereas impactor results are based on aerodynamic behavior (ACGIH 2001).

Chemical analysis of particles follows protocols for analysis of any solid material. At industrial concentrations, adequate samples can be obtained from ducts and dust collectors. Because larger particles settle faster than smaller particles, the size and nature of deposited particles often change as suspended particles move away from a source. For instance, near the inlet of an outside air intake, deposited particles will probably be larger and have a coarse composition (e.g., road dust might predominate), whereas further into the duct, fine-mode aerosols would predominate (e.g., condensed oil fume and soot). At the lower concentrations of workplaces, samples are usually collected onto filters, and the filter deposit is analyzed. The filter material must be chosen to not interfere with the analysis. After sample preparation, analysis methods for gaseous contaminant analysis generally apply.

Typical Particle Levels

Particle counters, which detect particles larger than about 0.1 μm, indicate that the number of suspended particles is enormous. A room with heavy cigarette smoke has a particle concentration of 10^9 particles per cubic metre. Even clean air typically contains over 35 × 10^6 particles/m^3. If smaller particles detectable by other means, such as an electron microscope or condensation nucleus counter, are also included, the total particle concentration would be greater than the above concentrations by a factor of 10 to 100. Indoor particle levels are influenced by the number of people and their activities, building materials and construction, outside conditions, ventilation rate, and the air-conditioning and filtration system.

Wallace (1996) reviewed the effect of outdoor particle penetration and activities on indoor concentrations, and Riley et al. (2002) discussed the influence of air exchange rates and filtration on indoor concentrations in residential and commercial buildings. For further information, see the section on Nonindustrial Indoor Air Contaminants, NRC (1981), and Spengler et al. (1982).

BIOAEROSOLS

Bioaerosol refers to any airborne biological (generally microscopic) particulate matter. Though often thought of as originating as microorganisms (fungi, bacteria, viruses, protozoa, algae), bioaerosols may also be derived from plants (pollen and plant fragments), and animals (hair, dander, and saliva from dogs and cats; dust mites). In addition to the intact organisms (e.g., bacteria), their parts (fungal spores and fragments), components (endotoxins, allergens), and products (dust mite antigen-containing fecal pellets and fungal mycotoxins) may be included in the definition. The antigen or toxin to which the body reacts may be quite small; trace amounts are all that are required for many allergic or toxic reactions. Public interest has focused on airborne microorganisms responsible for diseases and infections, primarily bacteria and viruses. These are discussed in more detail in Chapter 10, including sources, transmission and health effects.

Bioaerosols are universally present in both indoor and outdoor environments. Although the organisms that are sources of bioaerosols are living, reproducing organisms, bioaerosols themselves do not have to be alive to cause allergic, toxic, or inflammatory responses. In fact, as little as 1 to 10% of outdoor bioaerosol is thought to be viable (Jaenicke 1998; Tong and Lighthart 1999). Furthermore, fragments of bioaerosols may be transported while attached to inert particles, and may be important from an exposure standpoint.

Problems of concern to engineers occur when microorganisms grow and reproduce indoors, or when large amounts of bioaerosol enter a building from outdoors. Buildings are not sterile, nor are they meant to be. The presence of bacteria and fungi outdoors in soil, water, and atmospheric habitats is normal. For example, spores of the fungus *Cladosporium* are commonly found on leaves and dead vegetation and are almost always found in outdoor air samples. Often, they are found in variable numbers in indoor air, depending on the amount of outdoor air that infiltrates into interior spaces or is brought in by the HVAC system. Outdoor microorganisms and pollen can also enter on shoes and clothing and be transferred to other surfaces in buildings. Through infiltration, pollens can be quite problematic indoors, often depending on the season. Pollens discharged by weeds, grasses, and trees (Hewson et al. 1967; Jacobson and Morris 1977; Solomon and Mathews 1978) can cause hay fever. Bioaerosols have properties of special interest to air-cleaning equipment designers (see Chapter 28 of the 2008 *ASHRAE Handbook—HVAC Systems and Equipment*).

Some bioaerosols originate indoors. Many allergens, such as cat, dog, and dust mite allergens, either originate indoors or have indoor reservoirs (bedding and fleecy materials). Much attention has been given to fungi, which include yeasts, molds (filamentous fungi), and mildews, as well as large mushrooms, puffballs, and bracket fungi.

Table 3 Common Molds on Water-Damaged Building Materials

Mold Species	Mold Species
Alternaria alternata	*Memnoniella echinata*
Aspergillus sydowii	*Paecilomyces variotii*
Aspergillus versicolor	*Penicillium aurantogriseum*
Chaetomium globusum	*Penicillium chrysogenum*
Cladosporium cladosporioides	*Penicillium citrinum*
Cladosporium sphaerospermum	*Penicillium commune*
Eurotium herbariorum	*Stachybotrys chartarum*
Eurotium repens	*Ulocladium chartarum*

Source: Health Canada (2004).

All fungi depend on external sources of organic material for both energy requirements and carbon skeletons, but very small quantities can be sufficient. Thus, they increase in number when supplied with a suitable food source such as very small quantities of dirt/dust, paper, or wood. Sufficient nutrients are almost always readily available in buildings. For growth to occur, sufficient water must also be available in the material. Adequate moisture content of a material may be attained when the relative humidity is high (typically, the equilibrium relative humidity of a porous material with the surrounding air is greater than 60%), on water incursion from a roof leak or condensation, or when water spills. Note that controlling humidity in a space per se is not sufficient to limit fungal growth; the moisture content of the substrate material must be controlled. Some species of mold that often grow on water-damaged building materials are listed in Table 3.

Mycotoxins are secondary metabolites produced by some filamentous fungi, Some are very toxic (e.g., aflatoxin) and some are beneficial (e.g., penicillin). There are hundreds of different mycotoxins, and more are being identified all the time. Mycotoxins can cause disease and death in humans and other animals, primarily when consumed in foods. However, inhalation exposure of fungal spores and fragments containing mycotoxins has been raised as a potential concern as a bioaerosol contaminant.

Bacteria are much simpler organisms than fungi, and generally require more water for growth, often growing in liquids or periodically wetted surfaces. Whereas fungi actively release spores into the environment from contaminated surfaces, bacteria are generally aerosolized by reentrainment of the water in which they are growing. Cooling towers, evaporative condensers, and domestic water service systems all provide water and nutrients for amplification of bacteria such as *Legionella pneumophila*. Growth of bacterial populations to excessive concentrations is generally associated with inadequate preventive maintenance or leaks creating standing water. *Legionella* is well studied, and ASHRAE has issued a position paper on its control (ASHRAE 1998).

Drain pans and cooling coils may also be sources of bacteria. Growth can occur in the water and the organism then can become aerosolized in water droplets. The most common source of bacteria as bioaerosols, especially in closed occupied spaces, may be droplet nuclei caused by actions such as sneezing, or carried on human or animal skin scales.

Endotoxins are components of the cell walls of a fairly large group of bacteria classified as Gram-negative (i.e., crystal violet dye, used in a Gram stain test, does not affect their color). Endotoxin exposure has been associated with a number of adverse health effects. Humidifier fever has been associated with inhalation of endotoxins (Apter 1997; Teeuw 1994).

Units of Measurement

Microorganisms such as bacteria and molds are usually measured either as total culturable or total countable bioaerosol. **Culturable** (viable) bioaerosols are those that can be grown in a laboratory culture. Results are normally reported as number of colony-forming units (CFU) per unit sample volume (m^3 for air samples), area (cm^2 for surface samples) or mass (g for bulk samples).

Countable bioaerosols (viable plus nonviable) include all particles that can be identified and counted under a microscope. Results are reported as number of particles per unit sample volume, area, or mass, as above.

Allergens are usually expressed as their weight (in ng) per unit volume; endotoxins are expressed as EU or endotoxin units.

Sampling

Sampling when bioaerosols are suspected as a contaminant may include direct plating of observed microbial growth, collection of bulk or surface samples, or air sampling. Surface sampling is useful for bioaerosol detection, because the surface may constitute a long-time duration sampler. The principles of sampling and analysis for bioaerosols are presented in depth by Macher (1999). AIHA (1996) gives assessment guidelines for collecting microbiological particulates.

The same principles that affect collection of an inert particulate aerosol sample also govern air sampling for microorganisms. Air sampling is not likely to yield useful data and information unless the sample collected is representative of exposure, and appropriate control samples are collected. The most representative samples are those collected in breathing zones over the range of aerosol concentrations. Personal sampling (in the breathing zone of a worker) is generally preferable, but area sampling (e.g., on a table) over representative periods is more commonly performed. Some investigators attempt to replicate exposure conditions through disturbance of the environment (semiaggressive sampling), such as occurs when walking on carpets, slamming doors, and opening books or file cabinets.

The sampling method selected affects the measured count. Methods that rely on counting analysis usually report higher concentrations than those that use culturing analysis, because of the inclusion of nonviable particles. There is no single, ideal bioaerosol sampler, but rather several complementary techniques that may be appropriate in any particular application. Collection directly on **filter paper** is simple and direct, but may dehydrate some organisms and underestimate exposure for live counting techniques. **Glass impingers** are an effective and standard method, but may overestimate exposure because the liquid contact and agitation can break clusters into smaller individual organisms, which are then each counted as a separate entity. **Slit-to-agar samplers** may give a more accurate culturable colony count, but do not measure nonculturable organisms or fragments, parts, or components. In general, culture plate impactors, including multiple- and single-stage devices as well as slit-to-agar samplers, are most useful in office environments where low concentrations of bacteria and fungi are expected. Some multihole impactors require application of a positive hole correction factor to the raw counts to compensate for multiple organisms focused aerodynamically and landing in the same place on the media. Because not all microorganisms can grow on the same media, impactors that separate samples must be collected for each. Liquid impingement subculturing allows plating one sample on multiple media. Filter cassette samplers are useful for some hardy microorganisms or components (e.g., endotoxins) and allergen analyses. Filter cassettes can also be used for spore counts.

Nonculture methods for fungal spores and pollen grains generally involve exposing an adhesive-coated glass slide or plate for a specific time period, then counting calibrated areas under the microscope, and calculating the number in a measured volume of air. Measurement methods for pollen are not discussed further here, because data are widely available in the public domain.

Some viruses, bacteria, algae, and protozoa are more difficult to culture than fungi, and air-sampling methodology for these organisms may not be practical. For example, *Legionella* requires special nutrients and conditions for growth, and thus may be difficult to recover from air. To further complicate the issue, not all fungi grow on any one media, so media selection may be important.

Table 4 Example Case of Airborne Fungi in Building and Outdoor Air

Location	CFU/m^3	Rank Order Taxa
Outdoors	210	*Cladosporium* > *Fusarium* > *Epicoccum* > *Aspergillus*
Complainant office #1	2500	*Tritirachium* > *Aspergillus* > *Cladosporium*
Complainant office #2	3000	*Tritirachium* > *Aspergillus* > *Cladosporium*

Notes: CFU/m^3 = colony-forming units per cubic metre of air. Culture media, for this example, was malt extract agar (ACGIH 1989).

Rank-order assessment is used to interpret air-sampling data for microorganisms (Macher 1999). Individual organisms are listed in descending order of abundance for a complainant indoor site and for one or more control locations. The predominance of one or more microbes in the complainant site, but not in the control sites or outdoors, suggests the presence of a source for that organism. An example is shown in Table 4.

Control

Control of bioaerosols is a complex issue. Generally, particulate removal devices and controls are effective in collecting and removing bioaerosols, including allergens (Foarde et al. 1994). The key to effective removal is that the bioaerosol must reach the removal device. Surprisingly, this fact is often overlooked.

When maximum removal of airborne microorganisms is either necessary or desirable, high-efficiency particulate air (HEPA) or ultralow penetration air (ULPA) filters are used. These filters create atmospheres with very low particulate levels.

In many situations, total control of airborne microorganisms is not required. For these applications, there are various types of high-efficiency, dry-media, extended-surface filters that provide the necessary efficiency. These filters have lower pressure differentials than HEPA filters operating at the same face velocity, and, when properly selected, remove the contaminants of concern.

Ultraviolet (UV) radiation is also used for control of airborne microorganisms, to prevent cross-infection in hospitals, to protect cleanrooms, and to assemble and launch space probes under sterile conditions. The key to effective use of UV lights is ensuring that the organism receives a sufficient dose of irradiation. Microorganisms vary widely in their susceptibility of UVC. Vegetative bacteria are readily killed; bacterial spores are much more difficult; fungal spores are extremely hard to kill. Surface kill is generally readily achieved because time is not a factor in attaining a sufficient dose to kill. Achieving kill of airborne contaminants is much more complicated. Banks of lights may be required to achieve sufficient dose to kill bacterial or fungal spores in a moving airstream

Sometimes, chemicals (**biocides** or **antimicrobials**) are also used to control microbial growth. In the United States, biocides and antimicrobials should be registered with the EPA under the Federal Insecticide, Fungicide, and Rodenticide Act (FIFRA). Uses for which an antimicrobial is approved should be stated on the label. Label claims are approved by the EPA based on efficacy data from specific standardized tests submitted by the manufacturer on a specific product. Standard efficacy testing of an antimicrobial is frequently done only on the active ingredient in the antimicrobial, and not on the entire product as it is going to be used. Although not required, an effective assessment of antimicrobial efficacy on a material should also include a use test.

In a study of antifungal treated air filters, Foarde (1999) found that antifungal treatment may be masked by dust loading of the filters. Dust creates a physical barrier between the antifungal and the organism. Furthermore, only two of the three antimicrobial treatments inhibited growth. Clearly, it is helpful for industry and consumers to have information on how a particular product or material is expected to perform in a particular application.

GASEOUS CONTAMINANTS

The terms **gas** and **vapor** are both used to describe the gaseous state of a substance. *Gas* is the correct term for describing any pure substance or mixture that naturally exists in the gaseous state at normal atmospheric conditions. That is, its vapor pressure is greater than ambient pressure at ambient temperature. Examples are oxygen, helium, ammonia, and nitrogen. *Vapor* is used to describe a substance in the gaseous state whose natural state is a liquid or solid at normal atmospheric conditions. The vapor pressure is below ambient pressure at ambient temperature. Examples include benzene, carbon tetrachloride, and water. Differences between the two classes reflect their preferred states:

- For a strong source, the concentration of a gas in air in a confined space can rise above one atmosphere. Thus, even nontoxic gases can be lethal if they completely fill a space, displacing the oxygen necessary for survival.
- Vapors can never exceed their saturated vapor pressure in air. The most familiar example of a vapor is water, with relative humidity expressing the air concentration as a percentage of the saturated vapor pressure.
- Vapors, because their natural state is liquid or solid (low vapor pressure), tend to condense on surfaces and be adsorbed.

Gaseous contaminants can also usefully be divided into organic and inorganic types. **Organic** compounds include all chemicals based on a skeleton of carbon atoms. Because carbon atoms easily combine to form chain, branched, and ring structures, there is a wide variety of organic compounds. Despite the variety, they all have similarities that can be used in sampling, analysis, and removal. Chemists subclassify organic compounds based on families having similar structure and predictable properties. Organic gaseous contaminants include gases such as methane, but the majority are vapors.

All other gaseous contaminants are classified as **inorganic**. Most inorganic air contaminants of interest to ventilation engineers are gases (mercury is an important exception). Major chemical families of inorganic and organic gaseous contaminants, with examples of specific compounds, are shown in Table 5, along with information about occurrence and use. Some organics belong to more than one class and carry the attributes of both.

Another useful gaseous contaminant classification is polar versus nonpolar. There is a continuous distribution between the extremes. For **polar** compounds, charge separation occurs between atoms, which affects physical characteristics as well as chemical reactivity. Water is one of the best examples of a polar compound, and consequently polar gaseous contaminants tend to be soluble in water. **Nonpolar** compounds are much less soluble in water, but dissolve in nonpolar liquids. This classification provides the basis for dividing consumer products that contain organic compounds into water-based and solvent-based. Contaminant classes in Table 5 that are strongly polar include acid gases, chemicals containing oxygen (e.g., alcohols, aldehydes, ketones, esters, organic acids), and some nitrogen-containing chemicals. Nonpolar classes include all hydrocarbons (alkyl, alkene, cyclic, aromatic), chlorinated hydrocarbons, terpenes, and some sulfur-containing chemicals.

Because no single sampling and analysis method applies to every (or even most) potential contaminant, having some idea what the contaminants and their properties might be is very helpful. Contaminants have sources, and consideration of the locale, industries, raw materials, cleaners, and consumer products usually provides some guidance regarding probable contaminants. Material safety data sheets (MSDS) provide information on potentially harmful chemicals that a product contains, but the information is often incomplete. Once a potential contaminant has been identified, the *Merck Index* (Budavi 1996), the *Toxic Substances Control Act Chemical Substance Inventory* (EPA 1979), *Dangerous Properties of Industrial Materials* (Sax and Lewis 1988), and *Handbook of Environmental Data on Organic Chemicals* (Verschueren 1996) are all useful in identifying and gathering information on contaminant properties, including some known by trade names only. Chemical and physical properties can be found in reference books such as the *Handbook of Chemistry and Physics* (Lide 1996). Note that a single chemical compound, especially an organic one, may have several scientific names. To reduce confusion, the Chemical Abstracts Service (CAS) assigns each chemical a unique five- to nine-digit identifier number. Table 6 shows CAS numbers and some physical properties for selected gaseous contaminants. Boiling points and saturated vapor pressures are important in predicting airborne concentrations of gaseous contaminants in cases of spillage or leakage of liquids. For example, because of its much higher volatility, ammonia requires more rigorous safety precautions than ethylene glycol when used as a heat exchange fluid. In laboratories where several acids are stored, hydrochloric acid (hydrogen chloride) usually causes more corrosion than sulfuric or nitric acids because its greater gaseous concentration results in escape of more chemical. Additional chemical and physical properties for some of the chemicals in Tables 5 and 6 can be found in Chapter 33.

Harmful Effects of Gaseous Contaminants

Harmful effects may be divided into four categories: toxicity, irritation, odor, and material damage.

Toxicity. The harmful effects of gaseous pollutants on a person depend on both short-term peak concentrations and the time-integrated exposure received by the person. Toxic effects are generally considered to be proportional to the exposure dose, although individual response variation can obscure the relationship. The allowable concentration for short exposures is higher than that for long exposures. Safe exposure limits have been set for a number of common gaseous contaminants in industrial settings. This topic is covered in more detail in the section on Industrial Air Contaminants and in Chapter 10.

Irritation. Although gaseous pollutants may have no discernible continuing health effects, exposure may cause physical irritation to building occupants. This phenomenon has been studied principally in laboratories and nonindustrial work environments, and is discussed in more detail in the section on Nonindustrial Indoor Air Contaminants and in Chapter 10.

Odors. Gaseous contaminant problems often appear as complaints about odors, and these usually are the result of concentrations considerably below industrial exposure limits. Odors are discussed in more detail in Chapter 12. Note that controlling gaseous contaminants because they constitute a nuisance odor is fundamentally different from controlling a contaminant because it has a demonstrated health effect. Odor control frequently can use limited-capacity “peak-shaving” technology to drop peaks of odorous compounds below the odor threshold. Later reemission at a low rate is neither harmful nor noticed. Such an approach may not be acceptable for control of toxic materials.

Damage to Materials. Material damage from gaseous pollutants includes corrosion, embrittlement, or discoloration. Because these effects usually involve chemical reactions that need water, material damage from air pollutants is less severe in the relatively dry indoor environment than outdoors, even at similar gaseous contaminant concentrations. To maintain this advantage, indoor condensation should be avoided. However, some dry materials can be significantly damaged. These effects are most serious in museums, because any loss of color or texture changes the essence of the object. Libraries and archives are also vulnerable, as are pipe organs and textiles. Consult Chapter 21 in the 2007 *ASHRAE Handbook—HVAC Applications* for additional information and an exhaustive reference list.

Table 5 Major Chemical Families of Gaseous Air Contaminants

No. Family	Examples	Other Information
Inorganic Contaminants		
1. Single-element atoms and molecules	Chlorine, radon, mercury	Chlorine is a strong respiratory irritant used as a disinfectant. Radon is an important soil gas. Mercury is the vapor in fluorescent light bulbs and tubes.
2. Oxidants	Ozone, nitrogen dioxide	Both members are corrosive and act as respiratory irritants.
3. Reducing agents	Carbon monoxide	Carbon monoxide is a toxic fuel combustion product.
4. Acid gases	Carbon dioxide, hydrogen chloride, hydrogen fluoride, hydrogen sulfide, nitric acid, sulfur dioxide, sulfuric acid	Carbon dioxide and hydrogen sulfide are only weakly acidic. Hydrogen sulfide is the main agent in sewer gas. Other members are corrosive and respiratory irritants. Some are important outdoor contaminants.
5. Nitrogen compounds	Ammonia, hydrazine, nitrous oxide	Ammonia used in cleaning products. It is a strong irritant. Hydrazine is used as an anticorrosion agent. Nitrous oxide (laughing gas) is used as an anesthetic.
6. Miscellaneous	Arsine, phosphine	Arsine and phosphine are used in the semiconductor industry.
Organic Contaminants		
7. *n*-Alkanes	Methane, propane, *n*-butane, *n*-hexane, *n*-heptane, *n*-octane, *n*-nonane, *n*-decane, *n*-undecane, *n*-dodecane	*n*-Alkanes are linear molecules and relatively easily identified analytically. Along with the far more numerous branched alkanes, they are components of solvents such as mineral spirits.
8. Branched alkanes	2-methyl pentane, 2-methyl hexane	There are many different ways of linking atoms in the carbon skeleton, so this family is very numerous. Members are difficult to separate and identify. Many occur as components of products such as gasoline, kerosene, mineral spirits, etc.
9. Alkenes and cyclic hydrocarbons	Ethylene, butadiene, 1-octene, cyclohexene, 4-phenyl cyclohexene (4-PC)	Ethylene gas is produced by ripening fruit (and used in the fruit industry). Some liquid members are components of gasoline, etc. 4-PC is responsible for "new carpet" odor.
10. Chlorofluorocarbons	R-11 (trichlorofluoromethane), R-12 (dichlorodifluoromethane), R-114 (dichlorotetrafluoroethane)	These have been widely used as refrigerants, but are being phased out because of their ozone-depleting potential.
11. Chlorinated hydrocarbons	Carbon tetrachloride, chloroform, dichloromethane, 1,1,1-trichloroethane, trichloroethylene, tetrachloroethylene, *p*-dichlorobenzene	Dichlorobenzene, an aromatic chemical, is a solid used as an air freshener. The others shown here are liquids and are effective nonpolar solvents. Some are used as degreasers or in the dry-cleaning industry.
12. Halide compounds	Methyl bromide, methyl iodide	Members of this family are of low combustibility. Some are used as flame retardants.
13. Alcohols	Methanol, ethanol, 2-propanol (isopropanol), 3-methyl 1-butanol, ethylene glycol, 2-butoxyethanol, phenol	Alcohols are strongly polar. Some (including 2-butoxyethanol) are used as solvents in water-based products. Phenol is used as a disinfectant. 3-methyl 1-butanol is emitted by some molds.
14. Ethers	Ethyl ether, methyl tertiary butyl ether (MTBE), 2-butoxyethanol	Ethyl ether and 2-butoxyethanol are used as solvents. MTBE is added to gasoline to improve combustion in vehicle motors.
15. Aldehydes	Formaldehyde, acetaldehyde, acrolein, benzaldehyde	Formaldehyde, acetaldehyde, and acrolein have unpleasant odors and are strong irritants.
16. Ketones	2-propanone (acetone), 2-butanone (MEK), methyl isobutyl ketone (MIBK), 2-hexanone	Ketones are medium-polarity chemicals. Some are useful solvents. Acetone and 2-hexanone are emitted by some molds.
17. Esters	Ethyl acetate, vinyl acetate, butyl acetate	Esters are medium-polarity chemicals. Some have pleasant odors and are added as fragrances to consumer products.
18. Nitrogen compounds other than amines	Nitromethane, acetonitrile, acrylonitrile, urea, hydrogen cyanide, peroxyacetal nitrite (PAN)	This family includes several different types of chemicals, and there are few common properties. Acetonitrile is used as a solvent; urea is a metabolic product; PAN is found in vehicle exhaust.
19. Aromatic hydrocarbons	Benzene, toluene, *p*-xylene, styrene, 1,2,4 trimethyl benzene, naphthalene, benz-α-pyrene	Benzene, toluene, and xylene are widely used as solvents and in manufacturing, and are ubiquitous in indoor air. Naphthalene is used as moth repellent.
20. Terpenes	α-pinene, limonene	A variety of terpenes are emitted by wood. The two listed here have pleasant odors and are used as fragrances in cleaners, perfumes, etc.
21. Heterocyclics	Ethylene oxide, tetrahydrofuran, 3-methyl furan, 1, 4-dioxane, pyridine, nicotine	Most heterocyclics are of medium polarity. Ethylene oxide is used as a disinfectant. Tetrahydrofuran and pyridine are used as solvents. Nicotine is a component of tobacco smoke.
22. Organophosphates	Malathion, tabun, sarin, soman	The listed members are components of agricultural pesticides and occur as outdoor air contaminants.
23. Amines	Trimethylamine, ethanolamine, cyclohexylamine, morpholine	Amines typically have unpleasant odors detectable at very low concentrations. Some (cyclohexylamine and morpholine) are used as antioxidants in boilers.
24. Monomers	Vinyl chloride, ethylene, methyl methacrylate, styrene	These have the potential to be released from their respective polymers (PVC, polythene, perspex, polystyrene) if materials are heated.
25. Mercaptans and other sulfur compounds	Bis-2-chloroethyl sulfide (mustard gas), ethyl mercaptan, dimethyl disulfide	Sulfur-containing chemicals typically have unpleasant odors detectable at very low concentrations. Ethyl mercaptan is added to natural gas so that gas leaks can be detected by odor. Mustard gas has been used in chemical warfare.
26. Organic acids	Formic acid, acetic acid, butyric acid	Formic and acetic acids (vinegar) are emitted by some types of wood. Butyric acid is a component of "new car" odor.
27. Miscellaneous	Phosgene, siloxanes	Phosgene is a toxic gas released during combustion of some chlorinated organic chemicals. Siloxanes occur widely in consumer products, including adhesives, sealants, cleaners, and hair and skin care products.

Table 6 Characteristics of Selected Gaseous Air Contaminants

	Chemical and Physical Properties				
Contaminant	Family[a]	CAS[b] number	BP,[c] °C	Sat. VP[d]	M[e]
Acetaldehyde	15	75-07-0	20	120	44
Acetone	16	67-64-1	56	31	58
Acrolein	15	107-02-8	51	36	56
Ammonia	5	7664-41-7	−33	1000	17
Benzene	19	71-43-2	81	13	78
2-Butanone (MEK)	16	78-93-3	79	13	72
Carbon dioxide	4	124-38-9	Sub[f]	>4000	44
Carbon monoxide	3	630-08-0	−191	>6000	28
Carbon disulfide	25	75-15-0	47	48	76
Carbon tetrachloride	11	56-23-5	77	15	154
Chlorine	1	7782-50-5	−34	770	71
Chloroform	11	67-66-3	61	26	119
Dichlorodifluoromethane	10	75-71-8	−29	650	121
Dichloromethane	12	75-09-2	40	58	85
Ethylene glycol	13	107-21-1	197	0.01	62
Ethylene oxide	21	75-21-8	13	1700	44
Formaldehyde	15	50-00-0	−19	520	30
n-Heptane	7	142-82-5	98	6.1	100
Hydrogen chloride	4	7647-01-0	−85	4700	37
Hydrogen cyanide	18	74-90-8	26	100	27
Hydrogen fluoride	4	7664-39-3	19	120	20
Hydrogen sulfide	4	7783-06-4	−61	2100	34
Mercury	1	7439-97-6	357	<0.002	201
Methane	7	74-82-8	−164	>10,000	16
Methanol	13	67-56-1	65	17	32
Nitric acid	4	7697-37-2	86	7	63
Nitrogen dioxide	2	10102-44-0	21	110	46
Ozone	2	10028-15-6	−112	>6000	48
Phenol	13	108-95-2	182	0.055	94
Phosgene	27	75-44-5	8	190	90
Propane	7	74-98-6	−42	940	44
Sulfur dioxide	4	7446-09-5	−10	420	64
Sulfuric acid	4	7664-93-9	337		98
Tetrachloroethylene	11	127-18-4	121	2.4	166
Toluene	19	108-88-3	111	3.8	92
Toluene diisocyanate	18	584-84-9	251	0.001	174
1,1,1-Trichloroethane	11	71-55-6	74	16	133
Trichloroethylene	11	79-01-6	87	9.9	131
Vinyl chloride monomer	24	75-01-4	−13	350	63
Xylene	19	106-42-3	138	1	106

[a]Chemical family numbers are as given in Table 5.
[b]CAS = Chemical Abstracts Services.
[c]BP = boiling point at 101.325 kPa pressure.
[d]Sat. VP = saturated vapor pressure at 25°C, kPa.
[e]M = molar mass.
[f]Sub = solid sublimes at −78°C.

Units of Measurement

Concentrations of gaseous contaminants are usually expressed in the following units:

ppm = parts of contaminant by volume per million parts of air by volume
ppb = parts of contaminant by volume per billion parts of air by volume
1000 ppb = 1 ppm
mg/m^3 = milligrams of contaminant per cubic metre of air
$\mu g/m^3$ = micrograms of contaminant per cubic metre of air

Conversions between ppm and mg/m^3 are

$$\text{ppm} = [8.309(273.15 + t)/Mp]\ (\text{mg/m}^3) \qquad (1)$$

$$\text{mg/m}^3 = [0.1204(Mp)/(273.15 + t)]\ (\text{ppm}) \qquad (2)$$

where

M = relative molar mass of contaminant
p = mixture pressure, kPa
t = mixture temperature, °C

Concentration data are often reduced to standard temperature and pressure (i.e., 25°C and 101.325 kPa), in which case,

$$\text{ppm} = (24.45/M)\ (\text{mg/m}^3) \qquad (3)$$

Using the 21°C standard temperature more familiar to engineers results in a conversion factor between ppm and mg/m^3 of 24.12 in Equation (3).

Equations (1) to (3) are strictly true only for ideal gases, but generally are acceptable for dilute vaporous contaminants dispersed in ambient air.

Measurement of Gaseous Contaminants

The concentration of contaminants in air must be measured to determine whether indoor air quality conforms to occupational health standards (in industrial environments) and is acceptable (in nonindustrial environments).

Measurement methods for airborne chemicals that are important industrially have been published by several organizations, including NIOSH (1994) and OSHA (1995). Methods typically involve sampling air with pumps for several hours to capture contaminants on a filter or in an adsorbent tube, followed by laboratory analysis for detection and determination of contaminant concentration. Concentrations measured in this way can usefully be compared to 8 h industrial exposure limits.

Measurement of gaseous contaminants at the lower levels acceptable for indoor air is not always as straightforward. Relatively costly analytical equipment may be needed, and it must be calibrated and operated by experienced personnel.

Currently available sample collection techniques are listed in Table 7, with information about their advantages and disadvantages. Analytical measurement techniques are shown in Table 8, with information on the types of contaminants to which they apply. Tables 7 and 8 provide an overview of gaseous contaminant sampling and analysis, with the intent of allowing informed interaction with specialists.

Techniques 1, 2, and 8 in Table 7 combine sampling and analysis in one piece of equipment and give immediate, on-site results. The other sampling methods require laboratory analysis after the field work. Equipment using the first technique can be coupled with a data logger to perform continuous monitoring and to obtain average concentrations over a time period. Most of the sample collection techniques can capture several contaminants. Several allow pollutants to accumulate or concentrate over time so that very low concentrations can be measured.

Some analytical measurement techniques are specific for a single pollutant, whereas others can provide concentrations for many contaminants simultaneously. Note that formaldehyde requires different measurement methods from other volatile organic compounds.

Measurement instruments used in industrial situations should be able to detect contaminants of interest at about one-tenth of **threshold limit value (TLV)** levels, published annually by ACGIH. If odors are of concern, detection sensitivity must be at odor threshold levels. Procedures for evaluating odor levels are given in Chapter 12.

When sample collection and analytical procedures appropriate to the application have been selected, a building-specific pattern of sampling locations and times must be carefully planned. Building and air-handling system layout and space occupancy and use patterns must be considered so that representative concentrations will be measured. Nagda and Rector (1983) and Traynor (1987) offer guidance in planning such surveys. Note that information in Tables 7 and 8 is not sufficient in itself to allow preparation of a measurement protocol.

Table 7 Gaseous Contaminant Sample Collection Techniques

Technique*	Advantages	Disadvantages
Active Methods		
1. Direct flow to detectors	Real-time readout, continuous monitoring possible Several pollutants possible with one sample (when coupled with chromatograph, spectroscope, or multiple detectors)	Average concentration must be determined by integration No preconcentration possible before detector; sensitivity may be inadequate On-site equipment often complicated, expensive, intrusive, and requires skilled operator
2. Capture by pumped flow through colorimetric detector tubes, papers, or tapes	Very simple, relatively inexpensive equipment and materials Immediate readout Integration over time	One pollutant per sample Relatively high detection limit Poor precision Requires multiple tubes, papers, or tapes for high concentrations or long-term measurements
3. Capture by pumped flow through solid adsorbent; subsequent desorption for concentration measurement	On-site sampling equipment relatively simple and inexpensive Preconcentration and integration over time inherent in method Several pollutants possible with one sample	Sampling media and desorption techniques are compound-specific Interaction between captured compounds and between compounds and sampling media; bias may result Gives only average over sampling period, no peaks Subsequent concentration measurement required
4. Collection in evacuated containers	Very simple on-site equipment No pump (silent) Several pollutants possible with one sample	Subsequent concentration measurement required Gives average over sampling period; no peaks Finite volume requires multiple containers for long-term or continuous measurement
5. Collection in nonrigid containers (plastic bags) held in an evacuated box	Simple, inexpensive on-site equipment (pumps required) Several pollutants possible with one sample	Cannot hold some pollutants Subsequent concentration measurement required Gives average over sampling period; no peaks Finite volume requires multiple containers for long-term or continuous measurement
6. Cryogenic condensation	Wide variety of organic pollutants can be captured Minimal problems with interferences and media interaction Several pollutants possible with one sample	Water vapor interference Subsequent concentration measurement required Gives average over sampling period; no peaks
7. Liquid impingers (bubblers)	Integration over time Several pollutants possible with one sample if appropriate liquid chosen	May be noisy Subsequent concentration measurement required Gives average over sampling period; no peaks
Passive Methods		
8. Passive colorimetric badges	Immediate readout possible Simple, unobtrusive, inexpensive No pumps, mobile; may be worn by occupants to determine average exposure	One pollutant per sample Relatively high detection limit Poor precision May require multiple badges for higher concentrations or long-term measurement
9. Passive diffusional samplers	Simple, unobtrusive, inexpensive No pumps, mobile; may be worn by occupants to determine average exposure	Subsequent concentration measurement required Gives average over sampling period; no peaks Poor precision

Sources: ATC (1990), Lodge (1988), NIOSH (1977, 1994), and Taylor et al. (1977).

*All techniques except 1, 2, and 8 require laboratory work after completion of field sampling. Only first technique is adaptable to continuous monitoring and able to detect short-term excursions.

VOLATILE ORGANIC COMPOUNDS

The entire range of organic indoor pollutants has been categorized by volatility, as indicated in Table 9 (WHO 1989). No sharp limits exist between the categories, which are defined by boiling-point ranges. Volatile organic compounds (VOCs) have attracted considerable attention in nonindustrial environments. They have boiling points in the range of approximately 50 to 250°C and vapor pressures greater than about 0.1 to 0.01 Pa. [Note that the U.S. Environmental Protection Agency (EPA) has a specific regulatory definition of VOCs (*Code of Federal Regulations* 40CFR51.100) that must be consulted if regulated U.S. air emissions are the matter of interest. Although similar to the definition here, it is more complex, with some excluded compounds and specified test methods.]

Sources of VOCs include solvents, reagents, and degreasers in industrial environments; and furniture, furnishings, wall and floor finishes, cleaning and maintenance products, and office and hobby activities in nonindustrial environments. Which gas contaminants are likely in an industrial environment can usually best be identified from the nature of the industrial processes, and that is the recommended first step. This discussion focuses on indoor VOCs because they are usually more difficult to identify and quantify.

Berglund et al. (1988) found that the sources of VOCs in nonindustrial indoor environments are confounded by the variable nature of emissions from potential sources. Emissions of VOCs from indoor sources can be classified by their presence and rate patterns. For example, emissions are continuous and regular from building materials and furnishings (e.g., carpet and composite-wood furniture), whereas emissions from other sources can be continuous but irregular (e.g., paints used in renovation work), intermittent and regular (e.g., VOCs in combustion products from gas stoves or cleaning products), or intermittent and irregular (e.g., VOCs from carpet shampoos) (Morey and Singh 1991).

Many "wet" emission sources (paints and adhesives) have very high emission rates immediately after application, but rates drop steeply with time until the product has cured or dried. New "dry"

Table 8 Analytical Methods to Measure Gaseous Contaminant Concentration

Method	Description	Typical Application (Family)
Gas chromatography (using the following detectors)	Separation of gas mixtures by time of passage down absorption column	
Flame ionization	Change in flame electrical resistance caused by ions of pollutant	Volatile, nonpolar organics (7-27)
Flame photometry	Measures light produced when pollutant is ionized by a flame	Sulfur (25), phosphorous (22) compounds Most organics (7-27), except methane
Photoionization	Measures ion current for ions created by ultraviolet light	Halogenated organics (11, 12) Nitrogenated organics (18, 23)
Electronic capture	Radioactively generated electrons attach to pollutant atoms; current measured	
Mass spectroscopy	Pollutant molecules are charged, passed through electrostatic magnetic fields in vacuum; path curvature depends on mass of molecule, allowing separation and counting of each type	Volatile organics (7-27 with boiling point < 65°C)
Infrared spectroscopy, including Fourier transform IR (FTIR) and photoacoustic IR	Absorption of infrared light by pollutant gas in a transmission cell; a range of wavelengths is used, allowing identification and measurement of individual pollutants	Acid gases (4, 26), carbon monoxide (3) Many organics; any gas with an absorption band in the infrared (7-27)
High-performance liquid chromatography (HPLC)	Pollutant is captured in a liquid, which is then passed through a liquid chromatograph (analogous to a gas chromatograph)	Aldehydes (15), ketones (16) Phosgene (27) Nitrosamines (18, 23) Cresol, phenol (13)
Colorimetry	Chemical reaction with pollutant in solution yields a colored product whose light absorption is measured	Ozone (2) Oxides of nitrogen (2) Formaldehyde (15)
Fluorescence and pulsed fluorescence	Pollutant atoms are stimulated by a monochromatic light beam, often ultraviolet; they emit light at characteristic fluorescent wavelengths, whose intensity is measured	Sulfur dioxide (4) Carbon monoxide (3)
Chemiluminescence	Reaction (usually with a specific injected gas) results in photon emission proportional to concentration	Ozone (2) Nitrogen compounds (5, 18, 23) Some organics (7-27)
Electrochemical	Pollutant is bubbled through reagent/water solution, changing its conductivity or generating a voltage	Ozone (2) Hydrogen sulfide (4) Acid gases (4, 26)
Titration	Pollutant is absorbed into water and known quantities of acid or base are added to achieve neutrality	Acid gases (4, 26) Basic gases (5, 23)
Ultraviolet absorption	Absorption of UV light by a cell through which the polluted air passes is measured	Ozone (2) Aromatics (19) Sulfur dioxide (4) Oxides of nitrogen (2) Carbon monoxide (3)
Atomic absorption	Contaminant is burned in a hydrogen flame; a light beam with a spectral line specific to the pollutant is passed through the flame; optical absorption of the beam is measured	Mercury vapor (1)
Surface acoustic wave, flexural plate wave, etc.	Contaminant adsorption on a substrate alters the resonant vibration frequency or vibration transmittance characteristics	
Chemiresistor (metal oxide)	Contaminant interacts with coated metal oxide surface at high temperature, changing the resistance to electrical current	Carbon monoxide (3), hydrogen sulfide (4), organic vapors (7-27)

Sources: ATC (1990), Lodge (1988), NIOSH (1977,1994), and Taylor et al (1977).

Table 9 Classification of Indoor Organic Contaminants by Volatility

Description	Abbreviation	Boiling Point Range, °C
Very volatile (gaseous) organic compounds	VVOC	0 to 50–100
Volatile organic compounds	VOC	50–100 to 240–260
Semivolatile organics (pesticides, polynuclear aromatic compounds, plasticizers)	SVOC	240–260 to 380–400

Source: WHO (1989).
Notes:
Polar compounds and VOCs with higher mol masses appear at higher end of each boiling-point range.
The EPA use a different definition of VOC for regulatory purposes.

materials (carpets, wall coverings, and furnishings) also emit chemicals at higher rates until aged. Decay of these elevated VOC concentrations to normal constant-source levels can take weeks to months, depending on emission rates, surface areas of materials, and ventilation protocols. Renovation can cause similar increases of somewhat lower magnitude. The total VOC concentration in new office buildings at the time of initial occupancy can be 50 to 100 times that present in outdoor air (Sheldon et al. 1988a, 1988b). In new office buildings with adequate outdoor air ventilation, these ratios often fall to less than 5:1 after 4 or 5 months of aging. In older buildings with continuous, regular, and irregular emission sources, indoor/outdoor ratios of total VOCs may vary from nearly 1:1, when maximum amounts of outdoor air are being used in HVAC systems, to greater than 10:1 during winter and summer months, when minimum amounts of outdoor air are being used (Morey and Jenkins 1989; Morey and Singh 1991).

Although direct VOC emissions are usually the primary source of VOCs in a space, some materials act as sinks for emissions and then become secondary sources as they reemit adsorbed chemicals (Berglund et al. 1988). Adsorption may lower the peak concentrations achieved, but the subsequent desorption prolongs the presence of indoor air pollutants. Sink materials include carpet, fabric partitions, and other fleecy materials, as well as ceiling tiles and wallboard. The type of material and compound affects the rate of adsorption and desorption (Colombo et al. 1991). Indoor air quality models using empirically derived adsorption and desorption rates have been developed to predict the behavior of sinks. Experiments conducted in an IAQ test house confirmed the importance of sinks when trying to control the level of indoor VOCs (Tichenor et al. 1991). Longer periods of increased ventilation lessen sink and reemission effects. VanOsdell (1994) reviewed research studies of indoor VOCs as part of ASHRAE research project RP-674, and found more than 300 compounds had been identified indoors and that there was no agreement on a short list of key VOCs.

The large number of VOCs usually found indoors, and the impossibility of identifying all of them in samples, led to the concept of **total VOC (TVOC)**. Some researchers have used TVOC to represent the sum of all detected VOCs. TVOC concentrations are often reported as everything detected in the air by analysis methods such as photoionization detectors (PID) or flame ionization detectors (FID). Therefore, all methods for TVOC determination are intrinsically of low to moderate accuracy because of variations in detector response to different classes of VOCs. Despite the limitations, TVOC can be useful, and is widely used for mixed-contaminant atmospheres. Both theoretical and practical limitations of the TVOC approach have been discussed (Hodgson 1995; Otson and Fellin 1993). Wallace et al. (1991) showed that individual VOC concentrations in homes and buildings are 2 to 5 times those of outdoors, and personal TVOC exposures resulting from normal daily activities were estimated to be 2 to 3 times greater than general indoor air concentrations.

Personal activities frequently bring individuals close to air contaminant sources. In addition, exposure from contaminated air jets depends on the complex airflows around the body, including the main flow stream, air turbulence, and obstructions nearby (Rodes et al. 1991). Individual organic compounds seldom exceed 0.05 mg/m^3 (50 μg/m^3) in indoor air. An upper extreme average concentration of TVOCs in normally occupied houses is approximately 20 mg/m^3.

The Large Buildings Study by the U.S. EPA (Brightman et al. 1996) developed the VOC sample target list shown in Table 10 to identify common VOCs that should be measured. Lists of common indoor VOCs prepared by other organizations are similar.

Because chlorofluorocarbons (CFCs) are hydrocarbons with some hydrogen atoms replaced by chlorine and fluorine atoms, they are classed as organic chemicals. They have been widely used as heat transfer gases in refrigeration applications, blowing agents, and propellants in aerosol products (including medications and consumer products) and as expanders in plastic foams. Exposure to CFCs and HCFCs occurs mainly through inhalation, and can occur from leaks in refrigeration equipment or during HVAC maintenance.

Volatile organic compounds produced by microorganisms as they grow are referred to as **microbial VOCs (MVOCs)**. Of particular interest are those emitted by fungi contaminating water-damaged buildings. Most MVOCs produced are mixtures of compounds that are common to many different species (as well as to industrial chemicals). However, there are also compounds specific to a particular genus or species. Analysis for MVOCs is generally by gas chromatography/mass spectrometry (GC/MS) with thermal desorption.

Table 10 VOCs Commonly Found in Buildings

Benzene	Styrene
m-, *p*-xylene	*p*-dichlorobenzene
1,2,4-trimethylbenzene	*n*-undecane
n-octane	*n*-nonane
n-decane	Ethyl acetate
n-dodecane	Dichloromethane
Butyl acetate	1,1,1-trichloroethane
Chloroform	Tetrachloroethylene
Trichloroethylene	Carbon disulfide
Trichlorofluoromethane	Acetone
Dimethyl disulfide	2-butanone
Methyl isobutyl ketone	Methyl tertiary butyl ether
Limonene	Naphthalene
α-,β-pinene	4-phenyl cyclohexene
Propane	Butane
2-butoxyethanol	Ethanol
Isopropanol	Phenol
Formaldehyde	Siloxanes
Toluene	

Source: Brightman et al. (1996).

MVOCs include a variety of chemical classes including alcohols, ketones, organic acids, and heterocyclic compounds, among others. Many have extremely low odor thresholds. Examples in Table 5 include acetone, ethanol, 3-methyl 1-butanol, 2-hexanone, and 3-methyl furan. More information on MVOCs can be found in Horner and Miller (2003).

It is not known whether exposure to MVOCs is likely to cause adverse health effects on its own, because MVOCs are not likely to comprise the sole exposure. However, many are quite objectionable and may be irritating. At the very least, they may indicate a potential mold growth problem in a building, and often cause complaints about air quality. Note that MVOCs are distinct from fungal mycotoxins, which are nonvolatile and therefore nonodorous.

Controlling Exposure to VOCs

Much can be done to reduce building occupants' exposures to emissions of VOCs from building materials and products and to prevent outdoor VOCs from being brought into buildings. In most cases, the economically and technically preferred hierarchy for indoor contaminant reduction is (1) source control, (2) dilution with ventilation air, and (3) air filtration. With regard to VOCs, source control includes substitution of alternative products, isolation of contamination sources, and local ventilation. This requires careful planning; specifications; and selection, modification, and treatment of products, as well as special installation procedures and proper ventilation system operation. This chapter provides only a brief survey of contaminant control. Chapter 45 of the 2007 *ASHRAE Handbook—HVAC Applications* provides a full discussion.

Levin (1989, 1991) wrote extensively about designing new buildings for good indoor air quality, with an emphasis on **source control**. Reducing VOC emissions by careful selection and installation of building materials and furnishings is a very effective strategy for controlling IAQ. Advances in product formulation and emission testing are leading to products claimed to be low-polluting, nontoxic, and environmentally safe. Requiring submission of emission testing data by manufacturers for building products, whether for a new building, for a building renovation or remodeling, or for substitution of a consumable product (housekeeping supplies), is becoming accepted practice. Prudent practice and administrative control should be used to minimize generation of VOCs in indoor air during occupied hours whenever possible. Consider scheduling use of volatile organic products, housekeeping activities, and pesticide application when occupant density is lowest. VOC-containing supplies should be stored in well-ventilated areas other than HVAC mechanical rooms or plenums.

Local exhaust ventilation is another source control approach effective for controlling known, unavoidable point emissions sources. It is prudent to isolate office machines (e.g., photocopiers, laser printers), food service equipment (e.g., microwave ovens, coffee makers), and work areas (e.g., graphics and photographic labs) using dedicated local exhaust systems that vent to the outside and away from outdoor air intakes. Eliminating sources of VOCs (or air cleaning at the source) prevents them from becoming a problem.

Ventilation has traditionally been considered the primary means for controlling indoor VOC contaminants. General-ventilation **dilution** is routinely applied in buildings in which major sources are under control and no special measures are required; it is an effective way to control normal constant-emission sources present in buildings, assuming no unusually strong sources and good-quality ventilation air. Compliance with ASHRAE *Standards* 62.1 and 62.2 should satisfy indoor dilution ventilation requirements. Provision for large amounts of outdoor ventilation air affects the size of the heating/cooling system.

Gas-phase air **filtration** has been applied to control industrial gaseous contaminants for many years. Application of this technology to nonindustrial building HVAC is of interest for improving IAQ, whether it is to provide ventilation without the need to use more outdoor air or to help clean poor-quality outdoor air. ASHRAE *Standard* 62.1 provides a calculation procedure for application of air cleaners to reduce the required outdoor air ventilation rates where such a strategy is economically attractive. Additional information is provided in Chapter 45 of the 2007 *ASHRAE Handbook—HVAC Applications*. Activated carbon and potassium permanganate-impregnated alumina are effective and widely available adsorbents that can be used, based on the contaminant mixture present (Liu and Huza 1995; Muller and England 1995; VanOsdell and Sparks 1995). Portable air cleaners with sorbent sections are only marginally effective (Shaughnessy et al. 1994) because of low sorbent mass and inadequate mixing to clean all the air in a room. Photocatalytic reactors are able to destroy VOCs (Peral et al. 1997). These reactors use ultraviolet light and a catalytic surface, such as titanium dioxide, to convert organic pollutants to CO_2 and water.

VOC control in buildings begins before building occupancy. A good ventilation protocol during construction, renovation, or remodeling includes using building ventilation systems to flush the work area with extra outdoor air or setting up a single-pass (100% outdoor air) system during and after these activities, continuing until enough time has passed to lower emitted concentrations to near background. This practice minimizes sink effects and secondary emissions.

INORGANIC GASES

Several inorganic gases are of concern because of their effects on human health and comfort and on materials. These include carbon dioxide, carbon monoxide, oxides of nitrogen, sulfur dioxide, ozone, and ammonia. Most have both outdoor and indoor sources.

Carbon dioxide (CO_2) or **carbonic acid** gas is produced by human respiration. It is not normally considered to be a toxic air contaminant, but it can be a simple asphyxiant (by oxygen displacement) in confined spaces such as submarines. CO_2 is found in the ambient environment at 330 to 370 ppm. Levels in the urban environment may be higher because of emissions from gasoline and, more often, diesel engines. Measurement of CO_2 in occupied spaces has been widely used to evaluate the amount of outdoor air supplied to indoor spaces. In ASHRAE *Standard* 62.1, a level of 1000 to 1200 ppm (or 700 ppm above outdoor air) has been suggested as being representative of delivery rates of 7.5 L/s per person of outside air when CO_2 is measured at equilibrium concentrations and at occupant densities of 10 people per 100 m^2 of floor space. Measuring CO_2 level before it has reached steady-state conditions can lead to inaccurate conclusions about the amount of outside air used in the building.

Carbon monoxide (CO) is an odorless, colorless, and tasteless gas produced by incomplete combustion of hydrocarbons. It is a common ambient air pollutant and is very toxic. Common indoor sources of CO include gas stoves, kerosene lanterns and heaters, mainstream and sidestream tobacco smoke, woodstoves, and unvented or improperly vented combustion sources. Building makeup air intakes located at street level or near parking garages can entrain CO from automobiles and carry it to the indoor environment. Air containing carbon monoxide may also enter the building directly if the indoor space is at negative pressure relative to outdoors. Major predictors of indoor CO concentrations are indoor fossil fuel sources, such as gas furnaces, hot water heaters, and other combustion appliances; attached garages; and weather inversions. Carbon monoxide can be a problem in indoor ice skating arenas where gasoline- or propane-powered resurfacing machines are used. Levels in homes only rarely exceed 5 ppm. In one sample of randomly selected homes, 10% failed a backdrafting test (Conibear et al. 1996). Under backdrafting conditions, indoor CO sources may contribute to much higher, dangerous levels of CO.

Oxides of nitrogen (NO_x) indoors result mainly from cooking appliances, pilot lights, and unvented heaters. Sources generating CO often produce nitric oxide (NO) and nitrogen dioxide (NO_2), as well. Underground or attached parking garages can also contribute to indoor concentrations of NO_x. An unvented gas cookstove contributes approximately 0.025 ppm of nitrogen dioxide to a home. During cooking, 0.2 to 0.4 ppm peak levels may be reached (Samet et al. 1987). Ambient air pollution from vehicle exhausts in urban locations can contribute NO_x to the indoor environment in makeup air. Oxides of nitrogen also are present in mainstream and sidestream tobacco smoke; NO and NO_2 are of most concern.

Sulfur dioxide (SO_2) can result from emissions of kerosene space heaters; combustion of fossil fuels such as coal, heating oil, and gasoline; or burning any material containing sulfur. Thus, sulfur dioxide is a common ambient air pollutant in many urban areas.

Ozone (O_3) is a photochemical oxidant that forms at ground level when hydrocarbons and oxides of nitrogen react with ultraviolet radiation in sunlight to produce photochemical smog. Ozone can be emitted by electrical or coronal discharges from office equipment, including laser printers and photocopiers. It can also form when ozone-generating devices (often marketed as portable air cleaners and ionizers) are used in the indoor environment (Esswein and Boeniger 1994).

Ammonia (NH_3) is a colorless gas with a sharp and intensely irritating odor. It is lighter than air and readily soluble in water. Ammonia is itself a refrigerant and fertilizer and is also a high-volume industrial chemical used in the manufacture of a wide variety of products (e.g., nitrogen fertilizers, nitric acid, synthetic fibers, explosives, and many others). In nature, ammonia is an animal metabolism byproduct formed by decomposition of uric acid. As an indoor air contaminant, ammonia generally originates in synthetic cleaners and as a metabolic byproduct.

Controlling Exposures to Inorganic Gases

As for VOCs, the three methods of control for inorganic gaseous contaminants are (1) source control, (2) ventilation control, and (3) removal by filters. **Source control** for inorganic gases involves limiting (or removing) the source of the problem; for example, gas cookstoves should not be used for space heating (often a problem in low-income urban residences). Another example is limiting automobile parking around building makeup air intakes. Source control should always be the primary consideration, but is not always feasible when there are many diverse contaminant sources, as in new buildings where the building itself or building furnishings may be the prime contributors to the problem.

Ventilation control involves bringing clean dilution air into the occupied space or directly exhausting air contaminants at the point of generation. As for VOCs, ASHRAE *Standard* 62.1 provides guidance in applying the ventilation rate and indoor air quality procedures for ventilation control.

Where neither source control nor ventilation control appear likely to control gaseous air contaminants, air **filtration** should be investigated. Gas-phase air filtration involves dry scrubbing to remove contaminants by adsorption onto several sorbents, including granular activated carbon (GAC), potassium permanganate impregnated alumina (PIA), and impregnated carbon filters. Coutant et al. (1994), Liu and Huza (1995), Muller and England (1995), and VanOsdell and Sparks (1995) review various filtration procedures.

No single type of media is effective for the broad range of indoor gaseous contaminants. Granular activated charcoal is generally an agent of choice for nonpolar compounds, and is suitable for O_3 and NO_2, but not for SO_x and NO, for which permanganate-impregnated alumina is more appropriate.

Ozone can be best controlled by local exhaust ventilation for demonstrated sources of ozone, such as photocopiers and equipment creating coronal discharges. Routine cleaning of attractor plates in an electrostatic precipitator and ensuring adequate prefilters can reduce ozone generation and limit arcing in this type of particle removal equipment. Using ozone-generating devices for air cleaning or purification has not been documented as a prudent means of air contaminant control, considering the potential health effects of the use of ozone indoors (Esswein and Boeniger 1994). The Food and Drug Administration (FDA 1990) specifically limits the use of ozone in concentrations greater than 50 ppb in areas intended for continuous occupancy, such as residences, offices, schools, and hospitals.

Carbon monoxide exposure control strategies primarily involve identification and control of CO emissions directly at their source. Underground parking garages are normally vented directly to the outdoors, with exhaust fans usually controlled by CO sensors. Local exhaust ventilation is an appropriate and effective control in most occupational cases. For example, automobile repair garages commonly use a tailpipe exhaust extension to control CO exposure of mechanics working in the repair bays. In ice skating rinks, electric or lower-emitting natural-gas-powered resurfacing machines can be used. Relocating building makeup air intakes or limiting vehicle access are reasonable means to prevent entrainment of automobile exhausts into building HVAC systems.

Carbon monoxide, however, is a common pollutant of ambient air. As a result, direct control by dilution may not be feasible if ambient air is heavily contaminated with CO. Diesel or natural gas may be substituted for gasoline engines to reduce CO where specific sources from engine exhaust are identified or are a concern. Adequate venting of any combustion sources is critical to prevent CO build-up indoors. CO may be monitored by a properly calibrated, direct-reading CO monitor, colorimetric indicator tubes, or passive diffusion sampling badges.

Exposure controls for carbon dioxide are generally limited to situations where exposure concentrations are expected to exceed 3 to 5%. CO_2 is not encountered at levels harmful to humans in the ambient environment. It is normally present at 300 to 500 ppm, and slightly higher in congested cities. With the exception of an intentional or accidental CO_2 "dump" from a fire suppression system or in a dry ice manufacturing facility, CO_2 is not encountered in significant concentrations that require specific engineering controls. However, CO_2 is denser than air and can persist for some time in low areas such as trenches, depressions, and pits. This characteristic creates a simple asphyxiation hazard, because CO_2 displaces oxygen.

AIR CONTAMINANTS BY SOURCE

Some air contaminants are commonly encountered and addressed as groups or single components originating from a source or having other common characteristics. Outdoor air contaminants, though widely varied between locations, are regulated uniformly across the United States and can usefully be considered as a separate category worthy of common consideration. Radioactive air contaminants also vary widely, but they too have many commonalities. This section addresses the commonalities and characteristics of air contaminants as a function of source or their common characteristics.

OUTDOOR AIR CONTAMINANTS

The total amount of suspended particulate matter in the atmosphere can influence the loading rate of air filters and their selection. The amount of soot that falls in U.S. cities ranges from 7 to 70 Mg/km^2 per month. Soot fall data indicate effectiveness of smoke abatement and proper combustion methods, and serve as comparative indices of such control programs. However, the data are of limited value to the ventilating and air-conditioning engineer, because they do not accurately represent airborne soot concentrations.

Concentrations of outdoor pollutants are important, because they may determine indoor concentrations in the absence of indoor sources. Table 11 presents typical urban outdoor concentrations of some common gaseous pollutants. Higher levels might be found if the building under consideration were located near a major source of contamination, such as a power plant, a refinery, or a sewage treatment plant. Note that levels of sulfur dioxide and nitrogen dioxide, which are often attached to particles, may be reduced by about half by building filtration systems. Also, ozone is a reactive gas that can be significantly reduced by contact with ventilation system components (Weschler et al. 1989).

The U.S. Environmental Protection Agency identified several important outdoor contaminants as criteria pollutants. The list includes suspended particulate matter, lead particulate matter, ozone, nitrogen dioxide, sulfur dioxide, and carbon monoxide. Standards set for these contaminants are shown in Table 12, and levels measured at a large number of locations in the United States are published by the EPA each year (*Code of Federal Regulations* 40CFR50).

Daily concentrations of VOCs in outdoor air can vary drastically (Ekberg 1994). These variations derive from vehicle traffic density, wind direction, industrial emissions, and photochemical reactions.

Table 11 Typical Outdoor Concentrations of Selected Gaseous Air Pollutants

Pollutant	Typical Concentration, μg/m³	Pollutant	Typical Concentration, μg/m³
Acetaldehyde	20	Methylene chloride	2.4
Acetone	3	Nitric acid	6
Ammonia	1.2	Nitric oxide	10
Benzene	8	Nitrogen dioxide	51
2-butanone (MEK)	0.3	Ozone	40
Carbon dioxide	612 000	Phenol	20
Carbon monoxide	3000	Propane	18
Carbon disulfide	310	Sulfur dioxide	240
Carbon tetrachloride	2	Sulfuric acid	6
Chloroform	1	Tetrachloroethylene	2.5
Ethylene dichloride	10	Toluene	20
Formaldehyde	20	1,1,1-trichloroethane	4
n-heptane	29	Trichloroethylene	15
Mercury (vapor)	0.005	Vinyl chloride monomer	0.8
Methane	1100		
Methyl chloride	9	Xylene	10

Sources: Braman and Shelley (1980), Casserly and O'Hara (1987), Chan et al. (1990), Cohen et al. (1989), Coy (1987), Fung and Wright (1990), Hakov et al. (1987), Hartwell et al. (1985), Hollowell et al. (1982), Lonnemann et al. (1974), McGrath and Stele (1987), Nelson et al. (1987), Sandalls and Penkett (1977), Shah and Singh (1988), Singh et al. (1981), Wallace et al. (1985), and Weschler and Shields (1989).

Table 12 Primary Ambient Air Quality Standards for the United States

	Long-Term			Short-Term		
	Concentration		Averaging	Concentration		Averaging
Contaminant	μg/m³	ppm	Period	μg/m³	ppm	Period, h
Sulfur dioxide	80	0.03	1 year[b]	365	0.14	24[a]
Carbon monoxide				10,000	9	
				40,000	35	8[a]
						1[a]
Nitrogen dioxide	100	0.053	1 year[b]			
Ozone[c]				235	0.08	8
Total particulate (PM_{10})[d]				150		24
Total particulate ($PM_{2.5}$)[e]	15		1 year[b]			
Lead particulate	1.5		3 months			

Source: EPA (2008)
[a]Not to be exceeded more than once a year
[b]Annual arithmetic mean
[c]Standard is met when three-year average of fourth-highest daily maximum 8-h average ozone concentrations measured at each monitor in an area over each year is less than or equal to 0.08 ppm.
[d]PM_{10} = particulates below 10 μm diameter.
[e]$PM_{2.5}$ = particulates below 2.5 μm diameter.

INDUSTRIAL AIR CONTAMINANTS

Many industrial processes produce significant quantities of air contaminants in the form of dusts, fumes, smokes, mists, vapors, and gases. Particulate and gaseous contaminants are best controlled at the source, so that they are neither dispersed through the factory nor allowed to increase to toxic concentration levels. Dilution ventilation is much less effective than local exhaust for reducing contamination from point-source emissions, and is used for control only when sources are distributed and not amenable to capture by an exhaust hood. For sources generating high levels of contaminants, it may also be necessary to provide equipment that reduces the amount of material discharged to the atmosphere (e.g., a dust collector for particulate contaminants and/or a high-dwell-time gas-phase media bed for gaseous contaminants). Control methods are covered in Chapters 28 and 29 of the 2008 *ASHRAE Handbook—HVAC Systems and Equipment* and Chapters 30 and 45 of the 2007 *ASHRAE Handbook—HVAC Applications*.

Reduction of concentrations of all contaminants to the lowest level is not economically feasible. Absolute control of all contaminants cannot be maintained, and workers can assimilate small quantities of various toxic materials without injury. The science of industrial hygiene is based on the fact that most air contaminants become toxic only if their concentration exceeds a maximum allowable limit for a specified period. Allowable limits in industrial environments are covered in Chapter 10.

Although the immediately dangerous to life and health (IDLH) toxicity limit is rarely a factor in HVAC design, HVAC engineers should consider it when deciding how much recirculation is safe in a given system. Ventilation airflow must never be so low that the concentration of any gaseous contaminant could rise to the IDLH level. Another toxic effect that may influence design is loss of sensory acuity because of gaseous contaminant exposure. For example, high concentrations of hydrogen sulfide, which has a very unpleasant odor, effectively eliminate a person's ability to smell the gas. Carbon monoxide, which has no odor to alert people to its presence, affects psychomotor responses and could be a problem in working environments such as air traffic control towers and vehicle repair shops. Clearly, waste anesthetic gases should not be allowed to reach levels in operating suites such that the alertness of any of the personnel is affected. NIOSH recommendations are frequently based on such subtle effects.

NONINDUSTRIAL INDOOR AIR CONTAMINANTS

Indoor air quality in residences, offices, and other indoor, nonindustrial environments has become a widespread concern (NRC 1981; Spengler et al. 1982). Exposure to indoor pollutants can be as important as exposure to outdoor pollutants because a large portion of the population spends up to 90% of their time indoors and because indoor pollutant concentrations are frequently higher than corresponding outdoor contaminant levels.

Symptoms of exposure include coughing; sneezing; eye, throat, and skin irritation; nausea; breathlessness; drowsiness; headaches; and depression. Rask (1988) suggests that when 20% of a single building's occupants suffer such irritations, the structure is suffering from **sick building syndrome (SBS)**. Case studies of such occurrences have consisted of analyses of questionnaires submitted to building occupants, measurements of contaminant levels, or both. Some attempts to relate irritations to gaseous contaminant concentrations are reported (Berglund et al. 1986; Cain et al. 1986; Lamm 1986; Mølhave et al. 1982). The correlation of reported complaints with gaseous pollutant concentrations is not strong; many factors affect these less serious responses to pollution. In general, physical irritation does not occur at odor threshold concentrations.

Characterization of indoor air quality has been the subject of numerous recent studies. ASHRAE *Indoor Air Quality (IAQ) Conference Proceedings* discuss indoor air quality problems and some practical controls. ASHRAE *Standard* 62.1 addresses many indoor air quality concerns. Table 13 illustrates sources, levels, and indoor-to-outdoor concentration ratios of several contaminants found in indoor environments. Chapter 10 has further information on indoor health issues.

A knowledge of sources frequently present in different types of buildings can be useful when investigating the causes of SBS. Common nonindustrial indoor sources are discussed in some detail here. Technical advances allow generation rates to be measured for several of these sources. These rates are necessary inputs for design of control equipment; full details are given in Chapter 45 of the 2007 *ASHRAE Handbook—HVAC Applications*.

Building materials and **furnishing** sources have been well studied. Particleboard, which is usually made from wood chips bonded with a phenol-formaldehyde or other resin, is widely used in current construction, especially for mobile homes, carpet underlay, and case goods. These materials, along with ceiling tiles, carpeting, wall coverings, office partitions, adhesives, and paint finishes, emit formaldehyde and other VOCs. Latex paints containing mercury emit mercury vapor. Although emission rates for these materials decline steadily with age, the half-life of emissions is surprisingly long. Black and Bayer (1986), Mølhave et al. (1982), and Nelms et al. (1986) report on these sources.

Ventilation systems may be a source of VOCs (Mølhave and Thorsen 1990). The interior of the HVAC system can have large areas of porous material used as acoustical liner that can adsorb odorous compounds. This material can also hold nutrients and, with moisture, can become a reservoir for microorganisms. Microbial contaminants produce characteristic VOCs [microbial VOCs (MVOCs)] associated with their metabolism. Other HVAC components, such as condensate drain pans, fouled cooling coils, and some filter media, may support microbiological life. Deodorants, sealants, and encapsulants are also sources of VOCs in HVAC systems.

Equipment sources in commercial and residential spaces have generation rates that are usually substantially lower than in the industrial environment. Because these sources are rarely hooded, emissions go directly to the occupants. In commercial spaces, the chief sources of gaseous contaminants are office equipment, including dry-process copiers (ozone); liquid-process copiers (VOCs); diazo printers (ammonia and related compounds); carbonless copy paper (formaldehyde); correction fluids, inks, and adhesives (various VOCs); and

Table 13 Sources, Possible Concentrations, and Indoor-to-Outdoor Concentration Ratios of Some Indoor Contaminants

Pollutant	Sources of Indoor Pollution	Upper Possible Indoor Concentration*	I/O Concentration Ratio for Upper Concentration	Location
Carbon monoxide	Combustion equipment, engines, faulty heating systems	100 mg/m^3	>>1	Indoor ice rinks, homes, cars, vehicle repair shops, parking garages
Respirable particles	Stoves, fireplaces, cigarettes, condensation of volatiles, aerosol sprays, resuspension, cooking	100 to 500 μg/m^3	>>1	Homes, offices, cars, public facilities, bars, restaurants
Organic vapors	Combustion, solvents, resin products, pesticides, aerosol sprays, cleaning products	NA	>1	Homes, restaurants, public facilities, offices, hospitals
Nitrogen dioxide	Combustion, gas stoves, water heaters, gas-fired dryers, cigarettes, engines	200 to 1000 μg/m^3	>>1	Homes, indoor ice rinks
Sulfur dioxide	Heating system	20 μg/m^3	<1	Mechanical/furnace rooms
Total suspended particles (without smoking)	Combustion, resuspension, heating system	100 μg/m^3	1	Homes, offices, transportation, restaurants
Sulfate	Matches, gas stoves	5 μg/m^3	<1	Mechanical/furnace rooms
Formaldehyde	Insulation, product binders, pressed wood products	2 mg/m^3 (2000 μg/m^3)	>>1	Homes, schools, offices
Radon and progeny	Building materials, groundwater, soil	0.1 to 100 nCi/m^3	>>1	Homes, schools
Asbestos	Fireproofing	<10^6 fiber/m^3	1	Homes, schools, offices
Mineral and synthetic fibers	Carpets, clothes, rugs, furnishing materials, wallboard	NA	—	Homes, schools, offices
Carbon dioxide	Combustion appliances, humans, pets	9000 mg/m^3	>>1	Homes, schools, offices, hospitals, public facilities
Viable organisms	Humans, pets, rodents, insects, plants, fungi, humidifiers, air conditioners	NA	>1	Homes, hospitals, schools, offices, public facilities
Ozone	Electric arcing, electronic air cleaners, some copiers, and printers, some UV light sources	400 μg/m^3	<1 >1	Airplanes Offices, homes

Source: NRC (1981).
*Concentrations listed are only those reported indoors. Both higher and lower concentrations have been measured. No averaging times are given. NA indicates that it is not appropriate to list a concentration.

spray cans, cosmetics, and so forth (Miksch et al. 1982). Medical and dental activities generate pollutants from the escape of anesthetic gases (nitrous oxide and isoflurene) and from sterilizers (ethylene oxide). The potential for asphyxiation is always a concern when compressed gases are present, even if that gas is nitrogen. In residences, the main sources of equipment-derived pollutants are gas ranges, wood stoves, and kerosene heaters. Venting is helpful, but some pollutants escape into the occupied area. The pollutant contribution by gas ranges is somewhat mitigated by the fact that they operate for shorter periods than heaters. The same is true of showers, which can contribute to radon and halocarbon concentrations indoors.

Cleaning agents and **other consumer products** can act as contaminant sources. Commonly used liquid detergents, waxes, polishes, spot removers, and cosmetics contain organic solvents that volatilize slowly or quickly. Mothballs and other pest control agents emit organic vapors. Black and Bayer (1986), Knoeppel and Schauenburg (1989), and Tichenor (1989) report data on the release of these volatile organic compounds (VOCs). Field studies have shown that such products contribute significantly to indoor pollution; however, a large variety of compounds is in use, and few studies have been made that allow calculation of typical emission rates. Pesticides, both those applied indoors and those applied outdoors to control termites, also pollute building interiors.

Tobacco smoke is a prevalent and potent source of indoor air pollutants. Almost all tobacco smoke arises from cigarette smoking. **Environmental tobacco smoke (ETS)**, sometimes called secondhand smoke, is the aged and diluted combination of sidestream smoke (smoke from the lit end of a cigarette and smoke that escapes from the filter between puffs) and mainstream smoke (smoke exhaled by a smoker). Emission factors for ETS components, the ratio of ETS components to marker compounds, and apportionment of ETS components in indoor air are reported in the literature by Heavner et al. (1996), Hodgson et al. (1996), Martin et al. (1997), and Nelson et al. (1994).

Occupants, both humans and animals, emit a wide array of pollutants by breath, sweat, and flatus. Some of these emissions are conversions from solids or liquids within the body. Many volatile organics emitted are, however, reemissions of pollutants inhaled earlier, with the tracheobronchial system acting like a physical adsorber.

Floor dust, which typically contains much larger particles and fibers than the air, has been found to be a sink (adsorption medium) and secondary emission source for VOCs. Floor dust is a mixture of organic and inorganic particles, hair and skin scales, and textile fibers. The fiber portion of floor dust has been shown to contain 169 mg/kg TVOC, and the particle portion 148 mg/kg (Gyntelberg et al. 1994). These VOCs were correlated to the prevalence of irritative (sore throat) and cognitive (concentration problems) symptoms among building occupants. One hundred eighty-eight compounds were identified from thermal desorption of office dust at 121°C (Wilkins et al. 1993). Household dust was found to be similar in composition (Wolkoff and Wilkins 1994).

Contaminants from other sources include chloroform from water; tetrachloroethylene and 1,1,1-trichloroethane from cleaning solvents; methylene chloride from paint strippers, fresheners, cleaners, and polishers; α-pinene and limonene from floor waxes; and 1-methoxy-2-propanol from spray carpet cleaners. Formaldehyde, a major VOC, has many sources, but pressed-wood products appear to be the most significant.

FLAMMABLE GASES AND VAPORS

Use of flammable materials is widespread. Flammable gases and vapors (as defined in NFPA *Standard* 30) can be found in sewage treatment plants, sewage and utility tunnels, dry-cleaning plants, automobile garages, and industrial finishing process plants.

A flammable liquid's vapor pressure and volatility or rate of evaporation determine its ability to form an explosive mixture. These properties can be expressed by the **flash point**, which is the temperature to which a flammable liquid must be heated to produce a flash when a small flame is passed across the surface of the liquid. Depending on the test methods, either the open- or closed-cup flash point may be listed. The higher the flash point, the more safely the liquid can be handled. Liquids with flash points higher than 38°C are called **combustible**, whereas those under 38°C are described as **flammable**. Those with flash points less than 21°C should be regarded as highly flammable.

In addition to having a low flash point, the air/vapor or air/gas mixture must have a concentration in the flammable (explosive) range before it can be ignited. The **flammable (explosive) range** is the range between the upper and lower explosive limits, expressed as percent by volume in air. Concentrations of material above the higher range or below the lower range will not explode. Flashpoint and explosive range data for many chemicals are listed in the *Fire Protection Guide to Hazardous Materials*, published by the National Fire Protection Association (NFPA 2002). Data for a small number of representative chemicals are shown in Table 14.

In designing ventilation systems to control flammable gases and vapors, the engineer must consider the following:

Most safety authorities and fire underwriters prefer to limit concentrations to 20 to 25% of the lower explosive limit of a material. The resulting safety factor of 4 or 5 allows latitude for imperfections in air distribution and variations of temperature or mixture and guards against unpredictable or unrecognized sources of ignition. Operation at concentrations above the upper explosive limit should be allowed only in rare instances, and after taking appropriate precautions. Some guidance is provided in American Petroleum Institute documents. To reach the upper explosive limit, the flammable gas or vapor must pass through the active explosive range, in which any source of ignition can cause an explosion. In addition, a drop in gas concentration caused by unforeseen dilution or reduced evaporation rate may place a system in the dangerous explosive range.

In occupied places where ventilation is applied for proper health control, the danger of an explosion is minimized. In most instances, flammable gases and vapors are also toxic, and maximum allowable concentrations are far below the material's lower explosive limit (LEL). For example, proper ventilation for acetone vapors keeps the concentration below the occupational exposure limit of 500 ppm (0.05% by volume). Acetone's LEL is 2.5% by volume. Proper location of exhaust and supply ventilation equipment depends primarily on how a contaminant is given off and on other problems of the process, and secondarily on the relative density of flammable vapor.

If the specific density of the explosive mixture is the same as that of air, cross drafts, equipment movement, and temperature differentials may cause sufficient mixing to produce explosive concentrations and disperse these throughout the atmosphere. In reasonably still air, heavier-than-air vapors may pool at floor level. Therefore, the engineer must either provide proper exhaust and supply air patterns to control hazardous material, preferably at its source, or offset the effects of drafts, equipment movement, and convection currents by providing good distribution of exhaust and supply air for general dilution and exhaust. The intake duct should be positioned so that it does not bring in exhaust gases or emissions from ambient sources.

Adequate ventilation minimizes the risk of or prevents fires and explosions and is necessary, regardless of other precautions, such as elimination of the ignition sources, safe building construction, and the use of automatic alarm and extinguisher systems.

Chapter 30 of the 2007 *ASHRAE Handbook—HVAC Applications* gives more details about equipment for control of combustible materials. Some design, construction, and ventilation issues are also addressed by NFPA *Standard* 30.

Table 14 Flammable Limits of Some Gases and Vapors

Gas or Vapor	Flash Point, °C	Flammable Limits, % by Volume: Lower	Upper
Acetone	–17	2.5	12.8
Ammonia	Gas	15	28
Benzene (benzol)	–11	1.2	7.8
n-Butane	–32	1.9	8.5
Carbon disulfide	–30	1.3	50
Carbon monoxide	Gas	12.5	74
1,2-Dichloroethylene	2	5.6	12.8
Diethylether	–45	1.9	36
Ethyl alcohol	13	3.3	19
Ethylene	Gas	2.7	36
Gasoline	–43	1.4	7.6
Hydrogen	Gas	4.0	75
Hydrogen sulfide	Gas	4.3	44
Isopropyl alcohol	12	2.0	12.7
Methyl alcohol	11	6.0	36
Methyl ethyl ketone	–9	1.4	11.4
Natural gas (variable)	Gas	3.8 to 6.5	13 to 17
Naphtha	Less than –18	1.1	5.9
Propane	Gas	2.1	9.5
Toluene (toluol)	4	0.1	7.1
o-Xylene	32	0.9	6.7

COMBUSTIBLE DUSTS

Many organic and some mineral dusts can produce dust explosions (Bartnecht 1989). Explosive dusts are potential hazards whenever uncontrolled dust escapes, and often, a primary explosion results from a small amount of dust in suspension that has been exposed to a source of ignition. Explosibility limits for combustible dusts differ from those for flammable gases and flammable vapors because of the interaction between dust layers and suspended dust. In addition, the pressure and vibration created by an explosion can dislodge large accumulations of dust on horizontal surfaces, creating a larger secondary explosion.

For ignition, dust clouds require high temperatures and sufficient dust concentration. These temperatures and concentrations and the minimum spark energy can be found in Avallone and Baumeister (1987). Several methods can be used to prevent the ignition of dust material (Jaeger and Siwek 1999; Siwek 1997):

- Limit the temperature of deposited product.
- Avoid potentially explosive combustible substance/air mixtures.
- Introduce inert gas in the area to lower the oxygen volume content below the limiting oxygen concentration (LOC) or maximum allowable oxygen concentration (MOC), so that ignition of the mixture can no longer take place. Adding inert dusts (e.g., rock salt, sodium sulfate) also works; in general, inert dust additions of more than 50% by weight are necessary. It is also possible to replace flammable solvents and cleaning agents with nonflammable halogenated hydrocarbons or water, or flammable pressure transmission fluids with halocarbon oils.
- Avoid effective ignition sources: eliminate hot sources (hot surfaces or smoldering material) and sources of sparks or electrostatic discharge.

Proper exhaust ventilation design can also be used for preventing high-dust conditions. Forced ventilation allows use of greater amounts of air and selective air circulation in areas surrounding the equipment. Its use and calculation of the minimum volume flow rate for supply and exhaust air are subject to certain requirements, covered in Chapter 30 of the 2007 *ASHRAE Handbook—HVAC Applications*. Ventilation systems and equipment chosen must prevent dust pocketing inside the equipment. When local exhaust ventilation is used, separation equipment should be installed as close to the dust source as possible to prevent transport of dust in the exhaust system.

RADIOACTIVE AIR CONTAMINANTS

Radioactive contaminants (Jacobson and Morris 1977) can be particulate or gaseous, and are similar to ordinary industrial contaminants. Many radioactive materials would be chemically toxic if present in high concentrations; however, in most cases, the radioactivity necessitates limiting their concentration in air.

Most radioactive air contaminants affect the body when they are absorbed and retained. This is known as the **internal radiation hazard**. Radioactive particulates may settle to the ground, where they contaminate plants and eventually enter the food chain and the human body. Deposited material on the ground increases **external radiation exposure**. However, except for fallout from nuclear weapons or a serious reactor accident, such exposure is insignificant.

Radioactive air contaminants can emit alpha, beta, or gamma rays. Alpha rays penetrate poorly and present no hazard, except when the material is deposited inside or on the body. Beta rays are somewhat more penetrating and can be both an internal and an external hazard. Penetration of gamma rays depends on their energy, which varies from one type of radioactive element or isotope to another. Distinction should be made between the radioactive material itself and the radiation it gives off. Radioactive particles can be removed from air by devices such as HEPA and ULPA filters, and radioactive gases by impregnated carbon or alumina (radioactive iodine) and absorption traps, but the gamma radiation from such material can penetrate solid materials. This distinction is frequently overlooked. The amount of radioactive material in air is measured in becquerels per cubic metre (1 becquerel equals 2.702702×10^{-11} curies), and the dose of radiation from deposited material is measured in rads.

Radioactive materials present distinctive problems. High concentrations of radioactivity can generate enough heat to damage filtration equipment or ignite the material spontaneously. The concentrations at which most radioactive materials are hazardous are much lower than those of ordinary materials; as a result, special electronic instruments that respond to radioactivity must be used to detect these hazardous levels.

The ventilation engineer faces difficulty in dealing with radioactive air contamination because of the extremely low permissible concentrations for radioactive materials. For some sensitive industrial plants, such as those in the photographic industry, contaminants must be kept from entering the plant. If radioactive materials are handled inside the plant, the problem is to collect the contaminated air as close to the source as possible, and then remove the contaminant from the air with a high degree of efficiency, before releasing it to the outdoors. Filters are generally used for particulate materials, but venturi scrubbers, wet washers, and other devices can be used as prefilters to meet special needs.

Design of equipment and systems for control of radioactive particulates and gases in nuclear laboratories, power plants, and fuel-processing facilities is a highly specialized technology. Careful attention must be given to the reliability, as well as the contaminant-removal ability, of equipment under the special environmental stresses involved. Various publications of the U.S. Department of Energy can provide guidance in this field.

Radon

A major source of airborne radioactive exposure to the population comes from radon. Radon (Rn) is a naturally occurring, chemically inert, colorless, odorless, tasteless radioactive gas. It is produced from radioactive decay of radium, which is formed through several intermediate steps of decay of uranium and thorium. Radon is widely found in the natural environment, because uranium salt precursors are widespread. Radon-222 is the most common isotope of radon. Before it decays, radon can move limited distances through very small spaces, such as those between particles of soil and rock, and enter indoor environments (Nazaroff et al. 1988; Tanner 1980). Additional but secondary sources of indoor radon include groundwater (radon is quite soluble in water) and radium-containing building materials.

Radon gas enters a house or building primarily through cracks, joints, and other holes in concrete foundations; directly through porous concrete blocks; through joints and openings in crawlspace ceilings; and through leakage points in HVAC ductwork embedded in slab floors or located in crawlspaces. Pressure-driven flow is the dominant radon entry mechanism in houses with elevated radon concentrations (Nazaroff et al. 1987). Pressure differences are caused by several factors, including thermal stack effect, wind, and operation of HVAC equipment. Rn can also diffuse directly through substructural materials (e.g., concrete). The diffusive Rn entry rate is often a significant portion of the total entry rate in houses with low Rn concentrations.

Measurement. Indoor concentrations of radon can vary hourly, daily, and seasonally, in some cases by as much as a factor of 10 to 20 on a daily basis (Turk et al. 1990). Thus, long-term measurements (3 months to 1 year) made during normal home activities generally provide more reliable estimates of the average indoor concentration than do short-term measurements. Two techniques widely used for homeowner measurements are the short-term charcoal canister (up to 7 days), and the long-term alpha-track methods (90 days to 1 year). Generally, short-term measurements should only be used as a screening technique to determine whether long-term measurement is necessary. When interpreting results, consider the great uncertainties in measurement accuracy with these devices (up to 50% at the radon levels typically found in homes), as well as the natural variability of radon concentrations.

Ideally, long-term measurements should be the basis for decisions on installation of radon mitigation systems, and short-term measurements should only be used as a screening method to identify buildings with Rn concentrations that are very high, justifying immediate remedial action. In practice, short-term measurements at the time a building is sold are the basis for most decisions about remedial action.

Typical Levels. The outdoor radon concentration is about 15 Bq/m^3 (0.4 pCi/L). The annual average concentration of radon in U.S. homes is about 46 Bq/m^3 (1.25 pCi/L) (EPA 1989). Although several sources of radon may contribute to the annual indoor average, pressure-driven flow of soil gas is the principal source for elevated concentrations; nonmunicipal water supplies can be a source of elevated indoor radon, but only in isolated instances.

Control. Exposure to indoor Rn may be reduced by (1) inhibiting Rn entry into the building or (2) removing or diluting Rn decay products in indoor air. The most effective and energy-efficient control measures are generally those that reduce Rn entry rates (Henschel 1993). One of the most common effective techniques is active subslab depressurization, in which a fan and piping system draw soil gas from beneath the slab and exhaust the gas outside. This technique reduces or reverses the pressure gradient that normally draws soil gas and Rn into the building and often reduces indoor Rn concentrations by a large factor (e.g., 5 to 10). Passive control methods such as Rn-resistant construction techniques and/or passive stack subslab depressurization systems are also used; however, their performance is not well characterized, and average reductions in Rn concentrations may be 50% or less. Sealing cracks and joints in slab floors improves performance of subslab depressurization systems. Sealing by itself is often not very effective in reducing indoor Rn.

In houses with crawlspaces, active (fan-forced) or passive crawlspace ventilation is often effective in maintaining low indoor Rn concentrations, although other techniques are also used (Henschel 1988, 1993).

SOIL GASES

The radioactive gas radon (Rn) is the best-known soil gas, but other gaseous contaminants may enter buildings along with radon from surrounding soil. Methane from landfills has reached explosive levels in some buildings. Potentially toxic or carcinogenic VOCs, including chlorinated hydrocarbons in the soil because of spills, improper disposal, leaks from storage tanks, and disposal in landfills, can also be transported into buildings (Garbesi and Sextro 1989; Hodgson et al. 1992; Kullman and Hill 1990; Wood and Porter 1987). Pesticides applied to soil beneath or adjacent to houses have also been detected in indoor air (Livingston and Jones 1981; Wright and Leidy 1982). The broad significance of health effects of exposure to these soil contaminants is not well understood.

Although soil gases generally have limited effects when diffusion is the primary mechanism driving entry, there are situations where advective processes are dominant. In such cases, effects on indoor air can be significant (Adomait and Fugler 1997). Pressure-driven airflow produced by thermal or wind drivers on the building affects entry of soil gas into the structure. Soil permeability to vapors, soil gas concentration, and soil-to-building pressure differential are the largest factors influencing indoor concentrations of these gases.

Techniques that reduce Rn entry from soil should also be effective in reducing entry of other soil gases into buildings. Other approaches (e.g., increasing ventilation in the building, such as by slightly opening a window) may help reduce house negative pressure (created by stack effect) with respect to soil gas pressure. Increased ventilation should be used with caution, and only after establishing for the house in question that it will not increase negative pressure where the soil gas enters.

REFERENCES

ACGIH. 1989. *Guidelines for the assessment of bioaerosols in the indoor environment*. American Conference of Governmental Industrial Hygienists, Cincinnati, OH.

ACGIH. Annually. *TLVs® and BEIs®: Threshold limit values for chemical substances and physical agents*. American Conference of Governmental Industrial Hygienists, Cincinnati, OH.

ACGIH. 2001. *Air sampling instruments*, 9th ed. American Conference of Governmental Industrial Hygienists, Cincinnati, OH.

Adomait, M. and D. Fugler. 1997. Method to evaluate soil gas VOC influx into houses. *Proceedings of the Air and Waste Management Association's 90th Annual Meeting*, Toronto.

AIHA. 1996. *Field guide for the determination of biological contaminants in environmental samples*. American Industrial Hygiene Association, Fairfax, VA.

ASHRAE. 1998. *Legionellosis position paper*.

ASHRAE. 2007. Method of testing general ventilation air-cleaning devices for removal efficiency by particle size. ANSI/ASHRAE *Standard* 52.2-2007.

ASHRAE. 2007. Ventilation for acceptable indoor air quality. ANSI/ASHRAE *Standard* 62.1-2007.

ASTM. 2007. Practice for continuous sizing and counting of airborne particles in dust-controlled areas and clean rooms using instruments capable of detecting single sub-micrometer and larger particles. ASTM *Standard* F50-07. American Society for Testing and Materials, West Conshohocken, PA.

ATC. 1990. *Technical assistance document for sampling and analysis of toxic organic compounds in ambient air*. Environmental Protection Agency, Research Triangle Park, NC.

Avallone, E.A. and T. Baumeister. 1987. *Marks' standard handbook for mechanical engineers*. McGraw-Hill, New York.

Bartnecht, W. 1989. *Dust explosions: Course, prevention, protection*. Springer-Verlag, Berlin.

Berglund, B., U. Berglund, and T. Lindvall. 1986. Assessment of discomfort and irritation from the indoor air. *IAQ '86: Managing Indoor Air for Health and Energy Conservation*, pp. 138-149. ASHRAE.

Berglund, B., I. Johansson, and T. Lindvall. 1988. Adsorption and desorption of organic compounds in indoor materials. In *Healthy Buildings '88*, vol. 3, pp. 299-309. B. Berglund and T. Lindvall, eds. Swedish Council for Building Research, Stockholm.

Black, M.S. and C.W. Bayer. 1986. Formaldehyde and other VOC exposures from consumer products. *IAQ '86: Managing Indoor Air for Health and Energy Conservation*. ASHRAE.

Braman, R.S. and T.J. Shelley. 1980. *Gaseous and particulate and ammonia and nitric acid concentrations. Columbus, Ohio area—Summer 1980*. PB 81-125007. National Technical Information Service, Springfield, VA.

Brightman, H.S., S.E. Womble, E.L. Ronca, and J.R. Girman. 1996. Baseline information on indoor air quality in large buildings (BASE '95). *Proceedings of Indoor Air '96*, vol. 3, pp. 1033-1038.

Budavi, S., ed. 1996. *The Merck index*, 12th ed. Merck and Company, White Station, NJ.

Cain, W.S., L.C. See, and T. Tosun. 1986. Irritation and odor from formaldehyde chamber studies, 1986. *IAQ '86: Managing Indoor Air for Health and Energy Conservation*. ASHRAE.

Casserly, D.M. and K.K. O'Hara. 1987. Ambient exposures to benzene and toluene in southwest Louisiana. *Paper* 87-98.1. Air and Waste Management Association, Pittsburgh, PA.

CFR. Annually. National primary and secondary ambient air quality standards. 40CFR50. *Code of Federal Regulations,* U.S. Government Printing Office, Washington, D.C.

CFR. Annually. Protection of environment: Requirements for preparation, adoption, and submittal of implementation plans. 40CFR51.100. *Code of Federal Regulations*, Government Printing Office, Washington, D.C.

Chan, C.C., L. Vanier, J.W. Martin, and D.T. William. 1990. Determination of organic contaminants in residential indoor air using an adsorption-thermal desorption technique. *Journal of the Air and Waste Management Association* 40(1):62-67.

Cohen, M.A., P.B. Ryan, Y. Yanigisawa, J.D. Spengler, H. Ozkaynak, and P.S. Epstein. 1989. Indoor/outdoor measurements of volatile organic compounds in the Kanawha Valley of West Virginia. *Journal of the Air Pollution Control Association* 39(8):1986-1993.

Colombo, A., M. DeBortoli, H. Knöppel, H. Schauenburg, and H. Vissers. 1991. Small chamber tests and headspace analysis of volatile organic compounds emitted from household products. *Indoor Air* 1:13-21.

Conibear, S., S. Geneser, and B.W. Carnow. 1996. Carbon monoxide levels and sources found in a random sample of households in Chicago during the 1994-1995 heating season. *Proceedings of IAQ '95*, pp. 111-118. ASHRAE.

Coutant, R.W., G.F. Ward, C.W. Spicer, et al. 1994. Control of NO_2 and nitrogen acids using alkaline-impregnated carbon filters. *Proceedings of IAQ '94*, pp. 139-145. ASHRAE.

Coy, C.A. 1987. Regulation and control of air contaminants during hazardous waste site redemption. *Paper* 87-18.1. Air and Waste Management Association, Pittsburgh, PA.

Ekberg, L.E. 1994. Outdoor air contaminants and indoor air quality under transient conditions. *Indoor Air* 4:189-196.

EPA. 1979. *Toxic substances control act chemical substance inventory*, vol. I-IV. Environmental Protection Agency, Office of Toxic Substances, Washington, D.C.

EPA. 1982. *Air quality criteria for particulate matter and sulfur*. EPA-600/8-82-029b.

EPA. 1989. *Radon and radon reduction technology*. EPA-600/9-89/006a, 1:4-15.

EPA. 2008. Integrated science assessment for particulate matter. *First External Review Draft*. Environmental Protection Agency, Office of Research and Development, Washington, D.C. Available at http://cfpub.epa.gov/ncea/cfm/recordisplay.cfm?deid=201805.

EPA. 2008. *National ambient air quality standards (NAAQS)*. Environmental Protection Agency, Washington, D.C. Available at http://epa.gov/air/criteria.html.

Esswein, E.J. and M.F. Boeniger. 1994. Effect of an ozone generating air purifying device on reducing concentrations of formaldehyde in air. *Applied Occupational Environmental Hygiene* 9(2).

FDA. 1990. *Maximum acceptable level of ozone*. 21CFR Ch. 1. Sec. 801.415: 24-25. U.S. Food and Drug Administration, Washington, D.C.

Foarde, K.K. 1999. Determine the efficiency of antimicrobial treatments of fibrous air filters. *Final Report*, ASHRAE Research Project RP-909.

Foarde, K.K., D.W. VanOsdell, J.J. Fischer, and K.E. Lee. 1994. Investigate and identify indoor allergens and biological toxins that can be removed by filtration. *Final Report*, ASHRAE Research Project RP-760.

Fung, K. and B. Wright. 1990. Measurement of formaldehyde and acetaldehyde using 2-4 dinitrophenylhydrazine-impregnated cartridges. *Aerosol Science and Technology* 12(1):44-48.

Garbesi, K. and R.G. Sextro. 1989. Modeling and field evidence of pressure-driven entry of soil gas into a home through permeable below-grade walls. *Environment Science and Technology* 23:1481-1487.

GSA. 1992. Airborne particulate cleanliness classes in cleanrooms and clean zones. *Federal Standard* 209E. U.S. General Services Administration, Washington, D.C.

Gyntelberg, F., P. Suadicami, J.W. Nielsen, P. Skov, O. Valbjorn, T. Nielsen, T.O. Schneider, O. Jorgenson, P. Wolkoff, C. Wilkins, S. Gravesen, and S. Nom. 1994. Dust and the sick-building syndrome. *Indoor Air* 4:223-238.

Hakov, R.J., J. Kemlis, and C. Ruggeri. 1987. Volatile organic compounds in the air near a regional sewage treatment plant in New Jersey. *Paper* 87-95.1. Air and Waste Management Association, Pittsburgh, PA.

Hartwell, T.D., J.H. Crowder, L.S. Sheldon, and E.D. Pellizzari. 1985. Levels of volatile organics in indoor air. *Paper* 85-30B.3. Air and Waste Management Association, Pittsburgh, PA.

Health Canada. 2004. *Fungal contamination in public buildings: Health effects and investigation methods.* Health Canada, Ottawa.

Heavner, D.L., W.T. Morgan, and M.W. Ogden. 1996. Determination of volatile organic compounds and respirable particulate matter in New Jersey and Pennsylvania homes and workplaces. *Environment International* 22:159-183.

Henschel, D.B. 1988. *Radon reduction techniques for detached houses—Technical guidance*, 2nd ed. EPA/625/5-87/019.

Henschel, D.B. 1993. *Radon reduction techniques for existing detached houses—Technical guidance*, 3rd ed. EPA/625/R-93/011.

Hewson, E.W., W.W. Payne, A.L. Cole, J.B. Harrington, Jr., and W.R. Solomon. 1967. Air pollution by ragweed pollen. *Journal of the Air Pollution Control Association* 17(10):651.

Hodgson, A.T. 1995. A review and a limited comparison of methods for measuring total volatile organic compounds in indoor air. *Indoor Air* 5(4):247.

Hodgson, A.T., K. Garbesi, R.G. Sextro, and J.M. Daisey. 1988. Transport of volatile organic compounds from soil into a residential basement. *Paper* 88-95B.1, *Proceedings of the 81st Annual Meeting of the Air Pollution Control Association*. Also LBL *Report* 25267.

Hodgson, A.T., K. Garbesi, R.G. Sextro, and J.M. Daisey. 1992. Soil gas contamination and entry of volatile organic compounds into a house near a landfill. *Journal of the Air and Waste Management Association* 42:277-283.

Hodgson, A.T., J.M. Daisey, K.R.R. Mahanama, J.T. Brinke, and L.E. Alevantis. 1996. Use of volatile tracers to determine the contribution of environmental tobacco smoke to concentrations of volatile organic compounds in smoking environments. *Environment International* 22:295-307.

Hollowell, C.D., R.A. Young, J.V. Berk, and S.R. Brown. 1982. Energy-conserving retrofits and indoor air quality in residential housing. *ASHRAE Transactions* 88(l):875-893.

Horner, W.E. and J.D. Miller. 2003. Microbial volatile organic compounds with emphasis on those arising from filamentous fungal contaminants of buildings (RP-1072). *ASHRAE Transactions* 109(1):215-231.

ISO. 1999. Cleanrooms and associated controlled environments—Part 1: Classification of air cleanliness. *Standard* 14644-1. International Organization for Standardization, Geneva.

Jacobson, A.R. and S.C. Morris. 1977. The primary pollutants, viable particulates, their occurrence, sources and effects. In *Air pollution*, 3rd ed., p. 169. Academic Press, New York.

Jaeger, N. and R. Siwek. 1999. Prevent explosions of combustible dusts. *Chemical Engineering Progress* 95(6).

Jaenicke, R. 1998. Biological aerosols in the atmosphere. Plenary Lecture, Fifth International Aerosol Conference, Edinburgh, Scotland.

Knoeppel, H. and H. Schauenburg. 1989. Screening of household products for the emission of volatile organic compounds. *Environment International* 15:413-418.

Kullman, G.J. and R.A. Hill 1990. Indoor air quality affected by abandoned gasoline tanks. *Applied Occupational Environmental Hygiene* 5:36-37.

Lamm, S.H. 1986. Irritancy levels and formaldehyde exposures in U.S. mobile homes. In *Indoor air quality in cold climates*, pp. 137-147. Air and Waste Management Association, Pittsburgh, PA.

Levin, H. 1989. Building materials and indoor air quality. *Occupational Medicine: State of the Art Reviews—Problem Buildings* 4(4):667-694.

Levin, H. 1991. Critical building design factors for indoor air quality and climate: current status and predicted trends. *Indoor Air* 1(1):79-92.

Lide, D.R., ed. 1996. *Handbook of chemistry and physics*, 77th ed. CRC Press, Boca Raton, FL.

Liu, R. and M.A. Huza. 1995. Filtration and indoor air quality: A practical approach. *ASHRAE Journal* 37(2):18-23.

Livingston, J.M. and C.R. Jones. 1981. Living area contamination by chlordane used for termite treatment. *Bulletin of Environmental Contaminant Toxicology* 27:406-411.

Lodge, J.E., ed. 1988. *Methods of air sampling and analysis*, 3rd ed. Lewis, Chelsea, MD.

Lonnemann, W.A., S.L. Kopczynski, P.E. Darley, and P.D. Sutterfield. 1974. Hydrocarbon composition of urban air pollution. *Environmental Science and Technology* 8(3):229-235.

Macher, J., ed. 1999. *Bioaerosols: Assessment and control.* American Conference of Governmental Industrial Hygienists, Cincinnati, Ohio.

Martin, P., D.L. Heavner, P.R. Nelson, K.C. Maiolo, C.H. Risner, P.S. Simmons, W.T. Morgan, and M.W. Ogden. 1997. Environmental tobacco smoke (ETS): A market cigarette study. *Environment International* 23(1):75-90.

McGrath, T.R. and D.B. Stele. 1987. Characterization of phonemic odors in a residential neighborhood. *Paper* 87-75A.5. Air and Waste Management Association, Pittsburgh, PA.

Miksch, R.R., C.D. Hollowell, and H.E. Schmidt. 1982. Trace organic chemical contaminants in office spaces. *Atmospheric Environment* 8: 129-137.

Mølhave, L. and M. Thorsen. 1990. A model for investigations of ventilation systems as sources for volatile organic compounds in indoor climate. *Atmospheric Environment* 25A:241-249.

Mølhave, L., L. Anderson, G.R. Lundquist, and O. Nielson. 1982. Gas emission from building materials. *Report* 137. Danish Building Research Institute, Copenhagen.

Morey, P.R. and B.A. Jenkins. 1989. What are typical concentrations of fungi, total volatile organic compounds, and nitrogen dioxide in an office environment. *Proceedings of IAQ '89, The Human Equation: Health and Comfort*, pp. 67-71. ASHRAE.

Morey, P.R. and J. Singh. 1991. Indoor air quality in non-industrial occupational environments. In *Patty's industrial hygiene and toxicology*, 4th ed.

Muller, C.O. and W.G. England. 1995. Achieving your indoor air quality goals: Which filtration system works best? *ASHRAE Journal* 27(2):24-32.

Nagda, N.L. and H.E. Rector. 1983. *Guidelines for monitoring indoor-air quality.* EPA 600/4-83-046. Environmental Protection Agency, Research Triangle Park, NC.

Nazaroff, W.W., S.R. Lewis, S.M. Doyle, B.A. Moed, and A.V. Nero. 1987. Experiments on pollutant transport from soil into residential basements by pressure-driven air flow. *Environment Science and Technology* 21:459.

Nazaroff, W.W., B.A. Moed, and R.G. Sextro. 1988. Soil as a source of indoor radon: Generation, migration and entry. In *Radon and its decay products in indoor air*, pp. 57-112. Wiley, New York.

Nelms, L.H., M.A. Mason, and B.A. Tichenor. 1986. The effects of ventilation rates and product loading on organic emission rates from particleboard. *IAQ '86: Managing Indoor Air for Health and Energy Conservation*, pp. 469-485. ASHRAE.

Nelson, E.D.P., D. Shikiya and C.S. Liu. 1987. Multiple air toxins exposure and risk assessment in the south coast air basin. *Paper* 87-97.4. Air and Waste Management Association, Pittsburgh, PA.

Nelson, P.R., P. Martin, M.W. Ogden, D.L. Heavner, C.H. Risner, K.C. Maiolo, P.S. Simmons, and W.T. Morgan. 1994. Environmental tobacco smoke characteristics of different commercially available cigarettes. *Proceedings of the Fourth International Aerosol Conference*, vol. 1, pp. 454-455.

NFPA. 2002. *The fire protection guide to hazardous materials*, 13th ed. National Fire Protection Association, Quincy, MA.

NFPA. 2003. Flammable and combustible liquids code. NFPA *Standard* 30. National Fire Protection Association, Quincy, MA.

NIOSH. 1977. *NIOSH manual of sampling data sheets*. U.S. Department of Health and Human Services, National Institute for Occupational Safety and Health, Washington, D.C.

NIOSH. 1994. *NIOSH manual of analytical methods*, 4th ed. M.E. Cassellini and P.F. O'Connor, eds. DHHS (NIOSH) *Publication* 94-113.

NNI. 2008. *The scale of things—Nanometers and more.* National Nanotechnology Institute. http://www.nano.gov/html/facts/The_scale_of_things.html.

NRC. 1981. *Indoor pollutants*. National Research Council, National Academy Press, Washington, D.C.

OSHA. 1995. *OSHA computerized information system chemical sampling information*. U.S. Government Printing Office, Washington, D.C.

Otson, R. and P. Fellin. 1993. TVOC measurements: Relevance and limitations. *Proceedings of Indoor Air '93*, vol. 2, pp. 281-285.

Owen, M.K., D.S. Ensor, and L.E. Sparks. 1992. Airborne particle sizes and sources found in indoor air. *Atmospheric Environment* 26A(12):2149-2162.

Peral, J., X. Domenech, and D.F. Ollis. 1997. Heterogeneous photocatalysis for purification, decontamination and deodorization of air. *Journal of Chemical Technology and Biotechnology* 70:117-140.

Rask, D. 1988. Indoor air quality and the bottom line. *Heating, Piping and Air Conditioning* 60(10).

Riley, W.J., T.E. McCone, A.C.K. Lai and W.W. Nazaroff 2002. Indoor particulate matter of outdoor origin: Importance of size-dependent removal mechanisms. *Environmental Science & Technology* 36:200-207.

Rodes, C.E. and J. W. Thornburg. 2004. Breathing zone exposure assessment. Ch. 5 in *Aerosols handbook: Measurement, dosimetry, and health effects*. L.S. Ruzer and N.H. Harley, eds. CRC Press, Boca Raton, FL.

Rodes, C.E., R.M. Kamens, and R.W. Wiener. 1991. The significance and characteristics of the personal activity cloud on exposure assessment methods for indoor contaminants. *Indoor Air* 2:123-145.

Samet, J.M., M.C. Marbury, and J.D. Spengler. 1987. Health effects and sources of indoor air pollution. *American Review of Respiratory Disease* 136:1486-1508.

Sandalls, E.J. and S.A. Penkett. 1977. Measurements of carbonyl sulfide and carbon disulphide in the atmosphere. *Atmospheric Environment* 11: 197-199.

Sax, N.I. and R.J. Lewis, Sr. 1988. *Dangerous properties of industrial materials*, 6th ed, 3 vol. Van Nostrand Reinhold, New York.

Scala, G.F. 1963. A new instrument for the continuous measurement of condensation nuclei. *Analytical Chemistry* 35(5):702.

Shah, J.J. and H.B. Singh. 1988. Distribution of volatile organic chemicals in outdoor and indoor air. *Environmental Science and Technology* 22(12):1391-1388.

Shaughnessy, R.J., E. Levetin, J. Glocker, and K.L. Sublette. 1994. Effectiveness of portable indoor air cleaners: Sensory testing results. *Indoor Air* 4:179-188.

Sheldon, L., R.W. Handy, T. Hartwell, R.W. Whitmore, H. Zelon, and E.D. Pellizzari. 1988a. *Indoor air quality in public buildings*, vol. I. EPA/600/S6-88/009a. Environmental Protection Agency, Washington, D.C.

Sheldon, L., H. Zelon, J. Sickles, C. Easton, T. Hartwell, and L. Wallace. 1988b. *Indoor air quality in public buildings*, vol. II. EPA/600/S688/009b. Environmental Protection Agency, Research Triangle Park, NC.

Singh. H.B., L.J. Salas, A. Smith, R. Stiles, and H. Shigeishi. 1981. *Atmospheric measurements of selected hazardous organic chemicals*. PB 81200628. National Technical Information Service, Springfield, VA.

Siwek, R. 1997. Dusts: Explosion protection. In *Perry's chemical handbook for chemical engineering*, 7th ed. McGraw-Hill, New York.

Solomon, W.R. and K.P. Mathews. 1978. Aerobiology and inhalant allergens. In *Allergy: Principles and practices*. Mosley, St. Louis.

Spengler, J., C. Hallowell, D. Moschandreas, and O. Fanger. 1982. Environment international. *Indoor air pollution*. Pergamon Press, Oxford, U.K.

Tanner, A.B. 1980. Radon migration in the ground: A supplementary review. In *Natural radiation environment*, vol. III. U.S. Department of Commerce, NTIS, Springfield, VA.

Task Group on Lung Dynamics. 1966. Deposition and retention models for internal dosimetry of the human respiratory tract. *Health Physics* 12: 173-207.

Taylor, D.G., R.E. Kupel, and J.M. Bryant. 1977. *Documentation of the NIOSH validation tests*. U.S. National Institute for Occupational Safety and Health, Washington, D.C.

Teeuw, K.B., C.M.J.E. Vandenbroucke-Grauls, and J. Verhoef. 1994. Airborne gram-negative bacteria and endotoxin in sick building syndrome. *Archives of Internal Medicine* 154:2339-2345.

Tichenor, B.A. 1989. Measurement of organic compound emissions using small test chambers. *Environment International* 15:389-396.

Tichenor, B.A., G. Guo, J.E. Dunn, L.E. Sparks, and M.A. Mason. 1991. The interaction of vapour phase organic compounds with indoor sinks. *Indoor Air* 1:23-35.

Tong, Y. and B. Lighthart. 1999. Diurnal distribution of total and culturable atmospheric bacteria at a rural site. *Aerosol Science and Technology* 30:246-254.

Traynor, G.W. 1987. Field monitoring design considerations for assessing indoor exposures to combustion pollutants. *Atmospheric Environment* 21(2):377-383.

Turk, B.H., R.J. Prill, D.T. Grimsrud, B.A. Moed, and R.G. Sextro. 1990. Characterizing the occurrence, sources and variability of radon in Pacific Northwest homes. *Journal of the Air and Waste Management Association* 40:498-506.

VanOsdell, D.W. 1994. Evaluation of test methods for determining the effectiveness and capacity of gas-phase air filtration equipment for indoor air applications—Phase I: Literature review and test recommendations (RP-674). *ASHRAE Transactions* 100(2):511-523.

VanOsdell, D.W. and L.E. Sparks. 1995. Carbon absorption for indoor air cleaning. *ASHRAE Journal* 27(2):34-40.

Verschueren, K. 1996. *Handbook of environmental data on organic chemicals*, 3rd ed. Van Nostrand Reinhold, New York.

Wallace, L. 1996. Indoor particles: A review. *Journal of the Air Waste Management Association* 46:98-126.

Wallace, L.A., E.D. Pellizzari, T.D. Hartwell, C.M. Sparacino, L.S. Sheldon, and H. Zelon. 1985. Personal exposures, indoor-outdoor relationships, and breath levels of toxic air pollutants measured for 355 persons in New Jersey. *Atmospheric Environment* 19:1651-1661.

Wallace, L.A., E. Pellizzari, and C. Wendel. 1991. Total volatile organic concentrations in 2700 personal, indoor, and outdoor air samples collected in the US EPA Team Studies. *Indoor Air* 4:465-477.

Weschler, C.J. and H.C. Shields. 1989. The effects of ventilation, filtration, and outdoor air on the composition of indoor air at a telephone office building. *Environment International* 15:593-604.

Weschler, C.J., H.C. Shields, and D.V. Naik. 1989. Indoor ozone exposures. *Journal of the Air Pollution Control Association* 39:1562-1568.

Whitby, K.T. 1978. The physical characteristics of sulfur aerosols. *Atmospheric Environment* 12:135-159.

WHO. 1989. Indoor air quality: Organic pollutants. *Euro Report and Studies* 111. World Health Organization, Regional Office for Europe, Copenhagen.

Wilkins, C.K., P. Wolkoff, F. Gyntelberg, P. Skov, and O. Valbjørn. 1993. Characterization of office dust by VOCs and TVOC release—Identification of potential irritant VOCs by partial least squares analysis. *Indoor Air* 3:283-290.

Willeke, K. and P.A. Baron, eds. 1993. *Aerosol measurement—Principles, techniques and applications*. Van Nostrand Reinhold, New York.

Wolkoff, P. and C.K. Wilkins. 1994. Indoor VOCs from household floor dust: Comparison of headspace with desorbed VOCs; method for VOC release determination. *Indoor Air* 4:248-254.

Wood, J.A. and M.L. Porter. 1987. Hazardous pollutants in class II landfills. *Journal of the Air Pollution Control Association* 37:609-615.

Wright, C.G. and R.B. Leidy. 1982. Chlordane and heptachlor in the ambient air of houses treated for termites. *Bulletin of Environmental Contaminant Toxicology* 28:617-623.

BIBLIOGRAPHY

ACGIH. 1985. *Particle size-selective sampling in the workplace*. American Conference of Governmental Industrial Hygienists, Cincinnati, OH.

ASHRAE. 2007. Designation and safety classification of refrigerants. ANSI/ASHRAE *Standard* 34-2007.

ASTM. 1990. *Biological contaminants in indoor environments*. STP 1071. American Society for Testing and Materials, West Conshohocken, PA.

Barbaree, J.M., B.S. Fields, J.C. Feeley, G.W. Gorman, and W.T. Martin. 1986. Isolation of protozoa from water associated with a Legionellosis outbreak and demonstration of intracellular multiplication of *Legionella pneumophila*. *Applied Environmental Microbiology* 51:422-424.

Burge, H.A. 1995. *Bioaerosols*. Lewis, Chelsea, MA.

Code of Federal Regulations. Occupational safety and health standards. 29CFR1900. *Code of Federal Regulations*, U.S. Government Printing Office, Washington, D.C. Revised annually.

Fliermans, C.B. 1985. Ecological niche of *Legionella pneumophila*. *Critical Reviews of Microbiology* 11:75-116.

Milton, D.K., R.J. Gere, H.A. Feldman, and I.A. Greaves. 1990. Endotoxin measurement: Aerosol sampling and application of a new limulus method. *American Industrial Hygiene Association Journal* 51:331.

Wilson, W.E. and H.H. Suh. 1997. Fine particles and coarse particles: Concentration relationships relevant to epidemiological studies. *Journal of the Air & Waste Management Association* 47(12).

CHAPTER 12

ODORS

VARIOUS factors make odor control an important consideration in ventilation engineering: (1) contemporary construction methods result in buildings that allow less air infiltration through the building envelope; (2) indoor sources of odors associated with modern building materials, furnishings, and office equipment have increased; (3) outdoor air is often polluted; and (4) energy costs encourage lower ventilation rates at a time when requirements for a relatively odor-free environment are greater than ever.

Since Yaglou et al.'s (1936) classic studies, the philosophy behind ventilation of nonindustrial buildings has mainly been to provide indoor air that is acceptable to occupants. Air is evaluated by the olfactory sense, although the general chemical sense, which is sensitive to irritants in the air, also plays a role.

This chapter reviews how odoriferous substances are perceived. Chapter 45 of the 2007 *ASHRAE Handbook—HVAC Applications* covers control methods. Chapter 10 of this volume has more information on indoor environmental health.

ODOR SOURCES

Outdoor sources of odors include automotive and diesel exhausts, hazardous waste sites, sewage treatment plants, compost piles, refuse facilities, printing plants, refineries, chemical plants, and many other stationary and mobile sources. These sources produce both inorganic compounds (e.g., ammonia and hydrogen sulfide) and volatile organic compounds (VOCs), including some that evaporate from solid or liquid particulate matter. Odors emitted by outdoor sources eventually enter the indoor environment.

Indoor sources also emit odors. Sources include tobacco products, bathrooms and toilets, building materials (e.g., adhesives, paints, caulks, processed wood, carpets, plastic sheeting, insulation board), consumer products (e.g., food, toiletries, cleaning materials, polishes), hobby materials, fabrics, and foam cushions. In offices, offset printing processes, copiers, and computer printers may produce odors. Electrostatic processes may emit ozone. Humans emit a wide range of odorants, including acetaldehyde, ammonia, ethanol, hydrogen sulfide, and mercaptans.

Mildew and other decay processes often produce odors in occupied spaces (home and office), damp basements, and ventilation systems (e.g., from wetted air-conditioning coils and spray dehumidifiers).

Chapter 45 of the 2007 *ASHRAE Handbook—HVAC Applications* gives further information on contaminant sources and generation rates.

SENSE OF SMELL

Olfactory Stimuli

Organic substances with relative molecular masses greater than 300 are generally odorless. Some substances with relative molecular masses less than 300 are such potent olfactory stimuli that they can be perceived at concentrations too low to be detected with direct-reading instruments. Trimethylamine, for example, can be recognized as a fishy odor by a human at a concentration of about 10^{-4} ppm.

Table 1 shows **odor detection threshold concentrations** for selected compounds. The **threshold limit value** (TLV) is the concentration of a compound that should have no adverse health consequences if a worker is regularly exposed for 8 h periods (ACGIH, revised annually). Table 1 also includes the ratio of the TLV to the odor threshold for each compound. For ratios greater than 1, most occupants can detect the odor and leave the area long before the compound becomes a health risk. As the ratio increases, the safety factor provided by the odor also increases. Table 1 is not a comprehensive list of the chemicals found in indoor air. AIHA (1989) and EPA (1992) list odor thresholds for selected chemicals.

Olfactory sensitivity often makes it possible to detect potentially harmful substances at concentrations below dangerous levels so that they can be eliminated. Foul-smelling air is often assumed to be

Table 1 Odor Thresholds, ACGIH TLVs, and TLV/Threshold Ratios of Selected Gaseous Air Pollutants

Compound	Odor Threshold,[a] ppmv	TLV,[b] ppmv	Ratio
Acetaldehyde	0.067	25-C	360
Acetone	62	500	8.1
Acetonitrile	1600	20	0.013
Acrolein	1.8	0.1-C	0.06
Ammonia	17	25	1.5
Benzene	61	0.5	0.01
Benzyl chloride	0.041	1	24
Carbon tetrachloride	250	5	0.02
Chlorine	0.08	0.5	6
Chloroform	192	10	0.05
Dioxane	12	20	1.7
Ethylene dichloride	26	10	0.4
Hydrogen sulfide	0.0094	10	1064
Methanol	160	200	1.25
Methylene chloride	160	50	0.3
Methyl ethyl ketone	16	200	12.5
Phenol	0.06	5	83
Sulfur dioxide	2.7	2	0.74
Tetrachloroethane	7.3	1	0.14
Tetrachloroethylene	47	25	0.5
Toluene	1.6	20	13
Trichloroethylene	82	10	0.1
Xylene (isomers)	20	100	5

Sources: ACGIH (1998), AIHA (1989).
[a]All thresholds are detection thresholds (ED_{50}).
[b]All TLVs are 8 h time-weighted averages, except those shown with -C, which are 15 min ceiling values.

The preparation of this chapter is assigned to TC 2.3, Gaseous Air Contaminants and Gas Contaminant Removal Equipment.

unhealthy. In reality, however, there is little correlation between odor perception and toxicity, and there is considerable individual variation in the perception of pleasantness/unpleasantness of odors. When symptoms such as nausea, headache, and loss of appetite are caused by an unpleasant odor, it may not matter whether the air is toxic but whether the odor is perceived to be unpleasant, associated with an unpleasant experience, or simply felt to be out of appropriate context. The magnitude of the symptoms is related to the magnitude of the odor, but even a room with a low but recognizable odor can make occupants uneasy. Several papers review sensory irritation and its relation to indoor air pollution (Cain and Cometto-Muñiz 1995; Cometto-Muñiz and Cain 1992; Cometto-Muñiz et al. 1997; Shams Esfandabad 1993).

Anatomy and Physiology

The **olfactory receptors** lie in the **olfactory cleft**, which is high in the nasal cavity. About five million olfactory **neurons** (a small cluster of nerve cells inside the nasal cavity above the bridge of the nose) each send an **axon** (an extension of the neuron) into the olfactory bulb of the brain. Information received from the receptors is passed to various central structures of the brain (e.g., olfactory cortex, hippocampus, amygdala). One sniff of an odorant can often evoke a complex, emotion-laden memory, such as a scene from childhood.

The surrounding nasal tissue contains other diffusely distributed nerve endings of the trigeminal nerve that also respond to airborne vapors. These receptors mediate the chemosensory responses such as tickling, burning, cooling, and, occasionally, painful sensations that accompany olfactory sensations. Most odorous substances at sufficient concentration also stimulate these nerve endings.

Olfactory Acuity

The olfactory acuity of the population is normally distributed. Most people have an average ability to smell substances or to respond to odoriferous stimuli, a few people are very sensitive or hypersensitive, and a few others are insensitive, including some who are totally unable to smell (**anosmic**). The olfactory acuity of an individual varies with the odorant.

Hormonal factors, which often influence emotional states, can modulate olfactory sensitivity. Although the evidence is not uniformly compelling, research has found that (1) the sensitivity of females varies during the menstrual cycle, reaching a peak just before and during ovulation (Schneider 1974); (2) females are generally more sensitive than males, but this difference only emerges around the time of sexual maturity (Koelega and Koster 1974); (3) sensitivity is altered by some diseases (Schneider 1974); and (4) various hormones and drugs (e.g., estrogen, alcohol) alter sensitivity (Engen et al. 1975; Schneider 1974).

Other factors that may affect olfactory perception include the individual's olfactory acuity, the magnitude of flow rate toward olfactory receptors, temperature, and relative humidity. Olfactory acuity can also vary with age (Stevens et al. 1989; Wysocki and Gilbert 1989), genetics (Wysocki and Beauchamp 1984), exposure history (Dalton and Wysocki 1996; Wysocki et al. 1997), and disease or injury (Cowart et al. 1993, 1997). Humans are able to perceive a large number of odors, yet untrained individuals are able to name only a few (Ruth 1986).

Individuals who are totally unable to detect odors are relatively rare (Cowart et al. 1997). A more common occurrence is an inability to detect one or a very limited number of odors, a condition known as **specific anosmia**. Although the huge number of possible chemicals makes for an untestable hypothesis, it has been posited that most, if not all, individuals have a specific anosmia to one or more compounds (Wysocki and Beauchamp 1984). The fact that individuals with specific anosmias have normal olfactory acuity for all other odors suggests that such anosmias may be caused by genetic differences.

In olfactory science, **adaptation** refers to decreased sensitivity or responsiveness to an odor after prolonged exposure. This exposure can selectively impair the perception of the exposure odorant, but there are also examples of cross-adaptation, where exposure to one odorant can result in adaptation to other odors as well. Adaptation can occur in the short term, where perception of a room's odor begins to fade within seconds of entering the room (Cometto-Muñiz and Cain 1995; Pierce et al. 1996). With long-term adaptation, an individual who habitually returns to the same environment does not smell odors that are quite discernible to a naive observer. This effect appears to shift both the threshold and the **suprathreshold** (stimuli above the threshold level) response to the odor (Dalton and Wysocki 1996). This is an important phenomenon for indoor air quality (IAQ) personnel to be aware of because it is often one of the biggest reasons for variations in detectability or response in real-world environments and makes the choice of test population or panelists for air quality evaluations a critical one.

FACTORS AFFECTING ODOR PERCEPTION

Humidity and Temperature

Temperature and humidity can both affect the perception of odors. Cain et al. (1983) reported that a combination of high temperature (25.5°C) and high humidity exacerbates odor problems. Berglund and Cain (1989) found that air was generally perceived to be fresher and less stuffy with decreasing temperature and humidity. Fang et al. (1998a, 1998b) and Toftum et al. (1998) found little or no increase in odor intensity with increasing enthalpy (temperature and humidity), but reported a very significant decrease in odor acceptability with increasing enthalpy.

Not all researchers have supported these findings. Kerka and Humphreys (1956) reported a decrease in odor intensity with increasing humidity. Berg-Munch and Fanger (1982) found no increase in odor intensity with increasing temperature (23 to 32°C). Clausen et al. (1985) found no significant change in odor intensity with increasing relative humidity (30% to 80%).

Although the findings are not homogeneous, they do show that temperature and humidity can act together to affect one's perception of odors. Air that is cooler and drier is generally perceived to be fresher and more acceptable even if odor intensity is not affected.

Sorption and Release of Odors

Because furnishings and interior surfaces absorb (and later desorb) odors during occupancy, spaces frequently retain normal occupancy odor levels long after occupancy has ceased. This is observed when furnaces or radiators, after a long shutdown, are heated at winter start-up and when evaporator coils warm up. The rate of desorption can be decreased by decreasing temperature and relative humidity, and increased (as for cleaning) by the reverse.

Environmental tobacco smoke may desorb from surfaces long after smoking has taken place. This phenomenon has caused many hotels to establish nonsmoking rooms.

Where the odor source is intrinsic to the materials (as in linoleum, paint, rubber, and upholstery), reducing the relative humidity decreases the rate of odor release. Quantitative values should not be used without considering the sorption/desorption phenomenon.

Emotional Responses to Odors

There can be considerable variation between individuals regarding the perceived pleasantness or unpleasantness of a given odor. Responses to odors may be determined by prior experiences and can include strong emotional reactions. This is because one of the brain structures involved in the sense of smell is the **amygdala**, a regulator of emotional behaviors (Frey 1995). Some IAQ complaints can involve emotional responses completely out of proportion to the concentration of the odorant or the intensity of the odor it produces.

Two theories describe physiological reasons for these strong responses. One of these is **kindling**, in which repeated, intermittent stimuli amplify nerve responses. The other is **response facilitation**, in which an initial stimulus perceived as strong is facilitated (becomes greater) rather than adapted to (Frey 1995).

Because of this emotional aspect, IAQ complaints involving odors can be very difficult to solve, especially if they are coming from a few sensitized individuals. It is important to respond quickly to complaints to minimize the risk of kindling or response facilitation.

ODOR SENSATION ATTRIBUTES

Odor sensation has four components or attributes: detectability, intensity, character, and hedonic tone.

Detectability (or **threshold**) is the minimum concentration of an odorant that provokes detection by some predetermined segment of the population. Two types of thresholds exist: detection and recognition.

The **detection threshold** is the lowest level that elicits response by a segment of the population. If that segment is 50%, the detection threshold is denoted by ED_{50}. **Recognition threshold** is the lowest level at which a segment of the population can recognize a given odor. Thresholds can be attributed to 100%, which includes all olfactory sensitivities, or to 10%, which includes only the most sensitive segment of the population. Threshold values are not physical constants, but statistical measurements of best estimates.

Intensity is a quantitative aspect of a descriptive analysis, stating the degree or magnitude of the perception elicited. Intensity of the perceived odor is, therefore, the strength of the odoriferous sensation. Detection threshold values and, most often, odor intensity determine the need for indoor odor controls.

Character defines the odor as similar to some familiar smell (e.g., fishy, sour, flowery). **Hedonics**, or the hedonic tone of an odor, is the degree to which an odor is perceived as pleasant or unpleasant. Hedonic judgments include both a *category* judgment (pleasant, neutral, unpleasant) and a *magnitude* judgment (very unpleasant, slightly pleasant).

Important questions are

- What is the minimum concentration of odorant that can be detected?
- How does perceived odor magnitude grow with concentration above the threshold?

No universal method has been accepted to measure either the threshold or perceived magnitude of the odor above threshold. However, guidelines and conventions simplify the choice of methods.

Detectability

Perception of weak odoriferous signals is probabilistic: at one moment odor may be perceptible, and at the next moment it may not. Factors affecting this phenomenon include moment-to-moment variability in the number of molecules striking the olfactory receptors, variability in which of the receptors are stimulated, concentration of the odor, the individual's style of breathing, and the individual's previous experience with the odor. The combined effect of these factors may prevent an individual from perceiving an odor during the entire time of the stimulus. During odor evaluation, dilution to detection or recognition threshold values allows determination of the largest number of dilutions that still allows half of the panelists to detect or recognize the odor.

Determination of Odor Thresholds. Odor threshold testing is over a century old. The process is complex, and several different methods are used. Partly because of variations in measurement techniques, reported threshold values can vary by several orders of magnitude for a given substance. To minimize variation caused by experimental techniques, a standard set of criteria has been developed for the panel, presentation apparatus, and presentation method (AIHA 1989; EPA 1992).

The **panel** should

- Include at least six members per group.
- Be selected based on odor sensitivity. Factors to be considered include anosmia, pregnancy, drug use, and smoking.
- Be calibrated to document individual and group variability.

Considerations for the **presentation apparatus** include

- Vapor modality: choice of a gas/air mixture, water vapor, or other substance.
- Diluent: choice of diluent (e.g., air, nitrogen), how it is treated, and what its source is.
- Presentation mode: delivery systems can be nose ports, vents into which the head is inserted, flasks, or whole rooms.
- Analytic measurement of odorant concentration.
- System calibration: flow rate should be approximately 0.05 L/s; face velocity should be low enough to be barely perceptible to the panelists.

Criteria for the **presentation method** include

- Threshold type: detection or recognition.
- Concentration presentation: this must take adaptation into account. Presenting ascending concentrations or allowing longer periods between concentrations helps avoid adaptation.
- Number of trials: test/retest reliability for thresholds is low. Increasing the number of trials helps correct for this.
- Forced-choice procedure: panelists must choose between the stimuli and one or two blanks. This helps eliminate false positive responses.
- Concentration steps: odorant should be presented successively at concentrations no more than three times the preceding one.

For more details regarding psychophysical procedures, ways to sample odoriferous air, handling samples, means of stimulus presentation, and statistical procedures, consult ASTM (1996).

Intensity

Psychophysical Power Law. The relation between **perceived odor magnitude** ***S*** and **concentration** ***C*** conforms to a power function:

$$S = kC^n \tag{1}$$

where

S = perceived intensity (magnitude) of sensation
k = characteristic constant
C = odorant concentration
n = exponent of psychophysical function (slope on a log-log scale)

This exemplifies the psychophysical power law, also called **Stevens' law** (Stevens 1957). In the olfactory realm, $n < 1.0$. Accordingly, a given percentage change in odorant concentration causes a smaller percentage change in perceived odor magnitude.

Scaling Methods. There are various ways to scale perceived magnitude, but a **category scale**, which can be either number- or word-categorized, is common. Numerical values on this scale do not reflect ratio relations among magnitudes (e.g., a value of 2 does not represent a perceived magnitude twice as great as a value of 1). Table 2 gives four examples of category scales.

Although category scaling procedures can be advantageous in the field, **ratio scaling** is used frequently in the laboratory (Cain and Moskowitz 1974). Ratio scaling requires observers to assign numbers proportional to perceived magnitude. For example, if the observer is instructed to assign the number 10 to one concentration and a subsequently presented concentration seems three times as strong, the observer calls it 30; if another seems half as strong, the observer assigns it 5. This procedure, called **magnitude estimation**,

Table 2 Examples of Category Scales

Number Category		Word Category	
Scale I	**Scale II**	**Scale I**	**Scale II**
0	0	None	None at all
1	1	Threshold	Just detectable
2	2.5	Very slight	Very mild
3	5	Slight	Mild
4	7.5	Slight-moderate	Mild-distinct
5	10	Moderate	Distinct
6	12.5	Moderate-strong	Distinct-strong
7	15	Strong	Strong

Source: Meilgaard et al. (1987).

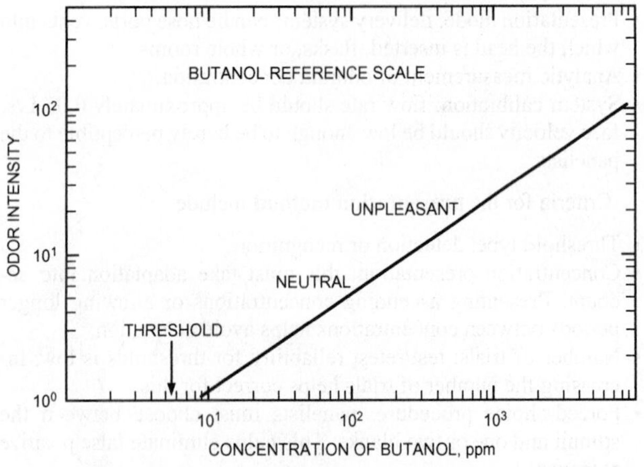

Fig. 1 Standardized Function Relating Perceived Magnitude to Concentration of 1-Butanol
(Moskowitz et al. 1974)

was used to derive the power function for butanol (Figure 1). Ratio scaling techniques allow for such relationships because they require subjects to produce numbers to match perceived sensations in which the numbers emitted reflect the ratio relations among the sensations.

The **labeled magnitude scale** is a hybrid of category and ratio scales (Green et al. 1996). This scale is intended to yield ratio-level data with a true zero and an orderly relationship among the scale values, such that any stimulus can be expressed as being proportionately more or less intense than another. Because it allows subjects to use natural-language descriptors to scale perceived experience, it often requires less training than ratio scales and produces absolute intensity estimates of perceived sensation (Figure 2).

A fourth way to measure suprathreshold odor intensity is to **match the intensity of odorants**. An observer can be given a concentration series of a matching odorant (e.g., 1-butanol) to choose the member that matches most closely the intensity of an *unknown* odorant. The matching odorant can be generated by a relatively inexpensive olfactometer such as that shown in Figure 3. Figure 4 shows, in logarithmic coordinates, functions for various odorants obtained by matching (Dravnieks and Laffort 1972). The left-hand ordinate expresses intensity in terms of concentration of butanol, and the right-hand ordinate expresses intensity in terms of perceived magnitude. The two ordinates are related by the function in Figure 1, the standardized function for butanol. The matching method illustrated here has been incorporated into ASTM *Standard* E544.

Character

The quality or character of an odor is difficult to assess quantitatively. A primary difficulty is that odors can vary along many dimensions. One way to assess quality is to ask panelists to judge the similarity between a test sample and various reference samples, using a five-point category scale. For some applications, reference

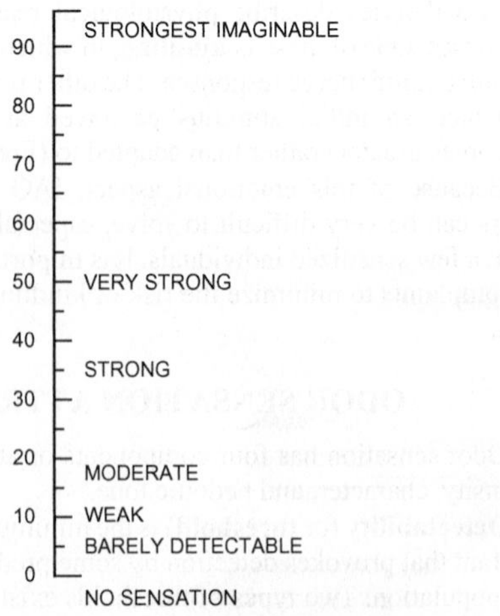

Subjects use a cursor (on a computer screen) or a pencil to mark the location on the scale that represents their judgment of intensity. They do not see numbers, only labels, and can place the mark anywhere on the scale.

Fig. 2 Labeled Magnitude Scale

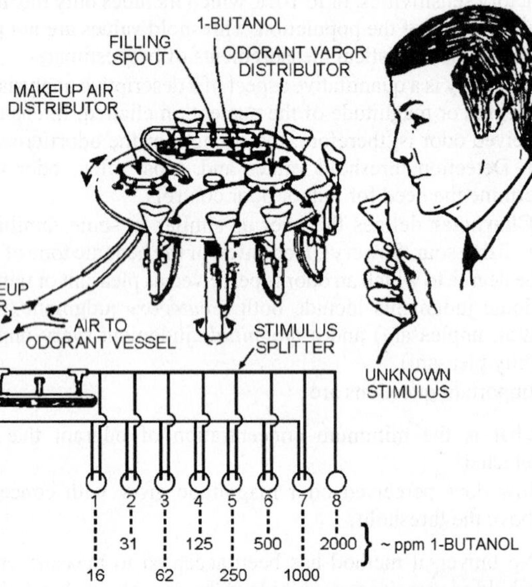

Fig. 3 Panelist Using Dravnieks Binary Dilution Olfactometer
(Dravnieks 1975)

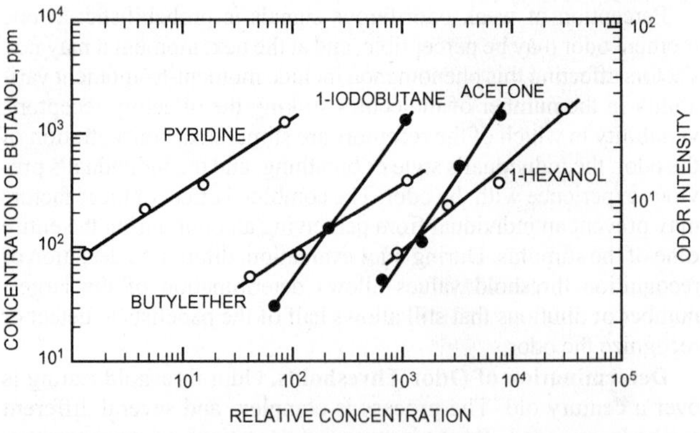

Fig. 4 Matching Functions Obtained with Dravnieks Olfactometer
(Cain 1978; Dravnieks and Laffort 1972)

odorants can be chosen to represent only the portion of the qualitative range relevant to the problem under investigation (e.g., animal odors). Another procedure is to ask panelists to assess the degree of association between a test sample's quality and certain verbal descriptors (e.g., sweaty, woody, chalky, sour).

The number of odorant descriptors and descriptors to be used have been subjects of disagreement (Harper et al. 1968). The number of descriptors varies from a minimum of seven (Amoore 1962) to as many as 830 used by an ASTM subcommittee. An atlas of odor characters, containing 146 descriptors, was compiled for 180 chemicals by ASTM (1985).

An odor can be characterized either by an open-ended word description or by multidimensional scaling. **Multidimensional scaling** is based on similarity and dissimilarity judgments in comparison to a set of standard odors or to various descriptors.

In some cases, the interest may be merely whether an odor's quality has changed as a result of some treatment (e.g., use of a bacteriostat). Under these circumstances, samples of air taken before and after treatment can be compared directly (using a simple scale of similarity) or indirectly (with appropriate verbal descriptors).

Hedonics

The acceptability or pleasantness of an odor can be measured psychophysically in the same way as odor intensity. Both ratio and category scaling procedures can be adapted to odor acceptability.

Odors do not always cause adverse reactions. Products are manufactured to elicit favorable responses. Acceptance tests may involve product comparison (frequently used in the perfume industry) or a hedonic scale. The premise of acceptance tests is that the larger the segment of subjects accepting the odor, the better the odor. A hedonic scale that allows for negative as well as positive responses is likely to better determine how acceptable the odor is.

All persons exposed to a given odor are not likely to agree on its acceptability. Acceptability of a given odor to a person is based on a complex combination of associations and is not simply a characteristic of the odor itself (Beck and Day 1991). Responses to odors are determined by both **bottom-up factors** (attributes or properties of the odorant) and **top-down factors** (expectations, attitudes, and associations from prior experience stored in memory, and appropriateness of the odor in its present context). Both factors are activated when an individual detects an odor, and the individual's ultimate response (e.g., perception of intensity, hedonics, irritation, or symptoms) is a joint function of both (Dalton 1996; Dalton et al. 1997). In some cases, the interpretation provided by the top-down process appears to override the outcome from the bottom-up process, resulting in complaints, symptoms, and reports of illness.

DILUTION OF ODORS BY VENTILATION

The size of the exponent n in Stevens' law [Equation (1)] varies from one odorant to another, ranging from less than 0.2 to about 0.7 (Cain and Moskowitz 1974). This determines the **slope** or **dose response** of the odor intensity/odorant concentration function and has important consequences for malodor control. A low slope value indicates an odor that requires greater relative dilution for the odor to dissipate; a high slope value indicates an odor that can be more quickly reduced by ventilation. For example, an exponent of 0.7 implies that, to reduce perceived intensity by a factor of 5, the concentration must be reduced by a factor of 10; an exponent of 0.2 would require a reduction in concentration by a factor of more than 3000 for the same reduction in perceived magnitude. Examples of compounds with low slope values include hydrogen sulfide, butyl acetate, and amines. Compounds with high slope values include ammonia and aldehydes.

The ability of ventilation to control odors also depends on the strength of the source generating the odorant(s) and the nature of the odor. An odorant with a stronger source requires proportionately more ventilation to achieve the same reduction in concentration. Odors that are perceived as unpleasant may require substantially greater reduction before being perceived as acceptable. In addition, some sources, such as painted walls and flooring materials, may show increased emission rates in response to increased ventilation rates, which further complicates the issue (Gunnarsen 1997).

ODOR CONCENTRATION

Analytical Measurement

Performance data on control of specific odorants can be obtained using suitable analytical methods. Detectors can sense substances in amounts as little as 1 ng. Air contains many minor components, so gas chromatographic separation of the components must precede detection. Because odor thresholds for some compounds are low, preconcentration of the minor components is necessary. **Preconcentration** consists of adsorption or absorption by a stable, sufficiently nonvolatile material, followed by thermal desorption or extraction. NIOSH (1993) reviews techniques for sampling and analysis of VOCs in indoor air.

Mass spectrometry can be used with **gas chromatography** to identify constituents of complex mixtures. The chromatograph resolves a mixture into its constituents, and the spectrometer provides identification and concentration of selected constituents.

Several other detectors are sufficiently sensitive and specific to detect resolved components. **Hydrogen flame ionization detectors** respond adequately and nearly mass-proportionally to almost all hydrocarbons, though their responses to organic chemicals containing other atoms (e.g., oxygen) are more variable. **Flame photometric detectors** can pinpoint with equal sensitivity compounds that contain sulfur; many sulfur compounds are strongly odorous and are of interest in odor work. A **Coulson conductometric detector** is specifically and adequately sensitive to ammonia and organic nitrogen compounds. **Thermal conductivity detectors** are generally not sensitive enough for analytical work on odors.

Frequently, a **sniffing port** (Dravnieks and Krotoszynski 1969; Dravnieks and O'Donnell 1971) is installed in parallel with the detector(s). Part of the resolved effluent exhausts through the port and allows components that are particularly odorous or carry some relevant odor quality to be annotated. Usually, only a fraction of all components studied exhibits odors.

Airborne VOCs cause odors, but the correlation between indoor VOC concentrations and odor complaints in indoor environments is poor. Considerable work has been done on **artificial noses**, which may offer objective determination of odorants (Bartlett et al. 1997; Freund and Lewis 1995; Moy et al. 1994; Taubes 1996). However, because the physicochemical correlates of olfaction are poorly understood, no simple analytical means to predict an odorant's perceived quality and intensity exists. Moreover, because acceptability of an odorant depends strongly on context, it is unlikely that analytical instruments will supplant human evaluation.

Odor Units

Odor concentration can be expressed as the number of unit volumes that a unit volume of odorous sample occupies when diluted to the odor threshold with nonodorous air. If a sample of odorous air can be reduced to threshold by a tenfold dilution with pure air, the concentration of the original sample is said to be 10 odor units. Hence, odor units are equivalent to multiples of threshold concentrations. Odor units are not units of perceived magnitude.

Odor units are widely used to express legal limits for emission of odoriferous materials. For example, the law may state that a factory operation may not cause the ambient odor level to exceed 15 odor units. For every odorant (chemical), odor units and parts per million (ppm) are proportional. The proportionality constant varies from one odorant to another, depending on the number of ppm needed to evoke a threshold response. Perceived odor magnitude (intensity), however, does not grow proportionally with concentration expressed in ppm. Therefore, it cannot grow proportionally with concentration expressed in odor units. For example, a sample of 20 odor units is always perceived as less than twice as strong as a sample of 10 odor units. Moreover, because the psychophysical function (slope) varies from one odorant to another, samples of two odorants, each at 20 odor units, may have unequal perceived intensities.

Although odor units are not equivalent to units of perceived magnitude, they can be useful. Most indoor and outdoor contaminants are complex mixtures, so that the actual concentration of the odoriferous portion of a sample cannot be expressed with certainty. Thus, the odor unit is a useful measure of concentration of the mixture when evaluating, for example, the efficiency of a filter or ventilation system to remove or dilute the odor.

OLF UNITS

Sometimes IAQ scientists cannot successfully resolve complaints about air in offices, schools, and other nonindustrial environments. Customarily, complaints are attributed to elevated pollutant concentrations; frequently, however, such high concentrations are not found, yet complaints persist.

Assuming that the inability to find a difference between air pollutant levels in buildings with registered complaints and those without complaints is due to inadequacies of prevailing measurement techniques, Fanger and others changed the focus from chemical analysis to sensory analysis (Fanger 1987, 1988; Fanger et al. 1988). Fanger quantified air pollution sources by comparing them with a well-known source: a sedentary person in thermal comfort. A new unit, the **olf**, was defined as the emission rate of air pollutants (bioeffluents) from a standard person. A **decipol** is one olf ventilated at a rate of 10 L/s of unpolluted air.

To use these units, Fanger generated a curve that relates the percentage of persons dissatisfied with air polluted by human bioeffluents as a function of the outdoor air ventilation rate and obtained the following expression:

$$D = 395\exp(-3.66q^{0.36}) \quad \text{for} \quad q \geq 0.332$$
$$D = 100 \quad \text{for} \quad q < 0.332 \qquad (2)$$

where

D = percentage of persons dissatisfied
q = ventilation/emission ratio, L/s per olf

This curve (Figure 5) is based on experiments involving more than 1000 European subjects (Fanger and Berg-Munch 1983). Experiments with American (Cain et al. 1983) and Japanese (Iwashita et al. 1990) subjects show very similar results.

The idea behind the olf is to express both human and nonhuman sensory sources in a single unit: equivalent standard persons (i.e., in olfs). A room should therefore be ventilated to handle the total sensory load from persons and building. The olf concept is used in European publications for ventilation (CEN 1998; ECA 1992) to determine required ventilation and in several national standards, including the Norwegian Building Code. Table 3 shows the sensory loads from different pollution sources used in CEN (1998).

Example. Office, low-polluting building, occupancy 0.07 persons/m^2

Occupants	0.07 olf/m^2
Building	0.1 olf/m^2
Total sensory load	0.17 olf/m^2

30% dissatisfied requires 4 L/s per olf ventilation rate (Figure 5)
Required ventilation: 4 × 0.17 = 0.7 L/(s·m^2)

The sensory load on the air in a space can be determined from Figure 5 by measuring the outdoor ventilation rate and determining the percent dissatisfied, using an untrained panel with a minimum of 20 impartial persons (Gunnarsen and Fanger 1992). The panel judges the acceptability of the air just after entering the space. The required ventilation rate depends on the desired percentage of occupant satisfaction. In ASHRAE *Standard* 62.1, 80% acceptability (20% dissatisfied) is the goal; European guidelines offer three quality levels: 15%, 20%, and 30% dissatisfied.

Although this system has much to offer from a theoretical standpoint, its use is controversial in some areas. Problems have been found in cultural differences among panel members and access to outdoor air for dilution (Aizlewood et al. 1996). The trend is now to use untrained panels, as described in the previous paragraph. Knudsen et al. (1998) showed that, for some building materials, the curve giving the relation between percent dissatisfied and ventilation rate is less steep than that in Figure 5, whereas it is steeper for others. The sensory load in this case depends on the ventilation rate. The constant sensory loads in Table 3 should therefore be seen as a first approximation.

Table 3 Sensory Pollution Load from Different Pollution Sources

Source	Sensory Load
Sedentary person (1 to 1.5 met)	1 olf
Person exercising	
Low level (3 met)	4 olf
Medium level (6 met)	10 olf
Children, kindergarten (3 to 6 yrs)	1.2 olf
Children, school (4 to 16 yrs)	1.3 olf
Low-polluting building	0.1 olf/m^2
Non-low-polluting building	0.2 olf/m^2

Source: CEN (1998).

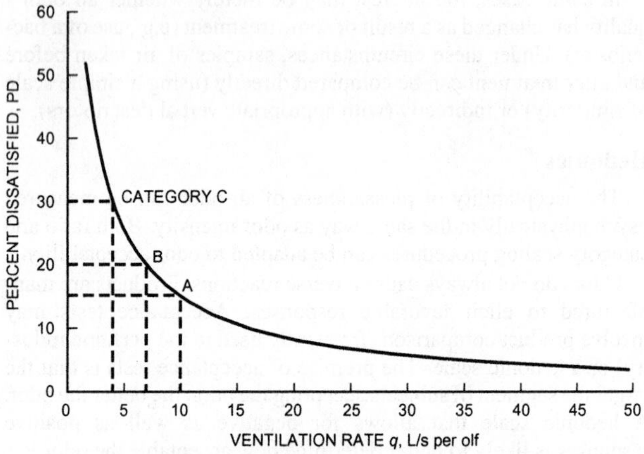

Fig. 5 Percentage of Dissatisfied Persons as a Function of Ventilation Rate per Standard Person (i.e., per Olf) (CEN 1998)

REFERENCES

ACGIH. Annually. *TLVs® and BEIs®*. American Conference of Governmental Industrial Hygienists, Cincinnati, OH.

AIHA. 1989. *Odor thresholds for chemicals with established occupational health standards*. American Industrial Hygiene Association, Akron, OH.

Aizlewood, C.E., G.J Raw, and N.A. Oseland. 1996. Decipols: Should we use them? *Indoor Built Environment* 5:263-269.

Amoore, J.E. 1962. The stereochemical theory of olfaction, 1: Identification of seven primary odors. *Proceedings of the Scientific Section of the Toilet Goods Association* 37:1-12.

ASHRAE. 2007. Ventilation for acceptable indoor air quality. ANSI/ASHRAE *Standard* 62.1-2007.

ASTM. 1985. Atlas of odor character profiles. *Data Series* 61. American Society for Testing and Materials, West Conshohocken, PA.

ASTM. 1996. Sensory testing methods, 2nd ed. E. Chambers IV and M.B. Wolf, eds. *Document* MNL26-EB. American Society for Testing and Materials, West Conshohocken, PA.

ASTM. 2004. Standard practices for referencing suprathreshold odor intensity. *Standard* E544-1999 (2004). American Society for Testing and Materials, West Conshohocken, PA.

Bartlett, P., J. Elliott, and J. Gardner. 1997. Electronic noses and their applications in the food industry. *Food Technology* 51(12):44-48.

Beck, L. and V. Day. 1991. New Jersey's approach to odor problems. *Transactions: Recent developments and current practices and odor regulations control and technology*, D.R. Derenzo and A. Gnyp, eds. Air and Waste Management Association, Pittsburgh, PA.

Berglund, L. and W.S. Cain. 1989. Perceived air quality and the thermal environment. *Proceedings of IAQ '89: The Human Equation: Health and Comfort*, San Diego, pp. 93-99.

Berg-Munch, B. and P.O. Fanger. 1982. The influence of air temperature on the perception of body odour. *Environment International* 8:333-335.

Cain, W.S. 1978. The odoriferous environment and the application of olfactory research. In *Handbook of perception*, vol. 6, *Tasting and smelling*, pp. 197-199, C.C. Carterette and M.P. Friedman, eds. Academic Press, New York.

Cain, W.S. and J.E. Cometto-Muñiz. 1995. Irritation and odors as indicators of indoor pollution. *Occupational Medicine* 10(1):133-135.

Cain, W.S. and H.R. Moskowitz. 1974. Psychophysical scaling of odor. In *Human responses to environmental odors*, pp. 1-32, A. Turk, J.W. Johnston, and D.G. Moulton, eds. Academic Press, New York.

Cain, W.S., B.P. Leaderer, R. Isseroff, L.G. Berglund, R.I. Huey, E.D. Lipsitt, and D. Perlman. 1983. Ventilation requirements in buildings—I: Control of occupancy odor and tobacco smoke odor. *Atmospheric Environment* 17:1183-1197.

CEN. 1998. Ventilation for buildings: Design criteria for the indoor environment. *Technical Report* CR1752. European Committee for Standardization, Brussels.

Clausen, G., P.O Fanger, W.S. Cain, and B.P. Leaderer. 1985. The influence of aging particle filtration and humidity on tobacco smoke odour. *Proceedings of CLIMA 2000*, vol. 4, pp. 345-349. Copenhagen.

Cometto-Muñiz, J.E. and W.S. Cain. 1992. Sensory irritation, relation to indoor air pollution in sources of indoor air contaminants—Characterizing emissions and health effects. In *Annals of the New York Academy of Sciences*, vol. 641: *Sources of indoor air contaminants: Characterizing emissions and health impacts*.

Cometto-Muñiz, J.E. and W.S. Cain. 1995. Olfactory adaptation. In *Handbook of olfaction and gustation*, R.L. Doty, ed. Marcel Dekker, New York.

Cometto-Muñiz, J.E., W.S. Cain, and H.K. Hudnell. 1997. Agonistic sensory effects of airborne chemicals in mixtures: Odor, nasal pungency and eye irritation. *Perception and Psychophysics* 59(5):665-674.

Cowart, B.J., K. Flynn-Rodden, S.J. McGeady, and L.D. Lowry. 1993. Hyposmia in allergic rhinitis. *Journal of Allergy and Clinical Immunology* 91:747-751.

Cowart, B.J., I.M. Young, R.S. Feldman, and L.D. Lowry. 1997. Clinical disorders of smell and taste. *Occupational Medicine* 12:465-483.

Dalton, P. 1996. Odor perception and beliefs about risk. *Chemical Senses* 21:447-458.

Dalton, P. and C.J. Wysocki. 1996. The nature and duration of adaptation following long-term exposure to odors. *Perception & Psychophysics* 58(5):781-792.

Dalton, P., C.J. Wysocki, M.J. Brody, and H.J. Lawley. 1997. The influence of cognitive bias on the perceived odor, irritation and health symptoms from chemical exposure. *International Archives of Occupational and Environmental Health* 69:407-417.

Dravnieks, A. 1975. Evaluation of human body odors, methods and interpretations. *Journal of the Society of Cosmetic Chemists* 26:551.

Dravnieks, A. and B. Krotoszynski. 1969. Analysis and systematization of data for odorous compounds in air. *ASHRAE Symposium Bulletin*: *Odor and odorants: The engineering view.*

Dravnieks, A. and P. Laffort. 1972. Physicochemical basis of quantitative and qualitative odor discrimination in humans. *Olfaction and Taste IV: Proceedings of the Fourth International Symposium*, pp. 142-148. D. Schneider, ed. Wissenschaftliche Verlagsgesellschaft mbH, Stuttgart.

Dravnieks, A. and A. O'Donnell. 1971. Principles and some techniques of high resolution headspace analysis. *Journal of Agricultural and Food Chemistry* 19:1049.

ECA. 1992. Guidelines for ventilation requirements in buildings. European Collaborative Action *Indoor Air Quality and its Impact on Man*: *Report* 11. EUR 14449 EN. Office for Official Publications of the European Committees, Luxembourg.

Engen, T., R.A. Kilduff, and N.J. Rummo. 1975. The influence of alcohol on odor detection. *Chemical Senses and Flavor* 1:323.

EPA. 1992. *Reference guide to odor thresholds for hazardous air pollutants listed in the* Clean Air Act Amendments of 1990. EPA/600/R-92/047. Office of Research and Development, U.S. Environmental Protection Agency, Washington, D.C.

Fang, L., G. Clausen, and P.O. Fanger. 1998a. Impact of temperature and humidity on the perception of indoor air quality. *Indoor Air* 8(2):80-90.

Fang, L., G. Clausen, and P.O. Fanger. 1998b. Impact of temperature and humidity on perception of indoor air quality during immediate and longer whole-body exposures. *Indoor Air* 8(4):276-284.

Fanger, P.O. 1987. A solution to the sick building mystery. *Indoor Air '87, Proceedings of the International Conference on Indoor Air and Climate*. Institute of Water, Soil and Air Hygiene, Berlin.

Fanger, P.O. 1988. Introduction of the olf and decipol units to quantify air pollution perceived by humans indoors and outdoors. *Energy and Buildings* 12:1-6.

Fanger, P.O. and B. Berg-Munch. 1983. Ventilation and body odor. *Proceedings of Engineering Foundation Conference on Management of Atmospheres in Tightly Enclosed Spaces,* pp. 45-50. ASHRAE.

Fanger, P.O., J. Lauridsen, P. Bluyssen, and G. Clausen. 1988. Air pollution sources in offices and assembly halls quantified by the olf unit. *Energy and Buildings* 12:7-19.

Freund, M.S. and N.S. Lewis. 1995. A chemically diverse conduction polymer-based "electronic nose." *Proceedings of the National Academy of Sciences* 92:2652-2656.

Frey, A.F. 1995. A review of the nature of odour perception and human response. *Indoor Environment* 4:302-305.

Green, B.G., P. Dalton, B. Cowart, G. Shaffer, K.R. Rankin, and J. Higgins. 1996. Evaluating the "labeled magnitude scale" for measuring sensations of taste and smell. *Chemical Senses* 21(3):323-334.

Gunnarsen, L. 1997. The influence of area-specific rate on the emissions from construction products. *Indoor Air* 7:116-120.

Gunnarsen, L. and P.O. Fanger. 1992. Adaptation to indoor air pollution. *Energy and Buildings* 18:43-54.

Harper, R., E.C. Bate Smith, and D.G. Land. 1968. *Odour description and odour classification.* American Elsevier, New York. Distributors for Churchill Livingston Publishing, Edinburgh, Scotland.

Iwashita, G., K. Kimura, S. Tanabe, S. Yoshizawa, and K. Ikeda. 1990. Indoor air quality assessment based on human olfactory sensation. *Journal of Architecture, Planning and Environmental Engineering* 410: 9-19.

Kerka, W.F. and C.M. Humphreys. 1956. Temperature and humidity effect on odour perception. *ASHRAE Transactions* 62:531-552.

Knudsen, H.N., O. Valbjørn, and P.A. Nielsen. 1998. Determination of exposure-response relationships for emissions from building products. *Indoor Air* 8(4):264-275.

Koelega, H.S. and E.P. Koster. 1974. Some experiments on sex differences in odor perception. In *Annals of the New York Academy of Sciences*, vol. 237: *Evaluation, Utilization, and Control*, p. 234.

Meilgaard, M., G.V. Civille, and B.T. Carr. 1987. *Sensory evaluation techniques.* CRC Press, Boca Raton, FL.

Moskowitz, H.R., A. Dravnieks, W.S. Cain, and A. Turk. 1974. Standardized procedure for expressing odor intensity. *Chemical Senses and Flavor* 1:235.

Moy, L., T. Tan, and J.W. Gardner. 1994. Monitoring the stability of perfume and body odors with an "electronic nose." *Perfumer and Flavorist* 19: 11-16.

NIOSH. 1993. Case studies—Indoor environmental quality "from the ground up." *Applied Occupational and Environmental Hygiene* 8: 677-680.

Norwegian Building Code. 1996. Oslo, Statens Hygningstekniske Eur.

Pierce, J.J.D., C.J. Wysocki, E.V. Aronov, J.B. Webb, and R.M. Boden. 1996. The role of perceptual and structural similarity in cross adaptation. *Chemical Senses* 21:223-227.

Ruth, J.H. 1986. Odor thresholds and irritation levels of several chemical substances: A review. *American Industrial Hygiene Association Journal* 47:142-151.

Schneider, R.A. 1974. Newer insights into the role and modifications of olfaction in man through clinical studies. In *Annals of the New York Academy of Sciences*, vol. 237: *Evaluation, Utilization, and Control*, p. 217.

Shams Esfandabad, H. 1993. *Perceptual analysis of odorous irritants in indoor air.* Ph.D. dissertation, Department of Psychology, Stockholm University.

Stevens, J.C., W.S. Cain, F.T. Schiet, and M.W. Oatley. 1989. Olfactory adaptation and recovery in old age. *Perception* 18(22):265-276.

Stevens, S.S. 1957. On the psychophysical law. *Psychological Review* 64:153.

Taubes, G. 1996. The electronic nose. *Discover* (September):40-50.

Toftum, J., A.S. Jørgensen, and P.O. Fanger. 1998. Upper limits for air humidity for preventing warm respiratory discomfort. *Energy and Buildings* 28(1):15-23.

Wysocki, C.J. and G.K. Beauchamp. 1984. Ability to smell androstenone is genetically determined. *Proceeding of the National Academy of Sciences of the United States of America* 81:4899-4902.

Wysocki, C.J. and A.N. Gilbert. 1989. *National Geographic* smell survey: Effects of age are heterogeneous. In *Annals of the New York Academy of Sciences*, vol. 561: *Nutrition and the Chemical Senses in Aging: Recent Advances and Current Research*, pp. 12-28. C.L. Murphy, W.S. Cain, and D.M. Hegsted, eds.

Wysocki, C.J., P. Dalton, P., M.J. Brody, and H.J. Lawley. 1997. Acetone odor and irritation thresholds obtained from acetone-exposed factory workers and from control (occupationally non-exposed) subjects. *American Industrial Hygiene Association Journal* 58:704-712.

Yaglou, C.P., E.C. Riley, and D.I. Coggins. 1936. Ventilation requirements. *ASHRAE Transactions* 42:133-162.

BIBLIOGRAPHY

ACGIH. 1988. *Advances in air sampling*. American Conference of Governmental Industrial Hygienists, Cincinnati, OH.

Clemens, J.B. and R.G. Lewis. 1988. Sampling for organic compounds. *Principles of Environmental Sampling* 20:147-157.

Moschandreas, D.J. and S.M. Gordon. 1991. Volatile organic compounds in the indoor environment: Review of characterization methods and indoor air quality studies. In *Organic chemistry of the atmosphere*. CRC Press, Boca Raton, FL.

CHAPTER 13

INDOOR ENVIRONMENTAL MODELING

THIS chapter presents two common indoor environmental modeling methods to calculate airflows and contaminant concentrations in buildings: computational fluid dynamics (CFD) and multizone network airflow modeling. Discussion of each method includes its mathematical background, practical modeling advice, model validation, and application examples.

Each modeling method has strengths and weaknesses for studying different aspects of building ventilation, energy, and indoor air quality (IAQ). CFD modeling can be used for a microscopic view of a building or its components by solving Navier-Stokes equations to obtain detailed flow field information and pollutant concentration distributions within a space. Its strengths include the rigorous application of fundamental fluid mechanics and the detailed nature of the airflow, temperature, and contaminant concentration results. However, these results require significant time, both for the analyst to create a model and interpret the results and for the computer to solve the equations. This time cost typically limits CFD to applications involving single rooms and steady-state solutions.

In contrast, multizone airflow and pollutant transport modeling can yield a macroscopic view of a building by solving a network of mass balance equations to obtain airflows and average pollutant concentrations in different zones of a whole building. This entire process takes much less time, making whole-building modeling, including various mechanical systems, possible over time periods as long as a year. This method's limitations include far less-detailed results (e.g., no internal-room airflow details, a single contaminant concentration for each room), which poorly approximate some modeling scenarios (e.g., atria, stratified rooms).

Although modeling software is widely available, successful application of either indoor environmental modeling method is still challenging. A strong grasp of fundamental building physics and detailed knowledge of the building space being modeled are both necessary. (Also see Chapters 1, 3, 4, 6, 9, 11, 16, and 24 of this volume.) Successful modeling also starts with planning that considers the project's objectives, resources, and available information. When modeling existing buildings, taking measurements may significantly improve the modeling effort. Modeling is particularly useful when known and unknown elements are combined, such as an existing building under unusual circumstances (e.g., fire, release of an airborne hazard). However, even for hypothetical buildings (e.g., in the design stage), knowledge gained from a good modeling effort can be valuable to planning and design efforts.

COMPUTATIONAL FLUID DYNAMICS

Computational fluid dynamic (CFD) modeling quantitatively predicts thermal/fluid physical phenomena in an indoor space. The conceptual model interprets a specific problem of the indoor environment through a mathematical form of the conservation law and situation-specific information (boundary conditions). The governing equations remain the same for all indoor environment applications of airflow and heat transfer, but boundary conditions change for each specific problem: for example, room layout may be different, or speed of the supply air may change. In general, a boundary condition defines the physical problem at specific positions. Often, physical phenomena are complicated by simultaneous heat flows (e.g., heat conduction through the building enclosure, heat gains from heated indoor objects, solar radiation through building fenestration), phase changes (e.g., condensation and evaporation of water), chemical reactions (e.g., combustion), and mechanical movements (e.g., fans, occupant movements).

CFD involves solving coupled partial differential equations, which must be worked simultaneously or successively. No analytical solutions are available for indoor environment modeling. Computer-based numerical procedures are the only means of generating complete solutions of these sets of equations.

CFD code is more than just a numerical procedure of solving governing equations; it can be used to solve fluid flow, heat transfer, chemical reactions, and even thermal stresses. Unless otherwise implemented, CFD does not solve acoustics and lighting, which are also important parameters in indoor environment analysis. Different CFD codes have different capabilities: a simple code may solve only laminar flow, whereas a complicated one can handle a far more complex (e.g., compressible) flow.

Mathematical and Numerical Background

Airflow in natural and built environments is predominantly turbulent, characterized by randomness, diffusivity, dissipation, and relatively large Reynolds numbers (Tennekes and Lumley 1972). Turbulence is not a fluid property, as are viscosity and thermal conductivity, but a phenomenon caused by flow motion. Research on turbulence began during the late nineteenth century (Reynolds 1895) and has been intensively pursued in academia and industry. For further information, see Corrsin's (1961) overview; Hinze's (1975) and Tennekes and Lumley's (1972) classic monographs; and Bernard and Wallace (2002), Mathieu and Scott (2000), and Pope (2000).

Indoor airflow, convective heat transfer, and species dispersion are controlled by the governing equations for mass, momentum in each flow direction, energy (**Navier-Stokes equation**), and contaminant distribution. A common form is presented in Equation (1), relating the change in time of a variable at a location to the amount of variable flux (e.g., momentum, mass, thermal energy). Essentially, transient changes plus convection equals diffusion plus sources:

$$\frac{\partial}{\partial t}(\rho\phi) + \frac{\partial}{\partial x_j}(\rho U_j \phi) = \frac{\partial}{\partial x_j}\left(\Gamma_\phi \frac{\partial \phi}{\partial x_j}\right) + S_\phi \qquad (1)$$

The preparation of this chapter is assigned to TC 4.10, Indoor Environmental Modeling.

where

t = time, s
ρ = density, kg/m³
ϕ = transport property (e.g., air velocity, temperature, species concentration) at any point
x_j = distance in j direction, m
U_j = velocity in j direction, m/s
Γ_ϕ = generalized diffusion coefficient or transport property of fluid flow
S_ϕ = source or sink

Local turbulence is expressed as a variable diffusion coefficient called the **turbulent viscosity**, often calculated from the equations for turbulent kinetic energy and its dissipation rate. The total description of flow, therefore, consists of eight differential equations, which are coupled and nonlinear. These equations contain first and second derivatives that express the convection, diffusion, and source of the variables. The equations can also be numerically solved [see the section on Large Eddy Simulation (LES)].

Direct solution of differential equations for the room's flow regime is not possible, but a numerical method can be applied. The differential equations are transformed into finite-volume equations formulated around each grid point, as shown in Figure 1. Convection and diffusion terms are developed for all six surfaces around the control volume, and the source term is formulated for the volume (see Figure 1B).

Assuming a room is typically divided into 90 × 90 × 90 cells, the eight differential equations are replaced by eight difference equations in each point, giving a total of 5.8 × 10⁶ equations with the same number of unknown variables.

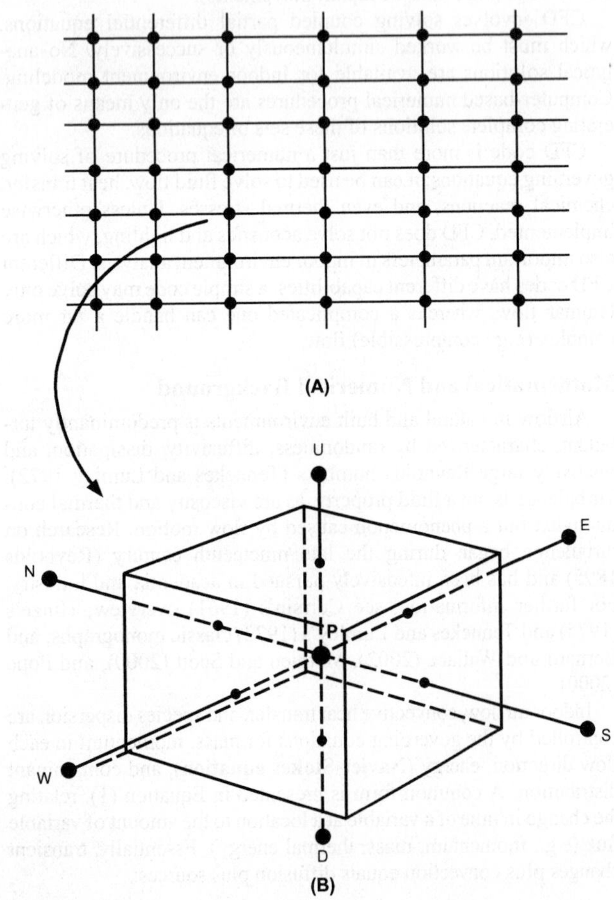

Fig. 1 (A) Grid Point Distribution and (B) Control Volume Around Grid Point P

The numerical method typically involves 3000 iterations, which means that a total of 17 × 10⁹ grid point calculations are made for the prediction of a flow field. This method obviously depends heavily on computers: the first predictions of room air movement were made in the 1970s, and have since increased dramatically in popularity, especially because computation cost has decreased by a factor of 10 every eight years. Baker et al. (1994), Chen and Jiang (1992), Nielsen (1975), and Williams et al. (1994a, 1994b) show early CFD predictions of flow in ventilated rooms, and Jones and Whittle (1992) discuss status and capabilities in the 1990s. Russell and Surendran (2000) review recent work on the subject.

Turbulent flow is a three-dimensional, random process with a wide spectrum of scales in time and space, initiated by flow instabilities at high Reynolds numbers; the energy involved dissipates in a cascading fashion (Mathieu and Scott 2000). Statistical analysis is used to quantify the phenomenon. At a given location and time, the instantaneous velocity u_i is

$$u_i = \bar{u}_i + u_i' \tag{2}$$

where $\bar{u}_i$ is the ensemble average of v for steady flow, and u_i' is fluctuation velocity. Through measurement, u_i' is obtained as the standard deviation of u_i. The turbulence intensity TI is

$$\mathrm{TI} \equiv \frac{u_i}{\bar{u}_i} \times 100 \text{ in percent} \tag{3}$$

The turbulent kinetic energy k per unit mass is

$$k = \frac{1}{2}\bar{u}_i'^2 = \frac{1}{2}(u_1'^2 + u_2'^2 + u_3'^2) \tag{4}$$

To quantify length and time, velocity correlations and higher moments of u_i are commonly used (Monin and Yaglom 1971). Those scales are essential to characterize turbulent flows and their energy transport mechanisms. With its turbulent kinetic energy extracted from the mean flow, large eddies cascade energy to smaller eddies. In the smallest eddies, viscous dissipation of the turbulent kinetic energy occurs. By equating the total amount of energy transfer to its dissipation rate ε, based on Kolmogorov's theory (Tennekes and Lumley 1972), a length scale η is defined as

$$\eta \equiv \left(\frac{\nu^3}{\varepsilon}\right)^{\frac{1}{4}} \tag{5}$$

where ν is the fluid's kinematic viscosity. The Kolmogorov length scale η is used to determine the smallest dissipative scale of a turbulent flow; it is important in determining the requirements of grid size [see the sections on Large Eddy Simulation (LES) and Direct Numerical Simulation (DNS)].

For an incompressible fluid, the governing equations of the turbulent flow motion are

$$\frac{\partial u_i}{\partial x_i} = 0 \tag{6}$$

$$\rho\frac{\partial u_i}{\partial t} + \rho u_j \frac{\partial u_i}{\partial x_j} = -\frac{\partial P}{\partial x_i} + \frac{\partial \tau_{ij}}{\partial x_j} \tag{7}$$

where t is time, ρ is the fluid density, P is pressure, and τ_{ij} is the viscous stress tensor defined as

$$\tau_{ij} \equiv 2\mu s_{ij} \tag{8}$$

where μ is the dynamic viscosity and s_{ij} is the strain rate tensor, defined as

$$s_{ij} \equiv \frac{1}{2}\left(\frac{\partial u_i}{\partial x_j} + \frac{\partial u_j}{\partial x_i}\right) \quad (9)$$

From Equations (6), (8), and (9), Equation (7) is rewritten as

$$\rho\frac{\partial u_i}{\partial t} + \rho\frac{\partial (u_i u_j)}{\partial x_j} = -\frac{\partial P}{\partial x_i} + \frac{\partial (2\mu s_{ij})}{\partial x_j} \quad (10)$$

Taking the ensemble average by using Equation (2), Equation (6) becomes

$$\frac{\partial \bar{u}_i}{\partial x_i} = 0 \quad (11)$$

Considering Equation (2), Equation (10) becomes the **Reynolds-averaged Navier-Stokes (RANS) equation** (Wilcox 1998):

$$\rho\frac{\partial \bar{u}_i}{\partial t} + \rho\bar{u}_j\frac{\partial \bar{u}_i}{\partial x_j} = -\frac{\partial \bar{P}}{\partial x_i} + \frac{\partial\left(2\mu\bar{s}_{ij} - \rho\overline{u_i'u_j'}\right)}{\partial x_j} \quad (12)$$

The right-hand term $-\rho\overline{u_i'u_j'}$ is called the **Reynolds stress tensor**. To compute the mean flow of turbulent fluid motion, this additional term causes the famous closure problem because of ensemble averaging, and must be calculated. Much turbulence research focuses on the closure problem by proposing various turbulence models.

Reynolds-Averaged Navier-Stokes (RANS) Approaches

The most intuitive approach to calculate Reynolds stresses is to adopt the mixing-length hypotheses originated by Prandtl. Many variants of the algebraic models and their applicability for various types of turbulent flows (e.g., free shear flows, wakes, jets) are collected and provided by Wilcox (1998).

Because of the importance of turbulent kinetic energy k in the turbulent energy budget, many researchers have developed models based on k and other derived turbulence quantities for calculating the Reynolds stresses. To solve the closure problem, the number of the additional equation(s) in turbulence models ranges from zero (Chen and Xu 1998) to seven [Reynolds stress model (RSM) for three-dimensional flows (Launder et al. 1975)]; all equations in these approaches are time-averaged. Two-equation variants of the k-ε model (where ε is the dissipation rate of turbulent kinetic energy) are popular in industrial applications, mostly for simulating steady mean flows and scalar species transport (Chen et al. 1990; Horstman 1988; Spalart 2000). A widely used method is predicting eddy viscosity μ_t from a two-equation k-ε turbulence model, as in Launder and Spalding (1974). Nielsen (1998) discusses modifications for room airflow. The k-ε turbulence model is only valid for fully developed turbulent flow.

Flow in a room will not always be at a high Reynolds number (i.e., fully developed everywhere in the room), but good predictions are generally obtained in areas with a certain velocity level. Low-turbulence effects can be predicted near wall regions with, for example, a Launder-Sharma (1974) low-Reynolds-number model.

More elaborate models, such as the Reynolds stress model (RSM), can also predict turbulence. This model closes the equation system with additional transport equations for Reynolds stresses [see Launder (1989)]; it is superior to the standard k-ε model because anisotropic effects of turbulence are taken into account. For example, the wall-reflection terms damp turbulent fluctuations perpendicular to the wall and convert energy to fluctuations parallel to the wall. This effect may be important for predicting a three-dimensional wall jet flow (Schälin and Nielsen 2003).

In general, RSM gives better results than the standard k-ε model for mean flow prediction, but improvements are not always significant, especially for the velocity fluctuations (Chen 1996; Kato et al. 1994). Murakami et al. (1994) compared the k-ε model, algebraic model (simplified RSM), and RSM in predicting room air movement induced by a horizontal nonisothermal jet. RSM's prediction of mean velocity and temperature profiles in the jet showed slightly better agreement with experiments than the k-ε model's prediction.

Large Eddy Simulation (LES)

For intrinsically transient flow fields, time-dependent RANS simulations often fail to resolve the flow field temporally. Large eddy simulation (LES) directly calculates the time-dependent large eddy motion while resolving the more universally small-scale motion using subgrid scale (SGS) modeling. LES has progressed rapidly since its inception four decades ago (Ferziger 1977; Smagorinsky 1963; Spalart 2000), when it was mainly a research tool that required enormous computing resources; modern computers can now implement LES for relatively simple geometries in building airflow applications (Emmerich and McGrattan 1998; Lin et al. 2001). For an excellent introduction to this promising CFD technique, see Ferziger (1977).

Filtering equations differentiate mathematically between large and small eddies. For example,

$$\bar{f}(r) = \int_{R^3} f(r')G_\Delta(r,r')dr' \quad (13)$$

where $G_\Delta(r,r')$ is a filter function with a filter with length scale Δ. $G_\Delta(r,r')$ integrates to 1 and decays to 0 for scales smaller than Δ (Chester et al. 2001). To resolve the SGS stresses, an analog to the RANS approach for the Reynolds stress is implemented as

$$u_i = \langle u_i\rangle + \langle u_i'\rangle \quad (14)$$

where $\langle u_i\rangle$ is the filtered average defined by Equation (13) and $\langle u_i'\rangle$ is the subgrid scale velocity, which is calculated through subgrid modeling. Filtering Equation (6) and (7) gives

$$\frac{\partial \langle u_i\rangle}{\partial x_i} = 0 \quad (15)$$

$$\rho\frac{\partial \langle u_i\rangle}{\partial t} + \rho\frac{\partial \langle u_i u_j\rangle}{\partial x_j} = -\frac{\partial \langle p\rangle}{\partial x_i} + \frac{\partial \langle 2\mu s_{ij}\rangle}{\partial x_j} \quad (16)$$

Based on Equation (14), the $\langle u_i u_j\rangle$ term in Equation (16) becomes,

$$\langle u_i u_j\rangle = \langle\langle u_i\rangle\langle u_j\rangle\rangle + \langle\langle u_i'\rangle\langle u_j\rangle\rangle + \langle\langle u_i\rangle\langle u_j'\rangle\rangle + \langle\langle u_i'\rangle\langle u_j'\rangle\rangle \quad (17)$$

The last three terms that contain the subgrid velocity are therefore the subject of modeling (Ferziger 1977). Breuer (1998) and Spalart (2000) describe some of the many other subgrid models and their performance. The latest developments of LES and its related techniques, such as the detached eddy simulation (DES), are described in detail by Spalart (2000).

Direction Numerical Simulation (DNS)

Direct numerical simulation (DNS) is used to study turbulent flow. This method is very accurate (sometimes better than experiments), and is used to benchmark performance of other CFD techniques. Because of its stringent requirements on grid, especially in the normal direction within the boundary layer (Grötzbach 1983), DNS is used to study spatially and temporally confined flows with simple geometry (Spalart 2000). Notwithstanding these limits, DNS also has been used to explore more complicated geometry, such as flow over a wavy wall (Cherukat et al. 1998), and flow mechanisms, such as multiphase flow (Ling et al. 1998) and droplet evaporation (Mashayek 1998).

MESHING FOR COMPUTATIONAL FLUID DYNAMICS

The first step in conducting a CFD analysis for a fluid region of interest is to divide the region into a large number of smaller regions called **cells**. The collection of cells that makes up the domain of interest is typically called the **mesh** or **grid**, and the process of dividing up the domain is called **meshing, gridding, grid generation**, or **discretization** of the computational domain.

Meshes can be structured or unstructured, depending on the connectivity of the cells in the mesh to one another. Individual cell shape varies, and each shape has advantages and disadvantages. These shapes range from triangles and quadrilaterals for two-dimensional (2D) geometry, to tetrahedrals (four-sided triangular-based shapes) and hexahedrons (typically six-sided boxes) for three-dimensional (3D) geometry. Wedges (a triangle swept into a three-dimensional shape) and rectangular-based pyramids can also be used to transition between the triangular sides of the tetrahedrals and quadrilateral sides of the hexahedrons.

Structured Grids

Structured grids have consistent geometrical regularity, wherein families of grid lines (in one direction) do not cross each other. Figure 2 shows examples of structured grids. These grids can be further subclassified as orthogonal and nonorthogonal.

Orthogonal structured grids, the simplest scheme, are based on Cartesian/polar-cylindrical coordinate systems. A curved or sloped boundary in the CFD domain is typically approximated by stepwise boundary. Figure 2A shows a meshed 2D domain for flow through a 90° elbow using a Cartesian orthogonal coordinate system. Cells outside the elbow are blocked from CFD analysis or turned into cells that do not participate in the flow field. The stairstep approach to representing the curved surface can lead to numerical errors at curved walls. Finer grids are needed to more accurately represent the curved/sloped boundary. The effect of reducing local grid size in one region (grid refinement) may propagate to other sections of the domain and result in an increase in the number of model cells. This, together with the blocked cells outside the flow domain, creates a burden on computing resources. The stepwise approximation of the boundary may also result in errors that negatively affect the CFD solution.

Modeling curved/sloped surfaces is possible by using the geometrical flexibility of the **nonorthogonal** grid, also known as **body-fitted** or **boundary-fitted grid**. An example of a 2D body-fitted nonorthogonal structured grid for a 90° elbow is shown in Figure 2B. Using the body-fitting method, geometric details are accurately represented without using stepwise approximation. An orthogonal grid can be structured (i.e., a single block, as in Figure 2), block-structured, or overlapping-structured.

A **block-structured** grid consists of a group of meshed regions (blocks) that collectively form the entire region of interest. This is typically referred to as a **multiblock domain**. The blocks may have a fine grid at the region of interest, to provide more details for flow field analysis, and a coarser grid away from the region of interest. Figure 3 shows block-structured grid for 2D flow through a 90° elbow connected to a rectangular duct. The grid is fine close to the solid surfaces, and is refined at point A, where flow separation is expected. This grid refinement is propagated through blocks 2 and 3. Interblock interfaces could have matching grids, as between blocks 1 and 2, or a nonmatching interface, as between blocks 2 and 3. The nonmatching interface is used to transfer from coarse to finer grid or vice versa. Numerical inaccuracies can occur where blocks are joined together with nonmatching mesh lines. The relative difference in mesh size on either side of the interface is important. Also, there is additional computational overhead associated with managing the nonconformal interface.

At the interface of the block-structured grid, the ratio of cell size change (i.e., large to small cells) between two blocks is recommended to be no more than two (Ferziger and Peric 1997), because transporting field variables from a fine to a coarse mesh or vice versa allows inaccuracies to enter the solution. If flow in a domain travels from a group of four cells to a single cell, the flow detail represented by the four cells is lost. In some cases, this rule can be bent, but this is best done by an experienced CFD modeler.

Structured grids simplify programming for the CFD code developer and provide regular structure for the matrix of algebraic equations. However, they may not adequately describe complex geometries, and it can be difficult to control grid distribution in the region of interest without propagating through the whole analyzed domain.

These structured grid types are mainly associated with finite-difference methods. The examples in Figures 2 and 3 are called the **physical planes**. Finite-difference methods require a uniform rectangular grid called the **computational plane**. The governing equations must be transformed to give one-to-one correspondences

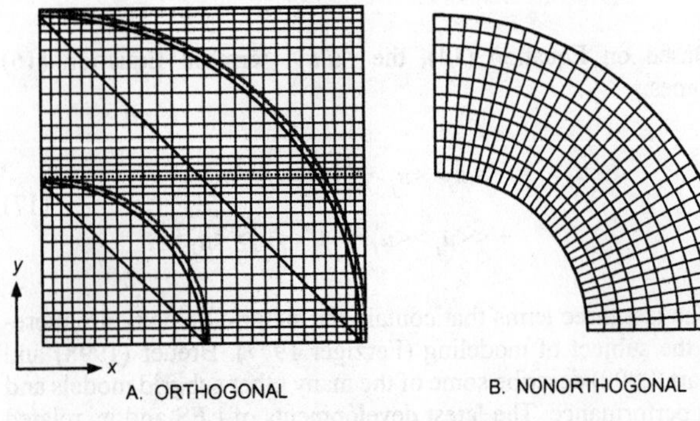

Fig. 2 Two-Dimensional CFD Structured Grid Model for Flow Through 90° Elbow

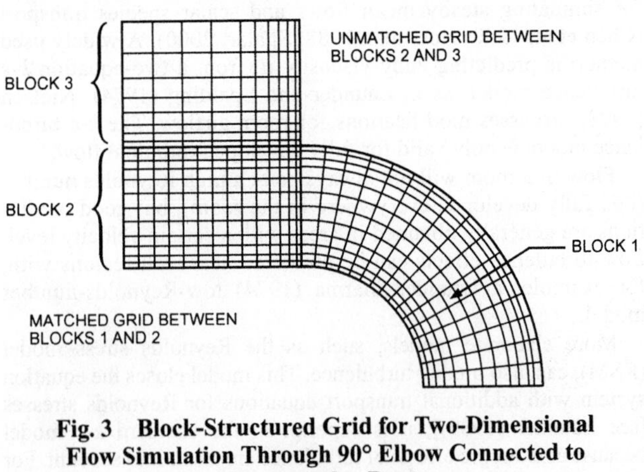

Fig. 3 Block-Structured Grid for Two-Dimensional Flow Simulation Through 90° Elbow Connected to Rectangular Duct

between the physical and computational planes. After analysis of the computational plane, the results are transferred back to the corresponding point on the physical plane. Using data transformation increases the programming efforts and computing costs for CFD. Anderson (1995) has more information on transformation methods.

Unstructured Grids

Unstructured grids (Figure 4) are flexible: they can represent complex geometry boundaries, and can be easily refined in the region of interest without propagating to the rest of the domain. Elements of different shapes can be used in the domain. Either matching or nonmatching nodes can be used between neighboring elements. Figure 4A is an unstructured grid using tetrahedral elements, whereas Figure 4B uses hexahedral elements; note that both have a meshing zone near the pipe wall to resolve the boundary layer. Unlike structured grids, the matrix of algebraic equation does not have a regular diagonal structure and has a slower solver than a structured grid solver (Ferzinger and Peric 1997).

Unstructured grids are mostly used for finite-element and finite-volume methods. No transformations are required for finite-volume methods, and analysis can be performed directly on the physical plane of the unstructured grid.

Grid Quality

Grid quality measures include the shape of the individual cells, the size of the cell relative to flow field features of interest, and the jump in grid size from one block to the next.

Cell quality is important. Values for variables stored at centers of cells must be interpolated to the face of the cell, which allows calculation of fluxes at faces of control volumes. A poor-quality mesh gives less accurate interpolations and can affect the quality of the simulation result by the introducing numerical inaccuracies. Mildly poor grids can increase convergence times; in extreme cases, local poor cell quality can result in overall flow field inaccuracies or cause the simulation to diverge and not reach a solution at all.

The examples in Figures 2 to 4 show clean, nonskewed cell shapes: the triangles do not lean over and the quadrilaterals have corners that do not vary significantly from 90°. In many practical meshes, the individual cells become distorted from these ideal shapes (e.g., because four-sided shapes may not fit well into wedge-shaped corners). The amount of distortion is typically referred to as **skewness**. Different CFD codes allow different levels of skewness, and the solver's overall sensitivity to skewness may be affected by the method of numerical discretization.

Grid cell size may be partially determined by the level of geometric detail needed. Cells need to be small enough to resolve the smallest geometric features of the domain. If cell size is too large, any curved elements cannot be represented by a series of straight lines.

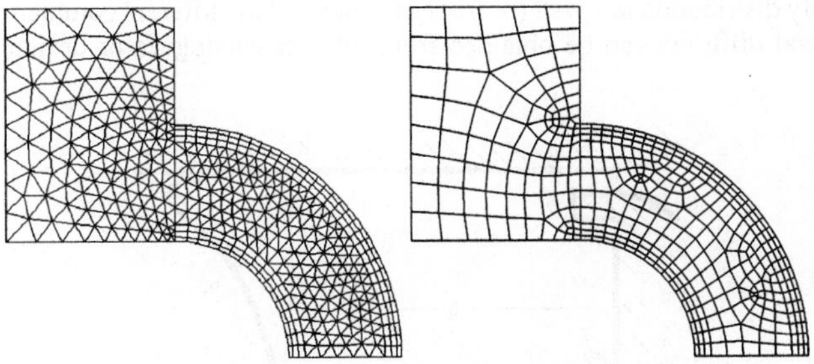

Fig. 4 Unstructured Grid for Two-Dimensional Meshing Scheme Flow Simulation Through 90° Elbow Connected to Rectangular Duct

In addition, a CFD solution's ability to resolve flow field features is limited by the grid resolution. If a grid has cell sizes of 10 mm, then flow field features smaller than 20 mm cannot be solved. Therefore, sharp gradients of flow field variables necessitate a finer mesh. The additional cells in the finer mesh are required to resolve the rapid change in the flow field variable. Additionally, fine grid resolution at walls is important for methods that use the law of the wall (see the Wall/Surface Boundary Conditions section), because fluxes and shear at the wall require accurate calculations of gradients.

Many CFD codes can start with a coarse mesh and add cells as necessary in particular regions, which can save computational time in the set-up and test simulation phases.

When generating a mesh, it is important to determine whether the mesh itself will affect the simulation and generate erroneous results. Figure 5 shows three circles with different meshing schemes. Figure 5A shows a grid on the circle that has a pincushion-like look; this mesh distorts the flow field in the "corners," because the four corner cells have two sides on the perimeter of the circle, whereas the rest of the cells around the circumference have only one. If this mesh is used to simulate flow down a pipe, flow velocity in the corner cells is adversely affected by the additional friction that these cells experience. Figure 5B shows the same geometry, but with a structured mesh created by placing a square in the center of the circle and drawing rays diagonally out from the corners. These rays and the circle's perimeter define other meshing blocks. If cut halfway through the horizontal or vertical centerline, the mesh can be stretched out into a rectangle. Finally, Figure 5C shows an unstructured mesh over the same geometry. The meshes in Figures 5B and 5C influence results less significantly than that in Figure 5A.

Immersed Boundary Grid Generation

The preceding discussion assumes that a 2- or 3-D computer model already exists for the geometry, architecture, or region of interest, and that the geometry can be imported into a gridding software package. The grid is then overlaid onto that geometry.

In immersed boundary grid generation, a model is not required to exist a priori. This simplifies gridding and geometry generation in one step: the orthogonal structured grid is created within a block and then the geometry (represented by blanked-out sections of cells within the meshed block) is overlaid (see Figure 1A). Groups of meshed blocks with overlaid architecture can be assembled to generate more complicated computational domains.

Although this technique can yield high-quality meshes for simple geometrical features (blocked representation), more sophisticated grid-generation techniques may be needed to grid complicated domains.

Grid Independence

The level of grid independence from the flow field solution is important to determine in advance. It may be sufficient to demonstrate that grids of similar resolution applied to similar problems give sufficiently low levels of uncertainty.

Grid independence can be achieved experimentally by using successive grid refinements in areas with sharp gradients or cell

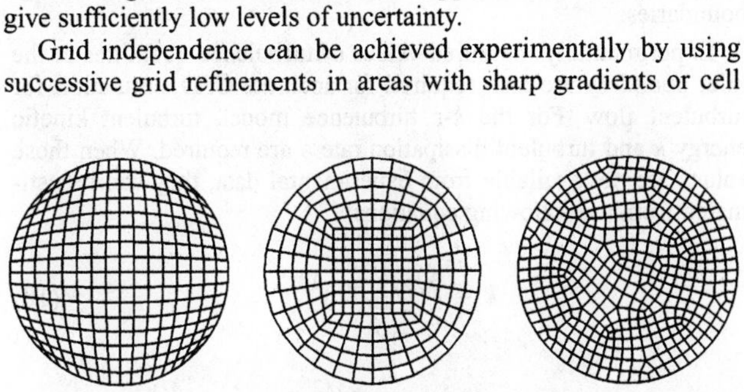

Fig. 5 Circle Meshing

skewness. This allows solutions obtained with coarser and finer grids to be compared. If results of two successive trials are comparable, then both models are grid-independent. In some cases, experienced CFD practitioners may be able to identify a sufficiently grid-independent solution without trials, but new CFD users should not assume a solution is grid-independent: different levels of grid can yield results different enough to make conclusions drawn from the flow field unreliable.

BOUNDARY CONDITIONS FOR COMPUTATIONAL FLUID DYNAMICS

Boundary conditions are integral to CFD modeling's ability to solve the general Navier-Stokes equations for a particular problem in an indoor environment. Boundary conditions specify physical and/or chemical characteristics at the model's perimeters. These characteristics could be constant throughout the analysis or time-dependent in transient analyses. This section discusses applying boundary conditions for CFD modeling of subsonic fluid flow.

Excluding free surface flow, most boundary conditions can be classified as either **Dirichlet** (variable values specified at the boundary node) or **Neumann** (variable derivatives are required at the boundary, and the boundary condition must be discretized to provide the required equation). Free surface flow requires moving boundary conditions, such as **kinematic** and **dynamic**.

Every model has walls, and most have at least one inlet and one outlet boundary. Some cases of natural convection heat transfer (e.g., CFD modeling of an enclosure with heated and cooled sides, modeling of convection from an object such as cylinder in a large fluid medium) may not require an inlet or outlet in the model. Typical boundary condition types for HVAC applications are inlets, outlets, walls or surfaces, symmetry surfaces, and fixed sources or sinks.

Inlet Boundary Conditions

Special attention must be paid to inlet boundary conditions, because supply diffusers are usually dominant sources of momentum that create airflow patterns responsible for temperature and concentration distributions.

Inlet boundary conditions may be velocity, pressure, or mass flow. When details of flow distribution are unknown, a constant-pressure boundary or constant flow rate can be specified. The pressure inlet boundary requires specifying static pressure for incompressible flow. Stagnation pressure and stagnation temperature should be specified at the pressure boundary for compressible flow. In both conditions, velocity components at the boundary are obtained by extrapolation.

The mass flow inlet condition requires specifying the mass flow rate and temperature for incompressible flow at the boundary. Velocities and pressure are calculated by extrapolation at inlet boundaries.

Experimentally measured values of turbulence quantities at the inlet boundary are also required for accurate CFD simulation for turbulent flow. For the k-ε turbulence model, turbulent kinetic energy k and turbulent dissipation rate ε are required. When these values are not available from experimental data, they can be estimated from the following equations:

$$k = \frac{3}{2}(U_{ref}\mathrm{TI})^2 \qquad (18)$$

$$\varepsilon = C_\mu^{3/4} \times \frac{k^{3/2}}{l} \qquad (19)$$

$$l = 0.07L \qquad (20)$$

where U_{ref} is the mean stream velocity, TI is turbulence intensity, l is the turbulence length scale, C_μ is the k-ε turbulence model constant ($C_\mu = 0.0845$), and L is the characteristic length of the inlet (for a duct, L is the equivalent radius).

For indoor environmental modeling, the inlet boundary is especially important because of the potentially complex geometry of supply diffusers designed to produce particular performance characteristics. Detailed diffuser modeling is possible for limited regions near the diffuser, but is not very practical in room-flow simulations: including the small geometric details of the diffuser in the room model results in a mesh with so many cells that current computation resources cannot efficiently find a solution. Therefore, most room airflow simulations should use simplified diffuser modeling that replicates diffuser performance without explicitly modeling the fine geometric details of the diffuser.

Other simplifications are possible. The most obvious method is replacing the actual diffuser with a less-complicated diffuser geometry, such as a slot opening, that supplies the same flow momentum and airflow rate to the space as the actual diffuser does (Nielsen 1992; Srebric and Chen 2002). Simplified methods are classified as jet momentum modeling either (1) at air supply devices or (2) in front of air supply devices (Fan 1995). Modeling at the supply device has several variations, including the slot and momentum models; variations of modeling in front of the diffuser include prescribed velocity, box, and diffuser specification (Srebric and Chen 2001, 2002). The most widely used methods are the momentum, box, and prescribed velocity methods.

The **momentum** method decouples the momentum and mass boundary conditions for the diffuser (Chen and Moser 1991). The diffuser is represented with an opening that has the same gross area, mass flux, and momentum flux as a real diffuser. This model allows source terms in the conservation equations to be specified over the real diffuser area. Air supply velocity for the momentum source is calculated from the mass flow rate $\dot{m}$ and the diffuser effective area A_0:

$$U_0 = \frac{\dot{m}}{\rho A_0} \qquad (21)$$

The momentum method is very simple, but might not work well for certain types of diffusers (Srebric and Chen 2002).

The **box** method is based on the wall jet flow generated close to the diffuser (Nielsen 1992; Srebric and Chen 2002). Figure 6 shows the location of boundary conditions around the diffuser. Details of flow immediately around the supply opening are ignored, and the supplied jet is described by values along surfaces a and b. There are two advantages of this method compared to the detailed diffuser simulations: (1) the box method does not require as fine a grid as fully numerical prediction of the wall jet development; and (2) two-dimensional predictions can be made for three-dimensional supply openings, provided that the jets develop into a two-dimensional wall jet or free jet at a certain distance from the openings. Data for velocity distribution in a wall (or free) jet generated by different commercial diffusers can be obtained from diffuser catalogues or design

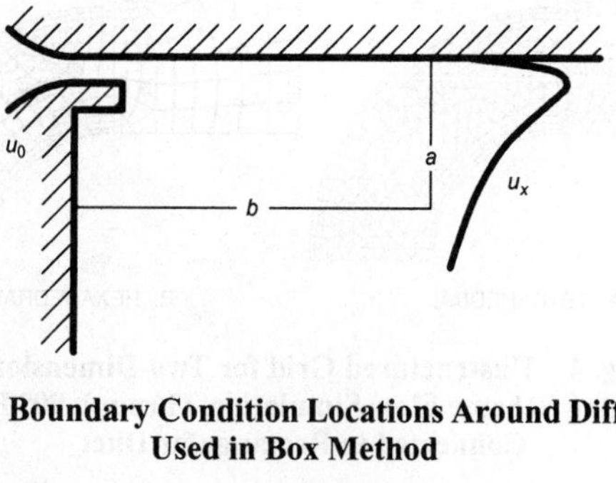

Fig. 6 Boundary Condition Locations Around Diffuser Used in Box Method

guide books, Chapter 20, and textbooks [e.g., Awbi (1991), Etheridge and Sandberg (1996), and Rajaratnam (1976)].

The **prescribed velocity** method has also been used in numerical prediction of room air movement. Figure 7 shows the method's details. Inlet profiles are given as boundary conditions of a simplified slot diffuser, represented by only a few grid points. All variables except velocities u and w are predicted in a volume close to the diffuser (x_a, y_b) as well as in the rest of the room. Velocities u and w are prescribed in the volume in front of the diffuser as the fixed analytical values obtained for a wall jet from the diffuser, or they are given as measured values in front of the diffuser (Gosman et al. 1980; Nielsen 1992).

For a more detailed description of simplified methods and their applicability to common supply diffusers, see Chen and Srebric (2000). Figure 8 shows how real diffusers can be simplified by the momentum method and box method in CFD simulations (Srebric 2000).

Outlet Boundary Conditions

A mass flow rate or constant pressure can be specified for an outlet boundary condition. The outlet flow rate or pressure boundary is extrapolated to determine the boundary velocity, which needs to be corrected during calculations to satisfy mass conservation in the analyzed domain. Some commercial CFD codes require turbulence values at outlet boundary conditions. These values are used when reversed flow occurs at the outlet pressure boundary.

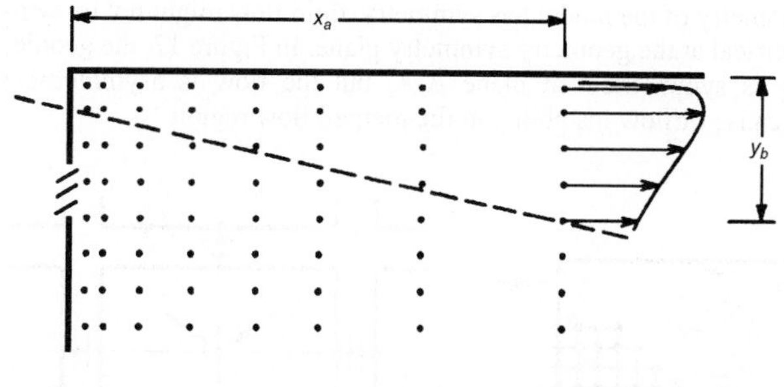

Fig. 7 Prescribed Velocity Field Near Supply Opening

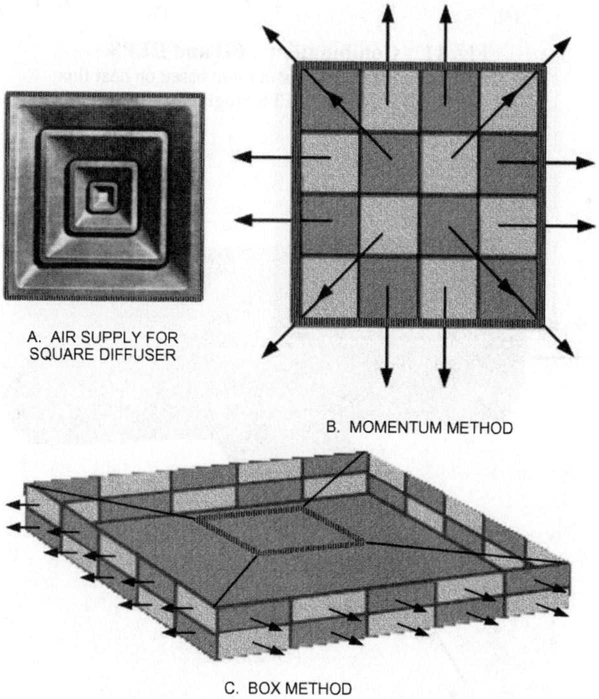

Fig. 8 Simplified Boundary Conditions for Supply Diffuser Modeling for Square Diffuser

Wall/Surface Boundary Conditions

Wall boundary conditions represent the wet, solid perimeter of the CFD model. All velocity components are set equal to wall velocity for no-slip wall conditions, and to zero for a stationary wall. This is an example of a Dirichlet boundary condition. Wall roughness for both types of flow regimes (laminar and turbulent) should be specified. At the wall, both regimes have laminar flow. For turbulent flow, the wall turbulent boundary layer consists of three sublayers as presented in Figure 9 (Wilcox 1998): a thin, viscous sublayer followed by the log-law layer and the defect layer. Turbulent flow modeling requires very fine mesh inside the boundary layer. This requires extensive computational hardware, which is very costly, but the resource requirements can be reduced by using empirical wall functions in the near wall region instead of directly applying the k-ε turbulence model with a very fine mesh.

Turbulent flow near a wall can be categorized as **laminar** (viscous sublayer) or **turbulent** (log-law layer), depending on the dimensionless distance Y^+ from the wall, defined as

$$Y^+ = \frac{\Delta Y_p}{\nu}\sqrt{\frac{\tau_w}{\rho}} \tag{22}$$

where ΔY_p is the distance from the wall to the center of the first cell, τ_w is wall shear stress, ρ is fluid density, and ν is the fluid kinematic viscosity.

The viscous sublayer is very thin ($Y^+ < 5$), and is typically smaller than the first cell ($2\Delta Y_p$). For the viscous sublayer, as shown in Figure 9,

$$u^+ = Y^+ \tag{23}$$

where u^+ is the dimensionless mean velocity ($u^+ = U_P/u_t$, $u_t = \sqrt{\tau_w/\rho}$, and U_P is the is the velocity parallel to the wall at ΔY_p).

In practical terms, most important layer is the turbulent log-law sublayer, which is characterized by the following dimensionless velocity profile:

$$u^+ = \frac{1}{\kappa}(\ln EY^+) \tag{24}$$

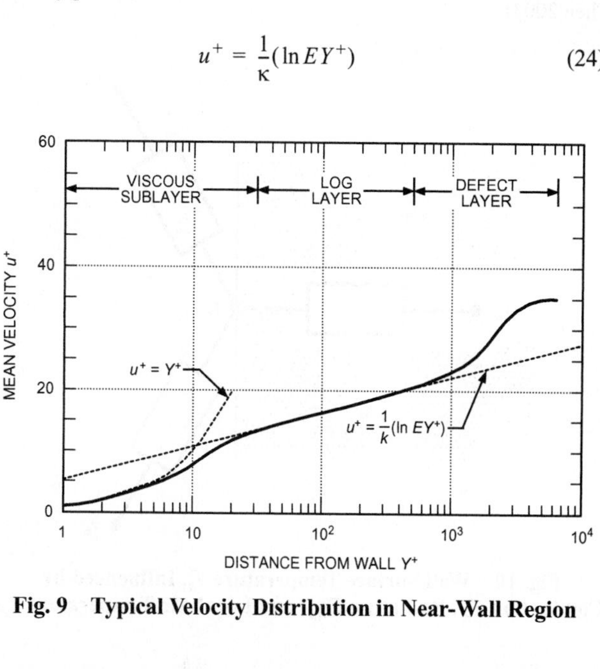

Fig. 9 Typical Velocity Distribution in Near-Wall Region

where κ is Von Karman's constant (κ = 0.41), and E is a constant depending on the wall roughness (E = 9.8 for hydraulically smooth walls).

The size of the log-law layer is typically $30 < Y^+ < 500$ (Versteeg and Malalasekera 1995). The turbulent kinetic energy k and turbulent dissipation rate ε use the following functions in the log-law layer:

$$k = \frac{u_\tau^2}{\sqrt{C_\mu}} \quad \text{and} \quad \varepsilon = \frac{u_\tau^3}{\kappa y} \tag{25}$$

where C_μ is the k-ε turbulence model constant.

Overall, wall functions are of great practical importance because they allow significant savings of computational time. However, assumptions used to derive the wall functions [i.e., Prandtl mixing hypothesis, Boussinesq eddy viscosity assumption, fully developed flow, and no pressure gradients or other momentum sources (constant shear stresses)] restrict their application to a certain class of flows. For indoor airflow applications, these assumptions are acceptable, and wall functions are widely used. However, predicted heat transfer in the near-wall region tends to be incorrect, depending on the control volume size at the wall (Yuan et al. 1994). Heat transfer calculation can be improved with more accurate temperature profile equations or use of prescribed empirical values for the convective heat transfer coefficient h.

Surface temperature and heat transfer are often complicated variables of time and position. However, many CFD simulations use steady-state boundary conditions for a typical or design day. Boundary conditions for surface temperature and heat transfer are illustrated in Figure 10, showing how surface temperature T_s depends on heat transfer to and from the surroundings, on radiation to and from the surfaces in the room, and on the air temperature close to the surface.

Boundary conditions for temperature or energy flux can be found from measurements, manual energy calculations, or a **building energy performance simulation (BEPS)** program. BEPS predicts both energy flow in the building structure and radiation plus detailed dynamic energy flow and consumption of the whole building during a period of time (Figure 11). There are different ways to exchange heat transfer information between BEPS and CFD programs (Zhai et al. 2002); the best method is to transfer surface temperatures from BEPS to CFD, and convective heat transfer coefficients and air temperature from CFD to BEPS, to achieve a unique solution (Zhai and Chen 2003).

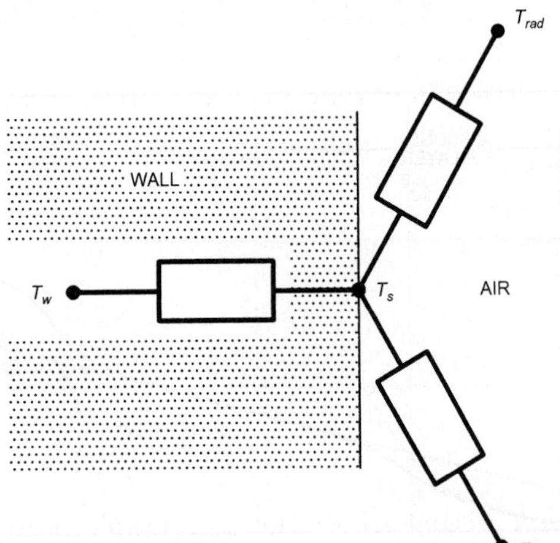

Fig. 10 Wall Surface Temperature T_s, Influenced by Conduction T_w, Radiation T_{rad}, and Local Air Temperature T_P

Dynamic simulations can be structured in different ways. A BEPS program can be connected to a separate CFD program, which predicts energy flow in selected situations. A CFD program can also be extended to find a combined solution of radiation, conduction, and thermal storage parallel to solving the flow field; this is often called a conjugate heat transfer model. Another possibility is to use additional CFD code in selected rooms as an extension of a large BEPS program. Examples of conjugate heat transfer and combined models are available in Beausoleil-Morrison (2000), Chen (1988), Kato et al. (1995), Moser et al. (1995), Nielsen and Tryggvason (1998), Srebric (2000), and Zhai and Chen (2003).

The simplest way to account for heat transfer at CFD boundaries is to prescribe wall temperatures obtained from on-site measurements. Using a turbulence model without wall functions is also recommended when heat and mass flows from surfaces are the important parameters. Predictions of actual flow at surfaces are more accurate than analytical values found from wall functions.

Symmetry Surface Boundary Conditions

For a model with symmetrical flow in at least one plane, the symmetry boundary condition represents no flow across the symmetry plane, and all scalar fluxes are set to zero.

Select symmetry boundary conditions cautiously. Although the geometry of the model has symmetry, fluid flow might not be symmetrical at the geometry symmetry plane. In Figure 12, the geometry is symmetrical at plane A-A, but the flow is asymmetrical because of flow instability at the merged flow region.

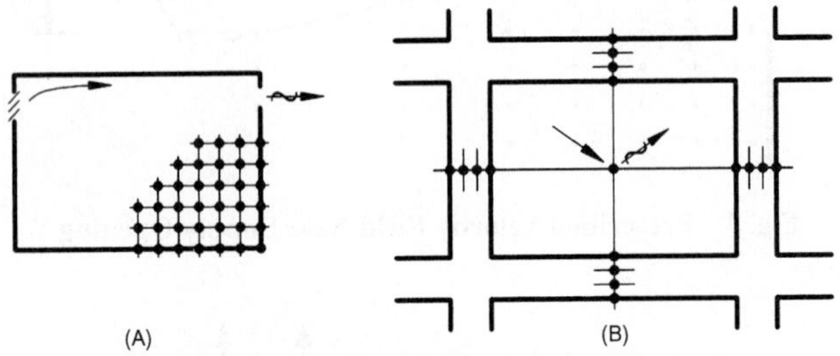

Fig. 11 Combination CFD and BEPS
The CFD program predicts flow in room based on heat flux calculated by BEPS program.

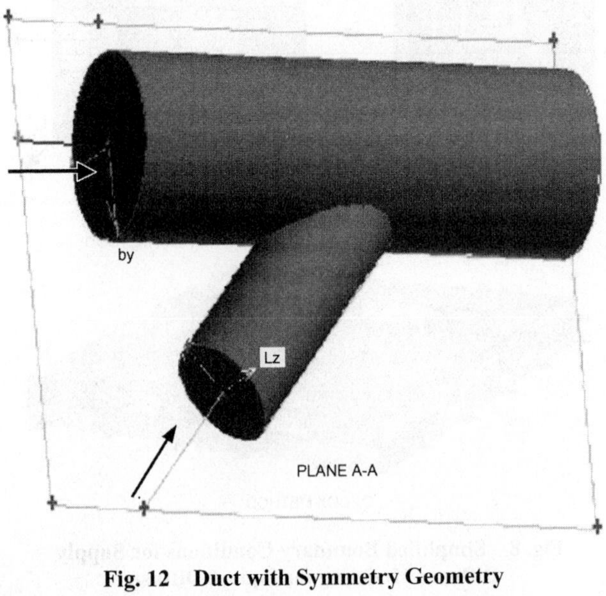

Fig. 12 Duct with Symmetry Geometry

Zhang et al. (2000) studied the symmetry pattern for a an 8.5 by 5 by 3 m room, with air supplied through a slot at the ceiling and along the 5 m long side. Return air exited through a slot at the floor along the same side wall as the inlet air. Velocity on one side of the symmetry plane was up to two times higher than on the other side, at the symmetrical location.

Fixed Sources and Sinks

Fixed sources are boundary conditions specified as fixed values of the calculated parameter or as mass/momentum/heat/contaminant fluxes. Examples include heat flux from a wall to simulate solar radiation, total heat flow in the occupied zone to simulate heat dissipation from occupants, momentum source from an operating fan, and species generation rate from contaminant sources. These sources could be placed anywhere in the CFD calculation domain, and can vary with time. Fixed-value sources/sinks usually use the wall functions if the source/sink is given as a fixed value, whereas fixed-flux sources/sinks do not use wall functions. These boundary conditions could also be associated with blockages in the flow domain (e.g., furniture, occupants, or other flow obstacles).

Modeling Considerations

Pressure boundary conditions are used when there is not enough information to specify the flow distribution, and the boundary pressure is known or assumed. Pressure boundaries are mostly used for buoyancy-driven flow and external flow applications. In inlet/outlet pressure boundary conditions, the stagnation pressure, temperature, concentration, and turbulence quantities k and ε are required. For external flow away from the wall, the free-stream k and ε can be set to zero. A pressure boundary velocity cannot be specified, but must be determined by the CFD code from interior conditions relative to the pressure boundary condition (inflow or outflow condition is possible).

When using different boundary conditions, be aware that most boundary conditions are just approximations of real physical phenomena. It is the user's responsibility to evaluate adequacy and influence of different boundary conditions on the accuracy of CFD simulation solutions.

CFD MODELING APPROACHES

Some steps are common to developing all types of CFD models and can increase the likelihood of getting a reasonable result with appropriate computing time.

Planning

Planning a CFD simulation is perhaps the most important step. During this phase, a clear understanding of what is being investigated is important. If the simulation is about thermal comfort in a room, some details about unoccupied space regions may be simplified: there may be little point in determining the thermal comfort in an unoccupied zone. If the purpose is to gain insight into a flow field, then some effort to estimate flow patterns helps during early modeling decisions and later evaluation of results.

During planning, a decision of whether to conduct a steady-state or transient simulation must be made. Transient simulations present time-accurate results, such as filling a tank, whereas steady-state simulations represent conditions after the flow field has been flowing long enough to reach equilibrium. It is important to recognize that some flows are inherently unsteady. The effect of choosing a steady-state solver to model unsteady flow should be considered during this process.

The physics to be examined should also be determined. Turbulence, heat transfer, species transport, and radiation phenomena can be evaluated during CFD modeling.

The final stage of planning is to determine how to represent the boundary conditions and flow physics. Diffusers, thermal sources leading to plumes, and contaminant sources are all important flow details that need to be appropriately represented.

Dimensional Accuracy and Faithfulness to Details

Highly detailed representation of architecture in a CFD model can significantly add to grid and computational costs. Often, high detail is not required. For instance, including doorknobs on a door will not likely change the simulation results greatly except immediately around the doorknob itself. However, if the room is negatively pressurized, significant flow through a crack beneath the door can cause a jet to propagate into the room, so accurately representing effects of flow through the crack is important. If the simulation is intended to assess thermal comfort in a laboratory with fume hoods, then the fume hood sash details may not be very important. However, if the purpose of the simulation is to evaluate fume hood capture performance, the sash opening detail can be important.

For complicated models, it can be helpful to evaluate and include the potential modifications for subsequent simulations before completing the geometry. This allows the simulation to be modified without breaking the grid and geometry, which can be the most time-consuming step of simulation. Preparing the grid for future simulations may reduce overall costs for later simulations.

CFD Simulation Steps

The basic mechanical steps in CFD simulation are as follows:

1. Create the geometry (a 3-D model of the simulation environment)
2. Generate the grid
3. Define surfaces and volumes and implement boundary conditions
4. Execute the simulation
5. Evaluate the simulation and conduct quality checks to determine whether CFD simulation is complete; refine the grid, change discretization, and continue to solve
6. Postprocess/analyze the simulation to extract desired information
7. Modify the simulation and redo as required

During planning, a large set of physical phenomena (e.g., turbulence, heat transfer, radiation, species transport, combustion) may need to be included within the simulation(s). When executing the simulation itself, starting with a minimal set of physics and then increasing the level of complexity has advantages. For example, for flow in a room with a large convective and radiant heat source from which a contaminant is escaping (e.g., an industrial furnace), (1) solve the fluid velocity field with turbulence, (2) calculate energy to get a temperature distribution, (3) add radiation to redistribute some thermal energy, and (4) track the contaminant by adding species transport equations to the simulation.

This stepped approach allows the modeler to build on previous flow field solutions and ensure that each new set of physics is starting from a reasonable estimate of the flow field. It has particular advantages for complicated models or increasing the probability of success for new users.

VERIFICATION, VALIDATION, AND REPORTING RESULTS

It is important to document and assess the credibility of CFD simulations through verification, validation, and reporting of results. The American Institute of Aeronautics and Astronautics (AIAA 1998) defines *verification* as "the process of determining that a (physical/mathematical) model implementation accurately represents the developer's conceptual description of the model and the solution on the model," and *validation* as "the process of determining the degree to which a (CFD) model is an accurate representation of the real world from the perspective of the intended uses of the model."

Verification ensures that a CFD code can accurately and correctly solve the equations used in the conceptual model; it does not imply that the computational results represent physical reality. Generally, verification is done during code development. Because very few HVAC engineers who do indoor environment analysis develop CFD codes, this section focuses mostly on code applications, not development. In addition, time and money available for simulation are usually limited, which requires that verification and validation be realistically achievable. Therefore, this section refines the definitions of verification, validation, and reporting of results:

- **Verification** identifies relevant physical phenomena for analysis and provides instructions on how to assess whether a particular CFD code can account for those physical phenomena.
- **Validation** provides instructions on how to demonstrate the coupled ability of a user and a CFD code to accurately conduct representative indoor environmental simulations with available experimental data.
- **Reporting** results provides instructions on how to summarize results so that others can make informed assessments of the value and quality of the CFD work.

Therefore, verification should represent physical realities, although the cases can be very simple, containing only one (or a few) flow and heat transfer features of the complete system. The validation cases should be close to reality and include the flow and heat transfer characteristics that need to be analyzed, although approximations may be used in the validation.

This section describes a procedure developed by Chen and Srebric (2002) for verification, validation, and reporting of CFD results, but its intent is not to develop standards. The extent of CFD's capability in modeling has not yet been developed to the point where standards can be written (AIAA 1998).

Verification

The basic physical phenomena of the indoor environment are airflow, heat transfer (conduction, convection, and radiation), mass transfer (species concentrations and solid and liquid particles), and chemical reactions (combustion). Therefore, the first step of verification is to identify benchmark cases with one or more flow and heat transfer features of those basic phenomena.

In some indoor regions, airflow can be laminar or weakly turbulent. The overall flow features are often considered as turbulent. Most indoor airflows are turbulent because of the high Rayleigh number Ra, and sometimes high Reynolds number Re, defined as

$$\mathrm{Ra} = \beta g \, \Delta T L^2 / \nu k \tag{26}$$

$$\mathrm{Re} = UL/\nu \tag{27}$$

In most rooms, Ra ranges from 10^9 to 10^{12} and Re from 10^4 to 10^7 if room height is used as the characteristic length L. Experiments have found that turbulence occurs when Ra > 10^9 and/or Re > 10^4.

Turbulence modeling approximations, which require more complex numerical schemes so that a converged solution can be achieved, must be made for CFD to solve the flow fields.

The ability of a CFD code to simulate airflow in an indoor environment and the fidelity of the computer model to the physical realities may vary, and should be assessed. Predicting indoor physical phenomena may require auxiliary flow and heat transfer models. The following aspects require special attention:

- Basic flow and heat transfer (convection, diffusion, conduction, and/or radiation)
- Turbulence models
- Auxiliary heat transfer and flow models
- Numerical methods
- Assessing CFD predictions

Whether a CFD code can be used to simulate an indoor environment depends on the flow and heat transfer features. For an indoor space with a baseboard heater, a CFD code that can solve natural convection flow may be sufficient. If a radiator replaces the baseboard heater, a radiation model is needed. When heat transfer through the walls must be considered, the code should have a conjugate heat transfer feature. When a duct supplies fresh air, room airflow becomes mixed convection, which requires the capability of mixed convection simulation. For indoor air quality studies, the code should be able to solve species concentrations. The more realistic the model is, the more complex the flow and heat transfer.

To verify a CFD code's capability of simulating the indoor environment of interest, review the code's manual and any libraries or examples provided by the developer to illustrate successful applications. Discussing the particular application with the code developer can ensure that the physical models required for the application are all available. However, even if a code has been found capable of simulating the physical phenomena in the indoor environment in the past, repeating the verification is helpful because success relies on the joint function of the user and the CFD code.

Hands-on verification usually starts with the simplest cases, which contain only one or two flow features and have been thoroughly tested to minimize uncertainties and errors. After successful verification, further simulations can be performed for more realistic cases, which may contain many key features of physical phenomena in an indoor space. The Reynolds or Rayleigh numbers can then be similar to those in reality.

Often, verification data are from high-precision experimental measurements. The quantity and quality of the experimental data are usually accompanied by quantified errors. They are generally accurate, have few human errors, cover a large area of interest in the CFD community, and are widely used for testing CFD simulations. These experimental data contain detailed information, such as boundary and initial conditions, and are usually two-dimensional.

Different cases represent different flow characteristics. Ideally, verification should be done for all flow features, but in practice, two to three important cases may be sufficient for most indoor environmental analyses.

Turbulence Model Identification. With a verification case identified, the next step is to identify a suitable turbulence model. These are divided into two groups: large eddy simulations (LES), and turbulent transport models [Reynolds-averaged Navier-Stokes (RANS) equation modeling]. LES divides turbulent flow into large-scale motion (calculated in LES) and small-scale motion (which must be modeled because of its effect on large-scale motion). Using a suitable subgrid scale model for the simulation is the most important factor, because the subgrid's accuracy and efficiency determines how correct and useful the LES is.

RANS models are more common in indoor airflow simulation. In general, eddy viscosity models are accurate for simple airflows, and Reynolds stress models are needed for complex flows. Complex flow exists in a flow domain with complex geometry, such as room and air supply diffuser geometry. Many CFD studies compare different turbulence models, so users may consult the literature for reported studies that are close to the case in question. The k-ε model is inaccurate for flows with adverse pressure gradient, which seriously limits its general usefulness. If comparisons for a particular case are not available, start with simple, popular models, such as the standard k-ε model (Launder and Spalding 1974), moving to progressively more complicated models if necessary. Vendors have made selecting different turbulence models as easy as a simple mouse click. However, a user should understand the principle of the model, its suitability for the problem to be solved, and the corresponding changes needed in using the model.

Identifying Auxiliary Heat Transfer and Flow Models. The indoor environment consists of very complicated physical phenomena, with radiative, conductive, and convective heat transfer almost always occurring simultaneously, and sometimes also including combustion, participating media radiation, and particle transport in multiple phases (air/liquid, air/solid, and air/liquid/solid). It is important to verify whether these physical phenomena can be modeled by a CFD code.

Separate verification of auxiliary models and turbulence models reduces the possibility of error. According to AIAA (1998), an error is "a recognizable deficiency in any phase or activity of modeling and simulation that is not due to lack of knowledge." A complex problem may be verified by separating it into several components that have analytical solutions. For example, a combined conductive, convective, and radiative heat transfer process can be verified by separating it into a conductive and radiative problem, and a convective problem. The two problems can then be verified by the relevant analytical solutions. Another example is liquid particle trajectory in indoor air quality simulations that involve condensation, evaporation, and collision, as well as strong interaction with airflow turbulence. The physical phenomena should be verified separately.

Verification does not ensure the correctness of the combined process. Therefore, uncertainty exists in the combined process. **Uncertainty** is a potential deficiency in any phase or activity of modeling caused by lack of knowledge; no highly accurate solutions are available. This may be addressed during validation.

Verification of numerical methods involves investigating the discretization of the continuous space and time (if transient) into finite intervals. The variables are computed at only a finite number of locations (**grid points**), so the continuous information contained in the solution of differential equations is replaced with discrete values. When a Cartesian mesh system is used for sloped or curved surfaces, the true geometry is not represented in the calculation because it would introduce an error. Thus, for sloped or curved surfaces, similar geometries must be verified rather restricting the simulation to empty rectangular rooms.

Different discretization schemes can be verified by comparing the results obtained from two different schemes. For example, to verify an unstructured grid system, Cartesian coordinates can be used as a reference. Case geometry should be simple, such as a rectangular room. Then, the two schemes should generate the same results. If the code has only one grid system, the discretization scheme verification can be combined with model verification.

Refining Grid Size and Time Step. Because CFD discretizes partial differential equations into discretized equations, this introduces an error. Verification of grid size and time step is done to reduce error to a level acceptable for the particular application. The time step applies only to transient flow simulation. Therefore, it is not sufficient to perform CFD computations on a single fixed grid. The difference in grid size and time step between two cases should be large enough to identify differences in CFD results. The common method is to repeat the computation by doubling the grid number, and compare the two solutions (Wilcox 1998). It is very important to separate numerical error from turbulence-model error, because the merits of different turbulence models cannot be objectively evaluated unless the discretization error of the numerical algorithm is known.

The geometry of an indoor space can be very complicated, and computer speed and capacity are still insufficient for simulating an indoor environment with very fine grid sizes (over a few million grids) and time steps (tens of thousands). Verification estimates the discretization error of the numerical solution. Theoretically, when grid size and time step approach zero, the discretization error of the numerical solution becomes negligible. For LES, when grid size and time step become small, flow in the subgrid scale is isotropic and the results become more accurate. When grid size is much smaller than the Kolmogorov length scale, the LES turns into a direct-numerical simulation.

Numerical Schemes, Iteration, and Convergence. A numerical scheme is important in CFD code to obtain a fast, accurate, and stable solution. A higher-order differencing scheme should be more accurate than a lower-order scheme for simple cases, such as those suggested for turbulence model verification. However, be aware of the limitations of various differencing schemes. For example, the central differencing scheme (accurate to the second order) is used for small Peclet numbers (Pe < 2), and the upwind scheme [accurate to the first order (but accounts for transportiveness)] is used for a high Peclet number. The Peclet number, the ratio of convection to conduction, is defined as

$$Pe = LU\rho C_p / k \qquad (28)$$

where C_p is specific heat.

Solution algorithms in CFD codes can be quite different, ranging from SIMPLE in conventional program with iteration, to the fast Fourier transformation for solving the Poisson pressure equation in LES without iteration. Iteration is normally needed in two situations: (1) globally for boundary value problems (i.e., over the entire domain), or (2) within each time step for transient physical phenomena. Criteria can be set to determine whether a converged solution is reached, such as a specified absolute and relative residual tolerance. The **residual** is the imbalance of solved variables (e.g., velocities, mass flow, energy, turbulence quantities, species concentrations). For indoor environment modeling, a CFD solution has converged if

$$\text{Residual for mass} = \frac{\text{Sum of absolute residuals in each cell}}{\text{Total mass inflow}} < 0.1\%$$

$$\text{Residual for energy} = \frac{\text{Sum of absolute residuals in each cell}}{\text{Total heat gains}} < 1\%$$

Similar convergence criteria can be defined for other solved variables, such as species concentration and turbulence parameters. Note that, for natural convection in a room, net mass flow is zero. Therefore, convergence has most likely been reached if there is little change (no change in the fourth digit) in the major dependent variables (temperature, velocities, and concentrations) within the last 100 iterations. However, a small relaxation factor can always give a false indication of convergence (Anderson et al. 1984).

To obtain stable and converged results, iteration often uses relaxation factors for different variables solved, such as underrelaxation factors and false time steps. Underrelaxation factors differ only slightly from false-time-steps.

Assessing CFD Predictions. A detailed qualitative and quantitative comparison of CFD results with data from experiments, analytical solutions, and direct numerical simulations is an important final step. All error analyses should be discussed in this section as well. The results indicate whether the CFD code can be used for indoor environment modeling.

Although this procedure divides verification into several parts, they often are integrated. The turbulence model and numerical technique must work together to obtain a correct CFD prediction for the flow features selected. However, it is necessary to break them down into individual items in some types of verifications, such as in CFD code development. Indoor environment designers often use commercial software, and it is logical to assume that the codes were verified during development. However, the verifications (if any) may have used different flows that are irrelevant to indoor airflow. In addition, a user may not fully understand the code's functions. It is imperative for the user to reverify a CFD code's capabilities for indoor environment simulations. This helps the user become more familiar with the code and eliminates human errors in using the code.

Generally, verification cases are not proprietary or restricted for security reasons; the data are usually available from the literature. It is strongly recommended that verification be reported when publishing CFD studies. This is especially helpful in eliminating user errors, because most CFD codes may have been validated by those cases. There are many examples of failed CFD simulations caused by user mistakes. Verification should be done for the following parameters:

- All variables solved by the governing equations (e.g., velocity, temperature, species concentrations)
- Boundary conditions (e.g., heat flux, mass inflow and outflow rates)

With these items verified, a CFD code should be able to correctly compute airflow and heat transfer encountered in an indoor environment. The level of accuracy depends on the criteria used in the verification. If the code failed to compute the flow correctly, the problem may be that (1) the code is incapable of solving the indoor airflows, (2) the code has bugs, or (3) there are errors in the user input data that defines the problem to be solved.

Validation

Validation demonstrates the ability of both the user and the code to accurately predict representative indoor environmental applications for which some sort of reliable data are available. It estimates how accurately the user can apply the code in simulating a full, real-world indoor environment problem, and gives the user the confidence to use the code for further applications, such as a design tool. A CFD code may solve the physical models selected to describe the real world, but may give inaccurate results because the selected models do not represent physical reality. For example, an indoor environment may simultaneously involve conduction, convection, and radiation, but a user may misinterpret the problem as purely convection. The CFD prediction may be correct for the convection part but fail to describe the complete physics involved. It is obviously a problem on the user's side, which validation process also tries to eliminate.

Note that *validation* addresses a complete flow and heat transfer system, or several subsystems that, together, represent a complete system. Although the procedure is almost the same, *verification* addresses only one of the flow aspects in an indoor environment.

The basic idea of validation is to identify suitable experimental data, to make sure that all important phenomena in the problem are correctly modeled, and to quantify the error and uncertainty in the CFD simulation. Because the primary role of CFD in indoor environment modeling is to serve as a high-fidelity tool for design and analysis, it is essential to have a systematic, rational, and affordable code validation process. Validation focuses on

- Confirming the capabilities of the turbulence model and other auxiliary models in predicting all the important physical phenomena associated with an indoor environment, before applying the CFD model for design and evaluation of a similar indoor environment category
- Confirming correctness of the discretization method, grid resolution, and numerical algorithm for flow simulation
- Confirming the user's knowledge of the CFD code and understanding of the basic physics involved

Ideally, validation should be performed for a complete indoor environment system that includes all important airflow and heat transfer physics and a full geometric configuration. Experimental data for a complete system can be obtained from on-site measurements or experiments in an environmental chamber. The data usually have a fairly high degree of uncertainty and large errors, and may contain little information about initial and boundary conditions. Reasonable assumptions are needed to make CFD simulation feasible.

Often, experimental data may not be available for a complete indoor environment system. In this case, validations for several subsystems or an incomplete system can be used. A subsystem represents some of the flow features in an indoor environment to be analyzed. The overall effect of several subsystems is equivalent to a complete system. For example, a complete indoor environment system consists of airflow and heat transfer in a room with occupants, furniture, and a forced air unit. If a user can correctly simulate several subsystems such as airflow and heat transfer (1) around a person, (2) in a room with obstacles, and (3) in a room with a forced air unit, the validation is acceptable. In the same example, an incomplete system for this environment can consist of airflow and heat transfer in a room with an occupant and a forced-air unit. Furniture, although it affects the indoor environment, is not as important as the other components, so validation with an incomplete system is acceptable. In either case, the key is that validation should lead to a solid confirmation of the combined capabilities of the user and code.

Although validation is for a complete indoor environment system, it is not necessary to start with a very complicated case if alternatives are available. Reliability is better

- For a simpler geometry, rather than a complicated one
- For convection, rather than combined convection, conduction, and radiation
- For single-phase flows, rather than multiphase flows
- For chemically inert materials, rather than chemically reactive materials

For complex physical phenomena in an indoor space, input data for CFD analysis may involve too much guesswork or imprecision. The available computer power may not be sufficient for high numerical accuracy, and the scientific knowledge base may be inadequate.

Complete system validation should be broken down into steps:

1. Setting up building geometry, and then placing inlets and outlets. Isothermal flow indicates the airflow pattern.
2. Adding heat transfer. Species concentration, particle trajectory, etc., should be considered later.

This progressive simulation procedure not only builds user confidence in performing the simulation, but also discovers some potential errors in the simulation.

If a CFD code has multiple choices, simple, popular models should be considered as the starting point for validation. The starting point can be as basic as

- Standard k-ε model
- No-auxiliary-flow and heat transfer models
- Structured mesh system
- Upwind scheme
- SIMPLE algorithm

The way of measuring real-world accuracy of the representation is to systematically compare CFD simulations to experimental data. The indoor environment systems used in validation are usually complicated, and the corresponding experimental data may contain bias errors and random errors, which should be reported as part of the validation. If the errors are unknown, a report on the equipment used in the measurements is helpful in assessing data quality. Although desirable, it is expensive and time-consuming to obtain good quality data for a complete system. Therefore, reporting the CFD validation of the complete system cannot be overemphasized.

The criteria for accuracy when conducting a validation depend on the application. Very high accuracy, although desirable, is not essential because most design changes are incremental variations from a baseline. As long as the predicted trends are consistent, then less-than-perfect accuracy should be acceptable. The validation process should be flexible, allowing varying levels of accuracy, and be tolerant of incremental improvements as time and funding permit. The level of agreement achieved with the test data, taking into the account measurement uncertainties, should be reviewed in light of the CFD application requirements. For example, validation for modeling air temperature in a fire simulation requires much lower minimum accuracy than that for a thermal comfort study for an indoor environment.

If validation cases are simple and represent a subsystem of a complex indoor airflow, the validation criteria should be more restrictive than those for the complete system. The criteria can also be selective. For example, if correct prediction of air velocity is more important, the criteria for heat transfer may be relaxed. Although air velocity and temperature are interrelated, one parameter's effect on the other may be second-order. This allows a fast, less detailed model to be used, such as standard k-ε model, rather than a detailed but slower model, such as low-Reynolds-number model for heat transfer calculation in boundary layers.

Reporting CFD Results

Reporting involves summarizing CFD simulation results, while providing sufficient information on the value and quality of the CFD work. This is an important quality assurance strategy for CFD analysis of the indoor environment.

It is recommended to start with verification and then proceed to validation. In principle, reports for technical audiences should include the information discussed in the verification and validation sections, such as

- Experimental design
- CFD models and auxiliary heat transfer and flow models
- Boundary conditions
- Numerical methods
- Comparison of the CFD results with the data
- Drawing conclusions

The reporting format, however, can be flexible. If a report were intended for nontechnical readers, including only the last two items would be sufficient.

Experimental Design. Thermal and flow conditions of the test environment should be described in enough detail that other people could repeat the simulation. This can be as simple as a reference to the literature or a description of cases in the report. An analysis of uncertainties and errors in the experimental data or a short description of the experimental procedure and equipment should also be included.

CFD Models and Auxiliary Heat Transfer and Flow Models. CFD includes hundreds of different models of LES and RANS. Many popular turbulence models have been widely used and reported, making it unnecessary to provide detailed formulation. When reporting CFD results, it is important to specify which turbulence model is used. If the model has not been widely reported, detailed information (including why the model was selected) should be presented.

Indoor environment analysis may require auxiliary heat transfer and flow models. For example, a building may use porous material as insulation. Heat transfer through the insulation combines conduction, convection, and radiation (too complex a process for limited computer resources to simulate in detail). Instead, a lumped-parameter model may be used to combine the heat transfer processes and obtain accurate CFD results for the indoor environment. Therefore, it should be described in the CFD analysis report.

Boundary Conditions. Accurate specification of boundary conditions is crucial, because they indicate how the user interprets the specific physical phenomena into a computer model or mathematical equations that can be solved by the code. This interpretation requires the most skill in CFD modeling. Therefore, detailed description of boundary conditions can help others make informed assessments of the simulation's quality. Include the following information:

- **Geometry settings** (the size of the computational domain along with sizes and locations of all solid objects represented in the model). If there is an external wall involved that cannot be considered adiabatic, external ambient conditions (e.g., ambient temperature, external radiation temperature, convective heat transfer coefficient) should be reported as well.
- **Inlet.** Airflow from a diffuser greatly affects a room's airflow pattern. Diffuser geometry, and approximations are often used in a complete system to make indoor airflow solvable. Therefore, the CFD report should give detailed information on the approximations used, as well as the set boundary conditions for the inlet. In some situations, the exact location of an inlet may be difficult to identify (e.g., air infiltration from the outdoors to an indoor space could be through the cracks of windows and doors). Conditions may differ from one window to another. Also, infiltration flow rate can be difficult to estimate because wind magnitude and direction change over time. Furthermore, turbulence parameters for the inlet are generally unknown, and should be estimated. Therefore, how these "inlet" conditions are specified should be clearly stated.
- **Outlet.** An outlet has little effect on room airflow. However, conditions set for the outlet often can significantly influence numerical stability. For example, the outlet may become an inlet during iteration of a calculation. If the default outlet temperature is 0°C, this could lead to a diverged solution.
- **Walls.** Rigid surfaces in an indoor space, such as walls, ceilings, floors, and furniture surfaces, are all considered as walls. Very close to the wall, airflow is laminar, and convective heat transfer often occurs in this region between the flow and surfaces. Many turbulence models cannot accurately handle the laminar sublayer, so ad hoc solutions, such as damping functions, are often used. How a CFD code treats wall boundary conditions greatly affects the accuracy of numerical results. Even if the indoor space is large and the wall effect seems small, accurate prediction of heat transfer from the walls to room air is still important.
- **Open boundary.** When the area of interest is a part of the indoor space, the computational domain does not have to align with a rigid surface; instead, an "open" boundary can be defined. Depending on the inside and outside pressure difference, air may flow in or out across the open boundary.
- **Source/sink.** This boundary condition fixes thermal or dynamic parameters (e.g., heat flux from a wall to simulate solar radiation, total heat flow in the occupied zone to simulate heat dissipation from occupants, momentum source from an operating fan, species generation rate from contaminant sources) in a defined region. Describe the location, size, and parameter being specified.
- **Coupling between a micro and a macro model.** For a large indoor space, CFD analysis may be divided into micro and macro simulations. The micro simulation zooms into a particular area to reveal details of flow and thermal characteristic on a small scale compared with that for the entire space of interest. This allows finer-resolution examination of details of flow in that area. The macro simulation is applied to the entire flow system, and may use the results of the micro simulation so that a coarser grid system can be used. This coupling is usually a complicated procedure that should be detailed in the report.
- **Other approximations.** Approximations are almost always involved when representing the real world in a computer model. For example, when the surface temperature distribution of a heated object is not uniform, the CFD simulation may choose to neglect temperature variation on the surface. When designing a large stadium, it may not be feasible to simulate each individual spectator; instead, the model may combine all the spectators into a human layer. There are numerous examples in indoor environment modeling that need to be approximated in a CFD simulation. All approximations should be reported.

Numerical Methods. It is essential to report the numerical methods used in the analysis, although the report can be brief if the technique is popular and widely available from the literature. The numerical technique includes discretization technique, grid size and quality, time step, numerical schemes, iteration number, and convergence criteria. The report should briefly state why the technique was used, and how suitable it is to the problem under consideration. It is also important to provide the quality indices of the mesh of a body-fitted coordinate, because mesh quality affects the prediction's accuracy. Typically, these indices include normal distances from solid surfaces to the centers of the first adjacent cells, maximum scale ratios of each two neighboring cells in each coordinate, and smallest angle of mesh cells. The first index determines the prediction of boundary layer flows, and the other two indicate whether unacceptable numerical errors are introduced into the simulation. Because a coarse grid introduces more numerical viscosity, grid-refinement study is essential to achieving a grid-independent solution, and should be included in the CFD report. Although it may not be realistic to conduct grid refinement for the complete system, it should be conducted for benchmark cases, to estimate the errors introduced in the complete system.

If different numerical schemes have been tested, the results should be reported. Knowing the performance of different numerical schemes helps identify whether a numerical scheme or turbulence model causes a discrepancy between the CFD results and experimental data. Iteration number and convergence criteria are interrelated. It is better to use the sum of the absolute residual at each cell for all the variables as convergence criteria. The relaxation method and values should also be reported.

Comparison of Results with Data. The most important part of the report is comparing experimental data with analysis results. Qualitative values, such as airflow pattern, should be compared first, followed by first-order parameters, such as air velocity, temperature, and species concentrations. In general, both CFD results and experimental data are more accurate for first-order parameters. Second-order parameters, such as turbulence kinetic energy, Reynolds stresses, and heat fluxes, usually have greater uncertainties and errors than the first-order parameters in both the results and the experimental data, so seeking perfect agreement for these parameters is unnecessary.

It is insufficient to describe the comparison between CFD results and experimental data as *excellent*, *good*, *fair*, *poor*, or *unacceptable*. For example, a 20% difference can be considered excellent for a complex flow problem, but rather poor for two-dimensional forced convection in an empty room. Therefore, the comparison should be quantitative. The most useful information from comparison is how to interpret discrepancies. If there is little discrepancy, it is important to know why a turbulence model that uses approximations can predict the physical phenomena so well. The comparison should clearly state the uncertainties and errors of the experimental data, if they are known.

Conclusions. The most important findings of the CFD analysis should be presented as its conclusions, which should have broad applicability to indoor environment simulation. The report may also recommend measures for further improvements in CFD analyses.

MULTIZONE NETWORK AIRFLOW AND CONTAMINANT TRANSPORT MODELING

Multizone or network models are used to address airflow, contaminant transport, heat transfer, or some combination thereof. This section presents the mathematical and numerical background of network airflow and contaminant transport models. Thermal network models are addressed in Chapter 19.

MULTIZONE AIRFLOW MODELING

Theory

Network airflow models idealize a building as a collection of zones, such as rooms, hallways, and duct junctions, joined by flow paths representing doors, windows, fans, ducts, etc. Thus, the user assembles a building description by connecting zones via the appropriate flow paths.

The network model predicts zone-to-zone airflows based on the pressure-flow characteristics of the path models, and pressure differences across the paths. Three types of forces drive flow through the paths: wind, temperature differences (stack effect), and mechanical devices such as fans.

As shown in Figure 13, airflow network models resemble electrical networks. Airflow corresponds to electric current, with zone pressure acting like the voltage at an electrical node. Flow paths correspond to resistors and other electrical elements, including active elements like batteries (fans).

Unlike CFD models, network models do not prescribe details of airflow in zones. Thus, at any given time, each network zone is characterized by a single pressure. Pressure in the zone varies according to height, for example, using the simple hydrostatic relationship $P + \rho gh$ = constant. Air density ρ is determined by the equation of state $\rho = P/R_{air}T$, based on the zone reference pressure P, temperature T, and the gas constant of the air mixture R_{air}. Zone temperature is given either directly by the user, or by an independent thermal model. The gas constant is typically assumed to be that of dry air, but can be made a function of other non-trace constituents as well (e.g., water vapor).

This lack of detail in the network zone models makes CFD preferable for predicting thermal comfort, or designing displacement ventilation systems, where airflow patterns in a room control the quantities of interest (Emmerich 1997).

In network airflow modeling, flow path models provide most of the modeling detail. Typically, the airflow rate $F_{j,i}$ from zone j to zone i, in kg/s, is some function of the pressure drop $P_j - P_i$ along the flow path:

$$F_{j,i} = f(P_j - P_i) \tag{29}$$

Various models represent different types of flow paths, but they are typically nonlinear. For example, the power-law model is commonly implemented as

$$Q = C(\Delta P)^n \tag{30}$$

where

Q = F/ρ = volumetric airflow rate, m³/s
ΔP = pressure drop across opening, Pa
C = flow coefficient, $(\text{Pa}^{1/n}\cdot\text{m}^3)$/s
n = flow exponent (typically 0.5 to 0.6)
ρ = density of air in flow path, kg/m³

$\Delta P_{j,i}$ is assumed to be governed by the Bernoulli equation, which accounts for static pressure on each side of the flow path and

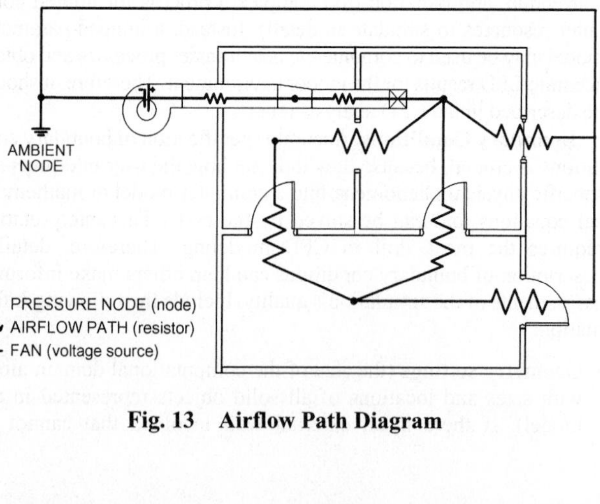

Fig. 13 Airflow Path Diagram

pressure differences through the flow path caused by density and height changes. Static pressure at flow path connections depends on the zone pressures, again after accounting for height-dependent pressure changes in the zones. Where a flow path connects to the building facade, the pressure also may depend on pressure imposed by wind (see Chapters 16 and 24). Typically, the calculated pressure drop through a flow path neglects heat transfer and changes in kinetic energy, but this is not an inherent limitation of the model.

The power law model is based on engineering equations for orifice flow (see Chapter 16). Models for duct system components (e.g., dampers, bends, transitions) also follow the power law, with flow coefficient C given by tables (see Chapter 21). Other models describe the flow through doors and windows, fans, and so on (Dols and Walton 2002; Fuestel 1998).

The network airflow model combines the flow element and zone relations by enforcing mass conservation at each zone. The mass of air m_i in zone i is given by the ideal gas law

$$m_i = \rho_i V_i = \frac{P_i V_i}{R_{air} T_i} \tag{31}$$

where

m_i = mass of air in zone i, kg
ρ_i = zone density, kg/m^3
V_i = zone volume, m^3
P_i = zone pressure, Pa
T_i = zone temperature, K
R_{air} = gas constant for air = 287.055 J/(kg·K)

For a transient solution, the principle of conservation of mass states that

$$\frac{\partial m_i}{\partial t} = \rho_i \frac{\partial V_i}{\partial t} + V_i \frac{\partial \rho_i}{\partial t} = \sum_j F_{j,i} + F_i \tag{32}$$

$$\frac{\partial m_i}{\partial t} \approx \frac{1}{\Delta t}\left[\left(\frac{P_i V_i}{R_{air} T_i}\right)_t - (m_i)_{t-\Delta t}\right] \tag{33}$$

where

$F_{j,i}$ = airflow rate between zones j and i (positive values indicate flows from j to i; negative values indicate flows from i to j), kg/s
F_i = nonflow processes that could add or remove significant quantities of air flows from j to i; negative values indicate flows from i to j

However, airflows are typically calculated for steady-state conditions. This is reasonable for most cases where driving forces change slowly compared to the airflow (e.g., because of the building's large thermal mass, or because rate-limited actuators change damper and fan settings slowly compared to the rate at which the airflow system reestablishes a steady state). Under this quasi-steady assumption, mass conservation in zone i reduces to

$$\sum_j F_{j,i} = 0 \tag{34}$$

This model was based on the assumption that airflows were quiescent and that the zones' resistance to airflow was negligible relative to the resistance imposed by the airflow paths that connect the zones. Hence, the model enforces conservation of mass in each zone, but does not conserve momentum. This means it cannot model some effects, such as the suction that develops in one branch of a duct junction because of flow in another branch (see Chapter 21), or effects of zone geometry (e.g., short-circuiting of a room when a ventilation supply duct blows air directly into a return air intake). For momentum-based effects, a CFD model of the room is preferable to a network model.

Solution Techniques

In a nodal formulation of the network airflow problem, zone pressures drive the problem. Specifically, the solution algorithm chooses one reference pressure for each zone, and then finds the driving pressure drops across each flow path, after accounting for changes of height in both zones and flow paths. Applying the element pressure/flow relations yields each path's mass flow. Finally, these flows are summed for each zone to determine whether mass conservation is satisfied.

This approach leads to a set of algebraic mass balance equations that must be satisfied simultaneously for any given point in time. Because airflows depend nonlinearly on node pressures, these equations are nonlinear, and therefore must be solved iteratively using a nonlinear equation solver. The simultaneous set of mass balance equations is typically solved using the **Newton-Raphson method** to "correct" the zone reference pressures until the simultaneous mass balance of all flows is achieved. This method requires a **correction vector**, which depends on the partial derivatives of relationships between flow and pressure for all flow connections. Therefore, these flow-pressure relationships must be first-order differentiable (Feustel 1998; Walton 1989).

The Newton-Raphson method begins with an initial guess of the pressures. A new estimated vector of all zone pressures $\{\mathbf{P}\}^*$ is computed from the current estimate of pressures $\{\mathbf{P}\}$ by

$$\{\mathbf{P}\}^* = \{\mathbf{P}\} - \{\mathbf{C}\} \tag{35}$$

where the correction vector $\{\mathbf{C}\}$ is computed by the matrix relationship

$$[\mathbf{J}]\{\mathbf{C}\} = \{\mathbf{B}\} \tag{36}$$

where $\{\mathbf{B}\}$ is a column vector of total flow into each zone, with each element given by

$$\mathbf{B}_i = \sum_j F_{j,i} \tag{37}$$

$[\mathbf{J}]$ is the square (i.e., N by N for a network of N zones) Jacobian matrix whose elements are given by

$$\mathbf{J}_{i,j} = \sum_i \frac{\partial F_{j,i}}{\partial P_j} \tag{38}$$

In Equations (37) and (38), $F_{j,i}$ and $\partial F_{j,i}/\partial P_j$ are evaluated using the current estimate of pressure $\{\mathbf{P}\}$.

Equation (35) represents a set of linear equations which must be solved iteratively until a convergent solution of the set of zone pressures is achieved. In its full form, $[\mathbf{J}]$ requires computer memory for N^2 values, and a standard Gauss elimination solution has execution time proportional to N^3. Sparse matrix methods can be used to reduce both the storage and execution time requirements. Two solution methods for the linear equations have been successfully implemented: **Skyline** (also called the **profile method**) and **preconditioned conjugate gradient (PCG)**, which may be useful for problems with many zones and junctions (Dols and Walton 2002). The number of iterations needed to find a solution may be reduced by applying descent-based techniques to Newton-Raphson (Dennis and Schnabel 1996). Under a fairly modest set of conditions, line search methods are guaranteed to converge to a unique solution (Lorenzetti 2002).

CONTAMINANT TRANSPORT MODELING

Fundamentals

Multizone contaminant transport models generally address transport of contaminants by advection via interzone airflows and mechanical system flows while accounting for some or all of the following: contaminant generation by various sources or chemical reaction, removal by filtration, chemical reaction, radiochemical decay, settling, or sorption of contaminants.

Unlike CFD models, the details of contaminant distribution within a zone are not modeled: each zone is considered well-mixed and characterized by a single concentration at any given point in time. Therefore, the well-mixed assumption's applicability to the mixing time and pattern of airflow in a zone should be considered. For example, the well-mixed assumption may be quite appropriate for zones with a mixing time well within the solution time step of interest (e.g., long-term off-gassing of building materials in common ventilation system configurations with relatively steady airflows). However, if a zone is characterized by steep concentration gradients and the time step of interest is relatively short (e.g., a chemical release in a relatively large zone), CFD analysis might be more appropriate. This is especially true if the reason for analysis is to resolve concentration gradients within the zone.

Solution Techniques

Generally, the goal is to solve a set of mass balance equations for each contaminant in each zone.

The mass of contaminant α in zone i is

$$m_{\alpha,i} = m_i C_{\alpha,i} \tag{39}$$

where m_i is the mass of air in zone i and $C_{\alpha,i}$ is the concentration mass fraction of α (kg of α/kg of air).

Contaminant is removed from zone i by

- Outward airflows from the zone at a rate of $\Sigma_j F_{i,j} C_{\alpha,j}$, where $F_{i,j}$ is the rate of air flow from zone i to zone j
- Removal at the rate $C_{\alpha,i} R_{\alpha,i}$ where $R_{\alpha,i}$ (kg of air/s) is a removal coefficient
- First-order chemical reactions with other contaminants $C_{\beta,i}$ (kg of β/kg of air) at rate $m_i \Sigma_\beta \kappa_{\alpha,\beta} C_{\beta,i}$, where $\kappa_{\alpha,\beta}$(1/s) is the kinetic reaction coefficient in zone i between species α and β

Contaminant is added to the zone by

- Inward airflows at rate $\Sigma_j (1 - \eta_{\alpha,j,i}) F_{j,i} C_{\alpha,j}$ where $\eta_{\alpha,j,i}$ is the filter efficiency in the path from zone j to zone i
- Generation at rate $G_{\alpha,i}$ (kg of α/s)
- Reactions of other contaminants

Conservation of contaminant mass for each species and assuming trace dispersal (i.e., $m_{\alpha,i} << m_i$) produces the following basic equation for contaminant dispersal for a given zone in a building:

$$\frac{dm_{\alpha,i}}{dt} = -R_{\alpha,i} C_{\alpha,i} - \sum_j F_{i,j} C_{\alpha,i} + \sum_j F_{i,j} (1 - \eta_{\alpha,j,i}) C_{\alpha,j} + m_i \sum_\beta \kappa_{\alpha,\beta} C_{\beta,i} + G_{\alpha,i} \tag{40}$$

This equation must be developed and solved for all zones to determine each contaminant's concentration. The various techniques for solving the ensuing set of equations can be categorized by the fundamental control volume used to develop them (i.e., Eulerian or Lagrangian), and by whether the analysis is geared towards solving the steady-state or dynamic system, or determining analytical solutions via eigen-analysis (Axley 1987, 1988; Dols and Walton 2002; Rodriguez and Allard 1992).

MULTIZONE MODELING APPROACHES

Simulation Planning

Planning can improve results and reduce the amount of input effort required in multizone simulations. The most important steps are determining what aspects of flow and contaminant transport are being studied, and what driving forces are likely to be most important.

One of the first decisions is defining zones in the model. The level of detail needed depends on both the building and scenario being modeled. For a study of contaminant transport from a garage into a house, separate zone models of clothes closets or kitchen cabinets are unnecessary and typically would only be needed if, for example, the source of the contaminant were inside the closet or cabinet. Because zones are typically broken where there are obstructions to air movement and/or differences in air properties, often a doorway between adjacent rooms is an appropriate place to define zones. Therefore, usually, a good starting point is to consider each room as a separate zone, and then model smaller enclosures in more detail or subdivide nonuniform rooms as necessary. On the other hand, sometimes the problem statement allows several rooms to be grouped together as a single zone. This is usually done to save user input time, because multizone models of even very large buildings can be quickly simulated on a desktop PC. HVAC system zoning also provides cues about how to group zones. Considering the primary driving forces (natural, mechanical, etc.) and the relative resistance of the flow elements that connect the zones to these forces can also be helpful. Starting with the assumption that each room is a zone, these changes can be made as the physics of the problem allow.

The type of simulation must also be determined. Are only airflow data necessary, or are contaminant concentrations also needed? Are the flow and contaminant transport problems steady-state, cyclical, or transient? Note that they may not be the same. Some models can simulate steady-state flow and transient contaminant transport.

During planning, the required model input data and boundary condition information must be specified, with the level of detail depending on the problem. Some items to consider are exterior envelope and interzonal leakage, weather conditions, wind pressure profiles, contaminant characteristics, contaminant source types and strengths, mechanical system flow rates, control algorithms, occupancy, and zone volumes.

Steps

The following process is typical of that used by experienced modelers to help catch mistakes and verify that the model is as intended. Always remember to save and test the model often.

1. **Input zones and building geometry**, using just enough detail to capture necessary information.
2. **Determine and specify building leakage**. This information may be obtained from blower door or tracer gas tests of the actual building, or estimated based on published data (see Chapter 16). Perform the following tests:
   - *Simulated blower door test*: Within the model, set all interior doors in the building to *open* and put a large pressurization fan in an exterior wall. Pressurize the building and use the fan's flow rate and consequent pressure difference across the exterior wall to calculate the leakage area per area of exterior wall. Verify specification of the proper amount of leakage on all walls by comparing inputs with data from an actual building or the literature. This is especially important when specifying individual leakage paths. If a result does not make sense, adjust leakage paths to see their effect on overall leakage.
   - *Simulation with typical weather boundary conditions*. Verify that the resulting infiltration rate is realistic.

3. **Check stack effects**. Remove the blower door fan from the model, specify a very cold outdoor temperature, and run a simulation. Check the location of the **neutral pressure level**, which is the collection of points on the building envelope where the pressure difference with the outdoors is zero. The points usually form a plane at the building's midheight, though it may be a bit higher if roof leakage occurs with no corresponding floor leakage. A very high or low neutral pressure level could indicate large unintended leaks, probably somewhere near the neutral pressure level. (Note that, in complex operating systems or scenarios, the neutral pressure level may not form a plane and could change with time.)
4. **Specify wind and wind pressure profiles** on exterior leakage paths: Some programs allow wind specification, but this has no effect unless the wind pressure profile for each path is also specified. Perform the following tests:
   - *Run a simulation with no stack effect or mechanical system, and a high wind.* Flow should be visible through each exterior path. This allows quick identification of paths that may be missing a wind pressure profile.
   - *Verify that inflows and outflows are as prescribed* for the wind pressure profile. (For example, inflow on the windward side, outflow for walls at negative pressure) This helps verify that the pressure profile is correctly input and that the building and wind are oriented properly.
   - *Try other terrain conditions* to see if changing this variable significantly affects results.
5. **Input air-handling system(s)** (if any). Again, use only as much detail as is necessary. For small buildings, it may be reasonable to represent the air-handling system as a simple fan through an exterior wall for ventilation. For internal distribution from zone to zone, HVAC system flows in and out of each zone must be specified. Duct details should be included only if they are an important aspect of the problem. Sometimes supply and return vents can be placed in plenums or other locations where duct leakage is expected, to approximate duct leakage. However, if pressure-driven leakage must be modeled, the ducts should be specified in detail. Keep in mind that leakage in VAV systems, for example, should be separately specified upstream and downstream of the VAV box. Perform the following tests:
   - *Run a simulation with no stack or wind driving forces* and check outdoor, return, and exhaust air volumes to verify that the outside air is properly defined. This is a common beginner's mistake because there are several ways to specify outside air (e.g., setting a percentage of outside air, or scheduling outside air when the default may be 100%), and they may override one another. Also note that the amount of return air specified must equal or exceed the recirculation air needed. Otherwise, outdoor air may be used to make up the difference.
   - *Verify a realistic pressure difference across walls.* For example, a 50 Pa pressure difference would not occur in a real house, and probably indicates problems with either the system or leakage input. It is important that the magnitude of the pressure differences makes sense for the situation being modeled.
6. **Specify contaminants.** Contaminant sources are usually specified on either a mass or volume basis, although numerical counts (e.g., of particles, spore counts, etc.) can also be modeled and can typically be interchanged with mass units. Model refinement is often most appropriate and desirable near the contaminant source, where large concentration gradients are present. Simulation tests for pressure and velocity suggest the expected accuracy when a contaminant is added to the system. Transport of contaminants, particularly aerosols, is also influenced by other mechanisms, for which coefficients are specified in the basic transport equations.
   - *Verify that the model predicts conservation of contaminant mass* across multiple zones.
   - *Use experimental tracer analysis* using dynamically similar, nontoxic materials (if desired and feasible).
7. **Run a sensitivity analysis**: Deviations in some variables may need to be considered. Depending on the source of the input data and type of simulation, it is often good to know how the system performs over a range of certain variables. Possible items to consider include
   - *Formal sensitivity analysis*, if resources permit.
   - *Leakage dependence*, tested under a range of values. If conclusions are too leakage-dependent and leakage test data are not available, then a range of possible results should be considered.
   - *System pressure balance.* In a building with multiple air-handling systems, their design flow rates may imply perfect balance between systems; however, in real buildings, the balance will never be perfect, which can drive contaminants into shafts and distribute them through the building. Pressurizing or depressurizing a floor slightly compared to others (by specifying slightly imbalanced system flows) can illustrate how big this effect is.
   - *Weather effects*, which can be particularly important when studying infiltration or trying to maintain a pressure differential somewhere in the system. Verify that the system can accommodate the expected range of outdoor conditions.

VERIFICATION AND VALIDATION

Verification and validation of multizone models are similar in many regards to that of CFD models. Because the number of cases a complex multizone model can simulate is unlimited, Herrlin (1992) concluded that absolute validation is impossible. However, validation is still important to identify and eliminate large errors and to establish the model's range of applicability. Therefore, a model's performance should be evaluated under a variety of situations, with the recognition that predictions will always have a degree of uncertainty.

Herrlin lists three techniques of model validation:

- **Analytical verification** (comparison to simple analytically solved cases)
- **Intermodel comparison** (comparison of one model to another)
- **Empirical validation** (comparison to experimental tests)

Herrlin also discussed some specific difficulties in validating multizone airflow models, including input uncertainty (particularly of air leakage distribution) and attempting to simulate processes that cannot be modeled (e.g., using a steady-state airflow model to simulate dynamic airflow).

ASTM *Standard* D5157, Standard Guide for Statistical Evaluation of Indoor Air Quality Models, provides information on establishing evaluation objectives, choosing data sets for evaluation, statistical tools for assessing model performance, and considerations in applying statistical tools. It stresses that data used for the evaluation process should be independent of the data used to develop the model. Also, sufficiently detailed information should be available for both the measured pollutant concentrations and the required input parameters. *Standard* D5157 also discusses the fact that model validation consists of multiple evaluations, with each evaluation assessing performance in specific situations.

Analytical Verification

Analytical verifications of multizone modeling tools are routinely performed to check the numerical solution. Analytical test cases are simple forms of problems that can be solved analytically to compare the model with an exact solution. For multizone models, these include airflow elements in series and parallel; stack effect; wind pressure effect; fan and duct elements; contaminant generation, dispersal, filtration, and deposition; and simple kinetic reactions. These tests are typically performed by model developers, but may be repeated by the user to develop confidence in the model and to verify the user's familiarity with the model. Such tests are not routinely published, but some were described by Walton (1989).

Unfortunately, most buildings are too complicated for the equations describing airflow and pollutant transport to be solved analytically. Therefore, analytical verification is of limited value in determining the adequacy of a multizone IAQ model for practical applications.

Intermodel Comparison

Intermodel comparison provides a relative check of different models' assumptions and numerical solutions. As with analytical verification, this is of limited value in evaluating a model's adequacy for practical applications. Generally, intermodel comparisons are not essential to a user, although good comparisons allow empirical validation conclusions to be generalized beyond the specific model studied.

Haghighat and Megri (1996) reported good agreement between CONTAM [the predecessor of CONTAMW (Dols and Walton 2002)], COMIS (Feustel et al. 1989), AIRNET (Walton 1989), CBSAIR (Haghighat and Rao 1991), and BUS (Tuomaala 1993) for airflow predictions for a four-zone model. The model building was two stories tall, with power-law flow elements for leakage. A single set of temperatures and wind-induced pressures was simulated. Model predictions for zone pressures and flow rates were within 5% and 13%, respectively.

Orme (2000) also found good agreement overall between CONTAM, COMIS, MZAP (unpublished), and BREEZE (BRE 1994) airflow predictions for a three-story building model. Power-law airflow elements were used to connect the four interior zones with each other and the ambient zone. A single wind speed and ambient temperature condition were applied. Note that both of these intermodel comparisons tested models for only a very limited range of conditions.

Empirical Validation

Empirical validation compares model assumptions and numerical solutions to indoor environmental problems of practical interest. However, the standard is only as accurate or realistic as the measurements used to produce it. Not only do all models have uncertainty, but all measurements do as well. Differences between model predictions and measurements could stem from errors in either set of data. As discussed in the section on CFD Modeling Approaches, comparison depends on the numerical model's capabilities and limiting assumptions, as well as the modeler's knowledge of both the model being applied and the indoor environment being modeled.

It is essential to apply valid statistical tools when interpreting comparisons of measurements and predictions. ASTM *Standard* D5157 provides three statistical tools for evaluating accuracy of IAQ predictions, and two additional statistical tools for assessing bias. Values for these statistical criteria are provided to indicate whether model performance is adequate. Note that the criteria and specific values in *Standard* D5157 are not ultimate arbiters of model accuracy, but they provide a useful template for the type of statistical analysis needed. Other valid statistical criteria may be substituted, with values appropriate for the accuracy needed for a specific project.

ASTM *Standard* D5157 suggests the following for assessing agreement between predictions:

- The correlation coefficient of predictions versus measurements should be 0.9 or greater.
- The line of regression between predictions and measurements should have a slope between 0.75 and 1.25 and an intercept less than 25% of the average measured concentration.

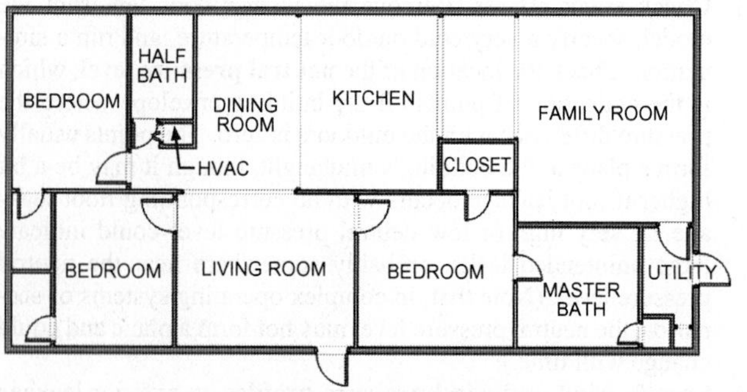

Fig. 14 Floor Plan of Living Area Level of Manufactured House

- The **normalized mean square error (NMSE)** should be less than 0.25. NMSE is calculated as

$$\text{NMSE} = \sum_{i=1}^{N} (C_{pi} - C_{oi})^2 / (n\bar{C}_o\bar{C}_p) \tag{41}$$

where C_p is the predicted concentration and C_o is the observed concentration.

For assessing bias,

1. The **normalized** or **fractional bias FB of mean concentrations** should be 0.25 or lower, and is calculated as

$$\text{FB} = 2(\bar{C}_p - \bar{C}_o)/(\bar{C}_p + \bar{C}_o) \tag{42}$$

2. The **fractional bias FS of variance** should be 0.5 or lower. FS is calculated as

$$\text{FS} = 2(\sigma^2\bar{C}_p - \sigma^2\bar{C}_o)/(\sigma^2\bar{C}_p + \sigma^2\bar{C}_o) \tag{43}$$

Emmerich (2001) reviewed the research literature for reports of empirical multizone model validation for residential-scale buildings. Few reviewed reports used either the ASTM *Standard* D5157 measures or other limited statistical evaluations to evaluate the results. However, for those cases with sufficient published data, Emmerich calculated several statistical measures from *Standard* D5157. Although these measures specifically address concentrations, they have been used to compare predicted and measured airflow rates also. Table 1 summarizes these published multizone model validation efforts.

There are many published validations for residential buildings, but far fewer for large commercial buildings because of the significant effort and cost involved in detailed measuring of a large building. Commercial studies are available by Furbringer et al. (1993), Said and MacDonald (1991), and Upham (1997).

Example 1. Ventilation Characterization of a New Manufactured House. Develop a multizone model to investigate various ventilation strategies of a new double-wide manufactured home consisting of three levels: crawlspace, living area, and attic. The crawlspace is divided into two sections by an insulated plastic belly; the region above the belly contains HVAC ductwork, and the volume below vents to the outdoors. The living area is shown in Figure 14. The attic comprises the volume above the vaulted ceiling, with five roof vents and eave vents spanning the perimeter of the house. Figure 15 provides a schematic of the house, showing connections between the levels and the air distribution system.

The building has an automated data acquisition system for monitoring air temperatures, building pressures, weather, and HVAC operation.

Table 1 Summary of Multizone Model Validation Reports

Reference	Test Building	Model	Parameter Evaluated	R	m	B	NMSE	FB
Bassett 1990	Five houses	CONTAM	Zone air change rates	0.91	1.31	–0.23	0.35	0.08
			Interzone airflows	0.27	0.10	1.34	2.98	0.37
Blomsterberg et al. 1999	Houses and apartment flats	COMIS	Average whole-house air change rates	0.98	1.04	–0.03	0.01	0.01
			Average room air change rates	0.72	0.70	0.32	0.24	0.03
Borchiellini et al. 1995	Two test houses	COMIS	Average interzone airflows	0.84	0.60	0.18	0.41	–0.24
Emmerich and Nabinger 2000	Single-zone test house	CONTAM	0.3 to 5.0 μm particle concentrations	0.94 to 0.99	0.84 to 1.02	–0.25 to 0.29	0.04 to 0.19	–0.26 to 0.16
Koontz et al. 1992	Test chamber	CONTAM	Methylene chloride concentration	0.98	1.08	0.07	0.20	0.16
	Two-zone research house	CONTAM	Transient CO concentration (zone 1)	0.94	0.70	0.14	0.15	0.06
			Transient CO concentration (zone 2)	0.98	0.85	0.26	0.02	–0.11
Haghighat and Megri 1996	Multizone laboratory	CONTAM	Interzone airflows	0.96	0.90	0.10	0.18	0.002
	House	CONTAM	Room airflows	0.96	0.84	0.14	0.04	–0.02
Lansari et al. 1996	Two-story house with garage	CONTAM	Tracer gas concentrations in garage	0.97	1.07	0.10	0.01	–0.03
			Tracer gas concentrations in other rooms	0.92	0.94	0.18	0.12	–0.27
Sextro et al. 1999	Three-story test building	CONTAM	Tracer gas concentrations	0.97	1.04	0.14	0.10	0.16
Yoshino et al. 1995	Three-room test house	COMIS	Air change rates	0.79	0.87	NA	NA	NA
			Tracer gas concentrations	0.98	1.06	NA	NA	NA
Zhao et al. 1998	Test house	COMIS	Room air change rates	0.72	0.92	NA	NA	NA
			Tracer gas concentrations	0.93	0.93	NA	NA	NA

Source: Emmerich (2001).
Note: R = correlation coefficient; m = slope of regression line; B = ratio of intercept of regression line to average measured value; NMSE = normalized mean square error; FB = fractional bias.

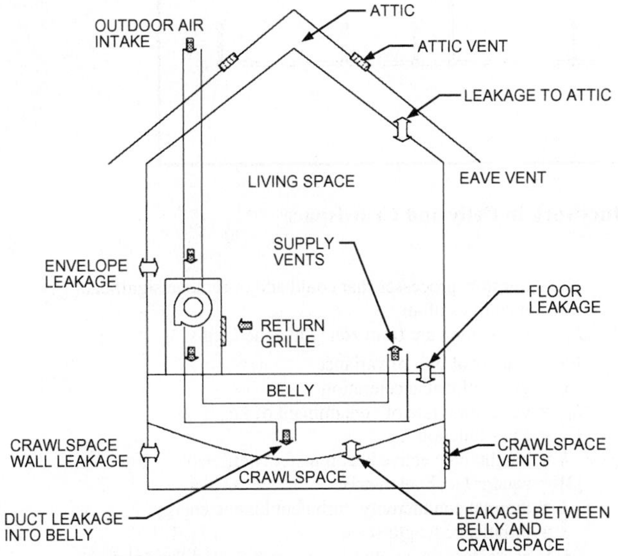

Fig. 15 Schematic of Ventilation System and Envelope Leakage

The instrumentation system also has an automated tracer gas system for continuous monitoring of building air change rates. The tracer gas system injects sulfur hexafluoride into the house every 4 to 6 h, allows it to mix to a uniform concentration, and then monitors the concentration decay in all the major zones of the building. Air change rates are then calculated based on the tracer gas decay rate in the living space.

Model Description. The model contains four levels: crawlspace, belly volume, living area (Figure 16), and attic. The duct modeling capabilities (see Figure 17 depicting belly level) were used to model the forced-air system. Leakage values of model airflow paths are listed in Table 2. Leaks in the living space envelope include the exterior wall and interfaces between the ceiling and wall, floor and wall, and the walls at the corners. In addition, there are two types of windows, the exterior doors, and the living space floor, which contains openings into the belly. There are also interior airflow paths, including leaks in the walls, doorframes, and open doors. Note that for all the tests and simulations performed, all interior doors were open. The attic has leakage in its floor (i.e., the ceiling of the living space), as well as the two types of attic vents to the outdoors. The crawlspace has leaks to the outdoors in the walls, vents in the front and rear of the house, and an access door. The model also includes a leak from the crawlspace into the belly. Finally, the duct leak into the belly, based on the described measurement, is included in the model.

Results. Tracer gas decay tests were simulated using the multizone model. Figure 18 shows the results of one of these simulations 30 min after injection of the tracer gas. The darker the shading, the higher the tracer gas concentration.

Figure 19A shows the measured and predicted air change rates with the forced-air system off as a function of indoor/outdoor air temperature difference under low wind speed conditions. Values predicted with the model are in good agreement with the measurements, particularly at low values of ΔT, but tend to underpredict by around 20% at higher values. Note that in all reported measurements and predictions, the outdoor air intake on the forced-air system and the window inlet vents are closed.

Figure 19B plots the measured and predicted air change rates with the forced-air system on, again for low wind speeds. Under positive temperature differences, the measured air change rates are actually lower than with the system off, which might not be expected with significant duct leakage. Airflow measurements indicate that the system moves about 450 L/s, but about 125 L/s is lost through duct leakage into the belly. Some of this airflow returns to the living space through leaks in the floor, but some flows through the crawlspace to the outdoors, which tends to depressurize the house. A significant air change rate is seen at zero ΔT, but this is not unexpected given the duct leakage.

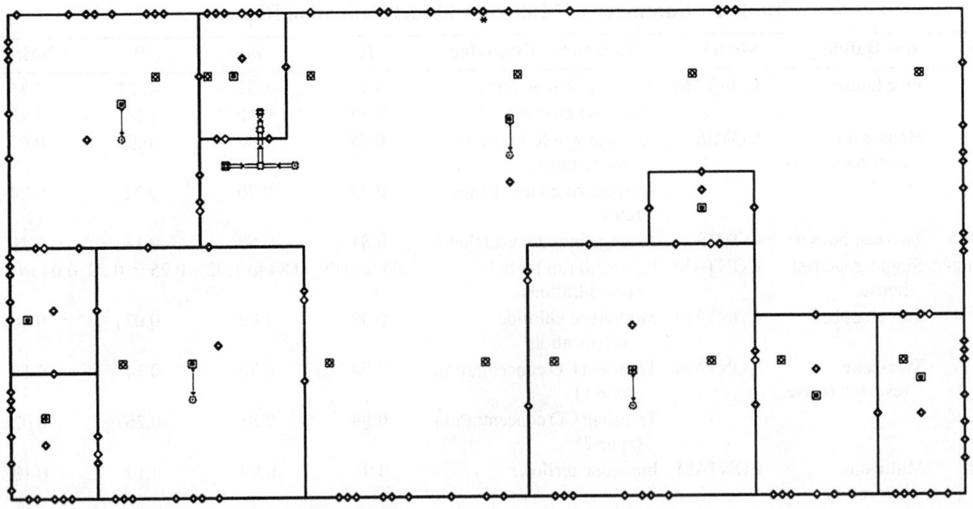

Fig. 16 Multizone Representation of First Floor

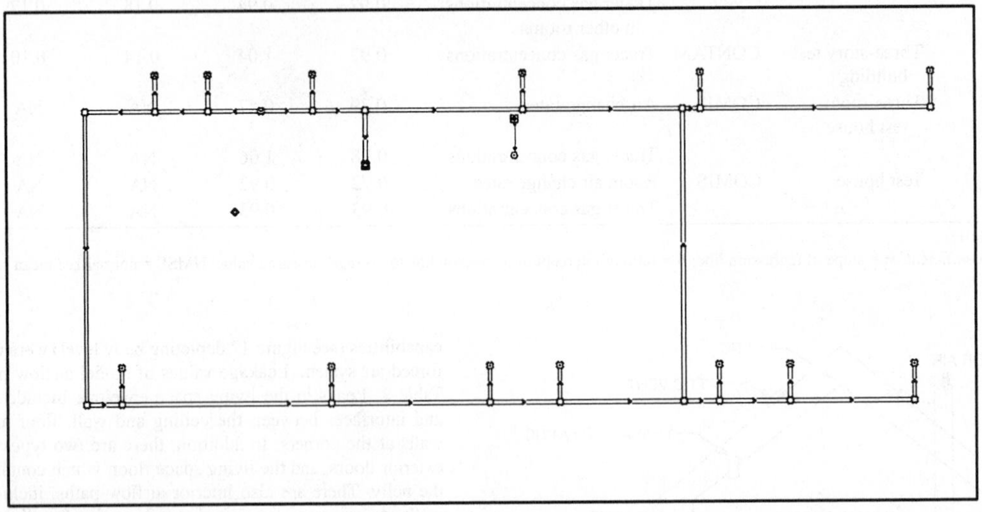

Fig. 17 Multizone Representation of Ductwork in Belly and Crawlspace

At higher values of ΔT, the stack effect "competes" with duct leakage into the belly, decreasing the air change rate into the house. This effect has actually been proposed as a means of controlling airflow and contaminant entry from crawl spaces (Phaff and De Gids 1994). Overall, with the fan on, the agreement between the predicted and measured air change rates is quite good.

SYMBOLS

A_0 = diffuser effective area
B = ratio of intercept of regression line to average measured value
{B} = column vector of total flow into each zone
{C} = correction vector
C = flow coefficient, $(\text{Pa}^{1/n}\cdot\text{m}^3)/\text{s}$; concentration mass fraction
C_o = observed concentration
c_p = concentration in air
C_p = specific heat; predicted concentration
c_R = mean concentration in return openings
$C_{\alpha,i}$ = concentration mass fraction of α, kg_α/kg of air
C_μ = k-ε turbulence model constant
E = constant depending on wall roughness (9.8 for hydraulically smooth walls)
f = [see Equation (29)]
FB = fractional bias of mean concentrations
F_i = nonflow processes that could add or remove significant quantities of air
$F_{j,i}$ = mass flow rate from zone j to zone i, kg/s
FS = fractional bias of variance
g = gravitational acceleration
$G_{\alpha,i}$ = generation rate of contaminant α, kg_α/s
G_Δ = filter function
h = height; convective heat transfer coefficient
[J] = square Jacobian matrix
k = thermal conductivity; turbulent kinetic energy
ℓ = turbulence length scale
L = characteristic length (e.g., room height, diffuser height)
m = mass of air, kg
M = slope of regression line
m_i = mass of air in zone i, kg
$\dot{m}$ = mass flow rate
n = flow exponent (typically 0.5 to 0.6)
NMSE = normalized mean square error
P = pressure
ΔP = pressure drop across opening, Pa
{P} = estimated pressures
{P*} = estimated vector of all zone pressures
Pe = Peclet number (ratio of convection to conduction)
P_i, P_j = zone pressure, Pa

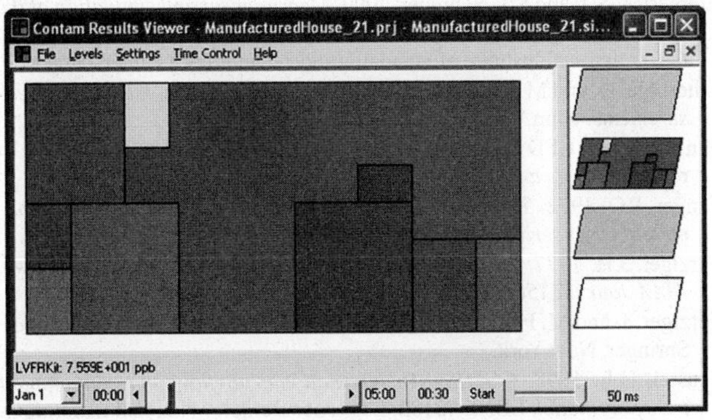

Fig. 18 Test Simulation of Concentration of Tracer Gas Decay in Manufactured House 30 min After Injection

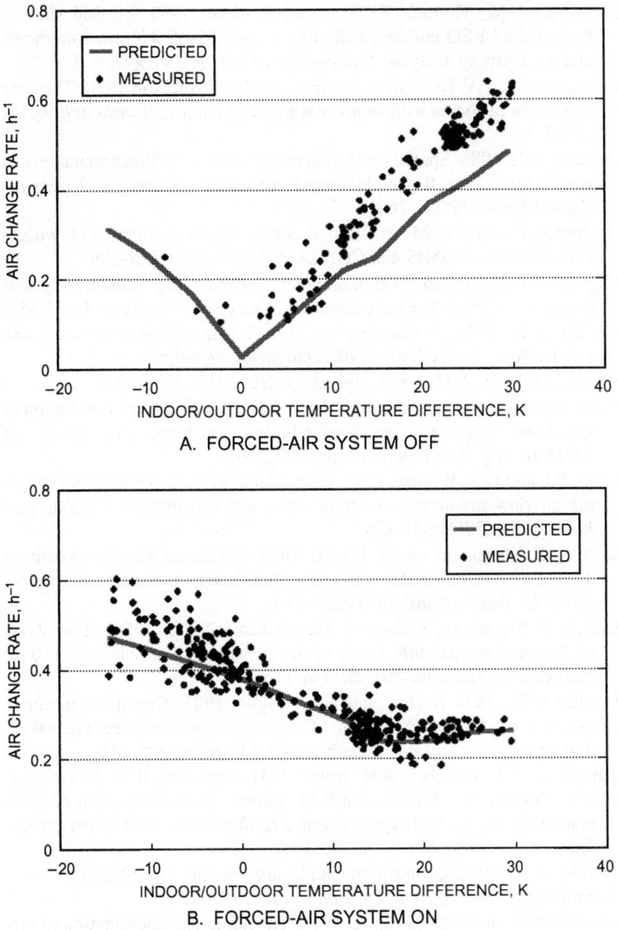

Fig. 19 Measured and Predicted Air Change Rates for Wind Speeds less than 2 m/s

Q = volumetric airflow rate, F/ρ, m³/s
R = removal coefficient; correlation coefficient
R_{air} = gas constant of air, 287.055 J/(kg·K)
Ra = Rayleigh number
Re = Reynolds number
s_{ij} = strain rate tensor
S_ϕ = source or sink
t = time, s
T = temperature, °C
ΔT = temperature change
TI = turbulence intensity, %

Table 2 Leakage Values of Model Airflow Components

	Exterior Airflow Paths	ELA at 4 Pa
Living space envelope	Exterior wall	14 mm²/m²
	Ceiling wall interface	81 mm²/m
	Floor wall interface	124 mm²/m
	Window #1	500 mm²
	Window #2	194 mm²
	Corner interface	80.8 mm²/m
	Exterior doors	1870 mm²
	Living space floor to belly volume	365 mm²/m²
Interior airflow paths	Interior walls	200 mm²/m²
	Bedroom doorframe	4100 mm²
	Open interior doors	2 by 0.9 m
	Bathroom doorframe	3300 mm²
	Interior doorframe	2500 mm²
	Closet doorframe	460 mm²
Attic	Attic floor	200 mm²/m²
	Roof vents	0.135 m²
	Eave vents	10 600 mm²/m
Crawlspace and belly	Exterior walls of crawlspace	2500 mm²/m²
	Rear crawlspace vents	32 300 mm²
	Front crawlspace vents	46 500 mm²
	Crawlspace access door	20 600 mm²
	Crawlspace to belly	25 800 mm²
	Duct leak into belly	3200 mm²

T_s = surface temperature
T_i = zone temperature, K
U = velocity
u_i = instantaneous velocity
$\bar{u}_i$ = ensemble average of v for steady flow
u_i' = fluctuation velocity
u_j = velocity in j direction, m/s
U_P = velocity parallel to wall at ΔY_p
U_{ref} = mean stream velocity
U_0 = air supply velocity for momentum source
V_i = zone volume, m³
x_i = distance in i direction, m
x_j = distance in j direction, m
Y^+ = dimensionless distance from wall
ΔY_p = distance from wall to center of first cell

Greek

α, β = contaminants
ε = dissipation rate of turbulent kinetic energy
ϕ = transport property (1 for mass continuity, momentum, temperature, or species concentration)
Γ_ϕ = generalized diffusion coefficient or transport property of fluid flow
η = Kolmogorov length scale; filter efficiency
κ = von Karmann's constant (0.41)
$\kappa_{\alpha,\beta}$ = kinetic reaction coefficient between α and β
μ = dynamic viscosity
μ_t = eddy viscosity
ν = kinematic viscosity
ρ = density, kg/m³
ρ_i = zone density, kg/m³
σ = standard deviation
τ_{ij} = viscous tensor stress
τ_w = wall shear stress

REFERENCES

AIAA. 1998. Guide for the verification and validation of computational fluid dynamics simulations. AIAA *Standard* G-077-1998. American Institute of Aeronautics and Astronautics, Reston, VA.

Anderson, J.D., Jr. 1995. *Computational fluid dynamics: The basics with applications*. McGraw-Hill, New York.

Anderson, D.A., J.C. Tannehill, and R.H. Pletcher. 1984. *Computational fluid dynamics and heat transfer*. Hemisphere, Washington, D.C.

ASTM. 1997. Standard guide for statistical evaluation of indoor air quality models. *Standard* D5157-97(2003)e1. American Society for Testing and Materials, West Conshohocken, PA.

Awbi, H.B. 1991. *Ventilation of buildings*. Chapman & Hall, London.

Axley, J.A. 1987. *Indoor air quality modeling, phase II report.* NBSIR 87-3661. National Institute of Standards and Technology, Gaithersburg, MD.

Axley, J.A. 1988. *Progress toward a general analytical method for predicting indoor air pollution in buildings—Indoor air quality modeling, phase III report.* NBSIR 88-3814. National Institute of Standards and Technology, Gaithersburg, MD.

Baker, A.J., P.T. Williams, and R.M. Kelso. 1994. Numerical calculation of room air motion—Part 1. *ASHRAE Transactions* 100(1):514-530.

Bassett, M. 1990. Infiltration and leakage paths in single family houses—A multizone infiltration case study. *AIVC Technical Note* 27. Air Infiltration and Ventilation Centre, Brussels, Belgium.

Beausoleil-Morrison, I. 2000. *The adaptive coupling of heat and air flow modelling with dynamic whole-building.* Ph.D. dissertation, Department of Mechanical Engineering, University of Strathclyde, Glasgow.

Bernard, P.S. and J.M. Wallace. 2002. *Turbulent flow: Analysis, measurement, and prediction.* John Wiley & Sons, Hoboken, NJ.

Blomsterberg, A., T. Carlsson, C. Svensson, and J. Kronvall. 1999. Air flows in dwellings—Simulations and measurements. *Energy and Buildings* 30:87-95.

Borchiellini, R., M. Cali, and M. Torchio. 1995. Experimental evaluation of COMIS results for ventilation of a detached house. *ASHRAE Transactions* 101(1).

BRE. 1994. *BREEZE 6.0 user manual.* Building Research Establishment, Garston, U.K.

Breuer, M. 1998. Large eddy simulation of the subcritical flow past a circular cylinder: Numerical and modeling aspects. *International Journal of Numerical Methods in Fluids* 28:1281-1302.

Chen, Q. 1988. *Indoor airflow, air quality and energy consumption of buildings*. Ph.D. dissertation, Delft University of Technology, The Netherlands.

Chen, Q. 1996. Prediction of room air motion by Reynolds-stress models. *Building and Environment* 31(3):233-244.

Chen, Q. and Z. Jiang. 1992. Significant questions in predicting room air motion. *ASHRAE Transactions* 98(1):929-939.

Chen, Q. and A. Moser. 1991. Simulation of a multiple-nozzle diffuser. *Proceedings of the 12th AIVC Conference* 2:1-14.

Chen, Q., A. Moser, and A. Huber. 1990. Prediction of buoyant, turbulent flow by a low Reynolds-number k-ε model. *ASHRAE Transactions* 96(1):564-573.

Chen, Q. and J. Srebric. 2000. *Simplified diffuser boundary conditions for numerical room airflow models.* ASHRAE Research Project (RP) 1009, Final Report.

Chen, Q. and J. Srebric. 2002. A procedure for verification, validation, and reporting of indoor environment CFD analyses. *International Journal of HVAC&R Research* 8(2):201-216.

Chen, Q. and W. Xu. 1998. A zero-equation turbulence model for indoor airflow simulation. *Energy and Buildings* 28(2):137-144.

Cherukat, P., Y. Na, and T. J. Hanratty. 1998. Direct numerical simulation of a fully developed turbulent flow over a wavy wall. *Theoretical and Computational Fluid Dynamics* 11:109-134.

Chester, S., F. Charlette, and C. Meneveau. 2001. Dynamic model for LES without test filtering: Quantifying the accuracy of Taylor series approximations. *Theoretical and Computational Fluid Dynamics* 15:165-181.

Corrsin, S. 1961. Turbulent flow. *American Scientist* 49:300-325.

Dennis, J.E. and R.B. Schnabel. 1996. *Numerical methods for unconstrained optimization and nonlinear equations.* Society for Industrial and Applied Mathematics, Philadelphia.

Dols, W.S. and G. Walton. 2002. *CONTAMW 2.0 user manual.* NISTIR 6921. National Institute of Standards and Technology, Gaithersburg, MD.

Emmerich, S.J. 1997. *Use of computational fluid dynamics to analyze indoor air quality issues.* NISTIR 5997. National Institute of Standards and Technology, Gaithersburg, MD.

Emmerich, S.J. 2001. Validation of multizone IAQ modeling of residential-scale buildings: A review. *ASHRAE Transactions* 107.

Emmerich, S.J. and K.B. McGrattan. 1998. Application of a large eddy simulation model to study room airflow *ASHRAE Transactions* 104(1):1-9.

Emmerich, S.J. and S.J. Nabinger. 2000. *Measurement and simulation of the IAQ impact of particle air cleaner in a single-zone building.* NISTIR 6461. National Institute of Standards and Technology, Gaithersburg, MD.

Etheridge, D. and M. Sandberg. 1996. *Building ventilation, theory and measurements.* John Wiley & Sons, Chichester.

Fan, Y. 1995. CFD modeling of the air and contaminant distribution in rooms. *Energy and Buildings* 23:33-39.

Fanger, P.O. 1972. *Thermal comfort: Analysis and application in environmental engineering*. McGraw-Hill.

Ferziger, J.H. 1977. Large eddy numerical simulations of turbulent flows. *AIAA Journal* 15(9):1261-1267.

Ferziger, J. and M. Peric. 1997. *Computational methods for fluid dynamics*. Springer, New York.

Feustel, H.E. 1998. *COMIS—An international air-flow and contaminant transport model.* LBNL 42182. Lawrence Berkeley National Laboratory.

Feustel, H.E., F. Allard, V.B. Dorer, M. Grosso, M. Herrlin, L. Mingsheng, J.C. Phaff, Y. Utsumi, and H. Yoshino. 1989. The COMIS infiltration model. *Proceedings of the 10th AIVC Conference,* Air Infiltration and Ventilation Centre.

Furbringer J.-M., V. Dorer, F. Huck, and A. Weber. 1993. Air flow simulation of the LESO building including a comparison with measurements and a sensitivity analysis. *Proceedings of Indoor Air 1993*, p. 5.

Gosman, A.D., P.V. Nielsen, A. Restivo, and J.H. Whitelaw. 1980. The flow properties of rooms with small ventilation openings. *Transactions of the ASME.*

Grötzbach, G. 1983. Spatial resolution requirements for direction numerical simulation of the Rayleigh-Bénard convection. *Journal of Computational Physics* 49:241-264.

Haghighat, F. and A.C. Megri. 1996. A comprehensive validation of two airflow models—COMIS and CONTAM. *Indoor Air* 6:278-288.

Haghighat, F. and J. Rao. 1991. Computer-aided building ventilation system design—A system theoretic approach. *Energy and Buildings* 1:147-155.

Herrlin, M.K. 1992. *Air-flow studies in multizone buildings—Models and applications.* Royal Institute of Technology, Stockholm.

Hinze, J.O. 1975. *Turbulence*, 2nd ed. McGraw-Hill, New York.

Horstman, R.H. 1988. Predicting velocity and contamination distribution in ventilated volumes using Navier-Stokes equations. *Proceedings of ASHRAE IAQ '88 Conference,* pp. 209-230.

Jones, P.J. and G.E. Whittle. 1992. Computational fluid dynamics for building air flow prediction—Current status and capabilities. *Building and Environment* 27(3):321-338.

Kato, S., S. Murakami, and Y. Kondo. 1994. Numerical simulation of two-dimensional room airflow with and without buoyancy by means of ASM. *ASHRAE Transactions* 100(1):238-255.

Kato, S., S. Murakami, S. Shoya, F. Hanyu, and J. Zeng. 1995. CFD analysis of flow and temperature fields in atrium with ceiling height of 130 m. *ASHRAE Transactions* 101(2):1144-1157.

Koontz, M.D., H.E. Rector, and N.L. Nagda. 1992. Consumer products exposure guidelines: Evaluation of indoor air quality models. GEOMET *Report* IE-1980. GEOMET Technologies, Germantown, MD.

Lansari, A., J.J. Streicher, A.H. Huber, G.H. Crescenti, R.B. Zweidinger, J.W. Duncan, C.P. Weisel, and R.M. Burton. 1996. Dispersion of automotive alternative fuel vapors within a residence and its attached garage. *Indoor Air* 6:118-126.

Launder, B.E. 1989. Second-moment closure: Present . . . and future? *International Journal of Heat and Fluid Flow* 10:282-300.

Launder, B.E. and D.B. Spalding. 1974. The numerical computation of turbulent flows. *Computer Methods in Applied Mechanics and Engineering* 3:269-289.

Launder, B.E., G.J. Reece, and W. Rodi. 1975. Progress in the development of a Reynolds-stress turbulence closure. *Journal of Fluid Mechanics* 68(3):537-566.

Launder, B.E. and B.I. Sharma. 1974. Application of the energy dissipation model of turbulence to the calculation of flow near a spinning disc. *Letters in Heat and Mass Transfer* 1(2):131-138.

Lin, C.H., M.F. Ahlers, A.K. Davenport, L.M. Sedgwick, R.H. Horstman, and J.C. Yu. 2001. *A numerical model for airborne disease transmission in a 767-300 passenger cabin.* Final report to the National Institute for Occupational Safety and Health, contract no. 200-2000-08001. Boeing Commercial Airplanes Group.

Lin, C.H., T. Han, and C.A. Koromilas. 1992. Effect of HVAC design parameters on passenger thermal comfort. SAE *Paper* No. 920264.Society of Automotive Engineers, Warrendale. PA.

Ling, W., J.N. Chung, T.R. Troutt, and C.T. Crowe. 1998. Direct numerical simulation of a three-dimensional temporal mixing layer with particle dispersion. *Journal of Fluid Mechanics* 358:61-85.

Lorenzetti, D.M. 2002. Computational aspects of nodal multizone airflow systems. *Building and Environment* 37:1083-1090.

Mashayek, F. 1998. Direct numerical simulation of evaporating droplet dispersion in forced low Mach number turbulence. *International Journal of Heat and Mass Transfer* 41(17):2601-2617.

Mathieu, J. and J. Scott. 2000. *An introduction to turbulent flow.* Cambridge University.

Monin, A.S. and A.M. Yaglom. 1971. *Statistical fluid mechanics*, vol. 1. MIT Press, Cambridge.

Moser, A., F. Off, A. Schälin, and X. Yuan. 1995. Numerical modeling of heat transfer by radiation and convection in an atrium with thermal inertia. *ASHRAE Transactions* 101(2):1136-1143.

Murakami, S. Kato, and R. Ooka. 1994. Comparison of numerical predictions of horizontal nonisothermal jet in a room with three turbulence models—*k*-ε, EVM, ASM, and DSM. *ASHRAE Transactions* 100(2): 697-706.

Nielsen, P.V. 1975. Prediction of air flow and comfort in air conditioned spaces. *ASHRAE Transactions* 81(2):247-259.

Nielsen, P.V. 1992. The description of supply openings in numerical models for room air distribution. *ASHRAE Transactions* 98(1):963-971.

Nielsen, P.V. 1995. Air flow in an exposition pavilion studied by scale-model experiments and computational fluid dynamics. *ASHRAE Transactions* 101(2):1118-1126.

Nielsen. P.V. 1998. The selection of turbulence models for prediction of room airflow. *ASHRAE Transactions* 104(1B):1119-1127.

Nielsen, P.V. and T. Tryggvason. 1998. Computational fluid dynamics and building energy performance simulation. *Proceedings of ROOMVENT '98: Sixth International Conference on Air Distribution in Rooms*, Stockholm, 1:101-107.

Orme, M. 2000. Applicable input data for a proposed ventilation modeling data guide. *ASHRAE Transactions* 106(2).

Phaff, H.J.C. and W.F. deGids. 1994. The air lock floor. *Proceedings of 5th Air Infiltration and Ventilation Centre Conference.* Air Infiltration and Ventilation Centre, Brussels, Belgium.

Pope, S.B. 2000. *Turbulent flows*. Cambridge University.

Rajaratnam, N. 1976. *Turbulent jets*. Elsevier, Amsterdam.

Reynolds, O. 1895. On the dynamical theory of incompressible viscous fluids and the determination of the criterion. *Philosophical Transactions of the Royal Society, London* A(186):123.

Rodriguez, E.A. and F. Allard. 1992. Coupling COMIS airflow model with other transfer phenomena. *Energy and Buildings* 18:147-157.

Russell, M.B. and P.N. Surendran. 2000. Use of computational fluid dynamics to aid studies of room air distribution: A review of some recent work. *Proceedings of CIBSE A: Building Services Engineering Research and Technology* 21(4):241-247.

Said, M.N. and R.A. MacDonald. 1991. An evaluation of a network smoke control model. *ASHRAE Transactions* 97(1):275-282.

Schälin, A. and P.V. Nielsen. 2003. Impact of turbulence anisotropy near walls in room air flow. (Accepted in 2003 for publication by *Indoor Air*).

Sextro, R.G., J.M. Daisey, H.E. Feustel, D.J. Dickerhoff, and C. Jump. 1999. Comparison of modeled and measured tracer gas concentrations in a multizone building. *Proceedings of Indoor Air '99*, vol. 1.

Smagorinsky, J. 1963. General circulation experiments with primitive equations. *Monthly Weather Review* 91:99-165.

Spalart, P.R. 2000. Strategies for turbulence modeling and simulations. *International Journal of Heat and Fluid Flow* 21:252-263.

Srebric, J. 2000. *Simplified methodology for indoor environment design.* Ph.D. dissertation, Department of Architecture, Massachusetts Institute of Technology, Cambridge.

Srebric, J. and Q. Chen. 2001. A method of test to obtain diffuser data for CFD modeling of room airflow. *ASHRAE Transactions* 107(2):108-116.

Srebric, J. and Q. Chen. 2002. Simplified numerical models for complex air supply diffusers. *International Journal of HVAC&R Research* 8(3): 277-294.

Tennekes, H. and J. L. Lumley. 1972. *A first course in turbulence.* MIT Press, Cambridge.

Tuomaala, P. 1993. New building air flow simulation model: Theoretical bases. *Building Services Engineering Research and Technology* 14: 151-157.

Upham, R.D. 1997. *A validation study of multizone air flow and contaminant migration simulation program CONTAM as applied to tall buildings.* M.S. thesis. The Pennsylvania State University, University Park.

Versteeg, H., and W. Malalasekera. 1995. *An introduction to computational fluid dynamics: The finite volume method.* Prentice Hall, Old Tappan, NJ.

Walton, G.N. 1989. *AIRNET—A computer program for building network airflow modeling.* NISTIR 89-4072. National Institute of Standards and Technology, Gaithersburg, MD.

Wilcox, D.C. 1998. *Turbulence modeling for CFD*, 2nd ed. DCW Industries, La Cañada, CA.

Williams, P.T., A.J. Baker, and R.M. Kelso. 1994a. Numerical calculation of room air motion—Part 2. *ASHRAE Transactions* 100(1):531-548.

Williams, P.T., A.J. Baker, and R.M. Kelso. 1994b. Numerical calculation of room air motion—Part 3. *ASHRAE Transactions* 100(1):549-564.

Yoshino, H., Z. Yun, H. Kobayashi and Y. Utsumi. 1995. Simulation and measurement of air infiltration and pollutant transport using a passive solar test house. *ASHRAE Transactions* 101(1).

Yuan, X., A. Moser, and P. Suter. 1994. Wall functions for numerical simulations of turbulent natural convection. *Proceedings of the 10th International Heat Transfer Conference*, Brighton, U.K., pp. 191-196.

Zhai, Z. and Q. Chen. 2003. Solution characters of iterative coupling between energy simulation and CFD programs. *Energy and Buildings* 35(5):493-505.

Zhai, Z., Q. Chen, P. Haves, and J.H. Klems. 2002. On approaches to couple energy simulation and computational fluid dynamics programs. *Building and Environment* 37:857-864.

Zhang, G., S. Morsing, B. Bjerg, K. Svidt, and J.S. Strom. 2000. Test room for validation of airflow patterns estimated by computational fluid dynamics. *Journal of Agricultural Engineering Research* 76: 141-148.

Zhao, Y., H. Yoshino, and H. Okuyama. 1998. Evaluation of the COMIS model by comparing simulation and measurement of airflow and pollutant concentration. *Indoor Air* 8:123-130.

BIBLIOGRAPHY

Feustel, H.E. and B.V. Smith. 1997. *COMIS 3.0 user's guide.* Lawrence Berkeley National Laboratory.

Jiang, Y., D. Alexander, H. Jenkins, R. Arthur, and Q. Chen. 2003. Natural ventilation in buildings: measurement in a wind tunnel and numerical simulation with large eddy simulation. *Journal of Wind Engineering and Industrial Aerodynamics* 91(3):331-353.

Jiang, Y. and Q. Chen. 2001. Study of natural ventilation in buildings by large eddy simulation. *Journal of Wind Engineering and Industrial Aerodynamics.* 89(13):1155-1178.

Jiang, Y. and Q. Chen. 2002. Effect of fluctuating wind direction on cross natural ventilation in building from large eddy simulation. *Building and Environment* 37(4):379-386.

Jiang, Y. and Q. Chen. 2003. Buoyancy-driven single-sided natural ventilation in buildings with large openings. *International Journal of Heat and Mass Transfer* 46(6):973-988.

Jiang, Y., M. Su, and Q. Chen. 2003. Using large eddy simulation to study airflows in and around buildings. *ASHRAE Transactions* 109(2).

Liddament, M. and C. Allen. 1983. The validation and comparison of mathematical models of air infiltration. *AIC Technical Note* 11. Air Infiltration Centre, Brussels, Belgium.

Spalart, P.R. and S.R. Allmaras. 1994. A one-equation turbulence model for aerodynamic flows. *La Recherche Aérospatiale* 1:5.

Su, M., Q. Chen, and C.-M. Chiang. 2001. Comparison of different subgrid-scale models of large eddy simulation for indoor airflow modeling. *Journal of Fluids Engineering* 123:628-639.

CHAPTER 14

CLIMATIC DESIGN INFORMATION

THIS chapter and the data on the accompanying CD-ROM provide the climatic design information for 5564 locations in the United States, Canada, and around the world. This is an increase of 1142 stations from the 2005 *ASHRAE Handbook—Fundamentals*. The large number of stations, along with the addition of several new table elements, made printing the whole tables impractical. Consequently, the complete table of design conditions for only Atlanta, GA, appears in this printed chapter to illustrate the table format. However, a subset of the table elements most often used is presented in the Appendix at the end of this chapter for selected stations representing major urban centers in the United States, Canada, and around the world. The complete data tables for all 5564 stations are contained on the CD-ROM that accompanies this book. On the CD-ROM, a StationFinder interactive mapping utility can be used to geographically locate stations. (Note: this utility requires Internet access.)

This climatic design information is commonly used for design, sizing, distribution, installation, and marketing of heating, ventilating, air-conditioning, and dehumidification equipment, as well as for other energy-related processes in residential, agricultural, commercial, and industrial applications. These summaries include values of dry-bulb, wet-bulb, and dew-point temperature, and wind speed with direction at various frequencies of occurrence. Also included in this edition are monthly degree-days to various bases, and parameters to calculate clear-sky irradiance. Sources of other climate information of potential interest to ASHRAE members are described later in this chapter.

Design information in this chapter was developed largely through research project RP-1453 (Thevenard 2009). The information includes design values of dry-bulb with mean coincident wet-bulb temperature, design wet-bulb with mean coincident dry-bulb temperature, and design dew-point with mean coincident dry-bulb temperature and corresponding humidity ratio. These data allow the designer to consider various operational peak conditions. Design values of wind speed facilitate the design of smoke management systems in buildings (Lamming and Salmon 1996, 1998).

Warm-season temperature and humidity conditions are based on annual percentiles of 0.4, 1.0, and 2.0. Cold-season conditions are based on annual percentiles of 99.6 and 99.0. The use of annual percentiles to define design conditions ensures that they represent the same probability of occurrence in any climate, regardless of the seasonal distribution of extreme temperature and humidity.

Monthly information including percentiles is compiled in addition to annual percentiles, to provide seasonally representative combinations of temperature, humidity, and solar conditions. Changes from the 2005 edition include the use of different percentiles for monthly design dry-bulb and mean coincident wet-bulb temperatures, and monthly design wet-bulb and mean coincident dry-bulb temperatures: 0.4, 2, 5, and 10% values are now used instead of the 0.4, 1, and 2% values listed in 2005. New elements in the 2009 edition are monthly average temperature and standard deviation of daily average temperature, which can be combined to estimate heating and cooling degree-days to any base, as explained later in this chapter. The tables also list heating and cooling degree-days for bases 18.3 and 10°C, as well as cooling degree-hours for bases 23.3 and 26.7°C. The calculation of daily dry-bulb and wet-bulb temperature profiles, which are useful for generating 24 h weather data sequences suitable as input to many HVAC analysis methods, has been significantly updated, with the inclusion of mean dry-bulb and wet-bulb temperature ranges coincident with the 5% monthly dry-bulb and wet-bulb design temperatures.

Finally, clear-sky solar radiation calculations have been moved to this chapter from other chapters. Two new parameters were included in the tables for that purpose: clear-sky optical depths for beam and diffuse irradiances. From these two parameters, clear-sky radiation for any time of any day of the year can be calculated, using a relatively simple method described later in the chapter. For convenience, the tables include noon-hour beam and diffuse irradiance values on the 21st day of each month.

Design conditions are provided for locations for which long-term hourly observations were available (1982-2006 for most stations in the United States and Canada). Compared to the 2005 chapter, the number of U.S. stations increased from 753 to 1085 (44% increase); Canadian stations increased from 307 to 480 (56% increase); and stations in the rest of the world increased from 3362 to 3999 (19% increase; see Figure 1 for map).

CLIMATIC DESIGN CONDITIONS

Table 1 shows climatic design conditions for Atlanta, GA, to illustrate the format of the data available on the CD-ROM. A limited subset of this data for 1450 of the 5564 locations for 21 annual data elements is provided for convenience in the Appendix.

The top part of the table contains station information as follows:

- Name of the observing station, state (USA) or province (Canada), country.
- World Meteorological Organization (WMO) station identifier.
- Weather Bureau Army Navy (WBAN) number (–99999 denotes missing).
- Latitude of station, °N/S.
- Longitude of station, °E/W.
- Elevation of station, m.
- Standard pressure at elevation, in kPa (see Chapter 1 for equations used to calculate standard pressure).
- Time zone, h ± UTC
- Time zone code (e.g., NAE = Eastern Time, USA and Canada). The CD-ROM contains a list of all time zone codes used in the tables.
- Period analyzed (e.g., 82-06 = data from 1982 to 2006 were used).

Annual Design Conditions

Annual climatic design conditions are contained in the first three sections following the top part of the table. They contain information as follows:

Annual Heating and Humidification Design Conditions.

- Coldest month (i.e., month with lowest average dry-bulb temperature; 1 = January, 12 = December).

The preparation of this chapter is assigned to TC 4.2, Climatic Information.

Table 1 Design Conditions for Atlanta, GA, USA

Lat: **33.64N** Long: **84.43W** Elev: **313** StdP: **97.62** Time Zone: **-5.00 (NAE)** Period: **82-06** WBAN: **13874**

Annual Heating and Humidification Design Conditions

Coldest Month	Heating DB 99.6%	Heating DB 99%	Humidification DP/MCDB and HR 99.6% DP	99.6% HR	99.6% MCDB	99% DP	99% HR	99% MCDB	Coldest month WS/MCDB 0.4% WS	0.4% MCDB	1% WS	1% MCDB	MCWS/PCWD to 99.6% DB MCWS	PCWD
1	-6.3	-3.5	-15.8	1.0	-2.6	-12.9	1.3	0.1	11.4	3.0	10.7	3.4	5.3	320

Annual Cooling, Dehumidification, and Enthalpy Design Conditions

Hottest Month	Hottest Month DB Range	Cooling DB/MCWB 0.4% DB	0.4% MCWB	1% DB	1% MCWB	2% DB	2% MCWB	Evaporation WB/MCDB 0.4% WB	0.4% MCDB	1% WB	1% MCDB	2% WB	2% MCDB	MCWS/PCWD to 0.4% DB MCWS	PCWD
7	9.5	34.4	23.5	33.0	23.3	31.9	23.0	25.1	31.2	24.5	30.3	24.0	29.4	4.0	300

Dehumidification DP/MCDB and HR 0.4% DP	0.4% HR	0.4% MCDB	1% DP	1% HR	1% MCDB	2% DP	2% HR	2% MCDB	Enthalpy/MCDB 0.4% Enth	0.4% MCDB	1% Enth	1% MCDB	2% Enth	2% MCDB	Hours 8 to 4 & 12.8/20.6
23.4	19.0	27.3	22.9	18.3	26.7	22.5	17.8	26.3	77.9	31.3	75.6	30.4	73.5	29.7	813

Extreme Annual Design Conditions

Extreme Annual WS 1%	2.5%	5%	Extreme Max WB	Extreme Annual DB Mean Min	Mean Max	Standard deviation Min	Standard deviation Max	n-Year Return Period Values of Extreme DB n=5 years Min	n=5 Max	n=10 years Min	n=10 Max	n=20 years Min	n=20 Max	n=50 years Min	n=50 Max
9.8	8.6	7.7	28.0	-11.2	35.9	4.2	1.8	-14.2	37.2	-16.7	38.2	-19.0	39.2	-22.1	40.6

Monthly Climatic Design Conditions

			Annual	Jan	Feb	Mar	Apr	May	Jun	Jul	Aug	Sep	Oct	Nov	Dec
Temperatures, Degree-Days and Degree-Hours		Tavg	17.0	6.6	8.8	12.6	16.6	21.2	24.8	26.7	26.2	22.9	17.5	12.4	7.7
		Sd		5.34	5.05	5.00	4.35	3.34	2.52	1.98	2.06	3.24	3.93	4.66	5.20
		HDD10.0	381	132	76	32	4	0	0	0	0	0	2	29	107
		HDD18.3	1497	365	268	185	81	13	1	0	0	6	63	184	331
		CDD10.0	2949	26	41	112	203	348	444	519	501	386	234	101	34
		CDD18.3	1023	0	1	7	29	102	195	261	243	142	37	6	1
		CDH23.3	8753	0	3	53	251	796	1712	2498	2196	1030	196	18	1
		CDH26.7	3266	0	0	4	46	215	668	1104	884	321	22	1	0
Monthly Design Dry Bulb and Mean Coincident Wet Bulb Temperatures	0.4%	DB		21.4	23.2	27.0	29.9	32.3	34.9	36.6	35.7	33.4	28.7	25.6	22.2
		MCWB		15.3	16.1	17.2	18.9	22.1	23.2	23.8	23.9	22.9	21.0	17.9	16.9
	2%	DB		18.9	20.7	24.8	28.0	30.5	33.2	34.8	33.8	31.3	27.1	23.3	20.0
		MCWB		14.6	15.0	15.7	17.9	21.0	22.6	23.8	23.8	22.2	19.5	17.2	16.1
	5%	DB		16.9	18.8	22.9	26.4	29.1	31.8	33.3	32.4	30.0	25.7	21.7	17.9
		MCWB		13.2	14.0	14.9	17.1	20.5	22.3	23.5	23.5	21.8	18.5	16.6	14.8
	10%	DB		14.9	17.0	20.9	24.4	27.6	30.5	31.9	31.1	28.6	24.0	20.0	16.0
		MCWB		11.5	12.8	14.3	16.4	19.8	21.9	23.5	23.1	21.5	18.0	15.8	12.6
Monthly Design Wet Bulb and Mean Coincident Dry Bulb Temperatures	0.4%	WB		17.8	18.6	19.3	21.6	23.9	25.0	26.1	25.7	24.6	22.6	20.7	19.0
		MCDB		19.7	19.8	23.2	26.1	28.8	31.0	32.3	32.0	30.0	26.7	22.4	20.6
	2%	WB		16.2	17.0	17.9	20.1	22.8	24.1	25.2	25.0	23.7	21.3	19.3	17.3
		MCDB		17.8	19.2	22.0	24.5	28.1	30.0	31.4	31.1	28.5	24.5	21.5	18.9
	5%	WB		14.2	15.5	16.8	19.0	21.9	23.6	24.7	24.4	23.1	20.4	18.1	15.5
		MCDB		16.0	17.8	20.8	23.4	27.0	29.1	30.6	29.9	27.5	23.4	20.3	17.7
	10%	WB		12.1	13.6	15.5	17.9	21.1	23.0	24.1	23.9	22.6	19.5	16.8	13.2
		MCDB		14.1	15.8	19.2	22.2	25.6	28.0	29.6	29.0	26.6	22.5	19.2	15.2
Mean Daily Temperature Range		MDBR		9.7	9.9	10.8	11.1	10.4	9.6	9.5	9.1	9.2	9.9	10.1	9.5
	5% DB	MCDBR		11.6	11.8	12.9	12.8	11.3	11.4	11.5	10.8	10.5	11.0	11.2	10.9
		MCWBR		8.0	7.2	6.6	5.5	4.4	3.7	3.5	3.4	3.7	4.9	6.4	7.4
	5% WB	MCDBR		9.4	9.5	10.2	10.0	9.7	9.6	10.0	9.5	8.7	8.3	8.7	9.3
		MCWBR		7.9	7.3	6.6	5.5	4.4	3.8	3.6	3.4	3.8	4.7	6.3	7.6
Clear Sky Solar Irradiance		taub		0.325	0.349	0.383	0.395	0.448	0.505	0.556	0.593	0.431	0.373	0.339	0.320
		taud		2.461	2.316	2.176	2.175	2.028	1.892	1.779	1.679	2.151	2.317	2.422	2.514
		Ebn,noon		888	898	890	893	845	794	751	714	832	859	862	874
		Edh,noon		95	117	143	148	173	198	220	239	144	115	97	87

CDD*n* Cooling degree-days base n°C, °C-day
CDH*n* Cooling degree-hours base n°C, °C-hour
DB Dry bulb temperature, °C
DP Dew point temperature, °C
Ebn,noon } Clear sky beam normal and diffuse hori-
Edh,noon } zontal irradiances at solar noon, W/m2
Elev Elevation, m
Enth Enthalpy, kJ/kg
HDD*n* Heating degree-days base n°C, °C-day
Hours 8/4 & 12.8/20.6 Number of hours between 8 a.m. and 4 p.m with DB between 12.8 and 20.6 °C
HR Humidity ratio, g of moisture per kg of dry air

Lat Latitude, °
Long Longitude, °
MCDB Mean coincident dry bulb temperature, °C
MCDBR Mean coincident dry bulb temp. range, °C
MCDP Mean coincident dew point temperature, °C
MCWB Mean coincident wet bulb temperature, °C
MCWBR Mean coincident wet bulb temp. range, °C
MCWS Mean coincident wind speed, m/s
MDBR Mean dry bulb temp. range, °C
PCWD Prevailing coincident wind direction, °, 0 = North, 90 = East

Period Years used to calculate the design conditions
Sd Standard deviation of daily average temperature, °C
StdP Standard pressure at station elevation, kPa
taub Clear sky optical depth for beam irradiance
taud Clear sky optical depth for diffuse irradiance
Tavg Average temperature, °C
Time Zone Hours ahead or behind UTC, and time zone code
WB Wet bulb temperature, °C
WBAN Weather Bureau Army Navy number
WMO# World Meteorological Organization number
WS Wind speed, m/s

- Dry-bulb temperature corresponding to 99.6 and 99.0% annual cumulative frequency of occurrence (cold conditions), °C.
- Dew-point temperature corresponding to 99.6 and 99.0% annual cumulative frequency of occurrence, °C; corresponding humidity ratio, calculated at standard atmospheric pressure at elevation of station, grams of moisture per kg of dry air; mean coincident dry-bulb temperature, °C.
- Wind speed corresponding to 0.4 and 1.0% cumulative frequency of occurrence for coldest month, m/s; mean coincident dry-bulb temperature, °C.
- Mean wind speed coincident with 99.6% dry-bulb temperature, m/s; corresponding most frequent wind direction, degrees from north (east = 90°).

Annual Cooling, Dehumidification, and Enthalpy Design Conditions.

- Hottest month (i.e., month with highest average dry-bulb temperature; 1 = January, 12 = December).
- Daily temperature range for hottest month, °C [defined as mean of the difference between daily maximum and daily minimum dry-bulb temperatures for hottest month].
- Dry-bulb temperature corresponding to 0.4, 1.0, and 2.0% annual cumulative frequency of occurrence (warm conditions), °C; mean coincident wet-bulb temperature, °C.
- Wet-bulb temperature corresponding to 0.4, 1.0, and 2.0% annual cumulative frequency of occurrence, °C; mean coincident dry-bulb temperature, °C.
- Mean wind speed coincident with 0.4% dry-bulb temperature, m/s; corresponding most frequent wind direction, degrees true from north (east = 90°).
- Dew-point temperature corresponding to 0.4, 1.0, and 2.0% annual cumulative frequency of occurrence, °C; corresponding humidity ratio, calculated at the standard atmospheric pressure at elevation of station, grams of moisture per kg of dry air; mean coincident dry-bulb temperature, °C.
- Enthalpy corresponding to 0.4, 1.0, and 2.0% annual cumulative frequency of occurrence, kJ/kg; mean coincident dry-bulb temperature, °C.
- Number of hours between 8 AM and 4 PM (inclusive) with dry-bulb temperature between 12.8 and 20.6°C.

Extreme Annual Design Conditions.

- Wind speed corresponding to 1.0, 2.5, and 5.0% annual cumulative frequency of occurrence, m/s.
- Extreme maximum wet-bulb temperature, °C.
- Mean and standard deviation of extreme annual minimum and maximum dry-bulb temperature, °C.
- 5-, 10-, 20-, and 50-year return period values for minimum and maximum extreme dry-bulb temperature, °C.

Monthly Design Conditions

Monthly design conditions are divided into subsections as follows:

Temperatures, Degree-Days, and Degree-Hours.

- Average temperature, °C. This parameter is a prime indicator of climate and is also useful to calculate heating and cooling degree-days to any base.
- Standard deviation of average daily temperature, °C. This parameter is useful to calculate heating and cooling degree-days to any base. Its use is explained in the section on Estimation of Degree-Days.
- Heating and cooling degree-days (bases 10 and 18.3°C). These parameters are useful in energy estimating methods. They are also used to classify locations into climate zones in ASHRAE *Standard* 169.
- Cooling degree-hours (bases 23.3 and 26.7°C). These are used in various standards, such as *Standard* 90.2-2004.

Monthly Design Dry-Bulb, Wet-Bulb, and Mean Coincident Temperatures. These values are derived from the same analysis that results in the annual design conditions. The monthly summaries are useful when seasonal variations in solar geometry and intensity, building or facility occupancy, or building use patterns require consideration. In particular, these values can be used when determining air-conditioning loads during periods of maximum solar radiation. The values listed in the tables include

- Dry-bulb temperature corresponding to 0.4, 2.0, 5.0, and 10.0% cumulative frequency of occurrence for indicated month, °C; mean coincident wet-bulb temperature, °C.
- Wet-bulb temperature corresponding to 0.4, 2.0, 5.0, and 10.0% cumulative frequency of occurrence for indicated month, °C; mean coincident dry-bulb temperature, °C.

For a 30-day month, the 0.4, 2.0, 5.0 and 10.0% values of occurrence represent the value that occurs or is exceeded for a total of 3, 14, 36, or 72 h, respectively, per month on average over the period of record. Monthly percentile values of dry- or wet-bulb temperature may be higher or lower than the annual design conditions corresponding to the same nominal percentile, depending on the month and the seasonal distribution of the parameter at that location. Generally, for the hottest or most humid months of the year, the monthly percentile value exceeds the design condition for the same element corresponding to the same nominal percentile. For example, Table 1 shows that the annual 0.4% design dry-bulb temperature at Atlanta, GA, is 34.4°C; the 0.4% monthly dry-bulb temperature exceeds 34.4°C for June, July, and August, with values of 34.9, 36.6, and 35.7°C, respectively. Two new percentiles were added to this chapter (5.0 and 10.0% values) to give a greater range in the frequency of occurrence, in particular providing less extreme options to select for design calculations.

A general, very approximate rule of thumb is that the *n*% annual cooling design condition is roughly equivalent to the *5n*% monthly cooling condition for the hottest month; that is, the 0.4% annual design dry-bulb temperature is roughly equivalent to the 2% monthly design dry-bulb temperature for the hottest month; the 1% annual value is roughly equivalent to the 5% monthly value for the hottest month, and the 2% annual value is roughly equivalent to the 10% monthly value for the hottest month.

Mean Daily Temperature Range. These values are useful in calculating daily dry- and wet-bulb temperature profiles, as explained in the section on Generating Design-Day Data. Three kinds of profile are defined:

- Mean daily temperature range for month indicated, °C (defined as mean of difference between daily maximum and minimum dry-bulb temperatures).
- Mean daily dry- and wet-bulb temperature ranges coincident with the 5% monthly design dry-bulb temperature. This is the difference between daily maximum and minimum dry- or wet-bulb temperatures, respectively, averaged over all days where the maximum daily dry-bulb temperature exceeds the 5% monthly design dry-bulb temperature.
- Mean daily dry- and wet-bulb temperature ranges coincident with the 5% monthly design wet-bulb temperature. This is the difference between daily maximum and minimum dry- or wet-bulb temperatures, respectively, averaged over all days where the maximum daily wet-bulb temperature exceeds the 5% monthly design wet-bulb temperature.

Clear-Sky Solar Irradiance. Clear-sky irradiance parameters are useful in calculating solar-related air conditioning loads for any time of any day of the year. Parameters are provided for the 21st day of each month. The 21st of the month is usually a convenient day for

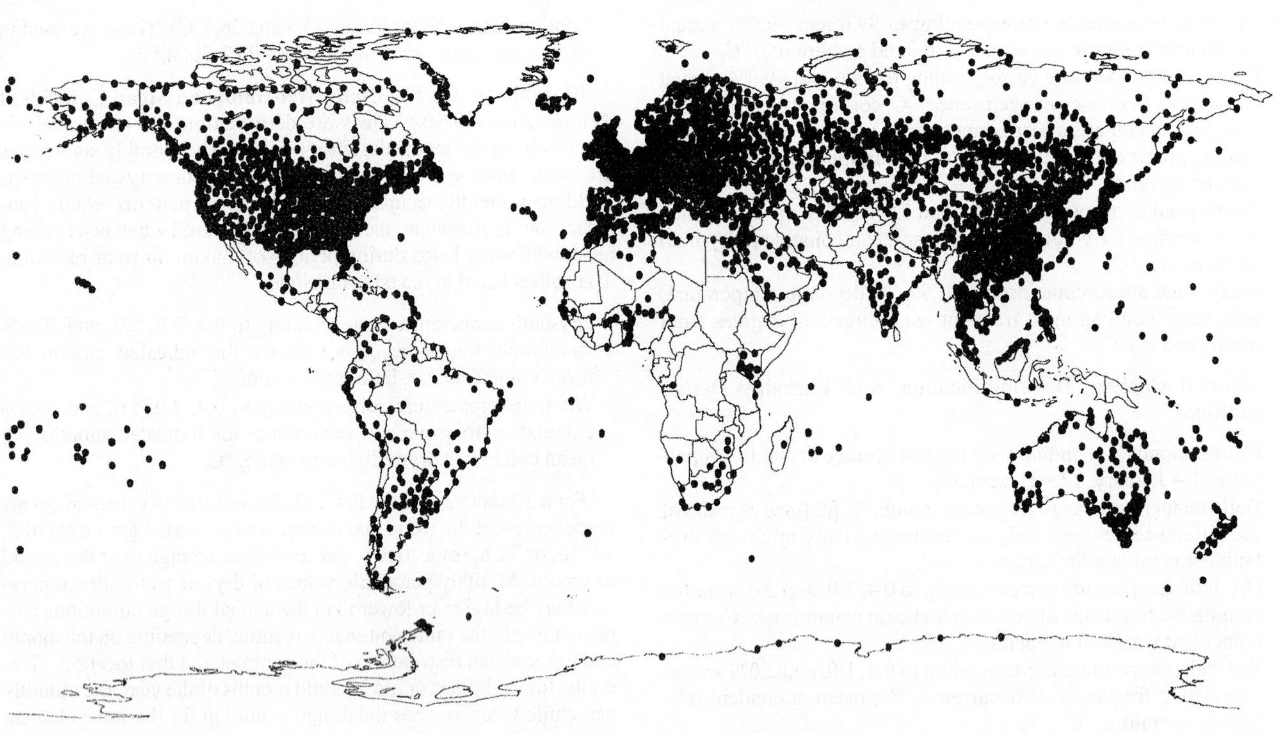

Fig. 1 Location of Weather Stations

solar calculations because June 21 and December 21 represent the solstices (longest and shortest days) and March 21 and September 21 are close to the equinox (days and nights have the same length). Parameters listed in the tables are

- Clear-sky optical depths for beam and diffuse irradiances, which are used to calculate beam and diffuse irradiance as explained in the section on Calculating Clear-Sky Solar Radiation.
- Clear-sky beam normal and diffuse horizontal irradiances at solar noon. These two values can be calculated from the clear-sky optical depths but are listed here for convenience.

Data Sources

The following two primary sources of observational data sets were used in calculating design values:

- Integrated Surface Dataset (ISD) data for stations from around the world provided by NCDC for the period 1982 to 2006 (Lott et al. 2001; NCDC 2003).
- Hourly weather records for the period 1982 to 2006 for 480 Canadian locations from Environment Canada (2003).

In most cases, the period of record used in the calculations spanned 25 years. This choice of period is a compromise between trying to derive design conditions from the longest possible period of record, and using the most recent data to capture climatic or land-use trends from the past two decades. The actual number of years used in the calculations for a given station depends on the amount of missing data, and, as discussed in the next section, may be as little as 8 years. The first and last years of the period of record used to calculate design conditions are listed in the top section of the tables of climatic design conditions, as shown in Table 1 for Atlanta.

Clear-sky solar irradiance parameters listed in the tables constitute a simple parameterization of a sophisticated broadband clear-sky radiation model called REST2 (Gueymard 2008, Thevenard 2009). The REST2 model requires detailed knowledge of various atmospheric constituents, such as aerosols, water vapor, ozone, etc. To extend applicability of the model to the whole world, multiple data sets, mainly derived from space observations, were used to obtain these inputs. Water vapor data were derived from the NVAP satellite/radiosonde assimilated dataset for 1988-1999 (Randel et al., 1996), corrected for elevation (Thevenard 2009). Total ozone amount was derived from observations of the TOMS instrument aboard the Nimbus 7 satellite (http://toms.gsfc.nasa.gov) for 1988-1992. A fixed NO_2 amount of 0.4 matm·cm was used throughout the world. Far-field ground albedo was obtained from the Surface and Atmospheric Radiation Budget (SARB) based on CERES data (Charlock et al. 2004) for 2000-2005. Aerosol turbidity data received special attention because they are the primary inputs that condition the accuracy of the direct and diffuse irradiance predictions under clear skies. Spaceborne data sets were used and were calibrated against a large number of ground-based sites. Six years (2000-2005) of simulated monthly-average aerosol optical depth at 550 nm were prepared with the MATCH model (Rasch et al. 1997; Clarke et al. 2001) by the Science Directorate/Climate Science Branch at NASA Langley Research Center, which also supplied aerosol single-scattering albedo estimates. Aerosol optical depth data from MATCH were combined with retrievals from two MODIS instruments (http://modis-atmos.gsfc.nasa.gov), and compared for ground-truthing with a large number of ground-based sites, mostly from the AERONET network (http://aeronet.gsfc.nasa.gov). Other details can be found in Thevenard (2009).

Results from the REST2 model were then fitted to the simple 2-parameter model described in this chapter. The fits enable a concise formulation requiring tabulation, on a monthly basis, of only two parameters per station, referred to here as the clear-sky beam and diffuse optical depths. Details about the fitting procedure can be found in Thevenard (2009).

Calculation of Design Conditions

Values of ambient dry-bulb, dew-point, and wet-bulb temperature and wind speed corresponding to the various annual percentiles represent the value that is exceeded on average by the indicated percentage of the total number of hours in a year (8760). The 0.4, 1.0, 2.0, and 5.0% values are exceeded on average 35, 88, 175, and 438 h per year, respectively, for the period of record. The design values occur more frequently than the corresponding nominal percentile in some years and less frequently in others. The 99.0 and 99.6% (cold-season) values are defined in the same way but are usually viewed as the values for which the corresponding weather element is less than the design condition for 88 and 35 h, respectively.

Simple design conditions were obtained by binning hourly data into *frequency vectors*, then deriving from the binned data the design condition having the probability of being exceeded a certain percentage of the time. Mean coincident values were obtained by double-binning the hourly data into *joint frequency matrices*, then calculating the mean coincident value corresponding to the simple design condition.

Coincident temperature ranges were also obtained by double-binning daily temperature ranges (daily maximum minus minimum) versus maximum daily temperature. The mean coincident daily range was then calculated by averaging all bins above the simple design condition of interest.

The weather data sets used for the calculations often contain missing values (either isolated records, or because some stations report data only every third hour). Gaps up to 6 h were filled by linear interpolation to provide as complete a time series as possible. Dry-bulb temperature, dew-point temperature, station pressure, and humidity ratio were interpolated. However, wind speed and direction were not interpolated because of their more stochastic and unpredictable nature.

Some stations in the ISD data set also provide data that were not recorded at the beginning of the hour. When data at the exact hour were missing, they were replaced by data up to 0.5 h before or after, when available.

Finally, psychrometric quantities such as wet-bulb temperature or enthalpy are not contained in the weather data sets. They were calculated from dry-bulb temperature, dew-point temperature, and station pressure using the psychrometric equations in Chapter 1.

Measures were taken to ensure that the number and distribution of missing data, both by month and by hour of the day, did not introduce significant biases into the analysis. Annual cumulative frequency distributions were constructed from the relative frequency distributions compiled for each month. Each individual month's data were included if they met the following screening criteria for completeness and unbiased distribution of missing data after data filling:

- The number of hourly dry-bulb temperature values for the month, after filling by interpolation, had to be at least 85% of the total hours for the month.
- The difference between the number of day and nighttime dry-bulb temperature observations had to be less than 60.

Although the nominal period of record selected for this analysis was 25 years (1982 through 2006 for most stations), some variation and gaps in observed data meant that some months' data were unusable because of incompleteness. Some months were also eliminated during additional quality control checks. A station's dry-bulb temperature design conditions were calculated only if there were data from at least 8 months that met the quality control and screening criteria from the period of record for each month of the year. For example, there had to be 8 months each of January, February, March, etc. for which data met the completeness screening criteria. These criteria were ascertained from results of RP-1171 (Hubbard et al. 2004) and were the same as used in calculating the design conditions in the 2001 and 2005 *ASHRAE Handbook—Fundamentals*.

Dew-point temperature, wet-bulb temperature, and enthalpy design conditions were calculated for a given month only if the number of dew-point, wet-bulb, or enthalpy values was greater than 85% of the minimum number of dry-bulb temperature values defined previously; wind speed and direction conditions were calculated for a given month only if the number of values was greater than 28.3% (i.e., one-third of 85%) the minimum number of dry-bulb temperature values. For example, a month of January was included in calculations if the number of dry-bulb temperature values exceeded 85% of 744 h, or 633 h. The month was included in calculation of dew-point temperature design conditions only if dew-point temperature was present for at least 85% of 633 h, or 538 h. The month was included in calculation of wind speed design conditions only if wind speed was present for at least 28.3% of 633 h, or 179 h.

Annual dry-bulb temperature extremes were calculated only for years that were 85% complete. At least 8 annual extremes were required to calculate the mean and standard deviation of extreme annual dry-bulb temperatures.

Daily minimum and maximum temperatures were calculated only for complete days; so were daily temperature ranges and mean coincident temperature ranges.

A final quality check was made of the calculated design values to identify potential errors. These checks included contour plots, consistency checks among the various parameters, and comparison to the 2005 chapter's values. About 32 stations from the 2005 edition have no equivalent within a 12 mile distance in the 2009 edition. These stations may have been dropped because of quality problems, or simply because they did not have enough data within the 1982-2006 period of record used for the present edition. Further details of the analysis procedures are available in Thevenard (2009).

Differences from Previously Published Design Conditions

- Climatic design conditions in this chapter are generally similar to those in previous editions, because similar if not identical analysis procedures were used. There are some differences, however, owing to a more recent period of record (generally 1982-2006 versus 1972-2001). For example, compared to the 2005 edition, 99.6% heating dry-bulb temperatures have increased by 0.11°C on average, and 0.4% cooling dry-bulb temperatures have increased by 0.14°C on average. Similar trends are observed for other design temperatures. The root mean square differences are 0.43°C for the 99.6% heating dry-bulb values and 0.30°C for 0.4% cooling dry-bulb. The increases noted here are generally consistent with the discussion in the section on Impacts of Climate Change.
- Further details concerning differences between design conditions in the 2005 edition and the 2001 edition are described in Thevenard et al. (2005). Differences between the 1993 and previous editions are described in Colliver et al. (2000).

Applicability and Characteristics of Design Conditions

Climatic design values in this chapter represent different psychrometric conditions. Design data based on dry-bulb temperature represent peak occurrences of the sensible component of ambient outdoor conditions. Design values based on wet-bulb temperature are related to the enthalpy of the outdoor air. Conditions based on dew point relate to the peaks of the humidity ratio. The designer, engineer, or other user must decide which set(s) of conditions and probability of occurrence apply to the design situation under consideration. Additional sources of information on frequency and duration of extremes of temperature and humidity are provided in the section on Other Sources of Climatic Information. Further information is available from Harriman et al. (1999). This section discusses the intended use of design conditions in the order they appear in Table 1.

Annual Heating and Humidification Design Conditions. The month with the lowest mean dry-bulb temperature is used, for example, to determine the time of year where the maximum heating load occurs.

The 99.6 and 99.0% design conditions are often used in sizing heating equipment.

The humidification dew point and mean coincident dry-bulb temperatures and humidity ratio provide information for cold-season humidification applications.

Wind design data provide information for estimating peak loads accounting for infiltration: extreme wind speeds for the coldest month, with the mean coincident dry-bulb temperature; and mean wind speed and direction coincident to the 99.6% design dry-bulb temperature.

Annual Cooling, Dehumidification, and Enthalpy Design Conditions. The month with the highest mean dry-bulb temperature is used, for example, to determine the time of year where the maximum sensible cooling load occurs, not taking into account solar loads.

The mean daily dry-bulb temperature range for the hottest month is the mean difference between the daily maximum and minimum temperatures during the hottest month and is calculated from the extremes of the hourly temperature observations. The true maximum and minimum temperatures for any day generally occur between hourly readings. Thus, the mean maximum and minimum temperatures calculated in this way are about 0.5°C less extreme than the mean daily extreme temperatures observed with maximum and minimum thermometers. This results in the true daily temperature range generally about 1°C greater than that calculated from hourly data. The mean daily dry-bulb temperature range is used in cooling load calculations.

The 0.4, 1.0, and 2.0% dry-bulb temperatures and mean coincident wet-bulb temperatures often represent conditions on hot, mostly sunny days. These are often used in sizing cooling equipment such as chillers or air-conditioning units.

Design conditions based on wet-bulb temperature represent extremes of the total sensible plus latent heat of outdoor air. This information is useful for design of cooling towers, evaporative coolers, and fresh-air ventilation systems.

The mean wind speed and direction coincident with the 0.4% design dry-bulb temperature is used for estimating peak loads accounting for infiltration.

Design conditions based on dew-point temperatures are directly related to extremes of humidity ratio, which represent peak moisture loads from the weather. Extreme dew-point conditions may occur on days with moderate dry-bulb temperatures, resulting in high relative humidity. These values are especially useful for humidity control applications, such as desiccant cooling and dehumidification, cooling-based dehumidification, and fresh-air ventilation systems. The values are also used as a check point when analyzing the behavior of cooling systems at part-load conditions, particularly when such systems are used for humidity control as a secondary function. Humidity ratio values are calculated from the corresponding dew-point temperature and the standard pressure at the location's elevation.

Annual enthalpy design conditions give the annual enthalpy for the cooling season; this is used for calculating cooling loads caused by infiltration and/or ventilation into buildings. Enthalpy represents the total heat content of air (the sum of its sensible and latent energies). Cooling loads can be calculated knowing the conditions of both the outdoor ambient and the building's interior air.

Extreme Annual Design Conditions. Extreme annual design wind speeds are used in designing smoke management systems.

The extreme maximum wet-bulb temperature provides the highest wet-bulb temperature observed over the entire period of record and is the most extreme condition observed during the data record for evaporative processes such as cooling towers. For most locations, the extreme maximum wet-bulb value is significantly higher than the 0.4% wet-bulb (see above) and should be used only for design of critical applications where an occasional short-duration capacity shortfall is not acceptable.

The mean and standard deviation of the extreme annual maximum and minimum dry-bulb temperatures are used to calculate the probability of occurrence of very extreme conditions. These can be required for design of equipment to ensure continuous operation and serviceability regardless of whether the heating or cooling loads are being met. These values were calculated from extremes of hourly temperature observations. The true maximum and minimum temperatures for any day generally occur between hourly readings. Thus, the mean maximum and minimum temperatures calculated in this way are about 0.5°C less extreme than the mean daily extreme temperatures observed with maximum and minimum thermometers.

The 5-, 10-, 20- and 50-year return periods for maximum and minimum extreme dry-bulb temperature are also listed in the table. Return period (or recurrence interval) is defined as the reciprocal of the annual probability of occurrence. For instance, the 50-year return period maximum dry-bulb temperature has a probability of occurring or being exceeded of 2.0% (i.e., 1/50) each year. This statistic does not indicate how often the condition will occur in terms of the number of hours each year (as in the design conditions based on percentiles) but describes the probability of the condition occurring at all in any year. The following method can be used to estimate the return period (recurrence interval) of extreme temperatures:

$$T_n = M + IFs \tag{1}$$

where

T_n = n-year return period value of extreme dry-bulb temperature to be estimated, years

M = mean of annual extreme maximum or minimum dry-bulb temperatures, °C

s = standard deviation of annual extreme maximum or minimum dry-bulb temperatures, °C

I = 1 if maximum dry-bulb temperatures are being considered

= −1 if minimum dry-bulb temperatures are being considered

$$F = -\frac{\sqrt{6}}{\pi}\left\{0.5772 + \ln\left[\ln\left(\frac{n}{n-1}\right)\right]\right\}$$

For example, the 50-year return period extreme maximum dry-bulb temperature estimated for Atlanta, GA, is 40.6°C (according to Table 1, M = 35.9°C, s = 1.8, and n = 50; I = 1). Similarly, the 50-year return period extreme minimum dry-bulb temperature for Atlanta, GA, is −22.1°C [M = −11.2°C, s = 4.2, and n = 50; I = −1]. The n-year return periods can be obtained for most stations using ASHRAE's Weather Data Viewer 4.0 (ASHRAE 2009), which is discussed in the section on Other Sources of Climatic Information.

Calculation of the n-year return period is based on assumptions that annual maxima and minima are distributed according to the Gumbel (Type 1 Extreme Value) distribution and are fitted with the method of moments (Lowery and Nash 1970). The uncertainty or standard error using this method increases with standard deviation, value of return period, and decreasing length of the period of record. It can be significant. For instance, the standard error in the 50-year return period maximum dry-bulb temperature estimated at a location with a 12-year period of record can be 3°C or more. Thus, the uncertainty of return period values estimated in this way are greater for stations with fewer years of data than for stations with the complete period of record from 1982-2006.

Temperatures, Degree-Days, and Degree-Hours. Monthly average temperatures and standard deviation of daily average temperatures are calculated using the averages of the minimum and maximum temperatures for each complete day within the period analyzed. They are used to estimate heating and cooling degree-days to any base, as explained in the section on Calculating Degree-Days.

Heating and cooling degree-days (base 10 or 18.3°C) are calculated as the sum of the differences between daily average temperatures and the base temperature. For example the number of **heating degree-days (HDD)** in the month is calculated as

$$HDD = \sum_{i=1}^{N} (T_{base} - \overline{T_i})^+ \quad (2)$$

where N is the number of days in the month, T_{base} is the reference temperature to which the degree-days are calculated, and $\overline{T_i}$ is the mean daily temperature calculated by adding the maximum and minimum temperatures for the day, then dividing by 2. The + superscript indicates that only positive values of the bracketed quantity are taken into account in the sum. Similarly, monthly **cooling degree-days (CDD)** are calculated as:

$$CDD = \sum_{i=1}^{N} (\overline{T_i} - T_{base})^+ \quad (3)$$

Degree-days are used in energy estimating methods, and to classify stations into climate zones for ASHRAE *Standard* 169.

Monthly Design Dry-Bulb and Mean Coincident Wet-Bulb Temperatures. These values provide design conditions for processes driven by dry-bulb air temperature. In particular, air-conditioning cooling loads are generally based on dry-bulb design conditions (plus clear-day solar radiation).

Monthly Design Wet-Bulb and Mean Coincident Dry-Bulb Temperatures. Wet-bulb design conditions are of use in analysis of evaporative coolers, cooling towers, and other equipment involving evaporative transfer. Note also that air wet-bulb temperature and enthalpy are closely related, so applications with large ventilation flow rates may have maximum cooling requirements under high wet-bulb conditions.

Mean Daily Temperature Range. Mean daily range values are computed using all days of the month, as opposed to coincident values that derive from design days. Mean daily range values have been published in previous Handbook editions and are included for completeness. Coincident daily range values should be used for generating design-day profiles.

Clear-Sky Solar Irradiance. Clear-sky solar irradiance data are used in load calculation methods. **Beam normal irradiance** refers to solar radiation emanating directly from the solar disk and measured perpendicularly to the rays of the sun. **Diffuse horizontal irradiance** refers to solar radiation emanating from the sky dome, sun excepted, and measured on a horizontal surface. Because beam and diffuse irradiance vary during the course of the day, new load calculation methods require their estimation at various times, a method for which is explained in the section on Calculating Clear-Sky Solar Radiation. The method uses the clear-sky optical depths, τ_b and τ_d, listed in Table 1 as *taub* and *taud*, respectively, as inputs. Clear-sky beam normal and diffuse horizontal irradiances at solar noon are also listed in Table 1 for convenience.

CALCULATING CLEAR-SKY SOLAR RADIATION

Knowledge of clear-sky solar radiation at various times of year and day is required by several calculation methods for heat gains in HVAC loads and solar energy applications. The tables of climatic design conditions now include the parameters required to calculate clear-sky beam and diffuse solar irradiance using the equations in the following section. The section on Transposition to Receiving Surfaces of Various Orientations explains how to use these values to calculate clear-sky solar radiation incident on arbitrary surfaces.

Note that in all equations in this section, *angles are expressed in degrees*. This includes the arguments appearing in trigonometric functions.

Solar Constant and Extraterrestrial Solar Radiation

The **solar constant E_{sc}** is defined as the intensity of solar radiation on a surface normal to the sun's rays, just beyond the earth's atmosphere, at the average earth-sun distance. One frequently used value is that proposed by the World Meteorological Organization in 1981, E_{sc} = 1367 W/m² (Iqbal 1983).

Because the earth's orbit is slightly elliptical, the **extraterrestrial radiant flux E_o** varies throughout the year, reaching a maximum of 1412 W/m² near the beginning of January, when the earth is closest to the sun (aphelion) and a minimum of 1322 W/m² near the beginning of July, when the earth is farthest from the sun (perihelion). Extraterrestrial solar irradiance incident on a surface normal to the sun's ray can be approximated with the following equation:

$$E_o = E_{sc}\left\{1 + 0.033\cos\left[360°\frac{(n-3)}{365}\right]\right\} \quad (4)$$

where n is the day of year (1 for January 1, 32 for February 1, etc.) and the argument inside the cosine is in degrees. Table 2 tabulates values of E_o for the 21st day of each month.

Equation of Time and Solar Time

The earth's orbital velocity also varies throughout the year, so **apparent solar time (AST)**, as determined by a solar time sundial, varies somewhat from the **mean time** kept by a clock running at a uniform rate. This variation is called the **equation of time (ET)** and is approximated by the following formula (Iqbal 1983):

$$ET = 2.2918(0.0075 + 0.1868\cos(\Gamma) - 3.2077\sin(\Gamma) - 1.4615\cos(2\Gamma) - 4.089\sin(2\Gamma)) \quad (5)$$

with ET expressed in minutes and

$$\Gamma = 360°\frac{n-1}{365} \quad (6)$$

Table 2 tabulates the values of ET for the 21st day of each month.

The conversion between local standard time and solar time involves two steps: the equation of time is added to the local standard time, and then a longitude correction is added. This longitude correction is four minutes of time per degree difference between the **local (site) longitude** and the longitude of the **local standard meridian (LSM)** for that time zone; hence, AST is related to the **local standard time (LST)** as follows:

$$AST = LST + ET/60 + (LON - LSM)/15 \quad (7)$$

where

AST = apparent solar time, decimal hours

Table 2 Approximate Astronomical Data for the 21st Day of Each Month

Month	Jan	Feb	Mar	Apr	May	Jun	Jul	Aug	Sep	Oct	Nov	Dec
Day of year	21	52	80	111	141	172	202	233	264	294	325	355
E_o, W/m²	1410	1397	1378	1354	1334	1323	1324	1336	1357	1380	1400	1411
Equation of time (ET), min	–10.6	–14.0	–7.9	1.2	3.7	–1.3	–6.4	–3.6	6.9	15.5	13.8	2.2
Declination δ, degrees	–20.1	–11.2	–0.4	11.6	20.1	23.4	20.4	11.8	–0.2	–11.8	–20.4	–23.4

Table 3 Time Zones in United States and Canada

Time Zone Name	TZ (Hours ± UTC)	Local Standard Meridian Longitude (°E)
Newfoundland standard time	−3.5	−52.5
Atlantic standard time	−4	−60
Eastern standard time	−5	−75
Central standard time	−6	−90
Mountain standard time	−7	−105
Pacific standard time	−8	−120
Alaska standard time	−9	−135
Hawaii-Aleutian standard time	−10	−150

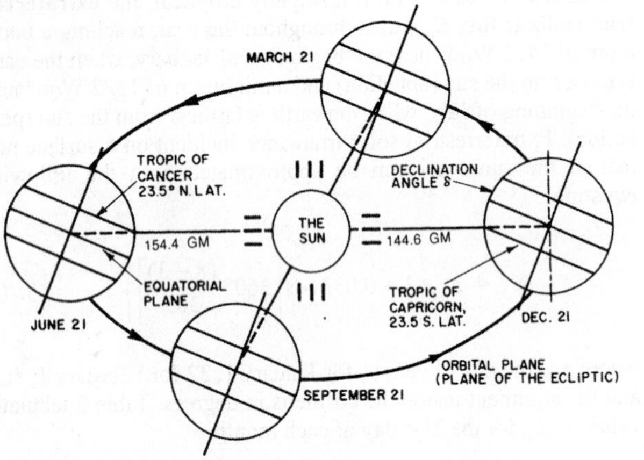

Fig. 2 Motion of Earth around Sun

LST = local standard time, decimal hours
ET = equation of time in minutes, from Table 2 or Equation (5)
LSM = longitude of local standard time meridian, °E of Greenwich (negative in western hemisphere)
LON = longitude of site, °E of Greenwich

Most standard meridians are found every 15° from 0° at Greenwich, U.K., with a few exceptions, such as the province of Newfoundland in Canada. Standard meridian longitude is related to time zone as follows:

$$LSM = 15TZ \tag{8}$$

where TZ is the time zone, expressed in hours ahead or behind **coordinated universal time (UTC)**. TZ is listed for each station on the CD-ROM accompanying this book. Table 3 lists time zones and standard time meridians for the United States and Canada.

If **daylight saving time** (DST) is to be used, rather than local standard time, an additional correction has to be performed. In most locales, local standard time can be obtained from daylight savings time by subtracting one hour:

$$LST = DST - 1 \tag{9}$$

where DST is in decimal hours.

Declination

Because the earth's equatorial plane is tilted at an angle of 23.45° to the orbital plane, the **solar declination** δ (the angle between the earth-sun line and the equatorial plane) varies throughout the year, as shown in Figure 2. This variation causes the changing seasons with their unequal periods of daylight and darkness. Declination can be obtained from astronomical or nautical almanacs; however, for most engineering applications, the following equation provides sufficient accuracy:

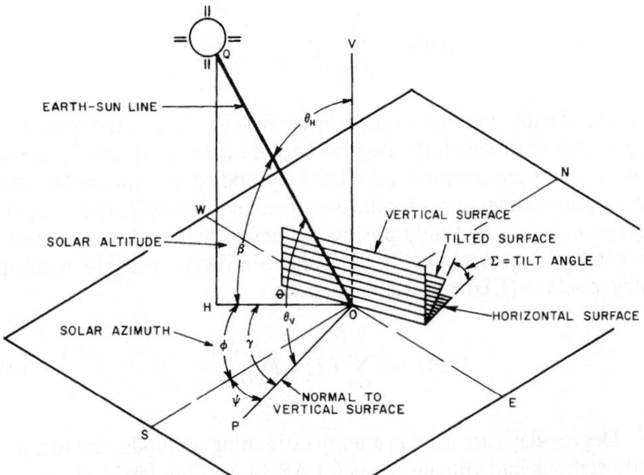

Fig. 3 Solar Angles for Vertical and Horizontal Surfaces

$$\delta = 23.45 \sin\left(360° \frac{n + 284}{365}\right) \tag{10}$$

where δ is in degrees and the argument inside the sine is also in degrees. Table 2 provides δ for the 21st day of each month.

Sun Position

The sun's position in the sky is conveniently expressed in terms of the solar altitude above the horizontal and the solar azimuth measured from the south (see Figure 3). The solar altitude angle β is defined as the angle between the horizontal plane and a line emanating from the sun. Its value ranges from 0° when the sun is on the horizon, to 90° if the sun is directly overhead. Negative values correspond to night times. The solar azimuth angle ϕ is defined as angular displacement from south of the projection, on the horizontal plane, of the earth-sun line. By convention, it is counted positive for afternoon hours and negative for morning hours.

Solar altitude and azimuth angles, in turn, depend on the local latitude L (°N, negative in the southern hemisphere); the solar declination δ, which is a function of the date [see Table 2 or Equation (10)]; and the hour angle H, defined as the angular displacement of the sun east or west of the local meridian due to the rotation of the earth, and expressed in degrees as

$$H = 15(AST - 12) \tag{11}$$

where AST is the apparent solar time [Equation (7)]. H is zero at solar noon, positive in the afternoon, and negative in the morning.

Equation (12) relates the solar altitude angle β to L, δ, and H:

$$\sin \beta = \cos L \cos \delta \cos H + \sin L \sin \delta \tag{12}$$

Note that at solar noon, $H = 0$ and the sun reaches its maximum altitude in the sky:

$$\beta_{max} = 90° - |L - \delta| \tag{13}$$

The azimuth angle ϕ is uniquely determined by its sine and cosine, given in Equations (14) and (15):

$$\sin \phi = \sin H \cos \delta / \cos \beta \tag{14}$$

$$\cos \phi = (\cos H \cos \delta \sin L - \sin \delta \cos L) / \cos \beta \tag{15}$$

Example 1. Calculate the position of the sun in Atlanta, GA, for July 21 at noon solar time.

Solution: From Table 1, Atlanta is at latitude $L = 33.64°N$. From Table 2 or Equation (10), declination $\delta = 20.44°$.

Solar altitude is given by Equation (13):

$$\beta = 90 - |33.64 - 20.44| = 76.80°$$

At solar noon, the sun is due south, so the azimuth angle ϕ is simply 0°.

Example 2. Perform the same calculation as in Example 1, but for 3:00 PM eastern daylight saving time.

Solution: Compared to Example 1, a few extra steps are required to calculate AST. From Table 1, for Atlanta, LON = 84.43°W = –84.43°E and TZ = –5.00. Also, from Table 1 or Equation (5), ET = –6.4 min. Then, from Equation (8):

$$LSM = 15(-5.00) = -75°$$

Because 3 PM daylight savings time is 2 PM standard time, or hour 14, Equation (7) leads to

$$AST = 14 - 6.4/60 + [(-84.43) - (-75)]/15 = 13.27 \text{ h}$$

Then, from Equation (11):

$$H = 15(13.27 - 12) = 18.97°$$

Solar altitude is given by Equation (12), using the same latitude and declination as in Example 1:

$$\sin\beta = \cos(33.64°)\cos(20.44°)\cos(18.97°) + \sin(33.64°)\sin(20.44°) = 0.931$$

Therefore, $\beta = 68.62°$.

Solar azimuth is obtained through Equations (14) and (15):

$$\sin\phi = \sin(18.97°)\cos(20.44°)/\cos(68.62°) = 0.836$$

$$\cos\phi = [\cos(18.97°)\cos(20.44°)\sin(33.64°) - \sin(20.44°)\cos(33.64°)]/\cos(68.62°) = 0.549$$

Therefore, $\phi = 56.69°$.

Air Mass

The relative air mass m is the ratio of the mass of atmosphere in the actual earth/sun path to the mass that would exist if the sun were directly overhead. Air mass is solely a function of solar altitude β and is obtained from (Kasten and Young, 1989)

$$m = 1/[\sin\beta + 0.50572(6.07995 + \beta)^{-1.6364}] \quad (16)$$

where β is expressed in degrees.

Clear-Sky Solar Radiation

Solar radiation on a clear day is defined by its beam (direct) and diffuse components. The direct component represents the part of solar radiation emanating directly from the solar disc, whereas the diffuse component accounts for radiation emanating from the rest of the sky. These two components are calculated as

$$E_b = E_o \exp[-\tau_b m^{ab}] \quad (17)$$

$$E_d = E_o \exp[-\tau_d m^{ad}] \quad (18)$$

where

E_b = beam normal irradiance (measured perpendicularly to rays of the sun)
E_d = diffuse horizontal irradiance (measured on horizontal surface)
E_o = extraterrestrial normal irradiance [Equation (4) or Table 2]
m = air mass [Equation 16)]
τ_b and τ_d = beam and diffuse optical depths (τ_b and τ_d are more correctly termed "pseudo" optical depths, because optical depth is usually employed when the air mass coefficient is unity; "optical depth" is used here for convenience.)
ab and ad = beam and diffuse air mass exponents

Values of τ_b and τ_d are location-specific, and vary during the year. They embody the dependence of clear-sky solar radiation upon local conditions, such as elevation, precipitable water content, and aerosols. Their average values were determined through ASHRAE research project RP-1453 (Thevenard 2009) and are tabulated for the 21st day of each month for all the locations in the tables of climatic design conditions. Values for other days of the year should be found by interpolation.

Air mass exponents ab and ad are correlated to τ_b and τ_d through the following empirical relationships:

$$ab = 1.219 - 0.043\tau_b - 0.151\tau_d - 0.204\tau_b\tau_d \quad (19)$$

$$ad = 0.202 - 0.852\tau_b - 0.007\tau_d - 0.357\tau_b\tau_d \quad (20)$$

Equations (17) to (20) describe a simple parameterization of a sophisticated broadband radiation model and provide accurate predictions of E_b and E_d, even at sites where the atmosphere is very hazy or humid most of the time.

Example 3. Calculate clear-sky beam and diffuse solar irradiance in Atlanta, GA, for July 21 at noon solar time. Note that Table 1 already lists clear-sky beam and diffuse solar irradiance for solar noon. Calculations are shown here to illustrate the application of the method.

Solution: From Example 1, at solar noon on July 21 in Atlanta solar altitude is $\beta = 76.80°$. From Equation (16):

$$m = 1/[\sin(76.80°) + 0.50572(6.07995 + 76.80)^{-1.6364}] = 1.027$$

From Table 1, the beam and diffuse optical depths for Atlanta in July are $\tau_b = 0.556$ and $\tau_d = 1.779$. From Table 2 or Equation (4), normal extraterrestrial irradiance on July 21 is $E_o = 1324$ W/m². Then, from Equations (19) and (20)

$$ab = 1.219 - 0.043 \times 0.556 - 0.151 \times 1.779 - 0.204 \times 0.556 \times 1.779 = 0.725$$

$$ad = 0.202 + 0.852 \times 0.556 - 0.007 \times 1.779 - 0.357 \times 0.556 \times 1.779 = 0.310$$

and from Equations (17) and (18),

$$E_b = 1324 \exp(-0.556 \times 1.027^{0.725}) = 751 \text{ W/m}^2$$

$$E_d = 1324 \exp(-1.779 \times 1.027^{0.310}) = 220 \text{ W/m}^2$$

These are the values listed for *Ebn,noon* and *Edh,noon* in Table 1.

Example 4. Perform the same calculation as in Example 3, but for 3 PM eastern daylight saving time.

Solution: This is the same calculation as in the solution of Example 3, but using the solar altitude $\beta = 68.62°$ calculated in Example 2 (ab and ad are unchanged from Example 3):

$$m = 1/[\sin(68.62°) + 0.50572(6.07995 + 68.62)^{-1.6364}] = 1.073$$

$$E_b = 1324 \exp(-0.556 \times 1.073^{0.725}) = 737 \text{ W/m}^2$$

$$E_d = 1324 \exp(-1.779 \times 1.073^{0.310}) = 215 \text{ W/m}^2$$

TRANSPOSITION TO RECEIVING SURFACES OF VARIOUS ORIENTATIONS

Calculations developed in the previous section are chiefly concerned with estimating clear-sky solar irradiance either normal to the rays of the sun (direct beam) or on a horizontal surface (diffuse). However, in many circumstances, calculation of clear-sky solar irradiance is required on surfaces of arbitrary orientations. Receiving surfaces can be vertical (e.g., walls and windows) or tilted (e.g., skylights or active solar devices). This section describes **transposition models** that enable calculating solar irradiance on any surface, knowing beam normal and diffuse horizontal irradiance.

Table 4 Surface Orientations and Azimuths, Measured from South

Orientation	N	NE	E	SE	S	SW	W	NW
Surface azimuth ψ	180°	−135°	−90°	−45°	0	45°	90°	135°

Solar Angles Related to Receiving Surfaces

The orientation of a receiving surface is best characterized by its tilt angle and its azimuth, shown in Figure 3. The tilt angle Σ (also called *slope*) is the angle between the surface and the horizontal plane. Its value lies between 0 and 180°. Most often, slopes are between 0° (horizontal) and 90° (vertical). Values above 90° correspond to surfaces facing the ground. The surface azimuth ψ is defined as the displacement from south of the projection, on the horizontal plane, of the normal to the surface. Surfaces that face west have a positive surface azimuth; those that face east have a negative surface azimuth. Surface azimuths for common orientations are summarized in Table 4. Note that, in this chapter, surface azimuth is defined as relative to south in both the northern and southern hemispheres. Other presentations and software use relative-to-north or relative-to-equator; care is required.

The surface-solar azimuth angle γ is defined as the angular difference between the solar azimuth ϕ and the surface azimuth ψ:

$$\gamma = \phi - \psi \tag{21}$$

Values of γ greater than 90° or less than −90° indicate that the surface is in the shade.

Finally, the angle between the line normal to the irradiated surface and the earth-sun line is called the angle of incidence θ. It is important in fenestration, load calculations, and solar technology because it affects the intensity of the direct component of solar radiation striking the surface and the surface's ability to absorb, transmit, or reflect the sun's rays. Its value is given by

$$\cos\theta = \cos\beta\cos\gamma\sin\Sigma + \sin\beta\cos\Sigma \tag{22}$$

Note that for vertical surfaces ($\Sigma = 90°$) Equation (22) simplifies to

$$\cos\theta = \cos\beta\cos\gamma \tag{23}$$

whereas for horizontal surfaces ($\Sigma = 0°$) it simplifies to

$$\theta = 90 - \beta \tag{24}$$

Example 5. For Atlanta, GA, on July 21 at 3 PM eastern daylight saving time, find the angle of incidence at a vertical widow facing 60° west of south.

Solution: The azimuth of the receiving surface is $\psi = +60°$. According to Example 2, solar azimuth angle is $\phi = 56.69°$. Then, Equation (21) gives the surface-solar azimuth angle as

$$\gamma = 56.69° - 60° = -3.31°$$

Still from Example 2, solar altitude angle is $\beta = 68.62°$. Equation (23) leads to

$$\cos\theta = \cos(68.62°)\cos(-3.31°) = 0.364$$

Therefore, $\theta = 68.66°$.

Example 6. For the same conditions as in Example 5, find the angle of incidence at a skylight tilted at 30° and facing 60° west of south.

Solution: The azimuth of the receiving surface is still $\psi = +60°$, but its slope is $\Sigma = 30°$. Other angles are unchanged from Example 5. Equation (22) now applies:

$$\cos\theta = \cos(68.62°)\cos(-3.31°)\sin(30°) + \sin(68.62°)\cos(30°) = 0.988$$

which leads to $\theta = 8.74°$.

Calculation of Clear-Sky Solar Irradiance Incident On Receiving Surface

Total clear-sky irradiance E_t reaching the receiving surface is the sum of three components: the beam component $E_{t,b}$ originating from the solar disc; the diffuse component $E_{t,d}$, originating from the sky dome; and the ground-reflected component $E_{t,r}$ originating from the ground in front of the receiving surface. Thus,

$$E_t = E_{t,b} + E_{t,d} + E_{t,r} \tag{25}$$

Only a simple method for computing all the factors on the right side of Equation (25) is presented here. More elaborate methods, particularly with regard to the calculating the diffuse component, can be found in Gueymard (1987) and Perez et al. (1990).

Beam Component. The beam component is obtained from a straightforward geometric relationship:

$$E_{t,b} = E_b\cos\theta \tag{26}$$

where θ is the angle of incidence. This relationship is valid when $\cos\theta > 0$; otherwise, $E_{t,b} = 0$.

Diffuse Component. The diffuse component is more difficult to estimate because of the nonisotropic nature of diffuse radiation: some parts of the sky, such as the circumsolar disc or the horizon, tend to be brighter than the rest of the sky, which makes the development of a simplified model challenging. For vertical surfaces, Stephenson (1965) and Threlkeld (1963) showed that the ratio Y of clear-sky diffuse irradiance on a vertical surface to clear-sky diffuse irradiance on the horizontal is a simple function of the angle of incidence θ:

$$E_{t,d} = E_d Y \tag{27}$$

with

$$Y = \max(0.45, 0.55 + 0.437\cos\theta + 0.313\cos^2\theta) \tag{28}$$

For a nonvertical surface with slope Σ, the following simplified relationships are sufficient for most applications described in this volume:

$$E_{t,d} = E_d(Y\sin\Sigma + \cos\Sigma) \qquad \text{if } \Sigma \le 90° \tag{29}$$

$$E_{t,d} = E_d Y\sin\Sigma \qquad \text{if } \Sigma > 90° \tag{30}$$

where Y is calculated for a *vertical surface* having the same azimuth as the receiving surface considered.

Note that Equations (27) to (30) are appropriate for clear-sky conditions, but should not be used for cloudy skies.

Ground-Reflected Component. Ground-reflected irradiance for surfaces of all orientations is given by

$$E_{t,r} = (E_b\sin\beta + E_d)\rho_g\frac{1-\cos\Sigma}{2} \tag{31}$$

where ρ_g is ground reflectance, often taken to be 0.2 for a typical mixture of ground surfaces. Table 5 provides estimates of ρ_g for other surfaces, including in the presence of snow.

Example 7. Find the direct, diffuse and ground-reflected components of clear-sky solar irradiance on the window in Example 5.

Solution: Clear-sky beam normal irradiance E_b and diffuse horizontal irradiance E_d were calculated in Example 4 as $E_b = 737$ W/m^2 and $E_d = 213$ W/m^2. Example 2 provided the solar altitude as $\beta = 68.62°$ and Example 5 provided the angle of incidence as $\theta = 68.66°$. The surface slope is $\Sigma = 90°$, and ground reflectance is assumed to be 0.2. Substituting these values into Equations (26), (27), (28), and (31) leads to

$$E_{t,b} = 737\cos(68.66°) = 268 \text{ W/m}^2$$

$$Y = \max[0.45, 0.55 + 0.437\cos(68.66°) + 0.313\cos^2(68.66°)] = 0.750$$

$$E_{t,d} = 215 \times 0.750 = 161 \text{ W/m}^2$$

$$E_{t,r} = [737\sin(68.62°) + 215]0.2\frac{1 - \cos(90°)}{2} = 90 \text{ W/m}^2$$

Example 8. Find the direct, diffuse and ground-reflected components of clear-sky solar irradiance on the skylight in Example 6.

Solution: This example uses the same values as Example 7, except that the surface slope is $\Sigma = 30°$ and the angle of incidence, calculated in Example 6, is $\theta = 8.74°$. The clear-sky irradiance components are then calculated from Equations (26), (29) and (31); the ratio Y is calculated for a *vertical* surface having the same azimuth as the receiving surface, so the value calculated in Example 7 is unchanged.

$$E_{t,b} = 737\cos(8.74°) = 729 \text{ W/m}^2$$

$$E_{t,d} = 215[0.750\sin(30°) + \cos(30°)] = 267 \text{ W/m}^2$$

$$E_{t,r} = [737\sin(68.62°) + 215]0.2\frac{1 - \cos(30°)}{2} = 12 \text{ W/m}^2$$

GENERATING DESIGN-DAY DATA

This section provides procedures for generating 24 h temperature data sequences suitable as input to many HVAC analysis methods, including the radiant time series (RTS) cooling load calculation procedure described in Chapter 18.

Temperatures. Table 6 gives a normalized daily temperature profile in fractions of daily temperature range. Recent research projects RP-1363 (Hedrick 2009) and RP-1453 (Thevenard 2009) have shown that this profile is representative of both dry-bulb and wet-bulb temperature variation on typical design days. To calculate hourly temperatures, subtract the Table 6 fraction of the dry- or wet-bulb daily range from the dry- or wet-bulb design temperature (limiting by saturation in the case of the wet-bulb). This procedure is applicable to annual or monthly data and is illustrated in Example 9. Table 7 specifies the input values to be used for generation of several design-day types.

Because daily temperature variation is driven by heat from the sun, the profile in Table 6 is, strictly speaking, specified in terms of solar time. Typical HVAC calculations (e.g., hourly cooling loads) are performed in local time, reflecting building operation schedules. The difference between local and solar time can easily be 1 or 2 h, depending on site longitude and whether daylight saving time is in effect. This difference can be included by accessing the temperature profile using apparent solar time (AST) calculated with Equation (7), as shown in the Example 9.

Additional Moist-Air Properties. Once hourly dry-bulb and wet-bulb temperatures are known, additional moist air properties (e.g., dew-point temperature, humidity ratio, enthalpy) can be derived using the psychrometric chart, equations in Chapter 1, or psychrometric software.

Example 9. Deriving Hourly Design-Day Temperatures. Calculate hourly temperatures for Atlanta, GA, for a July dry-bulb design day using the 5% design conditions.

Solution: From Table 1, the July 5% dry-bulb design conditions for Atlanta are DB = 33.3°C and MCWB = 23.5°C. Daily range values are MCDBR = 11.5°C and MCWBR = 3.5°C. Daylight saving time is in effect for Atlanta in July. Apparent solar time (AST) for hour 1 local daylight saving time (LDT) is −0.73. The nearest hour to the AST is 23, yielding a Table 6 profile value of 0.75. Then $t_{db,1} = 33.3 - 0.75 \times 11.5 = 24.7$°C. Similarly, $t_{wb,1} = 23.5 - 0.75 \times 3.5 = 20.9$°C. With psychrometric formulas, derive $t_{dp,1} = 19.2$°C. Table 8 shows results of this procedure for all 24 h.

Table 5 Ground Reflectance of Foreground Surfaces

Foreground Surface	Reflectance
Water (large angle of incidences)	0.07
Coniferous forest (winter)	0.07
Bituminous and gravel roof	0.13
Dry bare ground	0.2
Weathered concrete	0.22
Green grass	0.26
Dry grassland	0.2 to 0.3
Desert sand	0.4
Light building surfaces	0.6
Snow-covered surfaces:	
Typical city centre	0.2
Typical urban site	0.4
Typical rural site	0.5
Isolated rural site	0.7

Source: Adapted from Thevenard and Haddad (2006).

ESTIMATION OF DEGREE-DAYS

Monthly Degree-Days

The tables of climatic design conditions in this chapter list heating and cooling degree-days (bases 10 and 18.3°C). Although 10 and 18.3°C represent the most commonly used bases for the calculation of degree-days, calculation to other bases may be necessary. With that goal in mind, the tables also provide two parameters (monthly average temperature T, and standard deviation of daily average temperature s_d) that enable estimation of degree-days to any base with reasonable accuracy.

The calculation method was established by Schoenau and Kehrig (1990). Heating degree days HDD_b to base T_b are expressed as

Table 6 Fraction of Daily Temperature Range

Time, h	Fraction	Time, h	Fraction	Time, h	Fraction
1	0.88	9	0.55	17	0.14
2	0.92	10	0.38	18	0.24
3	0.95	11	0.23	19	0.39
4	0.98	12	0.13	20	0.50
5	1.00	13	0.05	21	0.59
6	0.98	14	0.00	22	0.68
7	0.91	15	0.00	23	0.75
8	0.74	16	0.06	24	0.82

Table 7 Input Sources for Design-Day Generation

Design Day Type	Design Conditions	Daily Ranges	Limits
Dry-bulb			
Annual	0.4, 1, or 2% annual cooling DB/MCWB	Hottest month 5% DB MCDBR/MCWBR	Hourly wet-bulb temp. = min(dry-bulb temp., wet-bulb temp.)
Monthly	0.4, 2, 5, or 10% DB/MCWB for month	5% DB MCDBR/MCWBR for month	
Wet-bulb			
Annual	0.4, 1, or 2% annual cooling WB/MCDB	Hottest month 5% WB MCDBR/MCWBR	Hourly dry-bulb temp. = max(dry-bulb temp. wet-bulb temp.)
Monthly	0.4, 2, 5, or 10% WB/MCDB for month	5% WB MCDBR/MCWBR for month	

Table 8 Derived Hourly Temperatures for Atlanta, GA for July for 5% Design Conditions, °C

Hour (LDT)	t_{db}	t_{wb}	t_{dp}	Hour (LDT)	t_{db}	t_{wb}	t_{dp}
1	24.7	20.9	19.2	13	30.7	22.7	19.4
2	23.9	20.6	19.2	14	31.8	23.0	19.5
3	23.2	20.4	19.2	15	32.7	23.3	19.6
4	22.7	20.3	19.2	16	33.3	23.5	19.6
5	22.4	20.2	19.2	17	33.3	23.5	19.6
6	22.0	20.1	19.2	18	32.6	23.3	19.6
7	21.8	20.0	19.2	19	31.7	23.0	19.5
8	22.0	20.1	19.2	20	30.5	22.7	19.4
9	22.8	20.3	19.2	21	28.8	22.1	19.4
10	24.8	20.9	19.2	22	27.5	21.8	19.3
11	27.0	21.6	19.3	23	26.5	21.4	19.3
12	28.9	22.2	19.4	24	25.5	21.1	19.2

LDT = Local daylight saving time

$$HDD_b = Ns_d[Z_bF(Z_b) + f(Z_b)] \quad (32)$$

where N is the number of days in the month and Z_b is the difference between monthly average temperature T and base temperature T_b, normalized by the standard deviation of the daily average temperature s_d:

$$Z_b = \frac{T_b - \overline{T}}{s_d} \quad (33)$$

Function f is the normal (Gaussian) probability density function with mean 0 and standard deviation 1, and function F is the equivalent cumulative normal probability function:

$$f(Z) = \frac{1}{\sqrt{2\pi}}\exp\left(\frac{-Z^2}{2}\right) \quad (34)$$

$$F(Z) = \sum_{-\infty}^{Z} f(z)dz \quad (35)$$

Both f and F are readily available as built-in functions in many scientific calculators or spreadsheet programs, so their manual calculation is rarely warranted.

Cooling degree days CDD_b to base T_b are calculated by the same equation:

$$CDD_b = Ns_d[Z_bF(Z_b) + f(Z_b)] \quad (36)$$

except that Z_b is now expressed as

$$Z_b = \frac{\overline{T} - T_b}{s_d} \quad (37)$$

Annual Degree-Days

Annual degree-days are simply the sum of monthly degree days over the twelve months of the year.

Example 10. Calculate heating and cooling degree-days (base 15°C) for Atlanta for the month of October.

Solution: For October in Atlanta, Table 1 provides $\overline{T}$ = 17.5°C and s_d = 3.93°C. For heating degree-days, Equation (33) provides Z_b = (15 – 17.5)/3.93 = –0.636. From a scientific calculator or a spreadsheet program $f(Z_b)$ = 0.326, and $F(Z_b)$ = 0.263. Equation (32) then gives

$$HDD_{15} = 31 \times 3.93[-0.636 \times 0.262 + 0.326] = 19.4°C\text{-day}.$$

For cooling degree-days, Z_b = 0.636. Note that $f(-Z_b) = f(Z_b)$ and $F(-Z_b) = 1 - F(Z_b)$, hence

$$f(Z_b) = 0.326 \quad \text{and} \quad F(Z_b) = 0.738$$

and

$$CDD_{15} = 31 \times 3.93(-0.636 \times 0.738 + 0.326) = 96.6°C\text{-day}.$$

For most stations, the monthly degree days calculated with this method are within 5°C-day of the observed values.

REPRESENTATIVENESS OF DATA AND SOURCES OF UNCERTAINTY

Representativeness of Data

The climatic design information in this chapter was obtained by direct analysis of observations from the indicated locations. Design values reflect an estimate of the cumulative frequency of occurrence of the weather conditions at the recording station, either for single or jointly occurring elements, for several years into the future. Several sources of uncertainty affect the accuracy of using the design conditions to represent other locations or periods.

The most important of these factors is spatial representativeness. Most of the observed data for which design conditions were calculated were collected from airport observing sites, the majority of which are flat, grassy, open areas, away from buildings and trees or other local influences. Temperatures recorded in these areas may be significantly different (3 to 5°C lower) compared to areas where the design conditions are being applied. Significant variations can also occur with changes in local elevation, across large metropolitan areas, or in the vicinity of large bodies of water. Judgment must always be exercised in assessing the representativeness of the design conditions. It is especially important to note the elevation of locations, because design conditions vary significantly for locations whose elevations differ by as little as a few hundred metres. Data representing psychrometric conditions are generally properties of air masses rather than local features, and tend to vary on regional scales. As a result, a particular value may reasonably represent an area extending several miles. Consult an applied climatologist regarding estimating design conditions for locations not listed in this chapter. For online references to applied climatologists, see http://www.ncdc.noaa.gov/oa/about/amscert.html. Also, GIS-compatible files (KML format) are provided on the CD-ROM accompanying this book. This allows use of the data in a GIS environment such as Google Earth or ArcGIS, which provides capabilities to overlay various layers of information such as elevation, land-use, bodies of water, etc. This type of information can greatly assist in determining the most representative location to use for an application.

The underlying data also depend on the method of observation. During the 1990s, most data gathering in the United States and Canada was converted to automated systems designated either an ASOS (Automated Surface Observation System) or an AWOS (Automated Weather Observing System). This change improved completeness and consistency of available data. However, changes have resulted from the inherent differences in type of instrumentation, instrumentation location, and processing procedures between the prior manual systems and ASOS. These effects were investigated in ASHRAE research project RP-1226 (Belcher and DeGaetano 2004). Comparison of one-year ASOS and manual records revealed some biases in dry-bulb temperature, dew-point temperature, and wind speed. These biases are judged to be negligible for HVAC engineering purposes; the tabulated design conditions in this chapter were derived from mixed automated and manual data as available. It has been recognized that changes in the location of the observing instruments often have a larger effect than the change in instrumentation. On the other hand, ASOS measurements of sky coverage and ceiling height differ markedly from manual observations and are incompatible with solar radiation models used in energy simulation software. An updated solar model, compatible with ASOS data, was developed as

Table 9 Locations Representing Various Climate Types

Cold Snow Forest	Dry	Warm Rainy	Tropical Rainy
Portland, ME	Amarillo, TX	Huntsville, AL	Key West, FL
Grand Island, NE	Bakersfield, CA	Wilmington, NC	West Palm Beach, FL
Minot, ND	Sacramento, CA	Portland, OR	
Indianapolis, IN	Phoenix, AZ	Quillayute, WA	

part of RP-1226. The ASOS-based model was found less accurate than models based on manually observed data when compared to measured solar radiation.

Weather conditions vary from year to year and, to some extent, from decade to decade because of the inherent variability of climate. Similarly, values representing design conditions vary depending on the period of record used in the analysis. Thus, because of short-term climatic variability, there is always some uncertainty in using design conditions from one period to represent another period. Typically, values of design dry-bulb temperature vary less than 1°C from decade to decade, but larger variations can occur. Differing periods used in the analysis can lead to differences in design conditions between nearby locations at similar elevations. Design conditions may show trends in areas of increasing urbanization or other regions experiencing extensive changes to land use. Longer-term climatic change brought by human or natural causes may also introduce trends into design conditions. This is discussed further in the section on Effects of Climate Change.

Wind speed and direction are very sensitive to local exposure features such as terrain and surface cover. The original wind data used to calculate the wind speed and direction design conditions in Table 1 are often representative of a flat, open exposure, such as at airports. Wind engineering methods, as described in Chapter 24, can be used to account for exposure differences between airport and building sites. This is a complex procedure, best undertaken by an experienced applied climatologist or wind engineer with knowledge of the exposure of the observing and building sites and surrounding regions.

Uncertainty from Variation in Length of Record

ASHRAE research project RP-1171 (Hubbard et al. 2004) investigated the uncertainty associated with the climatic design conditions in the 2001 *ASHRAE Handbook—Fundamentals*. The main objectives were to determine how many years are needed to calculate reliable design values and to look at the frequency and duration of episodes exceeding the design values.

Design temperatures in the 1997 and 2001 editions were calculated for locations for which there were at least 8 years of sufficient data; the criterion for using 8 years was based on unpublished work by TC 4.2. RP-1171 analyzed data records from 14 U.S. locations (Table 9) representing four different climate types. The dry-bulb temperatures corresponding to the five annual percentile design temperatures (99.6, 99, 0.4, 1, and 2%) from the 33-year period 1961-1993 (period used for the 2001 edition's U.S. stations) were calculated for each location. The temperatures corresponding to the same percentiles for each contiguous subperiod ranging from 1 to 33 years in length was calculated, and the standard deviation of the differences between the resulting design temperature from each subperiod and the entire 33-year period was calculated. For instance, for a 10-year period, the dry-bulb values corresponding to each of the 23 subperiods 1961-1970, 1962-1971, . . . , 1984-1993 were calculated and the standard deviation of differences with the dry-bulb value for the same percentile from the 33-year period calculated. The standard deviation values represent a measure of uncertainty of the design temperatures relative to the design temperature for the entire period of record.

The results for the five annual percentiles are summarized in Figures 4A to 4E, each of which shows how the uncertainty (the average standard deviation for each of the locations in each climate type) varies with length of period.

To the degree that the differences used to calculate the standard deviations are distributed normally, the short-period design temperatures can be expected to lie within one standard deviation of the long-term design temperature 68% of the time. For example, from Figure 4A, the uncertainty for the Cold Snow Forest for a 1-year period is 3.6°C. This can be interpreted that the probability is 68% that the difference in a 99.6% dry-bulb in any given year will be within 6.3°C of the long-term 99.6% dry-bulb. Similarly, there is a 68% probability that the 99.6% dry-bulb from any 10-year period will be within 1°C of the long-term value for a location of the Cold Snow Forest climate type.

The uncertainty for the cold season is higher than for the warm season. For example, the uncertainty for the 99.6% dry-bulb for a 10-year period ranges from 0.6 to 1.0°C for the five climate types, whereas the uncertainty for the 0.4% dry-bulb for a 10-year period ranges from 0.4 to 0.6°C.

A variety of other general characteristics of uncertainty are evident from an inspection of Figure 4. For example, the highest uncertainty of any climate type for a 10-year period is 1.1°C for the Cold Snow Forest 99% dry-bulb case. The smallest uncertainty is 0.2°C for the Tropical Rainy 1% and 2% dry-bulb cases.

Based on these results, it was concluded that using a minimum of 8 years of data would provide reliable (within ±1°C) climatic design calculations for most stations.

Effects of Climate Change

The evidence is unequivocal that the climate system is warming globally (IPCC 2007). The most frequently observed effects relate to increases in average, and to some degree, extreme temperatures.

This is partly illustrated by the results of an analysis of design conditions conducted as part of developing the updated values for this chapter (Thevenard 2009). For 1274 observing sites worldwide with suitably complete data from 1977 to 2006, selected design conditions were compared between the period 1977-1986 and 1997-2006. The results, averaged over all locations, are as follows:

- The 99.6% annual dry-bulb temperature increased 1.52°C
- The 0.4% annual dry-bulb increased 0.79°C
- Annual dew point increased by 0.55°C
- Heating-degree days (base 18.3°C) decreased by 237°C-days
- Cooling degree-days (base 10°C) increased by 136°C-days

Although these results are consistent with general warming of the world climate system, there are other effects that undoubtedly contribute, such as increased urbanization around many of the observing sites (airports, typically). There was no attempt in the analysis to determine the reasons for the changes.

Regardless of the reasons for increases, the general approach of developing design conditions based on analysis of the recent record (25 years, in this case) was specifically adopted for updating the values in this chapter as a balance between accounting for long-term trends and the sampling variation caused by year-to-year variation. Although this does not necessarily provide the optimum predictive value for representing conditions over the next one or two decades, it at least has the effect of incorporating changes in climate and local conditions as they occur, as updates are conducted regularly using recent data. Meteorological services worldwide are considering the many aspects of this complex issue in the calculation of climate "normals" (averages, extremes, and other statistical summary information of climate elements typically calculated for a 30-year period at the end of each decade). Livezey et al. (2007) and WMO (2007) provide detailed analyses and recommendations in this regard.

Extrapolating design conditions to the next few decades based on observed trends should only be done with attention to the particular climate element and the regional and temporal characteristics of observed trends (Livezey et al. 2007).

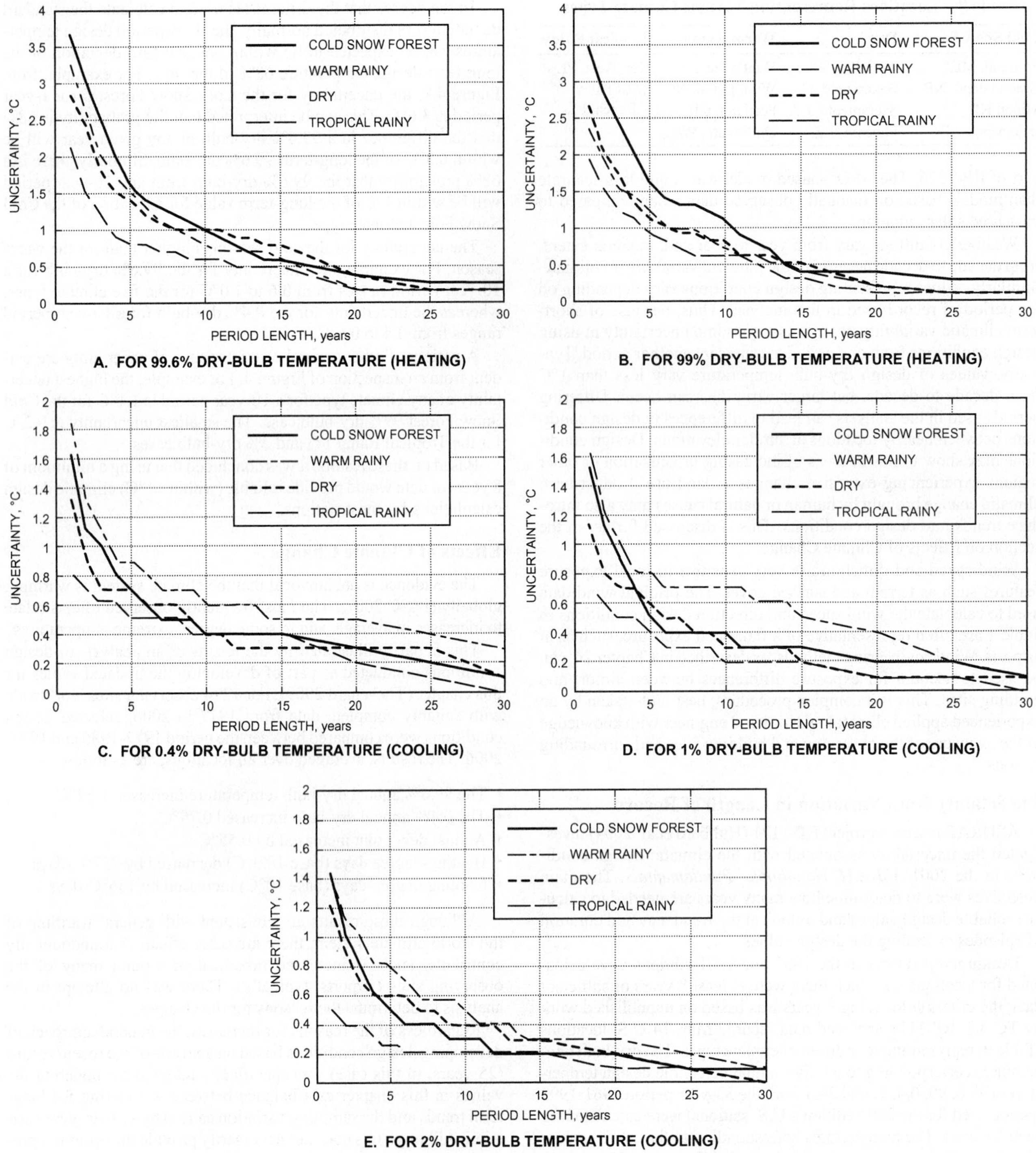

Fig. 4 Uncertainty versus Period Length for Various Dry-Bulb Temperatures, by Climate Type

Episodes Exceeding the Design Dry-Bulb Temperature

Design temperatures based on annual percentiles indicate how many hours each year on average the specific conditions will be exceeded, but do not provide any information on the length or frequency of such episodes. As reported by Hubbard et al. (2004), each episode and its duration for the locations in Table 9 during which the 2001 design conditions represented by the 99.6, 99, 0.4, 1, and 2% dry-bulb temperatures were exceeded (i.e., were more extreme) was tabulated and their frequency of occurrence analyzed. The measure of frequency is the average number of episodes per year or its reciprocal, the average period between episodes.

Cold- and warm-season results are presented in Figures 5A and 5B, respectively, for Indianapolis, IN, as a representative example. The duration for the 10-year period between episodes more extreme than the 99.6% design dry-bulb is 37 h, and 62 h for the 99% design dry-bulb. For the warm season, the 10-year period durations corresponding to the 0.4, 1, and 2% design dry-bulb, are about 10, 12, and 15 h, respectively.

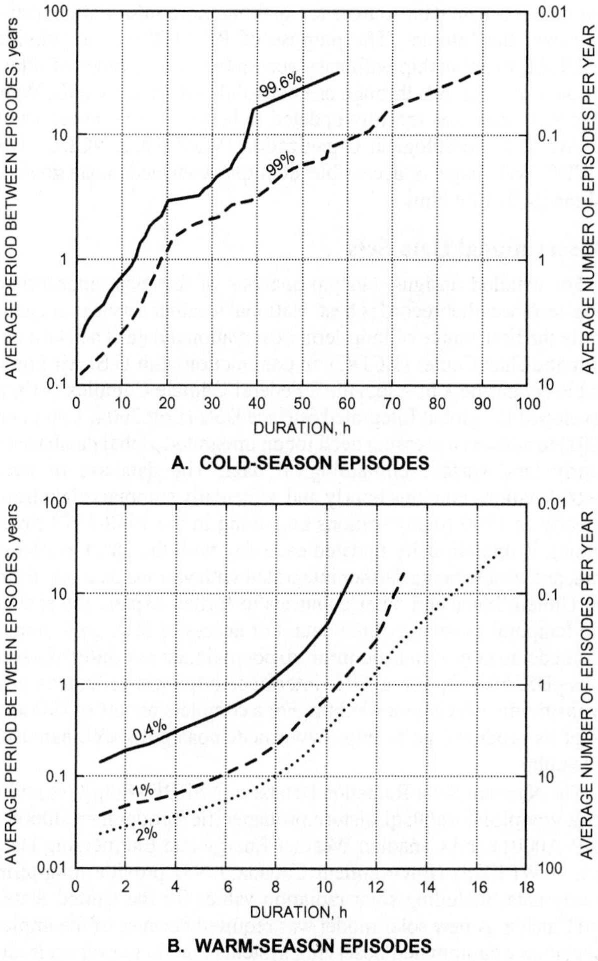

Fig. 5 Frequency and Duration of Episodes Exceeding Design Dry-Bulb Temperature for Indianapolis, IN

Although the results in Hubbard et al. (2004) varied somewhat among the locations analyzed, generally the longest cold-season episodes last days, whereas the longest warm-season episodes were always shorter than 24 h. These results were seen at almost all locations, and are general for the continental United States. The only exception was Phoenix, where the longest cold-season episodes were less than 24 h. This is likely the result of the southern latitude and dry climate, which produces a large daily temperature range, even in the cold season.

OTHER SOURCES OF CLIMATIC INFORMATION

Joint Frequency Tables of Psychrometric Conditions

Design values in this chapter were developed by ASHRAE research project RP-1453 (Thevenard 2009). The frequency vectors used to calculate the simple design conditions, and the joint frequency matrices used to calculate the coincident design conditions, are available in ASHRAE's Weather Data Viewer 4.0 (WDView 4.0) (ASHRAE 2009). WDView 4.0 gives users full access to the frequency vectors and joint frequency matrices for all 5564 stations in the 2009 *ASHRAE Handbook—Fundamentals* via a spreadsheet. WDView 4.0 provides the following capabilities:

- Select a station by WMO number or region/country/state/name or by proximity to a given latitude and longitude
- Retrieve design climatic conditions for a specified station, in SI or I-P units
- Display frequency vectors and joint frequency matrices in the form of numerical tables
- Display frequency distribution and the cumulative frequency distribution functions in graphical form
- Display joint frequency functions in graphical form
- Display the table of years and months used for the calculation
- Display hourly binned dry-bulb temperature data
- Calculate heating and cooling degree-days to any base, using the method of Schoenau and Kehrig (1990)

The **Engineering Weather Data CD** (NCDC 1999), an update of Air Force *Manual* 88-29, was compiled by the U.S. Air Force Combat Climatology Center. This CD contains several tabular and graphical summaries of temperature, humidity, and wind speed information for hundreds of locations in the United States and around the world. In particular, it contains detailed joint frequency tables of temperature and humidity for each month, binned at 0.5°C and 3 h local time-of-day intervals. This CD is available from NCDC: http: // ols.nndc.noaa.gov/ plolstore/ plsql/ olstore.prodspecific? prodnum=C00515-CDR-A0001.

The **International Station Meteorological Climate Summary (ISMCS)** is a CD-ROM containing climatic summary information for over 7000 locations around the world (NCDC 1996). A table providing the joint frequency of dry-bulb temperature and wet-bulb temperature depression is provided for the locations with hourly observations. It can be used as an aid in estimating design conditions for locations for which no other information is available. The CD is available here: http://ols.nndc.noaa.gov/plolstore/plsql/olstore.prodspecific?prodnum=C00268-CDR-A0001. A Web version of this product is now available free of charge from NCDC: http://cdo.ncdc.noaa.gov/pls/plclimprod/poemain.accessrouter?datasetabbv= DS3505.

Note that you should select the "advanced" option, then click on the "data summary" option. This service is also available via a GIS Web site: http://gis.ncdc.noaa.gov/website/ims-cdo/ish/viewer.htm.

The monthly frequency distribution of dry-bulb temperatures and mean coincident wet-bulb temperatures for 134 Canadian locations is available from Environment Canada (1983-1987).

Degree Days and Climate Normals

Heating and cooling degree-day summary data for over 4000 U.S. stations are available online at no cost at http://cdo.ncdc.noaa.gov/climatenormals/clim81_supp/CLIM81_Sup_02.pdf (NCDC 2002a, 2002b). This publication presents annual heating degree day normals to the following bases (°F): 65, 60, 57, 55, 50, 45, and 40; and annual cooling degree day normals to the following bases (°F): 70, 65, 60, 57, 55, 50, and 45.

The 1971-2000 climate normals for over 6000 United States locations are available online (free of charge) and on CD from the National Climatic Data Center: http://cdo.ncdc.noaa.gov/cgi-bin/climatenormals/climatenormals.pl. Also, users may generate normals/averages for any chosen period (dynamic normals) at http://www7.ncdc.noaa.gov/CDO/normals.

The Canadian Climate Normals for 1971-2000 are available from Environment Canada at http://climate.weatheroffice.ec.gc.ca (Environment Canada 2003).

The *Climatography of the United States* No. 20 (CLIM20), monthly station climate summaries for 1971-2000 are climatic station summaries of particular interest to engineering, energy, industry, and agricultural applications (NCDC 2004). These summaries contain a variety of statistics for temperature, precipitation, snow, freeze dates, and degree-day elements for 4273 stations. The statistics include means, median (precipitation and snow elements), extremes, mean number of days exceeding threshold values, and heating, cooling, and growing degree-days for various temperature bases. Also included are probabilities for monthly precipitation and freeze data. Information on this product can be found at http://www.ncdc.noaa.gov/oa/documentlibrary/pdf/eis/clim20eis.pdf.

Heating and cooling degree-day and degree-hour data for 3677 locations from 115 countries were developed by Crawley (1994) from the Global Daily Summary (GDS) version 1.0 and the International Station Meteorological Climate Summary (ISMCS) version 4.0 data.

Typical Year Data Sets

Software is available to simulate the annual energy performance of buildings requiring a 1-year data set (8760 h) of weather conditions. Many data sets in different record formats have been developed to meet this requirement. The data represent a typical year with respect to weather-induced energy loads on a building. No explicit effort was made to represent extreme conditions, so these files do not represent design conditions.

The National Renewable Energy Laboratory's (NREL) TMY3 data set (Wilcox and Marion 2008) contains data for 1020 U.S. locations. TMY3, along with the 1991-2005 National Solar Radiation Data Base (NSRDB) (NREL 2007), contains hourly solar radiation [global, beam (direct), and diffuse} and meteorological data for 1454 stations, and is available at http://ols.nndc.noaa.gov/plolstore/plsql/olstore.prodspecific?prodnum=C00668-TAP-A0001. These were produced using an objective statistical algorithm to select the most typical month from the long-term record.

Canadian Weather Year for Energy Calculation (CWEC) files for 47 Canadian locations were developed for use with the Canadian National Energy Code, using the TMY algorithm and software (Environment Canada 1993). Files for 75 locations are now available.

Examples of the use of these files for energy calculations in both residential and commercial buildings, including the differences among the files, are available in Crawley (1998) and Huang (1998).

Sequences of Extreme Temperature and Humidity Durations

Colliver (1997) and Colliver et al. (1998) compiled extreme sequences of 1-, 3-, 5-, and 7-day duration for 239 U.S. and 144 Canadian locations based independently on the following five criteria: high dry-bulb temperature, high dew-point temperature, high enthalpy, low dry-bulb temperature, and low wet-bulb depression. For the criteria associated with high values, the sequences are selected according to annual percentiles of 0.4, 1.0, and 2.0. For the criteria corresponding to low values, annual percentiles of 99.6, 99.0, and 98.0 are reported. Although these percentiles are identical to those used to select annual heating and cooling design temperatures, the maximum or minimum temperatures within each sequence are significantly more extreme than the corresponding design temperatures. The data included for each hour of a sequence are solar radiation, dry-bulb and dew-point temperature, atmospheric pressure, and wind speed and direction. Accompanying information allows the user to go back to the source data and obtain sequences with different characteristics (i.e., different probability of occurrence, windy conditions, low or high solar radiation, etc.). These extreme sequences are available on CD (ASHRAE 1997).

These sequences were developed primarily to assist the design of heating or cooling systems having a finite capacity before regeneration is required or of systems that rely on thermal mass to limit loads. The information is also useful where information on the hourly weather sequence during extreme episodes is required for design.

Global Weather Data Source Web Page

Because of growing demand for more comprehensive global coverage of weather data for HVAC applications around the world, ASHRAE sponsored research project RP-1170 (Plantico 2001) to construct a Global Weather Data Sources (GWDS) Web page. With the growth of the World Wide Web, many national climate services and other climate data sources are making more information available over the Internet. The purpose of RP-1170 was to provide ASHRAE membership with easy access to major sources of international weather data through one consolidated system via the Web. This Web page was recently updated to better use the resources of the World Meteorological Organization (WMO) and NCDC. The GWDS Web page is accessible at http://www.ncdc.noaa.gov/oa/ashrae/gwds-title.html.

Observational Data Sets

For detailed designs, custom analysis of the most appropriate long-term weather record is best. National weather services are generally the best source of long-term observational data. The National Climatic Data Center (NCDC), in conjunction with U.S. Air Force and Navy partners in Asheville's Federal Climate Complex (FCC), developed the global Integrated Surface Data (Lott 2004; Lott et al. 2001) to address a pressing need for an integrated global database of hourly land surface climatological data. The database of over 20,000 stations contains hourly and some daily summary data from as early as 1900 (many stations beginning in the 1948-1973 time-frame), is operationally updated each day with the latest available data, and is now being further integrated with various data sets from the United States and other countries to further expand the spatial and temporal coverage of the data. For access to ISD, go to http://cdo.ncdc.noaa.gov/pls/plclimprod/poemain.accessrouter?datasetabbv=DS3505 or, for a GIS interface, http://gis.ncdc.noaa.gov/website/ims-cdo/ish/viewer.htm. For a complete review of ISD and all of its products, go to http://www.ncdc.noaa.gov/oa/climate/isd/index.php.

The National Solar Radiation Database (NSRBD) (http://ols.nndc.noaa.gov/plolstore/plsql/olstore.prodspecific?prodnum=C00668-TAP-A0001) and Canadian Weather Energy and Engineering Data Sets (CWEEDS) (Environment Canada 1993) provide long-term hourly data, including solar radiation values for the United States and Canada. A new solar model was required because of the implementation of automated observing systems that do not report traditional cloud elements.

Considerable information about weather and climate services and data sets is available elsewhere through the World Wide Web. Information supplementary to this chapter may also be posted on the ASHRAE Technical Committee 4.2 Web site, the link to which is available from the ASHRAE Web site (www.ashrae.org).

REFERENCES

ASHRAE. 1997. *Design weather sequence viewer* 2.1. (CD-ROM).

ASHRAE. 2009. *Weather Data Viewer, version 4.0.* (CD-ROM).

Belcher, B.N. and A.T. DeGaetano. 2004. Integration of ASOS weather data into building energy calculations with emphasis on model-derived solar radiation (RP-1226). ASHRAE Research Project, *Final Report*.

Charlock T.P., F. Rose, D.A. Rutan, Z. Jin, D. Fillmore, and W.D. Collins. 2004. Global retrievals of the surface and atmosphere radiation budget and direct aerosol forcing. *Proceedings, 13th Conference on Satellite Meteorology and Oceanography.* American Meteorological Society, Norfolk, VA.

Clarke A.D., W.G. Collins, P.J. Rasch, V.N. Kapustin, K. Moore, S. Howell, and H.E. Fuelberg. 2001. Dust and pollution transport on global scales: Aerosol measurements and model predictions. *Journal of Geophysical Research* 106 (D23): 32555-32569.

Colliver, D.G. 1997. Sequences of extreme temperature and humidity for design calculations (RP-828). ASHRAE Research Project, *Final Report*.

Colliver D.G., R.S. Gates, H. Zhang, and K.T. Priddy. 1998. Sequences of extreme temperature and humidity for design calculations. *ASHRAE Transactions* 104(1A):133-144.

Colliver, D.G., R.S. Gates, T.F. Burkes, and H. Zhang. 2000. Development of the design climatic data for the 1997 *ASHRAE Handbook—Fundamentals. ASHRAE Transactions* 106(1).

Crawley, D.B. 1994. *Development of degree day and degree hour data for international locations.* D.B. Crawley Consulting, Washington, D.C.

Crawley, D.B. 1998. Which weather data should you use for energy simulations of commercial buildings? *ASHRAE Transactions* 104(2):498-515.

Environment Canada. 1983-1987. Principal station data. PSD 1 to 134. Atmospheric Environment Service, Downsview, Ontario.

Environment Canada. 1993. Canadian weather for energy calculations (CWEC files) user's manual. Atmospheric Environment Service, Downsview, Ontario.

Environment Canada. 2003. *Canadian 1971-2000 climate normals*. Meteorological Service of Canada, Downsview, Ontario. (Available at http://climate.weatheroffice.ec.gc.ca).

Gueymard, C.A. 1987. An anisotropic solar irradiance model for tilted surfaces and its comparison with selected engineering algorithms. *Solar Energy* 38:367-386. Erratum, *Solar Energy* 40:175 (1988).

Gueymard C.A. 2008. REST2: High performance solar radiation model for cloudless-sky irradiance, illuminance and photosynthetically active radiation—Validation with a benchmark dataset. *Solar Energy* 82:272-285.

Harriman, L.G., D.G. Colliver, and H.K. Quinn. 1999. New weather data for energy calculations. *ASHRAE Journal* 41(3):31-38.

Hedrick, R. 2009. Generation of hourly design-day weather data (RP-1363). ASHRAE Research Project, *Final Report* (Draft).

Huang, J. 1998. The impact of different weather data on simulated residential heating and cooling loads. *ASHRAE Transactions* 104(2):516-527.

Hubbard, K., K. Kunkel, A. DeGaetano, and K. Redmond. 2004. Sources of uncertainty in the calculation of the design weather conditions in the *ASHRAE Handbook of Fundamentals* (RP-1171). ASHRAE Research Project, *Final Report*.

IPCC. 2007. *Fourth assessment report: Summary for policy makers*. International Panel on Climate Change, World Meteorological Organization, Geneva. (Available at http://ipcc.cac.es/pdf/assessment-report/ar4/syr/ar4_syr_spm.pdf).

Iqbal, M. 1983. *An introduction to solar radiation*. Academic Press, Toronto.

Kasten, F. and T. Young. 1989. Revised optical air mass tables and approximation formula. *Applied Optics* 28:4735-4738.

Lamming, S.D. and J.R. Salmon. 1996. Wind data for design of smoke control systems (RP-816). ASHRAE Research Project, *Final Report*.

Lamming, S.D. and J.R. Salmon. 1998. Wind data for design of smoke control systems. *ASHRAE Transactions* 104(1A):742-751.

Livezey, R.E., K.Y.Vinnikov, M.M. Timofeyeva, R. Tinker, and H.M. Van Den Dool. 2007. Estimation and extrapolation of climate normals and climatic trends. *Journal of Applied Meteorology and Climatology* 46: 1759-1776.

Lott, J.N., R. Baldwin, and P. Jones. 2001. The FCC Integrated Surface Hourly Database, a new resource of global climate data. NCDC *Technical Report* 2001-01. National Climatic Data Center, Asheville, NC. (Available at ftp://ftp.ncdc.noaa.gov/pub/data/techrpts/tr200101/tr2001-01.pdf).

Lott, J.N. 2004. The quality control of the integrated surface hourly database. 84th American Meteorological Society Annual Meeting, Seattle, WA. (Available at http://ams.confex.com/ams/pdfpapers/71929.pdf).

Lowery, M.D. and J.E. Nash. 1970. A comparison of methods of fitting the double exponential distribution. *Journal of Hydrology* 10(3):259-275.

Machler, M.A. and M. Iqbal. 1985. A modification of the ASHRAE clear sky irradiation model. *ASHRAE Transactions* 91(1A):106-115.

NCDC. 1996. *International station meteorological climate summary (ISMCS)*. National Climatic Data Center, Asheville, NC.

NCDC. 1999. *Engineering weather data*. National Climatic Data Center, Asheville, NC.

NCDC. 2002a. Monthly normals of temperature, precipitation, and heating and cooling degree-days. In *Climatography of the United States* #81. National Climatic Data Center, Asheville, NC.

NCDC. 2002b. Annual degree-days to selected bases (1971-2000). In *Climatography of the United* States #81. National Climatic Data Center, Asheville, NC.

NCDC. 2003. *Data documentation for data set 3505 (DSI-3505) integrated surface hourly (ISH) data*. National Climatic Data Center, Asheville, NC.

NCDC. 2004. Monthly station climate summaries. In *Climatography of the U.S.* #20. National Climatic Data Center, Asheville, NC.

NREL. 2007. National solar radiation database, 1991-2005 update: User's manual. *Technical Report* NREL/TP-581-41364. National Renewable Energy Laboratory, Golden, CO. (Available at http://www.nrel.gov/docs/fy07osti/41364.pdf).

Perez, R., P. Ineichen, R. Seals, J. Michalsky, and R. Stewart. 1990. Modeling daylight availability and irradiance components from direct and global irradiance. *Solar Energy* 44(5):271-289.

Plantico, M. 2001. Identify and characterize international weather data sources (RP-1170). ASHRAE Research Project, *Final Report*.

Randel, D.L., T.J. Greenwald, T.H. Vonder Haar, G.L. Stephens, M.A. Ringerud, and C.L. Combs. 1996. A new global water vapor dataset. *Bulletin of the American Meteorological Society* 77:1233-1246.

Rasch, P.J., N.M. Mahowald, and B.E. Eaton. 1997. Representations of transport, convection, and the hydrologic cycle in chemical transport models: Implications for the modeling of short-lived and soluble species. *Journal of Geophysical Research* 102(D23):28127-28138.

Schoenau, G.J. and R.A. Kehrig. 1990. A method for calculating degree-days to any base temperature. *Energy and Buildings* 14:299-302.

Stephenson, D.G. 1965. Equations for solar heat gain through windows. *Solar Energy* 9(2):81-86.

Thevenard, D. 2009. Updating the ASHRAE climatic data for design and standards (RP-1453). ASHRAE Research Project, *Final Report*.

Thevenard, D., J. Lundgren, and R. Humphries. 2005. Updating the climatic design conditions in the *ASHRAE Handbook of Fundamentals* (RP-1273). ASHRAE Research Project, *Final Report*.

Thevenard, D. and K. Haddad. 2006. Ground reflectivity in the context of building energy simulation. *Energy and Buildings* 38(8):972-980.

Thevenard, D. and R. Humphries. 2005. The calculation of climatic design conditions in the 2005 *ASHRAE Handbook—Fundamentals*. *ASHRAE Transactions* 111(1):457-466.

Threlkeld, J.L. 1963. Solar irradiation of surfaces on clear days. *ASHRAE Transactions* 69:24.

Wilcox, S. and W. Marion. 2008. Users manual for TMY3 data sets. *Technical Report* NREL/TP-581-43156. National Renewable Energy Laboratory, Golden, CO. (Available at http://www.nrel.gov/docs/fy08osti/43156.pdf).

WMO. 2007. The role of climatological normals in a changing climate. *Technical Document* 1377. World Meteorological Organization, Geneva.

BIBLIOGRAPHY

ASHRAE. 2006. Weather data for building design standards. ANSI/ASHRAE *Standard* 169-2006.

APPENDIX: DESIGN CONDITIONS FOR SELECTED LOCATIONS

Meaning of acronyms:
DB: Dry bulb temperature, °C — *WB: Wet bulb temperature, °C*
MCWB: Mean coincident wet bulb temperature, °C
Lat: Latitude, ° — *DP: Dew point temperature, °C* — *MCDB: Mean coincident dry bulb temperature, °C*
Long: Longitude, ° — *HR: Humidity ratio, g of moisture per kg of dry air*
Elev: Elevation, m — *WS: Wind speed, m/s*
HDD and CDD 18.3: Annual heating and cooling degree-days, base 18.3°C, °C-day

Station	Lat	Long	Elev	Heating DB		Cooling DB/MCWB						Evaporation WB/MCDB				Dehumidification DP/HR/MCDB						Extreme Annual WS			Heat./Cool. Degree-Days	
						0.4%		1%		2%		0.4%		1%		0.4%			1%							
				99.6%	99%	DB	MCWB	DB	MCWB	DB	MCWB	WB	MCDB	WB	MCDB	DP	HR	MCDB	DP	HR	MCDB	1%	2.5%	5%	HDD	CDD 18.3
United States of America																									*541 sites, 544 more on CD-ROM*	
Alabama																									*11 sites, 3 more on CD-ROM*	
AUBURN-OPELIKA APT	32.62N	85.43W	236	-4.6	-2.4	33.9	23.0	32.6	23.1	32.0	23.1	25.2	30.7	24.7	29.9	23.7	19.1	27.4	22.9	18.2	26.6	7.8	6.8	5.7	1324	1033
BIRMINGHAM MUNICIPAL AP	33.56N	86.75W	192	-6.9	-4.5	35.0	24.0	33.7	23.8	32.5	23.6	25.8	31.3	25.3	30.9	24.5	19.9	28.2	23.8	19.1	27.7	8.2	7.3	6.5	1496	1082
CAIRNS AAF/OZARK	31.28N	85.72W	91	-2.8	-0.9	35.2	24.7	34.1	24.5	33.0	24.2	26.8	32.0	26.2	31.3	25.4	20.9	28.7	24.9	20.2	28.2	7.6	6.5	5.6	982	1342
DOTHAN MUNICIPAL	31.32N	85.45W	98	-2.6	-0.5	35.2	24.6	34.0	24.3	32.9	24.1	26.7	31.8	26.0	31.0	25.3	20.7	28.5	24.8	20.1	28.1	8.6	7.8	6.9	959	1378
GADSEN MUNI (AWOS)	33.97N	86.08W	173	-7.5	-5.5	34.1	23.7	32.9	23.6	32.2	23.5	25.6	31.6	25.0	30.9	23.8	19.1	28.7	23.0	18.1	27.8	7.5	6.4	5.5	1786	865
HUNTSVILLE INTL/JONES FIELD	34.64N	86.79W	196	-8.3	-5.8	34.8	23.9	33.4	23.7	32.3	23.4	25.7	31.2	25.2	30.7	24.3	19.7	28.1	23.7	19.0	27.5	9.6	8.4	7.6	1744	968
MAXWELL AFB/MONTGOM	32.38N	86.37W	53	-2.3	-0.3	36.2	24.7	35.1	24.8	34.0	24.6	26.9	32.7	26.4	32.1	25.5	20.9	29.4	25.0	20.2	29.0	8.0	7.0	5.9	1007	1443
MOBILE REGIONAL AP	30.69N	88.25W	67	-2.8	-0.7	34.2	24.9	33.2	24.7	32.4	24.5	26.7	31.3	26.1	30.6	25.5	20.9	28.5	25.0	20.2	28.0	9.2	8.3	7.5	923	1368
MONTGOMERY DANNELLY FIELD	32.30N	86.39W	62	-4.6	-2.6	35.7	24.7	34.5	24.5	33.4	24.4	26.5	32.7	25.9	31.8	24.9	20.0	29.1	24.3	19.4	28.5	8.3	7.4	6.4	1191	1268
MUSCLE SHOALS REGIONAL AP	34.75N	87.61W	171	-7.9	-5.5	35.3	24.1	33.9	24.0	32.7	23.8	25.9	31.7	25.4	31.2	24.4	19.8	28.3	23.9	19.1	27.8	8.3	7.5	6.5	1713	1012
TUSCALOOSA MUNICIPAL AP	33.21N	87.62W	57	-6.4	-3.9	35.4	24.7	34.1	24.6	33.0	24.4	26.5	32.3	25.9	31.6	25.1	20.3	28.7	24.4	19.5	28.3	7.8	6.6	5.8	1394	1167
Alaska																									*7 sites, 66 more on CD-ROM*	
FAIRBANKS INTL ARPT	64.82N	147.86W	138	-41.9	-38.9	27.4	16.1	25.6	15.5	23.7	14.7	17.2	24.7	16.4	23.3	14.7	10.6	18.4	13.7	9.9	17.8	7.9	6.9	5.7	7516	39
FT. RICHARDSON/BRYA	61.27N	149.65W	115	-28.1	-24.7	23.3	15.4	21.6	14.5	19.9	13.8	16.1	22.1	15.1	20.4	13.3	9.7	17.9	12.5	9.1	16.7	8.5	6.5	5.1	5959	2
ANCHORAGE/ELMENDORF	61.25N	149.80W	59	-26.0	-23.0	23.2	14.7	21.8	14.2	20.0	13.4	15.8	21.2	15.1	19.7	13.8	9.9	16.4	12.9	9.3	15.9	8.4	7.0	5.7	5756	6
LAKE HOOD SEAPLANE	61.18N	149.96W	40	-22.6	-20.1	23.6	15.4	21.9	14.8	20.1	13.9	16.2	22.2	15.4	20.2	13.8	9.9	17.1	12.9	9.3	16.8	8.4	7.3	6.1	5458	9
ANCHORAGE INTL AP	61.18N	149.99W	40	-22.7	-20.2	21.9	14.9	20.2	14.0	18.9	13.4	15.7	20.5	14.9	19.0	13.5	9.7	17.0	12.9	9.3	16.3	9.2	8.3	7.4	5623	3
ANCHORAGE MERRILL FIELD	61.22N	149.86W	42	-23.9	-21.6	22.7	15.2	21.3	14.5	19.9	13.8	16.2	21.3	15.4	19.7	14.0	10.0	17.2	13.1	9.4	16.7	6.8	5.6	4.8	5599	6
JUNEAU INT'L ARPT	58.36N	134.58W	7	-15.7	-13.2	23.1	15.4	21.1	14.6	19.2	13.8	16.2	21.8	15.3	19.8	14.0	10.0	16.7	13.3	9.6	16.0	11.9	10.6	8.9	4629	2
Arizona																									*9 sites, 7 more on CD-ROM*	
CASA GRANDA (AWOS)	32.95N	111.77W	446	0.0	1.4	42.5	20.7	41.4	20.4	40.2	20.2	23.3	33.9	22.8	34.2	21.1	16.7	26.3	19.9	15.4	26.2	9.1	7.8	6.6	853	1946
DAVIS-MONTHAN AFB	32.17N	110.88W	809	0.5	2.1	40.8	18.5	39.1	18.4	37.9	18.1	22.7	29.5	22.2	30.1	21.2	17.5	24.8	20.1	16.4	25.0	8.7	7.7	6.6	836	1724
FLAGSTAFF AIRPORT	35.13N	111.67W	2135	-15.6	-12.5	29.7	13.0	28.4	12.9	27.0	12.7	16.1	22.9	15.5	22.6	14.1	13.1	17.5	13.4	12.5	17.3	9.3	8.2	7.3	3840	60
LUKE AFB/PHOENIX	33.53N	112.38W	331	1.8	3.1	43.8	21.5	42.5	21.4	41.2	21.3	25.2	35.8	24.5	35.4	22.7	18.2	28.8	21.6	17.0	29.1	8.8	7.6	6.4	692	2179
PHOENIX SKY HARBOR INTL AP	33.44N	111.99W	337	3.7	5.2	43.4	21.1	42.3	21.0	41.2	20.9	24.5	35.8	24.0	35.4	21.8	17.2	28.1	21.0	16.3	29.1	8.2	7.1	5.8	523	2532
PRESCOTT LOVE FIELD	34.65N	112.42W	1540	-8.1	-6.3	34.6	16.2	33.0	15.9	32.0	15.6	19.5	27.4	18.7	26.7	17.4	15.1	21.6	16.4	14.1	21.3	9.3	8.3	7.5	2358	526
TUCSON INTERNATIONAL AP	32.13N	110.96W	779	-0.2	1.3	41.1	19.0	39.8	18.9	38.5	18.7	22.5	31.6	22.0	31.3	20.6	16.8	24.6	19.9	16.0	24.8	9.6	8.4	7.6	814	1767
YUMA INTL AIRPORT	32.65N	114.60W	63	5.5	7.1	43.8	23.1	42.6	22.9	41.5	22.6	26.6	36.0	25.8	35.6	24.1	19.2	30.8	23.2	18.1	31.3	9.3	8.2	7.2	378	2590
YUMA MCAS	32.65N	114.62W	65	5.4	7.0	43.8	23.2	42.6	22.9	41.6	22.6	26.6	36.0	25.8	35.5	24.1	19.2	30.6	23.1	18.0	31.2	9.3	8.2	7.3	378	2589
Arkansas																									*11 sites, 7 more on CD-ROM*	
BENTONVILLE (AWOS)	36.35N	94.22W	395	-12.1	-8.9	34.2	23.6	32.9	23.8	32.1	23.4	25.3	31.7	24.7	31.0	23.0	18.7	29.0	22.7	18.3	28.5	8.7	7.8	6.9	2251	742
FAYETTEVILLE DRAKE FIELD	36.01N	94.17W	384	-13.3	-9.6	35.1	24.0	33.7	23.8	32.4	23.5	25.6	32.1	25.0	31.3	23.7	19.4	28.8	23.0	18.6	28.2	9.2	8.4	7.8	2186	797
FORT SMITH REGIONAL AP	35.33N	94.37W	141	-9.6	-6.6	37.3	24.7	35.8	24.6	34.3	24.5	26.4	33.6	25.8	32.7	24.6	20.0	29.3	24.1	19.3	28.8	9.1	8.1	7.2	1797	1120
JONESBORO MUNI	35.83N	90.63W	82	-10.9	-7.5	35.8	25.0	34.2	24.5	33.1	24.3	26.7	32.8	26.1	32.2	25.1	20.4	29.8	24.1	19.2	28.9	9.3	8.4	7.7	1972	1063
LITTLE ROCK ADAMS FIELD	34.75N	92.23W	78	-8.2	-5.4	36.7	25.1	35.2	25.1	33.9	24.8	26.8	33.2	26.2	32.6	25.1	20.4	29.6	24.6	19.8	29.1	8.3	7.5	6.7	1653	1180
LITTLE ROCK AFB	34.92N	92.15W	103	-9.3	-6.4	37.4	25.2	35.7	25.3	34.1	25.0	27.3	32.8	26.7	32.4	26.1	21.7	29.5	25.2	20.5	29.1	7.9	6.7	5.7	1760	1131
LITTLE ROCK/ADAMS F	34.83N	92.25W	351	-8.7	-5.6	35.1	24.7	33.8	24.5	32.6	24.1	26.0	32.1	25.5	31.4	24.3	20.1	29.1	23.8	19.5	28.7	8.2	7.4	6.6	1792	1061
PINE BLUFF FAA AP	34.18N	91.94W	65	-6.1	-3.7	36.2	25.3	35.0	25.3	33.9	24.9	26.9	33.2	26.3	32.8	25.2	20.4	29.9	24.6	19.7	29.5	8.3	7.5	6.7	1475	1242
ROGERS (AWOS)	36.37N	94.10W	415	-12.2	-9.0	34.1	22.7	32.8	22.9	31.7	22.7	24.6	30.8	24.1	30.2	22.7	18.3	27.9	22.3	17.9	27.7	9.3	8.3	7.4	2256	752
SILOAM SPRING(AWOS)	36.18N	94.48W	364	-12.1	-8.8	35.3	23.4	33.7	23.4	32.4	23.2	24.9	31.9	24.4	31.2	22.7	18.3	29.0	22.4	17.8	28.7	10.2	8.9	8.0	2219	789
TEXARKANA WEBB FIELD	33.45N	94.01W	122	-5.8	-3.2	36.9	24.6	35.5	24.6	34.1	24.5	26.5	32.9	26.0	32.3	24.9	20.3	29.3	24.3	19.5	28.9	8.4	7.6	6.7	1351	1305
California																									*56 sites, 17 more on CD-ROM*	
ALAMEDA NAS	37.73N	122.32W	4	4.6	5.7	28.5	18.3	26.3	17.6	24.3	17.0	19.3	26.2	18.5	24.6	16.9	12.1	20.7	16.2	11.5	20.2	9.2	8.2	7.4	1199	126
BAKERSFIELD MEADOWS FIELD	35.43N	119.06W	150	0.1	1.6	39.5	21.7	38.1	21.2	36.8	20.7	23.3	36.2	22.4	35.3	18.9	14.0	30.3	17.5	12.7	29.8	8.2	7.1	5.9	1186	1242
BEALE AFB/MARYSVILE	39.13N	121.43W	38	0.1	1.4	38.1	21.4	36.7	20.7	35.1	20.1	22.8	35.6	21.8	34.2	18.1	13.1	28.3	17.3	12.4	26.9	9.6	8.2	7.0	1344	844
BURBANK-GLENDALE-PASSADENA AP	34.20N	118.36W	223	3.9	5.3	36.8	20.5	34.8	20.1	32.9	19.7	23.0	32.4	22.1	31.2	20.0	15.1	26.4	19.0	14.2	25.3	8.2	6.8	5.8	721	826
CAMARILLO (AWOS)	34.22N	119.08W	23	3.0	4.1	29.2	17.1	27.6	17.7	26.2	17.7	20.7	25.9	20.1	25.1	18.8	13.7	23.7	17.8	12.8	22.3	11.1	8.9	7.2	1031	201
CAMP PENDLETON MCAS	33.30N	117.35W	24	0.4	2.0	33.3	19.4	31.0	19.0	29.0	18.7	22.1	28.7	21.4	27.8	20.0	14.7	24.9	18.9	13.8	24.5	7.6	6.5	5.7	929	402
CARLSBAD/PALOMAR	33.13N	117.28W	100	6.1	7.2	27.6	18.0	26.3	17.9	24.1	18.1	21.3	24.8	20.5	23.9	19.9	14.8	23.4	19.0	13.9	22.6	6.3	5.5	4.9	971	241
CASTLE AFB/MERCED	37.38N	120.57W	60	-0.8	0.3	37.5	21.1	36.1	20.7	34.7	20.2	22.4	34.9	21.6	34.1	17.6	12.7	29.1	16.6	11.9	28.8	8.1	6.6	5.6	1461	819
EL TORO MCAS	33.68N	117.73W	117	4.6	6.2	33.4	20.1	31.4	19.7	29.8	19.2	22.2	30.0	21.4	28.8	19.4	14.4	25.8	18.6	13.6	25.2	6.4	5.2	4.5	676	594
FRESNO YOSEMITE INTL AP	36.78N	119.72W	100	-0.3	0.9	39.8	21.8	38.4	21.1	37.0	20.5	23.2	36.7	22.3	35.5	18.7	13.7	29.5	17.5	12.7	29.5	8.1	7.3	6.4	1278	1157
FULLERTON MUNICIPAL	33.87N	117.98W	29	4.0	6.0	33.7	20.3	32.3	19.8	30.8	20.1	22.7	30.4	21.9	29.0	20.2	14.9	26.5	19.0	13.8	25.8	6.0	5.0	4.6	692	655

Meaning of acronyms:
DB: Dry bulb temperature, °C *WB: Wet bulb temperature, °C*
MCWB: Mean coincident wet bulb temperature, °C
Lat: Latitude, °
DP: Dew point temperature, °C
MCDB: Mean coincident dry bulb temperature, °C
Long: Longitude, °
HR: Humidity ratio, g of moisture per kg of dry air
HDD and CDD 18.3: Annual heating and cooling degree-days, base 18.3°C, °C-day
Elev: Elevation, m
WS: Wind speed, m/s

Station	Lat	Long	Elev	Heating DB		Cooling DB/MCWB						Evaporation WB/MCDB				Dehumidification DP/HR/MCDB						Extreme Annual WS			Heat./Cool. Degree-Days	
						0.4%		1%		2%		0.4%		1%		0.4%			1%							
				99.6%	99%	DB / MCWB		DB / MCWB		DB / MCWB		WB / MCDB		WB / MCDB		DP / HR / MCDB			DP / HR / MCDB			1%	2.5%	5%	HDD / CDD 18.3	
IMPERIAL	32.83N	115.58W	-17	2.0	3.0	43.9	23.1	42.7	23.0	41.8	22.8	27.4	36.5	26.6	36.1	25.2	20.2	31.4	24.0	18.8	31.8	11.6	9.7	8.4	529	2292
JACK NORTHROP FLD H	33.92N	118.33W	21	7.0	7.6	29.9	16.7	27.8	17.9	27.0	17.8	21.2	26.0	20.5	25.0	19.1	13.9	23.6	18.7	13.6	23.2	7.3	6.3	5.6	657	394
LANCASTER GEN WM FOX FIELD	34.74N	118.22W	713	-5.9	-4.0	39.0	19.1	37.7	18.3	36.3	17.8	20.9	34.5	20.0	34.0	16.3	12.6	26.9	14.6	11.3	27.3	13.3	12.3	11.3	1663	981
LEMOORE REEVES NAS	36.33N	119.95W	71	-1.3	0.3	39.5	22.2	38.0	21.8	36.7	21.1	24.0	36.5	22.9	35.5	19.6	14.4	31.7	18.2	13.2	30.5	8.5	7.4	6.2	1243	1016
LIVERMORE MUNICIPAL	37.69N	121.82W	121	-1.0	0.5	37.1	20.7	34.9	19.6	32.7	18.8	21.6	35.0	20.4	32.9	16.3	11.8	26.9	15.3	11.0	23.9	8.8	8.0	7.3	1553	437
LOMPOC (AWOS)	34.67N	120.47W	27	0.2	1.8	27.4	16.2	25.1	16.3	23.2	15.9	18.6	24.1	17.8	23.1	16.4	11.7	20.7	15.8	11.3	20.3	9.1	8.3	7.6	1564	31
LONG BEACH DAUGHERTY FLD	33.83N	118.16W	12	5.1	6.4	32.9	20.0	30.9	19.6	29.1	19.1	22.5	28.8	21.7	27.5	20.6	15.3	24.7	19.7	14.5	24.2	7.8	6.7	5.7	663	608
LOS ANGELES INTL ARPT	33.94N	118.41W	99	6.9	8.0	28.7	17.9	26.9	18.2	25.4	18.2	21.2	25.6	20.6	24.5	19.7	14.6	23.3	19.0	13.9	22.8	8.9	7.8	7.2	713	343
MARCH AFB/RIVERSIDE	33.88N	117.27W	462	1.2	2.6	38.1	19.9	37.0	19.6	35.2	19.2	22.4	33.9	21.6	32.8	19.1	14.7	25.2	18.0	13.6	24.6	8.0	6.7	5.7	1011	888
MCCLELLAN AFB	38.67N	121.40W	25	-0.2	1.3	38.8	21.2	37.3	20.7	35.5	20.0	22.4	36.3	21.5	35.0	17.4	12.5	26.9	16.4	11.7	26.3	9.2	7.6	6.4	1304	883
MODESTO CITY-COUNTY AP	37.63N	120.95W	30	-0.5	0.9	38.4	21.5	36.8	20.7	35.2	19.9	22.5	36.0	21.6	34.6	17.4	12.5	30.4	16.3	11.6	28.5	8.4	7.5	6.9	1362	868
MONTEREY PENINSULA	36.58N	121.85W	50	2.6	3.7	25.2	15.7	22.7	15.2	21.3	15.0	17.2	22.2	16.6	21.1	15.2	10.8	18.1	14.1	10.1	17.5	7.6	6.7	5.7	1830	24
MOUNTAIN VIEW MOFFETT FLD NAS	37.42N	122.05W	10	2.5	3.7	31.2	18.9	28.7	18.3	27.0	17.9	20.3	28.1	19.5	26.7	17.4	12.4	23.8	16.4	11.7	22.4	8.4	7.6	6.8	1196	267
NAPA CO. AIRPORT	38.21N	122.28W	17	-1.1	0.3	32.9	19.2	30.3	18.5	27.9	17.8	20.5	30.5	19.5	28.5	16.4	11.7	24.4	15.9	11.3	23.5	9.5	8.5	7.8	1774	133
NORTON AFB/SAN BERN	34.10N	117.23W	353	1.1	2.5	39.4	20.9	37.9	20.8	36.3	20.4	23.6	35.0	22.8	34.2	20.0	15.4	28.4	19.0	14.4	28.5	7.5	5.8	4.9	918	1006
OAKLAND METROPOLITAN ARPT	37.76N	122.22W	27	2.9	4.2	27.7	18.3	25.4	17.8	23.5	17.3	19.8	25.5	18.8	24.0	17.6	12.7	21.6	16.8	12.0	20.7	10.3	8.7	8.1	1436	85
ONTARIO	34.07N	117.65W	304	2.2	3.8	38.1	21.6	36.6	21.1	34.9	20.6	23.7	34.2	22.9	33.2	20.9	16.1	27.3	19.7	14.9	26.4	10.3	8.3	7.5	811	951
PALM SPRINGS INTL	33.83N	116.50W	145	5.9	7.1	44.0	22.5	42.8	22.3	42.1	22.2	26.5	37.7	25.6	37.0	23.0	18.0	33.8	22.3	17.3	33.7	10.2	8.9	8.0	430	2382
PALM SPRINGS THERMAL AP	33.63N	116.16W	-36	-0.6	1.2	44.1	22.9	42.7	22.6	41.6	22.3	26.7	36.5	25.8	36.4	23.9	18.7	32.0	22.8	17.4	31.9	8.6	7.6	6.7	611	2144
POINT ARGUELLO	34.57N	120.63W	34	7.6	8.7	21.8	N/A	19.9	N/A	18.5	N/A	N/A	N/A	N/A	N/A	N/A	N/A	N/A	N/A	N/A	N/A	19.0	15.5	13.9	1838	12
POINT MUGU NF	34.12N	119.12W	4	3.8	5.1	27.8	16.6	26.0	17.5	24.4	17.7	21.2	24.5	20.3	23.6	20.0	14.7	22.9	18.9	13.7	22.4	10.2	8.4	7.3	1064	144
PORTERVILLE (AWOS)	36.03N	119.07W	135	-0.9	0.9	38.0	21.2	37.3	20.7	36.1	20.0	22.7	35.9	21.7	34.5	17.7	12.9	30.4	17.0	12.3	29.5	5.7	5.1	4.6	1412	919
REDDING MUNICIPAL ARPT	40.52N	122.31W	153	-2.0	-0.6	41.0	20.7	39.1	20.0	37.4	19.3	22.2	36.4	21.4	35.3	17.8	13.0	26.9	16.7	12.1	26.3	11.1	8.9	7.7	1508	1044
RIVERSIDE MUNI	33.95N	117.43W	256	2.2	2.9	37.6	21.3	36.3	20.6	34.7	20.2	23.0	34.3	22.2	33.1	19.0	14.3	27.6	17.9	13.3	26.5	9.3	7.6	6.4	901	861
SACRAMENTO EXECUTIVE ARPT	38.51N	121.49W	8	-0.4	1.0	37.9	21.3	36.2	20.5	34.3	19.8	22.6	35.5	21.5	34.0	17.7	12.7	29.1	16.5	11.8	26.9	9.1	8.2	7.3	1411	673
SACRAMENTO MATHER AIRPORT	38.55N	121.29W	29	-1.2	0.2	38.5	20.7	36.8	20.0	34.9	19.4	21.8	36.2	20.8	34.4	16.3	11.7	25.1	15.6	11.1	24.8	9.1	7.5	6.1	1499	695
SACRAMENTO METROPOLITAN AP	38.70N	121.59W	10	-0.3	1.1	38.0	21.5	36.6	20.9	34.9	20.3	22.9	35.9	21.9	34.5	17.9	12.9	29.4	17.0	12.2	28.4	10.4	8.7	7.8	1327	782
SALINAS MUNICIPAL AP	36.66N	121.61W	24	1.0	2.3	28.3	17.1	25.9	16.5	23.9	16.1	18.6	25.4	17.8	23.9	16.2	11.6	20.1	15.5	11.0	19.4	9.4	8.4	7.9	1511	63
SAN DIEGO LINDBERGH FIELD	32.74N	117.17W	9	7.1	8.2	28.9	19.9	27.3	19.7	25.9	19.4	22.7	26.3	21.8	25.3	21.4	16.0	25.1	20.5	15.2	24.2	7.9	7.1	6.2	621	423
SAN DIEGO MIRAMAR NAS	32.87N	117.15W	146	3.8	5.2	32.4	19.8	30.5	19.5	28.8	19.3	22.1	28.6	21.4	27.7	20.0	15.0	24.7	19.1	14.1	24.0	6.5	5.5	4.9	802	482
SAN DIEGO NORTH ISLAND NAS	32.70N	117.20W	8	7.0	7.8	28.0	18.9	26.4	19.2	25.1	19.1	22.0	25.2	21.3	24.6	21.0	15.7	24.4	20.0	14.7	23.5	8.4	7.4	6.5	681	372
SAN DIEGO/BROWN FLD	32.57N	116.98W	159	3.8	5.9	31.3	18.4	28.9	18.5	27.5	18.4	21.8	27.6	20.9	26.2	20.0	15.0	24.3	19.0	14.0	23.3	7.3	6.0	5.5	925	351
SAN DIEGO/MONTGOMER	32.82N	117.13W	129	4.9	6.2	31.3	19.0	29.0	18.7	27.6	18.3	22.0	27.4	21.2	26.2	20.2	15.1	24.3	19.2	14.2	23.6	7.1	5.9	5.5	828	437
SAN FRANCISCO INTL AP	37.62N	122.40W	6	3.8	4.9	28.3	17.2	25.7	16.7	23.6	16.2	18.6	25.7	17.8	23.9	16.1	11.5	19.9	15.3	10.9	19.2	12.8	11.5	10.6	1504	79
SAN JOSE INTL AP	37.36N	121.93W	15	2.1	3.2	33.5	19.4	31.4	19.0	29.3	18.4	20.8	30.6	20.1	29.1	17.3	12.4	24.8	16.4	11.7	23.9	8.9	8.1	7.4	1129	398
SAN LUIS CO RGNL	35.23N	120.63W	66	1.1	2.4	31.3	17.9	29.0	17.4	27.3	17.1	19.7	28.1	18.8	26.7	16.6	11.9	21.8	15.9	11.4	21.2	11.5	10.3	8.9	1223	153
SANTA BARBARA MUNICIPAL AP	34.43N	119.84W	6	1.5	2.7	28.3	17.8	26.4	17.8	25.0	17.5	20.4	25.2	19.6	24.2	18.6	13.5	22.6	17.8	12.8	21.5	8.7	7.5	6.2	1227	122
SANTA MARIA PUBLIC ARPT	34.92N	120.47W	73	0.1	1.5	29.0	17.1	26.8	16.6	24.9	16.2	19.1	26.0	18.2	24.7	16.4	11.8	20.7	15.6	11.2	20.1	10.6	9.0	8.1	1517	64
SANTA ROSA (AWOS)	38.51N	122.81W	45	-1.3	-0.1	35.2	19.5	32.8	19.2	30.9	18.5	21.0	32.8	20.0	31.1	16.2	11.5	26.9	15.1	10.8	24.1	7.6	6.7	5.7	1669	209
STOCKTON METROPOLITAN ARPT	37.89N	121.24W	8	-0.8	0.4	38.2	21.3	36.6	20.7	34.9	20.2	23.0	35.6	21.7	34.6	18.5	13.4	29.3	16.6	11.9	27.2	10.0	8.5	7.8	1392	770
TRAVIS AFB/FAIRFLD	38.27N	121.93W	18	-0.1	1.3	37.1	19.8	35.0	19.3	32.8	18.7	21.3	34.0	20.3	32.4	16.7	11.9	24.3	15.7	11.2	23.3	12.6	11.6	10.7	1387	547
TUSTIN MCAF	33.70N	117.83W	17	3.8	5.1	34.2	21.2	32.2	20.7	30.5	20.4	23.1	30.4	22.4	29.5	20.9	15.6	26.2	20.0	14.7	26.2	7.6	6.0	5.3	601	681
VISALIA MUNI (AWOS)	36.32N	119.40W	89	-1.1	0.4	37.7	22.3	36.6	21.7	35.1	20.9	23.9	35.0	22.9	33.8	20.3	15.1	29.9	18.9	13.8	29.0	6.6	5.5	4.8	1419	866
Colorado																									*10 sites, 15 more on CD-ROM*	
BUCKLEY ANGB/DENVER	39.72N	104.75W	1726	-17.9	-14.1	33.9	15.0	32.4	14.9	31.0	14.8	17.9	26.3	17.1	25.8	15.9	13.9	19.3	14.7	12.9	19.1	10.5	8.7	7.5	3289	381
COLORADO SPRINGS MUNI AP	38.81N	104.71W	1881	-18.2	-14.6	32.4	14.9	30.9	14.7	29.4	14.6	17.4	25.7	16.8	25.2	15.2	13.6	18.7	14.4	12.9	18.6	12.4	10.9	9.2	3488	244
DENVER INTL AP	39.83N	104.66W	1655	-17.4	-14.0	34.6	15.7	33.2	15.6	31.8	15.4	18.3	27.3	17.6	27.0	16.0	14.0	19.9	15.2	13.2	19.7	11.9	10.4	8.8	3301	432
DENVER STAPLETON INT'L ARPT	39.77N	104.87W	1611	-20.0	-16.0	34.1	15.9	32.6	15.6	31.1	15.4	18.1	27.7	17.5	26.9	15.7	13.6	20.0	14.7	12.7	19.8	10.9	8.8	7.7	3282	393
DENVER/CENTENNIAL	39.57N	104.85W	1793	-18.8	-15.5	33.0	15.7	32.0	15.5	30.2	15.3	18.4	27.3	17.5	26.4	16.1	14.3	20.2	14.9	13.2	19.9	11.1	9.5	8.4	3448	312
FORT COLLINS (AWOS)	40.45N	105.02W	1529	-17.7	-14.2	34.2	15.8	32.7	15.7	31.2	15.6	18.2	27.9	17.6	27.8	15.5	13.3	20.8	14.1	12.1	20.7	11.5	9.4	8.0	3451	338
FORT COLLINS(SAWRS)	40.58N	105.08W	1525	-20.4	-16.1	32.1	16.2	30.6	16.0	29.2	16.0	18.9	27.1	18.0	26.4	16.2	13.9	22.4	15.3	13.1	21.4	9.3	7.7	6.2	3492	274
GRAND JUNCTION WALKER FIELD	39.13N	108.54W	1475	-14.5	-11.3	36.3	16.6	34.9	16.1	33.5	15.6	18.6	29.7	18.0	28.8	16.1	13.7	20.4	15.0	12.8	20.8	10.3	8.5	7.5	2983	667
GREELEY/WELD (AWOS)	40.43N	104.63W	1420	-20.8	-17.2	35.2	16.8	33.4	16.7	32.1	16.7	19.5	29.1	18.7	28.7	17.0	14.5	22.6	16.0	13.5	22.0	12.4	10.4	8.5	3617	341
PUEBLO MEMORIAL AP	38.29N	104.50W	1439	-18.9	-14.8	36.9	17.1	35.4	16.9	33.9	16.7	19.6	29.5	19.0	29.2	17.3	14.8	21.2	16.4	14.0	20.9	12.9	11.1	9.2	3053	518
Connecticut																									*5 sites, 0 more on CD-ROM*	
BRIDGEPORT SIKORSKY MEMORIAL	41.18N	73.15W	5	-11.8	-9.2	30.8	22.9	29.1	22.0	27.8	21.4	24.4	28.3	23.8	27.1	23.2	18.0	26.3	22.7	17.4	25.6	10.9	9.3	8.4	2939	452
HARTFORD BRADLEY INTL AP	41.94N	72.68W	55	-16.0	-13.3	33.1	23.0	31.3	22.1	29.7	21.3	24.6	30.4	23.7	28.8	22.9	17.7	26.9	22.2	16.9	26.2	10.0	8.5	7.8	3329	411

Meaning of acronyms:
DB: Dry bulb temperature, °C *WB: Wet bulb temperature, °C*
MCWB: Mean coincident wet bulb temperature, °C

Lat: Latitude, °
DP: Dew point temperature, °C
MCDB: Mean coincident dry bulb temperature, °C

Long: Longitude, °
HR: Humidity ratio, g of moisture per kg of dry air

Elev: Elevation, m
WS: Wind speed, m/s
HDD and CDD 18.3: Annual heating and cooling degree-days, base 18.3°C, °C-day

Station	Lat	Long	Elev	Heating DB		Cooling DB/MCWB						Evaporation WB/MCDB				Dehumidification DP/HR/MCDB						Extreme Annual WS			Heat./Cool. Degree-Days	
				99.6%	99%	0.4%		1%		2%		0.4%		1%		0.4%			1%			1%	2.5%	5%	HDD / CDD 18.3	
						DB	MCWB	DB	MCWB	DB	MCWB	WB	MCDB	WB	MCDB	DP	HR	MCDB	DP	HR	MCDB				HDD	CDD
HARTFORD BRAINARD FD	41.74N	72.65W	6	-14.2	-11.9	32.5	23.0	31.0	22.6	29.1	21.6	25.1	29.8	24.1	28.3	23.7	18.5	27.4	22.7	17.5	26.7	9.0	8.3	7.6	3123	453
OXFORD (AWOS)	41.48N	73.13W	222	-16.1	-12.9	30.9	22.6	28.8	21.6	27.4	20.7	24.1	28.4	23.1	26.8	22.7	17.9	25.9	22.2	17.4	25.3	8.8	7.7	6.7	3560	256
WILLIMANTIC (ASOS)	41.73N	72.18W	76	-16.1	-12.7	32.2	23.1	30.2	22.4	28.7	21.7	24.6	29.5	23.7	28.0	22.9	17.8	26.4	22.5	17.3	25.9	8.8	7.8	7.0	3349	331
Delaware																										*2 sites, 1 more on CD-ROM*
DOVER AFB	39.13N	75.47W	7	-10.1	-7.7	33.4	24.3	32.1	23.8	30.5	23.3	25.9	30.6	25.3	29.6	24.7	19.8	28.1	24.0	18.8	27.5	10.8	9.1	8.1	2509	653
WILMINGTON NEW CASTLE CNTY AP	39.67N	75.60W	24	-11.3	-8.8	33.3	23.9	31.8	23.4	30.4	22.9	25.6	30.7	24.9	29.5	24.1	19.1	27.6	23.5	18.4	27.0	10.9	9.2	8.2	2659	623
Florida																										*32 sites, 15 more on CD-ROM*
CECIL FIELD	30.22N	81.87W	27	-1.2	0.8	35.7	24.7	34.6	24.5	33.7	24.3	26.3	32.2	25.8	31.6	24.9	20.1	28.3	24.3	19.3	27.9	8.3	7.4	6.5	648	1569
DAYTONA BEACH INTL AP	29.18N	81.06W	13	1.5	3.8	33.7	25.0	32.7	24.9	31.8	24.8	26.7	31.1	26.2	30.6	25.3	20.5	28.8	24.9	20.0	28.5	9.1	8.1	7.3	429	1626
FORT LAUDERDALE HOLLYWOOD INT	26.07N	80.15W	3	8.2	10.6	33.2	25.8	32.5	25.7	32.1	25.7	27.3	31.1	26.9	30.7	26.3	21.7	29.3	25.9	21.2	29.1	10.0	8.8	8.1	79	2506
FORT MYERS PAGE FIELD	26.59N	81.86W	6	5.8	8.0	34.3	25.0	33.6	25.0	33.0	25.0	26.9	31.3	26.6	30.9	25.9	21.2	28.6	25.4	20.6	28.3	8.5	7.8	7.0	152	2171
GAINESVILLE REGIONAL AP	29.69N	82.27W	50	-1.3	0.8	34.1	24.7	33.3	24.6	32.5	24.4	26.5	31.3	26.0	30.7	25.2	20.5	28.4	24.7	19.8	27.9	8.3	7.4	6.5	644	1467
HOMESTEAD AFB	25.48N	80.38W	5	8.0	10.2	32.9	26.2	32.4	26.1	32.0	26.0	27.5	30.6	27.2	30.4	26.9	22.6	29.0	26.2	21.7	28.8	8.4	7.5	6.7	80	2356
JACKSONVILLE INTL ARPT	30.49N	81.69W	10	-1.5	0.3	34.7	25.2	33.7	25.0	32.7	24.8	26.7	32.0	26.2	31.3	25.3	20.5	28.7	24.9	20.0	28.3	8.9	8.0	7.3	731	1458
JACKSONVILLE NAS	30.23N	81.68W	7	0.1	2.4	35.3	25.1	34.1	24.7	33.0	24.5	26.9	31.4	26.4	31.1	26.0	21.4	28.8	25.2	20.3	28.4	9.1	8.0	7.2	563	1714
JACKSONVILLE/CRAIG	30.34N	81.52W	13	-0.2	1.9	34.1	25.2	33.0	25.0	32.2	24.9	26.8	31.4	26.3	30.8	25.7	21.0	28.8	25.1	20.3	28.4	8.4	7.8	7.0	689	1428
MACDILL AFB/TAMPA	27.85N	82.52W	8	4.6	6.8	33.9	25.1	33.1	24.9	32.6	24.9	27.2	30.6	26.7	30.6	26.2	21.7	28.6	25.6	20.9	28.5	8.4	7.4	6.6	266	2024
MAYPORT NS	30.40N	81.42W	4	1.3	3.7	34.7	25.3	33.4	25.3	32.4	25.2	27.2	31.6	26.7	31.1	26.1	21.5	29.5	25.4	20.6	29.2	9.0	7.9	7.1	562	1683
MELBOURNE REGIONAL AP	28.10N	80.65W	8	3.9	6.3	33.7	25.9	32.7	25.8	32.1	25.7	27.6	31.3	27.0	30.8	26.5	22.0	29.6	26.0	21.4	29.4	9.3	8.5	8.0	250	1953
MIAMI INTL AP	25.82N	80.30W	9	8.7	10.9	33.2	25.3	32.6	25.3	32.1	25.2	26.8	30.5	26.4	30.4	25.8	21.1	28.6	25.3	20.4	28.5	9.2	8.4	7.7	72	2477
MIAMI/KENDALL-TAMIA	25.65N	80.43W	3	7.4	9.4	33.6	25.4	32.9	25.3	32.4	25.3	26.8	30.9	26.4	30.6	26.0	21.4	28.4	25.2	20.4	28.2	9.2	8.4	7.9	96	2268
NAPLES MUNICIPAL	26.15N	81.78W	7	6.6	8.6	32.7	25.2	32.3	25.2	31.8	25.2	26.8	30.6	26.4	30.4	25.8	21.1	28.7	25.2	20.4	28.6	8.4	7.5	6.6	155	2048
NASA SHUTTLE FCLTY	28.62N	80.72W	3	3.5	5.8	33.3	25.6	32.5	25.5	31.8	25.3	26.9	30.8	26.5	30.4	26.1	21.5	28.8	25.4	20.6	28.5	8.5	7.6	6.7	307	1750
OCALA MUNI (AWOS)	29.17N	82.22W	27	-1.3	1.1	34.0	24.0	33.0	24.0	32.6	23.9	25.9	30.9	25.6	30.6	24.6	19.6	28.1	24.0	19.0	27.7	8.0	6.7	5.6	575	1525
ORLANDO EXECUTIVE AP	28.55N	81.33W	34	4.4	6.8	34.2	24.4	33.7	24.4	32.8	24.4	26.5	30.6	26.0	30.1	25.7	21.0	27.9	25.1	20.2	27.5	8.5	7.9	7.1	265	1980
ORLANDO INTL ARPT	28.43N	81.33W	32	3.2	5.5	34.3	24.7	33.6	24.6	32.8	24.5	26.4	30.9	26.0	30.5	25.3	20.6	27.7	25.0	20.1	27.5	9.0	8.1	7.3	302	1877
ORLANDO SANFORD AIRPORT	28.78N	81.24W	17	3.7	5.7	34.9	24.1	33.9	23.9	32.9	23.9	25.8	31.3	25.5	30.8	24.1	19.1	27.8	24.0	18.9	27.7	9.1	8.1	7.2	342	1811
PANAMA CITY BAY CO	30.20N	85.68W	6	0.0	2.2	33.7	24.9	32.8	24.9	32.3	24.9	27.5	30.5	26.8	30.2	27.0	22.7	29.2	26.1	21.5	28.7	8.4	7.5	6.8	668	1582
PENSACOLA FOREST SHERMAN NAS	30.35N	87.32W	9	-2.1	0.1	34.0	25.8	33.0	25.6	32.3	25.4	27.7	31.3	26.9	30.9	26.6	22.2	29.7	26.0	21.4	29.3	10.5	8.7	7.8	827	1452
PENSACOLA REGIONAL AP	30.47N	87.19W	36	-1.4	0.7	34.3	25.4	33.1	25.1	32.2	25.0	27.2	31.3	26.7	30.7	26.2	21.7	29.2	25.6	20.9	28.6	9.0	8.1	7.4	817	1460
SARASOTA BRADENTON	27.38N	82.55W	10	4.0	6.5	33.4	26.2	32.8	26.1	32.4	26.0	28.1	31.6	27.5	31.1	27.3	23.2	30.3	26.5	22.1	29.7	9.7	8.4	7.6	250	1901
SOUTHWEST FLORIDA I	26.53N	81.75W	9	5.1	7.4	34.3	24.9	33.7	24.9	32.9	25.0	26.9	31.0	26.6	30.7	26.1	21.6	28.3	25.6	20.8	28.2	9.3	8.2	7.4	166	2101
ST PETERSBURG CLEAR	27.90N	82.68W	3	5.9	7.7	34.0	26.0	33.1	25.7	32.5	25.6	27.9	31.4	27.3	30.9	26.9	22.6	29.4	26.3	21.8	29.1	9.3	8.4	7.8	236	2104
TALLAHASSEE REGIONAL AF	30.39N	84.35W	21	-3.7	-1.7	35.3	24.8	34.2	24.5	33.3	24.3	26.5	31.8	26.1	31.2	25.2	20.4	28.2	24.7	19.8	27.9	8.0	7.1	6.1	852	1424
TAMPA INTERNATIONAL AP	27.96N	82.54W	3	3.6	5.8	33.6	25.2	33.0	25.2	32.4	25.1	26.9	31.1	26.6	30.9	25.8	21.1	29.3	25.3	20.5	28.9	8.1	7.2	6.3	293	1954
TYNDALL AFB	30.07N	85.58W	7	0.0	2.3	32.9	25.8	32.3	25.8	31.4	25.6	27.9	30.8	27.3	30.3	27.1	22.8	29.8	26.3	21.8	29.3	8.8	7.9	7.0	704	1470
VENICE PIER	27.07N	82.45W	5	5.7	7.9	30.9	N/A	30.3	N/A	29.9	N/A	N/A	N/A	N/A	N/A	N/A	N/A	N/A	N/A	N/A	N/A	12.6	10.6	8.8	263	1633
VERO BEACH MUNICIPAL ARPT	27.66N	80.42W	9	3.8	6.2	33.2	25.4	32.5	25.4	31.9	25.4	26.8	31.1	26.4	30.8	25.7	21.0	29.1	25.1	20.3	28.8	9.0	8.3	7.7	231	1925
WEST PALM BEACH INTL ARPT	26.69N	80.10W	6	6.8	9.0	33.0	25.3	32.4	25.4	31.8	25.4	26.7	30.9	26.4	30.6	25.5	20.8	28.7	25.2	20.3	28.6	10.3	9.0	8.3	121	2247
Georgia																										*19 sites, 2 more on CD-ROM*
ALBANY DOUGHERTY COUNTY AP	31.54N	84.19W	59	-3.1	-1.3	36.0	24.7	34.7	24.5	33.7	24.2	26.5	32.4	25.9	31.7	25.1	20.3	28.5	24.4	19.5	27.9	8.3	7.5	6.6	979	1394
ATHENS BEN EPPS AP	33.95N	83.33W	244	-5.7	-3.3	35.1	23.9	33.7	23.7	32.4	23.4	25.6	31.9	25.0	31.0	23.9	19.3	28.0	23.4	18.7	27.3	8.2	7.4	6.5	1534	994
ATLANTA (NEXRAD)	33.37N	84.55W	296	-7.2	-4.9	33.8	23.1	32.6	23.2	32.0	23.1	25.2	30.8	24.7	29.9	23.8	19.3	27.2	23.0	18.3	26.2	7.9	6.8	5.6	1692	823
ATLANTA HARTSFIELD INTL AF	33.64N	84.43W	313	-6.3	-3.5	34.4	23.5	33.0	23.3	31.9	23.0	25.1	31.2	24.5	30.3	23.4	19.0	27.3	22.9	18.3	26.7	9.8	8.6	7.7	1497	1023
AUGUSTA BUSH FIELD	33.37N	81.97W	45	-5.4	-3.4	36.2	24.6	34.8	24.4	33.6	24.2	26.3	32.8	25.7	31.9	24.7	19.8	28.5	24.1	19.1	28.1	8.4	7.4	6.5	1339	1146
AUGUSTA\DANIEL FLD	33.47N	82.03W	128	-2.5	-1.1	36.0	23.7	34.0	23.2	32.8	23.2	25.4	31.8	25.1	31.1	23.9	19.0	27.2	23.0	18.0	26.6	7.5	6.6	5.6	1168	1253
COLUMBUS METROPOLITAN ARPT	32.52N	84.94W	120	-3.8	-1.7	35.7	24.0	34.5	23.8	33.4	23.5	25.7	32.0	25.3	31.2	24.1	19.3	27.8	23.7	18.8	27.4	8.2	7.3	6.4	1151	1294
DEKALB PEACHTREE	33.87N	84.30W	313	-5.2	-2.9	34.0	23.0	32.9	23.1	32.3	22.8	25.1	31.2	24.5	30.3	23.0	18.5	26.3	22.8	18.2	26.1	8.2	7.3	6.1	1554	997
DOBBINS AFB/MARIETT	33.92N	84.52W	330	-6.9	-3.9	34.2	23.3	32.8	23.2	31.7	22.9	25.0	31.0	24.4	30.2	23.3	18.8	27.2	22.8	18.2	26.6	8.3	7.3	6.3	1607	960
FORT BENNING	32.33N	85.00W	88	-5.0	-3.0	36.0	24.4	34.6	24.3	33.4	24.1	26.6	32.2	25.9	31.5	25.1	20.5	28.8	24.5	19.7	28.1	7.4	6.2	5.3	1252	1171
FULTON CO ARPT BROW	33.77N	84.52W	263	-6.8	-3.9	34.2	23.7	33.0	23.5	32.1	23.2	25.3	31.6	24.8	30.7	23.5	18.9	27.7	23.0	18.3	27.2	8.1	7.1	6.2	1595	943
GAINESVILLE\LEE GIL	34.27N	83.83W	389	-5.0	-2.7	32.9	23.3	32.4	23.1	31.2	22.8	24.9	30.5	24.2	29.3	23.0	18.6	26.4	22.7	18.3	26.1	8.5	7.6	6.9	1649	884
HUNTER AAF	32.00N	81.13W	13	-2.2	-0.1	35.2	25.2	34.1	25.0	32.9	24.8	27.3	31.3	26.6	31.1	26.2	21.7	28.7	25.3	20.5	28.4	8.4	7.4	6.4	913	1411
MACON MIDDLE GA REGIONAL AP	32.69N	83.65W	110	-4.7	-2.6	35.9	24.3	34.6	24.2	33.5	23.9	26.2	32.5	25.6	31.7	24.5	19.8	28.6	24.0	19.2	28.0	8.1	7.2	6.2	1238	1216
MOODY AFB/VALDOSTA	30.97N	83.20W	71	-1.2	0.9	35.4	24.7	34.3	24.6	33.4	24.4	26.6	32.6	26.0	31.7	25.1	20.3	29.1	24.5	19.6	28.6	7.3	6.1	5.4	779	1481
ROME R B RUSSELL AP	34.35N	85.16W	196	-8.2	-5.5	35.8	23.7	34.0	23.5	32.8	23.3	25.6	32.1	25.1	31.5	23.9	19.2	28.5	23.1	18.3	27.9	6.8	5.6	4.9	1724	959

DB: Dry bulb temperature, °C | WB: Wet bulb temperature, °C | DP: Dew point temperature, °C | HR: Humidity ratio, g of moisture per kg of dry air | WS: Wind speed, m/s

MCWB: Mean coincident wet bulb temperature, °C | MCDB: Mean coincident dry bulb temperature, °C | HDD and CDD 18.3: Annual heating and cooling degree-days, base 18.3°C, °C-day

Station	Lat	Long	Elev	Heating DB		Cooling DB/MCWB						Evaporation WB/MCDB				Dehumidification DP/HR/MCDB						Extreme Annual WS			Heat./Cool. Degree-Days	
						0.4%		1%		2%		0.4%		1%		0.4%			1%							
				99.6%	99%	DB	MCWB	DB	MCWB	DB	MCWB	WB	MCDB	WB	MCDB	DP	HR	MCDB	DP	HR	MCDB	1%	2.5%	5%	HDD	CDD 18.3
VALDOSTA WB AIRPORT	30.78N	83.28W	60	-2.5	-0.6	35.2	25.2	34.1	24.8	33.2	24.5	26.9	32.1	26.3	31.5	25.7	21.1	28.5	25.1	20.3	28.1	7.6	6.7	5.9	838	1407
WARNER ROBINS AFB	32.63N	83.60W	92	-3.9	-2.1	36.3	24.5	35.0	24.4	33.8	24.1	26.5	32.7	25.9	31.9	24.9	20.2	29.1	24.2	19.3	28.3	8.5	7.4	6.2	1186	1248
Hawaii																										*4 sites, 4 more on CD-ROM*
BARBERS POINT NAS	21.30N	158.07W	10	15.2	16.5	32.7	22.8	32.2	22.8	31.6	22.7	25.4	29.8	24.7	29.5	24.0	18.9	28.2	23.1	17.9	27.8	8.8	7.9	7.3	0	2454
HILO INTERNATIONAL AP	19.72N	155.05W	11	16.4	17.1	29.8	23.4	29.2	23.3	28.8	23.2	24.8	27.8	24.4	27.5	23.9	18.8	26.2	23.4	18.3	25.9	7.9	7.1	6.0	0	1810
HONOLULU INTL ARPT	21.33N	157.94W	5	16.2	17.4	32.2	23.3	31.7	23.1	31.2	23.0	25.1	29.3	24.6	29.0	23.9	18.8	27.4	23.3	18.0	27.0	9.8	9.0	8.4	0	2583
KANEOHE BAY MCAS	21.45N	157.77W	6	17.9	19.0	29.6	23.7	29.1	23.4	28.7	23.3	25.2	27.9	24.7	27.6	24.2	19.1	27.0	23.7	18.5	26.7	8.6	7.9	7.2	0	2387
Idaho																										*7 sites, 7 more on CD-ROM*
BOISE AIR TERMINAL	43.57N	116.22W	874	-16.3	-11.9	36.7	17.9	35.0	17.3	33.3	16.7	19.1	33.2	18.3	32.2	14.3	11.3	22.4	13.0	10.4	22.4	9.7	8.5	7.6	3143	494
CALDWELL (AWOS)	43.63N	116.63W	740	-11.3	-8.7	36.1	19.1	33.9	18.3	32.4	17.7	20.2	33.4	19.3	32.1	15.9	12.4	25.3	13.9	10.9	25.1	9.6	8.4	7.4	3166	354
COEUR D`ALENE(AWOS)	47.77N	116.82W	707	-14.0	-11.3	33.0	17.1	31.4	16.8	29.0	16.0	18.7	30.1	17.7	28.8	14.1	10.9	21.6	13.0	10.2	20.9	10.0	8.5	7.5	3829	159
IDAHO FALLS FANNING FIELD	43.52N	112.07W	1446	-22.6	-19.1	33.2	16.3	31.9	16.0	30.2	15.4	18.3	28.7	17.3	27.9	14.9	12.6	21.6	13.7	11.6	20.7	12.2	10.9	9.3	4347	153
JOSLIN FLD MAGIC VA	42.48N	114.48W	1297	-12.5	-10.9	34.7	17.7	32.8	17.3	32.0	17.0	19.4	32.0	18.5	30.5	15.1	12.6	24.3	13.8	11.6	23.7	12.3	10.9	9.3	3421	389
LEWISTON NEZ PERCE CNTY AP	46.38N	117.01W	438	-12.1	-8.1	36.6	18.6	34.6	18.0	32.6	17.4	19.8	33.4	18.9	32.1	15.3	11.5	22.7	14.1	10.6	22.2	9.2	7.9	6.6	2847	452
POCATELLO REGIONAL AP	42.92N	112.57W	1365	-20.5	-17.1	34.7	16.6	32.9	16.2	31.3	15.7	18.5	30.3	17.6	29.1	14.9	12.5	21.8	13.5	11.4	21.5	12.5	11.2	9.8	3908	233
Illinois																										*14 sites, 6 more on CD-ROM*
AURORA MUNICIPAL	41.77N	88.47W	215	-18.9	-17.0	32.7	23.5	31.4	23.0	29.8	22.1	25.4	30.6	24.4	29.0	23.8	19.1	28.4	22.8	17.9	27.2	11.6	10.2	8.9	3557	395
CAHOKIA/ST. LOUIS	38.57N	90.15W	126	-12.5	-9.9	34.2	25.2	33.0	24.7	32.4	24.4	26.9	32.4	26.0	31.7	25.3	20.7	29.5	24.1	19.3	28.9	9.2	8.2	7.4	2473	776
CHICAGO MIDWAY AP	41.79N	87.75W	188	-18.7	-15.4	33.4	23.8	32.0	23.0	30.3	22.2	25.6	31.3	24.5	29.7	23.9	19.2	29.0	22.8	17.9	27.9	10.9	9.5	8.6	3294	568
CHICAGO OHARE INTL AP	41.99N	87.91W	205	-20.0	-16.6	33.3	23.7	31.6	23.0	30.1	22.1	25.5	31.2	24.5	29.6	23.8	19.2	28.9	22.9	18.0	27.7	11.1	9.4	8.6	3506	468
DECATUR	39.83N	88.87W	213	-18.0	-15.2	33.9	24.8	32.5	24.3	31.2	23.5	26.3	32.0	25.4	31.0	24.5	20.0	29.9	23.7	19.1	28.9	11.1	9.7	8.8	3072	592
GLENVIEW NAS	42.08N	87.82W	199	-20.3	-16.6	34.0	23.9	32.1	22.9	30.4	22.0	25.4	32.2	24.4	30.2	23.3	18.5	29.4	22.3	17.4	28.4	9.4	8.4	7.5	3459	501
MOLINE QUAD CITY INTL AP	41.47N	90.52W	181	-21.2	-17.8	34.1	24.6	32.6	24.0	31.0	23.0	26.2	32.1	25.2	30.8	24.5	19.9	29.6	23.6	18.8	28.4	11.0	9.2	8.3	3412	555
PEORIA GREATER PEORIA AP	40.67N	89.68W	202	-19.8	-16.5	33.7	24.7	32.3	24.1	30.8	23.2	26.3	31.7	25.4	30.6	24.7	20.2	29.5	23.8	19.1	28.4	10.6	9.0	8.2	3227	575
QUINCY MUNI BALDWIN FLD	39.94N	91.19W	234	-18.9	-15.9	34.0	24.7	32.4	24.1	31.0	23.4	25.9	31.7	25.2	31.0	24.2	19.7	29.3	23.4	18.8	28.4	11.0	9.4	8.6	3084	611
ROCKFORD GREATER ROCKFORD AP	42.20N	89.09W	227	-22.5	-18.7	33.1	23.9	31.4	23.2	29.9	22.2	25.7	31.0	24.6	29.4	24.1	19.5	28.9	23.1	18.3	27.8	11.0	9.4	8.6	3719	433
SCOTT AFB/BELLEVILL	38.55N	89.85W	135	-15.3	-12.0	35.0	25.2	33.7	24.8	32.4	24.2	26.8	32.4	26.0	31.6	25.2	20.7	29.9	24.4	19.6	29.0	9.6	8.4	7.5	2577	793
SPRINGFIELD CAPITAL AP	39.85N	89.68W	187	-19.0	-15.2	33.8	24.8	32.5	24.2	31.2	23.4	26.3	32.0	25.5	30.9	24.7	20.1	30.0	23.9	19.1	28.9	11.1	9.7	8.7	3016	631
UNIV OF ILLINOIS WI	40.03N	88.27W	236	-18.3	-15.4	33.6	24.7	32.3	24.1	30.9	23.5	26.5	31.7	25.5	30.4	25.0	20.7	30.2	24.0	19.4	28.6	12.3	11.0	9.8	3143	561
W. CHICAGO/DU PAGE	41.92N	88.25W	231	-20.8	-17.4	32.5	23.8	31.2	23.2	29.5	22.2	25.7	30.7	24.7	29.3	24.1	19.5	29.1	23.0	18.2	27.6	11.0	9.4	8.5	3617	409
Indiana																										*8 sites, 1 more on CD-ROM*
EVANSVILLE REGIONAL AP	38.04N	87.54W	118	-14.7	-11.1	34.4	24.6	33.1	24.3	32.0	23.8	26.3	32.1	25.6	31.1	24.7	20.0	29.5	24.0	19.2	28.7	9.2	8.3	7.4	2472	783
FORT WAYNE INTL AP	41.01N	85.21W	252	-19.2	-15.7	32.8	23.5	31.3	22.9	29.8	22.0	25.3	30.5	24.4	29.0	23.8	19.2	28.2	22.9	18.2	27.2	11.0	9.3	8.4	3339	462
GRISSOM ARB	40.65N	86.15W	253	-20.0	-15.9	33.5	24.3	31.9	23.8	30.4	22.7	26.2	31.7	25.2	30.0	24.6	20.3	29.7	23.6	19.0	28.4	11.2	9.2	8.2	3201	569
INDIANAPOLIS INTL AP	39.71N	86.27W	246	-18.0	-14.2	32.8	24.1	31.5	23.5	30.2	22.8	25.7	30.9	24.9	29.7	24.1	19.6	28.6	23.4	18.7	27.8	11.0	9.3	8.4	2957	586
LAFAYETTE PURDUE UNIV AP	40.41N	86.94W	194	-19.1	-15.5	33.6	24.2	32.2	23.6	30.9	22.9	26.0	31.5	25.1	30.2	24.4	19.8	29.3	23.6	18.8	28.3	10.3	9.0	8.2	3098	557
MONROE CO	39.13N	86.62W	264	-15.1	-12.1	32.5	24.5	32.0	24.5	30.8	23.7	26.0	30.4	25.3	30.0	24.8	20.5	28.7	23.8	19.3	28.0	8.7	7.8	7.1	2742	561
SOUTH BEND MICHIANA RGNL AP	41.71N	86.33W	236	-18.6	-15.3	32.7	23.5	31.2	22.6	29.6	21.9	25.2	30.4	24.2	28.9	23.7	19.0	28.5	22.7	18.0	27.2	10.8	9.2	8.3	3438	450
TERRE HAUTE/HULMAN	39.45N	87.32W	175	-17.9	-14.1	33.4	24.8	32.3	24.4	31.0	23.7	26.4	31.6	25.6	30.5	25.0	20.5	29.7	24.0	19.3	28.6	10.2	8.7	8.0	2886	603
Iowa																										*9 sites, 19 more on CD-ROM*
AMES MUNI ARPT	42.00N	93.62W	291	-21.0	-17.5	32.5	24.5	31.3	23.8	29.8	23.2	26.2	30.8	25.2	29.8	24.9	20.6	29.4	23.8	19.3	28.2	11.8	10.6	9.0	3549	441
ANKENY REGIONAL ARP	41.68N	93.55W	275	-20.8	-17.6	34.9	24.0	32.9	23.5	31.3	22.9	25.5	31.7	24.7	30.7	23.7	19.1	28.9	22.8	18.1	28.2	9.3	8.2	7.4	3308	591
BOONE MUNI	42.05N	93.85W	354	-21.0	-17.6	32.9	25.4	32.1	24.8	30.1	23.6	27.2	31.7	26.0	30.0	26.1	22.5	30.1	24.9	20.9	29.2	11.8	10.5	9.1	3516	497
CEDAR RAPIDS MUNICIPAL AP	41.88N	91.71W	266	-23.1	-19.9	33.1	24.4	31.4	23.7	29.9	22.8	25.9	30.8	25.0	29.8	24.6	20.2	29.1	23.5	18.9	27.9	11.8	10.4	9.0	3724	448
DAVENPORT NEXRAD	41.62N	90.58W	259	-19.6	-17.1	32.4	24.6	31.2	24.1	29.1	22.8	25.9	30.6	25.0	29.6	24.1	19.6	28.6	23.6	19.0	28.2	11.8	10.5	9.1	3438	449
DES MOINES INTL AP	41.54N	93.67W	294	-21.6	-18.7	34.1	24.6	32.3	23.9	30.7	23.0	25.8	31.6	25.0	30.7	24.1	19.7	29.3	23.3	18.7	28.5	11.5	10.0	8.8	3467	578
DUBUQUE REGIONAL AP	42.40N	90.70W	329	-22.3	-19.2	31.8	23.8	30.2	23.0	28.6	21.8	25.3	30.0	24.2	28.4	24.0	19.6	28.4	22.9	18.3	27.0	11.5	10.2	8.9	3882	361
SIOUX CITY SIOUX GATEWAY AP	42.39N	96.38W	336	-22.7	-19.8	34.1	24.0	32.5	23.6	31.0	22.8	25.9	31.4	25.0	30.6	24.4	20.1	29.4	23.3	18.8	28.7	12.8	11.4	10.1	3734	512
WATERLOO MUNICIPAL AP	42.55N	92.40W	268	-24.8	-21.3	33.2	24.2	31.6	23.2	30.0	22.4	25.8	31.0	24.8	29.7	24.4	20.0	29.1	23.3	18.7	27.9	11.7	10.5	9.1	3907	437
Kansas																										*10 sites, 16 more on CD-ROM*
FT RILEY/MARSHALL A	39.05N	96.77W	324	-18.5	-14.4	37.6	23.9	35.7	23.7	34.0	23.5	25.8	33.1	25.1	32.5	23.8	19.4	30.0	22.9	18.3	29.1	9.3	8.2	7.3	2806	843
LAWRENCE MUNI ARPT	39.00N	95.22W	254	-14.9	-12.3	37.3	24.9	35.1	24.6	33.0	24.1	26.7	33.5	25.8	32.6	24.8	20.5	30.7	23.8	19.3	29.7	11.2	9.7	8.5	2667	814
MANHATTAN RGNL	39.13N	96.67W	330	-16.4	-12.9	37.7	24.2	36.2	24.3	33.9	23.8	25.9	33.9	25.4	33.3	23.8	19.5	29.7	22.9	18.4	28.7	10.8	9.2	8.2	2823	809
MCCONNELL AFB	37.62N	97.27W	414	-14.9	-11.3	37.7	22.9	36.1	23.0	34.2	22.8	25.3	32.6	24.7	31.8	23.5	19.2	28.0	22.7	18.3	27.7	11.8	10.6	9.2	2415	959
OLATHE/JOHNSON CO.	38.85N	94.73W	334	-14.9	-12.3	35.9	24.6	33.6	24.4	32.3	24.1	26.1	32.2	25.5	31.7	24.1	19.8	29.7	23.7	19.3	29.1	10.5	9.0	8.2	2599	781
SALINA MUNICIPAL AP	38.81N	97.66W	391	-17.3	-13.7	38.5	23.3	36.8	23.2	34.9	22.9	25.2	33.6	24.6	32.7	22.9	18.5	29.0	22.3	17.9	28.4	12.3	11.1	9.9	2693	923
TOPEKA FORBES FIELD	38.95N	95.66W	329	-17.2	-13.9	35.9	23.8	33.9	23.6	32.4	23.3	25.7	32.2	25.0	31.4	23.9	19.5	29.5	23.0	18.4	28.5	11.3	10.4	9.1	2773	736

Meaning of acronyms:
DB: Dry bulb temperature, °C
WB: Wet bulb temperature, °C
MCWB: Mean coincident wet bulb temperature, °C
Lat: Latitude, °
DP: Dew point temperature, °C
MCDB: Mean coincident dry bulb temperature, °C
Long: Longitude, °
HR: Humidity ratio, g of moisture per kg of dry air
HDD and CDD 18.3: Annual heating and cooling degree-days, base 18.3°C, °C-day
Elev: Elevation, m
WS: Wind speed, m/s

Station	Lat	Long	Elev	Heating DB		Cooling DB/MCWB						Evaporation WB/MCDB				Dehumidification DP/HR/MCDB						Extreme Annual WS			Heat./Cool. Degree-Days	
						0.4%		1%		2%		0.4%		1%		0.4%			1%							
				99.6%	99%	DB / MCWB		DB / MCWB		DB / MCWB		WB / MCDB		WB / MCDB		DP / HR / MCDB			DP / HR / MCDB			1%	2.5%	5%	HDD / CDD 18.3	
TOPEKA MUNICIPAL AP	39.07N	95.63W	270	-17.4	-14.0	36.2	24.4	34.5	24.3	32.9	23.9	26.1	32.8	25.4	32.2	24.2	19.7	30.1	23.4	18.9	29.2	10.6	9.1	8.2	2768	788
WICHITA MID-CONTINENT AP	37.65N	97.43W	408	-15.6	-11.9	38.0	22.9	36.2	23.0	34.4	22.9	25.2	32.3	24.6	31.9	23.4	19.1	28.5	22.6	18.2	27.7	12.5	11.3	10.4	2536	932
WICHITA/COL. JABARA	37.75N	97.22W	433	-14.0	-11.4	37.6	23.2	36.2	23.3	33.8	23.2	25.2	32.7	24.6	32.0	22.9	18.6	28.4	22.5	18.1	27.9	12.2	11.1	9.9	2468	877
8 sites, 5 more on CD-ROM																										
Kentucky																										
BOWLING GREEN WARREN CO AP	36.98N	86.44W	164	-13.1	-9.4	34.0	24.1	32.7	24.1	31.5	23.7	25.8	31.5	25.2	30.7	24.2	19.4	28.6	23.6	18.8	28.0	9.0	8.2	7.4	2298	749
CINCINNATI NORTHERN KY AP	39.04N	84.67W	269	-16.1	-12.1	33.0	23.6	31.6	23.2	30.3	22.5	25.2	30.6	24.4	29.5	23.6	19.0	28.0	22.9	18.2	27.1	10.0	8.6	7.8	2769	599
FORT CAMPBELL (AAF)	36.67N	87.50W	173	-12.3	-8.9	34.7	24.8	33.3	24.5	32.3	24.2	26.6	31.9	25.8	31.1	25.1	20.7	28.9	24.3	19.6	28.4	8.5	7.5	6.6	2121	889
HENDERSON CITY	37.82N	87.68W	117	-13.7	-9.5	33.8	24.8	32.7	24.5	32.1	24.2	26.4	32.2	25.6	31.3	24.7	20.0	30.3	23.7	18.9	29.5	9.4	8.4	7.4	2455	746
LEXINGTON BLUEGRASS AP	38.04N	84.61W	301	-14.4	-10.7	33.2	23.3	31.9	23.2	30.6	22.7	25.2	30.7	24.5	29.6	23.5	18.9	28.1	22.8	18.2	27.3	9.0	8.0	7.3	2540	653
LOUISVILLE BOWMAN FIELD	38.23N	85.66W	170	-13.9	-10.2	34.1	24.0	32.8	23.8	31.6	23.4	25.8	31.4	25.2	30.7	24.1	19.4	28.5	23.5	18.7	28.0	8.4	7.7	6.7	2366	772
LOUISVILLE STANDIFORD FIELD	38.18N	85.73W	149	-13.3	-9.7	34.1	24.3	32.9	24.0	31.7	23.5	26.0	31.7	25.3	30.9	24.3	19.6	29.3	23.6	18.7	28.4	9.4	8.4	7.5	2316	831
SOMERSET(AWOS)	38.00N	84.60W	283	-10.2	-7.5	34.8	23.9	33.4	23.6	32.4	23.3	25.6	32.8	24.9	31.6	23.0	18.4	29.3	22.7	18.0	28.7	8.0	6.8	5.6	2102	809
12 sites, 5 more on CD-ROM																										
Louisiana																										
ALEXANDRIA ESLER REGIONAL AP	31.40N	92.30W	36	-3.0	-2.1	36.3	24.9	34.9	25.2	33.8	25.0	26.9	31.9	26.5	31.8	25.8	21.2	28.7	25.1	20.3	28.5	7.4	6.2	5.4	1114	1340
ALEXANDRIA INTERNATIONAL	31.33N	92.55W	27	-3.0	-1.3	35.9	25.3	34.2	25.1	33.5	25.0	27.1	32.0	26.6	31.9	26.0	21.4	29.3	25.2	20.3	29.1	8.3	7.2	6.1	1020	1427
BARKSDALE AFB	32.50N	93.67W	54	-5.3	-2.9	36.3	24.6	35.0	24.6	33.8	24.6	26.6	32.4	26.0	31.8	25.1	20.4	28.7	24.5	19.6	28.3	8.5	7.5	6.6	1271	1289
BATON ROUGE RYAN ARPT	30.54N	91.15W	23	-2.5	-0.5	34.6	25.3	33.8	25.1	33.0	24.9	26.9	31.7	26.5	31.1	25.7	21.0	28.8	25.2	20.4	28.4	8.4	7.5	6.8	894	1474
LAFAYETTE REGIONAL AP	30.21N	91.99W	13	-1.9	0.2	34.6	25.5	33.7	25.4	32.9	25.2	27.1	31.7	26.7	31.3	26.0	21.4	28.8	25.5	20.7	28.5	9.2	8.2	7.4	831	1535
LAKE CHARLES REGIONAL ARPT	30.13N	93.23W	3	-1.3	0.6	34.5	25.5	33.6	25.4	32.8	25.4	27.4	31.4	26.9	30.9	26.3	21.8	29.1	25.9	21.2	28.8	9.3	8.3	7.5	816	1539
MONROE REGIONAL AP	32.51N	92.04W	25	-4.7	-2.7	36.1	25.6	34.8	25.4	33.8	25.2	27.3	32.8	26.8	32.3	25.8	21.2	29.8	25.2	20.5	29.3	8.5	7.6	6.7	1243	1346
NEW ORLEANS ALVIN CALLENDER F	29.83N	90.03W	0	-1.1	1.0	33.6	25.8	32.9	25.6	32.2	25.5	27.8	30.8	27.1	30.4	26.9	22.6	29.3	26.3	21.7	28.8	7.9	7.0	5.9	791	1455
NEW ORLEANS INTL ARPT	29.99N	90.25W	6	-0.3	1.9	34.2	25.6	33.3	25.4	32.5	25.2	27.1	31.5	26.7	31.1	25.9	21.3	29.1	25.5	20.8	28.8	9.2	8.3	7.5	732	1581
NEW ORLEANS LAKEFRONT AP	30.04N	90.03W	3	2.0	3.8	34.1	26.0	33.3	25.7	32.6	25.5	27.4	31.9	26.9	31.3	26.3	21.7	29.7	25.9	21.2	29.4	10.7	9.1	8.3	617	1785
SHREVEPORT DOWNTOWN	32.54N	93.74W	55	-2.8	-1.2	37.4	24.7	36.0	24.7	34.5	24.5	26.4	33.1	26.0	32.4	24.8	20.0	28.5	24.2	19.2	28.3	8.4	7.5	6.6	1163	1473
SHREVEPORT REGIONAL ARPT	32.45N	93.82W	79	-4.6	-2.4	36.6	24.6	35.2	24.7	34.1	24.6	26.3	32.9	25.9	32.2	24.7	19.9	28.5	24.3	19.4	28.3	8.8	7.9	7.2	1198	1385
5 sites, 13 more on CD-ROM																										
Maine																										
AUBURN-LEWISTON	44.05N	70.28W	88	-21.5	-18.2	31.0	21.4	28.7	20.6	27.3	19.6	23.0	28.4	21.8	26.7	21.3	16.1	25.9	20.2	15.0	24.6	9.3	8.3	7.3	4262	171
BANGOR INTERNATIONAL AP	44.81N	68.82W	59	-21.9	-19.0	31.0	21.6	29.0	20.6	27.3	19.5	23.0	28.4	21.8	27.1	21.2	15.9	25.8	20.1	14.9	24.2	10.5	8.7	8.0	4263	199
BRUNSWICK NAS	43.90N	69.93W	23	-19.1	-16.8	30.2	21.5	28.4	20.5	26.9	19.6	23.0	28.1	21.9	26.6	21.3	16.0	25.6	20.5	15.2	24.4	9.9	8.5	7.6	3997	208
PORTLAND INTL JETPORT	43.64N	70.30W	19	-18.0	-15.4	30.4	21.7	28.6	20.9	26.9	20.0	23.3	28.3	22.2	26.7	21.6	16.3	25.9	20.7	15.4	24.6	10.4	8.8	7.9	3934	203
SANFORD MUNI (AWOS)	43.40N	70.72W	74	-21.6	-17.9	31.4	21.2	29.1	20.4	27.7	19.7	23.2	28.9	22.0	27.5	21.3	16.1	25.7	20.2	15.0	25.1	9.3	8.2	7.2	4189	186
3 sites, 2 more on CD-ROM																										
Maryland																										
ANDREWS AFB	38.82N	76.87W	86	-10.1	-7.6	34.4	24.0	32.8	23.5	31.4	22.9	25.7	31.4	24.9	30.2	24.0	19.1	27.9	23.3	18.2	27.2	10.5	8.9	7.9	2456	689
BALTIMORE BLT-WASHNGTN INT'L	39.17N	76.68W	47	-10.6	-8.2	34.4	23.9	32.9	23.5	31.4	22.8	25.6	31.4	24.9	30.3	24.0	19.0	27.8	23.4	18.3	27.1	10.0	8.6	7.7	2537	682
THOMAS POINT	38.90N	76.43W	12	-8.2	-6.0	30.4	N/A	29.3	N/A	28.3	N/A	N/A	N/A	N/A	N/A	N/A	N/A	N/A	N/A	N/A	N/A	17.2	14.4	12.0	2335	676
12 sites, 1 more on CD-ROM																										
Massachusetts																										
BARNSTABLE MUNI BOA	41.67N	70.27W	17	-12.5	-10.0	28.9	23.0	27.4	21.9	26.2	21.2	24.3	27.6	23.5	25.9	23.0	17.8	25.3	22.7	17.4	25.0	11.1	9.5	8.6	3293	271
BOSTON LOGAN INT'L ARPT	42.36N	71.01W	9	-13.6	-10.9	32.7	22.9	30.9	22.2	29.1	21.4	24.6	30.2	23.7	28.6	22.8	17.6	27.3	22.0	16.7	26.2	12.0	10.8	9.3	3123	417
BUZZARDS BAY	41.38N	71.03W	17	-11.2	-8.5	24.2	N/A	23.4	N/A	22.6	N/A	N/A	N/A	N/A	N/A	N/A	N/A	N/A	N/A	N/A	N/A	19.8	17.3	15.2	3092	156
CHATHAM MUNI ARPT	41.68N	70.00W	19	-12.0	-8.7	27.6	22.3	26.3	21.6	25.0	21.2	23.9	26.5	23.1	25.3	22.9	17.7	25.3	22.5	17.2	24.7	10.4	8.9	7.9	3151	238
LAWRENCE MUNI	42.72N	71.12W	46	-16.2	-12.6	32.3	23.1	31.0	22.5	28.8	21.8	24.5	29.6	23.7	28.3	22.8	17.6	26.5	22.4	17.2	26.2	9.0	8.0	7.2	3384	353
MARTHAS VINEYARD	41.40N	70.62W	21	-12.8	-10.9	28.0	22.1	27.2	21.6	26.0	21.0	23.9	26.8	23.1	25.4	22.8	17.6	25.4	22.5	17.2	24.7	11.7	10.5	9.1	3299	219
NEW BEDFORD RGNL	41.67N	70.95W	25	-13.7	-11.2	31.2	22.8	28.9	21.9	27.5	21.0	24.3	28.6	23.5	26.9	22.8	17.6	25.9	22.5	17.2	25.4	10.4	8.9	8.0	3243	307
NORWOOD MEMORIAL	42.18N	71.18W	15	-16.3	-12.9	32.4	23.5	31.1	23.0	28.9	22.0	25.1	30.3	24.1	28.4	23.1	17.8	26.5	22.7	17.5	26.1	9.2	8.1	7.3	3457	319
OTIS ANGB	41.65N	70.52W	40	-13.2	-10.6	29.2	22.3	27.7	21.7	26.3	21.0	24.2	27.2	23.4	25.9	23.1	17.9	25.3	22.5	17.3	24.8	12.2	10.8	9.2	3249	263
PLYMOUTH MUNICIPAL	41.92N	70.73W	45	-15.2	-12.4	31.3	22.8	29.0	22.1	27.7	21.1	24.4	29.0	23.6	27.2	22.9	17.8	25.9	22.5	17.3	25.5	10.4	8.9	8.0	3454	287
SOUTH WEYMOUTH NAS	42.15N	70.93W	49	-14.5	-12.0	32.9	23.2	31.0	22.4	29.3	21.5	25.0	30.5	23.8	28.8	23.4	18.3	27.7	22.3	17.1	26.3	8.3	7.4	6.5	3240	359
WORCESTER REGIONAL ARPT	42.27N	71.88W	310	-16.9	-14.3	29.8	21.8	28.4	21.1	26.9	20.2	23.4	27.7	22.5	26.4	22.1	17.4	25.6	21.2	16.5	24.6	11.5	10.2	8.7	3726	252
15 sites, 27 more on CD-ROM																										
Michigan																										
DETROIT CITY AIRPORT	42.41N	83.01W	191	-15.5	-12.9	32.7	23.2	31.3	22.4	29.8	21.6	24.9	30.3	23.9	29.0	23.1	18.3	27.9	22.2	17.3	27.0	9.1	8.3	7.7	3324	499
DETROIT METROPOLITAN ARPT	42.22N	83.35W	202	-17.0	-14.1	32.4	23.2	30.8	22.5	29.3	21.7	24.9	30.2	23.9	28.6	23.2	18.4	28.0	22.4	17.5	26.8	11.5	10.1	8.8	3435	431
DETROIT WILLOW RUN AP	42.23N	83.53W	218	-17.3	-14.4	32.4	23.6	31.0	22.6	29.2	21.6	25.1	30.6	24.0	28.9	23.2	18.4	27.7	22.4	17.6	26.8	11.0	9.6	8.5	3552	378
FLINT BISHOP INTL ARPT	42.97N	83.75W	234	-18.3	-15.7	31.9	23.3	30.3	22.3	28.8	21.3	24.7	29.7	23.7	28.3	23.1	18.4	27.9	22.2	17.3	26.4	10.8	9.2	8.4	3755	328
GRAND RAPIDS KENT COUNTY INT'	42.88N	85.52W	245	-17.0	-14.4	31.8	23.1	30.2	22.1	28.7	21.2	24.7	29.7	23.6	28.1	23.1	18.4	27.6	22.1	17.3	26.4	11.1	9.4	8.5	3715	348
GROSSE ISLE ARPT	42.10N	83.15W	176	-13.7	-12.0	32.1	23.6	30.0	23.3	28.6	22.6	25.7	29.1	24.7	28.3	24.1	19.5	27.3	23.7	18.9	26.9	9.3	8.3	7.5	3213	478

DB: Dry bulb temperature, °C | WB: Wet bulb temperature, °C | DP: Dew point temperature, °C | HR: Humidity ratio, g of moisture per kg of dry air | WS: Wind speed, m/s

MCWB: Mean coincident wet bulb temperature, °C | MCDB: Mean coincident dry bulb temperature, °C | HDD and CDD 18.3: Annual heating and cooling degree-days, base 18.3°C, °C-day

Station	Lat	Long	Elev	Heating DB		Cooling DB/MCWB						Evaporation WB/MCDB				Dehumidification DP/HR/MCDB						Extreme Annual WS			Heat./Cool. Degree-Days	
						0.4%		1%		2%		0.4%		1%		0.4%			1%							
				99.6%	99%	DB	MCWB	DB	MCWB	DB	MCWB	WB	MCDB	WB	MCDB	DP	HR	MCDB	DP	HR	MCDB	1%	2.5%	5%	HDD	CDD 18.3
KALAMAZOO BATTLE CR	42.23N	85.55W	273	-16.1	-12.8	32.3	23.0	31.0	22.4	28.8	21.5	24.5	29.5	23.7	28.3	22.8	18.1	27.4	22.3	17.6	26.8	9.7	8.5	7.7	3443	393
LANSING CAPITAL CITY ARPT	42.78N	84.58W	266	-19.1	-16.1	31.9	23.1	30.3	22.3	28.7	21.3	24.7	29.7	23.7	28.3	23.0	18.4	27.5	22.1	17.4	26.4	11.0	9.3	8.4	3827	317
MUSKEGON COUNTY ARPT	43.17N	86.24W	193	-15.5	-13.0	30.1	22.5	28.8	21.7	27.5	20.9	24.2	28.1	23.4	26.9	23.0	18.1	26.7	22.1	17.2	25.7	11.4	10.4	9.0	3724	287
OAKLAND CO INTL	42.67N	83.42W	306	-17.2	-14.7	32.0	23.1	30.1	22.0	28.6	21.2	24.2	29.6	23.2	28.1	22.5	17.9	27.3	21.8	17.1	26.2	10.9	9.4	8.5	3686	348
SAGINAW TRI CITY INTL AP	43.53N	84.08W	204	-17.8	-15.8	32.2	23.1	30.3	22.1	28.7	21.3	24.7	29.9	23.6	28.4	23.0	18.2	27.6	22.1	17.2	26.5	10.8	9.3	8.4	3871	314
SELFRIDGE ANGB	42.62N	82.83W	177	-16.3	-13.9	32.4	23.5	30.8	22.6	29.0	21.7	24.9	30.2	23.9	28.5	23.2	18.3	27.9	22.4	17.4	26.8	9.4	8.4	7.6	3574	373
ST.CLAIR COUNTY INT	42.92N	82.53W	198	-17.4	-14.8	32.4	23.4	30.2	22.0	28.7	21.4	24.7	29.8	23.5	28.0	22.9	18.1	26.9	22.3	17.4	26.2	8.3	7.4	6.6	3688	277
Minnesota																										*11 sites, 51 more on CD-ROM*
DULUTH HARBOR (CGS)	46.77N	92.08W	186	-24.5	-22.0	30.1	22.5	27.9	21.3	26.3	20.1	24.8	28.6	23.3	26.8	23.7	18.9	26.7	22.4	17.4	25.4	12.4	10.9	9.4	4752	177
DULUTH INTERNATIONAL ARPT	46.84N	92.19W	432	-28.6	-25.4	29.2	21.0	27.3	19.7	25.7	18.7	22.6	27.4	21.3	25.8	20.9	16.4	25.7	19.6	15.1	24.2	11.1	9.4	8.6	5236	116
FLYING CLOUD	44.82N	93.45W	283	-22.6	-20.0	32.7	23.6	31.3	23.1	29.1	21.9	25.5	30.7	24.3	29.1	23.8	19.3	28.9	22.7	18.0	27.6	9.9	8.6	7.8	4004	441
MANKATO(AWOS)	44.22N	93.92W	311	-25.1	-22.3	32.1	23.0	30.1	21.9	28.0	20.8	24.8	29.3	23.5	28.3	23.1	18.5	27.6	22.1	17.5	26.9	11.9	10.7	9.3	4272	332
MINNEAPOLIS/BLAINE	45.15N	93.22W	278	-22.6	-20.1	32.4	23.9	31.0	23.2	28.9	22.1	25.7	30.2	24.4	28.7	24.0	19.6	28.5	22.8	18.2	27.1	10.3	8.8	7.9	4147	351
MINNEAPOLIS/CRYSTAL	45.07N	93.35W	265	-22.6	-19.9	32.6	23.3	31.2	22.6	29.0	21.5	25.1	30.6	23.9	28.8	22.9	18.3	28.3	22.3	17.6	27.6	9.6	8.5	7.7	4128	383
MINNEAPOLIS-ST PAUL INT'L ARP	44.88N	93.23W	255	-25.2	-22.0	32.8	23.0	31.0	22.4	29.4	21.4	25.0	30.8	23.9	29.0	23.1	18.4	28.6	22.1	17.3	27.4	11.1	9.8	8.8	4203	417
ROCHESTER INTERNATIONAL ARPT	43.90N	92.49W	402	-26.2	-22.9	31.2	23.1	29.5	22.2	28.0	21.3	24.9	29.2	23.7	27.7	23.5	19.2	27.7	22.3	17.9	26.5	12.9	11.8	10.7	4431	284
SOUTH ST PAUL MUNI	44.85N	93.15W	250	-22.9	-20.9	32.6	23.1	31.2	22.5	29.0	21.4	25.2	30.0	24.0	28.4	23.8	19.2	28.2	22.6	17.8	26.6	8.2	7.2	6.2	4120	403
ST CLOUD REGIONAL ARPT	45.55N	94.05W	312	-28.5	-24.9	32.2	22.7	30.3	21.8	28.6	20.6	24.7	30.2	23.6	28.9	23.0	18.4	28.0	21.8	17.1	26.9	10.2	8.6	7.8	4733	263
ST PAUL DOWNTOWN AP	44.93N	93.05W	217	-24.4	-22.0	32.4	23.7	30.9	22.9	28.7	21.7	25.1	30.3	24.0	28.8	23.6	18.9	28.4	22.4	17.6	27.2	10.2	8.9	8.2	4183	372
Mississippi																										*6 sites, 5 more on CD-ROM*
HATTIESBURG LAUREL	31.47N	89.33W	93	-3.7	-2.2	35.4	24.3	34.0	23.9	32.9	23.8	25.8	32.2	25.4	31.6	24.0	19.1	28.3	23.7	18.7	28.1	6.9	5.7	5.0	1135	1273
JACKSON INTERNATIONAL AP	32.32N	90.08W	101	-5.6	-3.5	35.3	24.9	34.2	24.6	33.3	24.5	26.6	32.3	26.0	31.6	25.1	20.5	28.6	24.6	19.8	28.2	8.4	7.5	6.8	1284	1258
KEESLER AFB/BILOXI	30.42N	88.92W	8	-0.9	1.6	34.1	26.8	33.0	26.4	32.4	26.1	28.6	32.4	27.9	31.3	27.6	23.5	30.7	27.1	22.9	30.2	7.9	6.9	6.0	792	1532
MERIDIAN KEY FIELD	32.33N	88.75W	95	-5.6	-3.4	35.4	24.6	34.2	24.5	33.2	24.4	26.5	32.0	25.9	31.4	25.0	20.4	28.7	24.5	19.7	28.2	8.2	7.4	6.6	1289	1194
MERIDIAN NAAS	32.55N	88.57W	97	-6.2	-3.6	36.2	25.0	35.0	24.8	33.8	24.5	26.8	33.0	26.2	32.5	25.2	20.5	30.0	24.4	19.6	29.2	6.9	5.7	4.9	1309	1238
TUPELO C D LEMONS ARPT	34.26N	88.77W	110	-7.6	-5.1	35.5	24.5	34.2	24.2	33.0	24.2	26.2	32.0	25.7	31.4	24.6	19.9	28.7	24.1	19.2	28.2	8.4	7.6	6.9	1627	1094
Missouri																										*9 sites, 7 more on CD-ROM*
CAPE GIRARDEAU MUNICIPAL AP	37.23N	89.57W	107	-13.7	-10.1	34.9	25.2	33.6	25.0	32.4	24.5	26.8	32.5	26.1	31.7	25.2	20.6	30.2	24.4	19.7	29.2	9.5	8.5	7.9	2339	856
COLUMBIA REGIONAL AIRPORT	38.82N	92.22W	274	-17.0	-13.8	34.8	24.5	33.1	24.4	31.7	23.8	26.2	31.9	25.4	31.1	24.6	20.2	29.6	23.8	19.2	28.7	10.8	9.2	8.3	2772	686
JEFFERSON CITY MEM	38.58N	92.15W	167	-13.7	-11.0	35.1	24.6	33.0	24.1	32.3	23.9	26.3	31.7	25.5	31.3	24.9	20.4	29.3	23.8	19.1	28.2	9.3	8.3	7.3	2508	767
JOPLIN MUNICIPAL AP	37.15N	94.50W	300	-14.5	-10.9	35.9	24.2	34.4	24.2	33.0	23.8	25.9	32.4	25.3	31.9	24.1	19.7	29.6	23.4	18.9	29.0	11.0	9.4	8.5	2267	916
KANSAS CITY DOWNTOWN AP	39.12N	94.59W	229	-16.3	-13.0	36.2	24.4	34.4	24.3	33.0	24.0	26.5	33.0	25.7	32.0	24.7	20.3	30.4	23.9	19.3	29.7	10.1	8.8	8.2	2552	921
KANSAS CITY INT'L ARPT	39.30N	94.72W	312	-17.8	-14.8	35.7	24.6	33.7	24.4	32.1	23.9	26.4	32.4	25.6	31.6	24.7	20.5	30.2	23.8	19.4	29.3	11.5	10.4	9.0	2836	753
SPRINGFIELD REGIONAL ARPT	37.24N	93.39W	387	-15.4	-11.7	35.0	23.6	33.4	23.6	31.9	23.4	25.3	31.6	24.8	31.0	23.6	19.3	28.6	22.9	18.5	28.0	10.2	8.9	8.1	2477	759
ST LOUIS LAMBERT INT'L ARPT	38.75N	90.37W	216	-15.5	-12.1	35.4	24.9	34.0	24.5	32.6	23.9	26.3	32.7	25.7	31.8	24.6	20.1	29.7	23.9	19.3	29.2	10.8	9.1	8.2	2502	906
ST LOUIS SPIRIT OF ST LOUIS A	38.66N	90.66W	141	-15.0	-11.8	35.1	25.1	33.7	24.6	32.4	24.0	26.6	32.7	25.8	31.7	24.9	20.3	30.1	24.0	19.2	29.0	9.3	8.3	7.5	2593	765
Montana																										*7 sites, 11 more on CD-ROM*
BILLINGS LOGAN INT'L ARPT	45.81N	108.54W	1088	-24.2	-20.8	34.9	17.2	33.0	16.7	31.1	16.3	19.1	29.7	18.2	28.8	15.7	12.8	22.3	14.6	11.8	21.6	12.0	10.8	9.3	3766	353
BOZEMAN GALLATIN FIELD	45.79N	111.15W	1356	-27.8	-23.1	32.9	16.3	31.1	15.8	29.1	15.2	18.0	28.1	17.0	27.3	14.8	12.4	20.9	13.5	11.4	20.1	9.2	8.1	6.8	4651	118
BUTTE BERT MOONEY ARPT	45.95N	112.51W	1687	-29.1	-24.2	31.0	14.4	29.1	13.8	27.5	13.4	15.9	26.1	15.1	25.3	12.8	11.3	17.3	11.6	10.4	16.9	10.3	8.7	7.9	5116	42
GREAT FALLS	47.45N	111.38W	1130	-24.7	-21.3	32.5	15.9	30.5	15.3	28.7	14.9	17.5	28.3	16.6	27.0	14.1	11.5	19.0	13.0	10.7	19.6	N/A	N/A	N/A	4277	173
GREAT FALLS INTL ARPT	47.47N	111.38W	1115	-27.6	-24.0	33.4	16.3	31.5	15.7	29.5	15.3	17.9	29.2	16.9	27.9	14.4	11.7	19.7	13.3	10.9	19.5	14.0	12.3	11.1	4200	182
MALMSTROM AFB	47.52N	111.18W	1056	-27.2	-23.5	33.8	16.9	32.1	16.4	30.0	15.9	18.6	29.8	17.6	28.7	14.7	11.9	21.5	13.5	11.0	20.5	13.0	11.7	10.2	3896	235
MISSOULA INTERNATIONAL AP	46.92N	114.09W	972	-21.1	-16.8	33.6	16.9	31.8	16.5	29.8	15.9	18.6	29.4	17.6	28.3	15.2	12.2	20.7	14.0	11.2	20.2	9.7	8.4	7.5	4158	163
Nebraska																										*5 sites, 16 more on CD-ROM*
GRAND ISLAND CENTRAL NE REGIO	40.96N	98.31W	566	-21.2	-17.8	35.7	23.2	33.9	22.8	32.1	22.2	25.1	31.8	24.2	31.0	23.2	19.3	28.7	22.3	18.2	27.7	12.7	11.3	10.1	3424	581
LINCOLN MUNICIPAL ARPT	40.83N	96.76W	362	-20.8	-17.6	36.2	23.9	34.3	23.5	32.6	23.1	25.7	32.6	25.0	31.7	23.8	19.4	29.5	22.9	18.5	28.7	12.0	10.8	9.3	3329	658
OFFUTT AFB/BELLEVUE	41.12N	95.92W	319	-19.6	-16.9	35.0	24.9	32.9	24.2	31.6	23.4	26.4	32.1	25.5	31.0	24.9	20.7	29.6	23.9	19.5	28.7	10.9	9.1	8.1	3240	654
OMAHA EPPLEY AIRFIELD	41.31N	95.90W	299	-21.3	-18.2	35.0	24.5	33.2	23.9	31.6	23.1	26.1	32.0	25.2	31.0	24.5	20.1	29.7	23.5	18.9	28.7	11.6	10.4	9.0	3404	616
OMAHA WSFO	41.37N	96.02W	399	-22.1	-18.6	34.1	23.9	32.5	23.5	30.9	22.7	25.2	31.5	24.4	30.5	23.4	19.1	28.9	22.5	18.1	28.2	10.5	8.8	8.0	3441	586
Nevada																										*3 sites, 9 more on CD-ROM*
LAS VEGAS MCCARRAN INTL AP	36.08N	115.16W	665	-0.8	0.7	42.4	20.1	41.2	19.7	39.8	19.2	22.6	35.7	21.8	34.8	19.1	15.0	26.6	17.7	13.8	28.1	12.0	10.7	9.1	1169	1860
NELLIS AFB	36.23N	115.03W	573	-2.1	-0.3	42.9	19.8	41.8	19.5	40.4	19.0	22.5	35.0	21.8	35.0	19.1	14.9	26.8	17.6	13.5	28.6	11.7	10.2	8.7	1182	1857
RENO TAHOE INTERNATIONAL AP	39.48N	119.77W	1341	-11.2	-8.3	35.4	16.6	33.9	15.9	32.6	15.3	17.8	31.8	16.9	30.9	13.1	11.1	21.3	11.4	9.9	21.2	11.6	9.7	8.4	2889	386
New Hampshire																										*4 sites, 6 more on CD-ROM*
CONCORD MUNICIPAL ARPT	43.20N	71.50W	106	-20.4	-17.6	32.1	21.8	30.5	21.0	28.9	20.4	23.7	29.3	22.7	27.8	22.1	17.0	25.8	21.2	16.0	25.0	9.3	8.3	7.4	3989	256
JAFFREY MUNICIPAL	42.80N	72.00W	317	-19.9	-17.2	30.2	21.1	28.7	20.7	27.3	19.6	22.9	27.4	22.2	26.2	22.1	17.4	25.0	21.2	16.4	24.0	7.4	6.3	5.5	4059	201

Meaning of acronyms:
DB: Dry bulb temperature, °C — *WB: Wet bulb temperature, °C*
MCWB: Mean coincident wet bulb temperature, °C
Lat: Latitude, °
DP: Dew point temperature, °C
MCDB: Mean coincident dry bulb temperature, °C
Long: Longitude, °
HR: Humidity ratio, g of moisture per kg of dry air
Elev: Elevation, m
WS: Wind speed, m/s
HDD and CDD 18.3: Annual heating and cooling degree-days, base 18.3°C, °C-day

Station	Lat	Long	Elev	Heating DB		Cooling DB/MCWB						Evaporation WB/MCDB				Dehumidification DP/HR/MCDB						Extreme Annual WS			Heat./Cool. Degree-Days	
						0.4%		1%		2%		0.4%		1%		0.4%			1%							
				99.6%	99%	DB	MCWB	DB	MCWB	DB	MCWB	WB	MCDB	WB	MCDB	DP	HR	MCDB	DP	HR	MCDB	1%	2.5%	5%	HDD	CDD 18.3
MANCHESTER AIRPORT	42.93N	71.44W	71	-17.2	-14.0	32.9	22.3	31.5	21.5	29.9	20.9	24.3	30.2	23.4	28.6	22.5	17.3	27.0	21.9	16.8	26.2	8.5	7.9	6.9	3451	411
PEASE INTL TRADEPOR	43.08N	70.82W	31	-16.3	-13.5	31.8	22.6	29.9	21.7	28.0	20.8	24.1	29.2	23.1	27.8	22.5	17.3	26.9	21.7	16.4	25.7	10.1	8.7	7.7	3579	297
																									7 sites, 1 more on CD-ROM	
New Jersey																										
ATLANTIC CITY INTL AP	39.46N	74.46W	20	-12.3	-9.5	33.5	23.9	31.9	23.3	30.2	22.7	25.5	30.8	24.8	29.4	24.0	18.9	27.7	23.4	18.3	27.0	11.1	9.4	8.4	2750	553
BELMAR-FARMINGDALE	40.18N	74.13W	26	-11.8	-9.1	32.6	23.1	31.2	22.5	29.0	21.6	24.7	30.3	23.8	28.8	22.8	17.6	27.2	22.3	17.1	26.7	11.3	9.9	8.7	2843	482
MCGUIRE AFB	40.02N	74.60W	45	-12.1	-9.4	33.8	24.3	32.4	23.7	31.0	23.0	26.0	31.0	25.1	30.2	24.7	19.9	28.5	23.7	18.6	27.7	10.4	8.9	7.9	2721	597
MILLVILLE MUNICIPAL AF	39.37N	75.08W	23	-12.1	-9.3	33.3	23.8	31.9	23.4	30.5	22.8	25.5	30.6	24.9	29.4	24.1	19.0	27.5	23.5	18.4	26.9	8.9	8.1	7.4	2700	584
NEWARK INTERNATIONAL ARPT	40.72N	74.17W	9	-11.6	-9.1	34.5	23.8	32.8	23.0	31.2	22.3	25.4	31.5	24.6	29.9	23.7	18.6	27.8	23.1	17.8	27.1	11.2	9.8	8.7	2617	690
TETERBORO AIRPORT	40.85N	74.06W	2	-12.3	-9.7	33.5	23.9	32.1	23.3	30.5	22.4	25.6	31.1	24.6	29.7	24.0	18.8	28.2	23.0	17.7	26.9	9.2	8.4	7.7	2808	557
TRENTON MERCER COUNTY AP	40.28N	74.81W	65	-12.3	-9.9	33.6	23.6	32.1	23.2	30.7	22.6	25.3	31.6	24.4	29.8	23.2	18.1	27.7	22.7	17.6	27.3	10.5	8.9	8.2	2858	548
																									8 sites, 6 more on CD-ROM	
New Mexico																										
ALAMOGORDO WHITE SA	32.83N	105.98W	1313	-6.1	-3.8	37.8	17.8	37.1	17.8	35.9	18.1	21.9	30.7	21.1	29.8	19.1	16.3	24.5	18.7	15.9	24.6	9.6	8.2	7.2	1574	1089
ALBUQUERQUE INTL ARPT	35.04N	106.62W	1620	-7.9	-6.0	35.1	15.7	33.8	15.6	32.6	15.5	18.5	28.1	18.0	27.4	16.4	14.2	19.8	15.7	13.6	20.2	12.6	11.1	9.3	2261	749
CANNON AFB/CLOVIS	34.38N	103.32W	1309	-11.2	-8.1	36.4	17.6	34.9	17.7	33.5	17.9	21.4	28.5	20.7	28.1	19.8	17.1	22.8	18.8	16.0	22.8	12.5	11.0	9.5	2133	762
CLOVIS MUNI (AWOS)	34.43N	103.08W	1284	-10.1	-7.8	36.2	17.7	34.1	17.5	32.9	17.6	20.8	29.0	20.2	28.7	18.6	15.8	23.3	17.7	14.9	22.5	14.2	12.2	10.9	2273	661
FARMINGTON FOUR CORNERS REGL	36.74N	108.23W	1677	-13.6	-10.9	34.9	15.7	33.5	15.4	32.2	15.3	18.5	28.0	17.9	27.5	16.2	14.2	20.1	15.2	13.3	20.3	11.0	9.6	8.3	2983	496
HOLLOMAN AFB	32.85N	106.10W	1248	-7.2	-5.3	37.3	17.3	35.9	17.2	34.4	17.2	20.4	30.2	19.9	29.6	18.0	15.0	22.1	17.3	14.4	22.1	10.2	8.5	7.3	1809	934
ROSWELL INDUSTRIAL AIR PARK	33.31N	104.54W	1118	-8.7	-6.2	37.7	18.5	36.4	18.4	35.1	18.3	21.5	30.6	20.9	30.2	19.3	16.1	23.4	18.6	15.4	23.2	11.2	9.2	8.1	1761	1038
WHITE SANDS	32.38N	106.48W	1244	-7.6	-5.3	37.2	17.6	35.8	17.7	34.6	17.7	21.0	30.8	20.5	30.1	18.8	15.9	22.3	18.1	15.2	22.4	8.4	7.2	5.9	1637	1006
																									19 sites, 8 more on CD-ROM	
New York																										
ALBANY COUNTY AP	42.75N	73.80W	89	-18.8	-16.2	31.7	22.8	30.1	21.9	28.5	21.2	24.3	29.3	23.4	27.9	22.8	17.7	26.9	22.0	16.8	25.9	10.7	9.1	8.3	3671	329
AMBROSE LIGHT	40.45N	73.80W	21	-10.2	-8.0	28.8	N/A	27.1	N/A	25.8	N/A	N/A	N/A	N/A	N/A	N/A	N/A	N/A	N/A	N/A	N/A	19.0	16.5	14.9	2745	382
BINGHAMTON EDWIN A LINK FIELD	42.21N	75.98W	499	-18.3	-15.8	29.7	21.1	28.1	20.2	26.7	19.5	22.6	27.2	21.7	25.9	21.2	16.8	24.8	20.3	16.0	23.8	9.6	8.6	7.9	3947	222
BUFFALO NIAGARA INTL AF	42.94N	78.74W	215	-16.3	-14.1	30.3	21.8	28.9	21.1	27.6	20.5	23.8	27.8	22.9	26.7	22.4	17.6	26.2	21.5	16.6	25.4	12.6	11.1	9.6	3632	310
ELMIRA CORNING REGIONAL AP	42.16N	76.89W	291	-18.8	-15.9	32.2	22.4	30.3	21.3	28.7	20.7	24.0	29.4	23.0	28.0	22.4	17.7	26.8	21.3	16.6	25.5	9.2	8.3	7.5	3765	264
GRIFFISS AFB	43.23N	75.40W	158	-21.1	-17.9	31.5	22.2	29.8	21.1	28.2	20.5	23.8	29.1	22.7	27.5	22.1	17.1	26.8	21.1	16.0	25.6	9.9	8.4	7.4	3934	256
ISLIP LONG ISL MACARTHUR AP	40.79N	73.10W	33	-11.9	-9.4	31.4	23.0	29.8	22.3	28.2	21.6	24.8	28.7	24.1	27.3	23.7	18.6	26.5	23.0	17.8	25.7	10.6	9.0	8.3	2948	442
JAMESTOWN (AWOS)	42.15N	79.27W	525	-17.2	-14.9	28.0	20.9	27.2	20.4	25.9	19.4	22.4	26.7	21.4	25.4	21.2	16.9	25.4	20.0	15.7	24.0	9.6	8.5	7.7	3987	161
NEW YORK J F KENNEDY INT'L AR	40.66N	73.80W	7	-10.7	-8.2	32.1	23.1	30.3	22.3	28.7	21.9	25.0	29.1	24.3	27.7	23.8	18.7	27.0	23.2	18.0	26.1	12.2	11.0	9.6	2682	543
NEW YORK LAGUARDIA ARPT	40.78N	73.88W	9	-10.8	-8.2	33.5	23.5	31.8	22.8	30.3	22.2	25.1	30.7	24.4	29.2	23.5	18.4	27.2	22.9	17.6	26.7	12.2	11.0	9.7	2557	672
NEWBURGH/STEWART	41.50N	74.10W	177	-15.8	-12.8	32.1	22.5	30.2	22.0	28.8	21.2	24.5	29.2	23.5	28.1	22.9	18.0	27.1	22.2	17.2	26.2	10.9	9.2	8.3	3297	381
NIAGARA FALLS AF	43.11N	78.95W	179	-16.4	-14.1	31.0	22.7	29.5	21.8	28.1	21.0	24.2	28.9	23.3	27.5	22.7	17.8	26.8	22.0	17.0	25.8	11.7	10.4	9.0	3661	327
PLATTSBURGH AFB	44.65N	73.47W	72	-23.1	-20.6	30.3	21.8	28.4	20.8	26.8	20.1	23.4	27.9	22.3	26.7	21.9	16.7	26.1	20.8	15.6	24.8	9.2	8.2	7.3	4346	200
POUGHKEEPSIE DUTCHESS CO AP	41.63N	73.88W	49	-17.5	-14.4	33.0	23.3	31.4	22.6	29.7	21.8	24.9	30.8	23.9	29.2	23.0	17.8	27.9	22.3	17.1	27.1	8.2	7.5	6.4	3451	377
REPUBLIC	40.72N	73.40W	26	-11.2	-8.0	32.3	23.4	30.8	22.9	28.7	21.9	25.0	29.5	24.2	28.0	23.8	18.7	26.8	22.9	17.7	25.7	11.1	10.3	8.7	2798	508
ROCHESTER GREATER ROCHESTER I	43.12N	77.68W	169	-16.6	-14.4	31.3	22.9	29.7	21.8	28.2	21.0	24.2	29.2	23.1	27.6	22.5	17.6	27.1	21.6	16.6	25.7	11.3	9.6	8.5	3655	305
SYRACUSE HANCOCK INT'L ARPT	43.11N	76.10W	127	-19.3	-16.2	31.6	22.8	30.0	21.8	28.5	21.0	24.1	29.3	23.1	27.9	22.5	17.4	26.9	21.5	16.4	25.8	10.8	9.1	8.2	3686	314
UTICA ONEIDA COUNTY AP	43.15N	75.38W	227	-20.6	-17.3	30.9	22.4	29.1	21.4	27.8	20.6	23.8	28.5	22.9	27.2	22.4	17.6	26.1	21.4	16.5	25.2	9.3	8.4	7.7	3917	266
WHITE PLAINS WESTCHESTER CO A	41.07N	73.71W	121	-13.5	-11.1	32.2	23.4	30.3	22.5	28.8	21.6	24.8	29.7	23.9	28.2	23.1	18.1	26.5	22.6	17.6	26.0	9.1	8.1	7.1	3091	419
																									15 sites, 8 more on CD-ROM	
North Carolina																										
ASHEVILLE REGIONAL ARPT	35.43N	82.54W	661	-10.2	-7.5	31.2	22.0	29.9	21.6	28.7	21.2	23.4	28.5	22.8	27.6	22.0	18.1	25.3	21.3	17.4	24.7	10.4	8.8	7.9	2304	461
CHARLOTTE DOUGLAS INTL ARPT	35.21N	80.94W	234	-6.4	-4.1	34.5	23.7	33.1	23.4	31.9	23.0	25.1	31.3	24.5	30.4	23.4	18.7	27.1	22.9	18.1	26.6	8.3	7.4	6.5	1712	927
FAYETTEVILLE RGNL G	34.98N	78.88W	59	-5.9	-3.5	35.3	24.8	33.9	24.2	32.7	23.9	26.3	32.2	25.7	31.3	24.9	20.1	28.2	24.1	19.2	27.6	8.9	7.8	6.9	1538	1066
FORT BRAGG/SIMMONS	35.13N	78.93W	93	-5.7	-3.3	35.9	24.6	34.4	24.3	33.0	23.9	26.2	32.4	25.6	31.6	24.7	19.9	28.6	24.0	19.1	28.1	8.0	6.7	5.7	1533	1115
GREENSBORO PIEDMONT TRIAD INT	36.10N	79.94W	270	-8.3	-5.7	33.4	23.7	32.2	23.3	31.0	22.8	25.0	30.9	24.3	29.8	23.2	18.6	27.3	22.7	18.0	26.7	8.6	7.7	6.9	2037	759
HICKORY REGIONAL AP	35.74N	81.39W	362	-7.3	-4.9	33.6	22.7	32.3	22.7	31.0	22.4	24.6	30.1	24.0	29.3	23.0	18.5	26.5	22.4	17.9	25.9	7.8	6.6	5.8	1943	752
JACKSONVILLE (AWOS)	34.83N	77.62W	29	-6.7	-4.1	34.1	24.8	32.9	24.3	32.2	23.9	26.1	32.5	25.4	31.2	24.1	19.1	29.0	23.8	18.7	28.6	8.9	7.9	7.0	1663	932
NEW RIVER MCAF	34.70N	77.43W	8	-5.0	-2.9	34.0	25.6	32.8	25.3	31.8	24.9	27.0	31.8	26.3	31.0	25.9	21.2	29.6	25.0	20.1	28.9	8.9	7.8	7.0	1389	1083
PITT GREENVILLE ARP	35.63N	77.40W	8	-6.2	-4.0	35.1	24.9	33.9	24.1	32.8	23.8	26.2	33.7	25.4	32.0	24.0	18.9	29.5	23.2	18.0	28.3	8.4	7.4	6.4	1596	1077
POPE AFB	35.17N	79.02W	66	-6.0	-3.8	36.1	24.6	34.6	24.3	33.1	23.9	26.4	31.9	25.7	31.2	25.1	20.4	28.2	24.2	19.2	27.7	8.2	7.2	6.0	1563	1120
RALEIGH DURHAM INTERNATIONAL	35.87N	78.79W	133	-7.4	-5.0	34.5	24.4	33.2	24.2	31.9	23.6	25.7	31.8	25.2	31.0	24.1	19.3	28.1	23.5	18.6	27.4	8.5	7.5	6.8	1846	877
RICHMOND INTERNATIONAL AP	37.51N	77.32W	50	-8.4	-6.2	34.9	24.5	33.5	24.1	32.1	23.5	25.9	31.9	25.3	31.0	24.4	19.5	28.5	23.8	18.7	27.7	9.3	8.3	7.5	2089	827
SEYMOUR-JOHNSON AFB	35.33N	77.97W	33	-5.7	-3.2	35.8	25.0	34.2	24.5	32.8	24.2	26.5	32.3	25.9	31.3	25.1	20.3	28.6	24.5	19.5	28.0	8.2	7.1	6.1	1509	1087
WILMINGTON INTERNATIONAL ARPT	34.27N	77.91W	12	-4.5	-2.4	34.0	25.8	32.8	25.3	31.6	24.8	26.9	31.7	26.3	30.8	25.6	20.9	29.1	25.1	20.2	28.5	9.2	8.3	7.5	1327	1104
WINSTON-SALEM REYNOLDS AP	36.13N	80.22W	296	-7.7	-5.1	33.6	23.6	32.4	23.3	31.2	22.8	24.9	30.4	24.3	29.6	23.3	18.7	27.3	22.6	18.0	26.8	8.3	7.6	6.4	1919	794

Meaning of acronyms:
DB: Dry bulb temperature, °C — *WB: Wet bulb temperature, °C* — *MCWB: Mean coincident wet bulb temperature, °C*
Lat: Latitude, ° — *DP: Dew point temperature, °C* — *MCDB: Mean coincident dry bulb temperature, °C*
Long: Longitude, ° — *HR: Humidity ratio, g of moisture per kg of dry air*
Elev: Elevation, m — *WS: Wind speed, m/s* — *HDD and CDD 18.3: Annual heating and cooling degree-days, base 18.3°C, °C-day*

Station	Lat	Long	Elev	Heating DB		Cooling DB/MCWB						Evaporation WB/MCDB				Dehumidification DP/HR/MCDB						Extreme Annual WS			Heat./Cool. Degree-Days	
						0.4%		1%		2%		0.4%		1%		0.4%			1%							
				99.6%	99%	DB	MCWB	DB	MCWB	DB	MCWB	WB	MCDB	WB	MCDB	DP	HR	MCDB	DP	HR	MCDB	1%	2.5%	5%	HDD	CDD 18.3
North Dakota																										*6 sites, 6 more on CD-ROM*
BISMARCK MUNICIPAL ARPT	46.77N	100.75W	506	-28.9	-25.5	34.4	20.8	32.4	20.3	30.4	19.7	23.5	29.9	22.2	29.2	21.5	17.2	27.4	20.0	15.6	25.7	12.2	10.9	9.3	4706	299
FARGO HECTOR INTERNATIONAL AP	46.93N	96.81W	274	-29.1	-26.2	32.8	22.3	30.9	21.3	29.3	20.5	24.1	29.7	23.0	28.7	22.4	17.7	27.7	21.1	16.3	26.7	12.7	11.4	10.3	4885	307
GRAND FORKS AFB	47.97N	97.40W	276	-29.1	-26.6	32.6	21.9	30.9	21.2	29.0	20.2	24.6	29.1	23.1	28.1	23.0	18.3	26.7	21.9	17.1	26.0	12.7	11.3	9.9	5093	265
GRAND FORKS INTERNATIONAL AP	47.95N	97.18W	254	-30.1	-27.3	32.2	21.7	30.3	20.8	28.7	20.0	23.9	29.3	22.6	28.1	22.1	17.3	27.3	20.8	15.9	26.1	12.0	10.8	9.3	5172	241
MINOT AFB	48.42N	101.35W	497	-30.1	-27.4	34.0	20.3	31.8	19.9	29.8	19.2	22.8	30.2	21.6	28.6	20.8	16.4	26.6	19.1	14.7	25.0	12.9	11.6	10.1	5054	241
MINOT FAA AP	48.26N	101.28W	522	-28.8	-26.1	33.0	20.5	31.1	20.1	29.1	19.0	23.1	29.1	21.8	27.8	21.3	17.0	26.6	19.8	15.5	25.3	12.3	11.0	9.6	4868	250
Ohio																										*13 sites, 2 more on CD-ROM*
AKRON AKRON-CANTON REG AP	40.92N	81.44W	377	-16.8	-13.8	31.5	22.7	29.9	22.1	28.5	21.2	24.1	29.2	23.3	27.9	22.6	18.1	26.8	21.8	17.3	25.7	10.4	8.9	8.1	3358	376
CINCINNATI MUNICIPAL AP LUNKI	39.10N	84.42W	152	-14.3	-10.9	33.8	23.8	32.3	23.5	31.0	22.9	25.5	31.1	24.8	30.1	23.9	19.2	28.1	23.2	18.3	27.3	9.1	8.2	7.4	2641	639
CLEVELAND HOPKINS INTL AP	41.41N	81.85W	245	-16.4	-13.1	31.9	23.3	30.4	22.5	29.0	21.7	24.6	29.8	23.7	28.4	22.9	18.2	27.5	22.2	17.4	26.4	11.0	9.4	8.5	3280	413
COLUMBUS PORT COLUMBUS INTL A	39.99N	82.88W	249	-16.0	-12.7	32.8	23.2	31.5	22.7	30.2	22.0	24.8	30.5	24.0	29.2	23.1	18.4	27.3	22.4	17.6	26.8	9.8	8.4	7.5	2957	539
DAYTON INTERNATIONAL AIRPORT	39.91N	84.22W	306	-17.4	-14.0	32.4	23.1	31.0	22.7	29.7	21.9	24.7	30.1	23.9	28.9	23.0	18.4	27.7	22.3	17.7	26.9	10.9	9.2	8.4	3083	513
FINDLAY AIRPORT	41.01N	83.67W	248	-18.0	-14.7	32.4	23.1	31.0	22.6	29.3	21.6	24.9	30.1	23.9	28.5	23.2	18.5	27.9	22.4	17.6	26.7	10.9	9.3	8.4	3330	432
LANCASTER\FAIRFIEL	39.75N	82.65W	264	-16.0	-12.3	32.5	23.3	31.3	23.1	29.8	22.2	24.9	30.3	24.1	28.9	22.9	18.3	27.2	22.5	17.8	26.7	9.0	8.0	7.2	3041	431
MANSFIELD LAHM MUNICIPAL ARPT	40.82N	82.52W	400	-17.7	-14.6	31.1	22.8	29.7	22.1	28.4	21.4	24.4	29.2	23.5	28.1	22.8	18.4	27.1	22.0	17.5	26.3	11.0	9.5	8.5	3417	366
OHIO STATE UNIVERSI	40.07N	83.07W	283	-14.0	-11.3	32.4	23.2	31.2	22.8	29.6	22.2	24.7	30.1	23.9	28.8	22.8	18.1	27.3	22.4	17.7	26.7	9.7	8.5	7.7	2968	499
RICKENBACKER ANGB	39.82N	82.93W	230	-15.4	-12.1	33.6	24.3	32.3	23.9	30.9	23.3	26.5	30.4	25.4	30.0	25.9	21.8	29.0	24.0	19.4	27.4	9.9	8.4	7.5	2873	571
TOLEDO EXPRESS AIRPORT	41.59N	83.80W	211	-18.0	-14.8	32.9	23.5	31.3	22.6	29.8	21.9	25.1	30.5	24.1	29.0	23.4	18.7	28.3	22.6	17.7	27.1	10.9	9.2	8.3	3420	429
WRIGHT-PATERSON AFB	39.83N	84.05W	250	-17.0	-13.0	33.0	23.6	31.8	23.1	30.2	22.3	25.3	30.6	24.4	29.5	23.8	19.2	28.1	22.8	18.1	27.1	9.6	8.4	7.5	2989	541
YOUNGSTOWN REGIONAL AIRPORT	41.25N	80.67W	362	-16.8	-13.9	31.4	22.6	29.9	21.7	28.5	20.9	23.9	29.3	23.0	27.8	22.3	17.8	26.4	21.5	16.9	25.4	9.8	8.5	7.8	3454	321
Oklahoma																										*9 sites, 6 more on CD-ROM*
FORT SILL	34.65N	98.40W	369	-10.8	-7.3	38.0	22.7	36.8	22.8	35.3	22.9	25.2	32.6	24.7	32.0	23.4	19.0	28.1	22.7	18.2	27.6	11.1	9.5	8.6	1816	1173
LAWTON MUNICIPAL	34.57N	98.42W	338	-7.8	-6.2	39.1	23.0	37.9	23.2	37.2	23.2	25.6	33.8	25.1	33.1	23.0	18.5	28.8	22.7	18.2	28.5	11.6	10.3	9.0	1757	1249
OKLAHOMA CITY WILL ROGERS WOR	35.39N	97.60W	398	-11.4	-8.1	37.5	23.4	36.0	23.4	34.5	23.2	25.4	32.7	24.9	32.2	23.4	19.1	28.7	22.8	18.4	28.0	12.1	11.0	9.9	1953	1070
OKLAHOMA CITY/WILEY	35.53N	97.65W	396	-11.0	-7.8	37.5	23.2	36.2	23.3	34.6	23.2	25.2	32.8	24.7	32.1	23.0	18.6	28.5	22.5	18.1	28.1	11.8	10.8	9.5	1941	1136
STILLWATER RGNL	36.15N	97.08W	308	-10.2	-7.7	38.8	23.9	37.3	24.0	35.9	24.0	26.1	34.1	25.5	33.4	23.9	19.5	29.8	23.0	18.4	28.8	11.0	9.6	8.7	1984	1101
TINKER AFB	35.42N	97.38W	384	-11.1	-7.8	37.4	23.1	35.9	23.3	34.2	23.3	25.7	32.7	25.1	32.1	23.8	19.5	29.3	22.9	18.5	28.3	11.4	10.1	9.0	1893	1095
TULSA INTERNATIONAL AIRPORT	36.20N	95.89W	206	-11.7	-8.4	37.5	24.3	36.0	24.4	34.6	24.2	26.2	33.5	25.6	32.9	24.2	19.6	29.6	23.6	18.8	29.2	10.9	9.4	8.6	1941	1144
TULSA/LLOYD JONES	36.03N	95.98W	193	-9.0	-7.3	37.8	24.7	37.1	24.9	35.2	24.8	26.4	34.6	25.8	33.7	24.1	19.4	29.7	23.8	19.1	29.5	8.8	8.0	7.2	1934	1113
VANCE AFB	36.33N	97.92W	408	-14.1	-10.5	38.1	23.0	37.0	23.0	35.3	23.1	25.2	33.2	24.6	32.7	23.0	18.7	28.4	22.4	18.0	28.1	11.9	10.7	9.2	2220	1057
Oregon																										*9 sites, 12 more on CD-ROM*
AURORA STATE	45.25N	122.77W	60	-2.5	-1.3	32.9	19.6	31.2	19.5	28.9	18.8	21.2	29.8	20.2	28.8	17.8	12.9	24.7	17.3	12.5	23.4	8.1	7.1	5.8	2407	214
CORVALLIS MUNI	44.48N	123.28W	77	-3.9	-2.4	33.8	19.3	32.1	18.7	29.8	17.9	20.2	31.9	19.3	30.5	15.9	11.4	25.5	14.1	10.1	23.7	8.8	7.9	7.1	2336	229
EUGENE MAHLON SWEET ARPT	44.13N	123.21W	114	-5.3	-3.2	33.0	19.2	30.9	18.6	28.9	18.0	20.4	30.6	19.5	29.2	16.7	12.0	23.6	15.7	11.3	22.3	8.8	7.8	7.1	2598	144
MC MINNVILLE MUNI	45.18N	123.13W	51	-2.4	-1.2	33.0	18.8	32.0	19.0	29.0	18.1	20.3	30.8	19.4	29.7	16.4	11.7	22.3	15.9	11.4	22.1	9.3	8.1	7.1	2533	167
MEDFORD ROGUE VALLEY INTL AP	42.39N	122.87W	405	-5.1	-3.5	37.2	19.5	35.2	18.8	33.3	18.2	20.5	34.4	19.7	33.0	15.8	11.8	23.6	14.8	11.0	23.3	8.2	6.9	5.6	2402	439
PORTLAND INTERNATIONAL AP	45.59N	122.60W	33	-4.5	-1.9	32.9	19.7	30.6	19.2	28.6	18.5	20.8	30.6	19.9	29.2	17.1	12.3	24.0	16.3	11.7	22.9	10.6	8.8	7.9	2346	235
PORTLAND/HILLSBORO	45.53N	122.95W	62	-5.7	-3.0	33.2	20.1	31.1	19.5	28.8	18.7	21.4	31.1	20.2	29.5	17.7	12.7	25.2	16.5	11.9	23.4	8.4	7.7	6.5	2639	156
REDMOND ROBERTS FIELD	44.25N	121.15W	940	-14.8	-11.1	33.8	16.6	32.2	16.1	30.3	15.4	17.7	31.4	16.8	29.9	12.7	10.2	19.6	11.7	9.6	19.4	9.2	8.3	7.5	3633	127
SALEM MCNARY FIELD	44.91N	123.00W	61	-5.6	-3.2	33.3	19.4	31.1	18.8	29.0	18.1	20.4	31.2	19.5	29.5	16.4	11.7	23.3	15.5	11.1	22.6	9.3	8.2	7.3	2542	162
Pennsylvania																										*14 sites, 5 more on CD-ROM*
ALLENTOWN LEHIGH VALLEY INTL	40.65N	75.45W	117	-13.9	-11.4	32.8	23.2	31.2	22.5	29.8	21.8	24.8	30.2	24.0	28.8	23.2	18.3	27.3	22.5	17.4	26.5	10.8	9.1	8.1	3091	460
ALTOONA BLAIR CO ARPT	40.30N	78.32W	448	-15.2	-12.5	31.4	22.2	29.8	21.5	28.3	20.9	23.7	28.8	22.9	27.8	22.2	17.9	26.5	21.3	16.9	25.4	9.8	8.4	7.7	3311	343
BUTLER CO. (AWOS)	40.78N	79.95W	380	-16.1	-12.9	31.1	22.4	29.1	21.5	27.8	20.6	23.6	28.6	22.8	27.6	22.3	17.8	26.6	21.3	16.7	25.2	8.0	6.8	5.8	3388	297
ERIE INTERNATIONAL AP	42.08N	80.18W	225	-14.9	-12.4	30.2	22.7	28.9	22.0	27.6	21.5	24.1	28.1	23.2	27.2	22.7	17.9	26.9	21.8	17.0	25.9	11.0	9.7	8.7	3384	357
HARRISBURG CAPITAL CITY ARPT	40.22N	76.85W	106	-13.0	-10.4	33.5	23.2	32.0	22.5	30.4	21.9	24.7	30.4	24.0	29.2	23.0	18.0	26.9	22.4	17.4	26.3	9.2	8.2	7.4	2904	550
MIDDLETOWN HARRISBURG INTL AP	40.19N	76.76W	95	-11.8	-9.5	33.7	23.8	32.1	23.3	30.6	22.6	25.6	30.9	24.7	29.6	24.0	19.1	28.3	23.1	18.0	27.2	11.3	10.2	8.5	2797	619
PHILADELPHIA INTERNATIONAL AF	39.87N	75.23W	9	-10.8	-8.4	34.0	24.1	32.6	23.6	31.1	22.8	25.7	31.4	25.0	30.2	24.1	19.1	28.1	23.5	18.3	27.4	10.9	9.2	8.3	2544	707
PHILADELPHIA NE PHILADELPHIA	40.08N	75.01W	36	-11.7	-9.1	33.9	24.3	32.4	23.7	31.1	23.0	26.0	31.6	25.0	30.4	24.2	19.2	28.5	23.3	18.2	27.4	9.4	8.4	7.7	2679	629
PITTSBURGH ALLEGHENY CO AP	40.36N	79.92W	388	-15.4	-12.3	32.2	22.5	30.8	21.7	29.2	21.0	24.0	29.4	23.2	28.4	22.4	17.9	26.6	21.6	17.1	25.8	9.1	8.2	7.6	2976	486
PITTSBURGH INTERNATIONAL AP	40.50N	80.23W	367	-15.7	-12.5	31.9	22.5	30.4	21.7	29.0	21.0	24.0	29.3	23.1	28.1	22.3	17.8	26.6	21.6	17.0	25.7	10.5	8.8	7.9	3124	417
READING SPAATZ FIELD	40.37N	75.96W	108	-12.6	-10.4	33.5	23.4	32.0	22.8	30.3	22.2	25.1	30.8	24.2	29.2	23.1	18.1	27.9	22.6	17.5	27.1	10.1	8.6	8.0	2884	526
WASHINGTON (AWOS)	40.13N	80.28W	361	-16.3	-12.9	31.3	21.7	29.7	21.0	28.2	20.4	23.1	28.3	22.3	27.8	21.3	16.7	26.1	20.9	16.2	25.4	8.7	7.7	6.6	3327	301
WILKES-BARRE SCRANTON INTL AP	41.34N	75.73W	293	-15.9	-13.2	31.6	22.3	30.0	21.4	28.5	20.6	23.9	28.9	23.0	27.5	22.3	17.6	26.3	21.5	16.8	25.3	9.1	8.1	7.4	3392	347
WILLOW GROVE NAS	40.20N	75.15W	110	-12.1	-9.8	33.7	23.9	32.2	23.2	30.8	22.6	25.4	31.4	24.6	30.1	23.6	18.7	28.4	22.8	17.8	27.6	8.2	7.1	6.1	2755	588

Meaning of acronyms:
DB: Dry bulb temperature, °C *WB: Wet bulb temperature, °C*
MCWB: Mean coincident wet bulb temperature, °C
Lat: Latitude, °
DP: Dew point temperature, °C
MCDB: Mean coincident dry bulb temperature, °C
Long: Longitude, °
HR: Humidity ratio, g of moisture per kg of dry air
HDD and CDD 18.3: Annual heating and cooling degree-days, base 18.3°C, °C-day
Elev: Elevation, m
WS: Wind speed, m/s

Station	Lat	Long	Elev	Heating DB		Cooling DB/MCWB						Evaporation WB/MCDB				Dehumidification DP/HR/MCDB						Extreme Annual WS			Heat./Cool. Degree-Days	
						0.4%		1%		2%		0.4%		1%		0.4%			1%							
				99.6%	99%	DB / MCWB		DB / MCWB		DB / MCWB		WB / MCDB		WB / MCDB		DP / HR / MCDB			DP / HR / MCDB			1%	2.5%	5%	HDD / CDD 18.3	
Rhode Island																									*2 sites, 1 more on CD-ROM*	
PAWTUCKET (AWOS)	41.92N	71.50W	134	-16.0	-12.8	31.2	22.5	28.9	21.5	27.5	20.6	24.0	28.9	23.0	27.3	22.5	17.4	26.9	21.7	16.6	25.9	8.7	7.7	6.7	3482	271
PROVIDENCE T F GREEN STATE AR	41.72N	71.43W	19	-13.8	-11.2	32.3	23.0	30.4	22.1	28.8	21.3	24.7	29.6	23.8	27.8	23.3	18.1	26.8	22.6	17.3	25.9	10.9	9.2	8.4	3106	405
South Carolina																									*6 sites, 3 more on CD-ROM*	
CHARLESTON INTL ARPT	32.90N	80.04W	15	-2.8	-0.9	34.6	25.7	33.4	25.3	32.3	25.0	27.0	31.7	26.5	31.1	25.8	21.2	29.0	25.3	20.4	28.5	9.1	8.1	7.4	1049	1293
COLUMBIA METRO ARPT	33.94N	81.12W	69	-5.5	-3.4	36.1	24.1	34.7	23.9	33.5	23.7	25.8	32.2	25.3	31.5	24.2	19.3	27.8	23.7	18.7	27.3	8.5	7.6	6.8	1405	1171
FLORENCE REGIONAL AP	34.19N	79.73W	46	-4.8	-2.8	35.5	24.9	34.1	24.6	32.9	24.2	26.4	32.4	25.8	31.5	24.9	20.1	28.8	24.2	19.2	27.9	8.5	7.9	7.0	1351	1146
FOLLY ISLAND	32.68N	79.88W	5	-0.2	1.6	30.9	N/A	30.1	N/A	29.5	N/A	N/A	N/A	N/A	N/A	N/A	N/A	N/A	N/A	N/A	N/A	15.2	11.9	10.4	1057	1174
GREER GREENV'L-SPARTANBRG AP	34.90N	82.22W	296	-6.4	-4.0	34.4	23.4	33.0	23.3	31.7	22.9	25.0	31.2	24.4	30.2	23.3	18.8	26.9	22.8	18.2	26.4	8.7	7.8	7.1	1735	867
SHAW AFB/SUMTER	33.97N	80.47W	74	-4.4	-2.5	35.2	24.1	33.8	23.9	32.5	23.7	25.8	31.7	25.3	30.9	24.3	19.4	27.8	23.9	18.9	27.4	8.4	7.5	6.6	1374	1090
South Dakota																									*3 sites, 11 more on CD-ROM*	
ELLSWORTH AFB	44.15N	103.10W	980	-22.9	-19.8	35.8	18.9	33.5	18.6	31.5	18.2	21.6	30.0	20.6	29.2	19.0	15.5	25.5	17.8	14.4	24.2	15.3	12.8	11.2	3888	387
RAPID CITY REGIONAL ARPT	44.05N	103.05W	966	-23.6	-20.3	36.1	18.8	33.8	18.7	31.8	18.3	21.7	29.9	20.7	29.4	19.2	15.7	25.7	18.0	14.6	24.5	15.5	13.4	11.6	3904	377
SIOUX FALLS FOSS FIELD	43.58N	96.75W	435	-25.4	-22.4	33.8	23.3	31.9	23.0	30.2	22.0	25.2	30.9	24.2	29.9	23.6	19.4	28.7	22.4	18.1	27.7	12.3	11.0	9.5	4180	418
Tennessee																									*7 sites, 2 more on CD-ROM*	
BRISTOL TRI CITY AIRPORT	36.48N	82.40W	465	-11.5	-8.4	32.1	22.3	30.8	22.0	29.7	21.7	23.9	29.4	23.3	28.6	22.3	18.0	26.1	21.7	17.4	25.5	8.4	7.4	6.2	2352	553
CHATTANOOGA LOVELL FIELD AF	35.03N	85.20W	210	-7.9	-5.4	34.7	23.9	33.4	23.7	32.2	23.3	25.4	31.6	24.9	30.8	23.8	19.2	27.4	23.2	18.5	27.0	8.0	7.1	6.1	1776	933
JACKSON MCKELLAR-SIPES REGL A	35.59N	88.92W	129	-10.3	-7.4	34.8	25.0	33.7	24.8	32.6	24.4	26.5	32.5	25.8	31.6	24.8	20.2	29.6	24.1	19.3	28.9	8.7	8.0	7.2	1911	960
KNOXVILLE MCGHEE TYSON AP	35.82N	83.99W	299	-9.4	-6.6	33.7	23.5	32.3	23.3	31.2	22.9	25.1	30.9	24.5	30.0	23.3	18.8	27.6	22.8	18.2	26.9	9.0	7.8	6.8	2008	806
MEMPHIS INTERNATIONAL AP	35.06N	89.99W	101	-8.3	-5.7	35.6	25.2	34.4	24.9	33.4	24.7	26.8	32.8	26.2	32.2	25.1	20.5	29.9	24.6	19.8	29.4	9.1	8.2	7.4	1631	1230
MILLINGTON MUNI ARP	35.35N	89.87W	98	-10.0	-6.9	36.3	25.4	35.0	24.7	33.8	24.4	26.9	33.6	26.1	32.7	25.1	20.4	30.6	24.1	19.2	29.5	8.3	7.3	6.3	1769	1137
NASHVILLE INTERNATIONAL AF	36.12N	86.69W	184	-10.6	-7.6	34.7	23.9	33.4	23.8	32.2	23.4	25.6	31.5	25.1	31.0	24.0	19.4	28.2	23.4	18.6	27.6	8.9	7.9	7.2	1968	935
Texas																									*51 sites, 18 more on CD-ROM*	
ABILENE DYESS AFB	32.43N	99.85W	545	-8.8	-5.4	38.6	22.3	37.4	22.3	36.1	22.2	25.0	32.7	24.3	32.2	23.0	19.0	27.4	22.4	18.2	27.1	10.7	9.2	8.3	1444	1422
ABILENE REGIONAL AP	32.41N	99.68W	546	-7.8	-4.8	37.4	21.5	36.2	21.5	35.1	21.5	24.1	31.7	23.6	31.2	22.1	18.0	26.7	21.6	17.3	26.3	11.6	10.6	9.2	1409	1334
AMARILLO INTERNATIONAL AF	35.22N	101.71W	1099	-13.8	-10.2	36.3	19.0	34.9	19.0	33.5	19.0	21.7	30.0	21.1	29.6	19.5	16.3	24.0	18.8	15.6	23.6	12.9	11.7	10.7	2332	761
AUSTIN/BERGSTROM	30.18N	97.68W	151	-3.8	-1.3	37.6	23.9	36.6	24.0	35.5	24.1	26.2	32.1	25.7	31.7	24.9	20.3	27.6	24.4	19.7	27.3	9.4	8.4	7.6	919	1661
BROWNSVILLE S PADRE ISL INTL	25.91N	97.43W	7	2.4	4.9	35.3	25.4	34.7	25.4	34.0	25.4	27.0	31.0	26.8	30.9	26.2	21.7	28.3	25.8	21.1	28.2	11.7	10.6	9.3	314	2217
CAMP MABRY	30.32N	97.77W	201	-3.0	-0.4	37.4	23.6	36.4	23.6	35.3	23.7	25.8	31.6	25.5	31.2	24.6	20.1	27.2	24.1	19.5	26.9	9.0	8.1	7.3	858	1697
COLLEGE STATION EASTERWOOD FL	30.59N	96.36W	100	-3.3	-0.9	37.3	24.5	36.2	24.4	35.0	24.4	26.6	32.7	26.0	31.8	25.2	20.5	28.5	24.7	20.0	28.0	8.9	8.1	7.4	904	1653
CORPUS CHRISTI INTL ARPT	27.77N	97.51W	13	0.4	2.8	35.5	25.4	34.6	25.4	33.9	25.4	27.2	31.9	26.8	31.4	26.1	21.5	28.6	25.7	21.0	28.3	12.0	11.1	10.1	495	1941
CORPUS CHRISTI NAS	27.70N	97.28W	6	2.0	4.4	34.0	26.2	33.4	26.2	32.8	26.1	28.0	31.4	27.5	31.1	27.3	23.1	29.4	26.4	21.9	29.2	11.1	9.9	8.9	409	2110
DALLAS HENSLEY FIELD NAS	32.73N	96.97W	151	-7.5	-3.6	37.6	24.0	36.5	23.9	35.3	23.8	25.9	33.3	25.3	33.0	23.9	19.1	29.6	23.2	18.3	28.8	9.3	8.4	7.7	1251	1518
DALLAS LOVE FIELD	32.85N	96.85W	149	-5.8	-2.6	38.0	24.2	37.1	24.2	35.9	24.1	26.4	33.7	25.7	33.0	24.5	19.9	29.6	23.9	19.1	28.9	9.8	8.8	8.1	1169	1624
DALLAS/REDBIRD ARPT	32.68N	96.87W	201	-3.0	-2.1	37.9	23.8	37.2	23.8	36.1	23.7	25.8	33.3	25.3	32.7	23.9	19.3	28.0	23.0	18.2	27.4	10.1	8.7	7.9	1172	1524
DALLAS-FORT WORTH INTL AF	32.90N	97.04W	182	-6.5	-3.4	38.0	23.6	36.9	23.7	35.7	23.8	25.9	33.0	25.4	32.6	24.1	19.4	28.7	23.5	18.8	28.2	11.6	10.6	9.2	1264	1511
DEL RIO INTERNATIONAL AP	29.37N	100.92W	313	-0.7	1.2	38.6	22.4	37.4	22.4	36.4	22.3	25.3	31.9	24.8	31.5	23.7	19.2	27.5	23.0	18.4	27.3	9.2	8.2	7.4	708	1917
DRAUGHON MILLER CEN	31.15N	97.40W	213	-4.0	-2.1	37.5	23.4	36.4	23.4	35.3	23.5	25.5	32.6	25.1	32.1	23.8	19.2	27.4	23.1	18.3	27.0	11.1	9.9	8.8	1086	1516
EL PASO INTERNATIONAL AP	31.81N	106.38W	1194	-5.2	-3.1	38.1	18.1	36.8	18.0	35.5	17.9	21.3	30.1	20.7	29.6	19.4	16.4	22.8	18.7	15.6	22.8	11.4	9.3	8.1	1370	1286
FORT HOOD/GRAY AAF	31.07N	97.83W	312	-4.6	-2.1	37.7	23.0	36.7	23.0	35.5	23.1	25.4	32.2	24.9	31.7	23.9	19.5	27.2	23.1	18.6	26.7	9.8	8.7	8.0	1039	1565
FORT WORTH ALLIANCE	32.98N	97.32W	226	-5.8	-3.0	38.7	23.6	37.5	23.7	36.2	23.6	25.8	33.6	25.3	33.0	23.9	19.2	28.7	23.0	18.3	27.8	10.7	9.4	8.6	1320	1457
FORT WORTH MEACHAM	32.82N	97.36W	215	-6.7	-3.7	38.3	23.7	37.2	23.8	36.0	23.7	25.8	33.2	25.4	32.9	24.0	19.4	28.9	23.4	18.6	28.2	9.7	8.8	8.2	1256	1533
FORT WORTH NAS	32.77N	97.44W	198	-7.4	-3.6	37.9	23.9	36.9	24.0	35.7	24.0	26.3	33.5	25.7	33.0	24.4	19.8	29.2	23.8	19.1	28.8	10.5	9.1	8.3	1255	1512
GALVESTON/SCHOLES	29.27N	94.86W	3	0.6	2.9	33.0	26.0	32.5	25.9	32.2	25.9	27.5	30.4	27.2	30.3	27.1	22.8	28.9	26.3	21.7	29.1	11.4	10.0	8.9	608	1779
GEORGETOWN (AWOS)	30.68N	97.68W	240	-3.0	-2.0	37.3	22.7	36.1	22.7	34.8	22.7	24.9	31.3	24.5	30.9	23.0	18.3	26.5	22.8	18.0	26.5	9.4	8.5	7.7	1077	1502
HARLINGEN RIO GRANDE VALLEY I	26.23N	97.65W	11	2.5	4.9	37.1	25.4	36.2	25.4	35.5	25.4	27.4	32.8	26.9	32.1	26.3	21.8	28.7	26.0	21.4	28.6	12.4	11.1	10.4	311	2277
HOUSTON BUSH INTERCONTINENTAL	29.99N	95.36W	32	-1.6	0.5	36.0	24.8	35.0	24.8	34.0	24.8	26.7	31.7	26.3	31.2	25.5	20.8	28.3	25.1	20.3	28.0	8.6	7.8	7.2	786	1667
HOUSTON WILLIAM P HOBBY AP	29.65N	95.28W	14	-0.4	2.1	35.0	25.3	34.1	25.3	33.3	25.1	26.9	31.7	26.7	31.3	26.0	21.3	28.6	25.5	20.7	28.3	9.4	8.5	7.8	669	1724
HOUSTON/D.W. HOOKS	30.07N	95.55W	46	-1.0	1.1	37.0	24.4	35.2	24.8	33.9	24.8	26.8	31.2	26.4	30.9	26.2	21.7	28.1	25.2	20.5	28.0	7.9	7.1	6.1	775	1649
HOUSTON/ELLINGTON	29.60N	95.17W	12	0.0	2.3	35.6	25.7	34.7	25.8	33.8	25.7	27.8	31.5	27.3	31.1	27.2	23.0	29.0	26.3	21.8	28.6	8.9	8.0	7.3	676	1753
KELLY AFB	29.38N	98.58W	208	-2.0	0.4	37.9	23.6	37.0	23.5	35.9	23.5	26.4	30.4	25.8	30.4	25.6	21.4	27.4	24.9	20.5	27.2	8.9	8.0	7.1	767	1825
KILLEEN MUNI (AWOS)	31.08N	97.68W	258	-3.4	-1.3	37.5	23.4	36.4	23.4	35.2	23.6	25.5	33.2	25.1	32.6	23.4	18.7	28.2	22.9	18.2	27.9	9.8	8.8	8.1	1039	1571
LAREDO INTL AIRPORT	27.55N	99.47W	155	1.0	3.2	39.2	23.3	38.3	23.3	37.5	23.3	26.1	33.2	25.6	32.6	24.4	19.7	28.0	24.0	19.2	27.8	11.0	9.9	9.0	478	2354
LAUGHLIN AFB	29.37N	100.78W	327	-1.5	0.9	40.1	22.3	38.7	22.7	37.4	22.6	25.8	32.8	25.1	32.5	24.1	19.7	28.4	23.2	18.7	28.0	9.9	8.6	7.8	701	1957
LONGVIEW GREGG COUNTY AP	32.39N	94.71W	114	-5.8	-2.8	37.3	24.0	35.8	24.2	34.1	24.0	26.1	32.3	25.7	31.8	24.5	19.8	28.1	24.1	19.2	27.8	8.7	7.8	7.0	1171	1387
LUBBOCK INTERNATIONAL AP	33.67N	101.82W	988	-10.4	-7.3	37.1	19.5	35.7	19.7	34.4	19.7	22.8	30.8	22.2	30.2	20.7	17.4	25.0	20.1	16.7	24.5	12.9	11.6	10.5	1857	1016

Meaning of acronyms:

DB: Dry bulb temperature, °C — WB: Wet bulb temperature, °C — DP: Dew point temperature, °C — HR: Humidity ratio, g of moisture per kg of dry air — WS: Wind speed, m/s

MCWB: Mean coincident wet bulb temperature, °C — MCDB: Mean coincident dry bulb temperature, °C — HDD and CDD 18.3: Annual heating and cooling degree-days, base 18.3°C, °C-day

Station	Lat	Long	Elev	Heating DB 99.6%	Heating DB 99%	Cooling 0.4% DB	Cooling 0.4% MCWB	Cooling 1% DB	Cooling 1% MCWB	Cooling 2% DB	Cooling 2% MCWB	Evap 0.4% WB	Evap 0.4% MCDB	Evap 1% WB	Evap 1% MCDB	Dehum 0.4% DP	Dehum 0.4% HR	Dehum 0.4% MCDB	Dehum 1% DP	Dehum 1% HR	Dehum 1% MCDB	Extreme Annual WS 1%	WS 2.5%	WS 5%	HDD 18.3	CDD 18.3
MC GREGOR (AWOS)	31.48N	97.32W	180	-3.8	-2.2	37.7	23.8	37.1	23.8	36.0	23.7	26.0	33.2	25.6	32.9	24.1	19.4	28.4	23.7	19.0	28.2	10.1	9.0	8.2	1153	1494
MCALLEN MILLER INTL AP	26.18N	98.24W	34	2.5	4.9	37.8	24.7	37.1	24.8	36.2	24.7	26.9	32.7	26.5	32.0	25.9	21.3	28.1	25.3	20.5	27.9	11.1	10.0	9.1	320	2460
MCKINNEY MUNI ARPT	33.18N	96.58W	176	-5.9	-3.0	38.0	23.8	37.3	24.0	36.2	23.9	25.8	33.5	25.5	33.1	23.9	19.2	28.6	23.0	18.2	27.6	10.1	8.7	7.8	1337	1409
MIDLAND INTERNATIONAL AP	31.93N	102.21W	872	-7.6	-4.9	37.9	19.6	36.7	19.7	35.5	19.8	22.9	30.6	22.3	30.3	21.1	17.5	24.7	20.3	16.6	24.5	11.9	10.8	9.3	1475	1256
NACOGDOCHES (AWOS)	31.58N	94.72W	108	-3.7	-2.3	36.4	24.3	35.0	24.4	33.8	24.2	26.0	32.0	25.6	31.7	24.1	19.3	27.5	24.0	19.1	27.5	8.1	7.2	6.1	1177	1319
PORT ARANSAS	27.82N	97.05W	6	2.5	5.0	30.0	25.6	29.6	25.6	29.3	25.5	26.9	28.9	26.7	28.9	26.3	21.8	28.5	25.9	21.3	28.4	17.6	14.8	12.1	462	1679
PORT ARTHUR JEFFERSON COUNTY	29.95N	94.02W	5	-0.8	1.2	34.6	25.6	33.7	25.7	32.9	25.7	27.6	31.6	27.1	31.1	26.5	22.0	29.5	26.1	21.5	29.1	9.5	8.5	7.8	754	1596
RANDOLPH AFB	29.53N	98.28W	232	-2.5	-0.3	37.5	23.2	36.3	23.3	35.2	23.4	25.7	31.8	25.3	31.2	24.2	19.7	27.1	23.9	19.3	27.0	9.2	8.3	7.4	863	1652
REESE AFB	33.60N	102.05W	1014	-11.0	-7.8	37.8	19.6	36.1	19.5	34.5	19.5	22.7	30.6	21.9	30.3	20.6	17.3	25.8	19.7	16.3	25.2	12.1	10.6	9.1	1847	963
SABINE	29.67N	94.05W	6	0.1	2.2	31.3	24.9	30.6	25.1	30.1	25.2	27.3	29.6	26.8	29.3	26.6	22.2	28.8	26.0	21.4	28.7	16.0	13.1	10.8	799	1426
SAN ANGELO MATHIS FIELD	31.35N	100.49W	577	-6.6	-3.9	37.9	21.1	36.7	21.1	35.6	21.2	23.9	31.4	23.4	31.0	22.0	17.9	26.2	21.4	17.3	25.9	11.1	9.6	8.7	1276	1379
SAN ANTONIO INTL AP	29.53N	98.46W	247	-2.6	-0.2	37.0	23.1	36.1	23.1	35.1	23.2	25.6	31.1	25.2	30.6	24.4	19.9	26.7	24.0	19.4	26.6	9.0	8.1	7.4	822	1731
SAN ANTONIO/STINSON	29.34N	98.47W	176	-0.8	1.2	37.8	23.6	37.1	23.5	36.0	23.4	26.3	32.0	25.8	31.4	25.0	20.6	28.0	24.1	19.5	27.2	8.4	7.6	7.1	704	1821
SAN MARCOS MUNI	29.88N	97.87W	182	-2.3	-0.6	37.3	23.5	36.2	23.5	35.1	23.4	25.6	32.7	25.2	32.2	23.8	19.1	28.3	23.0	18.2	27.7	10.8	9.3	8.5	896	1636
VICTORIA REGIONAL AP	28.86N	96.93W	36	-1.2	1.1	35.9	24.6	34.9	24.8	34.1	24.8	26.8	31.1	26.4	30.7	25.8	21.1	27.9	25.3	20.6	27.7	10.9	9.3	8.5	668	1768
WACO REGIONAL AP	31.61N	97.23W	155	-5.1	-2.5	38.2	23.9	37.2	24.0	36.1	24.1	26.0	33.1	25.6	32.8	24.3	19.6	28.0	23.9	19.1	27.7	11.0	9.8	8.8	1141	1583
WICHITA FALLS MUNICIPAL ARPT	33.98N	98.49W	314	-9.3	-6.0	39.2	22.9	37.8	23.0	36.5	23.0	25.4	33.3	24.8	32.8	23.3	18.8	28.2	22.7	18.1	27.6	12.0	10.9	9.5	1609	1345
Utah																										*5 sites, 5 more on CD-ROM*
HILL AFB/OGDEN	41.12N	111.97W	1459	-13.0	-11.0	34.1	16.2	32.7	15.9	31.3	15.5	18.4	29.1	17.6	28.4	15.0	12.8	22.4	13.5	11.5	22.7	10.2	8.8	8.0	3363	508
LOGAN-CACHE AIRPORT	41.79N	111.85W	1358	-21.3	-17.7	35.0	17.2	33.0	16.4	32.2	16.1	18.5	30.6	17.8	29.8	15.2	12.8	20.8	13.6	11.5	21.5	8.8	7.4	5.9	3989	267
PROVO MUNI (AWOS)	40.22N	111.72W	1369	-12.8	-10.8	34.8	16.9	32.9	16.8	32.0	16.5	19.1	30.6	18.3	29.6	15.2	12.8	23.9	14.0	11.8	23.8	10.8	9.0	7.8	3307	426
SAINT GEORGE (AWOS)	37.08N	113.60W	896	-2.9	-2.0	41.2	18.9	39.7	18.2	38.0	17.8	20.4	34.1	19.8	34.1	17.1	13.7	24.5	15.2	12.0	25.7	11.9	10.3	8.7	1635	1506
SALT LAKE CITY INT'L ARPT	40.79N	111.97W	1288	-12.6	-9.9	36.3	17.5	34.9	17.0	33.5	16.6	19.5	30.5	18.7	30.1	16.4	13.6	22.9	15.0	12.5	23.2	11.2	9.3	8.3	3067	663
Vermont																										*1 site, 4 more on CD-ROM*
BURLINGTON INTERNATIONAL AP	44.47N	73.15W	104	-22.4	-19.7	31.3	21.7	29.6	20.9	28.0	20.1	23.4	28.8	22.4	27.3	21.7	16.6	25.9	20.8	15.6	25.1	10.6	9.1	8.3	4114	276
Virginia																										*17 sites, 13 more on CD-ROM*
DANVILLE FAA AP	36.57N	79.34W	180	-7.5	-5.5	34.0	23.7	32.8	23.5	32.0	23.2	25.5	31.5	24.8	30.5	23.8	19.1	28.3	23.0	18.1	27.2	8.3	7.3	6.4	1993	791
DINWIDDIE CO	37.18N	77.50W	60	-8.9	-7.1	36.3	25.5	34.8	24.9	33.1	24.1	27.2	33.3	26.3	32.9	25.9	21.4	30.7	24.1	19.2	29.0	8.1	7.0	5.8	2083	866
FORT BELVOIR/DAVISO	38.72N	77.18W	27	-10.8	-7.8	35.6	24.6	34.0	24.0	32.5	23.5	26.4	32.7	25.5	31.5	24.6	19.6	29.7	23.8	18.7	28.8	9.2	7.7	6.1	2396	752
LANGLEY AFB/HAMPTON	37.08N	76.37W	3	-6.4	-4.0	33.9	25.1	32.5	24.7	31.3	24.2	26.7	31.2	26.0	30.4	25.8	21.2	28.6	24.9	19.9	28.3	10.5	8.9	8.0	1896	875
LEESBURG/GODFREY	39.08N	77.57W	119	-9.9	-7.8	34.9	24.9	33.2	24.2	32.3	23.7	26.3	32.8	25.5	31.5	24.2	19.3	28.6	23.8	19.0	28.2	10.0	8.4	7.2	2501	704
LYNCHBURG REGIONAL ARPT	37.34N	79.21W	286	-9.8	-7.3	33.4	23.3	32.1	22.9	30.7	22.4	24.7	30.6	24.1	29.7	23.0	18.4	27.0	22.4	17.8	26.4	8.2	7.3	6.4	2328	624
MANASSAS MUNI(AWOS)	38.72N	77.52W	59	-11.2	-8.7	33.8	23.4	32.5	23.1	31.2	22.5	25.0	31.2	24.2	30.1	23.0	17.8	27.7	22.5	17.3	27.3	9.6	8.3	7.2	2672	574
NEWPORT NEWS	37.13N	76.49W	16	-7.4	-5.1	34.7	25.2	33.1	24.8	32.1	24.3	26.5	32.5	25.8	31.3	25.0	20.1	29.0	24.2	19.1	28.2	8.9	8.2	7.5	1977	862
NORFOLK INTERNATIONAL AP	36.90N	76.19W	9	-5.7	-3.6	34.3	24.8	32.9	24.4	31.6	23.9	26.1	31.4	25.5	30.6	24.7	19.8	28.2	24.2	19.1	27.5	11.2	9.7	8.7	1802	921
NORFOLK NAS	36.93N	76.28W	5	-5.1	-2.9	34.3	25.3	32.9	24.8	31.9	24.4	26.6	31.8	25.9	30.9	25.2	20.3	28.9	24.5	19.5	28.3	11.3	9.8	8.6	1728	977
OCEANA NAS	36.82N	76.03W	7	-6.0	-3.7	33.8	25.2	32.5	24.6	31.2	24.1	26.3	31.5	25.6	30.5	24.9	20.0	28.8	24.1	19.0	28.0	10.7	9.1	8.2	1834	863
QUANTICO MCAS	38.50N	77.30W	4	-8.8	-6.8	33.7	24.7	32.4	24.4	31.2	23.7	26.4	31.8	25.5	30.8	24.9	19.9	29.5	23.9	18.8	28.4	8.6	7.5	6.5	2299	761
ROANOKE REGIONAL AP	37.32N	79.97W	358	-9.9	-7.2	33.4	22.7	32.1	22.4	30.8	22.0	24.1	30.4	23.6	29.6	22.4	17.9	26.5	21.8	17.2	25.8	10.1	8.5	7.5	2277	658
STAUNTON/SHENANDOAH	38.27N	78.90W	366	-11.0	-8.5	34.0	23.4	32.8	23.3	32.0	23.0	25.8	30.8	25.1	30.1	24.1	19.9	28.2	23.7	19.4	27.8	7.9	6.8	5.7	2438	649
VIRGINIA TECH ARPT	37.22N	80.42W	650	-12.1	-9.0	31.3	21.8	30.0	21.5	28.7	20.9	23.5	28.9	22.7	27.9	22.0	18.1	26.9	21.2	17.2	25.8	9.2	8.2	7.2	2689	409
WASHINGTON DC DULLES INT'L AR	38.94N	77.45W	99	-11.8	-9.0	34.1	23.9	32.7	23.5	31.2	22.8	25.4	31.6	24.7	30.3	23.6	18.6	27.8	23.0	18.0	27.1	9.2	8.2	7.3	2631	622
WASHINGTON DC REAGAN AP	38.87N	77.03W	20	-8.7	-6.5	34.6	24.5	33.2	24.0	31.8	23.3	25.9	31.7	25.3	30.7	24.4	19.4	28.5	23.8	18.7	27.9	10.4	8.9	8.1	2223	847
Washington																										*20 sites, 13 more on CD-ROM*
ARLINGTON MUNI	48.17N	122.17W	42	-6.2	-4.1	27.9	18.8	26.3	17.9	24.1	17.2	19.6	26.9	18.6	25.2	16.8	12.0	22.6	16.0	11.4	21.7	9.3	8.1	6.9	2958	33
BELLINGHAM INTL AP	48.79N	122.54W	46	-7.8	-5.0	26.3	18.4	24.5	17.6	22.8	16.7	19.2	25.3	18.2	23.6	16.5	11.8	21.8	15.8	11.3	20.7	11.2	9.2	8.3	2983	28
BREMERTON NATIONAL	47.48N	122.75W	137	-4.6	-2.8	29.8	18.3	27.6	17.5	26.0	16.8	19.1	28.3	18.1	26.6	15.1	10.9	22.0	14.1	10.2	20.3	8.3	7.4	6.4	3057	56
FAIRCHILD AFB	47.62N	117.65W	743	-15.2	-11.9	33.0	16.8	31.4	16.4	29.6	15.8	18.3	29.6	17.4	28.4	14.7	11.4	20.1	13.4	10.5	19.7	10.6	8.9	7.8	3757	220
FELTS FLD	47.68N	117.32W	610	-13.9	-10.6	34.8	18.6	32.8	17.9	31.2	17.3	19.9	32.1	18.9	30.5	16.1	12.3	22.0	14.8	11.3	21.9	8.8	7.8	6.7	3401	248
GRAY AAF	47.08N	122.58W	92	-7.1	-4.2	30.2	18.2	28.0	17.5	26.2	16.8	19.1	28.1	18.2	26.4	16.1	11.5	20.4	15.1	10.8	20.1	7.8	6.6	5.7	2884	69
KELSO WB AP	46.12N	122.89W	6	-5.8	-3.1	31.1	19.7	28.0	18.8	26.4	17.8	20.4	29.2	19.3	27.4	17.1	12.2	24.3	16.1	11.5	22.8	7.9	6.8	5.8	2642	103
MC CHORD AFB/TACOMA	47.13N	122.48W	88	-6.3	-4.0	30.1	18.2	27.9	17.5	26.1	16.8	19.1	28.1	18.2	26.5	15.7	11.3	21.1	14.9	10.7	20.3	8.8	7.7	6.6	2838	69
OLYMPIA AIRPORT	46.97N	122.90W	61	-6.6	-4.4	30.7	18.9	28.5	18.2	26.6	17.5	19.9	29.3	18.8	27.3	16.3	11.7	22.0	15.5	11.1	21.0	8.4	7.5	6.6	2984	56
PASCO	46.27N	119.12W	123	-14.0	-9.7	37.5	21.1	35.8	20.3	33.6	19.5	22.3	34.7	21.2	33.4	17.9	13.1	26.5	17.1	12.4	25.6	11.0	9.3	8.2	2728	455
PEARSON FLD	45.62N	122.65W	8	-3.7	-2.3	32.6	19.0	30.9	19.0	28.0	18.2	20.7	29.8	19.8	28.9	17.3	12.4	23.8	16.3	11.6	22.7	7.5	6.4	5.5	2446	205
SEATTLE BOEING FIELD	47.53N	122.30W	9	-4.5	-2.2	30.0	18.7	27.9	17.7	26.3	17.1	19.4	28.6	18.5	26.6	16.1	11.4	20.8	15.2	10.8	20.6	8.4	7.6	6.6	2378	155
SEATTLE SEATTLE-TACOMA INTL A	47.46N	122.31W	132	-4.2	-1.6	29.4	18.3	27.4	17.5	25.5	17.0	19.2	27.9	18.2	26.0	15.9	11.4	20.8	15.1	10.9	19.9	9.0	8.1	7.3	2627	98

Meaning of acronyms:
DB: Dry bulb temperature, °C — *WB: Wet bulb temperature, °C*
MCWB: Mean coincident wet bulb temperature, °C
Lat: Latitude, ° — *DP: Dew point temperature, °C* — *MCDB: Mean coincident dry bulb temperature, °C*
Long: Longitude, ° — *HR: Humidity ratio, g of moisture per kg of dry air*
Elev: Elevation, m — *WS: Wind speed, m/s*
HDD and CDD 18.3: Annual heating and cooling degree-days, base 18.3°C, °C-day

Station	Lat	Long	Elev	Heating DB		Cooling DB/MCWB						Evaporation WB/MCDB				Dehumidification DP/HR/MCDB						Extreme Annual WS			Heat./Cool. Degree-Days	
						0.4%		1%		2%		0.4%		1%		0.4%			1%							
				99.6%	99%	DB	MCWB	DB	MCWB	DB	MCWB	WB	MCDB	WB	MCDB	DP	HR	MCDB	DP	HR	MCDB	1%	2.5%	5%	HDD	CDD 18.3
SHELTON/SANDERSON	47.24N	123.15W	82	-4.1	-2.8	30.9	18.2	28.2	18.1	26.3	17.2	19.5	28.8	18.5	27.0	16.2	11.6	21.3	15.2	10.9	20.3	9.1	8.2	7.3	2965	60
SNOHOMISH CO	47.90N	122.28W	189	-2.4	-1.1	26.3	17.1	24.0	16.7	22.7	16.1	18.4	24.4	17.5	23.0	16.2	11.8	20.1	15.1	11.0	19.5	10.8	8.9	7.8	2862	38
SPOKANE INTERNATIONAL AP	47.62N	117.53W	721	-16.2	-12.4	33.8	17.2	31.9	16.6	30.0	15.9	18.5	30.5	17.6	29.3	14.5	11.2	20.0	13.3	10.4	19.9	11.4	9.8	8.5	3715	235
TACOMA NARROWS	47.27N	122.57W	91	-1.4	0.3	28.7	17.8	27.1	17.2	25.0	16.5	18.8	27.1	17.9	25.2	16.1	11.5	20.3	15.1	10.8	19.5	8.8	7.9	7.0	2573	86
WALLA WALLA CITY COUNTY AP	46.10N	118.29W	367	-13.3	-8.8	37.2	19.3	34.9	18.6	32.8	17.9	20.5	34.0	19.5	32.8	16.0	11.9	23.3	14.6	10.9	22.9	10.6	8.9	8.0	2703	507
WEST POINT (LS)	47.67N	122.43W	9	-1.7	0.7	21.4	16.0	20.1	15.6	19.0	15.2	16.7	19.7	16.1	18.7	15.5	11.0	17.7	15.0	10.7	17.2	17.0	14.0	11.7	2713	5
YAKIMA AIR TERMINAL	46.56N	120.53W	325	-14.3	-11.1	35.4	19.2	33.6	18.5	31.7	17.7	20.2	32.6	19.2	31.4	15.7	11.6	24.6	14.5	10.7	23.8	10.5	8.6	7.5	3303	271
West Virginia																									*3 sites, 6 more on CD-ROM*	
CHARLESTON YEAGER ARPT	38.38N	81.59W	299	-13.0	-9.6	32.9	23.0	31.6	22.8	30.3	22.3	24.9	30.1	24.1	29.0	23.3	18.8	27.1	22.6	18.0	26.3	7.7	6.7	5.6	2468	592
HUNTINGTON TRI-STATE ARPT	38.38N	82.56W	255	-13.1	-9.7	33.3	23.2	31.9	23.0	30.6	22.6	25.2	30.4	24.4	29.4	23.6	19.0	27.5	22.9	18.2	26.7	7.6	6.8	5.7	2461	633
PARKERSBURG WOOD COUNTY AP	39.35N	81.44W	263	-14.8	-11.2	32.7	23.1	31.3	22.7	29.9	22.2	24.9	30.2	24.1	28.9	23.3	18.6	27.4	22.5	17.8	26.5	8.1	7.2	6.3	2726	536
Wisconsin																									*14 sites, 13 more on CD-ROM*	
APPLETON/OUTAGAMIE	44.25N	88.52W	280	-21.0	-17.8	31.4	23.8	29.7	22.8	27.9	21.5	25.3	29.8	24.1	28.0	23.9	19.4	27.5	22.7	18.1	26.4	11.0	9.5	8.5	3991	335
EAU CLAIRE COUNTY AP	44.87N	91.49W	273	-26.4	-23.1	32.7	23.0	30.7	21.9	29.1	20.9	24.5	30.1	23.4	28.7	22.7	18.0	27.8	21.7	16.9	26.5	8.8	8.0	7.3	4366	342
FOND DU LAC CO.	43.77N	88.49W	246	-20.0	-17.6	31.4	23.5	29.8	22.6	27.9	21.2	24.8	29.6	23.7	28.0	22.9	18.2	27.9	22.4	17.6	27.0	10.6	9.0	8.2	3884	328
GREEN BAY AUSTIN STRAUBEL INT	44.51N	88.12W	214	-23.3	-20.1	31.3	23.2	29.6	22.2	28.0	21.3	24.7	29.4	23.6	27.9	23.2	18.4	27.5	22.1	17.2	26.3	10.7	9.0	8.2	4269	261
KENOSHA RGNL	42.58N	87.92W	232	-17.5	-14.9	32.4	23.9	31.0	23.2	28.8	22.1	25.2	30.7	24.1	28.8	23.0	18.3	27.7	22.5	17.7	27.0	11.1	9.8	8.7	3641	350
LA CROSSE MUNICIPAL ARPT	43.75N	91.26W	200	-24.6	-21.0	33.4	23.9	31.7	23.0	30.0	22.0	25.5	31.1	24.4	29.4	23.9	19.2	28.9	22.8	17.9	27.5	10.3	8.7	8.1	3931	452
MADISON DANE CO REGIONAL ARPT	43.14N	89.35W	264	-22.8	-19.4	32.1	23.5	30.5	22.7	28.9	21.7	25.0	30.2	23.9	28.6	23.3	18.7	28.6	22.3	17.6	27.1	10.5	9.0	8.2	3998	338
MANITOWAC MUNI AWOS	44.13N	87.68W	198	-20.1	-17.5	29.2	21.9	27.6	21.1	26.3	20.1	23.6	28.0	22.3	26.3	22.3	17.4	26.8	21.2	16.2	25.4	10.8	9.3	8.4	4188	188
MILWAUKEE MITCHELL INTL AP	42.95N	87.90W	211	-20.0	-16.8	32.4	23.7	30.4	22.6	28.7	21.5	25.0	30.5	23.9	28.6	23.3	18.5	28.1	22.3	17.5	27.0	11.5	10.3	8.9	3763	380
MOSINEE/CENTRAL WI	44.78N	89.67W	389	-23.7	-21.3	30.9	22.5	28.8	21.5	27.4	20.1	23.6	28.6	22.4	27.2	22.1	17.6	27.2	21.0	16.4	26.0	10.3	8.8	7.9	4571	208
SHEBOYGAN	43.78N	87.85W	228	-18.8	-17.1	31.2	23.3	28.9	21.9	27.4	20.7	24.5	29.6	23.4	28.0	22.8	18.0	27.8	22.2	17.3	26.7	11.0	9.4	8.4	4061	240
SHEBOYGAN	43.75N	87.68W	189	-19.0	-16.4	28.4	22.3	26.3	21.4	24.7	21.1	24.8	26.8	23.6	25.3	24.2	19.6	25.6	23.0	18.2	24.8	18.7	15.2	12.7	4047	178
WAUSAU MUNICIPAL ARPT	44.93N	89.63W	365	-25.3	-22.2	31.2	22.1	29.4	21.1	27.8	19.9	23.6	28.5	22.6	27.4	22.1	17.6	26.2	21.0	16.4	25.3	8.6	7.8	7.0	4452	262
WITTMAN RGNL	43.98N	88.55W	253	-20.9	-17.9	31.3	23.3	29.1	22.4	27.8	21.2	24.8	29.4	23.6	27.9	22.9	18.2	27.4	22.4	17.6	26.7	10.4	9.0	8.1	4032	306
Wyoming																									*2 sites, 10 more on CD-ROM*	
CASPER NATRONA CO INTL AP	42.90N	106.47W	1612	-23.5	-19.0	34.3	15.5	32.8	15.1	31.2	14.8	17.5	28.5	16.7	27.8	14.4	12.5	19.2	13.3	11.6	19.2	14.4	12.6	11.5	4081	261
CHEYENNE MUNICIPAL ARPT	41.16N	104.81W	1872	-21.3	-16.8	31.8	14.8	30.2	14.4	28.6	14.1	17.2	25.3	16.5	24.9	15.0	13.4	18.8	14.0	12.6	18.5	15.1	12.9	11.6	3971	180
Canada																									*102 sites, 378 more on CD-ROM*	
Alberta																									*13 sites, 40 more on CD-ROM*	
CALGARY INT'L A	51.11N	114.02W	1084	-29.1	-25.7	28.6	15.7	26.6	15.1	24.8	14.5	17.3	25.4	16.2	24.1	14.3	11.6	20.1	13.2	10.8	18.9	12.2	10.5	9.2	5086	37
COP UPPER	51.08N	114.22W	1235	-28.0	-24.7	28.2	14.6	26.0	14.0	24.0	13.7	17.2	23.4	16.0	22.4	15.0	12.4	19.5	13.6	11.3	18.1	10.5	9.1	8.0	5039	42
EDMONTON CITY CENTRE A	53.57N	113.52W	671	-29.7	-26.9	28.1	17.8	26.2	16.7	24.6	15.8	18.9	25.9	17.8	24.5	16.3	12.6	22.3	15.2	11.7	20.8	9.7	8.3	7.3	5275	63
EDMONTON INT'L A	53.32N	113.58W	723	-32.5	-29.4	27.5	17.6	25.6	16.6	24.1	15.8	19.0	25.3	17.9	24.0	16.5	12.8	22.6	15.4	11.9	21.2	10.3	8.9	7.7	5755	23
EDMONTON NAMAO A	53.67N	113.47W	688	-30.6	-27.8	27.2	17.3	25.5	16.4	23.8	15.5	18.6	24.9	17.6	23.7	16.3	12.6	21.7	15.1	11.7	20.3	10.4	9.0	7.8	5494	35
FORT MCMURRAY A	56.65N	111.22W	369	-36.8	-34.0	28.9	17.7	26.9	16.5	25.0	15.7	18.9	26.6	17.8	24.9	16.1	12.0	21.4	15.0	11.2	20.2	8.3	7.3	6.3	6384	47
GRANDE PRAIRIE A	55.18N	118.88W	669	-36.4	-32.0	27.5	16.5	25.5	15.6	23.8	14.7	17.9	25.1	16.7	23.4	15.3	11.8	20.5	14.1	10.9	18.9	11.2	9.6	8.4	5886	24
LACOMBE CDA 2	52.45N	113.76W	860	-32.9	-28.9	28.3	17.9	26.2	17.0	24.4	16.0	19.1	26.0	18.0	24.7	16.4	13.0	22.8	15.2	12.0	21.4	9.4	8.1	7.0	5735	21
LETHBRIDGE A	49.63N	112.80W	929	-29.8	-26.4	31.4	16.5	29.4	16.1	27.4	15.6	18.6	27.1	17.5	26.3	15.5	12.3	21.9	14.3	11.4	20.5	16.2	14.0	12.5	4656	91
LETHBRIDGE CDA	49.70N	112.78W	921	-28.3	-25.1	32.0	16.7	29.8	16.2	27.8	15.8	18.7	27.5	17.7	26.3	15.7	12.5	22.0	14.5	11.5	20.8	13.3	11.8	10.4	4508	117
MEDICINE HAT A	50.02N	110.72W	717	-31.2	-27.7	32.5	17.6	30.6	17.0	28.7	16.3	18.9	29.1	17.9	27.9	15.6	12.1	21.8	14.4	11.2	21.0	11.1	9.6	8.4	4693	168
RED DEER A	52.18N	113.89W	905	-32.7	-28.9	27.9	17.0	26.0	16.2	24.3	15.4	18.4	25.6	17.3	24.1	15.7	12.4	21.7	14.6	11.6	20.5	9.2	8.2	7.5	5716	22
SPRINGBANK A	51.10N	114.37W	1201	-31.7	-27.9	26.8	15.5	24.9	14.6	23.1	14.1	16.8	24.2	15.8	22.9	14.0	11.5	20.0	12.9	10.7	18.5	11.1	9.5	8.3	5718	4
British Columbia																									*27 sites, 50 more on CD-ROM*	
ABBOTSFORD A	49.03N	122.36W	59	-8.6	-5.7	29.6	19.5	27.6	18.7	25.6	17.8	20.3	28.4	19.2	26.5	16.8	12.1	24.7	15.9	11.4	22.8	8.5	7.4	6.3	2963	67
AGASSIZ CS	49.25N	121.77W	15	-7.5	-4.8	30.1	20.1	28.3	19.5	26.5	19.0	21.5	28.2	20.4	26.8	18.9	13.7	25.7	17.8	12.8	24.1	10.4	8.2	6.4	2823	111
BALLENAS ISLAND	49.35N	124.16W	13	-0.7	0.9	23.9	19.5	22.6	18.9	21.6	18.2	20.4	23.2	19.5	22.1	19.2	14.0	22.2	18.3	13.2	21.3	15.9	13.7	12.0	2496	68
COMOX A	49.72N	124.90W	26	-5.4	-3.2	26.7	17.4	24.7	16.8	22.9	16.2	18.2	24.4	17.5	23.1	15.8	11.3	20.1	15.2	10.8	19.4	13.4	11.5	9.7	3097	49
DISCOVERY ISLAND	48.42N	123.23W	15	-0.1	2.7	23.1	N/A	21.2	N/A	19.6	N/A	N/A	N/A	N/A	N/A	N/A	N/A	N/A	N/A	N/A	N/A	16.4	13.1	10.1	2537	14
ENTRANCE ISLAND CS	49.22N	123.80W	5	-1.6	0.5	23.9	N/A	22.3	N/A	21.1	N/A	N/A	N/A	N/A	N/A	N/A	N/A	N/A	N/A	N/A	N/A	14.3	12.5	11.2	2641	62
ESQUIMALT HARBOUR	48.43N	123.44W	3	-2.1	-0.1	22.6	16.2	20.8	15.5	19.4	15.1	17.0	20.8	16.3	19.5	15.4	10.9	18.2	14.8	10.5	17.5	9.6	8.4	7.3	2886	8
HOWE SOUND - PAM ROCKS	49.49N	123.30W	5	-2.7	-0.2	25.1	19.4	23.3	18.4	22.1	17.8	20.2	23.6	19.2	22.4	18.7	13.6	22.6	17.8	12.8	21.5	18.1	15.9	13.5	2576	86
KAMLOOPS A	50.70N	120.44W	345	-20.8	-16.2	33.7	18.2	31.6	17.5	29.5	16.8	19.1	30.9	18.2	29.2	15.3	11.3	21.3	14.2	10.5	20.8	9.9	8.6	7.9	3567	256
KELOWNA A	49.96N	119.38W	430	-18.3	-14.4	32.7	18.0	30.8	17.5	28.7	16.7	19.2	29.7	18.2	28.4	15.7	11.7	21.3	14.6	11.0	20.7	7.5	6.3	5.2	3926	124

Meaning of acronyms:

DB: Dry bulb temperature, °C *WB: Wet bulb temperature, °C* *DP: Dew point temperature, °C* *HR: Humidity ratio, g of moisture per kg of dry air* *WS: Wind speed, m/s*

MCWB: Mean coincident wet bulb temperature, °C *MCDB: Mean coincident dry bulb temperature, °C* *HDD and CDD 18.3: Annual heating and cooling degree-days, base 18.3°C, °C-day*

Station	Lat	Long	Elev	Heating DB		Cooling DB/MCWB						Evaporation WB/MCDB				Dehumidification DP/HR/MCDB						Extreme Annual WS			Heat./Cool. Degree-Days	
						0.4%		1%		2%		0.4%		1%		0.4%			1%							
				99.6%	99%	DB / MCWB		DB / MCWB		DB / MCWB		WB / MCDB		WB / MCDB		DP / HR / MCDB			DP / HR / MCDB			1%	2.5%	5%	HDD / CDD 18.3	
PITT MEADOWS CS	49.21N	122.69W	5	-7.3	-4.7	30.5	20.3	28.5	19.5	26.6	18.7	21.0	28.6	19.9	27.1	18.0	13.0	24.6	17.1	12.2	23.0	5.5	4.7	4.0	2933	78
POINT ATKINSON	49.33N	123.26W	35	-0.4	1.7	25.0	N/A	23.7	N/A	22.7	N/A	N/A	N/A	N/A	N/A	N/A	N/A	N/A	N/A	N/A	N/A	13.7	11.7	10.0	2133	137
PRINCE GEORGE A	53.89N	122.68W	691	-31.0	-26.2	27.7	16.2	25.6	15.3	23.7	14.4	17.1	25.6	16.0	23.9	13.9	10.8	18.9	13.0	10.1	17.8	9.4	8.2	7.2	5142	19
SANDHEADS CS	49.11N	123.30W	0	-3.6	-0.7	22.3	N/A	21.3	N/A	20.4	N/A	N/A	N/A	N/A	N/A	N/A	N/A	N/A	N/A	N/A	N/A	13.6	12.0	10.7	2661	33
SUMMERLAND CS	49.56N	119.64W	454	-14.5	-10.3	33.0	17.9	31.1	17.4	29.2	16.7	19.5	29.6	18.4	28.2	16.0	12.0	22.5	14.8	11.1	22.1	8.3	6.7	5.4	3486	254
VANCOUVER HARBOUR CS	49.30N	123.12W	3	-2.9	-0.5	25.7	N/A	24.3	N/A	23.0	N/A	N/A	N/A	N/A	N/A	N/A	N/A	N/A	N/A	N/A	N/A	N/A	N/A	N/A	2622	69
VANCOUVER INT'L A	49.20N	123.18W	4	-7.0	-4.0	25.0	18.2	23.5	17.7	22.2	17.1	19.0	23.8	18.2	22.7	16.8	12.0	21.8	16.1	11.5	20.7	10.3	8.8	7.6	2932	41
VERNON CS	50.22N	119.19W	482	-14.8	-11.4	33.1	18.3	31.0	17.8	28.7	17.0	19.4	30.2	18.6	28.6	16.3	12.3	20.7	15.4	11.6	20.1	6.9	5.4	4.7	3722	205
VICTORIA GONZALES CS	48.41N	123.33W	70	-2.5	-0.2	24.7	17.1	22.3	16.3	20.6	15.5	17.7	22.8	16.9	21.2	15.8	11.3	18.9	15.1	10.8	18.3	12.3	10.5	9.2	2803	22
VICTORIA HARTLAND CS	48.53N	123.46W	154	-2.8	-0.8	28.5	19.2	26.7	18.4	25.1	17.7	20.2	26.6	19.3	25.3	17.9	13.1	22.8	17.0	12.4	21.6	9.8	8.5	7.4	2675	103
VICTORIA INT'L A	48.65N	123.43W	19	-4.7	-2.6	26.6	17.5	24.6	16.8	22.8	16.1	18.0	25.3	17.2	23.7	14.8	10.6	20.2	14.2	10.1	19.5	8.5	7.2	6.2	3022	22
VICTORIA MARINE	48.37N	123.75W	32	-5.6	-2.6	21.1	15.1	19.3	14.4	17.8	13.7	15.8	20.0	14.9	18.2	14.2	10.2	16.6	13.3	9.5	15.9	13.5	11.7	9.8	3394	1
VICTORIA UNIVERSITY CS	48.46N	123.30W	60	-2.1	0.1	27.0	18.4	25.2	17.8	23.5	17.3	19.6	25.2	18.7	23.7	17.6	12.7	21.4	16.7	12.0	20.4	5.9	5.1	4.4	2664	39
WEST VANCOUVER AUT	49.35N	123.19W	168	-5.8	-3.0	27.0	19.0	25.3	18.5	23.8	17.9	20.0	25.6	19.1	24.2	17.7	13.0	23.2	16.9	12.3	22.1	5.1	4.3	3.7	2956	71
WHITE ROCK CAMPBELL SCIENTIFI	49.02N	122.78W	13	-5.3	-2.7	24.9	18.7	23.3	18.1	22.1	17.5	19.7	23.4	18.8	22.2	18.2	13.1	21.8	17.3	12.4	20.7	6.4	5.4	4.4	2771	28
Manitoba																									*1 site, 32 more on CD-ROM*	
WINNIPEG RICHARDSON INT'L A	49.92N	97.23W	239	-32.2	-29.9	30.8	20.9	28.9	20.3	27.2	19.4	22.8	28.3	21.6	27.1	21.0	16.1	26.2	19.6	14.8	24.6	12.5	11.0	9.8	5750	168
New Brunswick																									*3 sites, 9 more on CD-ROM*	
FREDERICTON A	45.87N	66.53W	21	-23.6	-21.0	29.7	21.0	27.9	19.8	26.2	19.0	22.2	27.8	21.2	26.1	20.3	15.0	25.1	19.4	14.2	23.8	9.8	8.6	7.8	4692	132
MONCTON A	46.10N	64.69W	71	-22.6	-20.3	28.4	20.5	26.7	19.5	25.2	18.6	21.9	26.4	20.9	24.9	20.4	15.2	24.2	19.5	14.3	23.1	12.4	10.7	9.4	4792	95
SAINT JOHN A	45.32N	65.89W	109	-22.4	-19.9	26.0	18.5	24.4	17.7	22.8	16.8	20.0	24.0	19.0	22.6	18.6	13.6	21.5	17.6	12.8	20.3	11.9	10.3	9.1	4771	29
Newfoundland and Labrador																									*1 site, 29 more on CD-ROM*	
ST JOHN'S A	47.62N	52.74W	141	-15.7	-13.5	24.6	18.9	23.0	18.0	21.6	17.3	20.3	23.2	19.2	21.7	19.2	14.2	21.9	18.2	13.3	20.8	16.1	13.7	12.3	4907	28
Northwest Territories																									*1 site, 26 more on CD-ROM*	
YELLOWKNIFE A	62.46N	114.44W	206	-40.9	-38.9	25.2	15.9	23.5	15.1	21.8	14.4	17.0	22.9	16.1	21.9	14.7	10.7	19.2	13.6	9.9	18.4	9.5	8.4	7.7	8306	33
Nova Scotia																									*4 sites, 13 more on CD-ROM*	
HALIFAX STANFIELD INT'L A	44.88N	63.52W	145	-18.6	-16.5	27.6	20.0	25.9	19.1	24.3	18.2	21.5	25.3	20.5	24.0	20.3	15.2	23.1	19.3	14.3	22.0	12.0	10.3	9.1	4356	98
SHEARWATER A	44.63N	63.50W	51	-17.0	-14.9	26.0	19.4	24.3	18.4	22.8	17.8	21.0	23.6	20.0	22.5	20.1	14.9	22.0	19.1	14.0	21.0	11.9	10.3	9.1	4237	64
SHEARWATER JETTY	44.63N	63.52W	6	-13.9	-11.5	25.8	N/A	24.2	N/A	22.9	N/A	N/A	N/A	N/A	N/A	N/A	N/A	N/A	N/A	N/A	N/A	12.2	10.6	9.3	3883	72
SYDNEY A	46.17N	60.05W	62	-18.0	-15.7	27.3	20.0	25.7	19.3	23.9	18.3	21.4	25.6	20.3	24.0	20.0	14.8	23.5	19.0	13.9	22.2	12.6	11.0	9.7	4627	75
Nunavut																									*1 site, 34 more on CD-ROM*	
IQALUIT A	63.75N	68.55W	34	-40.1	-38.4	16.5	11.0	13.9	9.6	12.0	8.6	11.5	15.6	10.0	13.4	8.8	7.1	12.6	7.7	6.6	11.2	15.2	12.8	11.1	10076	0
Ontario																									*20 sites, 34 more on CD-ROM*	
BEAUSOLEIL	44.85N	79.87W	183	-23.9	-20.4	29.9	23.4	28.1	22.2	26.5	21.3	24.4	28.1	23.3	26.7	23.4	18.6	26.4	22.2	17.3	25.1	6.2	5.4	4.8	4362	211
BELLE RIVER	42.30N	82.70W	184	-14.6	-12.2	31.6	24.2	30.0	23.7	28.5	22.8	25.9	29.6	24.9	28.4	24.9	20.4	28.3	23.8	19.1	27.0	12.9	11.3	9.9	3324	450
BURLINGTON PIERS (AUT)	43.30N	79.80W	77	-15.3	-12.9	30.3	21.3	28.6	20.6	27.0	20.0	23.3	27.1	22.3	26.3	22.2	17.0	25.4	21.0	15.8	24.2	10.4	9.0	7.9	3557	310
ERIEAU (AUT)	42.25N	81.90W	178	-14.6	-12.4	26.9	23.0	25.9	22.5	25.0	22.0	24.7	25.6	23.9	25.0	24.4	19.8	25.3	23.6	18.8	24.6	13.0	11.4	10.1	3576	288
LAGOON CITY	44.55N	79.22W	221	-23.9	-20.7	27.5	22.9	26.2	22.0	25.1	21.2	24.1	26.4	23.0	25.3	23.3	18.5	25.6	22.2	17.4	24.7	12.7	11.2	9.9	4427	188
LONDON INT'L AIRPORT	43.03N	81.15W	278	-18.3	-15.9	30.1	22.3	28.5	21.5	27.1	20.6	23.6	28.2	22.6	26.9	22.1	17.4	26.1	21.2	16.4	25.1	10.8	9.5	8.5	3984	233
NORTH BAY A	46.36N	79.42W	370	-27.8	-24.9	27.8	20.0	26.1	19.1	24.7	18.3	21.7	25.8	20.6	24.0	20.4	15.7	23.7	19.4	14.8	22.6	9.5	8.4	7.5	5243	118
OTTAWA MACDONALD-CARTIER INT	45.32N	75.67W	114	-24.5	-21.8	30.6	21.6	28.9	20.6	27.3	19.8	23.1	28.2	22.1	26.7	21.5	16.4	25.7	20.5	15.4	24.7	10.0	8.8	7.8	4563	236
PETERBOROUGH A	44.23N	78.37W	191	-23.9	-20.4	29.5	21.7	28.1	20.8	26.7	20.1	23.3	27.6	22.2	26.2	21.9	17.0	25.5	20.9	16.0	24.2	8.9	7.7	6.7	4404	137
PORT WELLER (AUT)	43.25N	79.22W	79	-13.5	-11.3	29.3	23.6	27.7	22.8	26.3	22.2	24.8	27.6	23.9	26.4	24.0	19.1	26.5	23.2	18.2	25.5	14.5	12.8	11.3	3528	320
SAULT STE MARIE A	46.48N	84.51W	192	-25.1	-22.0	28.4	21.2	26.6	20.0	24.9	19.0	22.3	26.6	21.1	24.9	20.8	15.9	24.8	19.7	14.8	23.4	11.0	9.5	8.3	4994	91
SUDBURY A	46.62N	80.80W	348	-28.2	-25.2	29.2	20.1	27.3	19.0	25.7	18.1	21.5	27.0	20.5	25.2	19.8	15.2	23.5	18.8	14.2	22.8	10.4	9.2	8.2	5297	130
THUNDER BAY A	48.37N	89.33W	199	-30.0	-27.0	29.0	20.5	27.0	19.2	25.2	18.2	21.8	27.0	20.4	25.1	19.9	15.0	24.9	18.7	13.9	23.0	9.9	8.6	7.5	5633	69
TIMMINS VICTOR POWER A	48.57N	81.38W	295	-33.7	-30.6	29.4	19.8	27.4	18.4	25.6	17.7	21.3	27.1	20.1	25.1	19.3	14.6	23.8	18.2	13.6	22.8	8.4	7.9	6.9	6099	84
TORONTO BUTTONVILLE A	43.86N	79.37W	198	-20.1	-17.2	31.7	22.5	29.8	21.4	28.1	20.6	23.7	29.5	22.6	27.9	21.9	16.9	26.9	20.8	15.8	25.6	9.7	8.4	7.8	4108	251
TORONTO ISLAND A	43.63N	79.40W	77	-16.1	-13.3	28.5	21.8	26.8	21.4	25.3	20.8	23.5	26.3	22.6	25.3	22.7	17.5	25.1	21.8	16.6	24.2	13.3	11.8	10.5	3721	237
TORONTO LESTER B. PEARSON INT	43.68N	79.63W	173	-18.8	-16.1	31.2	22.2	29.4	21.2	27.8	20.4	23.6	29.0	22.6	27.6	21.9	16.9	26.5	20.9	15.9	25.4	11.9	10.3	9.1	3956	276
TRENTON A	44.12N	77.53W	86	-21.8	-18.9	29.2	22.1	27.7	21.3	26.4	20.5	23.5	27.5	22.6	26.2	22.2	17.1	26.0	21.3	16.2	25.0	10.8	9.3	8.2	4181	204
WELCOME ISLAND (AUT)	48.37N	89.12W	211	-26.0	-23.7	24.6	18.9	22.9	18.1	21.5	17.6	20.6	22.7	19.5	21.6	19.8	14.9	21.6	18.6	13.8	20.7	15.5	13.3	11.8	5378	43
WINDSOR A	42.28N	82.96W	190	-16.4	-13.7	31.9	22.8	30.3	22.2	28.9	21.4	24.4	29.7	23.4	28.2	22.7	17.8	27.6	21.8	16.9	26.2	11.4	10.0	8.9	3482	418
Prince Edward Island																									*1 site, 3 more on CD-ROM*	
CHARLOTTETOWN A	46.29N	63.13W	49	-20.5	-18.1	26.7	20.5	25.2	19.5	23.8	18.7	21.6	25.3	20.6	23.9	20.2	15.0	23.7	19.3	14.2	22.8	11.5	10.0	8.8	4703	94

Meaning of acronyms:
DB: Dry bulb temperature, °C | *WB: Wet bulb temperature, °C*
MCWB: Mean coincident wet bulb temperature, °C
Lat: Latitude, °
DP: Dew point temperature, °C
MCDB: Mean coincident dry bulb temperature, °C
Long: Longitude, °
HR: Humidity ratio, g of moisture per kg of dry air
HDD and CDD 18.3: Annual heating and cooling degree-days, base 18.3°C, °C-day
Elev: Elevation, m
WS: Wind speed, m/s

Station	Lat	Long	Elev	Heating DB		Cooling DB/MCWB						Evaporation WB/MCDB				Dehumidification DP/HR/MCDB						Extreme Annual WS			Heat./Cool. Degree-Days	
						0.4%		1%		2%		0.4%		1%		0.4%			1%							
				99.6%	99%	DB / MCWB		DB / MCWB		DB / MCWB		WB / MCDB		WB / MCDB		DP / HR / MCDB			DP / HR / MCDB			1%	2.5%	5%	HDD / CDD 18.3	
Québec																									*23 sites, 59 more on CD-ROM*	
BAGOTVILLE A	48.33N	71.00W	159	-30.1	-27.7	29.2	19.4	27.2	18.5	25.4	17.7	21.1	26.5	20.0	24.9	19.4	14.4	23.3	18.3	13.5	22.4	11.9	10.4	9.2	5758	95
JONQUIERE	48.42N	71.15W	128	-29.2	-26.8	29.0	19.8	27.2	18.9	25.3	18.3	21.9	26.7	20.8	24.9	20.3	15.2	24.2	19.3	14.3	23.0	10.6	9.5	8.5	5541	97
LA BAIE	48.30N	70.92W	152	-30.4	-28.0	29.1	19.5	27.2	18.9	25.3	18.2	21.8	26.6	20.7	24.7	20.3	15.2	24.0	19.2	14.2	22.9	10.3	9.2	8.1	5724	72
LAC SAINT-PIERRE	46.18N	72.92W	16	-25.5	-22.5	27.6	20.8	26.1	19.7	24.8	19.3	22.2	25.6	21.4	24.6	21.0	15.7	24.6	20.2	14.9	23.8	13.2	11.8	10.5	4782	171
L'ACADIE	45.29N	73.35W	44	-24.1	-21.7	30.1	21.7	28.7	21.1	27.2	20.3	23.7	27.8	22.6	26.3	22.4	17.1	26.1	21.4	16.1	24.9	10.4	9.0	7.8	4407	231
L'ASSOMPTION	45.81N	73.43W	21	-25.9	-22.9	30.4	21.8	28.7	20.8	27.2	20.0	23.4	28.0	22.2	26.4	21.8	16.5	25.7	20.9	15.6	24.6	8.5	7.5	6.6	4606	203
LENNOXVILLE	45.37N	71.82W	181	-26.0	-22.6	29.5	21.6	27.9	20.7	26.6	19.9	23.2	27.3	22.2	26.1	22.0	17.0	25.4	20.9	15.9	24.4	9.0	8.0	7.0	4598	149
MCTAVISH	45.50N	73.58W	73	-22.3	-19.5	30.2	21.9	28.6	20.9	27.3	20.0	23.3	28.2	22.2	26.4	21.7	16.5	26.0	20.8	15.6	25.1	5.1	4.4	4.0	4158	298
MONT-JOLI A	48.60N	68.22W	52	-23.9	-21.7	26.7	19.8	25.0	18.7	23.4	17.8	20.7	25.2	19.6	23.8	19.0	13.8	23.9	17.8	12.9	22.4	12.6	11.1	9.9	5424	67
MONT-ORFORD	45.31N	72.24W	846	-28.4	-24.9	25.1	18.5	23.5	17.7	22.0	17.1	20.5	23.1	19.3	21.5	19.7	16.0	21.8	18.6	14.9	20.5	15.7	13.6	12.2	5633	53
MONTREAL/MIRABEL INT'L A	45.67N	74.03W	82	-26.4	-23.6	29.4	21.8	27.9	20.7	26.3	19.9	22.9	27.7	21.8	26.3	21.3	16.1	25.8	20.2	15.1	24.4	8.9	7.6	6.6	4849	162
MONTREAL/PIERRE ELLIOTT TRUDE	45.47N	73.75W	36	-23.7	-21.1	30.0	22.1	28.5	21.1	27.1	20.2	23.2	28.1	22.2	26.6	21.6	16.3	26.0	20.7	15.5	25.2	11.1	9.7	8.6	4428	253
MONTREAL/ST-HUBERT A	45.52N	73.42W	27	-24.3	-21.8	30.1	21.8	28.5	21.0	27.1	20.2	23.3	28.0	22.3	26.5	21.8	16.5	25.8	20.8	15.5	24.9	11.4	10.0	8.9	4564	217
MONTREAL-EST	45.63N	73.55W	50	-23.4	-20.6	30.5	21.0	28.9	20.1	27.6	19.4	22.7	27.7	21.7	26.2	21.2	15.9	24.8	20.2	15.0	24.3	8.6	7.6	6.8	4319	283
NICOLET	46.23N	72.66W	8	-25.6	-22.9	28.8	22.6	27.2	21.4	25.8	20.6	23.7	27.2	22.5	25.8	22.5	17.2	25.9	21.4	16.1	24.6	9.6	8.2	7.2	4704	163
POINTE-AU-PERE (INRS)	48.51N	68.47W	5	-22.1	-19.6	23.1	18.7	21.5	17.5	20.2	16.6	19.6	22.3	18.3	20.7	18.4	13.3	21.6	17.1	12.2	20.1	13.2	11.6	10.3	5328	11
QUEBEC/JEAN LESAGE INTL A	46.80N	71.38W	74	-26.2	-23.6	28.9	21.3	27.3	20.2	25.7	19.2	22.7	26.9	21.5	25.5	21.3	16.1	25.3	20.1	14.9	24.0	11.1	9.7	8.7	5094	132
SHERBROOKE A	45.43N	71.68W	241	-28.3	-25.1	28.6	20.9	27.1	20.1	25.7	19.2	22.3	26.9	21.2	25.4	20.7	15.9	24.9	19.7	14.8	23.6	9.1	8.0	7.0	5058	93
ST-ANICET 1	45.12N	74.29W	49	-24.8	-22.0	30.1	22.5	28.6	21.5	27.2	20.7	24.1	28.4	23.0	26.9	22.7	17.5	26.6	21.7	16.4	25.4	9.4	8.3	7.3	4482	188
STE-ANNE-DE-BELLEVUE 1	45.43N	73.93W	39	-24.2	-21.3	30.0	21.8	28.5	21.0	27.1	20.2	23.5	28.0	22.4	26.4	22.1	16.8	25.8	21.2	15.9	24.6	9.0	7.9	7.1	4446	225
STE-FOY (U. LAVAL)	46.78N	71.29W	91	-25.0	-22.2	29.2	20.8	27.6	19.7	26.0	18.7	22.6	27.1	21.5	25.4	21.1	15.9	24.7	20.2	15.0	23.6	9.4	8.1	6.9	4851	145
TROIS-RIVIERES	46.35N	72.52W	6	-24.1	-21.5	27.4	21.4	26.3	20.9	25.1	20.3	23.0	25.7	22.1	24.9	22.1	16.8	24.9	21.2	15.8	23.9	10.7	9.4	8.3	4577	188
VARENNES	45.72N	73.38W	18	-23.8	-21.4	30.3	21.7	28.7	20.8	27.2	20.0	23.4	28.0	22.4	26.5	22.0	16.7	25.7	21.0	15.7	24.8	11.0	9.5	8.4	4493	206
Saskatchewan																									*6 sites, 38 more on CD-ROM*	
MOOSE JAW A	50.33N	105.55W	577	-33.3	-30.3	32.4	18.2	30.3	17.6	28.2	16.8	20.0	28.4	18.9	27.2	17.5	13.4	22.9	16.2	12.4	21.5	13.2	11.5	10.2	5343	158
MOOSE JAW CS	50.33N	105.56W	577	-29.7	-26.7	32.2	18.9	30.1	18.6	28.0	17.7	22.2	27.3	20.7	26.2	20.7	16.4	24.7	19.0	14.8	22.8	12.1	10.8	9.6	5244	127
PRINCE ALBERT A	53.22N	105.67W	428	-36.6	-33.5	29.3	18.6	27.3	17.7	25.6	16.6	19.9	26.8	18.8	25.4	17.5	13.2	23.0	16.3	12.2	21.7	9.5	8.4	7.6	6218	68
REGINA A	50.43N	104.67W	577	-34.0	-30.9	31.4	18.7	29.4	18.2	27.5	17.3	21.0	28.2	19.6	26.5	18.7	14.5	24.3	17.1	13.1	22.9	13.4	11.7	10.4	5701	126
SASKATOON DIEFENBAKER INT'L A	52.17N	106.72W	504	-35.0	-32.0	30.8	18.5	28.7	17.8	26.8	17.0	20.4	27.8	19.1	26.2	18.0	13.7	23.3	16.7	12.6	22.0	11.2	9.8	8.8	5861	105
SASKATOON KERNEN FARM	52.15N	106.55W	510	-33.5	-30.6	30.6	17.7	28.6	16.9	26.8	16.1	20.5	27.0	19.2	24.9	18.4	14.1	23.7	17.0	12.9	22.0	10.7	9.5	8.5	5903	101
Yukon Territory																									*1 site, 11 more on CD-ROM*	
WHITEHORSE A	60.71N	135.07W	706	-40.0	-35.3	25.6	14.1	23.2	13.2	21.2	12.3	14.7	23.5	13.7	21.7	11.2	9.0	16.2	10.2	8.4	15.6	10.4	9.4	8.4	6803	6
Albania																									*1 site, 0 more on CD-ROM*	
TIRANA	41.33N	19.78E	90	-2.2	-0.9	34.1	22.2	32.8	21.9	31.3	21.6	26.0	29.3	24.1	28.0	25.1	20.5	27.3	23.1	18.1	25.6	6.8	5.4	4.6	1644	633
Algeria																									*3 sites, 29 more on CD-ROM*	
CONSTANTINE	36.28N	6.62E	694	-0.5	0.5	38.2	19.8	36.6	19.7	34.8	19.6	22.2	32.5	21.4	31.5	19.3	15.3	25.2	18.4	14.4	24.9	10.2	8.7	7.5	1686	833
DAR-EL-BEIDA	36.68N	3.22E	29	1.9	3.0	35.2	22.2	33.4	22.4	31.9	22.5	25.5	30.6	24.7	29.7	24.1	19.0	28.1	23.2	18.0	27.4	10.7	9.3	8.1	999	884
ORAN-SENIA	35.63N	0.60W	91	2.1	3.6	33.9	20.8	32.0	21.2	30.7	21.2	24.4	29.1	23.7	28.2	23.0	17.9	26.9	22.2	17.1	26.5	12.2	10.2	9.0	936	851
Argentina																									*15 sites, 36 more on CD-ROM*	
AEROPARQUE BS. AS.	34.57S	58.42W	6	4.2	5.7	31.0	23.2	29.8	23.0	28.4	22.4	25.2	28.9	24.4	28.0	24.0	18.9	27.9	23.1	17.9	27.1	11.1	9.8	8.7	908	732
CORDOBA AERO	31.32S	64.22W	474	-0.1	1.8	34.5	22.3	33.0	21.9	31.5	21.5	25.0	31.1	24.0	29.8	23.3	19.2	28.2	22.2	17.9	27.1	11.8	10.3	9.2	973	737
CORRIENTES AERO.	27.45S	58.77W	62	4.8	6.0	36.2	24.5	35.1	24.6	33.9	24.3	27.2	32.3	26.6	31.6	26.0	21.5	30.4	25.2	20.5	29.3	10.3	8.9	7.9	392	1585
EZEIZA AERO	34.82S	58.53W	20	-0.1	1.3	33.7	22.5	32.1	22.0	30.7	21.6	24.6	30.1	23.8	29.0	23.1	17.9	27.1	22.2	16.9	26.2	10.0	8.7	7.8	1211	637
MAR DEL PLATA AERO	37.93S	57.58W	21	-1.1	0.2	31.0	21.3	29.0	20.6	27.1	20.1	23.2	27.5	22.3	26.2	22.0	16.7	24.8	21.1	15.8	23.9	11.5	10.2	9.2	1847	241
MENDOZA AERO	32.83S	68.78W	704	-0.5	0.9	35.4	19.9	34.0	19.7	32.8	19.5	22.7	31.3	21.9	30.5	20.0	16.1	27.2	19.1	15.1	26.7	8.8	7.4	6.3	1241	884
PARANA AERO	31.78S	60.48W	78	2.5	3.8	34.0	23.2	32.8	22.6	31.5	22.3	25.5	30.9	24.6	29.9	23.9	19.0	28.8	23.0	18.0	27.8	11.0	9.6	8.5	855	903
POSADAS AERO.	27.37S	55.97W	125	4.8	6.3	36.0	24.2	35.0	24.0	34.0	24.0	26.6	32.6	26.0	32.0	25.0	20.3	30.2	24.2	19.4	29.3	8.8	7.5	6.5	330	1708
RESISTENCIA AERO	27.45S	59.05W	52	2.0	3.9	36.9	24.0	35.5	24.2	34.2	24.1	27.0	32.5	26.4	31.9	25.5	20.8	29.9	24.9	20.1	29.4	9.0	7.7	6.9	459	1556
ROSARIO AERO	32.92S	60.78W	25	-0.6	0.9	34.1	23.2	32.8	22.7	31.4	22.3	25.5	30.7	24.6	29.7	24.0	19.0	28.5	23.1	17.9	27.5	11.9	10.3	9.4	1048	774
SALTA AERO	24.85S	65.48W	1221	-0.9	0.8	32.8	18.4	31.1	18.7	29.8	18.9	22.2	27.9	21.6	27.1	20.6	17.7	24.6	20.0	17.1	24.1	8.0	6.6	5.7	939	548
SAN JUAN AERO	31.40S	68.42W	598	-1.9	-0.3	37.9	20.0	36.3	19.8	35.0	19.4	22.6	33.5	21.8	32.4	19.2	15.1	27.7	18.3	14.2	27.3	13.9	11.8	10.2	1171	1118
SANTIAGO DEL ESTERO	27.77S	64.30W	199	-0.6	1.7	38.9	23.5	37.1	23.2	35.7	23.0	26.2	33.3	25.5	32.6	24.3	19.8	29.6	23.7	19.0	28.7	10.5	9.1	7.8	601	1446
SAUCE VIEJO AERO	31.70S	60.82W	18	0.5	2.2	34.8	24.8	33.2	24.0	32.0	23.5	26.8	32.0	25.9	30.8	25.4	20.6	29.8	24.5	19.5	29.0	15.2	12.4	11.5	816	1007
TUCUMAN AERO	26.85S	65.10W	450	3.2	4.8	36.0	23.4	34.4	23.3	33.1	23.1	26.2	32.1	25.4	31.3	24.6	20.7	30.1	23.8	19.8	29.2	9.1	7.5	6.1	588	1205

Meaning of acronyms:
DB: Dry bulb temperature, °C
WB: Wet bulb temperature, °C
MCWB: Mean coincident wet bulb temperature, °C
Lat: Latitude, °
DP: Dew point temperature, °C
MCDB: Mean coincident dry bulb temperature, °C
Long: Longitude, °
HR: Humidity ratio, g of moisture per kg of dry air
Elev: Elevation, m
WS: Wind speed, m/s
HDD and CDD 18.3: Annual heating and cooling degree-days, base 18.3°C, °C-day

Station	Lat	Long	Elev	Heating DB		Cooling DB/MCWB						Evaporation WB/MCDB				Dehumidification DP/HR/MCDB						Extreme Annual WS			Heat./Cool. Degree-Days	
						0.4%		1%		2%		0.4%		1%		0.4%			1%							
				99.6%	99%	DB / MCWB		DB / MCWB		DB / MCWB		WB / MCDB		WB / MCDB		DP / HR / MCDB			DP / HR / MCDB			1%	2.5%	5%	HDD / CDD 18.3	
Australia																									25 sites, 243 more on CD-ROM	
ADELAIDE AIRPORT	34.95S	138.53E	8	4.0	5.1	35.8	18.4	33.4	17.9	31.3	17.5	21.3	28.7	20.3	27.9	19.2	13.9	24.0	17.9	12.8	23.2	11.7	10.4	9.4	1202	451
ADELAIDE REGIONAL O	34.92S	138.62E	51	4.8	5.8	36.3	19.0	33.9	18.7	31.9	18.1	21.6	30.8	20.6	29.5	19.2	14.1	23.9	17.7	12.7	23.5	8.4	7.4	6.7	1108	522
ARCHERFIELD AIRPORT	27.57S	153.00E	13	5.2	6.5	33.1	23.0	31.7	22.8	30.4	22.4	25.3	30.0	24.7	28.9	24.2	19.1	27.0	23.5	18.3	26.6	9.1	8.1	7.3	368	1066
BANKSTOWN AIRPORT A	33.92S	150.98E	8	3.2	4.3	33.8	20.5	31.4	20.6	29.3	20.2	23.5	28.9	22.7	27.4	22.0	16.7	25.6	21.3	15.9	24.6	9.8	8.6	7.7	932	534
BRISBANE AERO	27.38S	153.13E	10	5.9	7.2	31.1	22.6	30.0	22.9	29.0	22.3	25.3	28.6	24.6	27.9	24.2	19.1	27.3	23.5	18.4	26.7	9.8	8.6	7.8	333	1024
CANBERRA AIRPORT	35.30S	149.20E	580	-3.3	-2.1	33.2	17.8	31.2	17.1	29.1	16.7	20.0	27.1	19.0	26.2	18.0	13.9	21.9	16.9	12.9	21.2	10.6	9.5	8.5	2113	246
CANTERBURY RACECOUR	33.90S	151.12E	3	3.7	4.7	32.8	19.9	30.5	20.1	28.6	20.0	23.3	27.7	22.6	26.7	22.1	16.8	25.3	21.3	16.0	24.6	11.5	9.2	7.8	894	516
COOLANGATTA AIRPORT	28.17S	153.50E	6	6.5	8.1	29.2	23.4	28.4	23.3	27.7	23.0	25.4	27.8	24.7	27.1	24.7	19.7	26.9	24.0	18.9	26.5	9.7	8.9	8.2	316	920
GOLD COAST SEAWAY	27.93S	153.43E	3	9.7	10.8	30.7	23.1	29.3	22.7	28.2	22.6	25.4	27.9	24.7	27.2	24.7	19.8	26.7	24.0	18.9	26.2	12.6	10.9	9.5	193	1079
HOMEBUSH (OLYMPIC SITE)	33.85S	151.07E	28	5.9	6.9	33.8	19.4	31.5	19.5	29.5	19.4	22.7	28.5	21.9	27.3	21.0	15.7	24.8	20.2	14.9	24.2	9.7	8.2	7.2	730	646
JANDAKOT AERO	32.10S	115.88E	31	1.8	3.2	36.0	19.8	34.1	19.7	32.2	19.1	22.9	30.2	21.5	29.2	20.9	15.6	25.1	19.3	14.1	23.7	10.5	9.3	8.4	983	642
LAVERTON AERODROME	37.87S	144.75E	20	1.8	3.0	34.1	19.0	31.1	18.3	28.4	17.8	20.9	27.8	19.9	26.8	18.9	13.7	23.3	17.8	12.8	22.0	12.2	10.6	9.5	1711	206
MELBOURNE	37.82S	144.97E	32	4.7	5.7	34.6	18.9	32.0	18.2	29.5	17.9	21.2	28.7	20.1	27.5	18.8	13.7	23.9	17.7	12.8	22.8	7.6	6.7	5.9	1309	315
MELBOURNE AIRPORT	37.67S	144.85E	119	2.8	3.8	34.6	18.0	31.9	17.6	29.1	17.2	20.6	27.9	19.5	26.7	18.4	13.4	22.4	17.2	12.5	21.2	13.8	12.3	10.8	1731	236
MOORABBIN AIRPORT	37.98S	145.10E	13	2.5	3.8	33.8	19.3	31.2	18.6	28.5	18.3	21.6	27.4	20.5	26.4	20.2	14.9	23.0	18.8	13.6	22.1	11.8	10.5	9.4	1668	195
MOUNT LAWLEY PERTH	31.92S	115.87E	25	3.9	5.2	36.2	20.2	34.1	19.8	32.2	19.4	22.5	30.8	21.6	29.5	20.1	14.9	24.9	19.3	14.1	24.1	8.4	7.4	6.6	753	744
MT LOFTY AWS	34.97S	138.70E	730	2.4	3.0	29.9	16.7	28.0	15.6	26.2	14.8	18.9	25.2	17.8	24.2	17.0	13.3	20.0	15.6	12.1	19.8	16.1	14.4	13.0	2675	154
NEWCASTLE NOBBYS SI	32.92S	151.78E	33	7.7	8.6	30.3	19.8	27.6	19.7	25.8	20.5	23.6	25.5	23.0	24.8	23.0	17.8	24.5	22.4	17.1	24.1	18.2	15.3	13.8	602	558
PERTH AIRPORT	31.93S	115.97E	20	4.2	5.6	37.1	19.3	35.1	19.2	33.1	18.8	22.1	30.8	21.2	29.8	19.7	14.4	24.3	18.8	13.6	23.7	11.0	9.7	8.8	782	767
SCORESBY RESEARCH	37.87S	145.25E	90	2.3	3.4	33.6	19.0	31.4	18.8	29.2	18.5	21.3	29.0	20.2	27.8	18.9	13.9	23.8	17.7	12.8	22.5	8.4	7.4	6.6	1674	238
SWANBOURNE	31.95S	115.77E	20	6.4	7.5	34.7	19.8	32.3	19.9	30.4	19.6	23.3	28.4	22.2	27.1	21.9	16.6	25.3	20.9	15.6	24.0	13.6	11.5	10.1	661	662
SYDNEY AIRPORT AMO	33.93S	151.18E	5	6.0	7.0	32.8	19.6	30.0	20.1	28.1	20.0	23.1	27.3	22.4	26.3	21.9	16.6	24.8	21.2	15.8	24.2	12.6	11.2	10.0	718	610
SYDNEY REGIONAL OFF	33.85S	151.20E	40	7.2	8.0	31.1	20.0	28.8	20.3	27.3	20.3	23.1	27.1	22.4	26.2	21.8	16.5	25.1	21.2	15.9	24.5	N/A	N/A	N/A	647	597
TUGGERANONG ISABELL	35.42S	149.10E	588	-4.0	-2.8	33.6	18.2	31.6	17.6	29.7	16.9	20.3	27.9	19.3	27.1	18.1	14.0	22.6	17.0	13.0	21.5	8.5	7.4	6.7	2091	281
WILLIAMTOWN RAAF	32.80S	151.83E	8	4.1	5.3	33.9	21.1	31.4	21.0	29.2	20.4	23.6	28.8	22.9	27.5	22.2	16.9	25.3	21.5	16.2	24.7	12.3	10.6	9.4	808	580
Austria																									5 sites, 63 more on CD-ROM	
GUMPOLDSKIRCHEN	48.03N	16.28E	233	-9.9	-7.7	30.9	21.0	29.1	20.2	27.4	19.4	21.7	29.5	20.8	27.9	19.0	14.2	24.8	18.2	13.5	24.4	7.9	6.6	5.7	3057	250
TULLN	48.32N	16.12E	176	-12.8	-9.6	30.9	21.0	29.0	20.0	27.3	19.2	21.8	29.3	20.7	27.5	19.1	14.2	25.6	18.2	13.4	24.1	11.8	10.2	8.9	3236	193
WIEN/CITY	48.20N	16.37E	171	-8.2	-6.1	31.5	21.8	29.8	21.1	28.2	20.2	22.6	30.0	21.8	28.3	20.2	15.2	25.9	19.4	14.5	25.4	9.0	7.8	7.0	2752	369
WIEN/HOHE WARTE	48.25N	16.37E	200	-10.3	-7.9	30.6	21.2	28.9	20.3	27.3	19.3	21.9	29.3	20.9	27.5	19.4	14.5	25.3	18.6	13.8	24.2	9.9	8.4	7.4	3041	242
WIEN/SCHWECHAT-FLUG	48.12N	16.57E	190	-11.5	-9.0	30.9	20.3	29.0	19.6	27.2	18.8	21.2	28.5	20.4	27.2	18.9	14.0	24.1	18.0	13.2	23.3	12.2	10.7	9.5	3180	212
Belarus																									6 sites, 12 more on CD-ROM	
BREST	52.12N	23.68E	146	-18.6	-15.1	29.6	19.6	27.7	18.8	25.9	17.9	20.7	26.9	19.7	25.6	18.6	13.7	23.0	17.7	12.9	22.1	7.6	6.5	5.7	3845	122
GOMEL	52.40N	30.95E	126	-21.1	-17.6	29.2	19.4	27.7	18.8	26.0	18.1	20.9	26.6	20.0	25.4	19.0	14.0	23.3	18.1	13.2	22.2	8.3	7.3	6.5	4224	134
GRODNO	53.60N	24.05E	134	-20.2	-16.8	28.3	19.2	26.4	18.4	24.8	17.5	20.5	26.1	19.5	24.7	18.6	13.6	23.1	17.6	12.8	21.7	10.8	9.4	8.3	4207	72
MINSK	53.93N	27.63E	231	-20.6	-17.2	28.2	18.8	26.8	18.2	25.0	17.5	20.1	26.1	19.2	24.8	18.1	13.4	22.5	17.1	12.6	21.4	8.0	6.9	6.1	4405	84
MOGILEV	53.95N	30.07E	192	-22.7	-19.1	27.7	19.0	26.0	18.5	24.4	17.7	20.4	25.5	19.4	24.3	18.6	13.8	23.1	17.6	12.9	21.8	10.0	8.9	7.9	4616	69
VITEBSK	55.17N	30.22E	176	-22.5	-18.7	27.4	19.1	25.8	18.4	24.3	17.6	20.4	25.4	19.4	24.1	18.5	13.7	23.0	17.6	12.9	21.8	8.3	7.1	6.2	4579	79
Belgium																									3 sites, 15 more on CD-ROM	
ANTWERPEN/DEURNE	51.20N	4.47E	14	-7.5	-5.0	29.2	20.7	27.2	19.8	25.3	18.9	21.5	27.5	20.5	25.9	19.4	14.1	24.4	18.4	13.3	23.2	10.2	8.9	7.8	2882	104
BRUXELLES NATIONAL	50.90N	4.53E	58	-7.7	-5.0	29.0	20.1	27.0	19.5	25.1	18.6	21.1	27.2	20.1	25.6	18.9	13.8	23.7	18.0	13.0	22.6	11.5	10.0	8.8	2933	96
UCCLE	50.80N	4.35E	104	-7.3	-4.8	28.7	19.9	26.9	19.2	25.0	18.4	20.9	26.9	19.9	25.4	18.8	13.8	23.7	17.8	12.9	22.4	9.7	8.3	7.2	2941	110
Benin																									1 site, 5 more on CD-ROM	
COTONOU	6.35N	2.38E	9	21.9	22.6	32.6	27.3	32.1	27.2	31.8	27.1	28.9	31.6	28.3	30.9	28.1	24.3	31.2	27.7	23.8	30.9	8.2	7.4	7.0	0	3339
Bolivia																									3 sites, 0 more on CD-ROM	
COCHABAMBA	17.42S	66.18W	2548	1.8	3.0	29.9	15.1	28.9	14.7	28.0	14.4	17.1	25.9	16.6	25.2	14.6	14.3	19.4	14.0	13.7	18.3	9.7	8.0	5.7	569	257
LA PAZ/ALTO	16.52S	68.18W	4038	-4.5	-3.4	17.4	6.3	16.8	6.1	16.0	6.0	9.1	14.0	8.7	13.4	7.2	10.5	10.2	6.9	10.3	9.9	8.7	7.7	6.5	3941	0
VIRU-VIRU	17.63S	63.13W	373	9.2	10.8	34.2	23.8	33.5	24.0	32.9	24.1	26.1	31.0	25.7	30.5	24.9	20.9	28.4	24.2	20.0	27.4	13.1	11.5	10.3	89	2142
Bosnia and Herzegovina																									3 sites, 3 more on CD-ROM	
BJELASNICA	43.72N	18.27E	2070	-19.8	-17.1	18.6	11.3	17.0	10.5	15.8	10.3	12.8	15.9	12.1	15.3	11.5	10.9	13.8	10.7	10.3	13.2	34.0	30.3	26.9	6120	1
SARAJEVO/BUTMIR	43.82N	18.33E	511	-13.6	-10.9	32.1	20.3	30.1	19.8	28.1	18.9	21.8	29.4	20.7	27.6	19.1	14.8	25.9	18.1	13.9	24.2	8.3	6.5	5.1	3241	189
SARAJEVO-BJELAVE	43.87N	18.43E	638	-12.4	-9.9	31.3	18.7	29.5	18.3	27.8	17.4	20.5	28.1	19.3	26.7	17.9	13.9	23.7	16.9	13.0	21.8	5.3	4.4	3.6	3186	217
Brazil																									30 sites, 7 more on CD-ROM	
ANAPOLIS (BRAZ-AFB)	16.23S	48.97W	1137	12.8	14.0	31.7	20.6	30.7	20.5	29.8	20.5	23.8	27.0	23.3	26.7	23.0	20.5	25.3	22.3	19.5	24.8	6.6	5.8	5.2	12	1516
ARACAJU (AEROPORTO)	10.98S	37.07W	9	21.1	21.9	32.1	26.6	31.8	26.4	31.1	26.2	27.3	30.6	27.0	30.5	26.2	21.7	29.5	26.1	21.4	29.5	7.3	6.4	6.0	0	3114
BELEM (AEROPORTO)	1.38S	48.48W	16	22.8	22.8	33.1	26.1	32.8	26.0	32.2	25.8	28.1	30.3	27.7	30.2	27.2	23.1	29.5	27.1	22.8	29.4	8.4	7.0	6.0	0	3338

Meaning of acronyms:
DB: Dry bulb temperature, °C *WB: Wet bulb temperature, °C*
MCWB: Mean coincident wet bulb temperature, °C
Lat: Latitude, °
DP: Dew point temperature, °C
MCDB: Mean coincident dry bulb temperature, °C
Long: Longitude, °
HR: Humidity ratio, g of moisture per kg of dry air
HDD and CDD 18.3: Annual heating and cooling degree-days, base 18.3°C, °C-day
Elev: Elevation, m
WS: Wind speed, m/s

Station	Lat	Long	Elev	Heating DB		Cooling DB/MCWB						Evaporation WB/MCDB				Dehumidification DP/HR/MCDB						Extreme Annual WS			Heat./Cool. Degree-Days	
						0.4%		1%		2%		0.4%		1%		0.4%			1%							
				99.6%	99%	DB	MCWB	DB	MCWB	DB	MCWB	WB	MCDB	WB	MCDB	DP	HR	MCDB	DP	HR	MCDB	1%	2.5%	5%	HDD	CDD 18.3
BELO HORIZONTE	19.93S	43.93W	850	11.0	12.1	32.1	20.6	31.1	20.7	30.2	20.8	24.0	27.4	23.4	27.2	23.1	19.8	25.5	22.2	18.8	24.7	7.9	6.9	6.1	37	1381
BELO HORIZONTE (AERO)	19.85S	43.95W	785	11.5	12.8	33.0	20.7	32.0	20.7	31.1	20.7	23.0	28.5	22.6	28.1	21.9	18.3	24.2	21.2	17.5	23.6	6.2	5.4	4.9	24	1644
BRASILIA (AEROPORTO)	15.87S	47.93W	1061	9.8	11.0	32.1	17.9	31.1	18.4	30.2	18.6	22.2	26.4	21.7	26.1	21.1	18.0	23.4	20.5	17.3	22.9	7.4	6.2	5.4	23	1346
CAMPINAS (AEROPORTO)	23.00S	47.13W	661	8.8	10.1	33.2	21.5	32.2	21.5	31.2	21.5	24.2	29.2	23.7	28.7	23.1	19.3	25.8	22.2	18.3	25.1	11.3	10.3	9.6	105	1439
CAMPO GRANDE (AERO)	20.47S	54.67W	567	8.5	10.8	36.2	22.7	35.2	22.9	34.2	23.0	26.1	32.0	25.7	31.5	24.9	21.4	28.8	24.2	20.5	27.9	10.4	9.7	8.8	58	2563
CUIABA (AEROPORTO)	15.65S	56.10W	187	13.1	15.0	38.0	22.9	37.0	23.1	36.1	23.4	28.1	31.7	27.3	30.9	27.2	23.5	29.7	26.8	22.9	29.3	7.7	6.4	5.5	12	3369
CURITIBA (AEROPORTO)	25.52S	49.17W	908	2.7	4.9	30.9	20.4	29.8	20.3	28.8	20.3	23.1	26.9	22.5	26.4	22.1	18.8	24.3	21.5	18.0	23.7	8.5	7.4	6.4	640	603
EDUARDO GOMES INTL	3.03S	60.05W	2	21.8	21.9	35.9	26.3	35.1	26.2	34.2	26.1	28.4	32.4	27.9	31.8	27.2	23.0	29.5	27.1	22.8	29.3	5.8	5.1	4.4	0	3446
FLORIANOPOLIS (AERO)	27.67S	48.55W	5	7.8	9.4	32.2	25.4	31.0	25.2	30.0	24.6	26.5	30.2	26.0	29.4	25.6	20.8	28.3	25.0	20.1	27.7	8.3	7.3	6.4	219	1320
FORTALEZA (AEROPORTO)	3.78S	38.53W	25	22.8	23.0	32.2	25.2	32.0	25.2	31.8	25.1	26.7	29.8	26.5	29.5	26.2	21.6	27.8	25.8	21.2	27.6	9.3	8.3	7.7	0	3423
GALEAO	22.82S	43.25W	6	14.9	15.9	37.9	25.6	36.1	25.3	34.8	25.1	28.0	32.6	27.4	31.8	27.1	22.8	30.1	26.2	21.6	29.3	8.3	7.2	6.3	6	2504
GOIANIA (AEROPORTO)	16.63S	49.22W	747	11.9	13.2	35.0	20.3	34.0	20.7	33.1	20.8	24.5	29.8	24.1	29.4	23.1	19.6	26.0	22.9	19.3	25.8	8.1	7.1	5.5	4	2248
GUARULHOS	23.43S	46.47W	768	7.2	9.0	32.8	22.1	31.2	21.8	30.2	21.5	24.7	28.5	24.0	27.8	24.0	20.7	25.7	23.1	19.6	25.1	7.6	6.8	6.1	232	1074
LONDRINA (AEROPORTO)	23.33S	51.13W	569	7.8	9.8	33.9	21.8	32.8	22.0	31.9	22.1	25.6	28.9	25.1	28.5	24.9	21.4	26.9	24.2	20.4	26.3	6.5	5.6	5.0	124	1613
MACAPA	0.03N	51.05W	15	22.8	22.9	34.0	26.2	33.2	26.0	33.0	26.0	27.5	31.6	27.0	31.4	26.2	21.7	29.7	26.0	21.4	29.4	8.4	7.4	6.6	0	3456
MACEIO (AEROPORTO)	9.52S	35.78W	117	19.1	19.8	33.0	25.4	32.2	25.1	31.8	24.9	26.8	30.2	26.5	29.8	26.1	21.8	28.4	25.7	21.3	28.1	7.6	6.8	6.2	0	2749
MANAUS (AEROPORTO)	3.15S	59.98W	84	22.1	22.8	34.7	25.9	34.0	25.9	33.2	25.8	27.2	31.5	27.0	31.3	26.2	21.8	29.2	26.0	21.5	29.1	6.2	5.3	4.8	0	3407
NATAL AEROPORTO	5.92S	35.25W	52	21.0	21.6	32.9	25.5	32.2	25.3	32.0	25.2	26.7	30.0	26.4	29.8	26.1	21.6	28.3	25.6	20.9	28.1	10.0	9.1	8.3	0	3176
PORTO ALEGRE (AERO)	30.00S	51.18W	3	4.1	5.9	34.9	24.6	33.1	24.0	31.9	23.5	26.3	31.6	25.5	30.5	25.0	20.1	28.3	24.1	19.0	27.5	9.2	8.0	6.9	462	1148
PORTO VELHO (AERO)	8.77S	63.92W	102	18.0	19.6	35.4	25.6	34.7	25.5	33.9	25.6	28.0	31.1	27.6	30.9	27.2	23.3	28.9	27.0	23.0	28.8	6.1	5.1	4.4	1	3266
RECIFE (AEROPORTO)	8.07S	34.85W	19	21.8	22.0	34.0	27.1	33.2	26.5	32.9	26.3	27.6	32.4	27.1	31.9	26.2	21.7	30.7	25.9	21.3	30.5	8.1	7.3	6.5	0	3432
RIO DE JANEIRO (AERO)	22.90S	43.17W	3	16.2	17.0	34.1	25.1	32.8	24.9	31.8	24.8	26.6	30.9	26.2	30.4	25.2	20.4	29.0	25.0	20.1	28.7	8.4	7.4	6.5	4	2297
SALVADOR (AEROPORTO)	12.90S	38.33W	6	20.2	21.1	32.4	26.6	32.0	26.4	31.2	26.0	27.4	30.9	27.0	30.6	26.4	21.9	29.5	26.1	21.5	29.4	9.1	8.2	7.4	0	3022
SAO LUIZ (AEROPORTO)	2.60S	44.23W	53	22.8	23.0	34.1	26.3	33.3	26.1	33.0	26.1	27.7	30.8	27.4	30.6	27.1	23.0	29.4	26.7	22.5	29.1	9.0	8.2	7.4	0	3616
SAO PAULO (AEROPORTO)	23.62S	46.65W	803	8.9	10.0	32.1	20.4	31.0	20.5	30.0	20.4	23.3	27.7	22.7	27.2	22.1	18.5	25.5	21.2	17.5	24.5	7.5	6.5	5.7	229	1123
TERESINA (AEROPORTO)	5.05S	42.82W	69	21.9	22.3	38.1	23.8	37.2	24.0	36.9	24.1	27.0	31.9	26.7	31.9	26.1	21.6	28.5	25.6	21.0	28.3	5.2	4.5	4.0	0	3944
VITORIA (AEROPORTO)	20.27S	40.28W	4	16.6	17.6	34.0	25.6	33.1	25.4	32.3	25.2	27.2	30.5	26.7	30.0	26.2	21.7	28.5	26.0	21.3	28.3	10.1	9.0	8.1	0	2585
Bulgaria																										*4 sites, 24 more on CD-ROM*
CHERNI VRAH (TOP/SOMMET)	42.58N	23.27E	2292	-19.9	-17.5	16.8	10.9	15.3	10.3	14.0	9.8	12.1	14.7	11.2	13.9	11.1	10.9	13.0	10.2	10.2	12.1	28.4	24.2	19.9	6503	0
PLOVDIV	42.13N	24.75E	185	-10.2	-7.4	34.2	20.9	32.6	20.7	31.0	20.1	22.8	31.3	21.8	29.9	20.1	15.1	27.0	19.1	14.2	25.5	12.1	10.3	9.3	2579	532
SOFIA (OBSERV.)	42.65N	23.38E	591	-12.5	-9.9	32.0	18.7	30.0	18.5	28.2	18.0	20.4	28.1	19.6	27.2	17.9	13.8	23.4	17.0	13.1	22.4	9.4	8.1	6.9	3169	239
VARNA	43.20N	27.92E	43	-8.9	-6.8	31.0	22.3	29.3	22.0	28.1	21.4	24.2	28.6	23.2	27.6	22.8	17.6	27.1	21.8	16.5	26.1	13.5	10.3	8.5	2607	383
Burkina Faso																										*2 sites, 3 more on CD-ROM*
BOBO-DIOULASSO	11.17N	4.32W	460	17.8	19.0	38.0	20.1	37.1	20.2	36.3	20.3	25.8	31.9	25.4	31.4	24.2	20.2	28.7	23.8	19.8	28.4	7.4	6.5	5.9	0	3354
OUAGADOUGOU	12.35N	1.52W	306	16.1	17.3	40.5	20.6	39.7	20.7	38.8	20.8	26.4	33.4	26.0	33.0	24.9	20.7	28.7	24.2	19.8	28.3	7.6	6.6	5.9	0	3802
Chad																										*1 site, 0 more on CD-ROM*
NDJAMENA	12.13N	15.03E	295	13.0	14.5	42.9	21.7	41.9	21.4	41.0	21.0	27.7	33.2	27.2	32.9	26.4	22.7	30.0	26.0	22.1	29.7	9.5	8.2	7.2	1	3829
Chile																										*2 sites, 10 more on CD-ROM*
ANTOFAGASTA	23.43S	70.45W	140	10.0	11.0	24.8	19.9	23.9	19.1	23.1	18.5	20.6	23.6	19.9	22.8	19.2	14.2	22.7	18.7	13.8	22.2	9.4	8.5	7.9	657	204
PUDAHUEL	33.38S	70.78W	474	-1.1	0.0	31.8	18.0	30.7	17.8	29.7	17.5	19.5	29.0	18.8	28.4	15.8	11.9	23.8	14.9	11.2	23.0	8.4	7.4	6.5	1523	227
China																										*89 sites, 308 more on CD-ROM*
ANQING	30.53N	117.05E	20	-1.9	-0.6	35.6	27.3	34.5	27.1	33.4	26.8	28.4	33.0	27.9	32.4	27.2	23.0	31.2	26.7	22.3	30.8	8.1	7.1	6.3	1618	1290
ANYANG	36.05N	114.40E	64	-8.0	-6.3	35.0	23.5	33.7	23.9	32.5	23.8	27.6	31.5	26.8	30.5	26.5	22.3	30.1	25.8	21.2	29.4	7.5	6.5	5.6	2353	985
BAODING	38.85N	115.57E	19	-10.0	-8.3	35.2	22.5	33.6	22.7	32.3	23.0	27.0	31.1	26.1	30.0	25.9	21.2	29.5	25.0	20.2	28.7	6.4	5.4	4.5	2643	942
BAOJI	34.35N	107.13E	610	-6.0	-4.6	34.7	21.7	33.3	21.5	31.8	21.4	24.7	30.7	23.9	29.5	23.1	19.2	28.0	22.2	18.2	27.2	6.2	5.2	4.4	2388	759
BEIJING	39.93N	116.28E	55	-10.8	-9.1	34.9	22.2	33.1	22.4	31.9	22.5	27.0	30.5	26.1	29.3	26.1	21.6	28.9	25.1	20.4	28.1	9.6	8.0	6.6	2830	848
BENGBU	32.95N	117.37E	22	-5.1	-3.6	35.6	26.6	34.2	26.2	32.9	25.4	28.3	32.9	27.8	32.3	27.2	23.0	31.1	26.6	22.2	30.6	7.2	6.2	5.4	1942	1129
BENXI	41.32N	123.78E	185	-22.8	-20.3	31.5	22.1	30.1	22.1	28.9	21.7	24.8	28.7	23.9	27.8	23.6	18.8	27.4	22.7	17.8	26.4	6.8	5.5	4.9	4097	487
BINHAI	39.12N	117.33E	2	-10.9	-9.1	34.2	23.5	33.0	23.6	31.9	23.2	27.7	30.5	26.8	29.8	27.0	22.7	29.5	26.1	21.5	28.5	10.2	8.6	7.4	2738	892
CANGZHOU	38.33N	116.83E	11	-10.1	-8.5	34.3	23.0	33.1	23.3	31.9	23.3	27.2	30.9	26.3	29.9	26.2	21.6	29.6	25.4	20.6	28.6	9.1	7.4	6.4	2686	923
CHANGCHUN	43.90N	125.22E	238	-24.8	-22.6	30.7	21.3	29.3	21.1	28.1	20.7	24.6	28.1	23.6	26.9	23.5	18.8	26.9	22.5	17.7	25.9	12.0	9.9	8.3	4823	403
CHANGDE	29.05N	111.68E	35	-0.9	0.1	36.1	27.3	35.0	27.1	33.7	26.8	28.7	33.2	28.1	32.7	27.6	23.6	31.5	26.9	22.7	31.0	6.0	5.0	4.2	1538	1279
CHANGSHA	28.23N	112.87E	68	-1.0	0.1	36.0	26.8	34.9	26.6	33.7	26.4	28.0	33.0	27.5	32.5	26.8	22.6	30.7	26.2	21.8	30.2	7.2	6.1	5.3	1521	1310
CHAOYANG	41.55N	120.45E	176	-19.7	-17.4	33.7	21.4	32.1	21.4	30.7	21.1	25.3	29.9	24.4	28.8	23.9	19.2	28.1	23.1	18.2	27.3	9.3	7.8	6.8	3725	623
CHENGDE	40.98N	117.95E	386	-17.9	-16.1	33.0	20.5	31.4	20.4	30.0	20.3	24.2	28.9	23.5	27.9	22.9	18.5	26.8	22.1	17.6	26.0	6.4	5.2	4.2	3783	526
CHENGDU	30.67N	104.02E	508	0.4	1.6	33.1	25.3	31.9	24.8	30.7	24.3	27.0	31.0	26.2	29.9	26.0	22.7	29.7	25.2	21.6	28.6	5.4	4.4	3.6	1455	923

Meaning of acronyms:

DB: Dry bulb temperature, °C; WB: Wet bulb temperature, °C; DP: Dew point temperature, °C; HR: Humidity ratio, g of moisture per kg of dry air; WS: Wind speed, m/s

MCWB: Mean coincident wet bulb temperature, °C; MCDB: Mean coincident dry bulb temperature, °C; HDD and CDD 18.3: Annual heating and cooling degree-days, base 18.3°C, °C-day

Station	Lat	Long	Elev	Heating DB		Cooling DB/MCWB						Evaporation WB/MCDB				Dehumidification DP/HR/MCDB						Extreme Annual WS			Heat./Cool. Degree-Days	
						0.4%		1%		2%		0.4%		1%		0.4%			1%							
				99.6%	99%	DB / MCWB		DB / MCWB		DB / MCWB		WB / MCDB		WB / MCDB		DP / HR / MCDB			DP / HR / MCDB			1%	2.5%	5%	HDD / CDD 18.3	
CHONGQING	29.58N	106.47E	260	3.2	4.2	36.9	25.6	35.5	25.6	34.2	25.4	27.4	32.7	26.9	32.2	26.1	22.2	30.2	25.6	21.5	29.8	5.1	4.3	3.6	1163	1278
DALIAN	38.90N	121.63E	97	-12.2	-10.3	31.1	23.4	29.9	23.0	28.4	22.4	26.0	28.7	25.2	27.6	25.2	20.5	27.4	24.4	19.6	26.6	11.2	9.8	8.6	3101	611
DANDONG	40.05N	124.33E	14	-16.4	-14.4	29.8	24.0	28.4	23.2	27.3	22.6	25.6	28.1	24.8	26.9	24.9	20.0	27.1	24.2	19.1	26.0	9.0	7.7	6.7	3641	439
DATONG	40.10N	113.33E	1069	-20.9	-18.9	31.5	17.2	29.9	17.0	28.5	16.9	21.2	26.5	20.3	25.5	19.6	16.4	23.4	18.7	15.4	22.9	9.9	8.3	7.2	4247	325
DEZHOU	37.43N	116.32E	22	-9.2	-7.7	34.2	23.6	33.0	24.0	31.9	23.7	27.6	31.3	26.7	30.3	26.5	22.1	30.2	25.6	20.9	29.4	7.4	6.4	5.5	2542	956
DIWOPU	43.90N	87.47E	664	-23.2	-21.2	35.4	18.2	34.0	18.0	32.8	17.6	20.5	30.3	19.7	29.4	18.0	14.0	22.2	16.9	13.1	22.2	7.3	5.6	4.5	4328	758
FUZHOU	26.08N	119.28E	85	4.4	5.5	35.5	26.9	34.4	26.7	33.3	26.4	27.9	33.6	27.4	32.8	26.3	22.0	31.3	25.9	21.5	30.5	8.3	7.1	6.2	741	1600
GANYU	34.83N	119.13E	10	-7.0	-5.4	33.1	26.4	31.6	25.7	30.3	25.3	28.2	31.6	27.5	30.5	27.2	23.0	30.5	26.6	22.2	29.7	7.5	6.5	5.7	2343	838
GAOYAO	23.05N	112.47E	12	6.5	7.6	35.0	26.6	34.2	26.5	33.3	26.4	27.7	32.3	27.3	31.7	26.6	22.1	29.7	26.2	21.7	29.4	6.9	5.9	5.1	390	2065
GUANGZHOU	23.17N	113.33E	42	5.8	7.0	35.0	26.3	34.1	26.2	33.2	26.1	27.7	31.6	27.4	31.1	26.8	22.6	29.5	26.3	21.8	29.1	6.8	5.9	5.1	402	2036
GUILIN	25.33N	110.30E	166	1.3	2.5	34.7	25.7	33.7	25.5	32.8	25.4	27.2	31.4	26.7	30.9	26.2	22.0	29.0	25.8	21.5	28.7	8.1	7.1	6.1	1064	1484
GUIYANG	26.58N	106.73E	1223	-2.3	-1.1	30.3	21.3	29.3	21.1	28.4	20.9	22.9	27.7	22.5	27.0	21.6	19.0	25.1	21.2	18.4	24.7	6.5	5.5	5.0	1684	691
HAIKOU	20.03N	110.35E	24	10.7	12.2	35.0	27.0	34.2	26.9	33.4	26.8	28.1	32.5	27.7	31.9	27.0	22.8	30.0	26.6	22.3	29.7	6.5	5.5	4.9	107	2494
HANGZHOU	30.23N	120.17E	43	-2.2	-1.0	36.1	26.8	35.1	26.7	33.8	26.5	28.2	32.9	27.7	32.3	27.1	23.0	30.4	26.5	22.2	30.0	7.2	6.1	5.3	1633	1213
HARBIN	45.75N	126.77E	143	-28.4	-25.9	31.1	20.8	29.6	20.6	28.2	20.4	24.1	28.0	23.2	26.8	23.0	18.0	26.5	22.1	17.0	25.7	9.1	7.5	6.6	5310	353
HEFEI	31.87N	117.23E	36	-4.1	-2.6	35.2	27.4	34.0	27.0	32.8	26.5	28.5	33.2	27.9	32.4	27.2	23.1	31.5	26.7	22.4	30.9	7.6	6.5	5.8	1873	1142
HOHHOT	40.82N	111.68E	1065	-21.9	-19.2	31.6	17.5	30.1	17.2	28.7	16.9	21.2	27.0	20.2	25.6	19.5	16.2	23.4	18.5	15.2	23.2	8.6	7.2	6.1	4429	319
HONG KONG INTERNATI	22.32N	113.92E	8	9.0	10.8	33.8	26.5	33.0	26.3	32.2	26.1	27.7	30.8	27.3	30.5	26.9	22.6	30.0	26.2	21.7	29.5	10.2	8.9	8.0	182	2253
HONG KONG OBSERVATO	22.30N	114.17E	62	9.6	10.9	32.2	26.5	31.7	26.4	31.2	26.3	27.4	30.5	27.1	30.1	26.6	22.3	29.3	26.2	21.8	29.1	8.6	7.4	6.5	237	1976
JIANGLING	30.33N	112.18E	33	-1.5	-0.5	34.8	27.6	33.8	27.1	32.8	26.6	28.6	33.1	28.0	32.5	27.4	23.4	31.6	26.8	22.6	31.1	7.1	6.0	5.2	1624	1199
JINAN	36.60N	117.05E	169	-8.2	-6.5	35.0	23.0	33.7	23.4	32.6	23.1	26.9	31.7	26.3	30.9	25.7	21.4	29.7	25.0	20.6	29.4	9.2	7.9	6.8	2284	1085
JINGDEZHEN	29.30N	117.20E	60	-1.7	-0.3	36.1	26.7	35.0	26.4	34.0	26.1	27.7	33.3	27.3	32.6	26.3	22.0	30.2	25.9	21.4	29.9	5.9	5.0	4.3	1396	1360
JINZHOU	41.13N	121.12E	70	-16.4	-14.5	31.6	22.1	30.2	21.9	29.0	21.6	25.6	28.7	24.7	27.6	24.7	19.9	27.6	23.9	18.9	26.6	10.1	8.6	7.4	3562	579
JIXI	45.28N	130.95E	234	-25.2	-23.1	30.5	20.9	28.9	20.3	27.4	19.9	23.5	27.8	22.5	26.3	22.1	17.3	25.9	21.2	16.3	25.1	10.5	9.2	7.9	5239	267
KUNMING	25.02N	102.68E	1892	0.3	1.7	27.1	16.6	26.1	16.8	25.3	16.8	20.0	24.2	19.5	23.5	18.7	17.1	21.9	18.2	16.6	21.3	8.0	7.0	6.0	1249	309
LANZHOU	36.05N	103.88E	1518	-11.7	-10.2	32.2	17.9	30.7	17.3	29.4	16.8	20.2	28.3	19.3	27.2	17.7	15.3	24.2	16.7	14.4	23.2	4.4	3.6	3.2	3147	411
LINGXIAN	37.33N	116.57E	19	-11.0	-8.8	35.1	23.3	33.7	23.9	32.3	24.1	27.7	31.2	27.0	30.5	26.8	22.4	30.0	26.0	21.4	29.3	8.6	7.5	6.5	2588	912
LIUZHOU	24.35N	109.40E	97	3.4	4.6	35.2	25.8	34.3	25.8	33.5	25.6	27.2	32.3	26.9	31.8	26.0	21.6	29.5	25.6	21.1	29.3	5.6	4.9	4.3	729	1849
MENGJIN	34.82N	112.43E	333	-6.8	-5.3	34.7	21.7	33.2	22.2	31.8	22.4	26.6	30.6	25.9	29.6	25.6	21.7	29.0	24.9	20.7	28.1	9.3	7.5	6.4	2265	890
MUDANJIANG	44.57N	129.60E	242	-26.4	-24.2	31.1	21.6	29.5	20.7	27.9	20.3	23.7	28.7	22.8	26.9	22.1	17.3	26.7	21.4	16.5	25.8	9.3	7.7	6.4	5174	317
NANCHANG	28.60N	115.92E	50	-0.8	0.3	35.7	27.0	34.6	26.8	33.5	26.7	28.2	32.6	27.8	32.2	27.2	23.1	30.7	26.7	22.4	30.4	6.4	5.5	4.9	1433	1395
NANJING	32.00N	118.80E	7	-4.8	-3.2	35.1	27.1	33.9	26.9	32.6	26.4	28.3	32.7	27.8	32.0	27.2	23.0	30.9	26.7	22.3	30.5	7.6	6.6	5.8	1914	1080
NANNING	22.82N	108.35E	126	5.2	6.5	35.0	26.3	34.1	26.2	33.2	26.0	27.7	31.9	27.4	31.4	26.7	22.7	29.7	26.3	22.1	29.3	6.2	5.3	4.4	489	1963
NEIJIANG	29.58N	105.05E	357	2.3	3.3	35.2	26.0	33.9	25.5	32.6	25.1	27.3	32.6	26.7	31.7	26.0	22.3	30.4	25.4	21.5	29.7	5.3	4.4	3.8	1241	1139
QINGDAO	36.07N	120.33E	77	-7.7	-6.1	32.0	23.5	30.6	23.4	29.1	23.2	26.6	29.0	25.9	28.0	26.0	21.6	27.9	25.2	20.6	27.2	11.8	10.2	9.0	2528	733
QINGJIANG	33.60N	119.03E	19	-6.2	-4.5	33.6	27.2	32.4	26.4	31.2	25.8	28.3	32.1	27.7	31.3	27.3	23.1	30.8	26.7	22.3	30.2	7.0	6.0	5.2	2166	921
QIQIHAR	47.38N	123.92E	148	-27.7	-25.6	31.7	20.9	30.0	20.3	28.5	19.9	23.8	27.9	22.7	27.0	22.6	17.6	26.4	21.5	16.4	25.3	9.9	8.3	7.2	5426	370
SHANGHAI	31.40N	121.47E	4	-1.9	-0.6	34.9	27.1	33.6	26.7	32.4	26.5	28.0	32.5	27.5	31.7	26.8	22.4	30.5	26.3	21.8	30.0	7.8	6.9	6.2	1599	1158
SHANGHAI/HONGQIAO	31.17N	121.43E	7	-3.0	-1.8	35.1	27.4	33.9	27.3	32.8	26.8	28.7	32.6	28.0	31.7	27.9	24.0	31.1	27.1	22.8	30.3	9.0	7.9	7.0	1684	1149
SHANTOU	23.40N	116.68E	3	7.1	8.5	33.5	27.1	32.6	26.9	31.9	26.6	28.2	31.4	27.7	30.7	27.2	23.0	30.0	27.0	22.7	29.7	8.2	7.2	6.3	380	1793
SHAOGUAN	24.80N	113.58E	68	2.6	3.9	35.5	26.0	34.5	26.0	33.6	25.8	27.2	32.4	26.9	31.8	26.0	21.5	29.3	25.6	21.1	29.0	6.7	5.7	5.0	776	1755
SHENYANG	41.73N	123.52E	43	-22.1	-19.7	31.6	23.3	30.4	22.7	29.2	22.2	25.6	29.5	24.7	28.4	24.4	19.5	28.0	23.6	18.5	27.1	9.7	8.2	7.1	4034	557
SHENZHEN	22.55N	114.10E	18	6.9	8.3	33.8	26.5	33.1	26.4	32.3	26.3	28.8	31.0	28.1	30.4	28.2	24.5	30.2	27.8	23.9	29.9	8.1	7.1	6.3	272	2141
SHIJIAZHUANG	38.03N	114.42E	81	-9.1	-7.4	35.7	22.2	34.1	22.8	32.7	22.9	27.0	31.2	26.2	30.2	25.9	21.4	29.8	25.0	20.3	28.9	6.6	5.3	4.4	2484	986
SIPING	43.18N	124.33E	167	-23.3	-21.2	31.0	22.1	29.7	21.7	28.6	21.2	24.8	28.5	24.0	27.5	23.7	18.9	27.3	22.9	18.0	26.5	9.3	7.9	6.8	4472	464
TAI SHAN	36.25N	117.10E	1536	-16.8	-14.8	22.5	16.9	21.6	17.1	20.8	17.3	20.6	21.0	19.9	20.3	20.5	18.4	20.8	19.8	17.6	20.2	18.4	16.3	14.6	4527	41
TAIYUAN	37.78N	112.55E	779	-15.1	-13.1	32.9	20.5	31.5	20.4	30.1	20.1	24.3	29.0	23.3	28.0	23.0	19.5	27.1	22.0	18.3	25.8	9.3	7.6	6.3	3263	503
TANGSHAN	39.67N	118.15E	29	-12.9	-11.0	33.2	22.9	31.8	23.0	30.7	22.7	26.6	30.2	25.7	29.1	25.5	20.8	29.0	24.7	19.8	28.1	8.2	6.7	5.6	2989	761
TAOXIAN	41.63N	123.48E	62	-25.0	-22.8	32.1	22.9	30.9	23.1	29.8	22.7	26.0	29.7	25.2	28.7	25.0	20.2	28.7	24.0	19.0	27.7	10.8	9.2	8.0	4148	562
TIANJIN	39.10N	117.17E	5	-10.2	-8.7	34.2	23.5	32.8	23.4	31.5	23.2	27.2	30.8	26.3	29.7	26.2	21.6	29.6	25.3	20.5	28.8	8.4	6.8	5.5	2724	911
WEIFANG	36.77N	119.18E	22	-11.1	-9.5	34.3	23.7	32.9	23.7	31.5	23.5	27.3	31.3	26.5	30.0	26.2	21.7	29.6	25.5	20.8	28.8	10.1	8.7	7.5	2734	794
WENZHOU	28.02N	120.67E	7	1.1	2.4	33.8	27.5	32.7	27.2	31.8	26.8	28.2	32.5	27.7	31.6	27.0	22.8	30.7	26.6	22.2	30.1	6.5	5.5	4.9	1139	1276
WU LU MU QI	43.80N	87.65E	947	-22.7	-20.2	33.4	16.4	31.8	16.1	30.4	15.7	18.0	28.6	17.4	27.8	15.0	11.9	20.2	13.9	11.1	20.3	7.8	6.1	5.1	4456	510
WUHAN	30.62N	114.13E	23	-2.2	-1.0	35.7	27.6	34.6	27.3	33.5	26.9	28.7	33.2	28.2	32.6	27.8	23.9	31.4	27.1	22.9	31.0	7.0	5.8	5.0	1647	1284
WUHU	31.33N	118.35E	16	-3.3	-1.9	35.8	27.4	34.6	27.1	33.3	26.8	28.5	33.4	27.9	32.8	27.3	23.1	31.4	26.7	22.3	30.8	7.9	6.7	5.9	1773	1157
XIAMEN	24.48N	118.08E	139	6.3	7.4	34.0	26.0	33.0	26.0	32.1	25.8	27.6	30.9	27.1	30.5	26.9	22.9	29.2	26.2	22.0	28.9	8.9	7.8	7.0	522	1656
XIAN	34.30N	108.93E	398	-6.3	-4.8	35.9	23.3	34.4	23.1	33.0	22.9	26.4	32.0	25.5	30.9	25.0	21.0	29.9	24.0	19.9	28.9	7.8	6.5	5.4	2350	891

Meaning of acronyms:
DB: Dry bulb temperature, °C *WB: Wet bulb temperature, °C* *Lat: Latitude, °* *Long: Longitude, °* *Elev: Elevation, m*
DP: Dew point temperature, °C *HR: Humidity ratio, g of moisture per kg of dry air* *WS: Wind speed, m/s*
MCWB: Mean coincident wet bulb temperature, °C *MCDB: Mean coincident dry bulb temperature, °C* *HDD and CDD 18.3: Annual heating and cooling degree-days, base 18.3°C, °C-day*

Station	Lat	Long	Elev	Heating DB		Cooling DB/MCWB						Evaporation WB/MCDB				Dehumidification DP/HR/MCDB						Extreme Annual WS			Heat./Cool. Degree-Days	
						0.4%		1%		2%		0.4%		1%		0.4%			1%							
				99.6%	99%	DB	MCWB	DB	MCWB	DB	MCWB	WB	MCDB	WB	MCDB	DP	HR	MCDB	DP	HR	MCDB	1%	2.5%	5%	HDD	CDD 18.3
XIHUA	33.78N	114.52E	53	-5.9	-4.4	35.0	25.3	33.7	25.5	32.4	25.0	28.5	32.5	27.7	31.4	27.5	23.5	31.3	26.7	22.4	30.3	6.7	5.5	4.7	2151	971
XINGTAI	37.07N	114.50E	78	-7.9	-6.4	35.5	22.4	34.1	22.9	32.8	23.0	27.2	31.3	26.4	30.4	26.1	21.6	29.7	25.3	20.7	29.2	5.9	4.9	4.2	2379	1023
XINING	36.62N	101.77E	2296	-16.2	-14.6	27.4	14.8	25.8	14.0	24.3	13.4	16.8	23.4	15.9	22.1	14.8	14.0	19.2	13.8	13.1	18.2	6.2	5.1	4.2	4193	47
XINYANG	32.13N	114.05E	115	-4.6	-3.2	34.5	26.4	33.3	25.7	32.1	25.2	27.7	32.4	27.1	31.6	26.5	22.4	30.3	26.0	21.6	29.8	8.4	7.2	6.2	1951	1024
XUZHOU	34.28N	117.15E	42	-6.6	-4.9	34.6	25.4	33.3	25.2	32.0	24.6	28.0	32.3	27.3	31.2	26.9	22.7	30.7	26.2	21.8	30.1	6.9	5.9	5.2	2182	998
YANGJIANG	21.87N	111.97E	22	7.2	8.4	33.0	26.6	32.2	26.4	31.6	26.3	27.7	30.6	27.5	30.3	27.1	22.9	29.3	26.7	22.4	29.1	8.1	6.8	5.9	288	2022
YANJI	42.87N	129.50E	178	-22.9	-20.9	31.0	21.9	29.4	21.2	27.8	20.5	24.1	28.9	23.1	27.0	22.7	17.8	26.9	21.8	16.9	25.8	10.1	8.5	7.3	4781	288
YICHANG	30.70N	111.30E	134	-0.8	0.2	35.6	26.6	34.2	26.1	33.0	25.4	28.0	33.1	27.4	32.2	26.7	22.7	31.0	26.2	21.9	30.3	4.7	4.0	3.4	1517	1189
YINCHUAN	38.47N	106.20E	1112	-17.0	-14.6	32.1	19.2	30.8	19.0	29.5	18.4	22.2	28.4	21.2	27.3	20.3	17.2	25.5	19.3	16.1	24.9	8.9	6.8	5.4	3568	455
YINGKOU	40.67N	122.20E	4	-17.7	-15.7	30.6	24.3	29.5	23.6	28.6	23.1	25.8	28.9	25.1	28.2	24.8	19.8	28.1	24.1	19.0	27.3	10.7	9.3	8.1	3666	601
YUEYANG	29.38N	113.08E	52	-0.9	0.1	34.4	27.4	33.6	27.0	32.8	26.7	28.5	32.9	27.8	32.2	27.2	23.1	31.8	26.6	22.3	31.1	7.2	6.3	5.5	1527	1297
YUNCHENG	35.05N	111.05E	365	-8.1	-6.4	36.3	22.6	34.9	22.6	33.5	22.4	25.9	32.4	25.2	31.5	24.2	20.0	29.8	23.4	19.1	29.2	9.4	7.9	6.8	2375	1013
ZHANGJIAKOU	40.78N	114.88E	726	-16.7	-15.1	32.6	18.9	31.0	18.6	29.6	18.5	22.7	28.1	21.9	27.2	21.2	17.3	25.7	20.2	16.3	25.1	7.3	6.1	5.3	3710	520
ZHANJIANG	21.22N	110.40E	28	7.8	9.2	33.9	26.7	33.1	26.8	32.4	26.7	28.1	31.3	27.7	30.8	27.2	23.1	29.8	26.9	22.7	29.6	8.0	6.6	5.8	223	2237
ZHENGZHOU	34.72N	113.65E	111	-6.7	-5.3	35.1	23.8	33.8	24.0	32.5	23.9	27.8	31.6	27.0	30.7	26.8	22.8	30.5	26.0	21.7	29.5	8.4	6.9	5.7	2226	962
ZUNYI	27.70N	106.88E	845	-1.2	-0.1	32.5	22.8	31.5	22.6	30.4	22.4	24.2	29.7	23.8	29.0	22.8	19.5	26.7	22.3	18.9	26.2	4.8	4.0	3.3	1683	838
Colombia																										*5 sites, 0 more on CD-ROM*
BARRANQUILLA/ERNEST	10.88N	74.78W	30	22.8	23.0	34.1	27.1	33.2	26.9	32.9	26.8	28.6	31.3	28.1	30.9	28.0	24.3	29.9	27.2	23.1	29.3	13.2	10.9	9.9	0	3609
BOGOTA/ELDORADO	4.70N	74.13W	2546	2.8	4.1	21.2	13.6	20.8	13.5	20.1	13.4	15.4	19.0	15.0	18.5	14.2	13.8	17.0	13.8	13.5	16.7	8.4	7.0	6.1	1752	0
CALI/ALFONSO BONILL	3.55N	76.38W	969	17.7	18.0	32.1	22.1	31.2	22.0	30.8	22.0	23.5	29.5	22.9	29.4	21.8	18.5	26.8	21.1	17.7	26.0	8.4	6.5	5.5	0	2139
CARTAGENA/RAFAEL NU	10.45N	75.52W	12	23.0	23.8	32.3	27.1	32.1	27.0	31.8	26.9	28.1	31.0	27.7	30.6	27.2	23.0	30.2	26.9	22.7	30.1	9.2	7.9	6.5	0	3533
RIONEGRO/J.M.CORDOV	6.13N	75.43W	2142	10.0	10.9	23.9	15.8	23.2	15.7	23.0	15.6	17.6	21.3	17.1	21.0	16.2	15.1	18.5	16.1	14.9	18.2	9.1	7.6	5.9	412	23
Congo																										*1 site, 0 more on CD-ROM*
BRAZZAVILLE/MAYA-M	4.25S	15.25E	316	18.0	18.9	34.0	24.7	33.1	24.6	32.7	24.5	26.1	31.0	25.7	30.6	24.9	20.8	28.2	24.2	19.9	27.8	5.9	5.0	4.3	0	2799
Costa Rica																										*1 site, 0 more on CD-ROM*
JUAN SANTAMARIA INT	9.98N	84.22W	934	16.6	17.1	30.9	21.0	30.0	20.7	29.2	20.7	24.2	26.9	23.7	26.6	23.8	20.9	25.9	22.9	19.8	25.3	12.7	10.6	9.9	0	1826
Côte d'Ivoire																										*1 site, 0 more on CD-ROM*
ABIDJAN	5.25N	3.93W	8	21.0	21.8	32.8	27.4	32.1	27.2	31.7	27.1	28.8	31.0	28.4	30.6	28.2	24.5	29.7	28.0	24.1	29.6	7.2	6.4	5.9	0	3197
Croatia																										*2 sites, 7 more on CD-ROM*
ZAGREB/MAKSIMIR	45.82N	16.03E	128	-11.1	-8.4	31.6	21.1	30.0	20.8	28.4	20.1	22.2	29.2	21.5	28.3	20.0	14.9	25.2	19.1	14.1	24.7	6.0	5.0	4.2	2873	301
ZAGREB/PLESO	45.73N	16.07E	107	-12.2	-9.1	31.9	22.0	30.2	21.5	28.8	20.7	23.0	29.9	22.2	28.6	20.9	15.8	26.4	20.0	14.9	25.5	8.5	7.2	5.9	2976	268
Cuba																										*3 sites, 2 more on CD-ROM*
AEROPUERTO JOSE MAR	22.98N	82.40W	75	11.0	13.0	33.1	25.5	32.3	25.4	32.0	25.4	27.7	30.5	27.2	30.4	27.1	23.0	29.6	26.2	21.8	29.1	10.4	9.3	8.0	21	2391
CAMAGUEY AEROPUERTO	21.42N	77.85W	118	15.2	16.9	33.3	24.4	33.0	24.5	32.2	24.5	26.7	30.8	26.3	30.3	25.8	21.5	29.1	25.2	20.6	28.3	10.4	9.3	8.2	3	2663
SANTIAGO DE CUBA	19.97N	75.85W	55	18.8	19.8	31.9	25.7	31.2	25.7	31.0	25.7	27.5	29.7	27.0	29.7	27.0	22.8	29.1	26.2	21.8	28.8	10.4	9.5	8.0	0	2836
Czech Republic																										*5 sites, 32 more on CD-ROM*
BRNO/TURANY	49.15N	16.70E	246	-13.5	-10.6	30.1	19.7	28.3	19.0	26.6	18.2	20.8	27.7	19.9	26.4	18.5	13.7	23.7	17.6	13.0	22.7	10.2	8.9	7.9	3498	162
OSTRAVA/MOSNOV	49.68N	18.12E	260	-16.1	-12.7	30.0	19.9	28.0	19.0	26.2	18.2	20.7	27.6	19.8	26.3	18.5	13.8	23.3	17.6	13.0	22.3	10.2	9.0	8.1	3644	107
PRAHA/RUZYNE	50.10N	14.25E	365	-14.6	-11.4	29.2	18.8	27.1	18.1	25.3	17.4	20.0	26.5	19.0	25.3	17.7	13.3	22.7	16.9	12.6	21.2	12.2	10.3	8.9	3754	89
PRAHA-KBELY	50.12N	14.53E	287	-13.0	-10.0	29.6	19.1	27.7	18.6	26.0	17.9	20.6	26.5	19.7	25.0	18.7	14.0	22.4	18.0	13.4	21.7	9.1	7.8	6.8	3458	132
PRAHA-LIBUS	50.02N	14.45E	303	-13.5	-10.4	30.1	18.9	28.1	18.3	26.3	17.5	20.1	27.2	19.2	25.8	17.8	13.2	22.0	17.0	12.6	21.2	8.7	7.2	6.1	3482	133
Denmark																										*4 sites, 27 more on CD-ROM*
DROGDEN	55.53N	12.72E	0	-8.0	-5.9	22.1	N/A	20.9	N/A	19.8	N/A	N/A	N/A	N/A	N/A	N/A	N/A	N/A	N/A	N/A	N/A	18.2	15.8	14.4	3606	23
KOEBENHAVN/KASTRUP	55.62N	12.65E	5	-9.2	-6.7	25.5	17.9	24.0	17.3	22.2	16.5	19.3	23.4	18.4	22.3	17.9	12.9	20.8	16.9	12.1	20.0	12.7	11.4	10.3	3653	45
ROSKILDE/TUNE	55.58N	12.13E	43	-10.1	-7.2	25.9	18.1	24.0	17.4	22.3	16.6	19.6	23.4	18.5	22.4	18.1	13.1	21.4	17.0	12.2	20.1	12.5	11.1	10.0	3784	29
VAERLOESE	55.77N	12.33E	31	-12.1	-8.8	26.2	18.1	24.5	17.6	22.8	16.9	19.6	23.5	18.6	22.7	18.3	13.2	20.8	17.2	12.3	19.7	12.3	10.7	9.4	3821	35
Dominican Republic																										*2 sites, 0 more on CD-ROM*
LAS AMERICAS	18.43N	69.67W	18	18.5	19.1	32.6	26.7	32.1	26.5	31.8	26.4	28.1	31.2	27.6	30.8	27.1	22.9	30.8	26.7	22.3	30.4	7.3	6.3	5.6	0	2860
SANTO DOMINGO	18.43N	69.88W	14	19.5	20.2	32.5	27.2	32.0	27.2	31.6	26.9	28.5	31.4	28.0	31.1	27.6	23.6	31.0	27.1	22.9	30.6	7.4	5.8	4.7	0	2982
Ecuador																										*2 sites, 1 more on CD-ROM*
GUAYAQUIL AEROPUERT	2.15S	79.88W	9	18.8	19.1	33.1	24.4	32.2	24.4	31.9	24.4	26.8	30.4	26.2	29.7	26.0	21.4	29.3	25.2	20.3	28.0	7.3	6.4	5.9	0	2780
QUITO AEROPUERTO	0.13S	78.48W	2812	6.8	7.8	21.9	12.2	21.1	12.2	20.6	12.1	14.5	18.9	14.1	18.4	13.1	13.3	16.1	12.5	12.8	15.3	7.7	6.8	6.0	1402	1
Egypt																										*6 sites, 12 more on CD-ROM*
ALEXANDRIA/NOUZHA	31.20N	29.95E	7	6.9	7.9	33.0	22.2	31.2	23.2	30.2	23.3	25.2	29.6	24.7	29.1	24.0	18.9	28.2	23.2	18.0	27.8	10.2	9.0	8.0	497	1267
ASYUT	27.05N	31.02E	70	4.3	5.4	40.7	20.3	39.3	20.2	38.0	19.9	22.4	35.6	21.7	34.8	18.4	13.4	27.2	17.3	12.4	27.5	10.6	9.4	8.5	539	2039

Meaning of acronyms:

DB: Dry bulb temperature, °C *WB: Wet bulb temperature, °C* *DP: Dew point temperature, °C* *HR: Humidity ratio, g of moisture per kg of dry air* *WS: Wind speed, m/s*

MCWB: Mean coincident wet bulb temperature, °C *MCDB: Mean coincident dry bulb temperature, °C* *HDD and CDD 18.3: Annual heating and cooling degree-days, base 18.3°C, °C-day*

Station	Lat	Long	Elev	Heating DB		Cooling DB/MCWB						Evaporation WB/MCDB				Dehumidification DP/HR/MCDB						Extreme Annual WS			Heat./Cool. Degree-Days	
						0.4%		1%		2%		0.4%		1%		0.4%			1%							
				99.6%	99%	DB / MCWB		DB / MCWB		DB / MCWB		WB / MCDB		WB / MCDB		DP / HR / MCDB			DP / HR / MCDB			1%	2.5%	5%	HDD / CDD 18.3	
PORT SAID	31.27N	32.30E	6	9.3	10.8	32.1	25.1	31.1	25.2	30.2	24.8	26.7	30.5	26.2	30.0	25.2	20.4	29.5	24.9	20.0	29.4	10.8	9.6	8.9	303	1567
PORT SAID/EL GAMIL	31.28N	32.23E	6	9.7	10.7	31.7	25.1	30.8	25.0	30.1	24.6	26.5	30.3	26.0	29.7	25.4	20.5	29.5	24.7	19.8	29.0	11.9	10.4	9.5	326	1482
Estonia																									*1 site, 8 more on CD-ROM*	
TALLINN	59.47N	24.82E	34	-19.1	-15.6	25.9	18.4	24.1	17.5	22.5	16.6	19.6	23.8	18.5	22.5	18.1	13.0	21.4	17.0	12.2	20.4	9.2	8.1	7.2	4649	31
Finland																									*2 sites, 46 more on CD-ROM*	
HELSINKI-VANTAA	60.32N	24.97E	56	-22.8	-19.1	26.7	17.9	24.9	16.8	23.2	16.0	19.1	24.0	18.1	22.8	17.2	12.4	20.5	16.2	11.6	19.5	10.0	8.8	7.8	4856	39
ISOSAARI	60.10N	25.07E	5	-20.2	-16.4	22.8	19.4	21.6	18.5	20.4	17.5	20.1	22.1	19.0	21.0	19.3	14.1	21.6	18.0	13.0	20.5	15.7	14.0	12.5	4655	29
France																									*14 sites, 125 more on CD-ROM*	
CAP COURONNE	43.33N	5.05E	27	-2.9	0.4	30.7	22.6	29.5	22.3	28.3	21.8	24.8	28.7	24.0	27.8	23.6	18.5	27.4	22.8	17.6	26.6	17.1	15.0	13.3	1578	568
CAP POMEGUES	43.27N	5.30E	70	-1.4	1.8	28.6	22.0	27.3	21.9	26.3	21.5	24.2	26.5	23.4	25.7	23.5	18.4	25.6	22.7	17.5	25.0	23.5	20.7	17.9	1523	457
CAPE FERRAT	43.68N	7.33E	144	3.2	4.8	29.0	22.6	28.0	22.5	27.1	22.2	24.5	27.3	23.9	26.7	23.6	18.8	26.5	22.9	18.0	25.9	13.4	10.4	8.4	1353	550
LE BOURGET	48.97N	2.43E	52	-4.2	-2.7	31.1	20.2	29.1	19.5	27.0	19.0	21.6	28.3	20.6	26.9	19.2	14.1	24.0	18.2	13.2	22.9	10.2	8.9	7.9	2548	176
LYON-BRON	45.72N	4.93E	202	-5.4	-3.9	33.6	19.8	31.7	19.7	30.0	19.3	21.6	29.6	20.9	28.7	19.0	14.1	24.5	18.2	13.4	23.7	11.5	10.0	8.6	2389	403
LYON-SATOLAS	45.73N	5.08E	240	-6.9	-4.5	32.4	20.3	30.7	19.9	28.9	19.4	21.7	29.0	20.9	28.0	19.2	14.4	24.5	18.5	13.7	23.6	10.8	9.2	7.9	2588	309
MARIGNANE	43.45N	5.23E	32	-3.1	-1.4	32.7	21.3	31.2	21.0	30.0	20.6	23.5	28.8	22.6	28.1	21.9	16.6	26.5	20.9	15.6	25.9	16.5	14.3	12.4	1692	600
NICE	43.65N	7.20E	27	1.8	2.9	29.5	22.9	28.5	22.6	27.7	22.3	25.0	27.7	24.1	27.1	24.0	19.0	27.1	23.1	17.9	26.5	11.7	9.9	8.2	1432	526
PARIS-AEROPORT CHAR	49.02N	2.53E	112	-6.2	-4.0	30.6	20.2	28.5	19.4	26.6	18.8	21.4	27.7	20.5	26.4	19.2	14.2	23.9	18.2	13.3	22.8	11.6	10.1	8.8	2649	164
PARIS-MONTSOURIS	48.82N	2.33E	77	-2.5	-1.3	31.5	20.3	29.5	19.7	27.5	19.0	21.6	29.3	20.5	27.3	19.2	14.1	24.6	18.2	13.2	23.3	7.3	6.4	5.7	2303	257
PARIS-ORLY	48.72N	2.38E	90	-5.9	-3.8	30.9	20.1	28.9	19.5	27.0	18.7	21.4	28.3	20.5	26.7	19.2	14.1	23.8	18.2	13.2	22.9	11.0	9.5	8.4	2642	182
TOULOUSE BLAGNAC	43.63N	1.37E	154	-4.3	-2.5	33.1	21.1	31.1	20.6	29.4	20.0	22.7	29.7	21.8	28.3	20.6	15.5	25.8	19.7	14.7	24.9	10.4	9.2	8.1	2075	380
TRAPPES	48.77N	2.00E	168	-4.1	-2.7	30.3	19.4	28.2	18.7	26.3	18.2	20.8	27.3	19.9	25.7	18.8	13.9	23.1	17.9	13.1	21.8	7.0	6.1	5.3	2677	151
VILLACOUBLAY	48.77N	2.20E	179	-5.9	-3.7	29.8	19.7	27.9	19.1	26.0	18.4	21.0	27.4	20.0	25.8	18.9	14.0	23.7	17.9	13.2	22.6	9.8	8.6	7.7	2787	154
Gabon																									*1 site, 0 more on CD-ROM*	
LIBREVILLE	0.45N	9.42E	15	21.9	22.4	31.4	27.1	31.0	27.0	30.6	26.8	28.0	30.1	27.6	29.7	27.2	23.1	29.4	27.1	22.8	29.3	7.1	6.3	5.7	0	2974
Gambia																									*1 site, 0 more on CD-ROM*	
BANJUL/YUNDUM	13.20N	16.63W	33	16.2	17.2	37.8	20.2	36.1	20.1	35.0	20.9	27.6	31.5	27.2	30.9	26.5	22.1	29.9	26.1	21.6	29.5	8.9	8.0	7.2	1	3113
Georgia																									*1 site, 4 more on CD-ROM*	
TBILISI	41.68N	44.95E	448	-5.7	-4.2	34.4	21.8	33.0	21.3	31.3	21.0	23.2	31.7	22.4	30.7	20.4	15.9	27.7	19.6	15.1	26.9	20.8	17.7	15.2	2371	659
Germany																									*28 sites, 107 more on CD-ROM*	
BERLIN/DAHLEM	52.47N	13.30E	51	-12.0	-9.1	29.3	19.0	27.3	18.2	25.6	17.4	20.2	26.5	19.3	25.2	18.1	13.1	22.3	17.1	12.3	21.1	7.4	6.5	5.9	3390	118
BERLIN/SCHONEFELD	52.38N	13.52E	47	-13.9	-10.8	29.6	19.0	27.7	18.3	25.8	17.6	20.2	26.5	19.3	25.7	18.1	13.1	22.6	17.1	12.2	21.3	11.1	9.6	8.4	3508	101
BERLIN/TEGEL (FAFB)	52.57N	13.32E	37	-12.4	-9.2	30.0	18.7	28.0	18.0	26.2	17.1	20.0	26.9	19.1	25.7	17.9	12.9	22.1	16.9	12.1	21.0	10.4	9.2	8.2	3317	147
BERLIN/TEMPELHOF	52.47N	13.40E	50	-11.8	-9.2	30.0	18.9	28.0	18.2	26.2	17.5	20.1	26.9	19.2	25.8	18.0	13.0	22.1	16.9	12.1	21.2	10.4	9.1	8.1	3284	147
BREMEN	53.05N	8.80E	3	-10.9	-8.4	28.4	19.4	26.4	18.4	24.5	17.5	20.3	26.1	19.3	24.6	18.3	13.2	22.4	17.3	12.4	21.4	11.4	10.0	8.9	3475	69
CELLE	52.60N	10.02E	52	-11.8	-8.9	30.1	18.9	28.1	18.3	26.2	17.4	20.1	27.8	19.1	26.2	17.4	12.5	22.1	16.5	11.8	21.6	9.3	8.1	7.0	3348	114
DRESDEN/KLOTZSCHE	51.13N	13.77E	230	-13.6	-10.6	29.4	18.7	27.3	18.1	25.7	17.4	20.0	26.6	19.0	25.2	17.5	12.9	22.1	16.7	12.3	21.4	9.6	8.3	7.3	3408	124
DUSSELDORF	51.28N	6.78E	45	-9.9	-6.8	29.6	19.6	27.8	18.7	26.1	17.9	20.5	27.3	19.7	26.0	18.3	13.2	22.9	17.4	12.5	21.9	10.4	9.2	8.1	2929	139
ESSEN/MULHEIM	51.40N	6.97E	154	-9.9	-6.9	28.2	19.3	26.6	18.4	24.8	17.6	20.1	26.2	19.2	25.1	18.0	13.2	22.4	17.1	12.4	21.2	9.7	8.4	7.4	3178	103
FRANKFURT MAIN ARPT	50.05N	8.60E	112	-10.5	-7.8	30.8	19.2	28.9	18.7	27.1	18.1	20.6	27.6	19.7	26.3	18.5	13.5	22.4	17.5	12.7	21.6	10.1	8.7	7.6	3143	166
FUERSTENFELDBRUCK	48.20N	11.27E	535	-15.1	-12.1	29.1	18.9	27.1	18.0	25.2	17.2	19.7	27.2	18.8	25.8	17.0	12.9	23.3	16.1	12.2	21.8	11.1	9.3	7.7	3706	82
GUETERSLOH	51.93N	8.32E	72	-9.9	-7.0	29.9	19.0	27.9	18.5	25.9	17.8	20.4	27.1	19.5	25.6	18.2	13.2	22.1	17.3	12.5	21.3	10.1	8.7	7.6	3117	114
HAMBURG/FUHLSBUTTEL	53.63N	10.00E	16	-11.6	-8.9	27.8	18.9	25.9	18.1	24.0	17.2	20.0	25.8	18.9	24.2	17.9	12.9	22.1	16.9	12.1	21.2	10.2	9.0	8.1	3514	61
HANNOVER	52.47N	9.70E	55	-12.7	-9.7	28.9	19.4	27.0	18.5	25.1	17.6	20.4	26.5	19.4	25.2	18.3	13.3	22.2	17.3	12.5	21.6	10.2	8.9	8.0	3368	80
HEIDELBERG (USA-AF)	49.40N	8.65E	109	-9.8	-6.2	32.0	20.6	30.1	19.9	28.2	18.9	21.7	29.2	20.8	27.9	19.2	14.1	24.3	18.2	13.3	23.7	7.8	6.6	5.7	2798	261
KOLN/BONN (CIV/MIL)	50.87N	7.17E	91	-10.6	-7.5	29.9	19.5	28.0	18.7	26.1	17.8	20.6	27.4	19.6	26.0	18.2	13.3	22.9	17.3	12.5	21.7	9.0	7.9	7.0	3126	107
LEIPZIG	51.32N	12.42E	151	-9.5	-7.2	30.4	19.3	28.4	18.4	26.6	17.9	20.5	27.5	19.6	25.8	18.2	13.4	22.2	17.4	12.7	21.7	6.8	5.9	5.1	3098	169
LEIPZIG/SCHKEUDITZ	51.42N	12.23E	133	-13.3	-10.4	29.8	19.2	27.7	18.5	25.9	17.7	20.2	27.1	19.3	25.7	17.8	13.0	22.7	17.0	12.3	21.8	12.5	10.8	9.4	3393	120
MUNICH	48.13N	11.55E	520	-11.9	-9.2	29.5	19.0	27.7	18.1	26.1	17.5	19.7	27.4	18.9	26.1	17.2	13.1	21.6	16.4	12.5	21.1	7.8	6.4	5.3	3337	157
MUNICH/RIEM	48.13N	11.70E	529	-14.2	-11.2	29.4	18.9	27.6	18.2	25.9	17.7	19.9	26.8	19.1	25.7	17.8	13.6	21.8	17.0	12.9	21.4	11.5	9.6	8.2	3613	96
NOERVENICH	50.83N	6.67E	135	-9.2	-6.4	30.2	19.6	28.2	18.7	26.2	18.0	20.6	27.9	19.7	26.4	18.2	13.3	23.2	17.2	12.5	22.2	10.2	8.7	7.5	3011	121
NURNBERG	49.50N	11.08E	319	-14.4	-10.9	30.2	18.5	28.3	17.9	26.5	17.0	19.7	26.8	18.9	25.5	17.6	13.1	21.3	16.8	12.4	20.6	9.2	7.9	6.8	3507	128
POTSDAM	52.38N	13.07E	81	-12.9	-10.3	29.3	18.9	27.4	18.3	25.6	17.7	20.2	26.6	19.3	25.4	18.3	13.3	22.1	17.1	12.3	21.3	10.8	9.4	8.3	3460	108
QUICKBORN	53.73N	9.88E	17	-9.6	-7.0	28.4	18.8	26.4	18.4	24.6	17.8	20.3	25.5	19.4	24.1	18.7	13.5	21.6	17.7	12.8	20.8	8.9	7.6	6.6	3456	58
ROTH	49.22N	11.10E	395	-14.2	-11.1	30.8	19.2	28.7	18.4	26.8	17.7	20.2	28.2	19.3	26.6	17.6	13.3	22.1	16.8	12.5	21.7	8.4	7.1	6.0	3643	100
STUTTGART/ECHTERDI	48.68N	9.22E	396	-12.7	-10.0	29.3	18.9	27.6	18.4	25.8	17.7	20.0	27.4	19.2	26.0	17.4	13.0	23.1	16.6	12.4	22.2	9.4	7.9	6.8	3490	106
STUTTGART/SCHNARREN	48.83N	9.20E	315	-11.5	-9.0	29.6	19.6	27.8	18.6	26.1	17.9	20.6	27.3	19.7	25.9	18.2	13.6	23.2	17.4	12.9	22.4	9.1	7.7	6.6	3152	160
WUNSTORF	52.47N	9.43E	51	-11.2	-8.6	30.2	19.2	28.0	18.5	26.0	17.5	20.3	27.8	19.3	26.1	17.8	12.9	22.5	16.9	12.1	22.1	10.8	9.4	8.4	3225	117

Meaning of acronyms:
DB: Dry bulb temperature, °C *WB: Wet bulb temperature, °C*
MCWB: Mean coincident wet bulb temperature, °C

Lat: Latitude, °
DP: Dew point temperature, °C
MCDB: Mean coincident dry bulb temperature, °C

Long: Longitude, °
HR: Humidity ratio, g of moisture per kg of dry air
HDD and CDD 18.3: Annual heating and cooling degree-days, base 18.3°C, °C-day

Elev: Elevation, m
WS: Wind speed, m/s

Station	Lat	Long	Elev	Heating DB		Cooling DB/MCWB						Evaporation WB/MCDB				Dehumidification DP/HR/MCDB						Extreme Annual WS			Heat./Cool. Degree-Days	
						0.4%		1%		2%		0.4%		1%		0.4%			1%							
				99.6%	99%	DB / MCWB		DB / MCWB		DB / MCWB		WB / MCDB		WB / MCDB		DP / HR / MCDB			DP / HR / MCDB			1%	2.5%	5%	HDD / CDD 18.3	
Greece																									*3 sites, 21 more on CD-ROM*	
ATHINAI (AIRPORT)	37.90N	23.73E	15	1.6	3.1	35.1	21.1	33.8	20.8	32.4	20.9	24.4	31.0	23.6	30.1	22.2	16.9	28.7	21.2	15.9	28.0	10.0	9.0	8.2	1165	1079
ELEFSIS (AIRPORT)	38.07N	23.55E	31	0.8	2.1	36.2	21.0	35.0	20.5	33.8	20.3	23.1	31.3	22.3	30.9	20.8	15.5	28.0	19.2	14.1	26.4	10.2	9.1	8.3	1266	1134
THESSALONIKI (AIRPORT)	40.52N	22.97E	4	-3.2	-1.9	34.1	21.6	32.8	21.6	31.2	21.0	23.6	30.9	22.7	29.9	21.1	15.8	28.0	20.2	14.9	27.0	12.4	10.0	8.5	1835	787
Guatemala																									*1 site, 0 more on CD-ROM*	
GUATEMALA (AEROPUERTO)	14.58N	90.52W	1489	10.8	11.8	28.0	17.6	27.1	17.7	26.2	17.7	20.1	24.6	19.6	23.9	19.0	16.5	21.2	18.2	15.8	20.6	12.2	10.4	9.6	71	645
Honduras																									*2 sites, 0 more on CD-ROM*	
LA MESA (SAN PEDRO SULA)	15.45N	87.93W	31	17.2	18.2	37.0	25.9	35.9	26.1	35.0	26.0	28.2	33.8	27.6	33.0	26.8	22.5	31.5	26.2	21.6	30.3	8.9	7.9	6.8	0	3237
TEGUCIGALPA	14.05N	87.22W	1007	11.5	12.9	32.0	19.4	31.1	19.8	30.1	19.7	22.5	27.8	22.1	27.5	21.1	17.8	24.5	20.5	17.2	23.7	9.3	8.2	7.1	12	1495
Hungary																									*3 sites, 23 more on CD-ROM*	
BUDAORS	47.45N	18.97E	132	-11.2	-9.0	31.0	20.1	29.3	19.7	27.8	19.2	21.3	28.9	20.5	27.5	18.6	13.7	24.3	17.9	13.1	23.6	13.9	11.6	9.3	3072	246
BUDAPEST/FERIHEGY I	47.43N	19.27E	185	-12.7	-10.0	32.2	21.8	30.6	21.0	28.9	20.0	23.0	30.6	21.7	28.5	20.2	15.2	26.9	19.2	14.3	25.1	13.9	11.1	9.1	3188	258
BUDAPEST/PESTSZENTL	47.43N	19.18E	139	-10.6	-8.6	32.3	20.2	30.6	19.7	28.9	19.0	21.3	29.1	20.6	28.2	18.9	13.9	23.9	18.0	13.2	23.3	7.7	6.5	5.6	3012	332
India																									*36 sites, 15 more on CD-ROM*	
AHMADABAD	23.07N	72.63E	55	10.9	12.2	42.0	23.2	40.9	22.9	39.7	23.1	28.6	33.9	28.1	32.9	27.4	23.5	30.8	27.0	22.8	30.3	6.4	5.5	5.0	11	3435
AKOLA	20.70N	77.07E	309	12.9	14.1	43.2	22.0	42.0	21.7	40.9	21.5	26.8	34.3	26.2	32.1	25.2	21.2	28.5	24.9	20.7	28.0	5.7	4.8	4.0	3	3382
AURANGABAD CHIKALTH	19.85N	75.40E	579	10.5	11.9	40.0	22.7	39.1	22.5	38.1	21.9	26.4	35.0	25.6	32.9	24.5	20.9	29.3	23.9	20.1	27.9	9.3	8.1	6.9	7	2707
BANGALORE	12.97N	77.58E	921	15.1	15.9	34.2	19.9	33.5	19.8	32.6	19.8	23.6	28.8	23.1	28.2	22.3	19.0	25.3	21.7	18.4	24.8	5.7	5.0	4.3	0	2121
BELGAUM/SAMBRA	15.85N	74.62E	747	13.3	14.5	36.3	19.1	35.3	19.2	34.4	19.2	23.9	29.0	23.5	28.1	22.7	19.1	25.4	22.3	18.6	25.0	8.4	7.7	6.7	0	2202
BHOPAL/BAIRAGARH	23.28N	77.35E	523	10.2	11.3	41.7	21.4	40.5	21.2	39.2	21.1	26.2	31.6	25.7	30.6	25.0	21.4	27.9	24.6	20.9	27.5	9.2	8.2	7.5	54	2707
BHUBANESWAR	20.25N	85.83E	46	14.0	15.1	38.5	26.5	37.2	26.5	36.1	26.4	29.3	34.0	28.9	33.5	28.3	24.6	31.3	27.9	24.1	31.0	10.3	9.0	8.0	1	3343
BIKANER	28.00N	73.30E	224	5.6	7.0	44.2	21.3	42.9	22.0	41.6	22.3	28.2	34.4	27.6	33.8	26.9	23.3	30.5	26.3	22.3	30.3	7.0	5.5	4.6	196	3360
BOMBAY/SANTACRUZ	19.12N	72.85E	14	16.5	17.8	35.8	23.0	34.6	23.2	33.8	23.5	27.7	31.4	27.4	31.0	26.8	22.4	29.9	26.3	21.8	29.5	6.9	6.2	5.5	0	3360
CALCUTTA/DUM DUM	22.65N	88.45E	6	11.6	12.8	37.2	26.8	36.2	26.8	35.2	26.7	29.5	34.2	29.1	33.7	28.3	24.6	32.0	28.0	24.1	31.8	5.7	4.9	4.2	16	3056
COIMBATORE/PEELAMED	11.03N	77.05E	399	18.0	18.9	36.7	22.7	35.7	22.8	34.8	22.8	26.0	31.8	25.5	31.0	24.7	20.7	27.6	24.2	20.1	27.1	10.2	8.7	8.0	0	3091
CWC VISHAKHAPATNAM	17.70N	83.30E	66	20.1	20.8	33.7	27.0	32.9	27.5	32.3	27.3	29.1	32.0	28.7	31.6	28.4	24.9	31.4	27.9	24.2	31.1	8.4	7.5	6.7	0	3379
GAUHATI	26.10N	91.58E	54	10.8	11.8	34.5	26.5	33.6	26.5	32.8	26.5	28.7	32.7	28.2	31.9	27.7	23.8	31.1	27.2	23.2	30.4	5.1	4.2	3.4	57	2344
GWALIOR	26.23N	78.25E	207	6.0	7.1	43.7	22.0	42.6	22.3	41.3	22.2	28.2	32.9	27.8	32.2	27.2	23.6	30.4	26.8	23.0	30.0	4.8	3.8	3.3	201	2969
HYDERABAD AIRPORT	17.45N	78.47E	545	13.9	15.2	40.2	22.1	39.1	22.0	38.0	21.9	25.7	31.7	25.1	30.9	24.2	20.5	27.8	23.8	19.9	27.2	8.2	7.1	6.1	0	3095
INDORE	22.72N	75.80E	567	9.1	10.4	40.8	19.7	39.6	19.8	38.4	19.7	25.6	30.3	25.1	29.6	24.5	20.9	27.5	24.1	20.3	26.9	11.2	9.6	8.8	46	2576
JABALPUR	23.20N	79.95E	393	8.4	9.6	42.4	20.7	41.1	20.7	39.7	21.0	26.7	31.4	26.2	30.4	25.6	21.8	28.6	25.1	21.3	28.0	4.2	3.4	3.0	89	2747
JAIPUR/SANGANER	26.82N	75.80E	390	7.1	8.4	42.4	21.3	41.1	21.3	39.8	21.3	27.2	31.4	26.8	30.9	26.3	22.8	29.0	25.9	22.3	28.6	7.1	5.8	5.0	174	2918
JAMSHEDPUR	22.82N	86.18E	142	10.0	11.2	42.3	22.3	40.5	22.6	38.8	23.0	28.1	32.9	27.6	32.2	27.1	23.2	29.8	26.6	22.6	29.4	3.6	3.1	2.5	27	3077
JODHPUR	26.30N	73.02E	224	8.9	10.1	42.6	21.2	41.3	21.7	40.2	21.9	27.5	32.4	27.0	32.0	26.5	22.6	29.6	25.9	21.9	29.1	5.8	4.9	4.1	69	3366
KOZHIKODE	11.25N	75.78E	5	22.1	22.8	33.7	27.8	33.2	27.4	32.7	27.1	28.7	32.7	28.2	32.1	27.5	23.4	31.8	27.1	22.9	31.3	6.7	5.8	5.0	0	3458
LUCKNOW/AMAUSI	26.75N	80.88E	128	6.8	8.0	42.1	23.1	40.8	23.1	39.2	23.6	29.2	33.7	28.8	33.1	28.2	24.8	31.4	27.9	24.3	31.1	7.4	6.1	5.2	188	2756
MADRAS/MINAMBAKKAM	13.00N	80.18E	16	20.0	20.7	38.5	25.7	37.2	25.6	36.2	25.6	28.3	32.9	27.9	32.3	27.2	23.1	30.5	26.8	22.5	30.2	8.3	7.5	6.5	0	3802
MANGALORE/BAJPE	12.92N	74.88E	102	20.6	21.4	34.3	24.9	33.8	24.9	33.2	24.7	27.1	31.3	26.7	30.8	26.1	21.8	28.9	25.7	21.2	28.5	8.0	7.0	6.2	0	3304
NAGPUR SONEGAON	21.10N	79.05E	310	11.7	12.9	43.7	22.1	42.5	21.9	41.2	21.7	26.9	32.2	26.5	31.4	25.7	21.8	28.9	25.2	21.2	28.3	8.0	6.5	5.6	6	3221
NELLORE	14.45N	79.98E	20	20.3	21.0	40.6	26.7	39.1	27.0	37.9	26.8	28.9	35.6	28.5	34.8	27.5	23.5	31.4	27.1	22.9	31.2	5.4	4.4	3.5	0	4047
NEW DELHI/PALAM	28.57N	77.12E	233	6.2	7.2	43.8	22.4	42.0	22.4	40.2	22.5	29.6	32.9	29.1	32.3	29.1	26.5	30.9	28.2	25.1	30.6	8.1	6.9	6.0	286	3011
NEW DELHI/SAFDARJUN	28.58N	77.20E	216	6.3	7.3	42.0	22.2	40.6	22.7	39.3	22.9	28.5	33.6	28.1	33.1	27.3	23.7	30.8	26.9	23.2	30.5	7.1	6.0	5.0	270	2762
PATIALA	30.33N	76.47E	251	5.0	6.0	41.4	24.3	39.8	24.2	38.2	24.5	29.3	33.5	29.0	33.3	28.4	25.4	31.6	28.0	24.8	31.4	4.4	3.4	2.8	414	2356
PATNA	25.60N	85.10E	60	8.2	9.3	41.0	23.4	39.5	23.4	37.9	23.8	28.9	33.7	28.6	33.0	28.0	24.2	30.9	27.6	23.7	30.6	6.4	5.6	5.0	129	2843
POONA	18.53N	73.85E	559	9.7	10.9	38.1	19.7	37.1	19.6	36.0	19.7	24.6	29.8	24.2	29.0	23.4	19.5	26.2	23.0	19.0	25.7	5.2	4.3	3.4	9	2298
RAJKOT	22.30N	70.78E	138	11.8	13.2	41.0	22.1	39.8	22.2	38.7	22.6	27.9	33.5	27.4	32.3	26.7	22.7	29.4	26.4	22.2	29.1	11.0	9.4	8.5	5	3410
SHOLAPUR	17.67N	75.90E	479	16.0	17.2	40.9	21.9	39.9	22.2	38.9	22.0	26.5	32.7	25.9	31.8	25.2	21.5	28.8	24.6	20.7	28.2	3.4	2.9	2.4	0	3461
SURAT	21.20N	72.83E	12	14.4	15.6	37.8	22.5	36.4	22.9	35.2	23.1	28.1	31.9	27.7	31.4	27.2	22.9	29.9	26.7	22.4	29.6	5.6	4.9	4.1	0	3418
THIRUVANANTHAPURAM	8.48N	76.95E	64	22.1	22.7	33.7	25.7	33.1	25.7	32.7	25.6	27.5	31.5	27.1	31.1	26.4	22.1	29.5	26.1	21.6	29.3	6.1	5.2	4.4	0	3374
TIRUCHCHIRAPALLI	10.77N	78.72E	88	20.0	20.8	38.9	25.4	38.1	25.4	37.2	25.2	27.7	34.6	27.2	33.8	26.2	21.9	30.1	25.8	21.3	29.7	11.6	10.6	9.2	0	3984
Indonesia																									*8 sites, 2 more on CD-ROM*	
DENPASAR/NGURAH RAI	8.75S	115.17E	1	21.8	22.6	32.6	26.6	32.1	26.4	31.7	26.3	27.6	30.8	27.2	30.5	26.9	22.5	29.8	26.2	21.6	29.2	8.0	6.9	6.0	0	3367
JAKARTA/SOEKARNO-HA	6.12S	106.65E	8	22.0	22.8	33.8	25.7	33.1	25.8	32.8	25.9	27.8	31.3	27.5	31.0	27.0	22.7	30.4	26.2	21.7	29.5	9.7	8.4	7.3	0	3398
MEDAN/POLONIA	3.57N	98.68E	25	22.3	22.8	34.1	26.2	33.4	26.2	33.0	26.2	27.6	32.0	27.2	31.5	26.2	21.7	29.9	26.0	21.5	29.7	6.1	5.3	4.8	0	3391
MENADO/ SAM RATULAN	1.53N	124.92E	80	20.3	21.2	32.9	24.0	32.5	24.2	32.0	24.4	26.4	30.2	26.1	29.9	25.3	20.6	28.0	25.1	20.4	27.8	7.6	5.9	4.9	0	3018

Meaning of acronyms:
DB: Dry bulb temperature, °C | *WB: Wet bulb temperature, °C* | *MCWB: Mean coincident wet bulb temperature, °C*
Lat: Latitude, ° | *DP: Dew point temperature, °C* | *MCDB: Mean coincident dry bulb temperature, °C*
Long: Longitude, ° | *HR: Humidity ratio, g of moisture per kg of dry air*
Elev: Elevation, m | *WS: Wind speed, m/s* | *HDD and CDD 18.3: Annual heating and cooling degree-days, base 18.3°C, °C-day*

Station	Lat	Long	Elev	Heating DB		Cooling DB/MCWB						Evaporation WB/MCDB				Dehumidification DP/HR/MCDB						Extreme Annual WS			Heat./Cool. Degree-Days	
						0.4%		1%		2%		0.4%		1%		0.4%			1%							
				99.6%	99%	DB	MCWB	DB	MCWB	DB	MCWB	WB	MCDB	WB	MCDB	DP	HR	MCDB	DP	HR	MCDB	1%	2.5%	5%	HDD	CDD 18.3
SURABAYA/JUANDA	7.37S	112.77E	3	20.9	21.8	34.2	24.5	33.6	24.6	33.1	24.7	27.0	31.1	26.7	30.8	26.0	21.3	28.8	25.6	20.8	28.6	8.3	7.3	6.1	0	3503
UJUNG PANDANG/HASAN	5.07S	119.55E	14	20.4	21.1	34.1	23.4	33.3	23.9	32.9	24.1	27.1	30.5	26.7	30.2	26.2	21.6	28.6	25.9	21.3	28.4	7.3	6.1	5.3	0	3221
Iran, Islamic Republic of																										*17 sites, 7 more on CD-ROM*
ABADAN	30.37N	48.25E	6	4.9	6.0	47.7	22.5	46.7	22.3	45.7	22.0	28.5	35.4	27.1	35.9	26.9	22.5	32.9	24.8	19.9	31.9	10.5	9.3	8.2	411	3263
AHWAZ	31.33N	48.67E	22	5.0	6.2	47.6	22.8	46.7	22.6	45.7	22.3	28.0	35.9	26.4	37.7	26.0	21.4	32.9	23.5	18.3	32.8	9.3	7.8	6.7	438	3269
ANZALI	37.47N	49.47E	-26	1.9	3.0	30.3	25.3	29.7	25.0	29.0	24.7	26.7	29.2	26.1	28.8	26.0	21.3	28.9	25.3	20.4	28.3	11.1	8.9	7.1	1521	833
ARAK	34.10N	49.77E	1708	-15.7	-11.8	36.2	16.4	35.1	15.9	34.0	15.5	19.1	32.4	17.8	31.8	14.1	12.3	27.2	12.3	11.0	25.3	8.4	7.5	6.4	2437	874
BANDARABBASS	27.22N	56.37E	10	9.3	10.9	41.8	23.7	40.1	25.2	38.8	25.9	31.2	35.1	30.7	34.7	30.2	27.6	33.8	29.9	27.0	33.6	8.6	7.5	6.8	71	3220
ESFAHAN	32.47N	51.67E	1550	-7.0	-5.1	39.0	17.7	38.0	17.2	36.8	16.8	19.0	36.5	18.1	35.9	12.1	10.6	28.0	10.6	9.6	26.5	10.2	8.6	7.4	1977	1074
HAMEDAN	34.85N	48.53E	1749	-16.8	-12.9	35.5	17.8	34.3	16.9	33.2	16.4	19.5	33.0	18.4	31.9	14.5	12.8	27.7	12.9	11.5	26.8	10.3	8.5	7.2	2804	551
KASHAN	33.98N	51.45E	982	-2.8	-1.0	41.7	20.0	40.5	19.5	39.3	19.1	21.9	38.5	21.0	37.8	16.0	12.8	32.6	14.4	11.6	31.7	6.2	4.6	3.4	1438	1833
KERMAN	30.25N	56.97E	1754	-6.8	-4.9	38.0	16.3	36.9	15.8	35.8	15.5	17.8	34.4	17.0	34.0	11.0	10.1	22.7	9.7	9.3	22.7	11.5	9.6	7.9	1619	1017
KERMANSHAH	34.27N	47.12E	1322	-7.3	-5.1	39.6	18.9	38.5	18.2	37.2	17.6	20.5	37.4	19.4	36.5	13.5	11.3	29.8	12.0	10.3	28.0	9.7	8.2	7.1	2070	1002
MASHHAD	36.27N	59.63E	999	-7.5	-5.1	37.1	19.1	35.9	18.8	34.8	18.3	22.0	33.6	20.8	33.0	17.9	14.6	30.6	16.2	13.0	28.2	9.1	7.8	6.8	2061	1014
ORUMIEH	37.53N	45.08E	1316	-10.7	-8.6	32.8	17.9	31.5	17.7	30.3	17.3	19.8	29.4	19.0	28.7	16.5	13.8	25.1	15.4	12.9	24.6	9.0	7.0	5.6	2899	451
SHIRAZ	29.53N	52.53E	1481	-1.8	-0.2	39.1	18.2	38.1	17.7	37.0	17.2	20.0	35.2	19.2	34.7	14.9	12.7	29.2	13.1	11.2	27.9	9.8	8.2	7.0	1356	1450
TABRIZ	38.08N	46.28E	1361	-10.9	-8.5	35.2	16.6	34.0	16.2	32.8	16.0	18.4	31.0	17.8	30.0	14.1	11.8	23.5	13.1	11.1	23.6	10.4	9.1	7.9	2667	802
TEHRAN-MEHRABAD	35.68N	51.32E	1191	-2.8	-1.3	38.5	19.0	37.2	18.7	36.1	18.3	22.5	33.0	21.0	33.2	18.9	15.9	31.0	16.9	13.9	29.6	11.4	9.7	7.9	1588	1540
ZAHEDAN	29.47N	60.88E	1370	-4.6	-2.7	39.1	16.5	38.0	16.0	36.9	15.4	19.0	34.1	17.5	34.8	12.9	10.9	25.3	10.8	9.5	20.6	12.0	10.1	8.7	1161	1456
ZANJAN	36.68N	48.48E	1663	-13.4	-10.7	34.0	15.6	32.7	15.6	31.4	15.1	18.0	29.8	17.2	28.9	13.7	12.0	23.3	12.8	11.3	22.1	9.8	8.0	6.9	2996	424
Ireland																										*2 sites, 13 more on CD-ROM*
CASEMENT AERODROME	53.30N	6.43W	93	-2.6	-1.2	23.1	17.5	21.4	16.7	20.1	16.1	18.4	21.6	17.4	20.3	17.1	12.3	19.8	16.2	11.6	18.9	15.2	13.3	11.9	3137	9
DUBLIN AIRPORT	53.43N	6.25W	85	-1.9	-0.7	22.1	17.1	20.7	16.4	19.5	15.8	18.0	20.8	17.1	19.7	16.8	12.1	19.4	16.0	11.5	18.5	13.4	12.0	10.6	3135	6
Israel																										*2 sites, 4 more on CD-ROM*
BEN-GURION INT. AIR	32.00N	34.90E	49	5.0	6.2	34.9	20.8	33.1	22.4	32.0	22.8	25.9	30.8	25.1	30.1	24.2	19.2	29.1	23.6	18.5	28.6	10.1	8.9	8.0	619	1289
SDE-DOV (TEL-AVIV)	32.10N	34.78E	4	7.1	8.4	31.2	23.8	30.2	24.2	29.7	24.1	26.8	29.3	26.0	29.0	26.0	21.4	29.0	25.1	20.2	28.5	12.0	9.7	8.3	519	1265
Italy																										*16 sites, 62 more on CD-ROM*
BARI/PALESE MACCHIE	41.13N	16.78E	49	0.9	2.0	33.8	22.8	31.9	22.5	30.2	21.9	25.3	29.5	24.3	28.7	24.1	19.1	27.6	23.0	17.9	26.9	9.5	8.3	7.2	1531	640
BOLOGNA/BORGO PANIG	44.53N	11.30E	49	-4.8	-3.1	34.1	23.1	32.8	22.9	31.2	22.2	24.9	31.3	24.0	30.2	23.0	17.8	28.4	22.0	16.8	27.4	7.2	6.1	5.2	2213	654
CATANIA/FONTANAROSS	37.47N	15.05E	17	1.6	2.9	35.0	23.1	33.1	23.3	31.9	23.0	26.4	29.9	25.6	29.5	25.4	20.6	28.1	24.5	19.5	27.6	9.9	8.4	7.3	1102	859
CATANIA/SIGONELLA	37.40N	14.92E	22	2.0	3.2	36.1	21.5	34.1	21.6	32.9	21.7	25.7	29.1	24.8	28.6	25.0	20.1	27.0	24.0	18.9	26.5	12.1	10.4	9.3	1122	924
FIRENZE/PERETOLA	43.80N	11.20E	38	-3.1	-1.4	35.1	23.0	33.6	22.6	32.1	21.8	24.6	31.8	23.7	30.5	22.8	17.6	27.1	21.8	16.5	26.9	8.7	7.3	6.2	1684	747
GENOVA/SESTRI	44.42N	8.85E	3	1.0	2.7	29.9	23.1	28.9	23.4	28.0	23.2	26.0	27.7	25.1	27.3	25.2	20.4	27.2	24.2	19.2	26.7	11.7	10.4	9.4	1411	638
GRAZZANISE	41.05N	14.07E	10	-0.9	0.2	32.1	22.7	31.0	22.6	30.0	22.7	25.9	29.2	25.0	28.6	24.9	20.0	28.3	23.9	18.8	27.5	10.0	8.4	7.1	1581	595
MILANO/LINATE	45.43N	9.28E	103	-5.1	-3.5	33.0	24.1	31.6	23.2	30.2	22.4	25.2	31.0	24.2	29.7	23.5	18.5	28.5	22.6	17.5	27.5	7.3	5.6	4.5	2265	588
NAPLES	40.90N	14.30E	93	2.0	3.2	33.5	23.6	32.1	23.2	31.0	22.9	25.9	30.9	24.9	30.2	24.2	19.3	29.3	23.1	18.1	28.4	8.2	6.8	5.7	1218	862
NAPOLI/CAPODICHINO	40.85N	14.30E	72	0.6	1.9	33.1	23.4	31.9	23.3	30.8	23.2	26.3	29.9	25.4	29.2	25.2	20.5	28.5	24.2	19.2	27.7	9.4	7.8	6.6	1368	742
PALERMO/PUNTA RAISI	38.18N	13.10E	21	6.8	7.8	33.5	22.3	31.6	22.9	30.1	24.0	26.9	29.3	26.2	28.8	26.1	21.6	28.8	25.2	20.4	28.2	13.1	11.4	9.9	801	1002
PRATICA DI MARE	41.65N	12.45E	21	0.8	1.9	30.9	23.2	29.8	23.4	28.9	23.8	26.2	28.4	25.3	28.0	25.2	20.4	28.0	24.2	19.2	27.3	10.1	8.5	7.4	1373	596
ROMA FIUMICINO	41.80N	12.23E	3	-0.8	0.7	31.0	22.8	30.0	22.9	29.0	22.9	25.9	28.5	25.1	27.9	25.1	20.2	27.6	24.1	19.0	27.0	11.5	9.8	8.4	1525	555
ROMA/CIAMPINO	41.78N	12.58E	105	-1.2	-0.1	33.2	21.9	32.1	21.7	30.9	21.4	24.7	28.8	23.9	28.2	23.8	18.9	26.7	22.8	17.8	26.0	11.3	9.3	7.8	1644	633
TORINO/BRIC DELLA C	45.03N	7.73E	710	-4.4	-3.1	28.2	20.4	27.1	19.9	25.9	19.4	22.8	25.8	21.9	24.9	21.9	18.1	24.3	20.9	17.0	23.9	8.7	7.0	5.4	2631	278
TORINO/CASELLE	45.22N	7.65E	287	-6.0	-4.6	31.0	22.5	29.8	21.9	28.3	21.1	24.0	28.6	23.1	27.6	22.7	18.1	26.4	21.8	17.1	25.6	6.3	4.6	3.7	2533	388
Jamaica																										*1 site, 1 more on CD-ROM*
KINGSTON/NORMAN MAN	17.93N	76.78W	14	22.1	22.8	33.3	25.9	33.0	25.9	32.5	25.7	28.1	30.4	27.6	30.3	27.6	23.6	29.3	27.0	22.8	29.2	14.4	13.2	12.1	0	3567
Japan																										*65 sites, 125 more on CD-ROM*
AKITA	39.72N	140.10E	21	-5.5	-4.4	31.5	24.2	30.0	23.7	28.5	23.1	25.1	29.5	24.5	28.6	23.9	18.8	27.4	23.2	18.1	26.9	12.3	10.7	9.3	2869	473
ASAHIKAWA	43.77N	142.37E	116	-18.4	-16.0	29.9	22.9	28.1	21.4	26.6	20.5	23.8	28.4	22.8	26.8	22.4	17.3	26.8	21.5	16.4	25.7	7.1	5.8	4.9	4343	226
ASHIYA AB	33.88N	130.65E	33	-1.1	0.0	32.2	25.7	31.2	25.7	30.1	25.4	26.7	30.1	26.2	29.5	25.9	21.3	29.0	25.2	20.4	28.1	10.4	9.2	8.1	1732	812
ATSUGI NAS	35.45N	139.45E	65	-1.2	-0.2	32.9	25.4	31.8	25.0	30.2	24.5	26.2	30.2	25.8	29.6	25.1	20.4	27.9	24.8	20.0	27.9	10.4	9.1	8.1	1727	824
CHIBA	35.60N	140.10E	19	0.4	1.1	32.3	25.6	31.3	25.4	30.4	25.0	26.5	30.5	26.1	29.8	25.5	20.7	28.9	25.0	20.1	28.4	12.3	10.5	9.0	1637	856
FUKUOKA	33.58N	130.38E	15	0.6	1.6	33.4	25.6	32.5	25.4	31.5	25.1	26.5	31.4	26.0	30.9	25.1	20.3	29.4	24.7	19.7	28.9	8.4	7.3	6.4	1473	1021
FUKUOKA AIRPORT	33.58N	130.45E	12	-0.7	0.8	33.9	25.6	32.9	25.4	31.9	25.1	26.6	31.2	26.2	30.7	25.2	20.4	29.0	24.9	20.0	28.8	9.3	8.3	7.4	1578	1014
FUKUYAMA	34.45N	133.25E	3	-2.7	-1.6	33.8	25.3	32.8	25.3	31.9	25.0	26.2	32.0	25.7	31.3	24.6	19.6	29.1	24.1	19.1	28.8	6.1	5.2	4.4	1842	951
FUSHIKI	36.80N	137.05E	13	-2.4	-1.5	33.4	24.6	31.8	24.5	30.3	24.1	25.7	30.4	25.2	29.9	24.5	19.5	28.2	23.9	18.8	27.6	7.5	6.4	5.5	2181	713
FUTENMA	26.27N	127.75E	84	10.8	11.8	32.2	26.6	31.9	26.5	31.1	26.3	27.9	30.5	27.3	29.9	27.1	23.1	29.6	26.2	21.9	28.8	11.2	9.7	8.5	202	1853
GIFU	35.40N	136.77E	17	-1.4	-0.5	35.1	25.3	33.8	24.9	32.4	24.5	26.3	32.2	25.8	31.3	24.9	20.0	28.3	24.5	19.5	28.1	8.0	7.0	6.2	1752	1029

Meaning of acronyms: *Lat: Latitude, °* *Long: Longitude, °* *Elev: Elevation, m*
DB: Dry bulb temperature, °C *WB: Wet bulb temperature, °C* *DP: Dew point temperature, °C* *HR: Humidity ratio, g of moisture per kg of dry air* *WS: Wind speed, m/s*
MCWB: Mean coincident wet bulb temperature, °C *MCDB: Mean coincident dry bulb temperature, °C* *HDD and CDD 18.3: Annual heating and cooling degree-days, base 18.3°C, °C-day*

Station	Lat	Long	Elev	Heating DB		Cooling DB/MCWB						Evaporation WB/MCDB				Dehumidification DP/HR/MCDB						Extreme Annual WS			Heat./Cool. Degree-Days	
						0.4%		1%		2%		0.4%		1%		0.4%			1%							
				99.6%	99%	DB / MCWB		DB / MCWB		DB / MCWB		WB / MCDB		WB / MCDB		DP / HR / MCDB			DP / HR / MCDB			1%	2.5%	5%	HDD / CDD 18.3	
GIFU AB	35.38N	136.87E	42	-3.2	-2.2	34.1	25.3	33.0	24.9	31.8	24.5	26.4	30.9	25.9	30.4	25.2	20.4	27.9	24.8	20.0	27.8	8.0	7.0	6.0	1982	888
HAMAMATSU	34.72N	137.72E	33	0.1	1.0	32.7	24.9	31.3	24.9	30.3	24.7	26.5	29.8	26.1	29.2	25.7	21.0	28.1	25.2	20.4	27.9	8.9	8.0	7.2	1515	931
HAMAMATSU AB	34.75N	137.70E	48	-1.1	-0.1	32.8	25.2	31.1	25.2	30.1	24.8	26.4	29.9	26.0	29.2	25.8	21.2	28.1	25.1	20.3	27.6	9.7	8.8	8.0	1648	842
HIMEJI	34.83N	134.67E	40	-2.3	-1.3	33.4	25.5	32.4	25.2	31.4	24.9	26.5	31.3	26.0	30.5	25.2	20.4	28.9	24.7	19.8	28.5	8.6	7.3	6.3	1879	918
HIROSHIMA	34.40N	132.47E	53	-1.1	-0.1	33.4	25.4	32.4	25.2	31.4	24.9	26.4	31.3	25.9	30.6	25.0	20.3	28.9	24.6	19.7	28.5	9.3	8.2	7.3	1698	964
IIZUKA	33.65N	130.70E	38	-1.8	-0.7	33.6	25.7	32.6	25.6	31.5	25.2	26.6	31.7	26.2	30.9	25.2	20.5	28.8	24.9	20.0	28.5	7.3	6.3	5.5	1720	941
IRUMA AB	35.83N	139.42E	93	-4.1	-2.9	33.9	25.6	32.2	25.0	30.9	24.6	26.4	31.4	25.8	30.4	25.1	20.4	28.4	24.2	19.4	27.7	9.7	8.4	7.2	2101	702
KADENA (USAF\NAVY)	26.35N	127.77E	45	10.0	11.1	33.2	27.0	32.8	27.0	32.1	26.8	28.3	31.0	27.9	30.6	27.8	24.0	30.1	27.1	23.0	29.8	11.6	9.8	8.6	197	1945
KAGOSHIMA	31.55N	130.55E	32	0.8	2.0	33.2	25.6	32.4	25.4	31.6	25.3	26.7	30.9	26.3	30.4	25.6	20.9	28.9	25.2	20.4	28.8	8.9	7.5	6.6	1142	1237
KANAZAWA	36.58N	136.63E	33	-1.8	-0.9	33.1	24.8	32.0	24.7	30.8	24.4	25.9	30.8	25.4	30.2	24.5	19.6	28.8	23.9	18.9	28.3	11.7	9.9	8.5	2060	776
KANSAI INTERNATIONA	34.43N	135.25E	8	1.8	2.2	33.0	25.8	32.0	25.6	31.1	25.6	26.8	30.4	26.5	30.0	26.0	21.4	29.0	25.2	20.4	28.6	12.8	11.1	9.7	1515	1082
KOBE	34.70N	135.22E	30	-0.5	0.6	32.9	24.9	31.8	24.7	30.8	24.5	26.2	30.2	25.7	29.6	25.1	20.3	28.4	24.7	19.7	28.2	9.4	8.1	7.1	1651	1003
KOCHI	33.57N	133.55E	5	-1.0	0.0	32.6	25.0	31.6	24.8	30.7	24.6	26.2	29.9	25.9	29.6	25.3	20.4	28.2	24.8	19.8	28.0	5.8	4.9	4.2	1429	999
KOMATSU AB	36.40N	136.40E	9	-2.2	-1.2	33.1	24.7	31.8	24.7	30.2	24.3	26.1	30.3	25.5	29.7	25.0	20.1	28.4	24.1	19.1	27.7	11.1	9.4	8.3	2161	698
KUMAGAYA	36.15N	139.38E	31	-2.2	-1.2	35.2	25.4	33.8	24.9	32.3	24.3	26.4	32.4	25.8	31.4	25.0	20.1	28.1	24.4	19.4	28.1	7.9	6.8	5.8	1863	867
KUMAMOTO	32.82N	130.70E	39	-1.9	-0.7	34.2	25.2	33.2	25.0	32.2	24.8	26.5	31.3	26.1	30.6	25.4	20.7	28.4	24.9	20.1	28.1	7.2	6.0	5.2	1537	1106
KURE	34.23N	132.55E	5	-0.1	0.9	32.4	25.2	31.6	25.0	30.7	24.7	25.9	30.6	25.5	30.0	24.6	19.6	28.5	24.2	19.1	28.2	7.0	6.0	5.2	1596	982
KYOTO	35.02N	135.73E	46	-1.1	-0.2	34.6	24.7	33.5	24.4	32.2	24.1	25.7	32.0	25.2	31.2	24.0	19.0	28.4	23.6	18.5	28.3	5.2	4.5	4.1	1775	1017
MATSUYAMA	33.85N	132.78E	34	-0.3	0.6	33.1	24.8	32.2	24.6	31.3	24.4	25.7	30.9	25.2	30.3	24.2	19.2	27.9	23.8	18.7	27.8	5.9	5.1	4.4	1611	969
MIYAZAKI	31.93N	131.42E	15	-0.4	0.8	33.7	25.7	32.5	25.6	31.3	25.4	26.9	31.0	26.4	30.4	25.8	21.1	28.9	25.4	20.6	28.6	9.1	7.7	6.6	1271	1077
NAGANO	36.67N	138.20E	419	-6.9	-5.7	32.6	23.4	31.2	23.0	29.7	22.5	24.3	30.3	23.7	29.3	22.6	18.2	27.3	22.0	17.5	26.8	7.9	7.0	6.2	2759	611
NAGASAKI	32.73N	129.87E	35	0.6	1.7	32.5	25.4	31.6	25.4	30.6	25.2	26.7	30.0	26.3	29.5	25.9	21.3	28.7	25.4	20.7	28.4	7.8	6.5	5.6	1386	1029
NAGOYA	35.17N	136.97E	56	-1.5	-0.6	34.3	24.8	33.0	24.6	31.7	24.2	26.0	31.2	25.6	30.5	24.8	20.0	28.0	24.2	19.3	27.7	8.6	7.5	6.6	1774	972
NAGOYA AIRPORT	35.25N	136.92E	17	-2.2	-1.2	34.5	25.0	33.2	24.8	32.0	24.3	26.2	31.1	25.8	30.5	25.1	20.2	28.1	24.2	19.2	27.8	9.8	8.4	7.3	1855	969
NAHA	26.20N	127.68E	53	11.7	12.5	32.1	26.3	31.6	26.2	31.1	26.1	27.2	30.2	27.0	30.0	26.5	22.1	29.1	26.1	21.7	28.9	13.1	11.0	9.7	162	1922
NAHA AIRPORT	26.20N	127.65E	6	12.0	12.9	32.2	26.4	31.9	26.4	31.1	26.5	27.6	30.1	27.2	29.9	27.0	22.7	29.9	26.2	21.7	29.3	13.3	11.6	10.3	132	1999
NARA	34.70N	135.83E	106	-2.2	-1.4	34.1	24.7	33.0	24.6	31.8	24.3	25.8	31.6	25.3	30.9	24.2	19.4	28.0	23.7	18.8	27.6	4.6	4.0	3.4	1937	872
NIIGATA	37.92N	139.05E	6	-2.2	-1.3	32.8	25.0	31.5	24.7	30.1	24.2	25.9	30.8	25.3	30.0	24.5	19.5	28.8	23.9	18.8	28.2	10.4	9.1	8.0	2276	698
NYUTABARU AB	32.08N	131.45E	82	-1.8	-0.1	32.2	25.4	31.1	25.6	30.0	25.4	26.7	29.7	26.2	29.2	26.1	21.7	28.4	25.2	20.6	27.8	9.9	8.3	7.0	1398	913
OITA	33.23N	131.62E	13	-0.7	0.3	33.2	25.3	32.1	25.2	31.0	24.9	26.3	30.9	25.8	30.2	25.1	20.2	28.6	24.6	19.6	28.2	7.2	6.2	5.4	1594	909
OKAYAMA	34.67N	133.92E	18	-1.2	-0.2	34.4	25.2	33.4	24.9	32.3	24.6	26.2	31.8	25.7	31.1	24.7	19.8	28.4	24.3	19.3	28.4	9.9	8.3	7.0	1727	1054
ONAHAMA	36.95N	140.90E	5	-2.7	-1.7	28.9	23.9	27.7	23.7	26.8	23.3	25.0	27.4	24.5	26.7	24.2	19.2	26.4	23.7	18.6	26.0	8.3	7.1	6.3	2224	457
OSAKA	34.68N	135.52E	83	0.3	1.2	34.2	24.8	33.2	24.7	32.2	24.4	26.1	31.6	25.6	31.0	24.6	19.8	28.9	24.1	19.2	28.7	9.2	8.0	6.9	1577	1114
OSAKA INTERNATIONAL	34.78N	135.43E	15	-1.8	-0.8	34.2	25.3	33.2	25.0	32.1	24.7	26.5	31.7	26.0	31.0	25.1	20.2	28.8	24.4	19.4	28.5	8.4	7.4	6.5	1775	1028
OTARU	43.18N	141.02E	26	-9.7	-8.5	28.0	22.3	26.4	21.1	24.9	20.5	23.1	26.9	22.2	25.4	21.7	16.4	25.4	21.0	15.7	24.7	8.0	6.9	6.1	3703	204
OZUKI AB	34.05N	131.05E	7	-0.9	0.1	32.2	25.7	31.2	25.7	30.2	25.4	26.7	30.3	26.4	29.8	25.9	21.3	29.6	25.1	20.3	28.6	11.0	9.3	8.1	1722	858
SAPPORO	43.07N	141.33E	26	-10.6	-9.2	29.2	22.8	27.6	21.8	26.1	20.7	23.7	27.8	22.8	26.5	22.3	17.1	26.6	21.4	16.1	25.6	9.1	7.7	6.6	3673	263
SENDAI	38.27N	140.90E	43	-4.2	-3.1	30.8	24.2	29.3	23.6	27.9	23.0	25.1	28.9	24.6	27.9	24.1	19.1	27.0	23.6	18.5	26.5	10.3	8.8	7.6	2571	448
SHIMOFUSA AB	35.80N	140.02E	33	-2.9	-1.8	33.2	25.5	32.0	25.1	30.9	24.9	26.5	31.0	26.0	30.2	25.2	20.4	28.5	24.9	20.1	28.3	10.6	9.0	7.6	1888	772
SHIMONOSEKI	33.95N	130.93E	19	1.1	2.2	31.8	25.5	30.9	25.2	30.1	24.9	26.3	30.0	25.8	29.6	25.2	20.4	28.8	24.7	19.8	28.4	10.3	8.9	7.7	1475	938
SHIZUHAMA AB	34.82N	138.30E	10	-0.9	0.2	32.8	25.9	31.2	25.6	30.2	25.3	26.9	30.3	26.5	29.7	26.1	21.5	28.7	25.4	20.6	28.2	10.8	9.7	8.7	1493	884
SHIZUOKA	34.98N	138.40E	15	-0.3	0.8	33.0	25.1	31.6	25.0	30.5	24.7	26.4	30.5	25.9	29.7	25.2	20.4	28.5	24.8	19.8	28.2	6.3	5.5	5.0	1454	918
SUMOTO	34.33N	134.90E	112	-0.1	0.8	31.8	25.1	30.8	25.0	29.8	24.8	26.2	29.9	25.7	29.2	25.2	20.6	28.3	24.7	20.0	27.9	7.2	6.1	5.3	1723	873
TADOTSU	34.28N	133.75E	5	-0.1	1.0	33.6	25.0	32.6	24.7	31.7	24.5	25.9	31.4	25.5	30.8	24.4	19.4	28.8	23.9	18.8	28.6	7.5	6.4	5.5	1631	1026
TAKAMATSU	34.32N	134.05E	10	-0.9	0.1	34.0	25.1	32.9	25.0	31.8	24.9	26.3	31.4	25.9	30.8	25.0	20.1	28.7	24.6	19.6	28.5	8.1	6.9	6.0	1712	988
TOKYO	35.68N	139.77E	36	0.5	1.3	33.2	25.0	32.0	24.7	31.0	24.3	26.0	30.8	25.5	30.2	24.6	19.7	28.5	24.1	19.1	28.5	8.6	7.5	6.6	1611	902
TOKYO INTERNATIONAL	35.55N	139.78E	9	0.1	1.1	32.9	25.8	31.8	25.4	30.4	25.0	26.6	30.6	26.1	29.8	25.2	20.4	28.8	25.0	20.1	28.6	12.5	11.1	9.9	1645	849
TOYAMA	36.72N	137.20E	17	-2.9	-1.9	33.2	25.1	31.9	24.8	30.6	24.4	26.1	30.9	25.5	30.1	24.7	19.8	28.7	24.2	19.1	28.1	9.2	7.8	6.6	2206	723
TSUIKI AB	33.68N	131.05E	20	-2.2	-1.2	32.1	26.0	31.1	26.0	30.1	25.6	27.1	30.2	26.6	29.6	26.2	21.6	29.1	25.8	21.2	28.8	10.0	8.7	7.7	1901	786
UTSUNOMIYA	36.55N	139.87E	140	-4.5	-3.3	33.0	25.2	31.5	24.6	30.1	24.0	25.9	31.1	25.3	30.0	24.5	19.9	28.2	24.0	19.2	27.9	9.2	7.6	6.4	2204	679
WAKAYAMA	34.23N	135.17E	18	0.4	1.2	33.1	24.7	32.0	24.8	31.1	24.7	26.2	30.7	25.8	30.2	25.0	20.1	29.2	24.5	19.5	28.8	10.8	9.1	7.9	1577	1024
YOKOHAMA	35.43N	139.65E	42	0.3	1.1	32.1	25.1	31.0	24.9	30.0	24.5	26.1	30.2	25.6	29.4	25.0	20.2	28.3	24.5	19.5	28.0	9.5	8.3	7.3	1659	812
YOKOSUKA	35.28N	139.67E	53	0.9	1.9	33.2	25.5	31.9	25.2	30.1	24.7	26.6	30.9	25.8	29.7	25.2	20.5	28.4	24.9	20.1	28.2	13.5	11.8	10.2	1508	872
YOKOTA (JASDF/USAF)	35.75N	139.35E	139	-4.0	-2.9	33.9	25.7	32.1	24.9	30.9	24.4	26.4	31.5	25.8	30.5	25.1	20.5	28.7	24.2	19.4	28.1	9.1	7.8	6.7	2048	702

Meaning of acronyms:
DB: Dry bulb temperature, °C
WB: Wet bulb temperature, °C
MCWB: Mean coincident wet bulb temperature, °C
Lat: Latitude,
DP: Dew point temperature, °C
MCDB: Mean coincident dry bulb temperature, °C
Long: Longitude,
HR: Humidity ratio, g of moisture per kg of dry air
WS: Wind speed, m/s
HDD and CDD 18.3: Annual heating and cooling degree-days, base 18.3°C, °C-day

Station	Lat	Long	Elev	Heating DB		Cooling DB/MCWB						Evaporation WB/MCDB				Dehumidification DP/HR/MCDB						Extreme Annual WS			Heat./Cool. Degree-Days	
						0.4%		1%		2%		0.4%		1%		0.4%			1%							
				99.6%	99%	DB	MCWB	DB	MCWB	DB	MCWB	WB	MCDB	WB	MCDB	DP	HR	MCDB	DP	HR	MCDB	1%	2.5%	5%	HDD	CDD 18.3
Jordan																										3 sites, 4 more on CD-ROM
AMMAN AIRPORT	31.98N	35.98E	779	1.0	2.1	35.3	19.1	34.0	18.8	32.8	18.5	22.4	30.2	21.5	29.3	20.1	16.3	25.4	19.1	15.3	24.5	10.2	8.8	7.7	1291	1037
IRBED	32.55N	35.85E	616	2.0	3.5	34.3	18.8	32.9	18.7	31.7	18.7	22.5	27.8	21.8	27.0	21.2	17.1	23.6	20.6	16.4	23.1	9.0	7.9	7.0	1147	1036
QUEEN ALIA AIRPORT	31.72N	35.98E	722	-0.8	0.5	36.8	20.3	35.1	19.5	33.9	19.3	23.1	32.4	22.1	31.6	20.2	16.3	26.9	19.1	15.1	26.4	12.2	10.2	9.2	1414	752
Kazakhstan																										6 sites, 64 more on CD-ROM
ALMATY	43.23N	76.93E	851	-19.9	-16.8	33.9	18.7	32.1	18.2	30.8	17.8	20.5	30.0	19.6	29.0	17.4	13.8	24.6	16.2	12.8	23.6	5.9	4.7	3.9	3628	459
ASTANA	51.13N	71.37E	350	-30.8	-28.2	31.9	17.8	29.9	17.3	28.1	16.7	19.6	27.2	18.7	26.2	17.2	12.8	21.7	16.2	12.0	21.1	11.4	9.9	8.6	5717	206
KARAGANDA	49.80N	73.15E	553	-29.4	-26.4	32.0	16.6	30.0	16.2	28.1	15.5	18.4	26.8	17.6	25.8	16.0	12.1	20.4	14.9	11.3	19.9	11.1	9.4	8.1	5537	194
PAVLODAR	52.30N	76.93E	122	-32.4	-29.8	32.6	18.6	30.7	18.3	28.9	17.6	20.6	28.0	19.7	27.0	18.3	13.4	23.2	17.2	12.5	22.5	9.4	8.2	7.2	5708	249
SHYMKENT	42.32N	69.70E	604	-13.9	-10.8	37.1	19.6	35.9	19.2	34.4	18.7	21.3	33.5	20.4	32.4	17.2	13.2	26.1	16.1	12.3	25.7	7.9	6.8	6.0	2544	802
ZHAMBYL	42.85N	71.38E	655	-19.6	-16.1	35.6	18.2	34.0	17.8	32.6	17.4	19.7	31.2	19.0	30.7	16.2	12.4	22.8	15.2	11.7	22.5	11.5	8.5	6.3	3237	593
Kenya																										2 sites, 12 more on CD-ROM
MOMBASA	4.03S	39.62E	55	19.9	20.6	33.0	25.2	32.2	25.0	31.9	25.0	26.4	30.1	26.1	29.7	25.3	20.6	27.8	25.2	20.4	27.6	8.7	8.0	7.1	0	2917
NAIROBI/KENYATTA AI	1.32S	36.92E	1624	9.8	11.0	29.0	15.7	28.1	15.8	27.3	16.0	18.8	23.4	18.4	23.0	17.7	15.5	19.6	17.2	15.0	19.1	9.8	8.7	7.7	104	523
Korea, Democratic People's Republic of																										7 sites, 20 more on CD-ROM
CHONGJIN	41.78N	129.82E	43	-13.4	-11.5	27.5	22.3	26.1	21.6	24.9	21.1	23.7	26.2	22.8	25.0	22.9	17.7	25.4	22.1	16.8	24.6	7.3	5.7	4.6	3828	214
HAMHEUNG	39.93N	127.55E	22	-13.4	-11.5	31.4	23.6	29.7	23.0	28.1	22.2	25.3	29.5	24.5	28.0	24.1	19.0	27.5	23.4	18.3	26.7	8.2	6.8	5.6	3246	394
KAESONG	37.97N	126.57E	70	-13.2	-11.3	30.9	25.0	29.5	23.9	28.3	23.3	26.1	29.1	25.4	28.0	25.2	20.6	27.6	24.6	19.8	26.9	8.3	6.8	5.6	3096	537
NAMPO	38.72N	125.38E	47	-12.9	-11.1	30.1	25.0	28.9	24.3	27.9	23.7	26.2	28.9	25.5	27.8	25.4	20.7	28.0	24.7	19.9	27.0	10.0	8.3	7.1	3192	555
PYONGYANG	39.03N	125.78E	36	-15.5	-13.2	31.2	24.2	30.0	23.7	28.8	23.0	25.8	29.2	25.1	28.1	24.8	19.9	27.7	24.2	19.2	27.0	6.7	5.7	4.8	3298	574
SINUIJU	40.10N	124.38E	7	-15.7	-13.7	30.8	24.2	29.3	23.3	28.0	22.9	25.8	29.0	25.0	27.4	24.9	20.0	27.5	24.2	19.1	26.5	7.8	6.5	5.6	3499	502
WONSAN	39.18N	127.43E	36	-10.5	-8.7	31.5	23.6	29.9	22.8	28.3	22.2	25.4	29.3	24.6	28.0	24.4	19.4	27.5	23.6	18.4	26.8	7.7	6.4	5.4	2961	431
Korea, Republic of																										28 sites, 23 more on CD-ROM
BUSAN	35.10N	129.03E	70	-5.6	-3.9	31.2	25.8	30.1	25.4	29.0	24.8	26.6	29.7	26.0	29.0	25.7	21.2	28.5	25.1	20.4	28.2	10.2	8.8	7.6	1903	684
CHEONGJU	36.63N	127.45E	59	-11.8	-9.6	32.8	24.7	31.5	24.0	30.2	23.2	26.0	30.2	25.3	29.4	24.9	20.1	27.9	24.2	19.3	27.5	6.7	5.6	4.9	2739	706
CHEONGJU INTL AIRPO	36.72N	127.50E	60	-14.0	-11.2	33.2	25.9	32.0	25.1	30.8	24.4	27.1	31.4	26.2	30.2	26.0	21.6	29.6	25.1	20.4	28.6	7.2	5.9	5.1	2843	704
DAEGU	35.88N	128.62E	59	-7.6	-5.9	34.1	24.6	32.6	24.1	31.2	23.4	26.0	31.1	25.4	30.2	24.7	19.8	28.6	24.1	19.1	28.0	8.4	7.3	6.4	2251	802
DAEGU INTL AIRPORT	35.90N	128.67E	35	-9.1	-7.6	35.0	25.7	33.2	25.0	32.0	24.2	26.8	32.4	26.2	31.2	25.2	20.4	29.3	24.9	20.0	29.1	8.5	7.4	6.4	2382	793
DAEJEON	36.37N	127.37E	72	-11.0	-9.1	32.7	24.9	31.3	24.3	30.1	23.5	26.3	30.2	25.6	29.3	25.2	20.5	28.3	24.6	19.7	27.6	7.1	5.8	5.0	2719	673
GIMHAE INTL AIRPORT	35.18N	128.93E	5	-6.8	-5.1	32.8	26.0	31.2	25.6	30.1	24.9	26.8	30.8	26.3	30.0	25.9	21.3	29.5	25.1	20.2	28.5	9.2	8.0	7.1	2142	747
GIMPO INTL AIRPORT	37.57N	126.78E	17	-13.8	-11.8	32.0	25.2	30.8	24.7	29.2	23.4	26.8	29.8	26.1	28.8	26.1	21.5	28.2	25.2	20.3	27.4	8.4	7.3	6.3	3025	614
GWANGJU	35.17N	126.90E	74	-6.8	-5.3	32.4	25.1	31.2	24.6	30.1	24.0	26.2	30.2	25.6	29.4	25.1	20.4	28.1	24.6	19.7	27.7	7.6	6.5	5.5	2312	764
GWANGJU AB	35.12N	126.82E	13	-7.8	-6.2	34.1	26.5	32.8	25.8	31.2	24.9	27.2	31.6	26.6	30.9	26.1	21.6	29.4	25.2	20.4	28.5	7.4	6.3	5.5	2416	833
INCHEON	37.47N	126.63E	70	-10.7	-8.9	31.1	24.7	29.8	23.9	28.6	23.3	25.7	29.1	25.1	28.2	24.8	20.0	27.6	24.2	19.3	27.1	9.5	8.0	6.8	2763	612
JEJU	33.52N	126.53E	23	0.0	0.9	31.7	25.3	30.7	25.2	29.7	25.1	26.7	29.8	26.1	29.3	25.7	21.1	29.0	25.1	20.3	28.5	11.1	9.5	8.2	1698	778
JEJU INTL AIRPORT	33.52N	126.50E	24	-0.8	0.2	31.9	26.5	30.8	26.6	29.8	26.2	28.2	30.1	27.4	29.3	27.8	23.9	29.8	27.0	22.7	29.0	12.3	10.9	9.8	1799	751
JEONJU	35.82N	127.15E	55	-8.9	-7.2	33.1	25.4	31.9	24.7	30.6	23.8	26.5	30.4	25.8	29.7	25.5	20.8	28.4	24.7	19.9	27.8	5.6	4.9	4.3	2481	774
JINJU	35.20N	128.12E	23	-8.6	-7.1	32.8	25.0	31.5	24.7	30.2	24.1	26.6	30.6	26.0	29.7	25.5	20.7	28.7	24.9	20.0	28.1	7.2	6.2	5.3	2413	694
MASAN	35.18N	128.57E	4	-4.7	-3.1	32.4	25.5	31.2	25.2	30.0	24.6	26.6	30.4	26.0	29.7	25.6	20.8	28.9	24.9	20.0	28.4	6.8	5.9	5.3	1941	787
OSAN AB	37.10N	127.03E	12	-13.1	-11.1	33.0	26.1	31.8	25.3	30.1	24.3	27.2	30.5	26.5	29.8	26.2	21.7	28.7	25.8	21.2	28.4	8.2	7.0	6.0	2892	698
POHANG	36.03N	129.38E	4	-6.7	-5.0	33.6	24.9	32.1	24.4	30.5	24.0	26.3	30.7	25.7	29.9	25.1	20.3	28.5	24.5	19.5	28.1	8.5	7.1	6.1	2113	713
POHANG AB	35.98N	129.42E	20	-7.1	-5.8	34.0	25.9	32.7	25.4	31.0	24.8	26.8	32.0	26.2	30.9	25.2	20.4	29.2	24.9	20.1	29.0	9.6	8.3	7.4	2237	686
PYONGTAEK (A-511)	36.97N	127.03E	14	-13.1	-11.0	32.9	26.1	31.4	25.3	30.1	24.4	27.0	31.0	26.2	29.9	26.1	21.5	29.1	25.1	20.3	28.3	7.9	6.6	5.8	2904	686
SACHON (KOR-AFB)	35.08N	128.08E	8	-10.0	-8.8	33.1	26.5	31.9	25.8	30.2	24.9	27.1	31.5	26.5	30.5	26.0	21.4	29.8	25.2	20.4	28.8	7.0	6.0	5.2	2451	700
SEOGWIPO	33.25N	126.57E	51	-0.1	1.0	31.3	26.4	30.4	26.1	29.6	25.6	27.3	30.0	26.7	29.4	26.6	22.2	29.2	26.0	21.5	28.7	8.4	7.3	6.4	1436	848
SEOUL	37.57N	126.97E	86	-11.6	-9.6	32.1	24.6	30.7	23.6	29.5	23.1	25.9	29.9	25.2	28.8	24.9	20.2	27.9	24.2	19.3	27.2	7.2	6.2	5.4	2721	699
SEOUL (KOR-AF HQ)	37.50N	126.93E	49	-11.8	-10.1	33.2	25.2	32.0	24.5	30.8	24.1	26.3	31.0	25.8	30.1	25.1	20.3	28.3	24.7	19.9	28.0	6.3	5.2	4.5	2620	796
SEOUL AB	37.43N	127.12E	20	-14.8	-12.0	33.2	25.3	31.9	24.6	30.2	23.5	26.3	31.1	25.7	30.0	25.1	20.2	28.7	24.2	19.2	27.6	6.2	5.3	4.5	2915	670
SUWON	37.27N	126.98E	35	-12.2	-10.1	32.1	24.9	30.7	24.1	29.5	23.3	26.0	29.7	25.3	28.8	25.0	20.1	27.9	24.3	19.3	27.3	6.4	5.4	4.7	2846	662
ULSAN	35.55N	129.32E	36	-6.2	-4.7	33.1	24.9	31.8	24.6	30.3	24.0	26.2	30.6	25.6	29.7	25.0	20.2	28.6	24.5	19.5	28.1	7.0	6.1	5.3	2119	696
YEOSU	34.73N	127.75E	67	-5.2	-3.8	30.5	24.9	29.4	24.6	28.4	24.2	26.2	28.7	25.6	28.1	25.4	20.8	27.7	24.8	20.1	27.2	12.1	10.5	9.2	2047	676
Kyrgyzstan																										1 site, 6 more on CD-ROM
BISHKEK	42.85N	74.53E	760	-20.4	-16.6	35.2	20.0	33.8	19.1	32.3	18.6	21.8	32.5	20.5	31.1	18.1	14.3	27.2	16.9	13.2	25.6	8.5	7.1	6.0	3218	596
Latvia																										2 sites, 8 more on CD-ROM
RIGA	56.97N	24.05E	26	-18.5	-14.6	27.4	19.1	25.4	18.2	23.7	17.3	20.2	25.2	19.2	23.7	18.5	13.4	22.3	17.5	12.6	21.4	10.0	8.5	7.6	4193	69
RIGA	56.92N	23.97E	11	-18.2	-14.1	28.9	20.1	27.1	19.6	25.8	18.6	21.6	26.8	20.4	25.1	19.8	14.6	24.4	18.8	13.6	22.9	9.1	8.1	7.3	4064	96

Meaning of acronyms:
DB: Dry bulb temperature, °C *WB: Wet bulb temperature, °C*
MCWB: Mean coincident wet bulb temperature, °C
Lat: Latitude, °
DP: Dew point temperature, °C
MCDB: Mean coincident dry bulb temperature, °C
Long: Longitude, °
HR: Humidity ratio, g of moisture per kg of dry air
HDD and CDD 18.3: Annual heating and cooling degree-days, base 18.3°C, °C-day
Elev: Elevation, m
WS: Wind speed, m/s

Station	Lat	Long	Elev	Heating DB		Cooling DB/MCWB						Evaporation WB/MCDB				Dehumidification DP/HR/MCDB						Extreme Annual WS			Heat./Cool. Degree-Days	
						0.4%		1%		2%		0.4%		1%		0.4%			1%							
				99.6%	99%	DB	MCWB	DB	MCWB	DB	MCWB	WB	MCDB	WB	MCDB	DP	HR	MCDB	DP	HR	MCDB	1%	2.5%	5%	HDD	CDD 18.3
Lebanon																										*1 site, 0 more on CD-ROM*
BEYROUTH (AEROPORT)	33.82N	35.48E	19	7.6	8.9	31.8	21.9	30.8	23.9	30.1	24.4	26.7	29.7	26.1	29.4	25.9	21.3	29.4	25.1	20.2	29.0	11.2	9.2	7.6	464	1383
Libyan Arab Jamahiriya																										*3 sites, 3 more on CD-ROM*
BENINA	32.10N	20.27E	132	6.8	7.8	37.2	21.8	35.2	21.6	33.8	21.2	25.4	31.1	24.6	29.8	24.0	19.2	27.4	23.2	18.2	27.0	14.5	12.9	10.5	637	1344
MISURATA	32.42N	15.05E	32	8.0	9.0	36.5	21.4	34.2	21.4	32.2	21.5	26.2	29.3	25.6	28.8	25.4	20.7	28.3	24.7	19.8	27.8	13.1	10.8	9.5	504	1313
TRIPOLI INTERNATION	32.70N	13.08E	63	4.2	5.2	41.9	24.0	39.9	23.6	38.0	23.0	27.3	36.9	26.0	34.1	25.0	20.3	30.7	23.9	19.0	29.7	10.4	9.5	8.5	668	1633
Lithuania																										*2 sites, 5 more on CD-ROM*
KAUNAS	54.88N	23.83E	770	-19.7	-16.0	27.8	19.0	26.1	18.3	24.4	17.3	20.5	25.8	19.4	24.2	18.7	14.8	22.9	17.6	13.9	21.8	9.8	8.7	7.7	4208	67
VILNIUS	54.63N	25.28E	156	-20.2	-16.8	28.0	18.5	26.1	17.9	24.4	17.1	20.2	25.4	19.2	24.0	18.5	13.6	22.0	17.4	12.7	21.0	10.3	9.0	7.9	4361	72
Macao																										*1 site, 0 more on CD-ROM*
TAIPA GRANDE	22.15N	113.60E	6	7.2	8.8	32.9	27.3	32.1	27.1	31.4	26.9	28.2	30.9	27.8	30.4	27.3	23.1	29.7	27.1	22.8	29.6	11.0	9.6	8.6	309	1987
Macedonia, the former Yugoslav Republic of																										*1 site, 3 more on CD-ROM*
SKOPJE- AIRPORT	41.97N	21.65E	239	-12.7	-9.0	35.6	20.6	33.8	20.2	32.1	19.7	21.9	32.2	21.2	31.0	18.8	14.0	24.8	18.0	13.3	24.1	8.9	7.6	6.2	2653	500
Madagascar																										*1 site, 2 more on CD-ROM*
ANTANANARIVO/IVATO	18.80S	47.48E	1276	7.9	8.9	29.2	18.9	28.2	18.9	27.5	18.8	21.6	26.3	20.9	25.7	20.2	17.4	23.4	19.7	16.8	22.7	8.1	7.2	6.4	330	643
Malaysia																										*6 sites, 8 more on CD-ROM*
KOTA KINABALU	5.93N	116.05E	3	22.7	22.9	33.3	27.7	33.0	27.5	32.5	27.2	28.8	32.4	28.2	32.0	27.8	23.9	32.1	27.1	22.9	31.5	7.0	5.6	4.7	0	3432
KUALA LUMPUR SUBANG	3.12N	101.55E	22	22.0	22.7	34.2	25.6	33.9	25.7	33.2	25.6	27.5	31.5	27.1	31.2	26.2	21.7	29.3	26.1	21.5	29.2	6.4	5.5	4.9	0	3559
KUANTAN	3.78N	103.22E	16	21.3	21.8	33.9	26.1	33.2	26.1	32.8	26.1	27.5	31.5	27.1	31.2	26.3	21.8	29.3	26.1	21.5	29.1	6.6	5.7	5.2	0	3257
KUCHING	1.48N	110.33E	27	21.9	22.2	33.9	25.8	33.2	25.8	32.8	25.8	27.2	31.5	26.8	30.9	26.1	21.6	29.6	25.8	21.1	29.1	5.3	4.5	4.0	0	3236
SANDAKAN	5.90N	118.07E	13	22.9	23.3	33.5	26.3	32.9	26.2	32.3	26.2	27.5	31.3	27.2	31.0	26.3	21.8	29.6	26.1	21.6	29.4	7.1	6.2	5.4	0	3439
TAWAU	4.27N	117.88E	20	22.0	22.5	32.3	25.7	32.0	25.8	31.6	25.8	27.4	30.6	27.1	30.4	26.5	22.0	29.7	26.1	21.6	29.4	6.0	5.2	4.6	0	3202
Mali																										*1 site, 0 more on CD-ROM*
BAMAKO/SENOU	12.53N	7.95W	381	15.2	16.8	40.1	20.1	39.2	20.3	38.6	20.4	27.1	31.5	26.3	31.1	26.1	22.5	28.8	25.2	21.3	28.0	8.5	7.3	6.4	0	3530
Mauritania																										*1 site, 1 more on CD-ROM*
NOUAKCHOTT	18.10N	15.95W	3	12.9	14.0	41.2	20.9	39.4	20.6	37.7	20.5	28.1	30.6	27.4	30.2	27.8	23.8	29.2	26.9	22.6	28.9	10.2	9.1	8.2	2	2959
Mexico																										*18 sites, 4 more on CD-ROM*
AEROP. INTERNACIONA	19.43N	99.13W	2235	4.1	5.6	29.0	13.8	27.9	13.7	26.9	13.6	16.6	23.4	16.1	23.0	14.8	13.9	18.2	14.1	13.3	17.4	21.1	9.6	7.9	563	190
AEROP.INTERNACIONAL	20.98N	89.65W	9	13.7	15.4	38.2	24.4	37.1	24.4	36.1	24.5	28.0	31.9	27.2	31.6	27.1	22.9	28.9	26.2	21.7	28.6	10.5	9.6	8.3	3	3214
CANCUN INTL	21.03N	86.87W	6	13.8	15.1	34.1	27.1	33.8	27.1	33.1	26.9	28.4	32.5	28.0	32.2	27.2	23.0	30.9	27.0	22.7	30.8	10.5	9.7	8.1	1	2973
DE GUANAJUATO INTL	20.98N	101.48W	1861	4.0	5.8	34.0	14.9	32.8	15.3	31.2	15.4	19.9	27.2	19.3	26.3	18.1	16.3	20.5	17.2	15.5	20.2	12.6	10.1	8.7	273	756
DON MIGUEL Y HIDALG	20.52N	103.30W	1566	1.9	3.2	33.6	16.1	32.2	15.7	31.2	15.4	20.1	26.8	19.7	26.2	18.2	15.9	21.8	18.0	15.7	21.6	10.3	8.5	7.6	327	743
GENERAL ABELARDO L	32.53N	116.97W	156	5.9	6.9	32.0	21.1	30.1	20.7	28.8	20.1	23.2	29.5	22.2	28.1	21.1	16.1	26.9	20.1	15.1	25.4	8.4	7.1	6.2	673	516
GENERAL FRANCISCO J	22.28N	97.87W	25	10.1	11.9	34.1	26.7	33.2	26.6	33.0	26.6	28.6	32.2	27.8	31.5	27.8	23.9	31.7	26.9	22.7	30.8	14.9	11.9	10.0	79	2579
GENERAL HERIBERTO J	19.13N	96.18W	33	14.9	16.0	35.2	27.0	34.1	27.0	33.2	26.7	28.2	33.4	27.6	32.5	27.0	22.7	30.8	26.2	21.7	30.0	20.1	15.3	12.6	3	2780
GENERAL JUAN N ALVA	16.75N	99.75W	5	19.8	20.8	33.7	26.8	33.1	26.6	32.9	26.5	28.0	32.4	27.5	31.9	26.9	22.6	31.3	26.2	21.6	30.5	8.7	7.8	6.5	0	3312
GENERAL MARIANO ESC	25.77N	100.10W	399	3.2	5.1	38.9	23.6	37.8	23.4	36.9	23.6	26.5	34.8	26.0	33.9	24.2	20.1	29.6	24.0	19.8	29.4	14.1	10.6	9.7	357	2165
GENERAL RAFAEL BUEL	23.15N	106.27W	12	8.9	10.1	34.1	25.4	33.2	25.3	33.0	25.2	27.7	31.8	27.2	31.2	26.8	22.5	30.8	26.1	21.5	30.0	9.1	7.6	6.6	23	2192
LICENCIADO ADOLFO L	19.33N	99.57W	2643	-2.0	-0.8	26.2	13.1	25.1	13.0	24.1	12.8	16.2	21.2	15.6	20.7	14.9	14.7	17.6	14.1	13.9	17.0	9.1	7.6	6.2	1764	3
LICENCIADO BENITO J	19.43N	99.07W	2286	3.0	4.8	29.2	12.9	28.1	12.6	27.0	12.5	16.1	22.9	15.7	22.3	14.2	13.4	17.2	13.9	13.2	17.1	11.6	9.8	8.3	601	189
MAZATLAN/G.BUELNA I	23.15N	106.25W	5	10.9	12.0	34.4	26.7	34.0	26.6	33.2	26.3	28.6	32.7	28.0	31.7	27.2	23.0	30.7	27.1	22.8	30.5	10.4	7.0	5.7	11	2397
MONTERREY (CITY)	25.73N	100.30W	515	4.3	5.9	38.2	23.3	37.1	23.3	36.1	23.5	26.7	34.1	25.9	33.3	24.7	21.0	31.6	23.8	19.9	30.1	5.5	4.5	4.0	336	2142
SAN LUIS POTOSI	22.18N	100.98W	1883	-0.2	1.9	32.3	15.7	30.9	15.6	29.6	15.6	18.8	25.8	18.2	25.1	17.1	15.4	20.0	16.3	14.6	19.5	10.0	8.6	7.6	707	408
TAMPICO/GEN FJ MINA	22.28N	97.85W	24	10.0	11.8	33.1	26.9	32.2	26.5	32.0	26.4	28.5	31.3	27.7	30.7	27.9	24.0	31.0	26.9	22.7	30.1	14.9	10.7	9.5	93	2392
VERACRUZ/GEN JARA	19.15N	96.18W	29	14.0	15.2	34.2	26.9	33.2	26.7	32.8	26.5	27.8	32.7	27.2	31.8	26.2	21.7	30.0	26.1	21.6	29.8	20.8	15.3	12.9	7	2571
Moldova, Republic of																										*1 site, 0 more on CD-ROM*
KISINEV	47.02N	28.98E	173	-14.3	-11.9	31.1	20.0	29.5	19.4	28.0	18.8	21.5	28.4	20.6	27.1	19.2	14.3	24.4	18.3	13.5	23.5	6.4	5.5	4.8	3337	325
Mongolia																										*1 site, 39 more on CD-ROM*
ULAANBAATAR	47.92N	106.87E	1306	-34.1	-31.1	29.9	15.8	27.5	15.0	25.5	14.5	17.6	25.3	16.6	24.0	15.1	12.6	19.7	14.0	11.7	19.3	10.3	9.0	7.6	6964	79
Morocco																										*11 sites, 9 more on CD-ROM*
AGADIR	30.38N	9.57W	23	5.0	6.5	35.2	19.4	31.8	18.9	29.0	18.4	22.5	28.7	21.8	26.6	21.0	15.7	24.0	20.2	15.0	23.2	10.6	8.7	7.2	521	648
AGADIR AL MASSIRA	30.32N	9.40W	23	5.1	6.7	37.6	19.6	34.1	19.1	31.8	19.0	22.6	30.4	22.1	29.3	20.2	15.0	24.4	20.0	14.7	24.2	9.5	8.1	7.1	385	906
CASABLANCA	33.57N	7.67W	57	6.0	7.1	29.5	22.0	27.3	22.1	26.2	21.9	24.0	26.8	23.4	25.9	23.1	18.0	25.5	22.6	17.4	24.9	7.8	6.6	5.6	694	591
FES-SAIS	33.93N	4.98W	579	0.8	2.0	39.1	20.2	37.1	20.2	35.2	19.7	22.6	33.9	21.6	32.9	19.0	14.8	27.8	18.0	13.9	26.1	9.9	8.1	6.7	1251	810
MARRAKECH	31.62N	8.03W	466	4.1	5.2	41.2	20.8	39.2	20.6	37.2	20.4	23.7	35.2	22.5	34.2	20.1	15.6	29.6	19.0	14.6	27.2	8.4	6.9	5.7	649	1362

Meaning of acronyms:
DB: Dry bulb temperature, °C | *WB: Wet bulb temperature, °C* | *MCWB: Mean coincident wet bulb temperature, °C*
Lat: Latitude, ° | *DP: Dew point temperature, °C* | *MCDB: Mean coincident dry bulb temperature, °C*
Long: Longitude, ° | *HR: Humidity ratio, g of moisture per kg of dry air*
Elev: Elevation, m | *WS: Wind speed, m/s*
HDD and CDD 18.3: Annual heating and cooling degree-days, base 18.3°C, °C-day

Station	Lat	Long	Elev	Heating DB		Cooling DB/MCWB						Evaporation WB/MCDB				Dehumidification DP/HR/MCDB						Extreme Annual WS			Heat./Cool. Degree-Days	
						0.4%		1%		2%		0.4%		1%		0.4%			1%							
				99.6%	99%	DB / MCWB		DB / MCWB		DB / MCWB		WB / MCDB		WB / MCDB		DP / HR / MCDB			DP / HR / MCDB			1%	2.5%	5%	HDD / CDD 18.3	
OUJDA	34.78N	1.93W	470	0.2	1.9	37.2	20.9	35.2	20.6	33.3	20.2	23.6	32.1	22.7	30.7	21.1	16.7	26.9	20.3	15.9	26.0	12.1	10.3	9.2	1179	802
RABAT-SALE	34.05N	6.77W	79	5.0	6.0	32.2	22.0	29.8	21.7	27.8	21.8	24.6	28.9	23.5	27.3	23.2	18.1	26.9	22.2	17.0	25.6	8.2	7.0	6.1	800	533
TANGER (AERODROME)	35.73N	5.90W	21	4.1	5.8	33.1	21.5	31.8	21.4	30.1	21.2	23.2	29.6	22.6	28.6	21.2	15.9	25.8	20.8	15.5	25.5	17.8	14.8	13.0	823	683
TETUAN/SANIA RAMEL	35.58N	5.33W	10	6.3	7.7	32.8	20.7	30.9	20.6	29.3	20.6	24.2	27.4	23.6	26.7	23.2	18.0	25.7	22.7	17.4	25.3	12.6	10.9	9.8	644	800
Mozambique																										*1 site, 0 more on CD-ROM*
MAPUTO/MAVALANE	25.92S	32.57E	44	12.0	13.0	35.2	24.0	33.3	23.9	31.9	24.0	26.6	31.0	26.1	30.3	25.5	20.8	28.7	25.0	20.2	28.2	16.0	13.9	11.9	22	1938
Netherlands																										*6 sites, 24 more on CD-ROM*
AMSTERDAM AP SCHIPH	52.30N	4.77E	-4	-7.3	-4.9	27.8	19.7	25.6	19.0	23.7	18.0	20.7	25.8	19.7	24.1	19.0	13.7	22.6	18.0	13.0	21.4	13.6	11.9	10.4	3038	65
HOEK VAN HOLLAND	51.98N	4.10E	14	-6.3	-3.8	27.2	19.4	24.6	18.5	22.7	18.1	20.6	24.8	19.7	23.1	19.3	14.1	22.2	18.5	13.3	21.1	16.3	14.7	13.3	2826	68
IJMUIDEN	52.47N	4.57E	13	-6.8	-4.5	25.5	18.7	23.5	17.9	21.7	17.6	20.0	23.3	19.1	21.5	18.9	13.7	21.1	18.2	13.1	20.2	18.6	16.3	14.8	2972	51
ROTTERDAM AP ZESTIE	51.95N	4.45E	-4	-7.3	-4.8	27.9	19.9	25.8	19.3	23.9	18.2	20.9	26.1	19.9	24.4	19.2	13.9	23.1	18.2	13.1	21.9	12.8	11.3	10.0	3009	68
VALKENBURG	52.18N	4.42E	2	-7.2	-4.8	27.1	19.5	24.9	18.7	22.9	17.8	20.5	25.1	19.4	23.4	18.9	13.7	22.4	17.9	12.9	21.2	13.8	12.2	10.9	3041	55
WOENSDRECHT	51.45N	4.33E	17	-7.2	-5.1	29.7	20.1	27.5	19.5	25.3	18.6	21.2	26.9	20.2	25.4	19.2	14.0	22.9	18.3	13.2	22.2	9.8	8.4	7.4	2976	91
New Zealand																										*4 sites, 34 more on CD-ROM*
AUCKLAND AERO AWS	37.00S	174.80E	7	4.5	5.6	25.3	20.0	24.3	19.3	23.5	18.8	21.2	23.8	20.5	23.0	20.2	14.9	22.6	19.5	14.3	22.1	13.0	11.3	10.0	1232	156
AUCKLAND AIRPORT	37.02S	174.80E	6	1.8	2.9	25.2	19.7	24.2	19.2	23.3	18.7	21.2	23.6	20.5	22.9	20.2	14.9	22.4	19.5	14.3	21.9	13.0	11.6	10.4	1326	151
CHRISTCHURCH	43.48S	172.55E	30	-2.6	-1.7	28.0	16.8	25.9	16.0	24.0	15.5	18.4	24.4	17.5	22.8	16.3	11.7	19.7	15.7	11.2	19.0	11.4	10.2	9.1	2604	59
CHRISTCHURCH AERO A	43.48S	172.52E	37	-2.5	-1.5	27.6	16.5	25.5	15.7	23.6	15.2	18.2	24.0	17.3	22.6	16.2	11.6	19.5	15.4	11.0	18.5	11.5	10.2	9.1	2612	51
Nicaragua																										*1 site, 0 more on CD-ROM*
MANAGUA A.C.SANDINO	12.15N	86.17W	56	19.8	20.4	36.0	24.2	35.1	24.1	34.5	24.0	26.6	31.4	26.2	31.0	25.2	20.5	28.3	25.1	20.3	28.2	7.9	6.9	6.1	0	3416
Niger																										*1 site, 11 more on CD-ROM*
NIAMEY-AERO	13.48N	2.17E	227	15.7	16.9	42.2	21.2	41.4	21.1	40.6	21.1	27.1	33.3	26.6	33.0	25.9	21.9	29.4	25.1	20.8	29.2	9.7	8.3	7.3	0	4151
Norway																										*2 sites, 43 more on CD-ROM*
OSLO/FORNEBU	59.90N	10.62E	17	-17.2	-14.5	26.8	17.8	25.0	17.0	23.2	15.9	19.2	24.1	18.2	23.1	17.7	12.7	20.6	16.2	11.5	19.4	8.5	7.3	6.4	4344	51
OSLO-BLINDERN	59.95N	10.72E	96	-13.9	-11.6	26.4	17.6	24.7	16.7	23.2	15.8	18.7	23.7	17.8	22.9	16.9	12.2	20.4	15.8	11.4	19.6	8.1	6.9	6.0	4186	56
Oman																										*1 site, 7 more on CD-ROM*
BURAIMI	24.23N	55.78E	299	9.4	10.9	45.4	22.2	44.4	21.7	43.4	21.5	28.0	33.4	27.1	34.0	26.8	23.3	30.8	25.6	21.6	31.2	8.4	7.3	6.4	77	3726
Pakistan																										*3 sites, 0 more on CD-ROM*
ISLAMABAD AIRPORT	33.62N	73.10E	508	2.2	3.3	41.1	22.4	39.2	22.7	38.0	22.7	28.1	34.0	27.5	33.2	26.7	23.7	31.3	26.1	22.9	30.9	12.0	9.9	8.6	652	1982
KARACHI AIRPORT	24.90N	67.13E	22	10.0	11.6	38.9	22.6	37.1	23.1	35.9	23.6	28.2	33.3	27.8	32.7	27.1	22.9	30.9	26.6	22.2	30.6	9.1	8.1	7.3	23	3180
LAHORE AIRPORT	31.52N	74.40E	217	3.9	5.0	43.2	23.2	41.8	23.5	40.0	23.6	29.3	34.2	28.7	33.6	28.1	25.0	32.1	27.8	24.5	31.9	8.1	6.4	5.4	411	2572
Palestinian Territory, Occupied																										*1 site, 0 more on CD-ROM*
JERUSALEM AIRPORT	31.87N	35.22E	759	0.8	2.0	32.9	18.7	31.2	18.5	30.1	18.2	21.8	28.7	21.0	27.2	19.9	16.0	24.4	19.1	15.2	23.0	9.9	8.7	7.9	1400	699
Panama																										*2 sites, 0 more on CD-ROM*
MARCOS A GELABERT I	8.97N	79.55W	10	22.8	22.9	34.8	25.3	34.1	25.2	33.2	25.2	27.7	31.4	27.2	31.0	26.8	22.4	30.3	26.2	21.6	29.8	7.8	6.9	6.1	0	3579
TOCUMEN	9.05N	79.37W	45	20.0	20.9	34.0	25.7	33.2	25.4	33.0	25.3	27.6	31.2	27.1	30.9	26.8	22.5	29.6	26.1	21.7	29.1	7.6	6.5	5.6	0	3241
Paraguay																										*1 site, 1 more on CD-ROM*
ASUNCION/AEROPUERTO	25.25S	57.52W	101	5.1	7.1	36.9	23.8	35.8	23.9	34.8	24.0	26.7	32.3	26.2	31.9	25.2	20.5	29.5	24.7	20.0	29.1	10.4	9.4	8.5	254	2049
Peru																										*8 sites, 5 more on CD-ROM*
AREQUIPA	16.33S	71.57W	2520	5.8	6.5	24.1	11.6	23.6	11.4	23.0	11.2	15.0	21.3	14.4	20.7	12.9	12.7	17.2	12.1	12.0	16.3	10.2	8.2	7.2	1098	2
CHICLAYO	6.78S	79.82W	30	15.0	15.6	32.2	24.5	31.8	24.3	30.8	23.7	25.9	30.4	25.3	29.4	24.5	19.5	28.3	24.0	19.0	28.3	10.5	9.7	9.0	3	1627
CUZCO	13.53S	71.93W	3249	0.0	1.0	22.9	11.0	22.1	10.8	21.2	10.4	12.7	20.2	12.2	19.6	10.0	11.4	15.3	9.2	10.9	14.5	9.2	7.2	5.8	2092	0
IQUITOS	3.78S	73.30W	126	19.0	20.2	34.1	26.6	33.2	26.5	33.0	26.5	27.4	32.5	27.2	32.1	26.1	21.8	30.8	25.8	21.4	30.6	6.2	4.8	3.9	0	3036
LIMA-CALLAO/AEROP.	12.00S	77.12W	13	14.0	14.6	29.3	23.6	28.2	22.8	27.1	22.2	24.2	27.7	23.7	27.0	23.1	17.9	26.8	22.4	17.1	26.4	9.4	8.1	7.1	165	822
PIURA	5.20S	80.60W	55	15.9	16.4	34.1	25.2	33.3	24.9	32.8	24.7	26.5	31.8	26.1	31.3	25.2	20.4	28.7	24.7	19.9	28.6	8.9	8.0	7.0	0	2426
PUCALLPA	8.37S	74.57W	149	17.6	18.9	34.8	26.3	34.0	26.2	33.3	26.0	27.0	33.1	26.7	32.6	25.2	20.7	30.1	25.0	20.5	30.1	6.6	5.4	4.5	0	3069
TRUJILLO	8.08S	79.10W	30	14.7	14.9	29.0	24.6	28.2	24.3	27.7	24.1	25.4	27.9	25.0	27.4	24.3	19.3	27.3	24.1	19.0	27.2	8.6	8.0	7.3	97	857
Philippines																										*10 sites, 24 more on CD-ROM*
CAGAYAN DE ORO	8.48N	124.63E	6	22.0	22.7	34.6	27.5	34.0	27.4	33.5	27.3	28.8	33.1	28.4	32.7	27.6	23.6	32.2	27.2	23.0	32.0	4.9	3.9	3.1	0	3573
DAVAO AIRPORT	7.12N	125.65E	18	22.4	22.9	33.7	26.2	33.1	26.3	32.7	26.3	27.7	31.7	27.4	31.4	26.6	22.1	30.3	26.2	21.7	30.0	8.0	6.1	5.2	0	3457
GEN. SANTOS	6.12N	125.18E	15	22.6	23.0	35.1	27.2	34.4	27.1	33.8	27.1	28.3	33.0	28.0	32.8	27.1	22.8	31.7	26.7	22.3	31.4	6.0	5.2	4.6	0	3592
ILOILO	10.70N	122.57E	8	22.8	23.3	34.7	27.4	34.0	27.3	33.3	27.2	28.6	32.8	28.2	32.4	27.5	23.4	31.5	27.1	22.9	31.3	7.6	6.5	5.8	0	3593
MACTAN	10.30N	123.97E	24	23.0	23.7	33.3	27.1	33.0	27.1	32.3	26.9	28.5	31.0	28.1	30.9	27.9	24.0	30.2	27.5	23.4	29.9	8.2	7.0	6.1	0	3535
MANILA	14.58N	120.98E	13	23.1	23.8	34.5	26.3	33.8	26.3	33.1	26.2	28.2	32.0	27.7	31.5	27.2	23.0	30.8	26.7	22.3	30.4	9.9	7.8	6.3	0	3695
NINOY AQUINO INTERN	14.52N	121.00E	15	20.9	21.9	34.9	26.2	34.1	26.0	33.4	25.9	28.2	31.7	27.7	31.2	27.2	23.0	30.0	27.0	22.7	29.8	16.3	13.8	10.4	0	3456
SANGLEY POINT	14.50N	120.92E	2	23.1	23.8	34.7	27.9	34.1	27.7	33.5	27.4	28.7	33.3	28.4	32.8	27.5	23.4	32.0	27.1	22.9	31.7	9.3	7.4	6.3	0	3776

Meaning of acronyms:
DB: Dry bulb temperature, °C — WB: Wet bulb temperature, °C
MCWB: Mean coincident wet bulb temperature, °C
Lat: Latitude, °
DP: Dew point temperature, °C
MCDB: Mean coincident dry bulb temperature, °C
Long: Longitude, °
HR: Humidity ratio, g of moisture per kg of dry air
HDD and CDD 18.3: Annual heating and cooling degree-days, base 18.3°C, °C-day
Elev: Elevation, m
WS: Wind speed, m/s

Station	Lat	Long	Elev	Heating DB		Cooling DB/MCWB						Evaporation WB/MCDB				Dehumidification DP/HR/MCDB						Extreme Annual WS			Heat./Cool. Degree-Days	
						0.4%		1%		2%		0.4%		1%		0.4%			1%							
				99.6%	99%	DB	MCWB	DB	MCWB	DB	MCWB	WB	MCDB	WB	MCDB	DP	HR	MCDB	DP	HR	MCDB	1%	2.5%	5%	HDD	CDD 18.3
SCIENCE GARDEN	14.63N	121.02E	46	20.2	21.0	35.2	26.2	34.6	26.2	33.8	26.1	27.7	32.4	27.4	31.9	26.6	22.2	30.3	26.2	21.7	29.8	5.9	5.0	4.2	0	3398
ZAMBOANGA	6.90N	122.07E	6	22.4	23.0	34.1	27.4	33.5	27.2	33.1	27.1	28.1	32.6	27.7	32.2	26.9	22.5	31.2	26.5	22.1	30.9	5.8	5.1	4.5	0	3586
Poland																										*13 sites, 47 more on CD-ROM*
GDANSK-REBIECHOWO	54.38N	18.47E	138	-16.1	-12.7	27.1	18.8	25.1	17.8	23.2	17.0	19.9	24.8	18.9	23.6	18.1	13.3	21.9	17.1	12.4	20.9	12.7	10.6	9.3	4059	42
GDANSK-SWIBNO	54.33N	18.93E	7	-17.0	-12.7	25.8	19.5	23.6	18.3	21.9	17.6	20.3	24.4	19.1	22.5	18.8	13.6	22.1	17.7	12.7	21.1	10.2	8.7	7.5	3891	34
HEL	54.60N	18.82E	3	-9.6	-7.3	25.2	20.0	23.6	19.1	22.1	18.3	20.7	24.0	19.8	22.7	19.5	14.2	22.6	18.6	13.5	21.6	10.3	8.9	7.8	3676	46
KATOWICE	50.23N	19.03E	284	-15.4	-12.3	29.1	19.7	27.2	18.6	25.5	17.9	20.6	26.9	19.6	25.6	18.4	13.7	22.9	17.5	13.0	21.8	8.3	7.3	6.4	3723	92
KRAKOW	50.08N	19.80E	237	-16.9	-13.8	29.7	20.3	27.8	19.6	25.9	18.5	21.2	27.8	20.2	26.1	19.0	14.2	24.0	18.1	13.4	22.6	9.3	8.2	7.3	3717	112
LODZ	51.73N	19.40E	190	-15.8	-12.5	29.5	19.2	27.4	18.4	25.7	17.6	20.5	26.5	19.5	25.2	18.6	13.7	22.5	17.6	12.9	21.5	9.2	8.0	7.1	3779	110
LUBLIN RADAWIEC	51.22N	22.40E	240	-17.6	-14.1	28.4	20.0	26.6	19.2	24.9	18.2	21.1	26.4	20.0	25.0	19.2	14.4	23.9	18.1	13.4	22.4	8.6	7.5	6.7	3985	81
POZNAN	52.42N	16.85E	84	-14.3	-11.1	30.0	19.2	28.0	18.3	26.2	17.6	20.5	27.3	19.6	25.8	18.2	13.3	22.4	17.3	12.5	21.6	9.8	8.4	7.4	3621	114
RACIBORZ	50.05N	18.20E	206	-16.0	-12.4	29.6	20.1	27.6	19.4	25.7	18.5	21.1	27.0	20.1	25.9	19.0	14.1	24.1	18.0	13.3	22.8	10.1	8.6	7.5	3594	104
SZCZECIN	53.40N	14.62E	7	-12.9	-9.7	28.9	20.0	27.0	19.1	25.2	18.3	21.2	26.7	20.1	25.2	19.2	14.0	23.8	18.2	13.1	22.3	9.5	8.4	7.5	3500	95
TERESPOL	52.07N	23.62E	137	-19.5	-15.5	29.2	19.8	27.2	19.3	25.5	18.3	21.3	26.5	20.1	25.5	19.4	14.4	24.2	18.3	13.4	22.5	7.4	6.5	5.9	3944	99
WARSZAWA-OKECIE	52.17N	20.97E	106	-16.6	-13.1	29.6	20.0	27.6	19.2	25.9	18.1	21.2	27.2	20.2	25.7	19.1	14.1	23.8	18.2	13.3	22.6	10.3	9.1	8.2	3771	112
WROCLAW II	51.10N	16.88E	124	-15.2	-11.5	29.8	19.8	27.9	19.0	26.1	18.2	20.7	27.4	19.8	25.9	18.5	13.6	23.2	17.6	12.8	22.1	8.9	7.8	6.9	3539	113
Portugal																										*1 site, 23 more on CD-ROM*
LISBOA/PORTELA	38.77N	9.13W	114	4.2	5.8	34.2	20.0	32.1	19.7	30.1	19.4	22.2	29.2	21.4	27.6	20.8	15.6	23.4	20.0	14.9	22.7	10.4	9.3	8.4	1012	599
Puerto Rico																										*2 sites, 2 more on CD-ROM*
SAN JUAN INTL ARPT	18.42N	66.00W	19	20.6	21.2	33.0	25.2	32.0	25.5	31.5	25.4	27.0	30.5	26.6	30.3	25.9	21.3	29.0	25.6	20.8	28.7	8.5	7.9	7.3	0	3118
SAN JUAN L M MARIN INTL AP	18.43N	66.00W	3	20.9	21.4	32.8	25.3	31.9	25.6	31.4	25.6	27.2	30.4	26.9	30.1	26.2	21.6	29.0	25.8	21.1	28.8	9.2	8.4	7.8	0	3108
Qatar																										*1 site, 0 more on CD-ROM*
DOHA INTERNATIONAL	25.25N	51.57E	10	11.1	12.5	43.7	22.1	42.3	22.4	41.1	22.7	31.1	35.2	30.5	34.8	30.1	27.4	34.0	29.4	26.2	33.7	10.8	9.5	8.4	73	3527
Romania																										*8 sites, 44 more on CD-ROM*
BUCURESTI AFUMATI	44.48N	26.18E	90	-14.0	-11.0	33.2	21.8	31.8	21.2	30.1	20.4	23.2	30.0	22.2	29.3	21.2	16.0	24.9	20.1	14.9	24.1	10.3	8.2	7.1	3069	382
BUCURESTI INMH-BANE	44.48N	26.12E	91	-12.9	-10.1	33.8	21.3	32.0	21.0	30.2	20.2	23.2	29.9	22.2	28.8	21.2	16.1	25.0	20.2	15.0	23.9	8.9	7.6	6.6	3055	376
CLUJ-NAPOCA	46.78N	23.57E	413	-15.4	-12.8	30.0	20.4	28.3	19.5	26.8	18.9	21.7	27.8	20.6	26.3	19.8	15.3	24.2	18.8	14.3	22.9	8.3	6.8	5.5	3618	148
CONSTANTA	44.22N	28.65E	14	-9.3	-7.1	29.7	23.7	28.2	22.9	27.1	22.2	25.4	27.9	24.1	26.9	24.7	19.7	27.0	23.2	18.0	25.9	13.4	11.6	10.1	2703	403
CRAIOVA	44.32N	23.87E	195	-12.3	-9.6	33.4	22.5	31.8	22.0	30.1	21.3	24.3	30.7	23.1	29.3	22.3	17.4	27.3	21.2	16.2	25.9	13.6	10.1	8.4	2937	433
IASI	47.17N	27.63E	104	-15.9	-12.9	32.0	21.3	30.2	20.6	28.8	19.9	22.8	29.1	21.7	27.9	20.9	15.7	25.7	19.8	14.7	24.1	9.8	8.2	7.2	3316	308
KOGALNICEANU	44.33N	28.43E	102	-11.3	-9.1	31.9	22.0	30.1	21.9	28.8	21.3	25.5	27.6	24.1	26.7	25.0	20.3	26.5	23.2	18.2	25.1	11.3	9.4	8.6	2956	357
TIMISOARA	45.77N	21.25E	88	-12.3	-9.4	33.5	21.2	31.9	20.7	30.0	20.0	22.6	30.0	21.7	28.8	20.8	15.6	24.1	19.7	14.6	23.5	8.5	7.2	6.0	2924	347
Russian Federation																										*62 sites, 497 more on CD-ROM*
ADLER	43.43N	39.90E	13	-2.3	-0.9	29.7	23.9	28.5	23.3	27.4	22.8	25.2	28.4	24.3	27.4	24.1	19.0	27.6	23.2	18.0	26.6	7.9	6.8	6.1	2079	411
ARHANGELSK	64.55N	40.58E	4	-33.8	-30.2	27.0	19.1	24.8	17.8	22.7	16.7	20.2	25.2	18.9	23.4	18.2	13.1	22.5	17.1	12.2	21.5	8.1	7.0	6.2	6350	41
ASTRAHAN	46.28N	48.05E	-23	-18.3	-15.2	34.8	21.5	33.2	21.1	31.7	20.5	23.5	30.7	22.6	29.7	21.5	16.1	26.3	20.5	15.1	25.5	10.3	9.0	8.2	3437	642
BARNAUL	53.43N	83.52E	184	-32.2	-28.8	29.9	19.0	28.1	18.4	26.5	17.7	20.8	27.0	19.8	25.7	18.8	13.9	23.7	17.7	13.0	22.8	11.3	9.3	8.1	5868	153
BRJANSK	53.25N	34.32E	216	-22.6	-19.4	28.1	19.1	26.5	18.5	24.9	17.7	20.4	26.0	19.5	24.7	18.5	13.7	22.9	17.5	12.9	21.9	9.4	8.3	7.4	4611	107
CEREPOVEC	59.25N	37.97E	114	-30.9	-27.2	27.3	19.7	25.4	18.7	23.6	17.5	20.7	25.7	19.6	23.9	19.0	14.0	23.4	17.9	13.0	21.9	9.3	7.9	6.6	5666	40
CHELJABINSK-BALANDI	55.30N	61.53E	227	-29.0	-26.1	30.1	19.6	28.2	18.8	26.5	18.0	20.9	27.6	19.9	26.3	18.7	13.9	23.2	17.7	13.0	22.5	11.2	9.5	8.3	5632	143
CHITA	52.08N	113.48E	671	-36.6	-34.5	30.4	19.4	28.3	18.2	26.2	17.2	20.9	28.0	19.6	25.8	18.7	14.7	23.7	17.4	13.5	22.4	10.2	8.9	7.8	7018	86
EKATERINBURG	56.83N	60.63E	283	-30.2	-27.3	29.1	19.3	27.2	18.4	25.5	17.6	20.8	27.0	19.7	25.4	18.7	14.0	23.7	17.7	13.1	22.4	9.0	7.9	7.1	5942	92
ELABUGA	55.77N	52.07E	192	-29.0	-25.6	29.6	19.7	27.8	19.0	26.0	18.1	21.0	27.3	20.1	26.0	19.0	14.1	23.9	18.0	13.2	22.9	13.4	11.9	9.8	5469	146
GOR'KIJ	56.22N	43.82E	82	-27.4	-23.9	28.4	19.5	26.7	18.8	25.0	17.8	20.9	26.3	19.8	24.8	19.1	14.0	23.5	17.9	13.0	22.2	9.3	8.3	7.3	5184	94
HABAROVSK	48.52N	135.17E	76	-30.0	-28.2	30.2	22.0	28.6	21.3	27.0	20.4	23.7	27.7	22.6	26.7	22.6	17.5	25.5	21.2	16.0	24.7	10.4	9.2	8.2	6119	214
IRKUTSK	52.27N	104.32E	469	-35.0	-31.8	28.1	18.0	26.3	17.3	24.7	16.8	19.8	25.5	18.7	24.1	17.9	13.6	22.1	16.9	12.7	21.0	10.1	8.9	7.8	6703	44
IZHEVSK	56.83N	53.45E	159	-30.1	-26.6	29.3	19.6	27.4	18.7	25.6	17.9	20.8	27.1	19.8	25.7	18.6	13.7	23.7	17.7	12.9	22.5	10.2	8.8	7.5	5749	112
KALININGRAD	54.72N	20.55E	21	-18.2	-13.9	27.7	19.3	25.8	18.3	24.0	17.4	20.6	25.6	19.5	24.1	18.9	13.7	22.7	17.8	12.8	21.7	8.5	7.5	6.6	3898	60
KALUGA	54.57N	36.40E	201	-25.2	-21.9	27.6	19.5	26.0	18.7	24.3	17.8	20.8	25.6	19.7	24.3	19.0	14.1	23.5	17.9	13.2	22.3	9.2	7.8	6.8	4944	64
KAZAN`	55.60N	49.28E	116	-28.4	-25.1	29.6	19.7	27.8	19.2	26.0	18.2	21.2	27.3	20.2	25.8	19.1	14.0	24.2	18.1	13.2	23.1	11.5	10.1	9.3	5362	148
KEMEROVO	55.23N	86.12E	260	-32.9	-29.6	28.7	19.1	26.9	18.2	25.1	17.4	20.7	25.8	19.6	24.7	18.9	14.2	23.3	17.8	13.1	22.1	10.9	9.6	8.7	6227	109
KIROV	58.65N	49.62E	164	-32.8	-28.2	27.8	19.8	25.7	18.4	23.9	17.4	20.7	25.9	19.5	24.2	18.8	13.9	23.8	17.7	12.9	22.0	9.9	8.7	7.8	5932	62
KIROV	58.60N	49.63E	158	-29.7	-26.5	29.1	20.2	27.4	19.0	25.6	18.1	21.0	27.1	20.2	25.9	18.9	13.9	24.2	18.0	13.2	22.8	6.3	5.5	5.1	5630	119
KRASNODAR	45.03N	39.15E	34	-14.9	-11.6	33.6	22.6	31.7	21.9	30.0	21.0	24.0	30.8	23.0	29.4	22.0	16.7	27.4	21.0	15.7	26.2	10.4	9.2	8.3	2947	461
KRASNOJARSK	56.00N	92.88E	277	-33.7	-31.1	28.4	18.3	26.6	17.6	24.8	16.8	20.0	25.7	19.0	24.3	18.1	13.4	22.4	17.0	12.6	21.3	10.1	8.4	7.0	6254	68
KRASNOJARSK OPYTNOE	[illegible]	[illegible]	[illegible]	[illegible]	[illegible]	[illegible]	[illegible]	[illegible]	[illegible]	[illegible]	[illegible]	[illegible]	[illegible]	[illegible]	[illegible]	[illegible]	[illegible]	[illegible]	[illegible]	[illegible]	[illegible]	[illegible]	[illegible]	[illegible]	[illegible]	[illegible]

DB: Dry bulb temperature, °C WB: Wet bulb temperature, °C DP: Dew point temperature, °C HR: Humidity ratio, g of moisture per kg of dry air WS: Wind speed, m/s
MCWB: Mean coincident wet bulb temperature, °C MCDB: Mean coincident dry bulb temperature, °C HDD and CDD 18.3: Annual heating and cooling degree-days, base 18.3°C, °C-day

Station	Lat	Long	Elev	Heating DB		Cooling DB/MCWB						Evaporation WB/MCDB				Dehumidification DP/HR/MCDB						Extreme Annual WS			Heat./Cool. Degree-Days	
						0.4%		1%		2%		0.4%		1%		0.4%			1%							
				99.6%	99%	DB	MCWB	DB	MCWB	DB	MCWB	WB	MCDB	WB	MCDB	DP	HR	MCDB	DP	HR	MCDB	1%	2.5%	5%	HDD	CDD 18.3
KURSK	51.77N	36.17E	247	-22.9	-19.6	29.0	19.1	27.3	18.7	25.8	18.0	20.8	26.5	19.9	25.3	18.8	14.0	23.5	17.9	13.2	22.6	10.2	8.4	7.5	4526	143
MAGNITOGORSK	53.35N	59.08E	382	-29.4	-26.5	30.1	18.6	28.2	17.8	26.5	17.2	20.0	27.2	19.1	25.9	17.6	13.2	23.0	16.6	12.3	22.2	10.2	8.9	7.5	5841	126
MAHACKALA	43.02N	47.48E	32	-11.1	-8.1	31.2	23.4	29.7	23.0	28.6	22.5	25.2	29.0	24.3	28.1	24.0	19.0	28.1	23.0	17.8	27.3	11.2	9.5	8.2	2774	551
MOSKVA	55.83N	37.62E	156	-23.1	-19.8	28.4	20.1	26.6	19.5	25.0	18.5	21.2	26.4	20.2	25.2	19.3	14.4	24.0	18.4	13.5	22.8	6.8	5.6	4.4	4747	107
MURMANSK	68.97N	33.05E	51	-31.9	-27.9	24.1	15.9	21.6	14.7	19.2	13.6	16.8	21.7	15.5	20.3	14.7	10.5	19.1	13.1	9.5	17.4	11.2	9.7	8.5	6635	10
NIZHNYJ TAGIL	57.88N	60.07E	258	-32.1	-29.3	28.4	19.0	26.7	18.4	24.9	17.6	20.5	26.1	19.4	24.8	18.5	13.8	22.7	17.5	12.9	21.7	7.4	6.6	5.7	6228	65
NIZNIJ NOVGOROD	56.27N	44.00E	157	-27.1	-23.5	29.3	20.0	27.9	19.6	26.1	18.7	21.2	27.0	20.3	25.9	19.2	14.3	23.6	18.2	13.4	22.5	7.2	6.3	5.5	5065	134
NOVOKUZNETSK	53.82N	86.88E	308	-31.9	-28.9	29.0	19.2	27.2	18.4	25.5	17.8	20.7	26.4	19.7	25.2	18.8	14.2	23.5	17.7	13.1	22.4	12.1	10.1	8.5	5978	98
NOVOSIBIRSK	55.08N	82.90E	176	-34.4	-30.8	29.2	19.0	27.4	18.2	25.9	17.5	20.7	26.3	19.7	25.1	19.0	14.1	22.7	17.9	13.1	21.8	10.7	9.3	8.0	6165	117
OMSK	55.02N	73.38E	122	-32.7	-29.5	31.0	18.8	29.1	18.2	27.3	17.6	20.6	27.8	19.7	26.6	18.2	13.3	23.2	17.1	12.4	22.4	10.6	9.1	8.0	6078	167
OREL	52.93N	36.00E	203	-24.2	-20.6	28.6	19.6	27.1	18.9	25.5	18.3	21.0	26.6	20.1	25.3	19.0	14.2	24.2	18.1	13.3	22.7	10.6	9.5	8.3	4629	121
ORENBURG	51.68N	55.10E	117	-29.2	-25.8	33.8	19.7	31.6	18.9	29.8	18.3	21.3	29.9	20.3	28.7	18.5	13.5	24.3	17.4	12.6	23.4	10.8	9.4	8.4	5146	297
PENZA	53.12N	45.02E	174	-27.0	-23.7	30.4	19.7	28.6	18.8	26.9	18.1	21.2	27.7	20.2	26.3	19.0	14.1	24.2	18.0	13.2	22.9	10.4	9.4	8.6	5043	153
PERM	57.95N	56.20E	170	-30.8	-27.3	29.5	20.1	27.7	19.2	25.7	18.2	21.2	27.5	20.1	26.2	18.9	14.0	25.2	17.8	13.0	23.3	10.0	8.8	7.8	5856	108
RJAZAN'	54.62N	39.72E	160	-23.5	-20.8	28.4	19.7	26.5	18.7	24.9	17.8	20.8	26.3	19.7	24.9	18.8	13.8	23.5	17.8	13.0	22.1	9.7	8.0	6.8	4896	118
RJAZAN'	54.63N	39.70E	158	-25.6	-21.7	29.1	19.3	27.4	18.8	25.8	18.3	21.1	26.4	20.1	25.2	19.3	14.3	23.6	18.3	13.4	22.3	6.7	5.9	5.2	4837	131
ROSTOV-NA-DONU	47.25N	39.82E	77	-17.0	-14.6	33.1	22.0	31.1	21.1	29.6	20.3	23.2	30.7	22.2	28.9	20.9	15.8	26.5	19.9	14.8	25.5	12.7	11.0	9.6	3526	427
SAMARA	53.25N	50.45E	40	-27.2	-24.5	31.5	20.1	29.6	19.6	27.8	18.9	21.8	28.5	20.9	27.4	19.7	14.4	24.7	18.6	13.5	23.7	10.6	9.4	8.3	5088	199
SARATOV	51.57N	46.03E	156	-23.1	-20.4	31.6	19.6	29.7	19.0	28.0	18.3	21.1	28.3	20.2	27.2	18.8	13.9	23.8	17.9	13.1	23.2	10.6	9.4	8.2	4618	304
SHEREMETYEVO	55.97N	37.42E	197	-25.2	-21.9	28.2	19.0	26.2	18.5	24.8	17.9	20.5	25.6	19.5	24.6	18.8	14.0	23.4	17.8	13.1	22.1	9.3	8.2	7.3	5029	78
SMOLENSK	54.75N	32.07E	239	-23.1	-19.8	26.9	19.4	25.3	18.7	23.8	17.8	20.5	25.2	19.5	23.9	18.8	14.1	23.0	17.8	13.2	21.8	7.4	6.4	5.6	4814	63
ST.PETERSBURG	59.97N	30.30E	6	-23.2	-19.8	27.3	19.1	25.5	18.2	23.8	17.3	20.2	25.4	19.2	24.0	18.2	13.1	22.4	17.2	12.3	21.4	8.8	7.4	6.5	4813	62
STAVROPOL	45.12N	42.08E	452	-17.1	-13.8	33.2	20.1	31.2	19.7	29.2	19.1	21.7	29.7	20.9	28.3	19.1	14.7	25.1	18.2	13.8	24.2	12.9	11.0	9.5	3367	377
SURGUT	61.25N	73.50E	56	-40.8	-37.9	28.3	18.6	26.7	17.7	24.6	17.2	20.0	25.9	19.0	24.4	17.9	13.0	22.4	16.9	12.1	21.5	10.2	9.1	8.1	7444	84
TJUMEN	57.12N	65.43E	104	-32.4	-29.3	29.4	19.4	27.6	18.7	25.9	18.1	21.0	26.9	20.0	25.7	18.9	13.8	23.6	17.9	13.0	22.9	6.5	5.8	5.2	6086	116
TOMSK	56.50N	84.92E	139	-36.2	-32.3	28.4	19.6	26.7	18.4	25.0	17.8	20.9	25.9	19.9	24.7	19.2	14.2	23.3	18.1	13.2	22.3	10.0	8.3	7.1	6453	84
TULA	54.23N	37.62E	204	-25.1	-21.4	29.0	19.8	27.3	18.9	25.6	18.3	21.1	26.8	20.1	25.3	19.1	14.3	24.0	18.2	13.4	22.9	7.3	6.3	5.5	4798	108
TVER	56.90N	35.88E	146	-26.2	-22.8	28.4	19.7	26.5	18.8	24.8	17.9	21.0	26.1	19.8	24.7	19.1	14.2	23.6	18.1	13.2	22.1	9.4	7.9	7.0	5019	80
UFA	54.72N	55.83E	104	-31.5	-28.0	30.8	20.6	28.9	19.5	27.1	18.9	21.8	28.5	20.8	27.1	19.5	14.4	25.1	18.5	13.5	24.1	10.3	9.0	7.8	5545	146
ULAN-UDE	51.83N	107.60E	515	-36.1	-33.5	30.8	18.2	28.6	17.6	26.7	16.9	20.0	27.4	19.0	25.7	17.5	13.4	22.7	16.6	12.6	21.8	11.8	9.7	8.2	6974	110
ULYANOVSK	54.32N	48.33E	127	-28.4	-24.9	30.3	20.3	28.5	19.2	26.8	18.6	21.4	27.8	20.6	26.8	19.3	14.3	24.3	18.3	13.4	23.4	11.3	10.0	9.0	5136	158
VLADIMIR	56.12N	40.35E	170	-26.7	-23.1	28.2	20.1	26.4	19.5	24.7	18.4	21.2	26.2	20.2	25.1	19.5	14.6	23.8	18.3	13.5	22.7	9.3	8.2	7.3	5123	97
VLADIVOSTOK	43.12N	131.93E	183	-24.5	-22.0	28.1	21.3	26.1	20.4	24.3	19.7	23.1	26.0	22.0	24.3	22.1	17.2	24.3	21.2	16.2	23.2	13.7	11.8	10.3	4989	145
VNUKOVO	55.58N	37.25E	214	-24.1	-21.0	28.1	19.2	26.2	18.6	24.8	18.0	20.6	25.8	19.6	24.5	18.9	14.0	23.3	17.8	13.1	22.4	9.9	8.7	7.9	4956	86
VOLGOGRAD	48.78N	44.37E	134	-21.8	-19.1	33.8	19.2	31.8	18.7	30.0	18.3	20.7	29.5	20.0	28.4	18.1	13.3	23.0	17.3	12.6	22.8	12.8	11.2	10.0	4184	399
VORONEZ	51.65N	39.25E	104	-23.9	-20.8	29.4	19.3	27.8	18.4	26.1	17.7	20.6	26.8	19.8	25.5	18.5	13.5	23.0	17.7	12.9	22.2	10.9	9.2	7.7	4593	137
VORONEZ	51.70N	39.22E	149	-23.7	-20.3	30.9	20.0	29.1	19.2	27.5	18.5	21.3	28.2	20.5	26.7	19.1	14.1	23.4	18.3	13.5	23.1	8.1	7.1	6.3	4344	228
WLADIKAVKAZ	43.05N	44.65E	703	-14.2	-11.6	29.9	20.3	28.1	19.7	26.6	19.0	21.9	27.5	20.9	26.2	20.1	16.1	24.9	19.1	15.2	23.9	5.1	4.2	3.4	3517	209
Saudi Arabia																										*9 sites, 17 more on CD-ROM*
ABHA	18.23N	42.65E	2093	5.9	7.1	30.9	13.0	30.1	13.1	29.3	13.3	19.6	24.1	19.0	23.5	18.2	17.0	21.8	17.8	16.5	21.7	9.7	8.6	7.7	560	712
AL-MADINAH	24.55N	39.70E	636	9.0	10.7	45.0	19.0	44.0	18.7	43.1	18.4	21.9	36.8	20.8	37.3	17.2	13.3	26.0	16.0	12.3	25.1	9.3	8.2	7.3	92	3662
DHAHRAN	26.27N	50.17E	17	7.8	9.0	44.2	23.1	43.1	22.9	42.1	23.0	30.6	35.6	29.8	35.1	29.3	26.2	33.8	28.8	25.3	33.5	11.1	9.9	8.9	205	3284
GASSIM	26.30N	43.77E	648	3.2	4.9	44.2	18.9	43.4	18.5	42.8	18.3	22.1	35.2	20.6	36.9	18.2	14.2	26.6	16.2	12.5	23.0	9.2	8.1	7.0	467	2806
JEDDAH (KING ABDUL AZIZ INTL)	21.70N	39.18E	17	15.1	16.2	40.9	23.5	39.6	24.1	38.4	24.5	29.8	35.0	29.1	34.4	28.8	25.3	33.5	27.9	24.0	32.7	10.0	8.9	8.1	1	3697
KHAMIS MUSHAIT	18.30N	42.80E	2056	5.8	7.5	31.8	15.1	31.1	14.9	30.3	14.5	19.4	24.7	18.8	23.9	18.0	16.7	22.3	17.1	15.7	21.8	9.4	8.4	7.4	391	936
MAKKAH	21.43N	39.77E	240	16.0	17.2	45.1	24.6	44.1	24.4	43.1	24.3	28.9	38.6	28.0	38.0	26.2	22.3	35.3	25.3	21.0	34.5	6.3	5.3	4.7	1	4701
RIYADH OBS. (O.A.P.)	24.70N	46.73E	620	5.9	7.2	44.2	18.7	43.8	18.5	42.9	18.2	20.9	36.4	20.0	36.6	17.2	13.3	22.3	16.1	12.3	21.7	9.5	8.3	7.3	301	3264
TABUK	28.38N	36.60E	768	1.8	3.0	40.8	18.8	39.2	18.1	38.2	17.7	20.8	36.3	19.9	35.3	15.2	11.8	26.5	14.1	11.0	26.5	10.4	8.7	7.2	708	2026
Senegal																										*1 site, 6 more on CD-ROM*
DAKAR/YOFF	14.73N	17.50W	24	16.5	16.9	32.1	23.5	31.2	25.0	30.7	25.3	27.9	29.7	27.3	29.3	27.2	23.1	28.9	27.0	22.8	28.6	9.9	9.0	8.2	1	2322
Serbia																										*2 sites, 31 more on CD-ROM*
BEOGRAD	44.80N	20.47E	132	-8.9	-6.7	33.7	21.2	32.1	20.8	30.4	20.1	22.3	30.7	21.6	29.7	19.7	14.6	25.6	18.9	13.9	24.6	7.4	6.3	5.3	2558	498
BEOGRAD/SURCIN	44.82N	20.28E	99	-11.0	-8.3	33.8	21.8	32.0	21.5	30.1	20.8	23.0	30.9	22.2	29.6	20.6	15.4	26.6	19.8	14.7	25.7	10.4	8.8	7.5	2755	396
Singapore																										*1 site, 0 more on CD-ROM*
SINGAPORE/CHANGI AI	1.37N	103.98E	16	23.0	23.5	33.2	26.4	32.8	26.3	32.2	26.2	27.7	30.7	27.4	30.4	27.0	22.8	29.5	26.6	22.2	29.1	7.5	6.6	5.8	0	3537
Slovakia																										*1 site, 18 more on CD-ROM*
BRATISLAVA-LETISKC	48.20N	17.20E	134	-11.9	-9.1	32.0	20.5	30.1	20.0	28.5	19.2	21.5	29.3	20.7	28.3	19.0	14.0	24.7	18.1	13.2	23.7	10.0	8.6	7.5	3099	265

Meaning of acronyms:
DB: Dry bulb temperature, °C
WB: Wet bulb temperature, °C
MCWB: Mean coincident wet bulb temperature, °C
Lat: Latitude, °
DP: Dew point temperature, °C
MCDB: Mean coincident dry bulb temperature, °C
Long: Longitude, °
HR: Humidity ratio, g of moisture per kg of dry air
HDD and CDD 18.3: Annual heating and cooling degree-days, base 18.3°C, °C-day
Elev: Elevation, m
WS: Wind speed, m/s

Station	Lat	Long	Elev	Heating DB		Cooling DB/MCWB						Evaporation WB/MCDB				Dehumidification DP/HR/MCDB						Extreme Annual WS			Heat./Cool. Degree-Days	
						0.4%		1%		2%		0.4%		1%		0.4%			1%							
				99.6%	99%	DB / MCWB		DB / MCWB		DB / MCWB		WB / MCDB		WB / MCDB		DP / HR / MCDB			DP / HR / MCDB			1%	2.5%	5%	HDD / CDD 18.3	
South Africa																									8 sites, 14 more on CD-ROM	
BLOEMFONTEIN AIRPOR	29.10S	26.30E	1354	-4.6	-3.1	33.9	15.5	32.8	15.4	31.3	15.5	19.6	26.4	19.0	26.0	17.8	15.1	21.6	17.0	14.3	21.0	9.4	8.2	7.2	1364	542
CAPE TOWN INTNL. AI	33.97S	18.60E	42	3.8	5.0	31.0	19.4	29.1	19.0	27.6	18.5	21.1	27.4	20.4	26.2	19.1	14.0	22.6	18.4	13.3	22.1	14.0	12.5	11.3	901	366
DURBAN INTNL. AIRPO	29.97S	30.95E	14	9.4	10.7	30.2	23.9	29.2	23.7	28.5	23.4	25.5	28.5	24.9	27.9	24.4	19.4	27.2	24.0	18.9	26.9	11.3	10.1	9.0	129	1132
EAST LONDON	33.03S	27.83E	125	8.1	9.1	30.2	20.1	28.6	20.5	27.2	20.6	23.8	27.2	23.1	26.2	22.8	17.8	25.7	22.1	17.0	24.9	12.8	11.2	9.9	419	576
JOHANNESBURG INTNL.	26.15S	28.23E	1720	0.2	2.1	29.0	15.4	27.9	15.5	26.9	15.6	19.4	24.0	18.6	23.5	18.0	16.0	21.4	17.1	15.1	20.6	9.3	8.3	7.4	1099	268
PORT ELIZABETH	33.98S	25.62E	63	5.4	6.8	29.2	18.9	27.3	19.5	26.1	19.7	22.7	25.7	22.0	24.9	21.9	16.7	24.3	21.1	15.9	23.6	14.5	12.8	11.4	645	413
PRETORIA (IRENE)	25.92S	28.22E	1523	2.7	3.9	30.6	16.1	29.3	16.4	28.2	16.4	20.2	26.0	19.7	25.2	18.5	16.1	22.2	18.0	15.7	21.7	8.9	7.6	6.6	811	473
PRETORIA-EENDRACHT	25.73S	28.18E	1326	3.0	4.2	32.1	17.5	31.0	17.4	30.0	17.5	21.0	27.0	20.4	26.4	19.4	16.7	22.7	18.8	16.0	22.5	5.7	4.8	4.1	589	847
Spain																									14 sites, 22 more on CD-ROM	
ALICANTE/EL ALTET	38.28N	0.55W	31	3.3	4.8	32.8	21.6	31.2	22.1	30.2	22.2	25.5	28.7	24.8	28.4	24.4	19.4	27.2	23.8	18.7	27.0	10.2	8.9	7.7	868	891
BARCELONA/AEROPUERT	41.28N	2.07E	6	0.9	2.1	30.2	23.8	29.1	23.6	28.2	23.0	25.4	28.7	24.6	28.0	24.2	19.1	27.8	23.3	18.1	27.1	9.5	8.2	7.2	1389	573
BILBAO/SONDICA	43.30N	2.90W	39	-0.2	1.1	32.7	21.0	29.9	20.2	27.9	19.4	23.0	28.6	21.9	26.7	21.3	16.0	24.3	20.3	15.0	23.2	9.8	8.3	7.1	1494	374
LAS PALMAS DE GRAN	27.93N	15.38W	47	13.2	14.1	30.1	20.2	28.3	20.4	27.2	20.7	24.4	26.6	23.5	25.9	23.7	18.7	25.9	22.8	17.6	25.3	14.4	13.5	12.7	73	1026
MADRID/BARAJAS RS	40.45N	3.55W	582	-4.1	-2.8	36.2	19.6	34.9	19.3	33.3	18.6	21.7	33.8	20.7	32.4	17.2	13.2	26.6	16.2	12.3	26.0	9.7	8.4	7.3	2023	612
MADRID/TORREJON	40.48N	3.45W	611	-4.2	-3.0	36.8	20.0	35.1	19.5	33.8	18.9	21.8	34.3	20.7	32.4	17.1	13.2	27.8	16.1	12.4	26.5	9.2	8.0	6.9	2133	573
MALAGA/AEROPUERTO	36.67N	4.48W	7	3.9	5.1	34.8	20.4	32.5	20.1	30.8	20.0	23.9	28.0	23.3	27.4	22.8	17.5	26.3	22.0	16.7	26.0	11.3	9.8	8.5	849	818
MURCIA	38.00N	1.17W	62	2.4	3.8	35.8	21.4	34.5	21.3	33.2	21.1	24.4	30.6	23.7	29.7	22.8	17.7	26.3	22.0	16.8	26.1	8.0	7.0	6.1	892	1082
PALMA DE MALLORCA/S	39.55N	2.73E	7	-0.1	1.1	33.2	22.9	31.9	23.0	30.6	22.8	25.8	29.5	25.0	29.0	24.8	19.9	28.1	23.9	18.8	27.6	10.2	9.0	8.0	1319	684
SEVILLA/SAN PABLC	37.42N	5.90W	31	1.3	2.9	39.9	23.8	38.0	22.6	36.1	21.9	25.1	36.6	23.8	34.7	22.0	16.7	28.9	20.9	15.6	27.4	8.8	7.8	6.7	913	1140
VALENCIA/AEROPUERTO	39.50N	0.47W	62	1.0	2.2	33.1	21.4	31.7	21.9	30.2	22.1	25.0	29.3	24.3	28.6	23.8	18.8	27.5	23.0	17.9	27.2	11.4	9.6	8.1	1088	801
VALLADOLID	41.65N	4.77W	735	-4.2	-2.8	34.3	18.1	32.8	17.8	31.0	17.3	19.6	30.9	18.7	29.7	16.0	12.4	22.3	15.1	11.7	21.4	8.3	7.1	6.0	2413	359
ZARAGOZA (USAFB)	41.67N	1.05W	263	-2.2	-0.9	36.1	20.7	34.0	20.4	32.2	20.0	22.4	32.1	21.6	31.0	19.2	14.5	25.3	18.8	14.1	25.2	12.5	10.8	9.6	1741	667
ZARAGOZA/AEROPUERTO	41.67N	1.00W	258	-2.9	-1.1	36.1	21.5	34.2	20.9	32.8	20.4	22.8	33.1	21.9	31.3	19.9	15.0	26.2	18.9	14.1	25.6	13.4	12.0	10.7	1734	685
Sri Lanka																									1 site, 0 more on CD-ROM	
KATUNAYAKE	7.17N	79.88E	8	20.9	22.0	33.1	25.2	32.6	25.5	32.1	25.6	27.7	30.9	27.4	30.7	26.9	22.6	30.2	26.4	21.9	29.7	9.0	8.2	7.5	0	3412
Sweden																									4 sites, 93 more on CD-ROM	
GOTEBORG	57.72N	12.00E	2	-11.7	-8.9	26.7	18.2	25.2	17.6	23.6	16.9	19.7	24.3	18.8	23.0	18.1	13.0	21.9	17.1	12.2	20.8	9.0	7.5	6.4	3633	62
GOTEBORG/LANDVETTER	57.67N	12.30E	169	-14.1	-11.0	26.0	16.8	24.1	16.1	22.3	15.2	18.3	23.2	17.3	22.0	16.9	12.3	19.8	15.8	11.5	18.6	11.2	10.0	8.9	4193	28
GOTEBORG/SAVE	57.78N	11.88E	16	-14.8	-11.3	25.8	17.8	24.0	17.1	22.2	16.3	19.5	23.2	18.4	22.0	18.2	13.1	20.9	17.1	12.2	19.8	11.3	10.0	8.9	4001	24
STOCKHOLM/BROMMA	59.37N	17.90E	14	-17.1	-13.9	27.0	17.9	25.1	16.9	23.2	16.0	19.2	24.1	18.3	22.7	17.6	12.7	20.7	16.6	11.8	20.0	9.0	8.0	7.1	4286	49
Switzerland																									3 sites, 32 more on CD-ROM	
LAEGERN	47.48N	8.40E	843	-11.7	-9.2	26.1	17.9	24.4	17.2	22.9	16.7	19.4	23.5	18.3	22.6	18.0	14.3	21.2	16.8	13.2	20.1	12.6	10.9	9.5	3917	71
ZUERICH METEOSCHWEI	47.38N	8.57E	569	-9.3	-7.0	28.8	19.1	27.0	18.4	25.4	17.7	20.0	26.7	19.2	25.4	17.7	13.6	22.2	17.0	13.0	21.3	8.9	7.3	5.8	3296	139
ZURICH-KLOTEN	47.48N	8.53E	432	-10.1	-7.6	30.1	19.9	28.2	19.1	26.5	18.5	20.7	27.9	19.9	26.6	18.2	13.8	23.0	17.5	13.2	22.2	8.5	7.1	6.0	3303	132
Syrian Arab Republic																									5 sites, 4 more on CD-ROM	
ALEPPO INT. AEROPOR	36.18N	37.20E	384	-2.0	-0.6	38.8	20.2	37.2	19.9	35.9	19.7	22.8	33.0	22.1	32.2	19.7	15.1	27.4	19.0	14.4	26.9	10.3	9.2	8.1	1533	1323
DAMASCUS INT. AIRPO	33.42N	36.52E	609	-3.5	-1.9	39.1	18.5	37.8	18.2	36.2	17.9	21.0	30.6	20.3	29.9	19.0	14.8	22.8	18.0	14.0	22.5	12.1	10.5	9.4	1527	1060
DARAA	32.60N	36.10E	543	1.0	2.5	35.8	19.2	34.2	19.4	32.9	19.4	22.5	30.8	21.8	29.4	20.4	16.1	24.4	19.7	15.4	24.2	8.3	6.9	5.5	1175	1022
HAMA	35.12N	36.75E	303	-1.4	0.2	38.9	20.5	37.3	20.1	36.0	19.8	22.6	34.0	21.9	33.2	19.1	14.4	27.9	18.2	13.6	26.9	7.1	5.7	4.8	1349	1324
LATTAKIA	35.53N	35.77E	7	4.1	5.6	32.2	22.2	31.1	23.8	30.2	24.0	26.2	29.9	25.8	29.4	25.1	20.2	29.2	24.5	19.5	28.8	9.9	8.0	6.5	744	1149
Taiwan, Province of China																									19 sites, 17 more on CD-ROM	
CHIANG KAI SHEK	25.08N	121.22E	33	8.9	10.0	34.2	27.0	33.5	26.9	32.9	26.8	28.5	32.1	27.9	31.5	27.3	23.2	30.5	27.0	22.8	30.2	12.8	11.7	10.8	300	1874
CHILUNG	25.15N	121.80E	3	10.2	11.1	33.8	26.1	32.9	26.0	32.1	26.0	27.2	31.1	27.0	30.8	26.3	21.8	29.3	26.0	21.3	29.2	9.3	8.0	7.0	255	1823
CHINMEM/SHATOU(AFB)	24.43N	118.37E	9	6.9	7.9	33.1	28.4	32.2	28.1	31.9	27.9	29.3	32.0	28.8	31.6	28.8	25.3	31.5	28.1	24.2	31.0	9.7	8.5	7.8	538	1589
HSINCHU (TW-AFB)	24.82N	120.93E	8	9.0	10.0	33.1	27.8	32.5	27.6	32.0	27.4	28.8	31.9	28.2	31.5	27.9	24.1	31.5	27.2	23.0	30.9	13.3	11.9	10.7	293	1842
HSINCHU CITY	24.83N	120.93E	27	8.8	10.0	33.9	27.2	33.2	27.0	32.5	26.8	28.0	32.6	27.6	32.1	26.7	22.4	31.2	26.3	21.8	30.7	9.8	8.5	7.4	298	1842
KANGSHAN (TW-AFB)	22.78N	120.27E	10	10.0	11.2	33.2	27.3	32.8	27.2	32.1	27.0	28.2	31.5	28.0	31.2	27.2	23.0	30.4	27.1	22.8	30.3	8.4	7.2	6.3	80	2237
KAOHSIUNG	22.63N	120.28E	29	12.4	13.6	32.8	27.2	32.2	27.1	31.8	26.9	28.1	31.6	27.7	31.2	27.1	23.0	30.3	26.7	22.4	30.1	7.5	6.4	5.6	38	2492
KAOHSIUNG INTL ARPT	22.58N	120.35E	9	11.8	12.9	33.2	26.5	32.9	26.4	32.2	26.2	27.6	31.0	27.2	30.9	26.7	22.3	29.5	26.2	21.6	29.5	8.9	7.4	6.4	43	2475
PINGTUNG NORTH(AFB)	22.70N	120.48E	29	11.1	12.3	34.2	27.2	33.9	27.2	33.2	26.9	28.2	32.6	27.7	32.1	27.1	22.9	30.5	26.8	22.4	30.2	7.2	6.0	5.1	41	2489
PINGTUNG SOUTH(AFB)	22.68N	120.47E	24	11.8	12.9	34.9	27.3	34.1	27.1	33.3	26.8	28.2	32.8	27.8	32.3	27.1	22.9	30.6	26.8	22.5	30.2	7.3	6.1	5.2	34	2577
SUNGSHAN/TAIPEI	25.07N	121.55E	6	9.0	10.4	34.9	26.8	34.0	26.9	33.2	26.7	28.0	32.7	27.6	32.0	27.0	22.7	30.5	26.2	21.7	29.9	8.8	7.8	7.1	242	2022
TAIBEI	25.03N	121.52E	9	9.6	10.8	34.9	26.7	34.1	26.6	33.3	26.4	27.8	32.9	27.3	32.2	26.6	22.1	30.2	26.1	21.5	30.0	7.9	7.0	6.3	237	2044
TAICHUNG (TW-AFB)	24.18N	120.65E	112	7.0	9.1	34.2	27.0	[illegible]	[illegible]	[illegible]	[illegible]	[illegible]	[illegible]	[illegible]	[illegible]	[illegible]	[illegible]	[illegible]	[illegible]	[illegible]	[illegible]	[illegible]	[illegible]	[illegible]	[illegible]	[illegible]

Meaning of acronyms:
DB: Dry bulb temperature, °C *WB: Wet bulb temperature, °C*
MCWB: Mean coincident wet bulb temperature, °C
Lat: Latitude, °
DP: Dew point temperature, °C
MCDB: Mean coincident dry bulb temperature, °C
Long: Longitude, °
HR: Humidity ratio, g of moisture per kg of dry air
Elev: Elevation, m
WS: Wind speed, m/s
HDD and CDD 18.3: Annual heating and cooling degree-days, base 18.3°C, °C-day

Station	Lat	Long	Elev	Heating DB		Cooling DB/MCWB						Evaporation WB/MCDB				Dehumidification DP/HR/MCDB						Extreme Annual WS			Heat./Cool. Degree-Days	
						0.4%		1%		2%		0.4%		1%		0.4%			1%							
				99.6%	99%	DB / MCWB		DB / MCWB		DB / MCWB		WB / MCDB		WB / MCDB		DP / HR / MCDB			DP / HR / MCDB			1%	2.5%	5%	HDD / CDD 18.3	
TAIZHONG	24.15N	120.68E	78	9.5	10.8	33.4	26.3	32.8	26.2	32.3	26.0	27.1	31.9	26.7	31.4	25.8	21.3	29.5	25.5	20.9	29.4	5.0	4.3	3.9	152	2137
TAOYUAN AB (=589650)	25.07N	121.23E	45	8.5	9.8	33.9	28.0	33.1	27.7	32.2	27.3	29.0	32.6	28.2	32.1	28.0	24.2	32.1	27.1	23.0	31.3	11.9	10.5	9.5	342	1798
WU-CHI OBSERVATORY	24.25N	120.52E	5	9.9	11.0	32.8	27.2	32.3	27.1	31.9	26.9	28.1	31.7	27.7	31.3	27.1	22.9	30.8	26.6	22.2	30.6	16.0	14.2	12.7	224	1954
WUCHIA OBSERVATORY	24.27N	120.62E	5	7.9	8.9	32.2	27.2	31.9	27.0	31.1	26.9	28.2	31.0	27.7	30.6	27.4	23.3	30.5	26.9	22.6	30.2	11.9	10.2	9.1	323	1668
Tajikistan																										*1 site, 2 more on CD-ROM*
DUSHANBE	38.55N	68.78E	800	-7.1	-4.9	37.4	19.8	36.2	19.5	35.1	19.1	22.7	33.7	21.4	32.7	18.9	15.1	30.1	17.5	13.8	28.6	6.3	5.1	4.1	1941	952
Tanzania, United Republic of																										*1 site, 0 more on CD-ROM*
DAR ES SALAAM AIRPO	6.87S	39.20E	53	17.7	18.3	33.1	25.6	32.6	25.4	32.1	25.2	26.7	30.7	26.4	30.2	25.9	21.3	28.3	25.4	20.7	27.9	8.6	7.8	7.0	0	2809
Thailand																										*2 sites, 60 more on CD-ROM*
BANGKOK METROPOLIS	13.73N	100.57E	4	19.0	20.6	35.8	26.5	35.1	26.4	34.5	26.2	28.1	33.0	27.7	32.5	26.9	22.5	30.5	26.5	22.1	30.2	6.3	5.5	4.9	0	3873
DON MUANG	13.92N	100.60E	12	19.0	20.4	37.2	26.7	36.4	26.7	35.7	26.6	29.6	34.2	29.1	33.4	28.7	25.2	32.1	28.1	24.3	31.6	8.1	7.0	6.2	0	3908
Togo																										*1 site, 0 more on CD-ROM*
LOME	6.17N	1.25E	25	21.0	21.9	33.1	26.2	32.7	26.4	32.2	26.4	28.2	30.9	28.0	30.6	27.8	23.9	29.6	27.2	23.1	29.3	8.3	7.4	6.7	0	3314
Tunisia																										*1 site, 13 more on CD-ROM*
TUNIS-CARTHAGE	36.83N	10.23E	4	5.0	6.0	37.3	22.8	35.2	22.8	33.6	22.5	25.8	31.3	25.1	30.4	24.3	19.2	28.1	23.7	18.6	27.8	11.8	10.4	9.3	814	1186
Turkey																										*19 sites, 28 more on CD-ROM*
ADANA	36.98N	35.30E	20	1.2	2.9	36.6	22.1	35.1	23.0	34.0	23.5	26.5	32.1	26.0	31.5	25.1	20.2	28.8	24.2	19.2	28.3	8.0	6.8	6.0	941	1485
ADANA/INCIRLIK AB	37.00N	35.43E	73	-0.1	1.2	36.8	22.4	35.1	22.6	34.0	23.0	26.6	32.1	26.1	31.4	25.1	20.4	29.0	24.2	19.3	28.7	8.4	7.2	6.2	1106	1294
ADANA/INCIRLIK AFB	37.00N	35.42E	76	0.2	1.9	36.1	21.9	34.8	22.2	33.6	22.7	26.3	31.6	25.7	30.7	25.0	20.2	29.0	24.2	19.3	28.3	8.5	7.3	6.3	1081	1280
ANTALYA	36.87N	30.73E	54	1.4	2.8	38.0	21.0	36.1	20.9	34.4	20.8	26.2	30.5	25.7	30.0	25.0	20.2	29.3	24.2	19.2	28.9	10.5	9.0	7.6	1076	1200
BURSA	40.18N	29.07E	100	-3.8	-2.2	34.1	22.1	32.6	21.7	31.2	21.2	23.6	31.5	22.8	30.5	21.0	15.9	28.4	20.1	15.0	27.2	7.4	6.2	5.4	1987	603
DIYARBAKIR	37.88N	40.18E	677	-9.0	-6.0	40.1	20.4	39.0	20.2	37.8	20.0	23.4	35.8	22.2	35.4	19.1	15.1	32.3	17.6	13.7	30.7	8.9	7.7	6.6	2188	1176
ERZURUM	39.95N	41.17E	1758	-29.6	-26.4	30.0	15.7	28.2	15.3	26.9	14.8	17.6	26.7	16.6	25.8	14.0	12.4	23.0	12.9	11.5	21.8	10.4	9.5	8.5	5081	63
ESENBOGA	40.12N	33.00E	949	-15.7	-11.9	33.0	17.6	31.2	17.3	29.8	16.9	19.2	29.4	18.3	28.5	15.2	12.1	23.6	14.2	11.3	22.9	8.9	7.7	6.7	3299	227
ESKISEHIR	39.78N	30.57E	786	-11.0	-8.6	33.0	20.0	31.2	19.6	29.9	19.0	21.8	30.3	20.8	28.8	19.0	15.2	26.0	18.0	14.2	25.4	8.8	7.9	7.0	2898	321
ETIMESGUT	39.95N	32.68E	806	-11.2	-9.0	34.1	18.5	32.2	18.2	30.9	17.6	20.2	30.4	19.4	29.4	16.8	13.2	25.3	15.5	12.2	24.2	9.2	8.0	6.8	2878	382
GAZIANTEP	37.08N	37.37E	701	-4.8	-3.0	38.7	22.2	37.1	21.4	35.9	21.0	23.5	36.2	22.6	35.3	19.2	15.2	32.1	18.0	14.1	31.3	8.1	7.0	6.0	1979	1139
ISTANBUL/ATATURK	40.97N	28.82E	37	-2.6	-1.0	31.1	21.4	30.0	21.3	28.9	20.9	24.3	27.6	23.3	27.0	23.2	18.0	26.2	22.1	16.8	25.4	11.1	9.9	9.1	1927	616
IZMIR/A. MENDERES	38.27N	27.15E	120	-2.8	-1.1	37.0	20.9	35.5	20.4	34.2	20.1	22.5	33.3	21.7	32.3	19.0	14.0	26.1	18.1	13.2	25.8	12.0	10.9	10.1	1585	997
IZMIR/CIGLI	38.52N	27.02E	5	-1.8	-0.2	36.2	21.9	34.9	21.6	33.8	21.2	23.5	33.1	22.7	32.2	20.2	14.9	28.3	19.4	14.2	27.6	10.9	9.7	8.7	1408	983
KAYSERI/ERKILET	38.82N	35.43E	1054	-16.0	-12.6	33.8	17.8	32.0	17.3	30.2	16.7	19.2	30.1	18.3	29.2	15.2	12.3	23.6	14.2	11.5	23.0	9.3	7.4	5.6	3137	264
KONYA	37.97N	32.55E	1031	-13.0	-10.1	33.8	17.1	32.1	16.8	30.6	16.4	19.1	29.9	18.0	28.9	15.0	12.0	25.2	13.5	10.9	23.5	11.5	9.8	8.7	2919	439
MALATYA/ERHAC	38.43N	38.08E	849	-11.5	-8.7	37.2	19.8	36.0	19.3	34.8	19.0	22.5	34.8	21.0	33.4	17.9	14.2	32.9	16.1	12.7	30.2	10.1	8.9	7.6	2650	786
SAMSUN	41.28N	36.30E	4	-1.3	0.0	28.0	22.4	27.1	22.2	26.3	21.8	23.8	26.9	23.1	26.3	22.7	17.4	26.3	22.0	16.6	25.8	8.3	7.0	5.9	1962	384
VAN	38.45N	43.32E	1662	-14.0	-11.9	29.0	19.1	27.9	19.0	26.9	18.6	21.9	26.9	20.7	26.3	20.1	18.2	26.1	18.8	16.7	25.6	8.2	6.5	5.3	3538	231
Turkmenistan																										*1 site, 17 more on CD-ROM*
ASHGABAT KESHI	37.92N	58.33E	312	-6.7	-4.6	40.1	19.8	38.8	19.6	37.5	19.5	23.1	34.7	22.2	33.6	19.1	14.4	29.9	18.1	13.5	29.6	9.4	8.2	7.2	1909	1454
Ukraine																										*15 sites, 29 more on CD-ROM*
CHERNIHIV	51.47N	31.25E	141	-20.7	-17.3	29.6	19.7	27.8	19.1	26.2	18.4	21.2	27.2	20.2	25.9	19.1	14.1	23.9	18.2	13.3	22.8	9.2	8.2	7.3	4168	147
DNIPROPETROVSK	48.37N	35.08E	143	-17.8	-15.1	31.9	20.6	30.2	19.9	28.5	19.3	22.2	29.5	21.2	27.9	19.8	14.7	25.3	18.9	13.9	24.1	11.6	9.9	8.9	3763	312
DONETSK	48.07N	37.77E	225	-18.9	-16.1	31.3	19.7	29.5	19.2	27.8	18.6	21.2	28.4	20.4	27.1	18.9	14.1	23.7	18.1	13.4	22.9	12.4	10.4	9.0	3937	253
KHARKIV	49.97N	36.13E	155	-19.6	-16.8	30.8	19.6	29.0	19.0	27.4	18.5	21.1	27.9	20.3	26.5	19.0	14.0	23.5	18.1	13.3	23.0	9.6	8.4	7.8	4058	231
KHERSON	46.63N	32.57E	54	-15.8	-13.1	32.7	20.7	30.9	20.2	29.2	19.3	22.2	29.5	21.4	28.2	20.1	14.9	24.4	19.2	14.0	23.9	9.8	8.4	7.4	3372	348
KRYVYI RIH	48.03N	33.22E	124	-18.0	-15.4	31.7	20.1	30.1	19.4	28.4	18.8	21.7	28.6	20.7	27.4	19.4	14.3	24.5	18.5	13.5	23.5	11.6	10.0	8.6	3745	271
KYIV	50.40N	30.57E	167	-18.1	-15.1	29.4	20.0	27.8	19.3	26.2	18.6	21.3	27.1	20.4	25.9	19.3	14.3	23.9	18.4	13.6	23.0	8.9	7.5	6.6	3907	180
LUHANSK	48.57N	39.25E	62	-20.6	-17.4	33.0	20.3	30.9	19.6	29.1	18.9	21.8	29.4	20.9	28.6	19.3	14.2	24.7	18.5	13.4	23.7	11.8	9.4	7.6	3868	297
LVIV	49.82N	23.95E	323	-17.3	-14.2	28.1	19.5	26.6	18.8	25.0	18.0	20.6	26.3	19.7	24.9	18.6	14.0	23.3	17.8	13.3	22.3	9.7	8.3	7.3	3957	87
MARIUPOL	47.03N	37.50E	70	-15.4	-13.0	30.4	22.1	28.8	21.5	27.5	20.8	23.5	28.2	22.6	27.2	22.1	16.9	26.0	21.1	15.8	25.5	14.4	12.8	11.7	3596	333
ODESA	46.43N	30.77E	42	-13.9	-11.1	31.2	20.2	29.8	19.9	28.0	19.4	22.6	27.2	21.6	26.4	21.1	15.8	24.8	20.1	14.8	24.0	11.2	9.6	8.4	3249	339
POLTAVA	49.60N	34.55E	160	-19.4	-16.3	30.4	19.9	28.7	19.2	27.1	18.6	21.5	28.0	20.5	26.5	19.3	14.3	24.5	18.4	13.5	23.5	10.1	8.5	7.2	4000	217
SIMFEROPOL	45.02N	33.98E	181	-12.7	-10.2	32.2	20.1	30.3	19.4	28.8	18.9	21.7	28.1	20.8	27.3	19.9	14.9	23.7	18.9	14.0	22.9	12.3	10.7	9.4	3096	317
VINNYTSIA	49.23N	28.60E	298	-19.1	-16.0	28.4	19.3	27.0	18.6	25.6	18.0	20.6	26.3	19.7	25.0	18.6	13.9	23.4	17.7	13.2	22.2	11.4	9.4	8.2	4083	117
ZAPORIZHZHIA	47.80N	35.02E	112	-17.7	-14.8	32.3	20.1	30.5	19.5	28.9	18.9	21.7	28.9	20.9	27.9	19.5	14.4	24.4	18.6	13.7	23.5	10.1	8.8	7.8	3658	319
United Arab Emirates																										*5 sites, 2 more on CD-ROM*
ABU DHABI BATEEN AI	24.43N	54.47E	3	13.0	14.1	43.0	23.9	41.6	24.0	40.2	24.4	30.8	34.6	30.3	34.3	30.0	27.3	33.4	29.3	26.1	33.2	9.5	8.4	7.5	21	3479
ABU DHABI INTER. AI	24.43N	54.65E	27	11.5	12.9	44.9	23.2	43.3	23.5	42.1	23.7	30.6	35.3	30.0	34.8	29.4	26.4	33.5	29.0	25.6	33.2	9.4	8.4	7.5	30	3565
AL AIN INTERNATIONA	24.27N	55.60E	262	11.1	12.1	45.9	22.3	45.0	22.5	44.1	22.4	28.6	35.6	27.7	35.5	27.1	23.6	32.1	26.0	22.0	31.5	10.4	9.1	8.1	37	3939

Meaning of acronyms:
DB: Dry bulb temperature, °C — *WB: Wet bulb temperature, °C*
MCWB: Mean coincident wet bulb temperature, °C
Lat: Latitude, °
DP: Dew point temperature, °C
MCDB: Mean coincident dry bulb temperature, °C
Long: Longitude, °
HR: Humidity ratio, g of moisture per kg of dry air
HDD and CDD 18.3: Annual heating and cooling degree-days, base 18.3°C, °C-day
Elev: Elevation, m
WS: Wind speed, m/s

Station	Lat	Long	Elev	Heating DB		Cooling DB/MCWB						Evaporation WB/MCDB				Dehumidification DP/HR/MCDB						Extreme Annual WS			Heat./Cool. Degree-Days	
						0.4%		1%		2%		0.4%		1%		0.4%			1%							
				99.6%	99%	DB	MCWB	DB	MCWB	DB	MCWB	WB	MCDB	WB	MCDB	DP	HR	MCDB	DP	HR	MCDB	1%	2.5%	5%	HDD	CDD 18.3
DUBAI INTERNATIONAL	25.25N	55.33E	5	12.7	13.6	42.8	23.8	41.1	24.1	40.0	24.4	30.3	34.9	29.8	34.5	29.2	25.9	33.2	28.8	25.3	33.2	9.2	8.2	7.4	24	3442
SHARJAH INTER. AIRP	25.33N	55.52E	33	9.9	11.1	44.0	23.9	42.8	23.9	41.3	24.3	30.0	36.4	29.3	35.7	28.8	25.4	33.1	28.0	24.2	32.8	8.3	7.3	6.4	56	3289
United Kingdom																									*26 sites, 172 more on CD-ROM*	
AUGHTON	53.55N	2.92W	56	-3.4	-1.9	24.4	17.7	22.4	16.8	20.6	16.0	18.5	23.1	17.6	21.3	16.8	12.1	19.8	16.0	11.5	19.0	11.5	10.2	9.1	3205	19
BINGLEY NO.2	53.82N	1.87W	267	-4.1	-2.9	23.8	17.3	21.7	16.3	19.9	15.4	18.0	21.9	16.9	20.5	16.6	12.2	19.5	15.5	11.4	18.4	12.7	11.0	9.6	3676	10
BIRMINGHAM AIRPORT	52.45N	1.73W	99	-5.2	-3.4	26.7	17.9	24.5	17.0	22.8	16.4	18.9	24.4	18.0	22.9	17.0	12.3	20.6	16.1	11.6	19.7	10.0	8.9	8.0	3167	31
BRISTOL	51.38N	2.72W	194	-3.2	-2.0	25.8	17.8	23.2	16.9	21.8	16.3	18.8	23.3	17.8	21.7	17.2	12.6	19.7	16.8	12.2	19.2	12.1	10.6	9.6	3019	28
BRISTOL WEA CENTER	51.47N	2.60W	11	-2.8	-1.1	26.6	18.5	24.7	17.4	23.0	16.7	19.4	24.5	18.3	22.8	17.4	12.5	21.1	16.6	11.8	20.1	10.4	9.0	7.9	2659	58
CARDIFF WEATHER CEN	51.48N	3.18W	52	-1.0	0.1	26.2	18.2	24.3	17.4	22.7	16.6	19.2	24.5	18.2	22.6	17.3	12.5	20.8	16.6	11.9	19.9	11.7	10.2	9.0	2531	57
CARDIFF-WALES ARPT	51.40N	3.35W	67	-3.0	-1.5	24.8	17.9	22.8	17.1	21.1	16.4	18.7	22.8	17.9	21.2	17.2	12.4	19.9	16.7	12.0	19.2	13.3	11.7	10.3	2958	24
CHURCH LAWFORD	52.37N	1.33W	106	-4.7	-3.1	26.6	18.7	24.4	17.6	22.6	16.8	19.7	24.2	18.4	23.0	18.3	13.3	20.5	16.8	12.1	19.7	10.0	8.6	7.6	3184	30
CILFYNYDD	51.63N	3.30W	194	-4.6	-2.9	25.6	18.4	23.6	17.2	21.8	16.4	19.2	23.9	18.0	22.0	17.6	12.9	20.8	16.5	12.0	19.4	11.6	9.9	8.6	3281	26
CROSBY	53.50N	3.07W	9	-3.4	-1.8	24.5	18.3	22.3	17.4	20.6	16.7	19.2	22.8	18.2	21.1	18.0	13.0	20.3	17.1	12.2	19.4	17.6	15.1	13.4	2977	20
EAST MIDLANDS	52.83N	1.32W	96	-4.0	-2.2	26.8	18.4	24.2	17.1	22.8	16.5	19.2	24.6	18.2	22.9	17.2	12.4	20.9	16.2	11.6	19.9	12.8	11.1	9.8	3114	39
EDINBURGH AIRPORT	55.95N	3.35W	41	-5.3	-3.4	22.4	16.6	20.8	16.0	19.3	15.1	17.7	21.1	16.7	19.7	16.2	11.6	18.9	15.4	11.0	18.1	12.4	10.8	9.5	3465	3
EMLEY MOOR	53.62N	1.67W	259	-3.2	-2.2	24.0	17.6	22.0	16.7	20.4	15.8	18.4	22.4	17.3	20.9	16.9	12.4	20.0	15.9	11.6	18.9	14.8	12.9	10.9	3485	16
GLASGOW AIRPORT	55.87N	4.43W	8	-5.9	-3.9	23.7	17.2	21.6	16.2	19.9	15.4	18.1	22.1	17.1	20.3	16.7	11.9	19.8	15.8	11.2	18.9	13.1	11.4	10.0	3435	8
GRAVESEND-BROADNESS	51.47N	0.30E	3	-1.7	-0.7	28.4	20.3	26.3	19.3	24.4	18.3	21.2	26.8	20.1	24.9	19.2	14.0	23.0	18.2	13.1	22.3	11.1	9.8	8.8	2552	94
HAWARDEN	53.17N	2.98W	9	-4.3	-2.6	25.3	18.4	23.3	17.6	21.5	16.8	19.5	23.5	18.4	22.1	18.0	13.0	21.0	16.9	12.1	20.1	10.4	9.2	8.1	3051	19
KENLEY AIRFIELD	51.30N	0.08W	170	-2.7	-1.6	26.7	18.1	24.7	17.2	23.0	16.5	19.1	24.4	18.2	23.0	17.2	12.5	20.7	16.4	11.9	19.9	11.0	9.5	8.4	2942	49
LECONFIELD	53.87N	0.43W	7	-3.7	-2.3	25.0	18.2	23.2	17.2	21.6	16.5	19.0	23.3	18.0	22.0	17.3	12.4	20.7	16.4	11.7	19.6	12.6	11.0	9.7	3229	17
LEEDS BRADFORD	53.87N	1.65W	213	-3.0	-1.9	24.2	17.7	22.2	16.6	20.7	16.0	18.4	22.4	17.4	21.2	17.0	12.5	20.2	16.0	11.7	18.9	12.9	11.1	9.8	3397	17
LEEDS WEATHER CTR	53.80N	1.55W	47	-2.3	-1.1	26.1	17.9	24.1	16.9	22.4	16.1	18.7	24.3	17.7	22.8	16.7	11.9	20.8	15.7	11.2	19.6	13.0	11.0	9.4	2943	39
LIVERPOOL	53.33N	2.85W	25	-3.1	-1.9	25.2	18.0	23.2	16.9	21.8	16.5	18.7	23.6	17.9	22.1	17.0	12.2	20.7	16.1	11.5	19.9	13.3	11.5	10.1	2983	30
LONDON WEA CENTER	51.52N	0.12W	23	-2.6	-1.0	27.2	18.9	25.6	18.0	24.1	17.4	19.9	25.8	18.9	23.9	17.5	12.6	22.3	16.8	12.0	21.6	11.7	10.3	9.4	2526	101
LONDON WEATHER CENT	51.52N	0.10W	43	-0.6	0.4	28.5	18.4	26.5	17.7	24.6	16.9	19.5	25.8	18.7	24.3	17.2	12.4	21.8	16.4	11.8	21.1	9.3	8.3	7.4	2344	129
LONDON/HEATHROW AIR	51.48N	0.45W	25	-3.1	-1.7	28.3	18.7	26.3	17.9	24.6	17.2	19.8	26.2	18.9	24.4	17.5	12.6	21.6	16.8	12.0	21.0	10.1	8.8	7.9	2661	94
MANCHESTER AIRPORT	53.35N	2.28W	69	-3.7	-2.2	25.8	17.9	23.7	17.0	21.9	16.1	18.7	23.7	17.8	22.2	16.9	12.2	20.4	16.0	11.5	19.4	11.1	9.9	8.8	3116	31
NORTHOLT	51.55N	0.42W	39	-4.1	-2.6	28.3	18.7	26.2	18.0	24.4	17.3	19.8	26.0	18.9	24.3	17.6	12.7	21.7	16.8	12.0	21.1	10.4	9.2	8.3	2826	75
Uruguay																									*2 sites, 7 more on CD-ROM*	
CARRASCO	34.83S	56.00W	32	1.4	2.9	31.3	21.7	29.9	21.4	28.1	20.9	24.0	28.2	23.2	26.9	23.0	17.8	25.8	22.1	16.8	24.8	13.2	11.1	9.9	1221	461
PRADO	34.85S	56.20W	16	3.0	4.3	31.6	22.5	30.1	22.0	28.8	21.7	24.2	29.1	23.5	27.8	22.7	17.5	26.5	22.1	16.8	25.9	10.2	8.6	7.6	1104	573
Uzbekistan																									*3 sites, 16 more on CD-ROM*	
NAMANGAN	40.98N	71.58E	474	-7.4	-5.3	36.4	21.6	35.2	21.1	34.0	20.8	23.3	33.1	22.4	32.6	20.0	15.6	30.1	18.9	14.5	29.1	7.4	5.6	4.4	2251	1064
SAMARKAND	39.57N	66.95E	724	-9.8	-7.1	36.0	19.2	34.8	18.8	33.6	18.4	20.9	33.0	20.0	31.9	16.8	13.1	26.2	15.7	12.2	24.9	10.4	9.1	7.9	2268	818
TASHKENT	41.27N	69.27E	466	-9.4	-7.0	38.2	20.5	37.0	20.2	35.8	19.9	23.6	34.6	22.2	33.4	19.8	15.4	31.7	18.2	13.8	29.1	6.2	5.3	4.5	2162	1019
Venezuela																									*2 sites, 1 more on CD-ROM*	
CARACAS/MAIQUETIA A	10.60N	66.98W	48	20.7	21.2	33.4	28.0	33.0	27.8	32.2	27.5	29.8	31.9	29.2	31.5	29.2	26.1	31.2	28.8	25.4	30.9	5.2	4.3	3.5	0	3242
SAN ANTONIO DEL TAC	7.85N	72.45W	378	19.9	20.8	35.0	23.6	34.2	23.4	33.8	23.4	26.3	31.5	25.7	31.1	25.0	21.1	28.8	24.2	20.0	27.8	12.3	10.8	9.9	0	3276
Viet Nam																									*4 sites, 16 more on CD-ROM*	
DA NANG	16.07N	108.35E	7	16.5	17.4	36.0	26.2	35.0	26.3	34.1	26.3	28.1	32.5	27.7	31.9	27.1	22.8	30.6	26.6	22.2	30.1	7.4	6.2	5.2	4	2907
HA NOI	21.03N	105.80E	6	10.0	11.1	35.7	27.5	34.7	27.6	33.8	27.5	29.3	32.6	28.7	32.1	28.8	25.3	31.2	28.0	24.2	30.7	6.9	5.9	5.1	168	2348
PHU LIEN	20.80N	106.63E	116	9.8	11.0	34.0	28.9	33.1	28.7	32.3	28.3	30.1	32.6	29.4	31.9	29.4	26.6	32.1	28.7	25.6	31.3	7.0	5.6	4.7	163	2191
TAN SON HOA	10.82N	106.67E	5	20.1	21.1	35.2	25.8	34.7	25.8	34.0	25.8	28.0	31.8	27.6	31.4	27.1	22.8	29.9	26.7	22.3	29.6	11.5	7.9	6.7	0	3594
Zimbabwe																									*1 site, 1 more on CD-ROM*	
HARARE (KUTSAGA)	17.92S	31.13E	1480	6.7	7.8	30.7	16.3	29.6	16.2	28.8	16.2	20.1	24.8	19.7	24.2	19.0	16.5	21.1	18.4	16.0	20.8	9.0	7.9	7.1	348	731

CHAPTER 15

FENESTRATION

FENESTRATION is an architectural term that refers to the arrangement, proportion, and design of window, skylight, and door systems in a building. Fenestration can serve as a physical and/or visual connection to the outdoors, as well as a means to admit solar radiation for natural lighting (**daylighting**), and for heat gain to a space. Fenestration can be fixed or operable, and operable units can allow natural ventilation to a space and egress in low-rise buildings.

Fenestration affects building energy use through four basic mechanisms: thermal heat transfer, solar heat gain, air leakage, and daylighting. The energy effects of fenestration can be minimized by (1) using daylight to offset lighting requirements, (2) using glazings and shading strategies to control solar heat gain to supplement heating through passive solar gain and minimize cooling requirements, (3) using glazing to minimize conductive heat loss, (4) specifying low-air-leakage fenestration products, and (5) integrating fenestration into natural ventilation strategies that can reduce energy use for cooling and fresh air requirements.

Today's designers, builders, energy codes, and energy-efficiency incentive programs [such as ENERGY STAR (www.energystar.gov) and the LEED Green Building Program (www.usgbc.org)] are asking more and more from fenestration systems. Window, skylight, and door manufacturers are responding with new and improved products to meet those demands. With the advent of computer simulation software, designing to improve thermal performance of fenestration products has become much easier. Through participation in rating and certification programs [such as those of the National Fenestration Rating Council (NFRC)] that require the use of this software, fenestration manufacturers can take credit for these improvements through certified ratings that are credible to designers, builders, and code officials. A designer should consider architectural requirements, thermal performance, economic criteria, and human comfort when selecting fenestration. Typically, a wide range of fenestration products are available that meet the specifications for a project. Refining the specifications to improve energy performance and enhance a living or work space can result in lower energy costs, increased productivity, and improved thermal and visual comfort. CEA (1995) provides guidance for carrying out these requirements.

FENESTRATION COMPONENTS

Fenestration components include glazing material, either glass or plastic; framing, mullions, muntin bars, dividers, and opaque door slabs; and shading devices such as louvered blinds, drapes, roller shades, and awnings. In this chapter, **fenestration** and **fenestration systems** refer to the basic assemblies and components of exterior window, skylight, and door systems within the building envelope.

Glazing Units

A glazing unit may consist of a single glazing or multiple glazings. Units with multiple glazing layers, sometimes called **insulating glazing units (IGUs)**, are hermetically sealed, multiple-pane assemblies consisting of two or more glazing layers held and bonded at their perimeter by a spacer bar typically containing a desiccant material. The desiccated spacer is surrounded on at least two sides by a sealant that adheres the glass to the spacer. Figure 1 shows the construction of a typical double-glazing unit.

Glazing. The most common glazing material is glass, although plastic is also used. Both may be clear, tinted, coated, laminated, patterned, or obscured. Clear glass transmits more than 75% of the incident solar radiation and more than 85% of the visible light. Tinted glass is available in many colors, all of which differ in the amount of solar radiation and visible light they transmit and absorb. Coatings on glass affect the transmission of solar radiation, and visible light may affect the absorptance of room-temperature radiation.

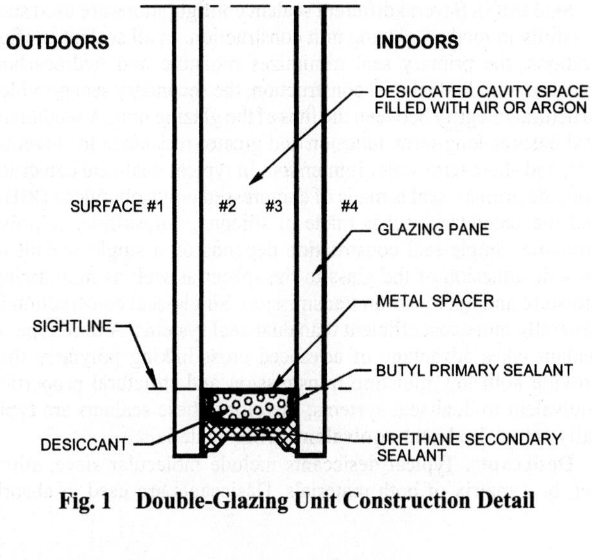

Fig. 1 Double-Glazing Unit Construction Detail

The preparation of this chapter is assigned to TC 4.5, Fenestration.

Some coatings are highly reflective (e.g., mirrors), whereas others have very low reflectance. Some coatings result in visible light transmittance as much as twice the solar heat gain coefficient (desirable for good daylighting while minimizing cooling loads). Laminated glass is made of two panes of glass adhered together. The interlayer between the two panes of glass is typically plastic and may be clear, tinted, or coated. Patterned glass is a durable ceramic frit applied to a glass surface in a decorative pattern. Obscured glass is translucent and is typically used in privacy applications.

Because of its energy efficiency, daylighting, and comfort benefits, low-emissivity (low-e) coated glass is now used in more than 50% of all fenestration products installed in the United States. Tinted and reflective glazing can also be used to reduce solar heat gain through fenestration products. Low-e coatings can also be applied to thin plastic films for use as one of the middle layers in glazing units with three or more layers. There are two types of low-e coating: **high-solar-gain** coatings primarily reduce heat conduction through the glazing system, and are intended for cold climates. **Low-solar-gain coatings**, for hot climates, reduce solar heat gain by blocking admission of the infrared portion of the solar spectrum. There are two ways of achieving low-solar-gain low-e performance: (1) with a special, multilayer solar-infrared-reflecting coating, and (2) with a solar-infrared-absorbing outer glass. To protect the inner glazing and building interior from the absorbed heat from this outer glass, a cold-climate-type low-e coating is also used to reduce conduction of heat from the outer pane to the inner one. In addition, argon and krypton gas are used in lieu of air in the gap between the panes in combination with low-e glazing to further reduce energy transfer. Some manufacturers construct glazing units with one or more suspended, low-e coated plastic films between glazing layers and with a spacer that has better insulating properties and a dual sealant that improves the seal around the gas spaces.

Spacer. The spacer separates the panes of glass and provides the surface for primary and secondary sealant adhesion. Several types of spacers are used today. Each type provides different heat transfer properties, depending on spacer material and geometry.

Heat transfer at the edge of the glazing unit is greater than at its center because of greater heat flow through the spacer system. To minimize this heat flow, **warm-edge spacers** have been developed that reduce edge heat transfer by using spacer materials that have lower thermal conductivity than the typical aluminum (e.g., stainless steel, galvanized steel, tin-plated steel, polymers, foamed silicone) from which spacers have often been made.

Fusing or bending the corners of the spacer minimizes moisture and hydrocarbon vapor transmission into the air space through the corners. Desiccants such as molecular sieve or silica gel are also used to absorb moisture initially trapped in the glazing unit during assembly or that gradually diffuses through the seals after construction.

Sealant(s). Several different sealant configurations are used successfully in modern glazing unit construction. In all sealant configurations, the primary seal minimizes moisture and hydrocarbon transmission. In dual-seal construction, the secondary seal provides structural integrity between the lites of the glazing unit. A secondary seal ensures long-term adhesion and greater resistance to solvents, oils, and short-term water immersion. In typical dual-seal construction, the primary seal is made of compressed polyisobutylene (PIB), and the secondary seal is made of silicone, polysulfide, or polyurethane. Single-seal construction depends on a single sealant to provide adhesion of the glass to the spacer as well as minimizing moisture and hydrocarbon transmission. Single-seal construction is generally more cost efficient than dual-seal systems. A third type of sealant takes advantage of advanced cross-linking polymers that provide both low moisture transmission and structural properties equivalent to dual-seal systems; therefore, these sealants are typically called **dual-seal-equivalent (DSE)** materials.

Desiccants. Typical desiccants include molecular sieve, silica gel, or a matrix of both materials. Desiccants are used to absorb moisture initially trapped in the glazing unit during assembly or that gradually diffused through the seals after construction.

Gas Fill. The hermetically sealed space between glass panes is most often filled with air. In some cases, argon and krypton gas are used instead, to further reduce energy transfer.

Framing

The three main categories of window framing materials are wood, metal, and polymers. **Wood** has good structural integrity and insulating value but low resistance to weather, moisture, warpage, and organic degradation (from mold and insects). **Metal** is durable and has excellent structural characteristics, but it has very poor thermal performance. The metal of choice in windows is almost exclusively aluminum, because of its ease of manufacture, low cost, and low mass, but aluminum has a thermal conductivity roughly 1000 times that of wood or polymers. The poor thermal performance of metal-frame windows can be improved with a thermal break (a nonmetal component that separates the metal frame exposed to the outside from the surfaces exposed to the inside). **Polymer** frames are made of extruded vinyl or poltruded fiberglass (glass-reinforced polyester). Their thermal and structural performance is similar to that of wood, although vinyl frames for large windows must be reinforced.

Manufacturers sometimes combine these materials as clad units (e.g., vinyl-clad aluminum, aluminum-clad wood, vinyl-clad wood) to increase durability, improve thermal performance, or improve aesthetics. In addition, curtain wall systems for commercial buildings may be structurally glazed, and the outdoor "framing" is simply rubber gaskets or silicone.

Residential windows can be categorized by operator type, as shown by the traditional basic types in Figure 2. The glazing system can be mounted either directly in the frame (a direct-glazed or direct-set window, which is not operable) or in a sash that moves in the frame (for an operating window). In operable windows, a weather-sealing system between the frame and sash reduces air and water leakage.

Shading

Shading can be located either outdoors or indoors, and in some cases, internal to the glazing system (between the glass). Materials used include metal, wood, plastic, and fabric. Shading devices are available in a wide range of products that differ greatly in their appearance and energy performance. They include indoor and outdoor blinds, integral blinds, indoor and outdoor screens, shutters, draperies, and roller shades. Shading devices on the outdoor side of the glazing reduce solar heat gain more effectively than indoor devices. However, indoor devices are easier to operate and adjust. Some products help insulate the indoors from the outdoors, whereas others redirect incoming solar radiation to minimize visual and thermal discomfort. Window reveals and side fins as well as awnings and overhangs can offer effective shading as well. Outdoor vegetative shading is particularly effective in reducing solar heat gain while enhancing the outdoor scene.

DETERMINING FENESTRATION ENERGY FLOW

Energy flows through fenestration via (1) conductive and convective heat transfer caused by the temperature difference between outdoor and indoor air, (2) net long-wave (above 2500 nm) radiative exchange between the fenestration and its surroundings and between glazing layers, and (3) short-wave (below 2500 nm) solar radiation incident on the fenestration product, either directly from the sun or reflected from the ground or adjacent objects. Simplified calculations are based on the observation that temperatures of the sky, ground, and surrounding objects (and hence their radiant emission) correlate with the outdoor air temperature. The radiative interchanges are then approximated by assuming that all the radiating surfaces (including the sky) are at the same temperature as the

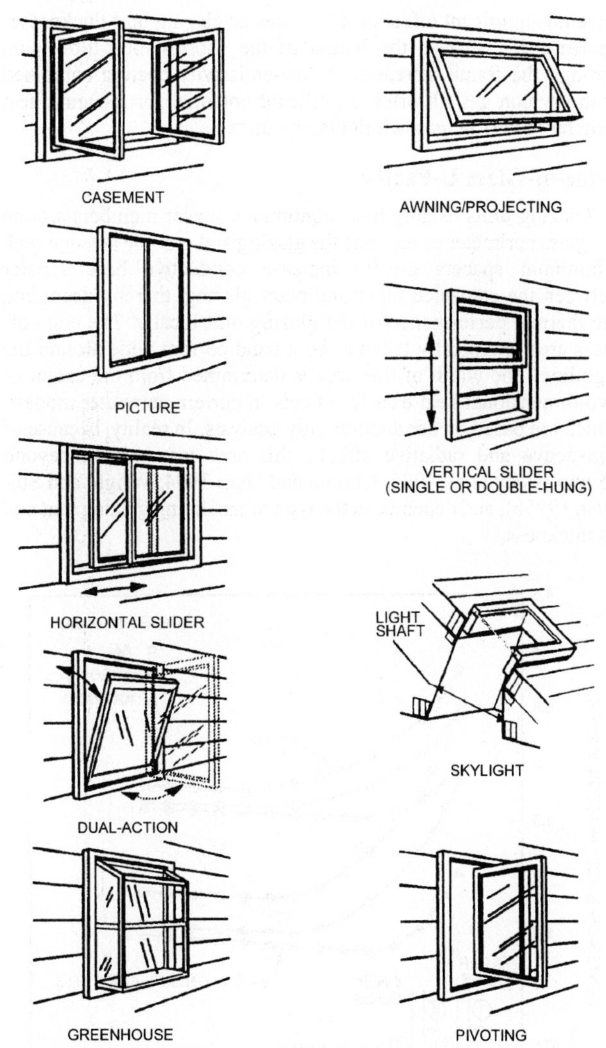

Fig. 2 Types of Residential Windows

outdoor air. With this assumption, the basic equation for the steady-state energy flow Q through a fenestration is

$$Q = UA_{pf}(t_{out} - t_{in}) + (\mathrm{SHGC})A_{pf}E_t \qquad (1)$$

where

Q = instantaneous energy flow, W
U = overall coefficient of heat transfer (U-factor), W/(m^2·K)
A_{pf} = total projected area of fenestration (the product's rough opening in the wall or roof less installation clearances), m^2
t_{in} = indoor air temperature, °C
t_{out} = outdoor air temperature, °C
SHGC = solar heat gain coefficient, dimensionless
E_t = incident total irradiance, W/m^2

U and SHGC are steady-state performance indices. The main justification for Equation (1) is its simplicity, achieved by collecting all the linked radiative, conductive, and convective energy transfer processes into *U* and SHGC. These quantities vary because (1) convective heat transfer rates vary as fractional powers of temperature differences or free-stream speeds, (2) variations in temperature caused by weather or climate are small on the absolute temperature scale (K) that controls radiative heat transfer rates, (3) fenestration systems always involve at least two thermal resistances in series, and (4) solar heat gain coefficients depend on solar incident angle and spectral distribution.

In this chapter, Q is divided into two parts:

$$Q = Q_{th} + Q_{sol} \qquad (2)$$

where

Q_{th} = steady-state heat transfer caused by indoor/outdoor temperature difference, W
Q_{sol} = steady-state heat transfer caused by solar radiation, W

The section on U-Factor (Thermal Transmittance) deals with Q_{th}, and the section on Solar Heat Gain and Visible Transmittance discusses Q_{sol}. In the latter section, the effects of both direct solar radiation and solar radiation scattered by the sky or ground are included.

Equation (1) presents a fenestration as it might appear on a building plan: a featureless, planar object filling an opening in the building envelope. Real fenestrations, however, are composite three-dimensional objects that may consist of multiple complex assemblies. Heat transfer through such an assembly of elements is calculated by dividing the fenestration area into parts, each of which has an energy flow that is more simply calculated than the total:

$$Q = \sum_v A_v q_v \qquad (3)$$

where

q_v = energy flux (energy flow per unit area) of *v*th part, W
A_v = area of *v*th part, m^2

This subdivision is applied to each term in Equation (2) separately; for example, heat transfer through glazings differs from that through frames, so it is useful to make the following separation:

$$Q_{th} = A_f q_f + A_g q_g \qquad (4)$$

where the subscript *f* refers to the frame, and *g* refers to the glazing (both for thermal energy flow). Similarly, solar radiation has different effects on the frame and the glazed area of a fenestration (because the frame is generally opaque), so that

$$Q_{sol} = A_{op} q_{op} + A_s q_s \qquad (5)$$

where the subscript *op* refers to the (opaque) frame (for solar energy flow), and *s* refers to the (solar-transmitting) glazing. This division into frame and glazing areas can be and usually is different for the solar and other thermal energy flows. Subdivisions of this sort, when Equation (3) is compared with Equation (1), effectively make the overall U-factor and solar heat gain coefficient area-averaged quantities. This area averaging is described explicitly in the appropriate sections of this chapter. Note that, in more complicated fenestrations, where the glazing portion may contain opaque shading elements, the opaque portion by definition can never under any conditions admit directly transmitted solar energy. A window with a closed, perfectly opaque blind would not be considered an opaque element because sometimes the blind may be open. A section of curtain wall consisting of wall or frame elements with an outdoor cover of glass (for uniform appearance) would be an opaque element despite its transparent covering.

A second type of subdivision occurs when, for a given part of the fenestration system, energy flow is driven by physical processes that are more complicated than those assumed in Equation (1). For example, heat transfer through a glazing consists of contact (i.e., glass-to-air) and radiative parts, and the latter (q_R) may depend on radiant temperatures that differ from the air temperatures in Equation (1):

$$q = q_C + q_R \qquad (6)$$

U-FACTOR (THERMAL TRANSMITTANCE)

In the absence of sunlight, air infiltration, and moisture condensation, the first term in Equation (1) represents the heat transfer rate through a fenestration system. Most fenestration systems consist of transparent multipane glazing units and opaque elements comprising the sash and frame (hereafter called **frame**). The glazing unit's heat transfer paths are subdivided into center-of-glass, edge-of-glass, and frame contributions (denoted by subscripts *cg*, *eg*, and *f*, respectively). Consequently, the total rate of heat transfer through a fenestration system can be calculated knowing the separate contributions of the these three paths. (When present, glazing dividers, such as decorative grilles and muntin bars, also affect heat transfer, and their contribution must be considered.) The overall U-factor is estimated using area-weighted U-factors for each contribution by

$$U_o = \frac{U_{cg}A_{cg} + U_{eg}A_{eg} + U_f A_f}{A_{pf}} \tag{7}$$

When a fenestration product has glazed surfaces in only one direction, the sum of the areas equals the projected area A_{pf}. Skylights, greenhouse/garden windows, bay/bow windows, etc., because they extend beyond the plane of the wall/roof, have greater surface area for heat loss than a window with a similar glazing option and frame material; consequently, U-factors for such products are expected to be greater.

DETERMINING FENESTRATION U-FACTORS

Center-of-Glass U-Factor

For single glass, U-factors depend strongly on indoor and outdoor film coefficients. The U-factor for single glass is

$$U = \frac{1}{1/h_o + 1/h_i + L/k} \tag{8}$$

where

h_o, h_i = outdoor and indoor respective glass surface heat transfer coefficients, W/(m²·K)
L = glass thickness, m
k = thermal conductivity, W/(m²·K)

For other fenestration, values for U_{cg} at standard indoor and outdoor conditions depend on glazing construction features such as the number of glazing lights, gas space dimensions, orientation relative to vertical, emissivity of each surface, and composition of fill gas. Several computer programs can be used to estimate glazing unit heat transfer for a wide range of glazing construction. The NFRC calls for WINDOW 5 (LBL 2001) as a standard calculation method for center glazing.

Heat flow across the central glazed portion of a multipane unit must consider both convective and radiative transfer in the gas space, and may be considered one-dimensional. Convective heat transfer is estimated based on high-aspect-ratio, natural convection correlations for vertical and inclined air layers (El Sherbiny et al. 1982; Shewen 1986; Wright 1996a). Radiative heat transfer (ignoring gas absorption) is quantified using a more fundamental approach. Computational methods solving the combined heat transfer problem have been devised (Hollands and Wright 1982; Rubin 1982a, 1982b).

Figure 3 shows the effect of gas space width on U_{cg} for vertical double- and triple-paned glazing units. U-factors are plotted for air, argon, and krypton fill gases and for high (uncoated) and low (coated) values of surface emissivity. The optimum gas space width is 12.7 mm for air and argon, and 8 mm for krypton. Greater widths have no significant effect on U_{cg}. Greater glazing unit thicknesses decrease U_o because the length of the shortest heat flow path through the frame increases. A low-emissivity coating combined with krypton gas fill offers significant potential for reducing heat transfer in narrow-gap-width glazing units.

Edge-of-Glass U-Factor

Glazing units usually have continuous spacer members around the glass perimeter to separate the glazing and provide an edge seal. Aluminum spacers greatly increase conductive heat transfer between the contacted inner and outer glazing, thereby degrading the thermal performance of the glazing unit locally. The edge-of-glass area is typically taken to be a band 65 mm wide around the sightline. The width of this area is determined from the extent of two-dimensional heat transfer effects in current computer models, which are based on conduction-only analysis. In reality, because of convective and radiative effects, this area may extend beyond 65 mm (Beck et al. 1995; Curcija and Goss 1994; Wright and Sullivan 1995b), and depends on the type of insulating glazing unit and its thickness.

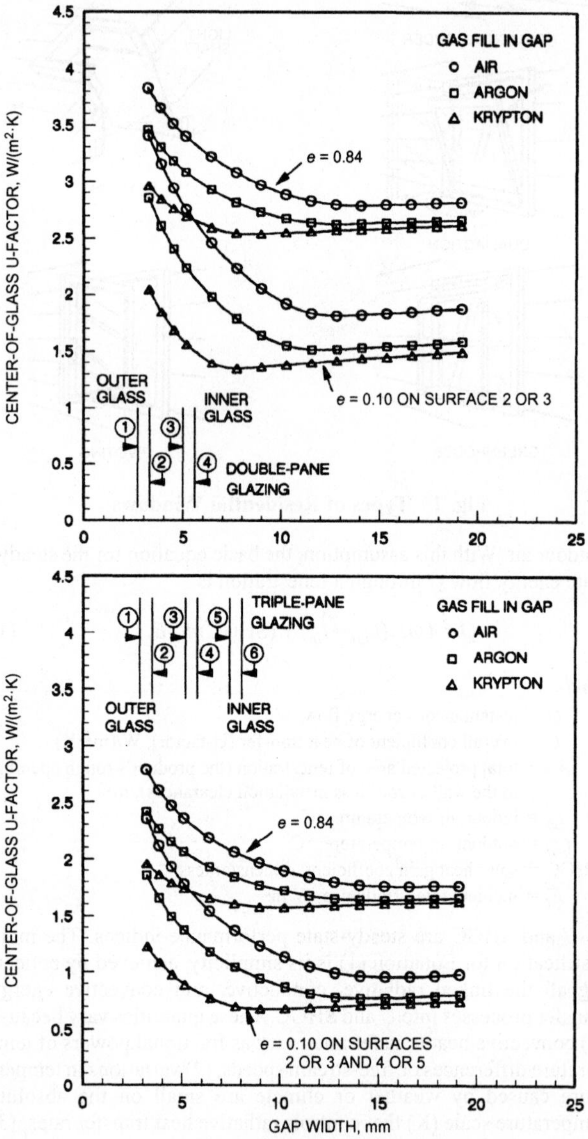

Fig. 3 Center-of-Glass U-Factor for Vertical Double- and Triple-Pane Glazing Units

Table 1 Representative Fenestration Frame U-Factors in W/(m²·K), Vertical Orientation

		Product Type/Number of Glazing Layers																
		Operable			Fixed			Garden Window		Plant-Assembled Skylight			Curtainwall[e]			Sloped/Overhead Glazing[e]		
Frame Material	Type of Spacer	1[b]	2[c]	3[d]	1[b]	2[c]	3[d]	1[b]	2[c]	1[b]	2[c]	3[d]	1[f]	2[g]	3[h]	1[f]	2[g]	3[h]
Aluminum without thermal break	All	13.51	12.89	12.49	10.90	10.22	9.88	10.67	10.39	44.57	39.86	39.01	17.09	16.81	16.07	17.32	17.03	16.30
Aluminum with thermal break[a]	Metal	6.81	5.22	4.71	7.49	6.42	6.30			39.46	28.67	26.01	10.22	9.94	9.37	10.33	9.99	9.43
	Insulated	N/A	5.00	4.37	N/A	5.91	5.79			N/A	26.97	23.39	N/A	9.26	8.57	N/A	9.31	8.63
Aluminum-clad wood/ reinforced vinyl	Metal	3.41	3.29	2.90	3.12	2.90	2.73			27.60	22.31	20.78						
	Insulated	N/A	3.12	2.73	N/A	2.73	2.50			N/A	21.29	19.48						
Wood/vinyl	Metal	3.12	2.90	2.73	3.12	2.73	2.38	5.11	4.83	14.20	11.81	10.11						
	Insulated	N/A	2.78	2.27	N/A	2.38	1.99	N/A	4.71	N/A	11.47	9.71						
Insulated fiber-glass/vinyl	Metal	2.10	1.87	1.82	2.10	1.87	1.82											
	Insulated	N/A	1.82	1.48	N/A	1.82	1.48											
Structural glazing	Metal												10.22	7.21	5.91	10.33	7.27	5.96
	Insulated												N/A	5.79	4.26	N/A	5.79	4.26

Note: This table should only be used as an estimating tool for early phases of design.
[a]Depends strongly on width of thermal break. Value given is for 9.5 mm.
[b]Single glazing corresponds to individual glazing unit thickness of 3 mm (nominal).
[c]Double glazing corresponds to individual glazing unit thickness of 19 mm (nominal).
[d]Triple glazing corresponds to individual glazing unit thickness of 34.9 mm (nominal).
[e]Glass thickness in curtainwall and sloped/overhead glazing is 6.4 mm.
[f]Single glazing corresponds to individual glazing unit thickness of 6.4 mm (nominal).
[g]Double glazing corresponds to individual glazing unit thickness of 25.4 mm (nominal).
[h]Triple glazing corresponds to individual glazing unit thickness of 44.4 mm (nominal).
N/A: Not applicable

In low-conductivity frames, heat flow at the edge-of-glass and frame area is through the spacer, and so the type of spacer has a greater impact on the edge-of-glass and frame U-factor. In metal frames, the edge-of-glass and frame U-factor varies little with the type of spacer (metal or insulating) because there is a significant heat flow through the highly conductive frame near the edge-of-glass area.

Frame U-Factor

Fenestration frame elements consist of all structural members exclusive of glazing units and include sash, jamb, head, and sill members; meeting rails and stiles; mullions; and other glazing dividers. Estimating the rate of heat transfer through the frame is complicated by the (1) variety of fenestration products and frame configurations, (2) different combinations of materials used for frames, (3) different sizes available, and, to a lesser extent, (4) glazing unit width and spacer type. Internal dividers or grilles have little effect on the fenestration U-factor, provided there is at least a 3 mm gap between the divider and each panel of glass.

Computer simulations found that frame heat loss in most fenestration is controlled by a single component or controlling resistance, and only changes in this component significantly affect frame heat loss (EEL 1990). For example, the frame U-factor for thermally broken aluminum fenestration products is largely controlled by the depth of the thermal break material in the heat flow direction. For aluminum frames without a thermal break, the inside film coefficient provides most of the resistance to heat flow. For vinyl- and wood-framed fenestrations, the controlling resistance is the shortest distance between the inside and outside surfaces, which usually depends on the thickness of the sealed glazing unit.

Carpenter and McGowan (1993) experimentally validated frame U-factors for a variety of fixed and operable fenestration product types, sizes, and materials using computer modeling techniques. Table 1 lists frame U-factors for a variety of frame and spacer materials and glazing unit thicknesses. Frame and edge U-factors are normally determined by two-dimensional computer simulation.

Curtain Wall Construction

A curtain wall is an outdoor building wall that carries no roof or floor loads and consists entirely or principally of glass and other surfacing materials supported by a framework. A curtain wall typically has a metal frame. To improve the thermal performance of standard metal frames, manufacturers provide both traditional thermal breaks as well as thermally improved products. The traditional thermal break is poured and debridged (i.e., urethane is poured into a metal U-channel in the frame and then the bottom of the channel is removed by machine). For this system to work well, there must be a thermal break between indoors and outdoors for all frame components, including those in any operable sash. Skip debridging (incomplete pour and debridging used for increased structural strength) can significantly degrade the U-factor. Bolts that penetrate the thermal break also degrade performance, but to a lesser degree. Griffith et al. (1998) showed that stainless steel bolts spaced 300 mm on center increased the frame U-factor by 18%. The paper also concluded that, in general, the isothermal planes method referenced in Chapter 27 provides a conservative approach to determining U-factors.

Thermally improved curtain wall products are a more recent development. In these products, most of the metal frame tends to be located on the indoor side with only a metal cap exposed on the outdoor side. Plastic spacers isolate the glazing assembly from both the outdoor metal cap and the indoor metal frame. These products can have significantly better thermal performance than standard metal frames, but it is important to minimize the number and area of the bolts that penetrate from outdoor to indoor.

SURFACE AND CAVITY HEAT TRANSFER COEFFICIENTS

Part of the overall thermal resistance of a fenestration system derives from convective and radiative heat transfer between the exposed surfaces and the environment, and in the cavity between panes of glass. Surface heat transfer coefficients h_o, h_i, and h_c at the outer and inner glazing surfaces, and in the cavity, respectively, combine the effects of radiation and convection.

Wind speed and building orientation are important in determining h_o. This relationship has long been studied, and many correlations have been proposed for h_o as a function of wind speed. However, no universal relationship has been accepted, and limited field measurements at low wind speeds by Klems (1989) differ significantly from values used by others.

Convective heat transfer coefficients are usually determined at standard temperature and air velocity conditions on each side. Wind speed can vary from less than 0.2 m/s for calm weather, free convection conditions, to over 29 m/s for storm conditions. A nominal

Table 2 Indoor Surface Heat Transfer Coefficient h_i in W/(m²·K), Vertical Orientation (Still Air Conditions)

			Winter Conditions[b]			Summer Conditions[c]		
Glazing ID[a]	Glazing Type	Glazing Height, m	Glass Temp., °C	Temp. Diff., °C	h_i, W/(m²·K)	Glass Temp., °C	Temp. Diff., °C	h_i, W/(m²·K)
1	Single glazing	0.6	–9	30	8.04	33	9	8.10
		1.2	–9	30	7.42	33	9	7.64
		1.8	–9	30	7.10	33	9	7.41
5	Double glazing with 12.7 mm airspace	0.6	7	14	7.72	35	11	8.30
		1.2	7	14	7.21	35	11	7.82
		1.8	7	14	6.95	35	11	7.58
23	Double glazing with e = 0.1 on surface 2 and 12.7 mm argon space	0.6	13	8	7.44	34	10	8.20
		1.2	13	8	7.00	34	10	7.73
		1.8	13	8	6.77	34	10	7.50
43	Triple glazing with e = 0.1 on surfaces 2 and 5 and 12.7 mm argon spaces	0.6	17	4	7.09	40	16	8.73
		1.2	17	4	6.72	40	16	8.20
		1.8	17	4	6.53	40	16	7.94

Notes:
[a]Glazing ID refers to fenestration assemblies in Table 4.
[b]Winter conditions: room air temperature t_i = 21°C, outdoor air temperature t_o = –18°C, no solar radiation
[c]Summer conditions: room air temperature t_i = 24°C, outdoor air temperature t_o = 32°C, direct solar irradiance E_D = 748 W/m²
$h_i = h_{ic} + h_{iR} = 1.46(\Delta T/L)^{0.25} + \varepsilon\sigma(T_i^4 - T_g^4)/\Delta T$, where $\Delta T = T_i - T_g$, K; L = glazing height, m; T_g = glass temperature, K; σ = Stefan-Boltzmann constant; and ε = surface emissivity.

value of 29 W/(m²·K) corresponding to a 6.7 m/s wind is often used to represent winter design conditions. At low wind speeds, h_o varies with outside air and surface temperature, orientation to vertical, and air moisture content. The overall surface heat transfer coefficient can be as low as 6.8 W/(m²·K) (Yazdanian and Klems 1993).

For natural convection and radiation at the indoor surface of a vertical fenestration product, surface coefficient h_i depends on the indoor air and glass surface temperatures and on the emissivity of the glass surface. Table 2 shows the variation of h_i for winter (t_i = 21°C) and summer (t_i = 24°C) design conditions, for a range of glass types and heights. Designers often use h_i = 8.3 W/(m²·K), which corresponds to t_i = 21°C, glass temperature of –9°C, and uncoated glass with e_g = 0.84. For summer conditions, the same value [h_i = 8.3 W/(m²·K)] is normally used, and it corresponds approximately to glass temperature of 35°C, t_i = 24°C, and e_g = 0.84. For winter conditions, this most closely approximates single glazing with clear glass that is 600 mm tall, but it overestimates the value as the glazing unit conductance decreases and height increases. For summer conditions, this value approximates all types of glass that are 600 mm tall but, again, is less accurate as glass height increases. If the indoor surface of the glass has a low-e coating, h_i values are about halved at both winter and summer conditions.

Heat transfer between the glazing surface and its environment is driven not only by local air temperatures but also by radiant temperatures to which the surface is exposed. The radiant temperature of the indoor environment is generally assumed to be equal to the indoor air temperature. This is a safe assumption where a small fenestration is exposed to a large room with surface temperatures equal to the air temperature, but it is not valid in rooms where the fenestration is exposed to other large areas of glazing surfaces (e.g., greenhouse, atrium) or to other cooled or heated surfaces (Parmelee and Huebscher 1947).

The radiant temperature of the outdoor environment is frequently assumed to be equal to the outdoor air temperature. This assumption may be in error, because additional radiative heat loss occurs between a fenestration and the clear sky (Berdahl and Martin 1984). Therefore, for clear-sky conditions, some effective outdoor temperature $t_{o,e}$ should replace t_o in Equation (1). For methods of determining $t_{o,e}$, see, for example, work by AGSL (1992). Note that a fully cloudy sky is assumed in ASHRAE design conditions.

The air space in a window constructed using glass with no reflective coating on the air space surfaces has a coefficient h_s of 7.4 W/(m²·K). When a reflective coating is applied to an air space surface, h_s can be selected from Table 3 by first calculating the effective air space emissivity $e_{s,e}$ by Equation (9):

$$e_{s,e} = \frac{1}{1/e_o + 1/e_i - 1} \tag{9}$$

where e_o and e_i are the hemispherical emissivities of the two air space surfaces. Hemispherical emissivity of ordinary uncoated glass is 0.84 over a wavelength range of 0.4 to 40 μm.

Table 4 lists computed U-factors, using winter design conditions, for a variety of generic fenestration products, based on ASHRAE-sponsored research involving laboratory testing and computer simulations. In the past, test data were used to provide more accurate results for specific products (Hogan 1988). Computer simulations (with validation by testing) are now accepted as the standard method for accurate product-specific U-factor determination. The simulation methodologies are specified in the National Fenestration Rating Council's NFRC *Technical Document* 100 (NFRC 2004a) and are based on algorithms published in ISO *Standard* 15099 (ISO 2000). The *International Energy Conservation Code* and various state energy codes in the United States, the National Energy Code in Canada, and ASHRAE *Standards* 90.1 and 90.2 all reference these standards. Fenestration must be rated in accordance with the NFRC standards for code compliance. Use of Table 4 should be limited to that of an estimating tool for the early phases of design.

Values in Table 4 are for vertical installation and for skylights and other sloped installations with glazing surfaces sloped 20° from the horizontal. Data are based on center-of-glass and edge-of-glass component U-factors and assume that there are no dividers. However, they apply only to the specific design conditions described in the table's footnotes, and are typically used only to determine peak load conditions for sizing heating equipment. Although these U-factors have been determined for winter conditions, they can also be used to estimate heat gain during peak cooling conditions, because conductive gain, which is one of several variables, is usually a small portion of the total heat gain for fenestration in direct sunlight. Glazing designs and framing materials may be compared in choosing a fenestration system that needs a specific winter design U-factor.

Table 4 lists 48 glazing types, with multiple glazing categories appropriate for sealed glazing units and the addition of storm sash to other glazing units. No distinction is made between flat and domed units such as skylights. For acrylic domes, use an average gas-space width to determine the U-factor. Note that garden window and sloped/pyramid/barrel vault skylight U-factors are approximately twice those of other similar products. Although this is partially due to the difference in slope in the case of sloped/pyramid/barrel vault skylights, it is largely because these products project out from the surface of the wall or roof. For instance, the skylight surface area,

Table 3 Air Space Coefficients for Horizontal Heat Flow

Air Space Thickness, mm	Air Space Temp., °C	Air Temp. Diff., K	Air Space Coefficient h_s, W/(m^2·K) Effective Emissivity $e_{s,e}$ 0.82	0.72	0.40	0.20	0.10	0.05
13	−15	5	5.0	4.6	3.3	2.6	2.2	2.0
		15	5.1	4.7	3.5	2.7	2.3	2.1
		30	5.7	5.3	4.0	3.2	2.8	2.7
		40	6.0	5.6	4.3	3.6	3.2	3.0
		50	6.3	5.9	4.6	3.8	3.4	3.2
	0	5	5.7	5.2	3.7	2.8	2.3	2.1
		15	5.7	5.3	3.8	2.9	2.4	2.2
		30	6.1	5.7	4.2	3.3	2.8	2.6
		40	6.4	6.0	4.5	3.5	3.1	2.8
		50	6.7	6.2	4.7	3.8	3.3	3.1
	10	5	6.1	5.6	4.0	3.0	2.4	2.2
		15	6.2	5.7	4.0	3.0	2.5	2.2
		30	6.5	6.0	4.3	3.3	2.8	2.5
		40	6.8	6.2	4.6	3.5	3.0	2.8
		50	7.0	6.5	4.8	3.8	3.3	3.0
	30	5	7.2	6.6	4.6	3.3	2.7	2.4
		15	7.3	6.6	4.6	3.3	2.7	2.4
		30	7.4	6.8	4.7	3.5	2.8	2.5
		40	7.6	6.9	4.9	3.6	3.0	2.7
		50	7.8	7.2	5.1	3.9	3.2	2.9
	50	5	8.4	7.7	5.2	3.7	2.9	2.5
		15	8.5	7.7	5.2	3.7	2.9	2.6
		30	8.5	7.8	5.3	3.8	3.0	2.6
		40	8.6	7.9	5.4	3.9	3.1	2.7
		50	8.8	8.0	5.5	4.0	3.2	2.8
10	−15	5	5.5	5.1	3.9	3.1	2.7	2.5
		30	5.7	5.3	4.0	3.2	2.9	2.7
		50	6.1	5.7	4.4	3.6	3.2	3.1
	0	5	6.2	5.7	4.3	3.3	2.9	2.6
		30	6.3	5.8	4.4	3.4	3.0	2.7
		50	6.6	6.1	4.6	3.7	3.2	3.0
	10	5	6.7	6.2	4.6	3.5	3.0	2.8
		30	6.8	6.3	4.6	3.6	3.1	2.8
		50	7.0	6.5	4.8	3.8	3.2	3.0
	30	5	7.8	7.2	5.2	3.9	3.3	3.0
		30	7.9	7.2	5.2	4.0	3.3	3.0
		50	8.0	7.3	5.3	4.0	3.4	3.1
	50	5	9.1	8.3	5.9	4.3	3.6	3.2
		30	9.1	8.4	5.9	4.4	3.6	3.2
		50	9.2	8.4	6.0	4.4	3.6	3.3
7	−15	<50	6.5	6.1	4.9	4.1	3.7	3.5
	0	<50	7.3	6.8	5.3	4.4	3.9	3.7
	10	<50	7.8	7.3	5.6	4.6	4.1	3.8
	30	<50	9.0	8.4	6.3	5.1	4.4	4.1
	50	<50	10.3	9.5	7.1	5.6	4.8	4.4
6	−15	<50	7.1	6.7	5.4	4.6	4.2	4.0
	0	<50	7.9	7.4	5.9	5.0	4.5	4.3
	10	<50	8.4	7.9	6.2	5.2	4.7	4.4
	30	<50	9.6	9.0	7.0	5.7	5.1	4.7
	50	<50	11.0	10.2	7.8	6.2	5.5	5.1
5	−15	<50	7.8	7.4	6.2	5.4	5.0	4.8
	0	<50	8.7	8.2	6.7	5.8	5.3	5.1
	10	<50	9.2	8.7	7.1	6.0	5.5	5.2
	30	<50	10.5	9.9	7.8	6.6	5.9	5.6
	50	<50	11.9	11.2	8.7	7.2	6.4	6.0

which includes the curb, can vary from 13 to 240% greater than the rough opening area, depending on the size and mounting method. Unless otherwise noted, all multiple-glazed units are filled with dry air. Argon units are assumed to be filled with 90% argon (Elmahdy and Yusuf 1995). U-factors for CO_2-filled units are similar to argon fills. For spaces up to 13 mm, argon/SF_6 (sulfur hexafluoride) mixtures up to 70% SF_6 are generally the same as argon fills. Use of krypton gas can provide U-factors lower than those for argon for glazing spaces less than 13 mm.

Table 4 provides data for six values of hemispherical emissivity and for 6.4 and 12.7 mm gas space widths. The emissivity of various low-e glasses varies considerably between manufacturers and processes. When the emissivity is between the listed values, interpolation may be used. When manufacturers' data are not available for low-e glass, assume that glass with a pyrolytic (hard) coating has a maximum emissivity of 0.20 and that glass with a sputtered (soft) coating has a maximum emissivity of 0.10. Tinted glass does not change the winter U-factor. Also, some reflective glass may have an emissivity less than 0.84. Values listed are for insulating glass units using aluminum edge spacers. If an insulated or nonmetallic spacer is used, the U-factors are approximately 0.17 W/(m^2·K) lower.

Fenestration product types are subdivided first by vertical versus sloped installation and then into two general categories: manufactured and site-assembled. "Manufactured" represents products delivered as a complete unit to the site. These products are typically installed in low-rise residential and small commercial/institutional/industrial buildings. Use the operable category for vertical sliders, horizontal sliders, casement, awning, pivoted, and dual-action windows, and for sliding and swinging glass doors. For picture windows, use the fixed category. For products that project out from the surface of the wall, use the garden window category. For skylights, use the sloped skylight category.

"Site-assembled" represents products where frame extrusions are assembled on site into a fenestration product and then glazing is added on site. These products are typically installed in high-rise residential and larger commercial/institutional/industrial buildings. Curtain walls are typically made up of vision (transparent) and spandrel (opaque) panels. Table 4 contains representative U-factors for the vision panel (including mullions) for these assemblies. The spandrel portion of curtain walls usually consists of a metal pan filled with insulation and covered with a sheet of glass or other weatherproof covering. Although the U-factor in the center of the spandrel panel can be quite low, the metal pan is a thermal bridge, significantly increasing the U-factor of the assembly. Two-dimensional simulation, validated by testing of a curtain wall having an aluminum frame with a thermal break, found that the U-factor for the edge of the spandrel panel (the 65 mm band around the perimeter adjacent to the frame) was 40% of the way toward the U-factor of the frame. The U-factor was 0.34 for the center of the spandrel, 2.56 for the edge of the spandrel, and 6.02 for the frame (Carpenter and Elmahdy 1994). Two-dimensional heat transfer analysis or physical testing is recommended to determine the U-factor of spandrel panels. Use the sloped/overhead glazing category for sloped glazing panels comparable to curtain walls.

Physical testing of double-glazed units showed U-factors of 5.74 W/(m^2·K) for a thermally broken aluminum pyramidal skylight and 7.4 W/(m^2·K) for an aluminum-frame half-round barrel vault (both normalized to a rough opening of 2.4 by 2.4 m). Until more conclusive results are available, U-factors for these systems can be estimated by multiplying the site-assembled sloped/overhead glazing values in Table 4 by the ratio of total product surface area (including curbs) to rough opening area. These ratios range from 1.2 to 2.0 for low-slope skylights, 1.4 to 2.1 for pyramid assemblies sloped at 45°, and 1.7 to 2.9 for semicircular barrel vault assemblies.

U-factors in Table 4 are based on definitions of the six product types, frame sizes, and proportion of frame to glass area shown in Figure 4. Four of the products are manufactured type. Sizes are as

Table 4 U-Factors for Various Fenestration Products in W/(m²·K)

Product Type		Glass Only		Vertical Installation: Operable (including sliding and swinging glass doors)					Vertical Installation: Fixed				
Frame Type		**Center of Glass**	**Edge of Glass**	**Aluminum Without Thermal Break**	**Aluminum With Thermal Break**	**Reinforced Vinyl/ Aluminum Clad Wood**	**Wood/ Vinyl**	**Insulated Fiberglass/ Vinyl**	**Aluminum Without Thermal Break**	**Aluminum With Thermal Break**	**Reinforced Vinyl/ Aluminum Clad Wood**	**Wood/ Vinyl**	**Insulated Fiberglass/ Vinyl**
ID	**Glazing Type**												
	Single Glazing												
1	3.2 mm glass	*5.91*	*5.91*	7.01	6.08	5.27	5.20	4.83	6.38	6.06	5.58	5.58	5.40
2	6.4 mm acrylic/polycarb	*5.00*	*5.00*	6.23	5.35	4.59	4.52	4.18	5.55	5.23	4.77	4.77	4.61
3	3.2 mm acrylic/polycarb	*5.45*	*5.45*	6.62	5.72	4.93	4.86	4.51	5.96	5.64	5.18	5.18	5.01
	Double Glazing												
4	6.4 mm airspace	*3.12*	*3.63*	4.62	3.61	3.24	3.14	2.84	3.88	3.52	3.18	3.16	3.04
5	12.7 mm airspace	*2.73*	*3.36*	4.30	3.31	2.96	2.86	2.58	3.54	3.18	2.85	2.83	2.72
6	6.4 mm argon space	*2.90*	*3.48*	4.43	3.44	3.08	2.98	2.69	3.68	3.33	3.00	2.98	2.86
7	12.7 mm argon space	*2.56*	*3.24*	4.16	3.18	2.84	2.74	2.46	3.39	3.04	2.71	2.69	2.58
	Double Glazing, e = 0.60 on surface 2 or 3												
8	6.4 mm airspace	*2.95*	*3.52*	4.48	3.48	3.12	3.02	2.73	3.73	3.38	3.04	3.02	2.90
9	12.7 mm airspace	*2.50*	*3.20*	4.11	3.14	2.80	2.70	2.42	3.34	2.99	2.67	2.65	2.53
10	6.4 mm argon space	*2.67*	*3.32*	4.25	3.27	2.92	2.82	2.54	3.49	3.13	2.81	2.79	2.67
11	12.7 mm argon space	*2.33*	*3.08*	3.98	3.01	2.68	2.58	2.31	3.20	2.84	2.52	2.50	2.39
	Double Glazing, e = 0.40 on surface 2 or 3												
12	6.4 mm airspace	*2.78*	*3.40*	4.34	3.35	3.00	2.90	2.61	3.59	3.23	2.90	2.88	2.77
13	12.7 mm airspace	*2.27*	*3.04*	3.93	2.96	2.64	2.54	2.27	3.15	2.79	2.48	2.46	2.35
14	6.4 mm argon space	*2.44*	*3.16*	4.07	3.09	2.76	2.66	2.38	3.30	2.94	2.62	2.60	2.49
15	12.7 mm argon space	*2.04*	*2.88*	3.75	2.79	2.48	2.38	2.11	2.95	2.60	2.29	2.27	2.16
	Double Glazing, e = 0.20 on surface 2 or 3												
16	6.4 mm airspace	*2.56*	*3.24*	4.16	3.18	2.84	2.74	2.46	3.39	3.04	2.71	2.69	2.58
17	12.7 mm airspace	*1.99*	*2.83*	3.70	2.75	2.44	2.34	2.07	2.91	2.55	2.24	2.22	2.12
18	6.4 mm argon space	*2.16*	*2.96*	3.84	2.88	2.56	2.46	2.19	3.05	2.70	2.38	2.36	2.26
19	12.7 mm argon space	*1.70*	*2.62*	3.47	2.53	2.24	2.14	1.88	2.66	2.30	2.00	1.98	1.88
	Double Glazing, e = 0.10 on surface 2 or 3												
20	6.4 mm airspace	*2.39*	*3.12*	4.02	3.05	2.72	2.62	2.34	3.25	2.89	2.57	2.55	2.44
21	12.7 mm airspace	*1.82*	*2.71*	3.56	2.62	2.32	2.22	1.96	2.76	2.40	2.10	2.08	1.98
22	6.4 mm argon space	*1.99*	*2.83*	3.70	2.75	2.44	2.34	2.07	2.91	2.55	2.24	2.22	2.12
23	12.7 mm argon space	*1.53*	*2.49*	3.33	2.40	2.12	2.02	1.76	2.51	2.16	1.86	1.84	1.74
	Double Glazing, e = 0.05 on surface 2 or 3												
24	6.4 mm airspace	*2.33*	*3.08*	3.98	3.01	2.68	2.58	2.31	3.20	2.84	2.52	2.50	2.39
25	12.7 mm airspace	*1.70*	*2.62*	3.47	2.53	2.24	2.14	1.88	2.66	2.30	2.00	1.98	1.88
26	6.4 mm argon space	*1.87*	*2.75*	3.61	2.66	2.36	2.26	2.00	2.81	2.45	2.15	2.12	2.02
27	12.7 mm argon space	*1.42*	*2.41*	3.24	2.31	2.04	1.94	1.69	2.42	2.06	1.76	1.74	1.65
	Triple Glazing												
28	6.4 mm airspace	*2.16*	*2.96*	3.78	2.78	2.46	2.42	2.17	3.02	2.68	2.36	2.36	2.25
29	12.7 mm airspace	*1.76*	*2.67*	3.46	2.47	2.18	2.14	1.90	2.68	2.34	2.03	2.03	1.92
30	6.4 mm argon space	*1.93*	*2.79*	3.60	2.60	2.30	2.26	2.02	2.82	2.49	2.17	2.17	2.06
31	12.7 mm argon space	*1.65*	*2.58*	3.36	2.39	2.10	2.06	1.83	2.58	2.24	1.93	1.93	1.83
	Triple Glazing, e = 0.20 on surface 2, 3, 4, or 5												
32	6.4 mm airspace	*1.87*	*2.75*	3.55	2.56	2.26	2.22	1.98	2.78	2.44	2.12	2.12	2.01
33	12.7 mm airspace	*1.42*	*2.41*	3.18	2.21	1.94	1.90	1.67	2.38	2.05	1.74	1.74	1.64
34	6.4 mm argon space	*1.59*	*2.54*	3.32	2.34	2.06	2.02	1.79	2.53	2.20	1.89	1.89	1.78
35	12.7 mm argon space	*1.25*	*2.28*	3.04	2.08	1.82	1.78	1.55	2.24	1.90	1.60	1.60	1.50
	Triple Glazing, e = 0.20 on surfaces 2 or 3 and 4 or 5												
36	6.4 mm airspace	*1.65*	*2.58*	3.36	2.39	2.10	2.06	1.83	2.58	2.24	1.93	1.93	1.83
37	12.7 mm airspace	*1.14*	*2.19*	2.95	1.99	1.74	1.69	1.48	2.14	1.80	1.50	1.50	1.40
38	6.4 mm argon space	*1.31*	*2.32*	3.09	2.12	1.86	1.82	1.59	2.29	1.95	1.65	1.65	1.55
39	12.7 mm argon space	*0.97*	*2.05*	2.81	1.86	1.62	1.57	1.36	1.99	1.65	1.36	1.36	1.26
	Triple Glazing, e = 0.10 on surfaces 2 or 3 and 4 or 5												
40	6.4 mm airspace	*1.53*	*2.49*	3.27	2.30	2.02	1.98	1.75	2.48	2.15	1.84	1.84	1.73
41	12.7 mm airspace	*1.02*	*2.10*	2.85	1.90	1.66	1.61	1.40	2.04	1.70	1.41	1.41	1.31
42	6.4 mm argon space	*1.19*	*2.23*	2.99	2.04	1.78	1.73	1.52	2.19	1.85	1.55	1.55	1.45
43	12.7 mm argon space	*0.80*	*1.92*	2.67	1.73	1.49	1.45	1.24	1.84	1.51	1.22	1.22	1.12
	Quadruple Glazing, e = 0.10 on surfaces 2 or 3 and 4 or 5												
44	6.4 mm airspaces	*1.25*	*2.28*	3.04	2.08	1.82	1.78	1.55	2.24	1.90	1.60	1.60	1.50
45	12.7 mm airspaces	*0.85*	*1.96*	2.71	1.77	1.54	1.49	1.28	1.89	1.55	1.26	1.26	1.17
46	6.4 mm argon spaces	*0.97*	*2.05*	2.81	1.86	1.62	1.57	1.36	1.99	1.65	1.36	1.36	1.26
47	12.7 mm argon spaces	*0.68*	*1.83*	2.57	1.64	1.41	1.37	1.16	1.74	1.41	1.12	1.12	1.03
48	6.4 mm krypton spaces	*0.68*	*1.83*	2.57	1.64	1.41	1.37	1.16	1.74	1.41	1.12	1.12	1.03

Notes:

1. All heat transmission coefficients in this table include film resistances and are based on winter conditions of –18°C outdoor air temperature and 21°C indoor air temperature, with 6.7 m/s outdoor air velocity and zero solar flux. With the exception of single glazing, small changes in the indoor and outdoor temperatures will not significantly affect overall U-factors. Coefficients are for vertical position except skylight values, which are for 20° from horizontal with heat flow up.
2. Glazing layer surfaces are numbered from outdoor to indoor. Double, triple, and quadruple refer to the number of glazing panels. All data are based on 3 mm glass, unless otherwise noted. Thermal conductivities are: 0.917 W/(m·K) for glass, and 0.19 W/(m·K) for acrylic and polycarbonate.
3. *Standard* spacers are metal. Edge-of-glass effects are assumed to extend over the 63.5 mm band around perimeter of each glazing unit.

Table 4 U-Factors for Various Fenestration Products in W/(m²·K) (*Concluded*)

Vertical Installation					Sloped Installation									
Garden Windows		Curtainwall			Glass Only (Skylights)		Manufactured Skylight				Site-Assembled Sloped/Overhead Glazing			
Aluminum Without Thermal Break	Wood/ Vinyl	Aluminum Without Thermal Break	Aluminum With Thermal Break	Structural Glazing	Center of Glass	Edge of Glass	Aluminum Without Thermal Break	Aluminum With Thermal Break	Reinforced Vinyl/ Aluminum Clad Wood	Wood/ Vinyl	Aluminum Without Thermal Break	Aluminum With Thermal Break	Structural Glazing	ID
14.21	11.94	6.86	6.27	6.27	*6.76*	*6.76*	10.03	9.68	9.16	8.05	7.66	7.64	7.10	1
12.70	10.42	6.03	5.44	5.44	*5.85*	*5.85*	9.09	8.74	8.23	7.45	6.83	6.80	6.27	2
13.45	11.18	6.44	5.86	5.86	*6.30*	*6.30*	9.56	9.21	8.70	7.89	7.24	7.22	6.68	3
9.78	7.50	4.38	3.79	3.56	*3.29*	*3.75*	6.23	5.46	5.21	4.79	4.54	4.71	3.75	4
9.19	6.92	4.03	3.45	3.22	*3.24*	*3.71*	6.17	5.41	5.16	4.74	4.49	4.68	3.70	5
9.44	7.17	4.18	3.60	3.37	*3.01*	*3.56*	5.96	5.19	4.94	4.54	4.30	4.52	3.51	6
8.94	6.67	3.89	3.30	3.07	*3.01*	*3.56*	5.96	5.19	4.94	4.54	4.30	4.52	3.51	7
9.53	7.25	4.23	3.65	3.41	*3.07*	*3.60*	6.01	5.24	4.99	4.59	4.35	4.56	3.55	8
8.86	6.58	3.84	3.25	3.02	*3.01*	*3.56*	5.96	5.19	4.94	4.54	4.30	4.52	3.51	9
9.11	6.84	3.99	3.40	3.17	*2.78*	*3.40*	5.74	4.97	4.72	4.34	4.10	4.37	3.31	10
8.61	6.33	3.69	3.11	2.88	*2.78*	*3.40*	5.74	4.97	4.72	4.34	4.10	4.37	3.31	11
9.28	7.00	4.08	3.50	3.27	*2.90*	*3.48*	5.85	5.08	4.83	4.44	4.20	4.45	3.41	12
8.52	6.25	3.64	3.06	2.83	*2.84*	*3.44*	5.79	5.02	4.78	4.39	4.15	4.41	3.36	13
8.77	6.50	3.79	3.21	2.97	*2.50*	*3.20*	5.46	4.69	4.45	4.09	3.86	4.18	3.07	14
8.18	5.91	3.45	2.86	2.63	*2.61*	*3.28*	5.57	4.80	4.56	4.19	3.96	4.25	3.17	15
8.94	6.67	3.89	3.30	3.07	*2.61*	*3.28*	5.57	4.80	4.56	4.19	3.96	4.25	3.17	16
8.10	5.82	3.40	2.81	2.58	*2.61*	*3.28*	5.57	4.80	4.56	4.19	3.96	4.25	3.17	17
8.35	6.08	3.54	2.96	2.73	*2.22*	*3.00*	5.19	4.42	4.18	3.84	3.61	3.98	2.83	18
7.67	5.39	3.15	2.56	2.33	*2.27*	*3.04*	5.24	4.47	4.24	3.89	3.66	4.02	2.88	19
8.69	6.42	3.74	3.16	2.92	*2.50*	*3.20*	5.46	4.69	4.45	4.09	3.86	4.18	3.07	20
7.84	5.57	3.25	2.66	2.43	*2.50*	*3.20*	5.46	4.69	4.45	4.09	3.86	4.18	3.07	21
8.10	5.82	3.40	2.81	2.58	*2.04*	*2.88*	5.02	4.25	4.02	3.69	3.46	3.86	2.68	22
7.41	5.14	3.00	2.42	2.18	*2.16*	*2.96*	5.13	4.36	4.13	3.79	3.56	3.94	2.78	23
8.61	6.33	3.69	3.11	2.88	*2.39*	*3.12*	5.35	4.58	4.34	3.99	3.76	4.10	2.97	24
7.67	5.39	3.15	2.56	2.33	*2.44*	*3.16*	5.41	4.64	4.40	4.04	3.81	4.14	3.02	25
7.93	5.65	3.30	2.71	2.48	*1.93*	*2.79*	4.91	4.14	3.91	3.58	3.37	3.77	2.58	26
7.24	4.96	2.90	2.32	2.09	*2.04*	*2.88*	5.02	4.25	4.02	3.69	3.46	3.86	2.68	27
see	see	3.48	2.91	2.62	*2.22*	*3.00*	5.13	4.24	4.03	3.63	3.55	3.92	2.70	28
note	note	3.14	2.57	2.27	*2.04*	*2.88*	4.96	4.07	3.87	3.48	3.40	3.80	2.56	29
7	7	3.28	2.71	2.42	*1.99*	*2.83*	4.91	4.01	3.81	3.43	3.35	3.76	2.51	30
		3.04	2.47	2.17	*1.87*	*2.75*	4.80	3.90	3.70	3.33	3.25	3.68	2.41	31
see	see	3.23	2.66	2.37	*1.93*	*2.79*	4.85	3.96	3.76	3.38	3.30	3.72	2.46	32
note	note	2.84	2.27	1.97	*1.76*	*2.67*	4.68	3.79	3.59	3.22	3.16	3.59	2.31	33
7	7	2.99	2.42	2.12	*1.59*	*2.54*	4.52	3.63	3.43	3.07	3.01	3.47	2.17	34
		2.69	2.12	1.83	*1.53*	*2.49*	4.46	3.57	3.37	3.02	2.96	3.43	2.12	35
see	see	3.04	2.47	2.17	*1.65*	*2.58*	4.57	3.68	3.48	3.12	3.06	3.51	2.22	36
note	note	2.59	2.02	1.73	*1.53*	*2.49*	4.46	3.57	3.37	3.02	2.96	3.43	2.12	37
7	7	2.74	2.17	1.87	*1.36*	*2.36*	4.29	3.40	3.21	2.86	2.81	3.30	1.97	38
		2.44	1.87	1.58	*1.25*	*2.28*	4.18	3.29	3.10	2.76	2.71	3.22	1.87	39
see	see	2.94	2.37	2.07	*1.53*	*2.49*	4.46	3.57	3.37	3.02	2.96	3.43	2.12	40
note	note	2.49	1.92	1.63	*1.42*	*2.41*	4.35	3.46	3.27	2.91	2.86	3.34	2.02	41
7	7	2.64	2.07	1.78	*1.19*	*2.23*	4.13	3.24	3.04	2.71	2.66	3.18	1.82	42
		2.29	1.72	1.43	*1.14*	*2.19*	4.07	3.18	2.99	2.66	2.61	3.13	1.77	43
		2.69	2.12	1.83	*1.25*	*2.28*	4.18	3.29	3.10	2.76	2.71	3.22	1.87	44
see	see	2.34	1.77	1.48	*1.08*	*2.14*	4.02	3.12	2.93	2.60	2.56	3.09	1.72	45
note	note	2.44	1.87	1.58	*1.02*	*2.10*	3.96	3.07	2.88	2.55	2.51	3.05	1.67	46
7	7	2.19	1.62	1.33	*0.91*	*2.01*	3.85	2.96	2.77	2.45	2.41	2.96	1.58	47
		2.19	1.62	1.33	*0.74*	*1.87*	3.68	2.79	2.60	2.29	2.26	2.83	1.43	48

4. Product sizes are described in Figure 4, and frame U-factors are from Table 1.
5. Use U = 3.40 W/(m²·K) for glass block with mortar but without reinforcing or framing.
6. Use of this table should be limited to that of an estimating tool for the early phases of design.
7. Values for triple- and quadruple-glazed garden windows are not listed, because these are not common products.
8. U-factors in this table were determined using NFRC 100-91. They have not been updated to the current rating methodology in NFRC 100-2004.

defined in NFRC *Technical Document* 100: operable and fixed (non-operable) glazing units are 1.8 m^2 in area, and the overall size corresponds to a 1200 by 1500 mm fenestration product. The garden window category is 1.8 m^2 in projected area (3.24 m^2 in surface area) and 1500 mm wide by 1200 mm high by 380 mm deep. The manufactured skylight category is a nominal 1.44 m^2 in area, corresponding to a 1200 by 1200 mm skylight. The nominal dimensions of a roof-mounted skylight correspond to centerline spacing of roof framing members; consequently, the rough opening dimensions are 1180 by 1180 mm. The curtain wall and sloped/overhead glazing categories are a nominal 4 m^2 in area, representing repeating 2000 by 2000 mm panels. The nominal dimensions correspond to centerline spacing of the head and sill and vertical mullions.

Six frame types are listed (although not all for any one category) in order of improving thermal performance. The most conservative assumption is to use the frame category of aluminum frame without a thermal break (although there are products on the market that have higher U-factors). The aluminum frame with a thermal break is for frames having at least a 10 mm thermal break between the inside and outside for all members including both the frame and the operable sash, if applicable. (Products are available with significantly wider thermal breaks, which achieve considerable improvement.) The aluminum-clad wood/reinforced vinyl category represents vinyl-frame products, such as sliding glass doors or large windows that have extensive metal reinforcing within the frame and wood products with extensive metal, usually on the outdoor surface of the frame. Both of these factors provide short circuits, which degrade the thermal performance of the frame material. The wood/vinyl frame category represents the improved thermal performance that is possible if the thermal short circuits from the previous frame category do not exist. Insulated fiberglass/vinyl represents fiberglass or vinyl frames that do not have metal reinforcing and whose frame cavities are filled with insulation. For several site-assembled product types, there is a structural glazing frame category that represents products where sheets of glass are butt-glazed to each other using a sealant only, and framing members are not exposed to the exterior. For glazing with a steel frame, use aluminum frame values. For aluminum window with wood trim or vinyl cladding, use the values for aluminum. Frame type refers to the primary unit; therefore, when storm sash is added over another fenestration product, use values given for the nonstorm product.

To estimate the overall U-factor of a fenestration product that differs significantly from the assumptions given in Table 4 and/or Figure 4, first determine the area that is frame/sash, center-of-glass, and edge-of-glass (based on a 65 mm band around the perimeter of each glazing unit). Next, determine the appropriate component U-factors. These can be taken either from the standard values listed in italics in Table 4 for glass, from the values in Table 1 for frames, or from some other source such as test data or computed factors. Finally, multiply the area and the component U-factors, sum these products, and then divide by the rough opening in the building envelope where this product will fit to obtain the overall U-factor U_o.

Table 5 provides approximate data to convert the overall U-factor at one wind condition to a U-factor at another.

Example 1. Estimate the design U-factor for a manufactured fixed fenestration product with a reinforced vinyl frame and double-glazing with a sputter-type low-e coating (e = 0.10). The gap is 13 mm wide and argon-filled, and the spacer is metal. The outdoor windspeed is 12 m/s.

Table 5 Glazing U-Factors for Various Wind Speeds in W/(m^2 · K)

Wind Speed, km/h		
24	**12**	**0**
0.5	0.46	0.42
1.0	0.92	0.85
1.5	1.33	1.27
2.0	1.74	1.69
2.5	2.15	2.12
3.0	2.56	2.54
3.5	2.98	2.96
4.0	3.39	3.38
4.5	3.80	3.81
5.0	4.21	4.23
5.5	4.62	4.65
6.0	5.03	5.08
6.5	5.95	5.50

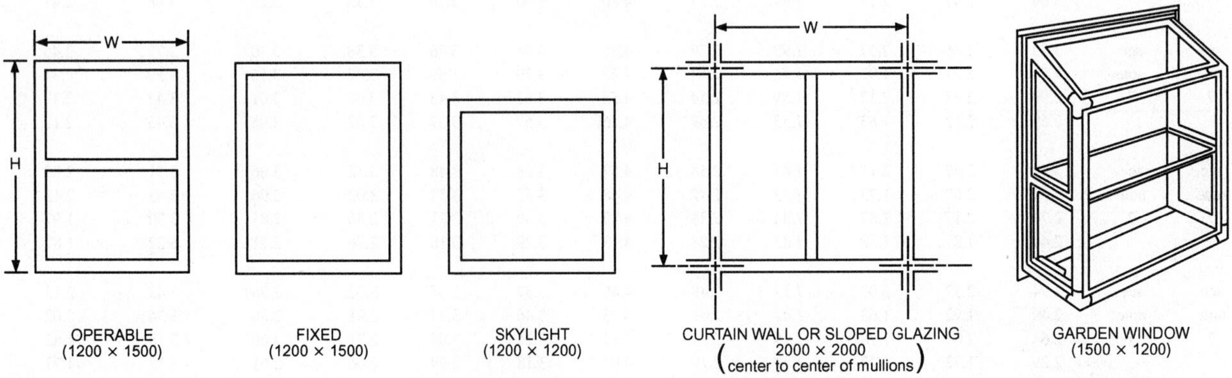

Frame Material	Frame Width, mm					
	Operable	**Fixed**	**Garden Window**	**Skylight**	**Curtainwall**	**Sloped/Overhead Glazing**
Aluminum without thermal break	38	33	44	18	57	57
Aluminum with thermal break	53	33	N/A	18	57	57
Aluminum-clad wood/reinforcing vinyl	71	41	N/A	23	N/A	N/A
Wood/vinyl	71	41	44	23	N/A	N/A
Insulated fiberglass/vinyl	79	46	N/A	N/A	N/A	N/A
Structural glazing	N/A	N/A	N/A	N/A	57	64

Fig. 4 Frame Widths for Standard Fenestration Units

Solution: Locate the glazing system type in the first column of Table 4 (ID = 23), then find the appropriate product type (fixed) and frame type (reinforced vinyl). The U-factor listed (in the tenth column of U-factors) is 1.86 W/(m²·K). This U-factor is for 24 m/s outdoor windspeed.

From Table 5, interpolate 1.86 in the 24 m/s column to the corresponding value in the 12 m/s column.

$$\frac{1.86 - 1.50}{2.00 - 1.50} = \frac{U_{12\ \mathrm{m/s}} - 1.33}{1.74 - 1.33}$$

$$U_{12\ \mathrm{m/s}} = 1.63\ \mathrm{W/(m^2{\cdot}K)}$$

Example 2. Estimate a representative U-factor for a wood-framed, 970 by 2080 mm swinging French door with eight 280 by 400 mm panes (true divided panels), each consisting of clear double-glazing with a 6.5 mm air space and a metal spacer.

Solution: Without more detailed information, assume that the dividers have the same U-factor as the frame and that the divider edge has the same U-factor as the edge-of-glass. Calculate center-of-glass, edge-of-glass, and frame areas:

$$A_{cg} = 8[(280 - 130)(400 - 130)]/10^6 = 0.324\ \mathrm{m^2}$$

$$A_{eg} = 8(280 \times 400)/10^6 - 0.324 = 0.572\ \mathrm{m^2}$$

$$A_f = (970 \times 2080)/10^6 - 8(280 \times 400)/10^6 = 1.122\ \mathrm{m^2}$$

Select center-of-glass, edge-of-glass, and frame U-factors. These component U-factors are 3.12 and 3.63 W/(m²·K) (from Table 4, glazing ID = 4, U-factor columns 1 and 2) and 2.90 W/(m²·K) (from Table 4, wood frame, metal spacer, operable, double-glazing), respectively. From Equation (7),

$$U_o = \frac{(3.12 \times 0.324) + (3.63 \times 0.572) + (2.90 \times 1.122)}{(0.97 \times 2.08)}$$

$$= 3.14\ \mathrm{W/(m^2{\cdot}K)}$$

Example 3. Estimate the overall average U-factor for a multifloor curtain wall assembly that is part vision glass and part opaque spandrel. The typical floor-to-floor height is 3.6 m, and the building module is 1.2 m as reflected in the spacing of the mullions both horizontally and vertically. For a representative section 1.2 m wide and 3.6 m tall, one of the modules is glazed and the other two are opaque. The mullions are aluminum frame with a thermal break 80 mm wide and centered on the module. The IGU is double glazing with a pyrolytic low-e coating (e = 0.40) and has a 13 mm gap filled with air and a metal spacer. The spandrel panel has a metal pan backed by R = 3.5 (m²·K)/W insulation and no intermediate reinforcing members.

Solution: It is necessary to calculate the U-factor for the glazed module and for the opaque spandrel modules, and then to do an area-weighted average to determine the average U-factor for the overall curtain wall assembly.

First, calculate the overall U-factor for the glazed module. Calculate center-of-glass, edge-of-glass, and frame areas. The glazed area is 1120 by 1120 mm (1200 mm module, 1200 mm of mullions on each edge).

$$A_{cg} = (1120 - 130)(1120 - 130)/10^6 = 0.9801\ \mathrm{m^2}$$

$$A_{eg} = (1120 \times 1120)/10^6 - 0.9801 = 0.2743\ \mathrm{m^2}$$

$$A_f = [(1200 \times 1200)/10^6 - (1120 \times 1120)]/10^6 = 0.1856\ \mathrm{m^2}$$

Select center-of-glass, edge-of-glass, and frame U-factors. These component U-factors are 2.27 and 3.04 W/(m²·K) (from Table 4, ID = 13, columns 1 and 2) and 9.94 W/(m²·K) (from Table 4, aluminum frame with a thermal break, metal spacer, curtain wall, double glazing), respectively. From Equation (7),

$$U_{glazing\ module} = \frac{(2.27 \times 0.9801) + (3.04 \times 0.2743) + (9.94 \times 0.1856)}{(1.2 \times 1.2)}$$

$$= 3.41\ \mathrm{W/(m^2{\cdot}K)}$$

Then, calculate the overall U-factor for the two opaque spandrel modules. The center-of-spandrel, edge-of spandrel, and frame areas are the same as the glazed module. The frame U-factor is the same. Calculate the center-of-spandrel U-factor. In this particular case, the R-value of the insulation does not need to be rated, because there are no intermediate framing members penetrating it and providing thermal short circuits. When the resistance of the insulation [3.5 (m²·K)/W] is added to the exterior air film resistance of 0.03 (m²·K)/W and the interior air film resistance of 0.12 (m²·K)/W (from Table 1, Chapter 26), the total resistance is 3.65 (m²·K)/W, and the U-factor is 1/3.65 = 0.274 W/(m²·K). The edge-of-spandrel U-factor is 40% of the way to the frame U-factor, which is 0.274 + [0.40(9.94 – 0.274)] = 4.14 W/(m²·K).

$$U_{opaque\ spandrel\ module} = \frac{(0.274 \times 0.9801) + (4.14 \times 0.2743) + (9.94 \times 0.1856)}{(1.2 \times 1.2)}$$

$$= 2.26\ \mathrm{W/(m^2{\cdot}K)}$$

Finally, calculate the overall average U-factor for the curtain wall assembly, including the one module of vision glass and the two modules of opaque spandrel.

$$U_{curtain\ wall} = \frac{[3.41 \times (1.2 \times 1.2)] + [2.26 \times 2 \times (1.2 \times 1.2)]}{3 \times (1.2 \times 1.2)}$$

$$= 2.64\ \mathrm{W/(m^2{\cdot}K)}$$

Note that even with double glazing having a low-e coating and with R-20 in the opaque areas, this curtain wall with metal pans only has an overall R-value of approximately 0.38 (m²·K)/W.

Example 4. Estimate the U-factor for a semicircular barrel vault that is 6 m wide, 3 m tall, and 10 m long mounted on a 150 mm curb. The barrel vault has an aluminum frame without a thermal break. The glazing is double with a 13 mm gap width filled with air and a low-e coating (e = 0.20).

Solution: An approximation can be made by multiplying the U-factor for a site-assembled sloped/overhead glazing product having the same frame and glazing features by the ratio of the surface area (including the curb) of the barrel vault to the rough opening area in the roof that the barrel vault fits over. First, determine the surface area (including the curb) of the barrel vault:

Area of the curved portion of the barrel vault
$= (\pi \times \text{diameter}/2) \times \text{length}$
$= (3.14 \times 6/2) \times 10 = 94.25\ \mathrm{m^2}$

Area of the two ends of the barrel vault
$= 2 \times (\pi \times \text{radius}^2)/2 = \pi r^2$
$= 3.14 \times 3^2 = 28.27\ \mathrm{m^2}$

Area of the curb
$= \text{perimeter} \times \text{curb height}$
$= (6 + 10 + 6 + 10) \times 0.150 = 4.8\ \mathrm{m^2}$

Total surface area of the barrel vault
$= 94.25 + 28.27 + 4.8 = 127.3\ \mathrm{m^2}$

Second, determine the rough opening area in the roof that the barrel vault fits over:
$= \text{length} \times \text{width}$
$= 6 \times 10 = 60\ \mathrm{m^2}$

Third, determine the ratio of the surface area to the rough opening area:
$= 127.3/60 = 2.12$

Fourth, determine the U-factor from Table 4 of a site-assembled sloped/overhead glazing product having the same frame and glazing features. The U-factor is 3.96 W/(m²·K) (ID = 17, 12th column on the second page of Table 4).

Fifth, determine the estimated U-factor of the barrel vault.

$U_{barrel\ vault}$
$= U_{sloped\ overhead\ glazing} \times$ surface area/rough opening for the barrel vault
$= 3.96 \times 2.12 = 8.40\ \mathrm{W/(m^2{\cdot}K)}$

REPRESENTATIVE U-FACTORS FOR DOORS

Doors are often an overlooked component in the thermal integrity of the building envelope. Although swinging and revolving doors represent a small portion of the shell in residential, commercial, and institutional buildings, their U-factor is usually many times higher than that of the walls or ceilings. In some storage and industrial buildings, loading bay doors (overhead doors) represent a significant area of high heat loss. Table 6 contains representative U-factors for swinging doors determined through computer simulation (Carpenter and Hogan 1996). These are generic values, and product-specific values determined in accordance with standards should be used whenever available. NFRC *Technical Document* 100 (NFRC 2004a), and CSA *Standard* A440 give procedures for evaluating the performance of swinging doors. Tables 7 to 9 contain representative U-factors for revolving, emergency exit, garage, and aircraft hangar doors determined through testing (McGowan et al. 2006).

Swinging doors can be divided into two categories: slab and stile-and-rail. A stile-and-rail door is a swinging door with a full-glass insert supported by horizontal rails and vertical stiles. The stiles and rails are typically either solid wood members or extruded aluminum or vinyl, as shown in Figure 5. Most residential doors are slab type with solid wood, steel, or a fiberglass skin over foam insulation in a wood frame with aluminum sill. The edges of the steel skin door are normally wood to provide a thermal break. In commercial construction, doors are either steel skin over foam insulation in a steel frame (i.e., utility doors) or a full glass door made up of aluminum stiles, rails, and frame (i.e., entrance doors). The most important factors affecting door U-factor are material construction, glass size, and glass type. Frame depth, slab width, and number of panels have a minor effect on door performance. Side lites and double doors have U-factors similar to a single door of the same construction. For wood slab doors in a wood frame, the glazing area has little effect on the U-factor. For an insulated steel slab in a wood frame, however, glazing area strongly affects U-factor. Typical commercial insulated slab doors have a U-factor approximately twice that of residential insulated doors, the prime reason being thermal bridging of the slab edge and the steel frame. Stile-and-rail doors, even if thermally broken, have U-factors 50% higher than a full-glass commercial steel slab door.

There are three generic types of overhead doors: roll-up, uninsulated sectional, and insulated sectional. Metal roll-up doors consist of small metal plates of approximately 65 mm in height that roll up around a metal rod to open. Sectional doors consist of a series of

Table 6 Design U-Factors of Swinging Doors in W/(m²·K)

Door Type (Rough Opening = 970 × 2080 mm)	No Glazing	Single Glazing	Double Glazing with 12.7 mm Air Space	Double Glazing with $e = 0.10$, 12.7 mm Argon
Slab Doors				
Wood slab in wood frame[a]	2.61			
6% glazing (560 × 200 lite)	—	2.73	2.61	2.50
25% glazing (560 × 910 lite)	—	3.29	2.61	2.38
45% glazing (560 × 1620 lite)	—	3.92	2.61	2.21
More than 50% glazing		Use Table 4 (operable)		
Insulated steel slab with wood edge in wood frame[b]	0.91			
6% glazing (560 × 200 lite)	—	1.19	1.08	1.02
25% glazing (560 × 910 lite)	—	2.21	1.48	1.31
45% glazing (560 × 1630 lite)	—	3.29	1.99	1.48
More than 50% glazing		Use Table 4 (operable)		
Foam-insulated steel slab with metal edge in steel frame[c]	2.10			
6% glazing (560 × 200 lite)	—	2.50	2.33	2.21
25% glazing (560 × 910 lite)	—	3.12	2.73	2.50
45% glazing (560 × 1630 lite)	—	4.03	3.18	2.73
More than 50% glazing		Use Table 4 (operable)		
Cardboard honeycomb slab with metal edge in steel frame	3.46			
Stile-and-Rail Doors				
Sliding glass doors/French doors		Use Table 4 (operable)		
Site-Assembled Stile-and-Rail Doors				
Aluminum in aluminum frame	—	7.49	5.28	4.49
Aluminum in aluminum frame with thermal break	—	6.42	4.20	3.58

Notes:
[a]Thermally broken sill [add 0.17 W/(m²·K) for non-thermally broken sill]
[b]Non-thermally broken sill
[c]Nominal U-factors are through center of insulated panel before consideration of thermal bridges around edges of door sections and because of frame.

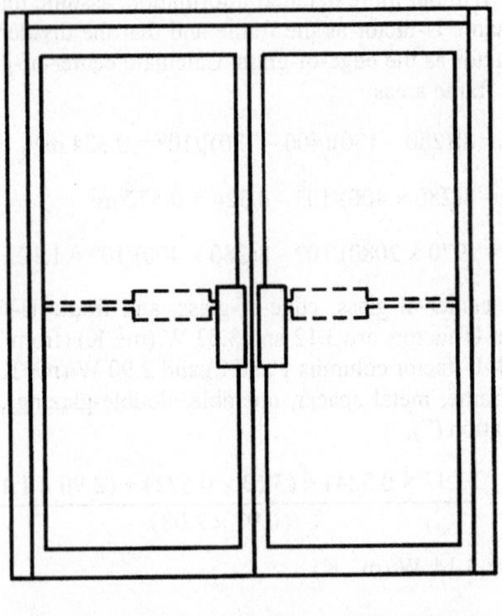

Fig. 5 Details of Stile-and-Rail Door

Table 7 Design U-factors for Revolving Doors in W/(m²·K)

Type	Size (Width × Height)	U-Factor
3-wing	2.44 × 2.13 m	4.46
	3.28 × 2.44 m	4.53
4-wing	2.13 × 1.98 m	3.56
	2.13 × 2.29 m	3.63
Open*	2.08 × 2.13 m	7.49

*U-factor of Open door determined using NFRC *Technical Document* 100-91. It has not been updated to current rating methodology in NFRC *Technical Document* 100-2004.

Table 8 Design U-factors for Double-Skin Steel Emergency Exit Doors in W/(m²·K)

Core Insulation Thickness, mm	Core Insulation Type	Rough Opening Size 0.9 × 2 m	Rough Opening Size 1.8 × 2 m
35*	Honeycomb kraft paper	3.23	2.97
	Mineral wool, steel ribs	2.50	2.05
	Polyurethane foam	1.92	1.60
44*	Honeycomb kraft paper	3.25	3.06
	Mineral wool, steel ribs	2.30	1.90
	Polyurethane foam	1.77	1.50
35	Honeycomb kraft paper	3.38	3.11
	Mineral wool, steel ribs	2.67	2.21
	Polyurethane foam	2.10	1.77
44	Honeycomb kraft paper	3.38	3.22
	Mineral wool, steel ribs	2.47	2.08
	Polyurethane foam	1.95	1.69

*With thermal break

Table 9 Design U-factors for Double-Skin Steel Garage and Aircraft Hanger Doors in W/(m²·K)

Insulation		One-Piece Tilt-Up[a]		Sectional Tilt-Up[b]	Aircraft Hangar	
Thickness, mm	Type	2.44 × 2.1 m	4.9 × 2.1 m	2.74 × 2.1 m	22 × 3.7 m[c]	73 × 15.2 m[d]
35	EPS, steel ribs[e]	2.03	1.90	1.94 to 2.19		
	XPS, steel ribs[f]	1.90	1.74	1.76 to 2.05		
50	EPS, steel ribs[e]	1.74	1.58	1.66 to 1.87		
	XPS, steel ribs[f]	1.62	1.46	1.53 to 1.77		
76	EPS, steel ribs[e]	1.46	1.29	1.43 to 1.60		
	XPS, steel ribs[f]	1.37	1.21	1.34 to 1.52		
102	EPS, steel ribs[e]	1.29	1.13	1.29 to 1.43		
	XPS, steel ribs[f]	1.22	1.06	1.22 to 1.36		
	EPS, steel ribs[e]	1.11	0.93	1.13 to 1.22		
	XPS, steel ribs[f]	1.06	0.88	1.08 to 1.17		
89	XPS				1.40	0.91
	Mineral wool, steel ribs				1.45	0.92
	EPS				1.32	0.83
140	XPS				1.18	0.72
	Mineral wool, steel ribs				1.28	0.73
	EPS				1.14	0.67
—	Uninsulated[g]				6,27	7.00
	All products[f]	6.53[g]				

Notes:
[a]Values are for thermally broken or thermally unbroken doors.
[b]Lower values are for thermally broken doors; upper values are for doors with no thermal break.
[c]Typical size for a small private airplane (single- or twin-engine).
[d]Typical hangar door for a midsized commercial jet airliner.
[e]EPS = extruded polystyrene; XPS = expanded polystyrene.
[f]U-factor determined using NFRC *Technical Document* 100-91. Not updated to current rating methodology in NFRC *Technical Document* 100-2004.
[g]U-factor determined for 3.05 × 3.05 m sectional door, but is representative of similar products of different size.

600 mm high sections that travel in a track to open. There is a wide range in the design of insulated overhead doors. Factors affecting heat transfer include width of insulation, thermal break design (if any), and design of indoor skin. For uninsulated sectional doors, there is very little difference between the center value and the total value: essentially the value of single glazing. The center of an insulated door has low U-factors, but thermal bridging at the door and section edges significantly increases the total U-factor. For doors without thermally broken edges, the total value is 2.5 to 3.3 times greater than the center value. Adding a good thermal break design reduces this increase to a 1.6 multiplier.

Many commercial buildings use revolving entrance doors. Most of these doors are of similar design: single glazing in an aluminum frame without thermal break. The door, however, can be in two positions: closed (X-shaped as viewed from above) or open (+-shaped). At nighttime, these doors are locked in the X position, effectively creating a double-glazed system. During the daytime, the door revolves and is often left positioned so that there is only one glazing between the inside and outside (+ position). U-factors are given in Table 7 for both positions.

SOLAR HEAT GAIN AND VISIBLE TRANSMITTANCE

Fenestration solar heat gain has two components. First is **directly transmitted solar radiation**. The quantity of radiation entering the fenestration directly is governed by the solar transmittance of the glazing system, and is determined by multiplying the incident irradiance by the glazing area and its solar transmittance. The second component is the inward flowing fraction of **absorbed solar radiation**, radiation that is absorbed in the glazing and framing materials of the window, some of which is subsequently conducted, convected, or radiated to the interior of the building.

Visible transmittance is the solar radiation transmitted through fenestration weighted with respect to the photopic response of the human eye. It physically represents the perceived clearness of the fenestration, and is likely different from the solar transmittance of the same fenestration.

The underlying physics behind solar heat gain and visible transmittance can be very complex, but a rudimentary understanding is required if technologies such as low-e coatings are to be discussed. Accurately calculating the solar heat gain and visible transmittance of a fenestration system, including the effects of angular and spectral dependence, in the presence of multiple glass and shade layers, is very complex. The reader is referred to ISO *Standard* 15099 (ISO 2000) or the ASHRAE HandbookCD+ for complete details of how to do this calculation. Software such as WINDOW 5.0 (LBL 2001) incorporate these advanced calculations and can be used for more detailed window analysis.

SOLAR-OPTICAL PROPERTIES OF GLAZING

Optical Properties of Single Glazing Layers

Radiation passing from one medium into another is partly transmitted and partly reflected at the interface between the two media. Further, as this radiation passes through either medium, an additional fraction is absorbed because of the absorptivity of the material. Materials that do not absorb radiation completely, such as air or glass, are classified as being transparent or translucent. Translucent glazings exhibit sufficient light-diffusing properties that images of objects viewed through it are blurred. Opaque glazings transmit no perceptible light.

If solar radiation incident on glazing is considered, the **transmittance** T, **reflectance** R, and **absorptance** $\mathcal{A}$ of the glazing layer contain the effects of multiple reflections between the two interfaces of the layer as well as the effects of absorption during the passage through the layer of each interreflection (Figure 6). For radiation incident on the front side of the glazing, the reflectance is called the **front reflectance** R^f. The **back reflectance** R^b (not shown in Figure 6) is the reflectance of the layer for radiation incident on back side b.

The transmittance, reflectance, and absorptance of a layer are formally defined as the fractions of incident flux that transmit, reflect, and are absorbed by the layer, respectively, including the

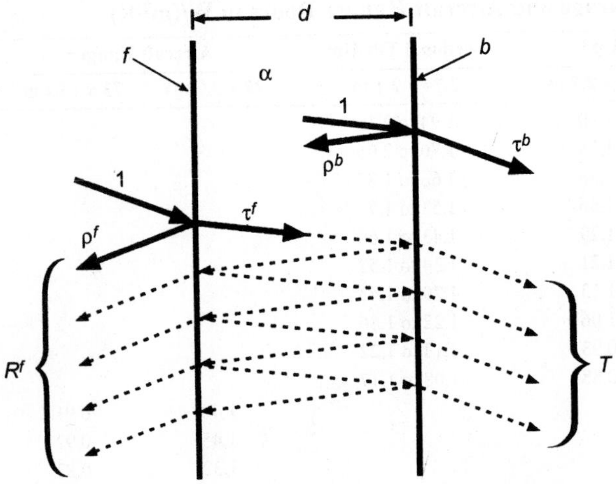

Fig. 6 Optical Properties of a Single Glazing Layer

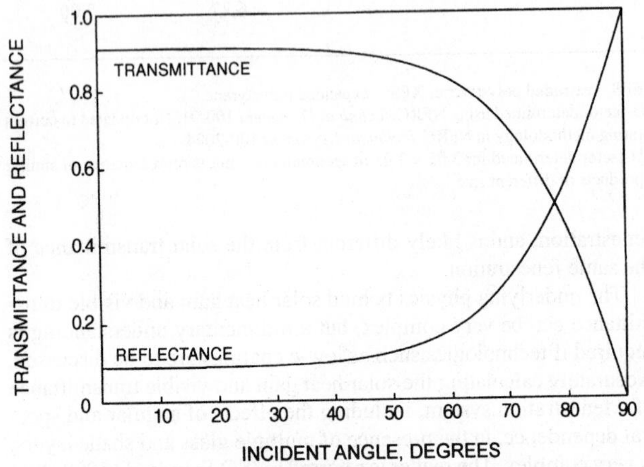

Fig. 7 Transmittance and Reflectance of Glass Plate
(Refractive index $n = 1.55$, thickness $t = 3.2$ mm, absorptivity $\alpha = 0.01$/m)

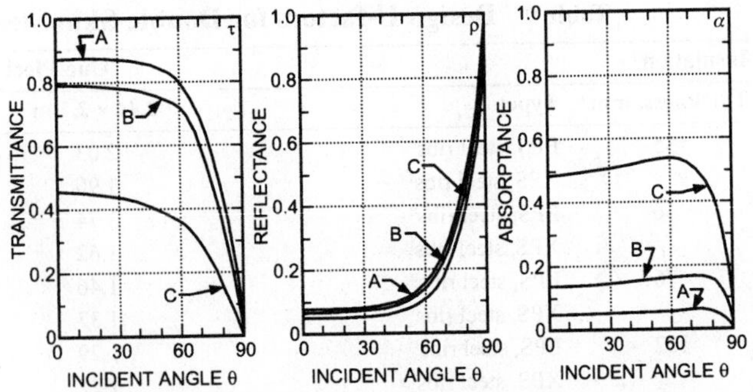

Fig. 8 Variations with Incident Angle of Solar-Optical Properties for (A) Double-Strength Sheet Glass, (B) Clear Plate Glass, and (C) Heat-Absorbing Plate Glass

effects of interreflection. Their sum equals unity, as shown in Equation (10).

$$T + R + \mathcal{A} = 1 \tag{10}$$

The layer has a thickness d and is characterized by **transmissivity** τ and **reflectivity** ρ of each of the two surfaces and by the **absorptivity** α of the glazing layer of thickness d. In general, τ and ρ are characteristics of the interface between the material and the adjacent medium; they may in principle be different for the two surfaces (e.g., for a coated surface, or where a material layer is adjacent to another material rather than air). Physical arguments, however, dictate that T^f and T^b for the layer be the same (and the f and b superscripts are therefore omitted). R^f and R^b will be different given similar variations in coatings or adjacent materials, and examination of Equation (10) shows that $\mathcal{A}^f$ and $\mathcal{A}^b$ may be different as well. Uncoated glass has the same front and back properties.

Angular Variations. The interfacial properties τ and ρ, and consequently layer properties T, R, and $\mathcal{A}$, also depend on the incident angle θ of the radiation incident on the layer. Figure 7 shows the optical properties of common window glass as a function of incidence angle. This variation of properties is small for incident angles below 40° but becomes significant at larger angles. Chapter 14 provides details on calculating the direction and magnitude of solar flux that is incident on a window.

Figure 8 compares the properties of glasses of different thickness and composition. As the incident angle increases from zero, transmittance decreases, reflectance increases, and absorptance first increases because of the lengthened optical path and then decreases as more incident radiation is reflected. Although the shapes of the property curves are superficially similar, note that both the magnitude of the transmittance at normal incidence and the angle at which the transmittance changes significantly vary with glass type and thickness. The three curves all have slightly different shapes. For coated glasses or for multiple-pane glazing systems, this difference is more pronounced. One cannot assume that all glazings or glazing systems have a universal angular dependence.

Angular performance is important when peak gains and annual energy performance are considered. In North America, peak summertime solar gains occur with east- and west-facing vertical windows at angles of incidence ranging from about 25 to 55°. The peak solar gain for horizontal glazings occurs typically at relatively small angles of incidence (midday sun high in sky in summer). For north- and south-facing vertical glazings, peak summertime solar gains occur at angles of incidence greater than about 40°. Angles of incidence important for annual energy performance calculations range from 5° to over 80° for east- and west-facing vertical and for horizontal windows. This range is only slightly diminished for south-facing windows. For north-facing windows, the direct beam solar gains are small and their angles of incidence range from 62 to 86° (McCluney 1994b).

Spectral Variations. Many glazing systems have optical properties that are *spectrally selective* (i.e., they vary across the electromagnetic spectrum with wavelength λ). Ordinary clear float glass possesses this property, but to a modest degree that is seldom of much concern in load calculations. Tinted and coated glass can exhibit strong spectral selectivity, a desirable property for certain applications, and this effect must be accounted for in solar heat gain determinations.

Figure 9 (McCluney 1993) shows the normal incidence spectral transmittances of several common commercially available glazings. Figure 10 (McCluney 1996) shows the normal incidence spectral transmittances and outdoor reflectances of a variety of additional coated and tinted glasses, indicating the strong spectral selectivity now available from some glass and window manufacturers. Actual transmittance varies with the amount of iron or other absorbers in the glass. Glass with low iron content has a relatively constant spectral transmittance over the entire solar spectrum.

Solar-Optical Property Data. Transmittance and reflectance are the basic measurable quantities for an isolated glazing layer in air. Measurements on glazing layers are typically made using a spectrophotometer at normal incidence, and the properties at other angles must be inferred from these measurements. A systematic compilation of these measured properties (for most glazings manufactured in the United States) called the International Glazing Database (IGDB) is maintained by the National Fenestration Rating Council and is available on the Internet at http://www.nfrc.org or at http://windows.lbl.gov/materials/IGDB/default.htm (LBL 2001; NFRC 2004h). For uncoated glazings, layer properties can also be determined from first principles [e.g., McCluney (1994a)].

Obtaining the necessary basic information about the solar-optical properties of coated glass requires spectrophotometric measurements. Alternatively, an approximation procedure is described by Finlayson and Arasteh (1993). Coated glazing properties should vary from these estimates by no more than ±20% at 60° incidence (Rubin et al. 1999). It is currently not practical to determine the solar-optical properties of coated glazings from first principles.

Optical Properties of Glazing Systems

The optical properties of glazing systems (multiple glazing layers) are affected by interreflections between layers in addition to the

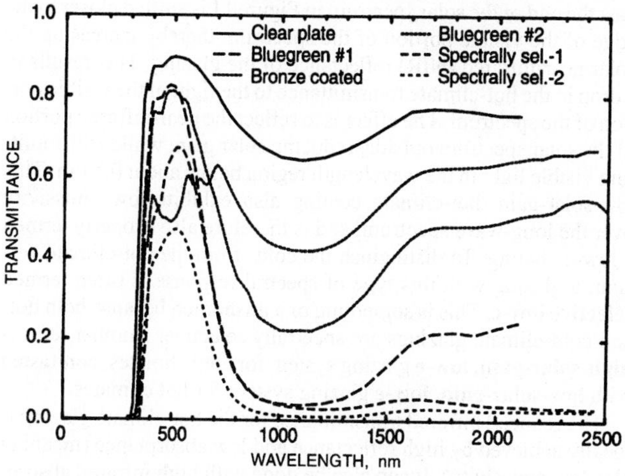

Fig. 9 Spectral Transmittances of Commercially Available Glazings
(McCluney 1993)

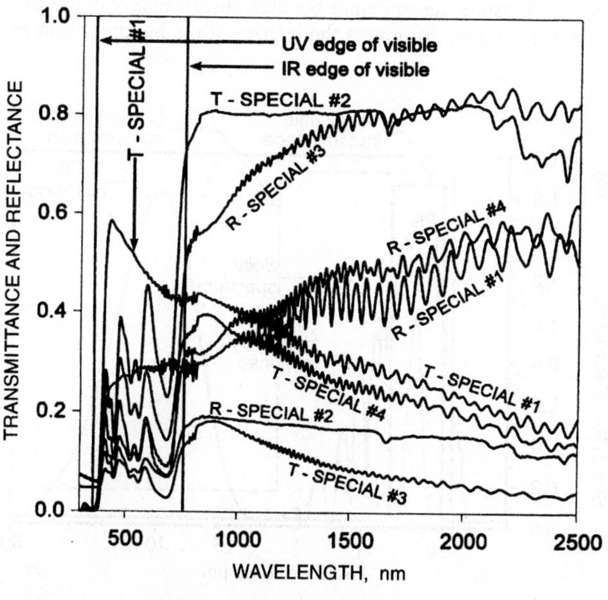

Fig. 10 Spectral Transmittances and Reflectances of Strongly Spectrally Selective Commercially Available Glazings
(McCluney 1996)

specular and angular properties of the individual layers. Consequently, the effect of a particular layer on the overall properties may not only depend on its solar-optical properties, but also on its position within the assembly. It is therefore necessary to expand glazing layer considerations to apply to the overall properties of systems and subsystems of glazing layers. The properties of any subsystem can be calculated by use of recursion relations (LBL 2003).

Spectral Averaging of Glazing System Properties. The solar-optical properties of a glazing are the wavelength-integrated (or total) transmittance, reflectance, and absorptance of the glazing to incident solar radiation. If the spectral optical properties $T(\lambda)$, $R(\lambda)$, and $\mathcal{A}(\lambda)$ of the glazing and the spectral irradiance $E(\lambda)$ incident on the glazing are known, the solar optical properties can be calculated using ASTM *Standards* E903, E971, E972, and E1084, as well as NFRC *Technical Document* 300.

$$X = \frac{\int_{\lambda_{min}}^{\lambda_{max}} E_{STD}(\lambda)X(\lambda)d\lambda}{\int_{\lambda_{min}}^{\lambda_{max}} E_{STD}(\lambda)d\lambda} \tag{11}$$

where

$X(\lambda) = T(\lambda), R(\lambda)$, or $\mathcal{A}(\lambda)$
$E_{STD}(\lambda)$ = standard solar distribution
X = total T, R, or $\mathcal{A}$ to standard solar distribution

For multiple-layer glazing systems, the spectral averaging should in general be applied to the system spectral properties at each angle. Because all glazing layer properties are to some extent both angle and wavelength dependent, and because these equations are nonlinear in the glazing properties, this is the only procedure that is valid in principle.

Many window glazings do not have strong spectral selectivity over the solar spectrum, so their spectral optical properties can be considered constant, even if the source spectrum changes substantially. In these cases, the transmitted spectral irradiance can be determined by multiplying the incident irradiance by the solar transmittance. For special combinations of climate and location, it may be desirable to use variant solar spectra as weighting functions. It is seldom either feasible or necessary to carry out heat transfer calculations using a detailed, time-dependent solar spectrum and the spectral glazing properties.

Angular Averaging of Glazing System Properties. It is relatively simple to account for angular dependence in beam solar radiation, because at a given time the radiation is incident from a single, easily determined direction. However, for diffuse solar and ground-reflected radiation, the situation is more complicated. In principle, energy flow through the glazing should equal the sum of individual energy flows caused by incident radiation from each direction.

Although such calculations can be done for specific sky conditions using detailed sky data or models, the labor involved is worthwhile only for very specific purposes. Usually, a drastically simplifying assumption is made. Both sky and ground radiation are assumed to be **ideally diffuse** (i.e., to have a sky radiance that is independent of direction). Diffuse properties are then determined by integrating over all directions. See the section on Diffuse Radiation under Solar Heat Gain Coefficient for more details. In addition, the spectral dependence is assumed to be the same as for beam solar radiation.

$$X_D = \frac{\iint_{hem} X(\theta)\cos\theta d\varpi}{\iint_{hem} \cos\theta d\varpi} = 2\int_0^{\pi/2} X(\theta)\cos\theta d\theta \tag{12}$$

where

$X(\theta)$ = $T(\theta)$, $R(\theta)$, or $\mathcal{A}(\theta)$
ϖ = solid angle of integration
X_D = total T, R, or $\mathcal{A}$ of standard solar distribution

More careful consideration must be given to these quantities for tilted glazings or for direction-dependent shading (e.g., overhangs, venetian blinds) greater accuracy is desired.

Spectrally Selective Glazing and Glazing Systems. Spectrally selective glazing shows strong changes in its optical properties with variations in wavelength over the spectrum. The spectral range from 300 nm to over 50 μm contains radiation from both the sun and sky incident on fenestration systems. The majority of this radiation is called **short-wave** or **solar** radiation. About 99% of the energy in the solar spectrum is between 0.3 to 3.5 μm. The spectral range from 3.5 to over 50 μm is called **long-wave, infrared**, or **thermal** radiation, which contains radiation from the sun and sky, but also from warm bodies both outside and inside the building. In Figure 11, the solar spectrum for an air mass m = 1.5 represents short-wave radiation, with thermal radiation represented by a blackbody source at 24°C. The latter has been scaled up to better compare it with the shape of the solar spectrum. The reflectance spectrum shown is an idealization of typical glazing reflectivity. Figure 11 clearly shows the separation of the solar spectrum from the long-wave spectrum characteristic of radiant emission from an indoor pane of a multiple-pane glazing system.

Figure 11 also shows the human eye spectral response (called the human photopic visibility function). To the human eye, the glazing represented in the figure does not appear very reflective. It is also strongly transmitting for solar radiation, including the visible portion. The glazing is, however, nearly opaque to long-wave radiation, demonstrating that visual perception of a material is a poor indicator of its overall spectral characteristics. The glazing system reflectance depicted in Figure 11 is good for admitting solar radiation while preventing the escape of long-wave radiation emitted by surfaces inside the room, a good design for cold sunny days.

Almost all window glass is opaque to the long-wave radiation emitted by surfaces at temperatures below about 1200°C. This characteristic produces the **greenhouse effect**, by which solar radiation passing through a window is partially retained inside by the following mechanism. Radiation absorbed by surfaces in the room is emitted as long-wavelength radiation, which cannot escape directly through the glass because of its opaqueness to radiation beyond 4.5 μm. Instead, radiation from room surfaces is absorbed and reemitted to both sides as determined by several parameters, such as the inside and outside film heat transfer coefficients, the surface emissivities, and other glazing properties.

A good long-wave reflector can be a poor short-wave reflector and a good short-wave transmitter. Because of the conservation of energy ($T + R + \mathcal{A} = 1.0$), high long-wave reflectance means low transmittance and absorptance. Kirchhoff's law shows that low absorptance means low emissivity as well. This is the principle of operation of the high-solar-gain (or cold-climate) **low-e coating** on window glass. Such a coating has high transmittance over the entire solar spectrum, producing high solar heat gain while being highly reflective to long-wave infrared radiation emitted by the indoor surfaces, reflecting this radiation inward. The term *low-e* refers to a low emissivity over the long-wavelength portion of the spectrum.

Figure 12 shows hypothetical glazing systems with performance tuned to specific climates. In this case, the sharp **reflectance edge** that the ideal high solar gain cold-climate low-e coating exhibits just past the end of the solar spectrum in Figure 11 is shifted closer to the edge of the visible portion of the spectrum, thereby increasing the solar near-infrared (NIR) reflectance of the glazing. This results in a drop in the hot-climate transmittance to the right of the visible portion of the spectrum. The effect is to reflect the near-infrared portion of the solar spectrum outside, reducing solar gain, while still admitting visible light in the wavelength region below about 0.8 μm. This low-solar-gain, hot-climate coating also exhibits low emissivity over the long-wave spectrum, and is therefore also properly termed a low-e coating. To distinguish the cold- from the hot-climate version, a glazing with this type of spectral response is often termed **selective low-e**. This is something of a misnomer, because both hot- and cold-climate glazings are spectrally selective. Another term is **high-solar-gain, low-e** glazing system for cold climates, contrasted with **low-solar-gain, low-e** glazing system for hot climates.

The reduced infrared transmittance for the hot-climate glazing is ideally achieved by high reflectance and low absorptance (meaning also low emissivity). It can also be done with high infrared absorptance, if the flow of absorbed solar radiation to the interior of the building can be reduced, introducing a second approach to the construction of a hot-climate, low-solar-gain glazing system. In this case, the outer pane of a multiple-pane glazing system is made to have good visible transmittance but high absorptance over the solar infrared spectrum. To protect the interior of the building from the

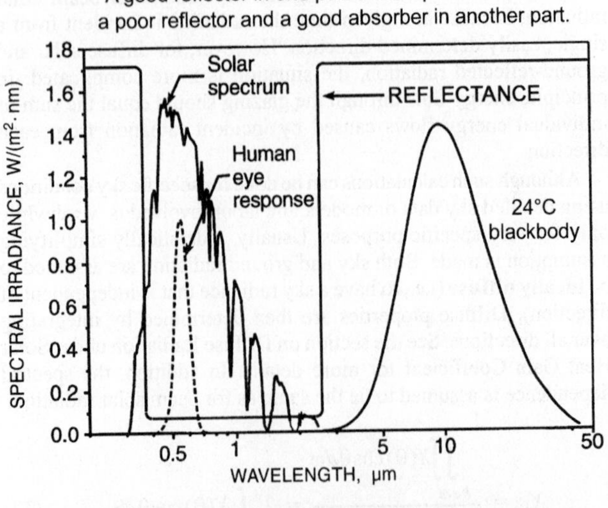

Fig. 11 Solar Spectrum, Human Eye Response Spectrum, Scaled Blackbody Radiation Spectrum, and Idealized Glazing Reflectance Spectrum

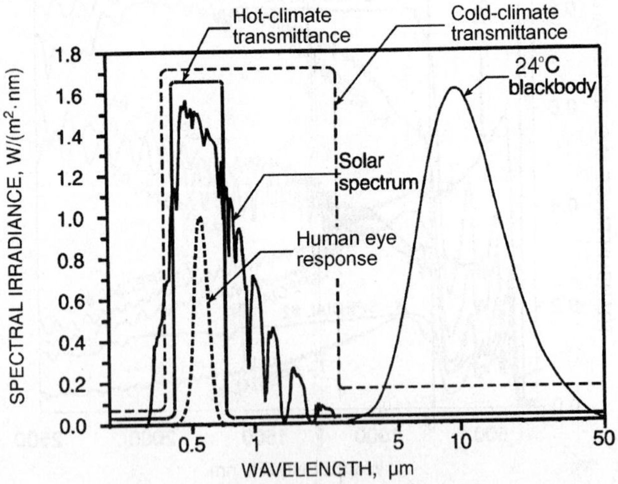

Fig. 12 Demonstration of Two Spectrally Selective Glazing Concepts, Showing Ideal Spectral Transmittances for Glazings Intended for Hot and Cold Climates

heat of this absorbed radiation, additional glazings, gas spaces, and cold-climate or low-solar-gain, low-e coatings are added.

By this means, radiation, conduction, and convection of heat from the hot outer pane to the interior ones and to the interior of the building are reduced because of the coating, the insulating gas space, and the additional panes. Such a glazing system for hot climates is insulated primarily *not* to protect the building from conductive heat losses in winter but to protect the interior from the solar radiant heat absorbed by the hot outer pane in summer. Several manufacturers offer this kind of nonreflecting, spectrally selective glazing system for commercial buildings having large cooling loads. Figure 12 shows that glazings intended for hot climates should have (1) high transmittance over the visible portion of the spectrum to let daylight in for both illumination and view and (2) low transmittance over all other portions of the spectrum to reduce solar heat gain. In contrast, glazings intended for very cold climates should have high transmittance over the whole solar spectrum, from 0.38 to over 3.5 μm, for maximum admission of solar radiant heat gain and light. In addition, glazings for cold climates should have low transmittance over the long-wavelength portion of the spectrum to block radiant heat emitted by the relatively warm indoor surfaces of buildings, preventing its escape to the outside.

Extreme spectral selectivity in glazing systems in the visible portion of the spectrum can produce an unwanted color shift in transmitted light. The color of transmitted light and its color-rendering properties should be considered in the design.

SOLAR HEAT GAIN COEFFICIENT

The concept of the solar heat gain coefficient is best illustrated for the case of a single glass pane in direct sunlight. If $E_D = E_{DN}\cos\theta$ is the direct solar irradiance incident on a single pane of glass, with T the solar transmittance, $\mathcal{A}$ the solar absorptance, and N the **inward-flowing fraction** of the absorbed radiation, then the total solar gain (per unit area) q_b that enters the space because of incident solar radiation is

$$q_b = E_D(T + N\mathcal{A}) \qquad (13)$$

in units of energy flux per unit area, W/m^2.

The inward-flowing fraction is thermal in origin; it depends on heat transfer properties of the assembly rather than on its optical properties. Absorbed solar radiation, including ultraviolet, visible, and infrared radiation from the sun and sky, is turned into heat inside the absorbing material. In a window, the glazing system temperature rises as a result to some approximately equilibrium value at which energy gains from absorbed radiation are balanced by equal losses. Absorbed solar radiation is dissipated through conduction, convection, and radiation. Some heat leaves the building, and the remainder goes inside, adding to the directly transmitted solar radiation. The magnitude of the inward-flowing fraction depends on the nature of the air boundary layers adjacent to both sides of the glazing, including any gas between the panes of a multiple-pane glazing system (N_i is often used to distinguish the inward-flowing fraction from the outward-flowing fraction, N_o. However, because only the inward-flowing fraction is used here, the subscript i is dropped for clarity).

The quantity in parenthesis in Equation (13) is called the **solar heat gain coefficient (SHGC)**. The total solar gain (from direct beam radiation) can therefore be computed using the following equation:

$$q_b = E_D \text{SHGC} \qquad (14)$$

The SHGC is needed to determine the solar heat gain through a window's glazing system, and should be included along with U-factor and other instantaneous performance properties in any manufacturer's description of a window's energy performance.

Calculation of Solar Heat Gain Coefficient

Because the optical properties $\mathcal{A}$ and T vary with the angle of incidence and wavelength, the solar heat gain coefficient is also a function of these variables. In the most general way, the solar heat gain $q(\theta)$ and the solar heat gain coefficient SHGC(θ,λ) are defined as

$$\begin{aligned} q(\theta) &= \int_{\lambda} E_D(\lambda)[T(\theta,\lambda) + N\mathcal{A}(\theta,\lambda)]d\lambda \\ &= \int_{\lambda} E_D(\lambda)\text{SHGC}(\theta,\lambda)d\lambda \end{aligned} \qquad (15)$$

where

$E_D(\lambda)$ = incident solar spectral irradiance
$T(\theta, \lambda)$ = spectral transmittance of glazing system
$\mathcal{A}(\theta, \lambda)$ = total spectral absorptance of glazing system

Here, the angle- and wavelength-dependent solar heat gain coefficient is given by

$$\text{SHGC}(\theta, \lambda) = T(\theta, \lambda) + N\mathcal{A}(\theta, \lambda) \qquad (16)$$

Combined with Equation (11), this becomes the wavelength-averaged solar heat gain coefficient:

$$\text{SHGC}(\theta) = \frac{\int_{\lambda_{min}}^{\lambda_{max}} E_D(\lambda)[T(\theta,\lambda) + N(\lambda)\mathcal{A}(\theta,\lambda)]d\lambda}{\int_{\lambda_{min}}^{\lambda_{max}} E_D(\lambda)d\lambda} \qquad (17)$$

Equations (15) to (17) indicate the preferred way of determining the solar gain of glazing systems and calculating the solar heat gain coefficient. Computer programs such as WINDOW (LBL 2003) are available to assist in the calculation. In WINDOW, the overall system optical properties at a given incident angle are calculated for each wavelength and the results averaged following Equation (17). The ASTM *Standard* E891 spectrum is used in the averaging. The wavelength-averaged properties (at a given incident angle) can then be used in Equation (14). This approach has been adopted by the National Fenestration Rating Council in NFRC *Technical Document* 200 for rating, certifying, and labeling windows for energy performance and by the Canadian Standards Association (CSA *Standard* A440.2). The method is valid for strongly spectrally selective (as well as nonselective) glazing systems.

When a glazing system is not strongly spectrally selective, the solar-weighted spectral broadband values of the optical properties can be used, and the integral over wavelength shown in Equations (15) and (17) is not needed. In this case, each glazing layer has its own individual inward-flowing fraction of the absorbed radiation for that layer. With the glazings numbered from the outside inward, and k the glazing index, the SHGC is given by

$$\text{SHGC}(\theta) = T^f(\theta) + \sum_{k=1}^{L} N_k \mathcal{A}_k^f(\theta) \qquad (18)$$

where

T^f = front transmittance of glazing system
L = number of glazing layers
$\mathcal{A}_k^f$ = absorptance of layer k
N_k = inward-flowing fraction for layer k

The inward-flowing fractions can be calculated from simplified heat transfer models, using the following equation:

$$N_k = U\sum_{j=k}^{1} R_{j-1,j} \tag{19}$$

This equation is essentially the U-factor of the fenestration times the thermal resistance from the kth layer to the outdoors. In more complicated multilayer glazing systems, it is advisable to perform a detailed heat transfer analysis of the system to determine the values of N_k, because the effective heat transfer coefficients and U depend (weakly) on the glazing layer temperatures and other environmental conditions [e.g., Finlayson and Arasteh (1993), LBL (2001), Wright (1995b)].

Diffuse Radiation

For incident diffuse radiation, the hemispherical average solar heat gain coefficient must be used. This may be calculated by combining Equation (17) with Equation (12) as follows:

$$\langle \text{SHGC}(\theta)\rangle_D = \frac{\int\int_{hem} \text{SHGC}(\theta)\cos\theta\, d\varpi}{\int\int_{hem} \cos\theta\, d\varpi} \tag{20}$$

$$= 2\int_0^{\pi/2} \text{SHGC}(\theta)\cos\theta\, d\theta$$

Equivalently, T and $\mathcal{A}$ in Equation (18) can be hemispherically averaged using Equation (12) so that

$$\langle \text{SHGC}\rangle_D = \langle T^f\rangle_D + \sum_{k=1}^{L} N_k \langle \mathcal{A}_k^f\rangle_D \tag{21}$$

In any case, N_k is unaffected in averaging, because it does not depend on incident angle or wavelength.

Solar Gain Through Frame and Other Opaque Elements

Figure 13 illustrates the mechanisms by which a window provides solar gain. It is assumed that all of the directly transmitted solar radiation is absorbed at indoor surfaces, where it is converted to heat. Solar gain also enters a building through opaque elements such as the frame and any mullion or dividers that are part of the fenestration system, because a portion of the solar energy absorbed at the surfaces of these elements is redirected to the indoor side by heat transfer.

The solar heat gain coefficient of the fenestration system can be calculated while accounting for solar gain through the opaque elements by area-weighting the solar heat gain coefficients of the glazing, frame, and M divider elements. Thus,

$$\text{SHGC} = \frac{\text{SHGC}_g A_g + \text{SHGC}_f A_f + \sum_{i=1}^{M} A_i \text{SHGC}_i}{A_g + A_f + \sum_{i=1}^{M} A_i} \tag{22}$$

where SHGC_g, SHGC_f, and SHGC_i are the solar heat gain coefficients of the glazed area, frame, and ith divider, respectively. A_g, A_f, and A_i are the corresponding projected areas.

In some cases, it is useful to have an overall SHGC for the opaque elements only, which is defined by

$$\text{SHGC}_{op} = \frac{\text{SHGC}_f A_f + \sum_{i=1}^{M} A_i \text{SHGC}_i}{A_{op}} \tag{23}$$

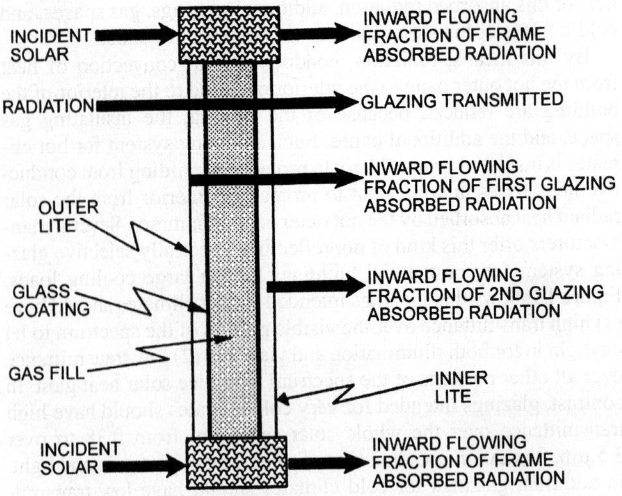

Fig. 13 Components of Solar Radiant Heat Gain with Double-Pane Window, Including Both Frame and Glazing Contributions

where

$$A_{op} = A_f + \sum_{i=1}^{M} A_i$$

SHGC_f can be estimated (Wright 1995a) using

$$\text{SHGC}_f = \alpha_f^s \left(\frac{U_f}{h_f}\right)\left(\frac{A_f}{A_{surf}}\right) \tag{24}$$

where α_f^s is the solar absorptivity of the outdoor surface of the frame, U_f is the frame U-factor, and h_f is the heat transfer coefficient (radiative plus convective) between the frame and the outdoor environment. The projected-to-surface area ratio (A_f/A_{surf}) corrects for the fact that U_f is based on projected area A_f and h_f is based on the exposed outdoor frame surface area A_{surf}. SHGC_i can be calculated in the same way:

$$\text{SHGC}_i = \alpha_i^s \left(\frac{U_i}{h_i}\right)\left(\frac{A_i}{A_{surf,\,i}}\right) \tag{25}$$

The outdoor-side heat transfer coefficients h_f and h_i can be estimated using ASHRAE (1996):

$$h_f \text{ or } h_i = h_{co} + 4\sigma e_f T_{out}^3 \tag{26}$$

where h_{co} is the convective heat transfer coefficient between the frame (or divider) surface and the outdoor environment, e_f is the emissivity (long-wave) of the outdoor frame (or divider) surface, T_{out} is the outdoor absolute temperature, and σ is the Stefan-Boltzmann constant.

Solar Heat Gain Coefficient, Visible Transmittance, and Spectrally Averaged Solar-Optical Property Values

Table 10 lists visible transmittance, solar transmittance, front and back reflectance, and solar heat gain coefficients for common glazing and window systems. The ID number for each entry in Table 10 refers to an ID number in Table 4, and the window systems therefore include windows with aluminum or metal frames and windows with other frames that have a lower conductivity (e.g., thermally broken aluminum, wood, vinyl, and fiberglass). As can be seen in Table 10, the total window solar heat gain coefficient varies with the type of operator, size of the fenestration product, and type of frame.

The glazing T_v, T_{sol}, R^f, R^b, and SHGC values have been calculated using manufacturers' spectral data following methods described in Finlayson and Arasteh (1993) and Wright (1995a), and using the 1.5 air mass spectrum found in ASTM *Standard* E891. Glazing values are given for 3 and 6 mm glass and vary with glass thickness and glass manufacturer. Values shown are average values and may vary by ±0.05. It is recommended that actual values be determined using detailed spectral data from NFRC (2004h). The front reflectance is the reflectance of the unit to the outside, and the back reflectance is the reflectance to the room side.

Visible transmittances are center-glazing values at normal incidence. A rule of thumb is to select a glazing unit whose visible transmittance is greater than its solar heat gain coefficient, especially if daylighting strategies will be used in the building. For maximum light with minimum solar gain, there are fenestration products available having visible transmittance that is 1.4 times their SHGC. For energy calculations on a daylit building, visible transmittance for the entire window should be used. The visible transmittance of a window can be calculated by multiplying the fraction of glazing area by the center-glazing visible transmittance.

Solar heat gain coefficients are provided for center-glazing and total window values. Center-glazing solar heat gain coefficients are given at normal incidence (0°) and at 40°, 50°, 60°, 70°, and 80° incidence angles. For angles other than those listed, straight-line interpolation can be used between the two closest angles for which values are shown. Total window solar heat gain coefficients assume normal incidence. The operable and fixed window sizes in Table 4 were used. To calculate the frame area, frame heights shown in Figure 4 for aluminum and aluminum-clad wood/wood/vinyl were used. The frame area for aluminum windows is 11% for operable size, and 10% for fixed. The frame area for other frames is 20% for the operable size and 12% for fixed. The ratio of projected frame area to frame surface area is assumed to be 1.0, based on Wright (1995a).

Frame solar heat gain coefficients used to determine the total window solar heat gain coefficients are calculated according to the section on Solar Gain Through Frame and Other Opaque Elements. Frame U-factors are taken from Table 1. Frame absorptance is assumed to be 0.5. The outside film coefficient is 22.2 W/(m^2·K), corresponding to a wind speed of 3.4 m/s. For the aluminum window, the frame solar heat gain coefficient is 0.14 for the operable window and 0.11 for the fixed. For the other frames, the frame solar heat gain coefficient varies between 0.02 and 0.07 for the various lower-conductivity frame types. A frame solar heat gain coefficient of 0.04 is used for the operable window, and 0.03 for the fixed. These values correspond directly to the aluminum-clad wood/reinforced vinyl frames.

Solar transmittances and front and back reflectances are also center-glazing values and are given at normal incidence (0°) and at 40°, 50°, 60°, 70°, and 80° incidence angles. The effective inward-flowing fraction of absorbed radiation for the entire system (not layer-specific values) can be determined from Equation (14) by inserting the solar transmittance and corresponding SHGC.

Example 5. Estimate the overall visible light transmittance for an operable wood casement window with clear, uncoated 6 mm double glazing. The operable window has 27% frame area with a wood frame.

Solution: The center-glazing visible light transmittance is 0.78 (see Table 10, glazing ID = 5b, first column). The overall visible light transmittance is

$$T_v = 0.27(0) + 0.73(0.78) = 0.57$$

Airflow Windows

If properly managed, airflow between panes of a double-glazed window can improve fenestration performance. In normal use, a venetian blind is located between the glazing layers. Ventilation air from the room enters the double-glazed cavity, flows over the blind, and can be exhausted from the building or returned through the ducts to the central HVAC system.

These systems can control window heat transfer under many different operating conditions. During sunny winter days, the blind acts as a solar air collector; heat removed by the moving air can be used elsewhere in the building. Further, the window acts as a heat exchanger when sunlit so that the indoor glass temperature nearly equals the room air temperature and improves thermal comfort. In the summer, the window can have a very low solar heat gain coefficient if the blinds are appropriately placed, because the majority of solar gains are removed from the window.

Brandle and Boehm (1982) and Sodergren and Bostrom (1971) give details on airflow windows.

Skylights

Skylight solar heat gain strongly depends on the configuration of the space below or adjacent to (i.e., in sloped applications) the skylight formed by the skylight curb and any associated light well.

Five aspects must be considered: (1) transmittance and absorptance of the skylight unit, (2) transmitted solar flux that reaches the aperture of the light well, (3) whether that aperture is covered by a diffuser, (4) transmitted solar flux that strikes the walls of the light well, and (5) reflectance of the walls of the light well. Data for flat skylights, which may be considered as sloped glazings, are found in Tables 4 and 11.

Domed Skylights. Solar and total heat gains for domed skylights can be determined by the same procedure used for windows. Table 11 gives SHGCs for plastic domed skylights at normal incidence (Shutrum and Ozisik 1961). Manufacturers' literature has further details. Given the poorly defined incident angle conditions for domed skylights, it is best to use these values without correction for incident angle, together with the correct (angle-dependent) value of incident solar irradiance. Results should be considered approximate. In the absence of other data, these values may also be used to make estimates for skylights on slanted roofs.

Glass Block Walls

Glass block can be used for light transmission through outdoor walls when optical clarity for view is unnecessary. Table 12 describes a variety of glass block patterns and gives solar heat gain coefficients to be applied to solar irradiances so that approximate instantaneous solar heat gains can be calculated (Smith and Pennington 1964).

Convection and low-temperature radiative heat gain for all hollow glass block panels fall within a narrow range. Differences in SHGCs are largely the result of differences in transmittance of glass blocks for solar radiation. Solar heat gain coefficients for any particular glass block pattern vary depending on orientation and time of day. The SHGC for western exposures in the morning (shaded) is depressed because of heat storage in the block, whereas the SHGC for eastern exposures in the afternoon (shaded) is elevated as stored heat is dissipated. Time lag effects from heat storage are estimated by using solar gains and air-to-air temperature differences for one hour earlier than the time for which the load calculation is made.

Calorimeter tests of Type 1A glass block showed little difference in solar heat gains between glass block with either black or white ceramic enamel on the exterior of the block. White and black ceramic enamel surfaces represent the two extremes for reflecting or absorbing solar energy; therefore, glass block with enamel surfaces of other colors should have solar heat gain coefficients between these values. Because glass blocks are good examples of strongly angularly selective fenestrations, appropriate caution must be taken.

Table 10 Visible Transmittance (T_v), Solar Heat Gain Coefficient (SHGC), Solar Transmittance (T), Front Reflectance (R^f), Back Reflectance (R^b), and Layer Absorptance ($\mathcal{A}^f_n$) for Glazing and Window Systems

	Glazing System				Center-of-Glazing Properties							Total Window SHGC at Normal Incidence				Total Window T_v at Normal Incidence			
					Incidence Angles							Aluminum		Other Frames		Aluminum		Other Frames	
ID	Glass Thick., mm		Center Glazing T_v		Normal 0.00	40.00	50.00	60.00	70.00	80.00	Hemis., Diffuse	Operable	Fixed	Operable	Fixed	Operable	Fixed	Operable	Fixed
Uncoated Single Glazing																			
1a	3	CLR	0.90	SHGC	0.86	0.84	0.82	0.78	0.67	0.42	0.78	0.78	0.79	0.70	0.76	0.80	0.81	0.72	0.79
				T	0.83	0.82	0.80	0.75	0.64	0.39	0.75								
				R^f	0.08	0.08	0.10	0.14	0.25	0.51	0.14								
				R^b	0.08	0.08	0.10	0.14	0.25	0.51	0.14								
				$\mathcal{A}^f_1$	0.09	0.10	0.10	0.11	0.11	0.11	0.10								
1b	6	CLR	0.88	SHGC	0.81	0.80	0.78	0.73	0.62	0.39	0.73	0.74	0.74	0.66	0.72	0.78	0.79	0.70	0.77
				T	0.77	0.75	0.73	0.68	0.58	0.35	0.69								
				R^f	0.07	0.08	0.09	0.13	0.24	0.48	0.13								
				R^b	0.07	0.08	0.09	0.13	0.24	0.48	0.13								
				$\mathcal{A}^f_1$	0.16	0.17	0.18	0.19	0.19	0.17	0.17								
1c	3	BRZ	0.68	SHGC	0.73	0.71	0.68	0.64	0.55	0.34	0.65	0.67	0.67	0.59	0.65	0.61	0.61	0.54	0.60
				T	0.65	0.62	0.59	0.55	0.46	0.27	0.56								
				R^f	0.06	0.07	0.08	0.12	0.22	0.45	0.12								
				R^b	0.06	0.07	0.08	0.12	0.22	0.45	0.12								
				$\mathcal{A}^f_1$	0.29	0.31	0.32	0.33	0.33	0.29	0.31								
1d	6	BRZ	0.54	SHGC	0.62	0.59	0.57	0.53	0.45	0.29	0.54	0.57	0.57	0.50	0.55	0.48	0.49	0.43	0.48
				T	0.49	0.45	0.43	0.39	0.32	0.18	0.41								
				R^f	0.05	0.06	0.07	0.11	0.19	0.42	0.10								
				R^b	0.05	0.68	0.66	0.62	0.53	0.33	0.10								
				$\mathcal{A}^f_1$	0.46	0.49	0.50	0.51	0.49	0.41	0.48								
1e	3	GRN	0.82	SHGC	0.70	0.68	0.66	0.62	0.53	0.33	0.63	0.64	0.64	0.57	0.62	0.73	0.74	0.66	0.72
				T	0.61	0.58	0.56	0.52	0.43	0.25	0.53								
				R^f	0.06	0.07	0.08	0.12	0.21	0.45	0.11								
				R^b	0.06	0.07	0.08	0.12	0.21	0.45	0.11								
				$\mathcal{A}^f_1$	0.33	0.35	0.36	0.37	0.36	0.31	0.35								
1f	6	GRN	0.76	SHGC	0.60	0.58	0.56	0.52	0.45	0.29	0.54	0.55	0.55	0.49	0.53	0.68	0.68	0.61	0.67
				T	0.47	0.44	0.42	0.38	0.32	0.18	0.40								
				R^f	0.05	0.06	0.07	0.11	0.20	0.42	0.10								
				R^b	0.05	0.06	0.07	0.11	0.20	0.42	0.10								
				$\mathcal{A}^f_1$	0.47	0.50	0.51	0.51	0.49	0.40	0.49								
1g	3	GRY	0.62	SHGC	0.70	0.68	0.66	0.61	0.53	0.33	0.63	0.64	0.64	0.57	0.62	0.55	0.56	0.50	0.55
				T	0.61	0.58	0.56	0.51	0.42	0.24	0.53								
				R^f	0.06	0.07	0.08	0.12	0.21	0.44	0.11								
				R^b	0.06	0.07	0.08	0.12	0.21	0.44	0.11								
				$\mathcal{A}^f_1$	0.33	0.36	0.37	0.37	0.37	0.32	0.35								
1h	6	GRY	0.46	SHGC	0.59	0.57	0.55	0.51	0.44	0.28	0.52	0.54	0.54	0.48	0.52	0.41	0.41	0.37	0.40
				T	0.46	0.42	0.40	0.36	0.29	0.16	0.38								
				R^f	0.05	0.06	0.07	0.10	0.19	0.41	0.10								
				R^b	0.05	0.06	0.07	0.10	0.19	0.41	0.10								
				$\mathcal{A}^f_1$	0.49	0.52	0.54	0.54	0.52	0.43	0.51								
1i	6	BLUGRN	0.75	SHGC	0.62	0.59	0.57	0.54	0.46	0.30	0.55	0.57	0.57	0.50	0.55	0.67	0.68	0.60	0.66
				T	0.49	0.46	0.44	0.40	0.33	0.19	0.42								
				R^f	0.06	0.06	0.07	0.11	0.20	0.43	0.11								
				R^b	0.06	0.06	0.07	0.11	0.20	0.43	0.11								
				$\mathcal{A}^f_1$	0.45	0.48	0.49	0.49	0.47	0.38	0.48								
Reflective Single Glazing																			
1j	6	SS on CLR 8%	0.08	SHGC	0.19	0.19	0.19	0.18	0.16	0.10	0.18	0.18	0.18	0.16	0.17	0.07	0.07	0.06	0.07
				T	0.06	0.06	0.06	0.05	0.04	0.03	0.05								
				R^f	0.33	0.34	0.35	0.37	0.44	0.61	0.36								
				R^b	0.50	0.50	0.51	0.53	0.58	0.71	0.52								
				$\mathcal{A}^f_1$	0.61	0.61	0.60	0.58	0.52	0.37	0.57								
1k	6	SS on CLR 14%	0.14	SHGC	0.25	0.25	0.24	0.23	0.20	0.13	0.23	0.24	0.24	0.21	0.22	0.12	0.13	0.11	0.12
				T	0.11	0.10	0.10	0.09	0.07	0.04	0.09								
				R^f	0.26	0.27	0.28	0.31	0.38	0.57	0.30								
				R^b	0.44	0.44	0.45	0.47	0.52	0.67	0.46								
				$\mathcal{A}^f_1$	0.63	0.63	0.62	0.60	0.55	0.39	0.60								

Table 10 Visible Transmittance (T_v), Solar Heat Gain Coefficient (SHGC), Solar Transmittance (T), Front Reflectance (R^f), Back Reflectance (R^b), and Layer Absorptance ($\mathcal{A}^f_n$) for Glazing and Window Systems (*Continued*)

ID	Glazing System: Glass Thick., mm	Glazing System	Center Glazing T_v		Center-of-Glazing Properties, Incidence Angles: Normal 0.00	40.00	50.00	60.00	70.00	80.00	Hemis., Diffuse	Total Window SHGC at Normal Incidence: Aluminum Operable	Aluminum Fixed	Other Frames Operable	Other Frames Fixed	Total Window T_v at Normal Incidence: Aluminum Operable	Aluminum Fixed	Other Frames Operable	Other Frames Fixed
1l	6	SS on CLR 20%	0.20	SHGC	0.31	0.30	0.30	0.28	0.24	0.16	0.28	0.29	0.29	0.26	0.28	0.18	0.18	0.16	0.18
				T	0.15	0.15	0.14	0.13	0.11	0.06	0.13								
				R^f	0.21	0.22	0.23	0.26	0.34	0.54	0.25								
				R^b	0.38	0.38	0.39	0.41	0.48	0.64	0.41								
				$\mathcal{A}^f_1$	0.64	0.64	0.63	0.61	0.56	0.40	0.60								
1m	6	SS on GRN 14%	0.12	SHGC	0.25	0.25	0.24	0.23	0.21	0.14	0.23	0.24	0.24	0.21	0.22	0.11	0.11	0.10	0.11
				T	0.06	0.06	0.06	0.06	0.04	0.03	0.06								
				R^f	0.14	0.14	0.16	0.19	0.27	0.49	0.18								
				R^b	0.44	0.44	0.45	0.47	0.52	0.67	0.46								
				$\mathcal{A}^f_1$	0.80	0.80	0.78	0.76	0.68	0.48	0.75								
1n	6	TI on CLR 20%	0.20	SHGC	0.29	0.29	0.28	0.27	0.23	0.15	0.27	0.27	0.27	0.24	0.26	0.18	0.18	0.16	0.18
				T	0.14	0.13	0.13	0.12	0.09	0.06	0.12								
				R^f	0.22	0.22	0.24	0.26	0.34	0.54	0.26								
				R^b	0.40	0.40	0.42	0.44	0.50	0.65	0.43								
				$\mathcal{A}^f_1$	0.65	0.65	0.64	0.62	0.57	0.40	0.62								
1o	6	TI on CLR 30%	0.30	SHGC	0.39	0.38	0.37	0.35	0.30	0.20	0.35	0.36	0.36	0.32	0.35	0.27	0.27	0.24	0.26
				T	0.23	0.22	0.21	0.19	0.16	0.09	0.20								
				R^f	0.15	0.15	0.17	0.20	0.28	0.50	0.19								
				R^b	0.32	0.33	0.34	0.36	0.43	0.60	0.36								
				$\mathcal{A}^f_1$	0.63	0.65	0.64	0.62	0.57	0.40	0.62								
Uncoated Double Glazing																			
5a	3	CLR CLR	0.81	SHGC	0.76	0.74	0.71	0.64	0.50	0.26	0.66	0.69	0.70	0.62	0.67	0.72	0.73	0.65	0.71
				T	0.70	0.68	0.65	0.58	0.44	0.21	0.60								
				R^f	0.13	0.14	0.16	0.23	0.36	0.61	0.21								
				R^b	0.13	0.14	0.16	0.23	0.36	0.61	0.21								
				$\mathcal{A}^f_1$	0.10	0.11	0.11	0.12	0.13	0.13	0.11								
				$\mathcal{A}^f_2$	0.07	0.08	0.08	0.08	0.07	0.05	0.07								
5b	6	CLR CLR	0.78	SHGC	0.70	0.67	0.64	0.58	0.45	0.23	0.60	0.64	0.64	0.57	0.62	0.69	0.70	0.62	0.69
				T	0.61	0.58	0.55	0.48	0.36	0.17	0.51								
				R^f	0.11	0.12	0.15	0.20	0.33	0.57	0.18								
				R^b	0.11	0.12	0.15	0.20	0.33	0.57	0.18								
				$\mathcal{A}^f_1$	0.17	0.18	0.19	0.20	0.21	0.20	0.19								
				$\mathcal{A}^f_2$	0.11	0.12	0.12	0.12	0.10	0.07	0.11								
5c	3	BRZ CLR	0.62	SHGC	0.62	0.60	0.57	0.51	0.39	0.20	0.53	0.57	0.57	0.50	0.55	0.55	0.56	0.50	0.55
				T	0.55	0.51	0.48	0.42	0.31	0.14	0.45								
				R^f	0.09	0.10	0.12	0.16	0.27	0.49	0.15								
				R^b	0.12	0.13	0.15	0.21	0.35	0.59	0.19								
				$\mathcal{A}^f_1$	0.30	0.33	0.34	0.36	0.37	0.34	0.33								
				$\mathcal{A}^f_2$	0.06	0.06	0.06	0.06	0.05	0.03	0.06								
5d	6	BRZ CLR	0.47	SHGC	0.49	0.46	0.44	0.39	0.31	0.17	0.41	0.45	0.45	0.40	0.43	0.42	0.42	0.38	0.41
				T	0.38	0.35	0.32	0.27	0.20	0.08	0.30								
				R^f	0.07	0.08	0.09	0.13	0.22	0.44	0.12								
				R^b	0.10	0.11	0.13	0.19	0.31	0.55	0.17								
				$\mathcal{A}^f_1$	0.48	0.51	0.52	0.53	0.53	0.45	0.50								
				$\mathcal{A}^f_2$	0.07	0.07	0.07	0.07	0.06	0.04	0.07								
5e	3	GRN CLR	0.75	SHGC	0.60	0.57	0.54	0.49	0.38	0.20	0.51	0.55	0.55	0.49	0.53	0.67	0.68	0.60	0.66
				T	0.52	0.49	0.46	0.40	0.30	0.13	0.43								
				R^f	0.09	0.10	0.12	0.16	0.27	0.50	0.15								
				R^b	0.12	0.13	0.15	0.21	0.35	0.60	0.19								
				$\mathcal{A}^f_1$	0.34	0.37	0.38	0.39	0.39	0.35	0.37								
				$\mathcal{A}^f_2$	0.05	0.05	0.05	0.04	0.04	0.03	0.04								
5f	6	GRN CLR	0.68	SHGC	0.49	0.46	0.44	0.39	0.31	0.17	0.41	0.45	0.45	0.40	0.43	0.61	0.61	0.54	0.60
				T	0.39	0.36	0.33	0.29	0.21	0.09	0.31								
				R^f	0.08	0.08	0.10	0.14	0.23	0.45	0.13								
				R^b	0.10	0.11	0.13	0.19	0.31	0.55	0.17								
				$\mathcal{A}^f_1$	0.49	0.51	0.05	0.53	0.52	0.43	0.50								
				$\mathcal{A}^f_2$	0.05	0.05	0.05	0.05	0.04	0.03	0.05								

Table 10 Visible Transmittance (T_v), Solar Heat Gain Coefficient (SHGC), Solar Transmittance (T), Front Reflectance (R^f), Back Reflectance (R^b), and Layer Absorptance ($\mathcal{A}^f_n$) for Glazing and Window Systems (*Continued*)

	Glazing System				Center-of-Glazing Properties							Total Window SHGC at Normal Incidence				Total Window T_v at Normal Incidence			
					Incidence Angles							Aluminum		Other Frames		Aluminum		Other Frames	
ID	Glass Thick., mm		Center Glazing T_v		Normal 0.00	40.00	50.00	60.00	70.00	80.00	Hemis., Diffuse	Operable	Fixed	Operable	Fixed	Operable	Fixed	Operable	Fixed
5g	3	GRY CLR	0.56	SHGC	0.60	0.57	0.54	0.48	0.37	0.20	0.51	0.55	0.55	0.49	0.53	0.50	0.50	0.45	0.49
				T	0.51	0.48	0.45	0.39	0.29	0.12	0.42								
				R^f	0.09	0.09	0.11	0.16	0.26	0.48	0.14								
				R^b	0.12	0.13	0.15	0.21	0.34	0.59	0.19								
				$\mathcal{A}^f_1$	0.34	0.37	0.39	0.40	0.41	0.37	0.37								
				$\mathcal{A}^f_2$	0.05	0.06	0.06	0.05	0.05	0.03	0.05								
5h	6	GRY CLR	0.41	SHGC	0.47	0.44	0.42	0.37	0.29	0.16	0.39	0.43	0.43	0.38	0.42	0.36	0.37	0.33	0.36
				T	0.36	0.32	0.29	0.25	0.18	0.07	0.28								
				R^f	0.07	0.07	0.08	0.12	0.21	0.43	0.12								
				R^b	0.10	0.11	0.13	0.18	0.31	0.55	0.17								
				$\mathcal{A}^f_1$	0.51	0.54	0.56	0.57	0.56	0.47	0.53								
				$\mathcal{A}^f_2$	0.07	0.07	0.07	0.06	0.05	0.03	0.06								
5i	6	BLUGRN CLR	0.67	SHGC	0.50	0.47	0.45	0.40	0.32	0.17	0.43	0.46	0.46	0.41	0.44	0.60	0.60	0.54	0.59
				T	0.40	0.37	0.34	0.30	0.22	0.10	0.32								
				R^f	0.08	0.08	0.10	0.14	0.24	0.46	0.13								
				R^b	0.11	0.11	0.14	0.19	0.31	0.55	0.17								
				$\mathcal{A}^f_1$	0.47	0.49	0.50	0.51	0.50	0.42	0.48								
				$\mathcal{A}^f_2$	0.06	0.06	0.06	0.05	0.04	0.03	0.05								
5j	6	HI-P GRN CLR	0.59	SHGC	0.39	0.37	0.35	0.31	0.25	0.14	0.33	0.36	0.36	0.32	0.35	0.53	0.53	0.47	0.52
				T	0.28	0.26	0.24	0.20	0.15	0.06	0.22								
				R^f	0.06	0.07	0.08	0.12	0.21	0.43	0.11								
				R^b	0.10	0.11	0.13	0.19	0.31	0.55	0.17								
				$\mathcal{A}^f_1$	0.62	0.65	0.65	0.65	0.62	0.50	0.63								
				$\mathcal{A}^f_2$	0.03	0.03	0.03	0.03	0.02	0.01	0.03								
Reflective Double Glazing																			
5k	6	SS on CLR 8%, CLR	0.07	SHGC	0.13	0.12	0.12	0.11	0.10	0.06	0.11	0.13	0.13	0.11	0.12	0.06	0.06	0.06	0.06
				T	0.05	0.05	0.04	0.04	0.03	0.01	0.04								
				R^f	0.33	0.34	0.35	0.37	0.44	0.61	0.37								
				R^b	0.38	0.37	0.38	0.40	0.46	0.61	0.40								
				$\mathcal{A}^f_1$	0.61	0.61	0.60	0.58	0.53	0.37	0.56								
				$\mathcal{A}^f_2$	0.01	0.01	0.01	0.01	0.01	0.01	0.01								
5l	6	SS on CLR 14%, CLR	0.13	SHGC	0.17	0.17	0.16	0.15	0.13	0.08	0.16	0.17	0.16	0.14	0.15	0.12	0.12	0.10	0.11
				T	0.08	0.08	0.08	0.07	0.05	0.02	0.07								
				R^f	0.26	0.27	0.28	0.31	0.38	0.57	0.30								
				R^b	0.34	0.33	0.34	0.37	0.44	0.60	0.36								
				$\mathcal{A}^f_1$	0.63	0.64	0.64	0.63	0.61	0.56	0.60								
				$\mathcal{A}^f_2$	0.02	0.02	0.02	0.02	0.02	0.02	0.02								
5m	6	SS on CLR 20%, CLR	0.18	SHGC	0.22	0.21	0.21	0.19	0.16	0.09	0.20	0.21	0.21	0.18	0.20	0.16	0.16	0.14	0.16
				T	0.12	0.11	0.11	0.09	0.07	0.03	0.10								
				R^f	0.21	0.22	0.23	0.26	0.34	0.54	0.25								
				R^b	0.30	0.30	0.31	0.34	0.41	0.59	0.33								
				$\mathcal{A}^f_1$	0.64	0.64	0.63	0.62	0.57	0.41	0.61								
				$\mathcal{A}^f_2$	0.03	0.03	0.03	0.03	0.02	0.02	0.03								
5n	6	SS on GRN 14%, CLR	0.11	SHGC	0.16	0.16	0.15	0.14	0.12	0.08	0.14	0.16	0.16	0.14	0.14	0.10	0.10	0.09	0.10
				T	0.05	0.05	0.05	0.04	0.03	0.01	0.04								
				R^f	0.14	0.14	0.16	0.19	0.27	0.49	0.18								
				R^b	0.34	0.33	0.34	0.37	0.44	0.60	0.36								
				$\mathcal{A}^f_1$	0.80	0.80	0.79	0.76	0.69	0.49	0.76								
				$\mathcal{A}^f_2$	0.01	0.01	0.01	0.01	0.01	0.01	0.01								
5o	6	TI on CLR 20%, CLR	0.18	SHGC	0.21	0.20	0.19	0.18	0.15	0.09	0.18	0.20	0.20	0.18	0.19	0.16	0.16	0.14	0.16
				T	0.11	0.10	0.10	0.08	0.06	0.03	0.09								
				R^f	0.22	0.22	0.24	0.27	0.34	0.54	0.26								
				R^b	0.32	0.31	0.32	0.35	0.42	0.59	0.35								
				$\mathcal{A}^f_1$	0.65	0.66	0.65	0.63	0.58	0.41	0.62								
				$\mathcal{A}^f_2$	0.02	0.02	0.02	0.02	0.02	0.01	0.02								
5p	6	TI on CLR 30%, CLR	0.27	SHGC	0.29	0.28	0.27	0.25	0.20	0.12	0.25	0.27	0.27	0.24	0.26	0.24	0.24	0.22	0.24
				T	0.18	0.17	0.16	0.14	0.10	0.05	0.15								
				R^f	0.15	0.15	0.17	0.20	0.29	0.51	0.19								
				R^b	0.27	0.27	0.28	0.31	0.40	0.58	0.31								
				$\mathcal{A}^f_1$	0.64	0.64	0.63	0.62	0.58	0.43	0.61								
				$\mathcal{A}^f_2$	0.04	0.04	0.04	0.04	0.03	0.02	0.04								

Table 10 Visible Transmittance (T_v), Solar Heat Gain Coefficient (SHGC), Solar Transmittance (T), Front Reflectance (R^f), Back Reflectance (R^b), and Layer Absorptance ($\mathcal{A}^f_n$) for Glazing and Window Systems (*Continued*)

	Glazing System				Center-of-Glazing Properties							Total Window SHGC at Normal Incidence				Total Window T_v at Normal Incidence			
					Incidence Angles							Aluminum		Other Frames		Aluminum		Other Frames	
ID	Glass Thick., mm		Center Glazing T_v		Normal 0.00	40.00	50.00	60.00	70.00	80.00	Hemis., Diffuse	Operable	Fixed	Operable	Fixed	Operable	Fixed	Operable	Fixed
Low-e Double Glazing, e = 0.2 on surface 2																			
17a	3	LE CLR	0.76	SHGC	0.65	0.64	0.61	0.56	0.43	0.23	0.57	0.59	0.60	0.53	0.58	0.68	0.68	0.61	0.67
				T	0.59	0.56	0.54	0.48	0.36	0.18	0.50								
				R^f	0.15	0.16	0.18	0.24	0.37	0.61	0.22								
				R^b	0.17	0.18	0.20	0.26	0.38	0.61	0.24								
				$\mathcal{A}^f_1$	0.20	0.21	0.21	0.21	0.20	0.16	0.20								
				$\mathcal{A}^f_2$	0.07	0.07	0.08	0.08	0.07	0.05	0.07								
17b	6	LE CLR	0.73	SHGC	0.60	0.59	0.57	0.51	0.40	0.21	0.53	0.55	0.55	0.49	0.53	0.65	0.66	0.58	0.64
				T	0.51	0.48	0.46	0.41	0.30	0.14	0.43								
				R^f	0.14	0.15	0.17	0.22	0.35	0.59	0.21								
				R^b	0.15	0.16	0.18	0.23	0.35	0.57	0.22								
				$\mathcal{A}^f_1$	0.26	0.26	0.26	0.26	0.25	0.19	0.25								
				$\mathcal{A}^f_2$	0.10	0.11	0.11	0.11	0.10	0.07	0.10								
Low-e Double Glazing, e = 0.2 on surface 3																			
17c	3	CLR LE	0.76	SHGC	0.70	0.68	0.65	0.59	0.46	0.24	0.61	0.64	0.64	0.57	0.62	0.68	0.68	0.1	0.67
				T	0.59	0.56	0.54	0.48	0.36	0.18	0.50								
				R^f	0.17	0.18	0.20	0.26	0.38	0.61	0.24								
				R^b	0.15	0.16	0.18	0.24	0.37	0.61	0.22								
				$\mathcal{A}^f_1$	0.11	0.12	0.13	0.13	0.14	0.15	0.12								
				$\mathcal{A}^f_2$	0.14	0.14	0.14	0.13	0.11	0.07	0.13								
17d	6	CLR LE	0.73	SHGC	0.65	0.63	0.60	0.54	0.42	0.21	0.56	0.59	0.60	0.53	0.58	0.65	0.66	0.58	0.64
				T	0.51	0.48	0.46	0.41	0.30	0.14	0.43								
				R^f	0.15	0.16	0.18	0.23	0.35	0.57	0.22								
				R^b	0.14	0.15	0.17	0.22	0.35	0.59	0.21								
				$\mathcal{A}^f_1$	0.17	0.19	0.20	0.21	0.22	0.22	0.19								
				$\mathcal{A}^f_2$	0.17	0.17	0.17	0.15	0.13	0.07	0.16								
17e	3	BRZ LE	0.58	SHGC	0.57	0.54	0.51	0.46	0.35	0.18	0.48	0.52	0.52	0.46	0.51	0.52	0.52	0.46	0.51
				T	0.46	0.43	0.41	0.36	0.26	0.12	0.38								
				R^f	0.12	0.12	0.14	0.18	0.28	0.50	0.17								
				R^b	0.14	0.15	0.17	0.23	0.35	0.60	0.21								
				$\mathcal{A}^f_1$	0.31	0.34	0.35	0.37	0.38	0.35	0.34								
				$\mathcal{A}^f_2$	0.11	0.11	0.10	0.10	0.08	0.04	0.10								
17f	6	BRZ LE	0.45	SHGC	0.45	0.42	0.40	0.35	0.27	0.14	0.38	0.42	0.42	0.37	0.40	0.40	0.41	0.36	0.40
				T	0.33	0.30	0.28	0.24	0.17	0.07	0.26								
				R^f	0.09	0.09	0.10	0.14	0.23	0.44	0.13								
				R^b	0.13	0.14	0.16	0.21	0.34	0.58	0.20								
				$\mathcal{A}^f_1$	0.48	0.51	0.52	0.54	0.53	0.45	0.50								
				$\mathcal{A}^f_2$	0.11	0.11	0.10	0.09	0.07	0.04	0.09								
17g	3	GRN LE	0.70	SHGC	0.55	0.52	0.50	0.44	0.34	0.17	0.46	0.50	0.51	0.45	0.49	0.62	0.63	0.56	0.62
				T	0.44	0.41	0.38	0.33	0.24	0.11	0.36								
				R^f	0.11	0.11	0.13	0.17	0.27	0.48	0.16								
				R^b	0.14	0.15	0.17	0.23	0.35	0.60	0.21								
				$\mathcal{A}^f_1$	0.35	0.38	0.39	0.41	0.42	0.37	0.38								
				$\mathcal{A}^f_2$	0.11	0.10	0.10	0.09	0.07	0.04	0.09								
17h	6	GRN LE	0.61	SHGC	0.41	0.39	0.36	0.32	0.25	0.13	0.34	0.38	0.38	0.34	0.36	0.54	0.55	0.49	0.54
				T	0.29	0.26	0.24	0.21	0.15	0.06	0.23								
				R^f	0.08	0.08	0.09	0.13	0.22	0.43	0.13								
				R^b	0.13	0.14	0.16	0.21	0.34	0.58	0.20								
				$\mathcal{A}^f_1$	0.53	0.57	0.58	0.59	0.58	0.48	0.56								
				$\mathcal{A}^f_2$	0.10	0.09	0.09	0.08	0.06	0.03	0.08								
17i	3	GRY LE	0.53	SHGC	0.54	0.51	0.49	0.44	0.33	0.17	0.46	0.50	0.50	0.44	0.48	0.47	0.48	0.42	0.47
				T	0.43	0.40	0.38	0.33	0.24	0.11	0.35								
				R^f	0.11	0.11	0.13	0.17	0.27	0.48	0.16								
				R^b	0.14	0.15	0.17	0.22	0.35	0.60	0.21								
				$\mathcal{A}^f_1$	0.36	0.39	0.40	0.42	0.42	0.38	0.39								
				$\mathcal{A}^f_2$	0.10	0.10	0.10	0.09	0.07	0.04	0.09								

Table 10 Visible Transmittance (T_v), Solar Heat Gain Coefficient (SHGC), Solar Transmittance (T), Front Reflectance (R^f), Back Reflectance (R^b), and Layer Absorptance ($\mathcal{A}^f_n$) for Glazing and Window Systems (*Continued*)

Glazing System					Center-of-Glazing Properties: Incidence Angles							Total Window SHGC at Normal Incidence				Total Window T_v at Normal Incidence			
												Aluminum		Other Frames		Aluminum		Other Frames	
ID	Glass Thick., mm		Center Glazing T_v		Normal 0.00	40.00	50.00	60.00	70.00	80.00	Hemis., Diffuse	Operable	Fixed	Operable	Fixed	Operable	Fixed	Operable	Fixed
17j	6	GRY LE	0.37	SHGC	0.39	0.37	0.35	0.31	0.24	0.13	0.33	0.36	0.36	0.32	0.35	0.33	0.33	0.30	0.33
				T	0.27	0.25	0.23	0.20	0.14	0.06	0.21								
				R^f	0.09	0.09	0.11	0.14	0.23	0.44	0.14								
				R^b	0.13	0.14	0.16	0.22	0.34	0.58	0.20								
				$\mathcal{A}^f_1$	0.55	0.58	0.59	0.59	0.58	0.48	0.56								
				$\mathcal{A}^f_2$	0.09	0.09	0.08	0.07	0.06	0.03	0.08								
17k	6	BLUGRN LE	0.62	SHGC	0.45	0.42	0.40	0.35	0.27	0.14	0.37	0.42	0.42	0.37	0.40	0.55	0.56	0.50	0.55
				T	0.32	0.29	0.27	0.23	0.17	0.07	0.26								
				R^f	0.09	0.09	0.10	0.14	0.23	0.44	0.13								
				R^b	0.13	0.14	0.16	0.21	0.34	0.58	0.20								
				$\mathcal{A}^f_1$	0.48	0.51	0.53	0.54	0.54	0.45	0.51								
				$\mathcal{A}^f_2$	0.11	0.10	0.10	0.09	0.07	0.03	0.09								
17l	6	HI-P GRN LE	0.55	0.241	0.34	0.31	0.30	0.26	0.20	0.11	0.28	0.32	0.32	0.28	0.30	0.49	0.50	0.44	0.48
				T	0.22	0.19	0.18	0.15	0.10	0.04	0.17								
				R^f	0.07	0.07	0.08	0.11	0.20	0.41	0.11								
				R^b	0.13	0.14	0.16	0.21	0.33	0.58	0.20								
				$\mathcal{A}^f_1$	0.64	0.67	0.68	0.68	0.66	0.53	0.65								
				$\mathcal{A}^f_2$	0.08	0.07	0.06	0.06	0.04	0.02	0.06								
Low-e Double Glazing, e = 0.1 on surface 2																			
21a	3	LE CLR	0.76	SHGC	0.65	0.64	0.62	0.56	0.43	0.23	0.57	0.59	0.60	0.53	0.58	0.68	0.68	0.61	0.67
				T	0.59	0.56	0.54	0.48	0.36	0.18	0.50								
				R^f	0.15	0.16	0.18	0.24	0.37	0.61	0.22								
				R^b	0.17	0.18	0.20	0.26	0.38	0.61	0.24								
				$\mathcal{A}^f_1$	0.20	0.21	0.21	0.21	0.20	0.16	0.20								
				$\mathcal{A}^f_2$	0.07	0.07	0.08	0.08	0.07	0.05	0.07								
21b	6	LE CLR	0.72	SHGC	0.60	0.59	0.57	0.51	0.40	0.21	0.53	0.55	0.55	0.49	0.53	0.64	0.65	0.58	0.63
				T	0.51	0.48	0.46	0.41	0.30	0.14	0.43								
				R^f	0.14	0.15	0.17	0.22	0.35	0.59	0.21								
				R^b	0.15	0.16	0.18	0.23	0.35	0.57	0.22								
				$\mathcal{A}^f_1$	0.26	0.26	0.26	0.26	0.25	0.19	0.25								
				$\mathcal{A}^f_2$	0.10	0.11	0.11	0.11	0.10	0.07	0.10								
Low-e Double Glazing, e = 0.1 on surface 3																			
21c	3	CLR LE	0.75	SHGC	0.60	0.58	0.56	0.51	0.40	0.22	0.52	0.55	0.55	0.49	0.53	0.67	0.68	0.60	0.66
				T	0.48	0.45	0.43	0.37	0.27	0.13	0.40								
				R^f	0.26	0.27	0.28	0.32	0.42	0.62	0.31								
				R^b	0.24	0.24	0.26	0.29	0.38	0.58	0.28								
				$\mathcal{A}^f_1$	0.12	0.13	0.14	0.14	0.15	0.15	0.13								
				$\mathcal{A}^f_2$	0.14	0.15	0.15	0.16	0.16	0.10	0.15								
21d	6	CLR LE	0.72	SHGC	0.56	0.55	0.52	0.48	0.38	0.20	0.49	0.51	0.52	0.46	0.50	0.64	0.65	0.58	0.63
				T	0.42	0.40	0.37	0.32	0.24	0.11	0.35								
				R^f	0.24	0.24	0.25	0.29	0.38	0.58	0.28								
				R^b	0.20	0.20	0.22	0.26	0.34	0.55	0.25								
				$\mathcal{A}^f_1$	0.19	0.20	0.21	0.22	0.23	0.22	0.21								
				$\mathcal{A}^f_2$	0.16	0.17	0.17	0.17	0.16	0.10	0.16								
21e	3	BRZ LE	0.57	SHGC	0.48	0.46	0.44	0.40	0.31	0.17	0.42	0.44	0.44	0.39	0.43	0.51	0.51	0.46	0.50
				T	0.37	0.34	0.32	0.27	0.20	0.08	0.30								
				R^f	0.18	0.17	0.19	0.22	0.30	0.50	0.21								
				R^b	0.23	0.23	0.25	0.29	0.37	0.57	0.28								
				$\mathcal{A}^f_1$	0.34	0.37	0.38	0.39	0.39	0.35	0.37								
				$\mathcal{A}^f_2$	0.11	0.12	0.12	0.12	0.11	0.07	0.11								
21f	6	BRZ LE	0.45	SHGC	0.39	0.37	0.35	0.31	0.24	0.13	0.33	0.36	0.36	0.32	0.35	0.40	0.41	0.36	0.40
				T	0.27	0.24	0.22	0.19	0.13	0.05	0.21								
				R^f	0.12	0.12	0.13	0.16	0.24	0.44	0.16								
				R^b	0.19	0.20	0.22	0.25	0.34	0.55	0.24								
				$\mathcal{A}^f_1$	0.51	0.54	0.55	0.56	0.55	0.46	0.53								
				$\mathcal{A}^f_2$	0.10	0.10	0.10	0.10	0.09	0.05	0.10								

Table 10 Visible Transmittance (T_v), Solar Heat Gain Coefficient (SHGC), Solar Transmittance (T), Front Reflectance (R^f), Back Reflectance (R^b), and Layer Absorptance ($\mathcal{A}^f_n$) for Glazing and Window Systems (*Continued*)

	Glazing System				Center-of-Glazing Properties							Total Window SHGC at Normal Incidence				Total Window T_v at Normal Incidence			
					Incidence Angles							Aluminum		Other Frames		Aluminum		Other Frames	
ID	Glass Thick., mm		Center Glazing T_v		Normal 0.00	40.00	50.00	60.00	70.00	80.00	Hemis., Diffuse	Operable	Fixed	Operable	Fixed	Operable	Fixed	Operable	Fixed
21g	3	GRN LE	0.68	SHGC	0.46	0.44	0.42	0.38	0.30	0.16	0.40	0.42	0.43	0.38	0.41	0.61	0.61	0.54	0.60
				T	0.36	0.32	0.30	0.26	0.18	0.08	0.28								
				R^f	0.17	0.16	0.17	0.20	0.29	0.48	0.20								
				R^b	0.23	0.23	0.25	0.29	0.37	0.57	0.27								
				$\mathcal{A}^f_1$	0.38	0.41	0.42	0.43	0.43	0.38	0.40								
				$\mathcal{A}^f_2$	0.10	0.11	0.11	0.11	0.10	0.06	0.10								
21h	6	GRN LE	0.61	SHGC	0.36	0.33	0.31	0.28	0.22	0.12	0.30	0.34	0.34	0.30	0.32	0.54	0.55	0.49	0.54
				T	0.24	0.21	0.19	0.16	0.11	0.05	0.18								
				R^f	0.11	0.10	0.11	0.14	0.22	0.43	0.14								
				R^b	0.19	0.20	0.22	0.25	0.34	0.55	0.24								
				$\mathcal{A}^f_1$	0.56	0.59	0.61	0.61	0.59	0.48	0.58								
				$\mathcal{A}^f_2$	0.09	0.09	0.09	0.08	0.08	0.04	0.08								
21i	3	GRY LE	0.52	SHGC	0.46	0.44	0.42	0.38	0.30	0.16	0.39	0.42	0.43	0.38	0.41	0.46	0.47	0.42	0.46
				T	0.35	0.32	0.30	0.25	0.18	0.08	0.28								
				R^f	0.16	0.16	0.17	0.20	0.28	0.48	0.20								
				R^b	0.23	0.23	0.25	0.29	0.37	0.57	0.27								
				$\mathcal{A}^f_1$	0.39	0.42	0.43	0.44	0.44	0.38	0.41								
				$\mathcal{A}^f_2$	0.10	0.11	0.11	0.11	0.10	0.06	0.10								
21j	6	GRY LE	0.37	SHGC	0.34	0.32	0.30	0.27	0.21	0.12	0.28	0.32	0.32	0.28	0.30	0.33	0.33	0.30	0.33
				T	0.23	0.20	0.18	0.15	0.11	0.04	0.17								
				R^f	0.11	0.11	0.12	0.15	0.23	0.44	0.15								
				R^b	0.20	0.20	0.22	0.25	0.34	0.55	0.24								
				$\mathcal{A}^f_1$	0.58	0.60	0.61	0.61	0.59	0.48	0.59								
				$\mathcal{A}^f_2$	0.08	0.08	0.08	0.08	0.07	0.04	0.08								
21k	6	BLUGRN LE	0.62	SHGC	0.39	0.37	0.34	0.31	0.24	0.13	0.33	0.36	0.36	0.32	0.35	0.55	0.56	0.50	0.55
				T	0.28	0.25	0.23	0.20	0.14	0.06	0.22								
				R^f	0.12	0.12	0.13	0.16	0.24	0.44	0.16								
				R^b	0.23	0.23	0.25	0.28	0.37	0.57	0.27								
				$\mathcal{A}^f_1$	0.51	0.54	0.56	0.56	0.55	0.46	0.53								
				$\mathcal{A}^f_2$	0.08	0.09	0.08	0.08	0.08	0.05	0.08								
21l	6	HI-P GRN W/LE CLR	0.57	SHGC	0.31	0.30	0.29	0.26	0.21	0.12	0.27	0.29	0.29	0.26	0.28	0.51	0.51	0.46	0.50
				T	0.22	0.21	0.19	0.17	0.12	0.06	0.18								
				R^f	0.07	0.07	0.09	0.13	0.22	0.46	0.12								
				R^b	0.23	0.23	0.24	0.28	0.37	0.57	0.27								
				$\mathcal{A}^f_1$	0.67	0.68	0.67	0.66	0.62	0.46	0.65								
				$\mathcal{A}^f_2$	0.04	0.05	0.05	0.05	0.04	0.03	0.04								
Low-e Double Glazing, e = 0.05 on surface 2																			
25a	3	LE CLR	0.72	SHGC	0.41	0.40	0.38	0.34	0.27	0.14	0.36	0.38	0.38	0.34	0.36	0.64	0.65	0.58	0.63
				T	0.37	0.35	0.33	0.29	0.22	0.11	0.31								
				R^f	0.35	0.36	0.37	0.40	0.47	0.64	0.39								
				R^b	0.39	0.39	0.40	0.43	0.50	0.66	0.42								
				$\mathcal{A}^f_1$	0.24	0.26	0.26	0.27	0.28	0.23	0.26								
				$\mathcal{A}^f_2$	0.04	0.04	0.04	0.04	0.03	0.03	0.04								
25b	6	LE CLR	0.70	SHGC	0.37	0.36	0.34	0.31	0.24	0.13	0.32	0.34	0.34	0.30	0.33	0.62	0.63	0.56	0.62
				T	0.30	0.28	0.27	0.23	0.17	0.08	0.25								
				R^f	0.30	0.30	0.32	0.35	0.42	0.60	0.34								
				R^b	0.35	0.35	0.35	0.38	0.44	0.60	0.37								
				$\mathcal{A}^f_1$	0.34	0.35	0.35	0.36	0.35	0.28	0.34								
				$\mathcal{A}^f_2$	0.06	0.07	0.07	0.06	0.06	0.04	0.06								
25c	6	BRZ W/LE CLR	0.42	SHGC	0.26	0.25	0.24	0.22	0.18	0.10	0.23	0.25	0.25	0.22	0.23	0.37	0.38	0.34	0.37
				T	0.18	0.17	0.16	0.14	0.10	0.05	0.15								
				R^f	0.15	0.16	0.17	0.21	0.29	0.51	0.20								
				R^b	0.34	0.34	0.35	0.37	0.44	0.60	0.37								
				$\mathcal{A}^f_1$	0.63	0.63	0.63	0.61	0.57	0.42	0.60								
				$\mathcal{A}^f_2$	0.04	0.04	0.04	0.04	0.03	0.03	0.04								

Table 10 Visible Transmittance (T_v), Solar Heat Gain Coefficient (SHGC), Solar Transmittance (T), Front Reflectance (R^f), Back Reflectance (R^b), and Layer Absorptance ($\mathcal{A}^f_n$) for Glazing and Window Systems (*Continued*)

	Glazing System				Center-of-Glazing Properties							Total Window SHGC at Normal Incidence				Total Window T_v at Normal Incidence			
					Incidence Angles							Aluminum		Other Frames		Aluminum		Other Frames	
ID	Glass Thick., mm		Center Glazing T_v		Normal 0.00	40.00	50.00	60.00	70.00	80.00	Hemis., Diffuse	Operable	Fixed	Operable	Fixed	Operable	Fixed	Operable	Fixed
25d	6	GRN W/LE CLR	0.60	SHGC	0.31	0.30	0.28	0.26	0.21	0.12	0.27	0.29	0.29	0.26	0.28	0.53	0.54	0.48	0.53
				T	0.22	0.21	0.20	0.17	0.13	0.06	0.18								
				R^f	0.10	0.10	0.12	0.16	0.25	0.48	0.15								
				R^b	0.35	0.34	0.35	0.37	0.44	0.60	0.37								
				$\mathcal{A}^f_1$	0.64	0.64	0.64	0.63	0.59	0.43	0.62								
				$\mathcal{A}^f_2$	0.05	0.05	0.05	0.05	0.04	0.03	0.05								
25e	6	GRY W/LE CLR	0.35	SHGC	0.24	0.23	0.22	0.20	0.16	0.09	0.21	0.23	0.23	0.20	0.21	0.31	0.32	0.28	0.31
				T	0.16	0.15	0.14	0.12	0.09	0.04	0.13								
				R^f	0.12	0.13	0.15	0.18	0.26	0.49	0.17								
				R^b	0.34	0.34	0.35	0.37	0.44	0.60	0.37								
				$\mathcal{A}^f_1$	0.69	0.69	0.68	0.67	0.62	0.45	0.66								
				$\mathcal{A}^f_2$	0.03	0.03	0.03	0.03	0.03	0.02	0.03								
25f	6	BLUE W/LE CLR	0.45	SHGC	0.27	0.26	0.25	0.23	0.18	0.11	0.24	0.26	0.25	0.22	0.24	0.40	0.41	0.36	0.40
				T	0.19	0.18	0.17	0.15	0.11	0.05	0.16								
				R^f	0.12	0.12	0.14	0.17	0.26	0.49	0.16								
				R^b	0.34	0.34	0.35	0.37	0.44	0.60	0.37								
				$\mathcal{A}^f_1$	0.66	0.66	0.65	0.64	0.60	0.44	0.63								
				$\mathcal{A}^f_2$	0.04	0.04	0.04	0.04	0.04	0.03	0.04								
25g	6	HI-P GRN W/LE CLR	0.53	SHGC	0.27	0.26	0.25	0.23	0.18	0.11	0.23	0.26	0.25	0.22	0.24	0.47	0.48	0.42	0.47
				T	0.18	0.17	0.16	0.14	0.10	0.05	0.15								
				R^f	0.07	0.07	0.09	0.13	0.22	0.46	0.12								
				R^b	0.35	0.34	0.35	0.38	0.44	0.60	0.37								
				$\mathcal{A}^f_1$	0.71	0.72	0.71	0.69	0.64	0.47	0.68								
				$\mathcal{A}^f_2$	0.04	0.04	0.04	0.04	0.03	0.02	0.04								
Triple Glazing																			
29a	3	CLR CLR CLR	0.74	SHGC	0.68	0.65	0.62	0.54	0.39	0.18	0.57	0.62	0.62	0.55	0.60	0.66	0.67	0.59	0.65
				T	0.60	0.57	0.53	0.45	0.31	0.12	0.49								
				R^f	0.17	0.18	0.21	0.28	0.42	0.65	0.25								
				R^b	0.17	0.18	0.21	0.28	0.42	0.65	0.25								
				$\mathcal{A}^f_1$	0.10	0.11	0.12	0.13	0.14	0.14	0.12								
				$\mathcal{A}^f_2$	0.08	0.08	0.09	0.09	0.08	0.07	0.08								
				$\mathcal{A}^f_3$	0.06	0.06	0.06	0.06	0.05	0.03	0.06								
29b	6	CLR CLR CLR	0.70	SHGC	0.61	0.58	0.55	0.48	0.35	0.16	0.51	0.56	0.56	0.50	0.54	0.62	0.63	0.56	0.62
				T	0.49	0.45	0.42	0.35	0.24	0.09	0.39								
				R^f	0.14	0.15	0.18	0.24	0.37	0.59	0.22								
				R^b	0.14	0.15	0.18	0.24	0.37	0.59	0.22								
				$\mathcal{A}^f_1$	0.17	0.19	0.20	0.21	0.22	0.21	0.19								
				$\mathcal{A}^f_2$	0.12	0.13	0.13	0.13	0.12	0.08	0.12								
				$\mathcal{A}^f_3$	0.08	0.08	0.08	0.08	0.06	0.03	0.08								
29c	6	HI-P GRN CLR CLR	0.53	SHGC	0.32	0.29	0.27	0.24	0.18	0.10	0.26	0.30	0.30	0.26	0.29	0.47	0.48	0.42	0.47
				T	0.20	0.17	0.15	0.12	0.07	0.02	0.15								
				R^f	0.06	0.07	0.08	0.11	0.20	0.41	0.11								
				R^b	0.13	0.14	0.16	0.22	0.35	0.57	0.20								
				$\mathcal{A}^f_1$	0.64	0.67	0.68	0.68	0.66	0.53	0.65								
				$\mathcal{A}^f_2$	0.06	0.06	0.05	0.05	0.05	0.03	0.05								
				$\mathcal{A}^f_3$	0.04	0.04	0.04	0.03	0.02	0.01	0.04								
Triple Glazing, e = 0.2 on surface 2																			
32a	3	LE CLR CLR	0.68	SHGC	0.60	0.58	0.55	0.48	0.35	0.17	0.51	0.55	0.55	0.49	0.53	0.61	0.61	0.54	0.60
				T	0.50	0.47	0.44	0.38	0.26	0.10	0.41								
				R^f	0.17	0.19	0.21	0.27	0.41	0.64	0.25								
				R^b	0.19	0.20	0.22	0.29	0.42	0.63	0.26								
				$\mathcal{A}^f_1$	0.20	0.20	0.20	0.21	0.21	0.17	0.20								
				$\mathcal{A}^f_2$	0.08	0.08	0.08	0.09	0.08	0.07	0.08								
				$\mathcal{A}^f_3$	0.06	0.06	0.06	0.06	0.05	0.03	0.06								

Table 10 Visible Transmittance (T_v), Solar Heat Gain Coefficient (SHGC), Solar Transmittance (T), Front Reflectance (R^f), Back Reflectance (R^b), and Layer Absorptance ($\mathcal{A}^f_n$) for Glazing and Window Systems (*Continued*)

	Glazing System				Center-of-Glazing Properties: Incidence Angles							Total Window SHGC at Normal Incidence: Aluminum		Other Frames		Total Window T_v at Normal Incidence: Aluminum		Other Frames	
ID	Glass Thick., mm		Center Glazing T_v		Normal 0.00	40.00	50.00	60.00	70.00	80.00	Hemis., Diffuse	Operable	Fixed	Operable	Fixed	Operable	Fixed	Operable	Fixed
32b	6	LE CLR CLR	0.64	SHGC	0.53	0.50	0.47	0.41	0.29	0.14	0.44	0.49	0.49	0.43	0.47	0.57	0.58	0.51	0.56
				T	0.39	0.36	0.33	0.27	0.17	0.06	0.30								
				R^f	0.14	0.15	0.17	0.21	0.31	0.53	0.20								
				R^b	0.16	0.16	0.19	0.24	0.36	0.57	0.22								
				$\mathcal{A}^f_1$	0.28	0.31	0.31	0.34	0.37	0.31	0.31								
				$\mathcal{A}^f_2$	0.11	0.11	0.11	0.11	0.10	0.08	0.11								
				$\mathcal{A}^f_3$	0.08	0.08	0.08	0.07	0.05	0.03	0.07								
Triple Glazing, e = 0.2 on surface 5																			
32c	3	CLR CLR LE	0.68	SHGC	0.62	0.60	0.57	0.49	0.36	0.16	0.52	0.57	0.57	0.50	0.55	0.61	0.61	0.54	0.60
				T	0.50	0.47	0.44	0.38	0.26	0.10	0.41								
				R^f	0.19	0.20	0.22	0.29	0.42	0.63	0.26								
				R^b	0.18	0.19	0.21	0.27	0.41	0.64	0.25								
				$\mathcal{A}^f_1$	0.11	0.12	0.13	0.14	0.15	0.15	0.13								
				$\mathcal{A}^f_2$	0.09	0.10	0.10	0.10	0.10	0.08	0.10								
				$\mathcal{A}^f_3$	0.11	0.11	0.11	0.10	0.08	0.04	0.10								
32d	6	CLR CLR LE	0.64	SHGC	0.56	0.53	0.50	0.44	0.32	0.15	0.47	0.51	0.52	0.46	0.50	0.57	0.58	0.1	0.56
				T	0.39	0.36	0.33	0.27	0.17	0.06	0.30								
				R^f	0.16	0.16	0.19	0.24	0.36	0.57	0.22								
				R^b	0.14	0.15	0.17	0.21	0.31	0.53	0.20								
				$\mathcal{A}^f_1$	0.17	0.19	0.20	0.21	0.22	0.22	0.19								
				$\mathcal{A}^f_2$	0.13	0.14	0.14	0.14	0.13	0.10	0.13								
				$\mathcal{A}^f_3$	0.15	0.16	0.15	0.14	0.12	0.05	0.14								
Triple Glazing, e = 0.1 on surface 2 and 5																			
40a	3	LE CLR LE	0.62	SHGC	0.41	0.39	0.37	0.32	0.24	0.12	0.34	0.38	0.38	0.34	0.36	0.55	0.56	0.50	0.55
				T	0.29	0.26	0.24	0.20	0.13	0.05	0.23								
				R^f	0.30	0.30	0.31	0.34	0.41	0.59	0.33								
				R^b	0.30	0.30	0.31	0.34	0.41	0.59	0.33								
				$\mathcal{A}^f_1$	0.25	0.27	0.28	0.30	0.32	0.27	0.28								
				$\mathcal{A}^f_2$	0.07	0.08	0.08	0.08	0.07	0.06	0.07								
				$\mathcal{A}^f_3$	0.08	0.09	0.09	0.09	0.07	0.04	0.08								
40b	6	LE CLR LE	0.59	SHGC	0.36	0.34	0.32	0.28	0.21	0.10	0.30	0.34	0.34	0.30	0.32	0.53	0.53	0.47	0.52
				T	0.24	0.21	0.19	0.16	0.10	0.03	0.18								
				R^f	0.34	0.34	0.35	0.38	0.44	0.61	0.37								
				R^b	0.23	0.23	0.25	0.28	0.36	0.56	0.27								
				$\mathcal{A}^f_1$	0.24	0.25	0.26	0.28	0.30	0.25	0.26								
				$\mathcal{A}^f_2$	0.10	0.11	0.11	0.11	0.10	0.07	0.10								
				$\mathcal{A}^f_3$	0.09	0.09	0.09	0.08	0.07	0.03	0.08								
Triple Glazing, e = 0.05 on surface 2 and 4																			
49	3	LE LE CLR	0.58	SHGC	0.27	0.25	0.24	0.21	0.16	0.08	0.23	0.26	0.25	0.22	0.25	0.52	0.52	0.46	0.51
				T	0.18	0.17	0.16	0.13	0.08	0.03	0.14								
				R^f	0.41	0.41	0.42	0.44	0.50	0.65	0.44								
				R^b	0.46	0.45	0.46	0.48	0.53	0.68	0.47								
				$\mathcal{A}^f_1$	0.27	0.28	0.28	0.29	0.30	0.24	0.28								
				$\mathcal{A}^f_2$	0.12	0.12	0.12	0.12	0.11	0.07	0.12								
				$\mathcal{A}^f_3$	0.02	0.02	0.02	0.02	0.01	0.01	0.02								
50	6	LE LE CLR	0.55	SHGC	0.26	0.25	0.23	0.21	0.16	0.08	0.22	0.25	0.25	0.21	0.24	0.49	0.0	0.44	0.48
				T	0.15	0.14	0.12	0.10	0.07	0.02	0.12								
				R^f	0.33	0.33	0.34	0.37	0.43	0.60	0.36								
				R^b	0.39	0.38	0.38	0.40	0.46	0.61	0.40								
				$\mathcal{A}^f_1$	0.34	0.36	0.36	0.37	0.36	0.28	0.35								
				$\mathcal{A}^f_2$	0.15	0.15	0.15	0.14	0.12	0.08	0.14								
				$\mathcal{A}^f_3$	0.03	0.03	0.03	0.03	0.02	0.01	0.03								

KEY:
CLR = clear, BRZ = bronze, GRN = green, GRY = gray, BLUGRN = blue-green, SS = stainless steel reflective coating, TI = titanium reflective coating
Reflective coating descriptors include percent visible transmittance as x%.
HI-P GRN = high-performance green tinted glass, LE = low-emissivity coating

T_v = visible transmittance, T = solar transmittance, SHGC = solar heat gain coefficient, and H. = hemispherical SHGC
ID #s refer to U-factors in Table 4, except for products 49 and 50.

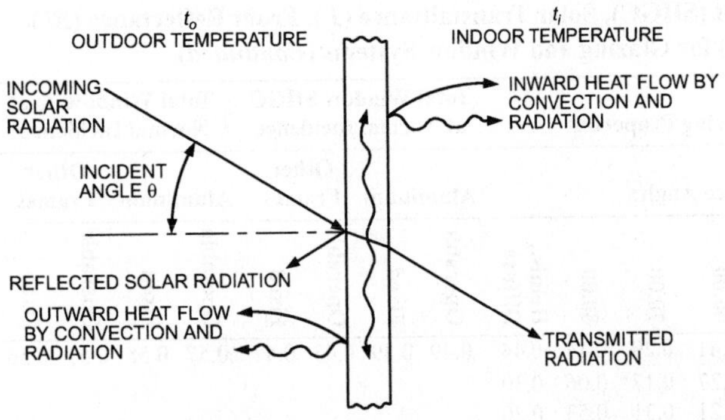

Fig. 14 Instantaneous Heat Balance for Sunlit Glazing Material

Plastic Materials for Glazing

Generally, factors outlined for glass apply also to glazing materials such as acrylic, polycarbonate, polystyrene, or other plastic panels. If solar transmittance, absorptance, and reflectance are known, an SHGC and a shading coefficient can be calculated in the same way as for glass. These properties can be obtained from the manufacturer or be determined by simple laboratory tests. The National Fenestration Rating Council has developed standards for testing the optical properties of glazing (NFRC 2004d, 2004e).

In selecting plastic panels for glazing, concerns include possible deterioration from the sun, expansion and contraction because of temperature extremes, and possible damage from abrasion.

CALCULATION OF SOLAR HEAT GAIN

To calculate solar energy fluxes, first calculate the incident angle θ from the local standard time and the longitude. The direct normal solar irradiance E_{DN}, diffuse sky irradiance E_d, ground-reflected radiation E_r, and total incident irradiance E_t can then be determined. Note that the latter two are assumed to be ideally diffuse radiation. Calculation methods for these parameters are described in Chapter 14.

Solar energy flow through a fenestration may be divided into two parts, opaque and glazing portions, q_{op} and q_s, respectively, as given in Equation (5). The glazing solar energy flux q_s can be split into that from incident beam radiation (q_b) and incident diffuse radiation (q_d), which includes both diffuse sky radiation and radiation scattered (reflected) from the ground:

$$q_s = q_b + q_d \quad (27)$$

The net heat balance that would occur for a sunlit glazing if there were no diffuse radiation is shown in Figure 14. This net heat balance does not include any of the heat flows contained in Q_{th} in Equation (1) (i.e., those resulting from inside/outside temperature differences). The heat balance is pictured as superimposed on the thermal effect. This superposition picture should not be carried too far, however, because the heat flows indicated in Figure 14 as resulting from convection and radiation depend in part on processes that are nonlinear with respect to temperature, so that in reality the two effects cannot be separated. To calculate them, the actual glazing (and other) temperatures are needed, not simply the incremental temperature rise caused by sunlight.

Figure 14 shows that the glazing solar energy flow from beam radiation consists of two parts:

$$q_b = q_{bt} + q_{ba} \quad (28)$$

where

q_{bt} = glazing solar energy flux caused by transmitted incident beam radiation

q_{ba} = glazing solar energy flux caused by inward heat flow of absorbed beam radiation

Table 11 Solar Heat Gain Coefficients for Domed Horizontal Skylights

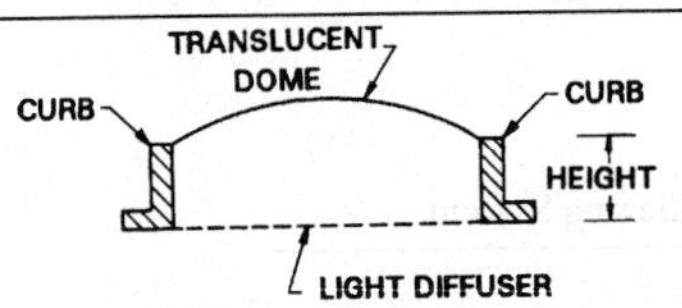

Dome	Light Diffuser (Translucent)	Curb Height, mm	Curb Width-to-Height Ratio	Solar Heat Gain Coefficient	Visible Transmittance
Clear	Yes	0	∞	0.53	0.56
τ = 0.86	τ = 0.58	225	5	0.50	0.58
		450	2.5	0.44	0.59
Clear		0	∞	0.86	0.91
τ = 0.86	None	225	5	0.77	0.91
		450	2.5	0.70	0.91
Translucent		0	∞	0.50	0.46
τ = 0.52	None	450	2.5	0.40	0.32
Translucent		0	∞	0.30	0.25
τ = 0.27	None	225	5	0.26	0.21
		450	2.5	0.24	0.18

Sources: Laouadi et al. (2003), Schutrum and Ozisik (1961).

The glazing solar energy flux caused by incident beam radiation is calculated from

$$q_b = E_{DN} \cos\theta \, \mathrm{SHGC}(\theta) \quad (29)$$

where the beam solar heat gain coefficient is given by Equation (17) or (18). If, instead, the solar radiant and heat fluxes are needed separately, calculate the glazing transmitted solar flux (solar radiation traveling in the incident direction) from

$$q_{bt} = E_{DN} \cos\theta \, T(\theta) \quad (30)$$

and the inward-flowing absorbed solar flux (heat) from

$$q_{ba} = E_{DN} \cos\theta \sum_{k=1}^{L} N_k \mathcal{A}_k^f(\theta) \quad (31)$$

Values of $T(\theta)$ and $\mathcal{A}^f(\theta)$ in these equations can be found in Table 10, and determination of N_k is discussed in the section on Calculation of Solar Heat Gain Coefficient.

For diffuse radiation,

$$q_d = q_{dt} + q_{da} \quad (32)$$

where

q_{dt} = glazing solar energy flux caused by transmitted incident diffuse radiation

q_{da} = glazing solar energy flux caused by inward heat flow of absorbed diffuse radiation

Glazing solar energy flux caused by diffuse incident radiation is calculated from

$$q_d = (E_d + E_r)\langle \mathrm{SHGC} \rangle_D \quad (33)$$

where the hemispherically averaged solar heat gain coefficient is calculated from Equation (20). Solar radiant and heat fluxes can be separately calculated from

$$q_{dt} = (E_d + E_r)\langle T \rangle_D \quad (34)$$

which is diffusely distributed solar radiation (note that effects of finite glazing size and thickness are neglected), and

Table 12 Shading Coefficients and U-Factors for Standard Hollow Glass Block Wall Panels

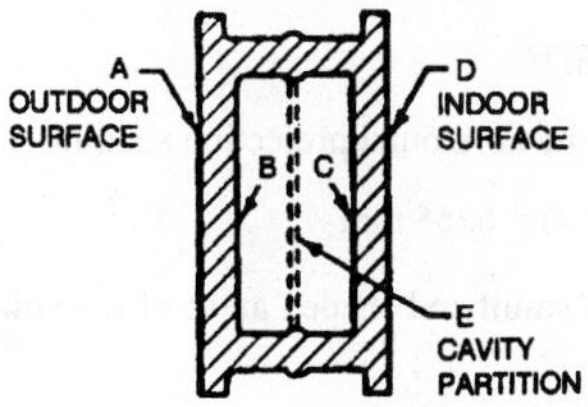

Type of Glass Block[a]	Description of Glass Block	Solar Heat Gain Coefficient In Sun	Solar Heat Gain Coefficient In Shade[b]	U-Factor,[c] W/(m²·K)
Type I	Glass colorless or aqua A, D: Smooth B, C: Smooth or wide ribs, or flutes horizontal or vertical, or shallow configuration E: None	0.57	0.35	2.9
Type IA	Same as type I except ceramic enamel on A	0.23	0.17	2.9
Type II	Same as type I except glass fiber screen partition E	0.38	0.30	2.7
Type III	Glass colorless or aqua A, D: Narrow vertical ribs or flutes. B, C: Horizontal light-diffusing prisms, or horizontal light-directing prisms E: Glass fiber screen	0.29	0.23	2.7
Type IIIA	Same as type III except E: Glass fiber screen with green ceramic spray coating or glass fiber screen and gray glass or glass fiber screen with light-selecting prisms	0.22	0.16	2.7
Type IV	Same as type I except reflective oxide coating on A	0.14	0.10	2.9

[a]All values are for 200 by 200 by 100 mm block, set in light-colored mortar. For 300 by 300 by 100 mm block, increase coefficients by 15%, and for 150 by 150 by 100 mm block, reduce coefficients by 15%.

[b]For NE, E, and SE panels in shade, add 50% to values listed for panels in shade.

[c]Values shown are identical for all size block.

$$q_{da} = (E_d + E_r)\sum_{k=1}^{L} N_k \langle \mathcal{A}_k^f \rangle_D \tag{35}$$

Opaque Fenestration Elements

The opaque portion solar energy flux is calculated from

$$q_{op} = (E_{DN}\cos\theta + E_d + E_r)\text{SHGC}_{op} \tag{36}$$

where SHGC_{op} is obtained from Equation (23).

Example 6. Calculate the solar energy flux through the glazing system ID 25a given $\theta = 60°$, $E_{DN} = 600$ W/m², and $E_d = 150$ W/m².

Solution: The solar heat gain coefficients are SHGC(60°) = 0.34, and $\text{SHGC}_D = 0.36$ (see Table 10, glazing ID 25a, 5th and 8th columns).

$$q_s = q_t + q_a$$

$$= E_{DN}\cos(60)\text{SHGC}(60) + (E_d + E_r)\langle\text{SHGC}\rangle_D$$

$$= (600.0)\cos(60)(0.34) + (150)(0.36) = 156 \text{ W/m}^2$$

SHADING AND FENESTRATION ATTACHMENTS

SHADING

The most effective way to reduce the solar load on fenestration is to intercept direct radiation from the sun before it reaches the glass. Fenestration products fully shaded from the outside reduce solar heat gain by as much as 80%. Fenestration can be shaded by roof overhangs, vertical and horizontal architectural projections, awnings, heavily proportioned outdoor louvers, or a variety of vegetative shades, including trees, hedges, and trellis vines. In all outdoor shading structures, it is necessary to consider the structures' geometry relative to changing sun position to determine the times and quantities of direct sunlight penetration. A detailed discussion of the effectiveness of outside shading is given in Ewing and Yellott (1976).

The general effect of shading is to attenuate solar radiation. Some of the beam radiation may reach the fenestration unaffected by the shade, and this is accounted for by the unshaded fraction F_u. Assuming that the shade does not transmit or diffuse solar radiation, the solar heat gain of the fenestration can be approximated by modifying Equation (27):

$$q_s = F_u q_b + q_{d,shaded} \tag{37}$$

Here, the term $q_{d,shaded}$ indicates that a new SHGC must be determined to account for the fact that the shading device restricts the amount of sky-diffuse radiation on the fenestration system. More complex models are required for situations where the shade is partially transmitting and diffusing in nature.

Roof Overhangs: Horizontal and Vertical Projections

In the northern hemisphere, horizontal projections can considerably reduce solar heat gain on south, southeast, and southwest exposures during late spring, summer, and early fall. On east and west exposures during the entire year, and on south exposures in winter, the solar altitude is generally so low that, to be effective, horizontal projections must be excessively long.

The ability of horizontal projections to intercept the direct component of solar radiation depends on their geometry and the profile or shadow-line angle Ω (Figure 15), defined as the angular difference between a horizontal plane and a plane tilted about a horizontal axis in the plane of the fenestration until it includes the sun. The vertical profile angle Ω can be calculated by

$$\tan\Omega = \tan\beta/\cos\gamma \tag{38}$$

where

β = solar altitude angle
γ = solar azimuth

The shadow width S_W and shadow height S_H (Figure 16) produced by the vertical and horizontal projections (P_V and P_H), respectively, can be calculated using the surface solar azimuth γ and the vertical profile angle Ω determined by Equation (38).

$$S_W = P_V|\tan\gamma| \tag{39}$$

$$S_H = P_H\tan\Omega \tag{40}$$

When the surface solar azimuth γ is greater than 90° and less than 270°, the fenestration product is completely in the shade; thus, $S_W = W + R_w$ and sunlit area $A_{SL} = 0$.

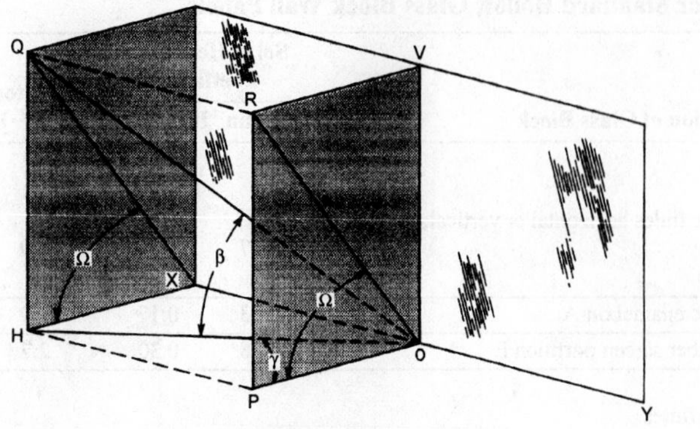

Fig. 15 Profile Angle for South-Facing Horizontal Projections

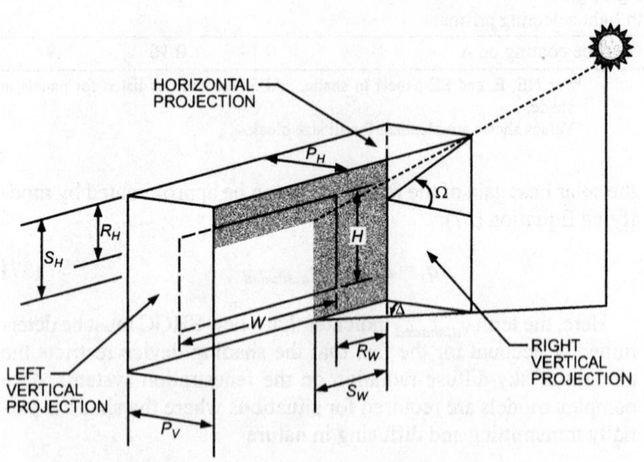

Fig. 16 Vertical and Horizontal Projections and Related Profile Angles for Vertical Surface Containing Fenestration

The sunlit (A_{SL}) and shaded (A_{SH}) areas of the fenestration product are variable during the day and can be calculated for each moment using the following relations:

$$A_{SL} = [W - (S_W - R_W)][H - (S_H - R_H)] \tag{41}$$

$$A_{SH} = A - A_{SL} \tag{42}$$

where A is total fenestration product area.

For software-based or multiple calculations, McCluney (1990) describes an algorithm that can be used to calculate the unshaded fraction of a window equipped with overhangs, awnings, or side fins.

Example 7. A window facing 30° south of west (wall azimuth y = +60°) in a building at 33.65°N latitude, and 84.42°W longitude is 1841.5 mm wide and 6286.5 mm high. The depth of the horizontal projection is 2438 mm. At 3:00 PM on July 21, it is calculated that the hour angle $H = 15 \times (13.27 - 12) = 19.03°$; and the declination $\delta = 20.60°$.

The solar altitude β is calculated to be:

$$\sin\beta = \cos(33.65)\cos(20.60)\cos(19.03) + \sin(33.65)\sin(20.60)$$

$$\beta = 68.7°$$

The solar azimuth ϕ is

$$\cos\phi = [\sin(68.68)\sin(33.65) - \sin(20.60)]/[\cos(68.68)\cos(33.65)]$$

$$\phi = 57.1°$$

Thus, the wall solar azimuth is $\gamma = 57.1 - 60 = -2.9°$.

(a) Find the sunlit and shaded area of the window.
(b) Find the depth of the projections necessary to fully shade the window.

Solution:
(a) Using Equation (39), the width of the vertical projection shadow is

$$S_W = 0\,|\tan(-2.9)| = 0 \text{ mm}$$

Using Equation (38), the profile angle for the horizontal projection is

$$\tan\Omega = \tan(68.7)/\cos(2.9)$$

$$\Omega = 68.7°$$

Using Equation (40), the height of the horizontal projection shadow is

$$S_H = 2438\tan(68.7) = 6255 \text{ mm}$$

Using Equations (41) and (42), the sunlit and shaded areas of the window are now

$$A_{SL} = [1841.5 - (0 - 0)][6286.5 - (6255 - 0)]/10^6 = 0.058 \text{ m}^2$$

$$A_{SH} = (1841.5 \times 6286.5)/10^6 - 0.058 = 11.519 \text{ m}^2$$

(b) The shadow length necessary to fully shade the given window $S_{H(fs)}$ and $S_{W(fs)}$ from the horizontal and vertical projection are given by (see Figure 16)

$$S_{H(fs)} = 6286.5 + 0 = 6286.5 \text{ mm}$$

$$S_{W(fs)} = 1841.5 + 0 = 1841.5 \text{ mm}$$

Thus, using Equations (39) and (40),

$$P_{H(fs)} = 6286.5\cot(68.7) = 2453.5 \text{ mm}$$

$$P_{W(fs)} = 1841.5|\cot(-2.9)| = 36\,351.7 \text{ mm}$$

For this example, because both horizontal and vertical projections do not need to fully shade the window, a horizontal projection of 2454 mm is satisfactory. Also, to accurately analyze the influence of external projections, an hour-by-hour calculation must be performed over the periods of the year for which shading is desired.

FENESTRATION ATTACHMENTS

Fenestration attachments generally consist of items that can be used as part of a system to provide solar and daylighting control, as well as privacy, aesthetics, and comfort for building occupants. Attachments also include other devices that, though not intended for solar control, affect the solar and visual performance of the fenestration system. Attachments to the indoor side of a window can include horizontal louvers (venetian blinds), vertical louvers, roller shades, insect screens, and drapery. Between glazings of multi-glazed windows, horizontal louvers and roller shades may be incorporated. On the outdoor side, insect screens can be added, as well as horizontal louvers in the plane of the window.

Fenestrations with shading devices have a degree of thermal and optical complexity far greater than that of unshaded fenestrations, and are referred to as **complex fenestration**.

In unshaded fenestration, individual glazing layers can only communicate thermally with adjacent layers. This is not the case for complex fenestration. A fenestration layer such as a screen or louvered blind is not sealed, and allows convective heat transfer between nonadjacent layers. Similarly, shading layers are inherently diathermanous (i.e., they transmit both long- and short-wave radiation). Radiative heat transfer, therefore, can also occur between nonadjacent layers. For example, for a window with indoor venetian blinds, heat transfer occurs between the indoor glass and the blind, the indoor glass and the room, and between the blind and the room. Therefore, methods described previously for determining the U-factor and inward-flowing fractions of fenestration systems cannot be applied to complex fenestration (Collins and Wright 2006; Wright 2008).

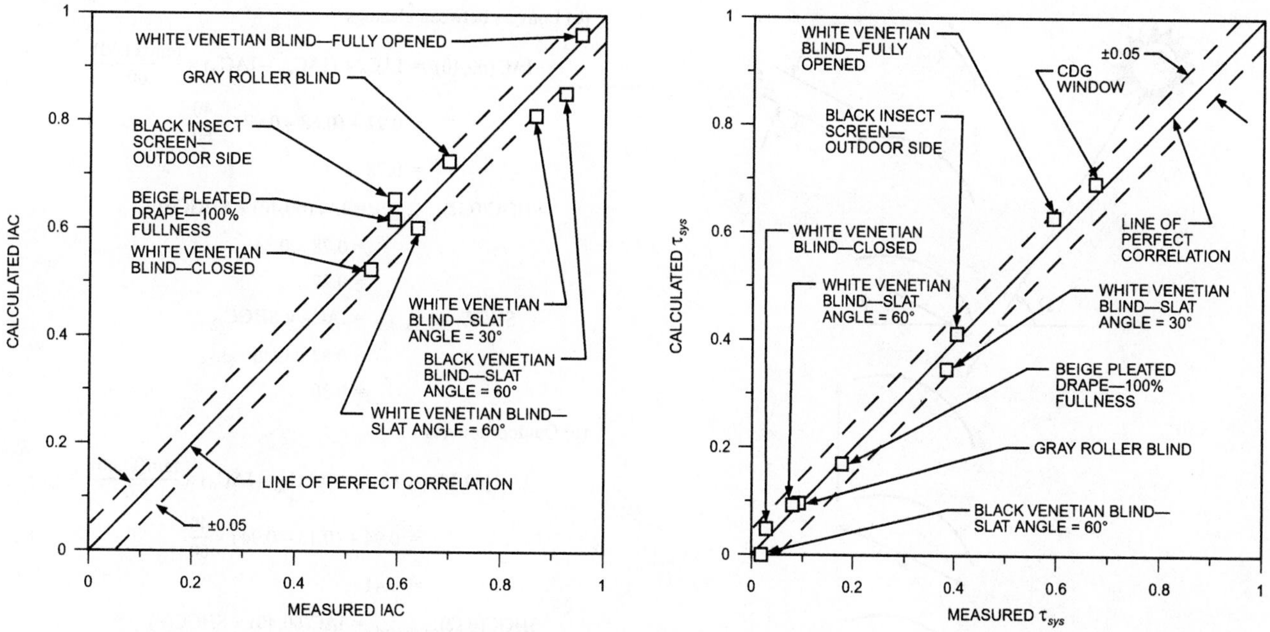

Fig. 17 Comparison of IAC and Solar Transmission Values from ASHWAT Model Versus Measurements
(Normal incidence; various shading layers attached to conventional double-glazed window)
(Wright et al. 2009)

Also, complex fenestration can have a **nonspecular optical element.** This is an element for which light (or short-wave infrared radiation) incident on the element from a single spatial direction does not emerge traveling in a single transmitted direction and/or a single reflected direction. Examples of nonspecular elements are shades, drapes, blinds, honeycombs, figured glass, ground glass, and other diffusers, lenses, prisms, and holographic glazings.

Two methods have been developed that allow the analysis of complex fenestration. The first method was proposed by Klems (1994a, 1994b, 2001), and relies on measurement of the bidirectional transmittance and reflectance of each glazing layer, and on calorimetrically determined values of inward flowing fraction, as input to a matrix calculation. It is a physically based and highly accurate approach that is also computationally and experimentally intensive. For details of this approach, see Chapter 31 of the 2005 *ASHRAE Handbook—Fundamentals*. The second method, developed through ASHRAE-sponsored research (Wright et al. 2008b), is an empirically based approach that uses readily available information about the system geometry and material properties, and is designed to fit into established window analysis methodology. The methodology has been shown to accurately predict complex fenestration performance from easily obtained data regarding shade geometry and material.

In contrast to these two methods, a simplified approach is presented in the following section for calculating the approximate SHGC for a selection of the more common shading elements and glazing systems.

Simplified Methodology

Considering only the approximate total heat flux through the fenestration, measurements made on a fenestration under one set of conditions can often be extrapolated to other fenestrations and conditions to give an adequate answer. In this case, the heat flux through the center-glass region is represented by

$$q = E_{DN}\cos(\theta)\text{SHGC}(\theta)\text{IAC}(\theta, \Omega) + (E_d + E_r)\langle\text{SHGC}\rangle_D\text{IAC}_D \tag{43}$$

where the solar heat gain coefficients in Equation (43) are for the center-glass region of an unshaded glazing, and may be calculated using methods described previously, or obtained from Table 10. The **indoor solar attenuation coefficient (IAC)** represents the fraction of heat flow that enters the room, some energy having been excluded by the shading. Depending on the type of shade, it may vary angularly and with shade type and geometry. The IAC is defined as

$$\text{IAC}(\theta, \Omega) = \frac{\text{SHGC}(\theta, \Omega)_{cg,\, shaded}}{\text{SHGC}(\theta)_{cg}} \qquad \text{IAC}_D = \frac{\langle\text{SHGC}\rangle_{D,\, cg,\, shaded}}{\langle\text{SHGC}\rangle_{D,\, cg}} \tag{44}$$

where Ω is either the horizontal or vertical profile angle.

IAC values presented in the following sections have been determined using the ASHWAT models (Wright et al. 2008b), which have been validated, with calorimetric results showing prediction of fenestration performance to within 5% (Figure 17).

Because shading layers generally have a small effect on the U-value of complex fenestration systems (Wright et al. 2008b), in this simplified analysis, the effects of shading devices on U-factor are ignored. System U-value is assumed to be similar to that of the same glazing (minus the shade) and can be determined from Table 4.

Note that this simplified approach applies only to the SHGC of the center-glass region of the fenestration product. Results from this analysis must be combined with the methods provided in the Solar Heat Gain Coefficient and Solar Heat Gain sections.

Slat-Type Sunshades

Slat-type sunshades consist of horizontal or vertically oriented louvers in located in the plane of the window. They can be installed on the outdoor and indoor side of the fenestration, or between glazings in a multilayered glazing system. The transmitted solar radiation may consist of straight-through, transmitted diffuse, and reflected through components.

The geometry considered is shown in Figure 18, with slat width *w*, slat crown *c*, slat spacing *s*, and slat angle ϕ. The ratios of *w/s* and

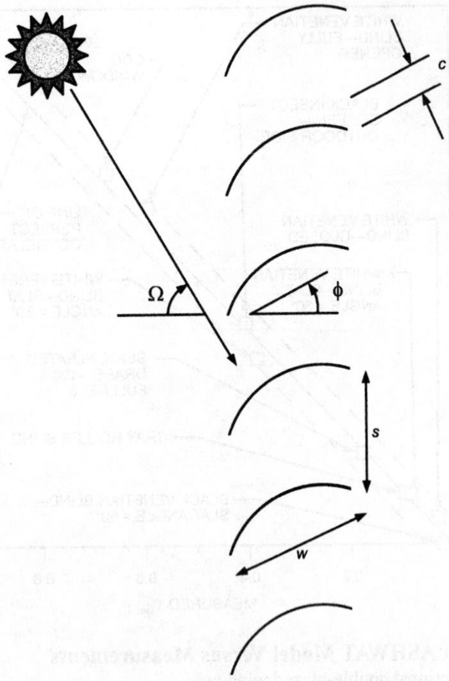

Fig. 18 Geometry of Slat-Type Sunshades

w/c are assumed constant at 1.2 and 16 respectively, which are representative of many commercially available products. The profile angle Ω can represent either the vertical profile Ω_V or the horizontal profile Ω_H. The vertical profile angle is used for horizontal louvered shades, and is calculated using Equation (38). The horizontal profile angle is used for vertical louvered shades and is equal to the wall solar azimuth γ.

Tables 13A to G presents IAC values at profile angles of 0 and 60° for various glazing and shade combinations. IAC varies with profile angle where the profile angle can be the vertical profile (for horizontal louvers) or horizontal profile (for vertical louvers). The variation of IAC with profile angle can be determined from

$$IAC(\theta,\Omega) = IAC_0 + IAC_x \times \min(1, 0.02 \times \Omega) \tag{45}$$

Collins et al. (2008), Huang et al. (2006), Kotey et al. (2009e), and Wright et al. (2008) contain more comprehensive discussions of models used to determine IACs of louvered sunshades.

Example 8. Calculate the SHGC of glazing system ID 25a if a horizontally louvered shade is added (a) on the indoor side, (b) between the glazings, and (c) on the outdoor side. The shade material has a reflectivity of 0.60 and the shades are installed in the open position (0°). θ = 60° and Ω_V = 40°. Also consider (d) vertical louvers located on the indoor side of the glazing with Ω_H = 40°.

Solution: Use Equations (44) and (45) and values from Table 13E. From Example 6, SHGC(60°) = 0.34, and $SHGC_D$ = 0.36.

(a) Indoor shade

$$IAC(60,40) = IAC_0 + (IAC_{60} - IAC_0) \times \frac{\min(\Omega,60)}{60}$$
$$= 0.99 + (0.87 - 0.99) \times \frac{40}{60}$$
$$= 0.91$$

$$SHGC(\theta,\Omega)_{cg,\,shaded} = IAC(60,40) \times SHGC(\theta)_{cg}$$
$$= 0.91 \times 0.34$$
$$= 0.31$$

$$SHGC_{D,\,cg,\,shaded} = IAC_D \times SHGC_{D,\,cg}$$
$$= 0.93 \times 0.36$$
$$= 0.33$$

(b) Louvers between glazings

$$IAC(60,40) = IAC_0 + (IAC_{60} - IAC_0) \times \frac{\min(\Omega,60)}{60}$$
$$= 0.97 + (0.68 - 0.97) \times \frac{40}{60}$$
$$= 0.78$$

$$SHGC(\theta,\Omega)_{cg,\,shaded} = IAC(60,40) \times SHGC(\theta)_{cg}$$
$$= 0.78 \times 0.34$$
$$= 0.27$$

$$SHGC_{D,\,cg,\,shaded} = IAC_D \times SHGC_{D,\,cg}$$
$$= 0.82 \times 0.36$$
$$= 0.30$$

(c) Outdoor louvers

$$IAC(60,40) = IAC_0 + (IAC_{60} - IAC_0) \times \frac{\min(\Omega,60)}{60}$$
$$= 0.94 + (0.15 - 0.94) \times \frac{40}{60}$$
$$= 0.41$$

$$SHGC(\theta,\Omega)_{cg,\,shaded} = IAC(60,40) \times SHGC(\theta)_{cg}$$
$$= 0.41 \times 0.34$$
$$= 0.14$$

$$SHGC_{D,\,cg,\,shaded} = IAC_D \times SHGC_{D,\,cg}$$
$$= 0.51 \times 0.36$$
$$= 0.18$$

(d) Vertical louvers

For the given conditions, results are the same as for part (a).

Drapery

Drapery fabrics can be classified in terms of their solar-optical properties as having specific values of fabric transmittance and reflectance. Fabric reflectance is the major factor in determining the ability of a fabric to reduce solar heat gain. Based on their appearance, draperies can also be classified by yarn color as dark, medium, and light and by weave as closed, semiopen, and open. The apparent color of a fabric is determined by the reflectance of the yarn itself. Drapery fabrics are classified into nine types, rated by openness and yarn reflectances (Figures 19 and 20).

The solar-optical properties of drapery fabrics can be determined accurately by laboratory tests (Kotey et al. 2009b; Yellott 1963), and manufacturers can usually supply solar transmittance and reflectance values for their products. In addition to these properties, the openness factor (ratio of the open area between the fibers to the total area of the fabric) is a useful property that can be measured exactly (Keyes 1967; Pennington and Moore 1967). Visual estimations of openness and yarn reflectance, interpreted through Figures 19 and 20, are valuable in judging the effectiveness of drapes for (1) protection from excessive radiant energy from either sunlight or sun-heated glass, (2) brightness control, (3) providing either outward view or privacy, and (4) sound control.

To understand drapery layer solar-optical properties, the **fullness** of the drapery is needed. As simplified in Figure 21, the pleating of the drape is assumed to be square, with pleat depth *w* and width *s*. For 100% fullness, the width of fabric used is twice the width of the fenestration. If the drapery is hung flat, like a fenestration product shade, the fullness is 0%.

Table 13G presents IAC and F_R values for typical glazing and shade combinations. For these types of shades, the IAC value is not strongly influenced by the incident angle of irradiation; therefore, a constant value of IAC can be used.

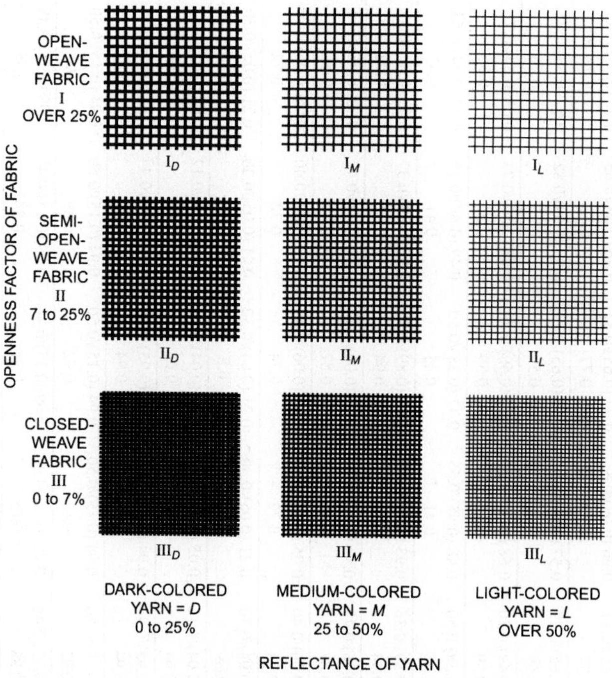

NOTE: Classes may be approximated by eye. With closed fabrics, no objects are visible through the material, but large light or dark areas may show. Semiopen fabrics do not allow details to be seen, and large objects are clearly defined. Open fabrics allow details to be seen, and the general view is relatively clear with no confusion of vision. The yarn color or shade of light or dark may be observed to determine whether the fabric is light, medium, or dark.

Fig. 19 Designation of Drapery Fabrics

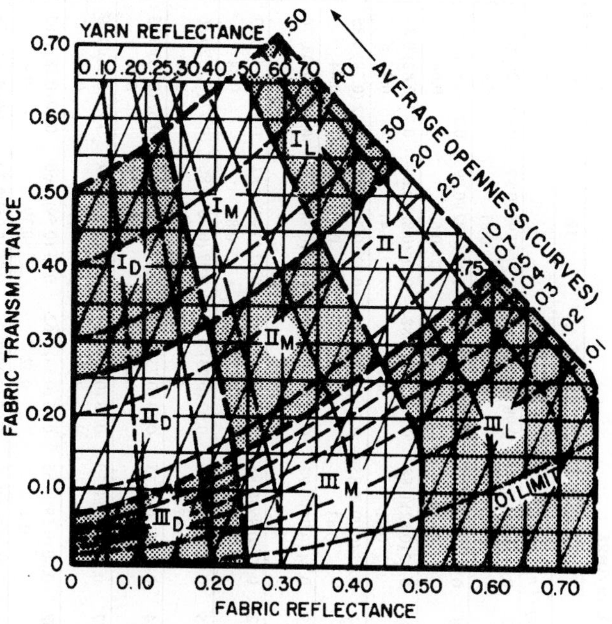

Fig. 20 Drapery Fabric Properties

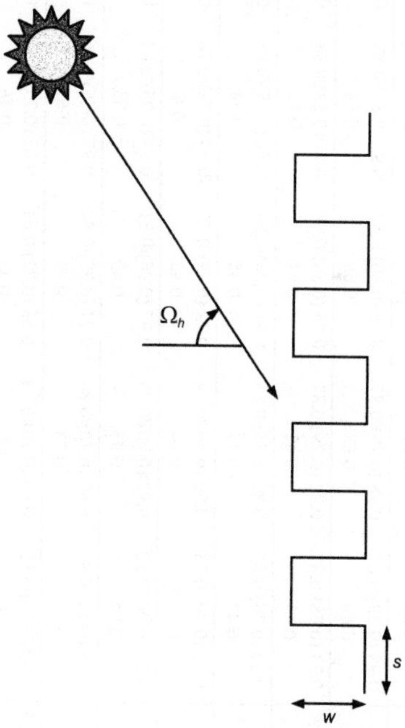

Fig. 21 Geometry of Drapery Fabrics

Kotey et al. (2009a, 2009b) and Wright et al. (2009) contain more comprehensive discussions of models used to determine IACs of draperies.

Example 9. Calculate the SHGC of glazing system ID 25a if a drapery is added on the indoor side. The fabric has an openness factor of 0.05 and a yarn reflectance of 0.60, and the drapery has 100% fullness.

Solution: In Figure 20, these lines intersect in the area of designator III_L. Fabric is closed and light in color, with probable fabric reflectance of 0.52 and fabric transmittance of 0.30.

From Table 13G, both IAC and $IAC_D = 0.68$.

$$SHGC(\theta,\Omega)_{cg,\,shaded} = IAC(60,40) \times SHGC(\theta)_{cg} = 0.68 \times 0.34 = 0.23$$

$$SHGC_{D,\,cg,\,shaded} = IAC_D \times SHGC_{D,\,cg} = 0.68 \times 0.36 = 0.25$$

Roller Shades and Insect Screens

In general, both roller shades and insect screens are equivalent to drapery of 0% fullness. Appropriately, much of the methodology applied to drapery fabrics applies for these devices as well.

Table 13G presents IAC for typical glazing and shade combinations. For these types of shades, the IAC value is not strongly influenced by the incident angle of irradiation; therefore, a constant value of IAC can be used.

For a more comprehensive discussion of models used to determine IACs, see Kotey et al. (2008, 2009c) for roller shades and Kotey et al. (2009d) for insect screens.

Example 10. Calculate the SHGC of glazing system ID 25a if a roller shade is added on the indoor side. The shade has an openness factor of 0.0 and a yarn reflectance of 0.65.

Solution: From Table 13G, both IAC and $IAC_D = 0.60$.

$$SHGC(\theta,\Omega)_{cg,\,shaded} = IAC(60,40) \times SHGC(\theta)_{cg} = 0.60 \times 0.34 = 0.20$$

$$SHGC_{D,\,cg,\,shaded} = IAC_D \times SHGC_{D,\,cg} = 0.60 \times 0.36 = 0.22$$

Table 13A IAC Values for Louvered Shades: Uncoated Single Glazings

		Glazing ID:	1a	1b	1c	1d	1e	1f	1g	1h	1i
Louver Location	Louver Reflection	ϕ	IAC_0 (IAC_{60})/IAC_{diff}, F_R								
Indoor Side	0.15	Worst[a]	0.98 (0.97)/0.86 0.92	0.98 (0.97)/0.86 0.91	0.98 (0.96)/0.86 0.88	0.97 (0.95)/0.87 0.82	0.98 (0.96)/0.87 0.87	0.97 (0.95)/0.87 0.82	0.98 (0.96)/0.87 0.87	0.97 (0.95)/0.87 0.81	0.97 (0.95)/0.87 0.83
		0°	0.98 (0.78)/0.87 0.69	0.98 (0.79)/0.87 0.68	0.98 (0.80)/0.88 0.66	0.97 (0.82)/0.88 0.64	0.98 (0.80)/0.88 0.66	0.97 (0.82)/0.89 0.63	0.98 (0.80)/0.88 0.66	0.97 (0.82)/0.89 0.63	0.97 (0.82)/0.88 0.64
		Excluded Beam[b]	0.73 (0.78)/0.87 0.43	0.74 (0.79)/0.87 0.43	0.75 (0.80)/0.88 0.42	0.77 (0.82)/0.88 0.41	0.76 (0.80)/0.88 0.42	0.77 (0.82)/0.88 0.41	0.76 (0.80)/0.88 0.42	0.78 (0.82)/0.88 0.41	0.77 (0.82)/0.88 0.41
		45°	0.80 (0.74)/0.83 0.47	0.80 (0.75)/0.83 0.46	0.81 (0.76)/0.84 0.45	0.82 (0.78)/0.85 0.44	0.81 (0.77)/0.84 0.45	0.83 (0.79)/0.85 0.43	0.81 (0.77)/0.84 0.45	0.83 (0.79)/0.85 0.43	0.82 (0.78)/0.85 0.44
		Closed	0.70 (0.70)/0.73 0.44	0.70 (0.70)/0.74 0.44	0.72 (0.72)/0.75 0.42	0.74 (0.74)/0.76 0.4	0.72 (0.72)/0.75 0.42	0.74 (0.74)/0.77 0.4	0.72 (0.72)/0.75 0.42	0.74 (0.74)/0.77 0.4	0.74 (0.74)/0.76 0.4
Indoor Side	0.50	Worst[a]	0.98 (0.96)/0.80 0.94	0.97 (0.96)/0.80 0.93	0.97 (0.96)/0.81 0.89	0.97 (0.95)/0.83 0.83	0.97 (0.96)/0.82 0.88	0.97 (0.95)/0.83 0.83	0.97 (0.96)/0.82 0.88	0.97 (0.95)/0.83 0.82	0.97 (0.95)/0.83 0.84
		0°	0.98 (0.70)/0.83 0.74	0.97 (0.70)/0.84 0.73	0.97 (0.72)/0.84 0.71	0.97 (0.75)/0.86 0.67	0.97 (0.73)/0.85 0.7	0.97 (0.76)/0.86 0.67	0.97 (0.73)/0.85 0.7	0.97 (0.76)/0.86 0.66	0.97 (0.75)/0.86 0.67
		Excluded Beam[b]	0.59 (0.70)/0.82 0.5	0.60 (0.70)/0.83 0.5	0.63 (0.72)/0.84 0.48	0.67 (0.75)/0.85 0.46	0.64 (0.73)/0.84 0.48	0.67 (0.76)/0.85 0.46	0.64 (0.73)/0.84 0.48	0.67 (0.76)/0.85 0.46	0.67 (0.75)/0.85 0.46
		45°	0.69 (0.58)/0.74 0.53	0.70 (0.59)/0.75 0.52	0.72 (0.62)/0.76 0.5	0.75 (0.66)/0.79 0.48	0.73 (0.63)/0.77 0.5	0.75 (0.67)/0.79 0.47	0.73 (0.63)/0.77 0.5	0.75 (0.67)/0.79 0.47	0.75 (0.66)/0.79 0.48
		Closed	0.51 (0.49)/0.58 0.46	0.52 (0.50)/0.58 0.45	0.55 (0.53)/0.61 0.43	0.60 (0.58)/0.65 0.4	0.56 (0.54)/0.62 0.42	0.60 (0.59)/0.65 0.4	0.56 (0.54)/0.62 0.42	0.61 (0.59)/0.66 0.39	0.60 (0.58)/0.65 0.4
Indoor Side	0.80	Worst[a]	0.97 (0.96)/0.73 0.95	0.97 (0.96)/0.74 0.94	0.97 (0.95)/0.76 0.9	0.96 (0.95)/0.78 0.85	0.97 (0.95)/0.76 0.89	0.96 (0.95)/0.79 0.84	0.97 (0.95)/0.76 0.89	0.96 (0.95)/0.79 0.83	0.96 (0.95)/0.78 0.85
		0°	0.97 (0.60)/0.78 0.82	0.97 (0.61)/0.79 0.81	0.97 (0.64)/0.80 0.78	0.96 (0.68)/0.82 0.73	0.97 (0.65)/0.81 0.77	0.96 (0.69)/0.83 0.72	0.97 (0.65)/0.81 0.77	0.96 (0.69)/0.83 0.72	0.96 (0.68)/0.82 0.73
		Excluded Beam[b]	0.45 (0.60)/0.77 0.66	0.47 (0.61)/0.77 0.65	0.51 (0.64)/0.79 0.61	0.57 (0.68)/0.81 0.56	0.52 (0.65)/0.79 0.59	0.57 (0.69)/0.81 0.55	0.52 (0.65)/0.79 0.59	0.58 (0.69)/0.82 0.55	0.57 (0.68)/0.81 0.56
		45°	0.59 (0.42)/0.66 0.66	0.60 (0.43)/0.67 0.65	0.63 (0.48)/0.69 0.61	0.67 (0.54)/0.73 0.56	0.64 (0.49)/0.70 0.59	0.68 (0.55)/0.73 0.55	0.64 (0.49)/0.70 0.59	0.68 (0.56)/0.73 0.55	0.68 (0.54)/0.73 0.56
		Closed	0.33 (0.29)/0.43 0.52	0.35 (0.31)/0.44 0.51	0.40 (0.37)/0.49 0.46	0.47 (0.44)/0.54 0.41	0.42 (0.38)/0.50 0.45	0.48 (0.45)/0.55 0.41	0.42 (0.38)/0.50 0.45	0.49 (0.46)/0.55 0.41	0.47 (0.44)/0.54 0.42
Between Glazings[c]	0.15	Worst[a]	0.93 (0.89)/0.36 0.98	0.93 (0.89)/0.36 0.97	0.93 (0.89)/0.36 0.95	0.93 (0.89)/0.37 0.92	0.93 (0.89)/0.36 0.94	0.93 (0.89)/0.37 0.91	0.93 (0.89)/0.36 0.94	0.93 (0.89)/0.37 0.91	0.93 (0.89)/0.37 0.92
		0°	0.93 (0.05)/0.41 0.9	0.93 (0.06)/0.41 0.89	0.93 (0.06)/0.42 0.87	0.93 (0.06)/0.42 0.84	0.93 (0.06)/0.42 0.87	0.93 (0.06)/0.42 0.84	0.93 (0.06)/0.42 0.87	0.93 (0.07)/0.42 0.83	0.93 (0.06)/0.42 0.84
		Excluded Beam[b]	0.04 (0.05)/0.39 0.77	0.04 (0.06)/0.40 0.76	0.04 (0.06)/0.40 0.74	0.05 (0.06)/0.40 0.72	0.04 (0.06)/0.40 0.74	0.05 (0.06)/0.40 0.72	0.04 (0.06)/0.40 0.74	0.05 (0.07)/0.40 0.72	0.05 (0.06)/0.40 0.72
		45°	0.20 (0.04)/0.29 0.83	0.20 (0.04)/0.30 0.82	0.21 (0.04)/0.30 0.81	0.21 (0.05)/0.30 0.78	0.21 (0.04)/0.30 0.8	0.21 (0.05)/0.30 0.78	0.21 (0.04)/0.30 0.8	0.21 (0.05)/0.30 0.77	0.21 (0.05)/0.30 0.78
		Closed	0.03 (0.03)/0.11 0.65	0.03 (0.04)/0.11 0.65	0.04 (0.04)/0.11 0.65	0.04 (0.05)/0.12 0.64	0.04 (0.04)/0.11 0.64	0.05 (0.05)/0.12 0.64	0.04 (0.04)/0.11 0.64	0.05 (0.05)/0.12 0.64	0.04 (0.05)/0.12 0.64
Between Glazings[c]	0.50	Worst[a]	0.94 (0.95)/0.44 0.98	0.94 (0.95)/0.44 0.97	0.94 (0.95)/0.44 0.95	0.94 (0.95)/0.44 0.92	0.94 (0.95)/0.44 0.94	0.94 (0.95)/0.44 0.91	0.94 (0.95)/0.44 0.94	0.94 (0.95)/0.44 0.91	0.94 (0.95)/0.44 0.92
		0°	0.94 (0.15)/0.50 0.96	0.94 (0.15)/0.50 0.96	0.94 (0.15)/0.50 0.93	0.94 (0.15)/0.50 0.9	0.94 (0.15)/0.50 0.92	0.94 (0.15)/0.50 0.89	0.94 (0.15)/0.50 0.92	0.94 (0.15)/0.50 0.89	0.94 (0.15)/0.50 0.9
		Excluded Beam[b]	0.08 (0.15)/0.48 0.92	0.08 (0.15)/0.48 0.91	0.09 (0.15)/0.48 0.89	0.09 (0.15)/0.48 0.85	0.09 (0.15)/0.48 0.88	0.09 (0.15)/0.48 0.85	0.09 (0.15)/0.48 0.88	0.09 (0.15)/0.48 0.84	0.09 (0.15)/0.48 0.85

Table 13A IAC Values for Louvered Shades: Uncoated Single Glazings (*Continued*)

		Glazing ID:	1a	1b	1c	1d	1e	1f	1g	1h	1i
		45°	0.26 (0.07)/0.36 0.93	0.26 (0.07)/0.36 0.92	0.26 (0.07)/0.36 0.89	0.26 (0.07)/0.37 0.86	0.26 (0.07)/0.36 0.89	0.26 (0.07)/0.37 0.85	0.26 (0.07)/0.36 0.89	0.26 (0.07)/0.37 0.85	0.26 (0.07)/0.37 0.86
		Closed	0.05 (0.03)/0.14 0.8	0.05 (0.03)/0.14 0.8	0.05 (0.03)/0.14 0.77	0.05 (0.04)/0.15 0.75	0.05 (0.04)/0.14 0.77	0.06 (0.04)/0.15 0.74	0.05 (0.04)/0.14 0.77	0.06 (0.04)/0.15 0.74	0.05 (0.04)/0.15 0.75
Between Glazings[c]	0.80	Worst[a]	0.95 (1.02)/0.54 0.98	0.95 (1.02)/0.54 0.98	0.95 (1.01)/0.54 0.95	0.95 (1.00)/0.54 0.92	0.95 (1.01)/0.54 0.95	0.95 (1.00)/0.54 0.91	0.95 (1.01)/0.54 0.95	0.95 (1.00)/0.54 0.91	0.95 (1.01)/0.54 0.92
		0°	0.95 (0.28)/0.61 0.98	0.95 (0.28)/0.61 0.97	0.95 (0.28)/0.61 0.95	0.95 (0.28)/0.61 0.91	0.95 (0.28)/0.61 0.94	0.95 (0.28)/0.61 0.91	0.95 (0.28)/0.61 0.94	0.95 (0.28)/0.61 0.91	0.95 (0.28)/0.61 0.91
		Excluded Beam[b]	0.17 (0.28)/0.59 0.97	0.17 (0.28)/0.59 0.96	0.17 (0.28)/0.58 0.94	0.17 (0.28)/0.58 0.9	0.17 (0.28)/0.58 0.93	0.17 (0.28)/0.58 0.89	0.17 (0.28)/0.58 0.93	0.17 (0.28)/0.59 0.89	0.17 (0.28)/0.59 0.9
		45°	0.34 (0.12)/0.46 0.97	0.34 (0.12)/0.46 0.96	0.34 (0.12)/0.46 0.94	0.34 (0.12)/0.46 0.9	0.34 (0.12)/0.46 0.93	0.34 (0.12)/0.46 0.9	0.34 (0.12)/0.46 0.93	0.34 (0.12)/0.46 0.89	0.35 (0.12)/0.46 0.9
		Closed	0.08 (0.04)/0.21 0.93	0.08 (0.04)/0.21 0.92	0.09 (0.04)/0.20 0.89	0.09 (0.04)/0.21 0.86	0.09 (0.04)/0.20 0.89	0.09 (0.04)/0.21 0.85	0.09 (0.04)/0.20 0.89	0.09 (0.04)/0.21 0.85	0.09 (0.04)/0.21 0.86
Outdoor Side	0.15	Worst[a]	0.93 (0.89)/0.36 0.98	0.93 (0.89)/0.36 0.97	0.93 (0.89)/0.36 0.95	0.93 (0.89)/0.37 0.92	0.93 (0.89)/0.36 0.94	0.93 (0.89)/0.37 0.91	0.93 (0.89)/0.36 0.94	0.93 (0.89)/0.37 0.91	0.93 (0.89)/0.37 0.92
		0°	0.93 (0.05)/0.41 0.9	0.93 (0.06)/0.41 0.89	0.93 (0.06)/0.42 0.87	0.93 (0.06)/0.42 0.84	0.93 (0.06)/0.42 0.87	0.93 (0.06)/0.42 0.84	0.93 (0.06)/0.42 0.87	0.93 (0.07)/0.42 0.83	0.93 (0.06)/0.42 0.84
		Excluded Beam[b]	0.04 (0.05)/0.39 0.77	0.04 (0.06)/0.40 0.76	0.04 (0.06)/0.40 0.74	0.05 (0.06)/0.40 0.72	0.04 (0.06)/0.40 0.74	0.05 (0.06)/0.40 0.72	0.04 (0.06)/0.40 0.74	0.05 (0.07)/0.40 0.72	0.05 (0.06)/0.40 0.72
		45°	0.20 (0.04)/0.29 0.83	0.20 (0.04)/0.30 0.82	0.21 (0.04)/0.30 0.81	0.21 (0.05)/0.30 0.78	0.21 (0.04)/0.30 0.8	0.21 (0.05)/0.30 0.78	0.21 (0.04)/0.30 0.8	0.21 (0.05)/0.30 0.77	0.21 (0.05)/0.30 0.78
		Closed	0.03 (0.03)/0.11 0.65	0.03 (0.04)/0.11 0.65	0.04 (0.04)/0.11 0.65	0.04 (0.05)/0.12 0.64	0.04 (0.04)/0.11 0.64	0.05 (0.05)/0.12 0.64	0.04 (0.04)/0.11 0.64	0.05 (0.05)/0.12 0.64	0.04 (0.05)/0.12 0.64
Outdoor Side	0.50	Worst[a]	0.94 (0.95)/0.44 0.98	0.94 (0.95)/0.44 0.97	0.94 (0.95)/0.44 0.95	0.94 (0.95)/0.44 0.92	0.94 (0.95)/0.44 0.94	0.94 (0.95)/0.44 0.91	0.94 (0.95)/0.44 0.94	0.94 (0.95)/0.44 0.91	0.94 (0.95)/0.44 0.92
		0°	0.94 (0.15)/0.50 0.96	0.94 (0.15)/0.50 0.96	0.94 (0.15)/0.50 0.93	0.94 (0.15)/0.50 0.9	0.94 (0.15)/0.50 0.92	0.94 (0.15)/0.50 0.89	0.94 (0.15)/0.50 0.92	0.94 (0.15)/0.50 0.89	0.94 (0.15)/0.50 0.9
		Excluded Beam[b]	0.08 (0.15)/0.48 0.92	0.08 (0.15)/0.48 0.91	0.09 (0.15)/0.48 0.89	0.09 (0.15)/0.48 0.85	0.09 (0.15)/0.48 0.88	0.09 (0.15)/0.48 0.85	0.09 (0.15)/0.48 0.88	0.09 (0.15)/0.48 0.84	0.09 (0.15)/0.48 0.85
		45°	0.26 (0.07)/0.36 0.93	0.26 (0.07)/0.36 0.92	0.26 (0.07)/0.36 0.89	0.26 (0.07)/0.37 0.86	0.26 (0.07)/0.36 0.89	0.26 (0.07)/0.37 0.85	0.26 (0.07)/0.36 0.89	0.26 (0.07)/0.37 0.85	0.26 (0.07)/0.37 0.86
		Closed	0.05 (0.03)/0.14 0.8	0.05 (0.03)/0.14 0.8	0.05 (0.03)/0.14 0.77	0.05 (0.04)/0.15 0.75	0.05 (0.04)/0.14 0.77	0.06 (0.04)/0.15 0.74	0.05 (0.04)/0.14 0.77	0.06 (0.04)/0.15 0.74	0.05 (0.04)/0.15 0.75
Outdoor Side	0.80	Worst[a]	0.95 (1.02)/0.54 0.98	0.95 (1.02)/0.54 0.98	0.95 (1.01)/0.54 0.95	0.95 (1.00)/0.54 0.92	0.95 (1.01)/0.54 0.95	0.95 (1.00)/0.54 0.91	0.95 (1.01)/0.54 0.95	0.95 (1.00)/0.54 0.91	0.95 (1.01)/0.54 0.92
		0°	0.95 (0.28)/0.61 0.98	0.95 (0.28)/0.61 0.97	0.95 (0.28)/0.61 0.95	0.95 (0.28)/0.61 0.91	0.95 (0.28)/0.61 0.94	0.95 (0.28)/0.61 0.91	0.95 (0.28)/0.61 0.94	0.95 (0.28)/0.61 0.91	0.95 (0.28)/0.61 0.91
		Excluded Beam[b]	0.17 (0.28)/0.59 0.97	0.17 (0.28)/0.59 0.96	0.17 (0.28)/0.58 0.94	0.17 (0.28)/0.58 0.9	0.17 (0.28)/0.58 0.93	0.17 (0.28)/0.58 0.89	0.17 (0.28)/0.58 0.93	0.17 (0.28)/0.59 0.89	0.17 (0.28)/0.59 0.9
		45°	0.34 (0.12)/0.46 0.97	0.34 (0.12)/0.46 0.96	0.34 (0.12)/0.46 0.94	0.34 (0.12)/0.46 0.9	0.34 (0.12)/0.46 0.93	0.34 (0.12)/0.46 0.9	0.34 (0.12)/0.46 0.93	0.34 (0.12)/0.46 0.89	0.35 (0.12)/0.46 0.9
		Closed	0.08 (0.04)/0.21 0.93	0.08 (0.04)/0.21 0.92	0.09 (0.04)/0.20 0.89	0.09 (0.04)/0.21 0.86	0.09 (0.04)/0.20 0.89	0.09 (0.04)/0.21 0.85	0.09 (0.04)/0.20 0.89	0.09 (0.04)/0.21 0.85	0.09 (0.04)/0.21 0.86
Sheer		100%	0.7 0.5	0.71 0.49	0.72 0.47	0.74 0.45	0.72 0.47	0.74 0.44	0.72 0.47	0.74 0.44	0.74 0.45

Notes:

[a] Louvers track so that profile angle equals negative slat angle and maximum direct beam is admitted.

[b] Louvers track to block direct beam radiation. When negative slat angles result, slat defaults to 0°.

[c] Glazing cavity width equals original cavity width plus slat width.

Table 13B IAC Values for Louvered Shades: Uncoated Double Glazings

		Glazing ID:	5a	5b	5c	5d	5e	5f	5g	5h	5i
Louver Location	**Louver Reflection**	ϕ	IAC_0 (IAC_{60})/IAC_{diff}, F_R								
Indoor Side	0.15	Worst[a]	0.99 (0.98)/0.92 0.87	0.99 (0.98)/0.92 0.84	0.99 (0.97)/0.92 0.84	0.98 (0.97)/0.93 0.79	0.99 (0.97)/0.92 0.83	0.98 (0.97)/0.93 0.78	0.99 (0.97)/0.92 0.83	0.98 (0.97)/0.93 0.78	0.98 (0.97)/0.93 0.79
		0°	0.99 (0.88)/0.93 0.67	0.99 (0.89)/0.93 0.65	0.99 (0.89)/0.93 0.65	0.98 (0.90)/0.93 0.62	0.99 (0.89)/0.93 0.65	0.98 (0.90)/0.94 0.62	0.99 (0.89)/0.93 0.65	0.98 (0.90)/0.94 0.62	0.98 (0.90)/0.93 0.62
		Excluded Beam[b]	0.84 (0.88)/0.93 0.42	0.84 (0.89)/0.93 0.41	0.84 (0.89)/0.93 0.41	0.86 (0.90)/0.93 0.4	0.85 (0.89)/0.93 0.41	0.86 (0.90)/0.93 0.4	0.85 (0.89)/0.93 0.41	0.86 (0.90)/0.93 0.4	0.86 (0.90)/0.93 0.4
		45°	0.88 (0.85)/0.90 0.45	0.88 (0.85)/0.90 0.44	0.88 (0.85)/0.90 0.44	0.89 (0.87)/0.91 0.42	0.88 (0.86)/0.90 0.44	0.89 (0.87)/0.91 0.42	0.88 (0.86)/0.90 0.44	0.89 (0.87)/0.91 0.42	0.89 (0.87)/0.91 0.42
		Closed	0.81 (0.81)/0.83 0.41	0.82 (0.82)/0.84 0.4	0.82 (0.82)/0.84 0.4	0.83 (0.84)/0.85 0.38	0.82 (0.82)/0.84 0.4	0.83 (0.84)/0.85 0.38	0.82 (0.82)/0.84 0.4	0.83 (0.84)/0.85 0.38	0.83 (0.84)/0.85 0.38
Indoor Side	0.50	Worst[a]	0.98 (0.97)/0.86 0.88	0.98 (0.97)/0.87 0.86	0.98 (0.97)/0.87 0.85	0.98 (0.97)/0.88 0.8	0.98 (0.97)/0.87 0.84	0.98 (0.97)/0.89 0.79	0.98 (0.97)/0.87 0.84	0.98 (0.97)/0.89 0.79	0.98 (0.97)/0.88 0.8
		0°	0.98 (0.80)/0.89 0.71	0.98 (0.82)/0.90 0.69	0.98 (0.81)/0.90 0.69	0.98 (0.84)/0.91 0.65	0.98 (0.82)/0.90 0.68	0.98 (0.84)/0.91 0.65	0.98 (0.82)/0.90 0.68	0.98 (0.84)/0.91 0.65	0.98 (0.84)/0.91 0.65
		Excluded Beam[b]	0.70 (0.80)/0.88 0.48	0.72 (0.82)/0.89 0.47	0.72 (0.81)/0.89 0.47	0.75 (0.84)/0.90 0.45	0.73 (0.82)/0.89 0.46	0.76 (0.84)/0.90 0.45	0.73 (0.82)/0.89 0.46	0.76 (0.84)/0.90 0.45	0.75 (0.84)/0.90 0.45
		45°	0.78 (0.70)/0.82 0.5	0.80 (0.72)/0.83 0.49	0.79 (0.72)/0.83 0.48	0.82 (0.76)/0.85 0.46	0.80 (0.73)/0.84 0.48	0.82 (0.76)/0.85 0.46	0.80 (0.73)/0.84 0.48	0.82 (0.76)/0.85 0.46	0.82 (0.76)/0.85 0.46
		Closed	0.63 (0.63)/0.69 0.42	0.66 (0.65)/0.71 0.4	0.65 (0.65)/0.71 0.4	0.70 (0.70)/0.74 0.38	0.66 (0.66)/0.71 0.4	0.70 (0.70)/0.75 0.38	0.66 (0.66)/0.71 0.4	0.70 (0.70)/0.75 0.38	0.70 (0.70)/0.74 0.38
Indoor Side	0.80	Worst[a]	0.97 (0.96)/0.80 0.9	0.97 (0.96)/0.81 0.87	0.97 (0.96)/0.81 0.87	0.97 (0.96)/0.84 0.81	0.97 (0.96)/0.82 0.86	0.97 (0.96)/0.84 0.8	0.97 (0.96)/0.82 0.86	0.97 (0.96)/0.84 0.8	0.97 (0.96)/0.84 0.81
		0°	0.97 (0.71)/0.84 0.78	0.97 (0.73)/0.85 0.75	0.97 (0.73)/0.85 0.75	0.97 (0.77)/0.87 0.7	0.97 (0.73)/0.85 0.74	0.97 (0.77)/0.87 0.7	0.97 (0.73)/0.85 0.74	0.97 (0.77)/0.87 0.7	0.97 (0.77)/0.87 0.71
		Excluded Beam[b]	0.57 (0.71)/0.83 0.6	0.60 (0.73)/0.84 0.58	0.60 (0.73)/0.84 0.58	0.65 (0.77)/0.86 0.54	0.61 (0.73)/0.84 0.57	0.66 (0.77)/0.86 0.53	0.61 (0.73)/0.84 0.57	0.66 (0.77)/0.86 0.53	0.65 (0.77)/0.86 0.54
		45°	0.68 (0.56)/0.74 0.6	0.71 (0.60)/0.76 0.58	0.70 (0.59)/0.76 0.58	0.74 (0.65)/0.79 0.54	0.71 (0.60)/0.76 0.57	0.75 (0.66)/0.79 0.53	0.71 (0.60)/0.76 0.57	0.75 (0.66)/0.79 0.53	0.74 (0.65)/0.79 0.54
		Closed	0.47 (0.45)/0.55 0.46	0.51 (0.50)/0.59 0.43	0.50 (0.49)/0.58 0.43	0.57 (0.56)/0.64 0.4	0.51 (0.50)/0.59 0.43	0.57 (0.57)/0.64 0.39	0.51 (0.50)/0.59 0.43	0.57 (0.57)/0.65 0.39	0.57 (0.56)/0.64 0.4
Between Glazings[c]	0.15	Worst[a]	0.97 (0.98)/0.66 0.93	0.97 (0.99)/0.67 0.91	0.96 (0.97)/0.67 0.91	0.95 (0.96)/0.69 0.88	0.95 (0.97)/0.67 0.91	0.95 (0.95)/0.69 0.88	0.95 (0.97)/0.67 0.91	0.95 (0.95)/0.69 0.88	0.95 (0.96)/0.69 0.88
		0°	0.97 (0.50)/0.70 0.81	0.97 (0.51)/0.71 0.8	0.96 (0.52)/0.70 0.8	0.95 (0.55)/0.72 0.78	0.95 (0.52)/0.70 0.79	0.95 (0.55)/0.72 0.78	0.95 (0.52)/0.70 0.79	0.95 (0.55)/0.72 0.78	0.95 (0.55)/0.72 0.78
		Excluded Beam[b]	0.43 (0.50)/0.69 0.66	0.45 (0.51)/0.69 0.66	0.46 (0.52)/0.69 0.66	0.49 (0.55)/0.71 0.65	0.46 (0.52)/0.69 0.65	0.49 (0.55)/0.71 0.65	0.46 (0.52)/0.69 0.65	0.49 (0.55)/0.71 0.65	0.49 (0.55)/0.71 0.65
		45°	0.54 (0.47)/0.62 0.7	0.55 (0.48)/0.63 0.7	0.56 (0.49)/0.63 0.7	0.58 (0.52)/0.65 0.69	0.56 (0.49)/0.63 0.69	0.58 (0.52)/0.65 0.68	0.56 (0.49)/0.63 0.69	0.59 (0.52)/0.65 0.68	0.58 (0.52)/0.65 0.69
		Closed	0.42 (0.45)/0.50 0.65	0.44 (0.47)/0.51 0.65	0.44 (0.47)/0.52 0.65	0.47 (0.50)/0.54 0.64	0.45 (0.48)/0.52 0.64	0.48 (0.51)/0.54 0.64	0.45 (0.48)/0.52 0.64	0.48 (0.51)/0.54 0.64	0.47 (0.50)/0.54 0.64
Between Glazings[c]	0.50	Worst[a]	0.97 (1.01)/0.67 0.94	0.97 (1.02)/0.67 0.92	0.96 (1.00)/0.67 0.92	0.95 (0.98)/0.69 0.89	0.95 (0.99)/0.68 0.92	0.95 (0.98)/0.69 0.89	0.95 (0.99)/0.68 0.92	0.95 (0.98)/0.69 0.89	0.95 (0.98)/0.69 0.89
		0°	0.97 (0.49)/0.71 0.84	0.97 (0.50)/0.72 0.83	0.96 (0.51)/0.72 0.83	0.95 (0.54)/0.73 0.8	0.95 (0.52)/0.72 0.82	0.95 (0.55)/0.73 0.8	0.95 (0.52)/0.72 0.82	0.95 (0.55)/0.73 0.8	0.95 (0.54)/0.73 0.8
		Excluded Beam[b]	0.38 (0.49)/0.70 0.72	0.39 (0.50)/0.70 0.71	0.40 (0.51)/0.70 0.71	0.44 (0.54)/0.72 0.69	0.41 (0.52)/0.71 0.71	0.45 (0.55)/0.72 0.69	0.41 (0.52)/0.71 0.71	0.45 (0.55)/0.72 0.69	0.44 (0.54)/0.72 0.69

Table 13B IAC Values for Louvered Shades: Uncoated Double Glazings (*Continued*)

		Glazing ID:	5a	5b	5c	5d	5e	5f	5g	5h	5i
		45°	0.51 (0.38)/0.61 0.75	0.52 (0.40)/0.62 0.74	0.53 (0.41)/0.62 0.73	0.56 (0.45)/0.64 0.72	0.53 (0.42)/0.62 0.73	0.56 (0.46)/0.64 0.71	0.53 (0.42)/0.62 0.73	0.56 (0.46)/0.64 0.71	0.56 (0.45)/0.64 0.72
		Closed	0.32 (0.32)/0.42 0.67	0.33 (0.33)/0.43 0.66	0.35 (0.35)/0.44 0.66	0.39 (0.39)/0.47 0.65	0.36 (0.36)/0.45 0.66	0.39 (0.40)/0.48 0.65	0.36 (0.36)/0.45 0.66	0.40 (0.40)/0.48 0.65	0.39 (0.39)/0.47 0.66
Between Glazings[c]	0.80	Worst[a]	0.97 (1.04)/0.68 0.94	0.97 (1.04)/0.68 0.93	0.96 (1.02)/0.69 0.93	0.95 (1.01)/0.70 0.9	0.96 (1.02)/0.69 0.93	0.95 (1.00)/0.70 0.9	0.96 (1.02)/0.69 0.93	0.95 (1.00)/0.70 0.89	0.95 (1.01)/0.70 0.9
		0°	0.97 (0.49)/0.73 0.89	0.97 (0.50)/0.74 0.88	0.96 (0.51)/0.74 0.87	0.95 (0.55)/0.75 0.84	0.96 (0.52)/0.74 0.87	0.95 (0.55)/0.75 0.84	0.96 (0.52)/0.74 0.87	0.95 (0.55)/0.75 0.84	0.95 (0.55)/0.75 0.84
		Excluded Beam[b]	0.35 (0.49)/0.72 0.82	0.36 (0.50)/0.72 0.81	0.37 (0.51)/0.72 0.8	0.42 (0.55)/0.74 0.76	0.38 (0.52)/0.72 0.79	0.42 (0.55)/0.74 0.76	0.38 (0.52)/0.72 0.79	0.42 (0.55)/0.74 0.76	0.42 (0.55)/0.74 0.77
		45°	0.50 (0.32)/0.60 0.83	0.51 (0.33)/0.61 0.81	0.52 (0.35)/0.62 0.8	0.55 (0.40)/0.64 0.77	0.53 (0.36)/0.62 0.8	0.55 (0.41)/0.64 0.77	0.53 (0.36)/0.62 0.8	0.56 (0.41)/0.64 0.77	0.55 (0.40)/0.64 0.77
		Closed	0.24 (0.20)/0.36 0.74	0.25 (0.22)/0.37 0.73	0.27 (0.25)/0.39 0.71	0.32 (0.30)/0.43 0.69	0.28 (0.26)/0.40 0.71	0.33 (0.31)/0.43 0.69	0.28 (0.26)/0.40 0.71	0.33 (0.31)/0.43 0.69	0.32 (0.30)/0.43 0.69
Outdoor Side	0.15	Worst[a]	0.93 (0.89)/0.35 0.95	0.93 (0.89)/0.36 0.94	0.93 (0.89)/0.36 0.93	0.93 (0.89)/0.36 0.9	0.93 (0.89)/0.36 0.93	0.93 (0.89)/0.36 0.89	0.93 (0.89)/0.36 0.93	0.93 (0.89)/0.36 0.89	0.93 (0.89)/0.36 0.9
		0°	0.93 (0.05)/0.41 0.9	0.93 (0.05)/0.41 0.88	0.93 (0.05)/0.41 0.88	0.93 (0.05)/0.41 0.84	0.93 (0.05)/0.41 0.87	0.93 (0.06)/0.41 0.84	0.93 (0.05)/0.41 0.87	0.93 (0.06)/0.41 0.84	0.93 (0.05)/0.41 0.84
		Excluded Beam[b]	0.03 (0.05)/0.39 0.78	0.03 (0.05)/0.39 0.77	0.03 (0.05)/0.39 0.76	0.03 (0.05)/0.39 0.73	0.03 (0.05)/0.39 0.76	0.03 (0.06)/0.39 0.73	0.03 (0.05)/0.39 0.76	0.04 (0.06)/0.40 0.73	0.03 (0.05)/0.39 0.73
		45°	0.19 (0.03)/0.29 0.84	0.19 (0.03)/0.29 0.82	0.20 (0.03)/0.29 0.82	0.20 (0.04)/0.29 0.79	0.20 (0.03)/0.29 0.81	0.20 (0.04)/0.29 0.78	0.20 (0.03)/0.29 0.81	0.20 (0.04)/0.30 0.78	0.20 (0.04)/0.29 0.79
		Closed	0.02 (0.02)/0.10 0.66	0.02 (0.02)/0.10 0.66	0.02 (0.03)/0.10 0.65	0.03 (0.03)/0.11 0.64	0.03 (0.03)/0.10 0.65	0.03 (0.03)/0.11 0.64	0.03 (0.03)/0.10 0.65	0.03 (0.03)/0.11 0.64	0.03 (0.03)/0.11 0.64
Outdoor Side	0.50	Worst[a]	0.94 (0.98)/0.44 0.95	0.94 (0.98)/0.44 0.94	0.94 (0.97)/0.44 0.93	0.94 (0.96)/0.44 0.9	0.94 (0.96)/0.44 0.93	0.94 (0.95)/0.44 0.9	0.94 (0.96)/0.44 0.93	0.94 (0.95)/0.44 0.89	0.94 (0.96)/0.44 0.9
		0°	0.94 (0.14)/0.50 0.94	0.94 (0.14)/0.50 0.93	0.94 (0.15)/0.50 0.92	0.94 (0.15)/0.50 0.89	0.94 (0.15)/0.50 0.92	0.94 (0.15)/0.50 0.88	0.94 (0.15)/0.50 0.92	0.94 (0.15)/0.50 0.88	0.94 (0.15)/0.50 0.89
		Excluded Beam[b]	0.07 (0.14)/0.48 0.91	0.07 (0.14)/0.48 0.9	0.08 (0.15)/0.48 0.89	0.08 (0.15)/0.48 0.85	0.08 (0.15)/0.48 0.88	0.08 (0.15)/0.48 0.85	0.08 (0.15)/0.48 0.88	0.08 (0.15)/0.48 0.84	0.08 (0.15)/0.48 0.85
		45°	0.25 (0.06)/0.36 0.92	0.25 (0.06)/0.36 0.9	0.25 (0.06)/0.36 0.9	0.25 (0.07)/0.36 0.86	0.25 (0.06)/0.36 0.89	0.25 (0.07)/0.36 0.85	0.25 (0.06)/0.36 0.89	0.25 (0.07)/0.36 0.85	0.25 (0.07)/0.36 0.86
		Closed	0.04 (0.02)/0.14 0.82	0.04 (0.03)/0.14 0.81	0.04 (0.03)/0.14 0.8	0.04 (0.03)/0.14 0.76	0.04 (0.03)/0.14 0.79	0.05 (0.03)/0.14 0.76	0.04 (0.03)/0.14 0.79	0.05 (0.03)/0.14 0.76	0.04 (0.03)/0.14 0.76
Outdoor Side	0.80	Worst[a]	0.95 (1.08)/0.55 0.95	0.95 (1.07)/0.55 0.94	0.95 (1.04)/0.55 0.93	0.95 (1.02)/0.54 0.9	0.95 (1.04)/0.55 0.93	0.95 (1.02)/0.54 0.9	0.95 (1.04)/0.55 0.93	0.95 (1.02)/0.54 0.89	0.95 (1.03)/0.54 0.9
		0°	0.95 (0.29)/0.62 0.95	0.95 (0.29)/0.61 0.94	0.95 (0.28)/0.61 0.94	0.95 (0.28)/0.61 0.9	0.95 (0.28)/0.61 0.93	0.95 (0.28)/0.61 0.9	0.95 (0.28)/0.61 0.93	0.95 (0.28)/0.61 0.89	0.95 (0.28)/0.61 0.9
		Excluded Beam[b]	0.16 (0.29)/0.59 0.94	0.16 (0.29)/0.59 0.93	0.16 (0.28)/0.59 0.92	0.16 (0.28)/0.59 0.89	0.16 (0.28)/0.59 0.92	0.16 (0.28)/0.59 0.88	0.16 (0.28)/0.59 0.92	0.16 (0.28)/0.59 0.88	0.16 (0.28)/0.59 0.89
		45°	0.34 (0.12)/0.47 0.95	0.34 (0.12)/0.47 0.93	0.33 (0.12)/0.47 0.93	0.33 (0.12)/0.46 0.89	0.33 (0.12)/0.46 0.92	0.33 (0.12)/0.46 0.88	0.33 (0.12)/0.46 0.92	0.33 (0.12)/0.46 0.88	0.34 (0.12)/0.46 0.89
		Closed	0.08 (0.04)/0.21 0.92	0.08 (0.04)/0.21 0.9	0.08 (0.04)/0.21 0.89	0.08 (0.04)/0.21 0.86	0.08 (0.04)/0.21 0.89	0.08 (0.04)/0.21 0.85	0.08 (0.04)/0.21 0.89	0.08 (0.04)/0.21 0.85	0.08 (0.04)/0.21 0.86

Notes:

[a] Louvers track so that profile angle equals negative slat angle and maximum direct beam is admitted.

[b] Louvers track to block direct beam radiation. When negative slat angles result, slat defaults to 0°.

[c] Glazing cavity width equals original cavity width plus slat width.

Table 13C IAC Values for Louvered Shades: Coated Double Glazings with 0.2 Low-e

Louver Location	Louver Reflection	Glazing ID: / ϕ	17a	17b	17c	17d	17e	17f	17g	17h	17i	17j	17k
			IAC_0 (IAC_{60})/IAC_{diff}, F_R										
Indoor Side	0.15	Worst[a]	0.99 (0.98)/0.94 0.86	0.99 (0.98)/0.94 0.83	0.99 (0.98)/0.94 0.83	0.99 (0.98)/0.94 0.79	0.99 (0.98)/0.94 0.81	0.99 (0.98)/0.95 0.76	0.99 (0.98)/0.94 0.8	0.99 (0.98)/0.95 0.75	0.99 (0.98)/0.94 0.8	0.99 (0.98)/0.95 0.75	0.99 (0.98)/0.95 0.76
		0°	0.99 (0.91)/0.95 0.66	0.99 (0.91)/0.95 0.64	0.99 (0.91)/0.95 0.65	0.99 (0.92)/0.95 0.63	0.99 (0.92)/0.95 0.63	0.99 (0.93)/0.95 0.61	0.99 (0.92)/0.95 0.63	0.99 (0.93)/0.95 0.6	0.99 (0.92)/0.95 0.63	0.99 (0.93)/0.95 0.6	0.99 (0.93)/0.95 0.61
		Excluded Beam[b]	0.87 (0.91)/0.94 0.41	0.88 (0.91)/0.95 0.41	0.88 (0.91)/0.95 0.41	0.89 (0.92)/0.95 0.41	0.88 (0.92)/0.95 0.41	0.90 (0.93)/0.95 0.4	0.88 (0.92)/0.95 0.41	0.90 (0.93)/0.95 0.4	0.88 (0.92)/0.95 0.41	0.90 (0.93)/0.95 0.4	0.90 (0.93)/0.95 0.4
		45°	0.90 (0.88)/0.92 0.44	0.91 (0.89)/0.93 0.43	0.91 (0.89)/0.93 0.44	0.92 (0.89)/0.93 0.43	0.91 (0.89)/0.93 0.43	0.92 (0.90)/0.93 0.42	0.91 (0.89)/0.93 0.43	0.92 (0.90)/0.93 0.42	0.91 (0.89)/0.93 0.43	0.92 (0.90)/0.93 0.42	0.92 (0.90)/0.93 0.42
		Closed	0.85 (0.85)/0.87 0.4	0.86 (0.86)/0.88 0.39	0.85 (0.86)/0.88 0.4	0.86 (0.87)/0.88 0.39	0.86 (0.86)/0.88 0.39	0.87 (0.88)/0.89 0.37	0.86 (0.86)/0.88 0.39	0.87 (0.88)/0.89 0.37	0.86 (0.86)/0.88 0.39	0.87 (0.88)/0.89 0.37	0.87 (0.88)/0.89 0.37
Indoor Side	0.50	Worst[a]	0.98 (0.98)/0.88 0.87	0.98 (0.98)/0.89 0.84	0.98 (0.98)/0.89 0.84	0.98 (0.98)/0.90 0.8	0.98 (0.98)/0.90 0.82	0.98 (0.98)/0.91 0.76	0.98 (0.98)/0.90 0.81	0.98 (0.98)/0.91 0.76	0.98 (0.98)/0.90 0.81	0.98 (0.98)/0.91 0.76	0.98 (0.98)/0.91 0.77
		0°	0.98 (0.83)/0.91 0.7	0.98 (0.85)/0.91 0.68	0.98 (0.85)/0.91 0.68	0.98 (0.86)/0.92 0.66	0.98 (0.85)/0.92 0.67	0.98 (0.87)/0.93 0.63	0.98 (0.85)/0.92 0.66	0.98 (0.87)/0.93 0.63	0.98 (0.85)/0.92 0.66	0.98 (0.87)/0.93 0.63	0.98 (0.87)/0.93 0.64
		Excluded Beam[b]	0.74 (0.83)/0.90 0.47	0.76 (0.85)/0.91 0.46	0.76 (0.85)/0.91 0.46	0.79 (0.86)/0.92 0.45	0.77 (0.85)/0.91 0.45	0.80 (0.87)/0.92 0.44	0.77 (0.85)/0.91 0.45	0.80 (0.87)/0.92 0.44	0.77 (0.85)/0.91 0.45	0.81 (0.87)/0.92 0.44	0.80 (0.87)/0.92 0.44
		45°	0.81 (0.74)/0.85 0.49	0.83 (0.76)/0.86 0.48	0.83 (0.76)/0.86 0.48	0.84 (0.79)/0.87 0.47	0.83 (0.77)/0.86 0.47	0.86 (0.81)/0.88 0.45	0.83 (0.77)/0.87 0.47	0.86 (0.81)/0.88 0.45	0.83 (0.77)/0.87 0.47	0.86 (0.81)/0.88 0.45	0.86 (0.81)/0.88 0.45
		Closed	0.67 (0.67)/0.73 0.41	0.70 (0.70)/0.75 0.39	0.70 (0.70)/0.75 0.4	0.73 (0.73)/0.78 0.38	0.71 (0.71)/0.76 0.39	0.75 (0.75)/0.79 0.37	0.72 (0.71)/0.76 0.38	0.76 (0.75)/0.79 0.37	0.72 (0.71)/0.76 0.38	0.76 (0.76)/0.80 0.37	0.75 (0.75)/0.79 0.37
Indoor Side	0.80	Worst[a]	0.98 (0.97)/0.82 0.88	0.98 (0.97)/0.83 0.85	0.98 (0.97)/0.83 0.85	0.98 (0.97)/0.85 0.82	0.98 (0.97)/0.84 0.83	0.98 (0.97)/0.86 0.78	0.98 (0.97)/0.84 0.83	0.98 (0.97)/0.87 0.77	0.98 (0.97)/0.84 0.83	0.98 (0.97)/0.87 0.77	0.98 (0.97)/0.87 0.78
		0°	0.98 (0.74)/0.86 0.76	0.98 (0.76)/0.87 0.74	0.98 (0.76)/0.87 0.74	0.98 (0.79)/0.88 0.71	0.98 (0.77)/0.88 0.72	0.98 (0.81)/0.89 0.68	0.98 (0.77)/0.88 0.72	0.98 (0.81)/0.89 0.68	0.98 (0.77)/0.88 0.72	0.98 (0.81)/0.89 0.68	0.98 (0.81)/0.89 0.68
		Excluded Beam[b]	0.61 (0.74)/0.84 0.59	0.64 (0.76)/0.86 0.56	0.64 (0.76)/0.86 0.56	0.68 (0.79)/0.87 0.54	0.66 (0.77)/0.86 0.55	0.71 (0.81)/0.88 0.51	0.66 (0.77)/0.87 0.54	0.71 (0.81)/0.89 0.51	0.66 (0.77)/0.87 0.54	0.72 (0.81)/0.89 0.51	0.71 (0.81)/0.88 0.51
		45°	0.71 (0.60)/0.77 0.59	0.74 (0.64)/0.79 0.56	0.74 (0.64)/0.79 0.56	0.77 (0.68)/0.81 0.54	0.75 (0.66)/0.80 0.55	0.79 (0.71)/0.83 0.51	0.75 (0.66)/0.80 0.54	0.79 (0.71)/0.83 0.51	0.75 (0.66)/0.80 0.54	0.79 (0.72)/0.83 0.51	0.79 (0.71)/0.83 0.51
		Closed	0.51 (0.50)/0.59 0.44	0.55 (0.54)/0.63 0.42	0.55 (0.55)/0.63 0.42	0.60 (0.60)/0.67 0.4	0.57 (0.57)/0.65 0.41	0.64 (0.64)/0.70 0.38	0.58 (0.57)/0.65 0.4	0.64 (0.64)/0.70 0.38	0.58 (0.57)/0.65 0.4	0.64 (0.64)/0.70 0.38	0.64 (0.64)/0.70 0.38
Between Glazings[c]	0.15	Worst[a]	0.97 (1.02)/0.78 0.92	0.98 (1.02)/0.78 0.9	0.96 (0.96)/0.59 0.91	0.96 (0.96)/0.60 0.89	0.95 (0.95)/0.60 0.9	0.95 (0.95)/0.62 0.87	0.95 (0.95)/0.60 0.9	0.95 (0.95)/0.62 0.87	0.95 (0.95)/0.60 0.9	0.95 (0.95)/0.62 0.87	0.95 (0.95)/0.62 0.87
		0°	0.97 (0.66)/0.80 0.8	0.98 (0.67)/0.81 0.79	0.96 (0.39)/0.63 0.79	0.96 (0.40)/0.64 0.78	0.95 (0.41)/0.64 0.79	0.95 (0.44)/0.65 0.77	0.95 (0.41)/0.64 0.79	0.95 (0.44)/0.65 0.77	0.95 (0.41)/0.64 0.79	0.95 (0.44)/0.65 0.77	0.95 (0.44)/0.65 0.77
		Excluded Beam[b]	0.59 (0.66)/0.79 0.66	0.60 (0.67)/0.80 0.66	0.33 (0.39)/0.62 0.66	0.34 (0.40)/0.62 0.66	0.35 (0.41)/0.62 0.65	0.38 (0.44)/0.64 0.65	0.36 (0.41)/0.63 0.65	0.39 (0.44)/0.64 0.65	0.36 (0.41)/0.63 0.65	0.39 (0.44)/0.64 0.65	0.38 (0.44)/0.64 0.65
		45°	0.67 (0.62)/0.74 0.69	0.68 (0.63)/0.75 0.69	0.46 (0.36)/0.54 0.7	0.46 (0.37)/0.55 0.7	0.47 (0.38)/0.55 0.7	0.50 (0.41)/0.57 0.69	0.47 (0.38)/0.56 0.7	0.50 (0.41)/0.57 0.69	0.47 (0.38)/0.56 0.7	0.50 (0.41)/0.58 0.69	0.49 (0.41)/0.57 0.69
		Closed	0.57 (0.60)/0.64 0.65	0.58 (0.61)/0.65 0.65	0.32 (0.34)/0.40 0.64	0.33 (0.35)/0.41 0.64	0.34 (0.36)/0.42 0.64	0.37 (0.40)/0.44 0.64	0.35 (0.37)/0.42 0.64	0.38 (0.40)/0.45 0.64	0.35 (0.37)/0.42 0.64	0.38 (0.40)/0.45 0.64	0.37 (0.39)/0.44 0.64
Between Glazings[c]	0.50	Worst[a]	0.97 (1.03)/0.75 0.92	0.97 (1.03)/0.75 0.91	0.96 (1.01)/0.61 0.91	0.96 (1.01)/0.62 0.89	0.96 (1.00)/0.62 0.91	0.95 (0.99)/0.64 0.87	0.95 (0.99)/0.62 0.9	0.95 (0.98)/0.64 0.87	0.95 (0.99)/0.62 0.9	0.95 (0.98)/0.64 0.87	0.95 (0.99)/0.64 0.88
		0°	0.97 (0.61)/0.79 0.83	0.97 (0.62)/0.79 0.82	0.96 (0.41)/0.66 0.83	0.96 (0.42)/0.67 0.82	0.96 (0.43)/0.67 0.82	0.95 (0.45)/0.68 0.8	0.95 (0.43)/0.67 0.82	0.95 (0.46)/0.68 0.8	0.95 (0.43)/0.67 0.82	0.95 (0.46)/0.69 0.8	0.95 (0.45)/0.68 0.8
		Excluded Beam[b]	0.49 (0.61)/0.77 0.7	0.50 (0.62)/0.78 0.7	0.31 (0.41)/0.65 0.72	0.32 (0.42)/0.65 0.72	0.33 (0.43)/0.65 0.71	0.36 (0.45)/0.67 0.7	0.33 (0.43)/0.66 0.71	0.37 (0.46)/0.67 0.7	0.33 (0.43)/0.66 0.71	0.37 (0.46)/0.67 0.7	0.36 (0.45)/0.67 0.7

Table 13C IAC Values for Louvered Shades: Coated Double Glazings with 0.2 Low-e (*Continued*)

		Glazing ID:	17a	17b	17c	17d	17e	17f	17g	17h	17i	17j	17k
		45°	0.61 (0.49)/0.69 0.73	0.62 (0.50)/0.70 0.72	0.45 (0.31)/0.55 0.75	0.46 (0.32)/0.56 0.74	0.47 (0.33)/0.56 0.74	0.49 (0.37)/0.58 0.72	0.47 (0.34)/0.56 0.74	0.50 (0.37)/0.58 0.72	0.47 (0.34)/0.56 0.74	0.50 (0.37)/0.58 0.72	0.49 (0.37)/0.58 0.72
		Closed	0.42 (0.42)/0.52 0.66	0.43 (0.43)/0.53 0.66	0.25 (0.25)/0.35 0.67	0.26 (0.26)/0.36 0.66	0.28 (0.27)/0.37 0.66	0.31 (0.31)/0.40 0.66	0.28 (0.28)/0.38 0.66	0.32 (0.32)/0.41 0.65	0.28 (0.28)/0.38 0.66	0.32 (0.32)/0.41 0.65	0.31 (0.31)/0.40 0.66
Between Glazings[c]	0.80	Worst[a]	0.97 (1.05)/0.72 0.94	0.97 (1.05)/0.72 0.92	0.97 (1.05)/0.65 0.92	0.97 (1.05)/0.66 0.9	0.96 (1.04)/0.66 0.91	0.96 (1.02)/0.67 0.88	0.96 (1.03)/0.66 0.91	0.95 (1.02)/0.67 0.88	0.96 (1.03)/0.66 0.91	0.95 (1.02)/0.68 0.88	0.96 (1.02)/0.67 0.88
		0°	0.97 (0.55)/0.77 0.88	0.97 (0.56)/0.78 0.86	0.97 (0.45)/0.71 0.88	0.97 (0.46)/0.72 0.86	0.96 (0.46)/0.72 0.87	0.96 (0.49)/0.73 0.84	0.96 (0.47)/0.72 0.86	0.95 (0.49)/0.73 0.83	0.96 (0.47)/0.72 0.86	0.95 (0.50)/0.73 0.83	0.96 (0.49)/0.73 0.84
		Excluded Beam[b]	0.40 (0.55)/0.75 0.8	0.41 (0.56)/0.76 0.78	0.31 (0.45)/0.69 0.82	0.32 (0.46)/0.70 0.81	0.33 (0.46)/0.70 0.8	0.37 (0.49)/0.71 0.77	0.34 (0.47)/0.70 0.8	0.37 (0.49)/0.71 0.77	0.34 (0.47)/0.70 0.8	0.37 (0.50)/0.71 0.77	0.37 (0.49)/0.71 0.77
		45°	0.55 (0.37)/0.65 0.81	0.56 (0.39)/0.65 0.79	0.47 (0.28)/0.58 0.83	0.48 (0.29)/0.58 0.81	0.49 (0.31)/0.59 0.81	0.51 (0.34)/0.61 0.77	0.49 (0.31)/0.59 0.8	0.51 (0.35)/0.61 0.77	0.49 (0.31)/0.59 0.8	0.52 (0.35)/0.61 0.77	0.51 (0.34)/0.61 0.78
		Closed	0.29 (0.25)/0.41 0.72	0.30 (0.27)/0.42 0.71	0.21 (0.17)/0.33 0.75	0.22 (0.18)/0.34 0.73	0.24 (0.20)/0.35 0.72	0.27 (0.25)/0.38 0.7	0.24 (0.21)/0.36 0.72	0.28 (0.25)/0.39 0.7	0.24 (0.21)/0.36 0.72	0.28 (0.26)/0.39 0.69	0.27 (0.25)/0.38 0.7
Outdoor Side	0.15	Worst[a]	0.93 (0.89)/0.35 0.95	0.93 (0.89)/0.35 0.93	0.93 (0.89)/0.35 0.93	0.93 (0.89)/0.35 0.91	0.93 (0.89)/0.35 0.92	0.93 (0.89)/0.35 0.88	0.93 (0.89)/0.35 0.91	0.93 (0.89)/0.35 0.88	0.93 (0.89)/0.35 0.91	0.93 (0.89)/0.36 0.88	0.93 (0.89)/0.35 0.88
		0°	0.93 (0.04)/0.41 0.9	0.93 (0.04)/0.41 0.88	0.93 (0.04)/0.41 0.89	0.93 (0.04)/0.41 0.87	0.93 (0.04)/0.41 0.87	0.93 (0.05)/0.41 0.84	0.93 (0.04)/0.41 0.87	0.93 (0.05)/0.41 0.83	0.93 (0.04)/0.41 0.87	0.93 (0.05)/0.41 0.83	0.93 (0.05)/0.41 0.84
		Excluded Beam[b]	0.02 (0.04)/0.39 0.8	0.02 (0.04)/0.39 0.79	0.02 (0.04)/0.39 0.8	0.02 (0.04)/0.39 0.78	0.02 (0.04)/0.39 0.77	0.03 (0.05)/0.39 0.74	0.02 (0.04)/0.39 0.77	0.03 (0.05)/0.39 0.74	0.02 (0.04)/0.39 0.77	0.03 (0.05)/0.39 0.74	0.03 (0.05)/0.39 0.74
		45°	0.19 (0.02)/0.28 0.84	0.19 (0.02)/0.29 0.83	0.19 (0.02)/0.28 0.84	0.19 (0.02)/0.29 0.82	0.19 (0.02)/0.29 0.82	0.19 (0.03)/0.29 0.79	0.19 (0.03)/0.29 0.81	0.20 (0.03)/0.29 0.78	0.19 (0.03)/0.29 0.81	0.20 (0.03)/0.29 0.78	0.19 (0.03)/0.29 0.79
		Closed	0.02 (0.02)/0.09 0.67	0.02 (0.02)/0.09 0.66	0.02 (0.02)/0.09 0.67	0.02 (0.02)/0.09 0.66	0.02 (0.02)/0.09 0.66	0.02 (0.02)/0.10 0.65	0.02 (0.02)/0.09 0.66	0.02 (0.03)/0.10 0.65	0.02 (0.02)/0.09 0.66	0.02 (0.03)/0.10 0.65	0.02 (0.02)/0.10 0.65
Outdoor Side	0.50	Worst[a]	0.94 (0.98)/0.43 0.95	0.94 (0.98)/0.43 0.93	0.94 (0.99)/0.44 0.93	0.94 (0.98)/0.44 0.91	0.94 (0.97)/0.43 0.92	0.94 (0.95)/0.43 0.88	0.94 (0.96)/0.43 0.91	0.94 (0.95)/0.43 0.88	0.94 (0.96)/0.43 0.91	0.94 (0.95)/0.43 0.88	0.94 (0.96)/0.43 0.88
		0°	0.94 (0.14)/0.50 0.94	0.94 (0.14)/0.50 0.92	0.94 (0.14)/0.50 0.92	0.94 (0.14)/0.50 0.9	0.94 (0.14)/0.49 0.91	0.94 (0.14)/0.49 0.87	0.94 (0.14)/0.49 0.91	0.94 (0.14)/0.49 0.87	0.94 (0.14)/0.49 0.91	0.94 (0.14)/0.49 0.87	0.94 (0.14)/0.49 0.88
		Excluded Beam[b]	0.07 (0.14)/0.47 0.91	0.07 (0.14)/0.47 0.9	0.07 (0.14)/0.48 0.9	0.07 (0.14)/0.48 0.88	0.07 (0.14)/0.47 0.88	0.07 (0.14)/0.47 0.85	0.07 (0.14)/0.47 0.88	0.07 (0.14)/0.47 0.84	0.07 (0.14)/0.47 0.88	0.08 (0.14)/0.47 0.84	0.07 (0.14)/0.47 0.85
		45°	0.25 (0.06)/0.36 0.92	0.25 (0.06)/0.36 0.9	0.25 (0.06)/0.36 0.91	0.25 (0.06)/0.36 0.88	0.25 (0.06)/0.36 0.89	0.25 (0.06)/0.36 0.85	0.25 (0.06)/0.36 0.88	0.25 (0.06)/0.36 0.85	0.25 (0.06)/0.36 0.88	0.25 (0.06)/0.36 0.85	0.25 (0.06)/0.36 0.85
		Closed	0.04 (0.02)/0.13 0.84	0.04 (0.02)/0.13 0.82	0.04 (0.02)/0.13 0.83	0.04 (0.02)/0.13 0.81	0.04 (0.02)/0.13 0.81	0.04 (0.03)/0.13 0.77	0.04 (0.02)/0.13 0.8	0.04 (0.03)/0.14 0.77	0.04 (0.02)/0.13 0.8	0.04 (0.03)/0.14 0.77	0.04 (0.03)/0.14 0.77
Outdoor Side	0.80	Worst[a]	0.95 (1.07)/0.55 0.95	0.95 (1.07)/0.55 0.93	0.95 (1.08)/0.55 0.93	0.95 (1.08)/0.55 0.91	0.95 (1.04)/0.55 0.92	0.95 (1.02)/0.54 0.88	0.95 (1.04)/0.54 0.91	0.95 (1.02)/0.54 0.88	0.95 (1.04)/0.54 0.91	0.95 (1.02)/0.54 0.88	0.95 (1.03)/0.54 0.88
		0°	0.95 (0.28)/0.61 0.95	0.95 (0.28)/0.61 0.93	0.95 (0.29)/0.62 0.93	0.95 (0.28)/0.61 0.91	0.95 (0.28)/0.61 0.92	0.95 (0.28)/0.61 0.88	0.95 (0.28)/0.61 0.91	0.95 (0.28)/0.61 0.88	0.95 (0.28)/0.61 0.91	0.95 (0.28)/0.61 0.88	0.95 (0.28)/0.61 0.88
		Excluded Beam[b]	0.16 (0.28)/0.59 0.94	0.16 (0.28)/0.59 0.92	0.16 (0.29)/0.59 0.92	0.16 (0.28)/0.59 0.9	0.16 (0.28)/0.59 0.91	0.16 (0.28)/0.58 0.87	0.16 (0.28)/0.59 0.9	0.16 (0.28)/0.58 0.87	0.16 (0.28)/0.59 0.9	0.16 (0.28)/0.58 0.87	0.16 (0.28)/0.59 0.87
		45°	0.34 (0.12)/0.47 0.94	0.34 (0.12)/0.47 0.92	0.34 (0.12)/0.47 0.92	0.34 (0.12)/0.47 0.9	0.33 (0.12)/0.46 0.91	0.33 (0.12)/0.46 0.88	0.33 (0.12)/0.46 0.91	0.33 (0.12)/0.46 0.87	0.33 (0.12)/0.46 0.91	0.33 (0.12)/0.46 0.87	0.33 (0.12)/0.46 0.88
		Closed	0.08 (0.04)/0.21 0.92	0.08 (0.04)/0.21 0.9	0.08 (0.04)/0.21 0.91	0.08 (0.04)/0.21 0.88	0.08 (0.04)/0.21 0.89	0.08 (0.04)/0.20 0.85	0.08 (0.04)/0.21 0.88	0.08 (0.04)/0.20 0.85	0.08 (0.04)/0.21 0.88	0.08 (0.04)/0.20 0.85	0.08 (0.04)/0.20 0.85

Notes:

[a]Louvers track so that profile angle equals negative slat angle and maximum direct beam is admitted.

[b] Louvers track to block direct beam radiation. When negative slat angles result, slat defaults to 0°.

[c] Glazing cavity width equals original cavity width plus slat width.

Table 13D IAC Values for Louvered Shades: Coated Double Glazings with 0.1 Low-e

		Glazing ID:	21a	21b	21c	21d	21e	21f	21g	21h	21i	21j	21k
Louver Location	Louver Reflection	ϕ	IAC_0 (IAC_{60})/IAC_{diff}, F_R										
Indoor Side	0.15	Worst[a]	0.99 (0.98)/0.94 0.85	0.99 (0.98)/0.95 0.82	0.99 (0.98)/0.95 0.82	0.99 (0.98)/0.95 0.8	0.99 (0.98)/0.95 0.8	0.99 (0.98)/0.95 0.75	0.99 (0.98)/0.95 0.79	0.99 (0.98)/0.95 0.75	0.99 (0.98)/0.95 0.79	0.99 (0.98)/0.95 0.75	0.99 (0.98)/0.95 0.76
		0°	0.99 (0.92)/0.95 0.66	0.99 (0.92)/0.95 0.64	0.99 (0.93)/0.96 0.64	0.99 (0.93)/0.96 0.63	0.99 (0.93)/0.96 0.63	0.99 (0.93)/0.96 0.61	0.99 (0.93)/0.96 0.63	0.99 (0.94)/0.96 0.6	0.99 (0.93)/0.96 0.63	0.99 (0.94)/0.96 0.6	0.99 (0.93)/0.96 0.61
		Excluded Beam[b]	0.89 (0.92)/0.95 0.41	0.89 (0.92)/0.95 0.41	0.90 (0.93)/0.95 0.41	0.90 (0.93)/0.96 0.41	0.90 (0.93)/0.95 0.4	0.91 (0.93)/0.96 0.4	0.90 (0.93)/0.96 0.4	0.91 (0.94)/0.96 0.4	0.90 (0.93)/0.96 0.4	0.91 (0.94)/0.96 0.4	0.91 (0.93)/0.96 0.4
		45°	0.92 (0.89)/0.93 0.44	0.92 (0.90)/0.93 0.43	0.92 (0.90)/0.93 0.43	0.93 (0.91)/0.94 0.43	0.92 (0.91)/0.94 0.43	0.93 (0.91)/0.94 0.42	0.93 (0.91)/0.94 0.42	0.93 (0.91)/0.94 0.41	0.93 (0.91)/0.94 0.42	0.93 (0.91)/0.94 0.41	0.93 (0.91)/0.94 0.42
		Closed	0.86 (0.87)/0.88 0.4	0.87 (0.87)/0.89 0.39	0.87 (0.88)/0.89 0.39	0.88 (0.88)/0.90 0.39	0.88 (0.88)/0.89 0.38	0.89 (0.89)/0.90 0.37	0.88 (0.88)/0.90 0.38	0.89 (0.89)/0.90 0.37	0.88 (0.88)/0.90 0.38	0.89 (0.89)/0.90 0.37	0.89 (0.89)/0.90 0.37
Indoor Side	0.50	Worst[a]	0.99 (0.98)/0.89 0.86	0.99 (0.98)/0.90 0.84	0.99 (0.98)/0.91 0.83	0.99 (0.98)/0.91 0.81	0.99 (0.98)/0.91 0.81	0.99 (0.98)/0.92 0.76	0.99 (0.98)/0.91 0.8	0.99 (0.98)/0.92 0.76	0.99 (0.98)/0.91 0.8	0.99 (0.98)/0.92 0.76	0.99 (0.98)/0.92 0.76
		0°	0.99 (0.85)/0.92 0.7	0.99 (0.86)/0.92 0.68	0.99 (0.87)/0.93 0.67	0.99 (0.87)/0.93 0.66	0.99 (0.87)/0.93 0.66	0.99 (0.89)/0.94 0.63	0.99 (0.87)/0.93 0.66	0.99 (0.89)/0.94 0.63	0.99 (0.87)/0.93 0.66	0.99 (0.89)/0.94 0.63	0.99 (0.89)/0.94 0.64
		Excluded Beam[b]	0.77 (0.85)/0.91 0.47	0.79 (0.86)/0.92 0.46	0.79 (0.87)/0.92 0.46	0.81 (0.87)/0.92 0.45	0.80 (0.87)/0.92 0.45	0.82 (0.89)/0.93 0.44	0.80 (0.87)/0.92 0.45	0.82 (0.89)/0.93 0.44	0.80 (0.87)/0.92 0.45	0.82 (0.89)/0.93 0.44	0.82 (0.89)/0.93 0.44
		45°	0.83 (0.77)/0.86 0.49	0.84 (0.79)/0.87 0.48	0.85 (0.79)/0.88 0.48	0.86 (0.81)/0.88 0.47	0.85 (0.80)/0.88 0.47	0.87 (0.82)/0.89 0.45	0.86 (0.80)/0.88 0.47	0.87 (0.83)/0.89 0.45	0.86 (0.80)/0.88 0.47	0.87 (0.83)/0.89 0.45	0.87 (0.82)/0.89 0.45
		Closed	0.71 (0.70)/0.75 0.41	0.73 (0.73)/0.77 0.39	0.74 (0.73)/0.78 0.39	0.75 (0.75)/0.79 0.38	0.75 (0.75)/0.79 0.39	0.77 (0.77)/0.81 0.37	0.75 (0.75)/0.79 0.38	0.78 (0.78)/0.81 0.37	0.75 (0.75)/0.79 0.38	0.78 (0.78)/0.81 0.37	0.77 (0.77)/0.81 0.37
Indoor Side	0.80	Worst[a]	0.98 (0.97)/0.84 0.88	0.98 (0.97)/0.85 0.85	0.98 (0.97)/0.86 0.84	0.98 (0.97)/0.87 0.82	0.98 (0.97)/0.86 0.82	0.98 (0.97)/0.88 0.77	0.98 (0.97)/0.86 0.81	0.98 (0.97)/0.88 0.77	0.98 (0.97)/0.86 0.81	0.98 (0.97)/0.88 0.77	0.98 (0.97)/0.88 0.78
		0°	0.98 (0.76)/0.87 0.76	0.98 (0.78)/0.88 0.74	0.98 (0.79)/0.89 0.73	0.98 (0.81)/0.89 0.71	0.98 (0.80)/0.89 0.72	0.98 (0.83)/0.90 0.68	0.98 (0.81)/0.89 0.71	0.98 (0.83)/0.90 0.68	0.98 (0.81)/0.89 0.71	0.98 (0.83)/0.90 0.68	0.98 (0.83)/0.90 0.68
		Excluded Beam[b]	0.64 (0.76)/0.86 0.59	0.67 (0.78)/0.87 0.56	0.69 (0.79)/0.88 0.56	0.71 (0.81)/0.89 0.54	0.70 (0.80)/0.88 0.55	0.73 (0.83)/0.90 0.52	0.70 (0.81)/0.88 0.54	0.74 (0.83)/0.90 0.52	0.70 (0.81)/0.88 0.54	0.74 (0.83)/0.90 0.52	0.73 (0.83)/0.90 0.52
		45°	0.74 (0.64)/0.79 0.59	0.76 (0.67)/0.81 0.57	0.77 (0.68)/0.81 0.56	0.79 (0.71)/0.83 0.54	0.78 (0.70)/0.82 0.55	0.80 (0.74)/0.84 0.52	0.78 (0.70)/0.82 0.55	0.81 (0.74)/0.84 0.52	0.78 (0.70)/0.82 0.55	0.81 (0.74)/0.84 0.51	0.81 (0.74)/0.84 0.52
		Closed	0.54 (0.53)/0.62 0.45	0.59 (0.58)/0.66 0.42	0.60 (0.59)/0.67 0.42	0.63 (0.62)/0.69 0.4	0.62 (0.61)/0.68 0.41	0.66 (0.66)/0.72 0.38	0.62 (0.62)/0.69 0.41	0.67 (0.66)/0.72 0.38	0.62 (0.62)/0.69 0.41	0.67 (0.67)/0.72 0.38	0.66 (0.66)/0.72 0.38
Between Glazings[c]	0.15	Worst[a]	0.98 (1.01)/0.80 0.91	0.98 (1.01)/0.80 0.9	0.96 (0.99)/0.60 0.9	0.96 (0.99)/0.61 0.89	0.96 (0.98)/0.61 0.89	0.95 (0.97)/0.63 0.87	0.95 (0.98)/0.61 0.89	0.95 (0.97)/0.63 0.86	0.95 (0.98)/0.61 0.89	0.95 (0.97)/0.63 0.86	0.95 (0.97)/0.62 0.87
		0°	0.98 (0.69)/0.82 0.8	0.98 (0.70)/0.83 0.79	0.96 (0.40)/0.64 0.79	0.96 (0.40)/0.65 0.78	0.96 (0.42)/0.65 0.78	0.95 (0.44)/0.66 0.77	0.95 (0.42)/0.65 0.78	0.95 (0.45)/0.66 0.77	0.95 (0.42)/0.65 0.78	0.95 (0.45)/0.66 0.77	0.95 (0.44)/0.66 0.77
		Excluded Beam[b]	0.63 (0.69)/0.81 0.66	0.64 (0.70)/0.82 0.66	0.34 (0.40)/0.63 0.66	0.35 (0.40)/0.63 0.65	0.36 (0.42)/0.64 0.65	0.39 (0.44)/0.65 0.65	0.37 (0.42)/0.64 0.65	0.39 (0.45)/0.65 0.65	0.37 (0.42)/0.64 0.65	0.40 (0.45)/0.65 0.65	0.39 (0.44)/0.65 0.65
		45°	0.71 (0.66)/0.77 0.69	0.71 (0.67)/0.78 0.69	0.47 (0.36)/0.55 0.7	0.47 (0.37)/0.56 0.7	0.48 (0.38)/0.56 0.69	0.50 (0.41)/0.58 0.69	0.49 (0.39)/0.57 0.69	0.51 (0.42)/0.58 0.68	0.49 (0.39)/0.57 0.69	0.51 (0.42)/0.58 0.68	0.50 (0.41)/0.58 0.69
		Closed	0.61 (0.64)/0.68 0.65	0.63 (0.65)/0.69 0.65	0.33 (0.35)/0.41 0.64	0.34 (0.36)/0.41 0.64	0.35 (0.37)/0.42 0.64	0.38 (0.40)/0.45 0.64	0.35 (0.37)/0.43 0.64	0.38 (0.40)/0.45 0.64	0.35 (0.37)/0.43 0.64	0.38 (0.40)/0.45 0.64	0.38 (0.40)/0.45 0.64
Between Glazings[c]	0.50	Worst[a]	0.97 (1.03)/0.77 0.92	0.97 (1.03)/0.78 0.9	0.97 (1.06)/0.63 0.91	0.97 (1.06)/0.63 0.89	0.96 (1.05)/0.64 0.9	0.95 (1.03)/0.65 0.87	0.96 (1.04)/0.64 0.89	0.95 (1.03)/0.65 0.87	0.96 (1.04)/0.64 0.89	0.95 (1.03)/0.65 0.87	0.95 (1.03)/0.65 0.87
		0°	0.97 (0.65)/0.81 0.83	0.97 (0.66)/0.81 0.82	0.97 (0.42)/0.68 0.83	0.97 (0.42)/0.68 0.82	0.96 (0.44)/0.69 0.82	0.95 (0.46)/0.69 0.8	0.96 (0.44)/0.69 0.81	0.95 (0.46)/0.70 0.8	0.96 (0.44)/0.69 0.81	0.95 (0.47)/0.70 0.79	0.95 (0.46)/0.69 0.8
		Excluded Beam[b]	0.54 (0.65)/0.80 0.7	0.55 (0.66)/0.80 0.7	0.32 (0.42)/0.66 0.72	0.32 (0.42)/0.67 0.71	0.34 (0.44)/0.67 0.71	0.37 (0.46)/0.68 0.7	0.34 (0.44)/0.67 0.71	0.37 (0.46)/0.68 0.7	0.34 (0.44)/0.67 0.71	0.38 (0.47)/0.68 0.7	0.37 (0.46)/0.68 0.7

Table 13E IAC Values for Louvered Shades: Double Glazings with 0.05 Low-e (*Continued*)

		Glazing ID:	25a	25b	25c	26d	25e	25f
		Excluded Beam[b]	0.58 (0.68)/0.81 0.7	0.60 (0.69)/0.81 0.7	0.64 (0.71)/0.81 0.68	0.63 (0.71)/0.81 0.69	0.65 (0.72)/0.81 0.68	0.63 (0.71)/0.81 0.69
		45°	0.68 (0.59)/0.74 0.73	0.69 (0.61)/0.75 0.72	0.71 (0.65)/0.76 0.7	0.71 (0.64)/0.76 0.71	0.72 (0.66)/0.77 0.7	0.71 (0.64)/0.76 0.71
		Closed	0.52 (0.52)/0.60 0.66	0.54 (0.54)/0.61 0.66	0.59 (0.59)/0.65 0.65	0.58 (0.58)/0.64 0.66	0.60 (0.60)/0.65 0.65	0.58 (0.58)/0.64 0.66
Between Glazings[c]	0.80	Worst[a]	0.97 (1.02)/0.77 0.93	0.97 (1.01)/0.78 0.91	0.95 (0.98)/0.79 0.87	0.95 (0.98)/0.79 0.88	0.94 (0.97)/0.79 0.86	0.95 (0.99)/0.79 0.88
		0°	0.97 (0.65)/0.81 0.87	0.97 (0.67)/0.82 0.86	0.95 (0.70)/0.82 0.83	0.95 (0.69)/0.82 0.83	0.94 (0.71)/0.82 0.82	0.95 (0.69)/0.82 0.84
		Excluded Beam[b]	0.51 (0.65)/0.80 0.8	0.53 (0.67)/0.81 0.79	0.59 (0.70)/0.81 0.76	0.58 (0.69)/0.81 0.76	0.60 (0.71)/0.81 0.75	0.58 (0.69)/0.81 0.76
		45°	0.64 (0.50)/0.71 0.81	0.65 (0.53)/0.73 0.8	0.69 (0.59)/0.74 0.76	0.68 (0.58)/0.74 0.77	0.69 (0.60)/0.75 0.76	0.68 (0.58)/0.74 0.77
		Closed	0.39 (0.36)/0.49 0.73	0.42 (0.39)/0.51 0.73	0.49 (0.47)/0.57 0.7	0.48 (0.46)/0.56 0.71	0.51 (0.49)/0.58 0.7	0.48 (0.46)/0.56 0.71
Outdoor Side	0.15	Worst[a]	0.93 (0.92)/0.36 0.94	0.93 (0.92)/0.36 0.92	0.93 (0.90)/0.36 0.87	0.93 (0.89)/0.36 0.88	0.93 (0.90)/0.36 0.86	0.93 (0.89)/0.36 0.89
		0°	0.93 (0.05)/0.41 0.89	0.93 (0.05)/0.41 0.87	0.93 (0.06)/0.41 0.82	0.93 (0.05)/0.41 0.83	0.93 (0.06)/0.42 0.81	0.93 (0.05)/0.41 0.84
		Excluded Beam[b]	0.03 (0.05)/0.39 0.78	0.03 (0.05)/0.39 0.77	0.04 (0.06)/0.40 0.72	0.03 (0.05)/0.39 0.73	0.04 (0.06)/0.40 0.71	0.03 (0.05)/0.39 0.74
		45°	0.20 (0.03)/0.29 0.83	0.20 (0.03)/0.29 0.82	0.20 (0.04)/0.30 0.77	0.20 (0.03)/0.29 0.78	0.20 (0.04)/0.30 0.76	0.20 (0.03)/0.29 0.78
		Closed	0.02 (0.02)/0.10 0.66	0.02 (0.02)/0.10 0.66	0.03 (0.03)/0.11 0.64	0.03 (0.03)/0.10 0.65	0.03 (0.04)/0.11 0.64	0.03 (0.03)/0.10 0.65
Outdoor Side	0.50	Worst[a]	0.94 (1.08)/0.45 0.94	0.94 (1.06)/0.45 0.92	0.94 (0.99)/0.44 0.87	0.94 (0.96)/0.44 0.88	0.94 (0.98)/0.44 0.86	0.94 (0.97)/0.44 0.89
		0°	0.94 (0.15)/0.51 0.93	0.94 (0.15)/0.51 0.91	0.94 (0.15)/0.50 0.86	0.94 (0.15)/0.50 0.87	0.94 (0.15)/0.50 0.85	0.94 (0.15)/0.50 0.88
		Excluded Beam[b]	0.08 (0.15)/0.49 0.9	0.08 (0.15)/0.49 0.88	0.08 (0.15)/0.48 0.83	0.08 (0.15)/0.48 0.84	0.08 (0.15)/0.48 0.82	0.08 (0.15)/0.48 0.85
		45°	0.26 (0.06)/0.38 0.91	0.26 (0.06)/0.38 0.89	0.26 (0.07)/0.37 0.84	0.25 (0.06)/0.36 0.85	0.26 (0.07)/0.37 0.82	0.25 (0.06)/0.36 0.85
		Closed	0.04 (0.03)/0.15 0.82	0.04 (0.03)/0.15 0.81	0.05 (0.03)/0.14 0.75	0.04 (0.03)/0.14 0.76	0.05 (0.03)/0.14 0.74	0.04 (0.03)/0.14 0.76
Outdoor Side	0.80	Worst[a]	0.95 (1.25)/0.59 0.94	0.95 (1.21)/0.58 0.92	0.95 (1.08)/0.56 0.87	0.95 (1.04)/0.55 0.88	0.95 (1.06)/0.55 0.86	0.95 (1.05)/0.55 0.89
		0°	0.95 (0.30)/0.64 0.94	0.95 (0.30)/0.64 0.92	0.95 (0.29)/0.62 0.88	0.95 (0.28)/0.61 0.88	0.95 (0.29)/0.61 0.86	0.95 (0.28)/0.61 0.89
		Excluded Beam[b]	0.18 (0.30)/0.62 0.93	0.18 (0.30)/0.62 0.91	0.17 (0.29)/0.60 0.86	0.16 (0.28)/0.59 0.87	0.17 (0.29)/0.59 0.85	0.17 (0.28)/0.59 0.88
		45°	0.37 (0.13)/0.51 0.93	0.37 (0.13)/0.50 0.91	0.35 (0.13)/0.48 0.86	0.34 (0.12)/0.47 0.87	0.35 (0.13)/0.47 0.85	0.34 (0.12)/0.47 0.88
		Closed	0.09 (0.04)/0.24 0.91	0.09 (0.04)/0.24 0.89	0.09 (0.04)/0.22 0.83	0.08 (0.04)/0.21 0.85	0.09 (0.04)/0.21 0.82	0.08 (0.04)/0.21 0.85

Notes:

[a] Louvers track so that profile angle equals negative slat angle and maximum direct beam is admitted.

[b] Louvers track to block direct beam radiation. When negative slat angles result, slat defaults to 0°.

[c] Glazing cavity width equals original cavity width plus slat width.

Table 13F IAC Values for Louvered Shades: Triple Glazings

		Glazing ID:	29a	29b	32a	32b	32c	32d	40a	40b	40c	40d
Louver Location	**Louver Reflection**	**ϕ**	IAC_0 (IAC_{60})/IAC_{diff}, F_R									
Indoor Side	0.15	Worst[a]	0.99 (0.98)/0.94 0.82	0.99 (0.98)/0.95 0.78	0.99 (0.98)/0.95 0.8	0.99 (0.98)/0.96 0.75	1.00 (1.00)/0.97 0.76	1.00 (1.00)/0.97 0.71	1.00 (1.00)/0.98 0.73	1.00 (1.00)/0.98 0.67	0.99 (0.99)/0.96 0.78	0.99 (0.99)/0.96 0.73
		0°	0.99 (0.92)/0.95 0.65	0.99 (0.93)/0.95 0.62	0.99 (0.94)/0.96 0.64	0.99 (0.94)/0.96 0.61	1.00 (0.96)/0.98 0.6	1.00 (0.96)/0.98 0.56	1.00 (0.96)/0.98 0.58	1.00 (0.97)/0.99 0.54	0.99 (0.95)/0.97 0.63	0.99 (0.95)/0.97 0.6
		Excluded Beam[b]	0.88 (0.92)/0.95 0.41	0.89 (0.93)/0.95 0.4	0.90 (0.94)/0.96 0.41	0.91 (0.94)/0.96 0.4	0.93 (0.96)/0.97 0.39	0.93 (0.96)/0.98 0.36	0.94 (0.96)/0.98 0.37	0.95 (0.97)/0.98 0.35	0.92 (0.95)/0.97 0.4	0.93 (0.95)/0.97 0.4
		45°	0.91 (0.89)/0.93 0.43	0.92 (0.90)/0.93 0.43	0.93 (0.91)/0.94 0.43	0.93 (0.92)/0.95 0.42	0.95 (0.93)/0.96 0.41	0.95 (0.94)/0.97 0.38	0.95 (0.94)/0.97 0.39	0.96 (0.95)/0.97 0.37	0.94 (0.92)/0.95 0.42	0.94 (0.93)/0.96 0.41
		Closed	0.86 (0.87)/0.88 0.39	0.87 (0.88)/0.89 0.38	0.88 (0.89)/0.90 0.39	0.89 (0.90)/0.91 0.37	0.91 (0.91)/0.93 0.37	0.92 (0.92)/0.94 0.35	0.92 (0.93)/0.94 0.36	0.93 (0.94)/0.95 0.33	0.90 (0.90)/0.92 0.38	0.91 (0.91)/0.92 0.37
Indoor Side	0.50	Worst[a]	0.98 (0.98)/0.90 0.83	0.98 (0.98)/0.91 0.79	0.99 (0.98)/0.91 0.81	0.99 (0.98)/0.92 0.76	0.99 (0.99)/0.92 0.77	1.00 (1.00)/0.93 0.72	0.99 (1.00)/0.93 0.74	1.00 (1.00)/0.95 0.68	0.99 (0.98)/0.92 0.79	0.99 (0.98)/0.93 0.74
		0°	0.98 (0.86)/0.92 0.68	0.98 (0.87)/0.93 0.65	0.99 (0.88)/0.93 0.67	0.99 (0.90)/0.94 0.64	0.99 (0.89)/0.94 0.62	1.00 (0.91)/0.95 0.58	0.99 (0.91)/0.95 0.6	1.00 (0.92)/0.96 0.56	0.99 (0.89)/0.94 0.66	0.99 (0.91)/0.95 0.63
		Excluded Beam[b]	0.77 (0.86)/0.91 0.46	0.80 (0.87)/0.92 0.45	0.80 (0.88)/0.93 0.45	0.83 (0.90)/0.94 0.44	0.81 (0.89)/0.94 0.42	0.83 (0.91)/0.95 0.39	0.83 (0.91)/0.95 0.4	0.86 (0.92)/0.96 0.37	0.82 (0.89)/0.93 0.45	0.84 (0.91)/0.94 0.44
		45°	0.83 (0.78)/0.87 0.48	0.85 (0.81)/0.88 0.46	0.85 (0.81)/0.89 0.47	0.87 (0.84)/0.90 0.45	0.86 (0.82)/0.90 0.43	0.88 (0.84)/0.91 0.4	0.88 (0.84)/0.91 0.41	0.90 (0.87)/0.93 0.38	0.87 (0.83)/0.90 0.46	0.89 (0.85)/0.91 0.45
		Closed	0.71 (0.72)/0.77 0.39	0.74 (0.75)/0.79 0.38	0.75 (0.76)/0.80 0.39	0.78 (0.79)/0.82 0.37	0.76 (0.76)/0.81 0.35	0.79 (0.80)/0.83 0.33	0.78 (0.80)/0.83 0.34	0.82 (0.83)/0.86 0.31	0.77 (0.78)/0.81 0.38	0.80 (0.81)/0.84 0.36
Indoor Side	0.80	Worst[a]	0.98 (0.97)/0.85 0.84	0.98 (0.97)/0.87 0.8	0.98 (0.97)/0.86 0.82	0.98 (0.97)/0.88 0.77	0.99 (0.99)/0.87 0.79	0.99 (0.99)/0.89 0.73	0.99 (0.99)/0.88 0.75	0.99 (0.99)/0.90 0.69	0.98 (0.98)/0.87 0.8	0.98 (0.98)/0.89 0.75
		0°	0.98 (0.78)/0.88 0.74	0.98 (0.81)/0.89 0.7	0.98 (0.81)/0.89 0.72	0.98 (0.84)/0.91 0.68	0.99 (0.81)/0.90 0.67	0.99 (0.83)/0.91 0.62	0.99 (0.83)/0.91 0.64	0.99 (0.86)/0.93 0.59	0.98 (0.82)/0.90 0.71	0.98 (0.85)/0.92 0.67
		Excluded Beam[b]	0.66 (0.78)/0.87 0.56	0.70 (0.81)/0.89 0.53	0.69 (0.81)/0.88 0.55	0.74 (0.84)/0.90 0.52	0.69 (0.81)/0.89 0.49	0.73 (0.83)/0.90 0.45	0.72 (0.83)/0.90 0.46	0.77 (0.86)/0.92 0.42	0.71 (0.82)/0.89 0.54	0.76 (0.85)/0.91 0.51
		45°	0.75 (0.67)/0.80 0.56	0.78 (0.71)/0.83 0.53	0.77 (0.71)/0.82 0.55	0.81 (0.75)/0.85 0.52	0.77 (0.70)/0.83 0.49	0.80 (0.74)/0.85 0.44	0.80 (0.74)/0.85 0.46	0.83 (0.78)/0.87 0.42	0.79 (0.73)/0.84 0.54	0.82 (0.77)/0.86 0.51
		Closed	0.57 (0.58)/0.65 0.42	0.62 (0.64)/0.70 0.4	0.61 (0.63)/0.69 0.41	0.67 (0.68)/0.74 0.38	0.60 (0.62)/0.69 0.35	0.66 (0.67)/0.73 0.31	0.65 (0.66)/0.72 0.33	0.71 (0.72)/0.77 0.29	0.64 (0.65)/0.71 0.4	0.69 (0.71)/0.76 0.38
Between Glazings[c]	0.15	Worst[a]	0.97 (1.01)/0.63 0.9	0.97 (1.02)/0.64 0.87	0.98 (1.05)/0.76 0.88	0.98 (1.05)/0.77 0.85	0.97 (1.01)/0.60 0.79	0.98 (1.02)/0.62 0.74	0.98 (1.05)/0.73 0.75	0.99 (1.05)/0.75 0.7	0.98 (1.04)/0.71 0.87	0.99 (1.04)/0.73 0.84
		0°	0.97 (0.44)/0.66 0.79	0.97 (0.46)/0.68 0.78	0.98 (0.62)/0.78 0.78	0.98 (0.63)/0.80 0.77	0.97 (0.40)/0.64 0.59	0.98 (0.42)/0.66 0.56	0.98 (0.57)/0.76 0.57	0.99 (0.60)/0.78 0.54	0.98 (0.55)/0.74 0.78	0.99 (0.58)/0.76 0.76
		Excluded Beam[b]	0.36 (0.44)/0.65 0.66	0.38 (0.46)/0.67 0.65	0.52 (0.62)/0.77 0.66	0.54 (0.63)/0.79 0.65	0.32 (0.40)/0.63 0.34	0.35 (0.42)/0.65 0.33	0.48 (0.57)/0.75 0.33	0.50 (0.60)/0.77 0.33	0.46 (0.55)/0.73 0.65	0.49 (0.58)/0.75 0.65
		45°	0.48 (0.41)/0.59 0.7	0.50 (0.43)/0.60 0.69	0.62 (0.58)/0.72 0.69	0.64 (0.60)/0.73 0.68	0.45 (0.37)/0.56 0.43	0.47 (0.40)/0.58 0.41	0.58 (0.54)/0.69 0.4	0.60 (0.57)/0.71 0.39	0.57 (0.52)/0.68 0.69	0.59 (0.55)/0.69 0.68
		Closed	0.36 (0.41)/0.46 0.64	0.38 (0.43)/0.48 0.64	0.51 (0.57)/0.61 0.65	0.53 (0.58)/0.63 0.65	0.32 (0.37)/0.43 0.31	0.34 (0.40)/0.45 0.31	0.46 (0.53)/0.57 0.32	0.49 (0.55)/0.60 0.32	0.45 (0.51)/0.56 0.64	0.48 (0.53)/0.58 0.64
Between Glazings[c]	0.50	Worst[a]	0.97 (1.06)/0.65 0.9	0.98 (1.06)/0.66 0.88	0.98 (1.08)/0.74 0.89	0.98 (1.08)/0.75 0.86	0.97 (1.07)/0.63 0.8	0.98 (1.07)/0.65 0.75	0.98 (1.09)/0.72 0.77	0.99 (1.09)/0.74 0.71	0.98 (1.08)/0.71 0.88	0.99 (1.08)/0.72 0.85
		0°	0.97 (0.45)/0.69 0.83	0.98 (0.47)/0.71 0.81	0.98 (0.58)/0.78 0.81	0.98 (0.60)/0.79 0.79	0.97 (0.42)/0.68 0.66	0.98 (0.44)/0.69 0.62	0.98 (0.55)/0.77 0.62	0.99 (0.57)/0.78 0.59	0.98 (0.54)/0.75 0.81	0.99 (0.56)/0.77 0.79

Table 13F IAC Values for Louvered Shades: Triple Glazings (*Continued*)

		Glazing ID:	29a	29b	32a	32b	32c	32d	40a	40b	40c	40d
		Excluded Beam[b]	0.33 (0.45)/0.68 0.71	0.34 (0.47)/0.69 0.7	0.44 (0.58)/0.77 0.7	0.46 (0.60)/0.78 0.69	0.30 (0.42)/0.66 0.46	0.32 (0.44)/0.68 0.43	0.41 (0.55)/0.75 0.42	0.43 (0.57)/0.77 0.4	0.40 (0.54)/0.74 0.7	0.42 (0.56)/0.75 0.69
		45°	0.47 (0.35)/0.59 0.74	0.49 (0.37)/0.60 0.73	0.57 (0.47)/0.68 0.72	0.59 (0.48)/0.69 0.71	0.45 (0.32)/0.57 0.51	0.47 (0.35)/0.59 0.48	0.55 (0.44)/0.66 0.47	0.56 (0.46)/0.68 0.44	0.54 (0.43)/0.65 0.72	0.56 (0.45)/0.67 0.71
		Closed	0.28 (0.29)/0.39 0.66	0.29 (0.31)/0.41 0.66	0.38 (0.40)/0.50 0.66	0.40 (0.41)/0.51 0.66	0.25 (0.27)/0.37 0.36	0.27 (0.29)/0.39 0.35	0.35 (0.37)/0.48 0.35	0.37 (0.39)/0.49 0.34	0.34 (0.36)/0.46 0.66	0.36 (0.38)/0.48 0.65
Between Glazings[c]	0.80	Worst[a]	0.97 (1.11)/0.68 0.91	0.98 (1.11)/0.69 0.89	0.97 (1.11)/0.73 0.9	0.98 (1.11)/0.73 0.87	0.98 (1.12)/0.67 0.81	0.98 (1.12)/0.69 0.76	0.98 (1.12)/0.72 0.79	0.99 (1.12)/0.73 0.73	0.98 (1.11)/0.71 0.89	0.99 (1.11)/0.72 0.86
		0°	0.97 (0.48)/0.74 0.87	0.98 (0.49)/0.75 0.85	0.97 (0.55)/0.78 0.85	0.98 (0.56)/0.79 0.83	0.98 (0.47)/0.73 0.75	0.98 (0.48)/0.74 0.7	0.98 (0.54)/0.78 0.71	0.99 (0.55)/0.79 0.66	0.98 (0.53)/0.77 0.85	0.99 (0.54)/0.78 0.82
		Excluded Beam[b]	0.32 (0.48)/0.72 0.81	0.33 (0.49)/0.73 0.79	0.38 (0.55)/0.76 0.78	0.39 (0.56)/0.77 0.76	0.31 (0.47)/0.71 0.63	0.32 (0.48)/0.72 0.59	0.37 (0.54)/0.76 0.58	0.38 (0.55)/0.77 0.54	0.36 (0.53)/0.75 0.78	0.38 (0.54)/0.76 0.76
		45°	0.48 (0.31)/0.61 0.82	0.49 (0.32)/0.62 0.79	0.54 (0.37)/0.65 0.79	0.55 (0.38)/0.66 0.77	0.47 (0.30)/0.60 0.65	0.49 (0.32)/0.62 0.6	0.52 (0.36)/0.65 0.59	0.54 (0.37)/0.66 0.55	0.52 (0.35)/0.64 0.79	0.53 (0.36)/0.65 0.77
		Closed	0.22 (0.19)/0.36 0.73	0.23 (0.21)/0.37 0.72	0.27 (0.24)/0.41 0.71	0.29 (0.26)/0.42 0.7	0.21 (0.18)/0.35 0.49	0.22 (0.20)/0.37 0.46	0.26 (0.23)/0.40 0.45	0.28 (0.25)/0.41 0.43	0.25 (0.23)/0.39 0.72	0.27 (0.24)/0.40 0.7
Outdoor Side	0.15	Worst[a]	0.93 (0.90)/0.35 0.92	0.93 (0.90)/0.35 0.9	0.93 (0.90)/0.35 0.91	0.93 (0.89)/0.35 0.88	0.93 (0.90)/0.35 0.83	0.93 (0.90)/0.35 0.78	0.93 (0.90)/0.35 0.81	0.93 (0.89)/0.35 0.75	0.93 (0.89)/0.35 0.9	0.93 (0.89)/0.35 0.87
		0°	0.93 (0.04)/0.41 0.88	0.93 (0.05)/0.41 0.86	0.93 (0.04)/0.40 0.88	0.93 (0.04)/0.41 0.85	0.93 (0.04)/0.41 0.77	0.93 (0.04)/0.41 0.72	0.93 (0.04)/0.40 0.76	0.93 (0.04)/0.41 0.7	0.93 (0.04)/0.40 0.87	0.93 (0.04)/0.40 0.84
		Excluded Beam[b]	0.02 (0.04)/0.39 0.78	0.02 (0.05)/0.39 0.76	0.02 (0.04)/0.39 0.79	0.02 (0.04)/0.39 0.77	0.02 (0.04)/0.39 0.59	0.02 (0.04)/0.39 0.55	0.02 (0.04)/0.39 0.59	0.02 (0.04)/0.39 0.55	0.02 (0.04)/0.39 0.79	0.02 (0.04)/0.39 0.77
		45°	0.19 (0.02)/0.29 0.83	0.19 (0.03)/0.29 0.81	0.19 (0.02)/0.28 0.83	0.19 (0.02)/0.28 0.81	0.19 (0.02)/0.29 0.67	0.19 (0.02)/0.29 0.63	0.19 (0.02)/0.28 0.66	0.19 (0.02)/0.28 0.62	0.19 (0.02)/0.28 0.83	0.19 (0.02)/0.28 0.8
		Closed	0.02 (0.02)/0.09 0.66	0.02 (0.02)/0.09 0.66	0.01 (0.02)/0.09 0.67	0.02 (0.02)/0.09 0.66	0.02 (0.02)/0.09 0.36	0.02 (0.02)/0.09 0.35	0.01 (0.01)/0.09 0.37	0.01 (0.02)/0.09 0.35	0.01 (0.01)/0.09 0.67	0.01 (0.02)/0.09 0.66
Outdoor Side	0.50	Worst[a]	0.94 (1.00)/0.44 0.92	0.94 (0.99)/0.44 0.9	0.94 (0.99)/0.44 0.91	0.94 (0.99)/0.44 0.88	0.94 (1.00)/0.44 0.84	0.94 (1.00)/0.44 0.79	0.94 (1.00)/0.44 0.81	0.94 (0.99)/0.44 0.75	0.94 (0.99)/0.44 0.9	0.94 (0.99)/0.43 0.87
		0°	0.94 (0.14)/0.50 0.92	0.94 (0.14)/0.50 0.89	0.94 (0.14)/0.50 0.91	0.94 (0.14)/0.50 0.88	0.94 (0.14)/0.50 0.83	0.94 (0.14)/0.50 0.78	0.94 (0.14)/0.50 0.81	0.94 (0.14)/0.50 0.75	0.94 (0.14)/0.50 0.9	0.94 (0.14)/0.50 0.87
		Excluded Beam[b]	0.07 (0.14)/0.48 0.89	0.07 (0.14)/0.48 0.86	0.07 (0.14)/0.48 0.88	0.07 (0.14)/0.48 0.85	0.07 (0.14)/0.48 0.78	0.07 (0.14)/0.48 0.73	0.07 (0.14)/0.48 0.76	0.07 (0.14)/0.48 0.7	0.07 (0.14)/0.48 0.88	0.07 (0.14)/0.47 0.85
		45°	0.24 (0.06)/0.36 0.9	0.25 (0.06)/0.36 0.87	0.24 (0.06)/0.36 0.89	0.24 (0.06)/0.36 0.86	0.24 (0.06)/0.36 0.8	0.24 (0.06)/0.36 0.74	0.24 (0.06)/0.36 0.78	0.24 (0.06)/0.36 0.72	0.24 (0.06)/0.36 0.88	0.24 (0.06)/0.36 0.85
		Closed	0.04 (0.02)/0.14 0.82	0.04 (0.02)/0.14 0.79	0.03 (0.02)/0.13 0.82	0.04 (0.02)/0.13 0.79	0.03 (0.02)/0.14 0.65	0.04 (0.02)/0.14 0.61	0.03 (0.02)/0.13 0.65	0.03 (0.02)/0.13 0.6	0.03 (0.02)/0.13 0.82	0.03 (0.02)/0.13 0.79
Outdoor Side	0.80	Worst[a]	0.95 (1.11)/0.56 0.92	0.95 (1.10)/0.56 0.9	0.95 (1.10)/0.56 0.91	0.95 (1.08)/0.55 0.88	0.95 (1.11)/0.56 0.84	0.95 (1.10)/0.56 0.79	0.95 (1.10)/0.56 0.81	0.95 (1.09)/0.55 0.75	0.95 (1.10)/0.55 0.9	0.95 (1.08)/0.55 0.87
		0°	0.95 (0.29)/0.62 0.93	0.95 (0.29)/0.62 0.9	0.95 (0.29)/0.62 0.92	0.95 (0.29)/0.62 0.89	0.95 (0.29)/0.62 0.84	0.95 (0.29)/0.62 0.79	0.95 (0.29)/0.62 0.82	0.95 (0.29)/0.62 0.76	0.95 (0.29)/0.62 0.9	0.95 (0.29)/0.62 0.87
		Excluded Beam[b]	0.16 (0.29)/0.60 0.91	0.16 (0.29)/0.60 0.88	0.16 (0.29)/0.60 0.9	0.16 (0.29)/0.59 0.87	0.15 (0.29)/0.60 0.82	0.15 (0.29)/0.60 0.76	0.15 (0.29)/0.60 0.79	0.15 (0.29)/0.60 0.73	0.15 (0.29)/0.60 0.89	0.15 (0.29)/0.59 0.86
		45°	0.33 (0.13)/0.48 0.92	0.33 (0.13)/0.48 0.89	0.33 (0.12)/0.48 0.91	0.33 (0.12)/0.47 0.88	0.33 (0.13)/0.48 0.83	0.33 (0.13)/0.48 0.77	0.33 (0.12)/0.48 0.8	0.33 (0.12)/0.47 0.74	0.33 (0.12)/0.48 0.9	0.33 (0.12)/0.47 0.87
		Closed	0.08 (0.04)/0.22 0.89	0.08 (0.04)/0.22 0.87	0.08 (0.04)/0.21 0.89	0.08 (0.04)/0.21 0.86	0.08 (0.04)/0.22 0.79	0.08 (0.04)/0.22 0.74	0.08 (0.04)/0.21 0.77	0.08 (0.04)/0.21 0.71	0.08 (0.04)/0.21 0.88	0.08 (0.04)/0.21 0.85

Notes:

[a] Louvers track so that profile angle equals negative slat angle and maximum direct beam is admitted.

[b] Louvers track to block direct beam radiation. When negative slat angles result, slat defaults to 0°.

[c] Glazing cavity width equals original cavity width plus slat width.

Table 13G IAC Values for Draperies, Roller Shades, and Insect Screens

Drapery

Shade	Fabric Designator	Fullness	Glazing ID: 1a	1b	1c	1d	1e	1f	1g	1h	1i
			IAC, F_R								
Dark Closed Weave	III_D	100%	0.71, 0.50	0.71, 0.49	0.72, 0.47	0.74, 0.45	0.72, 0.47	0.74, 0.44	0.72, 0.47	0.74, 0.44	0.74, 0.45
Medium Closed Weave	III_M	100%	0.59, 0.53	0.60, 0.52	0.62, 0.49	0.65, 0.46	0.63, 0.49	0.66, 0.46	0.63, 0.49	0.66, 0.45	0.65, 0.46
Light Closed Weave	III_L	100%	0.45, 0.62	0.46, 0.60	0.50, 0.56	0.55, 0.50	0.51, 0.54	0.56, 0.50	0.51, 0.54	0.56, 0.49	0.55, 0.51
Dark Semiopen Weave	II_D	100%	0.75, 0.55	0.75, 0.54	0.76, 0.52	0.78, 0.49	0.76, 0.52	0.78, 0.49	0.76, 0.52	0.78, 0.49	0.78, 0.49
Medium Semiopen Weave	II_M	100%	0.65, 0.63	0.66, 0.62	0.68, 0.59	0.70, 0.55	0.68, 0.58	0.71, 0.54	0.68, 0.58	0.71, 0.54	0.70, 0.55
Light Semiopen Weave	II_L	100%	0.56, 0.79	0.57, 0.77	0.60, 0.71	0.64, 0.65	0.61, 0.70	0.65, 0.64	0.61, 0.70	0.65, 0.63	0.64, 0.65
Dark Open Weave	I_D	100%	0.80, 0.63	0.80, 0.62	0.81, 0.60	0.82, 0.57	0.82, 0.59	0.83, 0.56	0.82, 0.59	0.83, 0.56	0.82, 0.57
Medium Open Weave	I_M	100%	0.71, 0.73	0.72, 0.72	0.73, 0.69	0.76, 0.64	0.74, 0.68	0.76, 0.63	0.74, 0.68	0.76, 0.63	0.76, 0.64
Light Open Weave	I_L	100%	0.64, 0.87	0.65, 0.85	0.68, 0.80	0.71, 0.73	0.68, 0.78	0.71, 0.72	0.68, 0.78	0.72, 0.71	0.71, 0.73
Sheer		100%	0.73, 0.89	0.73, 0.88	0.75, 0.83	0.77, 0.77	0.75, 0.82	0.78, 0.76	0.75, 0.82	0.78, 0.75	0.77, 0.77

Shade	Fabric Designator	Fullness	Glazing ID: 5a	5b	5c	5d	5e	5f	5g	5h	5i
Dark Closed Weave	III_D	100%	0.81, 0.46	0.82, 0.45	0.82, 0.44	0.83, 0.42	0.82, 0.44	0.83, 0.42	0.82, 0.44	0.84, 0.42	0.83, 0.42
Medium Closed Weave	III_M	100%	0.70, 0.48	0.72, 0.46	0.72, 0.46	0.75, 0.43	0.72, 0.46	0.75, 0.43	0.72, 0.46	0.75, 0.43	0.75, 0.43
Light Closed Weave	III_L	100%	0.57, 0.54	0.60, 0.52	0.59, 0.52	0.64, 0.47	0.60, 0.51	0.65, 0.47	0.60, 0.51	0.65, 0.47	0.64, 0.47
Dark Semiopen Weave	II_D	100%	0.84, 0.51	0.85, 0.50	0.85, 0.49	0.86, 0.47	0.85, 0.49	0.86, 0.47	0.85, 0.49	0.86, 0.46	0.86, 0.47
Medium Semiopen Weave	II_M	100%	0.75, 0.57	0.76, 0.55	0.76, 0.55	0.79, 0.51	0.76, 0.55	0.79, 0.51	0.76, 0.55	0.79, 0.51	0.79, 0.52
Light Semiopen Weave	II_L	100%	0.65, 0.70	0.68, 0.67	0.67, 0.67	0.71, 0.61	0.68, 0.66	0.72, 0.60	0.68, 0.66	0.72, 0.60	0.72, 0.61
Dark Open Weave	I_D	100%	0.88, 0.59	0.88, 0.57	0.88, 0.57	0.89, 0.54	0.88, 0.57	0.89, 0.54	0.88, 0.57	0.89, 0.54	0.89, 0.54
Medium Open Weave	I_M	100%	0.79, 0.68	0.80, 0.65	0.80, 0.65	0.82, 0.61	0.80, 0.65	0.82, 0.60	0.80, 0.65	0.82, 0.60	0.82, 0.61
Light Open Weave	I_L	100%	0.72, 0.79	0.74, 0.76	0.73, 0.76	0.77, 0.69	0.74, 0.75	0.77, 0.69	0.74, 0.75	0.77, 0.68	0.77, 0.69
Sheer		100%	0.78, 0.83	0.8, 0.8	0.8, 0.8	0.82, 0.73	0.8, 0.79	0.82, 0.73	0.8, 0.79	0.82, 0.73	0.82, 0.74

Shade	Fabric Designator	Fullness	Glazing ID: 17a	17b	17c	17d	17e	17f	17g	17h	17i	17j	17k
Dark Closed Weave	III_D	100%	0.85, 0.45	0.86, 0.43	0.86, 0.44	0.87, 0.43	0.86, 0.43	0.88, 0.41	0.87, 0.42	0.88, 0.40	0.87, 0.42	0.88, 0.40	0.88, 0.41
Medium Closed Weave	III_M	100%	0.74, 0.47	0.76, 0.45	0.76, 0.45	0.79, 0.44	0.77, 0.44	0.80, 0.42	0.78, 0.44	0.80, 0.41	0.78, 0.44	0.80, 0.41	0.80, 0.42
Light Closed Weave	III_L	100%	0.60, 0.52	0.64, 0.50	0.64, 0.50	0.68, 0.47	0.66, 0.48	0.71, 0.44	0.66, 0.48	0.71, 0.44	0.66, 0.48	0.71, 0.44	0.71, 0.45
Dark Semiopen Weave	II_D	100%	0.88, 0.50	0.89, 0.48	0.88, 0.49	0.89, 0.47	0.89, 0.48	0.90, 0.45	0.89, 0.47	0.90, 0.45	0.89, 0.47	0.90, 0.45	0.90, 0.45
Medium Semiopen Weave	II_M	100%	0.78, 0.56	0.8, 0.54	0.8, 0.54	0.82, 0.52	0.81, 0.52	0.83, 0.49	0.81, 0.52	0.83, 0.49	0.81, 0.52	0.83, 0.49	0.83, 0.49
Light Semiopen Weave	II_L	100%	0.68, 0.68	0.71, 0.64	0.71, 0.64	0.74, 0.61	0.72, 0.62	0.76, 0.57	0.73, 0.62	0.77, 0.57	0.73, 0.62	0.77, 0.57	0.76, 0.57
Dark Open Weave	I_D	100%	0.90, 0.58	0.91, 0.56	0.91, 0.56	0.91, 0.55	0.91, 0.55	0.92, 0.52	0.91, 0.55	0.92, 0.52	0.91, 0.55	0.92, 0.52	0.92, 0.52
Medium Open Weave	I_M	100%	0.81, 0.66	0.83, 0.64	0.83, 0.64	0.85, 0.61	0.84, 0.62	0.86, 0.58	0.84, 0.62	0.86, 0.58	0.84, 0.62	0.86, 0.58	0.86, 0.58
Light Open Weave	I_L	100%	0.74, 0.77	0.76, 0.73	0.76, 0.73	0.79, 0.69	0.77, 0.71	0.81, 0.65	0.78, 0.71	0.81, 0.65	0.78, 0.71	0.81, 0.65	0.81, 0.65
Sheer		100%	0.8, 0.81	0.82, 0.77	0.82, 0.78	0.84, 0.74	0.83, 0.75	0.85, 0.7	0.83, 0.75	0.85, 0.69	0.83, 0.75	0.85, 0.69	0.85, 0.7

Shade	Fabric Designator	Fullness	Glazing ID: 21a	21b	21c	21d	21e	21f	21g	21h	21i	21j	21k
Dark Closed Weave	III_D	100%	0.87, 0.44	0.88, 0.43	0.88, 0.43	0.88, 0.42	0.88, 0.42	0.89, 0.40	0.88, 0.42	0.89, 0.40	0.88, 0.42	0.89, 0.40	0.89, 0.40
Medium Closed Weave	III_M	100%	0.77, 0.46	0.79, 0.45	0.79, 0.45	0.81, 0.43	0.80, 0.43	0.82, 0.41	0.80, 0.43	0.82, 0.41	0.80, 0.43	0.82, 0.41	0.82, 0.41
Light Closed Weave	III_L	100%	0.64, 0.52	0.67, 0.49	0.68, 0.49	0.70, 0.47	0.69, 0.47	0.73, 0.45	0.70, 0.47	0.73, 0.44	0.70, 0.47	0.73, 0.44	0.73, 0.45
Dark Semiopen Weave	II_D	100%	0.89, 0.49	0.90, 0.48	0.90, 0.48	0.90, 0.47	0.90, 0.47	0.91, 0.45	0.90, 0.47	0.91, 0.45	0.90, 0.47	0.91, 0.45	0.91, 0.45
Medium Semiopen Weave	II_M	100%	0.8, 0.55	0.82, 0.53	0.82, 0.53	0.83, 0.51	0.83, 0.52	0.85, 0.49	0.83, 0.51	0.85, 0.49	0.83, 0.51	0.85, 0.49	0.85, 0.49
Light Semiopen Weave	II_L	100%	0.71, 0.67	0.74, 0.64	0.74, 0.63	0.76, 0.61	0.75, 0.61	0.78, 0.57	0.76, 0.61	0.78, 0.57	0.76, 0.61	0.78, 0.57	0.78, 0.57
Dark Open Weave	I_D	100%	0.92, 0.57	0.92, 0.56	0.92, 0.55	0.92, 0.54	0.92, 0.54	0.93, 0.52	0.92, 0.54	0.93, 0.52	0.92, 0.54	0.93, 0.52	0.93, 0.52
Medium Open Weave	I_M	100%	0.83, 0.65	0.85, 0.63	0.85, 0.63	0.86, 0.61	0.86, 0.61	0.87, 0.58	0.86, 0.61	0.87, 0.58	0.86, 0.61	0.87, 0.58	0.87, 0.58
Light Open Weave	I_L	100%	0.76, 0.77	0.78, 0.73	0.79, 0.72	0.81, 0.69	0.80, 0.70	0.82, 0.65	0.80, 0.69	0.82, 0.65	0.80, 0.69	0.82, 0.65	0.82, 0.66
Sheer		100%	0.82, 0.81	0.83, 0.77	0.84, 0.76	0.85, 0.74	0.85, 0.74	0.86, 0.7	0.85, 0.74	0.86, 0.69	0.85, 0.74	0.86, 0.69	0.86, 0.7

Table 13G IAC Values for Draperies, Roller Shades, and Insect Screens (*Continued*)

		Glazing ID:	25a	25b	25c	26d	25e	25f
Dark Closed Weave	III_D	100%	0.88, 0.43	0.89, 0.42	0.90, 0.40	0.90, 0.40	0.91, 0.39	0.90, 0.40
Medium Closed Weave	III_M	100%	0.80, 0.45	0.82, 0.44	0.85, 0.41	0.84, 0.41	0.85, 0.40	0.84, 0.42
Light Closed Weave	III_L	100%	0.68, 0.51	0.72, 0.48	0.76, 0.44	0.76, 0.45	0.77, 3	0.76, 0.45
Dark Semiopen Weave	II_D	100%	0.91, 0.48	0.91, 0.47	0.92, 0.44	0.92, 0.45	0.92, 0.43	0.92, 0.45
Medium Semiopen Weave	II_M	100%	0.83, 0.54	0.85, 0.52	0.87, 0.48	0.86, 0.49	0.87, 0.47	0.86, 0.49
Light Semiopen Weave	II_L	100%	0.75, 0.66	0.78, 0.63	0.81, 0.57	0.81, 0.58	0.82, 0.55	0.81, 0.58
Dark Open Weave	I_D	100%	0.93, 0.56	0.93, 0.55	0.94, 0.51	0.94, 0.52	0.94, 0.50	0.94, 0.52
Medium Open Weave	I_M	100%	0.86, 0.65	0.87, 0.62	0.89, 0.57	0.89, 0.58	0.89, 0.56	0.89, 0.59
Light Open Weave	I_L	100%	0.79, 0.75	0.82, 0.72	0.85, 0.65	0.84, 0.66	0.85, 0.63	0.84, 0.67
Sheer		100%	0.84, 0.8	0.86, 0.76	0.88, 0.69	0.88, 0.7	0.89, 0.67	0.88, 0.71

		Glazing ID:	29a	29b
Dark Closed Weave	III_D	100%	0.86, 0.44	0.87, 0.42
Medium Closed Weave	III_M	100%	0.77, 0.45	0.80, 0.43
Light Closed Weave	III_L	100%	0.65, 0.50	0.69, 0.47
Dark Semiopen Weave	II_D	100%	0.89, 0.48	0.90, 0.47
Medium Semiopen Weave	II_M	100%	0.81, 0.54	0.83, 0.51
Light Semiopen Weave	II_L	100%	0.72, 0.65	0.76, 0.60
Dark Open Weave	I_D	100%	0.91, 0.56	0.92, 0.54
Medium Open Weave	I_M	100%	0.84, 0.64	0.85, 0.60
Light Open Weave	I_L	100%	0.77, 0.73	0.80, 0.69
Sheer		100%	0.83, 0.78	0.85, 0.73

		Glazing ID:	32a	32b	32c	32d	40a	40b	40c	40d
Dark Closed Weave	III_D	100%	0.89, 0.43	0.90, 0.41	0.91, 0.42	0.92, 0.39	0.93, 0.41	0.94, 0.37	0.90, 0.42	0.91, 0.40
Medium Closed Weave	III_M	100%	0.80, 0.44	0.83, 0.42	0.82, 0.42	0.84, 0.39	0.84, 0.40	0.87, 0.37	0.82, 0.43	0.85, 0.41
Light Closed Weave	III_L	100%	0.69, 0.48	0.73, 0.45	0.69, 0.44	0.73, 0.40	0.73, 0.42	0.77, 0.38	0.71, 0.47	0.76, 0.44
Dark Semiopen Weave	II_D	100%	0.91, 0.47	0.92, 0.46	0.93, 0.46	0.94, 0.43	0.94, 0.45	0.95, 0.41	0.92, 0.46	0.93, 0.45
Medium Semiopen Weave	II_M	100%	0.83, 0.52	0.85, 0.50	0.84, 0.50	0.86, 0.46	0.86, 0.48	0.89, 0.44	0.85, 0.51	0.87, 0.48
Light Semiopen Weave	II_L	100%	0.75, 0.62	0.79, 0.58	0.75, 0.58	0.79, 0.52	0.78, 0.55	0.82, 0.49	0.77, 0.60	0.80, 0.56
Dark Open Weave	I_D	100%	0.93, 0.55	0.93, 0.53	0.95, 0.53	0.95, 0.50	0.96, 0.51	0.96, 0.47	0.94, 0.54	0.94, 0.52
Medium Open Weave	I_M	100%	0.86, 0.62	0.87, 0.59	0.87, 0.59	0.88, 0.54	0.88, 0.56	0.90, 0.51	0.87, 0.60	0.89, 0.57
Light Open Weave	I_L	100%	0.80, 0.71	0.83, 0.66	0.80, 0.66	0.82, 0.60	0.82, 0.63	0.85, 0.57	0.81, 0.69	0.84, 0.64
Sheer		100%	0.84, 0.75	0.87, 0.7	0.85, 0.71	0.87, 0.65	0.86, 0.68	0.89, 0.61	0.86, 0.73	0.88, 0.68

Roller Shades and Insect Screens

Shade/Screen	Openness	Refl./Trans.										
		Glazing ID:	1a	1b	1c	1d	1e	1f	1g	1h	1i
Light Translucent	0.14	0.60/0.25	0.44, 0.74	0.45, 0.72	0.49, 0.66	0.55, 0.59	0.51, 0.65	0.56, 0.59	0.51, 0.65	0.57, 0.58	0.55, 0.6
White Opaque	0.00	0.65/0.00	0.34, 0.45	0.35, 0.44	0.4, 0.41	0.47, 0.38	0.42, 0.4	0.48, 0.38	0.42, 0.4	0.49, 0.38	0.47, 0.38
Dark Opaque	0.00	0.20/0.00	0.64, 0.48	0.65, 0.47	0.67, 0.45	0.69, 0.43	0.67, 0.45	0.7, 0.42	0.67, 0.45	0.7, 0.42	0.69, 0.43
Light Gray Translucent	0.10	0.31/0.15	0.61, 0.57	0.62, 0.57	0.64, 0.54	0.68, 0.51	0.65, 0.53	0.68, 0.5	0.65, 0.53	0.69, 0.5	0.68, 0.51
Dark Gray Translucent	0.14	0.17/0.19	0.71, 0.58	0.72, 0.58	0.73, 0.55	0.76, 0.52	0.74, 0.55	0.76, 0.52	0.74, 0.55	0.76, 0.52	0.76, 0.52
Reflective White Opaque	0.00	0.84/0.00	0.3, 0.71	0.32, 0.68	0.38, 0.6	0.45, 0.53	0.39, 0.58	0.46, 0.52	0.39, 0.58	0.47, 0.52	0.45, 0.53
Reflective White Translucent	0.07	0.75/0.16	0.23, 0.42	0.25, 0.41	0.31, 0.38	0.39, 0.36	0.33, 0.37	0.4, 0.35	0.33, 0.37	0.41, 0.35	0.39, 0.36
Outdoor Insect Screen			0.64, 0.98	0.64, 0.98	0.64, 0.95	0.64, 0.92	0.64, 0.95	0.64, 0.91	0.64, 0.95	0.64, 0.91	0.64, 0.92
Indoor Insect Screen			0.88, 0.81	0.88, 0.8	0.89, 0.78	0.9, 0.75	0.89, 0.78	0.9, 0.75	0.89, 0.78	0.9, 0.75	0.9, 0.76
		Glazing ID:	5a	5b	5c	5d	5e	5f	5g	5h	5i
Light Translucent	0.14	0.60/0.25	0.55, 0.65	0.58, 0.62	0.58, 0.62	0.63, 0.56	0.58, 0.61	0.64, 0.56	0.58, 0.61	0.64, 0.56	0.63, 0.56
White Opaque	0.00	0.65/0.00	0.48, 0.4	0.52, 0.39	0.51, 0.39	0.57, 0.37	0.52, 0.39	0.58, 0.37	0.52, 0.39	0.58, 0.36	0.57, 0.37
Dark Opaque	0.00	0.20/0.00	0.76, 0.44	0.77, 0.43	0.77, 0.43	0.8, 0.41	0.78, 0.43	0.8, 0.41	0.78, 0.43	0.8, 0.4	0.8, 0.41
Light Gray Translucent	0.10	0.31/0.15	0.72, 0.53	0.74, 0.51	0.74, 0.51	0.77, 0.48	0.74, 0.51	0.77, 0.48	0.74, 0.51	0.77, 0.48	0.77, 0.48
Dark Gray Translucent	0.14	0.17/0.19	0.81, 0.54	0.82, 0.53	0.82, 0.53	0.84, 0.5	0.82, 0.52	0.84, 0.5	0.82, 0.52	0.84, 0.5	0.84, 0.5
Reflective White Opaque	0.00	0.84/0.00	0.43, 0.6	0.47, 0.55	0.46, 0.56	0.54, 0.5	0.47, 0.55	0.55, 0.49	0.47, 0.55	0.55, 0.49	0.54, 0.5
Reflective White Translucent	0.07	0.75/0.16	0.37, 0.38	0.42, 0.36	0.41, 0.36	0.49, 0.34	0.42, 0.36	0.5, 0.34	0.42, 0.36	0.5, 0.34	0.49, 0.34
Outdoor Insect Screen			0.64, 0.96	0.64, 0.94	0.64, 0.94	0.64, 0.91	0.64, 0.94	0.64, 0.9	0.64, 0.94	0.64, 0.9	0.64, 0.91
Indoor Insect Screen			0.92, 0.78	0.93, 0.77	0.93, 0.76	0.93, 0.74	0.93, 0.76	0.93, 0.74	0.93, 0.76	0.93, 0.73	0.93, 0.74

Table 13G IAC Values for Draperies, Roller Shades, and Insect Screens (*Continued*)

		Glazing ID:	17a	17b	17c	17d	17e	17f	17g	17h	17i	17j	17k
Light Translucent	0.14	0.60/0.25	0.58, 0.63	0.62, 0.6	0.62, 0.6	0.67, 0.56	0.64, 0.58	0.69, 0.53	0.64, 0.57	0.7, 0.53	0.64, 0.57	0.7, 0.53	0.7, 0.53
White Opaque	0.00	0.65/0.00	0.52, 0.39	0.56, 0.38	0.57, 0.38	0.61, 0.37	0.59, 0.37	0.65, 0.36	0.59, 0.37	0.65, 0.36	0.59, 0.37	0.65, 0.35	0.65, 0.36
Dark Opaque	0.00	0.20/0.00	0.8, 0.43	0.82, 0.42	0.82, 0.42	0.83, 0.41	0.82, 0.41	0.84, 0.39	0.82, 0.41	0.84, 0.39	0.82, 0.41	0.84, 0.39	0.84, 0.39
Light Gray Translucent	0.10	0.31/0.15	0.76, 0.52	0.78, 0.5	0.78, 0.5	0.8, 0.48	0.78, 0.49	0.81, 0.46	0.79, 0.49	0.82, 0.46	0.79, 0.49	0.82, 0.46	0.81, 0.46
Dark Gray Translucent	0.14	0.17/0.19	0.84, 0.53	0.85, 0.52	0.85, 0.52	0.86, 0.5	0.86, 0.51	0.87, 0.48	0.86, 0.51	0.88, 0.48	0.86, 0.51	0.88, 0.48	0.87, 0.48
Reflective White Opaque	0.00	0.84/0.00	0.46, 0.57	0.52, 0.53	0.52, 0.53	0.58, 0.5	0.54, 0.51	0.61, 0.47	0.55, 0.51	0.62, 0.46	0.55, 0.51	0.62, 0.46	0.61, 0.47
Reflective White Translucent	0.07	0.75/0.16	0.41, 0.37	0.47, 0.36	0.47, 0.36	0.53, 0.35	0.49, 0.35	0.57, 0.34	0.5, 0.35	0.58, 0.34	0.5, 0.35	0.58, 0.33	0.57, 0.34
Outdoor Insect Screen			0.64, 0.95	0.64, 0.93	0.64, 0.94	0.64, 0.91	0.64, 0.92	0.64, 0.89	0.64, 0.92	0.64, 0.89	0.64, 0.92	0.64, 0.89	0.64, 0.89
Indoor Insect Screen			0.94, 0.77	0.94, 0.76	0.94, 0.76	0.94, 0.74	0.94, 0.75	0.95, 0.72	0.94, 0.75	0.95, 0.72	0.94, 0.75	0.95, 0.72	0.95, 0.72

		Glazing ID:	21a	21b	21c	21d	21e	21f	21g	21h	21i	21j	21k
Light Translucent	0.14	0.60/0.25	0.61, 0.63	0.65, 0.59	0.66, 0.59	0.69, 0.56	0.68, 0.57	0.72, 0.53	0.68, 0.57	0.72, 0.53	0.68, 0.57	0.72, 0.53	0.72, 0.53
White Opaque	0.00	0.65/0.00	0.55, 0.39	0.6, 0.38	0.61, 0.38	0.64, 0.37	0.63, 0.37	0.67, 0.36	0.63, 0.37	0.67, 0.36	0.63, 0.37	0.68, 0.35	0.67, 0.36
Dark Opaque	0.00	0.20/0.00	0.82, 0.43	0.84, 0.42	0.84, 0.42	0.85, 0.41	0.85, 0.41	0.86, 0.39	0.85, 0.41	0.86, 0.39	0.85, 0.41	0.86, 0.39	0.86, 0.39
Light Gray Translucent	0.10	0.31/0.15	0.78, 0.51	0.8, 0.5	0.8, 0.5	0.82, 0.48	0.81, 0.48	0.83, 0.46	0.81, 0.48	0.83, 0.46	0.81, 0.48	0.83, 0.46	0.83, 0.46
Dark Gray Translucent	0.14	0.17/0.19	0.86, 0.53	0.87, 0.51	0.87, 0.51	0.88, 0.5	0.88, 0.5	0.89, 0.48	0.88, 0.5	0.89, 0.48	0.88, 0.5	0.89, 0.48	0.89, 0.48
Reflective White Opaque	0.00	0.84/0.00	0.5, 0.56	0.55, 0.53	0.56, 0.52	0.6, 0.5	0.58, 0.51	0.63, 0.47	0.59, 0.5	0.64, 0.47	0.59, 0.5	0.64, 0.47	0.64, 0.47
Reflective White Translucent	0.07	0.75/0.16	0.44, 0.36	0.5, 0.35	0.51, 0.35	0.56, 0.35	0.54, 0.35	0.6, 0.34	0.54, 0.35	0.6, 0.34	0.54, 0.35	0.6, 0.33	0.6, 0.34
Outdoor Insect Screen			0.64, 0.95	0.64, 0.93	0.64, 0.93	0.64, 0.91	0.64, 0.92	0.64, 0.89	0.64, 0.91	0.64, 0.89	0.64, 0.91	0.64, 0.89	0.64, 0.89
Indoor Insect Screen			0.94, 0.77	0.95, 0.75	0.95, 0.75	0.95, 0.74	0.95, 0.74	0.95, 0.72	0.95, 0.74	0.95, 0.72	0.95, 0.74	0.95, 0.72	0.95, 0.72

		Glazing ID:	25a	25b	25c	26d	25e	25f
Light Translucent	0.14	0.60/0.25	0.66, 0.62	0.71, 0.58	0.75, 0.53	0.75, 0.54	0.77, 0.52	0.74, 0.55
White Opaque	0.00	0.65/0.00	0.6, 0.38	0.66, 0.37	0.71, 0.35	0.7, 0.36	0.72, 0.35	0.7, 0.36
Dark Opaque	0.00	0.20/0.00	0.85, 0.42	0.86, 0.41	0.88, 0.39	0.88, 0.39	0.88, 0.38	0.87, 0.39
Light Gray Translucent	0.10	0.31/0.15	0.81, 0.5	0.83, 0.49	0.86, 0.46	0.85, 0.46	0.86, 0.45	0.85, 0.47
Dark Gray Translucent	0.14	0.17/0.19	0.88, 0.52	0.89, 0.51	0.9, 0.47	0.9, 0.48	0.91, 0.47	0.9, 0.48
Reflective White Opaque	0.00	0.84/0.00	0.55, 0.55	0.61, 0.52	0.68, 0.47	0.67, 0.48	0.69, 0.46	0.66, 0.48
Reflective White Translucent	0.07	0.75/0.16	0.5, 0.36	0.57, 0.35	0.64, 0.33	0.62, 0.34	0.65, 0.33	0.62, 0.34
Outdoor Insect Screen			0.65, 0.95	0.65, 0.93	0.64, 0.88	0.64, 0.89	0.64, 0.87	0.64, 0.89
Indoor Insect Screen			0.95, 0.76	0.96, 0.75	0.96, 0.72	0.96, 0.72	0.96, 0.71	0.96, 0.72

		Glazing ID:	29a	29b
Light Translucent	0.14	0.60/0.25	0.64, 0.6	0.68, 0.56
White Opaque	0.00	0.65/0.00	0.58, 0.38	0.63, 0.37
Dark Opaque	0.00	0.20/0.00	0.82, 0.42	0.84, 0.41
Light Gray Translucent	0.10	0.31/0.15	0.78, 0.5	0.81, 0.48
Dark Gray Translucent	0.14	0.17/0.19	0.86, 0.52	0.87, 0.5
Reflective White Opaque	0.00	0.84/0.00	0.53, 0.53	0.59, 0.49
Reflective White Translucent	0.07	0.75/0.16	0.48, 0.36	0.55, 0.35
Outdoor Insect Screen			0.64, 0.94	0.64, 0.91
Indoor Insect Screen			0.94, 0.76	0.95, 0.74

		Glazing ID:	32a	32b	32c	32d	40a	40b	40c	40d
Light Translucent	0.14	0.60/0.25	0.67, 0.58	0.72, 0.54	0.67, 0.52	0.71, 0.46	0.7, 0.49	0.75, 0.43	0.69, 0.56	0.74, 0.52
White Opaque	0.00	0.65/0.00	0.62, 0.37	0.68, 0.36	0.62, 0.33	0.67, 0.3	0.67, 0.31	0.72, 0.29	0.65, 0.37	0.71, 0.36
Dark Opaque	0.00	0.20/0.00	0.85, 0.41	0.87, 0.4	0.87, 0.4	0.89, 0.38	0.89, 0.39	0.91, 0.36	0.87, 0.41	0.88, 0.39
Light Gray Translucent	0.10	0.31/0.15	0.81, 0.49	0.84, 0.47	0.82, 0.46	0.85, 0.43	0.85, 0.44	0.87, 0.41	0.83, 0.48	0.85, 0.46
Dark Gray Translucent	0.14	0.17/0.19	0.88, 0.51	0.89, 0.49	0.9, 0.49	0.91, 0.45	0.91, 0.47	0.92, 0.43	0.89, 0.5	0.91, 0.48
Reflective White Opaque	0.00	0.84/0.00	0.57, 0.51	0.64, 0.47	0.57, 0.44	0.63, 0.39	0.61, 0.41	0.68, 0.36	0.6, 0.5	0.67, 0.46
Reflective White Translucent	0.07	0.75/0.16	0.53, 0.35	0.61, 0.34	0.52, 0.28	0.59, 0.26	0.58, 0.27	0.65, 0.25	0.56, 0.35	0.64, 0.34
Outdoor Insect Screen			0.64, 0.92	0.64, 0.9	0.64, 0.86	0.64, 0.8	0.64, 0.83	0.64, 0.77	0.64, 0.91	0.64, 0.88
Indoor Insect Screen			0.95, 0.75	0.96, 0.73	0.95, 0.7	0.95, 0.67	0.96, 0.68	0.96, 0.64	0.96, 0.74	0.96, 0.72

Notes:

[a] Louvers track so that profile angle equals negative slat angle and maximum direct beam is admitted.

[b] Louvers track to block direct beam radiation. When negative slat angles result, slat defaults to 0°.

[c] Glazing cavity width equals original cavity width plus slat width.

VISUAL AND THERMAL CONTROLS

The ideal fenestration system allows optimum lighting, heating, ventilation, and visibility; minimizes moisture and sound transfer between the outdoor and the indoor; and produces a satisfactory physiological and psychological environment. The controls of an optimum system react to varying climatological and occupant demands. Fixed controls may have operation or cost advantages or both but do not react to physical and psychological variations. Variable controls are, therefore, more effective in energy conservation and environmental satisfaction.

Operational Effectiveness of Shading Devices

Shading devices vary in their operational effectiveness. Some devices, such as overhangs, light shelves, and tinted glazings, do not require operation, have long life expectancies, and do not degrade significantly over their effective life. Other types of shading devices, especially operable indoor shades, may have reduced effectiveness because of less than optimal operation and degradation of effectiveness over time. It is important to evaluate operational effectiveness when considering the actual heat rejection potential of shading devices.

The performance of shading devices for reducing peak cooling loads and annual energy use should account for operational effectiveness or reliability in actual operation. Passive devices, such as architectural elements and glazing tinting, are considered 100% effective in operation. Glazing coatings and adherent films may degrade over time. Shade screens are removable and may be assumed to operate seasonally, but in any given population of users, some will remain in place all year long and some will not be installed or removed at optimum times. Automated shading devices controlled for optimum thermal operation are considered more effective than manual devices, but controls require ongoing maintenance, and some occupants may object to the lack of personal control with totally automated devices. Automated shading devices may also be operated for nonthermal purposes such as glare and daylighting optimization, and this may reduce thermal effectiveness. Manually operated devices are subject to wide variation in use effectiveness, and this diversity in effective use should be considered when evaluating performance.

Indoor Shading Devices

Although thermal comfort of occupants within the glazed space may be paramount to the HVAC designer, other factors that should be considered, some of which may be more important to the user, include the following:

Radiant Energy Protection. Unshaded fenestration products become sources of radiant heat by transmitting short-wave solar radiation and by emitting long-wave radiation to dissipate some of the absorbed solar energy. In winter, glass temperatures usually fall below room air temperature, which may produce thermal discomfort to occupants near the fenestration. In summer, individuals seated near the unshaded fenestration product may experience discomfort from both direct solar rays and long-wave radiation emitted by sun-heated glass. In winter, loss of heat by radiation to cold glass can also cause discomfort. Tightly woven, highly reflective drapes minimize such discomfort; drapes with high openness factors are less effective because they allow short- and long-wave radiation to pass more freely. Light-colored shading devices with maximum total surface usually provide the best protection because they absorb less heat and tend to lose heat readily by convection to the conditioned air.

Outward Vision. Outward vision is normally desirable in both business and living spaces. Open-weave, dark-colored fabrics of uniform pattern allow maximum outward vision, whereas uneven pattern weaves reduce the ability to see out. A semiopen weave modifies the view without completely obscuring the outdoors. Tightly woven fabrics block outward vision completely.

Privacy. Venetian blinds, either vertical or horizontal, can be adjusted and, when completely closed, afford full privacy. When draperies are closed, the degree of privacy is determined by their color and tightness of weave and the source of the principal illumination. To obscure the view so completely that not even shadows or silhouettes can be detected, fully opaque materials are used. Generally, the more brightly lit side of a partially shaded glazing is the most visible from the opposite side, making the indoor fairly private in daytime, but not at night.

Brightness Control. Visual comfort is essential in many occupied areas, and freedom from glare is an important factor in performing tasks. *Discomfort glare* is produced by uneven brightness in occupied spaces, with areas or spots that are much brighter than surrounding surfaces. Windows themselves, when they look out onto bright skies or brightly reflecting surfaces, can be glare sources if care is not taken to keep surround brightness comparable. A maximum brightness ratio of about 3 to 1 is sometimes quoted. Moderation of this ratio can be achieved through using indoor furnishings and wall coverings, which on average have moderately high diffuse reflectances and access to admitted daylight. Conversely, dark indoor surfaces, and those shaded from daylight illumination, accentuate the brightness difference between the window and its surroundings. Indoor surface brightness can also be elevated by ample use of indoor electric lighting, but this can have adverse consequences for the building's energy use. In general, larger window apertures admit more sunlight, increasing indoor brightness without affecting the perceived brightness of the window, all other factors being equal.

An important guideline is that direct sunlight must not strike the eye, and reflected sunlight from bright or shiny surfaces is equally disturbing and even disabling. A tightly woven white fabric with high solar transmittance attains such brilliance when illuminated by direct sunshine that, by contrast with its surroundings, it creates excessive glare. Off-white colors should be used so their surface brightness is not too great. Venetian blinds allow considerable light to enter by interreflection between slats. When two shading devices are used, the one on the inside (away from the fenestration product) should be darker and more open. With this arrangement, the inside device can be used to control brightness for the other shading devices and, when used alone, to reduce brightness while still allowing some view of the outside.

View Modification. When the view is unattractive or distracting, draperies modify the view to some degree, depending on fabric weave and color (summarized in Table 14), but the fenestration product remains as an effective connection to the outside.

Sound Control. Indoor shading devices, particularly draperies, can absorb some of the sounds originating within the room but have little or no effect in preventing outdoor sounds from entering. For excessive internally generated sound, the usual remedy is to apply acoustical treatment to the ceiling and other room surfaces. Although these materials can be effective in controlling sound, they are often located on the two horizontal surfaces (ceiling and floor) and leave the opposing vertical surfaces of glass and bare wall to reflect sound. The noise reduction coefficient (NRC = average absorptance coefficient at four frequencies) for venetian blinds is about 0.10, compared to 0.02 for glass and 0.03 for plaster. For drapery fabrics at 100% fullness, NRC ranges from 0.10 to 0.65, depending on the tightness of weave. Class III (tightly woven) fabrics have NRC values of 0.35 to 0.65. Figure 22 shows the relationship between NRC and openness factor for fabrics of normal weight.

Double Drapery

Double draperies (two sets of drapery covering the same area) have a light, open weave on the fenestration product side for outward vision and daylight when desired and a heavy, closed weave or opaque drapery on the room side to block out sunlight and provide privacy when desired. When properly selected and used, double draperies can provide a reduced U-factor and a lowered IAC. The

Table 14 Summary of Environmental Control Capabilities of Draperies

Item	Designator (Figure 19)								
	I_D	I_M	I_L	II_D	II_M	II_L	III_D	III_M	III_L
1. Protection from direct solar radiation and long-wave radiation to or from window areas	Fair	Fair	Fair	Fair	Good	Good	Fair	Good	Good
2. Effectiveness in allowing outward vision through fenestration	Good	Good	Fair	Fair	Fair	Some	None	None	None
3. Effectiveness in attaining privacy (limiting inward vision from outside)	None	None	Poor[a] Good[a]	Poor	Fair	Fair[a] Good[a]	Good[b]	Good[b]	Good[b]
4. Protection against excessive brightness and glare from sunshine and external objects	Mild	Mild	Mild[c] Poor[c]	Good	Good	Good[c] Poor[c]	Good	Good	Good[c] Poor[c]
5. Effectiveness in modifying unattractive or distracting view out of window	Little	Little	Some	Some	Good	Good	Blocks	Blocks	Blocks

[a]Good when bright illumination is on viewing side.
[b]To obscure view completely, material must be completely opaque.
[c]Poor rating applies to white fabric in direct sunlight. Use off-white color to avoid excessive transmitted light.

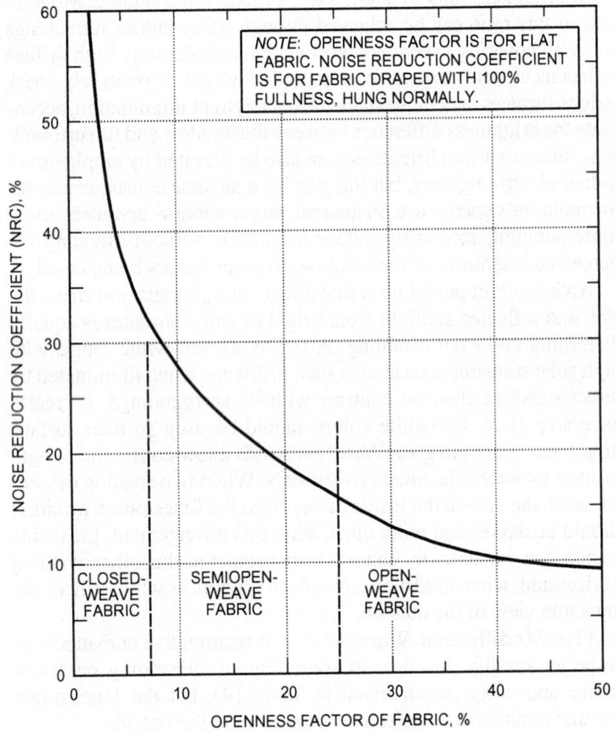

Fig. 22 Noise Reduction Coefficient Versus Openness Factor for Draperies

reduced U-factor results principally from adding a semiclosed air space to the barrier.

To most effectively reduce solar heat gain, drapery exposed to sunlight should have high reflectance and low transmittance. The light, open-weave drapery should be opened when the heavy drapery is closed to prevent entry of sunlight.

Properly used double draperies give (1) extreme flexibility of vision and light intensity, (2) a lowered U-factor and IAC, and (3) improved comfort, because the room-side drapery is more nearly at room temperature. Table 13 gives characteristics of individual draperies. For large areas, the IAC should be calculated in detail to determine the cooling load.

AIR LEAKAGE

Infiltration Through Fenestration

Air infiltration through fenestration products affects occupant comfort and energy consumption. Infiltration is the uncontrolled inward leakage of air caused by pressure effects of wind or differences in air density, such as stack effect. Infiltration should not be confused with ventilation. Although fenestration products can be operated to intentionally provide natural ventilation and increase comfort, infiltration should be reasonably minimized to avoid unpleasant accompanying problems. If additional air is required, controlled ventilation is preferable to infiltration. Mechanical ventilation provides air in a comfortable manner and when desired. For infiltration, however, peak supply is more likely to occur as an uncomfortable draft and when least desired, such as during a storm or the coldest weather.

ASHRAE/IESNA *Standard* 90.1, ASHRAE's energy standard for all buildings other than low-rise residential buildings, establishes an air leakage maximum of 2.0 L/s per square metre of gross fenestration product area (5.0 L/s per square metre for swinging entrance doors and revolving doors). This air leakage is as determined in accordance with NFRC *Technical Document* 400 and ASTM *Standard* E283 and allows direct comparison of all fenestration products: operable and fixed, windows and doors.

Most manufactured fenestration products achieve these reasonable standards of maximum air infiltration. However, products that do not completely seal, such as jalousie windows or doors, are not likely to do so and are most appropriate for installation in unconditioned spaces.

For products achieving this infiltration standard, energy consumption caused by infiltration is likely to be significantly less than energy associated with U-factor and solar heat gain coefficient. Also, although overall air infiltration is a significant component in determining a building's heating and cooling loads, infiltration through fenestration products meeting the standard is generally likely to be a small portion of that total.

Indoor Air Movement

Because supply air grilles are frequently located directly below fenestration products, air sweeps the indoor glass surface. Heated supply air should be directed away from the glass to prevent large temperature differences between the center and edges of the glass. These thermal effects must be considered, particularly when annealed glass is used and air is forced over the glass surface during the heating season. Direct flow of heated air over the glass surface can increase the heat transfer coefficient and temperature difference, causing a substantial increase in heat loss, as well as leading to thermally induced stress and risk of glass breakage.

Systems designed predominantly for cooling lower the glass temperature and rapidly pick up the cooling load. Both tend to improve comfort conditions. However, the air-conditioned space has an increased net heat gain caused by increases in (1) solar heat gain coefficient (SHGC) caused by delivery of more of the absorbed heat to the indoor space, (2) fenestration U-factor because of the greater convection effect at the indoor surface, and (3) air-to-air temperature difference because supply air rather than room air is in contact with the indoor glass surface. The principal increase in heat gain with clear glass is the result of increased U-factor and air-to-air temperature difference.

DAYLIGHTING

DAYLIGHT PREDICTION

Daylighting is the illumination of building interiors with sunlight and sky light and is known to affect visual performance, lighting quality, health, human performance, and energy efficiency. In many European countries with predominantly cloudy skies, codes regulate minimum window size, minimum daylight factor, and window position to provide views to all occupants and to create a minimum indoor brightness level. Daylighting also provides back-up indoor illumination in the event of power outages. Daylighting may have some positive or negative health effects on the skin, eyes, hormone secretion, and mood. Its temporal variation, intensity, spectral content, and diurnal and temporal variation may be used to combat jet lag, sick building syndrome, and other health problems.

In terms of energy efficiency, daylighting can provide substantial whole-building energy reductions in nonresidential buildings through the use of electric lighting controls. Daylight admission can displace the need for electric lighting at the perimeter zone with vertical windows (sidelighting) and at the core zone with skylights (toplighting). Lighting and its associated cooling energy use constitute 30 to 40% of a nonresidential building's energy use. Energy use reductions can be achieved, perhaps less reliably, in residential buildings with manual or automated switching of electric lights on and off to match space occupancy. For internal-load-dominated buildings, daylight admission must be balanced against solar heat admission to achieve optimum energy efficiency. Because heat gains from solar radiation typically define peak load conditions, daylighting is also a very effective method of decreasing peak demand. Daylighting can not only decrease annual operating costs through energy efficiency, but may also reduce capital cost by mechanical downsizing.

For daylighting designs using direct-beam sunlight entry, care must be taken to avoid overheating and glare. Such problems can be avoided by carefully controlling or eliminating direct beam entry through orientation and shading of daylighting apertures and other architectural features.

For conventional sidelit nonresidential buildings, three basic relationships for daylight optimization are given as a function of (1) glazing properties and (2) window area or the **window-to-wall area ratio (WWR),** which is defined as the ratio of the transparent glazing area to the outdoor floor-to-floor wall area:

1. Annual cooling energy use (including fan energy use) increases linearly with solar radiation admission, as indicated by the product of SHGC and WWR, but is affected by decreases in electric lighting heat gains.
2. Annual lighting energy use decreases exponentially/asymptotically with daylight admission, as indicated by the product of T_v and WWR.
3. Annual heating energy use (including fan energy use) increases linearly with decreased lighting heat gains.

Figure 23 illustrates the first two relationships for a prototypical nonresidential building. A similar relationship can be demonstrated with skylights.

The fenestration design that achieves an optimum balance between daylight admission and solar rejection can be determined by iterative calculations where the glazing area and/or glazing solar-optical properties are varied parametrically. For each case, the following general steps should be taken for each hour over a year:

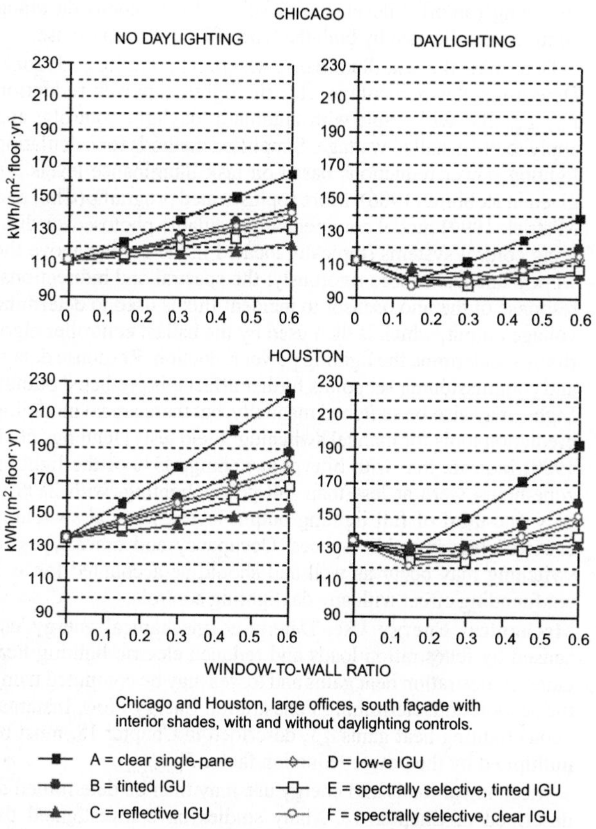

Fig. 23 Window-to-Wall Ratio Versus Annual Electricity Use in kWh/(m²·floor·year)

1. **Indoor Daylight Illuminance.** Determine the building characteristics, configuration, outdoor design conditions, and operating schedules as described in Chapter 18. These include building orientation, outdoor obstructions, ground reflectance, etc. Determine the depth from the window wall for each electric lighting zone. Typical sidelighting windows can effectively daylight the perimeter zone to a depth of 1.5 times the head height of the window. In private offices, one dimming zone is typically cost-effective, whereas in open-plan offices, two zones are cost-effective.

   Select a typical task location in each of the lighting zones. Determine indoor daylight illuminance from all window and skylight sources at these locations. Indoor illuminance may be determined using computer simulation tools or physical scale models. Comprehensive explanations of simple and computer-based tools are available (IEA 1999). The majority of these tools can model simple box geometry with noncomplex fenestration systems. Some advanced simulation tools, such as Radiance (Ward 1990) and Adeline (Erhorn and Dirksmöller 2000), can model complex geometry and fenestration systems with adequate bidirectional solar-optical data, but this capability is not routine.

2. **Lighting Energy Use.** Determine the type of lamps, ballasts, and control system to be used in the perimeter zones. Determine whether the lamp can be dimmed or switched. For example, fluorescent lamps can be dimmed, but metal halides cannot be switched or dimmed. Cold, outdoor applications of some lamps may prevent switching. For electronic dimming ballasts, obtain dimming power and light output characteristics. Obtain control specifications to determine how the system will respond to available light; dead-band ranges, response times, and commissioning affect the sensitivity and accuracy of the system. The type of

switching (on/off, bilevel, multilevel, and continuous dimming controls) are dictated by both the type of lamp and space use.

Determine the task illuminance design set point for each zone. Determine the percentage electric lighting power reduction $F_{daylight}$ that will result with automatic daylight controls, and apply to the installed wattage. Simplified methods for calculating lighting power reductions based on task illuminance levels are given in Robbins (1986). More sophisticated programs (Choi and Mistrick 1999) model commercially available photosensor dimming control systems (typically located in the ceiling above the work plane task) more rigorously; the spectral and bidirectional response of the photosensor to incident flux is used to determine voltage output, which is then used by the ballast controller algorithm to determine the lighting power reduction. Response delays and commissioning set points further affect this predicted output. Lights may also be switched manually, but there are no modeling prediction tools for manual switching. Field tests (Jennings et al. 1999) indicate that with bilevel switching, 45% of the lighting zone-hours were at less than full-power lighting, with 28% at only one-third of full lighting output levels. Manual switching occurred less in public spaces. Occupancy and other types of switching may occur as well and should be accounted for as a confounding effect with any daylighting controls.

3. **Mechanical Energy Use.** Determine mechanical energy use caused by fenestration loads and reduced electric lighting heat gains. Fenestration heat gains and losses may be computed using the section on Determining Fenestration Energy Flow. Instantaneous lighting heat gains q_{el}, described in Chapter 18, must be multiplied by the power reduction factor $F_{daylight}$.

   Mechanical loads and energy use may then be determined as described in Chapter 18. Many studies have investigated the magnitude of change in heating and cooling energy use associated with reductions of lighting energy use in nonresidential buildings, as will be realized with daylighting controls. In a DOE-2.1E simulation study (Sezgen and Koomey 2000), the greatest savings were generated in hospitals, large offices, and large hotels; for every \$1.00 saved through lighting energy efficiency, additional savings as a result of reduced HVAC were \$0.26, \$0.16, and \$0.14, respectively. These results emphasize the need to include HVAC effects when assessing the effects of daylighting. Simplified design tools are available to conduct such parametric runs for preliminary analysis. Skylighting tools based on regressions using DOE-2 data or simplified DOE-2 procedures are also available (AAMA 1987; Heschong et al. 1998). More comprehensive building energy prediction tools combined with daylighting algorithms, such as DOE-2.1E (Winkelmann 1983), implement hour-by-hour calculations using existing weather data and enable evaluation of glare, visual comfort, and quality of light as well.

In the United States, a general rule has been that the fenestration area should be at least 20% of the floor area. In Europe, a similar rule was based on a minimum illumination value on the normal work plane from a standard overcast sky condition. In general, it is more energy-efficient to use larger window areas to elevate indoor surface brightness as a glare reduction strategy than to increase indoor electric lighting levels. As window area increases, indoor brightness increases while window brightness remains the same. Of course, mitigating considerations include increased cost and heat transfer with larger windows. The latter problem can be mitigated with insulating multiple-pane windows and special coatings to reduce solar gain without serious loss of light transmission, as discussed in the section on Selecting Fenestration. Orientation and shading can also be effective at mitigating glare and overheating problems.

The secondary visual benefit of fenestration is the amount and quality of light it produces in the work environment. One general rule determined the need for auxiliary electric light by assuming that daylight was adequate for a depth of two and one-half times the height of the fenestration product into the room based on a normal sill height. To prevent excessive glare, all fenestration should have sun controls. Variable and removable controls are often more effective in daylighting than fixed controls.

For more accurate evaluation of daylight distribution in a space, several prediction tools, such as the *Recommended Practice of Daylighting* (IESNA 1999), are available. This practice shows a simple way of calculating the daylight distribution on the work plane from windows and skylights with and without controls. Many other daylight prediction tools calculate illuminance from radiant flux transfer or ray tracing.

Any or all of the various daylight prediction tools can be used to compare the relative value of daylight distribution from alternative fenestration systems, but ultimately the designer must evaluate costs and benefits to choose between alternative designs. This may be based on energy use or, more properly, on overall costs and benefits to the client. Also, the negative possibility of total loss of productivity from an electric brown-out in a space with no natural ventilation or daylight may be as important as the benefits of many energy-saving schemes.

LIGHT TRANSMITTANCE AND DAYLIGHT USE

When daylight is to be the primary lighting system, the minimum expected daylight in the building must be calculated for the building performance cycle and integrated into lighting calculations. IESNA (1999) gives daylight design and calculation procedures. In some glazing applications, such as artists' studios and showrooms, maximum transmittance may be required for adequate daylighting. Regular clear glass, produced by float, plate, or sheet process, may be the logical choice.

When daylight is a supplementary light source, the electric lighting can be designed independently of the daylight system. However, adequate switching must be included in the electric distribution to substitute available daylight for electric lighting by automatic or prescribed manual control whenever practical. Photosensitive controls automatically adjust shading devices to provide uniform illumination and reduce energy consumption. Manual control is less effective.

Buildings with large areas of glass usually have insulating glass units with clear, tinted, or reflective coatings. Tinted and reflecting units reduce the brightness contrast between fenestration products and other room surfaces and provide a relatively glare-free environment for most daylight conditions.

Table 10 lists typical approximate solar energy transmittances and daylight transmittances for various glass types. Manufacturers' literature has more appropriate type-specific values.

The color of glass chosen for a building depends largely on where and how it is used. For commercial building lobbies, showroom fenestration products, and other areas where maximum visibility from outdoor to indoor is required, regular clear glass is generally best. Clear glass with a low-e coating is also suitable for these locations, including for retail storefronts, because it only decreases light transmittance by about 10%. For other glass areas, tinted glass may best complement the indoor colors. Bronze, gray, and reflective-film glasses also give some privacy to building occupants during daylight hours. Patterned, etched, or sandblasted glass that diffuses lighting is available. In warm climates, tinted outer glass in an insulated double-pane system can have solar heat gain rejection benefits, while providing good color-rendering illumination of the interior without apparent color.

The primary purpose of a fenestration product is not just to save energy but to provide a view of the outdoors. One sees out of a fenestration product by virtue of the light from the outside that comes through that fenestration product into the occupant's eyes. The light from outside is valuable not only for views of the outdoors but for providing daylight illumination of the interior.

The light-transmitting properties of fenestration systems are therefore of great importance, not only for allowing views of the outdoors but also for admitting daylight to reduce electric lighting. It is conceivable that one could design a fenestration product with excellent solar heat gain performance for hot climates (meaning a very low solar heat gain coefficient) but very poor view and daylight illumination performance. If this problem is bad enough, it can cause occupants to turn on electric lights indoors during the daytime, which adds to the electric bill and possibly causes problems of thermal discomfort as well.

The light-transmitting property of a fenestration product is called the visible **transmittance** T_v. It is similar to the solar-weighted solar transmittance, except that an additional weighting function is needed, in this case to account for the spectral response of the human eye.

In most applications, it is important to have high visible transmittance. In northern climates, good solar heat gain is also important for offsetting wintertime heating costs. In southern climates, low solar heat gain is good for offsetting summertime cooling costs. In the latter situation, it is difficult to have both high visible transmittance and a low solar heat gain coefficient. Figures 24 and 25 show plots of visible transmittance versus SHGC for several glazing systems covering a range of spectral selectivities (McCluney 1996). The data are for normal incidence and a single, ASTM standard solar spectral distribution.

A rule of thumb is to select a glazing unit having a visible transmittance greater than its solar heat gain coefficient, especially if daylighting strategies will be used in the building. For maximum light with minimum solar gain, there are fenestration products available having a visible transmittance as high as 2.0 times the SHGC.

Three different zones are delineated in Figure 25. In the **neutral zone**, it is possible to have colorless glazing systems, meaning glazings with approximately uniform transmittance over the visible spectrum. Glazings in this zone can have some color, but this is not necessary. In the **color zone**, the only way to achieve higher visible transmittance for a given level of solar heat gain coefficient is by stripping off some of the red and blue wavelengths at the edges of the human spectral response function with a spectrally selective glazing transmittance, imparting color to the transmitted radiation (or by otherwise altering the spectral transmittance and hence the color over the visible portion of the spectrum). In the **forbidden zone**, no combination of visible transmittance and solar heat gain coefficient is possible for normal incidence and for the solar spectral distribution used. (Changing the solar spectral distribution used to calculate T_v and SHGC shifts the transition curves somewhat. A low solar altitude angle, direct-beam spectrum will move the curves to the left on the plot in Figure 25.) Glazings that transmit more solar radiant heat than light cluster on the lower portion of the plot.

The T_v versus SHGC chart can be a useful tool for illustrating the degree of spectral selectivity attained by a glazing system. These concepts lead to an index of spectral selectivity that can be useful. It is called the **light-to-solar-gain ratio (LSG)** defined as

$$\text{LSG} = \frac{T_v}{\text{SHGC}} \tag{46}$$

Some characteristic values for T_v, SHGC, and LSG are given in Table 15 for several different glazings, using the ASTM standard spectral distribution at normal incidence to calculate the values.

The LSG can be useful in spotting errors in calculating the SHGC. Values of SHGC that lie outside reasonable ranges can be spotted fairly quickly and used to identify possible problems in calculations or measurements. In general, it is very difficult and therefore unlikely to have a useful glazing system for buildings with an LSG value greater than 2.0. Values below 0.3 should be particularly suspect, because they indicate a glazing that transmits considerably more heat than light and would be unlikely candidates for general use. Generally, a high value of LSG is desired for residential buildings in hot climates, to maximize daylight admission with minimal solar heat gain. This is also true for internal-load-dominated nonresidential buildings in many climates, because solar gain rejection is often desired for such buildings, even in cool or cold climates. An LSG value somewhat below 1.0 is appropriate in cold climates for residential buildings and nonresidential buildings without strong internal cooling loads.

Table 15 Spectral Selectivity of Several Glazings

Glazing	T_v	SHGC	LSG
Reflective blue-green	0.33	0.38	0.87
Film on clear glass	0.19	0.22	0.86
Green tinted, medium	0.75	0.69	1.09
Green low-e	0.71	0.49	1.45
Sun-control low-e + green	0.36	0.23	1.56
Super low-e + clear	0.71	0.40	1.77
Super low-e + green	0.60	0.30	2.00

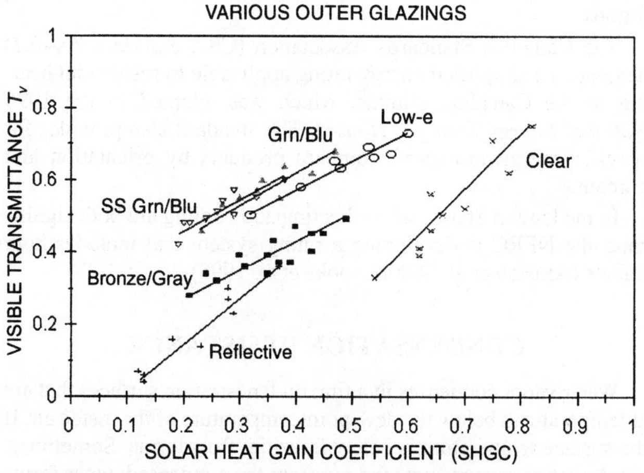

Fig. 24 Visible Transmittance Versus SHGC for Several Glazings with Different Spectral Selectivities

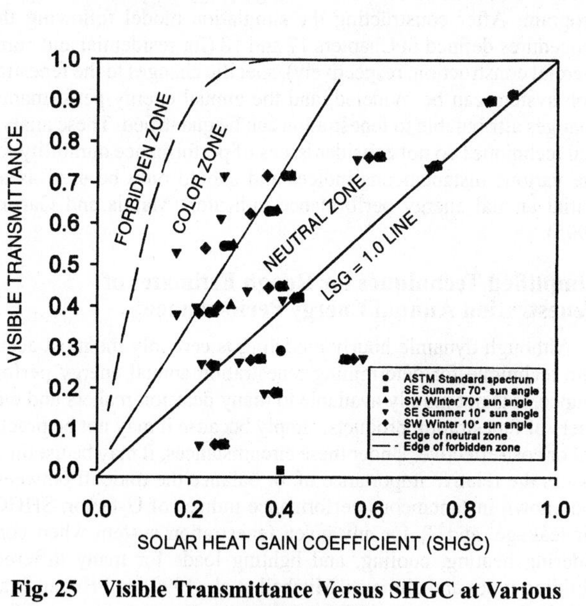

Fig. 25 Visible Transmittance Versus SHGC at Various Spectral Selectivities
(McCluney 1996)

SELECTING FENESTRATION

Because fenestration systems provide so many functions, and because environmental conditions and user needs vary widely, it is difficult to make a completely optimal selection of a fenestration system. Aesthetic and cost considerations are perhaps the most important to residential users, with visual and comfort performance also of interest. Considering annual energy costs, peak load consequences, and acoustic characteristics, the choice is seldom optimal. The HVAC system designer, fortunately, has a more restricted range of interests, mainly dealing with the energy consequences of a particular fenestration selection. This section therefore focuses on fenestration energy performance determination.

ANNUAL ENERGY PERFORMANCE

Instantaneous energy performance indices (U-factor, solar heat gain coefficient, air leakage, etc.) are typically used to compare fenestration systems under a fixed set of conditions. However, the absolute and relative effect of these indices on a building's heating and cooling load can fluctuate as environmental conditions change. As a result, these indices alone are not good indicators of the annual energy performance attributable to the fenestration. Furthermore, such energy performance is difficult to quantify in and of itself because of numerous dynamic responses between the fenestration system and the total environment in which it is installed. The four basic mechanisms of fenestration energy performance (thermal transfer, solar heat gains, air leakage, and daylighting) should all be taken into account but are not independent of many other parameters that influence performance. As a result, the annual energy performance of fenestration systems can be accurately determined only when many variables are considered. Building type and orientation, climate (weather, temperature, wind speed), microclimate (shading from adjacent buildings, trees, terrain), occupant usage patterns, and certain HVAC parameters can significantly affect the annual energy effects of fenestration systems.

For these reasons, the most effective means of establishing fenestration annual energy performance is through detailed, dynamic, hourly computer simulations for the specific building and climate of interest. Because the instantaneous performance of the fenestration often varies by differing magnitudes as climatic conditions change, the most accurate simulation results are obtained when these variances are accounted for in a building energy simulation computer program. After constructing the simulation model following the procedures defined in Chapters 17 and 18 (for residential and commercial construction, respectively), specific changes to the fenestration system can be modeled, and the annual energy performance changes attributable to fenestration can be quantified. These analytical techniques do not consider issues of performance durability for the various instantaneous indices and should only be used as an initial annual energy performance indicator (Mathis and Garries 1995).

Simplified Techniques for Rough Estimates of Fenestration Annual Energy Performance

Although dynamic hourly modeling is certainly the most accurate technique for determining fenestration annual energy performance, it is not readily available to many decision makers and end users of fenestration products, simply because it may not be practical or cost-effective. Under these circumstances, it may be useful to assess the relative importance of, or balance the tradeoff between, the known instantaneous performance indices of U-factor, SHGC, air leakage, and T_v for any given fenestration system when considering heating, cooling, and lighting loads for many different building types and climates. Mitchell et al. (1999) and Huang et al. (1999) describe personal computer programs to run this simplified analysis for residential windows.

Broad generalizations can be made for some classifications of building types and climates. For instance, with large commercial buildings, which require substantial cooling energy use during daytime occupied hours because of high internal loads, significant thermal mass, or high orientation dependency, the primary objective may be to place the most emphasis on low SHGC to reduce the cooling load. Also, an evaluation of commercial fenestration annual energy use can take into account the tradeoff between artificial lighting and the natural daylighting benefits associated with a particular fenestration system. However, low U-factor is also important because commercial buildings have bimodal operation: they can have significant heating energy consumption during morning warm-up, which occurs during unoccupied predawn hours, before people arrive and lights and equipment are turned on, and before any passive solar gain. In low-rise, detached residential buildings, electric lighting loads are typically very small in comparison to the heating and cooling loads because of high envelope-dependent energy use, egress requirements, and occupant usage patterns; therefore, the energy influence of daylighting may be neglected altogether. Despite these generalizations, the problem still exists of balancing and assessing the effect of each of the remaining parameters to establish seasonal or annual energy performance for cases in which detailed computer modeling is not performed.

Development of simplified annual energy performance indices for fenestration typically involves using instantaneous fenestration performance indices to quantify building- and climate-independent scalars of annual or seasonal energy performance for rating purposes. Many of these performance indices can be relatively independent of building type, climate, distribution of products, orientation, and other items needed for hourly dynamic building energy analyses. These normalized, scalar-based approaches are also limited in accuracy for the same reasons. A further limitation with the simplified techniques is that they do not have broad applicability to varied building types (e.g., commercial versus residential buildings). The usefulness of these scalar-based approaches can be increased when limiting the comparison to a single building type. Currently, the simplified techniques for characterizing fenestration annual energy performance are applicable only to fenestration systems for detached residential buildings and are not appropriate for use with multifamily residential or commercial building fenestration systems.

Simplified Residential Annual Energy Performance Ratings

Annual energy performance ratings can provide a simple means of product comparisons for consumers. These ratings have been derived with many assumptions, usually to suit local climatic conditions.

The Canadian Standards Association (CSA *Standard* A440.2) developed a simplified energy rating applicable to residential heating in the Canadian climate, which was adopted in the 1995 *National Energy Code for Houses*. The standard also provides for specific energy ratings to compare products by orientation and climate.

In the United States, where heating and cooling are both significant, the NFRC is developing a rating system that includes both effects (Arasteh et al. 2000; Crooks et al. 1995).

CONDENSATION RESISTANCE

Water vapor condenses in a film on fenestration surfaces that are at temperatures below the dew-point temperature of the inside air. If the surface temperature is below freezing, frost forms. Sometimes, condensation occurs first, and ice from the condensed water forms when temperatures drop below freezing. Condensation frequently occurs on single glazing and on aluminum frames without a thermal

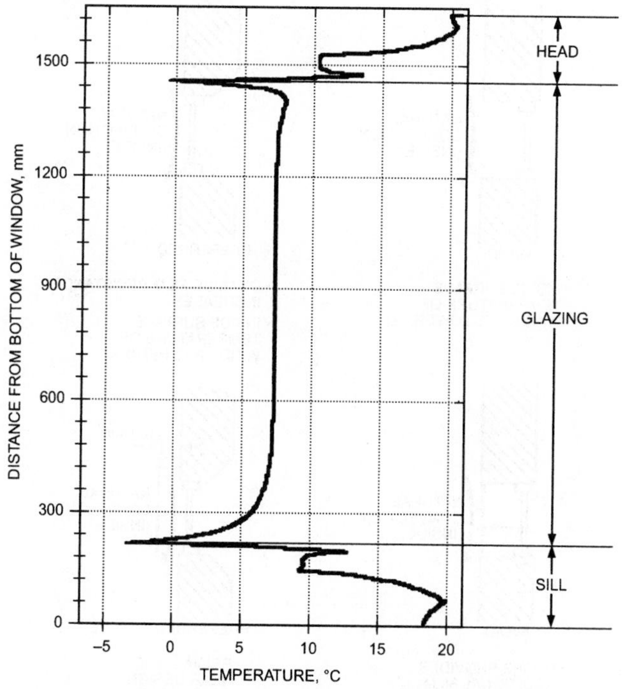

Fig. 26 Temperature Distribution on Indoor Surfaces of Glazing Unit

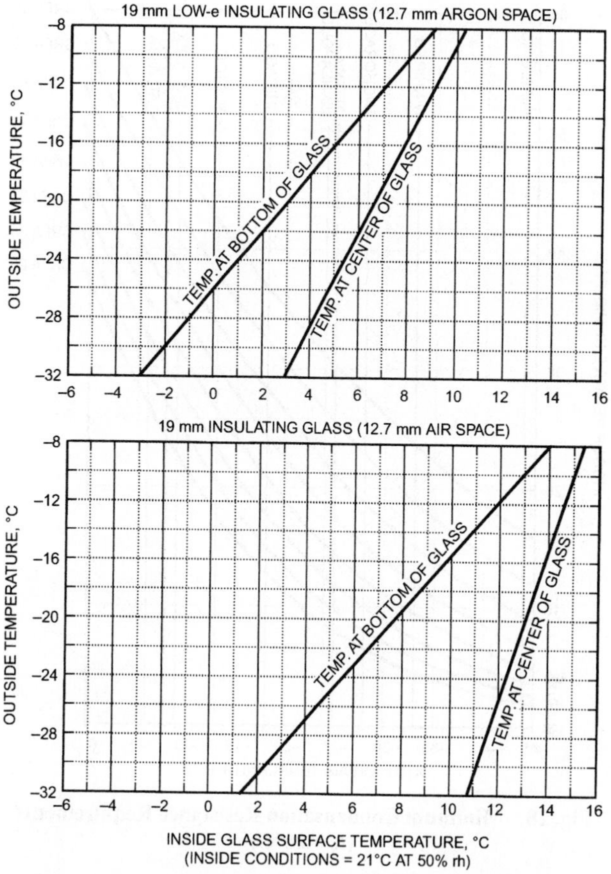

Fig. 27 Minimum Indoor Surface Temperatures Before Condensation Occurs

break. The edge-seal creates a thermal bridge at the perimeter of the glazing unit.

Circulation of fill gas caused by temperature differences in the glazing unit cavity contributes to the condensation problem at the bottom of the indoor glazing (Curcija and Goss 1994, 1995; Wright 1996b; Wright and Sullivan 1995a, 1995b). In winter, fill gas near the indoor glazing is warmed and flows up, while gas near the outdoor glazing is cooled and flows down. The descending gas becomes progressively colder until it reaches the bottom of the cavity. There, the gas turns and flows to the indoor glazing, resulting in higher heat transfer rates at the bottom. Thus, the bottom edge of the indoor glazing is cooled both by edge-seal conduction and by fill-gas convection. The combined effect of these two heat transfer mechanisms is shown in Figure 26. The surface isotherms show a wider band of cold glass at the bottom of the window. Typical condensation patterns match these isotherms. The vertical indoor surface temperature profile also shows the effect of edge-seal conduction and that the minimum indoor surface temperature is near the bottom edge of the glass.

Condensation on fenestration and surrounding structures can cause extensive structural, aesthetic, and health problems. Specific examples include peeling of paint, rotting of wood, saturation of insulation, and mold growth. Ice can render doors and windows inoperable and prevent egress during an emergency.

Energy-efficient housing has been accompanied by reduced ventilation. The resulting increase in indoor humidity has contributed to the condensation problem. However, the solution does not lie in the reduction of humidity levels to a minimum. Relative humidity below 20% and above 70% can increase health risks and reduce comfort. Generally, a minimum of 30% rh should be maintained, and 40% to 50% is more desirable (Sterling et al. 1985).

Minimum indoor surface temperatures can be quantified in a variety of ways. De Abreu et al. (1996), Elmahdy (1996), Griffith et al. (1996), Sullivan et al. (1996), and Zhao et al. (1996) demonstrated good agreement between detailed two-dimensional numerical simulation and surface temperature measurements using thermographs. Curcija et al. (1996) and Wright and Sullivan (1995c) developed simplified simulation models to predict condensation resistance. Center-glass and bottom-edge surface temperatures that can be expected for two different glazing systems exposed to a range of outdoor temperature are shown in Figure 27. Both glazing systems include insulating foam edge seals. High-performance glazing systems (e.g., low-e/argon and insulated spacers) allow significantly higher indoor humidity levels.

Current measures of condensation resistance of a fenestration system are the **condensation resistance (CR)** as defined by NFRC (2004g), the **condensation resistance factor (CRF)** as defined by AAMA (1988), or the **temperature index (I)**, as defined in CSA *Standards* A440 and A440.1.

Note that the temperature index method in CSA A440 stipulates that the test is performed on the window with all the cracks *not* sealed. This represents a major difference between the CSA A440 method and the AAMA and NFRC methods. There are some merits of leaving cracks unsealed during testing for condensation resistance. In particular, any inherent deficiencies in window design may result in uncontrolled air leakage through the window. This air leakage could not be detected or dealt with in the simulation models, and it can only be seen in the results of the determined temperature index. On the other hand, there is some financial benefit to the window manufacturer in testing the window for condensation resistance with cracks sealed, because one test can determine R-value and condensation resistance.

Research shows that air leakage does affect the temperature index (measure of condensation resistance as determined by CSA A440). Elmahdy (2001, 2003) showed that sealing cracks during testing artificially improves the temperature index, compared to the results of the same window tested with cracks unsealed.

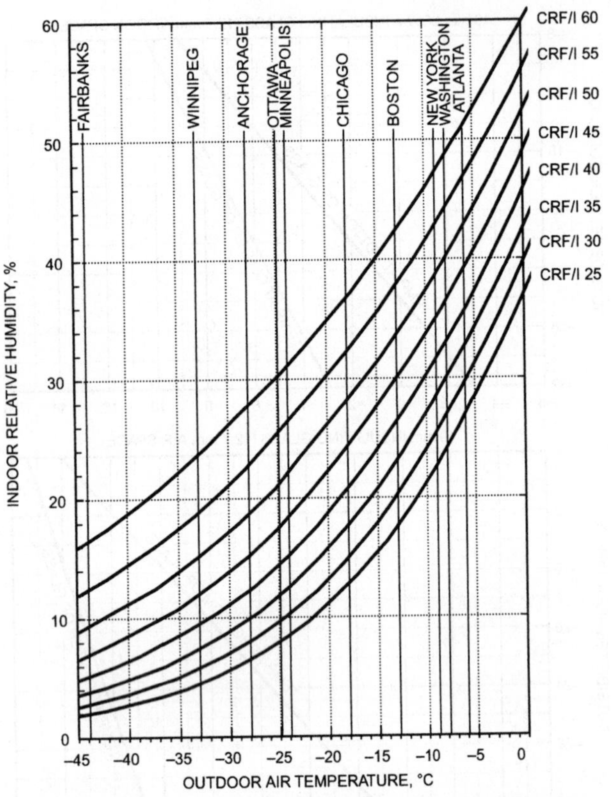

Fig. 28 Minimum Condensation Resistance Requirements (t_h = 20°C)

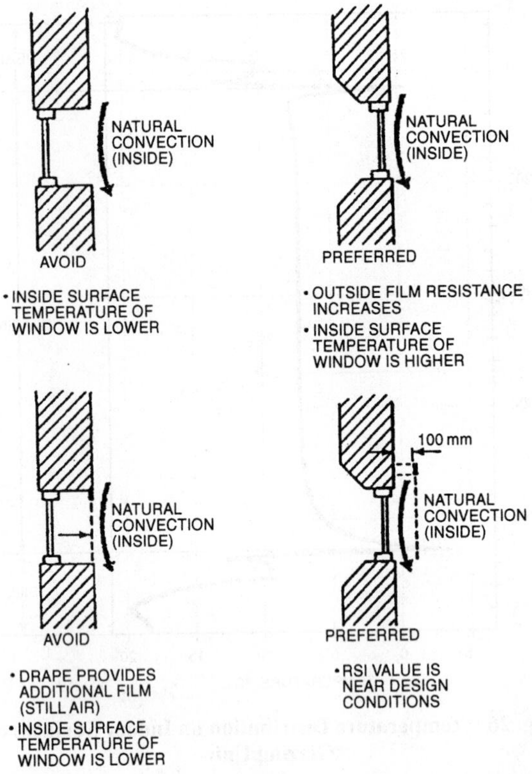

Fig. 29 Location of Fenestration Product Reveals and Blinds/Drapes and Their Effect on Condensation Resistance

Condensation resistance is a measure of condensation potential, based on both area and temperature weighting and expressed as a minimum of center-of-glazing, edge-of-glazing, and frame CRs. The novelty of this index is that it is determined using computer simulation tools unless the overall thermal performance cannot be validated with testing. If thermal performance cannot be validated, a testing option for determining CR is used.

The other two standards define the values by a single dimensionless number as

$$\text{CRF or } I = \frac{t - t_c}{t_h - t_c} \tag{47}$$

where t_h and t_c are the warm- and cold-side temperatures, respectively. Figure 28 can be used to determine the acceptable range of CRF/*I* for a specific climatic zone.

The two standards differ in the methods used to determine temperature. The CSA test procedure is based on thermocouple measurements at the coldest location on the frame plus three locations on the glass, each 10 mm above the bottom sightline. The AAMA procedure specifies two separate factors: one for the frame (CRF_F), which uses weighted frame temperature obtained from surface temperature measurements at predetermined and roving locations on the frame, and one for the glazing unit (CRF_G), which uses the average of six temperatures measured at predetermined locations near the top, middle, and bottom of the glazed area.

Inside details can significantly alter the potential for condensation on window surfaces. Items such as venetian blinds, roll blinds, insect screens, and drapes increase the thermal resistance between the indoor space and the window and lower the temperature of the window surfaces. These window treatments do not prevent migration of moisture, so they can cause increased condensation. Figure 29 shows different situations that affect the potential for condensation. Note that window reveal plays an important role. If the window is placed near the outside of the wall, the increase in the outdoor film coefficient and decrease in the indoor film coefficient cause colder window surfaces. This effect is more pronounced near the corners of the recess where the indoor film coefficient is locally suppressed because air movement is restricted. Also, blinds should be placed at least 100 mm from the plane of the wall to allow some natural convection between the window and the blind.

Air leakage, especially in operable sections of fenestration, is another important cause of low surface temperature. Leakage near edge-of-glass sections can further increase the potential for condensation. However, the drier outdoor air decreases relative humidity near leakage sites and, in some cases, offsets the undesirable effect of lower surface temperatures. The net effect of air leakage cannot readily be determined experimentally or with simulation.

OCCUPANT COMFORT AND ACCEPTANCE

Human thermal comfort is an immediate sensation that reflects building occupants' perceived response to many physical factors. Unlike much building design that is based primarily on long-term energy and economic considerations, comfort-related design focuses on, and must take heed of, short-term responses of the body's physiology to its surroundings.

Windows influence thermal comfort through a combination of three mechanisms: long-wave radiation exchange, absorption of solar radiation, and convective draft effects (Figure 30). An understanding of these phenomena is important to help designers evaluate the benefits of improved windows and create comfortable buildings. Although it is well understood that high-performance windows can reduce building energy consumption, a better understanding of their effect on comfort might lead to further savings. For example, Hawthorne and Reilly (2000) suggest that significant

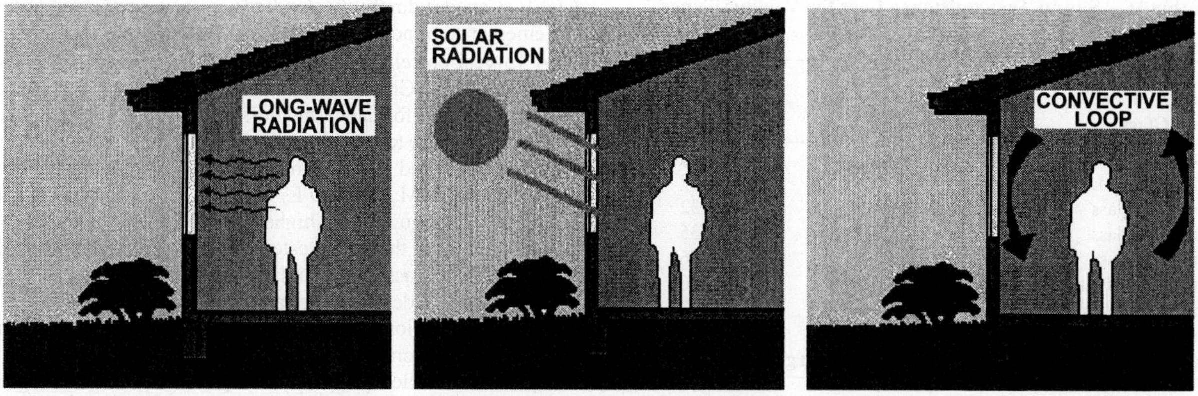

Fig. 30 Fenestration Effects on Thermal Comfort: Long-Wave Radiation, Solar Radiation, Convective Draft

energy consumption is caused by the standard practice of using perimeter duct distribution in houses to mitigate potential discomfort caused by windows. They found that perimeter heating is often not necessary when high-performance windows are installed and that heating energy savings of 10 to 15% could result from installing a simpler, less expensive duct system. Better windows can allow thermostat settings to be lowered with no loss of comfort. Another simulation study (Lyons et al. 2000) examined the relative magnitudes of a residential window's physical influences under a wide variety of winter and summer climates, glazing parameters, and clothing levels. They found that

- Long-wave, thermal radiation influences of the window dominate unless direct sun strikes the occupant
- Direct solar load has a major influence on perceptions of comfort
- For most residential-size windows, draft effects are generally small

With all but highly insulating windows, the inside surface temperature of the window is heavily influenced by outdoor conditions, and this temperature can significantly affect radiant heat exchange between an occupant and the environment. If this heat exchange moves outside the acceptable range, discomfort results. Mean radiant temperature (MRT) is commonly used to simplify the characterization of the radiant environment. On a cold day, the inside surface temperature can easily drop below –9°C for a clear single-pane window and below 4°C for a clear, double-pane window. If the occupant is sitting sufficiently near the window, MRT could drop to 13°C for the single-pane case and 17°C for the double-pane case. Based on ASHRAE *Standard* 55, even the use of the clear double-pane window could result in discomfort. [This example assumes an outdoor air temperature of –18°C, indoor air temperature of 22°C, nonwindow surface temperatures of 22°C, occupant-window view factor of 0.3, 0.9 clo (standard winter indoor clothing), and activity level of 1 met.] In addition to the MRT effect, a cold inside glass surface can induce a downward draft that increases air movement, contributing to further discomfort. If direct solar radiation strikes the glazing or occupant, the situation is much more complex.

In winter, the warming effect of sunlight on skin and clothing is often welcome, depending on the compounding effect of other factors such as air temperature. Windows also absorb and transmit a significant amount of solar radiation. Because of such absorption, a solar-heated window may improve MRT for a nearby person. The premise of passive solar design is that occupants will welcome, or at least tolerate, solar gain in exchange for savings on heating energy. However, it is desirable that the onset of discomfort be able to be predicted; otherwise, the energy-saving design may be defeated if occupants draw shades to prevent overheating.

In summer, solar-heated glass may become uncomfortably hot and, in commercial premises, actually devalue rented space near windows. The inside surface of body-tinted, heat-absorbing glass can routinely reach temperatures above 50°C in summer conditions, raising MRT by as much as 8 K. This can be ameliorated by adding a second pane of glass on the inside. Transmitted radiation often causes discomfort if it falls directly on the occupant. A person sitting near a window in direct solar radiation can experience heat gain equivalent to a 11 K rise in MRT (Arens et al. 1986). Similarly, in residential applications, the perceived need for solar control is affected both by the contribution of window surfaces to MRT and by overheating from direct solar load.

Advances in window technology, especially high-performance glazings, mean that the designer has a choice of potential glazing systems. On the basis of annual energy performance for heating, cooling, and lighting, these alternatives may give similar outcomes. However, because they represent different combinations of U-factor, SHGC, and inside glass surface temperature, their comfort outcomes may differ considerably. Research continues to develop tools that will help designers evaluate such difficult tradeoffs. In the meantime, several general rules of thumb may be followed:

- In heating-dominated climates, windows with the lowest U-factor tend to give the best comfort outcomes. However, there is likely to be a tradeoff between the twin goals of maximizing instantaneous comfort and minimizing annual energy consumption.
- In cooling-dominated climates or for orientations where cooling loads are of concern, windows with the lowest rise in surface temperature for a given SHGC tend to give the best comfort outcomes.

Sound Reduction

Proper acoustical treatment of outdoor walls can decrease noise levels in certain areas. The airtightness of a wall is the primary factor to consider in reducing sound transmission from outdoors. Once walls and fenestration products are tight, the choice of glass and draperies becomes important. Draperies do not prevent sound from coming through the fenestration; they act as an absorber for sound that does penetrate. Table 16 lists average sound transmission losses for various types of glass. These averages apply for the frequency range of 125 to 4000 Hz and were determined by tests based on ASTM *Standard* E90.

Strength and Safety

In addition to its thermal, visual, and aesthetic functions, glass for building exteriors must also perform well structurally. Wind loads are specified in most building codes, and these requirements may be adequate for many structures. However, detailed wind tunnel tests should be run for tall or unusually shaped buildings and for buildings where the surroundings create unusual wind patterns. The strength of annealed, heat-strengthened, tempered, laminated, and insulated glass is given in ASTM *Standard* E1300.

Table 16 Sound Transmittance Loss for Various Types of Glass

Type of Glass	Sound Transmittance Loss, dB
3 mm double-strength sheet glass	24
6 mm plate or float glass	27
13 mm plate glass	32
19 mm plate glass	35
25 mm plate glass	36
6 mm laminated glass (11 mm plastic interlayer)	30
25 mm insulating glass	32
13 mm laminated glass (11 mm plastic interlayer)	34
Insulating glass, 150 mm air space, 6 mm plate or float glass	40

Thermal expansion and contraction can break ordinary annealed glass. This expansion and contraction can be caused by solar radiation onto partly shaded glass, by heat traps from drop ceilings and tight-fitting drapes, or by HVAC ducts incorrectly directed toward the glazing. High-performance tinted and reflective glasses with low-e coatings are usually more vulnerable to thermal stress breakage than clear glass. Heat treating (heat strengthening or fully tempering) the glass resists thermal stress breakage. Heat-strengthened glass, although not a safety glass, is usually preferred to tempered (safety) glass because it typically has less distortion and is much less likely to have spontaneous breakage, which can occur on very rare occasions in tempered glass. The glass manufacturer or fabricator should be consulted for information on thermal stress performance.

Building codes may require glass in certain positions to perform with certain breakage characteristics, which can be satisfied by tempered, laminated, or wired glass. In this case, glass should meet *Code of Federal Regulations* 16CFR1201 or other appropriate breakage performance requirements.

Life-Cycle Costs

Alternative building shells should be compared to ensure satisfactory energy use and total energy budget compliance, if required. ASHRAE *Standards* 90.1 and 90.2 should be used as a starting point. A life-cycle cost model should be developed for each system considered. See Chapter 36 of the 2007 *ASHRAE Handbook—HVAC Applications*.

DURABILITY

Service life and long-term performance of fenestration systems depend on the durability of all the system's components. Representative samples of glazing units are usually tested (for seal durability) according to test methods to ensure the integrity of the seal. Failure of glazing units is usually indicated by loss of adhesion of sealant to the glass; as a result, fogging occurs inside the glazing cavity.

For argon-filled units, seal failure means a loss of argon and, hence, degradation in the unit's thermal characteristics. Extensive work at the National Research Council of Canada to study the durability of glazing units filled with argon gas (Elmahdy and Yusuf 1995) indicated that, under normal conditions, argon loss by diffusion through the sealant is very small. However, when cracks or pinholes exist in the sealant, most of the argon gas escapes, which implies that stringent quality control procedures are essential for the production of durable glazing units.

Degradation of organic materials and other chemical components in glazing units as a result of exposure to ultraviolet radiation is also a factor affecting durability and service life of fenestration systems. Low-e coatings on glass tend to enhance the appearance of chemical deposits on the glass surface. Also, inserting muntin bars in glazing cavities may result in excessive rates of unit failure during ultraviolet volatile (fogging) tests unless strict quality assurance processes are implemented. Current ASTM (United States) and CGSB (Canada) durability standards are being reviewed to reflect the emergence of new technologies in the fenestration industry.

A 15-year correlation study of insulating glass products by the Sealed Insulating Glass Manufacturers Association (SIGMA) found that long-term performance and durability of insulating glass correlated well with the test level to which such a unit's construction had been manufactured with regard to the ASTM *Standard* E773 test method and ASTM *Standard* E774 specification for sealed insulating glass. Units showing the highest percentage of resistance to seal failure were those that were tested in conformance with the ASTM *Standard* E774 Class CBA standard. Units that did not qualify to the A level showed a definite correlation to a higher percentage of failure. Field correlation studies found that units glazed in compliance with SIGMA recommendations perform for longer periods than units not constructed properly, having deficiencies in the glazing system, or not meeting ASTM requirements.

Durability of fenestration systems also depends on durability of other system components, such as weatherstripping, gaskets, glazing tapes, air seals, and hardware. Wear of these elements with time and use may result in excessive air and water leakage, which affects overall performance and service life of the system. Excessive water leakage may result in damage to the fenestration product, especially the edge seal, as well as the wall section where the product is mounted. Excessive air leakage may lead to frost build-up and condensation on fenestration surfaces.

Studies conducted at the National Research Council of Canada (Elmahdy 1995) and elsewhere (Patenaude 1995) showed that, when windows are tested at high pressure and temperature differentials, they experience air leakage rates exceeding those determined at 75 Pa and zero temperature differential (conditions used in rating window air leakage in U.S. and Canadian standards). In other studies (CANMET 1991, 1993), pressure and motion cycling on windows resulted in excessive degradation in almost all performance factors, particularly condensation resistance, ease of operation, and air and water leakage.

To predict long-term performance, unit construction for insulating glass should be tested and certified in accordance with ASTM *Standard* E774 Class CBA level and the requirements of the Insulating Glass Manufacturers Alliance (IGMA) or equivalent.

Durability may also affect long-term energy performance.

SUPPLY AND EXHAUST AIRFLOW WINDOWS

Airflow windows allow air to flow between glass panes of multilayered insulating glass units, to improve the window assembly's thermal performance.

Exhaust air windows allow indoor air to flow between the inner two panes of a triple-glazed window. In the cooling season, this airflow helps reduce the cooling load by transferring heat to the flowing air and discharging it to the outside. During the heating season, heat loss through the outer pane of the window comes mostly from exhaust airflow, which helps reduce thermal transmission loss through the window. In addition, exhaust airflow helps maintain the inner pane surface temperature close to the indoor air temperature, thus improving the thermal comfort of occupants (Haddad and Elmahdy 1998, 1999).

The supply air window allows outdoor air to flow between the outer two panes of a triple-glazed window and into the building. The airflow helps reduce the heating load when heat picked up by the flowing air finds its way back into the inside space. In the cooling season, the supply air window may increase the cooling load when heat is picked up from the outer glass pane and delivered into the inside space.

Haddad and Elmahdy (1998, 1999) provide results of computer models comparing thermal performance of supply and exhaust airflow windows with conventional windows in various locations in North America.

CODES AND STANDARDS

National Fenestration Rating Council (NFRC)

The National Fenestration Rating Council (NFRC) was formed in 1989 to respond to a need for fair, accurate, and credible ratings for fenestration products. NFRC has developed rating procedures for U-factor (NFRC *Technical Document* 100), solar heat gain coefficient and visible transmittance (NFRC *Technical Document* 200), optical properties (NFRC *Technical Document* 300), air leakage (NFRC *Technical Document* 400), and condensation resistance (NFRC *Technical Document* 500). To provide certified ratings, manufacturers follow the requirements in the NFRC Product Certification Program (PCP), which involves working with laboratories accredited to the NFRC Laboratory Accreditation Program (LAP), and independent certification and inspection agencies accredited through the NFRC Certification Agency Program (CAP).

NFRC *Technical Document* 100 was the first NFRC rating procedure approved and thus the first NFRC procedure adopted into energy codes in the United States. It requires using a combination of state-of-the-art computer simulations and improved thermal testing to determine U-factors for the whole product. The next step is product certification. NFRC has a series of checks and balances to ensure that the rating system is accurately and uniformly used. Products and their ratings are authorized for certification by an NFRC-licensed independent certification and inspection agency (IA). Finally, two labels are required: the temporary label, which contains the product ratings, and a permanent label, which allows tracking back to the IA and information in the NFRC *Product Directory.* In addition to informing the buyer, the temporary label provides the building inspector with the information necessary to verify energy code compliance. The permanent label provides access to energy rating information for a future owner, property manager, building inspector, lending agency, or building energy rating organization.

This process has noteworthy features that make it superior to previous fenestration energy rating systems and correct past problems:

- The procedures provide a means for manufacturers to take credit for all the nuances and refinement in their product design and a common basis for others to compare product claims.
- The involvement of independent laboratories and the IA provides architects, engineers, designers, contractors, consumers, building officials, and utility representatives with greater confidence that the information is unbiased.
- Requiring simulation and testing provides an automatic check on accuracy. This also remedies a shortcoming of previous energy code requirements that relied on testing alone, which allowed manufacturers to perform several tests and then use the best one for code purposes.
- The certification process indicates that the manufacturer is consistently producing the product that was rated. This corrects a past concern that manufacturers were able to make an exceptionally high quality sample and obtain a good rating in a test but not consistently produce that product.
- There is now a readily visible temporary label that can be used by the building inspector to quickly verify compliance with the energy code.
- There is now a permanent label that enables future access to energy rating information.

Although the NFRC program is similar for other fenestration characteristics, there are differences worth noting. Solar heat gain coefficient and visible transmittance ratings (NFRC *Technical Document* 200), which have been referenced in several codes, and condensation resistance ratings (NFRC *Technical Document* 500) are based on simulation alone. Optical properties (NFRC *Technical Document* 300) and emissivity (NFRC *Technical Document* 301) are based on measurements by the manufacturer, with independent verification. Air leakage ratings (NFRC *Technical Document* 400) are based on testing alone. For site-assembled fenestration products (such as curtain walls and window walls), an NFRC label certificate fulfills the labeling requirements and serves the certification purpose. A separate NFRC label certificate is required for each "individual product" in a particular project.

United States Energy Policy Act (EPAct)

In the United States, the 1992 Energy Policy Act (EPAct) required the development of national fenestration energy rating systems and specified NFRC as the preferred developer. (The U.S. Department of Energy was to establish procedures if the NFRC did not.) Although this recognition provided an impetus for NFRC to develop the desired procedures and programs, the EPAct sections on energy codes have been a key factor in their implementation.

EPAct set baselines for state energy codes. The ICC 2006 *International Energy Conservation Code (IECC)* and ASHRAE/IESNA *Standard* 90.1-2007, *Energy Standard for Buildings Except Low-Rise Residential Buildings*, are the current successors to the versions cited in the 1992 legislation. The majority of states have adopted the predecessors to the 2006 *IECC* (including the 2003, 2000, and 1998 *IECC* and the CABO 1995 *Model Energy Code*) and to ASHRAE/IESNA *Standard* 90.1-2007 (i.e., ASHRAE/IESNA *Standard* 90.1-2004/2001/1999/1989) into their codes either directly or by reference when adopting a building code published by one of the three national code organizations in the United States. The ICC 2006 *International Building Code* (the U.S. model building code jointly developed by ICBO, BOCA, and SBCCI) references the 2006 *International Energy Conservation Code.*

The ICC 2006 International Energy Conservation Code

The ICC 2006 *International Energy Conservation Code* (*IECC*) references NFRC *Technical Document* 100 for U-factor (as did the 2003, 2000, and 1998 *IECC* and the 1995 *Model Energy Code*) and NFRC *Technical Document* 200 for solar heat gain coefficient (SHGC) (as did the 2003, 2000, and 1998 *IECC*). Section 102.3, which applies to all occupancies, requires U-factors and SHGCs of fenestration products (windows, doors, and skylights) to be determined in accordance with NFRC *Technical Documents* 100 and 200 by an accredited independent laboratory and labeled and certified by the manufacturer. The language does not specify NFRC accreditation; however, it requires both the use of the NFRC rating procedure by an independent entity, and labeling and certification.

ASHRAE/IESNA *Standard* 90.1-2007

In 1999, ASHRAE and IESNA published a comprehensive update to *Standard* 90.1-1989 that included fenestration rating, labeling, and certification criteria in Sections 5.2.2 and 5.2.3. U-factors were to be determined in accordance with NFRC *Technical Document* 100, solar heat gain coefficient and visible transmittance in accordance with NFRC *Technical Document* 200, and air leakage in accordance with NFRC *Technical Document* 400.

In 2001, ASHRAE and IESNA made nominal modifications to *Standard* 90.1. The most significant changes for the 2004 version were in the lighting section, with fenestration rating, labeling, and certification criteria found in Sections 5.8.2.

The 2007 revision included substantial increases in stringency for the building envelope, including both opaque assemblies and fenestration. The NFRC references remained unchanged.

For further information on U.S. energy codes, the Building Codes Assistance Project (BCAP) publishes a bimonthly summary entitled "Status of State Energy Codes," which provides information on current codes and pending legislation. For additional information, contact BCAP at http://www.bcap-energy.org.

ASHRAE/USGBC/IESNA Draft *Standard* 189.1P

In 2006, ASHRAE, the U.S. Green Building Council (USGBC), and IESNA embarked on a project to develop a baseline standard for high-performance, green buildings that would apply to all buildings except low-rise residential buildings. Draft *Standard* 189.1P (ASHRAE 2008) addresses sustainable sites, energy and water efficiency, the building's effect on the atmosphere, materials and resources, and indoor environmental quality (IEQ). The standard is not a rating system, but it is hoped that organizations that do have building rating systems will integrate this standard into their rating process.

The energy-efficiency goals for the first version of *Standard* 189.1 are to achieve a 30% additional energy savings beyond that in ASHRAE/IESNA *Standard* 90.1-2007. *Standard* 189.1 builds on *Standard* 90.1, but the prescriptive option in *Standard* 189.1 substitutes more stringent values in the tables and adds other criteria. For example, the prescriptive option requires that vertical fenestration on the west, south, and east be shaded by an overhang, and that solar gain through east- and west-facing fenestration be less than that through north- and south-facing fenestration.

Canadian Standards Association (CSA)

In Canada, the Canadian Standards Association (CSA) promulgates fenestration energy rating standards. CSA *Standard* A440.2 addresses most fenestration products, and CSA *Standard* A453 addresses doors. These are companion standards to NFRC *Technical Document* 100. NFRC and CSA have established a Thermal Harmonization Task Force to attempt to harmonize their fenestration energy rating standards.

SYMBOLS

a = absorptance in a layer, considered as an isolated layer
A = total projected area of a fenestration product; apparent solar constant
$\mathcal{A}$ = absorptance in a layer or a collection of layers (system or subsystem)
e = hemispherical emissivity
E_d = diffuse sky irradiance
E_D = direct irradiance
E_{DN} = direct normal irradiance
E_r = diffuse ground reflected irradiance
E_t = total irradiance
h = surface heat transfer coefficient
k = thermal conductivity
L = glass thickness
n = refractive index
P_H = horizontal projection depth
P_V = vertical projection depth
q = instantaneous energy flux
Q = instantaneous energy flow
R = reflectance of a layer or collection of layers (system or subsystem)
R_H = height of opaque surface between fenestration product and horizontal projection
R_W = width of opaque surface between fenestration product and vertical projection
SHGC = solar heat gain coefficient
t = relative temperature
T = absolute temperature; transmittance of layer or collection of layers (system or subsystem)
U = overall coefficient of heat transfer
W = fenestration product width

Greek

α = material absorptivity
β = solar altitude angle
γ = surface solar azimuth
Δ = vertical projection profile angle
δ = declination
θ = incident angle
λ = wavelength
ξ = refractive angle
ρ_g = ground reflectance
Σ = surface tilt
ϕ = solar azimuth
Ω = horizontal projection profile angle
ϖ = solid angle

REFERENCES

AAMA. 1987. *Skylight handbook: Design guidelines.* American Architectural Manufacturers Association, Schamberg, IL.

AAMA. 1988. Voluntary test method for thermal transmittance and condensation resistance of windows, doors and glazed wall sections. *Publication* AAMA 1503.1-88. American Architectural Manufacturers Association, Schamberg, IL.

AGSL. 1992. *Vision3: Glazing system thermal analysis—User manual.* Department of Mechanical Engineering, University of Waterloo, Ontario.

Arasteh, D., J. Huang, R. Mitchell, B. Clear, and C. Kohler. 2000. A database of window annual energy use in typical North American single family houses. *ASHRAE Transactions* 106(1):562-574.

Arens, E.A., R. Gonzalez, and L. Berglund. 1986. Thermal comfort under an extended range of environmental conditions. *ASHRAE Transactions* 92(1).

ASHRAE. 2007. Energy standard for buildings except low-rise residential buildings. ASHRAE/IESNA *Standard* 90.1-2007.

ASHRAE. 1996. Standard method for determining and expressing the heat transfer and total optical properties of fenestration products. Draft *Standard* 142P, February.

ASHRAE. 2008. Standard for the design of high-performance green buildings except low-rise residential buildings. Draft ASHRAE/USGBC/IESNA *Standard* 189.1P.

ASTM. 2004. Recommended practice for laboratory measurements of airborne sound transmission loss of building partitions. *Standard* E90-04. American Society for Testing and Materials, West Conshohocken, PA.

ASTM. 2004. Standard test method for determining rate of air leakage through exterior windows, curtain walls, and doors under specified pressure differences across the specimen. *Standard* E283-04. American Society for Testing and Materials, West Conshohocken, PA.

ASTM. 2001. Standard test method for seal durability of sealed insulated glass units. *Standard* E773-01. American Society for Testing and Materials, West Conshohocken, PA.

ASTM. 1997. Standard specification for sealed insulated glass units. *Standard* E774-97. American Society for Testing and Materials, West Conshohocken, PA.

ASTM. 1992. Standard tables for terrestrial direct normal solar spectral irradiance for air mass 1.5. *Standard* E891-87 (1992) (now part of ASTM *Standard* G159-98). American Society for Testing and Materials, West Conshohocken, PA.

ASTM. 1996. Standard test method for solar absorptance, reflectance, and transmittance of materials using integrating spheres. *Standard* E903-96. American Society for Testing and Materials, West Conshohocken, PA.

ASTM. 2003. Standard practice for calculation of photometric transmittance and reflectance of materials to solar radiation. *Standard* E971-88 (2003). American Society for Testing and Materials, West Conshohocken, PA.

ASTM. 2007. Standard test method for solar photometric transmittance of sheet materials using sunlight. *Standard* E972-92 (2007). American Society for Testing and Materials, West Conshohocken, PA.

ASTM. 2003. Standard test method for solar transmittance (terrestrial) of sheet materials using sunlight. *Standard* E1084-86 (2003). American Society for Testing and Materials, West Conshohocken, PA.

ASTM. 2007. Standard practice for determining the minimum thickness and type of glass required to resist a specific load. *Standard* E1300-07e1. American Society for Testing and Materials, West Conshohocken, PA.

Beck, F.A., B.T. Griffith, D. Turler, and D. Arasteh. 1995. Using infrared thermography for the creation of a window surface temperature database to validate computer heat transfer models. *Proceedings of Windows Innovations Conference '95*, Toronto, ON.

Berdahl, P. and M. Martin. 1984. Emissivity of clear skies. *Solar Energy* 32(5).

Brandle, K. and R.F. Boehm. 1982. Air flow windows: Performance and applications. *Proceedings of Thermal Performance of the Exterior Envelopes of Buildings II*, ASHRAE/DOE Conference, ASHRAE Special Project SP-38.

CANMET. 1991. *A study of the long term performance of operating and fixed windows subjected to pressure cycling.* Catalogue No. M91-7/214-1993E. Efficiency and Alternative Energy Technology Branch, CANMET, Ottawa, ON.

CANMET. 1993. *Long term performance of operating windows subjected to motion cycling.* Catalogue No. M91-7/235-1993E. Efficiency and Alternative Energy Technology Branch, CANMET, Ottawa, ON.

Carpenter, S. and A. Elmahdy. 1994. Thermal performance of complex fenestration systems. *ASHRAE Transactions* 100(2):1179-1186.

Carpenter, S. and J. Hogan. 1996. Recommended U-factors for swinging, overhead and revolving doors. *ASHRAE Transactions* 102(1):955-959.

Carpenter, S. and A. McGowan. 1993. Effect of framing systems on the thermal performance of windows. *ASHRAE Transactions* 99(1):907-914.

CEA. 1995. *Energy-efficient residential and commercial windows reference guide.* Canadian Electricity Association, Montreal, QC.

Choi, A.-S. and R.G. Mistrick. 1999. Analysis of daylight responsive dimming system performance. *Building and Environment* 34:231-243.

Code of Federal Regulations. *Safety standard for architectural glazing materials.* 16CFR1201. U.S. Government Printing Office, Washington, D.C.

Collins, M.R. and J.L. Wright. 2006. Calculating center-glass performance indices of windows with a diathermanous layer. *ASHRAE Transactions* 112(2):22-29.

Collins, M.R., S.H. Tasnim, and J.L. Wright. 2008. Determination of convective heat transfer for glazing systems with between-the-glass louvered shades. *International Journal of Heat and Mass Transfer* 51: 2742-2751.

Crooks, B.P. et al. 1995. NFRC efforts to develop a residential fenestration annual energy rating methodology. *Proceedings of Windows Innovations Conference '95*, Toronto, ON.

CSA. 2000. *Windows.* CAN/CSA-A440-00. Canadian Standards Association, Etobicoke, ON.

CSA. 2005. *Windows/User selection guide to CSA* Standard *CAN/CSA-A440-00.* CAN/CSA *Special Publication* A440.1-00 (R2005). Canadian Standards Association, Etobicoke, ON.

CSA. 2000. Energy performance evaluation of swinging doors. CAN/CSA *Standard* A453-95 (R2000). Canadian Standards Association, Etobicoke, ON.

Curcija, D. and W.P. Goss. 1994. Two-dimensional finite-element model of heat transfer in complete fenestration systems. *ASHRAE Transactions* 100(2):1207-1221.

Curcija, D. and W.P. Goss. 1995. Three-dimensional finite element model of heat transfer in complete fenestration systems. *Proceedings of Windows Innovations Conference '95*, Toronto, ON.

Curcija, D., W.P. Goss, J.P. Power, and Y. Zhao. 1996. "Variable-h" model for improved prediction of surface temperatures in fenestration systems. *Technical Report*, University of Massachusetts at Amherst.

de Abreu, P., R.A. Fraser, H.F. Sullivan, and J.L. Wright. 1996. A study of insulated glazing unit surface temperature profiles using two-dimensional computer simulation. *ASHRAE Transactions* 102(2):497-507.

EEL. 1990. *FRAME/VISION window performance modelling and sensitivity analysis*. Institute for Research in Construction, National Research Council of Canada, Ottawa.

Elmahdy, A.H. 1995. Air leakage characteristics of windows subjected to simultaneous temperature and pressure differentials. *Proceedings of Windows Innovations Conference '95*, CANMET.

Elmahdy, H. 1996. Surface temperature measurement of insulating glass units using infrared thermography. *ASHRAE Transactions* 102(2):489-496.

Elmahdy, A.H. 2001. To seal or not to seal? A critical look at the effects of air leakage on the condensation resistance of windows. *The Whole-Life Performance of Façades*, Bath, U.K.

Elmahdy, A.H. 2003. Quantification of air leakage effects on the condensation resistance of windows. *ASHRAE Transactions* 109(1):600-606.

Elmahdy, A.H. and S.A. Yusuf. 1995. Determination of argon concentration and assessment of the durability of high-performance insulating glass units filled with argon gas. *ASHRAE Transactions* 101(2):1026-1037.

El Sherbiny, S.M., K.G.T. Hollands, and G.D. Raithby. 1982. Heat transfer by natural convection across vertical and inclined air layers. *Journal of Heat Transfer* 104:96-102.

Erhorn, H. and M. Dirksmöller, eds. 2000. *Documentation of the software package ADELINE 3.* Fraunhofer Institut für Bauphysik, Stuttgart.

Ewing, W.B. and J.I. Yellott. 1976. Energy conservation through the use of exterior shading of fenestration. *ASHRAE Transactions* 82(1):703-733.

Finlayson, E.U. and D. Arasteh. 1993. WINDOW 4.0: Documentation of calculation procedures. *Publication* LBL-33943/UC-350, Lawrence Berkeley Laboratory, Energy & Environment Division, Berkeley, CA.

Griffith, B.T., D. Turler, and D. Arasteh. 1996. Surface temperatures of insulated glazing units: Infrared thermography laboratory measurements. *ASHRAE Transactions* 102(2):479-488.

Griffith, B., E. Finlayson, M. Yazdanian, and D. Arasteh. 1998. The significance of bolts in the thermal performance of curtain-wall frames for glazed facades. *ASHRAE Transactions* 105(1):1063-1069.

Haddad, K.H. and A.H. Elmahdy. 1998. Comparison of the thermal performance of a conventional window and a supply-air window. *ASHRAE Transactions* 104(1A):1261-1270.

Haddad, K.H. and A.H. Elmahdy. 1999. Comparison of the thermal performance of an exhaust-air window and a supply-air window. *ASHRAE Transactions* 105(2):918-926.

Hawthorne, W.A. and S. Reilly. 2000. The impact of glazing selection on residential duct design and comfort. *ASHRAE Transactions* 106(1): 553-561.

Heschong, L., D. Mahone, F. Rubinstein, and J. McHugh. 1998. *Skylighting guidelines*. The Heschong Mahone Group, Sacramento, CA.

Hogan, J.F. 1988. A summary of tested glazing U-values and the case for an industry wide testing program. *ASHRAE Transactions* 94(2).

Hollands, K.G.T. and J.L. Wright. 1982. Heat loss coefficients and effective $\tau\alpha$ products for flat plate collectors with diathermous covers. *Solar Energy* 30:211-216.

Huang, J., R. Mitchell, D. Arasteh, and S. Selkowitz. 1999. Residential fenestration performance analysis using RESFEN 3.1. *Thermal Performance of the Exterior Envelopes of Buildings VII*, ASHRAE.

Huang, N.Y.T., J.L. Wright, and M.R. Collins. 2006. Thermal resistance of a window with an enclosed venetian blind: Guarded heater plate measurements. *ASHRAE Transactions* 112(2):13-21.

ICC. 2006. *International energy conservation code.* International Code Council, Falls Church, VA.

IEA. 1999. *Daylighting simulation: Methods, algorithms, and resources.* IEA SHC Task 21/ECBCS Annex 29. LBNL-44296, Lawrence Berkeley National Laboratory. Available at http://www.iea-shc.org.

IESNA. 1999. *IESNA recommended practice of daylighting.* IES RP-5-99. Illuminating Engineering Society of North America, New York.

ISO. 2000. Thermal performance of windows, doors and shading devices—Detailed calculations. ISO *Standard* 15099, Final Draft (FDIS). International Organization for Standardization, Geneva.

Jennings, J.D., F.M. Rubinstein, D. DiBartolomeo, and S. Blanc. 1999. *Comparison of control options in private offices in an advanced lighting controls testbed.* LBNL-43096, Lawrence Berkeley National Laboratory, Berkeley.

Keyes, M.W. 1967. Analysis and rating of drapery materials used for indoor shading. *ASHRAE Transactions* 73(1):8.4.1.

Klems, J.H. 1989. U-values, solar heat gain, and thermal performance: Recent studies using the MoWiTT. *ASHRAE Transactions* 95(1):609-617.

Klems, J.H. 1994a. A new method for predicting the solar heat gain of complex fenestration systems: I. Overview and derivation of the matrix layer calculation. *ASHRAE Transactions* 100(1):1065-1072.

Klems, J.H. 1994b. A new method for predicting the solar heat gain of complex fenestration systems: II. Detailed description of the matrix layer calculation. *ASHRAE Transactions* 100(1):1073-1086.

Klems, J.H. 2001. *Solar heat gain through fenestration systems containing shading: Procedures for estimating performance from minimal data.* LBNL-46682. Windows and Daylighting Group, Lawrence Berkeley National Laboratory, Berkeley, CA.

Kotey, N.A., J.L. Wright, and M.R. Collins. 2008. *Proceedings of the 3rd Annual Canadian Solar Buildings Conference*, Fredericton, NB. Solar Energy Society of Canada.

Kotey, N.A., J.L. Wright, and M.R. Collins. 2009a. A detailed model to determine the effective solar optical properties of draperies. *ASHRAE Transactions* 115(1).

Kotey, N.A., J.L. Wright, and M.R. Collins. 2009b. Determination of angle-dependent solar optical properties of drapery fabrics. *ASHRAE Transactions* 115(2).

Kotey, N.A., J.L. Wright, and M.R. Collins. 2009c. Determination of angle-dependent solar optical properties of roller blind materials. *ASHRAE Transactions* 115(1).

Kotey, N.A., J.L. Wright, and M.R. Collins. 2009d. Determination of angle-dependent solar optical properties of insect screens. *ASHRAE Transactions* 115(1).

Kotey, N.A., M.R. Collins, J.L. Wright, and T. Jiang. 2009e. A simplified method for calculating the effective solar optical properties of a venetian blind layer for building energy simulation. *ASME Journal of Solar Energy Engineering* 131.

LBL. 2003. *WINDOW 5.2: A PC program for analyzing window thermal performance for fenestration products*. LBL- 44789. Windows and Daylighting Group, Lawrence Berkeley Laboratory, Berkeley.

Lyons, P.R., D.A. Arasteh, and C. Huizenga. 2000. Window performance for human thermal comfort. *ASHRAE Transactions* 106(1):594-602.

Mathis, R.C. and R. Garries. 1995. Instant, annual life: A discussion on the current practice and evolution of fenestration energy performance rating. *Proceedings of Windows Innovations Conference '95*, Toronto, ON.

McCluney, R. 1990. Awning shading algorithm update. *ASHRAE Transactions* 96(1):34-38.

McCluney, R. 1993. Sensitivity of optical properties and solar gain of spectrally selective glazing systems to changes in solar spectrum. *Solar '93*, 22nd American Solar Energy Society Conference, Washington, D.C.

McCluney, R. 1994a. *Introduction to radiometry and photometry*. Artech House, Boston.

McCluney, R. 1994b. Angle of incidence and diffuse radiation influences on glazing system solar gain. *Proceedings Solar '94 Conference*, American Solar Energy Society, San Jose, CA.

McCluney, R. 1996. Sensitivity of fenestration solar gain to source spectrum and angle of incidence. *ASHRAE Transactions* 102(2):112-122.

McGowan, A, R. Jutras, G. Riopel, and M. Hanam. 2006. Heat transfer through roll-up doors, revolving doors and opaque non-residential swinging, sliding and rolling doors. ASHRAE Research Project RP-1236, *Final Report*.

Mitchell, R., J. Huang, D. Arasteh, R. Sullivan, and S. Phillip. 1999. *RESFEN 3.1: A PC program for calculating the heating and cooling energy use of windows in residential buildings—Program description*. LBNL-40682 Rev. BS-371. Lawrence Berkeley National Laboratory, Berkeley.

NFRC. 2004a. Procedure for determining fenestration product U-factors. *Technical Document* 100-2004. National Fenestration Rating Council, Silver Spring, MD.

NFRC. 2004b. Test procedure for measuring the steady-state thermal transmittance of fenestration systems. *Technical Document* 102-2004. National Fenestration Rating Council, Silver Spring, MD.

NFRC. 2004c. Procedure for determining fenestration product solar heat gain coefficient and visible transmittance at normal incidence. *Technical Document* 200-2004. National Fenestration Rating Council, Silver Spring, MD.

NFRC. 2004d. Standard test method for determining the solar optical properties of glazing materials and systems. *Technical Document* 300-2004. National Fenestration Rating Council, Silver Spring, MD.

NFRC. 2004e. Standard test method for emittance of specular surfaces using spectromteric measurements. *Technical Document* 301-2004. National Fenestration Rating Council, Silver Spring, MD.

NFRC. 2004f. Procedure for determining fenestration product air leakage. *Technical Document* 400-2004. National Fenestration Rating Council, Silver Spring, MD.

NFRC. 2004g. Procedure for determining fenestration product condensation resistance values. *Technical Document* 500-2004. National Fenestration Rating Council, Silver Spring, MD.

NFRC. 2004h. *Spectral data library*. Available through www.nfrc.org/software.aspx. National Fenestration Rating Council, Silver Spring, MD.

Parmelee, G.V. and R.G. Huebscher. 1947. Forced convection heat transfer from flat surfaces. *ASHVE Transactions*, pp. 245-284.

Patenaude, A. 1995. Air infiltration rate of windows under temperature and pressure differentials. *Proceedings of Windows Innovations Conference '95*, Toronto, ON.

Pennington, C.W. and G.L. Moore. 1967. Measurement and application of solar properties of drapery shading materials. *ASHRAE Transactions* 73(1):8.3.1.

Robbins, C.L. 1986. *Daylighting: Design and analysis*. Van Nostrand Reinhold, New York.

Rubin, M. 1982a. Solar optical properties of windows. *Energy Research* 6:122-133.

Rubin, M. 1982b. Calculating heat transfer through windows. *Energy Research* 6:341-349.

Rubin, M., R. Powles, and K. von Rottkay. 1999. Models for the angle-dependent optical properties of coated glazing materials. *Solar Energy* 66(4):267-276.

Schutrum, L.F. and N. Ozisik. 1961. Solar heat gains through domed skylights. *ASHRAE Journal*, pp. 51-60.

Sezgen, O. and J.G. Koomey. 1998. *Interactions between lighting and space conditioning energy use in U.S. commercial buildings*. LBNL-39795, Lawrence Berkeley National Laboratory, Berkeley.

Shewen, E.C. 1986. *A Peltier-effect technique for natural convection heat flux measurement applied to the rectangular open cavity*. Ph.D. dissertation. Department of Mechanical Engineering, University of Waterloo, ON.

Smith, W.A. and C.W. Pennington. 1964. Shading coefficients for glass block panels. *ASHRAE Journal* 5(12):31.

Sodergren, D. and T. Bostrom. 1971. Ventilating with the exhaust air window. *ASHRAE Journal* 13(4):51.

Sterling, E.M., A. Arundel, and T.D. Sterling. 1985. Criteria for human exposure in occupied buildings. *ASHRAE Transactions* 91(1).

Sullivan, H.F., J.L. Wright, and R.A. Fraser. 1996. Overview of a project to determine the surface temperatures of insulated glazing units: Thermographic measurement and two-dimensional simulation. *ASHRAE Transactions* 102(2):516-522.

Ward, G.W. 1990. Visualization. *Lighting Design + Application* 20(6):4-20.

Winkelmann, F.C. 1983. *Daylighting calculation in DOE-2*. LBNL-11353. Lawrence Berkeley National Laboratory.

Wright, J.L. 1995a. Summary and comparison of methods to calculate solar heat gain. *ASHRAE Transactions* 101(1):802-818.

Wright, J.L. 1995b. *VISION4 glazing system thermal analysis: Reference manual*. Advanced Glazing System Laboratory, University of Waterloo.

Wright, J.L. 1996a. A correlation to quantify convective heat transfer between window glazings. *ASHRAE Transactions* 102(1):940-946.

Wright, J.L. 1996b. A simplified numerical method for assessing the condensation resistance of windows. *ASHRAE Transactions* 104(1):1222-1229.

Wright, J.L. 2008. Calculating centre-glass performance indices of glazing systems with shading devices. *ASHRAE Transactions* 114(2):199-209.

Wright, J.L. and N.A. Kotey. 2006. Solar absorption by each element in a glazing/shading layer array. *ASHRAE Transactions* 112(2):3-12.

Wright, J.L. and H.F. Sullivan. 1995a. A two-dimensional numerical model for natural convection in a vertical, rectangular window cavity. *ASHRAE Transactions* 100(2):1193-1206.

Wright, J.L. and H.F. Sullivan. 1995b. A two-dimensional numerical model for glazing system thermal analysis. *ASHRAE Transactions* 101(1): 819-831.

Wright, J.L. and H.F. Sullivan. 1995c. A simplified method for the numerical condensation resistance analysis of windows. *Proceedings of Windows Innovations Conference '95*, Toronto, ON.

Wright, J.L., N.Y.T. Huang, and M.R. Collins. 2008. Thermal resistance of a window with an enclosed venetian blind: A simplified model. *ASHRAE Transactions* 114(1):471-482.

Wright, J.L., C. Barnaby, M.R. Collins, and N. Kotey. 2009. Improving load calculations for fenestrations with shading devices. ASHRAE Research Project RP-1311, *Final Report*.

Yazdanian, M. and J.H. Klems. 1993. Measurement of the exterior convective film coefficient for windows in low-rise buildings. *ASHRAE Transactions* 100(1):1087-1096.

Yellott, J.I. 1963. Selective reflectance—A new approach to solar heat control. *ASHRAE Transactions* 69:418.

Zhao, Y., D. Curcija, and W.P. Goss. 1996. Condensation resistance validation project—Detailed computer simulations using finite element methods. *ASHRAE Transactions* 102(2):508-515.

CHAPTER 16

VENTILATION AND INFILTRATION

PROVIDING a comfortable and healthy indoor environment for building occupants is the primary concern of HVAC engineers. Comfort and indoor air quality (IAQ) depend on many factors, including thermal regulation; control of internal and external sources of pollutants; supply of acceptable air; removal of unacceptable air; occupants' activities and preferences; and proper construction, operation, and maintenance of building systems. Ventilation and infiltration are only part of the acceptable indoor air quality and thermal comfort problem. HVAC designers, occupants, and building owners must be aware of and address other factors as well. Further information on indoor environmental health may be found in Chapter 10. Changing ventilation and infiltration rates to solve thermal comfort problems and reduce energy consumption can affect indoor air quality and may be against code, so any changes should be approached with care and be under the direction of a registered professional engineer with expertise in HVAC analysis and design.

HVAC design engineers and others concerned with building ventilation and indoor air quality should obtain a copy of ASHRAE *Standard* 62.1 or 62.2. These standards are reviewed regularly and contain ventilation design and evaluation requirements for commercial (62.1) and low-rise residential (62.2) buildings, respectively. In design of a new building or analysis of an existing building, the version of *Standard* 62 that has been adopted by the local code authority must be determined. An existing building may be required to meet current code, or allowed to comply with an older code. If a project involves infiltration in residences, then ASHRAE *Standards* 119 and 136 should be consulted. The last chapter of each year's *ASHRAE Handbook* (Chapter 39 of this volume) has a list of current standards.

This chapter addresses commercial and institutional buildings, where ventilation concerns usually dominate (though infiltration should not be ignored), and single- and multifamily residences, where infiltration has always been considered important but ventilation issues have received increased attention in recent years. Basic concepts and terminology for both are presented before more advanced analytical and design techniques are given. Ventilation of industrial buildings is covered in Chapter 29 of the 2007 *ASHRAE Handbook—HVAC Applications*. However, many of the fundamental ideas and terminology covered in this chapter can also be applied to industrial buildings.

Sustainability Rating Systems

Good indoor air quality is necessary for maintaining health and high productivity. Consequently, green and sustainable building rating systems, such as the U.S. Green Building Council's (USGBC) Leadership in Energy and Environmental Design (LEED®) program, place great importance on creating and maintaining acceptable IAQ. In fact, the LEED rating system was first developed to address IAQ concerns, and roughly one-third of the available credit points for new commercial buildings are still IAQ-related. Preparers of such rating systems, like others, have struggled with how to characterize complex ventilation and infiltration issues; many portions of this chapter; separate ASHRAE designer's guides, manuals, books, and standards; and the references cited address these issues in detail and provide methods for demonstrating the effectiveness of various HVAC systems and techniques in providing good IAQ in residential, commercial, and other buildings.

BASIC CONCEPTS AND TERMINOLOGY

Outdoor air that flows through a building is often used to dilute and remove indoor air contaminants. However, the energy required to condition this outdoor air can be a significant portion of the total space-conditioning load. The magnitude of outdoor airflow into the building must be known for proper sizing of the HVAC equipment and evaluation of energy consumption. For buildings without mechanical cooling and dehumidification, proper ventilation and infiltration airflows are important for providing comfort for occupants. ASHRAE *Standard* 55 specifies conditions under which 80% or more of the occupants in a space will find it thermally acceptable. Chapter 9 of this volume also addresses thermal comfort. Additionally, airflow into buildings and between zones affects fires and the movement of smoke. Smoke management is addressed in Chapter 52 of the 2007 *ASHRAE Handbook—HVAC Applications*.

Ventilation and Infiltration

Air exchange of outdoor air with air already in a building can be divided into two broad classifications: ventilation and infiltration.

Ventilation is intentional introduction of air from the outside into a building; it is further subdivided into natural and mechanical ventilation. **Natural ventilation** is the flow of air through open windows, doors, grilles, and other planned building envelope penetrations, and it is driven by natural and/or artificially produced pressure differentials. **Mechanical** (or **forced**) ventilation, shown in Figure 1, is the intentional movement of air into and out of a building using fans and intake and exhaust vents.

Infiltration is the flow of outdoor air into a building through cracks and other unintentional openings and through the normal use of exterior doors for entrance and egress. Infiltration is also known as **air leakage** into a building. **Exfiltration,** depicted in Figure 1, is leakage of indoor air out of a building through similar types of openings. Like natural ventilation, infiltration and exfiltration are driven by natural and/or artificial pressure differences. These forces are discussed in detail in the section on Driving Mechanisms for Ventilation and Infiltration. **Transfer air** is air that moves from one interior space to another, either intentionally or not.

The preparation of this chapter is assigned to TC 4.3, Ventilation Requirements and Infiltration.

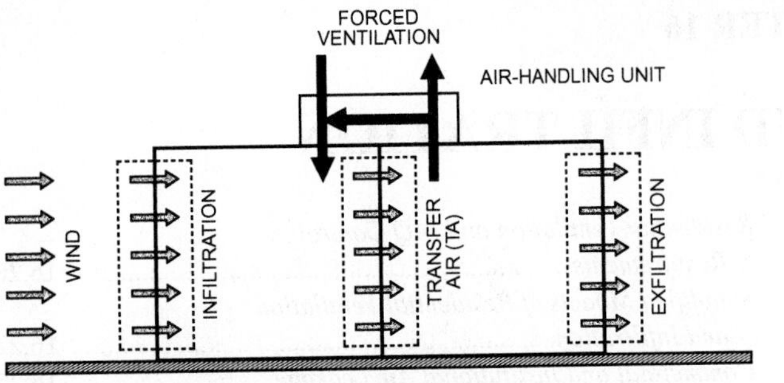

Fig. 1 Two-Space Building with Mechanical Ventilation, Infiltration, and Exfiltration

Ventilation and infiltration differ significantly in how they affect energy consumption, air quality, and thermal comfort, and they can each vary with weather conditions, building operation, and use. Although one mode may be expected to dominate in a particular building, all must be considered in the proper design and operation of an HVAC system.

Ventilation Air

Ventilation air is air used to provide acceptable indoor air quality. It may be composed of mechanical or natural ventilation, infiltration, suitably treated recirculated air, transfer air, or an appropriate combination, although the allowable means of providing ventilation air varies in standards and guidelines.

Modern commercial and institutional buildings normally have mechanical ventilation and are usually pressurized somewhat to reduce or eliminate infiltration. Mechanical ventilation has the greatest potential for control of air exchange when the system is properly designed, installed, and operated; it should provide acceptable indoor air quality and thermal comfort when ASHRAE *Standard* 55 and 62.1 requirements are followed. Mechanical ventilation equipment and systems are described in Chapters 1, 4, and 9 of the 2008 *ASHRAE Handbook—HVAC Systems and Equipment.*

In commercial and institutional buildings, natural ventilation (e.g., through operable windows) may not be desirable from the point of view of energy conservation and comfort. In commercial and institutional buildings with mechanical cooling and ventilation, an air- or water-side economizer may be preferable to operable windows for taking advantage of cool outdoor conditions when interior cooling is required. Infiltration may be significant in commercial and institutional buildings, especially in tall, leaky, or partially pressurized buildings and in lobby areas.

In most of the United States, residential buildings have historically relied on infiltration and natural ventilation to meet their ventilation air needs. Neither is reliable for ventilation air purposes because they depend on weather conditions, building construction, and maintenance. However, natural ventilation, usually through operable windows, is more likely to allow occupants to control airborne contaminants and interior air temperature, but it can have a substantial energy cost if used while the residence's heating or cooling equipment is operating.

In place of operable windows, small exhaust fans should be provided for localized venting in residential spaces, such as kitchens and bathrooms. Not all local building codes require that the exhaust be vented to the outside. Instead, the code may allow the air to be treated and returned to the space or to be discharged to an attic space. Poor maintenance of these treatment devices can make nonducted vents ineffective for ventilation purposes. Condensation in attics should be avoided. In northern Europe and in Canada, some building codes require general mechanical ventilation in residences, and heat recovery heat exchangers are popular for reducing energy consumption. Low-rise residential buildings with low rates of infiltration and natural ventilation, including most new buildings, require mechanical ventilation at rates given in ASHRAE *Standard* 62.2.

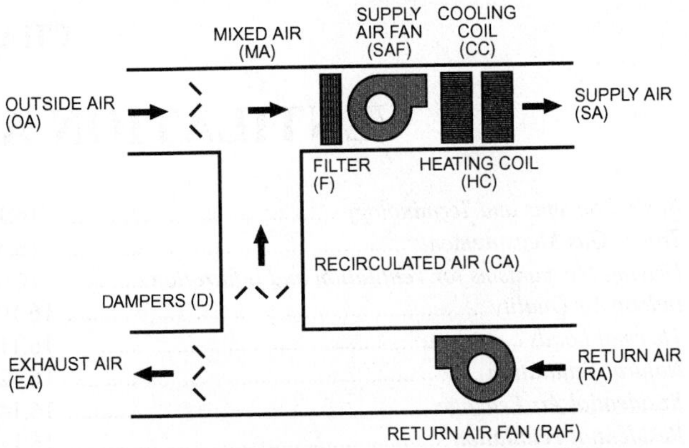

Fig. 2 Simple All-Air Air-Handling Unit with Associated Airflows

Forced-Air Distribution Systems

Figure 2 shows a simple **air-handling unit (AHU)** or **air handler** that conditions air for a building. Air brought back to the air handler from the conditioned space is **return air (RA)**. The return air either is discharged to the environment [**exhaust air (EA)**] or is reused [**recirculated air (CA)**]. Air brought in intentionally from the environment is **outdoor** or **outside air (OA)**. Because outdoor air may need treatment to be acceptable for use in a building, it should not be called "fresh air." Outside and recirculated air are combined to form **mixed air (MA)**, which is then conditioned and delivered to the thermal zone as **supply air (SA)**. Any portion of the mixed air that intentionally or unintentionally circumvents conditioning is **bypass air (BA)**. Because of the wide variety of air-handling systems, the airflows shown in Figure 2 may not all be present in a particular system as defined here. Also, more complex systems may have additional airflows.

Outside Air Fraction

The outside airflow introduced to a building or zone by an air-handling unit can also be described by the **outside air fraction X_{oa}**, which is the ratio of the volumetric flow rate of outside air brought in by the air handler to the total supply airflow rate:

$$X_{oa} = \frac{Q_{oa}}{Q_{sa}} = \frac{Q_{oa}}{Q_{ma}} = \frac{Q_{oa}}{Q_{oa} + Q_{ca}} \quad (1)$$

When expressed as a percentage, the outside air fraction is called the **percent outside air**. The design outside airflow rate for a building's or zone's ventilation system is found by applying the requirements of ASHRAE *Standard* 62.1 to that specific building. The supply airflow rate is that required to meet the thermal load. The outside air fraction and percent outside air then describe the degree of recirculation, where a low value indicates a high rate of recirculation, and a high value shows little recirculation. Conventional all-air air-handling systems for commercial and institutional buildings have approximately 10 to 40% outside air.

100% outside air means no recirculation of return air through the air-handling system. Instead, all the supply air is treated outside air, also known as **makeup air (KA)**, and all return air is discharged directly to the outside as **relief air (LA)**, via separate or centralized exhaust fans. An air-handling unit that provides 100% outside air to offset air that is exhausted is typically called a **makeup air unit (MAU)**.

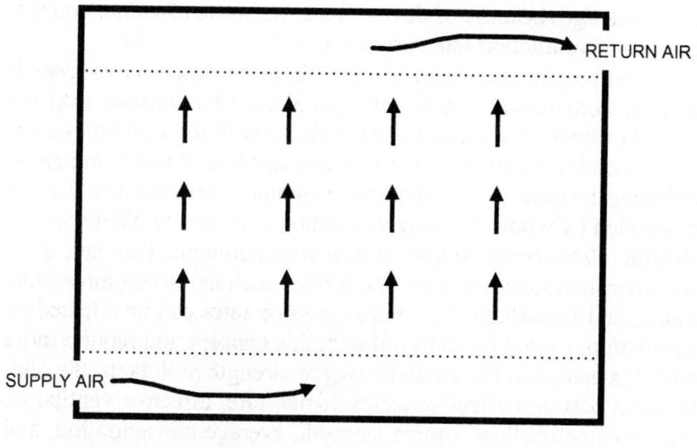

Fig. 3 Displacement Flow Within a Space

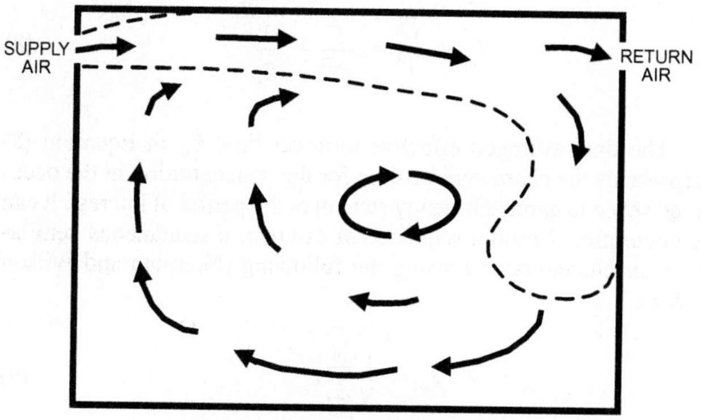

Fig. 4 Entrainment Flow Within a Space

When outside air via mechanical ventilation is used to provide ventilation air, as is common in commercial and institutional buildings, this outside air is usually delivered to spaces as all or part of the supply air. With a variable-air-volume (VAV) system, the outside air fraction of the supply air may need to be increased when supply airflow is reduced to meet a particular thermal load. In some HVAC systems, such as the dedicated outside air system (DOAS), conditioned outside air may be delivered separately from the way the spaces' loads are handled (Mumma and Shank 2001).

Room Air Movement

Air movement within spaces affects the diffusion of ventilation air and, therefore, indoor air quality and comfort. Two distinct flow patterns are commonly used to characterize air movement in rooms: displacement flow and entrainment flow. **Displacement flow**, shown in Figure 3, is the movement of air within a space in a piston- or plug-type motion. Ideally, no mixing of the room air occurs, which is desirable for removing pollutants generated within a space. A laminar-flow air distribution system that sweeps air across a space may produce displacement flow.

Entrainment flow, shown in Figure 4, is also known as **conventional mixing**. Systems with ceiling-based supply air diffusers and return air grilles are common examples of air distribution systems that produce entrainment flow. Entrainment flow with very poor mixing in the room has been called *short-circuiting flow* because much of the supply air leaves the room without mixing with room air. There is little evidence that properly designed, installed, and operated air distribution systems exhibit short-circuiting, although poorly designed, installed, or operated systems may short-circuit, especially ceiling-based systems in heating mode (Offermann and Int-Hout 1989).

Perfect mixing occurs when supply air is instantly and evenly distributed throughout a space. Perfect mixing is also known as

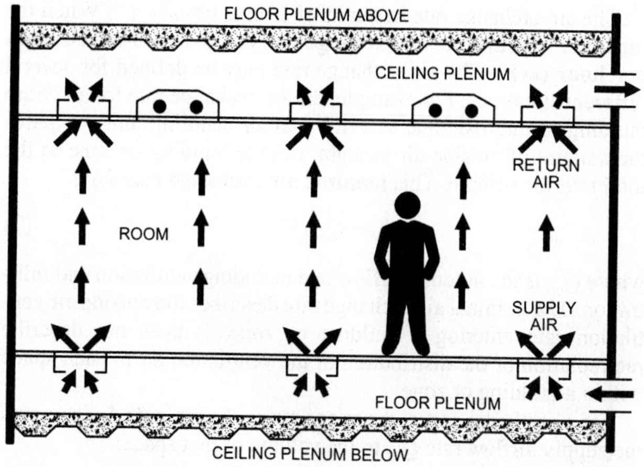

Fig. 5 Underfloor Air Distribution to Occupied Space Above
(Rock and Zhu 2002)

complete or **uniform mixing**; the air may be called **well stirred** or **well mixed**. This theoretical performance is approached by entrainment flow systems that have good mixing and by displacement flow systems that allow too much mixing (Rock et al. 1995). The outdoor air requirements given in Table 6.1 of ASHRAE *Standard* 62.1 assume delivery of ventilation air with perfect mixing within spaces. For more detailed information on space air diffusion, see Chapter 20.

Underfloor air distribution (UFAD or **UAD)**, as shown in Figure 5, is a hybrid method of conditioning and ventilating spaces (Bauman and Daly 2003). Air is introduced through a floor plenum, with or without branch ductwork or terminal units, and delivered to a space by floor-mounted diffusers. These diffusers encourage air mixing near the floor to temper the supply air. The combined air then moves vertically through the space, with reduced mixing, toward returns or exhausts placed in or near the ceiling. This vertical upward movement of the air is in the same direction as the thermal and contaminant plumes created by occupants and common equipment. Ventilation performance for UFAD systems is thus between floor-to-ceiling displacement flow and perfect mixing.

Supply air that enters a space through a diffuser is also known as **primary air**. A **jet** is formed as this primary air leaves the diffuser. **Secondary air** is the room air entrained into the jet. **Total air** is the combination of primary and secondary air at a specific point in a jet. The term *primary air* is also used to describe supply air provided to fan-powered mixing boxes by a central air-handling unit.

For evaluation of indoor air quality and thermal comfort, rooms are often divided into two portions: the **occupied zone** and the remaining volume of the space. Often, this remaining volume is solely the space above the occupants and is referred to as the **ceiling zone**. The occupied zone is usually defined as the lowest 1.8 m of a room, although layers near the floor and walls are sometimes deducted from it. Ceiling and floor plenums are not normally included in the occupied or ceiling zones. **Thermal zones** are different from these room air zones, and are defined for HVAC subsystems and their controls.

Air Exchange Rate

The **air exchange** (or **change**) **rate** I compares airflow to volume and is

$$I = Q/V \tag{2}$$

where

Q = volumetric flow rate of air into space, m³/s
V = interior volume of space, m³

The air exchange rate has units of 1/time, usually h^{-1}. When the time unit is hours, the air exchange rate is also called **air changes per hour (ach)**. The air exchange rate may be defined for several different situations. For example, the air exchange rate for an entire building or thermal zone served by an air-handling unit compares the amount of outside air brought into the building or zone to the total interior volume. This **nominal air exchange rate I_N** is

$$I_N = Q_{oa}/V \quad (3)$$

where Q_{oa} is the outdoor airflow rate including ventilation and infiltration. The nominal air exchange rate describes the outside air ventilation rate entering a building or zone. It does not describe recirculation or the distribution of the ventilation air to each space within a building or zone.

For a particular space, the **space air exchange rate I_S** compares the supply airflow rate Q_{sa} to the volume of that space:

$$I_S = Q_{sa}/V \quad (4)$$

The space air exchange rate for a particular space or zone includes recirculated as well as outside air in the supply air, and it is used frequently in the evaluation of supply air diffuser performance and space air mixing.

Time Constants

Time constants τ, which have units of time (usually in hours or seconds), are also used to describe ventilation and infiltration. One time constant is the time required for one air change in a building, zone, or space if ideal displacement flow existed. It is the inverse of the air exchange rate:

$$\tau = 1/I = V/Q \quad (5)$$

The **nominal time constant** compares the interior volume of a building or zone to the volumetric outdoor airflow rate:

$$\tau_N = V/Q_{oa} \quad (6)$$

Like the nominal air exchange rate, the nominal time constant does not describe recirculation of air within a building or zone. It also does not characterize the distribution of the outside air to individual spaces within a building or zone.

The **space time constant** compares the interior volume of a particular space to the total supply airflow rate to that space. The space time constant is the inverse of the space air exchange rate:

$$\tau_S = V/Q_{sa} \quad (7)$$

The space time constant includes the effect of recirculated air, if present, as well as that of outside air introduced to the space through the supply air. If infiltration is significant in a space, then the infiltration flow rate should be included when determining both the space air exchange rate and the space time constant.

Averaging Time-Varying Ventilation

When assessing time-varying ventilation in terms of controlling indoor air quality, the quantity of interest is often the temporal average rather than the peak. The concept of **effective ventilation** (Sherman and Wilson 1986; Yuill 1986, 1991) describes the proper ventilation rate averaging process. In this concept, the average (effective) rate is the steady-state rate that yields the same average contaminant concentration over the period of interest in the occupied space as does the actual sequence of time-varying discrete ventilation rates over the same period and in the same space. This effective rate is only equal to the simple arithmetic average rate when the discrete ventilation rates are constant over the period of interest and the contaminant concentration has reached its steady-state value. Simple arithmetic averaging of instantaneous ventilation rates or concentrations cannot generally be used to determine these averages because of the nonlinear response of indoor concentrations to ventilation rate variations.

An important constraint in the effective ventilation concept is that the contaminant source strength F must be constant over the period of interest or must be uncorrelated with the ventilation rate. These conditions are satisfied in many residential and commercial buildings because the emission rates of many contaminants that are controlled by whole-building ventilation vary slowly. Sherman and Wilson (1986) describe how to deal with pollutants that have stepwise constant emission rates. Pollutants such as carbon monoxide, radon, and formaldehyde, whose emission rates can be affected by ventilation, cannot be analyzed with this concept and require more complex analyses. For constant-source-strength pollutants, the relationship between effective air exchange rate, effective ventilation rate, volumetric flow, source strength, average concentration, and time-averaged effective turnover time is given by

$$I_m = \frac{\bar{Q}}{V} = \frac{F}{V\bar{C}} = \frac{1}{\bar{\tau}_e} \quad (8)$$

The time-averaged effective turnover time $\bar{\tau}_e$ in Equation (8) represents the characteristic time for the concentration in the occupied space to approach steady state over the period of interest. It can be determined from a sequence of discrete, instantaneous ventilation air change rates I_i using the following (Sherman and Wilson 1986):

$$\bar{\tau}_e = \frac{1}{N}\sum_{i=1}^{N} \tau_{e,i} \quad (9)$$

$$\text{for } I_i > 0, \tau_{e,i} = \frac{1 - \exp(-I_i \Delta t)}{I_i} + \tau_{e,i-1}\exp(-I_i \Delta t) \quad (10)$$

$$\text{for } I_i = 0, \tau_{e,i} = \Delta t + t_{e,i-1} \quad (11)$$

where

Δt = length of each discrete time period
$\bar{\tau}_e$ = time-averaged effective turnover time
$\tau_{e,i}$ = instantaneous turnover time in period i
$\tau_{e,i-1}$ = instantaneous turnover time in previous period

ASHRAE *Standard* 136 provides a set of factors to help calculate the annual effective air exchange rate.

Age of Air

The **age of air** θ_{age} (Sandberg 1981) is the length of time t that some quantity of outside air has been in a building, zone, or space. The "youngest" air is at the point where outside air enters the building by mechanical or natural ventilation or through infiltration (Grieve 1989). The "oldest" air may be at some location in the building or in the exhaust air. When the characteristics of the air distribution system are varied, age of air is inversely correlated with quality of outside air delivery. Units are of time, usually in seconds or minutes, so it is not a true efficiency or effectiveness measure. The age of air concept, however, has gained wide acceptance in Europe and is used increasingly in North America.

The age of air can be evaluated for existing buildings using tracer gas methods. Using either the decay (step-down) or growth (step-up) tracer gas method, the zone average or **nominal age of air** $\theta_{age,N}$ can be determined by taking concentration measurements in the exhaust air. The **local age of air** $\theta_{age,L}$ is evaluated through tracer gas measurements at any desired point in a space, such as at a worker's desk. When time-dependent data of tracer gas concentration are available, the age of air can be calculated from

$$\theta_{age} = \int_{\theta=0}^{\infty} \frac{C_{in} - C}{C_{in} - C_o} d\theta \qquad (12)$$

where C_{in} is the concentration of tracer gas being injected.

Because evaluation of the age of air requires integration to infinite time, an exponential tail is usually added to the known concentration data (Farrington et al. 1990).

Air Change Effectiveness

Ventilation effectiveness is a description of an air distribution system's ability to remove internally generated pollutants from a building, zone, or space. **Air change effectiveness** is a description of an air distribution system's ability to deliver ventilation air to a building, zone, or space. The HVAC design engineer usually does not have knowledge or control of actual pollutant sources within buildings, so Table 6.1 of ASHRAE *Standard* 62.1 defines outdoor air requirements for typical, expected building uses. For most projects, therefore, air change effectiveness is of more relevance to HVAC system design than ventilation effectiveness. Various definitions for air change effectiveness have been proposed. The specific measure that meets local code requirements must be determined, if any is needed at all.

Air change effectiveness measures ε_I are nondimensional gages of ventilation air delivery. One common definition of air change effectiveness is the ratio of a time constant to an age of air:

$$\varepsilon_I = \tau / \theta_{age} \qquad (13)$$

The **nominal air change effectiveness** $\varepsilon_{I,N}$ shows the effectiveness of outside air delivery to the entire building, zone, or space:

$$\varepsilon_{I,\,N} = \tau_N / \theta_{age,\,N} \qquad (14)$$

where the nominal time constant τ_N is usually calculated from measured airflow rates.

The **local air change effectiveness** $\varepsilon_{I,L}$ shows the effectiveness of outside air delivery to one specific point in a space:

$$\varepsilon_{I,\,L} = \tau_N / \theta_{age,\,L} \qquad (15)$$

where τ_N is found either through airflow measurements or from tracer gas concentration data. An $\varepsilon_{I,L}$ value of 1.0 indicates that the air distribution system delivers air equivalent to that of a system with perfectly mixed air in the spaces. A value less than 1.0 shows less than perfect mixing with some degree of stagnation. A value of $\varepsilon_{I,L}$ greater than 1.0 suggests that a degree of plug or displacement flow is present at that point (Rock 1992).

An HVAC design engineer often assumes that a properly designed, installed, operated, and maintained air distribution system provides an air change effectiveness of about 1. However, Table 6.1 of ASHRAE *Standard* 62.1 provides some estimates of effectiveness for operating in heating or cooling mode, and with various air distribution techniques. These values are then adjusted for commercial and institutional building design when the ventilation rate procedure is used. If the indoor air quality procedure of *Standard* 62.1 is used, then actual pollutant sources and the air change effectiveness must be known for the successful design of HVAC systems that have fixed ventilation airflow rates.

ASHRAE *Standard* 129 describes a method for measuring air change effectiveness of mechanically vented spaces and buildings with limited air infiltration, exfiltration, and air leakage with surrounding indoor spaces.

TRACER GAS MEASUREMENTS

The only reliable way to determine an existing building's air exchange rate is to measure it. Several tracer gas measurement procedures exist (including the ASTM *Standard* E741 test method), all involving an inert or nonreactive gas used to label the indoor air (Charlesworth 1988; Dietz et al. 1986; Fisk et al. 1989; Fortmann et al. 1990; Harrje et al. 1981, 1990; Hunt 1980; Lagus 1989; Lagus and Persily 1985; Persily 1988; Persily and Axley 1990; Sherman 1989a, 1989b, 1990; Sherman et al. 1980). The tracer is released into the building in a specified manner, and the concentration of the tracer in the building is monitored and related to the building's air exchange rate. Various tracer gases and associated concentration detection devices have been used. Desirable qualities of a tracer gas are detectability, nonreactivity, nontoxicity, neutral buoyancy, relatively low concentration in ambient air, and low cost (Hunt 1980).

All tracer gas measurement techniques are based on a mass balance of the tracer gas in the building. Assuming the outdoor concentration is zero and the indoor air is well mixed, this total balance takes the following form:

$$V\left(\frac{dC}{d\theta}\right) = F(\theta) - Q(\theta)C(\theta) \qquad (16)$$

where

V = volume of space being tested, m³
$C(\theta)$ = tracer gas concentration at time θ
$dC/d\theta$ = time rate of change of concentration, s^{-1}
$F(\theta)$ = tracer gas injection rate at time θ, m³/s
$Q(\theta)$ = airflow rate out of building at time θ, m³/s
θ = time, s

In Equation (16), density differences between indoor and outdoor air are generally ignored for moderate climates; therefore, Q also refers to the airflow rate into the building. Although Q is often referred to as the infiltration rate, any measurement includes both mechanical and natural ventilation in addition to infiltration. The ratio of Q to the volume V being tested has units of 1/time (often converted to ach) and is the air exchange rate I.

Equation (16) is based on the assumptions that (1) no unknown tracer gas sources exist, (2) airflow out of the building is the dominant means of removing the tracer gas from the space (i.e., the tracer gas does not react chemically in the space and/or is not adsorbed onto or by interior surfaces), and (3) the tracer gas concentration within the building can be represented by a single value (i.e., the tracer gas is uniformly mixed within the space). In such tracer gas experiments, box-type fans are often placed and operated within rooms to enhance mixing.

Three different tracer gas procedures are used to measure air exchange rates: (1) decay or growth, (2) constant concentration, and (3) constant injection.

Decay or Growth

Decay. The simplest tracer gas measurement technique is the decay method (also known as the step-down method). A small amount of tracer gas is injected into the space and is allowed to mix with the interior air. After the injection, $F = 0$ and then the solution to Equation (16) is

$$C(\theta) = C_o e^{-I\theta} \qquad (17)$$

where C_o is the concentration of the tracer in the space at $\theta = 0$.

Equation (17) is generally used to solve for I by measuring the tracer gas concentration periodically during the decay and fitting the data to the logarithmic form of Equation (17):

$$\ln C(\theta) = \ln C_o - I\theta \qquad (18)$$

Like all tracer gas techniques, the decay method has advantages and disadvantages. One advantage is that, because logarithms of concentration are taken, only relative concentrations are needed, which can simplify calibration of concentration-measuring equipment. Also, the tracer gas injection rate need not be measured, although it must be controlled so that the tracer gas concentrations are within the range of the concentration-measuring device. The concentration-measuring equipment can be located on site, or building samples can be collected in suitable containers, such as grab bags, and analyzed elsewhere.

The most serious problem with the decay technique is imperfect mixing of tracer gas with interior air, both at initial injection and during decay. Equations (16) and (17) assume that the tracer gas concentration within the building is uniform. If the tracer is not well mixed, this assumption is not appropriate and the determination of I is subject to errors. It is difficult to estimate the magnitude of errors caused by poor mixing, and there has been little analysis of this problem. Sometimes a two-zone model is applied to a room, and a mixing coefficient selected, to estimate the effect of poor mixing (e.g., Rock 1992).

Growth. The growth or step-up method is similar to the decay method except that the initial tracer gas concentration is low and the injected tracer gas is increased suddenly during the test.

Constant Concentration

In the constant concentration technique, the tracer gas injection rate is adjusted to maintain a constant concentration within the building. If the concentration is truly constant, then Equation (16) reduces to

$$Q(\theta) = F(\theta)/C \tag{19}$$

There is less experience with this technique than with the decay procedure, but an increasing number of applications exist (Bohac et al. 1985; Collet 1981; Fortmann et al. 1990; Kumar et al. 1979; Walker and Forest 1995; Walker and Wilson 1998; Wilson and Walker 1993).

Because tracer gas injection is continuous, no initial mixing period is required. Another advantage is that tracer gas injection into each zone of the building can be separately controlled; thus, the amount of outdoor air flowing into each zone can be determined. This procedure is best suited for longer-term continuous monitoring of fluctuating infiltration rates. One disadvantage is that it requires measurement of absolute tracer concentrations and injection rates. Also, imperfect mixing of the tracer and interior air causes a delay in the response of the concentration to changes in the injection rate.

Constant Injection

In the constant-injection procedure, the tracer is injected at a constant rate, and the solution to Equation (16) becomes

$$C(\theta) = (F/Q)(1 - e^{-I\theta}) \tag{20}$$

After sufficient time, the transient term reduces to zero, the concentration attains equilibrium, and Equation (20) reduces to

$$Q = F/C \tag{21}$$

Equation (21) is valid only when air exchange rate I and airflow rate Q are constant; thus, this technique is only appropriate for systems at or near equilibrium. It is particularly useful in spaces with mechanical ventilation or with high air exchange rates. Constant injection requires measurement of absolute concentrations and injection rates.

Dietz et al. (1986) used a special case of the constant-injection technique, using permeation tubes as a tracer gas source. The tubes release the tracer at an ideally constant rate into the building being tested, and a sampling tube packed with an adsorbent collects the tracer from the interior air at a constant rate by diffusion. After a sampling period of one week or more, the sampler is removed and analyzed to determine the average tracer gas concentration within the building during the sampling period.

Solving Equation (16) for C and taking the time average gives

$$\langle C\rangle = \langle F/Q\rangle = F\langle 1/Q\rangle \tag{22}$$

where $\langle \ldots \rangle$ denotes time average. Note that the time average of dC/dt is assumed to equal zero.

Equation (22) shows that the average tracer concentration $\langle C\rangle$ and injection rate F can be used to calculate the average of the inverse airflow rate. The average of the inverse is less than the inverse of the actual average, with the magnitude of this difference depending on the distribution of airflow rates during the measurement period. Sherman and Wilson (1986) calculated these differences to be about 20% for one-month averaging periods. Differences greater than 30% have been measured when occupant airing of houses caused large changes in air exchange rate; errors from 5 to 30% were measured when the variation was caused by weather effects (Bohac et al. 1987). Longer averaging periods and large changes in air exchange rates during the measurement periods generally lead to larger differences between the average inverse exchange rate and the inverse of the actual average rate.

Multizone Air Exchange Measurement

Equation (16) is based on the assumption of a single, well-mixed enclosure, and the techniques described are for single-zone measurements. Airflow between internal zones and between the exterior and individual internal zones has led to the development of multizone measurement techniques (Fortmann et al. 1990; Harrje et al. 1985; Harrje et al. 1990; Sherman and Dickerhoff 1989). These techniques are important when considering the transport of pollutants from one room of a building to another. A theoretical development is provided by Sinden (1978a). Multizone measurements typically use either multiple tracer gases for the different zones or the constant-concentration technique. A proper error analysis is essential in all multizone flow determination (Charlesworth 1988; D'Ottavio et al. 1988).

DRIVING MECHANISMS FOR VENTILATION AND INFILTRATION

Natural ventilation and infiltration are driven by pressure differences across the building envelope caused by wind and air density differences because of temperature differences between indoor and outdoor air (buoyancy, or the stack effect). Mechanical air-moving systems also induce pressure differences across the envelope through operation of appliances, such as combustion devices, leaky forced-air thermal distribution systems, and mechanical ventilation systems. The indoor/outdoor pressure difference at a location depends on the magnitude of these driving mechanisms as well as on the characteristics of the openings in the building envelope (i.e., their locations and the relationship between pressure difference and airflow for each opening).

Stack Pressure

Stack pressure is the hydrostatic pressure caused by the mass of a column of air located inside or outside a building. It can also occur within a flow element, such as a duct or chimney that has vertical separation between its inlet and outlet. The hydrostatic pressure in the air depends on density and the height of interest above a reference point.

Air density is a function of local barometric pressure, temperature, and humidity ratio, as described in Chapter 1. As a result, standard conditions should not be used to calculate the density. For example, a building site at 1500 m has air density that is about 20% less than if the building were at sea level. An air temperature increase from –30 to 20°C causes a similar air density difference. Combined, these elevation and temperature effects reduce air density about 45%. Moisture effects on density are generally negligible, so dry air density can be used instead, except in hot, humid climates when air is hot and close to saturation. For example, saturated air at 40°C has density about 5% less than that of dry air.

Assuming temperature and barometric pressure are constant over the height of interest, the stack pressure decreases linearly as the separation above the reference point increases. For a single column of air, the stack pressure can be calculated as

$$p_s = p_r - \rho g H \tag{23}$$

where

p_s = stack pressure, Pa
p_r = stack pressure at reference height, Pa
g = gravitational acceleration, 9.81 m/s²
ρ = indoor or outdoor air density, kg/m³
H = height above reference plane, m

For tall buildings or when significant temperature stratification occurs indoors, Equation (23) should be modified to include the density gradient over the height of the building.

Temperature differences between indoors and outdoors cause stack pressure differences that drive airflows across the building envelope; the **stack effect** is this buoyancy phenomenon. Sherman (1991) showed that any single-zone building can be treated as an equivalent box from the point of view of stack effect, if its leaks follow the power law as described in the section on Residential Air Leakage. The building is then characterized by an effective stack height and neutral pressure level (NPL) or leakage distribution, as described in the section on Neutral Pressure Level. Once calculated, these parameters can be used in physical, single-zone models to estimate infiltration.

Neglecting vertical density gradients, the stack pressure difference for a horizontal leak at any vertical location is given by

$$\Delta p_s = (\rho_o - \rho_i) g (H_{NPL} - H)$$
$$= \rho_o \left(\frac{T_i - T_o}{T_i} \right) g (H_{NPL} - H) \tag{24}$$

where

T_o = outdoor temperature, K
T_i = indoor temperature, K
ρ_o = outdoor air density, kg/m³
ρ_i = indoor air density, kg/m³
H_{NPL} = height of neutral pressure level above reference plane without any other driving forces, m

Chastain and Colliver (1989) showed that, when there is stratification, the average of the vertical distribution of temperature differences is more appropriate to use in Equation (24) than the localized temperature difference near the opening of interest.

By convention, stack pressure differences are positive when the building is pressurized relative to outdoors, which causes flow out of the building. Therefore, absent other driving forces and assuming no stack effect within the flow elements themselves, when indoor air is warmer than outdoors, the base of the building is depressurized and the top is pressurized relative to outdoors; when indoor air is cooler than outdoors, the reverse is true.

Absent other driving forces, the location of the NPL is influenced by leakage distribution over the building exterior and by interior compartmentation. As a result, the NPL is not necessarily located at the mid-height of the building; with effective horizontal barriers in tall buildings, it is also possible to have more than one NPL. NPL location and leakage distribution are described later in the section on Combining Driving Forces.

For a penetration through the building envelope for which (1) there is vertical separation between its inlet and outlet and (2) air inside the flow element is not at the indoor or outdoor temperature, such as in a chimney, more complex analyses than Equation (24) are required to determine the stack effect at any location on the building envelope.

Wind Pressure

When wind impinges on a building, it creates a distribution of static pressures on the building's exterior surface that depends on the wind direction, wind speed, air density, surface orientation, and surrounding conditions. Wind pressures are generally positive with respect to the static pressure in the undisturbed airstream on the windward side of a building and negative on the leeward sides. However, pressures on these sides can be negative or positive, depending on wind angle and building shape. Static pressures over building surfaces are almost proportional to the velocity pressure of the undisturbed airstream. The wind pressure or velocity pressure is given by the Bernoulli equation, assuming no height change or pressure losses:

$$p_w = C_p \rho \frac{U^2}{2} \tag{25}$$

where

p_w = wind surface pressure relative to outdoor static pressure in undisturbed flow, Pa
ρ = outside air density, kg/m³ (about 1.2 at or near sea level)
U = wind speed, m/s
C_p = wind surface pressure coefficient, dimensionless

C_p is a function of location on the building envelope and wind direction. Chapter 24 provides additional information on values of C_p.

Most pressure coefficient data are for winds normal to building surfaces. Unfortunately, for a real building, this fixed wind direction rarely occurs, and when the wind is not normal to the upwind wall, these pressure coefficients do not apply. Walker and Wilson (1994) developed a harmonic trigonometric function to interpolate between the surface average pressure coefficients on a wall that were measured with the wind normal to each of the four building surfaces. This function was developed for low-rise buildings three stories or less in height. For each wall of the building, C_p is given by

$$C_p(\phi) = 1/2\{[C_p(1) + C_p(2)](\cos^2\phi)^{1/4} + [C_p(1) - C_p(2)](\cos\phi)^{3/4} + [C_p(3) - C_p(4)](\sin^2\phi)^2 + [C_p(3) - C_p(4)]\sin\phi\} \tag{26}$$

where

$C_p(1)$ = pressure coefficient when wind is at 0°
$C_p(2)$ = pressure coefficient when wind is at 180°
$C_p(3)$ = pressure coefficient when wind is at 90°
$C_p(4)$ = pressure coefficient when wind is at 270°
ϕ = wind angle measured clockwise from the normal to wall 1

Because the cosine term in Equation (26) can be negative, its sign must be tracked. When $\cos(\phi)$ is negative, subtract the value of the absolute of $\cos(\phi)$ to the 3/4 power.

The measured data used to develop the harmonic function from Akins et al. (1979) and Wiren (1985) show that typical values for the pressure coefficients are $C_p(1) = 0.6$, $C_p(2) = -0.3$, $C_p(3) = C_p(4) = -0.65$. Because of geometry effects on flow around a building, application of this interpolation function is limited to low-rise buildings of rectangular plan form (i.e., not L-shaped) with the longest wall less than three times the length of the shortest wall. For less regular buildings, simple correlations are inadequate and building-specific pressure coefficients are required. Chapter 24 discusses wind pressures for complex building shapes and for high-rise buildings in more detail.

The wind speed most commonly available for infiltration calculations is that measured at the local weather station, typically the nearest airport. This wind speed needs to be corrected for reductions caused by the difference between the height where the wind speed is measured and the height of the building, and reductions caused by shelter effects.

The reference wind speed used to determine pressure coefficients is usually the wind speed at the eaves height for low-rise buildings and the building height for high-rise buildings. However, meteorological wind speed measurements are made at a different height (typically 10 m) and at a different location. The difference in terrain between the measurement station and the building under study must also be accounted for. Chapter 24 shows how to calculate the effective wind speed U_H from the reference wind speed U_{met} using boundary layer theory and estimates of terrain effects.

In addition to the reduction in wind pressures caused by reduced wind speed, the effects of local shelter also act to reduce wind pressures. The shielding effects of trees, shrubbery, and other buildings within several building heights of a particular building produce large-scale turbulence eddies that not only reduce effective wind speed but also alter wind direction. Thus, meteorological wind speed data must be reduced carefully when applied to low buildings.

Ventilation rates measured by Wilson and Walker (1991) for a row of houses showed reductions in ventilation rates of up to a factor of three when the wind changed direction from perpendicular to parallel to the row. They recommended estimating wind shelter for winds perpendicular to each side of the building and then using the interpolation function in Equation (27) to find the wind shelter for intermediate wind angles:

$$s = \frac{1}{2}\left\{\begin{array}{l}[s(1)+s(2)]\cos^2\phi + [s(1)-s(2)]\cos\phi \\ +[s(3)+s(4)]\sin^2\phi + [s(3)-s(4)]\sin\phi\end{array}\right\} \tag{27}$$

where

s = shelter factor for the particular wind direction ϕ
$s(i)$ = shelter factor when wind is normal to wall i (i = 1 to 4, for four sides of a building)

Although this method gives a realistic variation of wind shelter effects with wind direction, estimates for numerical values of wind shelter factor s for each of the four cardinal directions must be provided. Table 8 in the section on Residential Calculation Examples lists typical shelter factors. The wind speed used in Equation (25) is then given by

$$U = sU_H \tag{28}$$

The magnitude of pressure differences found on the surfaces of buildings varies rapidly with time because of turbulent fluctuations in the wind (Etheridge and Nolan 1979; Grimsrud et al. 1979). However, using average wind pressures to calculate pressure differences is usually sufficient to calculate average infiltration values.

Mechanical Systems

Operation of mechanical equipment, such as supply or exhaust systems and vented combustion devices, affects pressure differences across the building envelope. Interior static pressure adjusts such that the sum of all airflows through openings in the building envelope plus equipment-induced airflows balance to zero. To predict these changes in pressure differences and airflow rates caused by mechanical equipment, the location of each opening in the envelope and the relationship between pressure difference and airflow rate for each opening must be known. The interaction between mechanical ventilation system operation and envelope airtightness has been discussed for low-rise buildings (Nylund 1980) and for office buildings (Persily and Grot 1985a; Tamura and Wilson 1966, 1967a).

Air exhausted from a building by a whole-building exhaust system must be balanced by increasing airflow into the building through other openings. As a result, airflow at some locations changes from outflow to inflow. For supply fans, the situation is reversed and envelope inflows become outflows. Thus, the effects of a mechanical system on a building must be considered. Depressurization caused by an improperly designed exhaust system can increase the rate of radon entry into a building and interfere with proper operation of combustion device venting or other exhaust systems. Depressurization can also force moist outdoor air through the building envelope; for example, during the cooling season in hot, humid climates, moisture may condense within the building envelope and cause rust, rot, or mold. A similar phenomenon, but in reverse, can occur during the heating (and potentially humidifying) season in cold climates if the building is pressurized.

The interaction between mechanical systems and the building envelope also pertains to systems serving zones of buildings. Performance of zone-specific exhaust or pressurization systems is affected by leakage in zone partitions as well as in exterior walls.

Mechanical systems can also create infiltration-driving forces in single-zone buildings. Specifically, some single-family houses with central forced-air duct systems have multiple supply registers, yet only a central return grille. When internal doors are closed in these houses, large positive indoor/outdoor pressure differentials are created for rooms with only supply registers, whereas the room or hallway with the return grille tends to depressurize relative to outside. This is caused by the resistance of internal door undercuts, often partially blocked by carpeting, to flow from the supply register to the return (Modera et al. 1991). The magnitudes of the indoor/outdoor pressure differentials created have been measured to average 3 to 6 Pa (Modera et al. 1991). Balanced airflow systems, with ducted air return and distributed grilles, or adequately sized transfer grilles (where allowed by fire code) reduce this significantly.

Building envelope airtightness and interzonal airflow resistance can also affect performance of mechanical systems. The actual airflow rate delivered by these systems, particularly ventilation systems, depends on the pressure they work against. This effect is the same as the interaction of a fan with its associated ductwork, which is discussed in Chapter 21 of this volume and Chapter 20 of the 2008 *ASHRAE Handbook—HVAC Systems and Equipment*. The building envelope and its leakage must be considered part of the ductwork in determining the pressure drop of the system.

Duct leakage can cause similar problems. Supply leaks to the outside tend to depressurize the building; return leaks to the outside tend to pressurize it. Keeping ducts within the conditioned buildings, and sealing ducts well with durable materials and high-quality construction methods, significantly reduces this problem.

Combining Driving Forces

Pressure differences caused by wind, stack effect, and mechanical systems are considered in combination by adding them together and then determining the resulting airflow rate through each building envelope. The airflows must be determined in this manner, as opposed to adding the airflow rates due to the separate driving forces, because the airflow rate through each opening is not linearly related to pressure difference.

For uniform indoor air temperatures, the total pressure difference across each leak can be written in terms of a reference wind parameter P_U and stack effect parameter P_T common to all leaks:

$$P_U = \rho_o \frac{U_H^2}{2} \tag{29}$$

$$P_T = g\rho_o[(T_i - T_o)/T_i] \tag{30}$$

where T is air temperature, in K.

The pressure difference across each leak, with positive pressures for flow into the building, is then given by

$$\Delta p = s^2 C_p P_U + HP_T + \Delta p_I \tag{31}$$

where Δp_I is the pressure that acts to balance inflows and outflows, including mechanical system flows. Equation (31) can then be applied to every leak for the building with appropriate values of C_p, s, and H. Thus, each leak is defined by its pressure coefficient, shelter, and height. Where indoor pressures are not uniform, more complex analyses are required.

Neutral Pressure Level

The neutral pressure level (NPL) is that location or locations in the building envelope where there is no indoor-to-outdoor pressure difference. Internal partitions, stairwells, elevator shafts, utility ducts, chimneys, vents, operable windows, and mechanical supply and exhaust systems complicate the prediction of NPL location. An opening with a large area relative to the total building leakage causes the NPL to shift toward the opening. In particular, chimneys and openings at or above roof height raise the NPL in small buildings. Exhaust systems increase the height of the NPL; outdoor air supply systems lower it.

Figure 6 qualitatively shows the addition of driving forces for a building with uniform openings above and below mid-height and without significant internal resistance to airflow. The slopes of the pressure lines are a function of the densities of the indoor and outdoor air. In Figure 6A, with inside air warmer than outside and pressure differences caused solely by thermal forces, the NPL is at mid-height, with inflow through lower openings and outflow through higher openings. Direction of flow is always from the higher to the lower pressure region.

Figure 6B presents qualitative uniform pressure differences caused by wind alone, with opposing effects on the windward and leeward sides. When temperature difference and wind effects both exist, the pressures caused by each are added together to determine the total pressure difference across the building envelope. In Figure 6B, there is no NPL because no locations on the building envelope have zero pressure difference. Figure 6C shows the combination, where the wind force of Figure 6B has just balanced the thermal force of Figure 6A, causing no pressure difference at the top windward or bottom leeward side.

The relative importance of wind and stack pressures in a building depends on building height, internal resistance to vertical airflow, location and flow resistance characteristics of envelope openings, local terrain, and the immediate shielding of the building. The taller the building and the smaller its internal resistance to airflow, the stronger the stack effect. The more exposed a building is, the more susceptible it is to wind. For any building, there are ranges of wind speed and temperature difference for which the building's infiltration is dominated by stack effect, wind, or the driving pressures of both (Sinden 1978b). These building and terrain factors determine, for specific values of temperature difference and wind speed, in which regime the building's infiltration lies.

The effect of mechanical ventilation on envelope pressure differences is more complex and depends on both the direction of ventilation flow (exhaust or supply) and the differences in these ventilation flows among the zones of the building. If mechanically supplied outdoor air is provided uniformly to each story, the change in the exterior wall pressure difference pattern is uniform. With a nonuniform supply of outdoor air (for example, to one story only), the extent of pressurization varies from story to story and depends on internal airflow resistance. Pressurizing all levels uniformly has little effect on pressure differences across floors and vertical shaft enclosures, but pressurizing individual stories increases the pressure drop across these internal separations. Pressurizing the ground level is often used in tall buildings in winter to reduce negative air pressures across entries.

Available data on the NPL in various kinds of buildings are limited. The NPL in tall buildings varies from 0.3 to 0.7 of total building height (Tamura and Wilson 1966, 1967b). For houses, especially houses with chimneys, the NPL is usually above mid-height. Operating a combustion heat source with a flue raises the NPL further, sometimes above the ceiling (Shaw and Brown 1982).

Thermal Draft Coefficient

Compartmentation of a building also affects the NPL location. Equation (24) provides a maximum stack pressure difference, given no internal airflow resistance. The sum of pressure differences across the exterior wall at the bottom and top of the building, as calculated by these equations, equals the total theoretical draft for the building. The sum of actual top and bottom pressure differences, divided by the total theoretical draft pressure difference, equals the **thermal draft coefficient**. The value of the thermal draft coefficient depends on the airflow resistance of exterior walls relative to the airflow resistance between floors. For a building without internal partitions, the total theoretical draft is achieved across the exterior walls (Figure 7A), and the thermal draft coefficient equals 1. In a building with airtight separations at each floor, each story acts

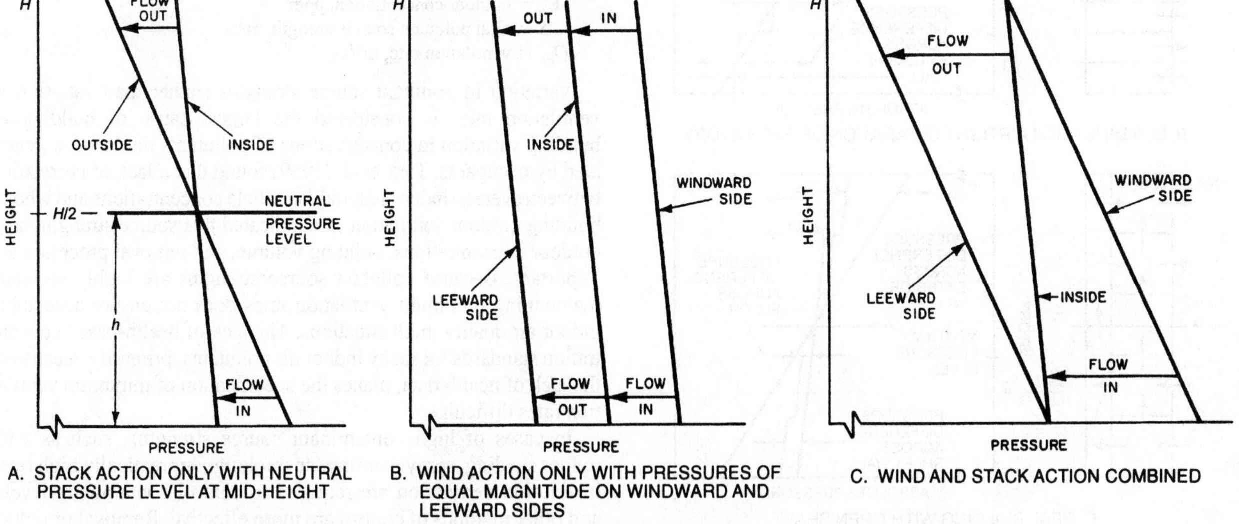

Fig. 6 Distribution of Inside and Outside Pressures over Height of Building

independently, its own stack effect being unaffected by that of any other floor (Figure 7B). The theoretical draft is minimized in this case, and each story has an NPL.

Real multistory buildings are neither open inside (Figure 7A), nor airtight between stories (Figure 7B). Vertical air passages, stairwells, elevators, and other service shafts allow airflow between floors. Figure 7C represents a heated building with uniform openings in the exterior wall, through each floor, and into the vertical shaft at each story. Between floors, the slope of the line representing the inside pressure is the same as that shown in Figure 7A, and the discontinuity at each floor (Figure 7B) represents the pressure difference across it. Some of the pressure difference maintains flow through openings in the floors and vertical shafts. As a result, the pressure difference across the exterior wall at any level is less than it would be with no internal flow resistance.

Maintaining airtightness between floors and from floors to vertical shafts is a way to control indoor/outdoor pressure differences because of the stack effect and, therefore, infiltration. Good separation is also conducive to proper operation of mechanical ventilation and smoke management systems. However, care is needed

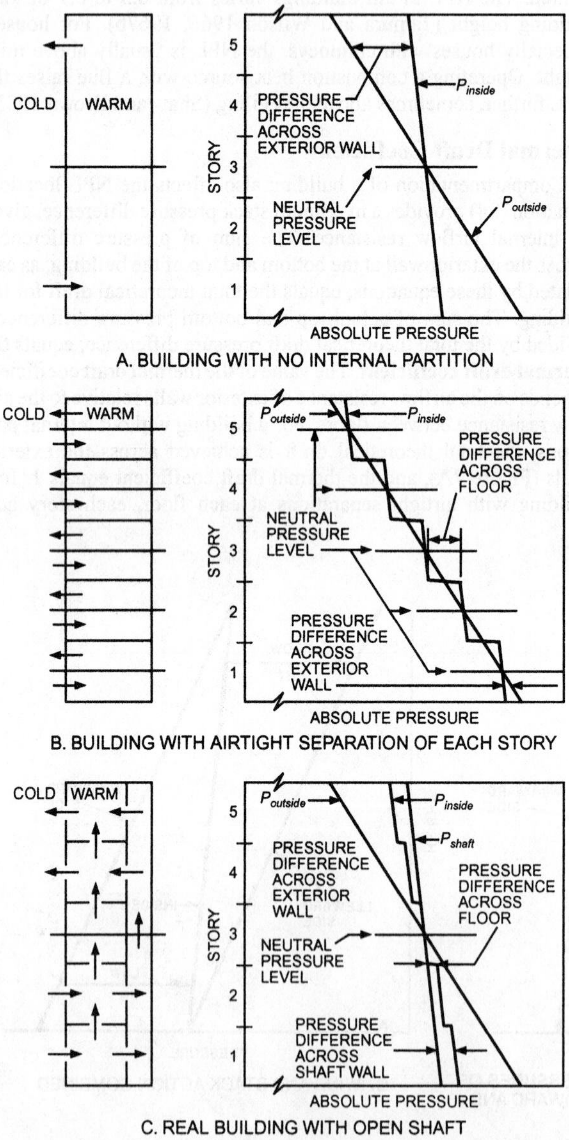

Fig. 7 Compartmentation Effect in Buildings

to avoid pressure differences that could prevent door opening in an emergency. Tamura and Wilson (1967a) showed that when vertical shaft leakage is at least two times envelope leakage, the thermal draft coefficient is almost one and the effect of compartmentation is negligible. Measurements of pressure differences in three tall office buildings by Tamura and Wilson (1967b) indicated that the thermal draft coefficient ranged from 0.8 to 0.9 with ventilation systems off.

INDOOR AIR QUALITY

Outdoor air requirements for acceptable indoor air quality (IAQ) have long been debated, and different rationales have produced radically different ventilation standards (Grimsrud and Teichman 1989; Janssen 1989; Klauss et al. 1970; Yaglou et al. 1936; Yaglou and Witheridge 1937). Historically, the major considerations have included the amount of outdoor air required to control moisture, carbon dioxide (CO_2), odors, and tobacco smoke generated by occupants. These considerations have led to prescriptions of a minimum rate of outdoor air supply per occupant. More recently, a major concern has been maintaining acceptable indoor concentrations of various additional pollutants that are not generated primarily by occupants. Engineering experience and field studies indicate that an outdoor air supply of about 10 L/s per person is very likely to provide acceptable perceived indoor air quality in office spaces, whereas lower rates may lead to increased sick building syndrome symptoms (Apte et al. 2000; Mendell 1993; Seppanen et al. 1999). Information on contaminants can be found in Chapter 11, and odors are covered in Chapter 12.

Indoor pollutant concentrations depend on the strength of pollutant sources and the total rate of pollutant removal. Pollutant sources include outdoor air; indoor sources such as occupants, furnishings, and appliances; dirty ventilation system ducts and filters; soil adjacent to the building; and building materials themselves, especially when new. Pollutant removal processes include dilution with outside air, local exhaust ventilation, deposition on surfaces, chemical reactions, and air-cleaning processes. If (1) general building ventilation is the only significant pollutant removal process, (2) indoor air is thoroughly mixed, and (3) pollutant source strength and ventilation rate have been stable for a sufficient period, then the steady-state indoor pollutant concentration is given by

$$C_i = C_o + 10^6 S/Q_{oa} \tag{32}$$

where

C_i = steady-state indoor concentration, ppm
C_o = outdoor concentration, ppm
S = total pollutant source strength, m^3/s
Q_{oa} = ventilation rate, m^3/s

Variation in pollutant source strengths (rather than variation in ventilation rate) is considered the largest cause of building-to-building variation in concentrations of pollutants that are not generated by occupants. Turk et al. (1989) found that a lack of correlation between average indoor respirable particle concentrations and whole-building outdoor ventilation rate indicated that source strength, high outdoor concentrations, building volume, and removal processes are important. Because pollutant source strengths are highly variable, maintaining minimum ventilation rates does not ensure acceptable indoor air quality in all situations. The lack of health-based concentration standards for many indoor air pollutants, primarily because of the lack of health data, makes the specification of minimum ventilation rates difficult.

In cases of high contaminant source strengths, such as with indoor sanding, spray painting, or smoking, impractically high rates of dilution ventilation are required to control contaminant levels, and other methods of control are more effective. Removal or reduction of contaminant sources is the most effective means of control. Controlling a localized source by means of local exhaust, such as range hoods or bathroom exhaust fans, as well as filtration and absorption, may also be effective [e.g., Rock (2006)].

Particles can be removed with various types of air filters. Gaseous contaminants with higher relative molecular mass can be controlled with activated carbon or alumina pellets impregnated with a substance such as potassium permanganate. Chapter 28 of the 2008 *ASHRAE Handbook—HVAC Systems and Equipment* has information on air cleaning.

Protection from Extraordinary Events

The design, operation and maintenance of a building's ventilation system, envelope, and other factors can significantly affect the building's potential vulnerability to extraordinary threats, which range from intentional releases of chemical or biological agents inside or outside a building, to releases of chemicals in industrial or transportation accidents, to natural disasters. ASHRAE (2003) addresses several key steps to manage risk from extraordinary incidents, including the following:

- Evaluate the risk to a facility of an extraordinary incident.
- Assess the building's vulnerability.
- Determine the degree of acceptable vulnerability.
- Consider protective measures or options in relation to new, renovated, and existing buildings.

Persily (2004) details how ventilation affects buildings' vulnerability to airborne chemical and biological releases, as well as some strategies for using ventilation (particularly involving airtightness and pressurizing the building interior to protect against outdoor releases) to increase the level of building protection against such incidents. Persily et al. (2007) evaluate retrofit options for building protection from airborne threats; approaches considered include enhanced particle filtration, sorbent-based gaseous air cleaning, ventilation system recommissioning, building envelope airtightening, building pressurization, relocation of outdoor air intakes, shelter-in-place (SIP), isolation of vulnerable spaces such as lobbies, and system shutdown and purge cycles. The filtration and air cleaning options have the advantage of always being operational as long as the systems are properly designed, installed, and maintained. However, the lack of standard test methods is a critical issue in application of some air-cleaning technologies. Building envelope air sealing and pressurization can be quite effective in protecting against outdoor releases as long as effective filtration against the contaminant of concern is also in place. The protection provided by operational changes such as system shutdown and purging depends heavily on timing; if timing is inappropriate, occupant exposure may increase. Isolating vulnerable zones and other system-related modifications depend on building layout and system design, and careful implementation is necessary for effectiveness under the range of conditions that exist in buildings. Finally, many retrofits also increase energy efficiency and improve indoor air quality, which should be included in a life-cycle cost comparison of different options to the degree possible. Chapter 58 of the 2007 *ASHRAE Handbook—HVAC Applications* addresses this topic of extraordinary events further.

THERMAL LOADS

Outdoor air introduced into a building constitutes a large part of the total space-conditioning (heating, cooling, humidification, and dehumidification) load, which is one reason to limit air exchange rates in buildings to the minimum required. Air exchange typically represents 20 to 50% of a building's thermal load. Chapters 17 and 18 cover thermal loads in more detail.

Air exchange increases a building's thermal load in several ways. First, incoming air must be heated or cooled from the outdoor air temperature to the indoor or supply air temperature. The rate of energy consumption by this sensible heating or cooling is given by

$$q_s = Q\rho c_p \Delta t \qquad (33)$$

where

q_s = sensible heat load, W
Q = airflow rate, m^3/s
ρ = air density, kg/m^3 (about 1.2 at or near sea level)
c_p = specific heat of air, J/(kg·K) (about 1000)
Δt = temperature difference between indoors and outdoors, K

and at or near sea-level air density, with an adjustment for typical room air humidity, this equation is commonly presented for design use as

$$q_s = 1230 Q\Delta t \qquad (34)$$

Equation (33) is known as the **sensible heat equation**. HVAC designers typically assume sea-level air pressure for locations with altitudes of 610 m or lower. A method to adjust for elevation is provided in Chapter 18.

Air exchange also modifies the moisture content of the air in a building. The rate of energy consumption associated with these latent loads (neglecting the energy associated with any condensate) is given by

$$q_l = Q\rho\Delta W(2501 + 1.805t) \qquad (35)$$

where

q_l = latent heat load, kW
ΔW = humidity ratio difference between indoors and outdoors, mass water/unit mass dry air, kg/kg
t = average of indoor and outdoor temperatures, °C

Equation (35) is known as the **latent heat equation**. When at or near sea level, and for common comfort air temperatures, the right-hand side of Equation (35) is approximately $3.01 \times 10^6\, Q\Delta W$.

Example 1. A makeup air unit (MAU) is to condition 2360 L/s of outdoor air in the winter for a building in Atlanta, Georgia. If the air is to be delivered directly to the occupied spaces at 24°C and 30% rh, how much sensible and latent heat must be added to this ventilation air at winter design conditions?

Solution: From the weather data tables provided on the CD included with this volume, Atlanta is at an elevation of about 305 m. Because this below the rule-of-thumb cutoff of 610 m for assuming sea-level conditions, air density is assumed to be 1.20 kg/m^3. Also from the Atlanta data table, the winter 99% design dry-bulb (db) temperature is –4.5°C, but a mean coincident wet bulb is not provided. However, for humidification design, a dew-point temperature of –16.7°C is given along with its –3.9°C mean coincident dry bulb (MCDB). Using these data, a –17.2°C dew point is assumed as the 99% mean coincident dew point.

From ASHRAE's sea-level psychrometric chart and the winter design conditions, the desired humidity ratio W of the 24°C, 30% rh makeup air is about 0.0056 kg_w/kg_{da}. For the very dry outside air, with a dew point of –17.2°C, a problem occurs: the standard sea-level psychrometric chart does not extend below 0°C. Designers often assume that air below this temperature has $W = 0$, and this assumption gives conservative results. However, both high- and low-temperature psychrometric charts are available from ASHRAE, as is a table of moist air properties at standard conditions in Chapter 1. From this table, saturated air at –17.2°C, which is also its dew point, has a humidity ratio of 0.0008298 kg_w/kg_{da}. With 2360 L/s of outdoor air to be conditioned, and using the sensible and latent heat equations for sea level, the energy needed to condition this outdoor air is

$$q_s = 1.23Q\Delta T = 1.23 \times 2360 \text{ L/s}[24 - (-4.5°C)]$$
$$= 82\,730 \text{ W} \approx 82.7 \text{ kW}$$

and

$$q_l = 3010Q\Delta W = 3010 \times 2360 \text{ L/s}(0.0056 - 0.0008298 \text{ kg}_w/\text{kg}_{da})$$
$$= 33\,886 \text{ W} \approx 33.9 \text{ kW}$$

Thus, the MAU's heating coil and humidifier, neglecting fan heat, need to be sized to provide at least a net 82.7 kW of sensible heat, and 33.9 kW of latent heat. Humidification can be provided by cold water, warm water, or steam, so a more precise psychrometric analysis is needed to size the heating coil correctly after the humidification method is selected and it is decided whether the humidifier will be placed before or after the heating coil.

As Example 1 shows, ventilation loads are substantial. They are often 50% or more of the total space conditioning loads in modern, well-insulated commercial buildings in less temperate climates. When cooling outdoor air, substantial moisture usually must be removed from the ventilation air; reheat or regenerative heat recovery may be required in all but dry climates.

Effect on Envelope Insulation

Air exchange also can affect a building's thermal load by altering performance of the envelope insulation system. Airflow through insulation can decrease thermal load through heat exchange between infiltrating or exfiltrating air and the insulation. Conversely, air moving in and out of the insulation from outside can increase the thermal load. Experimental and numerical studies have demonstrated that significant thermal coupling can occur between air leakage and insulation layers, thereby modifying the heat transmission in building envelopes. In particular, research (Bankvall 1987; Berlad et al. 1978; Lecompte 1987; Wolf 1966) has shown that convective airflow through air-permeable insulation in an envelope assembly may degrade its effective thermal resistance. This R-value degradation occurs when outside air moves through and/or around the insulation within the wall cavity and returns to the outdoors without reaching the conditioned space. A literature review by Powell et al. (1989) summarized the findings about air movement effects on the effective thermal resistance of porous insulation under various conditions. The effect of such airflow on insulation system performance is difficult to quantify, but should be considered. Airflow within the insulation system can also decrease the system's performance because of moisture condensation in and on the insulation.

Even if air flows only through cracks instead of through the insulation, the actual heating/cooling load from the combined effect of conduction and airflow heat transfer can be lower than the heating/cooling load calculated by Equation (33). This reduction in total heating/cooling load is a consequence of the thermal coupling between conduction and convection heat transfer and is called **infiltration heat recovery (IHR)**. Using a computer simulation, Kohonen et al. (1987) found that the conduction/infiltration thermal interaction reduced total heating load by 15%. Several experimental studies (e.g., Claridge and Bhattacharyya 1990; Claridge et al. 1988; Liu and Claridge 1992a, 1992b, 1992c, 1995; Timusk et al. 1992), using a test cell under both steady-state and dynamic conditions, found that the actual energy attributed to air infiltration can be 20 to 80% of the values given by Equation (35). Judkoff et al. (1997) measured heat recovery in a mobile home under steady-state conditions, and found that up to 40% heat recovery occurs during exfiltration through the envelope. Buchanan and Sherman (2000) performed two- and three-dimensional computational fluid dynamics (CFD) simulations to study the fundamental physics of the IHR process and developed a simple macro-scale mathematical model based on the steady-state one-dimensional convection-diffusion equation to predict a heat recovery factor. Their results show that the traditional method may overpredict the infiltration energy load. Using physical experiments, ASHRAE research project RP-1169 (Ackerman et al. 2006) showed that thermal resistances are affected by infiltration and exfiltration, but, on a net basis, the IHR effect can be neglected.

Infiltration Degree-Days

Heating and cooling degree-days are a simple way to characterize the severity of a particular climate. Heating and cooling degree-day values are based on sensible temperature data, but infiltration loads are both sensible and latent. **Infiltration degree days (IDDs)** more fully describe a climate and can be used to estimate heat loss or gain from infiltration in residences (Sherman 1986). Total infiltration degree-days is the sum of the heating and cooling infiltration degree-days and is calculated from hour-by-hour weather data and base conditions using weather weighted by infiltration rate. The selection of base conditions is an important part of the calculation of the IDDs. ASHRAE *Standard* 119 lists IDDs for many locations with a particular set of base conditions.

NATURAL VENTILATION

Natural ventilation is the flow of outdoor air caused by wind and thermal pressures through intentional openings in the building's shell. Under some circumstances, it can effectively control both temperature and contaminants in mild climates, but it is not considered practical in hot and humid climates or in cold climates. Temperature control by natural ventilation is often the only means of providing cooling when mechanical air conditioning is not available. The arrangement, location, and control of ventilation openings should combine the driving forces of wind and temperature to achieve a desired ventilation rate and good distribution of ventilation air through the building. However, intentional openings cannot always guarantee adequate temperature and humidity control or indoor air quality because of the dependence on natural (wind and stack) effects to drive the flow (Wilson and Walker 1992). Using night ventilation and the building's thermal mass effect may be effective for reducing conventional cooling energy consumption in some buildings and climates if moisture condensation can be controlled. Axley (2001a) and the Chartered Institute of Building Services Engineers (CIBSE 2005) review natural ventilation in commercial buildings, including potential advantages and problems, natural ventilation components and system designs, and recommended design and analysis approaches.

Natural Ventilation Openings

Natural ventilation openings include (1) windows, doors, dormer (monitor) openings, and skylights; (2) roof ventilators; (3) stacks; and (4) specially designed inlet or outlet openings.

Windows transmit light and provide ventilation when open. They may open by sliding vertically or horizontally; by tilting on horizontal pivots at or near the center; or by swinging on pivots at the top, bottom, or side. The type of pivoting used is important for weather protection and affects airflow rate.

Roof ventilators provide a weather-resistant air outlet. Capacity is determined by the ventilator's location on the roof; the resistance to airflow of the ventilator and its ductwork; the ventilator's ability to use kinetic wind energy to induce flow by centrifugal or ejector action; and the height of the draft.

Natural-draft or gravity roof ventilators can be stationary, pivoting, oscillating, or rotating. Selection criteria include ruggedness, corrosion resistance, stormproofing features, dampers and operating mechanisms, noise, cost, and maintenance. Natural ventilators can be supplemented with power-driven supply fans; the motors need only be energized when the natural exhaust capacity is too low. Gravity ventilator dampers can be manual or controlled by thermostat or wind velocity.

A natural-draft roof ventilator should be positioned so that it receives full, unrestricted wind. Turbulence created by surrounding obstructions, including higher adjacent buildings, impairs a ventilator's ejector action. Inlets can be conical or bell-mouthed to increase their flow coefficients. The opening area at any inlet should be increased if screens, grilles, or other structural members cause flow resistance. Building air inlets at lower levels should be larger than the combined throat areas of all roof ventilators.

Stacks or vertical flues should be located where wind can act on them from any direction. Without wind, stack effect alone removes air from the room with the inlets.

Ceiling Heights

In buildings that rely on natural ventilation for cooling, floor-to-ceiling heights are often increased well beyond the normal 2.5 to 3.2 m. Higher ceilings, as seen in buildings constructed before air conditioning was available, allow warm air and contaminants to rise above the occupied portions of rooms. Air is then exhausted from the ceiling zones, and cooler outside air is provided near the floors; a degree of floor-to-ceiling displacement airflow is thus desirable when using natural ventilation for cooling.

Required Flow for Indoor Temperature Control

The ventilation airflow rate required to remove a given amount of heat from a building can be calculated from Equations (33) and (35) if the quantity of heat to be removed and the indoor/outdoor temperature difference are known.

Airflow Through Large Intentional Openings

The relationship describing the airflow through a large intentional opening is based on the Bernoulli equation with steady, incompressible flow. The general form that includes stack, wind, and mechanical ventilation pressures across the opening is

$$Q = C_D A \sqrt{2\,\Delta p/\rho} \qquad (36)$$

where

Q = airflow rate, m^3/s
C_D = discharge coefficient for opening, dimensionless
A = cross-sectional area of opening, m^2
ρ = air density, kg/m^3
Δp = pressure difference across opening, Pa

The discharge coefficient C_D is a dimensionless number that depends on the geometry of the opening and the Reynolds number of the flow.

Flow Caused by Wind Only

Aspects of wind that affect the ventilation rate include average speed, prevailing direction, seasonal and daily variation in speed and direction, and local obstructions such as nearby buildings, hills, trees, and shrubbery. Liddament (1988) reviewed the relevance of wind pressure as a driving mechanism. A multiflow path simulation model was developed and used to illustrate the effects of wind on air exchange rate.

Wind speeds may be lower in summer than in winter; directional frequency is also a function of season. Natural ventilation systems are often designed for wind speeds of one-half the seasonal average. Equation (37) shows the rate of air forced through ventilation inlet openings by wind or determines the proper size of openings to produce given airflow rates:

$$Q = C_v A U \qquad (37)$$

where

Q = airflow rate, m^3/s
C_v = effectiveness of openings (C_v is assumed to be 0.5 to 0.6 for perpendicular winds and 0.25 to 0.35 for diagonal winds)
A = free area of inlet openings, m^2
U = wind speed, m/s

Inlets should face directly into the prevailing wind. If they are not advantageously placed, flow will be less than that predicted by Equation (37); if inlets are unusually well placed, flow will be slightly more. Desirable outlet locations are (1) on the leeward side of the building directly opposite the inlet; (2) on the roof, in the low-pressure area caused by a flow discontinuity of the wind; (3) on the side adjacent to the windward face where low-pressure areas occur; (4) in a dormer on the leeward side; (5) in roof ventilators; or (6) by stacks. Chapter 24 gives a general description of the wind pressure distribution on a building. Inlets should be placed in exterior high-pressure regions; outlets should be placed in exterior low-pressure regions.

Flow Caused by Thermal Forces Only

If building internal resistance is not significant, flow caused by stack effect can be expressed by

$$Q = C_D A \sqrt{2g\,\Delta H_{NPL}(T_i - T_o)/T_i} \qquad (38)$$

where

Q = airflow rate, m^3/s
C_D = discharge coefficient for opening
ΔH_{NPL} = height from midpoint of lower opening to NPL, m
T_i = indoor temperature, K
T_o = outdoor temperature, K

Equation (38) applies when $T_i > T_o$. If $T_i < T_o$, replace T_i in the denominator with T_o, and replace $(T_i - T_o)$ in the numerator with $(T_o - T_i)$. An average temperature should be used for T_i if there is thermal stratification. If the building has more than one opening, the outlet and inlet areas are considered equal. The discharge coefficient C_D accounts for all viscous effects such as surface drag and interfacial mixing.

Estimation of ΔH_{NPL} is difficult for naturally ventilated buildings. If one window or door represents a large fraction (approximately 90%) of the total opening area in the envelope, then the NPL is at the mid-height of that aperture, and ΔH_{NPL} equals one-half the height of the aperture. For this condition, flow through the opening is bidirectional (i.e., air from the warmer side flows through the top of the opening, and air from the colder side flows through the bottom). Interfacial mixing occurs across the counterflow interface, and the orifice coefficient can be calculated according to the following equation (Kiel and Wilson 1986):

$$C_D = 0.40 + 0.0045|T_i - T_o| \qquad (39)$$

If enough other openings are available, airflow through the opening will be unidirectional, and mixing cannot occur. A discharge coefficient of $C_D = 0.65$ should then be used. Additional information on stack-driven airflows for natural ventilation can be found in Foster and Down (1987).

Greatest flow per unit area of openings is obtained when inlet and outlet areas are equal; Equations (38) and (39) are based on this equality. Increasing the outlet area over inlet area (or vice versa) increases airflow but not in proportion to the added area. When openings are unequal, use the smaller area in Equation (38) and add the increase as determined from Figure 8.

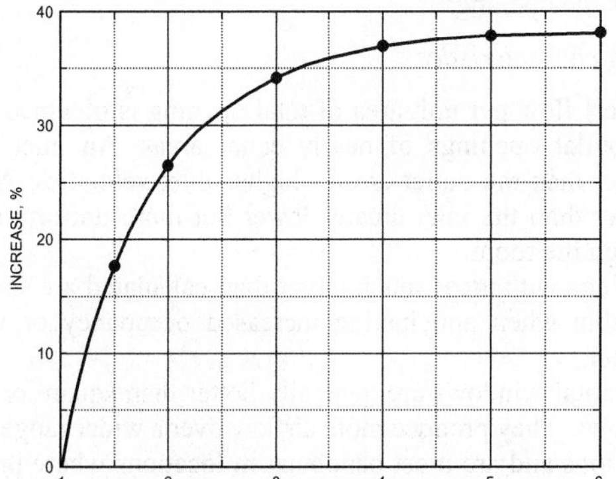

Fig. 8 Increase in Flow Caused by Excess Area of One Opening over the Other

Natural Ventilation Guidelines

Several general guidelines should be observed in designing for natural ventilation. Some of these may conflict with other climate-responsive strategies (such as using orientation and shading devices to minimize solar gain), with building codes that encourage compartmentalization to restrict fire and smoke movement, or with other design considerations.

System selection

- In hot, humid climates, use mechanical cooling. If mechanical cooling is not available, air velocities should be maximized in the occupied zones of rooms.
- In hot, arid climates, consider evaporative cooling. Airflow throughout the building should be maximized for structural cooling, particularly at night when the outside air temperature is low.

Building and surroundings characteristics

- Topography, landscaping, and surrounding buildings should be used to redirect airflow and give maximum exposure to breezes. Vegetation can funnel breezes and avoid wind dams, which reduce the driving pressure differential around the building. Site objects should not obstruct inlet openings.
- The building should be shaped to expose maximum shell openings to breezes.
- Architectural elements such as wing walls, parapets, and overhangs should be used to promote airflow into the building interior.
- The long façade of the building and the majority of door and window openings should be oriented with respect to prevailing summer breezes. If there is no prevailing direction, openings should be sufficient to provide ventilation regardless of wind direction.

Opening locations

- Windows should be located in opposing pressure zones. Two openings on opposite sides of a space increase ventilation flow. Openings on adjacent sides force air to change direction, providing ventilation to a greater area. The benefits of the window arrangement depend on the outlet location relative to the direction of the inlet airstream.
- If a room has only one external wall, better airflow is achieved with two widely spaced windows.
- If openings are at the same level and near the ceiling, much of the flow may bypass the occupied level and be ineffective in diluting contaminants there.
- Vertical distance between openings is required to take advantage of stack effect; the greater the vertical distance, the greater the ventilation rate.
- Openings in the vicinity of the NPL are least effective for thermally induced ventilation. If the building has only one large opening, the NPL tends to move to that level, which reduces pressure across the opening.

Opening characteristics

- Greatest flow per unit area of total opening is obtained by inlet and outlet openings of nearly equal areas. An inlet window smaller than the outlet creates higher inlet velocities. An outlet smaller than the inlet creates lower but more uniform airspeed through the room.
- Openings with areas much larger than calculated are sometimes desirable when anticipating increased occupancy or very hot weather.
- Horizontal windows are generally better than square or vertical windows. They produce more airflow over a wider range of wind directions and are most beneficial in locations where prevailing wind patterns shift.
- Window openings should be accessible to and operable by occupants, unless fully automated. For secondary fire egress, operable windows may be required.
- Inlet openings should not be obstructed by indoor partitions. Partitions can be placed to split and redirect airflow but should not restrict flow between the building's inlets and outlets. Vertical airshafts or open staircases can be used to increase and take advantage of stack effects. However, enclosed staircases intended for evacuation during a fire should not be used for ventilation.

Hybrid Ventilation

Application of purely natural ventilation systems may be limited in hot or humid climates, such as in much of the United States, by thermal comfort issues and the need for reliability. However, hybrid (or mixed-mode) ventilation systems or operational strategies offer the possibility of saving energy in a greater number of buildings and climates by combining natural ventilation systems with mechanical equipment (Emmerich 2006). The **air-side economizer** is one form of hybrid ventilation control scheme, and enjoys wide use in commercial, industrial, and institutional buildings in appropriate climates. The report of the International Energy Agency's (IEA) Annex 35 describes the principles of hybrid ventilation technologies, control strategies, design and analysis methods, and case studies (Heiselberg 2002). Integrated multizone airflow and thermal modeling is recommended when designing natural and hybrid ventilation systems (Axley 2001a; Li and Heiselberg 2003).

RESIDENTIAL AIR LEAKAGE

Most infiltration in U.S. residential buildings is dominated by envelope leakage. However, new construction tends toward tighter building envelopes.

Envelope Leakage Measurement

A building's envelope leakage can be measured with **pressurization testing,** commonly called a **blower-door test**. Fan pressurization is relatively quick and inexpensive, and it characterizes building envelope airtightness independent of weather conditions. In this procedure, a large fan or blower is mounted in a door or window and induces a large and roughly uniform pressure difference across the building shell [ASTM *Standards* E779 and E1827; Canadian General Standards Board (CGSB) *Standard* 149.10; ISO *Standard* 9972]. The airflow required to maintain this pressure difference is then measured. The leakier the building is, the more airflow is necessary to induce a specific indoor/outdoor pressure difference. The airflow rate is generally measured at a series of pressure differences ranging from about 10 Pa to 75 Pa.

The results of a pressurization test, therefore, consist of several combinations of pressure difference and airflow rate data. An example of typical data is shown in Figure 9. These data points characterize the air leakage of a building and are generally converted to a single value that serves as a measure of the building's airtightness. There are several different measures of airtightness, most of which involve fitting the data to a curve describing the relationship between the airflow Q through an opening in the building envelope and the pressure difference Δp across it. This relationship is called the **leakage function** of the opening. The form of the leakage function depends on the geometry of the opening. Background theoretical material relevant to leakage functions may be found in Chastain et al. (1987), Etheridge (1977), Hopkins and Hansford (1974), Kronvall (1980), and Walker et al. (1997).

Openings in a building envelope are not uniform in geometry and, generally, the flow never becomes fully developed. Each opening in the building envelope can be described by Equation (40), commonly called the **power law equation**:

$$Q = c(\Delta p)^n \tag{40}$$

where

Q = airflow through opening, m^3/s
c = flow coefficient, $m^3/(s \cdot Pa^n)$
n = pressure exponent, dimensionless

Sherman (1992a) showed how the power law can be developed analytically by looking at developing laminar flow in short pipes. Equation (40) only approximates the relationship between Q and Δp. Measurements of single cracks (Honma 1975; Kreith and Eisenstadt 1957) show that n can vary if Δp changes over a wide range. Additional investigation of pressure/flow data for simple cracks by Chastain et al. (1987) indicated the importance of adequately characterizing the three-dimensional geometry of openings and the entrance and exit effects. Walker et al. (1997) showed that, for the arrays of cracks in a building envelope over the range of pressures acting during infiltration, n is constant. A typical value for n is about 0.65. Values for c and n can be determined for a building by using fan pressurization testing.

Airtightness Ratings

In some cases, the predicted airflow rate is converted to an **equivalent** or **effective air leakage area** as follows:

$$A_L = 10\,000 Q_r \frac{\sqrt{\rho/2\Delta p_r}}{C_D} \tag{41}$$

where

A_L = equivalent or effective air leakage area, cm²
Q_r = predicted airflow rate at Δp_r (from curve fit to pressurization test data), m³/s
ρ = air density, kg/m³
Δp_r = reference pressure difference, Pa
C_D = discharge coefficient

All openings in the building shell are combined into an overall opening area and discharge coefficient for the building when the equivalent or effective air leakage area is calculated. Some users of the leakage area approach set $C_D = 1$. Others set $C_D \approx 0.6$ (i.e., the discharge coefficient for a sharp-edged orifice). The air leakage area of a building is, therefore, the area of an orifice (with an assumed value of C_D) that would produce the same amount of leakage as the building envelope at the reference pressure.

An airtightness rating, whether based on an air leakage area or a predicted airflow rate, is generally normalized by some factor to account for building size. Normalization factors include floor area, exterior envelope area, and building volume.

With the wide variety of possible approaches to normalization and reference pressure difference, and the use of the air leakage area concept, many different airtightness ratings are used. Reference pressure differences include 4, 10, 25, 50, and 75 Pa. Reference pressure differences of 4 and 10 Pa are advocated because they are closer to the pressure differences that actually induce air exchange and, therefore, better model the opening's flow characteristics. Although this may be true, they are outside the range of measured values in the test; therefore, predicted airflow rates at 4 and 10 Pa are subject to significant uncertainty. This uncertainty and its implications for quantifying airtightness are discussed in Chastain (1987), Modera and Wilson (1990), and Persily and Grot (1985b). Round-robin tests by Murphy et al. (1991) to determine the repeatability and reproducibility of fan pressurization devices found that subtle errors in fan calibration or operator technique are greatly exaggerated when extrapolating the pressure versus flow curve out to 4 Pa, with errors as great as ±40%, mainly because of fan calibration errors at low flow.

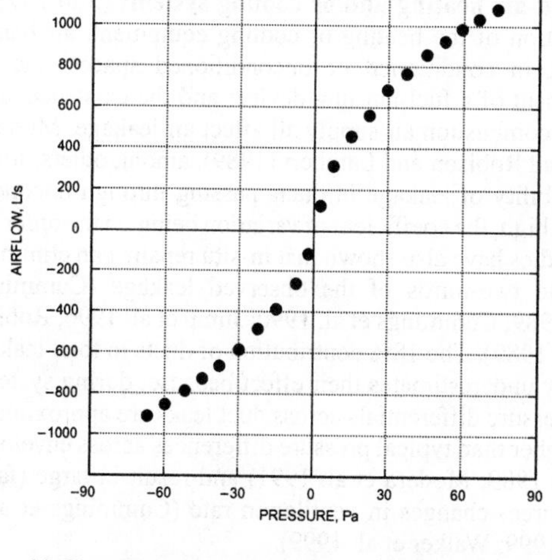

Fig. 9 Airflow Rate Versus Pressure Difference Data from Whole-House Pressurization Test

Some common airtightness ratings include the effective air leakage area at 4 Pa assuming $C_D = 1.0$ (Sherman and Grimsrud 1980); the equivalent air leakage area at 10 Pa assuming $C_D = 0.611$ (CGSB *Standard* 149.10); and the airflow rate at 50 Pa, divided by the building volume to give units of air changes per hour (Blomsterberg and Harrje 1979).

Conversion Between Ratings

Air leakage areas at one reference pressure difference can be converted to air leakage areas at another reference pressure difference according to

$$A_{r,2} = A_{r,1}\left(\frac{C_{D,1}}{C_{D,2}}\right)\left(\frac{\Delta p_{r,2}}{\Delta p_{r,1}}\right)^{n-0.5} \tag{42}$$

where

$A_{r,1}$ = air leakage area at reference pressure difference $\Delta p_{r,1}$, cm²
$A_{r,2}$ = air leakage area at reference pressure difference $\Delta p_{r,2}$, cm²
$C_{D,1}$ = discharge coefficient used to calculate $A_{r,1}$
$C_{D,2}$ = discharge coefficient used to calculate $A_{r,2}$
n = pressure exponent from Equation (40)

Air leakage area at one reference pressure difference can be converted to airflow rate at some other reference pressure difference according to

$$Q_{r,2} = \frac{C_{D,1}A_{r,1}}{10\,000}\sqrt{\frac{2}{\rho}}(\Delta p_{r,1})^{0.5-n}(\Delta p_{r,2})^n \tag{43}$$

where $Q_{r,2}$ is airflow rate at reference difference $\Delta p_{r,2}$, in m³/s.

Flow coefficient c in Equation (40) may be converted to air leakage area according to

$$A_L = \frac{10\,000c}{C_D}\sqrt{\frac{\rho}{2}}\Delta p_r^{(n-0.5)} \tag{44}$$

Finally, air leakage area may be converted to flow coefficient c in Equation (40) according to

$$c = \frac{C_D A_L}{10\,000}\sqrt{\frac{2}{\rho}}(\Delta p_r)^{0.5-n} \tag{45}$$

Equations (42) to (45) require assumption of a value of n, unless it is reported with the measurement results. When whole-building pressurization test data are fitted to Equation (40), the value of n generally lies between 0.6 and 0.7. Therefore, using a value of n in this range is reasonable.

Building Air Leakage Data

Fan pressurization measures a building property that ideally varies little with time and weather conditions. In reality, unless wind and temperature differences during the measurement period are suf-

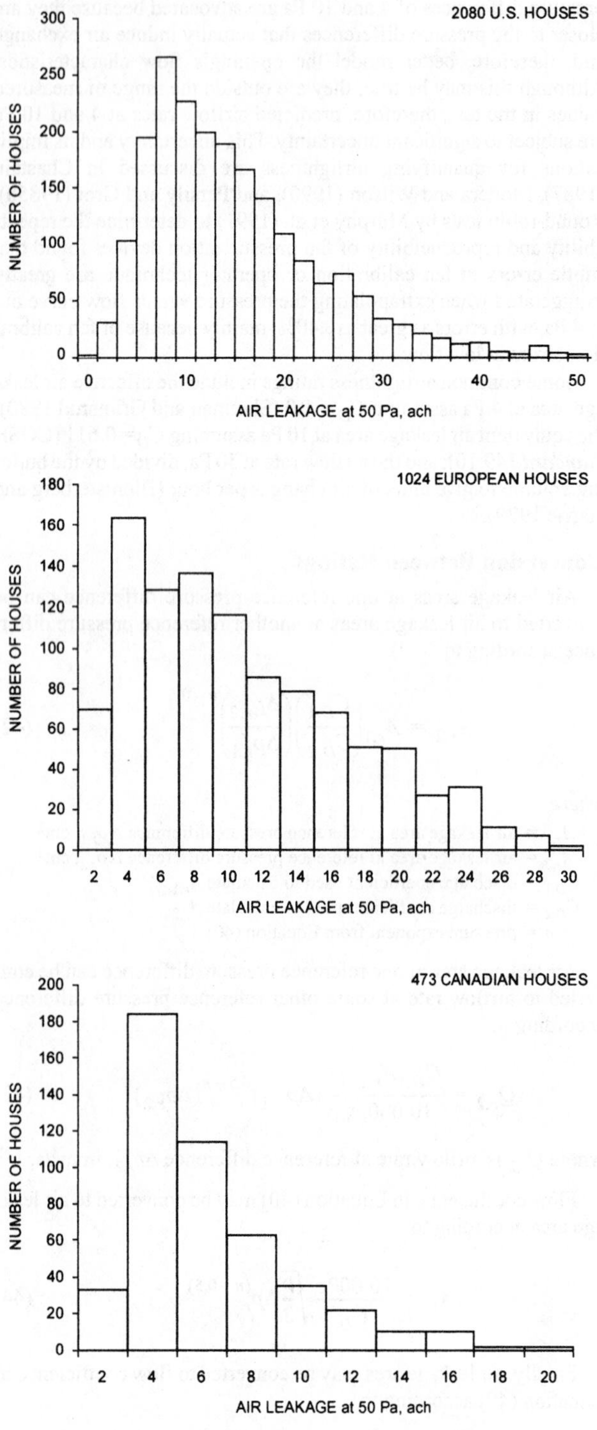

Fig. 10 Envelope Leakage Measurements

ficiently mild, pressure differences they induce during the test interfere with test pressures and cause measurement errors. Modera and Wilson (1990) and Persily (1982) studied the effects of wind speed on pressurization test results. Several experimental studies also showed variations on the order of 20 to 40% over a year in the measured airtightness in homes (Kim and Shaw 1986; Persily 1982; Warren and Webb 1986).

Figure 10 summarizes envelope leakage measured North American housing (Sherman and Dickerhoff 1998) and from several European and Canadian sources (AIVC 1994). This figure shows the large range of measured envelope tightness, but can still be used to illustrate typical and extreme values in the housing stock.

ASHRAE *Standard* 119 establishes air leakage performance levels for residential buildings. These levels are in terms of the normalized leakage area A_n:

$$A_n = 0.1\left(\frac{A_L}{A_f}\right)\left(\frac{H}{H_o}\right)^{0.3} \tag{46}$$

where

A_n = normalized leakage area, dimensionless
A_L = effective leakage area at 4 Pa (C_D = 1.0), cm²
A_f = gross floor area (within exterior walls), m²
H = building height, m
H_o = reference height of one-story building = 2.5 m

Air Leakage of Building Components

The fan pressurization procedure discussed in the section on Envelope Leakage Measurement allows whole-building air leakage to be measured. The location and size of individual openings in building envelopes are extremely important because they influence the air infiltration rate of a building as well as the envelope's heat and moisture transfer characteristics. Additional test procedures for pressure-testing individual building components such as windows, walls, and doors are discussed in ASTM *Standards* E283 and E783 for laboratory and field tests, respectively.

Leakage Distribution

Dickerhoff et al. (1982) and Harrje and Born (1982) studied air leakage of individual building components and systems. The following points summarize the percentages of whole-building air leakage area associated with various components and systems. Values in parentheses include the range determined for each component and the mean of the range.

Walls (18 to 50%; 35%). Both interior and exterior walls contribute to the leakage of the structure. Leakage can occur between the sill plate and foundation; through cracks below the bottom of the gypsum wallboard, electrical outlets, and plumbing penetrations; and into the attic at the top plates of walls.

Ceiling details (3 to 30%; 18%). Leakage across the top ceiling of the heated space is particularly insidious because it reduces the effectiveness of insulation on the attic floor and contributes to infiltration heat loss. Ceiling leakage also reduces the effectiveness of ceiling insulation in buildings without attics. Recessed lighting, plumbing, and electrical penetrations leading to the attic are some particular areas of concern.

Forced-air heating and/or cooling systems (3 to 28%; 18%). The location of the heating or cooling equipment, air handler, or ductwork in conditioned or unconditioned spaces; the venting arrangement of a fuel-burning device; and the existence and location of a combustion air supply all affect air leakage. Modera et al. (1991) and Robison and Lambert (1989), among others, found that the variability of leakage in ducts passing through unconditioned spaces is high, the coefficient of variation being on the order of 50%. Field studies have also shown that in-situ repairs can eliminate one-quarter to two-thirds of the observed leakage (Cummings and Tooley 1989; Cummings et al. 1990; Jump et al. 1996; Robison and Lambert 1989). The 18% contribution of ducts to total leakage significantly underestimates their effect because, during system operation, pressure differentials across duct leaks are approximately ten times higher than typical pressure differences across envelope leaks (Modera 1989; Modera et al. 1991) and result in large (factors of two to three) changes in ventilation rate (Cummings et al. 1990; Walker 1999; Walker et al. 1999).

Windows and doors (6 to 22%; 15%). More variation in window leakage is seen among window types (e.g., casement versus double-hung) than among new windows of the same type from different manufacturers (Weidt et al. 1979). Windows that seal by compressing the weather strip (casements, awnings) show significantly lower leakage than windows with sliding seals.

Fireplaces (0 to 30%; 12%). When a fireplace is not in use, poorly fitting dampers allow air to escape. Glass doors reduce excess air while a fire is burning, but rarely seal the fireplace structure more tightly than a closed damper does. Chimney caps or fireplace plugs (with signs that warn they are in place) effectively reduce leakage through a cold fireplace.

Vents in conditioned spaces (2 to 12%; 5%). Exhaust vents in conditioned spaces frequently have either no dampers or dampers that do not close properly.

Diffusion through walls (<1%). Compared to infiltration through holes and other openings in the structure, diffusion is not an important flow mechanism. At 5 Pa, the permeability of building materials produces an air exchange rate of less than 0.01 ach by wall diffusion in a typical house.

Component leakage areas. Individual building component leakage areas vary widely from house to house. Typical variability for an individual component is about a factor of 10, depending on the component's construction and installation. Testing should be used to establish the installed leakage of a component in applications where leakage is critical to building performance.

Multifamily Building Leakage

Leakage distribution is particularly important in multifamily apartment buildings. These buildings often cannot be treated as single zones because of the internal resistance between apartments. Moreover, leakage between apartments varies widely, from very small for well-constructed buildings with air/moisture retarders between units, to as high as 60% of the total apartment leakage in turn-of-the-century brick walk-up apartment buildings (Diamond et al. 1986; Modera et al. 1991).

Controlling Air Leakage

New Buildings. It is much easier to build a tight building than to tighten an existing building. Elmroth and Levin (1983), Eyre and Jennings (1983), Marbek Resource Consultants (1984), and Nelson et al. (1985) provide information and construction details on airtight building design for houses.

A continuous air infiltration retarder is one of the most effective means of reducing air leakage through walls, around window and door frames, and at joints between major building elements. Particular care must be taken to ensure its continuity at all wall, floor, and ceiling joints; at window and door frames; and at all penetrations of the retarder, such as electrical outlets and switches, plumbing connections, and utility service penetrations. Joints in the **air/vapor retarder** must be lapped and sealed. Plastic vapor retarders installed in the ceiling should be tightly sealed with the vapor retarder in the outside walls and should be continuous over the partition walls. A seal at the top of the partition walls prevents leakage into the attic; a plate on top of the studs generally gives a poor seal. The air infiltration retarder can be installed either on the inside of the wall framing, in which case it usually functions as a vapor retarder as well, or on the outside of the wall framing, in which case it should have a permeance rating high enough to allow diffusion of water vapor from the wall. For a discussion of moisture transfer in building envelopes, see Chapters 25 and 26.

Interior air/vapor retarders must be lapped and sealed at electrical outlets and switches, at joints between walls and floors and between walls and ceilings, and at plumbing connections penetrating the wall's interior finish. A continuous exterior air infiltration retarder installed on the outside of wall framing can cover these problem areas. Joints in the air infiltration retarder should be lapped and sealed or taped. Exterior air infiltration retarders are generally made of a material stronger than plastic film and are more likely to withstand damage during construction. Sealing the wall against air leakage at the exterior of the insulation also reduces convection currents within the wall cavity, allowing insulation to retain more of its effectiveness.

Existing Buildings. Air leakage sites must first be located to tighten the envelope of an existing building. As discussed earlier, air leakage in buildings is caused by not only windows and doors, but also a wide range of unexpected and unobvious construction defects. Many important leakage sites can be very difficult to find. A variety of techniques developed to locate leakage sites are described in ASTM *Standard* E1186 and Charlesworth (1988).

Once leakage sites are located, they can be repaired with materials and techniques appropriate to the size and location of the leak. Diamond et al. (1982), Energy Resource Center (1982), and Harrje et al. (1979) include information on airtightening or "weatherization" in existing residential buildings with caulking, sealing, weatherstripping, and use of door sweeps, for example. With these procedures, air leakage of residential buildings can be reduced dramatically: anywhere from 5% to more than 50%, depending on the extent of the tightening effort and the experience of those doing the work (Blomsterberg and Harrje 1979; Giesbrecht and Proskiw 1986; Harrje and Mills 1980; Jacobson et al. 1986; Verschoor and Collins 1986). Much less information is available for airtightening large, commercial buildings, but the same general principles apply (Parekh et al. 1991; Persily 1991).

RESIDENTIAL VENTILATION

Typical infiltration values in housing in North America vary by a factor of about ten, from tightly constructed housing with seasonal average air exchange rates as low as 0.1 air changes per hour (ach) to loosely constructed housing with air exchange rates as great as 2.0 ach. Figures 11 and 12 show histograms of infiltration rates measured in two different samples of North American housing (Grimsrud et al. 1982; Grot and Clark 1979). Figure 11 shows the average seasonal infiltration of 312 houses located in different areas in North America. The median infiltration value of this sample is 0.5 ach. Figure 12 represents measurements in 266 houses located in 16 U.S. cities. The median value of this sample is 0.9 ach. The group of houses in the Figure 11 sample is biased toward then-new, energy-efficient houses, whereas the group in Figure 12 represents older, low-income housing.

Additional studies have found average values for houses in regional areas. Palmiter and Brown (1989) and Parker et al. (1990) found a heating season average of 0.40 ach (range: 0.13 to 1.11 ach) for 134 houses in Pacific Northwest climates. In a comparison of 292

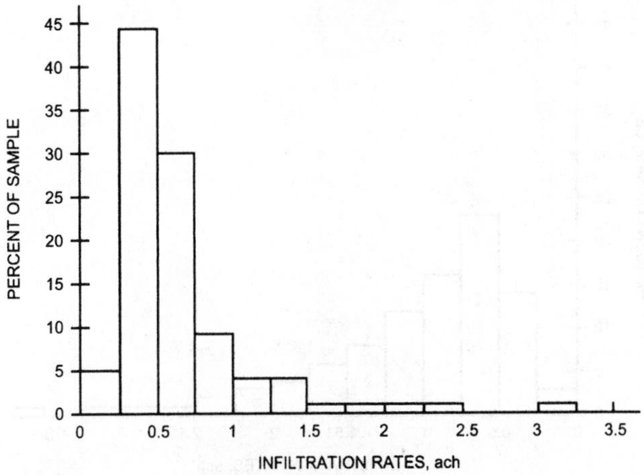

Fig. 11 Histogram of Infiltration Values for Then-New Construction

houses incorporating energy-efficient features (including measures to reduce air infiltration and provide ventilation heat recovery) with 331 control houses, Parker et al. (1990) found an average of about 0.25 ach (range: 0.02 to 1.63 ach) for the energy-efficient houses versus 0.49 (range: 0.05 to 1.63 ach) for the control. Ek et al. (1990) found an average of 0.5 ach (range: 0.26 to 1.09) for 93 double-wide manufactured homes in the Pacific Northwest. Canadian housing stock has been characterized by Riley (1990) and Yuill and Comeau (1989). Although these studies do not represent random samples of North American housing, they indicate the distribution of infiltration rates expected in a group of buildings.

Occupancy influences have not been measured directly and vary widely. Desrochers and Scott (1985) estimated that they add an average of 0.10 to 0.15 ach to unoccupied values. Kvisgaard and Collet (1990) found that, in 16 Danish dwellings, occupants on average provided 63% of the total air exchange rate.

Ventilation air requirements for houses in the United States have traditionally been met on the assumption that the building envelope is leaky enough that infiltration will suffice. Possible difficulties with this approach include low infiltration when natural forces (temperature difference and wind) are weak; unnecessary energy consumption when these forces are strong; drafts in cold climates; lack of control of ventilation rates to meet changing needs; poor humidity control; potential for interstitial condensation from exfiltration in cold climates or infiltration in hot humid climates; and lack of opportunity to recover energy used to condition ventilation air. The solution to these concerns is to have a tight building envelope and a properly designed and operated mechanical ventilation system.

ASHRAE *Standard* 119 and the National Building Code of Canada (NRCC 1995) encourage the transition to tighter envelope construction. Hamlin (1991) found a 30% increase in airtightness of tract-built Canadian houses between 1982 and 1989. Also, 82% of newer houses had natural air exchange rates below 0.3 ach in March. Yuill (1991) derived a procedure to show the extent to which infiltration contributes toward meeting ventilation air requirements. As a result, the National Building Code of Canada has requirements for mechanical ventilation capability in all new dwelling units.

Canadian Standards Association (CSA) *Standard* F326 expands the requirements for residential mechanical ventilation systems to cover air distribution within the house, thermal comfort, minimum temperatures for equipment and ductwork, system controls, pressurization and depressurization of the dwelling, installation requirements, and verification of compliance. Verification can be by design or by test, but the total rate of outside air delivery must be measured.

Mechanical ventilation is required by ASHRAE *Standard* 62.2 and by code in some U.S. states; some details of these requirement

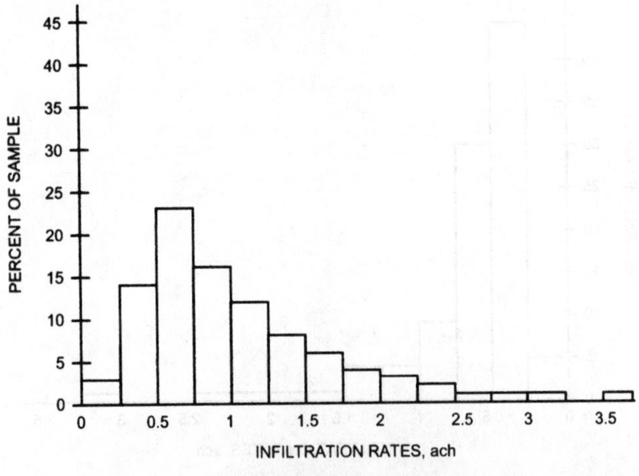

Fig. 12 Histogram of Infiltration Values for Low-Income Housing

are described in this chapter. The net benefit of using mechanical ventilation has been demonstrated and studied in various energy-efficient and advanced housing programs (Barley 2001; Palmiter et al. 1991; Riley 1990). Systems can be characterized as local or central; exhaust, supply, or balanced; with forced-air or radiant/ hydronic heating/cooling systems; with or without heat recovery; and with continuous operation or controlled by occupants, demand (i.e., by pollutant sensing), timers, or humidity. Note that not all combinations are viable. Various options are described by Fisk et al. (1984), Hekmat et al. (1986), Holton et al. (1997), Lubliner et al. (1997), Palmiter et al. (1991), Reardon and Shaw (1997), Sherman and Matson (1997), Sibbitt and Hamlin (1991), and Yuill et al. (1991).

The simplest systems use bathroom and kitchen fans to exhaust moisture and pollutants and to augment infiltration. Noise, installed capacity, durability under continuous operation, distribution to all rooms (especially bedrooms), envelope moisture, combustion safety, and energy efficiency issues need to be addressed. Many present bath and kitchen fans are ineffective ventilators because of poor installation and design, and many fail to exhaust outdoors. However, properly specified and installed exhaust fans can form part of good whole-house ventilation systems and are so specified in some Canadian building codes.

Some central supply systems use a central air-handling unit blower to induce air from the outdoors and distribute it. However, the blower operates intermittently if thermostatically controlled and provides little ventilation in mild weather. Continuous blower operation increases energy consumption. If the blower operates continuously when the heat source is off, the combination of lower mixed air temperature and high air speed can cause cold air drafts. To offset these problems, some systems use electronically commutated blower motors, which allow efficient continuous operation at lower speeds. Some others use a timer to cycle the blower when thermostatic demands are inadequate to cause the blower to operate when needed for ventilation (Rudd 1998).

Central exhaust systems use leakage sites and, in some cases, intentional and controllable openings in the building envelope as the supply. Such systems are suitable for retrofit in existing houses. Energy can be recovered from the exhaust airstream with a heat pump to supplement domestic hot-water and/or space heating.

For new houses with tightly constructed envelopes, balanced ventilation with passive heat recovery (air-to-air heat exchangers or heat recovery ventilators) can be appropriate in some climates. Fan-induced supply and exhaust air flows at nearly equal rates over a heat exchanger, where heat and sometimes moisture is transferred between the airstreams. This typically reduces the energy required to condition ventilation air by 60 to 80% (Cutter 1987). It also reduces the thermal discomfort that occurs when untempered air is introduced directly into the house. Airflow balance, leakage between streams, biological contamination of wet surfaces, frosting, and first cost are concerns associated with these systems.

Air-side economizers, which allow outside air to be up to 100% of the supply air at appropriate times, are not typically used in small buildings with low internal heat gains relative to the building envelope. Because of heat transfer through building envelopes, these small buildings quickly require heating or cooling as the outside air temperature falls or rises. Consequently, from an energy conservation point of view, small envelope-load-dominated buildings do not benefit as much as internal-load-dominated buildings from daytime use of air-side economizers; night ventilation during the cooling season may be very attractive. Also, ventilation rates increase dramatically when air-side economizers are in operation, so the extra moisture introduced or removed must be considered.

The type of ventilation system can be selected based on house leakage class as defined in ASHRAE *Standard* 119. Balanced air-to-air systems with heat recovery are optimal for tight houses (leakage classes A–C). The leakier the house is, the larger is the contribution from infiltration and the less effective is heat recovery ventilation. Tightening the envelope beyond the level of ASHRAE *Standard* 119 may be warranted in extreme climates to better use the heat recovery effect (Sherman and Matson 1997). In mild climates, these systems can also effectively be used in leakage classes D–F. Central exhaust systems should not be used for leakage classes A–C unless special provisions are made for air inlets; otherwise their operation may depressurize the house enough to cause backdrafting through fossil-fueled appliances. Unbalanced systems (either supply or exhaust) are optimal for leakage classes D–F. Ventilation systems are normally not needed for leakage classes G–J, but when they are needed, an unbalanced system is usually the best choice. More discussion of mechanical systems for residences is available in Russell et al. (2005); some information on practices outside North America can be found in McWilliams and Sherman (2005).

Residential Ventilation Zones

For guidance in the selection of residential ventilation systems, Sherman (1995) developed four climatic zones for the United States. These zones are shown in Figure 13 for the continental United States. Alaska is in zone 1, and Hawaii is in zone 4.

Zone 1 includes the severe climates of the northern tier of states. A zone 1 residence that meets airtightness and energy conservation standards probably cannot meet its ventilation needs through infiltration, and will require mechanical ventilation. Zone 2 includes moderate climates where careful design and construction may allow buildings to simultaneously meet energy standards and ventilation needs through infiltration and mechanical exhaust. The mild climates in zone 3 allow residences to meet both ASHRAE *Standards* 119 and 62.2 over a substantial range of airtightness. Zone 4 residences have relatively small energy penalties associated with infiltration or ventilation. In this zone, natural ventilation is usually preferred to mechanical ventilation as a technique to supplement infiltration.

Shelter in Place

The most fundamental function of a house is to provide shelter from outdoor conditions. The building is intended to be the first line of defense at separating the relatively uncontrolled outdoor environment from the desired indoor environment.

A first response to poor outdoor air quality is to go inside, close the windows, and turn off central heating, air-conditioning, and ventilating systems, as well as any other fans. Closing windows and other air intakes reduces air exchange with the outdoors, decreasing the immediate intrusion of outdoor air into the home. However, because no home is perfectly airtight, closing doors and windows does not eliminate intrusion. Because all indoor air ultimately comes from outdoors, all else being equal, indoor conditions eventually come to dynamic equilibrium with outdoor conditions. The tighter the building, the longer the time needed to come to equilibrium.

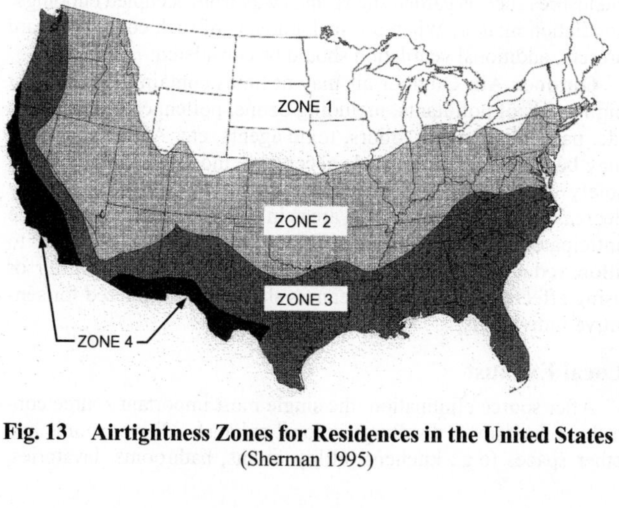

Fig. 13 Airtightness Zones for Residences in the United States (Sherman 1995)

The delay time (the time it takes to completely change the air in a building) is determined by the ventilation rate. The effectiveness of sheltering within the home thus depends on envelope tightness. For a home with 0.35 air changes per hour, the delay time is roughly 3 h. For a tight house without mechanical ventilation, the delay time can easily be twice as long. Most houses in the United States are leaky (i.e., typically one air change per hour) and thus could have a delay time on the order of one hour (Sherman and Matson 1997).

Reactive gases in outdoor air, such as ozone, can be decreased to some degree by the building envelope. For other outdoor contaminants, the building envelope serves to delay, not reduce, their introduction into the indoor environment. Such a delay is not very helpful at reducing exposures to outdoor contaminants that persist over days, but can be an effective strategy for short-duration (less than a few hours) sources. In houses without indoor ozone sources, ozone levels tend to be higher in houses that do not have air conditioners than in those with air conditioners; ozone levels also are higher when windows are open than when they are closed (Weschler 2000). For outdoor exposure times shorter than the delay time, the house serves as a reservoir of cleaner air. After the outdoor contaminant is gone, windows can be opened to flush out pollutants that entered during the exposure period.

Safe Havens

Simply going inside may not be sufficient for highly unusual but potentially lethal events. Chemical spills or fires, explosions, bioterrorism, or similar toxic air pollutant releases can temporarily create dangerous outdoor conditions that render other air quality issues insignificant. With sufficient warning, occupants should leave the vicinity, but the unexpected nature of these events means that the only viable alternative may be to shelter in place.

This strategy may work for short-term releases. Homes are often too leaky to provide the protection needed for longer-duration events, but individual rooms can be temporarily sealed to become safe havens. A safe haven should be chosen to have as little contact as possible with outside walls, and preferably be on the side of the house furthest downwind from the source. Duct tape can be used to seal leaks, cracks, seams, register grilles, and doors, with thick plastic sheeting used to span larger gaps (Sorensen and Vogt 2001). If such a shelter has an air change rate of 0.15 ach with the house, it will take 4 to 6 h for contaminated outdoor air to reach the safe haven.

There may, however, be a very small population of at-risk individuals or locations for which emergencies are somewhat more likely. In such cases, a safe haven can be designed in advance with a highly efficient particle/gas-phase filtration system capable of providing several hours, days, or weeks of protection (Ormerod 1983). A short-term safe haven might be effectively combined with other emergency shelters (e.g., tornado, hurricane, civil defense) to reduce cost.

RESIDENTIAL VENTILATION AND IAQ CONTROL REQUIREMENTS

ASHRAE *Standard* 62.2 presents minimum requirements for residential ventilation air and acceptable indoor air quality, and its user's manual (ASHRAE 2006) has detailed information for designing and constructing residential buildings in compliance with the standard. Best or good practice may require going beyond the standard's minima. This section describes good practice; however, this presumes that the minimum requirements of 62.2 are met as well.

Traditionally, ventilation air for residences has been provided by natural ventilation and infiltration. Sherman and Matson (1997) showed that most of the older building stock is sufficiently leaky that infiltration alone can meet the minimum requirements of ASHRAE *Standard* 62.2. Houses built or retrofitted to new standards have substantially tighter envelopes and insufficient infiltration to meet ventilation standards. Studies have shown that concerns over safety, noise, comfort, air quality, and energy minimize occupant use of operable windows (Johnson and Long 2005; Price and Sherman 2006). As a result, these houses require supplemental mechanical ventilation to satisfy current standards.

Simply meeting minimum residential ventilation rates is not always sufficient to adequately dilute all contaminants. For some buildings, such ventilation may not meet the requirements of individuals with allergies or chemical sensitivities or when there are unusual sources such as radon or mold. In these cases, source control or extra ventilation is required to manage the contaminant levels. Therefore, especially in single-family dwellings, occupants must be responsible for introducing, monitoring, and controlling the sources in the indoor environment, as well as for operating the dwelling unit to meet their individual needs. Increasingly, residences are also used for business or hobby purposes, which may introduce air contaminants not addressed in *Standard* 62.2; portions of these residences may require ventilation air as required by *Standard* 62.1 or industrial guidelines.

Source Control

When considering how much whole-house ventilation should be supplied, typical and unusual significant sources of indoor pollution need to be controlled. This can be done either by mitigating the source itself or by using local exhaust to extract contaminants before they can mix into the indoor environment. Typical sources that should be considered include the following:

Clothes Dryers and Central Vacuum Systems. Clothes dryer exhaust is heavily laden with moisture and laundry by-products such as flammable lint and various gaseous contaminants. Many moisture problems have been traced to clothes dryers vented indoors. Exhaust from clothes dryers, which is typically about 70 L/s, should be vented directly to the outdoors. Similarly, central vacuum systems should be vented directly outdoors to exhaust the finer particles that pass through their filters.

Combustion. Water and carbon dioxide are always emitted during combustion of hydrocarbons in air. Other dangerous compounds are created, as well. All these by-products should be vented directly outdoors, preferably using sealed combustion or direct-vent equipment. Venting should meet all applicable codes. For buildings with naturally aspirated combustion appliances, excessive depressurization by exhaust systems must be avoided, which can be done by keeping combustion equipment outside the pressure boundary. In addition, a depressurization safety test should be considered, such as described in ASTM *Standard* E1998 or CGSB *Standard* 51.71. Fireplace combustion products should be isolated from the occupied space using tight-fitting doors and outdoor air intakes, when necessary. Flues and chimneys must be designed and installed to disperse combustion products well away from air intakes and operable windows, for example. Chapter 34 of the 2008 *ASHRAE Handbook—HVAC Systems and Equipment* has more information on venting systems.

Carbon monoxide is one of the most pervasive indoor contaminants. It can come from virtually any source of combustion, including automobiles. Because even combustion appliances that meet manufacturers' specifications can interact with the building and emit carbon monoxide, at least one carbon monoxide alarm meeting safety standards such as CSA *Standard* 6.19 should be installed near sleeping areas in each dwelling, including each unit of multifamily residential buildings, that has combustion appliances (e.g., fireplaces, stoves, furnaces, water heaters) within the pressure boundary, or has attached garages or storage sheds. Carbon monoxide alarms also should be considered for nonresidential buildings: poisonings have occurred in many building types, including hotels, motels, stores, restaurants, nursing homes, dormitories, laundromats, and schools.

Garages. Garages and storage spaces contain many sources of contaminants. Doors between them and occupied space should be well sealed with gaskets or weatherstripping and possibly be self-closing. Depressurized sections of HVAC systems, such as air handlers or return or intake ducts, should not be located in garages. If such sections must pass through garages, they must be well sealed. Care should be taken to ensure that there is a good pressure barrier between the garage and the occupied space, typically using an air/moisture retarder such as heavy polyethylene, and other measures. Carbon monoxide sources may be present in garages, so pressure barriers, fire-rated compartmentation, and ventilation of attached residences are life-safety measures. Separate ventilation systems that slightly depressurize attached garages and storage spaces and exhaust directly outdoors should be considered, especially when these support spaces are tightly constructed or are in cold climates. Several studies (Batterman et al. 2006; Emmerich et al. 2003; Fugler 2004) of contaminant sources and transport in garages found that, in some cases, significant fractions of infiltration air enter houses from attached garages, and that modern residential garages are tighter than older garages, which were commonly assumed to be leaky enough to avoid many IAQ problems.

Particulates. The ventilation system should be designed such that return and outdoor air is filtered before passing through the thermal-conditioning components. Pressure drops associated with this filtration should be considered in the design of the air-handling system. Particulate filters or air cleaners should have a minimum efficiency of 60% for 3 μm particles, which is equivalent to a MERV 6 designated filter according to ASHRAE *Standard* 52.2.

Microbiologicals. Because ventilation can increase the source as well as removal rates of various air pollutants, it is, at best, moderately effective at reducing exposures to many airborne microbiologicals. Ventilation can, however, be part of the moisture balance that is critical to retarding fungal growth on surfaces and spores released into the air, depending on indoor/outdoor conditions.

Radon and Soil Gas. Buildings are exposed to gases that migrate from the soil through cracks or leaks. Soil gases vary with time and conditions, and can contain toxins from pesticides, landfill, fuel, or sewer gas, but the highest-profile pollutant in this category is radon and its radioactive-decay-produced "daughters." Source control measures, such as differential pressure control and airtightening, are far more effective than ventilation mechanisms at controlling exposure to soil gas. See Chapter 11 for more information.

Volatile Organic Compounds (VOCs). VOCs are ubiquitous in modern life. Products that emit VOCs include manufactured wood products, paints, stains, varnishes, solvents, pesticides, adhesives, wood preservatives, waxes, polishes, cleansers, lubricants, sealants, dyes, air fresheners, fuels, plastics, copy machines, printers, tobacco products, perfumes, cooking by-products, and dry-cleaned clothes. Whenever possible, VOCs and other toxic compounds should be stored outside the occupied space in loosely constructed or ventilated enclosures such as garden sheds, and away from occupied buildings' ventilation intakes. When unusual amounts of such compounds are present, additional ventilation should be considered.

Outdoor Air. Outdoor air may at times contain unacceptably high levels of pollutants, including ozone, pollen, carbon monoxide, particulate matter, odors, toxic agents, etc. At such times, it may be impossible to provide acceptable indoor air quality using solely outdoor air, and increased ventilation rates can actually decrease indoor air quality. In areas in which this problem may be anticipated, automatic or manual controls should be provided to allow reducing the ventilation rate. Cleaning recirculated air or using effective portable air cleaners should be considered for sensitive individuals.

Local Exhaust

After source elimination, the single most important source control mechanism in dwellings is local exhaust. All wet rooms and other spaces (e.g., kitchens, utility rooms, bathrooms, lavatories, toilets) designed to allow specific contaminant release should be provided with local exhaust. Workshops, recreation rooms, smoking areas, art studios, greenhouses, and hobby rooms may also require local ventilation and/or air cleaning to remove contaminants generated by the activities involved. Contaminants of concern should be evaluated to determine how much additional ventilation is required. Many of these rooms can be adequately ventilated by following the requirements for kitchens or bathrooms. If unvented combustion appliances must be used, rooms with these appliances should also meet general ventilation requirements for kitchens, because such appliances generate significant amounts of moisture and, often, ultrafine particles, even when burning properly.

Mechanical exhaust is the preferred method of providing local ventilation. Normally, it is designed to operate intermittently under manual control to exhaust contaminated air outside when the contaminant is being produced and occupants recognize the need for ventilation. However, in many circumstances, a continuous, lower-flow-rate exhaust can work as well.

Continuous Local Mechanical Exhaust. A continuously operating mechanical exhaust is intended to operate without occupant intervention. This exhaust may be part of a balanced mechanical ventilation system. The system should be designed to operate during all hours in which the dwelling is occupied. Override control should be provided if needed. The minimum delivered ventilation should be at least that given in Table 1.

Intermittent Local Mechanical Exhaust. An intermittently operating local mechanical exhaust is intended to be operated as needed by the occupant and should be designed with this intent. Shutoff timers, occupancy controls, multiple-speed fans, and switching integral with room lighting are helpful, provided they do not impede occupant control. The minimum airflow rate should be at least that given in Table 2.

Alternatives. Cleaning recirculated air can sometimes be substituted for local exhaust, if it can be shown to be effective in removing contaminants of concern. Natural ventilation is not generally a suitable method for local exhaust and ventilation air needs in most climates and spaces. Using natural ventilation can cause reentrainment problems when air flows into rather than out of the space, and contaminated exhaust or exfiltrating air reenters the building. In milder climates, natural ventilation may be acceptable when the contaminant of concern is related to odor rather than health or safety. Purpose-designed passive exhaust systems have shown acceptable ventilation in some European settings, and may be considered in lieu of mechanical systems. Axley (2001b) discusses evaluation and design of passive residential ventilation systems further.

Table 1 Continuous Exhaust Airflow Rates

Application	Airflow Rate	Notes
Kitchen	5 ach	Based on kitchen volume
Utility room, bathroom, toilet, lavatory	10 L/s	Not less than 2 ach

Table 2 Intermittent Exhaust Airflow Rates

Application	Airflow Rate	Notes
Kitchen	50 L/s	Vented range hood required if less than 5 ach
Utility room, bathroom, toilet, lavatory	25 L/s	Not less than 2 ach

Table 3 Total Ventilation Air Requirements

Area Based	Occupancy Based
0.15 L/s per square metre of floor space	3.5 L/s per person, based on normal occupancy

Whole-House Ventilation

Although control of significant sources of pollution in a dwelling is important, whole-house ventilation through centrally introduced, conditioned, and distributed outside air may still be needed. Each dwelling should be provided with outdoor air according to Table 3. The rate is the sum of the Area-Based and Occupancy-Based columns. Design occupancy can be based on the number of bedrooms as follows: first bedroom, two persons; each additional bedroom, one person. Additional ventilation should be considered when occupant densities exceed 1/25 m^3.

Natural whole-house ventilation that relies on occupant operation should not be used to make up any part of the minimum total whole-house ventilation air requirement. However, because occupancy and sources vary significantly, the capacity to ventilate above minimum rates can be provided by operable exterior openings such as doors and windows.

Air Distribution

Ventilation air should be provided to each habitable room through mechanical and natural air distribution. If a room does not have a balance between air supply and return or exhaust, pathways for transfer air should be provided. These pathways may be door undercuts, transfer ducts with grilles, or simply grilles where ducts are not necessary or required by code.

In houses without central air handlers, special provisions to distribute outdoor air may be required. Rooms in which occupants spend many continuous hours, such as bedrooms, may require special consideration. Local and whole-house ventilation equipment should be chosen to be energy efficient, easy to maintain, reliable, durable, and quiet. Heat recovery should be considered, especially in cold climates.

Selection Principles for Residential Ventilation Systems

Occupant comfort, energy efficiency, ease of use, service life, first and life-cycle cost, value-added features, and indoor environmental quality should be considered when selecting a strategy and system. HVAC and related systems can be a potential cause of poor indoor air quality. For example, occupants may not use the ventilation systems as intended if operation results in discomfort (e.g., drafts) or excessive energy use. The resulting lack of ventilation might produce poor indoor air quality. Therefore, careful design, construction, commissioning, operation, and maintenance is necessary to provide optimum effectiveness.

All exhaust, supply, or air-handler fans have the potential to change the pressure of the living space relative to the outside. High-volume fans, such as the air handler and some cooking exhaust fans, can cause high levels of depressurization, particularly in tightly constructed homes. Considering these effects is essential in design. Excessive depressurization of the living space relative to outside may cause backdrafting of combustion appliances and the migration of contaminants such as radon or other soil gases, car exhaust, or insulation particles into the living space. Depressurization can also result in moisture intrusion into building cavities in warm, moist climates, which may cause structural damage and fungal growth. Pressurization of the living space can cause condensation in building cavities in cold climates, also resulting in structural damage. Excess pressure can best be prevented by balanced ventilation systems and tightly sealed duct systems. In addition, adequate pathways must be available for all return air to the air-handling devices.

Occupant activities, operation of fans that exhaust air from the home, and leaky ducts on air conditioners, furnaces, or heat pumps may depressurize the structure. Options to address backdrafting concerns include

- Using combustion appliances with isolated (or sealed) combustion systems

- Locating combustion appliances in a ventilated room isolated from depressurized zones by well-sealed partitions
- Installing supply fans to balance or partially balance exhaust from the zone
- Testing to ensure that depressurization is not excessive

The system must be designed, built, operated, and maintained in a way that discourages growth of biological contaminants. Typical precautions include sloping condensate drain pans toward the drain, keeping condensate drains free of obstructions, keeping cooling coils free of dirt and other obstructions, maintaining humidifiers, and checking and eliminating any cause of moisture inside ducts.

Outside and exhaust airstreams of ventilation systems can be coupled using a heat pump or other device to recover thermal energy, when appropriate. Such heat pump or other equipment may reverse mode with the seasons or sensed temperature differences, for example. Heat can also be recovered from air to preheat potable water, for example.

SIMPLIFIED MODELS OF RESIDENTIAL VENTILATION AND INFILTRATION

This section describes several calculation procedures, ranging from simple estimation techniques to more physical models. Orme (1999) provides a more thorough review of simplified models. A building's air exchange rate cannot be reliably deduced from the building's construction or age, or from a simple visual inspection. Some measurement is necessary, such as a pressurization test of envelope airtightness or a detailed quantification of the leakage sites and their magnitude. The air exchange rate of a building may be calculated given (1) the location and leakage function for every opening in the building envelope and between major building zones, (2) the wind pressure coefficients over the building envelope, and (3) any mechanical ventilation airflow rates. These inputs are generally unavailable for all except very simple structures or extremely well studied buildings. Therefore, their values must be assumed. The appropriateness of these assumptions influences the accuracy of predictions of air exchange rates.

Empirical Models

These models of residential infiltration are based on statistical fits of infiltration rate data for specific houses. They use pressurization test results to account for house airtightness and take the form of simple relations between infiltration rate, an airtightness rating, and, in most cases, weather conditions. Empirical models account for envelope infiltration only and do not deal with intentional ventilation. In one approach, the calculated air exchange rate at 50 Pa based on a pressurization test is simply divided by a constant approximately equal to 20 (Sherman 1987). This technique does not account for the effect of infiltration-driving mechanisms on air exchange. Empirical models that do account for weather effects have been developed by Kronvall (1980), Reeves et al. (1979), and Shaw (1981).

The latter two models account for building air leakage using the values of c and n from Equation (40). The only other inputs required are wind speed and temperature difference. These empirical models predict long-term (one-week) infiltration rates very well in the houses from which they were developed; they do not, however, work as well in other houses because of the building-specific nature of leakage distribution, wind pressure, and internal partitioning. Persily (1986) and Persily and Linteris (1983) compared measured and predicted house infiltration rates for these and other models. The average long-term differences between measurements and predictions are generally on the order of 40%, although individual predictions can be off by 100% or more (Persily 1986; Walker and Wilson 1998).

Multizone Models

Multicell models of air exchange treat buildings as a series of interconnected zones and assume that air within each zone is well mixed. Several such models have been developed by Allard and Herrlin (1989), Etheridge and Alexander (1980), Feustel and Raynor-Hoosen (1990), Herrlin (1985), Liddament and Allen (1983), Walton (1984, 1989), and Walton and Dols (2003). They are all based on a mass balance for each zone of the building. These mass balances are used to solve for interior static pressures in the building by requiring that inflows and outflows for each zone balance to zero. The user must input information describing building envelope leakage, values to account for wind pressure on the building envelope, temperatures for each zone, and any mechanical ventilation airflow rates. Wind pressure coefficient data in the literature, air leakage measurement results from the building or its components, and air leakage data from the literature can be used as estimates. These models not only solve for whole-building and individual zone air exchange rates, but also determine airflow rates and pressure differences between zones. These interzone airflow rates are useful for predicting pollutant transport within buildings with well mixed zones. Chapter 13 has more details on multizone airflow and IAQ modeling.

Single-Zone Models

Several procedures have been developed to calculate building air exchange rates that are based on physical models of the building interior as a single zone. These single-zone models are only appropriate for buildings with no internal resistance to airflow, and are therefore inappropriate for large, multizone buildings. Some models of this type have been developed by Cole et al. (1980), Sherman and Grimsrud (1980), Walker and Wilson (1998), and Warren and Webb (1980). The section on Residential Calculation Examples uses both basic and enhanced models (Bradley 1993; CHBA 1994; Hamlin and Pushka 1994; Palmiter and Bond 1994; Walker and Wilson 1998).

The **basic model** uses effective air leakage area A_L at 4 Pa, which can be obtained from a whole-building pressurization test. The **enhanced model** uses pressurization test results to characterize house air leakage through leakage coefficient c and pressure exponent n. The enhanced model improves on the basic model by using a power law to represent envelope leakage, including a flue as a separate leakage site, and having separate wind effects for houses with crawlspaces or slab/basement foundations.

For both models, the user must input wind speed, temperature difference, information on distribution of leakage over the building envelope, a wind shelter (or local shielding for the basic model) parameter, and a terrain coefficient. The predictive accuracy of the enhanced model can be very good, typically ±10% when parameters are well known for the building in question (Palmiter and Bond 1994; Sherman and Modera 1986; Walker and Wilson 1998). All these single-zone models are sensitive to values of inputs, which are quite difficult to determine.

Superposition of Wind and Stack Effects

Simplified physical models of infiltration solve the problem of two natural driving forces, wind and stack, separately and then combine them in a process called **superposition**. Superposition is necessary because each physical process can affect internal and external pressures on the structure, which can cause interactions between physical processes that are otherwise independent. An exact solution is impossible because detailed properties of all the building leaks are unknown and because leakage is a nonlinear process. For this reason, most modelers have developed a simplified superposition process to combine stack and wind effects. Sherman (1992b) compared various superposition procedures and derived a generalized superposition equation involving simple leakage distribution parameters, and showed that the result is always subadditive.

Typically, only 35% of infiltration from the smaller effect can be added to the larger effect. Depending on details, that percentage could go as high as 85% or as low as zero. Walker and Wilson (1993) compared several superposition techniques to measured data. Sherman, as well as Walker and Wilson, found quadrature, shown in Equation (47), to be a robust superposition technique:

$$Q = \sqrt{Q_s^2 + Q_w^2} \qquad (47)$$

The following sections discuss how superposition is combined with calculation of wind and stack flows to determine total flow.

Residential Calculation Examples

Basic Model. The following calculations are based on the Sherman and Grimsrud (1980) model, which uses the effective air leakage area at 4 Pa. This leakage area can be obtained from a whole-building pressurization test. Using effective air leakage area, the airflow rate from infiltration is calculated according to

$$Q = \frac{A_L}{1000}\sqrt{C_s \Delta t + C_w U^2} \qquad (48)$$

where

Q = airflow rate, m^3/s
A_L = effective air leakage area, cm^2
C_s = stack coefficient, $(L/s)^2/(cm^4 \cdot K)$
Δt = average indoor-outdoor temperature difference for time interval of calculation, K
C_w = wind coefficient, $(L/s)^2/[cm^4 \cdot (m/s)^2]$
U = average wind speed measured at local weather station for time interval of calculation, m/s

Table 4 presents values of C_s for one-, two-, and three-story houses. The value of wind coefficient C_w depends on the local shelter class of the building (described in Table 5) and the building height. Table 6 presents values of C_w for one-, two-, and three-story houses in shelter classes 1 through 5. In calculating values in Tables 4 and 6, the following assumptions were made regarding input to the basic model:

Table 4 Basic Model Stack Coefficient C_s

	House Height (Stories)		
	One	Two	Three
Stack coefficient	0.000 145	0.000 290	0.000 435

Table 5 Local Shelter Classes

Shelter Class	Description
1	No obstructions or local shielding
2	Typical shelter for an isolated rural house
3	Typical shelter caused by other buildings across street from building under study
4	Typical shelter for urban buildings on larger lots where sheltering obstacles are more than one building height away
5	Typical shelter produced by buildings or other structures immediately adjacent (closer than one house height): e.g., neighboring houses on same side of street, trees, bushes, etc.

Table 6 Basic Model Wind Coefficient C_w

Shelter Class	House Height (Stories)		
	One	Two	Three
1	0.000 319	0.000 420	0.000 494
2	0.000 246	0.000 325	0.000 382
3	0.000 174	0.000 231	0.000 271
4	0.000 104	0.000 137	0.000 161
5	0.000 032	0.000 042	0.000 049

- Terrain used for converting meteorological to local wind speeds is that of a rural area with scattered obstacles
- $R = 0.5$ (half the building leakage in the walls)
- $X = 0$ (equal amounts of leakage in the floor and ceiling)
- Heights of one-, two-, and three-story buildings = 2.5, 5.0, and 7.5 m, respectively

Example 2. Estimate the infiltration at design conditions for a two-story house in Lincoln, Nebraska. The house has effective air leakage area of 500 cm^2 and volume of 340 m^3, and the predominant wind is perpendicular to the street (shelter class 3). The indoor air temperature is 20°C.

Solution: The 99% design temperature for Lincoln is −19°C. Assume a design wind speed of 6.7 m/s. From Equation (48), with $C_s = 0.000\,290$ from Table 4 and $C_w = 0.000\,231$ from Table 6, the airflow rate caused by infiltration is

$$Q = \frac{500}{1000}\sqrt{(0.000\,290 \times 39) + (0.000\,231 \times 6.7^2)}$$

$$= 0.0736\ m^3/s = 265\ m^3/h$$

From Equation (2), air exchange rate I is equal to Q divided by the building volume:

$$I = (265\ m^3/h)/340\ m^3 = 0.78\ h^{-1} = 0.78\ \text{ach}$$

Example 3. Predict the average infiltration during a one-week period in January for a one-story house in Portland, Oregon. During this period, the average indoor/outdoor temperature difference is 17 K, and average wind speed is 2.7 m/s. The house has volume of 255 m^3 and effective air leakage area of 690 cm^2, and it is located in an area with buildings and trees within 10 m in most directions (shelter class 4).

Solution: From Equation (48), the airflow rate caused by infiltration is

$$Q = \frac{690}{1000}\sqrt{(0.000\,145 \times 17) + (0.000\,104 \times 2.7^2)}$$

$$= 0.0392\ m^3/s = 141\ m^3/h$$

The air exchange rate is therefore

$$I = 141/255 = 0.55\ h^{-1} = 0.55\ \text{ach}$$

Example 4. Estimate the average infiltration over the heating season in a two-story house with volume of 310 m^3 and leakage area of 848 cm^2. The house is located on a lot with several large trees but no other close buildings (shelter class 3). Average wind speed during the heating season is 3.2 m/s, and the average indoor/outdoor temperature difference is 20 K.

Solution: From Equation (48), the airflow rate from infiltration is

$$Q = \frac{848}{1000}\sqrt{(0.000\,290 \times 20) + (0.000\,231 \times 3.2^2)}$$

$$= 0.077\ m^3/s = 276\ m^3/h$$

The average air exchange rate is therefore

$$I = 276/310 = 0.89\ h^{-1} = 0.89\ \text{ach}$$

Enhanced Model. This section presents a simple, single-zone approach to calculating air infiltration rates in houses based on the Walker and Wilson (1998) model. The airflow rate from infiltration is calculated using

$$Q_s = cC_s \Delta t^n \qquad (49)$$

$$Q_w = cC_w(sU)^{2n} \qquad (50)$$

where

Q_s = stack airflow rate, m^3/s
Q_w = wind airflow rate, m^3/s
c = flow coefficient, $m^3/(s/Pa^n)$
C_s = stack coefficient, $(Pa/K)^n$
C_w = wind coefficient, $(Pa \cdot s^2/m^2)^n$
s = shelter factor

In calculating tabulated values of C_s, C_w, and s, the following assumptions were made:

- Each story is 2.5 m high.
- The flue is 15 cm in diameter and reaches 2 m above the upper ceiling.
- The flue is unsheltered.
- Half of envelope leakage (not including the flue) is in the walls and one-quarter each is at the floor and ceiling, respectively.
- $n = 0.67$

Using typical values for terrain factors, house height, and wind speed measurement height, wind speed multiplier G (given in Table 7) uses a relationship based on equations found in Chapter 24 and used in the following examples.

Example 5. Estimate the infiltration at design conditions for a two-story slab-on-grade house with a flue in Lincoln, Nebraska. The house has a flow coefficient of $c = 0.051$ m³/(s·Paⁿ) and a pressure exponent of $n = 0.67$ (this corresponds to effective leakage area of 500 cm² at 4 Pa). The building volume is 340 m³. The 97.5% design temperature is −19°C, and design wind speed is 6.7 m/s.

Solution: For a slab-on-grade two-story house with a flue, Table 8 gives $C_s = 0.089$ (Pa/K)^{n}and $C_w = 0.156$ (Pa·s²/m²)^n. The house is maintained at 20°C indoors. The building wind speed is determined by taking design wind speed U_{met} and multiplying by the wind speed multiplier G from Table 7:

$$U = GU_{met} = 0.59(6.7) = 3.95 \text{ m/s}$$

From Table 5, the shelter class for a typical urban house is 4. Table 9 gives the shelter factor for a two-story house with a flue and shelter class 4 as $s = 0.64$. The stack flow is calculated using Equation (49):

$$Q_s = (0.051)(0.089)[20 - (-19)]^{0.67} = 0.053 \text{ m}^3\text{/s}$$

The wind flow is calculated using Equation (50):

$$Q_w = (0.051)(0.156)(0.64 \times 3.95)^{1.34} = 0.027 \text{ m}^3\text{/s}$$

Substituting Q_s and Q_w into Equation (47) gives $Q = 0.059$ m³/s = 214 m³/h. From Equation (2), air exchange rate I is equal to Q divided by building volume:

$$I = (214 \text{ m}^3\text{/h})/340 \text{ m}^3 = 0.63 \text{ h}^{-1} = 0.63 \text{ ach}$$

Example 6. Estimate the average infiltration over a one-week period for a single-story crawlspace house in Redmond, Washington. The house has a flow coefficient of $c = 0.078$ m³/(s·Paⁿ) and a pressure exponent of $n = 0.6$ (this corresponds to effective leakage area of 690 cm² at 4 Pa). The building volume is 255 m³. During this period, the average indoor/outdoor temperature difference is 16 K, and wind speed is 2.7 m/s. The house is electrically heated and has no flue.

Solution: For a single-story house with no flue, $C_s = 0.054$ (Pa/K)^n. For a crawlspace, $C_w = 0.128$ (Pa·s²/m²)^n. From Table 7, for a one-story house, $G = 0.48$.

$$U = GU_{met} = 0.48(2.7) = 1.3 \text{ m/s}$$

Table 9 gives shelter factor $s = 0.50$ for a house with no flue and shelter class 4. Stack flow is calculated using Equation (49):

$$Q_s = (0.078)(0.054)(16)^{0.6} = 0.022 \text{ m}^3\text{/s}$$

Wind flow is calculated using Equation (50):

$$Q_w = (0.078)(0.128)(0.50 \times 1.3)^{1.2} = 0.006 \text{ m}^3\text{/s}$$

Substituting Q_s and Q_w into Equation (47) gives $Q = 0.023$ m³/s = 83 m³/h. From Equation (2), air exchange rate I is equal to Q divided by building volume:

$$I = (83 \text{ m}^3\text{/h})/(255 \text{ m}^3) = 0.32 \text{ h}^{-1} = 0.32 \text{ ach}$$

Example 7. Estimate the infiltration for a three-story house in San Francisco, California. The house has a flow coefficient of $c = 0.102$ m³/(s·Paⁿ) and a pressure exponent of $n = 0.67$ (this corresponds to effective leakage area of 1000 cm² at 4 Pa). The building volume is 395 m³. The indoor/outdoor temperature difference is 5 K and wind speed is 4.47 m/s. The house has a flue and a crawlspace.

Solution: For a three-story house with a flue, $C_s = 0.107$(Pa/K)^n. For a crawlspace, $C_w = 0.154$ (Pa·s²/m²)^n. From Table 7, for a three-story house, $G = 0.67$.

$$U = GU_{met} = 0.67(4.47) = 3.0 \text{ m/s}$$

The prevailing wind blows along the row of houses parallel to the street, so the house has a shelter class of 5. Table 9 gives the shelter factor for a three-story house with a flue and shelter class 5 as $s = 0.43$.

$$Q_s = (0.102)(0.107)(5)^{0.67} = 0.032 \text{ m}^3\text{/s}$$

$$Q_w = (0.102)(0.154)(0.43 \times 3.0)^{1.34} = 0.022 \text{ m}^3\text{/s}$$

Substituting Q_s and Q_w in Equation (47) gives $Q = 0.039$ m³/s = 140 m³/h.

$$I = (140 \text{ m}^3\text{/h})/(395 \text{ m}^3) = 0.35 \text{ h}^{-1} = 0.35 \text{ ach}$$

Combining Residential Infiltration and Mechanical Ventilation

Significant infiltration and mechanical ventilation often occur simultaneously in residences. The pressure difference from Equation (31) can be used for each building leak, and the flow network (including mechanical ventilation) for the building can be solved to find the flow through all the leaks while accounting for the effect of the mechanical ventilation. However, for simplified models, natural infiltration and mechanical ventilation are usually determined separately and require a superposition method to combine the flow rates.

Sherman (1992b) compared various superposition procedures and derived a generalized superposition equation that involves simple leakage distribution parameters. The result is always subadditive. For small unbalanced fans, typically only half the flow contributes to the total, but this fraction can be anywhere between 0 and 100%, depending on leakage distribution. When fan flow is large, infiltration may be ignored.

Table 7 Enhanced Model Wind Speed Multiplier *G*

	House Height (Stories)		
	One	Two	Three
Wind speed multiplier G	0.48	0.59	0.67

Table 8 Enhanced Model Stack and Wind Coefficients

	One Story		Two Story		Three Story	
	No Flue	With Flue	No Flue	With Flue	No Flue	With Flue
C_s	0.054	0.069	0.078	0.089	0.098	0.107
C_w for basement slab	0.156	0.142	0.170	0.156	0.170	0.167
C_w for crawlspace	0.128	0.128	0.142	0.142	0.151	0.154

Table 9 Enhanced Model Shelter Factor *s*

Shelter Class	No Flue	One Story with Flue	Two Story with Flue	Three Story with Flue
1	1.00	1.10	1.07	1.06
2	0.90	1.02	0.98	0.97
3	0.70	0.86	0.81	0.79
4	0.50	0.70	0.64	0.61
5	0.30	0.54	0.47	0.43

In special cases when the leakage distribution is known and highly skewed, it may be necessary to work through the superposition method in more detail. For example, in a wind-dominated situation, a supply fan has a much bigger effect than an exhaust fan on changing the total ventilation rate; the same is true for houses with high neutral levels in cold climates. For the general case, when details are not known or can be assumed to be broad and typical, the following superposition gives good results:

$$Q_{comb} = Q_{bal} + \sqrt{Q_{unbal}^2 + Q_{infiltration}^2} \qquad (51)$$

Typical Practice

The preceding sections on estimating infiltration in low-rise residences represent current analytical techniques typically used for research and remediation purposes, but most small residential buildings are designed and constructed without direct involvement of ventilation engineers. Contractors, who typically prepare these buildings' designs, are required to follow mandates in various codes and standards, and they apply experience-based rules of thumb when determining, for example, exhaust needs. Often, leaky buildings or air quality problems result. Research and experience has shown that tightening building envelopes, and potentially using mechanical ventilation with heat recovery, can yield improved indoor air quality and reduced energy consumption. Retaining the services of a ventilation engineer before construction begins is advisable in some situations.

COMMERCIAL AND INSTITUTIONAL AIR LEAKAGE

Commercial Building Envelope Leakage

ASTM *Standard* E779 and CGSB *Standard* 149.10 include methods to measure the airtightness of building envelopes of single-zone buildings. Although many multizone buildings can be treated as single-zone buildings by opening interior doors or by inducing equal pressures in adjacent zones, these standards provide no guidelines for dealing with problems arising in tall buildings, such as stack and wind effects. Tall buildings require refinement and extensions of established procedures because they have obstacles to accurate measurement not present in small buildings, including large envelope leakage area, interfloor leakage, vertical shafts, and large wind and stack pressures. In conducting a fan pressurization test in a large building, the building's own air-handling equipment sometimes can be used to induce test pressures, as described in CGSB *Standard* 149.15. In other cases, a large fan is brought to the building to perform the test, as described by CIBSE *Standard* TM-23. Bahnfleth et al. (1999) also discuss how to address some of these issues.

Building envelopes of large commercial buildings are often assumed to be quite airtight. Tamura and Shaw (1976a) found that, assuming a flow exponent n of 0.65 in Equation (40), air leakage measurements in eight Canadian office buildings with sealed windows ranged from 610 to 2440 $cm^3/(s \cdot m^2)$. Persily and Grot (1986) ran whole-building pressurization tests in large office buildings that showed that pressurization airflow rate divided by building volume is relatively low compared to that of houses. However, if these airflow rates are normalized by building envelope area instead of by volume, the results indicate envelope airtightness levels similar to those in typical American houses. The same study also looked at eight U.S. office buildings and found air leakage ranging from 1080 to 5220 $cm^3/(s \cdot m^2)$ at 75 Pa. This means that office building envelopes are leakier than expected. Typical air leakage values per unit wall area at 75 Pa are 500, 1500, and 3000 $cm^3/(s \cdot m^2)$ for tight, average, and leaky walls, respectively (Tamura and Shaw 1976a).

Emmerich and Persily (2005) summarize available measured airtightness data for 203 U.S. commercial and institutional buildings. Sources of data included 9 buildings tested by the National Institute of Standards and Technology (Musser and Persily 2002; Persily and Grot 1986; Persily et al. 1991), 90 tested by the Florida Solar Energy Center (Cummings et al. 1996, 2000), 2 tested by Pennsylvania State University (Bahnfleth et al. 1999), 23 tested by Camroden Associates (Brennan et al. 1992 and previously unpublished data), and 79 buildings tested by the U.S. Army Corps of Engineers (previously unpublished data). Tested buildings were of a wide range of types and ages but were primarily low-rise buildings. The overall average airtightness of 28.4 $m^3/(h \cdot m^2)$ of above-grade envelope surface area at 75 Pa is in the same range as that reported for typical U.S. houses, and is similar to averages reported by Potter (2001) for U.K. commercial buildings built before recent airtightness regulations. The data show that taller buildings tend to be tighter, and a lack of correlation between year of construction and observed building air leakage. This study also found a trend, with considerable scatter, toward tighter buildings in colder climates. The authors caution that conclusions from this analysis are limited by the small sample size and a lack of random sampling. None of the buildings are known to have been constructed to meet a specified air leakage criterion, which has been identified as a key to achieving tight building envelopes in practice.

Grot and Persily (1986) also found that eight recently constructed office buildings had infiltration rates ranging from 0.1 to 0.6 ach with no outdoor air intake. The infiltration rates of these buildings exhibited varying degrees of weather dependence, generally much lower than that measured in houses. Infiltration in commercial buildings can have many negative consequences, including reduced thermal comfort, interference with proper operation of mechanical ventilation systems, degraded indoor air quality, moisture damage of building envelope components, and increased energy consumption. These results suggest strongly that commercial buildings' envelopes require tighter construction, and that continuous air barrier systems should be used in all conditioned buildings. Since 1997, the Building Environment and Thermal Envelope Council of the National Institute of Building Sciences has sponsored several symposia on air barriers for buildings in North American climates. Others have also published articles on the importance of limiting air leakage in commercial buildings (Anis 2001; Ask 2003; Fennell and Haehnel 2005).

Envelope leakage in commercial buildings also depends on HVAC system operation. Often, commercial buildings, and their HVAC systems, are in operation during normal daytime business hours but switch into "unoccupied" operation at nights and on weekends. If pressurized while their HVAC systems operate, infiltration is often very low or even eliminated in buildings with tight envelopes. However, in unoccupied mode, this pressurization is often lost, so infiltration and potentially moisture intrusion may be significant at times.

Air Leakage Through Internal Partitions

In large buildings, air leakage associated with internal partitions becomes very important. Elevator, stair, and service shaft walls; floors; and other interior partitions are the major separations of concern in these buildings. Their leakage characteristics are needed to determine infiltration through exterior walls and airflow patterns in a building. These internal resistances are also important in the event of a fire to predict smoke movement patterns and evaluate smoke management systems.

Table 10 gives air leakage areas calculated at 75 Pa with $C_D = 0.65$ for different internal partitions of commercial buildings (Klote and Milke 2002). Figure 14 presents examples of measured air leakage rates of elevator shaft walls (Tamura and Shaw 1976b), the type of data used to derive the values in Table 10. Consult Chapter 52 of the 2007 *ASHRAE Handbook—HVAC Applications* for performance models and applications of smoke management systems.

Leakage openings at the top of elevator shafts are equivalent to orifice areas of 0.4 to 1.0 m^2. Air leakage rates through stair shaft and

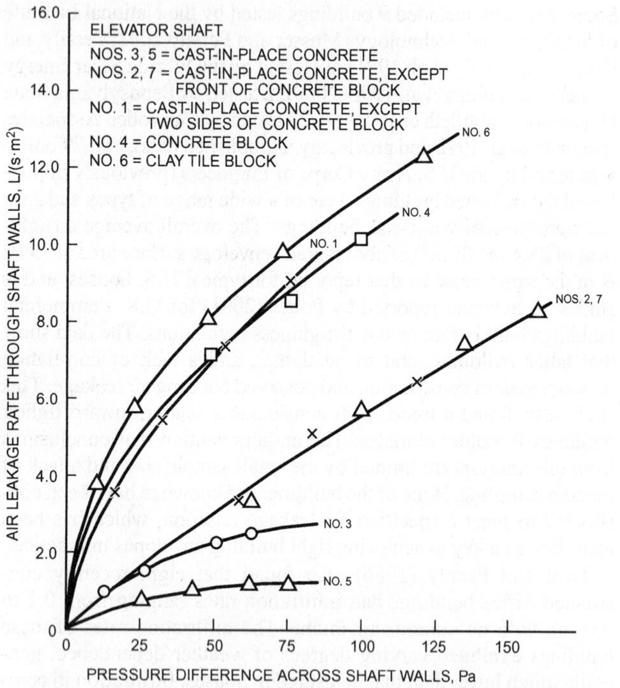

Fig. 14 Air Leakage Rates of Elevator Shaft Walls

Table 10 Air Leakage Areas for Internal Partitions in Commercial Buildings (at 75 Pa and C_D = 0.65)

Construction Element	Wall Tightness	Area Ratio
		A_L/A_w
Stairwell walls	Tight	0.14×10^{-4}
	Average	0.11×10^{-3}
	Loose	0.35×10^{-3}
Elevator shaft walls	Tight	0.18×10^{-3}
	Average	0.84×10^{-3}
	Loose	0.18×10^{-2}
		A_L/A_f
Floors	Average	0.52×10^{-4}

A_L = air leakage area A_w = wall area A_f = floor area

elevator doors are shown in Figure 15 as a function of average crack width around the door. Air leakage areas associated with other openings in commercial buildings are also important for air movement calculations. These include interior doors and partitions, suspended ceilings in buildings where space above the ceiling is used in air distribution, and other components of the air distribution system.

Air Leakage Through Exterior Doors

Door infiltration depends on the type and use of door, room, and building, and on air speed and pressure differentials. In residences and small buildings where doors are used infrequently, air exchange associated with a door can be estimated based on air leakage through cracks between door and frame. Airflow increases significantly as door-opening frequency increases. Vestibules or revolving doors should be considered for high-frequency applications.

Air Leakage Through Automatic Doors

Automatic swinging, sliding, rotating, or overhead doors are a major source of air leakage in buildings. They are normally installed where large numbers of people use the doors or bulk goods are transported through the doorways. These doors stay open longer with each use than manual doors. Air leakage through automatic doors can be reduced by installing a vestibule. However, pairs of automatic doors on the inside and outside of a vestibule normally have overlapping open periods, even when used by only one person

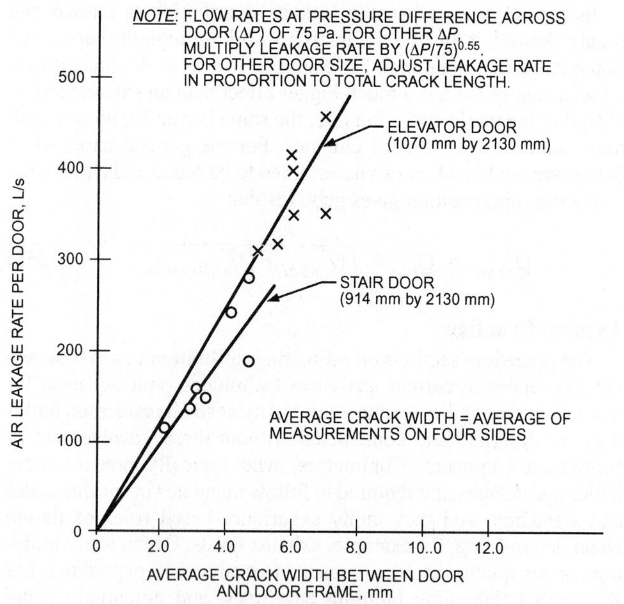

Fig. 15 Air Leakage Rate of Door Versus Average Crack Width

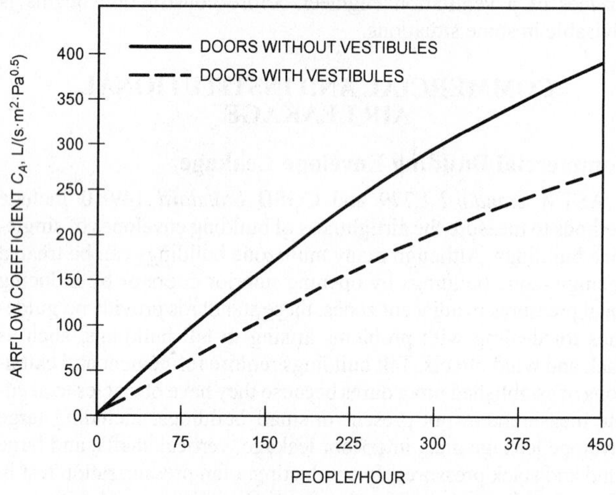

Fig. 16 Airflow Coefficient for Automatic Doors

at a time. Therefore, it is important that designers take into account airflow through automatic doors when calculating heating and cooling loads in adjacent spaces.

To calculate the average airflow rate through an automatic door, the designer must take into account the area of the door, the pressure difference across it, the discharge coefficient of the door when it is open, and the fraction of time that it is open. Obtaining the discharge coefficient is complicated by the fact that it changes as the door opens and closes.

To simplify this calculation, ASHRAE research project RP-763 (Yuill 1996) developed Figure 16 to combine the discharge coefficients of doors as they open and close with the fraction of time that doors are open at a particular level of use. This figure presents an overall airflow coefficient as a function of the number of people using a door per hour. To obtain the average infiltration rate through an automatic door, multiply this coefficient by the door's opening area and by the square root of the pressure difference between the outdoor and indoor air at the door's location. The pressure difference across a door in a building depends on wind pressure on the building, stack effect caused by the indoor/outdoor temperature difference, and effects of air-handling system operation. It also

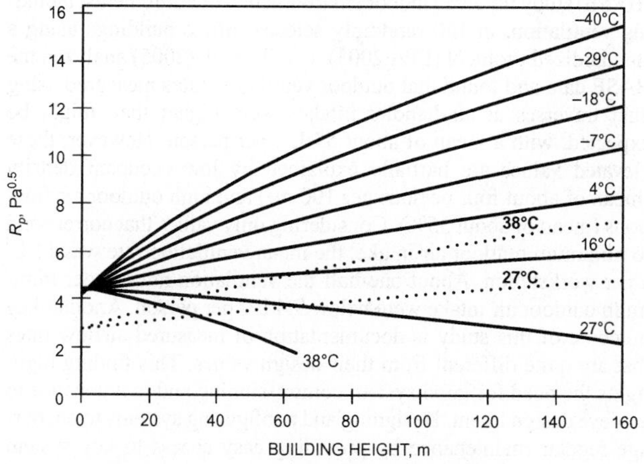

Fig. 17 Pressure Factor for Automatic Doors

depends on leakage characteristics of the building's exterior walls and of internal partitions.

Two simple methods are presented here. The first method uses simplifying assumptions to determine design values for R_p, the square root of the pressure difference across the automatic door, given in Figure 17. The second method requires explicit calculation of envelope pressures.

In Figure 17, airflows shown for outside air temperatures of 27 and 38°C, represented by dotted lines, are outward flows. They intercept the vertical axis at a lower point than the other lines because wind pressure coefficients on the building's downwind face, where the greatest outward flows occur, are lower than on the upward face. In many buildings, air pressure in the building is controlled by varying the flow rate through return fan(s) or by controlling the relief air dampers. These systems are usually set to maintain a pressure slightly above ambient in the lobby, but in a large building, multiple sensors may be used to regulate air pressure on each floor, for example. Subtracting the interior pressure maintained from the wind pressure gives the net pressure for estimating airflow through an exterior door.

Method 1. For the first method, the infiltration rate through the automatic door is given by

$$Q = C_A A R_p \tag{52}$$

where

Q = airflow rate, L/s
C_A = airflow coefficient from Figure 16, L/(s·m^2·Pa$^{0.5}$)
A = area of the door opening, m^2
R_p = pressure factor from Figure 17, Pa$^{0.5}$

Method 2. Airflow Q is given by

$$Q = C_A A \sqrt{\Delta p} \tag{53}$$

where

Q = airflow rate, L/s
C_A = airflow coefficient from Figure 16, L/(s·m^2·Pa$^{0.5}$)
A = area of the door opening, m^2
Δp = pressure difference across door, Pa

To find Δp, it is necessary to find the pressure differential from wind and that from stack effect. To give the largest possible pressure difference across the door, there are no interactions between the two natural pressures:

$$\Delta p = p_w - \Delta p_s \tag{54}$$

where

p_w = wind-induced surface pressure relative to static pressure, Pa
Δp_s = pressure difference due to stack effect, Pa

Example Calculations

Find the maximum possible infiltration through an automatic door located on the ground floor of a 20-story building. The area of the door is 0.91 × 2.1 m = 1.9 m^2. Each floor is 4 m high. Approximately 300 people per hour pass through the door. The design wind conditions are 6.7 m/s, indoor temperature is 21°C, and outdoor temperature is −7°C. The airflow coefficient from Figure 16, using the line for doors without vestibules, is approximately 306 L/(s·m^2·Pa$^{0.5}$).

Method 1:

The pressure factor from Figure 17 is 9.6 Pa$^{0.5}$. Equation (52) gives the door flow as

$$Q = 306(1.9)9.6 = 5600 \text{ L/s}$$

Method 2:

The worst possible case for wind surface pressure coefficient C_p at any point and in any position on the ground floor of the building is inferred from figures in Chapter 24 to be about 0.75. Using this in Equation (25), together with the specified wind speed, results in p_w = 20 Pa. Assume that H is one-half the door height (1.1 m). To have maximum pressure across the door, assume the neutral pressure plane is located halfway up the building such that

$$H_{NPL} = \frac{1}{2}(20 \text{ stories})\frac{4 \text{ m}}{\text{story}} = 40 \text{ m}$$

Substituting these values into Equation (24) gives Δp_s = −47 Pa. This is the maximum stack pressure difference given no internal resistance to airflow. To find the actual stack pressure difference, it is necessary to multiply this by a draft coefficient. For this example, the coefficient is assumed to be 0.9, which is the highest value that has been found for tall buildings. Therefore, Δp_s = 0.9(−47 Pa) = −42 Pa. The total pressure is then Δp = 20 − (−42) = 62 Pa. Substituting into Equation (53),

$$Q = 306(1.9)\sqrt{62} = 4580 \text{ L/s}$$

If the building has a vestibule, the airflow coefficient is read from Figure 16 using the line for doors with vestibules, and it is approximately 208 L/(s·m^2·Pa$^{0.5}$), reducing airflow to 3100 L/s into the building.

Air Exchange Through Air Curtains

Air curtains are jets of air projected across envelope openings with the intention of reducing air exchange and the entrance of dust and insects, for example. They are commonly applied to loading dock doorways and high-use building entrances. Performance of air curtains is highly dependent on factors such as jet characteristics, wind, and building pressurization. More discussion on air curtain performance is available in Chapter 17 of the 2004 *ASHRAE Handbook—HVAC Systems and Equipment*.

COMMERCIAL AND INSTITUTIONAL VENTILATION

ASHRAE *Standard* 62.1 contains requirements on ventilation and indoor air quality for commercial, institutional, and high-rise residential buildings. These requirements address system and equipment issues, design ventilation rates, commissioning and systems start-up, and operation and maintenance. The user's manual for *Standard* 62.1-2007 (ASHRAE 2007) provides details to help the user design, install, and operate buildings to meet requirements. The design requirements include two alternative procedures:

- The prescriptive **ventilation rate procedure (VRP)** contains a table of outdoor air ventilation requirements for a variety of space types, with adjustments for air distribution in rooms and systems serving multiple spaces. These requirements consist of both a per-person rate and a per-floor-area rate. Minimum outside air ventilation rates are based, in part, on research by Berg-Munch et al. (1986), Cain et al. (1983), Iwashita et al. (1989), and Yaglou et al. (1936), as well as years of experience of designers and building operators.

- The **indoor air quality procedure (IAQP)**, which achieves acceptable indoor air quality by controlling indoor contaminant concentrations through source control, air cleaning, and ventilation. It allows for either or both improved indoor air quality and reduced energy consumption. Chapter 28 of the 2008 *ASHRAE Handbook—HVAC Systems and Equipment* has information on air cleaning.

The ventilation rate procedure is by far the more commonly used.

Combining source control and local exhaust, as opposed to dilution with ventilation air, is the method of choice in many industrial environments. Industrial ventilation is discussed in Chapters 29 and 30 of the 2007 *ASHRAE Handbook—HVAC Applications* and in *Industrial Ventilation: A Manual of Recommended Practice* (ACGIH 2001). Ventilation of medical facilities, where high indoor air quality is expected, is discussed in ASHRAE *Standard* 62.1, Chapter 7 of the 2007 *ASHRAE Handbook—HVAC Applications*, and other publications [e.g., AIA et al. (2006)].

Commercial and institutional building ventilation systems are typically designed to provide slight pressurization to minimize infiltration. This pressurization is achieved by having the outside or makeup airflow rate higher than the exhaust or relief airflow rate. In these buildings, infiltration is usually neglected except in areas such as lobbies and loading docks, where infiltration can be important because of doors. However, as discussed previously, this may only be achieved in practice with tight envelope construction such as by including a continuous air barrier. As discussed in the section on Driving Mechanisms for Ventilation and Infiltration, wind and the stack effect can also cause significant infiltration and exfiltration. Ventilation airflow rates for commercial and institutional buildings are typically determined using procedures in ASHRAE *Standard* 62.1. In these procedures for designing mechanical ventilation systems, no credit is given for infiltration. However, weather-driven pressure differentials may be significant and need to be considered when designing the ventilation system.

Ventilation Rate Procedure

Per ASHRAE *Standard* 62.1, the design ventilation rate is determined based on a table of minimum ventilation requirements for different space types. These requirements are expressed as an outdoor airflow rate per occupant or per unit floor area, or often both, depending on space type. These ventilation rates are based on air pollutants generated by people, activities, and building materials and furnishings. The rates are then adjusted for various parameters (e.g., multiple zones, type of room air distribution).

The HVAC designer faces several challenges in designing an air distribution system to deliver outdoor air to building occupants. The first is to determine whether the outdoor air is acceptable for use, and to design a system for cleaning the air if it is not acceptable. A second is to design an air intake and distribution system that will *deliver* the required level of outdoor air to the occupied portions of the building, and not just *admit* it to an air handler. This outdoor air must be delivered not only at design conditions, but throughout the year. The task is complicated by weather-related variations in indoor/outdoor pressure difference. Other complications include pressure variations caused by building components such as exhaust fans or dirty filters, and probably most significantly by supply flow variations associated with variable-air-volume (VAV) systems (Janu et al. 1995; Mumma and Wong 1990). This delivery issue is related to the discussion in the section on Air Change Effectiveness.

Survey of Ventilation Rates in Office Buildings

Relatively few measurements of as-built office building ventilation performance have been conducted, and those data generally have not used consistent measurement methods or involved representative collections of buildings. The U.S. Environmental Protection Agency (EPA) Building Assessment Survey and Evaluation (BASE) study involved indoor environmental measurements, including ventilation, in 100 randomly selected office buildings using a standardized protocol (EPA 2003). Persily et al. (2005) analyzed the BASE data and found that outdoor ventilation rates measured using duct traverses at air handler intakes were higher than might be expected, with a mean of about 55 L/s per person. However, these elevated values are partially explained by low occupant density (mean of about four persons per 100 m^2) and high outdoor air fractions (mean of about 35%). Considering only values that correspond to minimum outdoor air intake, the mean ventilation rate was 11 L/s per workstation. About one-half the ventilation rates under minimum outdoor air intake were below 9.4 L/s per person. Another key outcome of this study is documentation of measured airflow rates that are quite different from their design values. This finding highlights the need for good system commissioning and maintenance to achieve design intent. Designing and configuring systems to encourage regular maintenance by providing easy access to key system components is also important.

OFFICE BUILDING EXAMPLE

Ventilation and infiltration principles from this chapter, *Standard* 62.1-2007, and elsewhere are applied to a conventional office building in Atlanta, Georgia. The building's floor plans, elevations, and wall sections are available in Chapter 18. The infiltration, local exhaust, or ventilation airflow rates in this example can be used later in the design process (1) as input for the heating and cooling load calculations; (2) for sizing fans, ducts, and dampers; and (3) for inclusion in the construction documents' air-handling units (AHUs) schedules and specifications.

This example relies on the 2007 edition of ASHRAE *Standard* 62.1; because this and other standards are updated frequently, users should check for the latest edition.

Location

The example building is about 13 km northeast of downtown Atlanta, and is close to a major highway and its access roads. Atlanta's climate is hot and humid in the summer, and has relatively mild winters. The average annual outdoor air temperature is about 15.9°C and the heating kelvin-days per year, base 18.3°C (HKD_{65}), are about 1814 (Rock 2005). From Chapter 14, the winter 99% design outdoor air (OA) temperature is –5°C, whereas the 1% cooling dry-bulb temperature is 32.8°C, with a mean coincident wet-bulb temperature of 23.3°C. The 99.6 and 0.4% design wind speeds are 5.4 m/s in the winter and 4 m/s in the summer, both out of the northwest. Warm and humid winds also travel north from the Gulf of Mexico, and occasionally the wind is from the Atlantic Ocean from the southeast.

Building

The approximately 2835 m^2 building is a two-story, flat-roofed, slab-on-grade commercial office building with a substantial roof overhang in each direction. Materials and construction quality are average commercial grade. The double-paned windows, and similar spandrel glass, are fixed in their metal curtain wall frames; all windows are nonoperable. The remaining portions of the exterior walls are brick. There are relatively few doors to the outside, as described later in this example. The building is surrounded by black asphalt driveways, a parking lot, and some vegetation. The nearby highway is across a parallel two-lane access road, to the northwest.

Occupancy

The building is occupied during normal weekday business hours, and occasionally for special weekend events. Night and weekend thermostat setbacks are used. On the perimeter of the building are mostly single-person offices and conference rooms. The core of the building is mainly open-plan with cubicle workspaces, as well as various support rooms, restrooms, two stair towers, and an elevator. There is a large mailroom on the first floor and a lunchroom on the second. Occupant density is high during workdays. The overhead fluorescent lighting is typical of such office buildings, and there are significant computing, printing, and copying equipment loads. Smoking is not allowed in the building.

The building is owner-occupied. Owners generally have long-term interests in minimizing costs, and in maximizing indoor air quality and thermal comfort so that productivity is high.

Infiltration

For this example, assume a conventional all-air overhead HVAC system, and that the building is well sealed. Consequently, a slightly positive overall building pressurization is assumed during occupied hours, because many existing commercial buildings are too leaky to be pressurized effectively. Because water condensation in the exterior envelope of the building is possible, air pressurization should be as low as is practical, and continuous vapor retarders should be installed. As a more expensive alternative to slight pressurization, the automatic control system could actively manage the dampers' positions and fans' operation to maintain an average neutral pressurization, relative to the outdoors. In either case, a good assumption is that infiltration is minimized, the windows and spandrel glass are fixed and well sealed, and the exterior doors are normally kept closed. During high-wind conditions beyond design, windward perimeter spaces may have some infiltration loads, but under non-peak outdoor temperatures, a well-zoned HVAC system should have enough capacity to handle these extra loads. If both the OA temperature and wind are extreme, then these upwind perimeter spaces may become slightly uncomfortable. These extreme conditions are expected to occur only a few hours in a typical year.

Spaces with exterior doors can experience significant infiltration loads when people enter and leave. The first-floor vestibules on the north and south sides of the building help limit this infiltration through the two main entrances. The double doors from stair tower #2 have infrequent use, and a high level of thermal comfort in stair towers is not typically expected. Thus, brief infiltration surges in stair tower #2 are deemed acceptable. However, the doors from the parking lot to the mailroom are frequently used by staff for shipping, receiving, entrance, and egress, and infiltration loads on the vestibules and mailroom are of concern. Many designers choose to ignore these extra loads in pressurized buildings, because they are transient and not easily characterized; the systems' capacities are likely sufficient to minimize uncomfortable conditions in these spaces. In this example, however, the HVAC designer is concerned about summertime airborne moisture, especially in the mailroom where books and other publications are stored, because strong, humid, southerly winds easily overcome a slight indoor pressurization when the large doors to the parking lot are open.

This chapter and many of its supporting references describe detailed methods for estimating infiltration or air leakage. Typically, pressure differences, openings' coefficients, and hour-by-hour weather data are required to perform these transient calculations, usually using a computer program separate from that used for thermal load calculations. For HVAC design purposes for a building similar to the example, an air exchange rate of unconditioned outside air through infiltration, per space, expressed in air changes per hour (ach) or airflow rate (L/s) is of more immediate use. Either value is then entered into the load calculation program. Unfortunately, accurate air changes per hour are difficult, if not impossible, to predict, so design estimates must be made. For example,

North Vestibule, Room 101

- Gross floor area ≈ 3.4 m × 4 m = 13.6 m^2
- Room volume ≈ 13.6 m^2 × 2.7 m = 36.7 m^3
- $ach_{inf} \approx 1.0$, so
- $Q_{inf} \approx (36.7\text{ m}^3 \times 1000\text{ L/m}^3 \times 1.0)/3660\text{ s/h} \approx 10.2\text{ L/s}_{oa}$

Either 1.0 ach or 10.2 L/s of infiltration is then used as input for the load calculation program for this space. The 1.0 ach assumption was made by the designer during on-site observation that these particular manually operated exterior doors have low usage. If passage rates were known, Yuill's (1996) flow rate estimation method would have been used instead.

South Vestibule, Room 115

- Gross floor area ≈ 2.4 m × 3 m = 7.2 m^2
- Room volume ≈ 7.2 m^2 × 2.7 m = 19.4 m^3
- $ach_{inf} \approx 2.0$, so
- $Q_{inf} \approx (19.4\text{ m}^3 \times 1000\text{ L/m}^3 \times 2.0)/3600\text{ s/h} \approx 10.8\text{ L/s}_{oa})$

In practice, this back entrance from the parking lot on the southeast side of the building is the primary means of entrance and egress, and as such, the estimated infiltration for it is increased to 2.0 ach, compared to the north vestibule's 1.0 ach.

In colder U.S. climates, it is common practice for low-cost commercial buildings to have only space heating, and not cooling, in stair towers and vestibules. However, for this building in the Southeast, the designer decided to provide cooling for these vestibules. Thus, the estimated infiltration rates are applied to both the heating and cooling load calculations for these spaces. The building's mailroom, which also has exterior doors, is to be heated and cooled, too.

Mailroom, Room 114

- Gross floor area ≈ (15.5 m × 6.7 m) + (10 m × 3 m) = 134 m^2
- Room volume ≈ 134 m^2 × 2.7 m = 362 m^3
- $ach_{inf} \approx 0.5$, so
- $Q_{inf} \approx (362\text{ m}^3 \times 1000\text{ L/m}^3 \times 0.5)/3600\text{ s/h} \approx 50.3\text{ L/s}_{oa}$

Even though the mailroom has only a single layer of doors to the outside, and not a vestibule, the designer estimated the infiltration at a lower rate (0.5 ach) than those for the vestibules. This is because of the mailroom's large interior volume relative to its exterior doorway's area.

Note that *no* estimate of air changes will be accurate at all times; this portion of HVAC design is still largely an art because of the many unknowns and variability of weather and building use. For improved energy conservation, all exterior doors must be extremely well weatherstripped and have automatic closers, and a sign indicating doors should be kept closed when not in use should be placed on the mailroom's doors. High-quality gaskets and sealants for the windows and spandrel glass are also required.

Local Exhausts

(This section assumes that ANSI/ASHRAE *Standard* 62.1-2007 has been adopted into the local building code without modification.) At least 10 rooms require direct, powered air exhaust: the two restrooms per floor, the darkroom, three designated photocopy spaces, and the two janitors' closets. The restrooms have three flushable fixtures each, so from Table 6.4 of *Standard* 62.1, with intermittent use, each restroom requires

$$Q_{ea} = 3\text{ units} \times 25\text{ L/s per unit} = 75\text{ L/s}$$

Also from Table 6.4, the darkroom (room 222) of the second floor needs

$$\text{Gross floor area} \approx 3\text{ m} \times 4.6\text{ m} = 13.8\text{ m}^2$$

$$Q_{ea} = 13.8\text{ m}^2 \times 5.0\text{ L/(s·m}^2) = 69\text{ L/s}$$

Similarly, the designated photocopy areas need 2.5 L/(s·m^2), so

$$\text{First floor, plan east: } \approx 7.4\text{ m}^2 \times 2.5\text{ L/(s·m}^2) = 18.5\text{ L/s}_{ea}$$

$$\text{First floor, plan southwest: } \approx 14.9\text{ m}^2 \times 2.5\text{ L/(s·m}^2) = 37.3\text{ L/s}_{ea}$$

Second floor, plan east: ≈10.4 m^2 × 2.5 L/(s·m^2) = 26 L/s_{ea}

The two small janitors' closets, one on each floor, also require exhaust:

$$5.6\ m^2 \times 5.0\ L/(s{\cdot}m^2) = 28\ L/s_{ea}$$

These local exhaust airflow rates are then entered into the load calculation program. They are room loads, attached to each particular space, and are *not* combined and entered as systems-level loads. The load calculation program evaluates the room loads, appropriately combines them, and then finds the systems-level loads for various peak hours.

Some local code authorities amend the requirements of *Standard* 62.1, or have not yet adopted the most current version, so significant deviations from these examples are possible. For example, in much of the United States, janitorial closets and photocopy rooms have not been required to have local exhausts. *Standard* 62.1-2007 recognized that these spaces can be significant sources of airborne pollutants, and some direct exhaust from them can be very beneficial for improving indoor air quality.

Ventilation

(This section assumes that ANSI/ASHRAE *Standard* 62.1-2007 has been adopted into local code without changes.) Ventilation air is needed to maintain acceptable indoor air quality. The example building is well sealed, natural ventilation is not used, and no credit for any infiltration is taken toward ventilation air requirements, as is typical for conventional commercial buildings. Thus, minimum ventilation air required by *Standard* 62.1 is provided mechanically through the AHUs. Because smoking is not allowed in the building, no extra ventilation for environmental tobacco smoke (ETS) is needed. However, considering outdoor air pollution from the major highway nearby as well as metropolitan Atlanta's smog, some outdoor air pretreatment may be considered later in the design process.

Standard 62.1 has two methods for determining needed ventilation airflow rates: the performance IAQ procedure (IAQP), and the prescriptive ventilation rate procedure (VRP). Most HVAC designers of conventional buildings with normal occupancies and outdoor air conditions use the VRP, which is appropriate for this example building.

Required ventilation air (conditioned outside air) is admitted to this building through two air-handling units; each AHU serves one floor. Flow rates of outside air are input values for, and carried through to the results of, the load calculation simulation. Energy needed to condition the outside air ultimately is a systems-level load, because all of this ventilation air is conditioned by the AHUs before its introduction to the building.

Commercial load calculation programs often provide suggested values of ventilation airflow rates and occupancy schedules, but may not have been updated to reflect the latest VRP requirements and procedures of *Standard* 62.1. As such, it is difficult to present an example here; instead, a sample check using some assumed values for the first-floor executive director's office (room 132) is given. It is assumed that this room is a separate thermal zone because of its use and its location on the southwest corner of the building and its two solar exposures.

Executive Director's Office, Room 132

- Gross floor area ≈ 3.7 m × 6.4 m = 23.7 m^2
- Room volume ≈ 23.7 m^2 × 2.7 m = 64 m^3
- Assumed supply air Q_{sa} = 194 L/s

The supply airflow rate was estimated at 7.93 m^2/kW, a sensible heat factor of 0.9, a cooling supply (12.8°C) to room (23.9°C) air temperature difference of 11.1 K, 1000 W per kW of cooling, and the sensible heat equation 1.23 × L/s × ΔT. From Table 6.1 of *Standard* 62.1, the office's population P can be estimated as

$$P = 23.7\ m^2 \times 5\ \text{occupants}/100\ m^2 = 1.19$$

In this case, however, there is only one regular occupant of the space. The needed ventilation airflow rate to the breathing zone V_{bz} is then found from the table as follows:

$$V_{bz} = R_p P_z + R_a A_z$$

$$V_{bz} = [2.5\ L/(s\cdot \text{person}) \times 1\ \text{person}] + [0.3\ L/(s\cdot m^2) \times 23.7\ m^2] = 9.61\ L/s$$

where

R_p = outdoor airflow rate required per person, from *Standard* 62.1's Table 6-1, L/s
P_z = zone population (largest number of people expected to occupy the zone during typical use)
R_a = outdoor airflow rate required per unit area, from *Standard* 62.1's Table 6-1, L/s
A_z = occupiable floor area of zone, m^2

Note that *Standard* 62.1's VRP includes a building component $R_a A_z$, as well as the traditional per-person people component.

Because this is a conventional office building, with ceiling plenums and no raised floors, overhead air supply and return is assumed. The cooling mode, not heating, is dominant in this and most other U.S. office buildings that have high internal heat gains as well as well-sealed envelopes. From the standard's Table 6.2, with ceiling supply of cool air, the zone air distribution effectiveness E_z is estimated as 1.0. From Equation (6-2) of the standard, the design zone outdoor airflow rate V_{oz} is then

$$V_{oz} = V_{bz}/E_z = (9.61\ L/s)/1.0 = 9.61\ L/s$$

But this is still not the amount of outside air that must be conditioned by the air handler: the rate must be adjusted for inefficiencies and recirculation in the air distribution system.

Because single-duct VAV with terminal reheat air distribution systems were initially planned by the designer, *Standard* 62.1's multiple-zone recirculating systems adjustment is needed. For this thermal zone, the primary outdoor air fraction Z_p for its VAV terminal unit and downstream is

$$Z_p = V_{oz}/V_{pz} = (9.61\ L/s)/(194\ L/s) = 0.05,\ \text{or}\ 5\%$$

However, for VAV systems, the minimum expected primary airflow rate should be used. In this case, 194 L/s is the peak design airflow rate. Designers often assume about 30% of this peak flow as the minimum in VAV systems, so for this space, 194 × 0.3 = 58.2 L/s. The adjusted primary outdoor air fraction is then

$$Z_p = V_{oz}/V_{pz} = (9.61\ L/s)/(58.2\ L/s) = 0.17,\ \text{or}\ 17\%$$

The preceding calculations need to be performed for every thermal zone on each air handler. Then, for each system, the highest primary outside air fraction is used to estimate the air distribution systems' ventilation effectiveness; ASHRAE (2007) includes a spreadsheet for doing these calculations.

For the purposes of this example, 0.17 is assumed to be the maximum Z_p, so, from Table 6.3 of *Standard* 62.1, the system ventilation efficiency E_v is 0.9. If, instead, the standard's Appendix A method for determining E_v were used, a value closer to 1.0 (perfect mixing) would likely result for this example's conventional overhead all-air cooling system. Table 6.3's value of 0.9 is likely somewhat conservative, but is obtained quickly for design purposes.

Next, the uncorrected outdoor air intake flow rate V_{ou} is needed; *Standard* 62.1's Equation (6-6) includes diversity factor D to adjust the people component of the flow rate. All zones' flow rates are needed to perform this calculation. For this example, the uncorrected outdoor air intake flow rate for the first floor's AHU was estimated from floor area, an occupancy of 5 people per 100 m^2, and

9.4 L/s per person, and is assumed to be 720 L/s. The adjusted outdoor air intake flow rate V_{ot} for this AHU is then

$$V_{ot} = V_{ou}/E_v = (720 \text{ L/s})/\ 0.9 = 800 \text{ L/s}_{oa}$$

After load calculations are complete, these assumed airflow rates can be replaced with actual values for each zone, and the outside airflow rate can be updated. Repeating the load calculations may be necessary. The final value of the adjusted outdoor air intake flow rate is then reported on the AHU's schedule so that testing, adjusting, and balancing (TAB) personnel and others can use this information to ensure that the system admits the desired flow rate of ventilation air. The information is also used to select air cleaners, dampers, coils, ducts, and fans.

For more examples on determining ventilation air rates for commercial buildings, see the user's manual for *Standard* 62.1 (ASHRAE 2007). For low-rise residential buildings, consult ASHRAE *Standard* 62.2 and its user's manual (ASHRAE 2006).

SYMBOLS

A = area, m^2 or cm^2
c = flow coefficient, $m^3/(s \cdot Pa^n)$
c_p = specific heat, J/(kg·K) or kJ/(kg·K)
C = concentration, ppm
$\overline{C}$ = time averaged concentration
C_A = airflow coefficient for automatic doors, $L/(s \cdot m^2 \cdot Pa^{0.5})$
C_D = discharge coefficient
C_p = pressure coefficient
C_s = stack flow coefficient, $(L/s)^2/(cm^4 \cdot K)$ or $(Pa/K)^n$
C_v = effectiveness of openings
C_w = wind flow coefficient, $(L/s)^2[cm^4 \cdot (m/s)^2]$ or $[Pa/(m/s)^2]^n$
E = system efficiency
F = tracer gas injection rate, m^3/s
$\overline{F}$ = time-averaged contaminant source strength, m^3/s
f = fractional on-time
g = gravitational acceleration, m/s^2
G = wind speed multiplier, Table 7
h = specific enthalpy, kJ/kg
H = height, m
i = hour of year
I = air exchange rate, 1/time
I_i = instantaneous air exchange rate, 1/time
I_m = effective air exchange rate, 1/time
IDD = infiltration degree-days, K·day
n = pressure exponent
N = number of discrete time periods in period of interest
p = pressure, Pa
P = parameter, or occupancy population
q = heat rate, W
Q = volumetric flow rate, m^3/s
$\underline{Q}$ = effective volumetric flow rate, m^3/s
R = outdoor airflow rate, L/s
s = shelter factor
S = source strength, m^3/s
t = time [Equations (9) to (11)]; temperature, °C or K
U = wind speed, m/s
V = volume, m^3, or ventilation airflow rate, L/s
W = humidity ratio, kg/kg
ε_I = air change effectiveness
θ = time
θ_{age} = age of air
ρ = air density, kg/m^3
τ = time constant
ϕ = wind angle, degrees

Subscripts

a = area
b = base
ba = bypass air
bz = breathing zone
c = calculated
ca = recirculated air
e = effective
ea = exhaust air
f = floor
i = indoor or time counter for summation (instantaneous)
inf = infiltration
H = building height, eaves or roof
ka = makeup air
l = latent
la = relief air
L = leakage or local
ma = mixed air
met = meteorological station location
n = normalized
N = nominal
NPL = neutral pressure level
o = outdoor, initial condition, or reference
oa = outdoor air
ot = adjusted outdoor air
ou = uncorrected outdoor air
oz = zone outdoor
p = pressure, or primary
r = reference
s = sensible or stack
sa = supply air
S = space or source
w = wind
v = ventilation
z = zone

REFERENCES

ACGIH. 2007. *Industrial ventilation: A manual of recommended practice*, 26th ed. American Conference of Governmental Industrial Hygienists, Cincinnati, OH.

Ackerman, M.Y., J.D. Dale, and D.J. Wilson. 2006. Infiltration heat recovery, part 1: Field studies in an instrumented test building (RP-1169). *ASHRAE Transactions* 112(2):597-608.

AIA, FGI, and DHHS. 2006. *Guidelines for design and construction of hospital and healthcare facilities*. American Institute of Architects, Facilities Guidelines Institute, and U.S. Department of Health and Human Services, Washington, D.C.

AIVC. 1994. An analysis and data summary of the AIVC's numerical database. *Technical Note* 44. International Energy Agency Air Infiltration and Ventilation Centre, Sint-Stevens-Woluwe, Belgium.

Akins, R.E., J.A. Peterka, and J.E. Cermak. 1979. Averaged pressure coefficients for rectangular buildings, vol. 1, *Proceedings of the Fifth International Wind Engineering Conference*, Fort Collins, pp. 369-380.

Allard, F. and M. Herrlin. 1989. Wind-induced ventilation. *ASHRAE Transactions* 95(2):722-728.

Anis, W. 2001. The impact of airtightness on system design. *ASHRAE Journal* 43(12):31-35.

Apte, M.G., W.J. Fisk, and J.M. Daisey. 2000. Associations between indoor CO_2 concentrations and sick building syndrome symptoms in US office buildings: An analysis of the 1994-1996 BASE study data. *Indoor Air* 10(4):246-257.

ASHRAE. 2007. Standard *62.1-2007 user's manual.*

ASHRAE. 2006. Standard *62.2 user's manual.*

ASHRAE. 2007. Method of testing general ventilation air-cleaning devices for removal efficiency by particle size. ANSI/ASHRAE *Standard* 52.2-2007.

ASHRAE. 2004. Thermal environmental conditions for human occupancy. ASHRAE *Standard* 55-2004.

ASHRAE. 2007. Ventilation for acceptable indoor air quality. ANSI/ASHRAE *Standard* 62.1-2007.

ASHRAE. 2007. Ventilation and acceptable indoor air quality in low-rise residential buildings. ANSI/ASHRAE *Standard* 62.2-2007.

ASHRAE. 2004. Air leakage performance for detached single-family residential buildings. ANSI/ASHRAE *Standard* 119-1988 (RA 2004).

ASHRAE. 2002. Measuring air-change effectiveness. ANSI/ASHRAE *Standard* 129-97 (RA 2002).

ASHRAE. 2006. A method of determining air change rates in detached dwellings. ANSI/ASHRAE *Standard* 136-1993 (RA 2006).

ASHRAE. 2003. Risk management guidance for health, safety and environmental security under extraordinary incidents. *Report*, Presidential Ad Hoc Committee for Building Health and Safety Under Extraordinary Incidents.

Ask, A. 2003. Ventilation and air leakage. *ASHRAE Journal* 45(11):28-36.

ASTM. 1999. Test method for determining rate of air leakage through exterior windows, curtain walls, and doors under specified pressure differences across the specimen. *Standard* E283-91 (R1999). American Society for Testing and Materials, West Conshohocken, PA.

ASTM. 2006. Test method for determining air change in a single zone by means of a tracer gas dilution. *Standard* E741-00 (R2006). American Society for Testing and Materials, West Conshohocken, PA.

ASTM. 2003. Test method for determining air leakage rate by fan pressurization. *Standard* E779-03. American Society for Testing and Materials, West Conshohocken, PA.

ASTM. 2002. Test method for field measurement of air leakage through installed exterior windows and doors. *Standard* E783-02. American Society for Testing and Materials, West Conshohocken, PA.

ASTM. 2003. Practices for air leakage site detection in building envelopes and air barrier systems. *Standard* E1186-2003. American Society for Testing and Materials, West Conshohocken, PA.

ASTM. 2007. Test methods for determining airtightness of buildings using an orifice blower door. *Standard* E1827-96 (R2007). American Society for Testing and Materials, West Conshohocken, PA.

ASTM. 2007. Guide for assessing depressurization-induced backdrafting and spillage from vented combustion appliances. *Standard* E1998-02 (R2007). American Society for Testing and Materials, West Conshohocken, PA.

Axley, J.W. 2001a. *Application of natural ventilation for U.S. commercial buildings—Climate suitability, design strategies and methods, modeling studies*. GCR-01-820, National Institute of Standards and Technology, Gaithersburg, MD.

Axley, J.W. 2001b. Residential passive ventilation systems: Evaluation and design. *Technical Note* 54. International Energy Agency Air Infiltration and Ventilation Centre, Sint-Stevens-Woluwe, Belgium.

Bahnfleth, W.P., G.K. Yuill, and B.W. Lee. 1999. Protocol for field testing of tall buildings to determine envelope air leakage rates. *ASHRAE Transactions* 105(2):27-38.

Bankvall, C.G. 1987. Air movements and thermal performance of the building envelope. In *Thermal insulation: Materials and systems*, pp. 124-131. F.J. Powell and S.L. Mathews, eds. American Society for Testing and Materials, West Conshohocken, PA.

Barley, D. 2001. *Overview of residential ventilation activities in the Building America Program (phase I)*. NREL/TP-550-30107, National Renewable Energy Laboratory, Golden, CO.

Batterman, S., G. Hatzivasilis, and C. Jia. 2006. Concentrations and emissions of gasoline and other vapors from residential vehicle garages. *Atmospheric Environment* 40:1828-1844.

Bauman, F. and A. Daly. 2003. *Underfloor air distribution design guide*. ASHRAE.

Berg-Munch, B., G. Clausen, and P.O. Fanger. 1986. Ventilation requirements for the control of body odor in spaces occupied by women. *Environmental International* 12(1-4):195.

Berlad, A.L., N. Tutu, Y. Yeh, R. Jaung, R. Krajewski, R. Hoppe and F. Salzano. 1978. Air intrusion effects on the performance of permeable insulation systems. In *Thermal insulation performance*, STP 718, pp. 181-194. D. McElroy and R. Tye, eds. American Society for Testing and Materials, West Conshohocken, PA.

Blomsterberg, A.K. and D.T. Harrje. 1979. Approaches to evaluation of air infiltration energy losses in buildings. *ASHRAE Transactions* 85(1):797.

Bohac, D.L., D.T. Harrje, and L.K. Norford. 1985. Constant concentration infiltration measurement technique: An analysis of its accuracy and field measurements, 176. *Proceedings of the ASHRAE/DOE/BTECC Conference on the Thermal Performance of the Exterior Envelopes of Buildings III,* Clearwater Beach, FL.

Bohac, D.L., D.T. Harrje, and G.S. Horner. 1987. Field study comparisons of constant concentration and PFT infiltration measurements. *Proceedings of the 8th IEA Conference of the Air Infiltration and Ventilation Centre*, Überlingen, Germany, pp. 47-62.

Bradley, B. 1993. Implementation of the AIM-2 infiltration model in HOT-2000. *Report*, for Natural Resources Canada.

Brennan, T., W. Turner, G. Fisher, B. Thompson, and B. Ligman. 1992. Fan pressurization of school buildings. *Proceedings of Thermal Performance of the Exterior Envelopes of Buildings V*, pp. 643-645. ASHRAE.

Buchanan, C.R. and M.H. Sherman. 2000. A mathematical model for infiltration heat recovery. *Proceedings of the 21st IEA Conference of the Air Infiltration and Ventilation Centre*, The Hague, Netherlands. *Report* LBNL-44294. Lawrence Berkeley National Laboratory, Berkeley, CA.

Cain, W.S., B. Leaderer, R. Isseroff, L. Berglund, R. Huey, and E. Lipsitt. 1983. Ventilation requirements in buildings—I. Control of occupancy odor and tobacco smoke odor. *Atmospheric Environment* 17(6):1183-1197.

CGSB. 2005. Depressurization test. CAN/CGSB *Standard* 51.71-2005. Canadian General Standards Board, Ottawa, ON.

CGSB. 1986. Determination of the airtightness of building envelopes by the fan depressurization method. *Standard* 149.10-M86. Canadian General Standards Board, Ottawa, ON.

CGSB. 1996. Determination of the overall envelope airtightness of buildings by the fan pressurization method using the building's air handling systems. *Standard* 149.15-96. Canadian General Standards Board, Ottawa, ON.

Charlesworth, P.S. 1988. Measurement of air exchange rates. Chapter 2 in *Air exchange rate and airtightness measurement techniques—An applications guide.* International Energy Agency Air Infiltration and Ventilation Centre, Sint-Stevens-Woluwe, Belgium.

Chastain, J.P. 1987. *Pressure gradients and the location of the neutral pressure axis for low-rise structures under pure stack conditions*. Unpublished M.S. thesis. University of Kentucky, Lexington.

Chastain, J.P. and D.G. Colliver. 1989. Influence of temperature stratification on pressure differences resulting from the infiltration stack effect. *ASHRAE Transactions* 95(1):256-268.

Chastain, J.P., D.G. Colliver, and P.W. Winner, Jr. 1987. Computation of discharge coefficients for laminar flow in rectangular and circular openings. *ASHRAE Transactions* 93(2):2259-2283.

CHBA. 1994. *HOT2000 technical manual.* Canadian Home Builders Association, Ottawa, ON.

CIBSE. 2000. Testing buildings for air leakage. *Standard* TM-23. Chartered Institution of Building Services Engineers, London.

CIBSE. 2005. *Natural ventilation in non-domestic buildings*. Chartered Institution of Building Services Engineers, London.

Claridge, D.E. and S. Bhattacharyya. 1990. The measured impact of infiltration in a test cell. *ASME Journal of Solar Energy Engineering* 112:123-126.

Claridge, D.E., M. Krarti, and S. Bhattacharyya. 1988. Preliminary measurements of the energy impact of infiltration in a test cell. *Proceedings of the Fifth Annual Symposium on Improving Building Energy Efficiency in Hot and Humid Climates*, pp. 308-317.

Cole, J.T., T.S. Zawacki, R.H. Elkins, J.W. Zimmer, and R.A. Macriss. 1980. Application of a generalized model of air infiltration to existing homes. *ASHRAE Transactions* 86(2):765.

Collet, P.F. 1981. Continuous measurements of air infiltration in occupied dwellings. *Proceedings of the 2nd IEA Conference of the Air Infiltration Centre*, Stockholm, p. 147.

CSA. 2006. Residential carbon monoxide alarming devices. CAN/CSA *Standard* C6.19-01 (R2006). Canadian Standards Association, Toronto.

CSA. 2005. Residential mechanical ventilation systems. CAN/CSA-F326-M91 (R2005). Canadian Standards Association, Toronto.

Cummings, J.B. and J.J. Tooley, Jr. 1989. Infiltration and pressure differences induced by forced air systems in Florida residences. *ASHRAE Transactions* 96(20):551-560.

Cummings, J.B., J.J. Tooley, Jr., and R. Dunsmore. 1990. Impacts of duct leakage on infiltration rates, space conditioning energy use and peak electrical demand in Florida homes. *Proceedings of the ACEEE Summer Study*, Pacific Grove, CA. American Council for an Energy-Efficient Economy, Washington, D.C.

Cummings, J.B., C.R. Withers, N. Moyer, P. Fairey, and B. McKendry. 1996. *Uncontrolled airflow in non-residential buildings*. FSEC-CR-878-96. Florida Solar Energy Center, Cocoa.

Cummings, J.B., D.B. Shirey, C. Withers, R. Raustad, and N. Moyer. 2000. Evaluating the impacts of uncontrolled air flow and HVAC performance problems on Florida's commercial and institutional buildings. *Final Report*, FSEC-CR-1210-00. Florida Solar Energy Center, Cocoa.

Cutter. 1987. Air-to-air heat exchangers. In *Energy design update.* Cutter Information Corporation, Arlington, MA.

Desrochers, D. and A.G. Scott. 1985. Residential ventilation rates and indoor radon daughter levels. *Transactions of the APCA Specialty Conference, Indoor Air Quality in Cold Climates: Hazards and Abatement Measures*, Ottawa, p. 362.

Diamond, R.C., J.B. Dickinson, R.D. Lipschutz, B. O'Regan, and B. Shohl. 1982. The house doctor's manual. *Report* PUB-3017. Lawrence Berkeley National Laboratory, Berkeley, CA.

Diamond, R.C., M.P. Modera, and H.E. Feustel. 1986. Ventilation and occupant behaviour in two apartment buildings. *Proceedings of the 7th IEA Conference of the Air Infiltration and Ventilation Centre*, Stratford-upon-Avon, U.K. *Report* LBL-21862. Lawrence Berkeley National Laboratory, Berkeley, CA.

Dickerhoff, D.J., D.T. Grimsrud, and R.D. Lipschutz. 1982. Component leakage testing in residential buildings. *Proceedings of the American Council for an Energy-Efficient Economy, 1982 Summer Study*, Santa Cruz, CA. *Report* LBL 14735. Lawrence Berkeley National Laboratory, Berkeley, CA.

Dietz, R.N., R.W. Goodrich, E.A. Cote, and R.F. Wieser. 1986. Detailed description and performance of a passive perfluorocarbon tracer system for building ventilation and air exchange measurement. In *Measured air leakage of buildings*, STP 904, p. 203. H.R. Trechsel and P.L. Lagus, eds. American Society for Testing and Materials, West Conshohocken, PA.

D'Ottavio, T.W., G.I. Senum, and R.N. Dietz. 1988. Error analysis techniques for perfluorocarbon tracer derived multizone ventilation rates. *Building and Environment* 23(40).

Ek, C.W., S.A. Anisko, and G.O. Gregg. 1990. Air leakage tests of manufactured housing in the Northwest United States. In *Air change rate and airtightness in buildings*, STP 1067, pp. 152-164. M.H. Sherman, ed. American Society for Testing and Materials, West Conshohocken, PA.

Elmroth, A. and P. Levin. 1983. *Air infiltration control in housing*. International Energy Agency Air Infiltration Centre, Sint-Stevens-Woluwe, Belgium.

Emmerich, S.J. 2006. Simulated performance of natural and hybrid ventilation systems in an office building. *HVAC&R Research* 12(4):975-1004.

Emmerich, S.J., and A.K. Persily. 2005. Airtightness of commercial buildings in the U.S. *Proceedings of the 26th IEA Conference of the Air Infiltration and Ventilation Centre*, Brussels, pp 65-70.

Emmerich, S.J., J.E. Gorfain, and C. Howard-Reed. 2003. Air and pollutant transport from attached garages to residential living spaces—Literature review and field test. *International Journal of Ventilation* 2(3):265-276.

Energy Resource Center. 1982. *How to house doctor*. University of Illinois, Chicago.

EPA. 2003. *A standardized EPA protocol for characterizing indoor air quality in large office buildings*. U.S. Environmental Protection Agency, Washington, D.C.

Etheridge, D.W. 1977. Crack flow equations and scale effect. *Building and Environment* 12:181.

Etheridge, D.W. and D.K. Alexander. 1980. The British gas multi-cell model for calculating ventilation. *ASHRAE Transactions* 86(2):808.

Etheridge, D.W. and J.A. Nolan. 1979. Ventilation measurements at model scale in a turbulent flow. *Building and Environment* 14(1):53.

Eyre, D. and D. Jennings. 1983. *Air-vapour barriers—A general perspective and guidelines for installation*. Energy, Mines, and Resources Canada, Ottawa, ON.

Farrington, R., D. Martin, and R. Anderson. 1990. A comparison of displacement efficiency, decay time constant, and age of air for isothermal flow in an imperfectly mixed enclosure. *Proceedings of the ACEEE 1990 Summer Study on Energy Efficiency in Buildings*, pp. 4.35-4.43. American Council for an Energy-Efficient Economy, Washington, D.C.

Fennell, H.C. and J. Haehnel. 2005. Setting airtightness standards. *ASHRAE Journal* 47(9):26-31.

Feustel, H.E. and A. Raynor-Hoosen, eds. 1990. Fundamentals of the multizone air flow model—COMIS. *Technical Note* 29. International Energy Agency Air Infiltration and Ventilation Centre, Sint-Stevens-Woluwe, Belgium.

Fisk, W.J., R.K. Spencer, D.T. Grimsrud, F.J. Offermann, B. Pedersen, and R. Sextro. 1984. Indoor air quality control techniques: A critical review. *Report* LBL-16493. Lawrence Berkeley National Laboratory, Berkeley, CA.

Fisk, W.J., R.J. Prill, and O. Steppanen. 1989. A multi-tracer technique for studying rates of ventilation, air distribution patterns and air exchange efficiencies. *Proceedings of Conference on Building Systems—Room Air and Air Contaminant Distribution*, pp. 237-240. ASHRAE.

Fortmann, R.C., N.L. Nagda, and H.E. Rector. 1990. Comparison of methods for the measurement of air change rates and interzonal airflows to two test residences. In *Air change rate and airtightness in buildings*, STP 1067, pp. 104-118. M.H. Sherman, ed. American Society of Testing and Materials, West Conshohocken, PA.

Foster, M.P. and M.J. Down. 1987. Ventilation of livestock buildings by natural convection. *Journal of Agricultural Engineering Research* 37:1.

Fugler, D. 2004. Garage performance testing. *CMHC Research Highlights* (April). Canada Mortgage and Housing Corporation, Ottawa, ON.

Giesbrecht, P. and G. Proskiw. 1986. An evaluation of the effectiveness of air leakage sealing. In *Measured air leakage of buildings*, STP 904, p. 312. H.R. Trechsel and P.L. Lagus, eds. American Society for Testing and Materials, West Conshohocken, PA.

Grieve, P.W. 1989. *Measuring ventilation using tracer-gases*. Brüel and Kjær, Denmark.

Grimsrud, D.T. and K.Y. Teichman. 1989. The scientific basis of *Standard* 62-1989. *ASHRAE Journal* 31(10):51-54.

Grimsrud, D.T., M.H. Sherman, R.C. Diamond, P.E. Condon, and A.H. Rosenfeld. 1979. Infiltration-pressurization correlations: Detailed measurements in a California house. *ASHRAE Transactions* 85(1):851.

Grimsrud, D.T., M.H. Sherman, and R.C. Sonderegger. 1982. Calculating infiltration: Implications for a construction quality standard. *Proceedings of the ASHRAE/DOE Conference on the Thermal Performance of the Exterior Envelope of Buildings II*, Las Vegas, p. 422.

Grot, R.A. and R.E. Clark. 1979. Air leakage characteristics and weatherization techniques for low-income housing. *Proceedings of the ASHRAE/DOE Conference on the Thermal Performance of the Exterior Envelopes of Buildings*, p. 178. Orlando, FL.

Grot, R.A. and A.K. Persily. 1986. Measured air infiltration and ventilation rates in eight large office buildings. In *Measured air leakage of buildings*, STP 904, p. 151. H.R. Trechsel and P.L. Lagus, eds. American Society for Testing and Materials, West Conshohocken, PA.

Hamlin, T.L. 1991. Ventilation and airtightness in new, detached Canadian housing. *ASHRAE Transactions* 97(2):904-910.

Hamlin, T. and W. Pushka. 1994. Predicted and measured air change rates in houses with predictions of occupant IAQ comfort. *Proceedings of the 15th IEA Air Infiltration and Ventilation Centre Conference*, Buxton, U.K., pp. 771-775.

Harrje, D.T. and G.J. Born. 1982. Cataloguing air leakage components in houses. *Proceedings of the ACEEE 1982 Summer Study*, Santa Cruz, CA. American Council for an Energy-Efficient Economy, Washington, D.C.

Harrje, D.T. and T.A. Mills, Jr. 1980. Air infiltration reduction through retrofitting. In *Building air change rate and infiltration measurements*. STP 719, p. 89. C.M. Hunt, J.C. King, and H.R. Trechsel, eds. American Society for Testing and Materials, West Conshohocken, PA.

Harrje, D.T., G.S. Dutt, and J. Beyea. 1979. Locating and eliminating obscure but major energy losses in residential housing. *ASHRAE Transactions* 85(2):521.

Harrje, D.T., R.A. Grot, and D.T. Grimsrud. 1981. Air infiltration site measurement techniques. *Proceedings of the 2nd IEA Conference of the Air Infiltration Centre*, p. 113. Stockholm, Sweden.

Harrje, D.T., G.S. Dutt, D.L. Bohac, and K.J. Gadsby. 1985. Documenting air movements and infiltration in multicell buildings using various tracer techniques. *ASHRAE Transactions* 91(2):2012-2027.

Harrje, D.T., R.N. Dietz, M. Sherman, D.L. Bohac, T.W. D'Ottavio, and D.J. Dickerhoff. 1990. Tracer gas measurement systems compared in a multifamily building. In *Air change rate and airtightness in buildings*, STP 1067, pp. 5-12. M.H. Sherman, ed. American Society for Testing and Materials, West Conshohocken, PA.

Heiselberg, P. 2002. Principles of hybrid ventilation. *Final Report*, International Energy Agency Energy Conservation in Buildings and Community Systems, Annex 35. Hybrid Ventilation Centre, Aalborg University, Denmark.

Hekmat, D., H.E. Feustel, and M.P. Modera. 1986. Impacts of ventilation strategies on energy consumption and indoor air quality in single-family residences. *Energy and Buildings* 9(3):239.

Herrlin, M.K. 1985. MOVECOMP: A static-multicell-airflow-model. *ASHRAE Transactions* 91(2B):1989.

Holton, J.K., M.J. Kokayko, and T.R. Beggs. 1997. Comparative ventilation system evaluations. *ASHRAE Transactions* 103(2):675-692.

Honma, H. 1975. *Ventilation of dwellings and its disturbances*. Faibo Grafiska, Stockholm, Sweden.

Hopkins, L.P. and B. Hansford. 1974. Air flow through cracks. *Building Service Engineer* 42(September):123.

Hunt, C.M. 1980. Air infiltration: A review of some existing measurement techniques and data. In *Building air change rate and infiltration measurements*, STP 719, p. 3. C.M. Hunt, J.C. King, and H.R. Trechsel, eds. American Society for Testing and Materials, West Conshohocken, PA.

ISO. 1995. Thermal insulation—Determination of building air tightness—Fan pressurization method. *Standard* 9972. International Organization for Standardization, Geneva.

Iwashita, G., K. Kimura., et al. 1989. Pilot study on addition of olf units for perceived air pollution sources. *Proceedings of the SHASE Annual Meeting*, pp. 3221-3324. Society of Heating, Air-Conditioning and Sanitary Engineers of Japan, Tokyo.

Jacobson, D.I., G.S. Dutt, and R.H. Socolow. 1986. Pressurization testing, infiltration reduction, and energy savings. In *Measured air leakage of buildings*, STP 904, p. 265. H.R. Trechsel and P.L. Lagus, eds. American Society for Testing and Materials, West Conshohocken, PA.

Janssen, J.E. 1989. Ventilation for acceptable indoor air quality. *ASHRAE Journal* 31(10):40-48.

Janu, G.J., J.D. Wegner, and C.G. Nesler. 1995. Outdoor air flow control for VAV systems. *ASHRAE Journal* 37(4):62-68.

Johnson, T. and T. Long. 2005. Determining the frequency of open windows in residences: A pilot study in Durham, North Carolina during varying temperature conditions. *Journal of Exposure Analysis and Environmental Epidemiology* 15(4):329-349.

Judkoff, R., J.D. Balcomb, C.E. Handcock, G. Barker, and K. Subbarao. 1997. Side-by-side thermal tests of modular offices: A validation study of the STEM method. *Report*. National Renewable Energy Laboratory, Golden, CO.

Jump, D.A., I.S. Walker, and M.P. Modera. 1996. Field measurements of efficiency and duct retrofit effectiveness in residential forced air distribution systems. *Proceedings of the 1996 ACEEE Summer Study*, pp. 1.147-1.156. American Council for an Energy-Efficient Economy, Washington, D.C.

Kiel, D.E. and D.J. Wilson. 1986. Gravity driven airflows through open doors, 15.1. *Proceedings of the 7th IEA Conference of the Air Infiltration and Ventilation Centre*, Stratford-upon-Avon, U.K.

Kim, A.K. and C.Y. Shaw. 1986. Seasonal variation in airtightness of two detached houses. In *Measured air leakage of buildings*, STP 904, p. 17. H.R. Trechsel and P.L. Lagus, eds. American Society for Testing and Materials, West Conshohocken, PA.

Klauss, A.K., R.H. Tull, L.M. Rootsd, and J.R. Pfafflino. 1970. History of the changing concepts in ventilation requirements. *ASHRAE Journal* 12(6):51-55.

Klote, J.H. and J.A. Milke. 2002. *Principles of smoke management.* ASHRAE.

Kohonen, R., T. Ojanen, and M. Virtanen. 1987. Thermal coupling of leakage flows and heating load of buildings. *Proceedings of the 8th IEA Air Infiltration and Ventilation Centre Conference*, Überlingen, Germany, pp. 10.1-10.22.

Kreith, F. and R. Eisenstadt. 1957. Pressure drop and flow characteristics of short capillary tubes at low Reynolds numbers. *ASME Transactions*, pp. 1070-1078.

Kronvall, J. 1980. *Correlating pressurization and infiltration rate data—Tests of an heuristic model*. Lund Institute of Technology, Division of Building Technology, Lund, Sweden.

Kumar, R., A.D. Ireson, and H.W. Orr. 1979. An automated air infiltration measuring system using SF6 tracer gas in constant concentration and decay methods. *ASHRAE Transactions* 85(2):385.

Kvisgaard, B. and P.F. Collet. 1990. The user's influence on air change. In *Air change rate and airtightness in buildings*, STP 1067, pp. 67-76. M.H. Sherman, ed. American Society for Testing and Materials, West Conshohocken, PA.

Lagus, P.L. 1989. Tracer measurement instrumentation suitable for infiltration, air leakage, and air flow pattern characterization. *Proceedings of the Conference on Building Systems—Room Air and Air Contaminant Distribution*, pp. 97-102. ASHRAE.

Lagus, P. and A.K. Persily. 1985. A review of tracer-gas techniques for measuring airflows in buildings. *ASHRAE Transactions* 91(2B):1075.

Lecompte, J.G.N. 1987. The influence of natural convection in an insulated cavity on thermal performance of a wall. In *Insulation materials, testing, and applications*. American Society for Testing and Materials, West Conshohocken, PA.

Li, Y. and P. Heiselberg. 2003. Analysis methods for natural and hybrid ventilation—A critical literature review and recent developments. *International Journal of Ventilation* 1(4):3-20.

Liddament, M.W. 1988. The calculation of wind effect on ventilation. *ASHRAE Transactions* 94(2):1645-1660.

Liddament, M. and C. Allen. 1983. The validation and comparison of mathematical models of air infiltration. *Technical Note* 11. International Energy Agency Air Infiltration and Ventilation Centre, Sint-Stevens-Woluwe, Belgium.

Liu, M. and D.E. Claridge. 1992a. The measured energy impact of infiltration under dynamic conditions. *Proceedings of the 8th Symposium on Improving Building Systems in Hot and Humid Climates*, Dallas.

Liu, M. and D.E. Claridge. 1992b. The measured energy impact of infiltration in a test cell. *Proceedings of the 8th Symposium on Improving Building Systems in Hot and Humid Climates*, Dallas.

Liu, M. and D.E. Claridge. 1992c. The energy impact of combined solar radiation/infiltration/conduction effects in walls and attics. *Proceedings of the Thermal Performance of Exterior Envelopes of Buildings, 5th ASHRAE/DOE/BTECC Conference*, Clearwater Beach, FL.

Liu, M. and D.E. Claridge. 1995. Experimental methods for identifying infiltration heat recovery in building. *Proceedings of the Thermal Performance of Exterior Envelopes of Buildings, 6th ASHRAE/DOE/BTECC Conference*, Clearwater Beach, FL.

Lubliner, M., D.T. Stevens, and B. Davis. 1997. Mechanical ventilation in HVD-code manufactured housing in the Pacific Northwest. *ASHRAE Transactions* 103(1):693-705.

Marbek Resource Consultants. 1984. *Air sealing homes for energy conservation*. Energy, Mines and Resources Canada, Buildings Energy Technology Transfer Program, Ottawa, ON.

McWilliams, J. and M. Sherman. 2005. Review of literature related to residential ventilation requirements. *Paper* LBNL-57236. Lawrence Berkeley National Laboratory, Berkeley, CA.

Mendell, M.J. 1993. Non-specific symptoms in office workers: A review and summary of the epidemiologic literature. *Indoor Air* 3 (4):227-236.

Modera, M.P. 1989. Residential duct system leakage: Magnitude, impacts, and potential for reduction. *ASHRAE Transactions*. 96(2):561-569.

Modera, M.P. and D.J. Wilson. 1990. The effects of wind on residential building leakage measurements. In *Air change rate and airtightness in buildings*, STP 1067, pp. 132-145. M.H. Sherman, ed. Lawrence Berkeley National Laboratory, Berkeley, CA. *Report* LBL-24195.

Modera, M.P., D. Dickerhoff, R. Jansky, and B. Smith. 1991. Improving the energy efficiency of residential air distribution systems in California. *Report* LBL-30866. Lawrence Berkeley National Laboratory, Berkeley, CA.

Mumma, S.A., and K.M. Shank. 2001. Achieving dry outside air in an energy efficient manner. *ASHRAE Transactions* 107(1):553-561.

Mumma, S.A. and Y.M. Wong. 1990. Analytical evaluation of outdoor airflow rate variation vs. supply airflow rate variation in VAV systems when the outside air damper position is fixed. *ASHRAE Transactions* 90(1):1197-1208.

Murphy, W.E., D.G. Colliver, and L.R. Piercy. 1991. Repeatability and reproducibility of fan pressurization devices in measuring building air leakage. *ASHRAE Transactions* 97(2):885-895.

Musser, A. and A. Persily. 2002. Multizone modeling approaches to contaminant-based design. *ASHRAE Transactions* 108(2):1-8.

Nelson, B.D., D.A. Robinson, and G.D. Nelson. 1985. Designing the envelope—Guidelines for buildings (SP-49). *Proceedings of the ASHRAE/DOE/BTECC Conference—Thermal Performance of the Exterior Envelopes of Buildings III*, Florida, pp. 1117-1122.

NRCC. 1995. *National Building Code of Canada*. National Research Council of Canada, Ottawa, ON.

Nylund, P.O. 1980. Infiltration and ventilation. *Report* D22:1980. Swedish Council for Building Research, Stockholm.

Offermann, F. and D. Int-Hout. 1989. Ventilation effectiveness measurements of three supply/return air configurations. *Environment International* 15(1-6):585-592.

Orme, M. 1999. Applicable models for air infiltration and ventilation calculations. *Technical Note* 51. International Energy Agency Air Infiltration and Ventilation Centre, Sint-Stevens-Woluwe, Belgium.

Ormerod, R. 1983. *Nuclear shelters: A guide to design*. Architectural Press, London.

Palmiter, L. and T. Bond. 1994. Modeled and measured infiltration II—A detailed case study of three homes. *Report* TR 102511. Electric Power Research Institute, Palo Alto, CA.

Palmiter, L. and I. Brown. 1989. The Northwest residential infiltration survey: Description and summary of results. *Proceedings of the ASHRAE/DOE/BTECC/CIBSE Conference—Thermal Performance of the Exterior Envelopes of Buildings IV*, Florida, pp. 445-457.

Palmiter, L., I.A. Brown, and T.C. Bond. 1991. Measured infiltration and ventilation in 472 all-electric homes. *ASHRAE Transactions* 97(2): 979-987.

Parekh, A., K. Ruest, and M. Jacobs. 1991. Comparison of airtightness, indoor air quality and power consumption before and after air-sealing of high-rise residential buildings. *Proceedings of the 12th IEA Conference of the Air Infiltration and Ventilation Centre*, Sint-Stevens-Woluwe, Belgium.

Parker, G.B., M. McSorley, and J. Harris. 1990. The Northwest residential infiltration survey: A field study of ventilation in new houses in the Pacific Northwest. In *Air change rate and airtightness in buildings*, STP 1067, pp. 93-103. M.H. Sherman, ed. American Society for Testing and Materials, West Conshohocken, PA.

Persily, A. 1982. Repeatability and accuracy of pressurization testing. *Proceedings of the ASHRAE/DOE Conference, Thermal Performance of the Exterior Envelopes of Buildings II*, Las Vegas.

Persily, A.K. 1986. Measurements of air infiltration and airtightness in passive solar homes. In *Measured air leakage of buildings*, STP 904, p. 46. H.R. Trechsel and P.L. Lagus, eds. American Society for Testing and Materials, West Conshohocken, PA.

Persily, A.K. 1988. Tracer gas techniques for studying building air exchange. *Report* NBSIR 88-3708. National Institute of Standards and Technology, Gaithersburg, MD.

Persily, A.K. 1991. Design guidelines for thermal envelope integrity in office buildings. *Proceedings of the 12th IEA Conference of the Air Infiltration and Ventilation Centre*, Ottawa, ON.

Persily, A.K. 2004. Building ventilation and pressurization as a security tool. *ASHRAE Journal* 46 (9):18-24.

Persily, A.K. and J. Axley. 1990. Measuring airflow rates with pulse tracer techniques. In *Air change rate and airtightness in buildings*, pp. 31-51. STP 1067. M.H. Sherman, ed. American Society for Testing and Materials, West Conshohocken, PA.

Persily, A.K. and R.A. Grot. 1985a. The airtightness of office building envelopes. *Proceedings of the ASHRAE/DOE/BTECC Conference on the Thermal Performance of the Exterior Envelopes of Buildings III*, Clearwater Beach, FL, p. 125.

Persily, A.K. and R.A. Grot. 1985b. Accuracy in pressurization data analysis. *ASHRAE Transactions* 91(2B):105.

Persily, A.K. and R.A. Grot. 1986. Pressurization testing of federal buildings. In *Measured air leakage of buildings*, STP 904, p. 184. H.R. Trechsel and P.L. Lagus, eds. American Society for Testing and Materials, West Conshohocken, PA.

Persily, A.K. and G.T. Linteris. 1983. A comparison of measured and predicted infiltration rates. *ASHRAE Transactions* 89(2):183.

Persily, A.K., W.S. Dols, S.J. Nabinger, and S. Kirchner. 1991. Preliminary results of the environmental evaluation of the Federal Records Center in Overland, Missouri. NISTIR *Report* 4634. National Institute of Standards and Technology, Gaithersburg, MD.

Persily, A.K., J. Gorfain, and G. Brunner. 2005. Ventilation design and performance in U.S. office buildings. *ASHRAE Journal* 47 (4):30-35.

Persily, A.K., R.E. Chapman, S. Emmerich, W.S. Dols, H. Davis, P. Lavappa, and A. Rushing. 2007. Building retrofits for increased protection against airborne chemical and biological releases. NISTIR *Report* 7379. National Institute of Standards and Technology, Gaithersburg, MD.

Potter, N. 2001. Air tightness testing—A guide for clients and contractors. *Technical Note* 19/2001. Building Services Research and Information Association, Bracknell, U.K.

Powell, F., M. Krarti, and A. Tuluca. 1989. Air movement influence on the effective thermal resistance of porous insulations: A literature survey. *Journal of Thermal Insulation* 12:239-251.

Price, P.N. and M.H. Sherman. 2006. Ventilation behavior and household characteristics in new California houses. *Report* LBNL-59620.

Reardon, J.T. and C.-Y. Shaw. 1997. Evaluation of five simple ventilation strategies suitable for houses without forced-air heating. *ASHRAE Transactions* 103(1):731-744.

Reeves, G., M.F. McBride, and C.F. Sepsy. 1979. Air infiltration model for residences. *ASHRAE Transactions* 85(1):667.

Riley, M. 1990. Indoor air quality and energy conservation: The R-2000 home program experience. *Proceedings of Indoor Air '90: International Conference on Indoor Air Quality and Climate*, Ottawa, vol. 5, p. 143.

Robison, P.E. and L.A. Lambert. 1989. Field investigation of residential infiltration and heating duct leakage. *ASHRAE Transactions* 95(2):542-550.

Rock, B.A. 1992. *Characterization of transient pollutant transport, dilution, and removal for the study of indoor air quality*. Ph.D. dissertation, University of Colorado at Boulder. University Microfilms International.

Rock, B.A. 2005. A user-friendly model and coefficients for slab-on-grade load and energy calculations. *ASHRAE Transactions* 111(2):122-136.

Rock, B.A. 2006. *Ventilation for environmental tobacco smoke*. Elsevier Science, New York, and ASHRAE.

Rock, B.A. and D. Zhu. 2002. *Designer's guide to ceiling-based air diffusion*. ASHRAE.

Rock, B.A., M.J. Brandemuehl, and R. Anderson. 1995. Toward a simplified design method for determining the air change effectiveness. *ASHRAE Transactions* 101(1):217-227.

Rudd, A.F. 1998. Design/sizing methodology and economic evaluation of central-fan-integrated supply ventilation systems. *ACEEE 1998 Summer Study on Energy Efficiency in Buildings*. 23-28 August, Pacific Grove, CA. American Council for an Energy Efficient Economy, Washington, D.C.

Russell, M., M. Sherman, and A. Rudd. 2005. Review of residential ventilation technologies. *Paper* LBNL-576. Lawrence Berkeley National Laboratory, Berkeley, CA.

Sandberg, M.H. 1981. What is ventilation efficiency? *Building and Environment* 16:123-135.

Seppanen, O.A., W.J. Fisk and M.J. Mendell. 1999. Association of ventilation rates and CO_2 concentrations with health and other responses in commercial and institutional buildings. *Indoor Air* 9(4):226-252.

Shaw, C.Y. 1981. A correlation between air infiltration and air tightness for a house in a developed residential area. *ASHRAE Transactions* 87(2):333.

Shaw, C.Y. and W.C. Brown. 1982. Effect of a gas furnace chimney on the air leakage characteristic of a two-story detached house. *Proceedings of the 3rd IEA Conference of the Air Infiltration Centre*, London.

Sherman, M.H. 1986. Infiltration degree-days: A statistic for quantifying infiltration-related climate. *ASHRAE Transactions* 92(2):161-181.

Sherman, M.H. 1987. Estimation of infiltration from leakage and climate indications. *Energy and Buildings* 10(1):81.

Sherman, M.H. 1989a. Uncertainty in airflow calculations using tracer gas measurements. *Building and Environment* 24(4):347-354.

Sherman, M.H. 1989b. On the estimation of multizone ventilation rates from tracer gas measurements. *Building and Environment* 24(4):355-362.

Sherman, M.H. 1990. Tracer gas techniques for measuring ventilation in a single zone. *Building and Environment* 25(4):365-374.

Sherman, M.H. 1991. Single-zone stack-dominated infiltration modeling. *Proceedings of the 12th IEA Conference of the Air Infiltration and Ventilation Centre*, Ottawa, ON, pp. 297-314.

Sherman, M.H. 1992a. A power law formulation of laminar flow in short pipes. *Journal of Fluids Engineering* 114:601-605. *Report* LBL-29414, Lawrence Berkeley National Laboratory, Berkeley, CA.

Sherman, M.H. 1992b. Superposition in infiltration modeling. *Indoor Air* 2:101-114.

Sherman, M.H. 1995. The use of blower door data. *Indoor Air* 5:215-224.

Sherman, M.H. and D. Dickerhoff. 1989. Description of the LBL multitracer measurement system. *Proceedings of the ASHRAE/DOE/BTECC/CIBSE Conference—Thermal Performance of the Exterior Envelopes of Buildings IV*, pp. 417-432.

Sherman, M.H. and D.J. Dickerhoff. 1998. Airtightness of U.S. dwellings. *ASHRAE Transactions* 104(2):1359-1367.

Sherman, M.H. and D.T. Grimsrud. 1980. Infiltration-pressurization correlation: Simplified physical modeling. *ASHRAE Transactions* 86(2):778.

Sherman, M.H. and N. Matson. 1997. Residential ventilation and energy characteristics. *ASHRAE Transactions* 103(1):717-730.

Sherman, M.H. and M.P. Modera. 1986. Comparison of measured and predicted infiltration using the LBL infiltration model. In *Measured air leakage of buildings*, STP 904, p. 325. H.R. Trechsel and P.L. Lagus, eds. American Society for Testing and Materials, West Conshohocken, PA.

Sherman, M.H. and D.J. Wilson. 1986. Relating actual and effective ventilation in determining indoor air quality. *Building and Environment* 21(3/4):135.

Sherman, M.H., D.T. Grimsrud, P.E. Condon, and B.V. Smith. 1980. Air infiltration measurement techniques. *Proceedings of the 1st IEA Conference of the Air Infiltration Centre*, London. *Report* LBL-10705. Lawrence Berkeley National Laboratory, Berkeley, CA.

Sibbitt, B.E. and T. Hamlin. 1991. *Meeting Canadian residential ventilation standard requirements with low-cost systems*. Canada Mortgage and Housing Corporation, Ottawa, ON.

Sinden, F.W. 1978a. Wind, temperature and natural ventilation—Theoretical considerations. *Energy and Buildings* 1(3):275.

Sinden, F.W. 1978b. Multi-chamber theory of air infiltration. *Building and Environment* 13:21-28.

Sorensen, J.H. and B.M. Vogt. 2001. Will duct tape and plastic really work? Issues related to expedient sheltering-in-place. *Report* ORNL/TM-2001/154. Oak Ridge National Laboratory, Oak Ridge, TN.

Tamura, G.T. and C.Y. Shaw. 1976a. Studies on exterior wall airtightness and air infiltration of tall buildings. *ASHRAE Transactions* 82(1):122.

Tamura, G.T. and C.Y. Shaw. 1976b. Air leakage data for the design of elevator and stair shaft pressurization system. *ASHRAE Transactions* 82(2):179.

Tamura, G.T. and A.G. Wilson. 1966. Pressure differences for a nine-story building as a result of chimney effect and ventilation system operation. *ASHRAE Transactions* 72(1):180.

Tamura, G.T. and A.G. Wilson. 1967a. Pressure differences caused by chimney effect in three high buildings. *ASHRAE Transactions* 73(2):II.1.1.

Tamura, G.T. and A.G. Wilson. 1967b. Building pressures caused by chimney action and mechanical ventilation. *ASHRAE Transactions* 73(2): II.2.1.

Timusk, J., A.L. Seskus, and K. Linger. 1992. A systems approach to extend the limit of envelope performance. *Proceedings of the 6th ASHRAE/DOE/BTECC Conference—Thermal Performance of Exterior Envelopes of Buildings*, Clearwater Beach, FL.

Turk, B.T., D.T. Grimsrud, J.T. Brown, K.L. Geisling-Sobotka, J. Harrison, and R.J. Prill. 1989. Commercial building ventilation rates and particle concentrations. *ASHRAE Transactions* 95(1):422-433.

Verschoor, J.D. and J.O. Collins. 1986. Demonstration of air leakage reduction program in navy family housing. In *Measured air leakage of buildings*, STP 904, p. 294. H.R. Trechsel and P.L. Lagus, eds. American Society for Testing and Materials, West Conshohocken, PA.

Walker, I.S. 1999. Distribution system leakage impacts on apartment building ventilation rates. *ASHRAE Transactions* 105(1):943-950.

Walker, I.S. and T.W. Forest. 1995. Field measurements of ventilation rates in attics. *Building and Environment* 30(3):333-347.

Walker, I.S. and D.J. Wilson. 1993. Evaluating models for superposition of wind and stack effects in air infiltration. *Building and Environment* 28(2):201-210.

Walker, I.S. and D.J. Wilson. 1994. Practical methods for improving estimates of natural ventilation rates. *Proceedings of the 15th IEA Conference of the Air Infiltration and Ventilation Centre*, Buxton, U.K., pp. 517-526.

Walker, I.S. and D.J. Wilson. 1998. Field validation of algebraic equations for stack and wind driven air infiltration calculations. *International Journal of HVAC&R Research* (now *HVAC&R Research*) 4(2):119-140.

Walker, I.S., D.J. Wilson., and M.H. Sherman. 1997. A comparison of the power law to quadratic formulations for air infiltration calculations. *Energy and Buildings* 27(3).

Walker, I., M. Sherman, J. Siegel, D. Wang, C. Buchanan, and M. Modera. 1999. Leakage diagnostics, sealant longevity, sizing and technology transfer in residential thermal distribution systems: Part II. *Report* LBNL-42691.

Walton, G.N. 1984. A computer algorithm for predicting infiltration and interroom airflows. *ASHRAE Transactions* 90(1B):601.

Walton, G.N. 1989. Airflow network models for element-based building airflow modeling. *ASHRAE Transactions* 95(2):611-620.

Walton, G., and W.S. Dols. 2003. CONTAM 2.1 supplemental user guide and program documentation. NISTIR *Report* 7049, National Institute of Standards and Technology, Gaithersburg, MD.

Warren, P.R. and B.C. Webb. 1980. The relationship between tracer gas and pressurization techniques in dwellings. *Proceedings of the 1st IEA Conference of the Air Infiltration Centre*, London.

Warren, P.R. and B.C. Webb. 1986. Ventilation measurements in housing. CIBSE Symposium, Natural Ventilation by Design. Chartered Institution of Building Services Engineers, London.

Weidt, J.L., J. Weidt, and S. Selkowitz. 1979. Field air leakage of newly installed residential windows. *Proceedings of the ASHRAE/DOE Conference—Thermal Performance of the Exterior Envelopes of Buildings* Orlando, FL, p. 149.

Weschler, C.J. 2000. Ozone in indoor environments: Concentration and chemistry. *Indoor Air* 10:269-288.

Wilson, D.J. and I.S. Walker. 1991. Wind shelter effects on air infiltration for a row of houses. *Proceedings of the 12th IEA Conference of the Air Infiltration and Ventilation Centre*, Ottawa, ON, pp. 335-346.

Wilson, D.J. and I.S. Walker. 1992. Feasibility of passive ventilation by constant area vents to maintain indoor air quality in houses. *Proceedings of Indoor Air Quality '92, ASHRAE/ACGIH/AIHA Conference*, San Francisco.

Wilson, D.J. and I.S. Walker. 1993. Infiltration data from the Alberta Home Heating Research Facility. *Technical Note* 41. Air Infiltration and Ventilation Centre, Sint-Stevens-Woluwe, Belgium.

Wiren, B.G. 1984. Wind pressure distributions and ventilation losses for a single-family house as influenced by surrounding buildings—A wind tunnel study. *Proceedings of the Air Infiltration Centre Wind Pressure Workshop*, Brussels, pp. 75-101.

Wolf, S. 1996. A theory of the effects of convective air flow through fibrous thermal insulation. *ASHRAE Transactions* 72(1):III 2.1-III 2.9.

Yaglou, C.P. and W.N. Witheridge. 1937. Ventilation requirements. *ASHVE Transactions* 43:423.

Yaglou, C.P., E.C. Riley, and D.I. Coggins. 1936. Ventilation requirements. *ASHVE Transactions* 42:133.

Yuill, G.K. 1986. The variation of the effective natural ventilation rate with weather conditions. *Proceedings of the Solar Energy Society of Canada Renewable Energy Conference '86*, pp. 70-75.

Yuill, G.K. 1991. The development of a method of determining air change rates in detached dwellings for assessing indoor air quality. *ASHRAE Transactions* 97(2):896-903.

Yuill, G.K. 1996. Impact of high use automatic doors on infiltration. ASHRAE Research Project RP-763, *Final Report*.

Yuill, G.K. and G.M. Comeau. 1989. Investigation of the indoor air quality, air tightness and air infiltration rates of a random sample of 78 houses in Winnipeg. *Proceedings of IAQ '89, The Human Equation—Health and Comfort*, pp. 122-127. ASHRAE.

Yuill, G.K., M.R. Jeanson, and C.P. Wray. 1991. Simulated performance of demand-controlled ventilation systems using carbon dioxide as an occupancy indicator. *ASHRAE Transactions* 97(2):963-968.

BIBLIOGRAPHY

AIVC. 2007. *AIRBASE bibliographic database*. International Energy Agency Air Infiltration and Ventilation Centre, Sint-Stevens-Woluwe, Belgium.

Colliver, D.G., W.E. Murphy, and W. Sun. 1992. Evaluation of the techniques for the measurement of air leakage of building components. ASHRAE Research Project RP-438, *Final Report*. University of Kentucky, Lexington.

Eto, J. 1990. The HVAC costs of increased fresh air ventilation rates in office buildings. *Proceedings of Indoor Air '90: International Conference on Indoor Air Quality and Climate*, Ottawa, ON, vol. 4, pp. 53-58.

Eto, J. and C. Meyer. 1988. The HVAC costs of increased fresh air ventilation rates in office buildings. *ASHRAE Transactions* 94(2):331-345.

Kohonen, R. and T. Ojanen. 1987. Non-steady state coupled diffusion and convection heat and mass transfer in porous media. *5th International Conference on Numerical Methods in Thermal Problems*, Montreal.

Lamming, S. and J. Salmon. 1998. Wind data for design of smoke control systems. *ASHRAE Transactions* 104(1):742-751.

Lstiburek, J.W. 2005. Understanding air barriers. *ASHRAE Journal* 47(7): 24-30.

Mumma, S.A. and R.J. Bolin. 1994. Real-time, on-line optimization of VAV system control to minimize the energy consumption rate and to satisfy ASHRAE *Standard* 62-1989 for all occupied zones. *ASHRAE Transactions* 94(1):168-179.

Subbarao, K., J.D. Burch, C.E. Handcock, A. Lekov, and J.D. Balcomb. 1990. Measuring the energy performance of buildings through short-term tests. *ACEEE 1990 Summer Study on Energy Efficiency in Buildings* 10:245-252.

Swedish Building Code. 1980. Thermal insulation and air tightness. *Svensk Byggnorm* (SBN) 1980.

CHAPTER 17

RESIDENTIAL COOLING AND HEATING LOAD CALCULATIONS

THIS chapter covers cooling and heating load calculation procedures for residential buildings, including detailed heat-balance methods that serve as the basis for cooling load calculation. Simple cooling-load procedures, suitable for hand calculations, are provided for typical cases. Straightforward heating load calculation procedures are also included.

Procedures in this chapter are based on the same fundamentals as the nonresidential methods in Chapter 18. However, many characteristics distinguish residential loads, and Chapter 18's procedures should be applied with care to residential applications.

Additional information about residential heating and cooling is found in Chapter 1 of the 2007 *ASHRAE Handbook—HVAC Applications* and Chapter 9 of the 2008 *ASHRAE Handbook—HVAC Systems and Equipment.*

RESIDENTIAL FEATURES

With respect to heating and cooling load calculation and equipment sizing, the following unique features distinguish residences from other types of buildings:

- **Smaller Internal Heat Gains.** Residential system loads are primarily imposed by heat gain or loss through structural components and by air leakage or ventilation. Internal heat gains, particularly those from occupants and lights, are small compared to those in commercial or industrial structures.
- **Varied Use of Spaces.** Use of spaces in residences is more flexible than in commercial buildings. Localized or temporary temperature excursions are often tolerable.
- **Fewer Zones.** Residences are generally conditioned as a single zone or, at most, a few zones. Typically, a thermostat located in one room controls unit output for multiple rooms, and capacity cannot be redistributed from one area to another as loads change over the day. This results in some hour-to-hour temperature variation or swing that has a significant moderating effect on peak loads, because of heat storage in building components.
- **Greater Distribution Losses.** Residential ducts are frequently installed in attics or other unconditioned buffer spaces. Duct leakage and heat gain or loss can require significant increases in unit capacity. Residential distribution gains and losses cannot be neglected or estimated with simple rules of thumb.
- **Partial Loads.** Most residential cooling systems use units of relatively small capacity (about 5 to 18 kW cooling, 18 to 32 kW heating). Because loads are largely determined by outside conditions, and few days each season are design days, the unit operates at partial load during most of the season; thus, an oversized unit is detrimental to good system performance, especially for cooling in areas of high wet-bulb temperature.
- **Dehumidification Issues.** Dehumidification occurs during cooling unit operation only, and space condition control is usually limited to use of room thermostats (sensible heat-actuated devices). Excessive sensible capacity results in short-cycling and severely degraded dehumidification performance.

In addition to these general features, residential buildings can be categorized according to their exposure:

- **Single-Family Detached.** A house in this category usually has exposed walls in four directions, often more than one story, and a roof. The cooling system is a single-zone, unitary system with a single thermostat. Two-story houses may have a separate cooling system for each floor. Rooms are reasonably open and generally have a centralized air return. In this configuration, both air and load from rooms are mixed, and a load-leveling effect, which requires a distribution of air to each room that is different from a pure commercial system, results. Because the amount of air supplied to each room is based on the load for that room, proper load calculation procedures must be used.
- **Multifamily.** Unlike single-family detached units, multifamily units generally do not have exposed surfaces facing in all directions. Rather, each unit typically has a maximum of three exposed walls and possibly a roof. Both east and west walls might not be exposed in a given living unit. Each living unit has a single unitary cooling system or a single fan-coil unit and the rooms are relatively open to one another. This configuration does not have the same load-leveling effect as a single-family detached house.
- **Other.** Many buildings do not fall into either of the preceding categories. Critical to the designation of a single-family detached building is well-distributed exposure so there is not a short-duration peak; however, if fenestration exposure is predominantly east or west, the cooling load profile resembles that of a multifamily unit. On the other hand, multifamily units with both east and west exposures or neither east nor west exposure exhibit load profiles similar to single-family detached.

CALCULATION APPROACH

Variations in the characteristics of residences can lead to surprisingly complex load calculations. Time-varying heat flows combine to produce a time-varying load. The relative magnitude and pattern of the heat flows depends on the building characteristics and exposure, resulting in a building-specific load profile. In general, an hour-by-hour analysis is required to determine that profile and find its peak.

In theory, cooling and heating processes are identical; a common analysis procedure should apply to either. Acceptable simplifications are possible for heating; however, for cooling, different approaches are used.

Heating calculations use simple worst-case assumptions: no solar or internal gains, and no heat storage (with all heat losses evaluated instantaneously). With these simplifications, the heating

The preparation of this chapter is assigned to TC 4.1, Load Calculation Data and Procedures.

problem is reduced to a basic $UA\Delta t$ calculation. The heating procedures in this chapter use this long-accepted approach, and thus differ only in details from prior methods put forth by ASHRAE and others.

In contrast, the cooling procedures in this edition are extensively revised, based on the results of ASHRAE research project RP-1199, also supported by the Air-Conditioning Contractors of America (ACCA) (Barnaby et al. 2004, 2005). Although the complexity of residential cooling load calculations has been understood for decades, prior methods used a cooling load temperature difference/cooling load factor (CLTD/CLF) form requiring only hand-tractable arithmetic. Without such simplification, the procedures would not have been used; an approximate calculation was preferable to none at all. The simplified approaches were developed using detailed computer models and/or empirical data, but only the simplifications were published. Now that computing power is routinely available, it is appropriate to promulgate 24 h, equation-based procedures.

OTHER METHODS

Several residential load calculation methods have been published in North America over the last 20 years. All use the $UA\Delta t$ heating formulation and some variation of the CLTD/CLF approach for cooling.

- **ACCA.** *Manual J*, 7th Edition (ACCA 1986) and 8th Edition (ACCA 2006) are widely used in the United States. Cooling loads are calculated using semiempirical heat gain factors derived from experimental data taken at the University of Illinois in the 1950s. These factors, associated overview, and references are found in the 1985 and earlier editions of the *ASHRAE Handbook—Fundamentals*. The 8th Edition retains the underlying factors but provides increased flexibility in their application, in addition to other extensions.
- **ASHRAE.** The 1989 to 2001 editions of the *ASHRAE Handbook—Fundamentals* contain an updated method based on ASHRAE research project RP-342 (McQuiston 1984). In this work, cooling factors were re-derived using a transfer-function building model that included temperature-swing effects.
- **F280.** This Canadian adaptation of the CLTD/CLF procedure (CAN/CSA-F280-M90 1990; HRAI 1996) also uses cooling methods based on ASHRAE RP-342. Heating procedures include detailed ground heat loss estimates.

A key common element of all cooling methods is attention to temperature swing, via empirical data or suitable models. Throughout the literature, it is repeatedly emphasized that direct application of nonresidential methods (based on a fixed set point) results in unrealistically high cooling loads for residential applications.

RESIDENTIAL HEAT BALANCE (RHB) METHOD

A 24 h procedure is required to accurately determine the cooling load profile of a residence. The heat balance (HB) method allows detailed simulation of space temperatures and heat flows. ASHRAE research project RP-1199 adapted HB to residential applications, resulting in the residential heat balance (RHB) method. Although RHB provides the technical basis for this chapter, it is a computer-only technique and is not documented here. HB is described in Chapter 18 and Pedersen et al. 1998; Barnaby et al. (2004, 2005) document RHB enhancements.

RP-1199 produced an implementation of the RHB method, called ResHB (Barnaby et al. 2004). This application is derived from the ASHRAE *Toolkit for Building Load Calculations* (Pedersen et al. 2001) and has the following features:

- **Multizone.** Whereas the original *Toolkit* code supported a single zone, ResHB can analyze projects that include multiple systems, zones, and rooms.
- **Temperature swing.** ResHB calculates cooling load with temperature swing. That is, the code searches for sensible capacity sufficient to hold the space temperature within a specified excursion above the set point.
- **Master/slave control.** ResHB allows control of cooling output in "slave" rooms based on the cooling requirements of a "master" room, where the thermostat is located. Rooms with incompatible load profiles will exhibit poor temperature control.
- **Residential defaults.** ResHB includes default values suitable for residential problems.

In its current form, ResHB is a research-oriented reference implementation of RHB. It is expected that ResHB will be incorporated into third-party software so the full RHB method will be available to practitioners. ResHB FORTRAN source code is available under license from ASHRAE.

RESIDENTIAL LOAD FACTOR (RLF) METHOD

The procedure presented in this chapter is the residential load factor (RLF) method. RLF is a simplified procedure derived from detailed ResHB analysis of prototypical buildings across a range of climates. The method is tractable by hand but is best applied using a spreadsheet. Two main applications are anticipated:

- **Education and training.** The transparency and simplicity of RLF make it suitable for use in introductory courses on building load calculations.
- **Quick load estimates.** In situations where detailed analysis is impractical, the RLF method is a possible alternative. For example, the method might be implemented as a spreadsheet on a handheld device and used for on-site sizing of replacement cooling equipment.

Note that, although room-by-room calculations are possible with the RLF method, computerized methods based on RHB are more suitable for performing full room-level calculations required for equipment selection and distribution system design.

RLF was derived from several thousand ResHB cooling load results (Barnaby and Spitler 2005; Barnaby et al. 2004). A range of climates and building types were analyzed. Statistical regression techniques were used to find values for the load factors tabulated in later sections. Factor values were validated by comparing ResHB versus RLF results for buildings not involved in the regression analysis. Within its range of applicability, RLF cooling loads are generally within 10% of those calculated with ResHB. The RLF derivation has been repeated for 2009 using the updated temperature profile and clear-sky model (see Chapter 14), resulting in minor revisions to load factors and other coefficients.

The RLF method should not be applied to situations outside the range of underlying cases, as shown in Table 1.

The RLF method appears more complex than the table-based procedure found in prior editions of this chapter. However, note that the RLF calculation sequence involves two distinct steps. First, the cooling and heating load factors (CFs and HFs) are derived for all project component types. These factors are then applied to the individual components by a single multiplication. (The two-step approach is clearly shown in the Load Calculation Example section.) For a specific location and representative constructions, CFs and HFs can be precalculated and used repeatedly. In essence, the structure of RLF allows assembling location-specific versions of the rigid tables found in prior editions. Further, this edition documents the equations used to generate tabulated values. Using these equations, a complete implementation of the RLF method, including CF and HF calculation, is well within the capabilities of current PC spreadsheet applications.

Table 1 RLF Limitations

Item	Valid Range	Notes
Latitude	20 to 60°N	Also approximately valid for 20 to 60°S with N and S orientations reversed for southern hemisphere.
Date	July 21	Application must be summer peaking. Buildings in mild climates with significant SE/S/SW glazing may experience maximum cooling load in fall or even winter. Use RHB if local experience indicates this is a possibility.
Elevation	Less than 2000 m	RLF factors assume 50 m elevation. With elevation-corrected C_s, method is acceptably accurate except at very high elevations.
Climate	Warm/hot	Design-day average outdoor temperature assumed to be above indoor design temperature.
Construction	Lightweight residential construction (wood or metal framing, wood or stucco siding)	May be applied to masonry veneer over frame construction; results are conservative. Use RHB for structural masonry or unconventional construction.
Fenestration area	0 to 15% of floor area on any façade, 0 to 30% of floor area total	Spaces with high fenestration fraction should be analyzed with RHB.
Fenestration tilt	Vertical or horizontal	Skylights with tilt less than 30° can be treated as horizontal. Buildings with significant sloped glazing areas should be analyzed with RHB.
Occupancy	Residential	Applications with high internal gains and/or high occupant density should be analyzed with RHB or nonresidential procedures.
Temperature swing	1.7 K	
Distribution losses	Typical	Applications with extensive duct runs in unconditioned spaces should be analyzed with RHB.

COMMON DATA AND PROCEDURES

The following guidelines, data requirements, and procedures apply to all load calculation approaches, whether heating or cooling, hand-tractable or computerized.

General Guidelines

Design for Typical Building Use. In general, residential systems should be designed to meet representative maximum-load conditions, not extreme conditions. Normal occupancy should be assumed, not the maximum that might occur during an occasional social function. Intermittently operated ventilation fans should be assumed to be off. These considerations are especially important for cooling-system sizing.

Building Codes and Standards. This chapter presentation is necessarily general. Codes and regulations take precedence; consult local authorities to determine applicable requirements.

Designer Judgment. Designer experience with local conditions, building practices, and prior projects should be considered when applying the procedures in this chapter. For equipment-replacement projects, occupant knowledge concerning performance of the existing system can often provide useful guidance in achieving a successful design.

Verification. Postconstruction commissioning and verification are important steps in achieving design performance. Designers should encourage pressurization testing and other procedures that allow identification and repair of construction shortcomings.

Uncertainty and Safety Allowances. Residential load calculations are inherently approximate. Many building characteristics are estimated during design and ultimately determined by construction quality and occupant behavior. These uncertainties apply to all calculation methods, including first-principles procedures such as RHB. It is therefore tempting to include safety allowances for each aspect of a calculation. However, this practice has a compounding effect and often produces oversized results. Typical conditions should be assumed; safety allowances, if applied at all, should be added to the final calculated loads rather than to intermediate components. In addition, temperature swing provides a built-in safety factor for sensible cooling: a 20% capacity shortfall typically results in a temperature excursion of at most about one or two degrees.

Basic Relationships

Common air-conditioning processes involve transferring heat via air transport or leakage. The sensible, latent, and total heat conveyed by air on a volumetric basis is

$$q_s = C_s Q \Delta t \quad (1)$$

$$q_l = C_l Q \Delta W \quad (2)$$

$$q_t = C_t Q \Delta h \quad (3)$$

$$q_t = q_s + q_l \quad (4)$$

where

q_s, q_l, q_t = sensible, latent, total heat transfer rates, W
C_s = air sensible heat factor, W/(L·s·K) (1.23 at sea level)
C_l = air latent heat factor, W/(L·s) (3010 at sea level)
C_t = air total heat factor, W/(L·s) per kJ/kg enthalpy h (1.2 at sea level)
Q = air volumetric flow rate, L/s
Δt = air temperature difference across process, K
ΔW = air humidity ratio difference across process, kg_w/kg_{da}
Δh = air enthalpy difference across process, kJ/kg

The heat factors C_s, C_l, and C_t are elevation dependent. The sea-level values in the preceding definitions are appropriate for elevations up to about 300 m. Procedures are provided in Chapter 18 for calculating adjusted values for higher elevations.

Design Conditions

The initial step in the load calculation is selecting indoor and outdoor design conditions.

Indoor Conditions. Indoor conditions assumed for design purposes depend on building use, type of occupancy, and/or code requirements. Chapter 9 and ASHRAE *Standard* 55 define the relationship between indoor conditions and comfort.

Typical practice for cooling is to design for indoor conditions of 24°C db and a maximum of 50 to 65% rh. For heating, 20°C db and 30% rh are common design values. These conditions are the default values used throughout this chapter.

Outdoor Conditions. Outdoor design conditions for load calculations should be selected from location-specific climate data in Chapter 14, or according to local code requirements as applicable.

Cooling. The 1% design dry-bulb temperature and mean coincident wet bulb temperature from Chapter 14 climate data are generally appropriate. As previously emphasized, oversized cooling equipment results in poor system performance. Extremely hot events are necessarily of short duration (conditions always moderate each night); therefore, sacrificing comfort under typical conditions to meet occasional extremes is not recommended.

Load calculations also require the hottest-month dry-bulb temperature daily range, and wind speed. These values can also be found in Chapter 14, although wind speed is commonly assumed to be 3.4 m/s.

Typical buildings in middle latitudes generally experience maximum cooling requirements in midsummer (July in the northern hemisphere and January in the southern hemisphere). For this reason, the RLF method is based on midsummer solar gains. However, this pattern does not always hold. Buildings at low latitudes or with significant south-facing glazing (north-facing in the southern hemisphere) should be analyzed at several times of the year using the RHB method. Local experience can provide guidance as to when maximum cooling is probable. For example, it is common for south-facing buildings in mild northern-hemisphere climates to have peak cooling loads in the fall because of low sun angles. Chapter 14 contains monthly temperature data to support calculations for any time of year.

Heating. General practice is to use the 99% design dry-bulb temperature from Chapter 14. Heating load calculations ignore solar and internal gains, providing a built-in safety factor. However, the designer should consider two additional factors:

- Many locations experience protracted (several-day) cold periods during which the outdoor temperature remains below the 99% value.
- Wind is a major determinant of infiltration. Residences with significant leakage (e.g., older houses) may have peak heating demand under conditions other than extreme cold, depending on site wind patterns.

Depending on the application and system type, the designer should consider using the 99.6% value or the mean minimum extreme as the heating design temperature. Alternatively, the heating load can be calculated at the 99% condition and a safety factor applied when equipment is selected. This additional capacity can also serve to meet pickup loads under nonextreme conditions.

Adjacent Buffer Spaces. Residential buildings often include unconditioned buffer spaces such as garages, attics, crawlspaces, basements, or enclosed porches. Accurate load calculations require the adjacent air temperature.

In many cases, a simple, conservative estimate is adequate, especially for heating calculations. For example, it is generally reasonable to assume that, under heating design conditions, adjacent uninsulated garages, porches, and attics are at outdoor temperature. Another reasonable assumption is that the temperature in an adjacent, unheated, *insulated* room is the mean of the indoor and outdoor temperatures.

In cases where a temperature estimate is required, a steady-state heat balance analysis yields the following:

$$t_b = \frac{C_s Q t_o + \sum A_x U_x t_x + q}{C_s Q + \sum A_x U_x} \tag{5}$$

where

t_b = buffer space temperature, °C
Q = buffer space infiltration/ventilation flow rate, L/s
t_o = outdoor air temperature, °C
A_x = area of xth buffer space surface, m²
U_x = U-factor of xth buffer space surface, W/(m²·K)
t_x = air temperature at outside of xth buffer space surface, °C (typically, outdoor air temperature for exterior surfaces, conditioned space temperature for surfaces between buffer space and house, or ground temperature for below-grade surfaces)
q = additional buffer space heat gains, W (e.g., solar gains or distribution system losses)

Building Data

Component Areas. To perform load calculations efficiently and reliably, standard methods must be used for determining building surface areas. For fenestration, the definition of component area must be consistent with associated ratings.

Gross area. It is both efficient and conservative to derive gross surface areas from outside building dimensions, ignoring wall and floor thicknesses. Thus, floor areas should be measured to the outside of adjacent exterior walls or to the center line of adjacent partitions. When apportioning to rooms, façade area should be divided at partition center lines. Wall height should be taken as floor-to-floor.

Using outside dimensions avoids separate accounting of floor edge and wall corner conditions. Further, it is standard practice in residential construction to define floor area in terms of outside dimensions, so outside-dimension takeoffs yield areas that can be readily checked against building plans (e.g., the sum of room areas should equal the plan floor area). Although outside-dimension procedures are recommended as expedient for load calculations, they are not consistent with rigorous definitions used in building-related standards [e.g., ASTM (1998)]. However, the inconsistencies are not significant in the load calculation context.

Fenestration area. Fenestration includes exterior windows, skylights, and doors. Fenestration U-factor and SHGC ratings (see Table 2) are based on the entire product area, including frames. Thus, for load calculations, fenestration area is the area of the rough opening in the wall or roof, less installation clearances (projected product area A_{pf}). Installation clearances can be neglected; it is acceptable to use the rough opening as an approximation of A_{pf}.

Net area. Net surface area is the gross surface area less fenestration area (rough opening or A_{pf}) contained within the surface.

Volume. Building volume is expediently calculated by multiplying floor area by floor-to-floor height. This produces a conservative estimate of enclosed air volume, because wall and floor volumes are included in the total. More precise calculations are possible but are generally not justified in this context.

Construction Characteristics.

U-factors. Except for fenestration, construction U-factors should be calculated using procedures in Chapter 27, or taken from manufacturer's data, if available. U-factors should be evaluated under heating (winter) conditions.

Fenestration. Fenestration is characterized by U-factor and solar heat gain coefficient (SHGC), which apply to the entire assembly (including frames). If available, rated values should be used, determined according to procedures set forth by National Fenestration Rating Council (NFRC), Canadian Standards Association (CSA), or other specifying body (see Chapter 15). Ratings can be obtained from product literature, product label, or published listings (NFRC 2009). For unrated products (e.g., in existing construction), the U-factor and SHGC can be estimated using Table 2 or tables in Chapter 15. Note that fenestration U-factors are evaluated under heating (winter) design conditions but are used in this chapter for both heating and cooling calculations.

Relatively few types of glazing are encountered in residential applications. Single-glazed clear, double-glazed clear, and double-glazed low-emissivity ("low-e") glass predominate. Single-glazed is now rare in new construction but common in older homes. Triple-glazing, reflective glass, and heat-absorbing glass are encountered occasionally. Acrylic or glass skylights are common. Multipane low-e insulated glazing is available in high- and low-solar-gain variants, as discussed in Chapter 15. Low-solar is now the more common for new construction in all parts of the United States.

Properties of windows equipped with storm windows should be estimated from data for a similar configuration with an additional pane. For example, data for clear, double-glazed should be used for a clear single-glazed window with a storm window.

Fenestration interior and exterior shading must be included in cooling load calculations, as discussed in the Cooling Load section.

Table 2 Typical Fenestration Characteristics

					Frame									
					Operable					Fixed				
Glazing Type	Glazing Layers	ID[b]	Property[c,d]	Center of Glazing	Aluminum	Aluminum with Thermal Break	Reinforced Vinyl/Aluminum Clad Wood	Wood/Vinyl	Insulated Fiberglass/Vinyl	Aluminum	Aluminum with Thermal Break	Reinforced Vinyl/Aluminum Clad Wood	Wood/Vinyl	Insulated Fiberglass/Vinyl
Clear	1	1a	*U*	5.91	7.24	6.12	5.14	5.05	4.61	6.42	6.07	5.55	5.55	5.35
			SHGC	0.86	0.75	0.75	0.64	0.64	0.64	0.78	0.78	0.75	0.75	0.75
	2	5a	*U*	2.73	4.62	3.42	3.00	2.87	5.83	3.61	3.22	2.86	2.84	2.72
			SHGC	0.76	0.67	0.67	0.57	0.57	0.57	0.69	0.69	0.67	0.67	0.67
	3	29a	*U*	1.76	3.80	2.60	2.25	2.19	1.91	2.76	2.39	2.05	2.01	1.93
			SHGC	0.68	0.60	0.60	0.51	0.51	0.51	0.62	0.62	0.60	0.60	0.60
Low-e, low-solar	2	25a	*U*	1.70	3.83	2.68	2.33	2.21	1.89	2.75	2.36	2.03	2.01	1.90
			SHGC	0.41	0.37	0.37	0.31	0.31	0.31	0.38	0.38	0.36	0.36	0.36
	3	40c	*U*	1.02	3.22	2.07	1.76	1.71	1.45	2.13	1.76	1.44	1.40	1.33
			SHGC	0.27	0.25	0.25	0.21	0.21	0.21	0.25	0.25	0.24	0.24	0.24
Low-e, high-solar	2	17c	U	1.99	4.05	2.89	2.52	2.39	2.07	2.99	2.60	2.26	2.24	2.13
			SHGC	0.70	0.62	0.62	0.52	0.52	0.52	0.64	0.64	0.61	0.61	0.61
	3	32c	*U*	1.42	3.54	2.36	2.02	1.97	1.70	2.47	2.10	1.77	1.73	1.66
			SHGC	0.62	0.55	0.55	0.46	0.46	0.46	0.56	0.56	0.54	0.54	0.54
Heat-absorbing	1	1c	*U*	5.91	7.24	6.12	5.14	5.05	4.61	6.42	6.07	5.55	5.55	5.35
			SHGC	0.73	0.64	0.64	0.54	0.54	0.54	0.66	0.66	0.64	0.64	0.64
	2	5c	*U*	2.73	4.62	3.42	3.00	2.87	2.53	3.61	3.22	2.86	2.84	2.72
			SHGC	0.62	0.55	0.55	0.46	0.46	0.46	0.56	0.56	0.54	0.54	0.54
	3	29c	*U*	1.76	3.80	2.60	2.25	2.19	1.91	2.76	2.39	2.05	2.01	1.93
			SHGC	0.34	0.31	0.31	0.26	0.26	0.26	0.31	0.31	0.30	0.30	0.30
Reflective	1	1l	*U*	5.91	7.24	6.12	5.14	5.05	4.61	6.42	6.07	5.55	5.55	5.35
			SHGC	0.31	0.28	0.28	0.24	0.24	0.24	0.29	0.29	0.27	0.27	0.27
	2	5p	*U*	2.73	4.62	3.42	3.00	2.87	2.53	3.61	3.22	2.86	2.84	2.72
			SHGC	0.29	0.27	0.27	0.22	0.22	0.22	0.27	0.27	0.26	0.26	0.26
	3	29c	*U*	1.76	3.80	2.60	2.25	2.19	1.91	2.76	2.39	2.05	2.01	1.93
			SHGC	0.34	0.31	0.31	0.26	0.26	0.26	0.31	0.31	0.30	0.30	0.30

[a]Data are from Chapter 15, Tables 4 and 13 for selected combinations.
[b]ID = Chapter 15 glazing type identifier.
[c]U = U-factor, W/(m^2·K)
[d]SHGC = solar heat gain coefficient

Table 2 shows representative window U-factor and SHGC values for common glazing and frame combinations. Consult Chapter 15 for skylight characteristics.

Load Components

Below-Grade Surfaces. For cooling calculations, heat flow into the ground is usually ignored because it is difficult to quantify. Surfaces adjacent to the ground are modeled as if well insulated on the outside, so there is no overall heat transfer, but diurnal heat storage effects are included. Heating calculations must include loss via slabs and basement walls and floors, as discussed in the Heating Load section.

Infiltration. Infiltration is generally a significant component of both cooling and heating loads. Refer to Chapter 16 for a detailed discussion of residential air leakage. The simplified residential models found in that chapter can be used to calculate infiltration rates for load calculations. Infiltration should be evaluated for the entire building, not individual rooms or zones.

Natural infiltration leakage rates are modified by mechanical pressurization caused by unbalanced ventilation or duct leakage. These effects are discussed in the section on Combined Ventilation and Infiltration Airflow.

Leakage rate. Air leakage rates are specified either as airflow rate Q_i, or air exchanges per hour (ACH), related as follows:

$$Q_i = \text{ACH}(V/3.6) \tag{6}$$

$$\text{ACH} = \frac{3.6Q_i}{V} \tag{7}$$

where

Q_i = infiltration airflow rate, L/s
ACH = air exchange rate, changes/h
V = building volume, m^3

Infiltration airflow rate depends on two factors:

- Building effective leakage area (envelope leaks plus other air leakage paths, notably flues) and its distribution among ceilings, walls, floors, and flues.
- Driving pressure caused by buoyancy (stack effect) and wind.

Using the simplifying assumptions presented in Chapter 16, these factors can be evaluated separately and combined using Equation (8).

$$Q_i = A_L \text{IDF} \tag{8}$$

where

A_L = building effective leakage area (including flue) at reference pressure difference = 4 Pa, assuming discharge coefficient C_D = cm^2
IDF = infiltration driving force, L/(s·cm^2)

The following sections provide procedures for determining A_L and IDF.

Leakage area. As discussed in Chapter 16, there are several interconvertible ways to characterize building leakage, depending on reference pressure differences and assumed discharge coefficient. This formulation uses the effective leakage area at 4 Pa, assuming $C_D = 1$, designated A_L (Sherman and Grimsrud 1980).

The only accurate procedure for determining A_L is by measurement using a pressurization test (commonly called a blower door test). Numerous field studies have shown that visual inspection is not adequate for obtaining even a crude estimate of leakage.

For buildings in design, a pressurization test is not possible and leakage area must be assumed for design purposes. Leakage can be estimated using tabulated component leakage areas found in Chapter 16. A simpler approach is based on an assumed average leakage per unit of building surface area:

$$A_L = A_{es} A_{ul} \tag{9}$$

where

A_{es} = building exposed surface area, m²

A_{ul} = unit leakage area, cm²/m² (from Table 3)

A_{ul} is the leakage area per unit surface area; suitable design values are found in Table 3. Field experience indicates that the level of care applied to reducing leakage often depends on winter conditions, because cold-air leakage is readily detected. Thus, lower A_{ul} values are expected in colder climates.

In Equation (9), A_{es} is the total building surface area at the envelope pressure boundary, defined as all above-grade surface area that separates the outdoors from conditioned or semiconditioned space. Table 4 provides guidance for evaluating A_{es}.

IDF. To determine IDF, use the Chapter 16 methods cited previously. As a further simplification, Barnaby and Spitler (2005) derived the following relationship that yields results approximately equal to the AIM-2 model (Walker and Wilson 1990, 1998; Chapter 16's enhanced model) at design conditions:

$$\text{IDF} = \frac{I_0 + H|\Delta t|[I_1 + I_2(A_{L,flue}/A_L)]}{1000} \tag{10}$$

where

I_0, I_1, I_2 = coefficients, as follows:

	Cooling 3.4 m/s	Heating 6.7 m/s
I_0	25	51
I_1	0.38	0.35
I_2	0.12	0.23

H = building average stack height, m (typically 2.5 m per story)

Δt = difference between indoor and outdoor temperatures, K

$A_{L,flue}$ = flue effective leakage area at reference pressure difference = 4 Pa, assuming $C_D = 1$, cm² (total for flues serving furnaces, domestic water heaters, fireplaces, or other vented equipment, evaluated assuming associated equipment is not operating and with dampers in closed position; see Chapter 16)

Building stack height H is the average height difference between the ceiling and floor (or grade, if the floor is below grade). Thus, for buildings with vented crawlspaces, the crawlspace height is not included. For basement or slab-on-grade construction, H is the average height of the ceiling above grade. Generally, there is significant leakage between basements and spaces above, so above-grade basement height should be included whether or not the basement is fully conditioned. With suitable adjustments for grade level, H can also be estimated as V/A_{cf} (conditioned floor area).

Table 3 Unit Leakage Areas

Construction	Description	A_{ul} (cm²/m²)
Tight	Construction supervised by air-sealing specialist	0.7
Good	Carefully sealed construction by knowledgeable builder	1.4
Average	Typical current production housing	2.8
Leaky	Typical pre-1970 houses	5.6
Very leaky	Old houses in original condition	10.4

Table 4 Evaluation of Exposed Surface Area

Situation	Include	Exclude
Ceiling/roof combination (e.g., cathedral ceiling without attic)	Gross surface area	
Ceiling or wall adjacent to attic	Ceiling or wall area	Roof area
Wall exposed to ambient	Gross wall area (including fenestration area)	
Wall adjacent to unconditioned buffer space (e.g., garage or porch)	Common wall area	Exterior wall area
Floor over open or vented crawlspace	Floor area	Crawlspace wall area
Floor over sealed crawlspace	Crawlspace wall area	Floor area
Floor over conditioned or semiconditioned basement	Above-grade basement wall area	Floor area
Slab floor		Slab area

Table 5 Typical IDF Values, L/(s·cm²)

H, m	Heating Design Temperature, °C					Cooling Design Temperature, °C			
	−40	−30	−20	−10	0	10	30	35	40
2.5	0.10	0.095	0.086	0.077	0.069	0.060	0.031	0.035	0.040
3	0.11	0.10	0.093	0.083	0.072	0.061	0.032	0.038	0.043
4	0.14	0.12	0.11	0.093	0.079	0.065	0.034	0.042	0.049
5	0.16	0.14	0.12	0.10	0.086	0.069	0.036	0.046	0.055
6	0.18	0.16	0.14	0.11	0.093	0.072	0.039	0.050	0.061
7	0.20	0.17	0.15	0.12	0.10	0.075	0.041	0.051	0.068
8	0.22	0.19	0.16	0.14	0.11	0.079	0.043	0.058	0.074

Equation (10) is valid for typical suburban residential wind sheltering, $A_{L,flue} < A_L/2$, and at any elevation. Table 5 shows IDF values derived with Equation (10), assuming $A_{L,flue} = 0$.

Verification of leakage. A postconstruction pressurization test is strongly recommended to verify that design leakage assumptions are actually achieved. Excess leaks can be located and repaired.

Allocation of infiltration to rooms. Total building infiltration should typically be allocated to rooms according to room volume; that is, it should be assumed that each room has the same air exchange rate as the whole building. In reality, leakage varies by room and over time, depending on outdoor temperature and wind conditions. These effects can either increase or decrease room leakage. In addition, system air mixing tends to redistribute localized leakage to all rooms. Thus, in most cases, there is no reasonable way to assign more or less leakage to specific rooms.

An exception is leaky, multistory houses. The preferable and cost-effective response is mitigation of the leakage. If repair is not possible, then for heating load calculation purposes, some leakage can be differentially assigned to lower story and/or windward rooms in proportion to exposed surface area (i.e., adjustment using an "exposure factor").

Multifamily buildings. Usually, the simplified methods in Chapter 16 and this section do not apply to multifamily residences. However, they can be used for row houses that are full building height and have more than one exposed façade. For apartment units subdivided within a former detached residence, the entire building should be analyzed and the resulting exchange rate applied to the apartment volume. In other multifamily structures, infiltration is determined by many factors, including overall building height and degree of sealing between apartments. For low-rise construction, an upper bound for the infiltration rate can be found by evaluating the entire building. As building height increases, leakage problems can be magnified, as discussed in Chapter 16. Estimating leakage rates may require advice from a high-rise infiltration specialist.

Ventilation.

Whole-building ventilation. Because of energy efficiency concerns, residential construction has become significantly tighter over the last several decades. Natural leakage rates are often insufficient to maintain acceptable indoor air quality. ASHRAE *Standard* 62.2-2004 specifies the required minimum whole-building ventilation rate as

$$Q_v = 0.01A_{cf}\, 0.05A_{cf} + 7.5\ 3.5(N_{br} + 1) \qquad (11)$$

where

Q_v = required ventilation flow rate, L/s
A_{cf} = building conditioned floor area, m^2
N_{br} = number of bedrooms (not less than 1)

Certain mild climates are exempted from this standard; local building authorities ultimately dictate actual requirements. Whole-building ventilation is expected to become more common because of a combination of regulation and consumer demand. The load effect of Q_v must be included in both cooling and heating calculations.

Heat recovery. Heat recovery devices should be considered part of mechanical ventilation systems. These appliances are variously called heat recovery ventilators (HRVs) or energy recovery ventilators (ERVs) and integrate with residential distribution systems, as described in Chapter 25 of the 2008 *ASHRAE Handbook—HVAC Systems and Equipment*. Either sensible heat or total heat (enthalpy) can be exchanged between the exhaust and intake airstreams. ERV/HRV units are characterized by their sensible and total effectiveness.

Local mechanical exhaust. Kitchen and bathroom exhaust fans are required by *Standard* 62.2 and are typically present. Exhaust fans that operate intermittently by manual control are generally not included in load calculations. Continuous systems should be included. Note that exhaust fans induce load only through enhanced infiltration because of building depressurization (see the section on Combined Ventilation and Infiltration Airflow for further discussion).

Combustion Air. Fuel-fired boilers, furnaces, and domestic water heaters require combustion air. If the combustion air source is within the building envelope (including in semiconditioned basements), additional infiltration and heating load are induced. Locating the equipment outside of conditioned space (e.g., in a garage or vented mechanical closet) or using sealed-combustion equipment eliminates this load.

Combustion air requirements for new forced-draft equipment can be estimated at 0.4 L/(s·kW) or about 12 L/s for a 30 kW heating appliance. The requirements for existing natural draft equipment should be estimated at twice that amount. In many cases, these quantities are relatively small and can be neglected.

For cooling load calculations, heating equipment is assumed to be not operating, leaving only any domestic water heaters, the combustion air requirements for which are generally neglected.

Combined Ventilation and Infiltration Airflow. Mechanical pressurization modifies the infiltration leakage rate. To assess this effect, overall supply and exhaust flow rates must be determined and then divided into "balanced" and "unbalanced" components.

$$Q_{bal} = \min(Q_{sup}, Q_{exh}) \qquad (12)$$

$$Q_{unbal} = \max(Q_{sup}, Q_{exh}) - Q_{bal} \qquad (13)$$

where

Q_{bal} = balanced airflow rate, L/s
Q_{sup} = total ventilation supply airflow rate, L/s
Q_{exh} = total ventilation exhaust airflow rate (including any combustion air requirements), L/s
Q_{unbal} = unbalanced airflow rate, L/s

Note that unbalanced duct leakage can produce additional pressurization or depressurization. This effect is discussed in the section on Distribution Losses.

Airflow components can be combined with infiltration leakage as follows (Palmiter and Bond 1991; Sherman 1992):

$$Q_{vi} = \max(Q_{unbal}, Q_i + 0.5Q_{unbal}) \qquad (14)$$

where

Q_{vi} = combined infiltration/ventilation flow rate (not including balanced component), L/s
Q_i = infiltration leakage rate assuming no mechanical pressurization, L/s

Ventilation/infiltration load. The cooling or heating load from ventilation and infiltration is calculated as follows:

$$q_{vi,s} = C_s[Q_{vi} + (1 - \varepsilon_s)Q_{bal,hr} + Q_{bal,oth}]\Delta t \qquad (15)$$

$$q_{vi,l} = C_l(Q_{vi} + Q_{bal,oth})\Delta W \quad \text{(no HRV/ERV)} \qquad (16)$$

$$q_{vi,t} = C_t[Q_{vi} + (1 - \varepsilon_t)Q_{bal,hr} + Q_{bal,oth}]\Delta h \qquad (17)$$

$$q_{vi,l} = q_{vi,t} - q_{vi,s} \qquad (18)$$

where

$q_{vi,s}$ = sensible ventilation/infiltration load, W
ε_s = HRV/ERV sensible effectiveness
$Q_{bal,hr}$ = balanced ventilation flow rate via HRV/ERV equipment, L/s
$Q_{bal,oth}$ = other balanced ventilation supply airflow rate, L/s
Δt = indoor/outdoor temperature difference, K
ΔW = indoor/outdoor humidity ratio difference
$q_{vi,t}$ = total ventilation/infiltration load, W
ε_t = HRV/ERV total effectiveness
Δh = indoor/outdoor enthalpy difference, kJ/kg
$q_{vnt,l}$ = latent ventilation/infiltration load, W

Distribution Losses. Air leakage and heat losses from duct systems frequently impose substantial equipment loads in excess of building requirements. The magnitude of losses depends on the location of duct runs, their surface areas, surrounding temperatures, duct wall insulation, and duct airtightness. These values are usually difficult to accurately determine at the time of preconstruction load calculations, and must be estimated using assumed values, so that selected equipment capacity is sufficient.

Good design and workmanship both reduce duct losses. In particular, locating duct runs within the conditioned envelope (above dropped hallway ceilings, for example) substantially eliminates duct losses. Specific recommendations are found in Chapter 9 of the 2008 *ASHRAE Handbook—HVAC Systems and Equipment*. Good workmanship and correct materials are essential to achieve low leakage. Many common sealing techniques, notably duct tape, have been shown to fail in a few years. Well-constructed duct systems show leakage rates of 5% of fan flow from supply and return runs, whereas 11% or more on each side is more typical. Because of the

Table 6 Typical Duct Loss/Gain Factors

		1 Story						2 or More Stories					
	Supply/Return Leakage	11%/11%			5%/5%			11%/11%			5%/5%		
Duct Location	Insulation ($m^2{\cdot}K$)/W	R-0	R-0.7	R-1.4	R-0	R-0.7	R-1.4	R-0	R-0.7	R-1.4	R-0	R-0.7	R-1.4
Conditioned space		No loss (F_{dl} = 0)											
Attic	C	1.26	0.71	0.63	0.68	0.33	0.27	1.02	0.66	0.60	0.53	0.29	0.25
	H/F	0.49	0.29	0.25	0.34	0.16	0.13	0.41	0.26	0.24	0.27	0.14	0.12
	H/HP	0.56	0.37	0.34	0.34	0.19	0.16	0.49	0.35	0.33	0.28	0.17	0.15
Basement	C	0.12	0.09	0.09	0.07	0.05	0.04	0.11	0.09	0.09	0.06	0.04	0.04
	H/F	0.28	0.18	0.16	0.19	0.10	0.08	0.24	0.17	0.15	0.16	0.09	0.08
	H/HP	0.23	0.17	0.16	0.14	0.09	0.08	0.20	0.16	0.15	0.12	0.08	0.07
Crawlspace	C	0.16	0.12	0.11	0.10	0.06	0.05	0.14	0.12	0.11	0.08	0.06	0.05
	H/F	0.49	0.29	0.25	0.34	0.16	0.13	0.41	0.26	0.24	0.27	0.14	0.12
	H/HP	0.56	0.37	0.34	0.34	0.19	0.16	0.49	0.35	0.33	0.28	0.17	0.15

Values calculated for ASHRAE *Standard* 152 default duct system surface area using model of Francisco and Palmiter (1999). Values are provided as guidance only; losses can differ substantially for other conditions and configurations. Assumed surrounding temperatures:

Cooling (C): t_o = 35°C, t_{attic} = 49°C, t_b = 20°C, t_{crawl} = 22°C Heating/furnace (H/F) and heating/heating pump (H/HP): t_o = 0°C, t_{attic} = 0°C, t_b = 18°C, t_{crawl} = 0°C

potentially large load impact of duct leakage, postconstruction verification of airtightness is strongly recommended.

Duct losses can be estimated using models specified in ASHRAE *Standard* 152, Francisco and Palmiter (1999), and Palmiter and Francisco (1997). The allowance for distribution losses is calculated as follows:

$$q_d = F_{dl} q_{bl} \quad (19)$$

where

q_d = distribution loss, W
F_{dl} = duct loss/gain factor, from Table 6 *or* ASHRAE *Standard* 152 design efficiencies *or* a detailed model
q_{bl} = total building load, W

Table 6 shows typical duct loss/gain factors calculated for the conditions indicated. These values can provide guidance for hand estimates, and illustrate the need for achieving low duct leakage. To the extent conditions differ from those shown, specific calculations should be made using a method cited previously. Note also that Table 6 cooling factors represent sensible gain only; duct leakage also introduces significant latent gain.

COOLING LOAD

A cooling load calculation determines total sensible cooling load from heat gain (1) through opaque surfaces (walls, floors, ceilings, and doors), (2) through transparent fenestration surfaces (windows, skylights, and glazed doors), (3) caused by infiltration and ventilation, and (4) because of occupancy. The latent portion of the cooling load is evaluated separately. Although the entire structure may be considered a single zone, equipment selection and system design should be based on room-by-room calculations. For proper design of the distribution system, the conditioned airflow required by each room must be known.

Peak Load Computation

To select a properly sized cooling unit, the peak or maximum load (block load) for each zone must be computed. The block load for a single-family detached house with one central system is the sum of all the room loads. If the house has a separate system for each zone, each zone block load is required. When a house is zoned with one central cooling system, the system size is based on the entire house block load, whereas zone components, such as distribution ducts, are sized using zone block loads.

In multifamily structures, each living unit has a zone load that equals the sum of the room loads. For apartments with separate systems, the block load for each unit establishes the system size. Apartment buildings having a central cooling system with fan-coils in each apartment require a block load calculation for the complete structure to size the central system; each unit load establishes the size of the fan-coil and air distribution system for each apartment. One of the methods for nonresidential buildings discussed in Chapter 18 may be used to calculate the block load.

Opaque Surfaces

Heat gain through walls, floors, ceilings, and doors is caused by (1) the air temperature difference across such surfaces and (2) solar gains incident on the surfaces. The heat capacity of typical construction moderates and delays building heat gain. This effect is modeled in detail in the computerized RHB method, resulting in accurate simultaneous load estimates.

The RLF method uses the following to estimate cooling load:

$$q_{opq} = A \times CF_{opq} \quad (20)$$

$$CF_{opq} = U(OF_t \Delta t + OF_b + OF_r DR) \quad (21)$$

where

q_{opq} = opaque surface cooling load, W
A = net surface area, m^2
CF = surface cooling factor, W/m^2
U = construction U-factor, W/($m^2{\cdot}K$)
Δt = cooling design temperature difference, K
OF_t, OF_b, OF_r = opaque-surface cooling factors (see Table 7)
DR = cooling daily range, K

OF factors, found in Table 7, represent construction-specific physical characteristics. OF_t values less than 1 capture the buffering effect of attics and crawlspaces, OF_b represents incident solar gain, and OF_r captures heat storage effects by reducing the effective temperature difference. Note also that CF can be viewed as CF = $U \times$ CLTD, the formulation used in prior residential and nonresidential methods.

As shown in Table 7, roof solar absorptance has a significant effect on ceiling cooling load contribution. Table 8 shows typical values for solar absorptance of residential roofing materials. Note that low absorptance cannot be achieved with asphalt shingles.

Slab Floors

Slab floors produce a slight reduction in cooling load, as follows:

$$q_{opq} = A \times CF_{slab} \quad (22)$$

Table 7 Opaque Surface Cooling Factor Coefficients

Surface Type	OF_t	OF_b, K	OF_r
Ceiling or wall adjacent to vented attic	0.62	$14.3\alpha_{roof} - 4.5$	–0.19
Ceiling/roof assembly	1	$38.3\alpha_{roof} - 7.0$	–0.36
Wall (wood frame) or door with solar exposure	1	8.2	–0.36
Wall (wood frame) or door (shaded)	1	0	–0.36
Floor over ambient	1	0	–0.06
Floor over crawlspace	0.33	0	–0.28
Slab floor (see Slab Floor section)			

α_{roof} = roof solar absorptance (see Table 8)

Table 8 Roof Solar Absorptance α_{roof}

	Color			
Material	White	Light	Medium	Dark
Asphalt shingles	0.75	0.75	0.85	0.92
Tile	0.30	0.40	0.80	0.80
Metal	0.35	0.50	0.70	0.90
Elastomeric coating	0.30			

Source: Summarized from Parker et al. 2000

$$CF_{slab} = 1.9 - 1.4h_{srf} \tag{23}$$

where

A = area of slab, m²
CF_{slab} = slab cooling factor, W/m²
h_{srf} = effective surface conductance, including resistance of slab covering material such as carpet $= 1/(R_{cvr} + 0.12)$, W/(m²·K). Representative R_{cvr} values are found in Chapter 6 of the 2008 *ASHRAE Handbook—HVAC Systems and Equipment.*
1.9 = constant, W/m²
1.4 = factor, K

Transparent Fenestration Surfaces

Cooling load associated with nondoor fenestration is calculated as follows:

$$q_{fen} = A \times CF_{fen} \tag{24}$$

$$CF_{fen} = U(\Delta t - 0.46DR) + PXI \times SHGC \times IAC \times FF_s \tag{25}$$

where

q_{fen} = fenestration cooling load, W
A = fenestration area (including frame), m²
CF_{fen} = surface cooling factor, W/m²
U = fenestration NFRC *heating* U-factor, W/(m²·K)
Δt = cooling design temperature difference, K
PXI = peak exterior irradiance, including shading modifications, W/m² [see Equations (26) or (27)]
SHGC = fenestration rated or estimated NFRC solar heat gain coefficient
IAC = interior shading attenuation coefficient, Equation (29)
FF_s = fenestration solar load factor, Table 13

Peak Exterior Irradiance (PXI). Although solar gain occurs throughout the day, RP-1199 regression studies (Barnaby et al. 2004) showed that the cooling load contribution of fenestration correlates well with the peak-hour irradiance incident on the fenestration exterior. PXI is calculated as follows:

$$PXI = T_x E_t \text{ (unshaded fenestration)} \tag{26}$$

$$PXI = T_x[E_d + (1 - F_{shd})E_D] \text{ (shaded fenestration)} \tag{27}$$

where

PXI = peak exterior irradiance, W/m²
E_t, E_d, E_D = peak total, diffuse, and direct irradiance (Table 9 or 10), W/m²
T_x = Transmission of exterior attachment (insect screen or shade screen)

Table 9 Peak Irradiance Equations

Horizontal surfaces

$$E_t = 952 + 6.49L - 0.166L^2$$
$$E_d = \min(E_t, 170)$$
$$E_D = E_t - E_d$$

Vertical surfaces

$$\phi = \left|\frac{\psi}{180}\right| \text{ (normalized exposure, 0 – 1)}$$

$$E_t = 453.4 + 1341\phi - 5279\phi^3 + 3260\phi^4 - 34.09\phi L + 0.2643\phi L^2 - 12.83L - 0.8425L^2 + [0.9835L^2/(\phi + 1)]$$

$$E_d = \min\left(E_t, 357 - 86.98\phi^2 + 1.764\phi L - \frac{108.4\sqrt[4]{L}}{\phi + 1}\right)$$

$$E_D = E_t - E_d$$

where

E_t, E_d, E_D = peak hourly total, diffuse, and direct irradiance, W/m²
L = site latitude, °N
ψ = exposure (surface azimuth), ° from south (–180 to +180)

Table 10 Peak Irradiance, W/m²

		Latitude								
Exposure		20°	25°	30°	35°	40°	45°	50°	55°	60°
North	E_D	125	106	92	84	81	85	96	112	136
	E_d	128	115	103	93	84	76	69	62	55
	E_t	253	221	195	177	166	162	164	174	191
Northeast/Northwest	E_D	460	449	437	425	412	399	386	374	361
	E_d	177	169	162	156	151	147	143	140	137
	E_t	637	618	599	581	563	546	529	513	498
East/West	E_D	530	543	552	558	560	559	555	547	537
	E_d	200	196	193	190	189	188	187	187	187
	E_t	730	739	745	748	749	747	742	734	724
Southeast/Southwest	E_D	282	328	369	405	436	463	485	503	517
	E_d	204	203	203	204	205	207	210	212	215
	E_t	485	531	572	609	641	670	695	715	732
South	E_D	0	60	139	214	283	348	408	464	515
	E_d	166	193	196	200	204	209	214	219	225
	E_t	166	253	335	414	487	557	622	683	740
Horizontal	E_D	845	840	827	806	776	738	691	637	574
	E_d	170	170	170	170	170	170	170	170	170
	E_t	1015	1010	997	976	946	908	861	807	744

Table 11 Exterior Attachment Transmission

Attachment	T_x
None	1.0
Exterior insect screen	0.64 (see Chapter 15, Table 13G)
Shade screen	Manufacturer shading coefficient (SC) value, typically 0.4 to 0.6

F_{shd} = fraction of fenestration shaded by permanent overhangs, fins, or environmental obstacles

For horizontal or vertical surfaces, peak irradiance values can be obtained from Table 9 for primary exposures, or from Table 10 equations for any exposure. Skylights with slope less than 30° from horizontal should be treated as horizontal. Steeper, nonvertical slopes are not supported by the RLF method.

Exterior Attachments. Common window coverings can significantly reduce fenestration solar gain. Table 11 shows transmission values for typical attachments.

Permanent Shading. The shaded fraction F_{shd} can be taken as 1 for any fenestration shaded by adjacent structures during peak hours. Simple overhang shading can be estimated using the following:

$$F_{shd} = \min\left[1, \max\left(0, \frac{\text{SLF} \times D_{oh} - X_{oh}}{h}\right)\right] \quad (28)$$

where

SLF = shade line factor from Table 12
D_{oh} = depth of overhang (from plane of fenestration), m
X_{oh} = vertical distance from top of fenestration to overhang, m
h = height of fenestration, m

The shade line factor (SLF) is the ratio of the vertical distance a shadow falls beneath the edge of an overhang to the depth of the overhang, so the shade line equals the SLF times the overhang depth. Table 12 shows SLFs for July 21 averaged over the hours of greatest solar intensity on each exposure.

More complex shading situations should be analyzed with the RHB method.

Fenestration Solar Load Factors. Fenestration solar load factors FF_s depend on fenestration exposure and are found in Table 13. The values represent the fraction of transmitted solar gain that contributes to peak cooling load. It is thus understandable that morning (east) values are lower than afternoon (west) values. Higher values are included for multifamily buildings with limited exposure.

Interior Shading. Interior shading significantly reduces solar gain and is ubiquitous in residential buildings. Field studies show that a large fraction of windows feature some sort of shading; for example, James et al. (1997) studied 368 houses and found interior shading in 80% of audited windows. Therefore, in all but special circumstances, interior shading should be assumed when calculating cooling loads. In the RLF method, the interior attenuation coefficient (IAC) model is used, as described in Chapter 15. Residential values from that chapter are consolidated in Table 14. IAC values for many other configurations are found in Chapter 15, Tables 13A to 13G.

In some cases, it is reasonable to assume that a shade is partially open. For example, drapes are often partially open to admit daylight. IAC values are computed as follows:

$$\text{IAC} = 1 + F_{cl}(\text{IAC}_{cl} - 1) \quad (29)$$

where

IAC = interior attenuation coefficient of fenestration with partially closed shade
F_{cl} = shade fraction closed (0 to 1)
IAC_{cl} = interior attenuation coefficient of fully closed configuration (from Table 14 or Chapter 15, Tables 13A to 13G)

Table 12 Shade Line Factors (SLFs)

	Latitude								
Exposure	**20°**	**25°**	**30°**	**35°**	**40°**	**45°**	**50°**	**55°**	**60°**
North	2.8	2.1	1.4	1.5	1.7	1.0	0.8	0.9	0.8
Northeast/Northwest	1.4	1.5	1.6	1.2	1.3	1.3	0.9	0.9	0.8
East/West	1.2	1.2	1.1	1.1	1.1	1.0	1.0	0.9	0.8
Southeast/Southwest	2.1	1.8	2.0	1.7	1.5	1.6	1.4	1.2	1.1
South	20.0	14.0	6.9	4.7	3.3	2.7	2.1	1.7	1.4

Note: Shadow length below overhang = SLF × D_{oh}

Table 13 Fenestration Solar Load Factors FF_s

Exposure	Single Family Detached	Multifamily
North	0.44	0.27
Northeast	0.21	0.43
East	0.31	0.56
Southeast	0.37	0.54
South	0.47	0.53
Southwest	0.58	0.61
West	0.56	0.65
Northwest	0.46	0.57
Horizontal	0.58	0.73

Infiltration and Ventilation

See the Common Data and Procedures section.

Internal Gain

The contributions of occupants, lighting, and appliance gains to peak sensible and latent loads can be estimated as

$$q_{ig,s} = 136 + 2.2A_{cf} + 22N_{oc} \quad (30)$$

$$q_{ig,l} = 20 + 0.22A_{cf} + 12N_{oc} \quad (31)$$

where

$q_{ig,s}$ = sensible cooling load from internal gains, W
$q_{ig,l}$ = latent cooling load from internal gains, W
A_{cf} = conditioned floor area of building, m²
N_{oc} = number of occupants (unknown, estimate as $N_{br} + 1$)

Equations (30) and (31) and their coefficients are derived from Building America (2004) load profiles evaluated at 4:00 P.M., as documented by Barnaby and Spitler (2005). Predicted gains are typical for U.S. homes. Further allowances should be considered when unusual lighting intensities or other equipment are in continuous use during peak cooling hours. In critical situations where intermittent high occupant density or other internal gains are expected, a parallel cooling system should be considered.

For room-by-room calculations, $q_{ig,s}$ should be evaluated for the entire conditioned area, and allocated to kitchen and living spaces.

Air Distribution System: Heat Gain

See the Common Data and Procedures section.

Total Latent Load

The latent cooling load is the result of three predominant moisture sources: outdoor air (infiltration and ventilation), occupants,

Table 14 Interior Attenuation Coefficients (IAC_{cl})

		Drapes			Roller Shades			Blinds	
		Open-Weave	Closed-Weave		Opaque		Translucent		
Glazing Layers	Glazing Type (ID*)	Light	Dark	Light	Dark	White	Light	Medium	White
1	Clear (1a)	0.64	0.71	0.45	0.64	0.34	0.44	0.74	0.66
	Heat absorbing (1c)	0.68	0.72	0.50	0.67	0.40	0.49	0.76	0.69
2	Clear (5a)	0.72	0.81	0.57	0.76	0.48	0.55	0.82	0.74
	Low-e high-solar (17c)	0.76	0.86	0.64	0.82	0.57	0.62	0.86	0.79
	Low-e low-solar (25a)	0.79	0.88	0.68	0.85	0.60	0.66	0.88	0.82
	Heat absorbing (5c)	0.73	0.82	0.59	0.77	0.51	0.58	0.83	0.76

*Chapter 15 glazing identifier

Table 15 Summary of RLF Cooling Load Equations

Load Source	Equation	Tables and Notes
Exterior opaque surfaces	$q_{opq} = A \times \text{CF}$ $\text{CF} = U(\text{OF}_t\Delta t + \text{OF}_b + \text{OF}_r\text{DR})$	OF factors from Table 7
Exterior transparent surfaces	$q_{fen} = A \times \text{CF}$ $\text{CF} = U(\Delta t - 0.46\text{DR}) + \text{PXI} \times \text{SHGC} \times \text{IAC} \times \text{FF}_s$	PXI from Table 9 plus adjustments FF_s from Table 13
Partitions to unconditioned space	$q = AU\Delta t$	Δt = temperature difference across partition
Ventilation/infiltration	$q_s = C_s Q\Delta t$	See Common Data and Procedures section
Occupants and appliances	$q_{ig,s} = 136 + 2.2A_{cf} + 22N_{oc}$	
Distribution	$q_d = F_{dl}\Sigma q$	F_{dl} from Table 6
Total sensible load	$q_s = q_d + \Sigma q$	
Latent load	$q_l = q_{vi,l} + q_{ig,l}$	
Ventilation/infiltration	$q_{vi,l} = C_l Q\Delta W$	
Internal gain	$q_{ig,l} = 20 + 0.22A_{cf} + 12N_{oc}$	

and miscellaneous sources, such as cooking, laundry, and bathing. These components, discussed in previous sections, combine to yield the total latent load:

$$q_l = q_{vi,l} + q_{ig,l} \tag{32}$$

where

q_l = total latent load, W
$q_{vi,l}$ = ventilation/infiltration latent gain, W, from Equation (16) or (18)
$q_{ig,l}$ = internal latent gain, W, from Equation (31)

Additional latent gains may be introduced through return duct leakage and specific atypical sources. These may be estimated and included. Lstiburek and Carmody (1993) provide data for household moisture sources; however, again note that Equation (31) adequately accounts for normal gains.

Because air conditioning systems are usually controlled by a thermostat, latent cooling is a side effect of equipment operation. During periods of significant latent gain but mild temperatures, there is little cooling operation, resulting in unacceptable indoor humidity. Multispeed equipment, combined temperature/humidity control, and dedicated dehumidification should be considered to address this condition.

Summary of RLF Cooling Load Equations

Table 15 contains a brief list of equations used in the cooling load calculation procedure described in this chapter.

HEATING LOAD

Calculating a residential heating load involves estimating the maximum heat loss of each room or space to be heated and the simultaneous maximum (block) heat loss for the building, while maintaining a selected indoor air temperature during periods of design outdoor weather conditions. As discussed in the section on Calculation Approach, heating calculations use conservative assumptions, ignoring solar and internal gains, and building heat storage. This leaves a simple steady-state heat loss calculation, with the only significant difficulty being surfaces adjacent to grade.

Exterior Surfaces Above Grade

All above-grade surfaces exposed to outdoor conditions (walls, doors, ceilings, fenestration, and raised floors) are treated identically, as follows:

$$q = A \times \text{HF} \tag{33}$$

$$\text{HF} = U\Delta t \tag{34}$$

where HF is the heating load factor in W/m²

Two ceiling configurations are common:

- For **ceiling/roof combinations** (e.g., flat roof or cathedral ceiling), the U-factor should be evaluated for the entire assembly.
- For **well-insulated ceilings (or walls) adjacent to vented attic space**, the U-factor should be that of the insulated assembly only (the roof is omitted) and the attic temperature assumed to equal the heating design outdoor temperature. The effect of attic radiant barriers can be neglected. In cases where the ceiling or wall is not well insulated, the adjacent buffer space procedure (see the section on Surfaces Adjacent to Buffer Space) can be used.

Below-Grade and On-Grade Surfaces

The Heating Load Calculations section of Chapter 18 includes simplified procedures for estimating heat loss through below-grade walls and below- and on-grade floors. Those procedures are applicable to residential buildings. In more detailed work, Bahnfleth and Pedersen (1990) show a significant effect of the area-to-perimeter ratio. For additional generality and accuracy, see also methods described or cited in Beausoleil-Morrison and Mitalas (1997), CAN/CSA *Standard* F280-M90 (1990), HRAI (1996), and Krarti and Choi (1996).

Surfaces Adjacent to Buffer Space

Heat loss to adjacent unconditioned or semiconditioned spaces can be calculated using a heating factor based on the partition temperature difference:

$$\text{HF} = U(t_i - t_b) \tag{35}$$

Buffer space air temperature t_b can be estimated using procedures discussed in the section on Adjacent Buffer Spaces. Generally, simple approximations are sufficient except where the partition surface is poorly insulated.

Crawlspaces and basements are cases where the partition (the house floor) is often poorly insulated; they also involve heat transfer to the ground. Most codes require crawlspaces to be adequately vented year round. However, work highlighting problems with venting crawlspaces (DeWitt 2003) has led to application of sealed crawlspaces with insulated perimeter walls. Equation (5) may be applied to basements and crawlspace by including appropriate ground-related terms in the heat balance formulation. For example, when including below-grade walls, $A_x = A_{bw}$, $U_x = U_{avg,bw}$, and $t_x = t_{gr}$ should be included as applicable in the summations in Equation (5). Losses from piping or ducting should be included as additional buffer space heat gain. Determining the ventilation or infiltration rate for crawlspaces and basements is difficult. Latta and Boileau (1969) estimated the air exchange rate for an uninsulated basement at 0.67 ach under winter conditions. Field measurements of eight ventilated crawlspaces summarized in Palmiter and Francisco (1996) yielded a median flow rate of 4.6 ach. Clearly, crawlspace infiltration rates vary widely, depending on vent configuration and operation.

Ventilation and Infiltration

Infiltration of outside air causes both sensible and latent heat loss. The energy required to raise the temperature of outdoor infiltrating air to indoor air temperature is the sensible component; energy associated with net loss of moisture from the space is the latent component. Determining the volumetric flow Q of outdoor air entering the building is discussed in the Common Data and Procedures section and in Chapter 16. Determining the resulting sensible and latent loads is discussed in the Ventilation/Infiltration Load subsection.

Humidification

In many climates, humidification is required to maintain comfortable indoor relative humidity under heating conditions. The latent ventilation and infiltration load calculated, assuming desired indoor humidity conditions, equals the sensible heat needed to evaporate water at a rate sufficient to balance moisture losses from air leakage. Self-contained humidifiers provide this heat from internal sources. If the heat of evaporation is taken from occupied space or the distribution system, the heating capacity should be increased accordingly.

Pickup Load

For intermittently heated buildings and night thermostat setback, additional heat is required to raise the temperature of air, building materials, and material contents to the specified temperature. The rate at which this additional heat must be supplied is the pickup load, which depends on the structure's heat capacity, its material contents, and the time in which these are to be heated.

Because the design outdoor temperature is generally much lower than typical winter temperatures, under most conditions excess heating capacity is available for pickup. Therefore, many engineers make no pickup allowance except for demanding situations. If pickup capacity is justified, the following guidance can be used to estimate the requirement.

Relatively little rigorous information on pickup load exists. Building simulation programs can predict recovery times and required equipment capacities, but a detailed simulation study is rarely practical. Armstrong et al. (1992a, 1992b) developed a model for predicting recovery from setback and validated it for a church and two office buildings. Nelson and MacArthur (1978) studied the relationship between thermostat setback, furnace capacity, and recovery time. Hedrick et al. (1992) compared Nelson and MacArthur's results to tests for two test houses. They found that the furnace oversizing required for a 2 h recovery time ranges from 20 to 120%, depending on size of setback, building mass, and heating Δt (colder locations require less oversizing on a percentage basis).

The designer should be aware that there are tradeoffs between energy savings from thermostat setback and energy penalties incurred by oversizing equipment. Koenig (1978) studied a range of locations and suggested that 30% oversizing allows recovery times less than 4 h for nearly the entire heating season and is close to optimum from an energy standpoint.

The preceding guidance applies to residential buildings with fuel-fired furnaces. Additional considerations may be important for other types of heating systems. For air-source heat pumps with electric resistance auxiliary heat, thermostat setback may be undesirable (Bullock 1978).

Thermostats with optimum-start algorithms, designed to allow both energy savings and timely recovery to the daytime set point, are becoming routinely available and should be considered in all cases.

Summary of Heating Load Procedures

Table 16 lists equations used in the heating load calculation procedures described in this chapter.

Table 16 Summary of Heating Load Calculation Equations

Load Source	Equation	Tables and Notes
Exterior surfaces above grade	$q = UA\Delta t$	$\Delta t = t_i - t_o$
Partitions to unconditioned buffer space	$q = UA\Delta t$	Δt = temp. difference across partition
Walls below grade	$q = U_{avg,bw}A(t_{in} - t_{gr})$	
Floors on grade	$q = F_p p \Delta t$	See Chapter 18, Equations (41) and (42)
Floors below grade	$q = U_{avg,bf}A(t_{in} - t_{gr})$	See Chapter 18, Equations (37) and (38)
Ventilation/infiltration	$q_{vi} = C_s Q \Delta t$	From Common Data and Procedures section
Total sensible load	$q_s = \Sigma q$	

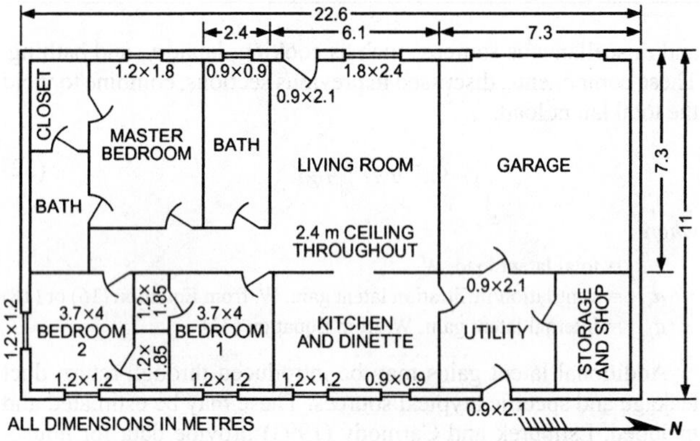

Fig. 1 Example House

LOAD CALCULATION EXAMPLE

A single-family detached house with floor plan shown in Figure 1 is located in Atlanta, GA, USA. Construction characteristics are documented in Table 17. Using the RLF method, find the block (whole-house) design cooling and heating loads. A furnace/air-conditioner forced-air system is planned with a well-sealed and well-insulated (R-8 wrap) attic duct system.

Solution

Design Conditions. Table 18 summarizes design conditions. Typical indoor conditions are assumed. Outdoor conditions are determined from Chapter 14.

Component Quantities. Areas and lengths required for load calculations are derived from plan dimensions (Figure 1). Table 19 summarizes these quantities.

Opaque Surface Factors. Heating and cooling factors are derived for each component condition. Table 20 shows the resulting factors and their sources.

Window Factors. Deriving cooling factors for windows requires identifying all unique glazing configurations in the house. Equation (25) input items indicate that the variations for this case are exposure, window height (with overhang shading), and frame type (which determines U-factor, SHGC, and the presence of insect screen). CF derivation for all configurations is summarized in Table 21.

For example, CF for operable 1 m high windows facing west (the second row in Table 21) is derived as follows:

- U-factor and SHGC are found in Table 2.
- Each operable window is equipped with an insect screen. From Table 11, $T_x = 0.64$ for this arrangement.
- Overhang shading is evaluated with Equation (28). For west exposure and latitude 34°, Table 12 shows SLF = 1.1. Overhang depth (D_{oh}) is 0.6 m and the window-overhang distance (X_{oh}) is 0 m. With window height h of 0.9 m, $F_s = 0.73$ (73% shaded).

Table 17 Example House Characteristics

Component	Description	Factors
Roof/ceiling	Flat wood frame ceiling (insulated with R-5.3 fiberglass) beneath vented attic with medium asphalt shingle roof	$U = 0.031\ 18$ W/(m²·K) $\alpha_{roof} = 0.85$ (Table 8)
Exterior walls	Wood frame, exterior wood sheathing, interior gypsum board, R-2.3 fiberglass insulation	$U = 51$ W/(m²·K)
Doors	Wood, solid core	$U = 2.3$ W/(m²·K)
Floor	Slab on grade with heavy carpet over rubber pad; R-0.9 edge insulation to 1 m below grade	$R_{cvr} = 0.21$ (m²·K)/W (Table 3, Chapter 6, 2008 *ASHRAE Handbook—HVAC Systems and Equipment*) $F_p = 85$ W/(m²·K) (estimated from Chapter 18, Table 24)
Windows	Clear double-pane glass in wood frames. Half fixed, half operable with insect screens (except living room picture window, which is fixed). 0.6 m eave overhang on east and west with eave edge at same height as top of glazing for all windows. Allow for typical interior shading, half closed.	Fixed: $U = 2.84$ W/(m²·K); SHGC = 0.67 (Table 2) Operable: $U = 2.87$ W/(m²·K); SHGC = 0.57 (Table 2); $T_x = 0.64$ (Table 11) $IAC_{cl} = 0.6$ (estimated from Table 14)
Construction	Good	$A_{ul} = 1.4$ cm²/m² (Table 3)

Table 18 Example House Design Conditions

Item	Heating	Cooling	Notes
Latitude	—	—	33.64°N
Elevation	—	—	315 m
Indoor temperature	20°C	24°C	
Indoor relative humidity	N/A	50%	No humidification
Outdoor temperature	−3.5°C	33°C	Cooling: 1% value Heating: 99%
Daily range	N/A	9.5 K	
Outdoor wet bulb	N/A	23.3°C	MCWB* at 1%
Wind speed	6.7 m/s	3.4 m/s	Default assumption
Design Δt	23.5 K	9 K	
Moisture difference		0.0052 kg/kg	Psychrometric chart

*MCWB = mean coincident wet bulb

Table 19 Example House Component Quantities

Component	Quantity	Notes
Ceiling	195.3 m²	Overall area less garage area (22.6 × 11) − (7.3 × 7.3)
Doors	3.8 m²	2 (each 0.9 by 2.1 m)
Windows	13.9 m²	
Walls, exposed exterior	126.2 m² gross, 108.5 m² net	Wall height = 2.4 m
Walls, garage	35.0 m²	
Floor area	95.3 m²	
Floor perimeter	67.2 m	Include perimeter adjacent to garage
Total exposed surface	67.2 m²	Wall gross area (including garage wall) plus ceiling area
Volume	356.5 m²	

Table 20 Example House Opaque Surface Factors

Component	U, W/(m²·K) or F_p, W/(m·K)	Heating HF	Heating Reference	Cooling OF_t	Cooling OF_b	Cooling OF_r	Cooling CF	Cooling Reference
Ceiling	0.18	4.2	Equation (34)	0.62	7.66	−0.19	2.06	Table 7 Equation (21)
Wall	0.51	12.0		1	8.20	−0.36	7.03	
Garage wall	0.51	12.0		1	0.00	−0.36	2.85	
Door	2.3	54.1		1	8.20	−0.36	31.69	
Floor perimeter	0.85	20.0	Chapter 18, Equation (42)					
Floor area				1.9	−1.4/(0.21 + 0.12) = −4.24		−2.34	Equation (23)

- PXI depends on peak irradiance and shading. Approximating site latitude as 35°N, Table 9 shows $E_D = 558$ and $E_d = 190$ W/m² for west exposure. Equation (27) combines these values with T_x and F_s to find PXI = 0.64[190 + (1 − 0.73)558] = 218 W/m².
- All windows are assumed to have some sort of interior shading in the half-closed position. Use Equation (29) with $F_{cl} = 0.5$ and $IAC_{cl} = 0.6$ (per Table 17) to derive IAC = 0.8.
- FF_s is taken from Table 13 for west exposure.
- Finally, inserting the preceding values into Equation (25) gives CF = 2.87(9 − 0.46 × 9.5) + 218 × 0.57 × 0.80 × 0.56 = 69 W/m².

Envelope Loads. Given the load factors and component quantities, heating and cooling loads are calculated for each envelope element, as shown in Table 22.

Infiltration and Ventilation. From Table 3, A_{ul} for this house is 1.4 cm²/m² of exposed surface area. Applying Equation (9) yields $A_L = A_{es} \times A_{ul} = 356.5 \times 1.1 = 499$ cm². Using Table 5, estimate heating and cooling IDF to be 0.035 (L·s)/cm², respectively [alternatively, Equation (10) could be used to find IDF values]. Apply Equation (8) to find the infiltration leakage rates and Equation (7) to convert the rate to air changes per hour:

$$Q_{i,h} = 499 \times 0.073 = 36 \text{ L/s (0.28 ach)}$$

$$Q_{i,c} = 499 \times 0.035 = 17 \text{ L/s (0.13 ach)}$$

Calculate the ventilation outside air requirement with Equation (11) using $A_{cf} = 195.3$ m² and $N_{br} = 3$, resulting in $Q_v = 24$ L/s. For design purposes, assume that this requirement is met by a mechanical system with balanced supply and exhaust flow rates ($Q_{unbal} = 0$).

Find the combined infiltration/ventilation flow rates with Equation (14):

$$Q_{vi,h} = 24 + \max(0, 36 + 0.5 \times 0) = 60 \text{ L/s}$$

$$Q_{vi,c} = 24 + \max(0, 17 + 0.5 \times 0) = 41 \text{ L/s}$$

At Atlanta's elevation of 313 m, elevation adjustment of heat factors results in a small (4%) reduction in air heat transfer; thus, adjustment is unnecessary, resulting in $C_s = 23$ W/(L·s·K). Use

Table 21 Example House Window Factors

Exposure	Height, m	Frame	U, W/(m²·K) Table 2	HF Eq. (34)	T_x Table 11	F_{shd} Eq. (28)	PXI Eq. (27)	SHGC Table 2	IAC Eq. (29)	FF_s Table 13	CF Eq. (25)
West	0.9	Fixed	2.84	66.7	1	0.73	341	0.67	0.80	0.56	115.4
	0.9	Operable	2.87	67.4	0.64	0.73	218	0.57	0.80	0.56	69.0
	1.8	Fixed	2.84	66.7	1	0.37	542	0.67	0.80	0.56	175.7
	1.8	Operable	2.87	67.4	0.64	0.37	347	0.57	0.80	0.56	101.8
	2.4	Fixed	2.84	66.7	1	0.28	592	0.67	0.80	0.56	190.8
South	1.2	Fixed	2.84	66.7	1	0.00	414	0.67	0.80	0.47	117.4
	1.2	Operable	2.87	67.4	0.64	0.00	265	0.57	0.80	0.47	70.1
East	0.9	Fixed	2.84	66.7	1	0.73	341	0.67	0.80	0.31	69.8
	0.9	Operable	2.87	67.4	0.64	0.73	218	0.57	0.80	0.31	44.1
	1.2	Fixed	2.84	66.7	1	0.55	441	0.67	0.80	0.31	86.4
	1.2	Operable	2.87	67.4	0.64	0.55	282	0.57	0.80	0.31	53.2

Table 22 Example House Envelope Loads

Component	HF	CF	Quantity, m² or m	Heating Load, W	Cooling Load, W
Ceiling	4.23	2.06	195.3	826	402
Wall	11.99	7.03	108.5	1301	763
Garage wall	11.99	2.85	35	420	100
Door	54.1	31.69	3.8	206	120
Floor perimeter	20.0		67.2	1344	
Floor area		−2.34	195.3		−457
W-Fixed-0.9	66.7	115.4	0.4	27	46
W-Operable-0.9	67.4	69.0	0.4	27	28
W-Fixed-1.8	66.7	175.7	1.1	73	193
W-Operable-1.8	67.4	101.8	1.1	74	112
W-Fixed-2.4	66.7	190.8	4.3	287	820
S-Fixed-1.2	66.7	117.4	0.7	47	82
S-Operable-1.2	67.4	70.1	0.7	47	49
E-Fixed-0.9	66.7	69.8	0.4	27	28
E-Operable-0.9	67.4	44.1	0.4	27	18
E-Fixed-1.2	66.7	86.4	2.2	147	190
E-Operable-1.2	67.4	53.2	2.2	148	117
Envelope totals				5027	2610

Table 23 Example House Total Sensible Loads

Item	Heating Load, W	Cooling Load, W
Envelope	5027	2610
Infiltration/ventilation	1734	454
Internal gain		654
Subtotal	6761	3718
Distribution loss	879	1004
Total sensible load	7640	4722

Equation (15) with $Q_{bal,hr} = 0$ and $Q_{bal,oth} = 0$ to calculate the sensible infiltration/ventilation loads:

$$q_{vi,s,h} = 1.23 \times 60 \times 23.5 = 1734 \text{ W}$$

$$q_{vi,s,c} = 1.23 \times 41 \times 9.1 = 454 \text{ W}$$

Internal Gain. Apply Equation (30) to find the sensible cooling load from internal gain:

$$q_{ig,s} = 136 + 2.2 \times 195.3 + 22(3 + 1) = 654 \text{ W}$$

Distribution Losses and Total Sensible Load. Table 23 summarizes the sensible load components. Distribution loss factors F_{dl} are estimated (from Table 6) at 0.13 for heating and 0.27 for cooling.

Latent Load. Use Equation (16) with $C_l = 3010$ W/(L·s), $Q_{vi,c} = 41$ L/s, $Q_{bal,oth} = 0$, and $\Delta W = 0.0052$ to calculate the infiltration/ventilation latent load = 641 W. Use Equation (31) to find the latent load from internal gains = 111 W. Therefore, the total latent cooling load is 752 W.

SYMBOLS

A = area, m²; ground surface temperature amplitude, °C
A_L = building effective leakage area (including flue) at 4 Pa, assuming $C_D = 1$, cm²
C_l = air latent heat factor, 3010 W/(L·s) at sea level
C_s = air sensible heat factor, 23 W/(L·s·K) at sea level
C_t = air total heat factor, 1.2 W/(L·s) (kJ/kg) at sea level
CF = cooling load factor, W/m²
D_{oh} = depth of overhang (from plane of fenestration), m
DR = daily range of outdoor dry-bulb temperature, K
E = peak irradiance for exposure, W/m²
F_{dl} = distribution loss factor
F_p = heat loss coefficient per unit length of perimeter, W/(m·K)
F_{shd} = shaded fraction
FF = coefficient for CF_{fen}
G = internal gain coefficient
h_{srf} = effective surface conductance, including resistance of slab covering material such as carpet, $1/(R_{cvr} + 0.12)$ W/(m²·K)
Δh = indoor/outdoor enthalpy difference, kJ/kg
H = height, m
HF = heating (load) factor, W/m²
I = infiltration coefficient
IAC = interior shading attenuation coefficient
IDF = infiltration driving force, L/(s·cm²)
k = conductivity, W/(m·K)
LF = load factor, W/m²
OF = coefficient for CF_{opq}
p = perimeter or exposed edge of floor, m
PXI = peak exterior irradiance, including shading modifications, W/m²
q = heating or cooling load, W
Q = air volumetric flow rate, L/s
R = insulation thermal resistance, (m²·K)W
SHGC = fenestration rated or estimated NFRC solar heat gain coefficient
SLF = shade line factor
t = temperature, °C
T_x = solar transmission of exterior attachment
Δt = design dry-bulb temperature difference (cooling or heating), K
U = construction U-factor, W/(m²·K) (for fenestration, NFRC rated *heating* U-factor)
w = width, m
ΔW = indoor-outdoor humidity ratio difference, kg_w/kg_{da}
V = building volume, m³
X_{oh} = vertical distance from top of fenestration to overhang, m
z = depth below grade, m
α_{roof} = roof solar absorptance
ε = heat/energy recovery ventilation (HRV/ERV) effectiveness

Subscripts

avg = average
b = base (as in OF_b), basement, building, buffer
bal = balanced

bf = basement floor
bl = building load
bw = basement wall
br = bedrooms
ceil = ceiling
cf = conditioned floor
cl = closed
cvr = floor covering
d = diffuse, distribution
D = direct
da = dry air
dl = distribution loss
env = envelope
es = exposed surface
exh = exhaust
fen = fenestration
floor = floor
gr = ground
hr = heat recovery
i = infiltration
in = indoor
ig = internal gain
l = latent
o = outdoor
oc = occupant
oh = overhang
opq = opaque
oth = other
pf = projected product
r = daily range (as in OF_r)
rhb = calculated with RHB method
s = sensible or solar
shd = shaded
slab = slab
srf = surface
sup = supply
t = total or temperature (as in OF_t)
ul = unit leakage
unbal = unbalanced
v = ventilation
vi = ventilation/infiltration
w = water
wall = wall
x = *x*th buffer space surface

REFERENCES

ACCA. 1986. *Load calculation for residential winter and summer air conditioning—Manual J*, 7th ed. Air Conditioning Contractors of America, Arlington, VA.

ACCA. 2006. *Manual J residential load calculations*, 8th ed., v. 2. Air Conditioning Contractors of America, Arlington, VA.

Armstrong, P.R., C.E. Hancock, and J.R. Seem. 1992a. Commercial building temperature recovery—Part 1: Design procedure based on a step response model (RP-491). *ASHRAE Transactions* 98(1):381-396.

Armstrong, P.R., C.E. Hancock, and J.R. Seem. 1992b. Commercial building temperature recovery—Part 2: Experiments to verify step response model (RP-491). *ASHRAE Transactions* 98(1):397-410.

ASHRAE. 2004. Thermal environmental conditions for human occupancy. ANSI/ASHRAE *Standard* 55-2004.

ASHRAE. 2007. Ventilation and acceptable indoor air quality in low-rise residential buildings. ANSI/ASHRAE *Standard* 62.2-2007.

ASHRAE. 2004. Air leakage performance of detached single-family residential buildings. ANSI/ASHRAE *Standard* 119-1988 (RA 2004).

ASHRAE. 2004. Method of test for determining the design and seasonal efficiencies of residential thermal distribution systems. ANSI/ASHRAE *Standard* 152-2004.

ASTM. 1998. Standard terminology of building constructions. *Standard* E631-93a(1998)e1. American Society for Testing and Materials, West Conshohocken, PA.

Bahnfleth, W.P. and C.O. Pedersen 1990. A three-dimensional numerical study of slab-on-grade heat transfer. *ASHRAE Transactions* 96(2):61-72.

Barnaby, C.S. and J.D. Spitler. 2005. Development of the residential load factor method for heating and cooling load calculations. *ASHRAE Transactions* 111(1):291-307.

Barnaby, C.S., J.D. Spitler, and D. Xiao. 2004. Updating the ASHRAE/ACCA residential heating and cooling load calculation procedures and data (RP-1199). ASHRAE Research Project, *Final Report*.

Barnaby, C.S., J.D. Spitler, and D. Xiao. 2005. The residential heat balance method for heating and cooling load calculations (RP-1199). *ASHRAE Transactions* 111(1):308-319.

Beausoleil-Morrison, I. and G. Mitalas. 1997. BASESIMP: A residential-foundation heat-loss algorithm for incorporating into whole-building energy-analysis programs. *Proceedings of Building Simulation '97*, Prague.

Building America. 2004. *Building America research benchmark definition* v. 3.1. Available at http://www.nrel.gov/docs/fy05osti/36429.pdf.

Bullock, C.E. 1978. Energy savings through thermostat setback with residential heat pumps. *ASHRAE Transactions* 84(2):352-363.

CSA. 2004. Determining the required capacity of residential space heating and cooling appliances. CAN/CSA *Standard* F280-M90 (R2004). Canadian Standards Association, Toronto.

DeWitt, C. 2003. Crawlspace myths. *ASHRAE Journal* 45:20-26.

Franciso, P.W. and L. Palmiter. 1999 (rev. 2003). *Improvements to ASHRAE* Standard *152P.* Ecotope, Inc., Seattle, WA.

Hedrick, R.L., M.J. Witte, N.P. Leslie, and W.W. Bassett. 1992. Furnace sizing criteria for energy-efficient setback strategies. *ASHRAE Transactions* 98(1):1239-1246.

Houghten, F.C., S.I. Taimuty, C. Gutberlet, and C.J. Brown. 1942. Heat loss through basement walls and floors. *ASHVE Transactions* 48:369.

HRAI. 1996. *Residential heat loss and gain calculations: Student reference guide.* Heating, Refrigerating and Air Conditioning Institute of Canada. Mississauga, ON.

James, P., J. Cummings, J. Sonne, R. Vieira, and J. Klongerbo. 1997. The effect of residential equipment capacity on energy use, demand, and run-time. *ASHRAE Transactions* 103(2):297-303.

Koenig, K. 1978. Gas furnace sizing requirements for residential heating using thermostat night setback. *ASHRAE Transactions* 84(2):335-351.

Krarti, M. and S. Choi 1996. Simplified method for foundation heat loss calculation. *ASHRAE Transactions* 102(1):140-152.

Latta, J.K. and G.G. Boileau. 1969. Heat losses from house basements. *Canadian Building* 19(10):39.

Lstiburek, J.L. and J. Carmody. 1993. *Moisture control handbook.* Van Nostrand Reinhold, New York.

McQuiston, F.C. 1984. A study and review of existing data to develop a standard methodology for residential heating and cooling load calculations (RP-342). *ASHRAE Transactions* 90(2A):102-136.

Nelson, L.W. and J.W. MacArthur. 1978. Energy savings through thermostat setback. *ASHRAE Transactions* 84(2):319-334.

NFRC. 2009. *NFRC certified products directory.* National Fenestration Rating Council, Silver Spring, MD. www.nfrc.org.

Palmiter, L. and T. Bond. 1991. Interaction of mechanical systems and natural infiltration. *Proceedings of the 12th AIVC Conference on Air Movement and Ventilation Control Within Buildings.* Air Infiltration and Ventilation Centre, Coventry, U.K.

Palmiter, L. and P. Francisco. 1996. Modeled and measured infiltration: Phase III. A detailed case study of three homes. Electric Power Research Institute *Report* TR-106288. Palo Alto, CA.

Palmiter, L. and P. Francisco. 1997. Development of a practical method of estimating the thermal efficiency of residential forced-air distribution systems. Electric Power Research Institute *Report* TR-107744. Palo Alto, CA.

Parker, D.S., J.E.R. McIlvaine, S.F. Barkaszi, D.J. Beal, and M.T. Anello. 2000. *Laboratory testing of the reflectance properties of roofing materials.* FSEC-CR670-00. Florida Solar Energy Center, Cocoa.

Pedersen, C.O., D.E. Fisher, J.D. Spitler, and R.J. Liesen. 1998. *Cooling and heating load calculation principles.* ASHRAE.

Pedersen, C.O., R.J. Liesen, R.K. Strand, D.E. Fisher, L. Dong, and P.G. Ellis. 2001. *Toolkit for building load calculations.* ASHRAE.

Sherman, M.H. 1992. Superposition in infiltration modeling. *Indoor Air* 2: 101-114.

Walker, I.S. and D.J. Wilson. 1990. The Alberta air infiltration model. The University of Alberta, Department of Mechanical Engineering, *Technical Report* 71.

Walker, I.S. and D.J. Wilson. 1998. Field validation of equations for stack and wind driven air infiltration calculations. *International Journal of HVAC&R Research* (now *HVAC&R Research*) 4(2).

BIBLIOGRAPHY

Bligh, T.P., P. Shipp, and G. Meixel. 1978. Energy comparisons and where to insulate earth sheltered buildings and basements. Earth Covered Settlements: U.S. Department of Energy Conference, Fort Worth, TX.

Chang, J.H. 1958. *Ground temperature*. Bluehill Meteorological Observatory, Harvard University, Cambridge, MA.

Harrje, D.T., G.S. Dutt, and J. Beyea. 1979. Locating and eliminating obscure but major energy losses in residential housing. *ASHRAE Transactions* 85(2).

Hite, S.C. and J.L. Dry. 1948. Research in home humidity control. *Research Bulletin* 106. Engineering Experiment Station, Purdue University, West Lafayette, IN.

Joy, F.A. 1958. Improving attic space insulating values. *Heating, Piping and Air Conditioning* 30(1):223.

Joy, F.A., J.J. Zabrony, and S. Bhaduri. 1956. Insulating value of reflective elements in an attic under winter conditions. Pennsylvania State University, University Park.

Machler, M.A. and M. Iqbal. 1985. A modification of the ASHRAE clear sky irradiation model. *ASHRAE Transactions* 91(1A):106-115.

McQuiston, F.C. and J.D. Spitler. 1992. *Cooling and heating load calculation manual*, 2nd ed. ASHRAE.

Peony, B.A., F.J. Powell, and D.M. Burch. 1979. Dynamic thermal performance of an experimental masonry building. NBS *Report* 10 664, National Institute of Standards and Technology, Gaithersburg, MD.

Rowley, F.B., A.B. Algren, and C.E. Lund. 1940. Methods of moisture control and their application to building construction. *Bulletin* No. 17 XLIII(4):28. University of Minnesota Engineering Experiment Station.

Sherman, M.H. 1980. Infiltration-pressurization correlation: Simplified physical modeling. *ASHRAE Transactions* 86(2):778.

Sobotka, P., H. Yoshino, and S. Matsumoto. 1994. Thermal performance of three deep basements: a comparison of measurements with ASHRAE *Fundamentals* and the Mitalas method, the European Standard and the two-dimensional FEM program. *Energy and Buildings* 21(1):23-34.

Wang, F.S. 1979. Mathematical modeling and computer simulation of insulation systems in below grade applications. ASHRAE/DOE Conference on Thermal Performance of the Exterior Envelopes of Buildings, Orlando, FL.

CHAPTER 18

NONRESIDENTIAL COOLING AND HEATING LOAD CALCULATIONS

HEATING and cooling load calculations are the primary design basis for most heating and air-conditioning systems and components. These calculations affect the size of piping, ductwork, diffusers, air handlers, boilers, chillers, coils, compressors, fans, and every other component of systems that condition indoor environments. Cooling and heating load calculations can significantly affect first cost of building construction, comfort and productivity of occupants, and operating cost and energy consumption.

Simply put, heating and cooling loads are the rates of energy input (heating) or removal (cooling) required to maintain an indoor environment at a desired temperature and humidity condition. Heating and air conditioning systems are designed, sized, and controlled to accomplish that energy transfer. The amount of heating or cooling required at any particular time varies widely, depending on external (e.g., outside temperature) and internal (e.g., number of people occupying a space) factors.

Peak design heating and cooling load calculations, which are this chapter's focus, seek to determine the maximum rate of heating and cooling energy transfer needed at any point in time. Similar principles, but with different assumptions, data, and application, can be used to estimate building energy consumption, as described in Chapter 19.

This chapter discusses common elements of cooling load calculation (e.g., internal heat gain, ventilation and infiltration, moisture migration, fenestration heat gain) and two methods of heating and cooling load estimation: heat balance (HB) and radiant time series (RTS).

COOLING LOAD CALCULATION PRINCIPLES

Cooling loads result from many conduction, convection, and radiation heat transfer processes through the building envelope and from internal sources and system components. Building components or contents that may affect cooling loads include the following:

- **External:** Walls, roofs, windows, skylights, doors, partitions, ceilings, and floors
- **Internal:** Lights, people, appliances, and equipment
- **Infiltration:** Air leakage and moisture migration
- **System:** Outside air, duct leakage and heat gain, reheat, fan and pump energy, and energy recovery

TERMINOLOGY

The variables affecting cooling load calculations are numerous, often difficult to define precisely, and always intricately interrelated. Many cooling load components vary widely in magnitude, and possibly direction, during a 24 h period. Because these cyclic changes in load components often are not in phase with each other, each component must be analyzed to establish the maximum cooling load for a building or zone. A **zoned system** (i.e., one serving several independent areas, each with its own temperature control) needs to provide no greater total cooling load capacity than the largest hourly sum of simultaneous zone loads throughout a design day; however, it must handle the peak cooling load for each zone at its individual peak hour. At some times of day during heating or intermediate seasons, some zones may require heating while others require cooling. The zones' ventilation, humidification, or dehumidification needs must also be considered.

Heat Flow Rates

In air-conditioning design, the following four related heat flow rates, each of which varies with time, must be differentiated.

Space Heat Gain. This instantaneous rate of heat gain is the rate at which heat enters into and/or is generated within a space. Heat gain is classified by its mode of entry into the space and whether it is sensible or latent. **Entry modes** include (1) solar radiation through transparent surfaces; (2) heat conduction through exterior walls and roofs; (3) heat conduction through ceilings, floors, and interior partitions; (4) heat generated in the space by occupants, lights, and appliances; (5) energy transfer through direct-with-space ventilation and infiltration of outdoor air; and (6) miscellaneous heat gains. **Sensible heat** is added directly to the conditioned space by conduction, convection, and/or radiation. **Latent heat** gain occurs when moisture is added to the space (e.g., from vapor emitted by occupants and equipment). To maintain a constant humidity ratio, water vapor must condense on the cooling apparatus and be removed at the same rate it is added to the space. The amount of energy required to offset latent heat gain essentially equals the product of the condensation rate and latent heat of condensation. In selecting cooling equipment, distinguish between sensible and latent heat gain: every cooling apparatus has different maximum removal capacities for sensible versus latent heat for particular operating conditions. In extremely dry climates, humidification may be required, rather than dehumidification, to maintain thermal comfort.

Radiant Heat Gain. Radiant energy must first be absorbed by surfaces that enclose the space (walls, floor, and ceiling) and objects in the space (furniture, etc.). When these surfaces and objects become warmer than the surrounding air, some of their heat transfers to the air by convection. The composite heat storage capacity of these surfaces and objects determines the rate at which their respective surface temperatures increase for a given radiant input, and thus governs the relationship between the radiant portion of heat gain and its corresponding part of the space cooling load (Figure 1). The thermal storage effect is critical in differentiating between instantaneous heat gain for a given space and its cooling load at that moment. Predicting the nature and magnitude of this phenomenon in order to estimate a realistic cooling load for a particular set of circumstances has long

The preparation of this chapter is assigned to TC 4.1, Load Calculation Data and Procedures.

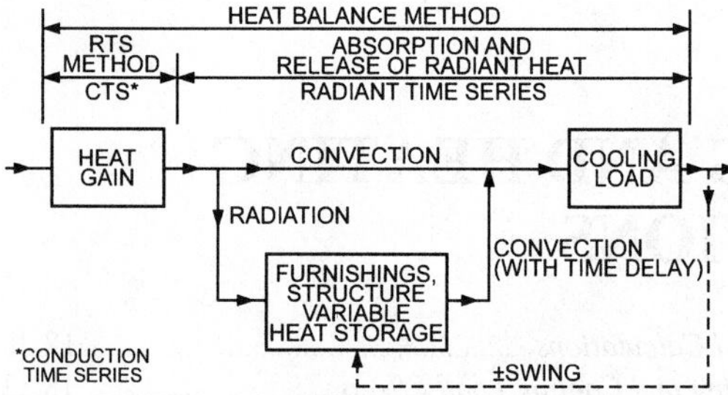

Fig. 1 Origin of Difference Between Magnitude of Instantaneous Heat Gain and Instantaneous Cooling Load

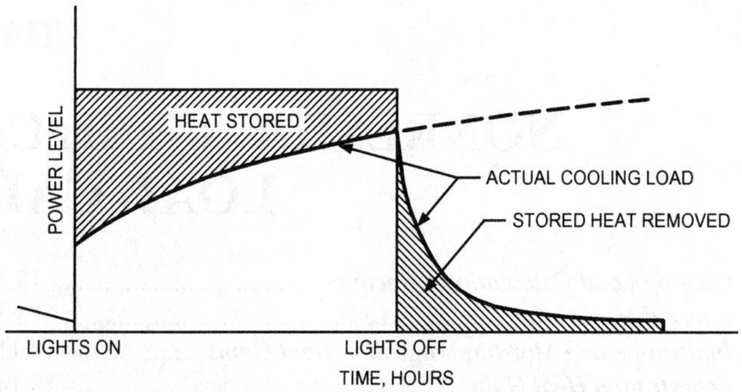

Fig. 2 Thermal Storage Effect in Cooling Load from Lights

been of interest to design engineers; the Bibliography lists some early work on the subject.

Space Cooling Load. This is the rate at which sensible and latent heat must be removed from the space to maintain a constant space air temperature and humidity. The sum of all space instantaneous heat gains at any given time does not necessarily (or even frequently) equal the cooling load for the space at that same time.

Space Heat Extraction Rate. The rates at which sensible and latent heat are removed from the conditioned space equal the space cooling load only if the room air temperature and humidity are constant. Along with the intermittent operation of cooling equipment, control systems usually allow a minor cyclic variation or swing in room temperature; humidity is often allowed to float, but it can be controlled. Therefore, proper simulation of the control system gives a more realistic value of energy removal over a fixed period than using values of the space cooling load. However, this is primarily important for estimating energy use over time; it is not needed to calculate design peak cooling load for equipment selection.

Cooling Coil Load. The rate at which energy is removed at a cooling coil serving one or more conditioned spaces equals the sum of instantaneous space cooling loads (or space heat extraction rate, if it is assumed that space temperature and humidity vary) for all spaces served by the coil, plus any system loads. System loads include fan heat gain, duct heat gain, and outdoor air heat and moisture brought into the cooling equipment to satisfy the ventilation air requirement.

Time Delay Effect

Energy absorbed by walls, floor, furniture, etc., contributes to space cooling load only after a time lag. Some of this energy is still present and reradiating even after the heat sources have been switched off or removed, as shown in Figure 2.

There is always significant delay between the time a heat source is activated, and the point when reradiated energy equals that being instantaneously stored. This time lag must be considered when calculating cooling load, because the load required for the space can be much lower than the instantaneous heat gain being generated, and the space's peak load may be significantly affected.

Accounting for the time delay effect is the major challenge in cooling load calculations. Several methods, including the two presented in this chapter, have been developed to take the time delay effect into consideration.

COOLING LOAD CALCULATION METHODS

This chapter presents two load calculation methods that vary significantly from previous methods. The technology involved, however (the principle of calculating a heat balance for a given space) is not new. The first of the two methods is the **heat balance (HB) method**; the second is **radiant time series (RTS)**, which is a simplification of the HB procedure. Both methods are explained in their respective sections.

Cooling load calculation of an actual, multiple-room building requires a complex computer program implementing the principles of either method.

Cooling Load Calculations in Practice

Load calculations should accurately describe the building. All load calculation inputs should be as accurate as reasonable, without using safety factors. Introducing compounding safety factors at multiple levels in the load calculation results in an unrealistic and oversized load.

Variation in heat transmission coefficients of typical building materials and composite assemblies, differing motivations and skills of those who construct the building, unknown filtration rates, and the manner in which the building is actually operated are some of the variables that make precise calculation impossible. Even if the designer uses reasonable procedures to account for these factors, the calculation can never be more than a good estimate of the actual load. Frequently, a cooling load must be calculated before every parameter in the conditioned space can be properly or completely defined. An example is a cooling load estimate for a new building with many floors of unleased spaces for which detailed partition requirements, furnishings, lighting, and layout cannot be predefined. Potential tenant modifications once the building is occupied also must be considered. Load estimating requires proper engineering judgment that includes a thorough understanding of heat balance fundamentals.

Perimeter spaces exposed to high solar heat gain often need cooling during sunlit portions of traditional heating months, as do completely interior spaces with significant internal heat gain. These spaces can also have significant heating loads during nonsunlit hours or after periods of nonoccupancy, when adjacent spaces have cooled below interior design temperatures. The heating loads involved can be estimated conventionally to offset or to compensate for them and prevent overheating, but they have no direct relationship to the spaces' design heating loads.

Correct design and sizing of air-conditioning systems require more than calculation of the cooling load in the space to be conditioned. The type of air-conditioning system, ventilation rate, reheat, fan energy, fan location, duct heat loss and gain, duct leakage, heat extraction lighting systems, type of return air system, and any sensible or latent heat recovery all affect system load and component sizing. Adequate system design and component sizing require that system performance be analyzed as a series of psychrometric processes.

System design could be driven by either sensible or latent load, and both need to be checked. When a space is sensible-load-driven, which is generally the case, the cooling supply air will have surplus capacity to dehumidify, but this is commonly permissible. For a space driven by latent load, (e.g., an auditorium), supply airflow based on sensible load is likely not have enough dehumidifying capability, so subcooling and reheating or some other dehumidification process is needed.

This chapter is primarily concerned with a given space or zone in a building. When estimating loads for a group of spaces (e.g., for an air-handling system that serves multiple zones), the assembled zones must be analyzed to consider (1) the simultaneous effects taking place; (2) any diversification of heat gains for occupants, lighting, or other internal load sources; (3) ventilation; and/or (4) any other unique circumstances. With large buildings that involve more than a single HVAC system, simultaneous loads and any additional diversity also must be considered when designing the central equipment that serves the systems. Methods presented in this chapter are expressed as hourly load summaries, reflecting 24 h input schedules and profiles of the individual load variables. Specific systems and applications may require different profiles.

DATA ASSEMBLY

Calculating space cooling loads requires detailed building design information and weather data at design conditions. Generally, the following information should be compiled.

Building Characteristics. Building materials, component size, external surface colors, and shape are usually determined from building plans and specifications.

Configuration. Determine building location, orientation, and external shading from building plans and specifications. Shading from adjacent buildings can be determined from a site plan or by visiting the proposed site, but its probable permanence should be carefully evaluated before it is included in the calculation. The possibility of abnormally high ground-reflected solar radiation (e.g., from adjacent water, sand, or parking lots) or solar load from adjacent reflective buildings should not be overlooked.

Outdoor Design Conditions. Obtain appropriate weather data, and select outdoor design conditions. Chapter 14 provides information for many weather stations; note, however, that these design dry-bulb and mean coincident wet-bulb temperatures may vary considerably from data traditionally used in various areas. Use judgment to ensure that results are consistent with expectations. Also, consider prevailing wind velocity and the relationship of a project site to the selected weather station.

Recent research projects have greatly expanded the amount of available weather data (e.g., ASHRAE 2004). In addition to the conventional dry-bulb with mean coincident wet-bulb, data are now available for wet-bulb and dew point with mean coincident dry-bulb. Peak space load generally coincides with peak solar or peak dry-bulb, but peak system load often occurs at peak wet-bulb temperature. The relationship between space and system loads is discussed further in following sections of the chapter.

To estimate conductive heat gain through exterior surfaces and infiltration and outdoor air loads at any time, applicable outdoor dry- and wet-bulb temperatures must be used. Chapter 14 gives monthly cooling load design values of outdoor conditions for many locations. These are generally midafternoon conditions; for other times of day, the daily range profile method described in Chapter 14 can be used to estimate dry- and wet-bulb temperatures. Peak cooling load is often determined by solar heat gain through fenestration; this peak may occur in winter months and/or at a time of day when outside air temperature is not at its maximum.

Indoor Design Conditions. Select indoor dry-bulb temperature, indoor relative humidity, and ventilation rate. Include permissible variations and control limits. Consult ASHRAE *Standard* 90.1 for energy-savings conditions, and *Standard* 55 for ranges of indoor conditions needed for thermal comfort.

Internal Heat Gains and Operating Schedules. Obtain planned density and a proposed schedule of lighting, occupancy, internal equipment, appliances, and processes that contribute to the internal thermal load.

Areas. Use consistent methods for calculation of building areas. For fenestration, the definition of a component's area must be consistent with associated ratings.

Gross surface area. It is efficient and conservative to derive gross surface areas from outside building dimensions, ignoring wall and floor thicknesses and avoiding separate accounting of floor edge and wall corner conditions. Measure floor areas to the outside of adjacent exterior walls or to the center line of adjacent partitions. When apportioning to rooms, façade area should be divided at partition center lines. Wall height should be taken as floor-to-floor height.

The outside-dimension procedure is expedient for load calculations, but it is not consistent with rigorous definitions used in building-related standards. The resulting differences do not introduce significant errors in this chapter's procedures.

Fenestration area. As discussed in Chapter 15, fenestration ratings [U-factor and solar heat gain coefficient (SHGC)] are based on the entire product area, including frames. Thus, for load calculations, fenestration area is the area of the rough opening in the wall or roof.

Net surface area. Net surface area is the gross surface area less any enclosed fenestration area.

INTERNAL HEAT GAINS

Internal heat gains from people, lights, motors, appliances, and equipment can contribute the majority of the cooling load in a modern building. As building envelopes have improved in response to more restrictive energy codes, internal loads have increased because of factors such as increased use of computers and the advent of dense-occupancy spaces (e.g., call centers). Internal heat gain calculation techniques are identical for both heat balance (HB) and radiant time series (RTS) cooling-load calculation methods, so internal heat gain data are presented here independent of calculation methods.

PEOPLE

Table 1 gives representative rates at which sensible heat and moisture are emitted by humans in different states of activity. In high-density spaces, such as auditoriums, these sensible and latent heat gains comprise a large fraction of the total load. Even for short-term occupancy, the extra sensible heat and moisture introduced by people may be significant. See Chapter 9 for detailed information; however, Table 1 summarizes design data for common conditions.

The conversion of sensible heat gain from people to space cooling load is affected by the thermal storage characteristics of that space because some percentage of the sensible load is radiant energy. Latent heat gains are usually considered instantaneous, but research is yielding practical models and data for the latent heat storage of and release from common building materials.

LIGHTING

Because lighting is often a major space cooling load component, an accurate estimate of the space heat gain it imposes is needed. Calculation of this load component is not straightforward; the rate of cooling load from lighting at any given moment can be quite different from the heat equivalent of power supplied instantaneously to those lights, because of heat storage.

Instantaneous Heat Gain from Lighting

The primary source of heat from lighting comes from light-emitting elements, or lamps, although significant additional heat may be generated from ballasts and other appurtenances in the luminaires. Generally, the instantaneous rate of sensible heat gain from electric lighting may be calculated from

$$q_{el} = WF_{ul}F_{sa} \tag{1}$$

where

q_{el} = heat gain, W
W = total light wattage, W
F_{ul} = lighting use factor
F_{sa} = lighting special allowance factor

Table 1 Representative Rates at Which Heat and Moisture Are Given Off by Human Beings in Different States of Activity

Degree of Activity		Total Heat, W Adult Male	Total Heat, W Adjusted, M/F[a]	Sensible Heat, W	Latent Heat, W	% Sensible Heat that is Radiant[b] Low V	% Sensible Heat that is Radiant[b] High V
Seated at theater	Theater, matinee	115	95	65	30		
Seated at theater, night	Theater, night	115	105	70	35	60	27
Seated, very light work	Offices, hotels, apartments	130	115	70	45		
Moderately active office work	Offices, hotels, apartments	140	130	75	55		
Standing, light work; walking	Department store; retail store	160	130	75	55	58	38
Walking, standing	Drug store, bank	160	145	75	70		
Sedentary work	Restaurant[c]	145	160	80	80		
Light bench work	Factory	235	220	80	140		
Moderate dancing	Dance hall	265	250	90	160	49	35
Walking 4.8 km/h; light machine work	Factory	295	295	110	185		
Bowling[d]	Bowling alley	440	425	170	255		
Heavy work	Factory	440	425	170	255	54	19
Heavy machine work; lifting	Factory	470	470	185	285		
Athletics	Gymnasium	585	525	210	315		

Notes:
1. Tabulated values are based on 24°C room dry-bulb temperature. For 27°C room dry bulb, total heat remains the same, but sensible heat values should be decreased by approximately 20%, and latent heat values increased accordingly.
2. Also see Table 4, Chapter 9, for additional rates of metabolic heat generation.
3. All values are rounded to nearest 5 W.

[a]Adjusted heat gain is based on normal percentage of men, women, and children for the application listed, and assumes that gain from an adult female is 85% of that for an adult male, and gain from a child is 75% of that for an adult male.

[b]Values approximated from data in Table 6, Chapter 9, where V is air velocity with limits shown in that table.

[c]Adjusted heat gain includes 18 W for food per individual (9 W sensible and 9 W latent).

[d]Figure one person per alley actually bowling, and all others as sitting (117 W) or standing or walking slowly (231 W).

The **total light wattage** is obtained from the ratings of all lamps installed, both for general illumination and for display use. Ballasts are not included, but are addressed by a separate factor. Wattages of magnetic ballasts are significant; the energy consumption of high-efficiency electronic ballasts might be insignificant compared to that of the lamps.

The **lighting use factor** is the ratio of wattage in use, for the conditions under which the load estimate is being made, to total installed wattage. For commercial applications such as stores, the use factor is generally 1.0.

The **special allowance factor** is the ratio of the lighting fixtures' power consumption, including lamps and ballast, to the nominal power consumption of the lamps. For incandescent lights, this factor is 1. For fluorescent lights, it accounts for power consumed by the ballast as well as the ballast's effect on lamp power consumption. The special allowance factor can be less than 1 for electronic ballasts that lower electricity consumption below the lamp's rated power consumption. Use manufacturers' values for system (lamps + ballast) power, when available.

For high-intensity-discharge lamps (e.g. metal halide, mercury vapor, high- and low-pressure sodium vapor lamps), the actual lighting system power consumption should be available from the manufacturer of the fixture or ballast. Ballasts available for metal halide and high pressure sodium vapor lamps may have special allowance factors from about 1.3 (for low-wattage lamps) down to 1.1 (for high-wattage lamps).

An alternative procedure is to estimate the lighting heat gain on a per square foot basis. Such an approach may be required when final lighting plans are not available. Table 2 shows the maximum lighting power density (LPD) (lighting heat gain per square metre) allowed by ASHRAE *Standard* 90.1-2007 for a range of space types.

In addition to determining the lighting heat gain, the fraction of lighting heat gain that enters the conditioned space may need to be distinguished from the fraction that enters an unconditioned space; of the former category, the distribution between radiative and convective heat gain must be established.

Fisher and Chantrasrisalai (2006) experimentally studied 12 luminaire types and recommended five different categories of luminaires, as shown in Table 3. The table provides a range of design data for the conditioned space fraction, short-wave radiative fraction, and long-wave radiative fraction under typical operating conditions: airflow rate of 5 L/(s·m^2), supply air temperature between 15 and 16.7°C, and room air temperature between 22 and 24°C. The recommended fractions in Table 3 are based on lighting heat input rates range of 9.7 to 28 W/m^2. For higher design power input, the lower bounds of the space and short-wave fractions should be used; for design power input below this range, the upper bounds of the space and short-wave fractions should be used. The **space fraction** in the table is the fraction of lighting heat gain that goes to the room; the fraction going to the plenum can be computed as 1 – the space fraction. The **radiative fraction** is the radiative part of the lighting heat gain that goes to the room. The convective fraction of the lighting heat gain that goes to the room is 1 – the radiative fraction. Using values in the middle of the range yields sufficiently accurate results. However, values that better suit a specific situation may be determined according to the notes for Table 3.

Table 3's data are applicable for both ducted and nonducted returns. However, application of the data, particularly the ceiling plenum fraction, may vary for different return configurations. For instance, for a room with a ducted return, although a portion of the lighting energy initially dissipated to the ceiling plenum is quantitatively equal to the plenum fraction, a large portion of this energy would likely end up as the conditioned space cooling load and a small portion would end up as the cooling load to the return air.

If the space airflow rate is different from the typical condition [i.e., about 5 L/(s·m^2)], Figure 3 can be used to estimate the lighting heat gain parameters. Design data shown in Figure 3 are only applicable for the recessed fluorescent luminaire without lens.

Although design data presented in Table 3 and Figure 3 can be used for a vented luminaire with side-slot returns, they are likely not applicable for a vented luminaire with lamp compartment returns, because in the latter case, all heat convected in the vented luminaire is likely to go directly to the ceiling plenum, resulting in zero convective fraction and a much lower space fraction. Therefore, the design data should only be used for a configuration where conditioned air is returned through the ceiling grille or luminaire side slots.

Table 2 Lighting Power Densities Using Space-by-Space Method

Common Space Types*	LPD, W/m²	Building-Specific Space Types	LPD, W/m²
Office—enclosed	12	Gymnasium/exercise center	
Office—open plan	12	Playing Area	15
Conference/meeting/multipurpose	14	Exercise Area	10
Classroom/lecture/training	15	Courthouse/police station/penitentiary	
For penitentiary	14	Courtroom	20
Lobby	14	Confinement cells	10
For hotel	12	Judges' chambers	14
For performing arts theater	36	Fire Stations	
For motion picture theater	12	Engine room	9
Audience/seating Area	10	Sleeping quarters	3
For gymnasium	4	Post office—sorting area	13
For exercise center	3	Convention center—exhibit space	14
For convention center	8	Library	
For penitentiary	8	Card file and cataloging	12
For religious buildings	18	Stacks	18
For sports arena	4	Reading area	13
For performing arts theater	28	Hospital	
For motion picture theater	13	Emergency	29
For transportation	5	Recovery	9
Atrium—first three floors	6	Nurses' station	11
Atrium—each additional floor	2	Exam/treatment	16
Lounge/recreation	13	Pharmacy	13
For hospital	9	Patient room	8
Dining Area	10	Operating room	24
For penitentiary	14	Nursery	6
For hotel	14	Medical supply	15
For motel	13	Physical therapy	10
For bar lounge/leisure dining	15	Radiology	4
For family dining	23	Laundry—washing	6
Food preparation	13	Automotive—service/repair	8
Laboratory	15	Manufacturing	
Restrooms	10	Low bay (<7.6 m floor to ceiling height)	13
Dressing/locker/fitting room	6	High bay (≥7.6 m floor to ceiling height)	18
Corridor/transition	5	Detailed manufacturing	23
For hospital	11	Equipment room	13
For manufacturing facility	5	Control room	5
Stairs—active	6	Hotel/motel guest rooms	12
Active storage	9	Dormitory—living quarters	12
For hospital	10	Museum	
Inactive storage	3	General exhibition	11
For museum	9	Restoration	18
Electrical/mechanical	16	Bank/office—banking activity area	16
Workshop	20	Religious buildings	
Sales area [for accent lighting, see Section 9.6.2(B) of ASHRAE *Standard* 90.1]	18	Worship pulpit, choir	26
		Fellowship hall	10
		Retail	
		Sales area for accent lighting, see Section 9.6.3(C) of ASHRAE *Standard* 90.1]	18
		Mall concourse	18
		Sports arena	
		Ring sports area	29
		Court sports area	25
		Indoor playing field area	15
		Warehouse	
		Fine material storage	15
		Medium/bulky material storage	10
		Parking garage—garage area	2
		Transportation	
		Airport—concourse	6
		Air/train/bus—baggage area	11
		Terminal—ticket counter	16

Source: ASHRAE *Standard* 90.1-2007.
*In cases where both a common space type and a building-specific type are listed, the building-specific space type applies.

For other luminaire types, it may be necessary to estimate the heat gain for each component as a fraction of the total lighting heat gain by using judgment to estimate heat-to-space and heat-to-return percentages.

Because of the directional nature of downlight luminaires, a large portion of the short-wave radiation typically falls on the floor. When converting heat gains to cooling loads in the RTS method, the solar radiant time factors (RTF) may be more appropriate than nonsolar RTF. (Solar RTF are calculated assuming most solar radiation is intercepted by the floor; nonsolar RTF assume uniform distribution by area over all interior surfaces.) This effect may be significant for rooms where lighting heat gain is high and for which solar RTF are significantly different from nonsolar RTF.

ELECTRIC MOTORS

Instantaneous sensible heat gain from equipment operated by electric motors in a conditioned space is calculated as

$$q_{em} = (P/E_M)F_{UM}F_{LM} \quad (2)$$

where

q_{em} = heat equivalent of equipment operation, W
P = motor power rating, W
E_M = motor efficiency, decimal fraction <1.0
F_{UM} = motor use factor, 1.0 or decimal fraction <1.0
F_{LM} = motor load factor, 1.0 or decimal fraction <1.0

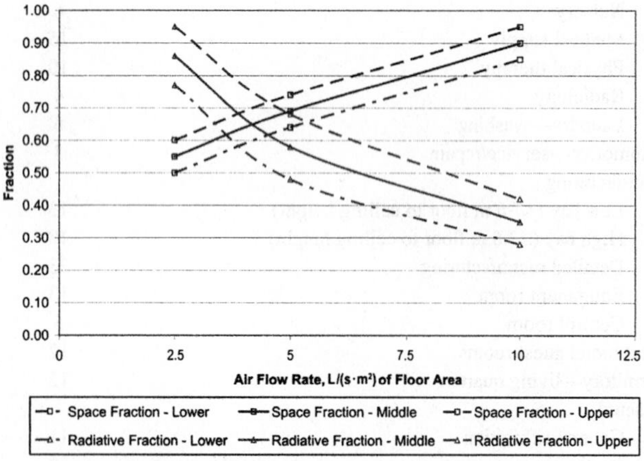

Fig. 3 Lighting Heat Gain Parameters for Recessed Fluorescent Luminaire Without Lens
(Fisher and Chantrasrisalai 2006)

The motor use factor may be applied when motor use is known to be intermittent, with significant nonuse during all hours of operation (e.g., overhead door operator). For conventional applications, its value is 1.0.

The motor load factor is the fraction of the rated load delivered under the conditions of the cooling load estimate. In Equation (2), it is assumed that both the motor and driven equipment are in the conditioned space. If the motor is outside the space or airstream,

$$q_{em} = PF_{UM}F_{LM} \quad (3)$$

When the motor is inside the conditioned space or airstream but the driven machine is outside,

$$q_{em} = P\left(\frac{1.0 - E_M}{E_M}\right)F_{UM}F_{LM} \quad (4)$$

Equation (4) also applies to a fan or pump in the conditioned space that exhausts air or pumps fluid outside that space.

Table 4 gives minimum efficiencies and related data representative of typical electric motors from ASHRAE *Standard* 90.1-2007. If electric motor load is an appreciable portion of cooling load, the motor efficiency should be obtained from the manufacturer. Also, depending on design, maximum efficiency might occur anywhere between 75 to 110% of full load; if under- or overloaded, efficiency could vary from the manufacturer's listing.

Overloading or Underloading

Heat output of a motor is generally proportional to motor load, within rated overload limits. Because of typically high no-load motor current, fixed losses, and other reasons, F_{LM} is generally assumed to be unity, and no adjustment should be made for underloading or overloading unless the situation is fixed and can be accurately established, and reduced-load efficiency data can be obtained from the motor manufacturer.

Radiation and Convection

Unless the manufacturer's technical literature indicates otherwise, motor heat gain normally should be equally divided between radiant and convective components for the subsequent cooling load calculations.

APPLIANCES

A cooling load estimate should take into account heat gain from all appliances (electrical, gas, or steam). Because of the variety of appliances, applications, schedules, use, and installations, estimates can be very subjective. Often, the only information available about

Table 3 Lighting Heat Gain Parameters for Typical Operating Conditions

Luminaire Category	Space Fraction	Radiative Fraction	Notes
Recessed fluorescent luminaire without lens	0.64 to 0.74	0.48 to 0.68	• Use middle values in most situations • May use higher space fraction, and lower radiative fraction for luminaire with side-slot returns • May use lower values of both fractions for direct/indirect luminaire • May use higher values of both fractions for ducted returns
Recessed fluorescent luminaire with lens	0.40 to 0.50	0.61 to 0.73	• May adjust values in the same way as for recessed fluorescent luminaire without lens
Downlight compact fluorescent luminaire	0.12 to 0.24	0.95 to 1.0	• Use middle or high values if detailed features are unknown • Use low value for space fraction and high value for radiative fraction if there are large holes in luminaire's reflector
Downlight incandescent luminaire	0.70 to 0.80	0.95 to 1.0	• Use middle values if lamp type is unknown • Use low value for space fraction if standard lamp (i.e. A-lamp) is used • Use high value for space fraction if reflector lamp (i.e. BR-lamp) is used
Non-in-ceiling fluorescent luminaire	1.0	0.5 to 0.57	• Use lower value for radiative fraction for surface-mounted luminaire • Use higher value for radiative fraction for pendant luminaire

Source: Fisher and Chantrasrisalai (2006).

Table 4 Minimum Nominal Efficiency for General Purpose Design A and Design B Motors*

	Minimum Nominal Full-Load Efficiency, %					
	Open Motors			Enclosed Motors		
Number of Poles ⇒	2	4	6	2	4	6
Synchronous Speed (RPM) ⇒	3600	1800	1200	3600	1800	1200
Motor Kilowatts						
0.8	—	82.5	80.0	75.5	82.5	80.0
1.1	82.5	84.0	84.0	82.5	84.0	85.5
1.5	84.0	84.0	85.5	84.0	84.0	86.5
2.2	84.0	86.5	86.5	85.5	87.5	87.5
3.7	85.5	87.5	87.5	87.5	87.5	87.5
5.6	87.5	88.5	88.5	88.5	89.5	89.5
7.5	88.5	89.5	90.2	89.5	89.5	89.5
11.1	89.5	91.0	90.2	90.2	91.0	90.2
14.9	90.2	91.0	91.0	90.2	91.0	90.2
18.7	91.0	91.7	91.7	91.0	92.4	91.7
22.4	91.0	92.4	92.4	91.0	92.4	91.7
29.8	91.7	93.0	93.0	91.7	93.0	93.0
37.3	92.4	93.0	93.0	92.4	93.0	93.0
44.8	93.0	93.6	93.6	93.0	93.6	93.6
56.0	93.0	94.1	93.6	93.0	94.1	93.6
74.6	93.0	94.1	94.1	93.6	94.5	94.1
93.3	93.6	94.5	94.1	94.5	94.5	94.1
111.9	93.6	95.0	94.5	94.5	95.0	95.0
149.2	94.5	95.0	94.5	95.0	95.0	95.0

Source: ASHRAE *Standard* 90.1-2007.
*Nominal efficiencies established in accordance with NEMA *Standard* MG1. Designs A and B are National Electric Manufacturers Association (NEMA) design class designations for fixed-frequency small and medium AC squirrel-cage induction motors.

heat gain from equipment is that on its nameplate, which can overestimate actual heat gain for many types of appliances, as discussed in the section on Office Equipment.

Cooking Appliances

These appliances include common heat-producing cooking equipment found in conditioned commercial kitchens. Marn (1962) concluded that appliance surfaces contributed most of the heat to commercial kitchens and that when appliances were installed under an effective hood, the cooling load was independent of the fuel or energy used for similar equipment performing the same operations.

Gordon et al. (1994) and Smith et al. (1995) found that gas appliances may exhibit slightly higher heat gains than their electric counterparts under wall-canopy hoods operated at typical ventilation rates. This is because heat contained in combustion products exhausted from a gas appliance may increase the temperatures of the appliance and surrounding surfaces, as well as the hood above the appliance, more so than the heat produced by its electric counterpart. These higher-temperature surfaces radiate heat to the kitchen, adding moderately to the radiant gain directly associated with the appliance cooking surface.

Marn (1962) confirmed that, where appliances are installed under an effective hood, only radiant gain adds to the cooling load; convective and latent heat from cooking and combustion products are exhausted and do not enter the kitchen. Gordon et al. (1994) and Smith et al. (1995) substantiated these findings. Chapter 31 of the 2007 ASHRAE *Handbook—HVAC Applications* has more information on kitchen ventilation.

Sensible Heat Gain for Hooded Cooking Appliances. To establish a heat gain value, nameplate energy input ratings may be used with appropriate usage and radiation factors. Where specific rating data are not available (nameplate missing, equipment not yet purchased, etc.), representative heat gains listed in Tables 5A to E (Swierczyna et al. 2008, 2009) for a wide variety of commonly encountered equipment items. In estimating appliance load, probabilities of simultaneous use and operation for different appliances located in the same space must be considered.

Radiant heat gain from hooded cooking equipment can range from 15 to 45% of the actual appliance energy consumption (Gordon et al. 1994; Smith et al. 1995; Swierczyna et al. 2008; Talbert et al. 1973). This ratio of heat gain to appliance energy consumption may be expressed as a radiation factor, and it is a function of both appliance type and fuel source. The radiation factor F_R is applied to the average rate of appliance energy consumption, determined by applying usage factor F_U to the nameplate or rated energy input. Marn (1962) found that radiant heat temperature rise can be substantially reduced by shielding the fronts of cooking appliances. Although this approach may not always be practical in a commercial kitchen, radiant gains can also be reduced by adding side panels or partial enclosures that are integrated with the exhaust hood.

Heat Gain from Meals. For each meal served, approximately 15 W of heat, of which 75% is sensible and 25% is latent, is transferred to the dining space.

Heat Gain for Generic Appliances. The average rate of appliance energy consumption can be estimated from the nameplate or rated energy input q_{input} by applying a duty cycle or usage factor F_U. Thus, sensible heat gain q_s for generic electric, steam, and gas appliances installed under a hood can be estimated using one of the following equations:

$$q_s = q_{input} F_U F_R \tag{5}$$

or

$$q_s = q_{input} F_L \tag{6}$$

where F_L is the ratio of sensible heat gain to the manufacturer's rated energy input. However, recent ASHRAE research (Swierczyna et al. 2008, 2009) showed the design value for heat gain from a hooded appliance at idle (ready-to-cook) conditions based on its energy consumption rate is, at best, a rough estimate. When appliance heat gain measurements during idle conditions were regressed against energy consumption rates for gas and electric appliances, the appliances' emissivity, insulation, and surface cooling (e.g., through ventilation rates) scattered the data points widely, with large deviations from the average values. Because large errors could occur in the heat load calculation for specific appliance lines by using a general radiation factor, heat gain values in Table 5 should be applied in the HVAC design.

Table 5 lists usage factors, radiation factors, and load factors based on appliance energy consumption rate for typical electrical, steam, and gas appliances under standby or idle conditions, hooded and unhooded.

Recirculating Systems. Cooking appliances ventilated by recirculating systems or "ductless" hoods should be treated as unhooded appliances when estimating heat gain. In other words, all energy consumed by the appliance and all moisture produced by cooking is introduced to the kitchen as a sensible or latent cooling load.

Recommended Heat Gain Values. Table 5 lists recommended rates of heat gain from typical commercial cooking appliances. Data in the "hooded" columns assume installation under a properly designed exhaust hood connected to a mechanical fan exhaust system operating at an exhaust rate for complete capture and containment of the thermal and effluent plume. Improperly operating hood systems load the space with a significant convective component of the heat gain.

Table 5A Recommended Rates of Radiant and Convective Heat Gain from Unhooded Electric Appliances During Idle (Ready-to-Cook) Conditions

	Energy Rate, W		Rate of Heat Gain, W					
Appliance	Rated	Standby	Sensible Radiant	Sensible Convective	Latent	Total	Usage Factor F_u	Radiation Factor F_r
Cabinet: hot serving (large), insulated*	1993	352	117	234	0	352	0.18	0.33
Cabinet: hot serving (large), uninsulated	1993	1026	205	821	0	1026	0.51	0.2
Cabinet: proofing (large)*	5099	410	352	0	59	410	0.08	0.86
Cabinet: proofing (small-15 shelf)	4191	1143	0	264	879	1143	0.27	0
Coffee brewing urn	3810	352	59	88	205	352	0.08	0.17
Drawer warmers, 2-drawer (moist holding)*	1202	147	0	0	59	59	0.12	0
Egg cooker	3194	205	88	117	0	205	0.06	0.43
Espresso machine*	2403	352	117	234	0	352	0.15	0.33
Food warmer: steam table (2-well-type)	1495	1026	88	176	762	1026	0.69	0.08
Freezer (small)	791	322	147	176	0	322	0.41	0.45
Hot dog roller*	996	703	264	440	0	703	0.71	0.38
Hot plate: single burner, high speed	1114	879	264	615	0	879	0.79	0.3
Hot-food case (dry holding)*	9115	733	264	469	0	733	0.08	0.36
Hot-food case (moist holding)*	9115	967	264	528	176	967	0.11	0.27
Microwave oven: commercial (heavy duty)	3194	0	0	0	0	0	0	0
Oven: countertop conveyorized bake/finishing*	6008	3693	645	3048	0	3693	0.61	0.17
Panini*	1700	938	352	586	0	938	0.55	0.38
Popcorn popper*	586	59	29	29	0	59	0.1	0.5
Rapid-cook oven (quartz-halogen)*	12 016	0	0	0	0	0	0	0
Rapid-cook oven (microwave/convection)*	7297	1202	293	909	0	293	0.16	0.24
Reach-in refrigerator*	1407	352	88	264	0	352	0.25	0.25
Refrigerated prep table*	586	264	176	88	0	264	0.45	0.67
Steamer (bun)	1495	205	176	29	0	205	0.14	0.86
Toaster: 4-slice pop up (large): cooking	1788	879	59	410	293	762	0.49	0.07
Toaster: contact (vertical)	3312	1553	791	762	0	1553	0.47	0.51
Toaster: conveyor (large)	9613	3019	879	2139	0	3019	0.31	0.29
Toaster: small conveyor	1700	1084	117	967	0	1084	0.64	0.11
Waffle iron	909	352	234	117	0	352	0.39	0.67

Source: Swierczyna et al. (2008, 2009).

Hospital and Laboratory Equipment

Hospital and laboratory equipment items are major sources of sensible and latent heat gains in conditioned spaces. Care is needed in evaluating the probability and duration of simultaneous usage when many components are concentrated in one area, such as a laboratory, an operating room, etc. Commonly, heat gain from equipment in a laboratory ranges from 50 to 220 W/m^2 or, in laboratories with outdoor exposure, as much as four times the heat gain from all other sources combined.

Medical Equipment. It is more difficult to provide generalized heat gain recommendations for medical equipment than for general office equipment because medical equipment is much more varied in type and in application. Some heat gain testing has been done, but the equipment included represents only a small sample of the type of equipment that may be encountered.

Data presented for medical equipment in Table 6 are relevant for portable and bench-top equipment. Medical equipment is very specific and can vary greatly from application to application. The data are presented to provide guidance in only the most general sense. For large equipment, such as MRI, heat gain must be obtained from the manufacturer.

Laboratory Equipment. Equipment in laboratories is similar to medical equipment in that it varies significantly from space to space. Chapter 14 of the 2007 *ASHRAE Handbook—HVAC Applications* discusses heat gain from equipment, which may range from 50 to 270 W/m^2 in highly automated laboratories. Table 7 lists some values for laboratory equipment, but, with medical equipment, it is for general guidance only. Wilkins and Cook (1999) also examined laboratory equipment heat gains.

Office Equipment

Computers, printers, copiers, etc., can generate very significant heat gains, sometimes greater than all other gains combined. ASHRAE research project RP-822 developed a method to measure the actual heat gain from equipment in buildings and the radiant/convective percentages (Hosni et al. 1998; Jones et al. 1998). This methodology was then incorporated into ASHRAE research project RP-1055 and applied to a wide range of equipment (Hosni et al. 1999) as a follow-up to independent research by Wilkins and McGaffin (1994) and Wilkins et al. (1991). Komor (1997) found similar results. Analysis of measured data showed that results for office equipment could be generalized, but results from laboratory and hospital equipment proved too diverse. The following general guidelines for office equipment are a result of these studies.

Nameplate Versus Measured Energy Use. Nameplate data rarely reflect the actual power consumption of office equipment. Actual power consumption is assumed to equal total (radiant plus convective) heat gain, but its ratio to the nameplate value varies widely. ASHRAE research project RP-1055 (Hosni et al. 1999) found that, for general office equipment with nameplate power consumption of less than 1000 W, the actual ratio of total heat gain to nameplate ranged from 25% to 50%, but when all tested equipment is considered, the range is broader. Generally, if the nameplate value is the only information known and no actual heat gain data are available for similar equipment, it is conservative to use 50% of nameplate as heat gain and more nearly correct if 25% of nameplate is used. Much better results can be obtained, however, by considering heat gain to be predictable based on the type of equipment. However, if the device has a mainly resistive internal electric load (e.g.,

Table 5B Recommended Rates of Radiant Heat Gain from Hooded Electric Appliances During Idle (Ready-to-Cook) Conditions

Appliance	Energy Rate, W Rated	Energy Rate, W Standby	Rate of Heat Gain, W Sensible Radiant	Usage Factor F_u	Radiation Factor F_r
Broiler: underfired 900 mm	10 814	9056	3165	0.84	0.35
Cheesemelter*	3605	3488	1348	0.97	0.39
Fryer: kettle	29 014	528	147	0.02	0.28
Fryer: open deep-fat, 1-vat	14 008	821	293	0.06	0.36
Fryer: pressure	13 511	791	147	0.06	0.19
Griddle: double sided 900 mm (clamshell down)*	21 218	2022	410	0.1	0.2
Griddle: double sided 900 mm (clamshell up)*	21 218	3370	1055	0.16	0.31
Griddle: flat 900 mm	17 115	3370	1319	0.2	0.39
Griddle-small 900 mm*	8997	1788	791	0.2	0.44
Induction cooktop*	21 013	0	0	0	0
Induction wok*	3488	0	0	0	0
Oven: combi: combi-mode*	16 411	1612	234	0.1	0.15
Oven: combi: convection mode	16 412	1612	410	0.1	0.25
Oven: convection full-size	12 103	1964	440	0.16	0.22
Oven: convection half-size*	5510	1084	147	0.2	0.14
Pasta cooker*	22 010	2491	0	0.11	0
Range top: top off/oven on*	4865	1172	293	0.24	0.25
Range top: 3 elements on/oven off	15 005	4513	1846	0.3	0.41
Range top: 6 elements on/oven off	15 005	9730	4074	0.65	0.42
Range top: 6 elements on/oven on	19 870	10 668	4250	0.54	0.4
Range: hot-top	15 826	15 035	3458	0.95	0.23
Rotisserie*	11 107	4044	1319	0.36	0.33
Salamander*	7004	6829	2051	0.97	0.3
Steam kettle: large (225 L), simmer lid down*	32 414	762	29	0.02	0.04
Steam kettle: small (150 L), simmer lid down*	21 599	528	88	0.02	0.17
Steamer: compartment: atmospheric*	9789	4484	59	0.46	0.01
Tilting skillet/braising pan	9642	1553	0	0.16	0

Source: Swierczyna et al. (2008, 2009).

a space heater), the nameplate rating may be a good estimate of its peak energy dissipation.

Computers. Based on tests by Hosni et al. (1999) and Wilkins and McGaffin (1994), nameplate values on computers should be ignored when performing cooling load calculations. Table 8 presents typical heat gain values for computers with varying degrees of safety factor.

Monitors. Based on monitors tested by Hosni et al. (1999), heat gain for cathode ray tube (CRT) monitors correlates approximately with screen size as

$$q_{mon} = 0.2S - 20 \tag{7}$$

where

q_{mon} = sensible heat gain from monitor, W
S = nominal screen size, mm

Table 8 shows typical values.

Flat-panel monitors have replaced CRT monitors in many workplaces. Power consumption, and thus heat gain, for flat-panel displays are significantly lower than for CRTs. Consult manufacturers' literature for average power consumption data for use in heat gain calculations.

Laser Printers. Hosni et al. (1999) found that power consumption, and therefore the heat gain, of laser printers depended largely on the level of throughput for which the printer was designed. Smaller printers tend to be used more intermittently, and larger printers may run continuously for longer periods.

Table 9 presents data on laser printers. These data can be applied by taking the value for continuous operation and then applying an appropriate diversity factor. This would likely be most appropriate for larger open office areas. Another approach, which may be appropriate for a single room or small area, is to take the value that most closely matches the expected operation of the printer with no diversity.

Copiers. Hosni et al. (1999) also tested five photocopy machines, including desktop and office (freestanding high-volume copiers) models. Larger machines used in production environments were not addressed. Table 9 summarizes the results. Desktop copiers rarely operate continuously, but office copiers frequently operate continuously for periods of an hour or more. Large, high-volume photocopiers often include provisions for exhausting air outdoors; if so equipped, the direct-to-space or system makeup air heat gain needs to be included in the load calculation. Also, when the air is dry, humidifiers are often operated near copiers to limit static electricity; if this occurs during cooling mode, their load on HVAC systems should be considered.

Miscellaneous Office Equipment. Table 10 presents data on miscellaneous office equipment such as vending machines and mailing equipment.

Diversity. The ratio of measured peak electrical load at equipment panels to the sum of the maximum electrical load of each individual item of equipment is the usage diversity. A small, one- or two-person office containing equipment listed in Tables 8 to 10 usually contributes heat gain to the space at the sum of the appropriate listed values. Progressively larger areas with many equipment items always experience some degree of usage diversity resulting from whatever percentage of such equipment is not in operation at any given time.

Wilkins and McGaffin (1994) measured diversity in 23 areas within five different buildings totaling over 25 600 m^2. Diversity was found to range between 37 and 78%, with the average (normalized based on area) being 46%. Figure 4 illustrates the relationship

Table 5C Recommended Rates of Radiant Heat Gain from Hooded Gas Appliances During Idle (Ready-to-Cook) Conditions

	Energy Rate, W		Rate of Heat Gain, W		
Appliance	Rated	Standby	Sensible Radiant	Usage Factor F_u	Radiation Factor F_r
Broiler: batch*	27 842	20 280	2374	0.73	0.12
Broiler: chain (conveyor)	38 685	28 340	3869	0.73	0.14
Broiler: overfired (upright)*	29 307	25 761	733	0.88	0.03
Broiler: underfired 900 mm	28 135	21 658	2638	0.77	0.12
Fryer: doughnut	12 895	3634	850	0.28	0.23
Fryer: open deep-fat, 1 vat	23 446	1377	322	0.06	0.23
Fryer: pressure	23 446	2638	234	0.11	0.09
Griddle: double sided 900 mm (clamshell down)*	31 710	2345	528	0.07	0.23
Griddle: double sided 900 mm (clamshell up)*	31 710	4308	1436	0.14	0.33
Griddle: flat 900 mm	26 376	5979	1084	0.23	0.18
Oven: combi: combi-mode*	22 185	1758	117	0.08	0.07
Oven: combi: convection mode	22 185	1700	293	0.08	0.17
Oven: convection full-size	12 895	3488	293	0.27	0.08
Oven: conveyor (pizza)	49 822	20 017	2286	0.4	0.11
Oven: deck	30 772	6008	1026	0.2	0.17
Oven: rack mini-rotating*	16 500	1319	322	0.08	0.24
Pasta cooker*	23 446	6946	0	0.3	0
Range top: top off/oven on*	7327	2169	586	0.3	0.27
Range top: 3 burners on/oven off	35 169	17 614	2081	0.5	0.12
Range top: 6 burners on/oven off	35 169	35 403	3370	1.01	0.1
Range top: 6 burners on/oven on	42 495	36 018	3986	0.85	0.11
Range: wok*	29 014	25 614	1524	0.88	0.06
Rethermalizer*	26 376	6829	3370	0.26	0.49
Rice cooker*	10 257	147	88	0.01	0.6
Salamander*	10 257	9759	1553	0.95	0.16
Steam kettle: large (225 L) simmer lid down*	42 495	1583	0	0.04	0
Steam kettle: small (38 L) simmer lid down*	15 240	967	88	0.06	0.09
Steam kettle: small (150 L) simmer lid down	29 307	1260	0	0.04	0
Steamer: compartment: atmospheric *	7620	2432	0	0.32	0
Tilting skillet/braising pan	30 479	3048	117	0.1	0.04

Source: Swierczyna et al. (2008, 2009).

Table 5D Recommended Rates of Radiant Heat Gain from Hooded Solid Fuel Appliances During Idle (Ready-to-Cook) Conditions

	Energy Rate, W	Rate of Heat Gain, W		Usage Factor	Radiation
Appliance	Rated	Standby	Sensible	F_u	Factor F_r
Broiler: solid fuel: charcoal	18 kg	12 309	1817	N/A	0.15
Broiler: solid fuel: wood (mesquite)*	18 kg	14 536	2051	N/A	0.14

Source: Swierczyna et al. (2008, 2009).

between nameplate, sum of peaks, and actual electrical load with diversity accounted for, based on the average of the total area tested. Data on actual diversity can be used as a guide, but diversity varies significantly with occupancy. The proper diversity factor for an office of mail-order catalog telephone operators is different from that for an office of sales representatives who travel regularly.

ASHRAE research project RP-1093 derived diversity profiles for use in energy calculations (Abushakra et al. 2004; Claridge et al. 2004). Those profiles were derived from available measured data sets for a variety of office buildings, and indicated a range of peak weekday diversity factors for lighting ranging from 70 to 85% and for receptacles (appliance load) between 42 and 89%.

Heat Gain per Unit Area. Wilkins and Hosni (2000) and Wilkins and McGaffin (1994) summarized research on a heat gain

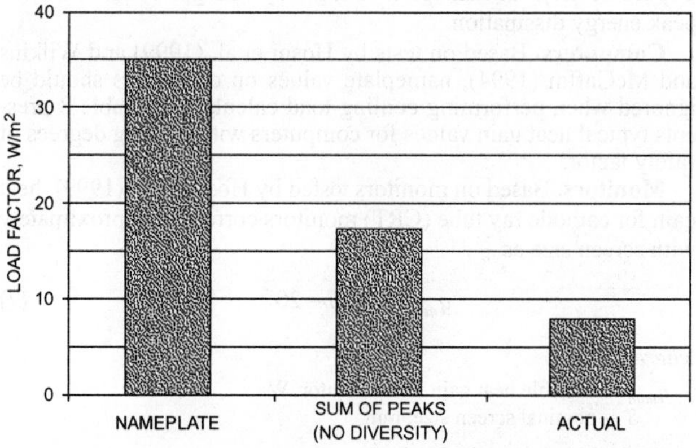

Fig. 4 Office Equipment Load Factor Comparison
(Wilkins and McGaffin 1994)

per unit area basis. Diversity testing showed that the actual heat gain per unit area, or load factor, ranged from 4.7 to 11.6 W/m^2, with an average (normalized based on area) of 8.7 W/m^2. Spaces tested were fully occupied and highly automated, comprising 21 unique areas in five buildings, with a computer and monitor at every workstation. Table 11 presents a range of load factors with a subjective description of the type of space to which they would apply. Table 12 presents more specific data that can be used to better quantify the amount of equipment in a space and expected load factor. The medium load density is likely to be appropriate for most standard office spaces. Medium/heavy or heavy load densities may be

Table 5E Recommended Rates of Radiant and Convective Heat Gain from Warewashing Equipment During Idle (Standby) or Washing Conditions

	Energy Rate, Btu/h		Rate of Heat Gain, W						
			Unhooded				Hooded		
Appliance	Rated	Standby/ Washing	Sensible Radiant	Sensible Convective	Latent	Total	Sensible/ Radiant	Usage Factor F_u	Radiation Factor F_r
Dishwasher (conveyor type, chemical sanitizing) standby	13 716	1671/12 778	0	1304	3954	5258	0	0.36	0.00
Dishwasher (conveyor type, hot-water sanitizing) standby	13 716	1671/N/A	0	1392	4973	6366	0	N/A	0.00
Dishwasher (door-type, hot-water sanitizing) standby	5393	352/3898	0	580	818	1398	0	0.26	0.00
Dishwasher (door-type, chemical sanitizing) washing	5393	352/3898	0	580	818	1398	0	0.26	0.00
Dishwasher* (under-counter type, chemical sanitizing) standby	7796	352/5480	0	668	1222	1890	0	0.35	0.00
Dishwasher* (under-counter type, hot-water sanitizing) standby	7796	498/5774	234	305	882	1421	234	0.27	0.34
Booster heater*	38 099	0	147	0	0	147	0	N/A	

Source: Swierczyna et al. (2008, 2009).

Note: Heat load values are prorated for 30% washing and 70% standby.

Table 6 Recommended Heat Gain from Typical Medical Equipment

Equipment	Nameplate, W	Peak, W	Average, W
Anesthesia system	250	177	166
Blanket warmer	500	504	221
Blood pressure meter	180	33	29
Blood warmer	360	204	114
ECG/RESP	1440	54	50
Electrosurgery	1000	147	109
Endoscope	1688	605	596
Harmonical scalpel	230	60	59
Hysteroscopic pump	180	35	34
Laser sonics	1200	256	229
Optical microscope	330	65	63
Pulse oximeter	72	21	20
Stress treadmill	N/A	198	173
Ultrasound system	1800	1063	1050
Vacuum suction	621	337	302
X-ray system	968		82
	1725	534	480
	2070		18

Source: Hosni et al. (1999).

Table 7 Recommended Heat Gain from Typical Laboratory Equipment

Equipment	Nameplate, W	Peak, W	Average, W
Analytical balance	7	7	7
Centrifuge	138	89	87
	288	136	132
	5500	1176	730
Electrochemical analyzer	50	45	44
	100	85	84
Flame photometer	180	107	105
Fluorescent microscope	150	144	143
	200	205	178
Function generator	58	29	29
Incubator	515	461	451
	600	479	264
	3125	1335	1222
Orbital shaker	100	16	16
Oscilloscope	72	38	38
	345	99	97
Rotary evaporator	75	74	73
	94	29	28
Spectronics	36	31	31
Spectrophotometer	575	106	104
	200	122	121
	N/A	127	125
Spectro fluorometer	340	405	395
Thermocycler	1840	965	641
	N/A	233	198
Tissue culture	475	132	46
	2346	1178	1146

Source: Hosni et al. (1999).

encountered but can be considered extremely conservative estimates even for densely populated and highly automated spaces.

Radiant Convective Split. ASHRAE research project RP-1482 (Hosni and Beck 2008) is examining the radiant/convective split for common office equipment; the most important differentiating feature is whether the equipment had a cooling fan. Footnotes in Tables 8 and 9 summarizes those results.

INFILTRATION AND MOISTURE MIGRATION HEAT GAINS

Two other load components contribute to space cooling load directly without time delay from building mass: (1) infiltration, and (2) moisture migration through the building envelope.

INFILTRATION

Principles of estimating infiltration in buildings, with emphasis on the heating season, are discussed in Chapter 16. When economically feasible, somewhat more outdoor air should be introduced to a building than the total of that exhausted, to create a slight overall positive pressure in the building relative to the outdoors. Under these conditions, air usually exfiltrates, rather than infiltrates, through the building envelope and thus effectively eliminates infiltration sensible and latent heat gains. However, there is concern, especially in some climates, that water may condense within the building envelope; actively managing space air pressures to reduce this condensation problem, as well as infiltration, may be needed.

When positive air pressure is assumed, most designers do not include infiltration in cooling load calculations for commercial buildings. However, including some infiltration for spaces such entry areas or loading docks may be appropriate, especially when those spaces are on the windward side of buildings. But the downward

Table 8 Recommended Heat Gain from Typical Computer Equipment

Equipment	Description	Nameplate Power Consumption, W	Average Power Consumption, W
Desktop computer[a]	Manufacturer A (model A); 2.8 GHz processor, 1 GB RAM	480	73
	Manufacturer A (model B); 2.6 GHz processor, 2 GB RAM	480	49
	Manufacturer B (model A); 3.0 GHz processor, 2 GB RAM	690	77
	Manufacturer B (model B); 3.0 GHz processor, 2 GB RAM	690	48
	Manufacturer A (model C); 2.3 GHz processor, 3 GB RAM	1200	97
Laptop computer[b]	Manufacturer 1; 2.0 GHz processor, 2 GB RAM, 430 mm screen	130	36
	Manufacturer 1; 1.8 GHz processor, 1 GB RAM, 430 mm screen	90	23
	Manufacturer 1; 2.0 GHz processor, 2 GB RAM, 355 mm screen	90	31
	Manufacturer 2; 2.13 GHz processor, 1 GB RAM, 355 mm screen, tablet PC	90	29
	Manufacturer 2; 366 MHz processor, 130 MB RAM, 355 mm screen)	70	22
	Manufacturer 3; 900 MHz processor, 256 MB RAM (265 mm screen)	50	12
Flat-panel monitor[c]	Manufacturer X (model A); 760 mm screen	383	90
	Manufacturer X (model B); 560 mm screen	360	36
	Manufacturer Y (model A), 480 mm screen	288	28
	Manufacturer Y (model B), 430 mm screen	240	27
	Manufacturer Z (model A), 430 mm screen	240	29
	Manufacturer Z (model C), 380 mm screen	240	19

Source: Hosni and Beck (2008).

[a]Power consumption for newer desktop computers in operational mode varies from 50 to 100 W, but a conservative value of about 65 W may be used. Power consumption in sleep mode is negligible. Because of cooling fan, approximately 90% of load is by convection and 10% is by radiation. Actual power consumption is about 10 to 15% of nameplate value.

[b]Power consumption of laptop computers is relatively small: depending on processor speed and screen size, it varies from about 15 to 40 W. Thus, differentiating between radiative and convective parts of the cooling load is unnecessary and the entire load may be classified as convective. Otherwise, a 75/25% split between convective and radiative components may be used. Actual power consumption for laptops is about 25% of nameplate values.

[c]Flat-panel monitors have replaced cathode ray tube (CRT) monitors in many workplaces, providing better resolution and being much lighter. Power consumption depends on size and resolution, and ranges from about 20 W (for380 mm size) to 90 W (for 760 mm). The most common sizes in workplaces are 480 and 560 mm, for which an average 30 W power consumption value may be used. Use 60/40% split between convective and radiative components. In idle mode, monitors have negligible power consumption. Nameplate values should not be used.

Table 9 Recommended Heat Gain from Typical Laser Printers and Copiers

Equipment	Description	Nameplate Power Consumption, W	Average Power Consumption, W
Laser printer, typical desktop, small-office type[a]	Printing speed up to 10 pages per minute	430	137
	Printing speed up to 35 pages per minute	890	74
	Printing speed up to 19 pages per minute	508	88
	Printing speed up to 17 pages per minute	508	98
	Printing speed up to 19 pages per minute	635	110
	Printing speed up to 24 page per minute	1344	130
Multifunction (copy, print, scan)[b]	Small, desktop type	600	30
		40	15
	Medium, desktop type	700	135
Scanner[b]	Small, desktop type	19	16
Copy machine[c]	Large, multiuser, office type	1750	800 (idle 260 W)
		1440	550 (idle 135 W)
		1850	1060 (idle 305 W)
Fax machine	Medium	936	90
	Small	40	20
Plotter	Manufacturer A	400	250
	Manufacturer B	456	140

Source: Hosni and Beck (2008).

[a]Various laser printers commercially available and commonly used in personal offices were tested for power consumption in print mode, which varied from 75 to 140 W, depending on model, print capacity, and speed. Average power consumption of 110 W may be used. Split between convection and radiation is approximately 70/30%.

[b]Small multifunction (copy, scan, print) systems use about 15 to 30 W; medium-sized ones use about 135 W. Power consumption in idle mode is negligible. Nameplate values do not represent actual power consumption and should not be used. Small, single-sheet scanners consume less than 20 W and do not contribute significantly to building cooling load.

[c]Power consumption for large copy machines in large offices and copy centers ranges from about 550 to 1100 W in copy mode. Consumption in idle mode varies from about 130 to 300 W. Count idle-mode power consumption as mostly convective in cooling load calculations.

stack effect, as occurs when indoor air is denser than the outdoor, might eliminate infiltration to these entries on lower floors of tall buildings; infiltration may occur on the upper floors during cooling conditions if makeup air is not sufficient.

Infiltration also depends on wind direction and magnitude, temperature differences, construction type and quality, and occupant use of exterior doors and operable windows. As such, it is impossible to accurately predict infiltration rates. Designers usually predict overall

Table 10 Recommended Heat Gain from Miscellaneous Office Equipment

Equipment	Maximum Input Rating, W	Recommended Rate of Heat Gain, W
Mail-processing equipment		
Folding machine	125	80
Inserting machine, 3600 to 6800 pieces/h	600 to 3300	390 to 2150
Labeling machine, 1500 to 30 000 pieces/h	600 to 6600	390 to 4300
Postage meter	230	150
Vending machines		
Cigarette	72	72
Cold food/beverage	1150 to 1920	575 to 960
Hot beverage	1,725	862
Snack	240 to 275	240 to 275
Other		
Bar code printer	440	370
Cash registers	60	48
Check processing workstation, 12 pockets	4800	2470
Coffee maker, 10 cups	1500	1050 sens., 450 latent
Microfiche reader	85	85
Microfilm reader	520	520
Microfilm reader/printer	1150	1150
Microwave oven, 28 L	600	400
Paper shredder	250 to 3000	200 to 2420
Water cooler, 30 L/h	700	350

Table 11 Recommended Load Factors for Various Types of Offices

Load Density of Office	Load Factor, W/m²	Description
Light	5.4	Assumes 15.5 m²/workstation (6.5 workstations per 100 m²) with computer and monitor at each plus printer and fax. Computer, monitor, and fax diversity 0.67, printer diversity 0.33.
Medium	10.8	Assumes 11.6 m²/workstation (8.5 workstations per 100 m²) with computer and monitor at each plus printer and fax. Computer, monitor, and fax diversity 0.75, printer diversity 0.50.
Medium/ Heavy	16.1	Assumes 9.3 m²/workstation (11 workstations per 100 m²) with computer and monitor at each plus printer and fax. Computer and monitor diversity 0.75, printer and fax diversity 0.50.
Heavy	21.5	Assumes 7.8 m²/workstation (13 workstations per 100 m²) with computer and monitor at each plus printer and fax. Computer and monitor diversity 1.0, printer and fax diversity 0.50.

Source: Wilkins and Hosni (2000).

rates of infiltration using the number of **air changes per hour (ach)**. A common guideline for climates and buildings typical of at least the central United States is to estimate the achs for winter heating conditions, and then use half that value for the cooling load calculations.

Standard Air Volumes

Because the specific volume of air varies appreciably, calculations are more accurate when made on the basis of air mass instead of volume. However, volumetric flow rates are often required for selecting coils, fans, ducts, etc.; basing volumes on measurement at standard conditions may be used for accurate results. One standard

Table 12 Cooling Load Estimates for Various Office Load Densities

Load Density*	Number	Each, W	Total, W	Diversity	Load, W
Light					
Computers	6	55	330	0.67	220
Monitors	6	55	330	0.67	220
Laser printer—small desk top	1	130	130	0.33	43
Fax machine	1	15	15	0.67	10
Total Area Load					494
Recommended equipment load factor = 5.4 W/m²					
Medium					
Computers	8	65	520	0.75	390
Monitors	8	70	560	0.75	420
Laser printer—desk	1	215	215	0.5	108
Fax machine	1	15	15	0.75	11
Total Area Load					929
Recommended equipment load factor = 10.8 W/m²					
Medium/Heavy					
Computers	10	65	650	1	650
Monitors	10	70	700	1	700
Laser printer—small office	1	320	320	0.5	160
Facsimile machine	1	30	30	0.5	15
Total Area Load					1525
Recommended equipment load factor = 16.1 W/m²					
Heavy Load Density[a]					
Computers	12	75	900	1	900
Monitors	12	80	960	1	960
Laser printer-small office	1	320	320	0.5	160
Facsimile machine	1	30	30	0.5	15
Total Area Load					2035
Recommended equipment load factor = 21.5 W/m²					

Source: Wilkins and Hosni (2000).
[a]See Table 11 for descriptions of load densities.

value is 1.2 kg_{da}/m^3 (0.833 m^3/kg). This density corresponds to about 16°C at saturation and 21°C dry air (at 101.325 kPa). Because air usually passes through the equipment at a density close to standard for locations below about 300 m, the accuracy desired normally requires no correction. When airflow is to be measured at a particular condition or point, such as at a coil entrance or exit, the corresponding specific volume can be read from the sea-level psychrometric chart. For higher elevations, the mass flow rates of air must be adjusted and higher-elevation psychrometric charts or algorithms must be used.

Heat Gain Calculations Using Standard Air Values

Air-conditioning design often requires the following information:

1. Total heat

Total heat gain q_t corresponding to the change of a given standard flow rate Q_s through an enthalpy difference Δh is

$$q_t = 1.2 Q_s \Delta h \quad (8)$$

where 1.2 = kg_{da}/m^3.

This total heat equation can also be expressed as

$$q_t = C_t Q_s \Delta h$$

where C_t = 1.2 is the air total heat factor, in W/(L/s) per kJ/kg enthalpy h.

2. Sensible heat

Sensible heat gain q_s corresponding to the change of dry-bulb temperature Δt for given airflow (standard conditions) Q_s is

$$q_s = 1.2(1.006 + 1.84W)Q_s\Delta t \quad (9)$$

where

0.24 = specific heat of dry air, kJ/(kg·K)
W = humidity ratio, kg_w/kg_{da}
0.45 = specific heat of water vapor, kJ/(kg·K)

The specific heats are for a range from about −75 to 90°C. When $W = 0$, the value of $1.20(1.006 + 1.84W) = 1.21$; when $W = 0.01$, the value is 1.23; when $W = 0.02$, the value is 1.25; and when $W = 0.03$, the value is 1.27. Because a value of $W = 0.01$ approximates conditions found in many air-conditioning problems, the sensible heat change (in W) has traditionally been found as

$$q_s = 1.23Q_s\Delta t \quad (10)$$

This sensible heat equation can also be expressed as

$$q_s = C_s Q_s \Delta t$$

where C_s = is the air sensible heat factor, in W/(L·s·K).

3. Latent heat

Latent heat gain q_l corresponding to the change of humidity ratio ΔW (in kg_w/kg_{da}) for given airflow (standard conditions) Q_s is

$$q_l = 1.20 \times 2500Q_s\Delta W = 3010Q_s\Delta W \quad (11)$$

where 2500 is the approximate heat content of 50% rh vapor at 24°C less the heat content of water at 10°C. A common design condition for the space is 50% rh at 24°C, and 10°C is normal condensate temperature from cooling and dehumidifying coils.

This latent heat equation can also be expressed as

$$q_l = C_l Q_s \Delta W$$

where $C_l = 3010$ is the air latent heat factor, in W/(L/s).

4. Altitude correction for total, sensible, and latent heat equations

The constants 1.2, 1.23, and 3010 are useful in air-conditioning calculations at sea level (101.325 kPa) and for normal temperatures and moisture ratios. For other conditions, more precise values should be used. For an altitude of 1525 m (84.1 kPa), appropriate values are 1.00, 1.03, and 2500. Equations (9) to (11) can be corrected for altitudes other than sea level by multiplying them by the ratio of pressure at sea level divided by the pressure at actual altitude. This can be derived from Equation (3) in Chapter 1 as

$$C_{x,alt} = C_{x,0}P/P_0$$

where $C_{x,0}$ is any of the sea-level C values and $P/P_0 = [1 - \text{elevation} \times (2.25577 \times 10^{-5})]^{5.2559}$, where elevation is in metres.

LATENT HEAT GAIN FROM MOISTURE DIFFUSION

Diffusion of moisture through building materials is a natural phenomenon that is always present. Chapters 25 to 27 cover principles, materials, and specific methods used to control moisture. Moisture transfer through walls and roofs is often neglected in comfort air conditioning because the actual rate is quite small and the corresponding latent heat gain is insignificant. Permeability and permeance values for various building materials are given in Chapter 26. Vapor retarders should be specified and installed in the proper location to keep moisture transfer to a minimum, and to minimize condensation within the envelope. Moisture migration up through slabs-on-grade and basement floors has been found to be significant, but has historically not been addressed in cooling load calculations. Under-slab continuous moisture retarders and drainage can reduce upward moisture flow.

Some industrial applications require low moisture to be maintained in a conditioned space. In these cases, the latent heat gain accompanying moisture transfer through walls and roofs may be greater than any other latent heat gain. This gain is computed by

$$q_{l_m} = MA\Delta p_v(h_g - h_f) \quad (12)$$

where

q_{l_m} = latent heat gain from moisture transfer, W
M = permeance of wall or roof assembly, ng/(s·m²·Pa)
A = area of wall or roof surface, m²
Δp_v = vapor pressure difference, Pa
h_g = enthalpy at room conditions, kJ/kg
h_f = enthalpy of water condensed at cooling coil, kJ/kg
$h_g - h_f$ = 2500 kJ/kg when room temperature is 24°C and condensate off coil is 10°C

OTHER LATENT LOADS

Moisture sources within a building (e.g., shower areas, swimming pools or natatoriums, arboretums) can also contribute to latent load. Unlike sensible loads, which correlate to supply air quantities required in a space, latent loads usually only affect cooling coils sizing or refrigeration load. Because air from showers and some other moisture-generating areas is exhausted completely, those airborne latent loads do not reach the cooling coil and thus do not contribute to cooling load. However, system loads associated with ventilation air required to make up exhaust air must be recognized, and any recirculated air's moisture must be considered when sizing the dehumidification equipment.

For natatoriums, occupant comfort and humidity control are critical. In many instances, size, location, and environmental requirements make complete exhaust systems expensive and ineffective. Where recirculating mechanical cooling systems are used, evaporation (latent) loads are significant. Chapter 4 of the 2007 *ASHRAE Handbook—HVAC Applications* provides guidance on natatorium load calculations.

FENESTRATION HEAT GAIN

For spaces with neutral or positive air pressurization, the primary weather-related variable affecting cooling load is solar radiation. The effect of solar radiation is more pronounced and immediate on exposed, nonopaque surfaces. Chapter 14 includes procedures for calculating clear-sky solar radiation intensity and incidence angles for weather conditions encountered at specific locations. That chapter also includes some useful solar equations. Calculation of solar heat gain and conductive heat transfer through various glazing materials and associated mounting frames, with or without interior and/or exterior shading devices, is discussed in Chapter 15. This chapter covers application of such data to overall heat gain evaluation, and conversion of calculated heat gain into a composite cooling load for the conditioned space.

FENESTRATION DIRECT SOLAR, DIFFUSE SOLAR, AND CONDUCTIVE HEAT GAINS

For fenestration heat gain, use the following equations:

Direct beam solar heat gain q_b:

$$q_b = AE_{t,b}\,\text{SHGC}(\theta)\text{IAC}(\theta,\Omega) \quad (13)$$

Diffuse solar heat gain q_d:

$$q_d = A(E_{t,d} + E_{t,r})\langle\text{SHGC}\rangle_D\,\text{IAC}_D \quad (14)$$

Conductive heat gain q_c:

$$q_c = UA(T_{out} - T_{in}) \qquad (15)$$

Total fenestration heat gain Q:

$$Q = q_b + q_d + q_c \qquad (16)$$

where

A = window area, m^2

$E_{t,b}$, $E_{t,d}$, and $E_{t,r}$ = beam, sky diffuse, and ground-reflected diffuse irradiance, calculated using equations in Chapter 14

SHGC(θ) = beam solar heat gain coefficient as a function of incident angle θ; may be interpolated between values in Table 10 of Chapter 15

$\langle SHGC \rangle_D$ = diffuse solar heat gain coefficient (also referred to as hemispherical SHGC); from Table 10 of Chapter 15

T_{in} = inside temperature, °C

T_{out} = outside temperature, °C

U = overall U-factor, including frame and mounting orientation from Table 4 of Chapter 15, $W/(m^2 \cdot K)$

IAC($\theta.\Omega$) = indoor solar attenuation coefficient for beam solar heat gain coefficient; = 1.0 if no inside shading device. IAC($\theta.\Omega$) is a function of shade type and, depending on type, may also be a function of beam solar angle of incidence θ and shade geometry

IAC_D = indoor solar attenuation coefficient for diffuse solar heat gain coefficient; = 1.0 if not inside shading device. IAC_D is a function of shade type and, depending on type, may also be a function of shade geometry

If specific window manufacturer's SHGC and U-factor data are available, those should be used. For fenestration equipped with inside shading (blinds, drapes, or shades), the indoor solar attenuation coefficients IAC($\theta.\Omega$) and IAC_D are listed in Tables 13A to 13G of Chapter 15.

Note that, as discussed in Chapter 15, fenestration ratings (U-factor and SHGC) are based on the entire product area, including frames. Thus, for load calculations, fenestration area is the area of the entire opening in the wall or roof.

EXTERIOR SHADING

Nonuniform exterior shading, caused by roof overhangs, side fins, or building projections, requires separate hourly calculations for the externally shaded and unshaded areas of the window in question, with the inside shading SHGC still used to account for any internal shading devices. The areas, shaded and unshaded, depend on the location of the shadow line on a surface in the plane of the glass. Sun (1968) developed fundamental algorithms for analysis of shade patterns. McQuiston and Spitler (1992) provide graphical data to facilitate shadow line calculation.

Equations for calculating shade angles [Chapter 15, Equations (39) to (42)] can be used to determine the shape and area of a moving shadow falling across a given window from external shading elements during the course of a design day. Thus, a subprofile of heat gain for that window can be created by separating its sunlit and shaded areas for each hour.

HEAT BALANCE METHOD

Cooling load estimation involves calculating a surface-by-surface conductive, convective, and radiative heat balance for each room surface and a convective heat balance for the room air. These principles form the foundation for all methods described in this chapter. The heat balance (HB) method solves the problem directly instead of introducing transformation-based procedures. The advantages are that it contains no arbitrarily set parameters, and no processes are hidden from view.

Some computations required by this rigorous approach require the use of computers. The heat balance procedure is not new. Many energy calculation programs have used it in some form for many years. The first implementation that incorporated all the elements to form a complete method was NBSLD (Kusuda 1967). The heat balance procedure is also implemented in both the BLAST and TARP energy analysis programs (Walton 1983). Before ASHRAE research project RP-875, the method had never been described completely or in a form applicable to cooling load calculations. The papers resulting from RP-875 describe the heat balance procedure in detail (Liesen and Pedersen 1997; McClellan and Pedersen 1997; Pedersen et al. 1997).

The HB method is codified in the software called Hbfort that accompanies Cooling and Heating Load Calculation Principles (Pedersen et al. 1998).

ASHRAE research project RP-1117 constructed two model rooms for which cooling loads were physically measured using extensive instrumentation (Chantrasrisalai et al. 2003; Eldridge et al. 2003; Iu et al. 2003). HB calculations closely approximated measured cooling loads when provided with detailed data for the test rooms.

ASSUMPTIONS

All calculation procedures involve some kind of model; all models require simplifying assumptions and, therefore, are approximate. The most fundamental assumption is that air in the thermal zone can be modeled as **well mixed**, meaning its temperature is uniform throughout the zone. ASHRAE research project RP-664 (Fisher and Pedersen 1997) established that this assumption is valid over a wide range of conditions.

The next major assumption is that the surfaces of the room (walls, windows, floor, etc.) can be treated as having

- Uniform surface temperatures
- Uniform long-wave (LW) and short-wave (SW) irradiation
- Diffuse radiating surfaces
- One-dimensional heat conduction within

The resulting formulation is called the **heat balance (HB) model**. Note that the assumptions, although common, are quite restrictive and set certain limits on the information that can be obtained from the model.

ELEMENTS

Within the framework of the assumptions, the HB can be viewed as four distinct processes:

1. Outside-face heat balance
2. Wall conduction process
3. Inside-face heat balance
4. Air heat balance

Figure 5 shows the relationship between these processes for a single opaque surface. The top part of the figure, inside the shaded box, is repeated for each surface enclosing the zone. The process for transparent surfaces is similar, but the absorbed solar component appears in the conduction process block instead of at the outside face, and the absorbed component splits into inward- and outward-flowing fractions. These components participate in the surface heat balances.

Outside-Face Heat Balance

The heat balance on the outside face of each surface is

$$q''_{\alpha sol} + q''_{LWR} + q''_{conv} - q''_{ko} = 0 \qquad (17)$$

where

$q''_{\alpha sol}$ = absorbed direct and diffuse solar radiation flux (q/A), W/m^2

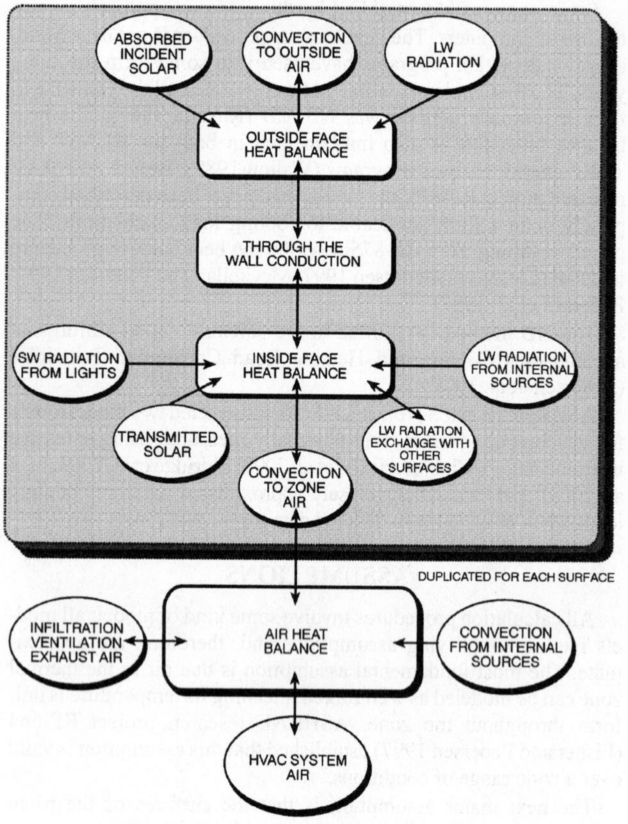

Fig. 5 Schematic of Heat Balance Processes in Zone

q''_{LWR} = net long-wave radiation flux exchange with air and surroundings, W/m^2

q''_{conv} = convective exchange flux with outside air, W/m^2

q''_{ko} = conductive flux (q/A) into wall, W/m^2

All terms are positive for net flux to the face except q''_{ko}, which is traditionally taken to be positive from outside to inside the wall.

Each term in Equation (17) has been modeled in several ways, and in simplified methods the first three terms are combined by using the sol-air temperature.

Wall Conduction Process

The wall conduction process has been formulated in more ways than any of the other processes. Techniques include

- Numerical finite difference
- Numerical finite element
- Transform methods
- Time series methods

This process introduces part of the time dependence inherent in load calculation. Figure 6 shows surface temperatures on the inside and outside faces of the wall element, and corresponding conductive heat fluxes away from the outside face and toward the inside face. All four quantities are functions of time. Direct formulation of the process uses temperature functions as input or known quantities, and heat fluxes as outputs or resultant quantities.

In some models, surface heat transfer coefficients are included as part of the wall element, making the temperatures in question the inside and outside air temperatures. This is not a desirable formulation, because it hides the heat transfer coefficients and prohibits changing them as airflow conditions change. It also prohibits treating the internal long-wave radiation exchange appropriately.

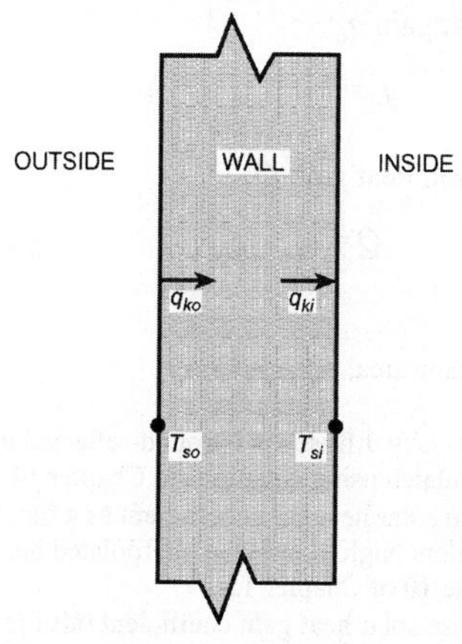

Fig. 6 Schematic of Wall Conduction Process

Because heat balances on both sides of the element induce both the temperature and heat flux, the solution must deal with this simultaneous condition. Two computational methods that have been used widely are finite difference and conduction transfer function methods. Because of the computational time advantage, the conduction transfer function formulation has been selected for presentation here.

Inside-Face Heat Balance

The heart of the HB method is the internal heat balance involving the inside faces of the zone surfaces. This heat balance has many heat transfer components, and they are all coupled. Both long-wave (LW) and short-wave (SW) radiation are important, as well as wall conduction and convection to the air. The inside face heat balance for each surface can be written as follows:

$$q''_{LWX} + q''_{SW} + q''_{LWS} + q''_{ki} + q''_{sol} + q''_{conv} = 0 \qquad (18)$$

where

q''_{LWX} = net long-wave radiant flux exchange between zone surfaces, W/m^2

q''_{SW} = net short-wave radiation flux to surface from lights, W/m^2

q''_{LWS} = long-wave radiation flux from equipment in zone, W/m^2

q''_{ki} = conductive flux through wall, W/m^2

q''_{sol} = transmitted solar radiative flux absorbed at surface, W/m^2

q''_{conv} = convective heat flux to zone air, W/m^2

These terms are explained in the following paragraphs.

LW Radiation Exchange Among Zone Surfaces. The limiting cases for modeling internal LW radiation exchange are

- Zone air is completely transparent to LW radiation
- Zone air completely absorbs LW radiation from surfaces in the zone

Most HB models treat air as completely transparent and not participating in LW radiation exchange among surfaces in the zone. The second model is attractive because it can be formulated simply using a combined radiative and convective heat transfer coefficient from each surface to the zone air and thus decouples radiant exchange among surfaces in the zone. However, because the transparent air model allows radiant exchange and is more realistic, the second model is inferior.

Furniture in a zone increases the amount of surface area that can participate in radiative and convective heat exchanges. It also adds thermal mass to the zone. These two changes can affect the time response of the zone cooling load.

SW Radiation from Lights. The short-wavelength radiation from lights is usually assumed to be distributed over the surfaces in the zone in some manner. The HB procedure retains this approach but allows the distribution function to be changed.

LW Radiation from Internal Sources. The traditional model for this source defines a radiative/convective split for heat introduced into a zone from equipment. The radiative part is then distributed over the zone's surfaces in some manner. This model is not completely realistic, and it departs from HB principles. In a true HB model, equipment surfaces are treated just as other LW radiant sources within the zone. However, because information about the surface temperature of equipment is rarely known, it is reasonable to keep the radiative/convective split concept even though it ignores the true nature of the radiant exchange. ASHRAE research project RP-1055 (Hosni et al. 1999) determined radiative/convective splits for many additional equipment types, as listed in footnotes for Tables 8 and 9.

Transmitted Solar Heat Gain. Chapter 15's calculation procedure for determining transmitted solar energy through fenestration uses the solar heat gain coefficient (SHGC) directly rather than relating it to double-strength glass, as is done when using a shading coefficient (SC). The difficulty with this plan is that the SHGC includes both transmitted solar and inward-flowing fraction of the solar radiation absorbed in the window. With the HB method, this latter part should be added to the conduction component so it can be included in the inside-face heat balance.

Transmitted solar radiation is also distributed over surfaces in the zone in a prescribed manner. It is possible to calculate the actual position of beam solar radiation, but this involves partial surface irradiation, which is inconsistent with the rest of the zone model, which assumes uniform conditions over an entire surface.

Using SHGC to Calculate Solar Heat Gain

The total solar heat gain through fenestration consists of directly transmitted solar radiation plus the inward-flowing fraction of solar radiation that is absorbed in the glazing system. Both parts contain beam and diffuse contributions. Transmitted radiation goes directly onto surfaces in the zone and is accounted for in the surface inside heat balance. The zone heat balance model accommodates the resulting heat fluxes without difficulty. The second part, the inward-flowing fraction of the absorbed solar radiation, interacts with other surfaces of the enclosure through long-wave radiant exchange and with zone air through convective heat transfer. As such, it is dependent both on geometric and radiative properties of the zone enclosure and convection characteristics inside and outside the zone. The solar heat gain coefficient (SHGC) combines the transmitted solar radiation and the inward-flowing fraction of the absorbed radiation. The SHGC is defined as

$$\text{SHGC} = \tau + \sum_{k=1}^{n} N_k \alpha_k \tag{19}$$

where

τ = solar transmittance of glazing
α_k = solar absorptance of the *k*th layer of the glazing system
n = number of layers
N_k = inward-flowing fraction of absorbed radiation in the *k*th layer

Note that Equation (19) is written generically. It can be written for a specific incidence angle and/or radiation wavelength and integrated over the wavelength and/or angle, but the principle is the same in each case. Refer to Chapter 15 for the specific expressions.

Unfortunately, the inward-flowing fraction *N* interacts with the zone in many ways. This interaction can be expressed as

$N = f$(inside convection coefficient, outside convection coefficient, glazing system overall heat transfer coefficient, zone geometry, zone radiation properties)

The only way to model these interactions correctly is to combine the window model with the zone heat balance model and solve both simultaneously. This has been done recently in some energy analysis programs, but is not generally available in load calculation procedures. In addition, the SHGC used for rating glazing systems is based on specific values of the inside, outside, and overall heat transfer coefficients and does not include any zonal long-wavelength radiation considerations. So, the challenge is to devise a way to use SHGC values within the framework of heat balance calculation in the most accurate way possible, as discussed in the following paragraphs.

Using SHGC Data. The normal incidence SHGC used to rate and characterize glazing systems is not sufficient for determining solar heat gain for load calculations. These calculations require solar heat gain as a function of the incident solar angle in order to determine the hour-by-hour gain profile. Thus, it is necessary to use angular SHGC values and also diffuse SHGC values. These can be obtained from the WINDOW 5.2 program (LBL 2003). This program does a detailed optical and thermal simulation of a glazing system and, when applied to a single clear layer, produces the information shown in Table 13.

Table 13 shows the parameters as a function of incident solar angle and also the diffuse values. The specific parameters shown are

V_{tc} = transmittance in visible spectrum
R_{fv} and R_{bv} = front and back surface visible reflectances
T_{sol} = solar transmittance [τ in Equations (19), (20), and (21)]
R_f and R_b = front and back surface solar reflectances
A_{bs1} = solar absorptance for layer 1, which is the only layer in this case [α in Equations (19), (20), and (21)]
SHGC = solar heat gain coefficient at the center of the glazing

The parameters used for heat gain calculations are T_{sol}, A_{bs}, and SHGC. For the specific convective conditions assumed in WINDOW

Table 13 Single-Layer Glazing Data Produced by WINDOW 5.2

Parameter	Incident Angle 0	10	20	30	40	50	60	70	80	90	Diffuse (Hemis.)
Vt_c	0.899	0.899	0.898	0.896	0.889	0.870	0.822	0.705	0.441	0	0.822
R_{fv}	0.083	0.083	0.083	0.085	0.091	0.109	0.156	0.272	0.536	1	0.148
R_{bv}	0.083	0.083	0.083	0.085	0.091	0.109	0.156	0.272	0.536	1	0.148
T_{sol}	0.834	0.833	0.831	0.827	0.818	0.797	0.749	0.637	0.389	0	0.753
R_f	0.075	0.075	0.075	0.077	0.082	0.099	0.143	0.253	0.506	1	0.136
R_b	0.075	0.075	0.075	0.077	0.082	0.099	0.143	0.253	0.506	1	0.136
A_{bs1}	0.091	0.092	0.094	0.096	0.100	0.104	0.108	0.110	0.105	0	0.101
SHGC	0.859	0.859	0.857	0.854	0.845	0.825	0.779	0.667	0.418	0	0.781

Source: LBL (2003).

5.2 program, the inward-flowing fraction of the absorbed solar can be obtained by rearranging Equation (19) to give

$$N_k \alpha_k = \text{SHGC} - \tau \quad (20)$$

This quantity, when multiplied by the appropriate incident solar intensity, provides the amount of absorbed solar radiation that flows inward. In the heat balance formulation for zone loads, this heat flux is combined with that caused by conduction through glazing and included in the surface heat balance.

The outward-flowing fraction of absorbed solar radiation is used in the heat balance on the outside face of the glazing and is determined from

$$(1 - N_k)\, \alpha_k = \alpha_k - N_k \alpha_k = \alpha_k - (\text{SHGC} - \tau) \quad (21)$$

If there is more than one layer, the appropriate summation of absorptances must be done.

There is some potential inaccuracy in using the WINDOW 5.2 SHGC values because the inward-flowing fraction part was determined under specific conditions for the inside and outside heat transfer coefficients. However, the program can be run with inside and outside coefficients of one's own choosing. Normally, however, this effect is not large, and only in highly absorptive glazing systems might cause significant error.

For solar heat gain calculations, then, it seems reasonable to use the generic window property data that comes from WINDOW 5.2. Considering Table 13, the procedure is as follows:

1. Determine angle of incidence for the glazing.
2. Determine corresponding SHGC.
3. Evaluate $N_k \alpha_k$ using Equation (19).
4. Multiply T_{sol} by incident beam radiation intensity to get transmitted beam solar radiation.
5. Multiply $N_k \alpha_k$ by incident beam radiation intensity to get inward-flowing absorbed heat.
6. Repeat steps 2 to 5 with diffuse parameters and diffuse radiation.
7. Add beam and diffuse components of transmitted and inward-flowing absorbed heat.

This procedure is incorporated into the HB method so the solar gain is calculated accurately for each hour.

Table 10 in Chapter 15 contains SHGC information for many additional glazing systems. That table is similar to Table 13 but is slightly abbreviated. Again, the information needed for heat gain calculations is T_{sol}, SHGC, and A_{bs}.

The same caution about the inside and outside heat transfer coefficients applies to the information in Table 13 in Chapter 31. Those values were also obtained with specific inside and outside heat transfer coefficients, and the inward-flowing fraction N is dependent upon those values.

Convection to Zone Air. Inside convection coefficients presented in past editions of this chapter and used in most load calculation procedures and energy programs are based on very old, natural convection experiments and do not accurately describe heat transfer coefficients in a mechanically ventilated zone. In previous load calculation procedures, these coefficients were buried in the procedures and could not be changed. A heat balance formulation keeps them as working parameters. In this way, research results such as those from ASHRAE research project RP-664 (Fisher 1998) can be incorporated into the procedures. It also allows determining the sensitivity of the load calculation to these parameters.

Air Heat Balance

In HB formulations aimed at determining cooling loads, the capacitance of air in the zone is neglected and the air heat balance is done as a quasisteady balance in each time period. Four factors contribute to the air heat balance:

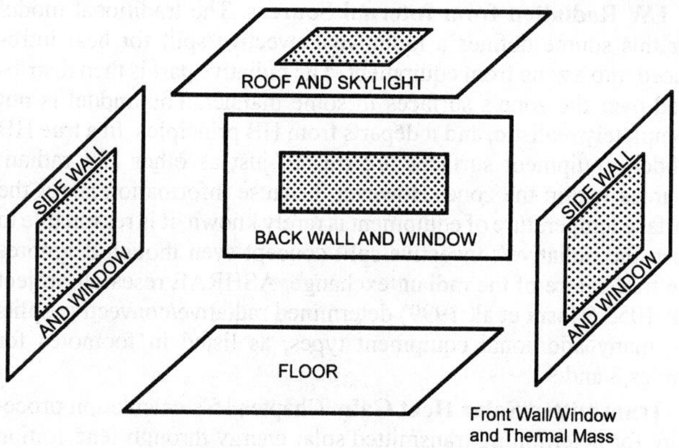

Fig. 7 Schematic View of General Heat Balance Zone

$$q_{conv} + q_{CE} + q_{IV} + q_{sys} = 0 \quad (22)$$

where

q_{conv} = convective heat transfer from surfaces, W
q_{CE} = convective parts of internal loads, W
q_{IV} = sensible load caused by infiltration and ventilation air, W
q_{sys} = heat transfer to/from HVAC system, W

Convection from zone surfaces q_{conv} is the sum of all the convective heat transfer quantities from the inside-surface heat balance. This comes to the air through the convective heat transfer coefficient on the surfaces.

The **convective parts of the internal loads q_{CE}** is the companion to q''_{LWS}, the radiant contribution from internal loads [Equation (18)]. It is added directly to the air heat balance. This also violates the tenets of the HB approach, because surfaces producing internal loads exchange heat with zone air through normal convective processes. However, once again, this level of detail is generally not included in the heat balance, so it is included directly into the air heat balance instead.

In keeping with the well-mixed model for zone air, any air that enters directly to a space through **infiltration or ventilation q_{IV}** is immediately mixed with the zone's air. The amount of infiltration or natural ventilation air is uncertain. Sometimes it is related to the indoor/outdoor temperature difference and wind speed; however it is determined, it is added directly to the air heat balance.

Conditioned air that enters the zone from the HVAC system and provides q_{sys} is also mixed directly with the zone air. For commercial HVAC systems, ventilation air is most often provided using outside air as part of this mixed-in conditioned air; ventilation air is thus normally a system load rather than a direct-to-space load. An exception is where infiltration or natural ventilation is used to provide all or part of the ventilation air, as discussed in Chapter 16.

GENERAL ZONE FOR LOAD CALCULATION

The HB procedure is tailored to a single thermal zone, shown in Figure 7. The definition of a thermal zone depends on how the fixed temperature is controlled. If air circulated through an entire building or an entire floor is uniformly well stirred, the entire building or floor could be considered a thermal zone. On the other hand, if each room has a different control scheme, each room may need to be considered as a separate thermal zone. The framework needs to be flexible enough to accommodate any zone arrangement, but the heat balance aspect of the procedure also requires that a complete zone be described. This zone consists of four walls, a roof or ceiling, a floor, and a "thermal mass surface" (described in the section on Input Required). Each wall and the roof can include a window (or skylight in the case of the roof). This makes a total of 12 surfaces, any of which may have zero area if it is not present in the zone to be modeled.

The heat balance processes for this general zone are formulated for a 24 h steady-periodic condition. The variables are the inside and outside temperatures of the 12 surfaces plus either the HVAC system energy required to maintain a specified air temperature or the air temperature, if system capacity is specified. This makes a total of $25 \times 24 = 600$ variables. Although it is possible to set up the problem for a simultaneous solution of these variables, the relatively weak coupling of the problem from one hour to the next allows a double iterative approach. One iteration is through all the surfaces in each hour, and the other is through the 24 h of a day. This procedure automatically reconciles nonlinear aspects of surface radiative exchange and other heat flux terms.

MATHEMATICAL DESCRIPTION

Conduction Process

Because it links the outside and inside heat balances, the wall conduction process regulates the cooling load's time dependence. For the HB procedure presented here, wall conduction is formulated using **conduction transfer functions (CTFs)**, which relate conductive heat fluxes to current and past surface temperatures and past heat fluxes. The general form for the inside heat flux is

$$q''_{ki}(t) = -Z_o T_{si,\theta} - \sum_{j=1}^{nz} Z_j T_{si,\theta-j\delta} + Y_o T_{so,\theta} + \sum_{j=1}^{nz} Y_j T_{so,\theta-j\delta} + \sum_{j=1}^{nq} \Phi_j q''_{ki,\theta-j\delta} \tag{23}$$

For outside heat flux, the form is

$$q''_{ko}(t) = -Y_o T_{si,\theta} - \sum_{j=1}^{nz} Y_j T_{si,\theta-j\delta} + X_o T_{so,\theta} + \sum_{j=1}^{nz} X_j T_{so,\theta-j\delta} + \sum_{j=1}^{nq} \Phi_j q''_{ko,\theta-j\delta} \tag{24}$$

where

X_j = outside CTF, $j = 0,1,\ldots nz$
Y_j = cross CTF, $j = 0,1,\ldots nz$
Z_j = inside CTF, $j = 0,1,\ldots nz$
Φ_j = flux CTF, $j = 1,2,\ldots nq$
θ = time
δ = time step
T_{si} = inside-face temperature, °C
T_{so} = outside-face temperature, °C
q''_{ki} = conductive heat flux on inside face, W/m²
q''_{ko} = conductive heat flux on outside face, W/m²

The subscript following the comma indicates the time period for the quantity in terms of time step δ. Also, the first terms in the series have been separated from the rest to facilitate solving for the current temperature in the solution scheme.

The two summation limits *nz* and *nq* depend on wall construction and also somewhat on the scheme used for calculating the CTFs. If $nq = 0$, the CTFs are generally referred to as **response factors**, but then theoretically *nz* is infinite. Values for *nz* and *nq* are generally set to minimize the amount of computation. A development of CTFs can be found in Hittle and Pedersen (1981).

Heat Balance Equations

The primary variables in the heat balance for the general zone are the 12 inside face temperatures and the 12 outside face temperatures at each of the 24 h, assigning *i* as the surface index and *j* as the hour index, or, in the case of CTFs, the sequence index. Thus, the primary variables are

$T_{so_{i,j}}$ = outside face temperature, $i = 1,2,\ldots,12; j = 1,2,\ldots, 24$
$T_{si_{i,j}}$ = inside face temperature, $i = 1,2,\ldots,12; j = 1,2,\ldots, 24$

In addition, q_{sys_j} = cooling load, $j = 1,2,\ldots, 24$

Equations (17) and (24) are combined and solved for T_{so} to produce 12 equations applicable in each time step:

$$T_{so_{i,j}} = \left(\sum_{k=1}^{nz} T_{si_{i,j-k}} Y_{i,k} - \sum_{k=1}^{nz} T_{so_{i,j-k}} Z_{i,k} - \sum_{k=1}^{nq} \Phi_{i,k} q''_{ko_{i,j-k}} + q''_{\alpha sol_{i,j}} + q''_{LWR_{i,j}} + T_{si_{i,j}} Y_{i,0} + T_{o_j} h_{co_{i,j}} \right) / (Z_{i,0} + h_{co_{i,j}}) \tag{25}$$

where

T_o = outside air temperature
h_{co} = outside convection coefficient, introduced by using $q''_{conv} = h_{co}(T_o - T_{so})$

Equation (25) shows the need to separate $Z_{i,0}$, because the contribution of current surface temperature to conductive flux can be collected with the other terms involving that temperature.

Equations (18) and (23) are combined and solved for T_{si} to produce the next 12 equations:

$$T_{si_{i,j}} = \left(T_{si_{i,j}} Y_{i,0} + \sum_{k-1}^{nz} T_{so_{i,j-k}} Y_{i,k} - \sum_{k=1}^{nz} T_{si_{i,j-k}} Z_{i,k} + \sum_{k=1}^{nq} \Phi_{i,k} q''_{ki_{i,j-k}} + T_{a_j} h_{ci_j} + q''_{LWS} + q''_{LWX} + q''_{SW} + q''_{sol}\, e \right) / (Z_{i,0} + h_{ci_{i,j}}) \tag{26}$$

where

T_a = zone air temperature
h_{ci} = convective heat transfer coefficient on the inside, obtained from $q''_{conv} = h_{ci}(T_a - T_{si})$

Note that in Equations (25) and (26), the opposite surface temperature at the current time appears on the right-hand side. The two equations could be solved simultaneously to eliminate those variables. Depending on the order of updating the other terms in the equations, this can have a beneficial effect on solution stability.

The remaining equation comes from the air heat balance, Equation (22). This provides the cooling load q_{sys} at each time step:

$$q_{sys_j} = \sum_{i=1}^{12} A_i h_{ci}(T_{si_{i,j}} - T_{a_j}) + q_{CE} + q_{IV} \tag{27}$$

In Equation (27), the convective heat transfer term is expanded to show the interconnection between the surface temperatures and the cooling load.

Overall HB Iterative Solution

The iterative HB procedure consists of a series of initial calculations that proceed sequentially, followed by a double iteration loop, as shown in the following steps:

1. Initialize areas, properties, and face temperatures for all surfaces, 24 h.
2. Calculate incident and transmitted solar flux for all surfaces and hours.
3. Distribute transmitted solar energy to all inside faces, 24 h.
4. Calculate internal load quantities for all 24 h.

5. Distribute LW, SW, and convective energy from internal loads to all surfaces for all hours.
6. Calculate infiltration and direct-to-space ventilation loads for all hours.
7. Iterate the heat balance according to the following scheme:

```
For Day = 1 to Maxdays
    For j = 1 to 24                {hours in the day}
        For SurfaceIter = 1 to MaxIter
            For i = 1 to 12                {The twelve zone surfaces}
                Evaluate Equations (34) and (35)
            Next i
        Next SurfaceIter
        Evaluate Equation (36)
    Next j
If not converged, Next Day
```

8. Display results.

Generally, four or six surface iterations are sufficient to provide convergence. The convergence check on the day iteration should be based on the difference between the inside and the outside conductive heat flux terms q_k. A limit, such as requiring the difference between all inside and outside flux terms to be less than 1% of either flux, works well.

INPUT REQUIRED

Previous methods for calculating cooling loads attempted to simplify the procedure by precalculating representative cases and grouping the results with various correlating parameters. This generally tended to reduce the amount of information required to apply the procedure. With heat balance, no precalculations are made, so the procedure requires a fairly complete description of the zone.

Global Information. Because the procedure incorporates a solar calculation, some global information is required, including latitude, longitude, time zone, month, day of month, directional orientation of the zone, and zone height (floor to floor). Additionally, to take full advantage of the flexibility of the method to incorporate, for example, variable outside heat transfer coefficients, things such as wind speed, wind direction, and terrain roughness may be specified. Normally, these variables and others default to some reasonable set of values, but the flexibility remains.

Wall Information (Each Wall). Because the walls are involved in three of the fundamental processes (external and internal heat balance and wall conduction), each wall of the zone requires a fairly large set of variables. They include

- Facing angle with respect to solar exposure
- Tilt (degrees from horizontal)
- Area
- Solar absorptivity outside
- Long-wave emissivity outside
- Short-wave absorptivity inside
- Long-wave emissivity inside
- Exterior boundary temperature condition (solar versus nonsolar)
- External roughness
- Layer-by-layer construction information

Again, some of these parameters can be defaulted, but they are changeable, and they indicate the more fundamental character of the HB method because they are related to true heat transfer processes.

Window Information (Each Window). The situation for windows is similar to that for walls, but the windows require some additional information because of their role in the solar load. Necessary parameters include

- Area
- Normal solar transmissivity
- Normal SHGC
- Normal total absorptivity
- Long-wave emissivity outside
- Long-wave emissivity inside
- Surface-to-surface thermal conductance
- Reveal (for solar shading)
- Overhang width (for solar shading)
- Distance from overhang to window (for solar shading)

Roof and Floor Details. The roof and floor surfaces are specified similarly to walls. The main difference is that the ground outside boundary condition will probably be specified more often for a floor.

Thermal Mass Surface Details. An "extra" surface, called a thermal mass surface, can serve several functions. It is included in radiant heat exchange with the other surfaces in the space but is only exposed to the inside air convective boundary condition. As an example, this surface would be used to account for movable partitions in a space. Partition construction is specified layer by layer, similar to specification for walls, and those layers store and release heat by the same conduction mechanism as walls. As a general definition, the extra thermal mass surface should be sized to represent all surfaces in the space that are exposed to the air mass, except the walls, roof, floor, and windows. In the formulation, both sides of the thermal mass participate in the exchange.

Internal Heat Gain Details. The space can be subjected to several internal heat sources: people, lights, electrical equipment, and infiltration. Infiltration energy is assumed to go immediately into the air heat balance, so it is the least complicated of the heat gains. For the others, several parameters must be specified. These include the following fractions:

- Sensible heat gain
- Latent heat gain
- Short-wave radiation
- Long-wave radiation
- Energy that enters the air immediately as convection
- Activity level of people
- Lighting heat gain that goes directly to the return air

Radiant Distribution Functions. As mentioned previously, the generally accepted assumptions for the HB method include specifying the distribution of radiant energy from several sources to surfaces that enclose the space. This requires a distribution function that specifies the fraction of total radiant input absorbed by each surface. The types of radiation that require distribution functions are

- Long-wave, from equipment and lights
- Short-wave, from lights
- Transmitted solar

Other Required Information. Additional flexibility is included in the model so that results of research can be incorporated easily. This includes the capability to specify such things as

- Heat transfer coefficients/convection models
- Solar coefficients
- Sky models

The amount of input information required may seem extensive, but many parameters can be set to default values in most routine applications. However, all parameters listed can be changed when necessary to fit unusual circumstances or when additional information is obtained.

RADIANT TIME SERIES (RTS) METHOD

The radiant time series (RTS) method is a simplified method for performing design cooling load calculations that is derived from the heat balance (HB) method. It effectively replaces all other simplified (non-heat-balance) methods, such as the transfer function method (TFM), the cooling load temperature difference/cooling load factor (CLTD/CLF) method, and the total equivalent temperature difference/time averaging (TETD/TA) method.

This method was developed to offer a method that is rigorous, yet does not require iterative calculations, and that quantifies each component's contribution to the total cooling load. In addition, it is desirable for the user to be able to inspect and compare the coefficients for different construction and zone types in a form illustrating their relative effect on the result. These characteristics of the RTS method make it easier to apply engineering judgment during cooling load calculation.

The RTS method is suitable for peak design load calculations, but it should not be used for annual energy simulations because of its inherent limiting assumptions. Although simple in concept, RTS involves too many calculations for practical use as a manual method, although it can easily be implemented in a simple computerized spreadsheet, as illustrated in the examples. For a manual cooling load calculation method, refer to the CLTD/CLF method in Chapter 28 of the 1997 *ASHRAE Handbook—Fundamentals*.

ASSUMPTIONS AND PRINCIPLES

Design cooling loads are based on the assumption of **steady-periodic conditions** (i.e., the design day's weather, occupancy, and heat gain conditions are identical to those for preceding days such that the loads repeat on an identical 24 h cyclical basis). Thus, the heat gain for a particular component at a particular hour is the same as 24 h prior, which is the same as 48 h prior, etc. This assumption is the basis for the RTS derivation from the HB method.

Cooling load calculations must address two time-delay effects inherent in building heat transfer processes:

(1) Delay of conductive heat gain through opaque massive exterior surfaces (walls, roofs, or floors)

(2) Delay of radiative heat gain conversion to cooling loads.

Exterior walls and roofs conduct heat because of temperature differences between outdoor and indoor air. In addition, solar energy on exterior surfaces is absorbed, then transferred by conduction to the building interior. Because of the mass and thermal capacity of the wall or roof construction materials, there is a substantial time delay in heat input at the exterior surface becoming heat gain at the interior surface.

As described in the section on Cooling Load Principles, most heat sources transfer energy to a room by a combination of convection and radiation. The convective part of heat gain immediately becomes cooling load. The radiative part must first be absorbed by the finishes and mass of the interior room surfaces, and becomes cooling load only when it is later transferred by convection from those surfaces to the room air. Thus, radiant heat gains become cooling loads over a delayed period of time.

OVERVIEW

Figure 8 gives an overview of the RTS method. When calculating solar radiation, transmitted solar heat gain through windows, sol-air temperature, and infiltration, RTS is exactly the same as previous simplified methods (TFM and TETD/TA). Important areas that differ from previous simplified methods include

- Computation of conductive heat gain
- Splitting of all heat gains into radiant and convective portions
- Conversion of radiant heat gains into cooling loads

The RTS method accounts for both conduction time delay and radiant time delay effects by multiplying hourly heat gains by 24 h time series. The time series multiplication, in effect, distributes heat gains over time. Series coefficients, which are called **radiant time factors** and **conduction time factors**, are derived using the HB method. Radiant time factors reflect the percentage of an earlier radiant heat gain that becomes cooling load during the current hour. Likewise, conduction time factors reflect the percentage of an earlier heat gain at the exterior of a wall or roof that becomes heat gain at the inside during the current hour. By definition, each radiant or conduction time series must total 100%.

These series can be used to easily compare the time-delay effect of one construction versus another. This ability to compare choices is of particular benefit during design, when all construction details may not have been decided. Comparison can illustrate the

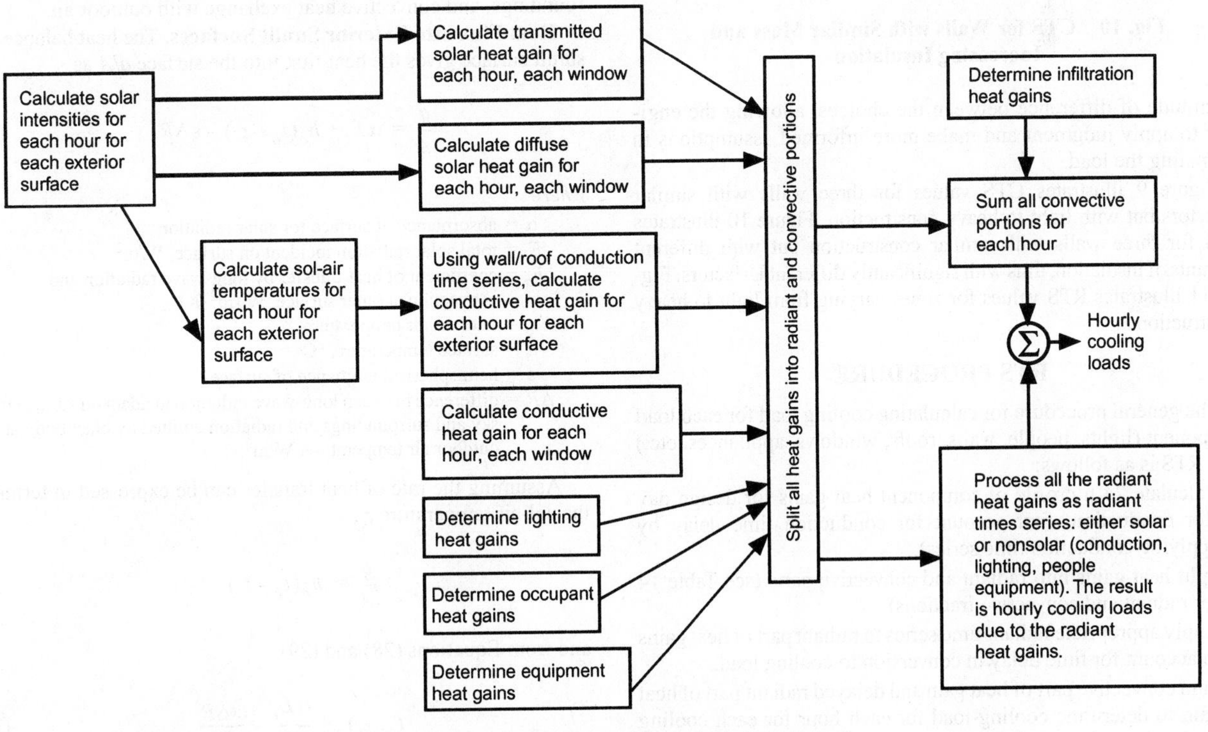

Fig. 8 Overview of Radiant Time Series Method

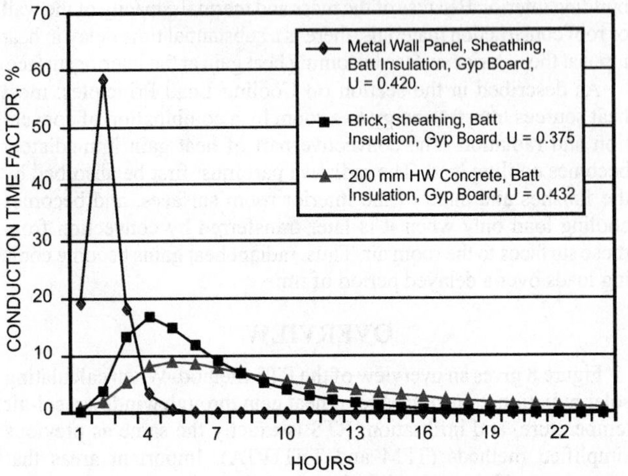

Fig. 9 CTS for Light to Heavy Walls

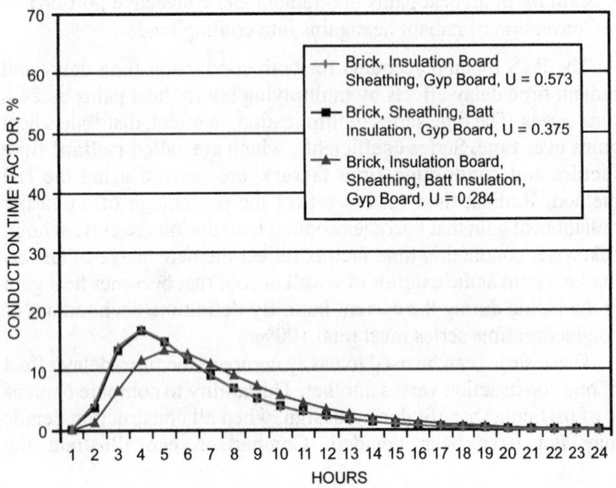

Fig. 10 CTS for Walls with Similar Mass and Increasing Insulation

magnitude of difference between the choices, allowing the engineer to apply judgment and make more informed assumptions in estimating the load.

Figure 9 illustrates CTS values for three walls with similar U-factors but with light to heavy construction. Figure 10 illustrates CTS for three walls with similar construction but with different amounts of insulation, thus with significantly different U-factors. Figure 11 illustrates RTS values for zones varying from light to heavy construction.

RTS PROCEDURE

The general procedure for calculating cooling load for each load component (lights, people, walls, roofs, windows, appliances, etc.) with RTS is as follows:

1. Calculate 24 h profile of component heat gains for design day (for conduction, first account for conduction time delay by applying conduction time series).
2. Split heat gains into radiant and convective parts (see Table 14 for radiant and convective fractions).
3. Apply appropriate radiant time series to radiant part of heat gains to account for time delay in conversion to cooling load.
4. Sum convective part of heat gain and delayed radiant part of heat gain to determine cooling load for each hour for each cooling load component.

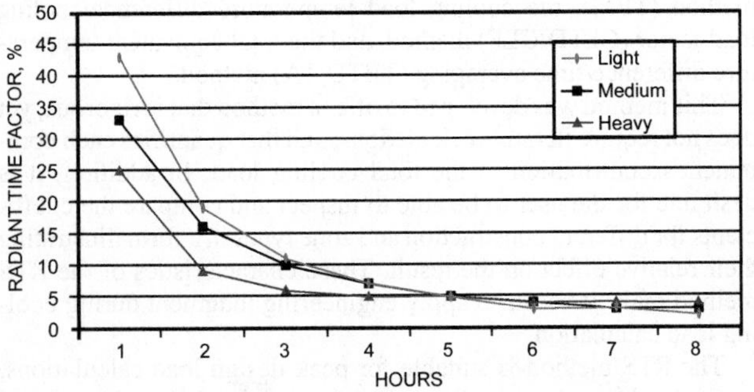

Fig. 11 RTS for Light to Heavy Construction

After calculating cooling loads for each component for each hour, sum those to determine the total cooling load for each hour and select the hour with the peak load for design of the air-conditioning system. Repeat this process for multiple design months to determine the month when the peak load occurs, especially with windows on southern exposures (northern exposure in southern latitudes), which can result in higher peak room cooling loads in winter months than in summer.

HEAT GAIN THROUGH EXTERIOR SURFACES

Heat gain through exterior opaque surfaces is derived from the same elements of solar radiation and thermal gradient as that for fenestration areas. It differs primarily as a function of the mass and nature of the wall or roof construction, because those elements affect the rate of conductive heat transfer through the composite assembly to the interior surface.

Sol-Air Temperature

Sol-air temperature is the outdoor air temperature that, in the absence of all radiation changes gives the same rate of heat entry into the surface as would the combination of incident solar radiation, radiant energy exchange with the sky and other outdoor surroundings, and convective heat exchange with outdoor air.

Heat Flux into Exterior Sunlit Surfaces. The heat balance at a sunlit surface gives the heat flux into the surface q/A as

$$\frac{q}{A} = \alpha E_t + h_o(t_o - t_s) - \varepsilon \Delta R \tag{28}$$

where

α = absorptance of surface for solar radiation
E_t = total solar radiation incident on surface, W/m²
h_o = coefficient of heat transfer by long-wave radiation and convection at outer surface, W/(m²·K)
t_o = outdoor air temperature, °C
t_s = surface temperature, °C
ε = hemispherical emittance of surface
ΔR = difference between long-wave radiation incident on surface from sky and surroundings and radiation emitted by blackbody at outdoor air temperature, W/m²

Assuming the rate of heat transfer can be expressed in terms of the sol-air temperature t_e,

$$\frac{q}{A} = h_o(t_e - t_s) \tag{29}$$

and from Equations (28) and (29),

$$t_e = t_o + \frac{\alpha E_t}{h_o} - \frac{\varepsilon \Delta R}{h_o} \tag{30}$$

Table 14 Recommended Radiative/Convective Splits for Internal Heat Gains

Heat Gain Type	Recommended Radiative Fraction	Recommended Convective Fraction	Comments
Occupants, typical office conditions	0.6	0.4	See Table 1 for other conditions.
Equipment	0.1 to 0.8	0.9 to 0.2	See Tables 6 to 12 for details of equipment heat gain and recommended radiative/convective splits for motors, cooking appliances, laboratory equipment, medical equipment, office equipment, etc.
Office, with fan	0.10	0.9	
Without fan	0.3	0.7	
Lighting			Varies; see Table 3.
Conduction heat gain			
Through walls and floors	0.46	0.54	
Through roof	0.60	0.40	
Through windows	0.33 (SHGC > 0.5) 0.46 (SHGC < 0.5)	0.67 (SHGC > 0.5) 0.54 (SHGC < 0.5)	
Solar heat gain through fenestration			
Without interior shading	1.0	0.0	
With interior shading			Varies; see Tables 13A to 13G in Chapter 15.
Infiltration	0.0	1.0	

Source: Nigusse (2007).

Table 15 Solar Absorptance Values of Various Surfaces

Surface	Absorptance
Brick, red (Purdue) [a]	0.63
Paint	
Red[b]	0.63
Black, matte[b]	0.94
Sandstone[b]	0.50
White acrylic[a]	0.26
Sheet metal, galvanized	
New[a]	0.65
Weathered[a]	0.80
Shingles	0.82
Gray[b]	
Brown[b]	0.91
Black[b]	0.97
White[b]	0.75
Concrete[a,c]	0.60 to 0.83

[a]Incropera and DeWitt (1990).
[b]Parker et al. (2000).
[c]Miller (1971).

For **horizontal surfaces** that receive long-wave radiation from the sky only, an appropriate value of ΔR is about 63 W/m^2, so that if $\varepsilon = 1$ and $h_o = 17$ W/(m^2·K), the long-wave correction term is about 4 K (Bliss 1961).

Because **vertical surfaces** receive long-wave radiation from the ground and surrounding buildings as well as from the sky, accurate ΔR values are difficult to determine. When solar radiation intensity is high, surfaces of terrestrial objects usually have a higher temperature than the outdoor air; thus, their long-wave radiation compensates to some extent for the sky's low emittance. Therefore, it is common practice to assume $\varepsilon\Delta R = 0$ for vertical surfaces.

Tabulated Temperature Values. The sol-air temperatures in Example Cooling and Heating Load Calculations section have been calculated based on $\varepsilon\Delta R/h_o$ values of 4 K for horizontal surfaces and 0°C for vertical surfaces; total solar intensity values used for the calculations were calculated using equations in Chapter 14.

Surface Colors. Sol-air temperature values are given in the Example Cooling and Heating Load Calculations section for two values of the parameter α/h_o; the value of 0.026 is appropriate for a light-colored surface, whereas 0.052 represents the usual maximum value for this parameter (i.e., for a dark-colored surface or any surface for which the permanent lightness cannot reliably be anticipated). Solar absorptance values of various surfaces are included in Table 15.

This procedure was used to calculate the sol-air temperatures included in the Examples section. Because of the tedious solar angle and intensity calculations, using a simple computer spreadsheet or other software for these calculations can reduce the effort involved.

Calculating Conductive Heat Gain Using Conduction Time Series

In the RTS method, conduction through exterior walls and roofs is calculated using conduction time series (CTS). Wall and roof conductive heat input at the exterior is defined by the familiar conduction equation as

$$q_{i,\theta-n} = UA(t_{e,\theta-n} - t_{rc}) \tag{31}$$

where

$q_{i,\theta-n}$ = conductive heat input for the surface *n* hours ago, W
U = overall heat transfer coefficient for the surface, W/(m^2·K)
A = surface area, m^2
$t_{e,\theta-n}$ = sol-air temperature *n* hours ago, °C
t_{rc} = presumed constant room air temperature, °C

Conductive heat gain through walls or roofs can be calculated using conductive heat inputs for the current hours and past 23 h and conduction time series:

$$q_\theta = c_0 q_{i,\theta} + c_1 q_{i,\theta-1} + c_2 q_{i,\theta-2} + c_3 q_{i,\theta-3} + \ldots + c_{23} q_{i,\theta-23} \tag{32}$$

where

q_θ = hourly conductive heat gain for the surface, W
$q_{i,\theta}$ = heat input for the current hour
$q_{i,\theta-n}$ = heat input *n* hours ago
c_0, c_1, etc. = conduction time factors

Conduction time factors for representative wall and roof types are included in Tables 16 and 17. Those values were derived by first calculating conduction transfer functions for each example wall and roof construction. Assuming steady-periodic heat input conditions for design load calculations allows conduction transfer functions to be reformulated into periodic response factors, as demonstrated by Spitler and Fisher (1999a). The periodic response factors were further simplified by dividing the 24 periodic response factors by the respective overall wall or roof U-factor to form the conduction time series (CTS). The conduction time factors can then be used in Equation (32) and provide a way to compare time delay characteristics

Table 16 Wall Conduction Time Series (CTS)

	CURTAIN WALLS			STUD WALLS				EIFS			BRICK WALLS									
Wall Number =	**1**	**2**	**3**	**4**	**5**	**6**	**7**	**8**	**9**	**10**	**11**	**12**	**13**	**14**	**15**	**16**	**17**	**18**	**19**	**20**
U-Factor, W/(m²·K)	0.428	0.429	0.428	0.419	0.417	0.406	0.413	0.668	0.305	0.524	0.571	0.377	0.283	0.581	0.348	0.628	0.702	0.514	0.581	0.389
Total *R*	2.3	2.3	2.3	2.4	2.4	2.5	2.4	1.5	3.3	1.9	1.7	2.7	3.5	1.7	2.9	1.6	1.4	1.9	1.7	2.6
Mass, kg/m²	31.0	20.9	80.0	25.5	84.6	25.6	66.7	36.6	38.3	130.9	214.1	214.7	215.8	290.6	304.0	371.7	391.5	469.3	892.2	665.1
Thermal Capacity, kJ/(m²·K)	30.7	20.4	67.5	24.5	73.6	32.7	61.3	36.7	38.8	120.6	177.8	177.8	177.8	239.1	253.5	320.9	312.7	388.4	784.9	580.5
Hour	**Conduction Time Factors, %**																			
0	18	25	8	19	6	7	5	11	2	1	0	0	0	1	2	2	1	3	4	3
1	58	57	45	59	42	44	41	50	25	2	5	4	1	1	2	2	1	3	4	3
2	20	15	32	18	33	32	34	26	31	6	14	13	7	2	2	2	3	3	4	3
3	4	3	11	3	13	12	13	9	20	9	17	17	12	5	3	4	6	3	4	4
4	0	0	3	1	4	4	4	3	11	9	15	15	13	8	5	5	7	3	4	4
5	0	0	1	0	1	1	2	1	5	9	12	12	13	9	6	6	8	4	4	4
6	0	0	0	0	1	0	1	0	3	8	9	9	11	9	7	6	8	4	4	5
7	0	0	0	0	0	0	0	0	2	7	7	7	9	9	7	7	8	5	4	5
8	0	0	0	0	0	0	0	0	1	6	5	5	7	8	7	7	8	5	4	5
9	0	0	0	0	0	0	0	0	0	6	4	4	6	7	7	6	7	5	4	5
10	0	0	0	0	0	0	0	0	0	5	3	3	5	7	6	6	6	5	4	5
11	0	0	0	0	0	0	0	0	0	5	2	2	4	6	6	6	6	5	5	5
12	0	0	0	0	0	0	0	0	0	4	2	2	3	5	5	5	5	5	5	5
13	0	0	0	0	0	0	0	0	0	4	1	2	2	4	5	5	4	5	5	5
14	0	0	0	0	0	0	0	0	0	3	1	2	2	4	5	5	4	5	5	5
15	0	0	0	0	0	0	0	0	0	3	1	1	1	3	4	4	3	5	4	4
16	0	0	0	0	0	0	0	0	0	3	1	1	1	3	4	4	3	5	4	4
17	0	0	0	0	0	0	0	0	0	2	1	1	1	2	3	4	3	4	4	4
18	0	0	0	0	0	0	0	0	0	2	0	0	1	2	3	3	2	4	4	4
19	0	0	0	0	0	0	0	0	0	2	0	0	1	2	3	3	2	4	4	4
20	0	0	0	0	0	0	0	0	0	2	0	0	0	1	3	3	2	4	4	4
21	0	0	0	0	0	0	0	0	0	1	0	0	0	1	2	2	1	4	4	4
22	0	0	0	0	0	0	0	0	0	1	0	0	0	1	2	2	1	4	4	3
23	0	0	0	0	0	0	0	0	0	0	0	0	0	0	1	1	1	3	4	3
Total Percentage	100	100	100	100	100	100	100	100	100	100	100	100	100	100	100	100	100	100	100	100
Layer ID from outside to inside (see Table 19)	F01	F01	F01	F01	F01	F01	F01	F01	F01	F01	F01	F01	F01	F01	F01	F01	F01	F01	F01	F01
	F09	F08	F10	F08	F10	F11	F07	F06	F06	F06	M01	M01	M01	M01	M01	M01	M01	M01	M01	M01
	F04	F04	F04	G03	G03	G02	G03	I01	I01	I01	F04	F04	F04	F04	F04	F04	F04	F04	F04	F04
	I02	I02	I02	I04	I04	I04	I04	G03	G03	G03	I01	G03	I01	I01	M03	I01	I01	I01	I01	M15
	F04	F04	F04	G01	G01	G04	G01	F04	I04	M03	G03	I04	G03	M03	I04	M05	M01	M13	M16	I04
	G01	G01	G01	F02	F02	F02	F02	G01	G01	F04	F04	G01	I04	F02	G01	G01	F02	F04	F04	G01
	F02	F02	F02	0	0	0	0	F02	F02	G01	G01	F02	G01	0	F02	F02	0	G01	G01	F02
	0	0	0	0	0	0	0	0	0	F02	F02	0	F02	0	0	0	0	F02	F02	0

Wall Number Descriptions

1. Spandrel glass, insulation board, gyp board
2. Metal wall panel, insulation board, gyp board
3. 25 mm stone, insulation board, gyp board
4. Metal wall panel, sheathing, batt insulation, gyp board
5. 25 mm stone, sheathing, batt insulation, gyp board
6. Wood siding, sheathing, batt insulation, 13 mm wood
7. 25 mm stucco, sheathing, batt insulation, gyp board
8. EIFS finish, insulation board, sheathing, gyp board
9. EIFS finish, insulation board, sheathing, batt insulation, gyp board
10. EIFS finish, insulation board, sheathing, 200 mm LW CMU, gyp board
11. Brick, insulation board, sheathing, gyp board
12. Brick, sheathing, batt insulation, gyp board
13. Brick, insulation board, sheathing, batt insulation, gyp board
14. Brick, insulation board, 200 mm LW CMU
15. Brick, 200 mm LW CMU, batt insulation, gyp board
16. Brick, insulation board, 200 mm HW CMU, gyp board
17. Brick, insulation board, brick
18. Brick, insulation board, 200 mm LW concrete, gyp board
19. Brick, insulation board, 300 mm HW concrete, gyp board
20. Brick, 200 mm HW concrete, batt insulation, gyp board

between different wall and roof constructions. Construction material data used in the calculations for walls and roofs in Tables 16 and 17 are listed in Table 18.

Heat gains calculated for walls or roofs using periodic response factors (and thus CTS) are identical to those calculated using conduction transfer functions for the steady periodic conditions assumed in design cooling load calculations. The methodology for calculating periodic response factors from conduction transfer functions was originally developed as part of ASHRAE research project RP-875 (Spitler and Fisher 1999b; Spitler et al. 1997). For walls and roofs that are not reasonably close to the representative constructions in Tables 16 and 17, CTS coefficients may be computed with a computer program such as that described by Iu and Fisher (2004). For walls and roofs with thermal bridges, the procedure described by Karambakkam et al. (2005) may be used to determine an equivalent wall construction, which can then be used as the basis for finding the CTS coefficients. When considering the level of detail needed to make an adequate approximation, remember that, for buildings with windows and internal heat gains, the conduction heat gains make up a relatively small part of the cooling load. For heating load calculations, the conduction heat loss may be more significant.

The tedious calculations involved make a simple computer spreadsheet or other computer software a useful labor saver.

Table 16 Wall Conduction Time Series (CTS) (*Concluded*)

	CONCRETE BLOCK WALL						PRECAST AND CAST-IN-PLACE CONCRETE WALLS								
Wall Number =	**21**	**22**	**23**	**24**	**25**	**26**	**27**	**28**	**29**	**30**	**31**	**32**	**33**	**34**	**35**
U-Factor, W/(m²·K)	0.383	0.335	0.414	1.056	0.834	0.689	0.673	0.418	0.434	0.650	0.387	0.467	0.434	0.266	3.122
Total *R*	2.6	3.0	2.4	0.9	1.2	1.5	1.5	2.4	2.3	1.5	2.6	2.1	2.3	3.8	0.3
Mass, kg/m²	108.8	108.8	224.3	94.3	107.1	168.9	143.9	144.6	262.5	291.8	274.7	488.1	469.9	698.9	683.2
Thermal Capacity, kJ/(m²·K)	98.1	98.1	204.4	83.8	96.1	151.3	124.7	124.7	220.8	247.3	233.0	441.5	425.2	631.6	615.2
Hour	**Conduction Time Factors, %**														
0	0	1	0	1	0	1	1	0	1	2	1	3	1	2	1
1	4	1	2	11	3	1	10	8	1	2	2	3	2	2	2
2	13	5	8	21	12	2	20	18	3	3	3	4	5	3	4
3	16	9	12	20	16	5	18	18	6	5	6	5	8	3	7
4	14	11	12	15	15	7	14	14	8	6	7	6	9	5	8
5	11	10	11	10	12	9	10	11	9	6	8	6	9	5	8
6	9	9	9	7	10	9	7	8	9	6	8	6	8	6	8
7	7	8	8	5	8	8	5	6	9	6	7	5	7	6	8
8	6	7	7	3	6	8	4	4	8	6	7	5	6	6	7
9	4	6	6	2	4	7	3	3	7	6	6	5	6	6	6
10	3	5	5	2	3	6	2	2	7	5	6	5	5	6	6
11	3	4	4	1	3	6	2	2	6	5	5	5	5	5	5
12	2	4	3	1	2	5	1	2	5	5	5	4	4	5	4
13	2	3	2	1	2	4	1	1	4	5	4	4	4	5	4
14	2	3	2	0	1	4	1	1	4	4	4	4	3	4	4
15	1	3	2	0	1	3	1	1	3	4	3	4	3	4	3
16	1	2	1	0	1	3	0	1	2	4	3	4	3	4	3
17	1	2	1	0	1	2	0	0	2	3	3	4	2	4	3
18	1	2	1	0	0	2	0	0	1	3	2	4	2	4	2
19	0	1	1	0	0	2	0	0	1	3	2	3	2	3	2
20	0	1	1	0	0	2	0	0	1	3	2	3	2	3	2
21	0	1	1	0	0	2	0	0	1	3	2	3	2	3	1
22	0	1	1	0	0	1	0	0	1	3	2	3	1	3	1
23	0	1	0	0	0	1	0	0	1	2	2	2	1	3	1
Total Percentage	100	100	100	100	100	100	100	100	100	100	100	100	100	100	100
Layer ID from outside to inside (see Table 19)	F01 M03 I04 G01 F02 —	F01 M08 I04 G01 F02 —	F01 F07 M05 I04 G01 F02	F01 M08 F02 — — —	F01 M08 F04 G01 F02 —	F01 M09 F04 G01 F02 —	F01 M11 I01 F04 G01 F02	F01 M11 I04 G01 F02 —	F01 M11 I02 M11 F02 —	F01 F06 I01 M13 G01 F02	F01 M13 I04 G01 F02 —	F01 F06 I02 M15 G01 F02	F01 M15 I04 G01 F02 —	F01 M16 I05 G01 F02 —	F01 M16 F02 — — —

Wall Number Descriptions

21. 200 mm LW CMU, batt insulation, gyp board
22. 200 mm LW CMU with fill insulation, batt insulation, gyp board
23. 25 mm stucco, 200 mm HW CMU, batt insulation, gyp board
24. 200 mm LW CMU with fill insulation
25. 200 mm LW CMU with fill insulation, gyp board
26. 300 mm LW CMU with fill insulation, gyp board
27. 100 mm LW concrete, board insulation, gyp board
28. 100 mm LW concrete, batt insulation, gyp board
29. 100 mm LW concrete, board insulation, 100 mm LW concrete
30. EIFS finish, insulation board, 200 mm LW concrete, gyp board
31. 200 mm LW concrete, batt insulation, gyp board
32. EIFS finish, insulation board, 200 mm HW concrete, gyp board
33. 200 mm HW concrete, batt insulation, gyp board
34. 300 mm HW concrete, batt insulation, gyp board
35. 300 mm HW concrete

HEAT GAIN THROUGH INTERIOR SURFACES

Whenever a conditioned space is adjacent to a space with a different temperature, heat transfer through the separating physical section must be considered. The heat transfer rate is given by

$$q = UA(t_b - t_i) \tag{33}$$

where

q = heat transfer rate, W
U = coefficient of overall heat transfer between adjacent and conditioned space, W/(m²·K)
A = area of separating section concerned, m²
t_b = average air temperature in adjacent space, °C
t_i = air temperature in conditioned space, °C

U-values can be obtained from Chapter 27. Temperature t_b may differ greatly from t_i. The temperature in a kitchen or boiler room, for example, may be as much as 8 to 28 K above the outdoor air temperature. Actual temperatures in adjoining spaces should be measured, when possible. Where nothing is known except that the adjacent space is of conventional construction, contains no heat sources, and itself receives no significant solar heat gain, $t_b - t_i$ may be considered the difference between the outdoor air and conditioned space design dry-bulb temperatures minus 3 K. In some cases, air temperature in the adjacent space corresponds to the outdoor air temperature or higher.

Floors

For floors directly in contact with the ground or over an underground basement that is neither ventilated nor conditioned, sensible heat transfer may be neglected for cooling load estimates because usually there is a heat loss rather than a gain. An exception is in hot climates (i.e., where average outdoor air temperature exceeds

Table 17 Roof Conduction Time Series (CTS)

	SLOPED FRAME ROOFS						WOOD DECK		METAL DECK ROOFS					CONCRETE ROOFS					
Roof Number	1	2	3	4	5	6	7	8	9	10	11	12	13	14	15	16	17	18	19
U-Factor, W/(m²·K)	0.249	0.227	0.255	0.235	0.239	0.231	0.393	0.329	0.452	0.370	0.323	0.206	0.297	0.304	0.296	0.288	0.315	0.313	0.239
Total *R*	4.0	4.4	3.9	4.2	4.2	4.3	2.5	3.0	2.2	2.7	3.1	4.9	3.4	3.3	3.4	3.5	3.2	3.2	4.2
Mass, kg/m²	26.7	21.0	14.0	34.7	55.5	34.9	48.9	55.9	23.9	30.9	25.0	27.2	57.6	149.2	214.3	279.3	360.7	474.5	362.3
Thermal Capacity, kJ/(m²·K)	26.6	16.4	12.3	47.0	73.5	47.0	75.6	79.7	28.6	32.7	28.6	32.7	57.2	134.9	190.1	245.2	333.2	437.4	331.1
Hour	**Conduction Time Factors, %**																		
0	6	10	27	1	1	1	0	1	18	4	8	1	0	1	2	2	2	3	1
1	45	57	62	17	17	12	7	3	61	41	53	23	10	2	2	2	2	3	2
2	33	27	10	31	34	25	18	8	18	35	30	38	22	8	3	3	5	3	6
3	11	5	1	24	25	22	18	10	3	14	7	22	20	11	6	4	6	5	8
4	3	1	0	14	13	15	15	10	0	4	2	10	14	11	7	5	7	6	8
5	1	0	0	7	6	10	11	9	0	1	0	4	10	10	8	6	7	6	8
6	1	0	0	4	3	6	8	8	0	1	0	2	7	9	8	6	6	6	7
7	0	0	0	2	1	4	6	7	0	0	0	0	5	7	7	6	6	6	7
8	0	0	0	0	0	2	5	6	0	0	0	0	4	6	7	6	6	6	6
9	0	0	0	0	0	1	3	5	0	0	0	0	3	5	6	6	5	5	5
10	0	0	0	0	0	1	3	5	0	0	0	0	2	5	5	6	5	5	5
11	0	0	0	0	0	1	2	4	0	0	0	0	1	4	5	5	5	5	5
12	0	0	0	0	0	0	1	4	0	0	0	0	1	3	5	5	4	5	4
13	0	0	0	0	0	0	1	3	0	0	0	0	1	3	4	5	4	4	4
14	0	0	0	0	0	0	1	3	0	0	0	0	0	3	4	4	4	4	3
15	0	0	0	0	0	0	1	3	0	0	0	0	0	2	3	4	4	4	3
16	0	0	0	0	0	0	0	2	0	0	0	0	0	2	3	4	3	4	3
17	0	0	0	0	0	0	0	2	0	0	0	0	0	2	3	4	3	4	3
18	0	0	0	0	0	0	0	2	0	0	0	0	0	1	3	3	3	3	2
19	0	0	0	0	0	0	0	2	0	0	0	0	0	1	2	3	3	3	2
20	0	0	0	0	0	0	0	1	0	0	0	0	0	1	2	3	3	3	2
21	0	0	0	0	0	0	0	1	0	0	0	0	0	1	2	3	3	3	2
22	0	0	0	0	0	0	0	1	0	0	0	0	0	1	2	3	2	2	2
23	0	0	0	0	0	0	0	0	0	0	0	0	0	1	1	2	2	2	2
	100	100	100	100	100	100	100	100	100	100	100	100	100	100	100	100	100	100	100
Layer ID from outside to inside (see Table 19)	F01	F01	F01	F01	F01	F01	F01	F01	F01	F01	F01	F01	F01	F01	F01	F01	F01	F01	F01
	F08	F08	F08	F12	F14	F15	F13	F13	F13	F13	F13	F13	M17	F13	F13	F13	F13	F13	F13
	G03	G03	G03	G05	G05	G05	G03	G03	G03	G03	G03	G03	F13	G03	G03	G03	G03	G03	M14
	F05	F05	F05	F05	F05	F05	I02	I02	I02	I02	I03	I02	G03	I03	I03	I03	I03	I03	F05
	I05	I05	I05	I05	I05	I05	G06	G06	F08	F08	F08	I03	I03	M11	M12	M13	M14	M15	I05
	G01	F05	F03	F05	F05	F05	F03	F05	F03	F05	F03	F08	F08	F03	F03	F03	F03	F03	F16
	F03	F16	—	G01	G01	G01	—	F16	—	F16	—	—	F03	—	—	—	—	—	F03
	—	F03	—	F03	F03	F03	—	F03	—	F03	—	—	—	—	—	—	—	—	—

Roof Number Descriptions

1. Metal roof, batt insulation, gyp board
2. Metal roof, batt insulation, suspended acoustical ceiling
3. Metal roof, batt insulation
4. Asphalt shingles, wood sheathing, batt insulation, gyp board
5. Slate or tile, wood sheathing, batt insulation, gyp board
6. Wood shingles, wood sheathing, batt insulation, gyp board
7. Membrane, sheathing, insulation board, wood deck
8. Membrane, sheathing, insulation board, wood deck, suspended acoustical ceiling
9. Membrane, sheathing, insulation board, metal deck
10. Membrane, sheathing, insulation board, metal deck, suspended acoustical ceiling
11. Membrane, sheathing, insulation board, metal deck
12. Membrane, sheathing, plus insulation boards, metal deck
13. 50 mm concrete roof ballast, membrane, sheathing, insulation board, metal deck
14. Membrane, sheathing, insulation board, 100 mm LW concrete
15. Membrane, sheathing, insulation board, 150 mm LW concrete
16. Membrane, sheathing, insulation board, 200 mm LW concrete
17. Membrane, sheathing, insulation board, 150 mm HW concrete
18. Membrane, sheathing, insulation board, 200 mm HW concrete
19. Membrane, 150 mm HW concrete, batt insulation, suspended acoustical ceiling

indoor design condition), where the positive soil-to-indoor temperature difference causes sensible heat gains (Rock 2005). In many climates and for various temperatures and local soil conditions, moisture transport up through slabs-on-grade and basement floors is also significant, and contributes to the latent heat portion of the cooling load.

CALCULATING COOLING LOAD

The **instantaneous cooling load** is the rate at which heat energy is convected to the zone air at a given point in time. Computation of cooling load is complicated by the radiant exchange between surfaces, furniture, partitions, and other mass in the zone. Most heat gain sources transfer energy by both convection and radiation. Radiative heat transfer introduces a time dependency to the process that is not easily quantified. Radiation is absorbed by thermal masses in the zone and then later transferred by convection into the space. This process creates a time lag and dampening effect. The convective portion, on the other hand, is assumed to immediately become cooling load in the hour in which that heat gain occurs.

Heat balance procedures calculate the radiant exchange between surfaces based on their surface temperatures and emissivities, but they typically rely on estimated "radiative/convective splits" to determine the contribution of internal loads, including people,

Table 18 Thermal Properties and Code Numbers of Layers Used in Wall and Roof Descriptions for Tables 16 and 17

Layer ID	Description	Thickness, mm	Conductivity, W/(m·K)	Density, kg/m³	Specific Heat, kJ/(kg·K)	Resistance, (m²·K)/W	R	Mass, kg/m²	Thermal Capacity, kJ/(m²·K)	Notes
F01	Outside surface resistance	—	—	—	—	0.04	0.04	—	—	1
F02	Inside vertical surface resistance	—	—	—	—	0.12	0.12	—	—	2
F03	Inside horizontal surface resistance	—	—	—	—	0.16	0.16	—	—	3
F04	Wall air space resistance	—	—	—	—	0.15	0.15	—	—	4
F05	Ceiling air space resistance	—	—	—	—	0.18	0.18	—	—	5
F06	EIFS finish	9.5	0.72	1856	0.84	—	0.01	17.7	14.92	6
F07	25 mm stucco	25.4	0.72	1856	0.84	—	0.04	47.2	39.45	6
F08	Metal surface	0.8	45.28	7824	0.50	—	0.00	6.0	3.07	7
F09	Opaque spandrel glass	6.4	0.99	2528	0.88	—	0.01	16.1	14.10	8
F10	25 mm stone	25.4	3.17	2560	0.79	—	0.01	65.1	51.71	9
F11	Wood siding	12.7	0.09	592	1.17	—	0.14	7.5	8.79	10
F12	Asphalt shingles	3.2	0.04	1120	1.26	—	0.08	3.6	4.50	
F13	Built-up roofing	9.5	0.16	1120	1.46	—	0.06	10.7	15.74	
F14	Slate or tile	12.7	1.59	1920	1.26	—	0.01	24.4	30.67	
F15	Wood shingles	6.4	0.04	592	1.30	—	0.17	3.8	4.91	
F16	Acoustic tile	19.1	0.06	368	0.59	—	0.31	7.0	4.09	11
F17	Carpet	12.7	0.06	288	1.38	—	0.22	3.7	5.11	12
F18	Terrazzo	25.4	1.80	2560	0.79	—	0.01	65.1	51.71	13
G01	16 mm gyp board	15.9	0.16	800	1.09	—	0.10	12.7	13.90	
G02	16 mm plywood	15.9	0.12	544	1.21	—	0.14	8.6	10.42	
G03	13 mm fiberboard sheathing	12.7	0.07	400	1.30	—	0.19	5.1	6.54	14
G04	13 mm wood	12.7	0.15	608	1.63	—	0.08	7.7	12.67	15
G05	25 mm wood	25.4	0.15	608	1.63	—	0.17	15.5	25.35	15
G06	50 mm wood	50.8	0.15	608	1.63	—	0.33	30.9	50.49	15
G07	100 mm wood	101.6	0.15	608	1.63	—	0.66	61.8	100.97	15
I01	25 mm insulation board	25.4	0.03	43	1.21	—	0.88	1.1	1.43	16
I02	50 mm insulation board	50.8	0.03	43	1.21	—	1.76	2.2	2.66	16
I03	75 mm insulation board	76.2	0.03	43	1.21	—	2.64	3.3	4.09	16
I04	89 mm batt insulation	89.4	0.05	19	0.96	—	1.94	1.7	1.64	17
I05	154 mm batt insulation	154.4	0.05	19	0.96	—	3.34	3.0	2.86	17
I06	244 mm batt insulation	243.8	0.05	19	0.96	—	5.28	4.7	4.50	17
M01	100 mm brick	101.6	0.89	1920	0.79	—	0.11	195.2	155.34	18
M02	150 mm LW concrete block	152.4	0.49	512	0.88	—	0.31	78.1	68.68	19
M03	200 mm LW concrete block	203.2	0.50	464	0.88	—	0.41	94.3	82.99	20
M04	300 mm LW concrete block	304.8	0.71	512	0.88	—	0.43	156.2	137.36	21
M05	200 mm concrete block	203.2	1.11	800	0.92	—	0.18	162.7	149.83	22
M06	300 mm concrete block	304.8	1.40	800	0.92	—	0.22	244.0	224.84	23
M07	150 mm LW concrete block (filled)	152.4	0.29	512	0.88	—	0.53	78.1	68.68	24
M08	200 mm LW concrete block (filled)	203.2	0.26	464	0.88	—	0.78	94.3	82.99	25
M09	300 mm LW concrete block (filled)	304.8	0.29	512	0.88	—	1.04	156.2	137.36	26
M10	200 mm concrete block (filled)	203.2	0.72	800	0.92	—	0.28	162.7	149.83	27
M11	100 mm lightweight concrete	101.6	0.53	1280	0.84	—	0.19	130.1	108.95	
M12	150 mm lightweight concrete	152.4	0.53	1280	0.84	—	0.29	195.2	163.52	
M13	200 mm lightweight concrete	203.2	0.53	1280	0.84	—	0.38	260.3	218.10	
M14	150 mm heavyweight concrete	152.4	1.95	2240	0.90	—	0.08	341.6	307.62	
M15	200 mm heavyweight concrete	203.2	1.95	2240	0.90	—	0.10	455.5	410.23	
M16	300 mm heavyweight concrete	304.8	1.95	2240	0.90	—	0.16	683.2	615.24	
M17	50 mm LW concrete roof ballast	50.8	0.19	640	0.84	—	0.27	32.5	27.19	28

Notes: The following notes give sources for the data in this table.

1. Chapter 26, Table 1 for 3.4 m/s wind
2. Chapter 26, Table 1 for still air, horizontal heat flow
3. Chapter 26, Table 1 for still air, downward heat flow
4. Chapter 26, Table 3 for 40 mm space, 32.2°C, horizontal heat flow, 0.82 emittance
5. Chapter 26, Table 3 for 90 mm space, 32.2°C, downward heat flow, 0.82 emittance
6. EIFS finish layers approximated by Chapter 26, Table 4 for 10 mm cement plaster, sand aggregate
7. Chapter 33, Table 3 for steel (mild), 22 gage
8. Chapter 26, Table 4 for architectural glass
9. Chapter 26, Table 4 for marble and granite
10. Chapter 26, Table 4, density assumed same as Southern pine
11. Chapter 26, Table 4 for mineral fiberboard, wet molded, acoustical tile
12. Chapter 26, Table 4 for carpet and rubber pad, density assumed same as fiberboard
13. Chapter 26, Table 4, density assumed same as stone
14. Chapter 26, Table 4 for nail-base sheathing
15. Chapter 26, Table 4 for Southern pine
16. Chapter 26, Table 4 for expanded polystyrene
17. Chapter 26, Table 4 for glass fiber batt, specific heat per glass fiber board
18. Chapter 26, Table 4 for clay fired brick
19. Chapter 26, Table 4, 7.3 kg block, 200 × 400 mm face
20. Chapter 26, Table 4, 8.6 kg block, 200 × 400 mm face
21. Chapter 26, Table 4, 14.5 kg block, 200 × 400 mm face
22. Chapter 26, Table 4, 15 kg normal weight block, 200 × 400 mm face
23. Chapter 26, Table 4, 22.7 kg normal weight block, 200 × 400 mm face
24. Chapter 26, Table 4, 7.3 kg block, vermiculite fill
25. Chapter 26, Table 4, 8.6 kg block, 200 × 400 mm face, vermiculite fill
26. Chapter 26, Table 4, 14.5 kg block, 200 × 400 mm face, vermiculite fill
27. Chapter 26, Table 4, 15 kg normal weight block, 200 × 400 mm face, vermiculite fill
28. Chapter 26, Table 4 for 640 kg/m³ LW concrete

lighting, appliances, and equipment, to the radiant exchange. RTS further simplifies the HB procedure by also relying on an estimated radiative/convective split of wall and roof conductive heat gain instead of simultaneously solving for the instantaneous convective and radiative heat transfer from each surface, as is done in the HB procedure.

Thus, the cooling load for each load component (lights, people, walls, roofs, windows, appliances, etc.) for a particular hour is the sum of the convective portion of the heat gain for that hour plus the time-delayed portion of radiant heat gains for that hour and the previous 23 h. Table 14 contains recommendations for splitting each of the heat gain components into convective and radiant portions.

RTS converts the radiant portion of hourly heat gains to hourly cooling loads using radiant time factors, the coefficients of the radiant time series. Radiant time factors are used to calculate the cooling load for the current hour on the basis of current and past heat gains. The radiant time series for a particular zone gives the time-dependent response of the zone to a single pulse of radiant energy. The series shows the portion of the radiant pulse that is convected to zone air for each hour. Thus, r_0 represents the fraction of the radiant pulse convected to the zone air in the current hour r_1 in the previous hour, and so on. The radiant time series thus generated is used to convert the radiant portion of hourly heat gains to hourly cooling loads according to the following equation:

$$Q_{r,\theta} = r_0 q_{r,\theta} + r_1 q_{r,\theta-1} + r_2 q_{r,\theta-2} + r_3 q_{r,\theta-3} + \ldots + r_{23} q_{r,\theta-23} \quad (34)$$

where

$Q_{r,\theta}$ = radiant cooling load Q_r for current hour θ, W
$q_{r,\theta}$ = radiant heat gain for current hour, W
$q_{r,\theta-n}$ = radiant heat gain *n* hours ago, W
r_0, r_1, etc. = radiant time factors

The radiant cooling load for the current hour, which is calculated using RTS and Equation (34), is added to the convective portion to determine the total cooling load for that component for that hour.

Radiant time factors are generated by a heat balance based procedure. A separate series of radiant time factors is theoretically required for each unique zone and for each unique radiant energy distribution function assumption. For most common design applications, RTS variation depends primarily on the overall massiveness of the construction and the thermal responsiveness of the surfaces the radiant heat gains strike.

One goal in developing RTS was to provide a simplified method based directly on the HB method; thus, it was deemed desirable to generate RTS coefficients directly from a heat balance. A heat balance computer program was developed to do this: Hbfort, which is included as part of *Cooling and Heating Load Calculation Principles* (Pedersen et al. 1998). The RTS procedure is described by Spitler et al. (1997). The procedure for generating RTS coefficients may be thought of as analogous to the custom weighting factor generation procedure used by DOE 2.1 (Kerrisk et al. 1981; Sowell 1988a, 1988b). In both cases, a zone model is pulsed with a heat gain. With DOE 2.1, the resulting loads are used to estimate the best values of the transfer function method weighting factors to most closely match the load profile. In the procedure described here, a unit periodic heat gain pulse is used to generate loads for a 24 h period. As long as the heat gain pulse is a unit pulse, the resulting loads are equivalent to the RTS coefficients.

Two different radiant time series are used: **Solar**, for direct transmitted solar heat gain (radiant energy assumed to be distributed to the floor and furnishings only) and **nonsolar**, for all other types of heat gains (radiant energy assumed to be uniformly distributed on all internal surfaces). Nonsolar RTS apply to radiant heat gains from people, lights, appliances, walls, roofs, and floors. Also, for diffuse solar heat gain and direct solar heat gain from fenestration with inside shading (blinds, drapes, etc.), the nonsolar RTS should be used. Radiation from those sources is assumed to be more uniformly distributed onto all room surfaces. Effect of beam solar radiation distribution assumptions is addressed by Hittle (1999).

Representative solar and nonsolar RTS data for light, medium, and heavyweight constructions are provided in Tables 19 and 20. Those were calculated using the Hbfort computer program (Pedersen et al. 1998) with zone characteristics listed in Table 21. Customized RTS values may be calculated using the HB method where the zone is not reasonably similar to these typical zones or where more precision is desired.

ASHRAE research project RP-942 compared HB and RTS results over a wide range of zone types and input variables (Rees et al. 2000; Spitler et al. 1998). In general, total cooling loads calculated using RTS closely agreed with or were slightly higher than those of the HB method with the same inputs. The project examined more than 5000 test cases of varying zone parameters. The dominating variable was overall thermal mass, and results were grouped into lightweight, U.S. medium-weight, U.K. medium-weight, and heavyweight construction. Best agreement between RTS and HB results was obtained for light- and medium-weight construction. Greater differences occurred in heavyweight cases, with RTS generally predicting slightly higher peak cooling loads than HB. Greater differences also were observed in zones with extremely high internal radiant loads and large glazing areas or with a very lightweight exterior envelope. In this case, heat balance calculations predict that some of the internal radiant load will be transmitted to the outdoor environment and never becomes cooling load within the space. RTS does not account for energy transfer out of the space to the environment, and thus predicted higher cooling loads.

ASHRAE research project RP-1117 constructed two model rooms for which cooling loads were physically measured using extensive instrumentation. The results agreed with previous simulations (Chantrasrisalai et al. 2003; Eldridge et al. 2003; Iu et al. 2003). HB calculations closely approximated the measured cooling loads when provided with detailed data for the test rooms. RTS overpredicted measured cooling loads in tests with large, clear, single-glazed window areas with bare concrete floor and no furnishings or internal loads. Tests under more typical conditions (venetian blinds, carpeted floor, office-type furnishings, and normal internal loads) provided good agreement between HB, RTS, and measured loads.

HEATING LOAD CALCULATIONS

Techniques for estimating design heating load for commercial, institutional, and industrial applications are essentially the same as for those estimating design cooling loads for such uses, with the following exceptions:

- Temperatures outside conditioned spaces are generally lower than maintained space temperatures.
- Credit for solar or internal heat gains is not included
- Thermal storage effect of building structure or content is ignored.
- Thermal bridging effects on wall and roof conduction are greater for heating loads than for cooling loads, and greater care must be taken to account for bridging effects on U-factors used in heating load calculations.

Heat losses (negative heat gains) are thus considered to be instantaneous, heat transfer essentially conductive, and latent heat treated only as a function of replacing space humidity lost to the exterior environment.

This simplified approach is justified because it evaluates worst-case conditions that can reasonably occur during a heating season. Therefore, the near-worst-case load is based on the following:

- Design interior and exterior conditions
- Including infiltration and/or ventilation
- No solar effect (at night or on cloudy winter days)

Table 19 Representative Nonsolar RTS Values for Light to Heavy Construction

	Light						Medium						Heavy						Interior Zones					
	With Carpet			No Carpet			With Carpet			No Carpet			With Carpet			No Carpet			Light		Medium		Heavy	
% Glass	10%	50%	90%	10%	50%	90%	10%	50%	90%	10%	50%	90%	10%	50%	90%	10%	50%	90%	With Carpet	No Carpet	With Carpet	No Carpet	With Carpet	No Carpet
Hour	Radiant Time Factor, %																							
0	47	50	53	41	43	46	46	49	52	31	33	35	34	38	42	22	25	28	46	40	46	31	33	21
1	19	18	17	20	19	19	18	17	16	17	16	15	9	9	9	10	9	9	19	20	18	17	9	9
2	11	10	9	12	11	11	10	9	8	11	10	10	6	6	5	6	6	6	11	12	10	11	6	6
3	6	6	5	8	7	7	6	5	5	8	7	7	4	4	4	5	5	5	6	8	6	8	5	5
4	4	4	3	5	5	5	4	3	3	6	5	5	4	4	4	5	5	4	4	5	3	6	4	5
5	3	3	2	4	3	3	2	2	2	4	4	4	4	3	3	4	4	4	3	4	2	4	4	4
6	2	2	2	3	3	2	2	2	2	4	3	3	3	3	3	4	4	4	2	3	2	4	3	4
7	2	1	1	2	2	2	1	1	1	3	3	3	3	3	3	4	4	4	2	2	1	3	3	4
8	1	1	1	1	1	1	1	1	1	3	2	2	3	3	3	4	3	3	1	1	1	3	3	4
9	1	1	1	1	1	1	1	1	1	2	2	2	3	3	2	3	3	3	1	1	1	2	3	3
10	1	1	1	1	1	1	1	1	1	2	2	2	3	2	2	3	3	3	1	1	1	2	3	3
11	1	1	1	1	1	1	1	1	1	2	2	2	2	2	2	3	3	3	1	1	1	2	2	3
12	1	1	1	1	1	1	1	1	1	1	1	1	2	2	2	3	3	3	1	1	1	1	2	3
13	1	1	1	0	1	0	1	1	1	1	1	1	2	2	2	3	3	2	1	1	1	1	2	3
14	0	0	1	0	1	0	1	1	1	1	1	1	2	2	2	3	2	2	1	0	1	1	2	3
15	0	0	1	0	0	0	1	1	1	1	1	1	2	2	2	2	2	2	0	0	1	1	2	3
16	0	0	0	0	0	0	1	1	1	1	1	1	2	2	2	2	2	2	0	0	1	1	2	3
17	0	0	0	0	0	0	1	1	1	1	1	1	2	2	2	2	2	2	0	0	1	1	2	2
18	0	0	0	0	0	0	1	1	1	1	1	1	2	2	1	2	2	2	0	0	1	1	2	2
19	0	0	0	0	0	0	0	1	0	0	1	1	2	2	1	2	2	2	0	0	1	0	2	2
20	0	0	0	0	0	0	0	0	0	0	1	1	2	1	1	2	2	2	0	0	0	0	2	2
21	0	0	0	0	0	0	0	0	0	0	1	1	2	1	1	2	2	2	0	0	0	0	2	2
22	0	0	0	0	0	0	0	0	0	0	1	0	1	1	1	2	2	2	0	0	0	0	1	2
23	0	0	0	0	0	0	0	0	0	0	0	0	1	1	1	2	2	1	0	0	0	0	1	2
	100	100	100	100	100	100	100	100	100	100	100	100	100	100	100	100	100	100	100	100	100	100	100	100

Table 20 Representative Solar RTS Values for Light to Heavy Construction

	Light						Medium						Heavy					
	With Carpet			No Carpet			With Carpet			No Carpet			With Carpet			No Carpet		
% Glass	10%	50%	90%	10%	50%	90%	10%	50%	90%	10%	50%	90%	10%	50%	90%	10%	50%	90%
Hour	Radiant Time Factor, %																	
0	53	55	56	44	45	46	52	54	55	28	29	29	47	49	51	26	27	28
1	17	17	17	19	20	20	16	16	15	15	15	15	11	12	12	12	13	13
2	9	9	9	11	11	11	8	8	8	10	10	10	6	6	6	7	7	7
3	5	5	5	7	7	7	5	4	4	7	7	7	4	4	3	5	5	5
4	3	3	3	5	5	5	3	3	3	6	6	6	3	3	3	4	4	4
5	2	2	2	3	3	3	2	2	2	5	5	5	2	2	2	4	4	4
6	2	2	2	3	2	2	2	1	1	4	4	4	2	2	2	3	3	3
7	1	1	1	2	2	2	1	1	1	4	3	3	2	2	2	3	3	3
8	1	1	1	1	1	1	1	1	1	3	3	3	2	2	2	3	3	3
9	1	1	1	1	1	1	1	1	1	3	3	3	2	2	2	3	3	3
10	1	1	1	1	1	1	1	1	1	2	2	2	2	2	2	3	3	3
11	1	1	1	1	1	1	1	1	1	2	2	2	2	2	1	3	3	2
12	1	1	1	1	1	0	1	1	1	2	2	2	2	1	1	2	2	2
13	1	1	0	1	0	0	1	1	1	2	2	2	2	1	1	2	2	2
14	1	0	0	0	0	0	1	1	1	1	1	1	2	1	1	2	2	2
15	1	0	0	0	0	0	1	1	1	1	1	1	1	1	1	2	2	2
16	0	0	0	0	0	0	1	1	1	1	1	1	1	1	1	2	2	2
17	0	0	0	0	0	0	1	1	1	1	1	1	1	1	1	2	2	2
18	0	0	0	0	0	0	1	1	1	1	1	1	1	1	1	2	2	2
19	0	0	0	0	0	0	0	0	0	1	1	1	1	1	1	2	2	2
20	0	0	0	0	0	0	0	0	0	1	1	1	1	1	1	2	2	2
21	0	0	0	0	0	0	0	0	0	0	0	0	1	1	1	2	2	2
22	0	0	0	0	0	0	0	0	0	0	0	0	1	1	1	2	1	1
23	0	0	0	0	0	0	0	0	0	0	0	0	1	1	1	2	1	1
	100	100	100	100	100	100	100	100	100	100	100	100	100	100	100	100	100	100

Table 21 RTS Representative Zone Construction for Tables 19 and 20

Construction Class	Exterior Wall	Roof/Ceiling	Partitions	Floor	Furnishings
Light	steel siding, 50 mm insulation, air space, 19 mm gyp	100 mm LW concrete, ceiling air space, acoustic tile	19 mm gyp, air space, 19 mm gyp	acoustic tile, ceiling air space, 100 mm LW concrete	25 mm wood @ 50% of floor area
Medium	100 mm face brick, 50 mm insulation, air space, 19 mm gyp	100 mm HW concrete, ceiling air space, acoustic tile	19 mm gyp, air space, 19 mm gyp	acoustic tile, ceiling air space, 100 mm HW concrete	25 mm wood @ 50% of floor area
Heavy	100 mm face brick, 200 mm HW concrete air space, 50 mm insulation, 19 mm gyp	200 mm HW concrete, ceiling air space, acoustic tile	19 mm gyp, 200 mm HW concrete block, 19 mm gyp	acoustic tile, ceiling air space, 200 mm HW concrete	25 mm wood @ 50% of floor area

- Before the periodic presence of people, lights, and appliances has an offsetting effect

Typical commercial and retail spaces have nighttime unoccupied periods at a setback temperature where little to no ventilation is required, building lights and equipment are off, and heat loss is primarily through conduction and infiltration. Before being occupied, buildings are warmed to the occupied temperature (see the following discussion). During occupied time, building lights, equipment, and people cooling loads can offset conduction heat loss, although some perimeter heat may be required, leaving the infiltration and ventilation loads as the primary heating loads. Ventilation heat load may be offset with heat recovery equipment. These loads (conduction loss, warm-up load, and ventilation load) may not be additive when sizing building heating equipment, and it is prudent to analyze each load and their interactions to arrive at final equipment sizing for heating.

HEAT LOSS CALCULATIONS

The general procedure for calculation of design heat losses of a structure is as follows:

1. Select outdoor design conditions: temperature, humidity, and wind direction and speed.
2. Select indoor design conditions to be maintained.
3. Estimate temperature in any adjacent unheated spaces.
4. Select transmission coefficients and compute heat losses for walls, floors, ceilings, windows, doors, and foundation elements.
5. Compute heat load through infiltration and any other outdoor air introduced directly to the space.
6. Sum the losses caused by transmission and infiltration.

Outdoor Design Conditions

The ideal heating system would provide enough heat to match the structure's heat loss. However, weather conditions vary considerably from year to year, and heating systems designed for the worst weather conditions on record would have a great excess of capacity most of the time. A system's failure to maintain design conditions during brief periods of severe weather usually is not critical. However, close regulation of indoor temperature may be critical for some occupancies or industrial processes. Design temperature data and discussion of their application are given in Chapter 14. Generally, the 99% temperature values given in the tabulated weather data be used. However, caution should be used, and local conditions always investigated. In some locations, outdoor temperatures are commonly much lower and wind velocities higher than those given in the tabulated weather data.

Indoor Design Conditions

The main purpose of the heating system is to maintain indoor conditions that make most of the occupants comfortable. It should be kept in mind, however, that the purpose of heating load calculations is to obtain data for sizing the heating system components. In

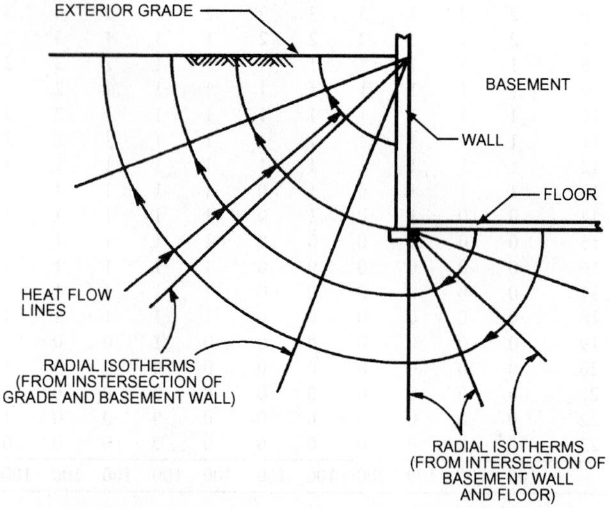

Fig. 12 Heat Flow from Below-Grade Surface

many cases, the system will rarely be called upon to operate at the design conditions. Therefore, the use and occupancy of the space are general considerations from the design temperature point of view. Later, when the building's energy requirements are computed, the actual conditions in the space and outdoor environment, including internal heat gains, must be considered.

The indoor design temperature should be selected at the lower end of the acceptable temperature range, so that the heating equipment will not be oversized. Even properly sized equipment operates under partial load, at reduced efficiency, most of the time; therefore, any oversizing aggravates this condition and lowers overall system efficiency. A maximum design dry-bulb temperature of 21°C is recommended for most occupancies. The indoor design value of relative humidity should be compatible with a healthful environment and the thermal and moisture integrity of the building envelope. A minimum relative humidity of 30% is recommended for most situations.

Calculation of Transmission Heat Losses

Exterior Surface Above Grade. All above-grade surfaces exposed to outdoor conditions (walls, doors, ceilings, fenestration, and raised floors) are treated identically, as follows:

$$q = A \times \mathrm{HF} \tag{35}$$

$$\mathrm{HF} = U\,\Delta t \tag{36}$$

where HF is the heating load factor in W/m^2.

Below-Grade Surfaces. An approximate method for estimating below-grade heat loss [based on the work of Latta and Boileau (1969)] assumes that the heat flow paths shown in Figure 12 can be used to find the steady-state heat loss to the ground surface, as follows:

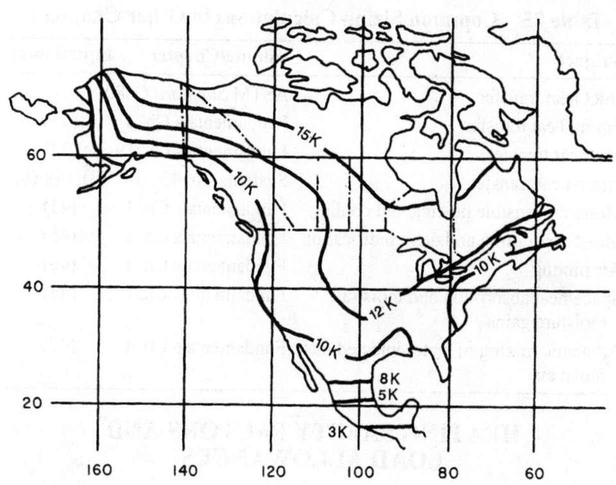

Fig. 13 Ground Temperature Amplitude

$$HF = U_{avg}(t_{in} - t_{gr}) \quad (37)$$

where

U_{avg} = average U-factor for below-grade surface from Equation (39) or (40), W/(m²·K)
t_{in} = below-grade space air temperature, °C
t_{gr} = design ground surface temperature from Equation (38), °C

The effect of soil heat capacity means that none of the usual external design air temperatures are suitable values for t_{gr}. Ground surface temperature fluctuates about an annual mean value by amplitude A, which varies with geographic location and surface cover. The minimum ground surface temperature, suitable for heat loss estimates, is therefore

$$t_{gr} = \bar{t}_{gr} - A \quad (38)$$

where

$\bar{t}_{gr}$ = mean ground temperature, °C, estimated from the annual average air temperature or from well-water temperatures, shown in Figure 17 of Chapter 32 in the 2007 *ASHRAE Handbook—HVAC Applications*
A = ground surface temperature amplitude, °C, from Figure 13 for North America

Figure 14 shows depth parameters used in determining U_{avg}. For walls, the region defined by z_1 and z_2 may be the entire wall or any portion of it, allowing partially insulated configurations to be analyzed piecewise.

The below-grade wall average U-factor is given by

$$U_{avg,bw} = \frac{2k_{soil}}{\pi(z_1 - z_2)} \times \left[\ln\left(z_2 + \frac{2k_{soil}R_{other}}{\pi}\right) - \ln\left(z_1 + \frac{2k_{soil}R_{other}}{\pi}\right)\right] \quad (39)$$

where

$U_{avg,bw}$ = average U-factor for wall region defined by z_1 and z_2, W/(m²·K)
k_{soil} = soil thermal conductivity, W/(m·K)
R_{other} = total resistance of wall, insulation, and inside surface resistance, (m²·K)/W
z_1, z_2 = depths of top and bottom of wall segment under consideration, m (Figure 14)

The value of soil thermal conductivity k varies widely with soil type and moisture content. A typical value of 1.4 W/(m·K) has been used previously to tabulate U-factors, and R_{other} is approximately 0.259 (m²·K)/W for uninsulated concrete walls. For these parameters, representative values for $U_{avg,bw}$ are shown in Table 22.

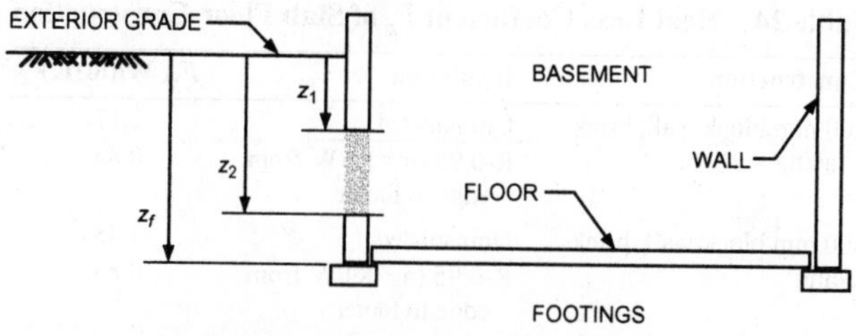

Fig. 14 Below-Grade Parameters

Table 22 Average U-Factor for Basement Walls with Uniform Insulation

	$U_{avg,bw}$ from Grade to Depth, W/(m²·K)			
Depth, m	**Uninsulated**	**R-0.88**	**R-1.76**	**R-2.64**
0.3	2.468	0.769	0.458	0.326
0.6	1.898	0.689	0.427	0.310
0.9	1.571	0.628	0.401	0.296
1.2	1.353	0.579	0.379	0.283
1.5	1.195	0.539	0.360	0.272
1.8	1.075	0.505	0.343	0.262
2.1	0.980	0.476	0.328	0.252
2.4	0.902	0.450	0.315	0.244

Soil conductivity = 1.4 W/(m·K); insulation is over entire depth. For other soil conductivities and partial insulation, use Equation (39).

Table 23 Average U-Factor for Basement Floors

	$U_{avg,bf}$, W/(m²·K)			
	w_b (Shortest Width of Basement), m			
z_f (Depth of Floor Below Grade), m	**6**	**7**	**8**	**9**
0.3	0.370	0.335	0.307	0.283
0.6	0.310	0.283	0.261	0.242
0.9	0.271	0.249	0.230	0.215
1.2	0.242	0.224	0.208	0.195
1.5	0.220	0.204	0.190	0.179
1.8	0.202	0.188	0.176	0.166
2.1	0.187	0.175	0.164	0.155

Soil conductivity is 1.4 W/(m·K); floor is uninsulated. For other soil conductivities and insulation, use Equation (39).

The average below-grade floor U-factor (where the entire basement floor is uninsulated or has uniform insulation) is given by

$$U_{avg,bf} = \frac{2k_{soil}}{\pi w_b} \times \left[\ln\left(\frac{w_b}{2} + \frac{z_f}{2} + \frac{k_{soil}R_{other}}{\pi}\right) - \ln\left(\frac{z_f}{2} + \frac{k_{soil}R_{other}}{\pi}\right)\right] \quad (40)$$

where

w_b = basement width (shortest dimension), m
z_f = floor depth below grade, m (see Figure 14)

Representative values of $U_{avg,bf}$ for uninsulated basement floors are shown in Table 23.

At-Grade Surfaces. Concrete slab floors may be (1) unheated, relying for warmth on heat delivered above floor level by the heating system, or (2) heated, containing heated pipes or ducts that constitute a radiant slab or portion of it for complete or partial heating of the house.

The simplified approach that treats heat loss as proportional to slab perimeter allows slab heat loss to be estimated for both unheated and heated slab floors:

$$q = p \times HF \quad (41)$$

Table 24 Heat Loss Coefficient F_p of Slab Floor Construction

Construction	Insulation	F_p, W/(m·K)
200 mm block wall, brick facing	Uninsulated	1.17
	R-0.95 (m²·K)/W from edge to footer	0.86
200 mm block wall, brick facing	Uninsulated	1.45
	R-0.95 (m²·K)/W from edge to footer	0.85
Metal stud wall, stucco	Uninsulated	2.07
	R-0.95 (m²·K)/W from edge to footer	0.92
Poured concrete wall with duct near perimeter*	Uninsulated	3.67
	R-0.95 (m²·K)/W from edge to footer	1.24

*Weighted average temperature of heating duct was assumed at 43°C during heating season (outdoor air temperature less than 18°C).

$$HF = F_p \Delta t \tag{42}$$

where

q = heat loss through perimeter, W
F_p = heat loss coefficient per metre of perimeter, W/(m·K), Table24
p = perimeter (exposed edge) of floor, m

Surfaces Adjacent to Buffer Space. Heat loss to adjacent unconditioned or semiconditioned spaces can be calculated using a heating factor based on the partition temperature difference:

$$HF = U(t_{in} - t_b) \tag{43}$$

Infiltration

All structures have some air leakage or infiltration. This means a heat loss because the cold, dry outdoor air must be heated to the inside design temperature and moisture must be added to increase the humidity to the design value. Procedures for estimating the infiltration rate are discussed in Chapter 16.

Once the infiltration rate has been calculated, the resulting sensible heat loss, equivalent to the sensible heating load from infiltration, is given by

$$q_s = 60[(\text{m/s})/v]c_p(t_{in} - t_o) \tag{44}$$

where

m³/s = volume flow rate of infiltrating air
c_p = specific heat capacity of air, kJ/(kg·K)
v = specific volume of infiltrating air, m³/kg

Assuming standard air conditions (15°C and sea-level conditions) for v and c_p, Equation (44) may be written as

$$q_s = 1.10(\text{m/s})(t_{in} - t_o) \tag{45}$$

The infiltrating air also introduces a latent heating load given by

$$q_l = 60[(\text{m/s})/v](W_{in} - W_o)D_h \tag{46}$$

where

W_{in} = humidity ratio for inside space air, kg_w/kg_a
W_o = humidity ratio for outdoor air, kg_w/kg_a
D_h = change in enthalpy to convert 1 kg water from vapor to liquid, kJ/kg

For standard air and nominal indoor comfort conditions, the latent load may be expressed as

$$q_l = 4840(\text{m/s})(W_{in} - W_o) \tag{47}$$

The coefficients 1.10 in Equation (45) and 4840 in Equation (47) are given for standard conditions. They depend on temperature and altitude (and, consequently, pressure).

Table 25 Common Sizing Calculations in Other Chapters

Subject	Volume/Chapter	Equation(s)
Duct heat transfer	ASTM *Standard* C680	
Piping heat transfer	Fundamentals Ch. 3	(35)
Fan heat transfer	Fundamentals Ch. 19	(22)
Pump heat transfer	Systems Ch. 43	(3), (4), (5)
Moist-air sensible heating and cooling	Fundamentals Ch. 1	(43)
Moist-air cooling and dehumidification	Fundamentals Ch. 1	(45)
Air mixing	Fundamentals Ch. 1	(46)
Space heat absorption and moist-air moisture gains	Fundamentals Ch. 1	(48)
Adiabatic mixing of water injected into moist air	Fundamentals Ch. 1	(47)

HEATING SAFETY FACTORS AND LOAD ALLOWANCES

Before mechanical cooling became common in the second half of the 1900s, and when energy was less expensive, buildings included much less insulation; large, operable windows; and generally more infiltration-prone assemblies than the energy-efficient and much tighter buildings typical of today. Allowances of 10 to 20% of the net calculated heating load for piping losses to unheated spaces, and 10 to 20% more for a warm-up load, were common practice, along with other occasional safety factors reflecting the experience and/or concern of the individual designer. Such measures are less conservatively applied today with newer construction. A combined warm-up/safety allowance of 20 to 25% is fairly common but varies depending on the particular climate, building use, and type of construction. Engineering judgment must be applied for the particular project. Armstrong et al. (1992a, 1992b) provide a design method to deal with warm-up and cooldown load.

OTHER HEATING CONSIDERATIONS

Calculation of design heating load estimates has essentially become a subset of the more involved and complex estimation of cooling loads for such spaces. Chapter 19 discusses using the heating load estimate to predict or analyze energy consumption over time. Special provisions to deal with particular applications are covered in the 2007 *ASHRAE Handbook—HVAC Applications* and the 2008 *ASHRAE Handbook—HVAC Systems and Equipment.*

The 1989 *ASHRAE Handbook—Fundamentals* was the last edition to contain a chapter dedicated only to heating load. Its contents were incorporated into this volume's Chapter 17, which describes steady-state conduction and convection heat transfer and provides, among other data, information on losses through basement floors and slabs.

SYSTEM HEATING AND COOLING LOAD EFFECTS

The heat balance (HB) or radiant time series (RTS) methods are used to determine cooling loads of rooms within a building, but they do not address the plant size necessary to reject the heat. Principal factors to consider in determining the plant size are ventilation, heat transport equipment, and air distribution systems. Some of these factors vary as a function of room load, ambient temperature, and control strategies, so it is often necessary to evaluate the factors and strategies dynamically and simultaneously with the heat loss or gain calculations.

The detailed analysis of system components and methods calculating their contribution to equipment sizing are beyond the scope of this chapter, which is general in nature. Table 25 lists the most frequently used calculations in other chapters and volumes.

ZONING

The organization of building rooms as defined for load calculations into zones and air-handling units has no effect on room cooling loads. However, specific grouping and ungrouping of rooms into zones may cause peak system loads to occur at different times during the day or year and may significantly affected heat removal equipment sizes.

For example, if each room is cooled by a separate heat removal system, the total capacity of the heat transport systems equals the sum of peak room loads. Conditioning all rooms by a single heat transport system (e.g., a variable-volume air handler) requires less capacity (equal to the simultaneous peak of the combined rooms load, which includes some rooms at off-peak loads). This may significantly reduce equipment capacity, depending on the configuration of the building.

VENTILATION

Consult ASHRAE *Standard* 62.1 and building codes to determine the required quantity of ventilation air for an application, and the various methods of achieving acceptable indoor air quality. The following discussion is confined to the effect of mechanical ventilation on sizing heat removal equipment. Where natural ventilation is used, through operable windows or other means, it is considered as infiltration and is part of the direct-to-room heat gain. Where ventilation air is conditioned and supplied through the mechanical system its sensible and latent loads are applied directly to heat transport and central equipment, and do not affect room heating and cooling loads. If the mechanical ventilation rate sufficiently exceeds exhaust airflows, air pressure may be positive and infiltration from envelope openings and outside wind may not be included in the load calculations. Chapter 16 includes more information on ventilating commercial buildings.

AIR HEAT TRANSPORT SYSTEMS

Heat transport equipment is usually selected to provide adequate heating or cooling for the peak load condition. However, selection must also consider maintaining desired inside conditions during all occupied hours, which requires matching the rate of heat transport to room peak heating and cooling loads. Automatic control systems normally vary the heating and cooling system capacity during these off-peak hours of operation.

On/Off Control Systems

On/off control systems, common in residential and light commercial applications, cycle equipment on and off to match room load. They are adaptable to heating or cooling because they can cycle both heating and cooling equipment. In their purest form, their heat transport matches the combined room and ventilation load over a series of cycles.

Variable-Air-Volume Systems

Variable-air-volume (VAV) systems have airflow controls that adjust cooling airflow to match the room cooling load. Damper leakage or minimum airflow settings may cause overcooling, so most VAV systems are used in conjunction with separate heating systems. These may be duct-mounted heating coils, or separate radiant or convective heating systems.

The amount of heat added by the heating systems during cooling becomes part of the room cooling load. Calculations must determine the minimum airflow relative to off-peak cooling loads. The quantity of heat added to the cooling load can be determined for each terminal by Equation (9) using the minimum required supply airflow rate and the difference between supply air temperature and the room inside heating design temperature.

Constant-Air-Volume Reheat Systems

In constant-air-volume (CAV) reheat systems, all supply air is cooled to remove moisture and then heated to avoid overcooling rooms. *Reheat* refers to the amount of heat added to cooling supply air to raise the supply air temperature to the temperature necessary for picking up the sensible load. The quantity of heat added can be determined by Equation (9).

With a constant-volume reheat system, heat transport system load does not vary with changes in room load, unless the cooling coil discharge temperature is allowed to vary. Where a minimum circulation rate requires a supply air temperature greater than the available design supply air temperature, reheat adds to the cooling load on the heat transport system. This makes the cooling load on the heat transport system larger than the room peak load.

Mixed Air Systems

Mixed air systems change the supply air temperature to match the cooling capacity by mixing airstreams of different temperatures; examples include multizone and dual-duct systems. Systems that cool the entire airstream to remove moisture and to reheat some of the air before mixing with the cooling airstream influence load on the heat transport system in the same way a reheat system does. Other systems separate the air paths so that mixing of hot- and cold-deck airstreams does not occur. For systems that mix hot and cold airstreams, the contribution to the heat transport system load is determined as follows.

1. Determine the ratio of cold-deck flow to hot-deck flow from

$$\frac{Q_h}{Q_c} = (T_c - T_r)/(T_r - T_h)$$

2. From Equation (10), the hot-deck contribution to room load during off-peak cooling is

$$q_{rh} = 1.23 Q_h (T_h - T_r)$$

where

Q_h = heating airflow, L/s
Q_c = cooling airflow, L/s
T_c = cooling air temperature, °C
T_h = heating air temperature, °C
T_h = room or return air temperature, °C
q_{rh} = heating airflow contribution to room load at off-peak hours, W

Heat Gain from Fans

Fans that circulate air through HVAC systems add energy to the system through the following processes:

- Increasing velocity and static pressure adds kinetic and potential energy
- Fan inefficiency in producing airflow and static pressure adds sensible heat (fan heat) to the airflow
- Inefficiency of motor and drive dissipates sensible heat

The power required to provide airflow and static pressure can be determined from the first law of thermodynamics with the following equation:

$$P_A = 0.009804 V p$$

where

P_A = air power, kW
V = flow rate, m³/s
p = pressure, kPa

at standard air conditions with air density = 1.2 kg/m³ built into the multiplier 0.009804. The power necessary at the fan shaft must account for fan inefficiencies, which may vary from 50 to 70%. This may be determined from

$$P_F = P_A/\eta_F$$

where

P_F = power required at fan shaft, kW
η_F = fan efficiency, dimensionless

The power necessary at the input to the fan motor must account for fan motor inefficiencies and drive losses. Fan motor efficiencies generally vary from 80 to 95%, and drive losses for a belt drive are 3% of the fan power. This may be determined from

$$P_M = (1 + \mathrm{DL})\, P_F/E_M E_D$$

where

P_M = power required at input to motor, kW
E_D = belt drive efficiency, dimensionless
E_M = fan motor efficiency, dimensionless
P_F = power required at fan shaft, kW
DL = drive loss, dimensionless

Almost all the energy required to generate airflow and static pressure is ultimately dissipated as heat within the building and HVAC system; a small portion is discharged with any exhaust air. Generally, it is assumed that all the heat is released at the fan rather than dispersed to the remainder of the system. The portion of fan heat released to the airstream depends on the location of the fan motor and drive: if they are within the airstream, all the energy input to the fan motor is released to the airstream. If the fan motor and drive are outside the airstream, the energy is split between the airstream and the room housing the motor and drive. Therefore, the following equations may be used to calculate heat generated by fans and motors:

If motor and drive are **outside** the airstream,

$$q_{fs} = P_F$$

$$q_{fr} = (P_M - P_F)$$

If motor and drive are **inside** the airstream,

$$q_{fs} = P_M$$

$$q_{fr} = 0.0$$

where

P_F = power required at fan shaft, kW
P_M = power required at input to motor, kW
q_{fs} = heat release to airstream, kW
q_{fr} = heat release to room housing motor and drive, kW

Supply airstream temperature rise may be determined from psychrometric formulas or Equation (9).

Variable- or adjustable-frequency drives (VFDs or AFDs) often drive fan motors in VAV air-handling units. These devices release heat to the surrounding space. Refer to manufacturers' data for heat released or efficiencies. The disposition of heat released is determined by the drive's location: in the conditioned space, in the return air path, or in a nonconditioned equipment room. These drives, and other electronic equipment such as building control, data processing, and communications devices, are temperature sensitive, so the rooms in which they are housed require cooling, frequently year-round.

Duct Surface Heat Transfer

Heat transfer across the duct surface is one mechanism for energy transfer to or from air inside a duct. It involves conduction through the duct wall and insulation, convection at inner and outer surfaces, and radiation between the duct and its surroundings. Chapter 4 presents a rigorous analysis of duct heat loss and gain, and Chapter 23 addresses application of analysis to insulated duct systems.

The effect of duct heat loss or gain depends on the duct routing, duct insulation, and its surrounding environment. Consider the following conditions:

- For duct run within the area cooled or heated by air in the duct, heat transfer from the space to the duct has no effect on heating or cooling load, but beware of the potential for condensation on cold ducts.
- For duct run through unconditioned spaces or outdoors, heat transfer adds to the cooling or heating load for the air transport system but not for the conditioned space.
- For duct run through conditioned space not served by the duct, heat transfer affects the conditioned space as well as the air transport system serving the duct.
- For an extensive duct system, heat transfer reduces the effective supply air differential temperature, requiring adjustment through air balancing to increase airflow to extremities of the distribution system.

Duct Leakage

Air leakage from supply ducts can considerably affect HVAC system energy use. Leakage reduces cooling and/or dehumidifying capacity for the conditioned space, and must be offset by increased airflow (sometimes reduced supply air temperatures), unless leaked air enters the conditioned space directly. Supply air leakage into a ceiling return plenum or leakage from unconditioned spaces into return ducts also affects return air temperature and/or humidity.

Determining leakage from a duct system is complex because of the variables in paths, fabrication, and installation methods. Refer to Chapter 21 and publications from the Sheet Metal and Air Conditioning Contractors' National Association (SMACNA) for methods of determining leakage. In general, good-quality ducts and post-installation duct sealing provide highly cost-effective energy savings, with improved thermal comfort and delivery of ventilation air.

Ceiling Return Air Plenum Temperatures

The space above a ceiling, when used as a return air path, is a ceiling return air plenum, or simply a **return plenum**. Unlike a traditional ducted return, the plenum may have multiple heat sources in the air path. These heat sources may be radiant and convective loads from lighting and transformers; conduction loads from adjacent walls, roofs, or glazing; or duct and piping systems within the plenum.

As heat from these sources is picked up by the unducted return air, the temperature differential between the ceiling cavity and conditioned space is small. Most return plenum temperatures do not rise more than 0.6 to 1.7 K above space temperature, thus generating only a relatively small thermal gradient for heat transfer through plenum surfaces, except to the outdoors. This yields a relatively large-percentage reduction in space cooling load by shifting plenum loads to the system. Another reason plenum temperatures do not rise more is leakage into the plenum from supply air ducts, and, if exposed to the roof, increasing levels of insulation.

Where the ceiling space is used as a return air plenum, energy balance requires that heat picked up from the lights into the return air (1) become part of the cooling load to the return air (represented by a temperature rise of return air as it passes through the ceiling space), (2) be partially transferred back into the conditioned space through the ceiling material below, and/or (3) be partially lost from the space through floor surfaces above the plenum. If the plenum has one or more exterior surfaces, heat gains through them must be considered; if adjacent to spaces with different indoor temperatures, partition loads must be considered, too. In a multistory building, the conditioned space frequently gains heat through its floor from a similar plenum below, offsetting the floor loss. The radiant component of heat leaving the ceiling or floor surface of a plenum is normally so small, because of relatively small temperature differences,

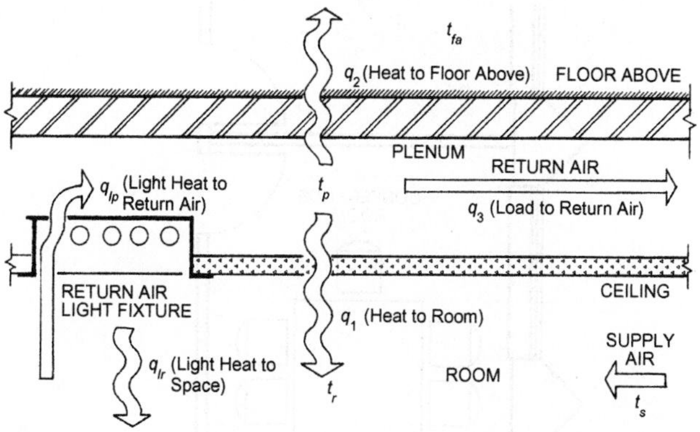

Fig. 15 Schematic Diagram of Typical Return Air Plenum

that all such heat transfer is considered convective for calculation purposes (Rock and Wolfe 1997).

Figure 15 shows a schematic of a typical return air plenum. The following equations, using the heat flow directions shown in Figure 15, represent the heat balance of a return air plenum design for a typical interior room in a multifloor building:

$$q_1 = U_c A_c (t_p - t_r) \tag{48}$$

$$q_2 = U_f A_f (t_p - t_{fa}) \tag{49}$$

$$q_3 = 1.1Q(t_p - t_r) \tag{50}$$

$$q_{lp} - q_2 - q_1 - q_3 = 0 \tag{51}$$

$$Q = \frac{q_r + q_1}{1.23(t_r - t_s)} \tag{52}$$

where

q_1 = heat gain to space from plenum through ceiling, kW
q_2 = heat loss from plenum through floor above, kW
q_3 = heat gain "pickup" by return air, kW
Q = return airflow, L/s
q_{lp} = light heat gain to plenum via return air, kW
q_{lr} = light heat gain to space, kW
q_f = heat gain from plenum below, through floor, kW
q_w = heat gain from exterior wall, kW
q_r = space cooling load, including appropriate treatment of q_{lr}, q_f, and/or q_w, kW
t_p = plenum air temperature, °C
t_r = space air temperature, °C
t_{fa} = space air temperature of floor above, °C
t_s = supply air temperature, °C

By substituting Equations (48), (49), (50), and (52) into heat balance Equation (51), t_p can be found as the resultant return air temperature or plenum temperature. The results, although rigorous and best solved by computer, are important in determining the cooling load, which affects equipment size selection, future energy consumption, and other factors.

Equations (48) to (52) are simplified to illustrate the heat balance relationship. Heat gain into a return air plenum is not limited to heat from lights. Exterior walls directly exposed to the ceiling space can transfer heat directly to or from return air. For single-story buildings or the top floor of a multistory building, roof heat gain or loss enters or leaves the ceiling plenum rather than the conditioned space directly. The supply air quantity calculated by Equation (52) is only for the conditioned space under consideration, and is assumed to equal the return air quantity.

The amount of airflow through a return plenum above a conditioned space may not be limited to that supplied into the space; it will, however, have no noticeable effect on plenum temperature if the surplus comes from an adjacent plenum operating under similar conditions. Where special conditions exist, Equations (48) to (52) must be modified appropriately. Finally, although the building's thermal storage has some effect, the amount of heat entering the return air is small and may be considered as convective for calculation purposes.

Ceiling Plenums with Ducted Returns

Compared to those in unducted plenum returns, temperatures in ceiling plenums that have well-sealed return or exhaust air ducts float considerably. In cooling mode, heat from lights and other equipment raises the ceiling plenum's temperature considerably. Solar heat gain through a poorly insulated roof can drive the ceiling plenum temperature to extreme levels, so much so that heat gains to uninsulated supply air ducts in the plenum can dramatically decrease available cooling capacity to the rooms below. In cold weather, much heat is lost from warm supply ducts. Thus, insulating supply air ducts and sealing them well to minimize air leaks are highly desirable, if not essential. Appropriately insulating roofs and plenums' exterior walls and minimizing infiltration are also key to lowering total building loads and improving HVAC system performance.

Floor Plenum Distribution Systems

Underfloor air distribution (UFAD) systems are designed to provide comfort conditions in the occupied level and allow stratification to occur above this level of the space. In contrast, room cooling loads determined by methods in this chapter assume uniform temperatures and complete mixing of air within the conditioned space, typically by conventional overhead air distribution systems. Ongoing research projects have identified several factors relating to the load calculation process:

- Heat transfer from a conditioned space with a conventional air distribution system is by convection; radiant loads are converted to convection and transferred to the airstream within the conditioned space.
- A significant fraction of heat transfer with a UFAD system is by radiation directly to the floor surface and, from there, by convection to the airstream in the supply plenum.
- Load at the cooling coil is similar for identical spaces with alternative distribution systems.

Plenums in Load Calculations

Currently, most designers include ceiling and floor plenums within neighboring occupied spaces when thermally zoning a building. However, temperatures in these plenums, and the way that they behave, are significantly different from those of occupied spaces. Thus, they should be defined as a separate thermal zone. However, most hand and computer-based load calculation routines currently do not allow floating air temperatures or humidities; assuming a constant air temperature in plenums, attics, and other unconditioned spaces is a poor, but often necessary, assumption. The heat balance method does allow floating space conditions, and when fully implemented in design load software, should allow more accurate modeling of plenums and other complex spaces.

CENTRAL PLANT

Piping

Losses must be considered for piping systems that transport heat. For water or hydronic piping systems, heat is transferred through the piping and insulation (see Chapter 23 for ways to determine this transfer). However, distribution of this transferred heat depends on the fluid in the pipe and the surrounding environment.

Consider a heating hot-water pipe. If the pipe serves a room heater and is routed through the heated space, any heat loss from the pipe adds heat to the room. Heat transfer to the heated space and heat loss from the piping system is null. If the piping is exposed to ambient conditions en route to the heater, the loss must be considered when selecting the heating equipment; if the pipe is routed through a space requiring cooling, heat loss from the piping also becomes a load on the cooling system.

In summary, the designer must evaluate both the magnitude of the pipe heat transfer and the routing of the piping.

Pumps

Calculating heat gain from pumps is addressed in the section on Electric Motors. For pumps serving hydronic systems, disposition of heat from the pumps depends on the service. For chilled-water systems, energy applied to the fluid to generate flow and pressure becomes a chiller load. For condenser water pumps, pumping energy must be rejected through the cooling tower. The magnitude of pumping energy relative to cooling load is generally small.

EXAMPLE COOLING AND HEATING LOAD CALCULATIONS

To illustrate the cooling and heating load calculation procedures discussed in this chapter, an example problem has been developed based on building located in Atlanta, Georgia. This example is a two-story office building of approximately 2800 m^2, including a variety of common office functions and occupancies. In addition to demonstrating calculation procedures, a hypothetical design/construction process is discussed to illustrate (1) application of load calculations and (2) the need to develop reasonable assumptions when specific data is not yet available, as often occurs in everyday design processes.

SINGLE-ROOM EXAMPLE

Calculate the peak heating and cooling loads for the conference room shown in Figure 16, for Atlanta, Georgia. The room is on the second floor of a two-story building and has two vertical exterior exposures, with a flat roof above.

Room Characteristics

Area: 25.47 m^2

Floor: Carpeted 127 mm concrete slab on metal deck above a conditioned space.

Roof: Flat metal deck topped with rigid mineral fiber insulation and perlite board (R = 2.2), felt, and light-colored membrane roofing. Space above 2.75 m suspended acoustical tile ceiling is used as a return air plenum. Assume 30% of the cooling load from the roof is directly absorbed in the return airstream without becoming room load. Use roof U = 0.40 W/(m^2·K).

Spandrel wall: Spandrel bronze-tinted glass, opaque, backed with air space, rigid mineral fiber insulation (R = 0.88), mineral fiber batt insulation (R = 0.88), and 16 mm gypsum wall board. Use spandrel wall U = 0.45 W/(m^2/K).

Brick wall: Light-brown-colored face brick (102 mm), mineral fiber batt insulation (R = 1.76), lightweight concrete block (152 mm) and gypsum wall board (16 mm). Use brick wall U = 0.45 W/(m^2·K).

Windows: Double glazed, 6 mm bronze-tinted outside pane, 13 mm air space and 6 mm clear inside pane with light-colored interior miniblinds. Window normal solar heat gain coefficient (SHGC) = 0.49. Windows are nonoperable and mounted in aluminum frames with thermal breaks having overall combined U = 3.18 W/(m^2·K) (based on Type 5d from Tables 4 and 10 of Chapter 15). Inside attenuation coefficients (IACs) for inside miniblinds are based on light venetian blinds (assumed louver reflectance = 0.8 and louvers positioned at 45° angle) with heat-absorbing double glazing (Type 5d from Table 13B of Chapter 15), IAC(0) = 0.74, IAC(60) = 0.65, IAD(diff) = 0.79, and radiant fraction = 0.54. Each window is 1.91 m wide by 1.95 m tall for an area per window = 3.72 m^2.

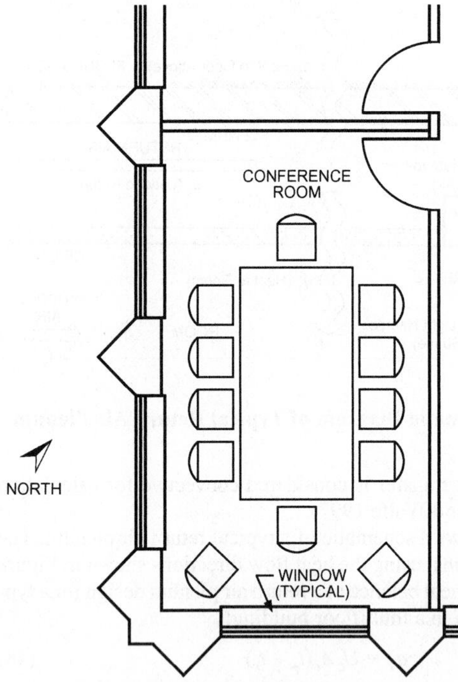

Fig. 16 Single-Room Example Conference Room

South exposure:	Orientation	= 30° east of true south
	Window area	= 3.72 m^2
	Spandrel wall area	= 5.57 m^2
	Brick wall area	= 5.57 m^2
West exposure:	Orientation	= 60° west of south
	Window area	= 7.43 m^2
	Spandrel wall area	= 11.15 m^2
	Brick wall area	= 6.97 m^2

Occupancy: 12 people from 8:00 AM to 5:00 PM.

Lighting: Four 3-lamp recessed fluorescent 600 by 1200 mm parabolic reflector (without lens) type with side slot return-air-type fixtures. Each fixture has three 32 W T-8 lamps plus electronic ballasts, for a total of 110 W per fixture or 440 W total for the room. Operation is from 7:00 AM to 7:00 PM. Assume 26% of the cooling load from lighting is directly absorbed in the return air stream without becoming room load, per Table 3.

Equipment: Several computers and a video projector may used, for which an allowance of 10.76 W/m^2 is to be accommodated by the cooling system, for a total of 274 W for the room. Operation is from 8:00 AM to 5:00 PM.

Infiltration: For purposes of this example, assume the building is maintained under positive pressure during peak cooling conditions and therefore has no infiltration. Assume that infiltration during peak heating conditions is equivalent to one air change per hour.

Weather data: Per Chapter 14, for Atlanta, Georgia, latitude = 33.64, longitude = 84.43, elevation = 313 m above sea level, 99.6% heating design dry-bulb temperature = –6.3°C. For cooling load calculations, use 5% dry-bulb/coincident wet-bulb monthly design day profile calculated per Chapter 14. See Table 26 for temperature profiles used in these examples.

Inside design conditions: 22.2°C for heating; 23.9°C with 50% rh for cooling.

Cooling Loads Using RTS Method

Traditionally, simplified cooling load calculation methods have estimated the total cooling load at a particular design condition by independently calculating and then summing the load from each component (walls, windows, people, lights, etc). Although the actual heat transfer processes for each component do affect each other, this simplification is appropriate for design load calculations and useful to the designer in understanding the relative contribution of each component to the total cooling load.

Cooling loads are calculated with the RTS method on a component basis similar to previous methods. The following example parts illustrate cooling load calculations for individual components of this single room for a particular hour and month.

Part 1. Internal cooling load using radiant time series. Calculate the cooling load from lighting at 3:00 PM for the previously described conference room.

Solution: First calculate the 24 h heat gain profile for lighting, then split those heat gains into radiant and convective portions, apply the appropriate RTS to the radiant portion, and sum the convective and radiant cooling load components to determine total cooling load at the designated time. Using Equation (1), the lighting heat gain profile, based on the occupancy schedule indicated is

$q_1 = (440\text{ W})(0\%) = 0$	$q_{13} = (440\text{ W})(100\%) = 440$
$q_2 = (440\text{ W})(0\%) = 0$	$q_{14} = (440\text{ W})(100\%) = 440$
$q_3 = (440\text{ W})(0\%) = 0$	$q_{15} = (440\text{ W})(100\%) = 440$
$q_4 = (440\text{ W})(0\%) = 0$	$q_{16} = (440\text{ W})(100\%) = 440$
$q_5 = (440\text{ W})(0\%) = 0$	$q_{17} = (440\text{ W})(100\%) = 440$
$q_6 = (440\text{ W})(0\%) = 0$	$q_{18} = (440\text{ W})(100\%) = 440$
$q_7 = (440\text{ W})(100\%) = 440$	$q_{19} = (440\text{ W})(0\%) = 0$
$q_8 = (440\text{ W})(100\%) = 440$	$q_{20} = (440\text{ W})(0\%) = 0$
$q_9 = (440\text{ W})(100\%) = 440$	$q_{21} = (440\text{ W})(0\%) = 0$
$q_{10} = (440\text{ W})(100\%) = 440$	$q_{22} = (440\text{ W})(0\%) = 0$
$q_{11} = (440\text{ W})(100\%) = 440$	$q_{23} = (440\text{ W})(0\%) = 0$
$q_{12} = (440\text{ W})(100\%) = 440$	$q_{24} = (440\text{ W})(0\%) = 0$

The convective portion is simply the lighting heat gain for the hour being calculated times the convective fraction for recessed fluorescent lighting fixtures without lens and with side slot return air, from Table 3:

$$Q_{c,15} = (1500)(52\%) = 229\text{ W}$$

The radiant portion of the cooling load is calculated using lighting heat gains for the current hour and past 23 h, the radiant fraction from Table 3 (48%), and radiant time series from Table 19, in accordance with Equation (34). From Table 19, select the RTS for medium-weight construction, assuming 50% glass and carpeted floors as representative of the described construction. Thus, the radiant cooling load for lighting is

$$Q_{r,15} = r_0(0.48)q_{15} + r_1(0.48)q_{14} + r_2(0.48)q_{13} + r_3(0.48)q_{12} + \ldots + r_{23}(0.48)q_{16}$$

$$= (0.49)(0.48)(440) + (0.17)(0.48)(440)$$
$$+ (0.09)(0.48)(440) + (0.05)(0.48)(440) + (0.03)(0.48)(440)$$
$$+ (0.02)(0.48)(440) + (0.02)(0.48)(440) + (0.01)(0.48)(440)$$
$$+ (0.01)(0.48)(440) + (0.01)(0.48)(0) + (0.01)(0.48)(0)$$
$$+ (0.01)(0.48)(0) + (0.01)(0.48)(0) + (0.01)(0.48)(0)$$
$$+ (0.01)(0.48)(0) + (0.01)(0.48)(0) + (0.01)(0.48)(0)$$
$$+ (0.01)(0.48)(0) + (0.01)(0.48)(0)+ (0.01)(0.48)(0)$$
$$+ (0.00)(0.48)(0) + (0.00)(0.48)(440) + (0.00)(0.48)(440)$$
$$+ (0.00)(0.48)(440) = 188\text{ W}$$

The total lighting cooling load at the designated hour is thus

$$Q_{light} = Q_{c,15} + Q_{r,15} = 229 + 188 = 417\text{ W}$$

As noted in the example definition, if it is assumed that 26% of the total lighting load is absorbed by the return air stream, the net lighting cooling load to the room is

$$Q_{light\text{-}room,\,15} = Q_{light,15}\,(74\%) = 417(0.74) = 309\text{ W}$$

See Table 27 for the conference room's lighting usage, heat gain, and cooling load profiles.

Part 2. Wall cooling load using sol-air temperature, conduction time series and radiant time series. Calculate the cooling load contribution from the spandrel wall section facing 60° west of south at 3:00 PM local standard time in July for the previously described conference room.

Solution: Determine the wall cooling load by calculating (1) sol-air temperatures at the exterior surface, (2) heat input based on sol-air temperature, (3) delayed heat gain through the mass of the wall to the interior surface using conduction time series, and (4) delayed space cooling load from heat gain using radiant time series.

First, calculate the sol-air temperature at 3:00 PM local standard time (LST) (4:00 PM daylight saving time) on July 21 for a vertical, dark-colored wall surface, facing 60° west of south, located in Atlanta, Georgia (latitude = 33.64, longitude = 84.43), solar taub = 0.556 and taud = 1.779 from monthly Atlanta weather data for July (Table 1 in Chapter 14). From Table 26, the calculated outdoor design temperature for that month and time is 33.3°C. The ground reflectivity is assumed $\rho_g = 0.2$.

Sol-air temperature is calculated using Equation (30). For the dark-colored wall, $\alpha/h_o = 0.053$, and for vertical surfaces, $\varepsilon\Delta R/h_o = 0$. The solar irradiance E_t on the wall must be determined using the equations in Chapter 14:

Solar Angles:

ψ = southwest orientation = +60°

Σ = surface tilt from horizontal (where horizontal = 0°) = 90° for vertical wall surface

3:00 PM LST = hour 15

Calculate solar altitude, solar azimuth, surface solar azimuth, and incident angle as follows:

From Table 2 in Chapter 14, solar position data and constants for July 21 are

ET = –6.4 min

δ = 20.4°

E_o = 1324 W/m²

Local standard meridian (LSM) for Eastern Time Zone = 75°.

Apparent solar time AST

$$\text{AST} = \text{LST} + \text{ET}/60 + (\text{LSM} - \text{LON})/15$$
$$= 15 + (-6.4/60) + [(75 - 84.43)/15]$$
$$= 14.2647$$

Hour angle H, degrees

$$H = 15(\text{AST} - 12)$$
$$= 15(14.2647 - 12)$$
$$= 33.97°$$

Solar altitude β

$$\sin\beta = \cos L \cos\delta \cos H + \sin L \sin\delta$$
$$= \cos(33.64)\cos(20.4)\cos(33.97) + \sin(33.64)\sin(20.4)$$
$$= 0.841$$
$$\beta = \sin^{-1}(0.841) = 57.2°$$

Solar azimuth ϕ

$$\cos\phi = (\sin\beta \sin L - \sin\delta)/(\cos\beta \cos L)$$
$$= [(\sin(57.2)\sin(33.64) - \sin(20.4)]/[\cos(57.2)\cos(33.64)]$$
$$= 0.258$$
$$\phi = \cos^{-1}(0.253) = 75.05°$$

Surface-solar azimuth γ

$$\gamma = \phi - \psi$$
$$= 75.05 - 60$$
$$= 15.05°$$

Incident angle θ

$$\cos\theta = \cos\beta \cos g \sin\Sigma + \sin\beta \cos\Sigma$$
$$= \cos(57.2)\cos(15.05)\sin(90) + \sin(57.2)\cos(90)$$
$$= 0.523$$
$$\theta = \cos^{-1}(0.523) = 58.5°$$

Table 26 Monthly/Hourly Design Temperatures (5% Conditions) for Atlanta, GA, °C

	January		February		March		April		May		June		July		August		September		October		November		December	
Hour	db	wb	db	wb	db	wb	db	wb	db	wb	db	wb	db	wb	db	wb	db	wb	db	wb	db	wb	db	wb
1	6.7	6.1	8.4	7.7	11.6	9.1	15.1	12.3	19.1	16.6	21.8	19.1	23.2	20.5	22.9	20.5	20.8	18.6	16.1	14.2	11.8	11.0	8.4	8.3
2	6.3	5.8	8.0	7.4	11.1	8.8	14.6	12.1	18.6	16.4	21.3	18.9	22.8	20.3	22.5	20.4	20.3	18.4	15.6	14.1	11.4	10.7	7.9	7.9
3	5.9	5.6	7.7	7.2	10.7	8.6	14.2	11.9	18.3	16.3	21.0	18.8	22.4	20.2	22.2	20.3	20.0	18.3	15.3	13.9	11.1	10.6	7.6	7.6
4	5.6	5.3	7.3	7.1	10.3	8.4	13.8	11.8	17.9	16.2	20.7	18.7	22.1	20.1	21.8	20.2	19.7	18.2	14.9	13.8	10.7	10.3	7.3	7.3
5	5.3	5.2	7.1	6.9	10.0	8.3	13.6	11.7	17.7	16.1	20.4	18.6	21.8	20.1	21.6	20.1	19.5	18.1	14.7	13.7	10.5	10.2	7.1	7.1
6	5.6	5.3	7.3	7.1	10.3	8.4	13.8	11.8	17.9	16.2	20.7	18.7	22.1	20.1	21.8	20.2	19.7	18.2	14.9	13.8	10.7	10.3	7.3	7.3
7	6.4	5.9	8.1	7.6	11.2	8.9	14.7	12.2	18.7	16.5	21.4	18.9	22.9	20.4	22.6	20.4	20.4	18.4	15.7	14.1	11.5	10.8	8.1	8.1
8	8.3	7.3	10.1	8.8	13.4	10.0	16.9	13.1	20.7	17.3	23.4	19.6	24.8	20.9	24.4	21.0	22.2	19.1	17.6	14.9	13.4	11.9	9.9	9.3
9	10.6	8.8	12.3	10.1	15.8	11.3	19.3	14.1	22.8	18.1	25.6	20.3	27.0	21.6	26.4	21.6	24.2	19.8	19.7	15.8	15.6	13.1	11.9	10.7
10	12.5	10.2	14.3	11.3	18.0	12.4	21.5	15.1	24.7	18.8	27.5	20.9	28.9	22.2	28.3	22.2	26.0	20.4	21.5	16.7	17.4	14.2	13.8	12.0
11	14.2	11.4	16.1	12.4	19.9	13.4	23.4	15.8	26.4	19.5	29.2	21.4	30.7	22.8	29.9	22.7	27.6	21.0	23.2	17.4	19.2	15.2	15.4	13.1
12	15.4	12.2	17.3	13.1	21.3	14.1	24.7	16.4	27.6	19.9	30.3	21.8	31.8	23.1	31.0	23.1	28.6	21.3	24.2	17.9	20.3	15.8	16.6	13.9
13	16.3	12.8	18.2	13.7	22.3	14.6	25.7	16.8	28.5	20.3	31.3	22.1	32.8	23.4	31.8	23.3	29.5	21.7	25.1	18.3	21.2	16.3	17.4	14.4
14	16.9	13.2	18.8	14.1	22.9	14.9	26.3	17.1	29.1	20.5	31.8	22.3	33.3	23.6	32.4	23.5	30.0	21.8	25.7	18.5	21.7	16.6	17.9	14.8
15	16.9	13.2	18.8	14.1	22.9	14.9	26.3	17.1	29.1	20.5	31.8	22.3	33.3	23.6	32.4	23.5	30.0	21.8	25.7	18.5	21.7	16.6	17.9	14.8
16	16.2	12.7	18.1	13.6	22.2	14.5	25.6	16.8	28.4	20.2	31.2	22.1	32.7	23.3	31.7	23.3	29.4	21.6	25.0	18.2	21.1	16.2	17.3	14.4
17	15.3	12.1	17.2	13.1	21.1	13.9	24.6	16.3	27.4	19.9	30.2	21.8	31.7	23.1	30.9	23.0	28.6	21.3	24.1	17.8	20.2	15.7	16.4	13.8
18	14.1	11.3	16.0	12.3	19.8	13.3	23.3	15.8	26.3	19.4	29.1	21.4	30.6	22.7	29.8	22.7	27.5	20.9	23.1	17.3	19.1	15.1	15.3	13.1
19	12.4	10.1	14.2	11.3	17.9	12.3	21.3	15.0	24.6	18.8	27.4	20.8	28.8	22.2	28.2	22.2	25.9	20.4	21.4	16.6	17.3	14.1	13.7	11.9
20	11.1	9.2	12.9	10.5	16.5	11.6	19.9	14.4	23.4	18.3	26.2	20.4	27.6	21.8	27.0	21.8	24.8	20.0	20.2	16.1	16.1	13.4	12.5	11.1
21	10.1	8.4	11.9	9.8	15.3	11.0	18.8	13.9	22.4	17.9	25.1	20.1	26.6	21.5	26.1	21.5	23.8	19.6	19.2	15.7	15.1	12.8	11.5	10.4
22	9.1	7.7	10.8	9.2	14.2	10.4	17.7	13.4	21.3	17.5	24.1	19.8	25.5	21.2	25.1	21.2	22.8	19.3	18.2	15.2	14.1	12.3	10.6	9.8
23	8.1	7.1	9.9	8.6	13.1	9.9	16.6	13.0	20.4	17.2	23.2	19.5	24.6	20.9	24.2	20.9	22.0	19.0	17.3	14.8	13.2	11.8	9.7	9.2
24	6.7	6.1	9.2	8.2	12.3	9.4	15.8	12.7	19.8	16.9	22.5	19.3	23.9	20.7	23.6	20.7	21.4	18.8	16.7	14.6	12.5	11.4	9.0	8.7

Table 27 Cooling Load Component: Lighting, W

		Heat Gain, kW							
	Usage Profile,		Convective	Radiant	Nonsolar RTS Zone Type 8,	Radiant Cooling	Total Sensible	% Lighting to Return	Room Sensible
Hour	%	Total	52%	48%	%	Load	Cooling Load	26%	Cooling Load
1	0	—	—	—	49	25	25	7	19
2	0	—	—	—	17	25	25	7	19
3	0	—	—	—	9	23	23	6	17
4	0	—	—	—	5	21	21	5	16
5	0	—	—	—	3	19	19	5	14
6	0	—	—	—	2	17	17	4	12
7	100	440	229	211	2	118	347	90	257
8	100	440	229	211	1	152	381	99	282
9	100	440	229	211	1	169	398	103	294
10	100	440	229	211	1	177	406	106	300
11	100	440	229	211	1	182	410	107	304
12	100	440	229	211	1	184	412	107	305
13	100	440	229	211	1	186	414	108	307
14	100	440	229	211	1	186	414	108	307
15	100	440	229	211	1	188	417	108	309
16	100	440	229	211	1	190	419	109	310
17	100	440	229	211	1	192	421	109	311
18	100	440	229	211	1	194	423	110	313
19	0	—	—	—	1	93	93	24	69
20	0	—	—	—	1	59	59	15	44
21	0	—	—	—	0	42	42	11	31
22	0	—	—	—	0	34	34	9	25
23	0	—	—	—	0	30	30	8	22
24	0	—	—	—	0	27	27	7	20
Total		5277	2744	2533		2533	5277	1372	3906

Beam normal irradiance E_b

$$E_b = E_o \exp(-\tau_b m^{ab})$$

m = relative air mass

$= 1/[\sin\beta + 0.50572(6.07995 + \beta)^{-1.6364}]$, β expressed in degrees

$= 1.18905$

ab = beam air mass exponent

$= 1.219 - 0.043\tau_b - 0.151\tau_d - 0.204\tau_b\tau_d$

$= 0.72468$

$$E_b = 1324\exp[-0.556(1.8905^{0.72468})] = 705 \text{ W/m}^2$$

Surface beam irradiance $E_{t,b}$

$$E_{t,b} = E_b \cos\theta = (705)\cos(58.5) = 368 \text{ W/m}^2$$

Ratio Y of sky diffuse radiation on vertical surface to sky diffuse radiation on horizontal surface

$$Y = 0.55 + 0.437\cos\theta + 0.313\cos^2\theta = 0.55 + 0.437\cos(58.5) + 0.313\cos^2(58.5) = 0.864$$

Diffuse irradiance E_d – Horizontal surfaces

$$E_d = E_o \exp(-\tau_d m^{ad})$$

ad = diffuse air mass exponent

$= 0.202 + 0.852\tau_b - 0.007\tau_d - 0.357\tau_b\tau_d$

$= 0.3101417$

$$E_d = E_o \exp(-\tau_d m^{ad}) = 1324\exp(-1.779(1.8905^{0.3101})] = 203 \text{ W/m}^2$$

Diffuse irradiance E_d – Vertical surfaces

$$E_{t,d} = E_d Y = (203)(0.864) = 175 \text{ W/m}^2$$

Ground reflected irradiance $E_{t,r}$

$$E_{t,r} = (E_b \sin\beta + E_d)\rho_g(1 - \cos\Sigma)/2 = [705\sin(57.2) + 203](0.2)[1 - \cos(90)]/2 = 80 \text{ W/m}^2$$

Total surface irradiance E_t

$$E_t = E_D + E_d + E_r = 368 + 175 + 80 = 623 \text{ W/m}^2$$

Sol–air temperature [from Equation (30)]:

$$T_e = t_o + \alpha E_t/h_o - \varepsilon\Delta R/h_o = 33.3 + (0.053)(623) - 0 = 66.3°\text{C}$$

This procedure is used to calculate the sol-air temperatures for each hour on each surface. Because of the tedious solar angle and intensity calculations, using a simple computer spreadsheet or other computer software can reduce the effort involved. A spreadsheet was used to calculate a 24 h sol-air temperature profile for the data of this example. See Table 28A for the solar angle and intensity calculations and Table 28B for the sol-air temperatures for this wall surface and orientation.

Conductive heat gain is calculated using Equations (31) and (32). First, calculate the 24 h heat input profile using Equation (31) and the sol-air temperatures for a southwest-facing wall with dark exterior color:

$$q_{i,1} = (0.45)(11.15)(23.2 - 23.9) = -3 \text{ W}$$
$$q_{i,2} = (0.45)(11.15)(22.8 - 23.9) = -6$$
$$q_{i,3} = (0.45)(11.15)(22.4 - 23.9) = -8$$
$$q_{i,4} = (0.45)(11.15)(22.1 - 23.9) = -9$$
$$q_{i,5} = (0.45)(11.15)(21.8 - 23.9) = -10$$
$$q_{i,6} = (0.45)(11.15)(22.6 - 23.9) = -7$$
$$q_{i,7} = (0.45)(11.15)(25.8 - 23.9) = 10$$
$$q_{i,8} = (0.45)(11.15)(29.9 - 23.9) = 31$$
$$q_{i,9} = (0.45)(11.15)(34.0 - 23.9) = 51$$
$$q_{i,10} = (0.45)(11.15)(37.4 - 23.9) = 68$$
$$q_{i,11} = (0.45)(11.15)(40.3 - 23.9) = 83$$
$$q_{i,12} = (0.45)(11.15)(42.9 - 23.9) = 96$$
$$q_{i,13} = (0.45)(11.15)(51.9 - 23.9) = 142$$
$$q_{i,14} = (0.45)(11.15)(60.8 - 23.9) = 187$$
$$q_{i,15} = (0.45)(11.15)(66.3 - 23.9) = 215$$
$$q_{i,16} = (0.45)(11.15)(67.1 - 23.9) = 219$$
$$q_{i,17} = (0.45)(11.15)(62.7 - 23.9) = 196$$
$$q_{i,18} = (0.45)(11.15)(52.6 - 23.9) = 145$$
$$q_{i,19} = (0.45)(11.15)(36.7 - 23.9) = 65$$
$$q_{i,20} = (0.45)(11.15)(27.6 - 23.9) = 19$$
$$q_{i,21} = (0.45)(11.15)(26.6 - 23.9) = 14$$
$$q_{i,22} = (0.45)(11.15)(25.5 - 23.9) = 8$$
$$q_{i,23} = (0.45)(11.15)(24.6 - 23.9) = 4$$
$$q_{i,24} = (0.45)(11.15)(23.9 - 23.9) = 0$$

Next, calculate wall heat gain using conduction time series. The preceding heat input profile is used with conduction time series to calculate the wall heat gain. From Table 16, the most similar wall construction is wall number 1. This is a spandrel glass wall that has similar mass and thermal capacity. Using Equation (32), the conduction time factors for wall 1 can be used in conjunction with the 24 h heat input profile to determine the wall heat gain at 3:00 PM LST:

$$\begin{aligned} q_{15} &= c_0 q_{i,15} + c_1 q_{i,14} + c_2 q_{i,13} + c_3 q_{i,12} + \cdots + c_{23} q_{i,14} \\ &= (0.18)(215) + (0.58)(187) + (0.20)(142) + (0.04)(96) \\ &\quad + (0.00)(83) + (0.00)(68) + (0.00)(51) + (0.00)(31) \\ &\quad + (0.00)(10) + (0.00)(-7) + (0.00)(-10) + (0.00)(-9) \\ &\quad + (0.00)(-8) + (0.00)(-6) + (0.00)(-3) + (0.00)(0) \\ &\quad + (0.00)(4) + (0.00)(8) + (0.00)(14) + (0.00)(19) \\ &\quad + (0.00)(65) + (0.00)(145) + (0.00)(196) + (0.00)(219) \\ &= 179 \text{ W} \end{aligned}$$

Because of the tedious calculations involved, a spreadsheet is used to calculate the remainder of a 24 h heat gain profile indicated in Table 28B for the data of this example.

Finally, calculate wall cooling load using radiant time series. Total cooling load for the wall is calculated by summing the convective and radiant portions. The convective portion is simply the wall heat gain for the hour being calculated times the convective fraction for walls from Table 14 (54%):

$$Q_c = (179)(0.54) = 97 \text{ W}$$

The radiant portion of the cooling load is calculated using conductive heat gains for the current and past 23 h, the radiant fraction for walls from Table 14 (46%), and radiant time series from Table 19, in accordance with Equation (34). From Table 19, select the RTS for medium-weight construction, assuming 50% glass and carpeted floors as representative for the described construction. Use the wall heat gains from Table 28B for 24 h design conditions in July. Thus, the radiant cooling load for the wall at 3:00 PM is

$$\begin{aligned} Q_{r,15} &= r_0(0.46)q_{i,15} + r_1(0.46)\, q_{i,14} + r_2(0.46)\, q_{i,13} + r_3(0.46)\, q_{i,12} \\ &\quad + \cdots + r_{23}(0.46)\, q_{i,16} \\ &= (0.49)(0.46)(179) + (0.17)(0.46)(138) + (0.09)(0.46)(101) \\ &\quad + (0.05)(0.46)(81) + (0.03)(0.46)(66) + (0.02)(0.46)(48) \\ &\quad + (0.02)(0.46)(29) + (0.01)(0.46)(9) + (0.01)(0.46)(-5) \\ &\quad + (0.01)(0.46)(-9) + (0.01)(0.46)(-9) + (0.01)(0.46)(-7) \\ &\quad + (0.01)(0.46)(-5) + (0.01)(0.46)(-3) + (0.01)(0.46)(0) \\ &\quad + (0.01)(0.46)(4) + (0.01)(0.46)(9) + (0.01)(0.46)(16) \\ &\quad + (0.01)(0.46)(32) + (0.01)(0.46)(78) + (0.00)(0.46)(144) \\ &\quad + (0.00)(0.46)(192) + (0.00)(0.46)(213) + (0.00)(0.46)(207) \\ &= 59 \text{ W} \end{aligned}$$

The total wall cooling load at the designated hour is thus

$$Q_{wall} = Q_c + Q_{r15} = 97 + 59 = 156 \text{ W}$$

Again, a simple computer spreadsheet or other software is necessary to reduce the effort involved. A spreadsheet was used with the heat gain profile to split the heat gain into convective and radiant portions, apply RTS to the radiant portion, and total the convective and radiant loads to determine a 24 h cooling load profile for this example, with results in Table 28B.

Part 3. Window cooling load using radiant time series. Calculate the cooling load contribution, with and without inside shading (venetian blinds) for the window area facing 60° west of south at 3:00 PM in July for the conference room example.

Solution: First, calculate the 24 h heat gain profile for the window, then split those heat gains into radiant and convective portions, apply the appropriate RTS to the radiant portion, then sum the convective and radiant cooling load components to determine total window cooling

Table 28A Wall Component of Solar Irradiance

				Direct Beam Solar			Diffuse Solar Heat Gain						
Local Standard Hour	Apparent Solar Time	Hour Angle H	Solar Altitude β	Solar Azimuth ϕ	Beam Normal E_b, W/m²	Surface Incident Angle θ	Surface Direct W/m²	Diffuse Horizontal E_d, W/m²	Ground Diffuse, W/m²	Y Ratio	Sky Diffuse W/m²	Subtotal Diffuse W/m²	Total Surface Irradiance, W/m²
1	0.26	−176	−36	−175	0.0	117.4	0.0	0.0	0.0	0.4500	0.0	0.0	0.0
2	1.26	−161	−33	−159	0.0	130.9	0.0	0.0	0.0	0.4500	0.0	0.0	0.0
3	2.26	−146	−27	−144	0.0	144.5	0.0	0.0	0.0	0.4500	0.0	0.0	0.0
4	3.26	−131	−19	−132	0.0	158.1	0.0	0.0	0.0	0.4500	0.0	0.0	0.0
5	4.26	−116	−9	−122	0.0	171.3	0.0	0.0	0.0	0.4500	0.0	0.0	0.0
6	5.26	−101	3	−113	17.7	172.5	0.0	18.4	1.9	0.4500	8.3	10.2	10.2
7	6.26	−86	14	−105	291.6	159.5	0.0	86.3	15.8	0.4500	38.8	54.7	54.7
8	7.26	−71	27	−98	490.3	145.9	0.0	135.4	35.5	0.4500	60.9	96.4	96.4
9	8.26	−56	39	−90	609.1	132.3	0.0	170.0	55.3	0.4500	76.5	131.9	131.9
10	9.26	−41	51	−81	681.8	118.8	0.0	194.3	72.7	0.4500	87.4	160.2	160.2
11	10.26	−26	63	−67	725.0	105.6	0.0	210.1	85.9	0.4553	95.6	181.5	181.5
12	11.26	−11	74	−39	746.9	92.6	0.0	218.5	93.5	0.5306	115.9	209.4	209.4
13	12.26	4	76	16	750.9	80.2	127.5	220.1	95.0	0.6332	139.4	234.3	361.8
14	13.26	19	69	57	737.7	68.7	268.4	214.9	90.2	0.7505	161.3	251.5	519.9
15	14.26	34	57	75	705.2	58.4	368.0	202.7	79.5	0.8644	175.2	254.7	622.7
16	15.26	49	45	86	647.8	50.4	412.7	182.6	64.0	0.9555	174.5	238.4	651.2
17	16.26	64	32	94	553.6	45.8	386.2	153.2	45.0	1.0073	154.3	199.3	585.5
18	17.26	79	20	102	398.2	45.5	279.0	111.5	24.8	1.0100	112.7	137.5	416.5
19	18.26	94	8	109	140.9	49.7	91.0	52.4	7.2	0.9631	50.4	57.6	148.7
20	19.26	109	−3	117	0.0	57.5	0.0	0.0	0.0	0.8755	0.0	0.0	0.0
21	20.26	124	−14	127	0.0	67.5	0.0	0.0	0.0	0.7630	0.0	0.0	0.0
22	21.26	139	−23	138	0.0	79.0	0.0	0.0	0.0	0.6452	0.0	0.0	0.0
23	22.26	154	−30	151	0.0	91.3	0.0	0.0	0.0	0.5403	0.0	0.0	0.0
24	23.26	169	−35	167	0.0	104.2	0.0	0.0	0.0	0.4618	0.0	0.0	0.0

Table 28B Conduction: Wall Component of Sol-Air Temperatures, Heat Input, Heat Gain, Cooling Load

							Heat Gain, W					
								Convective	Radiant			
Local Standard Hour	Total Surface Irradiance W/m²	Outside Temp., °C	Sol-Air Temp., °C	Inside Temp., °C	Heat Input, W	CTS Type 1, %	Total	37%	63%	Nonsolar RTS Zone Type 8, %	Radiant Cooling Load, W	Total Cooling Load, W
1	0.0	23.2	23.2	23.9	−3	18	0	0	0	49	9	10
2	0.0	22.8	22.8	23.9	−6	58	−3	−2	−1	17	7	6
3	0.0	22.4	22.4	23.9	−8	20	−5	−3	−2	9	6	3
4	0.0	22.1	22.1	23.9	−9	4	−7	−4	−3	5	5	1
5	0.0	21.8	21.8	23.9	−10	0	−9	−5	−4	3	4	−1
6	10.2	22.1	22.6	23.9	−7	0	−9	−5	−4	2	3	−2
7	54.7	22.9	25.8	23.9	10	0	−5	−2	−2	2	4	2
8	96.4	24.8	29.9	23.9	31	0	9	5	4	1	7	12
9	131.9	27.0	34.0	23.9	51	0	29	15	13	1	12	28
10	160.2	28.9	37.4	23.9	68	0	48	26	22	1	18	44
11	181.5	30.7	40.3	23.9	83	0	66	36	30	1	24	60
12	209.4	31.8	42.9	23.9	96	0	81	44	37	1	29	73
13	361.8	32.8	51.9	23.9	142	0	101	54	46	1	35	90
14	519.9	33.3	60.8	23.9	187	0	138	75	64	1	46	121
15	623.8	33.3	66.3	23.9	215	0	179	97	82	1	59	156
16	651.2	32.7	67.1	23.9	219	0	207	112	95	1	71	183
17	585.5	31.7	62.7	23.9	196	0	213	115	98	1	78	193
18	416.5	30.6	52.6	23.9	145	0	192	104	88	1	77	181
19	148.7	28.8	36.7	23.9	65	0	144	78	66	1	67	144
20	0.0	27.6	27.6	23.9	19	0	78	42	36	1	49	91
21	0.0	26.6	26.6	23.9	14	0	32	17	15	0	32	50
22	0.0	25.5	25.5	23.9	8	0	16	8	7	0	22	30
23	0.0	24.6	24.6	23.9	4	0	9	5	4	0	16	21
24	0.0	23.9	23.9	23.9	0	0	4	2	2	0	12	14

Table 29 Window Component of Heat Gain (No Blinds or Overhang)

	Beam Solar Heat Gain						Diffuse Solar Heat Gain							Conduction		
Local Std. Hour	Beam Normal, W/m²	Surface Incident Angle	Surface Beam, W/m²	Beam SHGC	Adjusted Beam IAC	Beam Solar Heat Gain, W	Diffuse Horiz. E_d, W/m²	Ground Diffuse, W/m²	Y Ratio	Sky Diffuse, W/m²	Subtotal Diffuse, W/m²	Hemis. SHGC	Diff. Solar Heat Gain, W	Outside Temp., °C	Conduction Heat Gain, W	Total Window Heat Gain, W
1	0.0	117.4	0.0	0.000	1.000	0	0.0	0.0	0.4500	0.0	0.0	0.410	0	23.2	–16	–16
2	0.0	130.9	0.0	0.000	1.000	0	0.0	0.0	0.4500	0.0	0.0	0.410	0	22.8	–26	–26
3	0.0	144.5	0.0	0.000	1.000	0	0.0	0.0	0.4500	0.0	0.0	0.410	0	22.4	–35	–35
4	0.0	158.1	0.0	0.000	1.000	0	0.0	0.0	0.4500	0.0	0.0	0.410	0	22.1	–43	–43
5	0.0	171.3	0.0	0.000	1.000	0	0.0	0.0	0.4500	0.0	0.0	0.410	0	21.8	–49	–49
6	17.7	172.5	0.0	0.000	0.000	0	18.4	1.9	0.4500	8.3	10.2	0.410	31	22.1	–43	–12
7	291.6	159.5	0.0	0.000	0.000	0	86.3	15.8	0.4500	38.8	54.7	0.410	167	22.9	–24	143
8	490.3	145.9	0.0	0.000	0.000	0	135.4	35.5	0.4500	60.9	96.4	0.410	294	24.8	22	316
9	609.1	132.3	0.0	0.000	0.000	0	170.0	55.3	0.4500	76.5	131.9	0.410	402	27.0	74	475
10	681.8	118.8	0.0	0.000	0.000	0	194.3	72.7	0.4500	87.4	160.2	0.410	488	28.9	119	608
11	725.0	105.6	0.0	0.000	0.000	0	210.1	85.9	0.4553	95.6	181.5	0.410	553	30.7	160	713
12	746.9	92.6	0.0	0.000	0.000	0	218.5	93.5	0.5306	115.9	209.4	0.410	638	31.8	188	826
13	750.9	80.2	127.5	0.166	1.000	157	220.1	95.0	0.6332	139.4	234.3	0.410	714	32.8	210	1082
14	737.7	68.7	268.4	0.321	1.000	640	214.9	90.2	0.7505	161.3	251.5	0.410	766	33.3	223	1629
15	705.2	58.4	369.0	0.398	1.000	1091	202.7	79.5	0.8644	175.2	254.7	0.410	776	33.3	223	2090
16	647.8	50.4	412.7	0.438	1.000	1343	182.6	64.0	0.9555	174.5	238.4	0.410	727	32.7	207	2277
17	553.6	45.8	386.2	0.448	1.000	1287	153.2	45.0	1.0073	154.3	199.3	0.410	607	31.7	185	2080
18	398.2	45.5	279.0	0.449	1.000	931	111.5	24.8	1.0100	112.7	137.5	0.410	419	30.6	158	1507
19	140.9	49.7	91.0	0.441	1.000	298	52.4	7.2	0.9631	50.4	57.6	0.410	176	28.8	117	591
20	0.0	57.5	0.0	0.403	0.000	0	0.0	0.0	0.8755	0.0	0.0	0.410	0	27.6	88	88
21	0.0	67.5	0.0	0.330	0.000	0	0.0	0.0	0.7630	0.0	0.0	0.410	0	26.6	63	63
22	0.0	79.0	0.0	0.185	0.000	0	0.0	0.0	0.6452	0.0	0.0	0.410	0	25.5	38	38
23	0.0	91.3	0.0	0.000	1.000	0	0.0	0.0	0.5403	0.0	0.0	0.410	0	24.6	17	17
24	0.0	104.2	0.0	0.000	1.000	0	0.0	0.0	0.4618	0.0	0.0	0.410	0	23.9	0	0

load for the time. The window heat gain components are calculated using Equations (13) to (15). From Part 2, at hour 15 LST (3:00 PM):

$$E_{t,b} = 368 \text{ W/m}^2$$
$$E_{t,d} = 175 \text{ W/m}^2$$
$$E_r = 80 \text{ W/m}^2$$
$$\theta = 58.5°$$

From Chapter 15, Table 10, for glass type 5d,

$$\text{SHGC}(\theta) = \text{SHGC}(58.5) = 0.3978 \text{ (interpolated)}$$

$$\langle \text{SHGC} \rangle_D = 0.41$$

From Chapter 15, Table 13B, for light-colored blinds (assumed louver reflectance = 0.8 and louvers positioned at 45° angle) on double-glazed, heat-absorbing windows (Type 5d from Table 13B of Chapter 15), IAC(0) = 0.74, IAC(60) = 0.65, IAC(diff) = 0.79, and radiant fraction = 0.54. Without blinds, IAC = 1.0. Therefore, window heat gain components for hour 15, without blinds, are

$$q_{b15} = AE_{t,b}\,\text{SHGC}(\theta)(\text{IAC}) = (7.43)(368)(0.3978)(1.00) = 1088 \text{ W}$$

$$q_{d15} = A(E_{t,d} + E_r)\langle \text{SHGC} \rangle_D(\text{IAC}) = (7.43)(175 + 80)(0.41)(1.00) = 777 \text{ W}$$

$$q_{c15} = UA(t_{out} - t_{in}) = (3.18)(7.43)(33.3 - 23.9) = 222 \text{ W}$$

This procedure is repeated to determine these values for a 24 h heat gain profile, shown in Table 29.

Total cooling load for the window is calculated by summing the convective and radiant portions. For windows with inside shading (blinds, drapes, etc.), the direct beam, diffuse, and conductive heat gains may be summed and treated together in calculating cooling loads. However, in this example, the window does not have inside shading, and the direct beam solar heat gain should be treated separately from the diffuse and conductive heat gains. The direct beam heat gain, without inside shading, is treated as 100% radiant, and solar RTS factors from Table 20 are used to convert the beam heat gains to cooling loads. The diffuse and conductive heat gains can be totaled and split into radiant and convective portions according to Table 14, and nonsolar RTS factors from Table 19 are used to convert the radiant portion to cooling load.

The solar beam cooling load is calculated using heat gains for the current hour and past 23 h and radiant time series from Table 20, in accordance with Equation (39). From Table 20, select the solar RTS for medium-weight construction, assuming 50% glass and carpeted floors for this example. Using Table 29 values for direct solar heat gain, the radiant cooling load for the window direct beam solar component is

$$\begin{aligned} Q_{b,15} &= r_0 q_{b,15} + r_1 q_{b,14} + r_2 q_{b,13} + r_3 q_{b,12} + \ldots + r_{23} q_{b,14} \\ &= (0.54)(1091) + (0.16)(640) + (0.08)(157) + (0.04)(0) \\ &\quad + (0.03)(0) + (0.02)(0) + (0.01)(0) + (0.01)(0) + (0.01)(0) \\ &\quad + (0.01)(0) + (0.01)(0) + (0.01)(0) + (0.01)(0) + (0.01)(0) \\ &\quad + (0.01)(0) + (0.01)(0) + (0.01)(0) + (0.01)(0) + (0.01)(0) \\ &\quad + (0.00)(0) + (0.00)(298) + (0.00)(931) + (0.00)(1287) \\ &\quad + (0.00)(1343) = 704 \text{ W} \end{aligned}$$

This process is repeated for other hours; results are listed in Table 30.

For diffuse and conductive heat gains, the radiant fraction according to Table 14 is 46%. The radiant portion is processed using nonsolar RTS coefficients from Table 19. The results are listed in Tables 29 and 30. For 3:00 PM, the diffuse and conductive cooling load is 922 W.

The total window cooling load at the designated hour is thus

$$Q_{window} = Q_b + Q_{diff + cond} = 704 + 922 = 1626 \text{ W}$$

Again, a computer spreadsheet or other software is commonly used to reduce the effort involved in calculations. The spreadsheet illustrated in Table 29 is expanded in Table 30 to include splitting the heat gain into convective and radiant portions, applying RTS to the radiant portion, and totaling the convective and radiant loads to determine a 24 h cooling load profile for a window without inside shading.

If the window has an inside shading device, it is accounted for with the inside attenuation coefficients (IAC), the radiant fraction, and the RTS type used. If a window has no inside shading, 100% of the direct beam energy is assumed to be radiant and solar RTS factors are used. However, if an inside shading device is present, the direct beam is assumed to be interrupted by the shading device, and a portion immediately becomes cooling load by convection. Also, the energy is assumed

Table 30 Window Component of Cooling Load (No Blinds or Overhang)

	Unshaded Direct Beam Solar (if AC = 1)						Shaded Direct Beam (AC < 1.0) + Diffuse + Conduction									
Local Standard Hour	Beam Heat Gain, W	Convective 0%, W	Radiant 100%, W	Solar RTS, Zone Type 8, %	Radiant W	Cooling Load, W	Beam Heat Gain, W	Diffuse Heat Gain, W	Conduction Heat Gain, W	Total Heat Gain, W	Convective 54%, W	Radiant 46%, W	Nonsolar RTS, Zone Type 8	Radiant W	Cooling Load, W	Window Cooling Load, W
1	0	0	0	54	57	57	0	0	−16	−16	−9	−7	49	41	32	89
2	0	0	0	16	57	57	0	0	−26	−26	−14	−12	17	35	20	78
3	0	0	0	8	57	57	0	0	−35	−35	−19	−16	9	30	11	68
4	0	0	0	4	57	57	0	0	−43	−43	−23	−20	5	25	1	59
5	0	0	0	3	57	57	0	0	−49	−49	−26	−22	3	20	−7	51
6	0	0	0	2	57	57	0	31	−43	−12	−7	−6	2	24	17	75
7	0	0	0	1	57	57	0	167	−24	143	77	66	2	57	135	192
8	0	0	0	1	56	56	0	294	22	316	171	145	1	106	276	332
9	0	0	0	1	50	50	0	402	74	475	257	219	1	158	415	464
10	0	0	0	1	39	39	0	488	119	608	328	279	1	207	535	573
11	0	0	0	1	25	25	0	553	160	713	385	328	1	249	634	659
12	0	0	0	1	12	12	0	638	188	826	446	380	1	291	737	750
13	157	0	157	1	88	88	0	714	210	924	499	425	1	331	830	918
14	640	0	640	1	371	371	0	766	223	990	534	455	1	364	898	1269
15	1091	0	1091	1	704	704	0	776	223	999	540	460	1	382	922	1626
16	1343	0	1343	1	957	957	0	727	207	934	504	430	1	378	883	1840
17	1287	0	1287	1	1028	1028	0	607	185	792	428	364	1	349	777	1805
18	931	0	931	1	882	882	0	419	158	576	311	265	1	293	604	1486
19	298	0	298	1	514	514	0	176	117	293	158	135	1	210	368	882
20	0	0	0	0	244	244	0	0	88	88	48	40	1	134	181	425
21	0	0	0	0	145	145	0	0	63	63	34	29	0	97	131	277
22	0	0	0	0	98	98	0	0	38	38	21	18	0	75	95	193
23	0	0	0	0	73	73	0	0	17	17	9	8	0	59	69	141
24	0	0	0	0	60	60	0	0	0	0	0	0	0	49	49	109

to be radiated to all surfaces of the room, therefore nonsolar RTS values are used to convert the radiant load into cooling load.

IAC values depend on several factors: (1) type of shading device, (2) position of shading device relative to window, (3) reflectivity of shading device, (4) angular adjustment of shading device, as well as (5) solar position relative to the shading device. These factors are discussed in detail in Chapter 15. For this example with venetian blinds, the IAC for beam radiation is treated separately from the diffuse solar gain. The direct beam IAC must be adjusted based on the profile angle of the sun. At 3:00 PM in July, the profile angle of the sun relative to the window surface is 58°. Calculated using Equation (45) from Chapter 15, the beam IAC = 0.653. The diffuse IAC is 0.79. Thus, the window heat gains, with light-colored blinds, at 3:00 PM are

$$q_{b15} = AE_D\,\text{SHGC}(\theta)(\text{IACb}) = (7.43)(368)(0.3978)(0.653) = 710\text{ W}$$

$$q_{d15} = A(E_d + E_r)\langle\text{SHGC}\rangle_D(\text{IACd}) = (7.43)(175 + 80)(0.41)(0.79) = 614\text{ W}$$

$$q_{c15} = UA(t_{out} - t_{in}) = (3.18)(7.43)(33.3 - 23.9) = 222\text{ W}$$

Because the same radiant fraction and nonsolar RTS are applied to all parts of the window heat gain when inside shading is present, those loads can be totaled and the cooling load calculated after splitting the radiant portion for processing with nonsolar RTS. This is illustrated by the spreadsheet results in Table 31. The total window cooling load with venetian blinds at 3:00 PM = 1319 W.

Part 4. Window cooling load using radiant time series for window with overhang shading. Calculate the cooling load contribution for the previous example with the addition of a overhang shading the window.

Solution: In Chapter 15, methods are described and examples provided for calculating the area of a window shaded by attached vertical or horizontal projections. For 3:00 PM LST IN July, the solar position calculated in previous examples is

Solar altitude $\beta = 57.2°$

Solar azimuth $\phi = 75.1°$

Surface-solar azimuth $\gamma = 15.1°$

From Chapter 15, Equation (106), profile angle Ω is calculated by

$$\tan\Omega = \tan\beta/\cos\gamma = \tan(57.2)/\cos(15.1) = 1.6087$$

$$\Omega = 58.1°$$

From Chapter 15, Equation (40), shadow height S_H is

$$S_H = P_H \tan\Omega = 3.05(1.6087) = 4.9\text{ m}$$

Because the window is 1.95 m tall, at 3:00 PM the window is completely shaded by the 3 m deep overhang. Thus, the shaded window heat gain includes only diffuse solar and conduction gains. This is converted to cooling load by separating the radiant portion, applying RTS, and adding the resulting radiant cooling load to the convective portion to determine total cooling load. Those results are in Table 32. The total window cooling load = 771 W.

Part 5. Room cooling load total. Calculate the sensible cooling loads for the previously described conference room at 3:00 PM in July.

Solution: The steps in the previous example parts are repeated for each of the internal and external loads components, including the southeast facing window, spandrel and brick walls, the southwest facing brick wall, the roof, people, and equipment loads. The results are tabulated in Table 33. The total room sensible cooling load for the conference room is 2937 W at 3:00 PM in July. When this calculation process is repeated for a 24 h design day for each month, it is found that the peak room sensible cooling load actually occurs in August at hour 15 (3:00 PM solar time) at 2968 W as indicated in Table 34.

Although simple in concept, these steps involved in calculating cooling loads are tedious and repetitive, even using the "simplified" RTS method; practically, they should be performed using a computer spreadsheet or other program. The calculations should be repeated for multiple design conditions (i.e., times of day, other months) to determine the maximum cooling load for mechanical equipment sizing. Example spreadsheets for computing each cooling load component using conduction and radiant time series have

Table 31 Window Component of Cooling Load (With Blinds, No Overhang)

	Unshaded Direct Beam Solar (if AC = 1)						Shaded Direct Beam (AC < 1.0) + Diffuse + Conduction									
Local Standard Hour	Beam Heat Gain, W	Convective 0%, W	Radiant 100%, W	Solar RTS, Zone Type 8, %	Radiant W	Cooling Load, W	Beam Heat Gain, W	Diffuse Heat Gain, W	Conduction Heat Gain, W	Total Heat Gain, W	Convective 54%, W	Radiant 46%, W	Nonsolar RTS, Zone Type 8	Radiant W	Cooling Load, W	Window Cooling Load, W
1	0	0	0	1	0	0	0	0	–16	–16	–7	–9	49%	62	55	55
2	0	0	0	0	0	0	0	0	–26	–26	–12	–14	17%	54	42	42
3	0	0	0	0	0	0	0	0	–35	–35	–16	–19	9%	48	32	32
4	0	0	0	0	0	0	0	0	–43	–43	–20	–23	5%	43	23	23
5	0	0	0	0	0	0	0	0	–49	–49	–22	–26	3%	37	15	15
6	0	0	0	0	0	0	0	25	–43	–19	–9	–10	2%	41	32	32
7	0	0	0	0	0	0	0	132	–24	108	50	58	2%	73	123	123
8	0	0	0	0	0	0	0	232	22	254	117	137	1%	121	238	238
9	0	0	0	0	0	0	0	317	74	391	180	211	1%	172	352	352
10	0	0	0	0	0	0	0	386	119	505	232	273	1%	219	451	451
11	0	0	0	0	0	0	0	437	160	597	275	322	1%	258	532	532
12	0	0	0	0	0	0	0	504	188	692	318	374	1%	295	614	614
13	0	0	0	0	0	0	102	564	210	876	403	473	1%	357	760	760
14	0	0	0	0	0	0	416	605	223	1244	572	672	1%	478	1050	1050
15	0	0	0	0	0	0	710	614	222	1549	712	836	1%	607	1319	1319
16	0	0	0	0	0	0	897	574	207	1679	772	907	1%	697	1470	1470
17	0	0	0	0	0	0	880	480	185	1545	711	834	1%	706	1417	1417
18	0	0	0	0	0	0	653	331	158	1141	525	616	1%	613	1138	1138
19	0	0	0	0	0	0	215	139	117	471	217	254	1%	410	627	627
20	0	0	0	0	0	0	0	0	88	88	40	48	1%	239	279	279
21	0	0	0	0	0	0	0	0	63	63	29	34	0%	163	192	192
22	0	0	0	0	0	0	0	0	38	38	18	21	0%	119	136	136
23	0	0	0	0	0	0	0	0	17	17	8	9	0%	92	100	100
24	0	0	0	0	0	0	0	0	0	0	0	0	0%	75	75	75

Table 32 Window Component of Cooling Load (With Blinds and Overhang)

	Overhang and Fins Shading					Shaded Direct Beam (AC < 1.0) + Diffuse + Conduction									
Local Standard Hour	Surface Solar Azimuth	Profile Angle	Shadow Width, m	Shadow Height, m	Direct Sunlit Area, m^2	Beam Heat Gain, W	Diffuse Heat Gain, W	Conduction Heat Gain, W	Total Heat Gain, W	Convective 54%, W	Radiant 46%, W	Nonsolar RTS, Zone Type 8	Radiant W	Cooling Load, W	Window Cooling Load, W
1	–235	52	0.0	0.0	0.0	0	0	–16	–16	–9	–7	49%	36	27	27
2	–219	40	0.0	0.0	0.0	0	0	–26	–26	–14	–12	17%	30	15	15
3	–204	29	0.0	0.0	0.0	0	0	–35	–35	–19	–16	9%	25	6	6
4	–192	19	0.0	0.0	0.0	0	0	–43	–43	–23	–20	5%	20	–3	–3
5	–182	9	0.0	0.0	0.0	0	0	–49	–49	–26	–22	3%	15	–11	–11
6	–173	–3	0.0	0.0	0.0	0	25	–43	–19	–10	–9	2%	18	8	8
7	–165	–15	0.0	0.0	0.0	0	132	–24	108	58	50	2%	46	104	104
8	–158	–28	0.0	0.0	0.0	0	232	22	254	137	117	1%	86	224	224
9	–150	–43	0.0	0.0	0.0	0	317	74	391	211	180	1%	131	342	342
10	–141	–58	0.0	0.0	0.0	0	386	119	505	273	232	1%	172	445	445
11	–127	–73	0.0	0.0	0.0	0	437	160	597	322	275	1%	209	531	531
12	–99	–87	0.0	0.0	0.0	0	504	188	692	374	318	1%	245	619	619
13	–44	80	0.0	2.0	0.0	0	564	210	774	418	356	1%	279	697	697
14	–3	69	0.0	2.0	0.0	0	605	223	829	447	381	1%	305	752	752
15	15	58	0.0	2.0	0.0	0	613	223	836	452	385	1%	320	771	771
16	26	48	0.0	2.0	0.0	0	574	207	781	422	359	1%	316	738	738
17	34	38	0.0	2.0	0.0	0	480	185	665	359	306	1%	292	651	651
18	42	26	0.0	1.5	1.8	154	331	158	642	347	296	1%	281	628	628
19	49	12	0.0	0.7	4.9	143	139	117	398	215	183	1%	223	438	438
20	57	–6	0.0	0.0	0.0	0	0	88	88	48	40	1%	133	181	181
21	67	–32	0.0	0.0	0.0	0	0	63	63	34	29	0%	95	129	129
22	78	–64	0.0	0.0	0.0	0	0	38	38	21	18	0%	71	91	91
23	91	87	0.0	0.0	0.0	0	0	17	17	9	8	0%	55	64	64
24	107	67	0.0	0.0	0.0	0	0	0	0	0	0	0%	44	44	44

Table 33 Single-Room Example Cooling Load (July 3:00 PM) for ASHRAE Example Office Building, Atlanta, GA

		Per Unit Cooling	Room Sensible Cooling, W	Return Air Sensible Cooling, W	Room Latent Cooling, W	Room Sensible Heating, W
Internal Loads:						
	No.	W/person				
People:	12	69	821	—	703	—
		W/m²				
Lighting:	440 W	12.0	308	—	—	—
Lighting 26% to RA:		4.1	—	109	—	—
Equipment:	274 W	10.4	265	—	—	—
Envelope Loads:						
Roof:	Roof area, m²	W/m²				
Area, m²:	25.5	7.3	184	—	—	288
Roof 30% to RA:			—	79	—	—
Walls:	Wall area, m²	W/m²				
Wall Type 1: Brick						
North	0.0	0.0	—	—	—	—
South	5.6	5.7	32	—	—	72
East	0.0	0.0	—	—	—	—
West	7.0	3.8	27	—	—	90
Wall Type 2: Spandrel						
North	0.0	0.0	—	—	—	—
South	5.6	10.0	57	—	—	72
East	0.0	0.0	—	—	—	—
West	11.1	13.9	156	—	—	144
Windows:	Window area, m²	W/m²				
Window Type 1						
North	0.0	0.0	—	—	—	—
South	0.0	0.0	—	—	—	—
East	0.0	0.0	—	—	—	—
West	0.0	0.0	—	—	—	—
Window Type 2						
North	0.0	0.0	—	—	—	—
South	3.7	85.2	316	—	—	337
East	0.0	0.0	—	—	—	—
West	7.4	103.8	771	—	—	674
Infiltration Loads:	Airflow, L/s	W/(L·s)				
Cooling, sensible:	0	0.0	—	—	—	—
Cooling, latent:	0	0.0	—	—	—	—
Heating:	19	35.0	—	—	—	678
		Room Load Totals:	2937	188	703	2355
		Cooling L/s:	239		Heating L/s:	123
		L/(s·m²):	9.1			

been compiled and are available from ASHRAE. To illustrate the full building example discussed previously, those individual component spreadsheets have been compiled to allow calculation of cooling and heating loads on a room by room basis as well as for a "block" calculation for analysis of overall areas or buildings where detailed room-by-room data is not available.

SINGLE-ROOM EXAMPLE PEAK HEATING LOAD

Although the physics of heat transfer that creates a heating load is identical to that for cooling loads, a number of traditionally used simplifying assumptions facilitate a much simpler calculation procedure. As described in the Heating Load Calculations section, design heating load calculations typically assume a single outside temperature, with no heat gain from solar or internal sources, under steady-state conditions. Thus, space heating load is determined by computing the heat transfer rate through building envelope elements ($UA\Delta T$) plus heat required because of outside air infiltration.

Part 6. Room heating load. Calculate the room heating load for the previous described conference room, including infiltration airflow at one air change per hour.

Solution: Because solar heat gain is not considered in calculating design heating loads, orientation of similar envelope elements may be ignored and total areas of each wall or window type combined. Thus, the total spandrel wall area = 5.57 + 11.15 = 16.72 m², total brick wall area = 5.57 + 6.97 = 12.54 m², and total window area = 3.72 + 7.43 = 11.15 m². For this example, use the U-factors that were used for cooling load conditions. In some climates, higher prevalent winds in winter should be considered in calculating U-factors (see Chapter 25 for information on calculating U-factors and surface heat transfer coefficients appropriate for local wind conditions). The 99.6% heating design dry-bulb temperature for Atlanta is –6.3°C and the inside design temperature is 22.2°C. The room volume with a 2.74 m ceiling = 2.74 × 25.47 = 69.8 m³ = 69 800 L. At one air change per hour, the infiltration airflow = 69 800/3600 = 19 L/s. Thus, the heating load is

Windows:	3.18 × 11.15 × [22.2 – (–6.3)]	=	1011 W
Spandrel Wall:	0.51 × 16.72 × [22.2 – (–6.3)]	=	243
Brick Wall:	0.45 × 12.54 × [22.2 – (–6.3)]	=	161
Roof:	0.40 × 25.47 × [22.2 – (–6.3)]	=	293
Infiltration:	19 × 1.23 × [22.2 – (–6.3)]	=	666
Total Room Heating Load:			2374 W

Table 34 Single-Room Example Peak Cooling Load (August 3:00 PM) for ASHRAE Example Office Building, Atlanta, GA

		Per Unit Cooling	Room Sensible Cooling, W	Return Air Sensible Cooling, W	Room Latent Cooling, W	Room Sensible Heating, W
Internal Loads:						
	No.	W/person				
People:	12	69	821	—	703	—
		W/m²				
Lighting:	440 W	12.0	308	—	—	—
Lighting 20% to RA:		4.1	—	108	—	—
Equipment:	274 W	10.4	265	—	—	—
Envelope Loads:						
Roof:	Roof area, m²	W/m²				
Area, m²:	25.5	6.6	168	—	—	288
Roof 30% to RA:			—	51	—	—
Walls:	Wall area, m²	W/m²				
Wall Type 1: Brick						
North	0.0	0.0	—	—	—	—
South	5.6	6.0	34	—	—	72
East	0.0	0.0	—	—	—	—
West	7.0	3.8	26	—	—	90
Wall Type 2: Spandrel						
North	0.0	0.0	—	—	—	—
South	5.6	11.7	64	—	—	72
East	0.0	0.0	—	—	—	—
West	11.1	15.1	167	—	—	144
Windows:	Window area, m²	W/m²				
Window Type 1						
North	0.0	0.0	—	—	—	—
South	0.0	0.0	—	—	—	—
East	0.0	0.0	—	—	—	—
West	0.0	0.0	—	—	—	—
Window Type 2						
North	0.0	0.0	—	—	—	—
South	3.7	85.5	318	—	—	337
East	0.0	0.0	—	—	—	—
West	7.4	106.9	796	—	—	674
Infiltration Loads:	Airflow, L/s	W/(L·s)				
Cooling, sensible:	0	0.0	—	—	—	—
Cooling, latent:	0	0.0	—	—	—	—
Heating:	19	35.0	—	—	—	678
		Room Load Totals:	2968	180	703	2355
		Cooling L/s:	241		Heating L/s:	123
		L/(s·m²):	9.5			

WHOLE-BUILDING EXAMPLE

Because a single-room example does not illustrate the full application of load calculations, a multistory, multiple-room example building has been developed to show a more realistic case. A hypothetical project development process is described to illustrate its effect on the application of load calculations.

Design Process and Shell Building Definition

A development company has acquired a piece of property in Atlanta, GA, to construct an office building. Although no tenant or end user has yet been identified, the owner/developer has decided to proceed with the project on a speculative basis. They select an architectural design firm, who retains an engineering firm for the mechanical and electrical design.

At the first meeting, the developer indicates the project is to proceed on a fast-track basis to take advantage of market conditions; he is negotiating with several potential tenants who will need to occupy the new building within a year. This requires preparing **shell-and-core** construction documents to obtain a building permit, order equipment, and begin construction to meet the schedule.

The shell-and-core design documents will include finished design of the building exterior (the **shell**), as well as permanent interior elements such as stairs, restrooms, elevator, electrical rooms and mechanical spaces (the **core**). The primary mechanical equipment must be sized and installed as part of the shell-and-core package in order for the project to meet the schedule, even though the building occupant is not yet known.

The architect selects a two-story design with an exterior skin of tinted, double-glazed vision glass; opaque, insulated spandrel glass, and brick pilasters. The roof area extends beyond the building edge to form a substantial overhang, shading the second floor windows. Architectural drawings for the shell-and-core package (see Figures 17 to 22) include plans, elevations, and skin construction details, and are furnished to the engineer for use in "block" heating and cooling load calculations. Mechanical systems and equipment must be specified and installed based on those calculations. (*Note*: Full-size, scalable electronic versions of the drawings in Figures 17 to 22, as well as detailed lighting plans, are available from ASHRAE at www.ashrae.org.)

Table 35 Block Load Example: Envelope Area Summary, m²

	Floor Area	Brick Areas				Spandrel/Soffit Areas				Window Areas			
		North	South	East	West	North	South	East	West	North	South	East	West
First Floor	1398	63.17	63.17	37.16	37.16	65.03	65.03	33.44	33.44	55.74	52.02	33.44	33.44
Second Floor	1398	47.38	47.38	27.87	27.87	96.62	92.90	50.17	50.17	52.02	55.74	33.44	33.44
Building Total	2796	110.55	110.55	65.03	65.03	161.65	157.93	83.61	83.61	107.76	107.76	66.89	66.89

The HVAC design engineer meets with the developer's operations staff to agree on the basic HVAC systems for the project. Based on their experience operating other buildings and the lack of specific information on the tenant(s), the team decides on two variable-volume air-handling units (AHUs), one per floor, to provide operating flexibility if one floor is leased to one tenant and the other floor to someone else. Cooling will be provided by an air-cooled chiller located on grade across the parking lot. Heating will be provided by electric resistance heaters in parallel-type fan-powered variable-air-volume (VAV) terminal units. The AHUs must be sized quickly to confirm the size of the mechanical rooms on the architectural plans. The AHUs and chiller must be ordered by the mechanical subcontractor within 10 days to meet the construction schedule. Likewise, the electric heating loads must be provided to the electrical engineers to size the electrical service and for the utility company to extend services to the site.

The mechanical engineer must determine the (1) peak airflow and cooling coil capacity for each AHU, (2) peak cooling capacity required for the chiller, and (3) total heating capacity for sizing the electrical service.

Solution: First, calculate "block" heating and cooling loads for each floor to size the AHUs, then calculate a block load for the whole building determine chiller and electric heating capacity.

Based on the architectural drawings, the HVAC engineer assembles basic data on the building as follows:

Location: Atlanta, GA. Per Chapter 14, latitude = 33.64, longitude = 84.43, elevation = 313 m above sea level, 99.6% heating design dry-bulb temperature = –6.3°C. For cooling load calculations, use 5% dry-bulb/coincident wet-bulb monthly design day profile from Chapter 14 (on CD-ROM). See Table 26 for temperature profiles used in these examples.

Inside design conditions: 22.2°C for heating; 23.9°C with 50% rh for cooling.

Building orientation: Plan north is 30° west of true north.

Gross area per floor: 1398 m²

Total building gross area: 2796 m²

Windows: Bronze-tinted, double-glazed. Solar heat gain coefficients, U-factors are as in the single-room example.

Walls: Part insulated spandrel glass and part brick-and-block clad columns. The insulation barrier in the soffit at the second floor is similar to that of the spandrel glass and is of lightweight construction; for simplicity, that surface is assumed to have similar thermal heat gain/loss to the spandrel glass. Construction and insulation values are as in single-room example.

Roof: Metal deck, topped with board insulation and membrane roofing. Construction and insulation values are as in the single-room example.

Floor: 127 mm lightweight concrete slab on grade for first floor and 127 mm lightweight concrete on metal deck for second floor

Total areas of building exterior skin, as measured from the architectural plans, are listed in Table 35.

The engineer needs additional data to estimate the building loads. Thus far, no tenant has yet been signed, so no interior layouts for population counts, lighting layouts or equipment loads are available. To meet the schedule, assumptions must be made on these load components. The owner requires that the system design must be flexible enough to provide for a variety of tenants over the life of the building. Based on similar office buildings, the team agrees to base the block load calculations on the following assumptions:

Occupancy: 7.54 people per 100 m² = 13.3 m²/person
Lighting: 16.15 W/m²
Tenant's office equipment: 10.76 W/m²

Normal use schedule is assumed at 100% from 7:00 AM to 7:00 PM and unoccupied/off during other hours.

With interior finishes not finalized, the owner commits to using light-colored interior blinds on all windows. The tenant interior design could include carpeted flooring or acoustical tile ceilings in all areas, but the more conservative assumption, from a peak load standpoint, is chosen: carpeted flooring and no acoustical tile ceilings (no ceiling return plenum).

For block loads, the engineer assumes that the building is maintained under positive pressure during peak cooling conditions and that infiltration during peak heating conditions is equivalent to one air change per hour in a 3.5 m deep perimeter zone around the building.

To maintain indoor air quality, outside air must be introduced into the building. Air will be ducted from roof intake hoods to the AHUs where it will be mixed with return air before being cooled and dehumidified by the AHU's cooling coil. ASHRAE *Standard* 62.1 is the design basis for ventilation rates; however, no interior tenant layout is available for application of *Standard* 62.1 procedures. Based on past experience, the engineer decides to use 9.44 L/s of outside air per person for sizing the cooling coils and chiller.

Block load calculations were performed using the RTS method, and results for the first and second floors and the entire building are summarized in Tables 36, 37, and 38. Based on these results, the engineer performs psychrometric coil analysis, checks capacities versus vendor catalog data, and prepares specifications and schedules for the equipment. This information is released to the contractor with the shell-and-core design documents. The air-handling units and chiller are purchased, and construction proceeds.

Tenant Fit Design Process and Definition

About halfway through construction, a tenant agrees to lease the entire building. The tenant will require a combination of open and enclosed office space with a few common areas, such as conference/training rooms, and a small computer room that will operate on a 24 h basis. Based on the tenant's space program, the architect prepares interior floor plans and furniture layout plans (Figures 23 and 24), and the electrical engineer prepares lighting design plans. Those drawings are furnished to the HVAC engineer to prepare detailed design documents. The first step in this process is to prepare room-by-room peak heating and cooling load calculations, which will then be used for design of the air distribution systems from each of the VAV air handlers already installed.

The HVAC engineer must perform a room-by-room "takeoff" of the architect's drawings. For each room, this effort identifies the floor area, room function, exterior envelope elements and areas, number of occupants, and lighting and equipment loads.

The tenant layout calls for a dropped acoustical tile ceiling throughout, which will be used as a return air plenum. Typical 600 by 1200 mm fluorescent, recessed, return-air-type lighting fixtures are selected. Based on this, the engineer assumes that 20% of the

Table 36 Block Load Example—First Floor Loads for ASHRAE Example Office Building, Atlanta, GA

Room Loads:[a]		Per Unit Cooling	Room Sensible Cooling, W	Return Air Sensible Cooling, W	Room Latent Cooling, W	Room Sensible Heating, W
Internal Loads:						
	No.	W/person				
People:	105	69.8	7232	—	6155	—
		W/m²				
Lighting:	22 575 W	15.5	21 480	—	—	—
Lighting 0% to RA:		0.0	—	—	—	—
Equipment:	15 050 W	10.4	14 589	—	—	—
Envelope Loads:						
Roof:	Roof area, m²	W/m²		—		
Area, m²:	—	0.0	—	—	—	—
Roof 0% to RA:			—	—	—	—
Walls:	Wall area, m²	W/m²				
Wall Type 1: Brick						
North	63.2	4.1	262	—	—	818
South	63.2	6.0	380	—	—	818
East	37.2	6.0	218	—	—	481
West	37.2	5.1	187	—	—	481
Wall Type 2: Spandrel						
North	65.0	10.1	664	—	—	842
South	65.0	8.8	576	—	—	842
East	33.4	8.2	276	—	—	433
West	33.4	16.4	549	—	—	433
Windows:	Window area, m²	W/m²				
Window Type 1:						
North	55.7	115.1	6425	—	—	5052
South	52.0	76.9	4005	—	—	4715
East	33.4	76.7	2566	—	—	3031
West	33.4	201.9	6752	—	—	3031
Window Type 2:						
North	0.0	0.0	—	—	—	—
South	0.0	0.0	—	—	—	—
East	0.0	0.0	—	—	—	—
West	0.0	0.0	—	—	—	—
Infiltration Loads:	Airflow, L/s	W/(L·s)				
Cooling, sensible:	0	0.0	—	—	—	—
Cooling, latent:	0	0.0	—	—	—	—
Heating:	407	35.0	—	—	—	14 272
		Room Load Totals:	66 161	—	6155	35 249
		Cooling L/s:	5380		Heating L/s:	1843
		L/(s·m²):	4.1			

Block Loads:[b]					
		Total Room Sensible + RA + Latent:	72 316	Room heating:	35 249
		Outside air (OA) sensible:	10 697	OA heating:	34 729
OA L/s:	991	OA latent:	14 732	Total heating, W:	69 978
Fan kW:	7.5	Fan heat to supply air:	7462	Heating W/m²:	50.2
Pump kW:	0	Pump heat to chilled water:	—		
				kW	m²/kW
		Total Block Cooling Load, W:	105 207	105.2	13.3

[a]Peak room sensible load occurs in month 7 at hour 16.
[b]Peak block load occurs in month 7 at hour 16.

heat gain from lighting will be to the return air plenum and not enter rooms directly. Likewise, some portion of the heat gain from the roof will be extracted via the ceiling return air plenum. From experience, the engineer understands that return air plenum paths are not always predictable, and decides to credit only 30% of the roof heat gain to the return air, with the balance included in the room cooling load.

For the open office areas, some areas along the building perimeter will have different load characteristics from purely interior spaces because of heat gains and losses through the building skin. Although those perimeter areas are not separated from other open office spaces by walls, the engineer knows from experience that they must be served by separate control zones to maintain comfort conditions. The data compiled from the room-by-room takeoff are included in Tables 39 and 40.

Room by Room Cooling and Heating Loads

The room by room results of RTS method calculations, including the month and time of day of each room's peak cooling load, are tab-

Table 37 Block Load Example—Second Floor Loads for ASHRAE Example Office Building, Atlanta, GA

Room Loads:[a]		Per Unit Cooling	Room Sensible Cooling, W	Return Air Sensible Cooling, W	Room Latent Cooling, W	Room Sensible Heating, W
Internal Loads:						
	No.	W/person				
People:	105	69	7186	—	6155	—
		W/m²				
Lighting:	22 575 W	15.1	21 369	—	—	—
Lighting 0% to RA:		0.0	—	—	—	—
Equipment:	15 050 W	10.4	14 544	—	—	—
Envelope Loads:						
Roof:	Roof area, m²	W/m²		—		
Area, m²:	1398.1	10.4	14 420	—	—	15 839
Roof 0% to RA:			—	—	—	—
Walls:	Wall area, m²	W/m²				
Wall Type 1: Brick						
North	47.4	3.5	166	—	—	613
South	47.4	5.7	268	—	—	613
East	27.9	5.7	160	—	—	361
West	27.9	3.8	109	—	—	361
Wall Type 2: Spandrel						
North	96.6	8.8	840	—	—	1251
South	92.9	10.1	945	—	—	1203
East	50.2	8.8	437	—	—	649
West	50.2	13.9	703	—	—	649
Windows:	Window area, m²	W/m²				
Window Type 1:						
North	0.0	0.0	—	—	—	—
South	0.0	0.0	—	—	—	—
East	0.0	0.0	—	—	—	—
West	0.0	0.0	—	—	—	—
Window Type 2:						
North	52.0	89.6	4665	—	—	4715
South	55.7	85.2	4744	—	—	5052
East	33.4	82.3	2752	—	—	3031
West	33.4	103.8	3470	—	—	3031
Infiltration Loads:	Airflow, L/s	W/(L·s)				
Cooling, sensible:	0	0.0	—	—	—	—
Cooling, latent:	0	0.0	—	—	—	—
Heating:	407	35.0	—	—	—	14 272
		Room Load Totals:	76 778	—	6155	51 640
		Cooling L/s:	6244		Heating L/s:	2700
		L/(s·m²):	4.6			

Block Loads:[b]					
		Total Room Sensible + RA + Latent:	82 933	Room heating:	51 640
		Outside air (OA) sensible:	11 509	OA heating:	34 730
OA L/s:	991	OA latent:	14 920	Total heating, W:	86 370
Fan kW:	7.5	Fan heat to supply air:	7462	Heating W/m²:	61.8
Pump kW:	0	Pump heat to chilled water:	—		
				kW	m²/kW
		Total Block Cooling Load, W:	116 824	116.8	12.0

[a]Peak room sensible load occurs in month 7 at hour 16.
[b]Peak block load occurs in month 7 at hour 16.

ulated in supplemental Tables 41 and 42 (available at www.ashrae.org), as well as peak heating loads for each room. These results are used by the HVAC engineer to select and design room air distribution devices and to schedule airflow rates for each space. That information is incorporated into the tenant fit drawings and specifications issued to the contractor.

Conclusions

The example results illustrate issues which should be understood and accounted for in calculating heating and cooling loads:

- First, peak room cooling loads occur at different months and times depending on the exterior exposure of the room. Calculation of cooling loads for a single point in time may miss the peak and result in inadequate cooling for that room.
- Often, in real design processes, all data is not known. Reasonable assumptions based on past experience must be made.
- Heating and air-conditioning systems often serve spaces whose use changes over the life of a building. Assumptions used in heating and cooling load calculations should consider reasonable possible uses over the life of the building, not just the first use of the space.

Table 38 Block Load Example—Overall Building Loads for ASHRAE Example Office Building, Atlanta, GA

				Room Sensible Cooling, W	Return Air Sensible Cooling, W		Room Latent Cooling, W	Room Sensible Heating, W
Room Loads[a]			Room Load Totals:	141 715	—		12 310	86 889
			Cooling L/s:	11 525		Heating L/s:		4543
			L/(s·m²):	4.1				
Block Loads:[b]			Total Room Sensible + RA + Latent:	154 025		Room heating:		86 889
			Outside air (OA) sensible:	26 828		OA heating:		69 459
	OA L/s:	1982	OA latent:	29 839		Total heating, W:		156 348
	Fan kW:	15	Fan heat to supply air:	14 924		Heating W/m²:		55.8
	Pump kW:	3.7	Pump heat to chilled water:	3731				
							kW	m²/kW
			Total Block Cooling Load, W:	229 347			229.4	12.2

[a]Peak room sensible load occurs in month 7 at hour 15.
[b]Peak block load occurs in month 7 at hour 15.

- The relative importance of each cooling and heating load component varies depending on the portion of the building being considered. Characteristics of a particular window may have little effect on the entire building load, but could have a significant effect on the supply airflow to the room where the window is located and thus on the comfort of the occupants of that space.

PREVIOUS COOLING LOAD CALCULATION METHODS

Procedures described in this chapter are the most current and scientifically derived means for estimating cooling load for a defined building space, but methods in earlier editions of the ASHRAE Handbook are valid for many applications. These earlier procedures are simplifications of the heat balance principles, and their use requires experience to deal with atypical or unusual circumstances. In fact, any cooling or heating load estimate is no better than the assumptions used to define conditions and parameters such as physical makeup of the various envelope surfaces, conditions of occupancy and use, and ambient weather conditions. Experience of the practitioner can never be ignored.

The primary difference between the HB and RTS methods and the older methods is the newer methods' direct approach, compared to the simplifications necessitated by the limited computer capability available previously.

The **transfer function method (TFM)**, for example, required many calculation steps. It was originally designed for energy analysis with emphasis on daily, monthly, and annual energy use, and thus was more oriented to average hourly cooling loads than peak design loads.

The **total equivalent temperature differential method with time averaging (TETD/TA)** has been a highly reliable (if subjective) method of load estimating since its initial presentation in the 1967 *Handbook of Fundamentals*. Originally intended as a manual method of calculation, it proved suitable only as a computer application because of the need to calculate an extended profile of hourly heat gain values, from which radiant components had to be averaged over a time representative of the general mass of the building involved. Because perception of thermal storage characteristics of a given building is almost entirely subjective, with little specific information for the user to judge variations, the TETD/TA method's primary usefulness has always been to the experienced engineer.

The **cooling load temperature differential method with solar cooling load factors (CLTD/CLF)** attempted to simplify the two-step TFM and TETD/TA methods into a single-step technique that proceeded directly from raw data to cooling load without intermediate conversion of radiant heat gain to cooling load. A series of factors were taken from cooling load calculation results (produced by more sophisticated methods) as "cooling load temperature differences" and "cooling load factors" for use in traditional conduction ($q = UA\Delta t$) equations. The results are approximate cooling load values rather than simple heat gain values. The simplifications and assumptions used in the original work to derive those factors limit this method's applicability to those building types and conditions for which the CLTD/CLF factors were derived; the method should not be used beyond the range of applicability.

Although the TFM, TETD/TA, and CLTD/CLF procedures are not republished in this chapter, those methods are not invalidated or discredited. Experienced engineers have successfully used them in millions of buildings around the world. The accuracy of cooling load calculations in practice depends primarily on the availability of accurate information and the design engineer's judgment in the assumptions made in interpreting the available data. Those factors have much greater influence on a project's success than does the choice of a particular cooling load calculation method.

The primary benefit of HB and RTS calculations is their somewhat reduced dependency on purely subjective input (e.g., determining a proper time-averaging period for TETD/TA; ascertaining appropriate safety factors to add to the rounded-off TFM results; determining whether CLTD/CLF factors are applicable to a specific unique application). However, using the most up-to-date techniques in real-world design still requires judgment on the part of the design engineer and care in choosing appropriate assumptions, just as in applying older calculation methods.

REFERENCES

Abushakra, B., J.S. Haberl, and D.E. Claridge. 2004. Overview of literature on diversity factors and schedules for energy and cooling load calculations (1093-RP). *ASHRAE Transactions* 110(1):164-176.

Armstrong, P.R., C.E. Hancock, III, and J.E. Seem. 1992a. Commercial building temperature recovery—Part I: Design procedure based on a step response model. *ASHRAE Transactions* 98(1):381-396.

Armstrong, P.R., C.E. Hancock, III, and J.E. Seem. 1992b. Commercial building temperature recovery—Part II: Experiments to verify the step response model. *ASHRAE Transactions* 98(1):397-410.

ASHRAE. 2004. Thermal environmental conditions for human occupancy. ANSI/ASHRAE *Standard* 55-2004.

ASHRAE. 2001. Ventilation for acceptable indoor air quality. ANSI/ASHRAE *Standard* 62-2001.

ASHRAE. 2007. Energy standard for building except low-rise residential buildings. ANSI/ASHRAE/IESNA *Standard* 90.1-2007.

ASHRAE. 2004. Updating the climatic design conditions in the *ASHRAE Handbook—Fundamentals* (RP-1273). ASHRAE Research Project, *Final Report*.

ASTM. 2008. Practice for estimate of the heat gain or loss and the surface temperatures of insulated flat, cylindrical, and spherical systems by use of computer programs. *Standard* C680-08. American Society for Testing and Materials, West Conshohocken, PA.

Table 39 Tenant Fit Example: First Floor Room Data

Room No.	Room Name	Area, m^2	Brick Area (Wall), m^2				Spandrel/Soffit Area (Wall), m^2				Window Area, m^2				No. of People	Lights, W	Equip., W
			North	South	East	West	North	South	East	West	North	South	East	West			
101	Vestibule	13.62	5.57	0.00	0.00	0.00	1.86	0.00	0.00	0.00	7.43	0.00	0.00	0.00	0	210	0
102	Reception	29.17	0.00	0.00	0.00	0.00	0.00	0.00	0.00	0.00	0.00	0.00	0.00	0.00	4	540	314
103	Coats	0.84	0.00	0.00	0.00	0.00	0.00	0.00	0.00	0.00	0.00	0.00	0.00	0.00	0	0	0
104	Meeting Room	11.85	3.72	0.00	0.00	0.00	3.72	0.00	0.00	0.00	3.72	0.00	0.00	0.00	6	220	128
105	Mgr. Mtgs./Conf.	11.85	3.72	0.00	0.00	0.00	3.72	0.00	0.00	0.00	3.72	0.00	0.00	0.00	3	220	128
106	Mgr. Ed./Ch. Prog.	11.85	3.72	0.00	0.00	0.00	3.72	0.00	0.00	0.00	3.72	0.00	0.00	0.00	1	220	128
107	Admin. Asst.	11.85	3.72	0.00	0.00	0.00	3.72	0.00	0.00	0.00	3.72	0.00	0.00	0.00	1	220	128
108	Director	25.17	9.29	0.00	7.43	0.00	7.43	0.00	3.72	0.00	7.43	0.00	3.72	0.00	9	440	271
109	Open Office	177.26	0.00	0.00	0.00	0.00	0.00	0.00	0.00	0.00	0.00	0.00	0.00	0.00	12	2850	1908
109A	E. Open Office	26.10	0.00	0.00	13.01	0.00	0.00	0.00	14.86	0.00	0.00	0.00	14.86	0.00	3	390	281
110	Member Mgr.	12.54	0.00	0.00	3.72	0.00	0.00	0.00	3.72	0.00	0.00	0.00	3.72	0.00	1	220	135
111	Member. Files	29.06	0.00	0.00	0.00	0.00	0.00	0.00	0.00	0.00	0.00	0.00	0.00	0.00	0	660	313
112	Prod./Misc./Stor.	23.63	0.00	0.00	0.00	0.00	0.00	0.00	0.00	0.00	0.00	0.00	0.00	0.00	0	300	254
113	Storage	20.21	0.00	0.00	3.72	0.00	0.00	0.00	3.72	0.00	0.00	0.00	3.72	0.00	0	150	0
114	Mailroom	136.01	0.00	22.30	9.29	0.00	0.00	18.58	7.43	0.00	0.00	14.86	7.43	0.00	2	2090	2928
115	Vestibule	7.11	0.00	1.86	0.00	0.00	0.00	1.86	0.00	0.00	0.00	7.43	0.00	0.00	0	60	0
116	Stair 2	16.26	0.00	7.43	0.00	0.00	0.00	14.86	0.00	0.00	0.00	0.00	0.00	0.00	0	0	0
117	Elevator Lobby	42.83	0.00	0.00	0.00	0.00	0.00	0.00	0.00	0.00	0.00	0.00	0.00	0.00	0	610	0
118	Computer/Tel.	36.84	0.00	0.00	0.00	0.00	0.00	0.00	0.00	0.00	0.00	0.00	0.00	0.00	2	880	397
119	Electrical Equip.	3.97	0.00	0.00	0.00	0.00	0.00	0.00	0.00	0.00	0.00	0.00	0.00	0.00	0	30	0
120	Storage	2.81	0.00	0.00	0.00	0.00	0.00	0.00	0.00	0.00	0.00	0.00	0.00	0.00	0	30	0
121	Data Proc. Mgr.	11.98	0.00	3.72	0.00	0.00	0.00	3.72	0.00	0.00	0.00	3.72	0.00	0.00	1	220	129
122	Open Office	168.34	0.00	0.00	0.00	0.00	0.00	0.00	0.00	0.00	0.00	0.00	0.00	0.00	7	2860	1812
122A	S. Open Office	23.69	0.00	11.15	0.00	0.00	0.00	11.15	0.00	0.00	0.00	11.15	0.00	0.00	4	660	255
123	Comm. Mgr.	11.38	0.00	3.72	0.00	0.00	0.00	3.72	0.00	0.00	0.00	3.72	0.00	0.00	1	220	123
123A	Acct. Supervisor	11.38	0.00	3.72	0.00	0.00	0.00	3.72	0.00	0.00	0.00	3.72	0.00	0.00	2	220	123
124	Acct. Mgr.	11.38	0.00	3.72	0.00	0.00	0.00	3.72	0.00	0.00	0.00	3.72	0.00	0.00	2	220	123
125	Director	23.50	0.00	5.57	0.00	9.29	0.00	3.72	0.00	7.43	0.00	3.72	0.00	7.43	5	440	253
126	Admin. Asst.	11.85	0.00	0.00	0.00	3.72	0.00	0.00	0.00	3.72	0.00	0.00	0.00	3.72	1	220	128
127	Meeting Room	11.85	0.00	0.00	0.00	3.72	0.00	0.00	0.00	3.72	0.00	0.00	0.00	3.72	6	220	128
128	Assist. B.O.D.	11.85	0.00	0.00	0.00	3.72	0.00	0.00	0.00	3.72	0.00	0.00	0.00	3.72	1	220	128
129	President	11.85	0.00	0.00	0.00	3.72	0.00	0.00	0.00	3.72	0.00	0.00	0.00	3.72	2	220	128
130	Conference	20.90	0.00	0.00	0.00	3.72	0.00	0.00	0.00	3.72	0.00	0.00	0.00	3.72	8	220	225
131	Storage	2.42	0.00	0.00	0.00	0.00	0.00	0.00	0.00	0.00	0.00	0.00	0.00	0.00	0	0	0
132	Ex. Director	22.70	5.57	0.00	0.00	9.29	3.72	0.00	0.00	7.43	3.72	0.00	0.00	7.43	5	440	244
133	Ex. Secretary	12.26	3.72	0.00	0.00	0.00	3.72	0.00	0.00	0.00	3.72	0.00	0.00	0.00	1	220	132
134	Asst. Ex. Dir.	11.85	3.72	0.00	0.00	0.00	3.72	0.00	0.00	0.00	3.72	0.00	0.00	0.00	1	220	128
135	Storage	1.28	0.00	0.00	0.00	0.00	0.00	0.00	0.00	0.00	0.00	0.00	0.00	0.00	0	0	0
136	Waiting	28.89	0.00	0.00	0.00	0.00	0.00	0.00	0.00	0.00	0.00	0.00	0.00	0.00	2	390	311
137	Storage	1.30	0.00	0.00	0.00	0.00	0.00	0.00	0.00	0.00	0.00	0.00	0.00	0.00	0	0	0
138	Open Office Sec'y	23.69	0.00	0.00	0.00	0.00	0.00	0.00	0.00	0.00	0.00	0.00	0.00	0.00	3	770	255
139	Conf. A	54.81	7.43	0.00	0.00	0.00	7.43	0.00	0.00	0.00	7.43	0.00	0.00	0.00	28	780	590
140	Conf. B	53.88	7.43	0.00	0.00	0.00	7.43	0.00	0.00	0.00	7.43	0.00	0.00	0.00	20	750	580
141	Stair 1	21.91	5.57	0.00	0.00	0.00	14.86	0.00	0.00	0.00	0.00	0.00	0.00	0.00	0	90	0
142	Conf. C	15.79	0.00	0.00	0.00	0.00	0.00	0.00	0.00	0.00	0.00	0.00	0.00	0.00	8	440	170
143	Janitor	5.07	0.00	0.00	0.00	0.00	0.00	0.00	0.00	0.00	0.00	0.00	0.00	0.00	0	75	0
144	Storage	9.96	0.00	0.00	0.00	0.00	0.00	0.00	0.00	0.00	0.00	0.00	0.00	0.00	0	150	0
145	Men	16.17	0.00	0.00	0.00	0.00	0.00	0.00	0.00	0.00	0.00	0.00	0.00	0.00	0	420	0
146	Women	16.17	0.00	0.00	0.00	0.00	0.00	0.00	0.00	0.00	0.00	0.00	0.00	0.00	0	420	0
147	Electrical	5.33	0.00	0.00	0.00	0.00	0.00	0.00	0.00	0.00	0.00	0.00	0.00	0.00	0	0	0
148	Mechanical	20.44	0.00	0.00	0.00	0.00	0.00	0.00	0.00	0.00	0.00	0.00	0.00	0.00	0	0	0
149	Hall of Fame	71.16	0.00	0.00	0.00	0.00	0.00	0.00	0.00	0.00	0.00	0.00	0.00	0.00	0	900	766
150	Personnel Mgr.	11.18	0.00	0.00	0.00	0.00	0.00	0.00	0.00	0.00	0.00	0.00	0.00	0.00	1	220	120
151	Personnel Clerk	11.18	0.00	0.00	0.00	0.00	0.00	0.00	0.00	0.00	0.00	0.00	0.00	0.00	2	220	120
Total		**1398.20**	**63.17**	**63.17**	**37.16**	**37.16**	**65.03**	**65.03**	**33.44**	**33.44**	**55.74**	**52.02**	**33.44**	**33.44**	**154**	**22 785**	**14 279**

Table 40 Tenant Fit Example: Second Floor Room Data

Room No.	Room Name	Area, m²	Brick Area (Wall), m²				Spandrel/Soffit Area (Wall), m²				Window Area, m²				No. of People	Lights, W	Equip. W
			North	South	East	West	North	South	East	West	North	South	East	West			
201	Mgr. Stds.	12.14	2.79	0.00	0.00	0.00	5.57	0.00	0.00	0.00	3.72	0.00	0.00	0.00	1	220	131
201A	Admin. Asst.	15.79	0.00	0.00	0.00	0.00	0.00	0.00	0.00	0.00	0.00	0.00	0.00	0.00	3	330	170
202	Stds. Admin.	11.85	2.79	0.00	0.00	0.00	5.57	0.00	0.00	0.00	3.72	0.00	0.00	0.00	1	220	128
203	Asst. Mgr. Stds.	11.85	2.79	0.00	0.00	0.00	5.57	0.00	0.00	0.00	3.72	0.00	0.00	0.00	1	220	128
204	Asst. Mgr. Stds.	11.85	2.79	0.00	0.00	0.00	5.57	0.00	0.00	0.00	3.72	0.00	0.00	0.00	2	220	128
205	Mgr. Tech. Serv.	11.85	2.79	0.00	0.00	0.00	5.57	0.00	0.00	0.00	3.72	0.00	0.00	0.00	2	220	128
206	Admin. Asst./Dir.	11.85	2.79	0.00	0.00	0.00	5.57	0.00	0.00	0.00	3.72	0.00	0.00	0.00	1	220	128
207	Director	23.41	4.18	0.00	6.97	0.00	5.57	0.00	11.15	0.00	3.72	0.00	7.43	0.00	5	440	252
208	Open Office	126.07	0.00	0.00	0.00	0.00	0.00	0.00	0.00	0.00	0.00	0.00	0.00	0.00	8	2480	1357
209	Mgr. Research	11.85	0.00	0.00	2.79	0.00	0.00	0.00	5.57	0.00	0.00	0.00	3.72	0.00	2	220	128
220	Mgr. Res. Prom.	11.85	0.00	0.00	2.79	0.00	0.00	0.00	5.57	0.00	0.00	0.00	3.72	0.00	2	220	128
211	Future	11.85	0.00	0.00	2.79	0.00	0.00	0.00	5.57	0.00	0.00	0.00	3.72	0.00	2	220	128
212	Copy/Storage	10.66	0.00	0.00	0.00	0.00	0.00	0.00	0.00	0.00	0.00	0.00	0.00	0.00	0	150	115
213	Rare Books Arch.	10.27	0.00	0.00	0.00	0.00	0.00	0.00	0.00	0.00	0.00	0.00	0.00	0.00	0	150	111
214	Library	74.51	0.00	0.00	0.00	0.00	0.00	0.00	0.00	0.00	0.00	0.00	0.00	0.00	13	1430	802
215	Corridor	73.49	0.00	0.00	0.00	0.00	0.00	0.00	0.00	0.00	0.00	0.00	0.00	0.00	0	1480	791
216	Conf. Room	23.69	0.00	0.00	5.57	0.00	0.00	0.00	11.15	0.00	0.00	0.00	7.43	0.00	12	440	255
217	Storage	52.03	0.00	8.36	6.97	0.00	0.00	16.72	11.15	0.00	0.00	11.15	7.43	0.00	0	550	560
218	Breakroom	43.66	0.00	9.75	0.00	0.00	0.00	16.72	0.00	0.00	0.00	11.15	0.00	0.00	16	770	470
219	Stair 2	16.26	0.00	5.57	0.00	0.00	0.00	14.86	0.00	0.00	0.00	3.72	0.00	0.00	0	220	0
220	Elevator Lobby	11.52	0.00	0.00	0.00	0.00	0.00	0.00	0.00	0.00	0.00	0.00	0.00	0.00	0	120	0
221	Supplies	14.88	0.00	0.00	0.00	0.00	0.00	0.00	0.00	0.00	0.00	0.00	0.00	0.00	0	150	160
222	Cam./Darkroom	13.94	0.00	0.00	0.00	0.00	0.00	0.00	0.00	0.00	0.00	0.00	0.00	0.00	1	150	150
223	Open Office	106.47	0.00	0.00	0.00	0.00	0.00	0.00	0.00	0.00	0.00	0.00	0.00	0.00	8	1760	1146
224	S. Open Office	16.66	0.00	5.57	0.00	0.00	0.00	11.15	0.00	0.00	0.00	7.43	0.00	0.00	6	440	179
226	Prod. Mgr.	11.85	0.00	2.79	0.00	0.00	0.00	5.57	0.00	0.00	0.00	3.72	0.00	0.00	2	220	128
227	Graphics Mgr.	11.85	0.00	2.79	0.00	0.00	0.00	5.57	0.00	0.00	0.00	3.72	0.00	0.00	1	220	128
228	Editor (Handbook)	11.85	0.00	2.79	0.00	0.00	0.00	5.57	0.00	0.00	0.00	3.72	0.00	0.00	2	220	128
229	Open Office	154.59	0.00	0.00	0.00	0.00	0.00	0.00	0.00	0.00	0.00	0.00	0.00	0.00	7	2750	1664
229A	S. Open Office	14.81	0.00	4.18	0.00	0.00	0.00	11.15	0.00	0.00	0.00	7.43	0.00	0.00	5	440	159
229	W. Open Office	21.60	0.00	0.00	0.00	8.36	0.00	0.00	0.00	16.72	0.00	0.00	0.00	11.15	5	660	233
230	Conf. Room	25.47	0.00	5.57	0.00	6.97	0.00	5.57	0.00	11.15	0.00	3.72	0.00	7.43	12	440	274
231	Editor	11.85	0.00	0.00	0.00	2.79	0.00	0.00	0.00	5.57	0.00	0.00	0.00	3.72	1	220	128
232	Editor	11.85	0.00	0.00	0.00	2.79	0.00	0.00	0.00	5.57	0.00	0.00	0.00	3.72	2	220	128
233	Director	23.41	4.18	0.00	0.00	6.97	5.57	0.00	0.00	11.15	3.72	0.00	0.00	7.43	7	440	252
234	Admin. Asst.	11.85	2.79	0.00	0.00	0.00	5.57	0.00	0.00	0.00	3.72	0.00	0.00	0.00	1	220	128
235	Adv. Sales Mgr.	11.85	2.79	0.00	0.00	0.00	5.57	0.00	0.00	0.00	3.72	0.00	0.00	0.00	1	220	128
235A	Adv. Prod. Mgr.	11.85	2.79	0.00	0.00	0.00	5.57	0.00	0.00	0.00	3.72	0.00	0.00	0.00	1	220	128
236	Comm/P.R. Mgr.	11.85	2.79	0.00	0.00	0.00	5.57	0.00	0.00	0.00	3.72	0.00	0.00	0.00	1	220	128
237	Conf. Room	11.85	2.79	0.00	0.00	0.00	5.57	0.00	0.00	0.00	3.72	0.00	0.00	0.00	6	220	128
238	Marketing Mgr.	11.85	2.79	0.00	0.00	0.00	5.57	0.00	0.00	0.00	3.72	0.00	0.00	0.00	1	220	128
239	Open Office	93.00	0.00	0.00	0.00	0.00	0.00	0.00	0.00	0.00	0.00	0.00	0.00	0.00	6	2200	1001
240	Storage	21.32	0.00	0.00	0.00	0.00	0.00	0.00	0.00	0.00	0.00	0.00	0.00	0.00	0	225	0
241	Stair 1	23.39	5.57	0.00	0.00	0.00	18.58	0.00	0.00	0.00	0.00	0.00	0.00	0.00	0	440	0
242	Corridor	10.27	0.00	0.00	0.00	0.00	0.00	0.00	0.00	0.00	0.00	0.00	0.00	0.00	0	90	0
243	Hall of Fame	50.63	0.00	0.00	0.00	0.00	0.00	0.00	0.00	0.00	0.00	0.00	0.00	0.00	0	690	0
244	Janitor	5.07	0.00	0.00	0.00	0.00	0.00	0.00	0.00	0.00	0.00	0.00	0.00	0.00	0	75	0
245	Storage	9.96	0.00	0.00	0.00	0.00	0.00	0.00	0.00	0.00	0.00	0.00	0.00	0.00	0	75	0
246	Men	16.17	0.00	0.00	0.00	0.00	0.00	0.00	0.00	0.00	0.00	0.00	0.00	0.00	0	420	0
247	Women	16.17	0.00	0.00	0.00	0.00	0.00	0.00	0.00	0.00	0.00	0.00	0.00	0.00	0	420	0
248	Electrical	5.33	0.00	0.00	0.00	0.00	0.00	0.00	0.00	0.00	0.00	0.00	0.00	0.00	0	0	0
249	Mechanical	20.44	0.00	0.00	0.00	0.00	0.00	0.00	0.00	0.00	0.00	0.00	0.00	0.00	0	0	0
250	Storage	16.10	0.00	0.00	0.00	0.00	0.00	0.00	0.00	0.00	0.00	0.00	0.00	0.00	0	225	0
Total		**1398.17**	**47.38**	**47.38**	**27.87**	**27.87**	**96.62**	**92.90**	**50.17**	**50.17**	**52.02**	**55.74**	**33.44**	**33.44**	**147**	**25 050**	**12 654**

Bliss, R.J.V. 1961. Atmospheric radiation near the surface of the ground. *Solar Energy* 5(3):103.

Chantrasrisalai, C., D.E. Fisher, I. Iu, and D. Eldridge. 2003. Experimental validation of design cooling load procedures: The heat balance method. *ASHRAE Transactions* 109(2):160-173.

Claridge, D.E., B. Abushakra, J.S. Haberl, and A. Sreshthaputra. 2004. Electricity diversity profiles for energy simulation of office buildings (RP-1093). *ASHRAE Transactions* 110(1):365-377.

Eldridge, D., D.E. Fisher, I. Iu, and C. Chantrasrisalai. 2003. Experimental validation of design cooling load procedures: Facility design (RP-1117). *ASHRAE Transactions* 109(2):151-159.

Fisher, D.R. 1998. New recommended heat gains for commercial cooking equipment. *ASHRAE Transactions* 104(2):953-960.

Fisher, D.E. and C. Chantrasrisalai. 2006. Lighting heat gain distribution in buildings (RP-1282). ASHRAE Research Project, *Final Report*.

Fisher, D.E. and C.O. Pedersen. 1997. Convective heat transfer in building energy and thermal load calculations. *ASHRAE Transactions* 103(2): 137-148.

Gordon, E.B., D.J. Horton, and F.A. Parvin. 1994. Development and application of a standard test method for the performance of exhaust hoods with commercial cooking appliances. *ASHRAE Transactions* 100(2).

Hittle, D.C. 1999. The effect of beam solar radiation on peak cooling loads. *ASHRAE Transactions* 105(2):510-513.

Hittle, D.C. and C.O. Pedersen. 1981. Calculating building heating loads using the frequency of multi-layered slabs. *ASHRAE Transactions* 87(2):545-568.

Hosni, M.H. and B.T. Beck. 2008. Update to measurements of office equipment heat gain data (RP-1482). ASHRAE Research Project, *Progress Report*.

Hosni, M.H., B.W. Jones, J.M. Sipes, and Y. Xu. 1998. Total heat gain and the split between radiant and convective heat gain from office and laboratory equipment in buildings. *ASHRAE Transactions* 104(1A):356-365.

Hosni, M.H., B.W. Jones, and H. Xu. 1999. Experimental results for heat gain and radiant/convective split from equipment in buildings. *ASHRAE Transactions* 105(2):527-539.

Incropera, F.P. and D.P DeWitt. 1990. *Fundamentals of heat and mass transfer*, 3rd ed. Wiley, New York.

Iu, I. and D.E. Fisher. 2004. Application of conduction transfer functions and periodic response factors in cooling load calculation procedures. *ASHRAE Transactions* 110(2):829-841.

Iu, I., C. Chantrasrisalai, D.S. Eldridge, and D.E. Fisher. 2003. experimental validation of design cooling load procedures: The radiant time series method (RP-1117). *ASHRAE Transactions* 109(2):139-150.

Jones, B.W., M.H. Hosni, and J.M. Sipes. 1998. Measurement of radiant heat gain from office equipment using a scanning radiometer. *ASHRAE Transactions* 104(1B):1775-1783.

Karambakkam, B.K., B. Nigusse, and J.D. Spitler. 2005. A one-dimensional approximation for transient multi-dimensional conduction heat transfer in building envelopes. *Proceedings of the 7th Symposium on Building Physics in the Nordic Countries*, The Icelandic Building Research Institute, Reykjavik, vol. 1, pp. 340-347.

Kerrisk, J.F., N.M. Schnurr, J.E. Moore, and B.D. Hunn. 1981. The custom weighting-factor method for thermal load calculations in the DOE-2 computer program. *ASHRAE Transactions* 87(2):569-584.

Komor, P. 1997. Space cooling demands from office plug loads. *ASHRAE Journal* 39(12):41-44.

Kusuda, T. 1967. *NBSLD, the computer program for heating and cooling loads for buildings*. BSS 69 and NBSIR 74-574. National Bureau of Standards.

Latta, J.K. and G.G. Boileau. 1969. Heat losses from house basements. *Canadian Building* 19(10):39.

LBL. 2003. *WINDOW 5.2: A PC program for analyzing window thermal performance for fenestration products*. LBL-44789. Windows and Daylighting Group. Lawrence Berkeley Laboratory, Berkeley.

Liesen, R.J. and C.O. Pedersen. 1997. An evaluation of inside surface heat balance models for cooling load calculations. *ASHRAE Transactions* 103(2):485-502.

Marn, W.L. 1962. Commercial gas kitchen ventilation studies. *Research Bulletin* 90(March). Gas Association Laboratories, Cleveland, OH.

McClellan, T.M. and C.O. Pedersen. 1997. Investigation of outside heat balance models for use in a heat balance cooling load calculation procedure. *ASHRAE Transactions* 103(2):469-484.

McQuiston, F.C. and J.D. Spitler. 1992. *Cooling and heating load calculation manual*, 2nd ed. ASHRAE.

Miller, A. 1971. *Meteorology*, 2nd ed. Charles E. Merrill, Columbus.

Nigusse, B.A. 2007. *Improvements to the radiant time series method cooling load calculation procedure*. Ph.D. dissertation, Oklahoma State University.

Parker, D.S., J.E.R. McIlvaine, S.F. Barkaszi, D.J. Beal, and M.T. Anello. 2000. *Laboratory testing of the reflectance properties of roofing material*. FSEC-CR670-00. Florida Solar Energy Center, Cocoa.

Pedersen, C.O., D.E. Fisher, and R.J. Liesen. 1997. Development of a heat balance procedure for calculating cooling loads. *ASHRAE Transactions* 103(2):459-468.

Pedersen, C.O., D.E. Fisher, J.D. Spitler, and R.J. Liesen. 1998. *Cooling and heating load calculation principles*. ASHRAE.

Rees, S.J., J.D. Spitler, M.G. Davies, and P. Haves. 2000. Qualitative comparison of North American and U.K. cooling load calculation methods. *International Journal of Heating, Ventilating, Air-Conditioning and Refrigerating Research* 6(1):75-99.

Rock, B.A. 2005. A user-friendly model and coefficients for slab-on-grade load and energy calculation. *ASHRAE Transactions* 111(2):122-136.

Rock, B.A. and D.J. Wolfe. 1997. A sensitivity study of floor and ceiling plenum energy model parameters. *ASHRAE Transactions* 103(1):16-30.

Smith, V.A., R.T. Swierczyna, and C.N. Claar. 1995. Application and enhancement of the standard test method for the performance of commercial kitchen ventilation systems. *ASHRAE Transactions* 101(2).

Sowell, E.F. 1988a. Cross-check and modification of the DOE-2 program for calculation of zone weighting factors. *ASHRAE Transactions* 94(2).

Sowell, E.F. 1988b. Load calculations for 200,640 zones. *ASHRAE Transactions* 94(2):716-736.

Spitler, J.D. and D.E. Fisher. 1999a. Development of periodic response factors for use with the radiant time series method. *ASHRAE Transactions* 105(2):491-509.

Spitler, J.D. and D.E. Fisher. 1999b. On the relationship between the radiant time series and transfer function methods for design cooling load calculations. *International Journal of Heating, Ventilating, Air-Conditioning and Refrigerating Research* (now *HVAC&R Research*) 5(2):125-138.

Spitler, J.D., D.E. Fisher, and C.O. Pedersen. 1997. The radiant time series cooling load calculation procedure. *ASHRAE Transactions* 103(2).

Spitler, J.D., S.J. Rees, and P. Haves. 1998. Quantitive comparison of North American and U.K. cooling load calculation procedures—Part 1: Methodology, Part II: Results. *ASHRAE Transactions* 104(2):36-46, 47-61.

Sun, T.-Y. 1968. Shadow area equations for window overhangs and side-fins and their application in computer calculation. *ASHRAE Transactions* 74(1):I-1.1 to I-1.9.

Swierczyna, R., P. Sobiski, and D. Fisher. 2008. Revised heat gain and capture and containment exhaust rates from typical commercial cooking appliances (RP-1362). ASHRAE Research Project, *Final Report*.

Swierczyna, R., P.A. Sobiski, and D.R. Fisher. 2009 (forthcoming). Revised heat gain rates from typical commercial cooking appliances from RP-1362. *ASHRAE Transactions* 115(2).

Talbert, S.G., L.J. Canigan, and J.A. Eibling. 1973. An experimental study of ventilation requirements of commercial electric kitchens. *ASHRAE Transactions* 79(1):34.

Walton, G. 1983. *Thermal analysis research program reference manual*. National Bureau of Standards.

Wilkins, C.K. and M.R. Cook. 1999. Cooling loads in laboratories. *ASHRAE Transactions* 105(1):744-749.

Wilkins, C.K. and M.H. Hosni. 2000. Heat gain from office equipment. *ASHRAE Journal* 42(6):33-44.

Wilkins, C.K. and N. McGaffin. 1994. Measuring computer equipment loads in office buildings. *ASHRAE Journal* 36(8):21-24.

Wilkins, C.K., R. Kosonen, and T. Laine. 1991. An analysis of office equipment load factors. *ASHRAE Journal* 33(9):38-44.

BIBLIOGRAPHY

Alereza, T. and J.P. Breen, III. 1984. Estimates of recommended heat gain due to commercial appliances and equipment. *ASHRAE Transactions* 90(2A):25-58.

Alford, J.S., J.E. Ryan, and F.O. Urban. 1939. Effect of heat storage and variation in outdoor temperature and solar intensity on heat transfer through walls. *ASHVE Transactions* 45:387.

American Gas Association. 1948. *A comparison of gas and electric use for commercial cooking*. Cleveland, OH.

American Gas Association. 1950. *Gas and electric consumption in two college cafeterias*. Cleveland, OH.

ASHRAE. 1975. *Procedure for determining heating and cooling loads for computerized energy calculations, algorithms for building heat transfer subroutines*.

ASHRAE. 1979. *Cooling and heating load calculation manual*.

BLAST Support Office. 1991. *BLAST user reference*. University of Illinois, Urbana–Champaign.

Brisken, W.R. and G.E. Reque. 1956. Thermal circuit and analog computer methods, thermal response. *ASHAE Transactions* 62:391.

Buchberg, H. 1958. Cooling load from thermal network solutions. ASHAE *Standard* 64:111.

Buchberg, H. 1955. Electric analog prediction of the thermal behavior of an inhabitable enclosure. *ASHAE Transactions* 61:339-386.

Buffington, D.E. 1975. Heat gain by conduction through exterior walls and roofs—Transmission matrix method. *ASHRAE Transactions* 81(2):89.

Burch, D.M., B.A. Peavy, and F.J. Powell. 1974. Experimental validation of the NBS load and indoor temperature prediction model. *ASHRAE Transactions* 80(2):291.

Burch, D.M., J.E. Seem, G.N. Walton, and B.A. Licitra. 1992. Dynamic evaluation of thermal bridges in a typical office building. *ASHRAE Transactions* 98:291-304.

Butler, R. 1984. The computation of heat flows through multi-layer slabs. *Building and Environment* 19(3):197-206.

Ceylan, H.T. and G.E. Myers. 1985. Application of response-coefficient method to heat-conduction transients. *ASHRAE Transactions* 91:30-39.

Chiles, D.C. and E.F. Sowell. 1984. A counter-intuitive effect of mass on zone cooling load response. *ASHRAE Transactions* 91(2A):201-208.

Chorpening, B.T. 1997. The sensitivity of cooling load calculations to window solar transmission models. *ASHRAE Transactions* 103(1).

Clarke, J.A. 1985. *Energy simulation in building design*. Adam Hilger Ltd., Boston.

Consolazio, W. and L.J. Pecora. 1947. Minimal replenishment air required for living spaces. ASHVE *Standard* 53:127.

Colliver, D.G., H. Zhang, R.S. Gates, and K.T. Priddy. 1995. Determination of the 1%, 2.5%, and 5% occurrences of extreme dew-point temperatures and mean coincident dry-bulb temperatures. *ASHRAE Transactions* 101(2):265-286.

Colliver, D.G., R.S. Gates, H. Zhang, and K.T. Priddy. 1998. Sequences of extreme temperature and humidity for design calculations. *ASHRAE Transactions* 104(1A):133-144.

Colliver, D.G., R.S. Gates, T.F. Burke, and H. Zhang. 2000. Development of the design climatic data for the 1997 ASHRAE Handbook—Fundamentals. *ASHRAE Transactions* 106(1):3-14.

Davies, M.G. 1996. A time-domain estimation of wall conduction transfer function coefficients. *ASHRAE Transactions* 102(1):328-208.

DeAlbuquerque, A.J. 1972. Equipment loads in laboratories. *ASHRAE Journal* 14(10):59.

Falconer, D.R., E.F. Sowell, J.D. Spitler, and B.B. Todorovich. 1993. Electronic tables for the ASHRAE load calculation manual. *ASHRAE Transactions* 99(1):193-200.

Harris, S.M. and F.C. McQuiston. 1988. A study to categorize walls and roofs on the basis of thermal response. *ASHRAE Transactions* 94(2): 688-714.

Headrick, J.B. and D.P. Jordan. 1969. Analog computer simulation of heat gain through a flat composite roof section. *ASHRAE Transactions* 75(2):21.

Hittle, D.C. 1981. Calculating building heating and cooling loads using the frequency response of multilayered slabs, Ph.D. dissertation, Department of Mechanical and Industrial Engineering, University of Illinois, Urbana-Champaign.

Hittle, D.C. and R. Bishop. 1983. An improved root-finding procedure for use in calculating transient heat flow through multilayered slabs. *International Journal of Heat and Mass Transfer* 26:1685-1693.

Houghton, D.G., C. Gutherlet, and A.J. Wahl. 1935. ASHVE Research Report No. 1001—Cooling requirements of single rooms in a modern office building. *ASHVE Transactions* 41:53.

Kimura and Stephenson. 1968. Theoretical study of cooling loads caused by lights. *ASHRAE Transactions* 74(2):189-197.

Kusuda, T. 1969. Thermal response factors for multilayer structures of various heat conduction systems. *ASHRAE Transactions* 75(1):246.

Leopold, C.S. 1947. The mechanism of heat transfer, panel cooling, heat storage. *Refrigerating Engineering* 7:33.

Leopold, C.S. 1948. Hydraulic analogue for the solution of problems of thermal storage, radiation, convection, and conduction. *ASHVE Transactions* 54:3-9.

Livermore, J.N. 1943. Study of actual vs predicted cooling load on an air conditioning system. *ASHVE Transactions* 49:287.

Mackey, C.O. and N.R. Gay. 1949. Heat gains are not cooling loads. *ASHVE Transactions* 55:413.

Mackey, C.O. and N.R. Gay. 1952. Cooling load from sunlit glass. *ASHVE Transactions* 58:321.

Mackey, C.O. and N.R. Gay. 1954. Cooling load from sunlit glass and wall. *ASHVE Transactions* 60:469.

Mackey, C.O. and L.T. Wright, Jr. 1944. Periodic heat flow—homogeneous walls or roofs. *ASHVE Transactions* 50:293.

Mackey, C.O. and L.T. Wright, Jr. 1946. Periodic heat flow—composite walls or roofs. *ASHVE Transactions* 52:283.

Mast, W.D. 1972. Comparison between measured and calculated hour heating and cooling loads for an instrumented building. ASHRAE *Symposium Bulletin* 72(2).

McBridge, M.F., C.D. Jones, W.D. Mast, and C.F. Sepsey. 1975. Field validation test of the hourly load program developed from the ASHRAE algorithms. *ASHRAE Transactions* 1(1):291.

Mitalas, G.P. 1968. Calculations of transient heat flow through walls and roofs. *ASHRAE Transactions* 74(2):182-188.

Mitalas, G.P. 1969. An experimental check on the weighting factor method of calculating room cooling load. *ASHRAE Transactions* 75(2):22.

Mitalas, G.P. 1972. Transfer function method of calculating cooling loads, heat extraction rate, and space temperature. *ASHRAE Journal* 14(12):52.

Mitalas, G.P. 1973. Calculating cooling load caused by lights. *ASHRAE Transactions* 75(6):7.

Mitalas, G.P. 1978. Comments on the Z-transfer function method for calculating heat transfer in buildings. *ASHRAE Transactions* 84(1):667-674.

Mitalas, G.P. and J.G. Arsenault. 1970. Fortran IV program to calculate Z-transfer functions for the calculation of transient heat transfer through walls and roofs. *Use of Computers for Environmental Engineering Related to Buildings*, pp. 633-668. National Bureau of Standards, Gaithersburg, MD.

Mitalas, G.P. and K. Kimura. 1971. A calorimeter to determine cooling load caused by lights. *ASHRAE Transactions* 77(2):65.

Mitalas, G.P. and D.G. Stephenson. 1967. Room thermal response factors. *ASHRAE Transactions* 73(2): III.2.1.

Nevins, R.G., H.E. Straub, and H.D. Ball. 1971. Thermal analysis of heat removal troffers. *ASHRAE Transactions* 77(2):58-72.

NFPA. 1999. Standard for health care facilities. *Standard* 99-99. National Fire Protection Association, Quincy, MA.

Nottage, H.B. and G.V. Parmelee. 1954. Circuit analysis applied to load estimating. *ASHVE Transactions* 60:59.

Nottage, H.B. and G.V. Parmelee. 1955. Circuit analysis applied to load estimating. *ASHAE Transactions* 61(2):125.

Ouyang, K. and F. Haghighat. 1991. A procedure for calculating thermal response factors of multi-layer walls—State space method. *Building and Environment* 26(2):173-177.

Parmelee, G.V., P. Vance, and A.N. Cherny. 1957. Analysis of an air conditioning thermal circuit by an electronic differential analyzer. *ASHAE Transactions* 63:129.

Paschkis, V. 1942. Periodic heat flow in building walls determined by electric analog method. *ASHVE Transactions* 48:75.

Peavy, B.A. 1978. A note on response factors and conduction transfer functions. *ASHRAE Transactions* 84(1):688-690.

Peavy, B.A., F.J. Powell, and D.M. Burch. 1975. Dynamic thermal performance of an experimental masonry building. NBS *Building Science Series* 45 (July).

Romine, T.B., Jr. 1992. Cooling load calculation: Art or science? *ASHRAE Journal*, 34(1):14.

Rudoy, W. 1979. Don't turn the tables. *ASHRAE Journal* 21(7):62.

Rudoy, W. and F. Duran. 1975. Development of an improved cooling load calculation method. *ASHRAE Transactions* 81(2):19-69.

Seem, J.E., S.A. Klein, W.A. Beckman, and J.W. Mitchell. 1989. Transfer functions for efficient calculation of multidimensional transient heat transfer. *Journal of Heat Transfer* 111:5-12.

Sowell, E.F. and D.C. Chiles. 1984a. Characterization of zone dynamic response for CLF/CLTD tables. *ASHRAE Transactions* 91(2A):162-178.

Sowell, E.F. and D.C. Chiles. 1984b. Zone descriptions and response characterization for CLF/CLTD calculations. *ASHRAE Transactions* 91(2A): 179-200.

Spitler, J.D. 1996. *Annotated guide to load calculation models and algorithms*. ASHRAE.

Spitler, J.D., F.C. McQuiston, and K.L. Lindsey. 1993. The CLTD/SCL/CLF cooling load calculation method. *ASHRAE Transactions* 99(1):183-192.

Spitler, J.D. and F.C. McQuiston. 1993. Development of a revised cooling and heating calculation manual. *ASHRAE Transactions* 99(1):175-182.

Stephenson, D.G. 1962. Method of determining non-steady-state heat flow through walls and roofs at buildings. *Journal of the Institution of Heating and Ventilating Engineers* 30:5.

Stephenson, D.G. and G.P. Mitalas. 1967. Cooling load calculation by thermal response factor method. *ASHRAE Transactions* 73(2):III.1.1.

Stephenson, D.G. and G.P. Mitalas. 1971. Calculation of heat transfer functions for multi-layer slabs. *ASHRAE Transactions* 77(2):117-126.

Stewart, J.P. 1948. Solar heat gain through walls and roofs for cooling load calculations. *ASHVE Transactions* 54:361.

Sun, T.-Y. 1968. Computer evaluation of the shadow area on a window cast by the adjacent building. *ASHRAE Journal* (September).

Todorovic, B. 1982. Cooling load from solar radiation through partially shaded windows, taking heat storage effect into account. *ASHRAE Transactions* 88(2):924-937.

Todorovic, B. 1984. Distribution of solar energy following its transmittal through window panes. *ASHRAE Transactions* 90(1B):806-815.

Todorovic, B. 1987. The effect of the changing shade line on the cooling load calculations. In ASHRAE videotape, *Practical applications for cooling load calculations*.

Todorovic, B. 1989. *Heat storage in building structure and its effect on cooling load; Heat and mass transfer in building materials and structure*. Hemisphere Publishing, New York.

Todorovic, B. and D. Curcija. 1984. Calculative procedure for estimating cooling loads influenced by window shading, using negative cooling load method. *ASHRAE Transactions* 2:662.

Todorovic, B., L. Marjanovic, and D. Kovacevic. 1993. Comparison of different calculation procedures for cooling load from solar radiation through a window. *ASHRAE Transactions* 99(2):559-564.

Vild, D.J. 1964. Solar heat gain factors and shading coefficients. *ASHRAE Journal* 6(10):47.

Wilkins, C.K. 1998. Electronic equipment heat gains in buildings. *ASHRAE Transactions* 104(1B):1784-1789.

York, D.A. and C.C. Cappiello. 1981. *DOE-2 engineers manual* (Version 2.1A). Lawrence Berkeley Laboratory and Los Alamos National Laboratory.

BUILDING EXAMPLE DRAWINGS

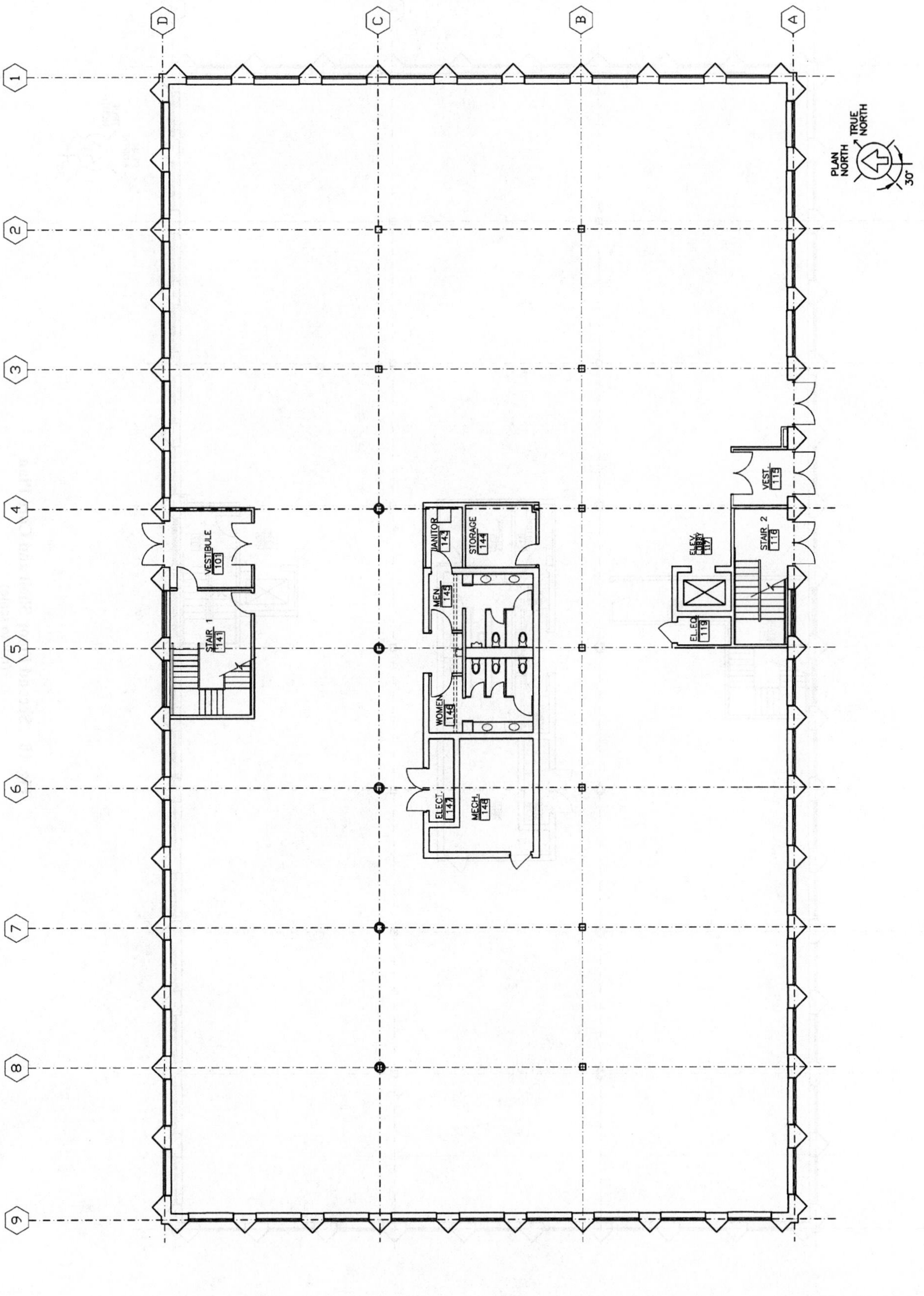

Fig. 17 First Floor Shell and Core Plan
(not to scale)

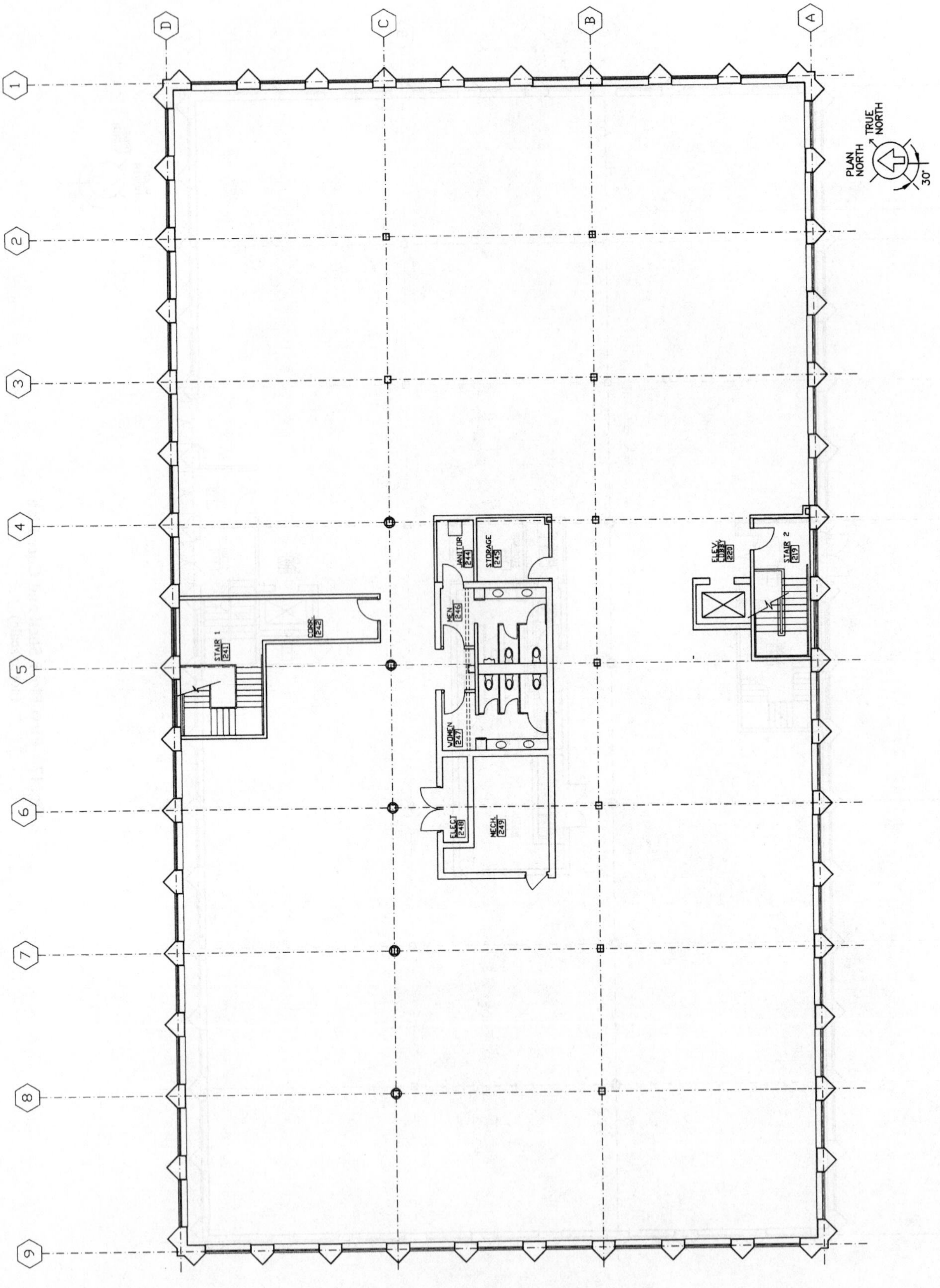

Fig. 18 Second Floor Shell and Core Plan
(not to scale)

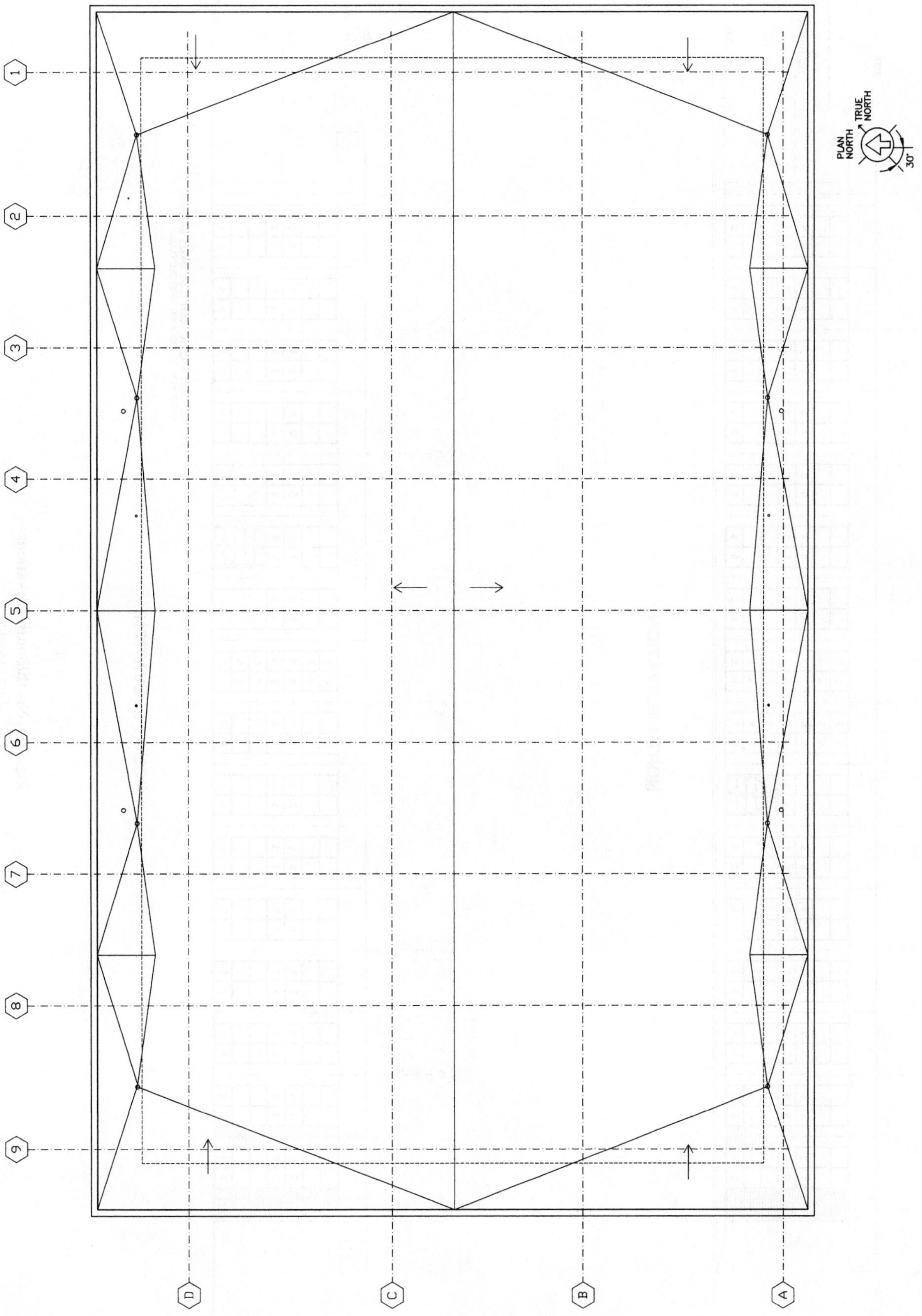

Fig. 19 Roof Plan
(not to scale)

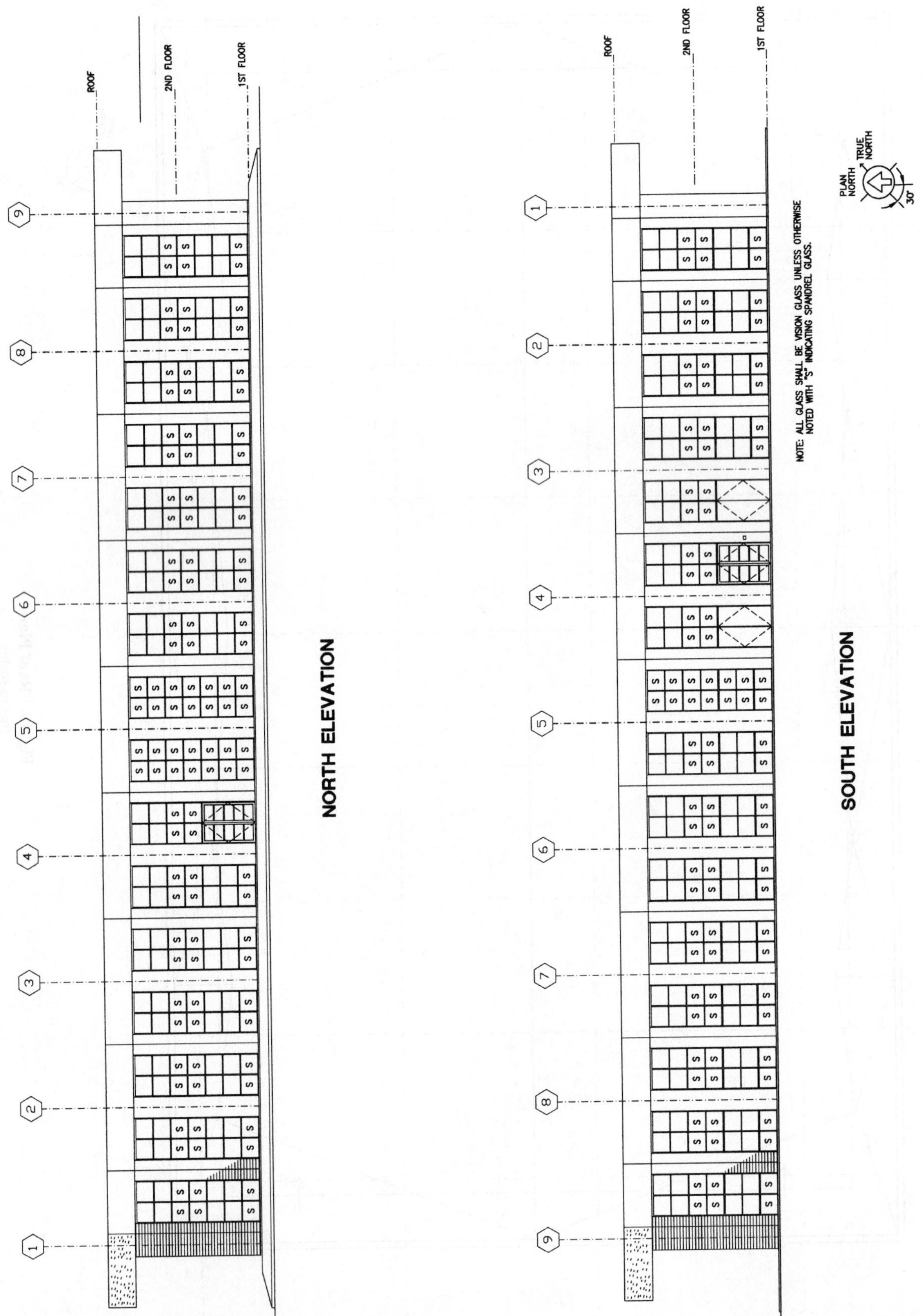

Fig. 20 North/South Elevations
(not to scale)

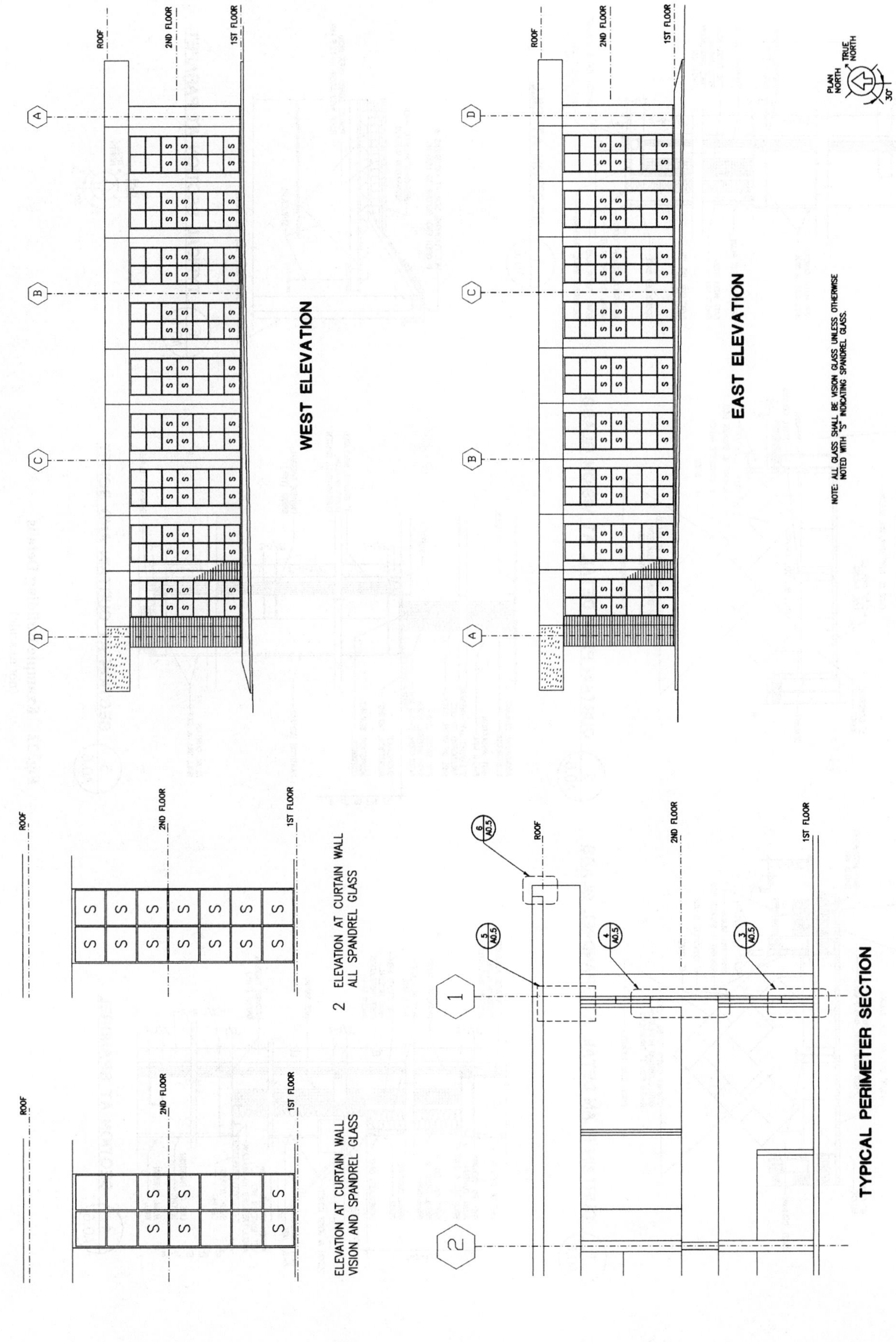

Fig. 21 East/West Elevations, Elevation Details, and Perimeter Section
(not to scale)

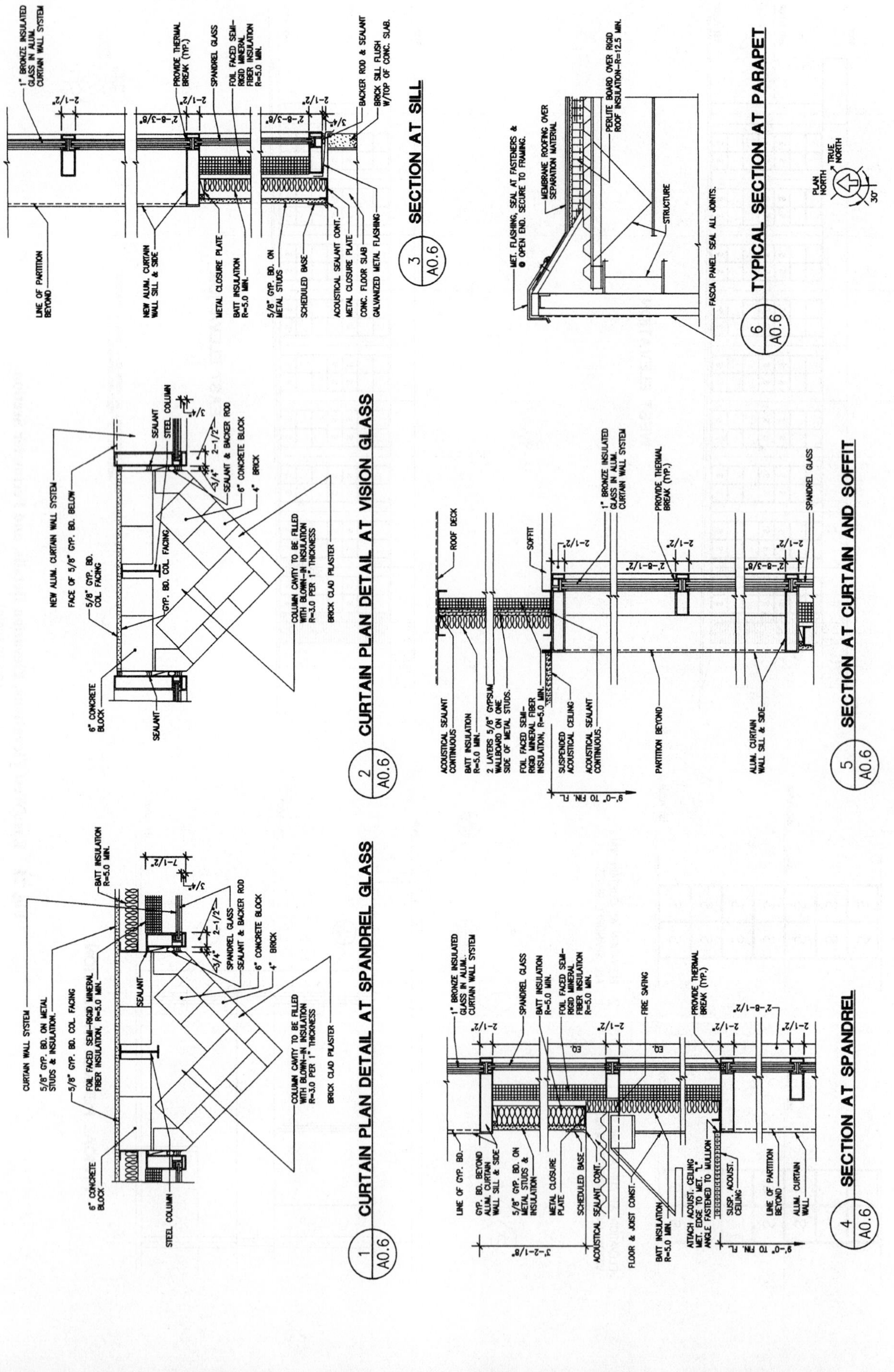

Fig. 22 Example Building Details
(not to scale)

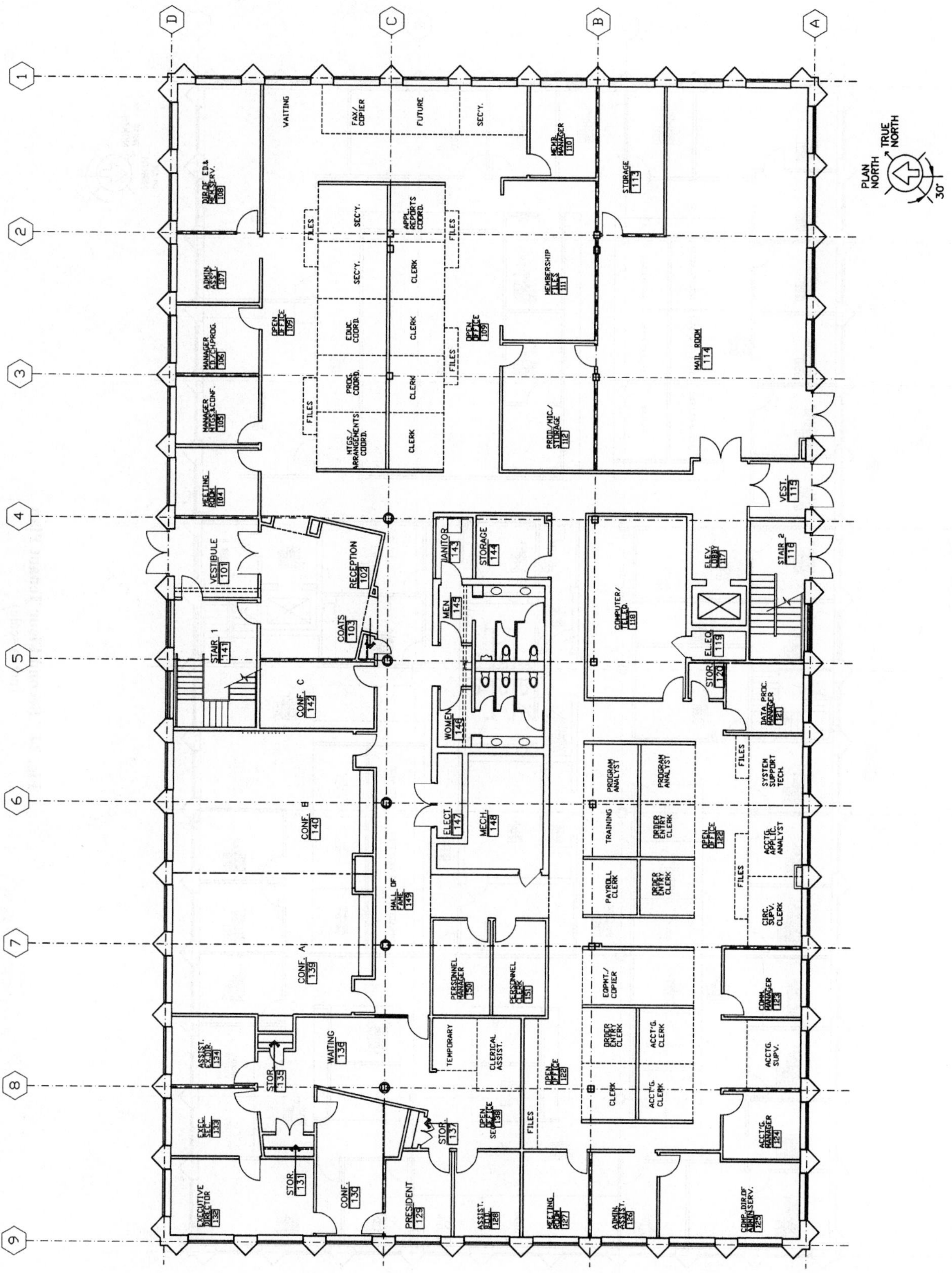

Fig. 23 First Floor Tenant Plan
(not to scale)

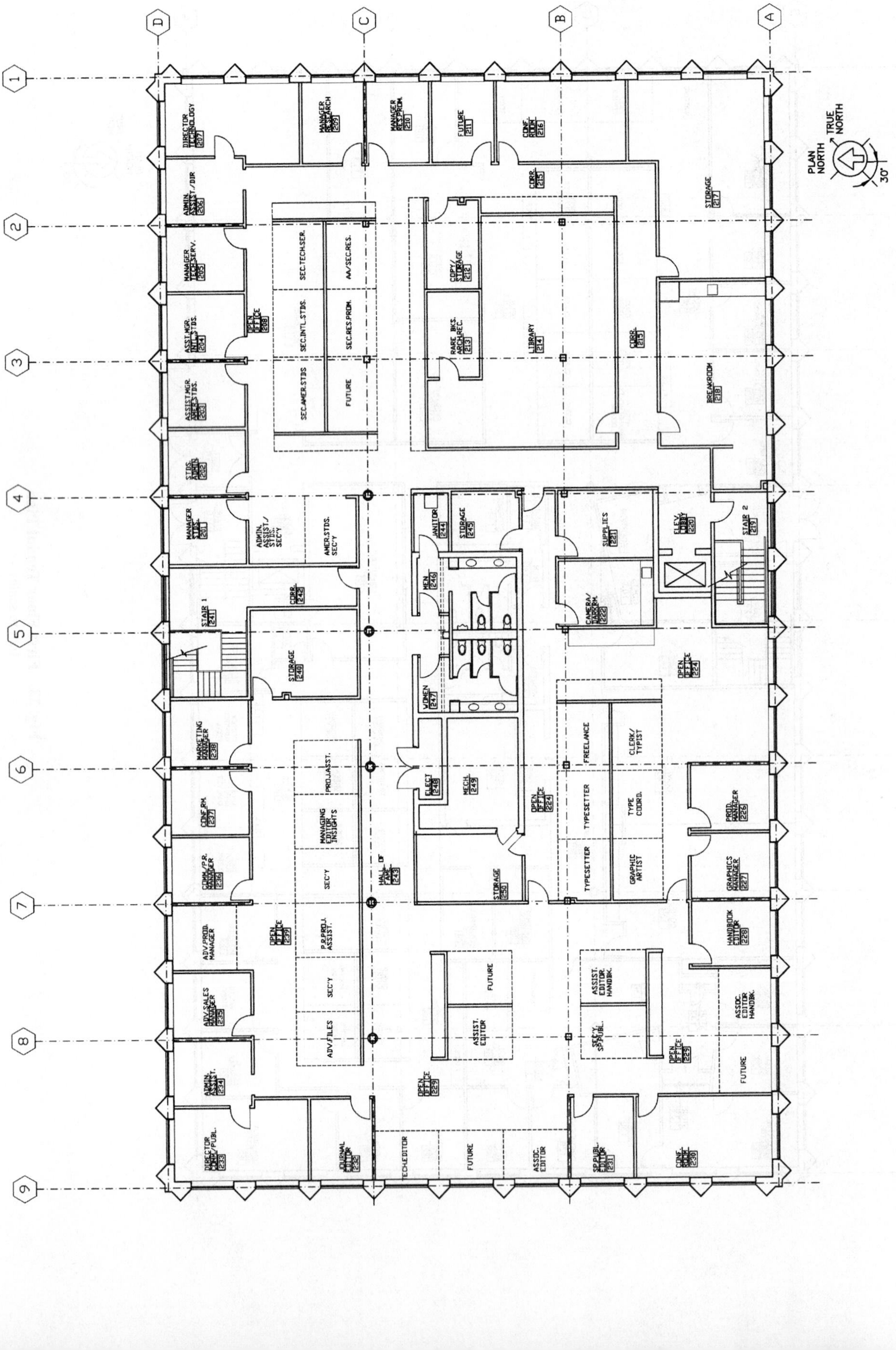

Fig. 24 Second Floor Tenant Plan
(not to scale)

CHAPTER 19

ENERGY ESTIMATING AND MODELING METHODS

ENERGY requirements and fuel consumption of HVAC systems directly affect a building's operating cost and indirectly affect the environment. This chapter discusses methods for estimating energy use for two purposes: modeling for building and HVAC system design and associated design optimization (**forward modeling**), and modeling energy use of existing buildings for establishing baselines and calculating retrofit savings (**data-driven modeling**).

GENERAL CONSIDERATIONS

MODELS AND APPROACHES

A mathematical **model** is a description of the behavior of a system. It is made up of three components (Beck and Arnold 1977):

1. **Input variables** (statisticians call these *regressor variables*, whereas physicists call them *forcing variables*), which act on the system. There are two types: controllable by the experimenter, and uncontrollable (e.g., climate).
2. **System structure and parameters/properties**, which provide the necessary physical description of the system (e.g., thermal mass or mechanical properties of the elements).
3. **Output** (*response*, or *dependent*) variables, which describe the reaction of the system to the input variables. Energy use is often a response variable.

The science of mathematical modeling as applied to physical systems involves determining the third component of a system when the other two components are given or specified. There are two broad but distinct approaches to modeling; which to use is dictated by the objective or purpose of the investigation (Rabl 1988).

Forward (Classical) Approach. The objective is to predict the output variables of a specified model with known structure and known parameters when subject to specified input variables. To ensure accuracy, models have tended to become increasingly complex, especially with the advent of cheap and powerful computing power. This approach presumes detailed knowledge not only of the various natural phenomena affecting system behavior but also of the magnitude of various interactions (e.g., effective thermal mass, heat and mass transfer coefficients, etc.). The main advantage of this approach is that the system need not be physically built to predict its behavior. Thus, this approach is ideal in the preliminary design and analysis stage and is most often used then.

Forward modeling of building energy use begins with a physical description of the building system or component of interest. For example, building geometry, geographical location, physical characteristics (e.g., wall material and thickness), type of equipment and operating schedules, type of HVAC system, building operating schedules, plant equipment, etc., are specified. The peak and average energy use of such a building can then be predicted or simulated by the forward simulation model. The primary benefits of this method are that it is based on sound engineering principles usually taught in colleges and universities, and consequently has gained widespread acceptance by the design and professional community. Major government-developed simulation codes, such as BLAST, DOE-2, and EnergyPlus, are based on forward simulation models. Figure 1 illustrates the ordering of the analysis typically performed by a building energy simulation program.

Data-Driven (Inverse) Approach. In this case, input and output variables are known and measured, and the objective is to determine a mathematical description of the system and to estimate system parameters. In contrast to the forward approach, the data-driven approach is relevant when the system has already been built and actual performance data are available for model development and/or identification. Two types of performance data can be used: nonintrusive and intrusive. **Intrusive data** are gathered under conditions of predetermined or planned experiments on the system to elicit system response under a wider range of system performance than would have occurred under normal system operation. These performance data allow more accurate model specification and identification. When constraints on system operation do not permit such tests to be performed, the model must be identified from **nonintrusive data** obtained under normal operation.

Data-driven modeling often allows identification of system models that are not only simpler to use but also are more accurate predictors of future system performance than forward models. The data-driven approach arises in many fields, such as physics, biology, engineering, and economics. Although several monographs, textbooks, and even specialized technical journals are available in this area, the approach has not yet been widely adopted in energy-related curricula and by the building professional community.

CHARACTERISTICS OF MODELS

Forward Models

Although procedures for estimating energy requirements vary considerably in their degree of complexity, they all have three common elements: calculation of (1) space load, (2) secondary

The preparation of this chapter is assigned to TC 4.7, Energy Calculations.

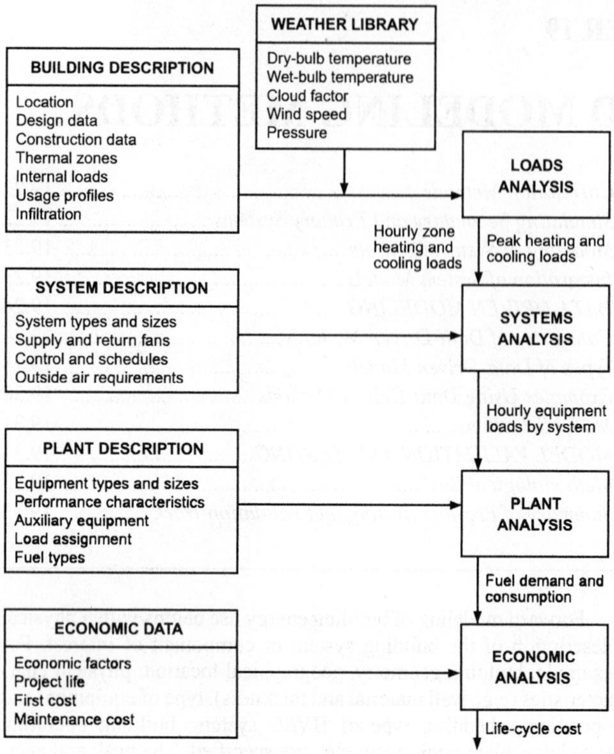

Fig. 1 Flow Chart for Building Energy Simulation Program
(Ayres and Stamper 1995)

equipment load, and (3) primary equipment energy requirements. Here, *secondary* refers to equipment that distributes the heating, cooling, or ventilating medium to conditioned spaces, whereas *primary* refers to central plant equipment that converts fuel or electric energy to heating or cooling effect.

The first step in calculating energy requirements is to determine the **space load**, which is the amount of energy that must be added to or extracted from a space to maintain thermal comfort. The simplest procedures assume that the energy required to maintain comfort is only a function of the outdoor dry-bulb temperature. More detailed methods consider solar effects, internal gains, heat storage in the walls and interiors, and the effects of wind on both building envelope heat transfer and infiltration. Chapters 17 and 18 discuss load calculation in detail.

Although energy calculations are similar to the heating and cooling load calculations used to size equipment, they are not the same. Energy calculations are based on average use and typical weather conditions rather than on maximum use and worst-case weather. Currently, the most sophisticated procedures are based on hourly profiles for climatic conditions and operational characteristics for a number of typical days of the year or on 8760 h of operation per year.

The second step translates the space load to a **load on the secondary equipment**. This can be a simple estimate of duct or piping losses or gains or a complex hour-by-hour simulation of an air system, such as variable-air-volume with outdoor-air cooling. This step must include calculation of all forms of energy required by the secondary system (e.g., electrical energy to operate fans and/or pumps, as well as energy in the form of heated or chilled water).

The third step calculates the fuel and **energy required by the primary equipment** to meet these loads and the peak demand on the utility system. It considers equipment efficiencies and part-load characteristics. It is often necessary to keep track of the different forms of energy, such as electrical, natural gas, or oil. In some cases, where calculations are required to ensure compliance with codes or standards, these energies must be converted to source energy or resource consumed, as opposed to energy delivered to the building boundary.

Often, energy calculations lead to an economic analysis to establish the cost-effectiveness of conservation measures (ASHRAE *Standard* 90.1). Thus, thorough energy analysis provides intermediate data, such as time of energy usage and maximum demand, so that utility charges can be accurately estimated. Although not part of the energy calculations, estimated capital equipment costs should be included.

Complex and often unexpected interactions can occur between systems or between various modes of heat transfer. For example, radiant heating panels affect space loads by raising the mean radiant temperature in the space (Howell and Suryanarayana 1990). As a result, air temperature can be lowered while maintaining comfort. Compared to a conventional heated-air system, radiant panels create a greater temperature difference from the inside surface to the outside air. Thus, conduction losses through the walls and roof increase because the inside surface temperatures are greater. At the same time, the heating load caused by infiltration or ventilation decreases because of the reduced indoor-to-outdoor-air temperature difference. The infiltration rate may also decrease because the reduced air temperature difference reduces the stack effect.

Data-Driven Models

The data-driven model has to meet requirements very different from the forward model. The data-driven model can only contain a relatively small number of parameters because of the limited and often repetitive information contained in the performance data. (For example, building operation from one day to the next is fairly repetitive.) It is thus a much simpler model that contains fewer terms representative of aggregated or macroscopic parameters (e.g., overall building heat loss coefficient and time constants). Because model parameters are deduced from actual building performance, it is much more likely to accurately capture as-built system performance, thus allowing more accurate prediction of future system behavior under certain specific circumstances. Performance data collection and model formulation need to be appropriately tailored for the specific circumstance, which often requires a higher level of user skill and expertise. In general, data-driven models are less flexible than forward models in evaluating energy implications of different design and operational alternatives, and so are not a substitute in this regard.

To better understand the uses of data-driven models, consider some of the questions that a building professional may ask about an existing building with known energy consumption (Rabl 1988):

- How does consumption compare with design predictions (and, in case of discrepancies, are they caused by anomalous weather, unintended building operation, improper operation, or other causes)?
- How would consumption change if thermostat settings, ventilation rates, or indoor lighting levels were changed?
- How much energy could be saved by retrofits to the building shell, changes to air handler operation from CV to VAV, or changes in the various control settings?
- If retrofits are implemented, can one verify that the savings are due to the retrofit and not to other causes (e.g., the weather)?
- How can one detect faults in HVAC equipment and optimize control and operation?

All these questions are better addressed by the data-driven approach. The forward approach could also be used, for example, by going back to the blueprints of the building and of the HVAC system, and repeating the analysis performed at the design stage using actual building schedules and operating modes, but this is tedious and labor-intensive, and materials and equipment often perform differently in reality than as specified. Tuning the forward-simulation model is often awkward and labor intensive, although it is still an option (as adopted in the calibrated data-driven approach).

CHOOSING AN ANALYSIS METHOD

The most important step in selecting an energy analysis method is matching method capabilities with project requirements. The method must be capable of evaluating all design options with sufficient accuracy to make correct choices. The following factors apply generally (Sonderegger 1985):

- **Accuracy.** The method should be sufficiently accurate to allow correct choices. Because of the many parameters involved in energy estimation, absolutely accurate energy prediction is not possible (Waltz 1992). ANSI/ASHRAE *Standard* 140, Method of Test for the Evaluation of Building Energy Analysis Computer Programs, was developed to identify and diagnose differences in predictions that may be caused by algorithmic differences, modeling limitations, coding errors, or input errors. More information on model validation and testing can be found in the Model Validation and Testing section of this chapter and in ANSI/ASHRAE *Standard* 140.
- **Sensitivity.** The method should be sensitive to the design options being considered. The difference in energy use between two choices should be adequately reflected.
- **Versatility.** The method should allow analysis of all options under consideration. When different methods must be used to consider different options, an accurate estimate of the differential energy use cannot be made.
- **Speed and cost.** The total time (gathering data, preparing input, calculations, and analysis of output) to make an analysis should be appropriate to the potential benefits gained. With greater speed, more options can be considered in a given time. The cost of analysis is largely determined by the total time of analysis.
- **Reproducibility.** The method should not allow so many vaguely defined choices that different analysts would get completely different results (Corson 1992).
- **Ease of use.** This affects both the economics of analysis (speed) and the reproducibility of results.

Selecting Energy Analysis Computer Programs

Selecting a building energy analysis program depends on its application, number of times it will be used, experience of the user, and hardware available to run it. The first criterion is the capability of the program to deal with the application. For example, if the effect of a shading device is to be analyzed on a building that is also shaded by other buildings part of the time, the ability to analyze detached shading is an absolute requirement, regardless of any other factors.

Because almost all manual methods are now implemented on a computer, selection of an energy analysis method is the selection of a computer program. The cost of the computer facilities and the software itself are typically a small part of running a building energy analysis; the major costs are of learning to use the program and of using it. Major issues that influence the cost of learning a program include (1) complexity of input procedures, (2) quality of the user's manual, and (3) availability of a good support system to answer questions. As the user becomes more experienced, the cost of learning becomes less important, but the need to obtain and enter a complex set of input data continues to consume the time of even an experienced user until data are readily available in electronic form compatible with simulation programs.

Complexity of input is largely influenced by the availability of default values for the input variables. Default values can be used as a simple set of input data when detail is not needed or when building design is very conventional, but additional complexity can be supplied when needed. Secondary defaults, which can be supplied by the user, are also useful in the same way. Some programs allow the user to specify a level of detail. Then the program requests only the information appropriate to that level of detail, using default values for all others.

Quality of output is another factor to consider. Reports should be easy to read and uncluttered. Titles and headings should be unambiguous. Units should be stated explicitly. The user's manual should explain the meanings of data presented. Graphic output can be very helpful. In most cases, simple summaries of overall results are the most useful, but very detailed output is needed for certain studies and also for debugging program input during the early stages of analysis.

Before a final decision is made, manuals for the most suitable programs should be obtained and reviewed, and, if possible, demonstration versions of the programs should be obtained and run, and support from the software supplier should be tested. The availability of training should be considered when choosing a more complex program.

Availability of weather data and a weather data processing subroutine or program are major features of a program. Some programs include subroutine or supplementary programs that allow the user to create a weather file for any site for which weather data are available. Programs that do not have this capability must have weather files for various sites created by the program supplier. In that case, the available weather data and the terms on which the supplier will create new weather data files must be checked. More information on weather data can be found in Chapter 14.

Auxiliary capabilities, such as economic analysis and design calculations, are a final concern in selecting a program. An economic analysis may include only the ability to calculate annual energy bills from utility rates, or it might extend to calculations or even to life-cycle cost optimization. An integrated program may save time because some input data have been entered already for other purposes.

The results of computer calculations should be accepted with caution, because the software vendor does not accept responsibility for the correctness of calculations or use of the program. Manual calculation should be done to develop a good understanding of underlying physical processes and building behavior. In addition, the user should (1) review the computer program documentation to determine what calculation procedures are used, (2) compare results with manual calculations and measured data, and (3) conduct sample tests to confirm that the program delivers acceptable results.

Tools for Energy Analysis

The most accurate methods for calculating building energy consumption are the most costly because of their intense computational requirements and the expertise needed by the designer or analyst. Simulation programs that assemble component models into system models and then exercise those models with weather and occupancy data are preferred by experts for determining energy use in buildings.

Often, energy consumption at a system or whole-building level must be estimated quickly to study trends, compare systems, or study building effects such as envelope characteristics. For these purposes, simpler methods, such as degree-day and bin, may be used.

Table 1 classifies methods for analyzing building energy use as either forward or data-driven, and either steady-state or dynamic. The U.S. Department of Energy maintains an up-to-date listing of building energy software with links to other sites that describe energy modeling tools at http://www.energytoolsdirectory.gov.

COMPONENT MODELING AND LOADS

CALCULATING SPACE SENSIBLE LOADS

Calculating instantaneous space sensible load is a key step in any building energy simulation. The **heat balance** and **weighting-factor methods** are used for these calculations. A third method, the **thermal-network method**, is not widely used but shows promise.

The **instantaneous space sensible load** is the rate of heat flow into the space air mass. This quantity, sometimes called the *cooling load*, differs from heat gain, which usually contains a radiative

Table 1 Classification of Analysis Methods For Building Energy Use

Method	Forward	Data-Driven: Empirical or Black-Box	Data-Driven: Calibrated Simulation	Data-Driven: Physical or Gray-Box	Comments
Steady-State Methods					
Simple linear regression (Kissock et al. 1998; Ruch and Claridge 1991)	—	X	—	—	One dependent parameter, one independent parameter. May have slope and *y*-intercept.
Multiple linear regression (Dhar 1995; Dhar et al. 1998, 1999a, 1999b; Katipamula et al. 1998; Sonderegger 1998)	—	X	—	—	One dependent parameter, multiple independent parameters.
Modified degree-day method	X	—	—	—	Based on fixed reference temperature of 18.3°C.
Variable-base degree-day method, or 3-P change point models (Fels 1986; Reddy et al. 1997; Sonderegger 1998)	X	X	—	X	Variable base reference temperatures.
Change-point models: 4-P, 5-P (Fels 1986; Kissock et al. 1998)	—	X	—	X	Uses daily or monthly utility billing data and average period temperatures.
ASHRAE bin method and data-driven bin method (Thamilseran and Haberl 1995)	X	X	—	—	Hours in temperature bin times load for that bin.
ASHRAE TC 4.7 modified bin method (Knebel 1983)	X	—	—	—	Modified bin method with cooling load factors.
Multistep parameter identification (Reddy et al. 1999)	—	—	—	X	Uses daily data to determine overall heat loss and ventilation of large buildings.
Dynamic Methods					
Thermal network (Rabl 1988; Reddy 1989; Sonderegger 1977)	X	—	—	X	Uses equivalent thermal parameters (data-driven mode).
Response factors (Kusuda 1969; Mitalas 1968; Mitalas and Stephenson 1967; Stephenson and Mitalas 1967)	X	—	—	—	Tabulated or as used in simulation programs.
Fourier analysis (Shurcliff 1984; Subbarao 1988)	X	—	X	X	Frequency domain analysis convertible to time domain.
ARMA model (Rabl 1988; Reddy 1989; Subbarao 1986)	—	—	—	X	Autoregressive moving average (ARMA) model.
PSTAR (Subbarao 1988)	X	—	X	X	Combination of ARMA and Fourier series; includes loads in time domain.
Modal analysis (Bacot et al. 1984; Rabl 1988)	X	—	—	X	Building described by diagonalized differential equation using nodes.
Differential equation (Rabl 1988)	—	—	—	X	Analytical linear differential equation.
Computer simulation: DOE-2, BLAST, EnergyPlus (Crawley et al. 2001; Haberl and Bou-Saada 1998; Manke et al. 1996; Norford et al. 1994)	X	—	X	—	Hourly and subhourly simulation programs with system models.
Computer emulation (HVACSIM+, TRNSYS) (Clark 1985; Klein et al. 1994)	X	—	—	—	Subhourly simulation programs.
Artificial neural networks (Kreider and Haberl 1994; Kreider and Wang 1991)	—	X	—	—	Connectionist models.

component that passes through the air and is absorbed by other bounding surfaces. Instantaneous space sensible load is entirely convective; even loads from internal equipment, lights, and occupants enter the air by convection from the surface of such objects or by convection from room surfaces that have absorbed the radiant component of energy emitted from these sources. However, some adjustment must be made when radiant cooling and heating systems are evaluated because some of the space load is offset directly by radiant transfer without convective transfer to the air mass.

For equilibrium, the instantaneous space sensible load must match the heat removal rate of the conditioning equipment. Any imbalance in these rates changes the energy stored in the air mass. Customarily, however, the thermal mass (heat capacity) of the air itself is ignored in analysis, so the air is always assumed to be in thermal equilibrium. Under these assumptions, the instantaneous space sensible load and rate of heat removal are equal in magnitude and opposite in sign.

The weighting-factor and heat balance methods use conduction transfer functions (or their equivalents) to calculate transmission heat gain or loss. The main difference is in the methods used to calculate the subsequent internal heat transfers to the room. Experience with both methods has indicated largely the same results, provided the weighting factors are determined for the specific building under analysis.

Heat Balance Method

The heat balance method for calculating net space sensible loads, as described in the *ASHRAE Toolkit for Building Load Calculations* (Pedersen et al. 2001, 2003), is more fundamental than the weighting-factor method. Its development relies on the first law of thermodynamics (conservation of energy) and the principles of matrix algebra. Because it requires fewer assumptions than the weighting-factor method, it is also more flexible. However, the heat balance method requires more calculations at each point in the simulation process, using more computer time. The weighting factors used are determined with a heat balance procedure. Although not necessary, linearization is commonly used to simplify the radiative transfer formulation.

The heat balance method allows the net instantaneous sensible heating and/or cooling load to be calculated on the space air mass.

Generally, a heat balance equation is written for each enclosing surface, plus one equation for room air. This set of equations can then be solved for the unknown surface and air temperatures. Once these temperatures are known, they can be used to calculate the convective heat flow to or from the space air mass. The heat balance method is developed in Chapter 18 for use in design cooling load calculations, so a fuller description is omitted here.

However, the heat balance procedure described in Chapter 18 is aimed at obtaining the design cooling load for a fixed zone air temperature. For building energy analysis purposes, it is preferable to know the actual heat extraction rate. This may be determined by recasting Equation (27) of Chapter 18 so that the system heat transfer is determined simultaneously with the zone air temperature. The system heat transfer is the rate at which heat is transferred to the space by the system. Although this can be done by simultaneously modeling the zone and the system (Taylor et al. 1990, 1991), it is convenient to make a simple, piecewise-linear representation of the system known as a *control profile*. This usually takes the form

$$q_{sys_j} = a + bt_{a_j} \tag{1}$$

where

q_{sys_j} = system heat transfer at time step j, W
a, b = coefficients that apply over a certain range of zone air temperatures
t_{a_j} = zone air temperature at time step j, °C

System heat transfer q_{sys_j} may be considered positive when heating is provided to the space and negative when cooling is provided. It is equal in magnitude but opposite in sign to the zone cooling load, as defined in Chapter 18, when zone air temperature is fixed.

Substituting Equation (1) into Equation (27) of Chapter 18 and solving for zone air temperature,

$$t_{a_j} = \frac{a + \sum_{i=1}^{N} A_i h_{ci} t_{si_{i,j}} + \rho c V_{infil_j} t_{o_j} + \rho c V_{vent_j} t_{v_j} + q_{c,int_j}}{-b + \sum_{i=1}^{N} A_i h_{ci} + \rho c V_{infil_j} + \rho c V_{vent_j}} \tag{2}$$

where

N = number of zone surfaces
A_i = area of ith surface, m²
h_{ci} = convection coefficient for ith surface, W/(m²·K)
$t_{si_{i,j}}$ = surface temperature for ith surface at time step j, °C
ρ = density, kg/m³
c = specific heat of air, J/(kg·K)
V = volumetric flow rate of air, m³/s
t_{o_j} = outdoor air temperature at time step j, °C
t_{v_j} = ventilation air temperature at time step j, °C
q_{c,int_j} = sum of convective portions of all internal heat gains at time step j, W

The zone air heat balance equation [Equation (2)] must be solved simultaneously with the interior and exterior surface heat balance equations [Equations (26) and (25) in Chapter 18]. Also, the correct temperature range must be found to use the proper set of a and b coefficients; this may be done iteratively. Once the zone air temperature is found, the actual system heat transfer rate may be found directly from Equation (1).

Beyond treatment of system heat transfer, other considerations that may be important in building energy analysis programs include simulations over periods as long as a year, treatment of radiant cooling and heating systems, treatment of interzone heat transfer, modeling convection heat transfer, and modeling radiation heat transfer.

The heat balance method in Chapter 18 assumes the use of a single design day. In a building energy analysis program, it is most commonly used with a year's worth of design weather data. In this case, the first day of the year is usually simulated several times until a steady-periodic response is obtained. Then, each day is simulated sequentially, and, where needed, historical data for surface temperatures and heat fluxes from the previous day are used.

When radiant cooling and heating systems are evaluated, the radiant source should be identified as a room surface. The calculation procedure considers the radiant source in the heat balance analysis. Therefore, the heat balance method is preferred over the weighting-factor method for evaluating radiant systems. Strand and Pedersen (1997) describe implementation of heat source conduction transfer functions, which may be used for modeling radiant panels, into a heat balance-based building simulation program.

In principle, this method extends directly to multiple spaces, with heat transfer between zones. In this case, some surface temperatures appear in the surface heat balance equations for two different zones. In practice, however, the size of the coefficient array required for solving the simultaneous equations becomes prohibitively large, and the solution time excessive. For this reason, many programs solve only one space at a time and assume that adjacent space temperatures are either the same as the space in question or some assigned, constant value. Other approaches may remove this limitation (Walton 1980).

Relatively simple exterior and interior convection models may be used for design cooling load calculation procedures. However, more sophisticated exterior convection models (Cooper and Tree 1973; Fracastoro et al. 1982; Melo and Hammond 1991; Walton 1983; Yazdanian and Klems 1994) that incorporate the effects of wind speed, wind direction, surface orientation, etc., may be preferable. More detailed interior convection correlations for use in buildings are also available (Alamdari and Hammond 1982, 1983; Altmayer et al. 1983; Bauman et al. 1983; Bohn et al. 1984; Chandra and Kerestecioglu 1984; Khalifa and Marshall 1990; Spitler et al. 1991; Walton 1983).

Also, more detailed models of exterior [e.g., Cole (1976); Walton (1983)] and interior [e.g., Carroll (1980); Davies (1988); Kamal and Novak (1991); Steinman et al. (1989); Walton (1980)] long-wave radiation transfer have been implemented in detailed building simulation programs.

Weighting-Factor Method

The weighting-factor method of calculating instantaneous space sensible load is a compromise between simpler methods (e.g., steady-state calculation) that ignore the ability of building mass to store energy, and more complex methods (e.g., complete energy balance calculations). With this method, space heat gains at constant space temperature are determined from a physical description of the building, ambient weather conditions, and internal load profiles. Along with the characteristics and availability of heating and cooling systems for the building, space heat gains are used to calculate air temperatures and heat extraction rates. This discussion is in terms of heat gains, cooling loads, and heat extraction rates. Heat losses, heating loads, and heat addition rates are merely different terms for the same quantities, depending on the direction of the heat flow.

The weighting factors represent Z-transfer functions (Kerrisk et al. 1981; York and Cappiello 1982). The Z-transform is a method for solving differential equations with discrete data. Two groups of weighting factors are used: heat gain and air temperature.

Heat gain weighting factors represent transfer functions that relate space cooling load to instantaneous heat gains. A set of weighting factors is calculated for each group of heat sources that differ significantly in the (1) relative amounts of energy appearing as convection to the air versus radiation, and (2) distribution of radiant energy intensities on different surfaces.

Air temperature weighting factors represent a transfer function that relates room air temperature to the net energy load of the room. Weighting factors for a particular heat source are determined by introducing a unit pulse of energy from that source into the room's network. The network is a set of equations that represents a heat balance for the room. At each time step (1 h intervals), including the initial introduction, the energy flow to the room air represents the amount of the pulse that becomes a cooling load. Thus, a long sequence of cooling loads can be generated, from which weighting factors are calculated. Similarly, a unit pulse change in room air temperature can be used to produce a sequence of cooling loads.

A two-step process is used to determine the air temperature and heat extraction rate of a room or building zone for a given set of conditions. First, the room air temperature is assumed to be fixed at some reference value, usually the average air temperature expected for the room over the simulation period. Instantaneous heat gains are calculated based on this constant air temperature. Various types of heat gains are considered. Some, such as solar energy entering through windows or energy from lighting, people, or equipment, are independent of the reference temperature. Others, such as conduction through walls, depend directly on the reference temperature.

A space sensible cooling load for the room, defined as the rate at which energy must be removed from the room to maintain the reference value of the air temperature, is calculated for each type of instantaneous heat gain. The cooling load generally differs from the instantaneous heat gain because some energy from heat gain is absorbed by walls or furniture and stored for later release to the air. At time θ, the calculation uses present and past values of the instantaneous heat gain (q_θ, $q_{\theta-1}$), past values of the cooling load ($Q_{\theta-1}$, $Q_{\theta-2}$, ...), and the **heat gain weighting factors** (v_0, v_1, v_2, ..., w_1, w_2, ...) for the type of heat gain under consideration. Thus, for each type of heat gain q_θ, cooling load Q_θ is calculated as

$$Q_\theta = v_0 q_\theta + v_1 q_{\theta-1} + \cdots - w_1 Q_{\theta-1} - w_2 Q_{\theta-2} - \cdots \quad (3)$$

The heat gain weighting factors are a set of parameters that determine how much of the energy entering a room is stored and how rapidly stored energy is released later. Mathematically, the weighting factors are parameters in a Z-transfer function relating the heat gain to the cooling load.

These weighting factors differ for different heat gain sources because the relative amounts of convective and radiative energy leaving various sources differ and because the distribution of radiative energy can differ. Heat gain weighting factors also differ for different rooms because room construction affects the amount of incoming energy stored by walls or furniture and the rate at which it is released. Sowell (1988) showed the effects of 14 zone design parameters on zone dynamic response. After the first step, cooling loads from various heat gains are added to give a total cooling load for the room.

In the second step, the total cooling load is used (with information on the room's HVAC system and a set of **air temperature weighting factors**) to calculate the actual heat extraction rate and air temperature. The actual heat extraction rate differs from the cooling load (1) because, in practice, air temperature can vary from the reference value used to calculate the cooling load, or (2) because of HVAC system characteristics. Deviation of air temperature t_θ from the reference value at hour θ is calculated as

$$t_\theta = 1/g_0 + [(Q_\theta - ER_\theta) + P_1(Q_{\theta-1} - ER_{\theta-1}) + P_2(Q_{\theta-2} - ER_{\theta-2}) + \cdots - g_1 t_{\theta-1} - g_2 t_{\theta-2} - \cdots] \quad (4)$$

where ER_θ is the energy removal rate of the HVAC system at hour θ, and g_0, g_1, g_2, ..., P_1, P_2, ... are air temperature weighting factors, which incorporate information about the room, particularly thermal coupling between the air and the storage capacity of the building mass.

Values of weighting factors for typical building rooms are presented in the following table. One of the three groups of weighting factors, for light, medium, and heavy construction rooms, can be used to approximate the behavior of any room. Some automated simulation techniques allow weighting factors to be calculated specifically for the building under consideration. This option improves the accuracy of the calculated results, particularly for a building with an unconventional design. McQuiston and Spitler (1992) provided electronic tables of weighting factors for a large number of parametrically defined zones.

Normalized Coefficients of Space Air Transfer Functions

Room Envelope Construction	g_0^*	g_1^*	g_2^*	p_0	p_1
	W/(m²·K)			Dimensionless	
Light	+9.54	−9.82	+0.28	1.0	−0.82
Medium	+10.28	−10.73	+0.45	1.0	−0.87
Heavy	+10.50	−11.07	+0.57	1.0	−0.93

Two assumptions are made in the weighting-factor method. First, the processes modeled are linear. This assumption is necessary because heat gains from various sources are calculated independently and summed to obtain the overall result (i.e., the superposition principle is used). Therefore, nonlinear processes such as radiation or natural convection must be approximated linearly. This assumption is not a significant limitation because these processes can be linearly approximated with sufficient accuracy for most calculations. The second assumption is that system properties influencing the weighting factors are constant (i.e., they are not functions of time). This assumption is necessary because only one set of weighting factors is used during the entire simulation period. This assumption can limit the use of weighting factors in situations where important room properties vary during the calculation (e.g., the distribution of solar radiation incident on the interior walls of a room, which can vary hourly, and inside surface heat transfer coefficients).

When the weighting-factor method is used, a combined radiative/convective heat transfer coefficient is used as the inside surface heat transfer coefficient. This value is assumed constant even though, in a real room, (1) radiant heat transferred from a surface depends on the temperature of other room surfaces (not on room air temperature) and (2) the combined heat transfer coefficient is not constant. Under these circumstances, an average value of the property must be used to determine the weighting factors. Cumali et al. (1979) investigated extensions to the weighting-factor method to eliminate this limitation.

Thermal-Network Methods

Although implementations of the thermal-network method vary, they all have in common the discretization of the building into a network of nodes, with interconnecting paths through which energy flows. In many respects, thermal-network models may be considered a refinement of the heat balance method. Where the heat balance model generally uses one node for zone air, the thermal-network method might use multiple nodes. For each heat transfer element (wall, roof, floor, etc.), the heat balance model generally has one interior and one exterior surface node; the thermal-network model may include additional nodes. Heat balance models generally use simple methods for distributing radiation from lights; thermal-network models may model the lamp, ballast, and luminaire housing separately. Furthermore, thermal-network models depend on a heat balance at each node to determine node temperature and energy flow between all connected nodes. Energy flows may include conduction, convection, and short- or long-wave radiation.

For any mode of energy flow, a range of techniques may be used to model the energy flow between two nodes. Taking conduction heat transfer as an example, the simplest thermal-network model would be a resistance/capacitance network (Sowell 1990). By refining network discretization, the models become what are commonly thought of as finite-difference or finite-volume models (Clarke 2001; Lewis and Alexander 1990; Walton 1993).

Thermal-network models generally use a set of algebraic and differential equations. In most implementations, the solution procedure is separated from the models so that, in theory, different solvers might be used to perform the simulation. In contrast, most heat balance and weighting factor programs interweave the solution technique with the models. Various solution techniques have been used in conjunction with thermal-network models. Examples include graph theory combined with Newton-Raphson and predictor/corrector ordinary differential equation integration (Buhl et al. 1990) and the use of Euler explicit integration combined with sparse matrix techniques (Walton 1993).

Of the three zone models discussed, thermal-network models are the most flexible and have the greatest potential for high accuracy. However, they also require the most computation time, and, in current implementations, require more user effort to take advantage of the flexibility.

GROUND HEAT TRANSFER

The thermal performance of building foundations, including guidelines for placement of insulation, is described in Chapter 25 of this volume and Chapter 43 of the 2007 *ASHRAE Handbook—HVAC Applications*. Chapter 18 provides information for calculating transmission heat losses through slab foundations and through basement walls and floors. These calculations are appropriate for design loads but are not intended for estimating annual energy usage. This section provides simplified calculation methods suitable for energy estimates over time periods of arbitrary length.

Thermal performance of building foundations has been largely ignored. It is estimated that, in the early 1970s, only 10% of the total energy use of a typical U.S. home was attributed to heat transfer from its foundation (Labs et al. 1988). Since then, thermal performance of above-grade building elements has improved significantly, and the contribution of ground-coupled heat transfer to total energy use in a typical U.S. home has increased. Shipp and Broderick (1983) estimated that heat transfer from an uninsulated basement in Columbus, Ohio, can represent up to 67% of the total building envelope heating load.

Earth-contact heat transfer, rated at 1 to 3 EJ of energy annually in U.S. buildings, has an effect similar to infiltration on annual heating and cooling loads in residential buildings (Claridge 1988a). Adding insulation to building foundations is estimated to save up to 0.5 EJ of annual energy use in the U.S. (Labs et al. 1988).

Simplified Calculation Method for Slab Foundations and Basements

The design tool for slab-on-grade floors developed by Krarti and Chuangchid (1999) can be modified to a simplified design tool for calculating heat loss for slabs and basements. The design tool is easy to use and requires straightforward input parameters with continuously variable values, including foundation size, insulation R-values, soil thermal properties, and indoor and outdoor temperatures. The simplified method provides a set of equations suitable for estimating the design, seasonal, and annual total heat loss of a slab or a basement as a function of a wide range of variables.

When the indoor temperature of the building is maintained constant, the ground-coupled heat transfer $q(\theta)$ varies with time according to the following equation:

$$q(\theta) = q_{mean} + q_{amp}\sin(\omega\theta + \phi) \tag{5}$$

where

q_{mean} = annual-mean heat loss/gain, W
q_{amp} = heat loss/gain amplitude, W
θ = time, s
ω = annual angular frequency ($\omega = 1.992 \times 10^{-7}$ rad/s)
ϕ = phase lag between total slab heat loss/gain and soil surface temperature, radians

Equation (5) is convenient and flexible because it can be used to calculate the foundation heat loss/gain not only at any time but also at design conditions and for any time period (such as a heating season or 1 year). In particular, the design heat loss/gain load q_{des} for a slab foundation is obtained as follows:

$$q_{des} = q_{mean} + q_{amp} \tag{6}$$

Parameters q_{mean} and q_{amp} are functions of variables such as building dimensions, soil properties, and insulation R-values. Expressions developed by nondimensional analysis allow calculation of q_{mean} and q_{amp}.

The soil conductivity is normalized to form four parameters (U_o, G, H, and D):

$$U_o = \frac{k_s}{(A/P)_{eff,\,b}} \tag{7}$$

where

k_s = soil thermal conductivity, W/(m·K)
P = slab perimeter, m
A = slab area, m²

For mean calculations,

$$(A/P)_{eff,\,b,\,mean} = [1 + b_{eff}(-0.4 + e^{-H_b})](A/P)_b \tag{8}$$

For annual calculations,

$$(A/P)_{eff,\,b,\,amp} = (1 + b_{eff}e^{-H_b})(A/P)_b \tag{9}$$

where

$$H_b = \frac{(A/P)_b}{k_s R_{eq}} \tag{10}$$

$$b_{eff} = \frac{B}{(A/P)_b} \tag{11}$$

where B = basement depth, m (0 m for slab).

$$G = k_s R_{eq}\sqrt{\frac{\omega}{\alpha_s}} \tag{12}$$

where

R_{eq} = equivalent thermal resistance for entire slab, (m²·K)/W
α_s = soil thermal diffusivity, m²/s

For uniform insulation configurations (placed horizontally beneath the slab floor),

$$R_{eq} = R_f + R_i \tag{13}$$

where

R_f = thermal resistance of floor, (m²·K)/W
R_i = thermal resistance of insulation, (m²·K)/W

For partial insulation configurations (both horizontal and vertical),

$$R_{eq} = \frac{R_f}{\left[1 - \left(\frac{c}{A/P}\frac{R_i}{(R_i + R_f)}\right)\right]} \tag{14}$$

Table 2 Coefficients *m* and *a* for Slab-Foundation Heat Transfer Calculations

Insulation Placement	*m*	*a*
Uniform horizontal	0.40	0.25
Partial horizontal	0.34	0.20
Vertical	0.28	0.13

where c = insulation length of slab, m.

$$H = \frac{(A/P)_{eff,b}}{k_s R_{eq}} \quad (15)$$

$$D = \ln\left[(1+H)\left(1+\frac{1}{H}\right)^H\right] \quad (16)$$

The effective heat-transfer coefficients for mean heat flow $U_{eff,mean}$ and heat-flow amplitude $U_{eff,amp}$, W/(m²·K), are

$$U_{eff,mean} = mU_o D \quad (17)$$

$$U_{eff,amp} = aU_o D^{0.16} G^{-0.6} \quad (18)$$

where the dimensionless coefficients *m* and *a* depend on the insulation placement configurations and are provided in Table 2.

The annual-mean slab foundation and basement heat loss/gain can now be defined as

$$q_{mean} = U_{eff,mean} A(t_a - t_r) \quad (19)$$

where

t_a = annual average ambient dry-bulb temperature, °C
t_r = annual average indoor dry-bulb temperature, °C

The heat loss/gain amplitude for slab foundations and basements is

$$q_{amp} = U_{eff,amp} A t_{amp} \quad (20)$$

where t_{amp} = annual amplitude ambient temperature, K.

This simplified model for slab-foundation and basement heat flows provides accurate predictions when *A*/*P* is larger than 0.5 metre. To illustrate the use of the simplified models, two examples are presented: one for a slab-on-grade floor for a building insulated with uniform horizontal insulation, and one for a basement structure insulated with uniform insulation.

Example 1. Calculation for Slab Foundations. Determine the annual mean and annual amplitude of total slab heat loss for the slab foundation illustrated in Figure 2. The building is located in Denver, Colorado.

Solution:

Step 1. Provide the required input data.

Dimensions
Slab width = 10.0 m
Slab length = 15.0 m
Ratio of slab area to slab perimeter, A/P = 3.0 m

102mm thick reinforced concrete slab, thermal resistance R_f = 0.5 (m²·K)/W

Soil Thermal Properties
Soil thermal conductivity k_s = 1.21 W/(m·K)
Soil density ρ = 700 kg/m³
Soil thermal diffusivity $\alpha_s = 5.975 \times 10^{-7}$ m²/s

Insulation
Uniform insulation R-value R_i = 3.52 (m²·K)/W

Temperatures
Indoor temperature t_r = 20°C
Annual average ambient temperature t_a = 6.3°C
Annual amplitude ambient temperature t_{amp} = 20 K
Annual angular frequency $\omega = 1.992 \times 10^{-7}$ rad/s

Step 2. Calculate q_{mean} and q_{amp} values.

The various normalized parameters are first calculated using Equations (7) to (18). Then, the annual mean and amplitude of the foundation slab heat loss/gain are determined using Equations (19) and (20).

$$U_o = \frac{k_s P}{A} = \frac{1.21}{3.0} = 0.4033$$

$$H = \frac{A}{Pk_s R_{eq}} = \frac{3.0}{1.21(0.5+3.52)} = 0.6168$$

$$D = \ln\left[(1+H)\left(1+\frac{1}{H}\right)^H\right] = 1.0748$$

$$G = k_s R_{eq}\sqrt{\frac{\omega}{\alpha_s}} = 1.21(0.5+3.52)\sqrt{\frac{1.992\times10^{-7}}{5.975\times10^{-7}}} = 2.8086$$

Therefore,

$$Q_m = U_{eff,m} A(T_r - T_a)$$
$$= 0.4 \times 0.4033 \times 1.0748 \times 150 \times (20 - 6.3)$$
$$= 357.00 \text{ W}$$

and

$$Q_A = U_{eff,a} A T_a$$
$$= 0.25 \times 0.4033 \times 1.0748^{0.16} \times 2.8086^{-0.6} \times 150 \times 20$$
$$= 165.00 \text{ W}$$

Example 2. Calculation for Basements. Determine the annual mean and amplitude of total basement heat loss for a building located in Denver, Colorado.

Solution:

Step 1. Provide the required input data.

Dimensions
Basement width = 10.0 m
Basement length = 15.0 m
Basement wall height B = 1.5 m
Basement slab and wall total area = 225.0 m²
Ratio of slab and wall area to slab and wall perimeter, $(A/P)_b$ = 3.629 m
102 mm thick reinforced concrete slab, thermal resistance R_f = 0.5 (m²·K)/W

Soil Thermal Properties
Soil thermal conductivity k_s = 1.21 W/(m·K)
Soil thermal diffusivity $\alpha_s = 4.47 \times 10^{-7}$ m²/s

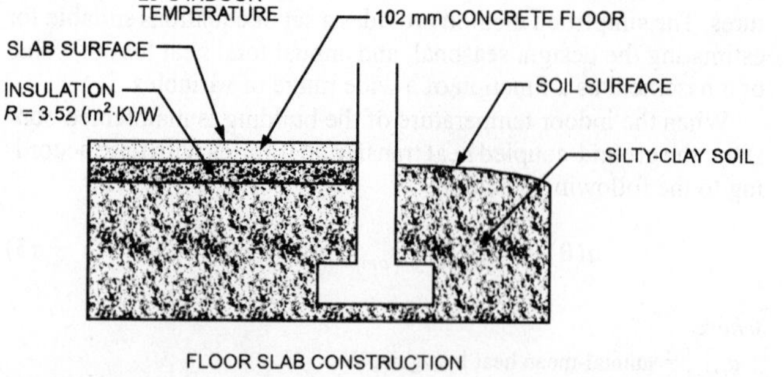

Fig. 2 Slab Foundation for Example 1

Insulation
Uniform insulation R-value $R_i = 1.152$ (m²·K)/W

Temperatures
Indoor temperature, $t_r = 22°C$
Annual average ambient temperature, $t_a = 10°C$
Annual amplitude ambient temperature, $t_{amp} = 12.7$ K
Annual angular frequency, $\omega = 1.992 \times 10^{-7}$ rad/s

Step 2. Calculate q_{mean} and q_{amp} values.

The normalized parameters are first calculated using Equations (7) to (18). Then, the annual mean and amplitude of the basement heat loss are determined using Equations (19) and (20).

$$H_b = \frac{(A/P)_b}{k_s R_{eq}} = \frac{3.629}{1.21(0.5 + 1.152)} = 1.8155$$

$$b_{eff} = \frac{B}{(A/P)_b} = \frac{1.5}{3.629} = 0.4133$$

$$(A/P)_{eff,\,b,\,mean} = [1 + 0.4133 \times (-0.4 + e^{-1.8155})] \times 3.629 = 3.2731$$

$$(A/P)_{eff,\,b,\,amp} = (1 + 0.4131 e^{-1.8139}) \times 11.91 = 12.7120$$

$$U_{o,m} = \frac{k_s}{(A/P)_{eff,\,b,\,mean}} = \frac{1.21}{3.2731} = 0.3697$$

$$U_{o,a} = \frac{k_s}{(A/P)_{eff,\,b,\,mean}} = \frac{1.21}{3.8731} = 0.3124$$

$$H_{mean} = \frac{(A/P)_{eff,\,b,\,mean}}{k_s R_{eq}} = \frac{3.2731}{1.21(0.5 + 1.152)} = 1.6374$$

$$H_{amp} = \frac{(A/P)_{eff,\,b,\,amp}}{k_s R_{eq}} = \frac{3.8731}{1.21(0.5 + 1.152)} = 1.9376$$

$$D_{mean} = \ln\left[(1 + H_{mean})\left(1 + \frac{1}{H_{mean}}\right)^{H_{mean}}\right] = 1.7503$$

$$D_{amp} = \ln\left[(1 + H_{amp})\left(1 + \frac{1}{H_{amp}}\right)^{H_{amp}}\right] = 1.8839$$

$$G = k_s R_{eq}\sqrt{\frac{\omega}{\alpha_s}} = 1.21(0.5 + 1.152)\sqrt{\frac{1.992 \times 10^{-7}}{4.47 \times 10^{-7}}} = 1.3344$$

Therefore,

$$Q_m = U_{eff,\,m} A(T_a - T_r)$$
$$= 0.4 \times 0.3697 \times 1.7503 \times 225 \times (22.0 - 10.0) = 698.85 \text{ W}$$

and

$$Q_a = U_{eff,\,a} A T_a = 0.25 \times 0.3124 \times 1.8839^{0.16}$$
$$\times 1.3344^{-0.6} \times 225 \times 12.7 = 207.72 \text{ W}$$

Table 3 compares results of the simplified method presented here and the more exact interzone temperature profile estimation (ITPE) (Krarti 1994a, 1994b; Krarti et al. 1988a, 1988b).

Table 3 Example 2 Heat Loss per Unit Area for the Simplified and ITPE Methods

Method	Mean (q_{mean}), W	Amplitude (q_{amp}), W
Simplified	699	208
ITPE solution	658	212

SECONDARY SYSTEM COMPONENTS

Secondary HVAC systems generally include all elements of the overall building energy system between a central heating and cooling plant and the building zones. The precise definition depends heavily on the building design. A secondary system typically includes air-handling equipment; air distribution systems with associated ductwork; dampers; fans; and heating, cooling, and humidity-conditioning equipment. They also include liquid distribution systems between the central plant and the zone and air-handling equipment, including piping, valves, and pumps.

Although the exact design of secondary systems varies dramatically among buildings, they are composed of a relatively small set of generic HVAC components. These components include distribution components (e.g., pumps/fans, pipes/ducts, valves/dampers, headers/plenums, fittings) and heat and mass transfer components (e.g., heating coils, cooling and dehumidifying coils, liquid heat exchangers, air heat exchangers, evaporative coolers, steam injectors). Most secondary systems can be described by simply connecting these components to form the complete system.

Energy estimation through computer simulation often mimics the modular construction of secondary systems by using modular simulation elements [e.g., the ASHRAE *HVAC2 Toolkit* (Brandemuehl 1993; Brandemuehl and Gabel 1994), the simulation program TRNSYS (Klein et al. 1994), and Annex 10 activities of the International Energy Agency]. To the extent that the secondary system consumes energy and transfers energy between the building and central plant, an energy analysis can be performed by characterizing the energy consumption of the individual components and the energy transferred among system components. In fact, few secondary components consume energy directly, except fans, pumps, furnaces, direct-expansion air-conditioning package units with gas-fired heaters, and inline heaters. In this chapter, secondary components are divided into two categories: distribution components and heat and mass transfer components.

Fans, Pumps, and Distribution Systems

The distribution system of an HVAC system affects energy consumption in two ways. First, fans and pumps consume electrical energy directly, based on the flow and pressures under which the device operates. Ducts and dampers, or pipes and valves, and the system control strategies affect the flow and pressures at the fan or pump. Second, thermal energy is often transferred to (or from) the fluid by (1) heat transfer through pipes and ducts and (2) electrical input to fans and pumps. Analysis of system components should, therefore, account for both direct electrical energy consumption and thermal energy transfer.

Fan and pump performance are discussed in Chapters 20 and 43 of the 2008 *ASHRAE Handbook—HVAC Systems and Equipment*. In addition, Chapter 21 of this volume covers pressure loss calculations for airflow in ducts and duct fittings. Chapter 22 presents a similar discussion for fluid flow in pipes. Although these chapters do not specifically focus on energy estimation, energy use is governed by the same performance characteristics and engineering relationships. Strictly speaking, performance calculations of a building's fan and air distribution systems require a detailed pressure balance on the entire network. For example, in an air distribution system, airflow through the fan depends on its physical characteristics, operating speed, and pressure differential across the fan. Pressure drop through the duct system depends on duct design, position of all dampers, and airflow through the fan. Interaction between the fan and duct system results in a set of coupled, nonlinear algebraic equations. Models and subroutines for performing these calculations are available in the ASHRAE *HVAC2 Toolkit* (Brandemuehl 1993).

Detailed analysis of a distribution system requires flow and pressure balancing among the components, but nearly all commercially available energy analysis methods approximate the effect of the interactions with part-load performance curves. This eliminates the need to calculate pressure drop through the distribution system at off-design conditions. Part-load curves are often expressed in terms of a **power input ratio** as a function of the part-load ratio, defined as the ratio of part-load flow to design flow:

$$\text{PIR} = \frac{W}{W_{full}} = f_{plr}\left(\frac{Q}{Q_{full}}\right) \tag{21}$$

where

PIR = power input ratio
W = fan motor power at part load, W
W_{full} = fan motor power at full load or design, W
Q = fan airflow rate at part load, cfm
Q_{full} = fan airflow rate at full load or design, cfm
f_{plr} = regression function, typically polynomial

The exact shape of the part-load curve depends on the effect of flow control on the pressure and fan efficiency and may be calculated using a detailed analysis or measured field data. Figure 3 shows the relationship for three typical fan control strategies, as represented in a simulation program (York and Cappiello 1982). In the simulation program, the curves are represented by polynomial regression equations. Models and subroutines for performing these calculations are also available in the ASHRAE *HVAC2 Toolkit* (Brandemuehl 1993).

Figure 4 shows an example of a similar curve for the part-load operation of a fan system in a monitored building (Brandemuehl and Bradford 1999). In this particular case, the fan system represents ten separate air handlers, each with supply and return fans, operating with variable-speed fan control to maintain a set duct static pressure. Notice that, although the shape of the curve is similar to the variable-speed curve of Figure 3, the measured data for this particular system exhibit a more linear relationship between power and flow.

Heat transferred to the airstream because of fan operation increases air temperature. Although fan shaft power directly affects heat transfer, motor inefficiencies also heat the air if the motor is mounted inside the airstream. For pumps, this contribution is typically assumed to be zero.

The following equation provides a convenient and general model to calculate the heat transferred to the fluid:

$$q_{fluid} = [\eta_m + (1 - \eta_m) f_{m,\,loss}]W \tag{22}$$

where

q_{fluid} = heat transferred to fluid, W
$f_{m,\,loss}$ = fraction of motor heat loss transferred to fluid stream, dimensionless (= 1 if fan mounted in airstream, = 0 if fan mounted outside airstream)
W = fan motor power, W
η_m = motor efficiency

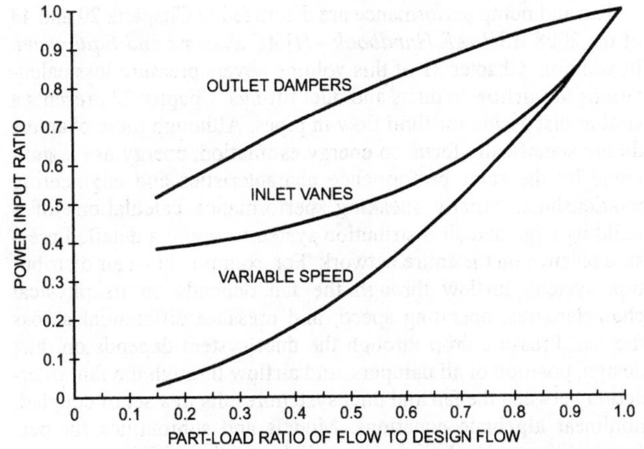

Fig. 3 Part-Load Curves for Typical Fan Operating Strategies
(York and Cappiello 1982)

Heat and Mass Transfer Components

Secondary HVAC systems comprise heat and mass transfer components (e.g., steam-based air-heating coils, chilled-water cooling and dehumidifying coils, shell-and-tube liquid heat exchangers, air-to-air heat exchangers, evaporative coolers, steam injectors). Although these components do not consume energy directly, their thermal performance dictates interactions between building loads and energy-consuming primary components (e.g., chillers, boilers). In particular, secondary component performance determines the entering fluid conditions for primary components, which in turn determine energy efficiencies of primary equipment. Accurate energy calculations cannot be performed without appropriate models of the system heat and mass transfer components.

For example, load on a chiller is typically described as the sum of zone sensible and latent loads, plus any heat gain from ducts, plenums, fans, pumps, and piping. However, the chiller's energy consumption is determined not only by the load but also by the return chilled-water temperature and flow rate. The return water condition is determined by cooling coil performance and part-load operating strategy of the air and water distribution system. The cooling coil might typically be controlled to maintain a constant leaving air temperature by modulating water flow through the coil. In such a scenario, the cooling coil model must be able to calculate the leaving air humidity, water temperature, and water flow rate given the cooling coil design characteristics and entering air temperature and humidity, airflow, and water temperature.

Virtually all building energy simulation programs include, and require, models of heat and mass transfer components. These models are generally relatively simple. Whereas a coil designer might use a detailed tube-by-tube analysis of conduction and convection heat transfer and condensation on fin surfaces to develop an optimal combination of fin and tube geometry, an energy analyst is more interested in determining changes in leaving fluid states as operating conditions vary during the year. In addition, the energy analyst is likely to have limited design data on the equipment and, therefore, requires a model with very few parameters that depend on equipment geometry and detailed design characteristics.

A typical approach to modeling heat and mass transfer components for energy calculations is based on an **effectiveness-NTU heat exchanger model** (Kays and London 1984). The effectiveness-NTU (number of transfer units) model is described in most heat transfer textbooks and briefly discussed in Chapter 4.

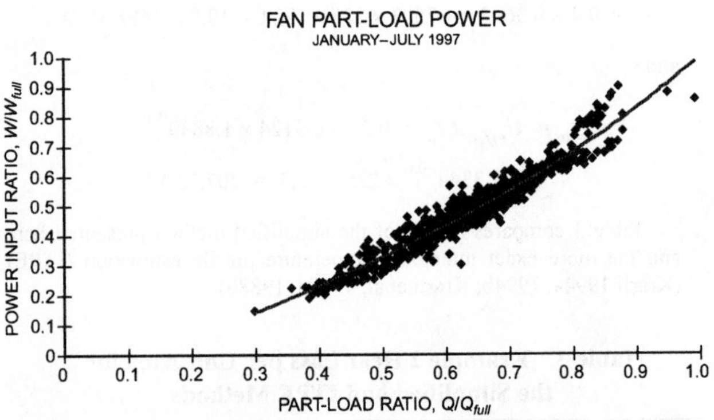

Fig. 4 Fan Part-Load Curve Obtained from Measured Field Data under ASHRAE RP-823
(Brandemuehl and Bradford 1999)

It is particularly appropriate for describing leaving fluid conditions when entering fluid conditions and equipment design characteristics are known. Also, this model requires only a single parameter to describe the characteristics of the exchanger: the overall transfer coefficient *UA*, which can be determined from limited design performance data.

Because the classical effectiveness methods were developed for sensible heat exchangers, they are used to perform energy calculations for a variety of sensible heat exchangers in HVAC systems. For typical finned-tube air-heating coils, the crossflow configuration with both fluid streams unmixed is most appropriate. The same configuration typically applies to air-to-air heat exchangers. For liquid-to-liquid exchangers, tube-in-tube equipment can be modeled as parallel or counterflow, depending on flow directions; shell-and-tube equipment can be modeled as either counter- or crossflow, depending on the extent of baffling and the number of tube passes.

The energy analyst must determine the *UA* to describe the operations of a specific heat exchanger. There are typically two approaches to determine this important parameter: direct calculation and manufacturers' data. Given detailed information about the materials, geometry, and construction of the heat exchanger, fundamental heat transfer principles can be applied to calculate the overall heat transfer coefficient. However, the method most appropriate for energy estimation is using manufacturers' performance data or direct measurements of installed performance. In reporting the design performance of a heat exchanger, a manufacturer typically gives the heat transfer rate under various operating conditions, with operating conditions described in terms of entering fluid flow rates and temperatures. The effectiveness and *UA* can be calculated from the given heat transfer rate and entering fluid conditions.

Example 3. An energy analyst seeks evaluate a hot-water heating system that includes a hot-water heating coil. The energy analysis program uses an effectiveness-NTU model of the coil and requires the *UA* of the coil as an input parameter. Although detailed information on the coil geometry and heat transfer surfaces is not available, the manufacturer states that the one-row hot-water heating coil delivers 240 kW of heat under the following design conditions:

Design Performance
Entering water temperature $t_{hi} = 80°C$
Water mass flow rate $\dot{m}_h = 5.0$ kg/s
Entering air temperature $t_{ci} = 20°C$
Air mass flow rate $\dot{m}_c = 8.0$ kg/s
Design heat transfer $q = 240$ kW

Solution: First determine the heat exchanger *UA* from design data, then use *UA* to predict performance at off-design conditions. Effectiveness-NTU relationships are used for both steps. The key assumption is that the *UA* is constant for both operating conditions.

a) An examination of flow rates and fluid specific heats allows calculation of the hot-fluid capacity rate C_h and the cold-fluid capacity rate C_c at design conditions, and the capacity rate ratio *Z*.

$$C_h = (\dot{m}c_p)_h = (5.0)(4.195) = 20.97 \text{ kW/K}$$

$$C_c = (\dot{m}c_p)_c = (8.0)(1.007) = 8.05 \text{ kW/K}$$

$$C_{max} = C_h \qquad C_{min} = C_c$$

$$Z = \frac{C_{min}}{C_{max}} = 0.384$$

where c_p is specific heat and c_{max} and c_{min} are the larger and smaller of the capacity rates, respectively,

b) Effectiveness can be directly calculated from the heat transfer definition.

$$\varepsilon = \frac{(t_{co} - t_{ci})}{(t_{hi} - t_{ci})} = \frac{q/C_c}{(t_{hi} - t_{ci})} = \frac{240/8.05}{(80 - 20)} = 0.497$$

where t_{co} is the leaving air temperature.

c) The effectiveness-NTU relationships for a crossflow heat exchanger with both fluids unmixed allow calculation of the effectiveness in terms of the capacity rate ratio *Z* and the NTU [the relationships are available from most heat transfer textbooks and, specifically, in Kays and London (1984)]. Given the effectiveness and capacity rate ratio, NTU = 0.804.

d) The heat transfer *UA* is then determined from the definition of the NTU.

$$UA = C_{min}\text{NTU} = (8.05)(0.804) = 6.472 \text{ kW/K}$$

Application to Cooling and Dehumidifying Coils

Analysis of air-cooling and dehumidifying coils requires coupled, nonlinear heat and mass transfer relationships. These relationships form the basis for all HVAC components with moisture transfer, including cooling coils, cooling towers, air washers, and evaporative coolers. Although the complex heat and mass transfer theory presented in many textbooks is often required for cooling coil design, simpler models based on effectiveness concepts are usually more appropriate for energy estimation. For example, the bypass factor is a form of effectiveness in the approach of the leaving air temperature to the apparatus dew-point, or coil surface, temperature.

The effectiveness-NTU method is typically developed and applied in analysis of sensible heat exchangers, but it can also be used to analyze other types of exchangers, such as cooling and dehumidifying coils, that couple heat and mass transfer. By redefining the state variables, capacity rates, and overall exchange coefficient of these enthalpy exchangers, the effectiveness concept may be used to calculate heat transfer rates and leaving fluid states. For sensible heat exchangers, the state variable is temperature, the capacity is the product of mass flow and fluid specific heat, and the overall transfer coefficient is the conventional overall heat transfer coefficient. For cooling and dehumidifying coils, the state variable becomes moist air enthalpy, the capacity has units of mass flow, and the overall heat transfer coefficient is modified to reflect enthalpy exchange. This approach is the basis for models by Brandemuehl (1993), Braun (1988), Elmahdy and Mitalas (1977), and Threlkeld (1970). The same principles also underlie the coil model described in Chapter 22 of the 2008 *ASHRAE Handbook—HVAC Systems and Equipment*.

The effectiveness model is based on the observation that, for a given set of entering air and liquid conditions, the heat and mass transfer are bounded by thermodynamic maximum values. Figure 5 shows the limits for leaving air states on a psychrometric chart. Specifically, the leaving chilled-water temperature cannot be warmer than the entering air temperature, and the leaving air temperature and humidity cannot be lower than the conditions of saturated moist air at the temperature of the entering chilled water.

Figure 5 also shows that performance of a cooling coil requires evaluating two different effectivenesses to identify the leaving air temperature and humidity. An overall effectiveness can be used to describe the approach of the leaving air enthalpy to the minimum possible value. An air-side effectiveness, related to the coil bypass factor, describes the approach of the leaving air temperature to the effective wet-coil surface temperature.

Effectiveness analysis is accomplished for wet coils by establishing a common state variable for both the moist air and liquid streams. As implied by the lower limit of the entering chilled-water temperature, this common state variable is the moist air enthalpy. In other words, all liquid and coil temperatures are transformed to the enthalpy of saturated moist air at the liquid or coil temperature. Changes in liquid temperature can similarly be expressed in terms of changes in saturated moist air enthalpy through a saturation specific heat $c_{p,sat}$ defined by the following:

$$c_{p,sat} = \frac{\Delta h_{l,sat}}{\Delta t_l} \tag{23}$$

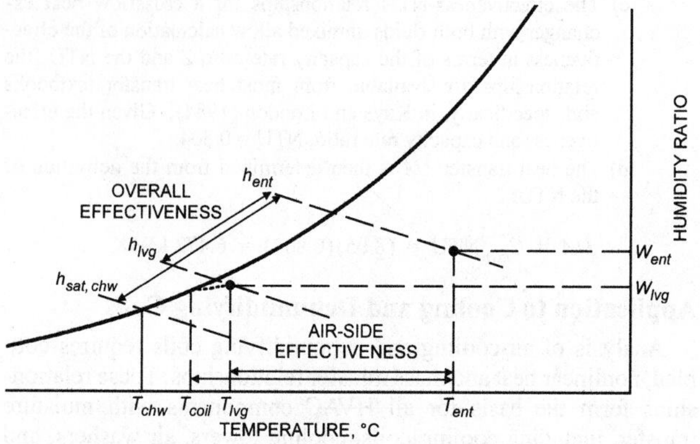

Fig. 5 Psychrometric Schematic of Cooling Coil Processes

Using the definition of Equation (23), the basic effectiveness relationships discussed in Chapter 4 can be written as

$$q = C_a(h_{a,ent} - h_{a,lvg}) = C_l(h_{l,sat,lvg} - h_{l,sat,ent}) \quad (24)$$

$$q = \varepsilon C_{min}(h_{a,ent} - h_{l,sat,ent}) \quad (25)$$

$$C_a = \dot{m}_a \quad (26)$$

$$C_l = \frac{(\dot{m}c_p)_l}{c_{p,sat}} \quad (27)$$

$$C_{min} = \min(C_a, C_l) \quad (28)$$

where

q = heat transfer from air to water, W
C = fluid capacity, kg/h
$\dot{m}_a$ = dry air mass flow rate, kg/s
$\dot{m}_l$ = liquid mass flow rate, kg/s
$c_{p,l}$ = liquid specific heat, kJ/(kg·K)
$c_{p,sat}$ = saturation specific heat, defined by Equation (23), kJ/(kg·K)
h_a = enthalpy of moist air, kJ/kg
$h_{l,sat}$ = enthalpy of saturated moist air at the temperature of the liquid, kJ/kg

The cooling coil effectiveness of Equation (25) is defined, then, as the ratio of moist air enthalpies in Figure 5. As with sensible heat exchangers, effectiveness is also a function of the physical coil characteristics and can be obtained by modeling the coil as a counterflow heat exchanger. However, because heat transfer calculations are performed based on enthalpies, the overall transfer coefficient must be based on enthalpy potential rather than temperature potential. The enthalpy-based heat transfer coefficient UA_h is related to the conventional temperature-based coefficient by the specific heat:

$$q = UA\Delta t = UA_h\Delta h$$
$$UA_h = \frac{UA\Delta t}{\Delta h} = \frac{UA}{c_p} \quad (29)$$

A similar analysis can be performed to evaluate the air-side effectiveness, which identifies the leaving air temperature. Whereas the overall enthalpy-based effectiveness is based on an overall heat transfer coefficient between the chilled water and air, air-side effectiveness is based on a heat transfer coefficient between the coil surface and air.

As with sensible heat exchangers, the overall heat transfer coefficients UA can be determined either from direct calculation from coil properties or from manufacturers' performance data. A sensible heat exchanger is modeled with a single effectiveness and can be described by a single parameter UA, but a wet cooling and dehumidifying coil requires two parameters to describe the two effectivenesses shown in Figure 5. These parameters are the internal and external UAs: one describes heat transfer between the chilled water and the air-side surface through the pipe wall, and the other between the surface and the moist air. UA values can be determined from the sensible and latent capacity of a cooling coil at a single rating condition. A significant advantage of the effectiveness-NTU method is that the component can be described with as little as one measured data point or one manufacturer's design calculation.

PRIMARY SYSTEM COMPONENTS

Primary HVAC systems consume energy and deliver heating and cooling to a building, usually through secondary systems. Primary equipment generally includes chillers, boilers, cooling towers, cogeneration equipment, and plant-level thermal-storage equipment. In particular, primary equipment generally represents the major energy-consuming equipment of a building, so accurate characterization of building energy use relies on accurate modeling of primary equipment energy consumption.

Modeling Strategies

Energy consumption characteristics of primary equipment generally depend on equipment design, load conditions, environmental conditions, and equipment control strategies. For example, chiller performance depends on the basic equipment design features (e.g., heat exchange surfaces, compressor design), temperatures and flow through the condenser and evaporator, and methods for controlling the chiller at different loads and operating conditions (e.g., inlet guide vane control on centrifugal chillers to maintain leaving chilled-water temperature set point). In general, these variables vary constantly and require calculations on an hourly basis.

Regression Models. Although many secondary components (e.g., heat exchangers, valves) are readily described by fundamental engineering principles, the complex nature of most primary equipment has discouraged the use of first-principle models for energy calculations. Instead, energy consumption characteristics of primary equipment have traditionally been modeled using simple equations developed by regression analysis of manufacturers' published design data. Because published data are often available only for full-load design conditions, additional correction functions are used to correct the full-load data to part-load conditions. The functional form of the regression equations and correction functions takes many forms, including exponentials, Fourier series, and, most of the time, second- or third-order polynomials. Selection of an appropriate functional form depends on the behavior of the equipment. In some cases, energy consumption is calculated using direct interpolation from tables of data, but this often requires excessive data input and computer memory.

The typical approach to modeling primary equipment in energy simulation programs is to assume the following functional form for equipment power consumption:

$$P = \text{PIR} \times \text{Load}$$
$$\text{PIR} = \text{PIR}_{nom} f_1(t_a, t_b, \ldots) f_2(\text{PLR}) \quad (30)$$

$$C_{avail} = C_{nom} f_3(t_a, t_b, \ldots)$$
$$\text{PLR} = \frac{\text{Load}}{C_{avail}} \quad (31)$$

where

P = equipment power, kW
PIR = energy input ratio
PIR_{nom} = energy input ratio under nominal full-load conditions

Load = power delivered to load, kW
C_{avail} = available equipment capacity, kW
C_{nom} = nominal equipment capacity, kW
f_1 = function relating full-load power at off-design conditions (t_a, t_b, ...) to full-load power at design conditions
f_2 = fraction full-load power function, relating part-load power to full-load power
f_3 = function relating available capacity at off-design conditions (t_a, t_b, ...) to nominal capacity
t_a, t_b = various operating temperatures that affect power
PLR = part-load ratio

The part-load ratio is the ratio of the load to the available equipment capacity at given off-design operating conditions. Like the power, the available, or full-load, capacity is a function of operating conditions.

The particular forms of off-design functions f_1 and f_3 depend on the specific type of primary equipment. For example, for fossil-fuel boilers, full-load capacity and power (or fuel use) can be affected by thermal losses to ambient temperature. However, these off-design functions are typically considered to be unity in most building simulation programs. For chillers, both capacity and power are affected by condenser and evaporator temperatures, which are often characterized in terms of their secondary fluids. For direct-expansion air-cooled chillers, operating temperatures are typically the wet-bulb temperature of air entering the evaporator and the dry-bulb temperature of air entering the condenser. For liquid chillers, the temperatures are usually the leaving chilled-water temperature and the entering condenser water temperature.

As an example, consider the performance of a direct-expansion (DX) packaged single-zone rooftop unit. The nominal rated performance of these units is typically given for an outdoor air temperature of 35°C and evaporator entering coil conditions of 26.7°C db and 19.4°C wb. However, performance changes as outdoor temperature and entering coil conditions vary. To account for these effects, the DOE-2.1E simulation program expresses the off-design functions f_1 and f_3 with biquadratic functions of the outdoor dry-bulb temperature and the coil entering wet-bulb temperature.

$$f_1(t_{wb,ent}, t_{oa}) = a_0 + a_1 t_{wb,ent} + a_2 t_{wb,ent}^2 + a_3 t_{oa} + a_4 t_{oa}^2 + a_5 t_{wb,ent} t_{oa} \quad (32)$$

$$f_3(t_{wb,ent}, t_{oa}) = c_0 + c_1 t_{wb,ent} + c_2 t_{wb,ent}^2 + c_3 t_{oa} + c_4 t_{oa}^2 + c_5 t_{wb,ent} t_{oa} \quad (33)$$

The constants in Equations (32) and (33) are given in Table 4.

The fraction full-load power function f_2 represents the change in equipment efficiency at part-load conditions and depends heavily on the control strategies used to match load and capacity. Figure 6 shows several possible shapes of these functional relationships. (Notice that these curves are similar to the fan part-load curves of Figure 3.) Curve 1 represents equipment with constant efficiency, independent of load. Curve 2 represents equipment that is most efficient in the middle of its operating range. Curve 3 represents equipment that is most efficient at full load. Note that these types of curves apply to both boilers and chillers.

First-Principle Models. As with the secondary components, engineering first principles can also be used to develop models of primary equipment. Gordon and Ng (1994, 1995), Gordon et al. (1995), Lebrun et al. (1999), and others have sought to develop such models in which unknown model parameters are extracted from measured or published manufacturers' data.

The energy analyst often must choose the appropriate model for the job. For example, a complex boiler model is not appropriate if the boiler operates at virtually constant efficiency. Similarly, a regression-based model might be appropriate when the user has a

Table 4 Correlation Coefficients for Off-Design Relationships

Corr.	0	1	2	3	4	5
f_1	−1.063931	0.0306584	0.0001269	0.0154213	0.0000497	0.0002096
f_3	0.8740302	0.0011416	0.0001711	−0.002957	0.0000102	0.0000592

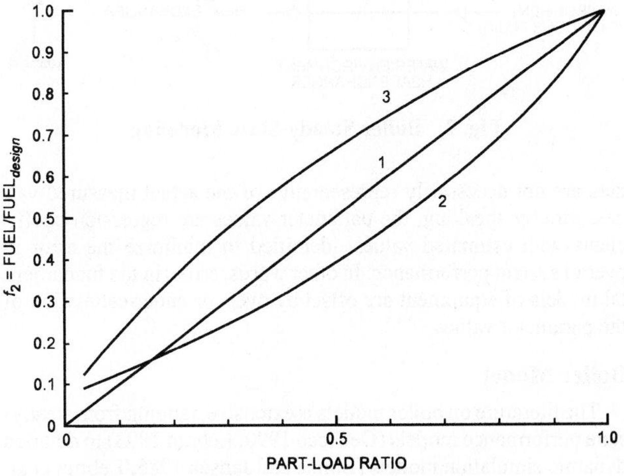

Fig. 6 Possible Part-Load Power Curves

full dataset of reliable in-situ measurements of the plant. However, first-principle physical models generally have several advantages over pure regression models:

- Physical models allow confident extrapolation outside the range of available data.
- Regression is still required to obtain values for unknown physical parameters. However, the values of these parameters usually have physical significance, which can be used to estimate default parameter values, diagnose errors in data analysis through checks for realistic parameter values, and even evaluate potential performance improvements.
- The number of unknown parameters is generally much smaller than the number of unknown coefficients in the typical regression model. For example, the standard ARI compressor model requires as many as 30 coefficients, 10 each for regressions of capacity, power, and refrigerant flow. By comparison, a physical compressor model may have as few as four or five unknown parameters. Thus, physical models require fewer measured data.
- Data on part-load operation of chillers and boilers are notoriously difficult to obtain. Part-load corrections often represent the greatest uncertainty in the regression models, while causing the greatest effect on annual energy predictions. By comparison, physical models of full-load operation often allow direct extension to part-load operation with little additional required data.

Physical models of primary HVAC equipment are generally based on fundamental engineering analysis and found in many HVAC textbooks, but the models described here are specifically based on the work of Bourdouxhe et al. (1994a, 1994b, 1994c) in developing the ASHRAE *HVAC 1 Toolkit* (Lebrun et al. 1999). Each elementary component's behavior is characterized by a limited number of physical parameters, such as heat exchanger heat transfer area or centrifugal compressor impeller blade angle. Values of these parameters are identified, or tuned, based on regression fits of overall performance compared to measured or published data.

Although physical models are based on physical characteristics, values obtained through a regression analysis of manufacturers'

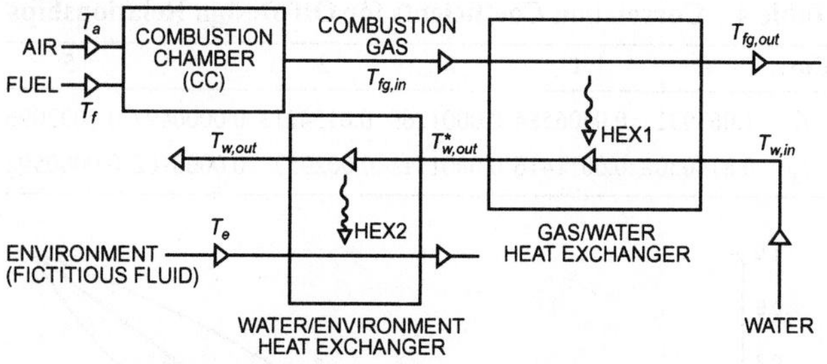

Fig. 7 Boiler Steady-State Modeling

data are not necessarily representative of the actual measured values. Strictly speaking, the parameter values are regression coefficients with estimated values, identified to minimize the error in overall system performance. In other words, errors in the fundamental models of equipment are offset by over- or under-estimation of the parameter values.

Boiler Model

The literature on boiler models is extensive, ranging from steady-state performance models (DeCicco 1990; Lebrun 1993) to detailed dynamic simulation models (Bonne and Jansen 1985; Lebrun et al. 1985), to a combination of these two schemes (Laret 1991; Malmström et al. 1985).

Dynamic models are meant to describe transient behavior of the equipment. Consequently, these models need to accurately capture the combustion process and the complex energy exchange that occurs inside the combustion chamber. Usually, this kind of model is very detailed and demanding to formulate and use. Hence, a dynamic boiler model should be considered only in more complex situations (e.g., large boilers in large buildings, district heating systems, cogeneration systems), where a complete, detailed representation of heat distribution, emission, and operation and control under varying external conditions is warranted.

Although all major variables of a boiler may vary with load and environmental conditions, assuming steady-state conditions during burner-on and burner-off times results in a relationship between input and output variables that is much simpler than those in dynamic models. Model evaluation against actual measurements shows that the steady-state model can be sufficiently accurate for energy calculations over relatively long time periods (e.g., weeks or months) with regard to the measuring accuracy.

In steady-state modeling, it is assumed that, during continuous operation, the boiler can be disaggregated into one adiabatic combustion chamber and two heat exchangers (Figure 7). The following fluid streams flow across the

- Combustion chamber (CC): air (subscript *a*) and fuel (subscript *f*) streams at the inlet, and combustion gas (subscript *fg*) at the outlet
- First heat exchanger (HEX1): combustion gas outlet and supply water streams (subscript *in*)
- Second heat exchanger (HEX2): heated water stream (subscript *out*) and a fluid representing the environment

The boiler model is characterized by three parameters, which represent the following heat transfer coefficients:

- UA_{ge}: between the flue gas and the environment in CC
- UA_{gw}: between the flue gas and the water in HEX1
- UA_{we}: between the water and the environment in HEX2

Primary model inputs to the model are the leaving water set-point temperature ($T_{w,out}$) and control model and the load characteristics (i.e., entering water temperature $T_{w,in}$ and water flow rate $\dot{m}_w$). Secondary model inputs include the air, fuel, and ambient temperatures (T_a, T_f, and T_e) as well as the fuel/air ratio *f*.

Modern boilers are airtight, so there is almost no air circulation across the combustion chamber when the burner is off. In this case, the boiler behaves as a simple water/environment heat exchanger (i.e., HEX1 and HEX2 are combined) and the thermal model is reduced to that of a simple heat exchanger.

Combustion Chamber Model. Mathematical description of this model allows the flue gas mass flow rate and enthalpy $h_{fg,in1}$ (in J/kg$_{fg}$) at the flue gas/water heat exchanger (HEX1) inlet to be calculated. The calculated flue gas mass flow rate is not necessarily the one associated with the specified value of the flue gas/water heat transfer coefficient/area product. Therefore, the following empirical relationship is used to adjust the value of this coefficient to the calculated value of the flue gas mass flow rate.

$$\dot{m}_{fg} = 1 + \frac{1}{f}\dot{m}_f \tag{34}$$

$$h_{fg,in} = \frac{h_{fg,in1}}{1 + \frac{1}{f}} \tag{35}$$

$$(UA_{gw})_{calc} = UA_{gw}\left[\frac{\dot{m}_{fg}}{(\dot{m}_{fg})_{rated}}\right]^{0.65} \tag{36}$$

where

$h_{fg,in1}$ = known function of composition of combustion products and flue gas temperature at inlet of gas/water heat exchanger, J/kg$_{fg}$

$h_{fg,in}$ = gas enthalpy at outlet of gas/water heat exchanger, J/kg$_f$

$(\dot{m}_{fg})_{rated}$=flue gas mass flow rate associated with specified value of gas/water heat transfer coefficient/area product, kg/s

Flue Gas-Water Heat Exchanger Model. The first step is to calculate the heat transfer rate q_{gw} across HEX1:

$$q_{gw} = \varepsilon_{gw}C_{fg}(T_{fg,in} - T_{w,in}) \tag{37}$$

where

$C_{fg} = c_{p,fg}\dot{m}_{fg}$ = heat capacity flow rate of flue gas

$\varepsilon_{gw} = \dfrac{1-\exp[-\text{NTU}(1-C)]}{1-C\exp[-\text{NTU}(1-C)]}$ = effectiveness for HEX1

For a counterflow heat exchanger,

$$\text{NTU} = \frac{UA_{gw}}{C_{fg}} \quad \text{and} \quad C = \frac{C_{fg}}{C_w} \tag{38}$$

where $C_{fg} \le C_w$ and $C_w = c_{p,w}\dot{m}_w$.

The temperature of flue gas leaving HEX1 ($T_{fg,out}$) can be calculated from

$$\varepsilon_{gw}(T_{fg,in} - T_{w,in}) = (T_{fg,in} - T_{fg,out}) \tag{39}$$

Other unknowns need also to be calculated. In HEX1, heat is transferred from hot flue gas to the water

$$q_{gw} = C_w(T^*_{w,out} - T_{w,in}) \tag{40}$$

from which the temperature of water leaving HEX1 and entering HEX2 is

$$T^*_{w,out} = \frac{q_{gw}}{C_w} + T_{w,in} \tag{41}$$

Water-Environment Heat Exchanger Model. In HEX2,

$$\varepsilon_{we}(T^*_{w,out} - T_e) = (T^*_{w,out} - T_{w,out}) \quad (42)$$

where $\varepsilon_{we} = 1 - \exp(-UA_{we}/C_w)$. Then water temperature at the outlet of HEX2 is

$$T_{w,out} = T_e + \frac{T^*_{w,out} - T_e}{\exp\left(\frac{UA_{we}}{C_w}\right)} \quad (43)$$

Consequently, heat loss from hot water in HEX2 is

$$q_{we} = C_w(T^*_{w,out} - T_{w,out}) \quad (44)$$

Useful heat given to the water stream is

$$q_b = q_{gw} - q_{we} \quad (45)$$

Finally, boiler efficiency is given by

$$\eta = \frac{q_b}{\dot{m}_f \times \text{FLHV}} \quad (46)$$

where FLHV is fuel lower heating value.

The main outputs of this model are

- The "useful" boiler output: its leaving water temperature (to be compared with its set point), or its corresponding "useful" power (i.e., net rate of heat transfer q_b by the heated water)
- Its energy consumption: burner fuel flow rate $\dot{m}_f$ or corresponding efficiency η

Secondary model outputs include

- Flue gas temperature, specific heat, and corresponding enthalpy flow in the chimney
- Environmental loss q_{we} in boiler room

The three-parameter model allows simulation of boilers using most conventional fuels under a wide range of operating conditions with less than 1% error. A two-exchanger model appears to be flexible enough to describe boiler behavior at different load conditions and water temperatures. This simple model is stated to accurately predict the sensitivity of a boiler to variations of burner fuel rate and airflow rates as well as water/environment losses.

Vapor Compression Chiller Models

Figure 8 shows a schematic of a vapor compression chiller. In this case, the components include two heat exchangers, an expansion valve, and a compressor with a motor and transmission. Chiller components are linked through the refrigerant. For energy estimating, a simplified approach is sufficient to represent the refrigerant as a "perfect" fluid with fictitious property values. That is, refrigerant liquid is modeled as incompressible, and vapor properties are described by ideal gas laws with effective average values of property parameters, such as specific heat.

Condenser and Evaporator Modeling. Both condensers and evaporators are modeled as classical heat exchangers. The two heat exchangers are each assumed to have a constant overall heat transfer coefficient. In addition, the models used in chiller systems suffer from one additional assumption: the refrigerant fluid is assumed to be isothermal for both heat exchangers, which effectively ignores the superheated and subcooled regions of the heat exchanger. The assumption of an isothermal refrigerant is particularly crude for the condenser, which sees very high refrigerant

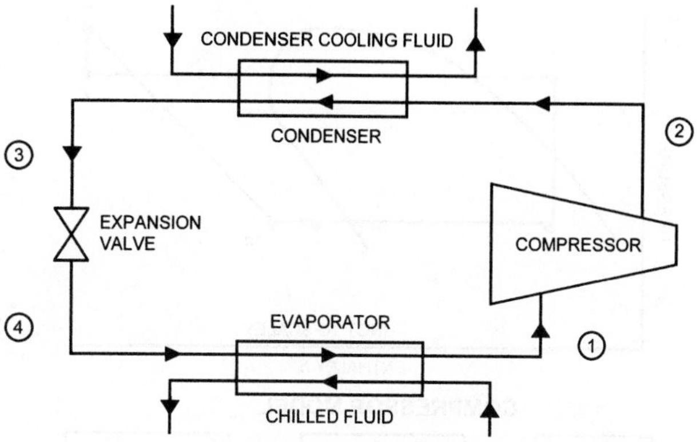

Fig. 8 Chiller Model Using Elementary Components
(See Figure 10 for description of points 1 to 4)

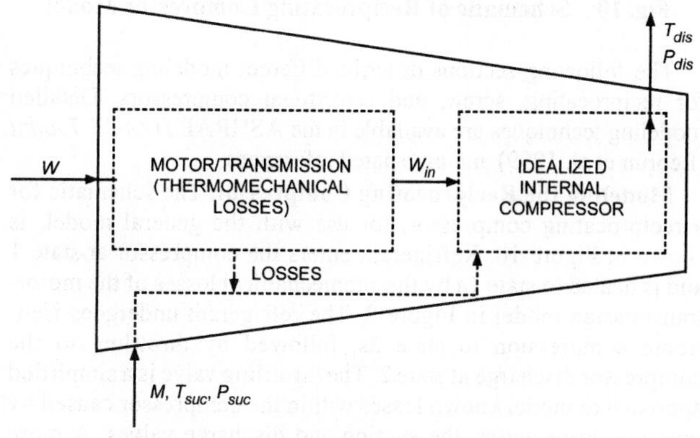

Fig. 9 General Schematic of Compressor

temperatures from the compressor discharge; thus, the mean temperature difference between refrigerant and water in the heat exchanger is significantly underestimated. Fortunately, this systematic error is offset by a significant overestimate of the corresponding heat transfer coefficient.

General Compressor Modeling. Modeling real compressors requires description of many thermomechanical losses (e.g., heat loss, fluid friction, throttling losses in valves, motor and transmission inefficiencies) within the compressor. Some of these losses can be modeled within the compressor, but others are too complex or unknown to describe in a model for energy calculations.

The general approach used here for compressor modeling is described in Figure 9. The compressor is described by two distinct internal elements: an idealized internal compressor and a motor-transmission element to account for unknown losses. Schematically, the motor-transmission subsystem represents an inefficiency of energy conversion. Losses from these inefficiencies are assumed to heat the fluid before compression. Mathematically, it can be modeled by the following linear relationship:

$$W = W_{lo} + (1 + \alpha)W_{int} \quad (47)$$

where

W = electrical power for a hermetic or semihermetic compressor, or shaft power for an open compressor
W_{lo} = constant electromechanical loss
W_{int} = idealized internal compressor power (depends on type of compressor)
α = proportional power loss factor

W_{lo} and α are empirical parameters determined by performing a regression analysis on manufacturers' data. Other parameters are also required to model W_{int}, depending on the type of compressor.

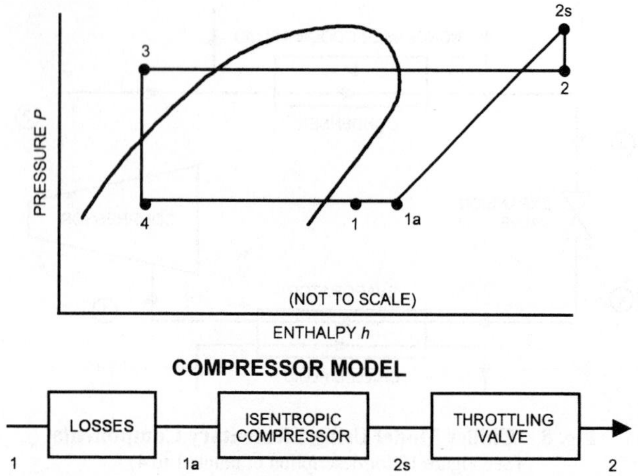

Fig. 10 Schematic of Reciprocating Compressor Model

The following sections describe different modeling techniques for reciprocating, screw, and centrifugal compressors. Detailed modeling techniques are available in the ASHRAE *HVAC 1 Toolkit* (Lebrun et al. 1999) and associated references.

Modeling the Reciprocating Compressor. The schematic for a reciprocating compressor, for use with the general model, is shown in Figure 10. Refrigerant enters the compressor at state 1 and is heated to state 1a by thermomechanical losses of the motor-transmission model in Figure 9. The refrigerant undergoes isentropic compression to state 2s, followed by throttling to the compressor discharge at state 2. The throttling valve is a simplified approach to model known losses within the compressor caused by pressure drops across the suction and discharge valves. A more accurate model might include pressure losses at both the compressor inlet and outlet, but analysis of compressor data reveals that the simpler model is adequate for modeling of typical reciprocating compressors. In fact, many compressors can be adequately modeled with no throttling valve at all.

The refrigerant flow rate through the system must be determined to predict chiller and compressor performance. In general, volumetric flow depends on the pressure difference across the compressor. The compressor refrigerant flow rate is a decreasing function of the pressure ratio because of vapor re-expansion in the clearance volume. With refrigerant vapor modeled as an ideal gas, the volumetric flow rate is given by

$$V = V_s\left[1 + C_f - C_f\left(\frac{p_{ex}}{p_{suc}}\right)^{1/\gamma}\right] \tag{48}$$

where

V = volumetric flow rate
V_s = swept volumetric flow rate (geometric displacement of the compressor)
C_f = clearance factor = $V_{clearance}/V_s$
p_{ex}/p_{suc} = cylinder pressure ratio
γ = specific heat ratio

V_s and C_f must be identified using data for the actual reciprocating compressor.

Although the models discussed apply to full-load operation, Equation (48) is also valid at part-load conditions. However, the internal power use can be different at part load depending on the particular strategy for capacity modulation, such as on-off cycling, cylinder unloading, hot-gas bypass, or variable-speed motor. In most cases, simple physical models can be developed to describe these methods, which generally vary the swept volumetric rate. Additional thermomechanical losses can also be modeled but often involve additional parameters. For example, the effect of cylinder unloading can be modeled by the following relationship:

$$W_{int} = W_s + \left(1 - \frac{N_c}{N_{c,FL}}\right)W_{pump} \tag{49}$$

where

W_{int} = idealized internal compressor power
N_c = number of cylinders in use
$N_{c,FL}$ = number of cylinders in use in full-load regime
W_{pump} = internal power of the compressor when all the cylinders are unloaded (pumping power)
W_s = isentropic power

The variable W_{pump} characterizes the part-load regime of the reciprocating compressor, and is assumed to be constant throughout the entire part-load range.

In summary, a realistic physical model of a reciprocating compressor, covering both full- and part-load operations, can be developed based on six parameters: the constant and proportional loss terms of the motor-transmission model W_{lo} and α, the swept volumetric flow rate V_s of the compressor cylinders, the cylinder clearance volume factor C_f, the fictitious exhaust valve flow area A_{ex}, and the zero-load pumping power of the unloaded compressor W_{pump}. The entire chiller can then be modeled with two additional parameters for the overall heat transfer coefficients of the condenser and evaporator.

Modeling Other Compressors and Chillers. From a modeling perspective, the thermodynamic processes of a screw compressor are similar to those of a reciprocating compressor. Physically, the screw compressor transports an initial volumetric flow rate of refrigerant vapor to a higher pressure and density by squeezing it into a smaller space. A realistic physical model of a variable-volume-ratio, twin-screw compressor, covering both full- and part-load operations, can be developed based on five parameters: the (1) constant and (2) proportional loss terms of the motor-transmission model of Equation (47), (3) swept volumetric flow rate of the compressor screw, (4) internal leakage area, and (5) pumped pressure differential for diverted flow at part load (Lebrun et al. 1999). The entire chiller can then be modeled with two additional parameters for the overall heat transfer coefficients of the condenser and evaporator.

An idealized internal model of a centrifugal compressor, to be used in conjunction with Equation (47) and Figure 9, can be based on an ideal analysis of a single-stage compressor composed of an isentropic impeller and isentropic diffuser. In addition to the thermomechanical loss parameters of Equation (47), only three additional parameters are required: the (1) peripheral speed of the impeller, (2) vane inclination at the impeller exhaust, and (3) impeller exhaust area.

The refrigerant cycle of an absorption chiller is the same as for a vapor compression cycle, except for the absorption-generation subsystem in place of the compressor (see Chapter 2 for more information). The absorption-generation subsystem includes an absorber, steam-fired generator, recovery heat exchanger, pump, and control valve. All components except the pump and control valve can be modeled as heat exchangers.

Cooling Tower Model

A cooling tower is used in primary systems to reject heat from the chiller condenser. Controls typically manage tower fans and pumps to maintain a desired water temperature entering the condenser. Like cooling and dehumidifying coils in secondary systems, cooling tower performance has a strong influence on the chiller's energy consumption. In addition, tower fans consume electrical energy directly.

Fundamentally, a cooling tower is a direct contact heat and mass exchanger. Equations describing the basic processes are given in

Chapter 6 and in many HVAC textbooks. Chapter 39 of the 2008 *ASHRAE Handbook—HVAC Systems and Equipment* describes the specific performance of cooling towers. Performance subroutines are also available in Klein et al. (1994) and Lebrun et al. (1999).

For energy calculations, cooling tower performance is typically described in terms of the outdoor wet-bulb temperature, temperature drop of water flowing through the tower (range), and difference between leaving water and air wet-bulb temperatures (approach). Simple models assume constant range and approach, but more sophisticated models use rating performance data to relate leaving water temperature to the outdoor wet-bulb temperature, water flow, and airflow. Simple cooling tower models, such as those based on a single overall transfer coefficient that can be directly inferred from a single tower rating point, are often appropriate for energy calculations.

SYSTEM MODELING

OVERALL MODELING STRATEGIES

In developing a simulation model for building energy prediction, two basic issues must be considered: (1) modeling components or subsystems and (2) overall modeling strategy. Modeling components, discussed in the section on Component Modeling and Loads, results in sets of equations describing the individual components. The overall modeling strategy refers to the **sequence** and **procedures** used to solve these equations. The accuracy of results and the computer resources required to achieve these results depend on the modeling strategy.

In most building energy programs, load models are executed for every space for every hour of the simulation period. (Practically all models use 1 h as the time step, which excludes any information on phenomena occurring in a shorter time span.) The load model is followed by running models for every secondary system, one at a time, for every hour of the simulation. Finally, the plant simulation model is executed again for the entire period. Each sequential execution processes the fixed output of the preceding step.

This procedure is illustrated in Figure 11. Solid lines represent data passed from one model to the next; dashed lines represent information, usually provided by the user, about one model passed to the preceding model. For example, the system information consists of a piecewise-linear function of zone temperature that gives the system capacity.

Because of this loads-systems-plants sequence, certain phenomena cannot be modeled precisely. For example, if the heat balance method for computing loads is used, and some component in the system simulation model cannot meet the load, the program can only report the current load. In actuality, the space temperature should readjust until the load matches equipment capacity, but this cannot be modeled because loads have been precalculated and fixed. If the weighting-factor method is used for loads, this problem is partially overcome, because loads are continually readjusted during the system simulation. However, the weighting factor technique is based on linear mathematics, and wide departures of room temperatures from those used during execution of the load program can introduce errors.

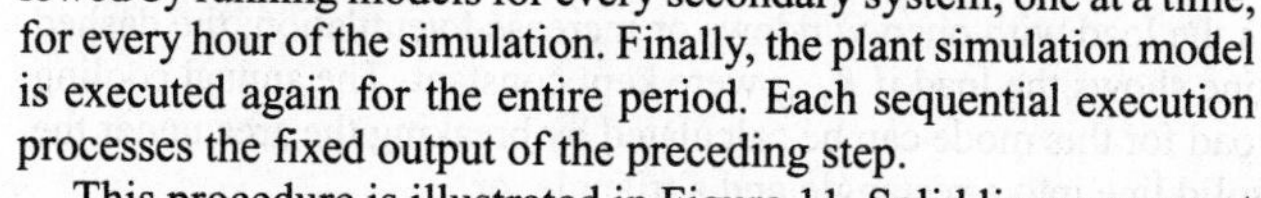

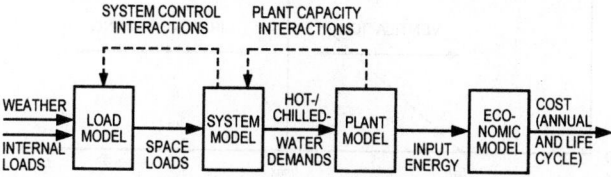

Fig. 11 Overall Modeling Strategy

A similar problem arises in plant simulation. For example, in an actual building, as the load on the central plant varies, the supply chilled-water temperature also varies. This variation in turn affects the capacity of secondary system equipment. In an actual building, when the central plant becomes overloaded, space temperatures should rise to reduce load. However, in most energy estimating programs, this condition cannot occur; thus, only the overload condition can be reported. These are some of the penalties associated with decoupling of the load, system, and plant models.

An alternative strategy, in which all calculations are performed at each time step, is possible. Here, the load, system, and plant equations are solved simultaneously at each time interval. With this strategy, unmet loads and imbalances cannot occur; conditions at the plant are immediately reflected to the secondary system and then to the load model, forcing them to readjust to the instantaneous conditions throughout the building. The results of this modeling strategy are superior, although the magnitude and importance of the improvement are uncertain.

The principal disadvantage of this approach, and the reason that it was not widely used in the past, is that it demands more computing resources. However, most current desktop computers can now run programs using the alternative approach in a reasonable amount of time. Programs that, to one degree or another, implement simultaneous solution of the loads, system, and plant models have been developed by Clarke (2001), Crawley et al. (2001), Klein et al. (1994), Park et al. (1985), and Taylor et al. (1990, 1991). Some of these programs simulate the loads, systems, and plants using subhourly time steps.

An economic model, as shown in Figure 11, calculates energy costs (and sometimes capital costs) based on the estimated required input energy. Thus, the simulation model calculates energy use and cost for any given input weather and internal loads. By applying this model (i.e., determining output for given inputs) at each hour (or other suitable interval), the hour-by-hour energy consumption and cost can be determined. Maintaining running sums of these quantities yields monthly or annual energy usage and costs.

These models only compare design alternatives; a large number of uncontrolled and unknown factors usually rule out such models for accurate prediction of utility bills. For example, Miller (1980) found that the dynamics of control of components may have at least minor effects on predicted energy use. The Bibliography lists several models, which are also described in Walton (1983) and York and Cappiello (1982). Generally, load models tend to be the most complex and time-consuming, whereas the central plant model is the least complex.

Because detailed models are computationally intensive, several simplified methods have been developed, including the degree-day, bin, and correlation methods.

DEGREE-DAY AND BIN METHODS

Degree-day methods are the simplest methods for energy analysis and are appropriate if building use and HVAC equipment efficiency are constant. Where efficiency or conditions of use vary with outdoor temperature, consumption can be calculated for different values of the outdoor temperature and multiplied by the corresponding number of hours; this approach is used in various **bin methods**. When the indoor temperature is allowed to fluctuate or when interior gains vary, simple steady-state models must not be used.

Although computers can easily calculate the energy consumption of a building, the concepts of degree-days and balance point temperature remain valuable tools. A climate's severity can be characterized concisely in terms of degree-days. Also, the degree-day method and its generalizations can provide a simple estimate of annual loads, which can be accurate if the indoor temperature and internal gains are relatively constant and if the heating or cooling systems operate for a complete season.

Balance Point Temperature

The balance point temperature t_{bal} of a building is defined as that value of the outdoor temperature t_o at which, for the specified value of the interior temperature t_i, the total heat loss q_{gain} is equal to the heat gain from sun, occupants, lights, and so forth.

$$q_{gain} = K_{tot}(t_i - t_{bal}) \tag{50}$$

where K_{tot} is the total heat loss coefficient of the building in W/K. For any steady-state method described in this section, heat gains must be the average for the period in question, not for the peak values. In particular, solar radiation must be based on averages, not peak values. The balance point temperature is therefore

$$t_{bal} = t_i - \frac{q_{gain}}{K_{tot}} \tag{51}$$

Heating is needed only when t_o drops below t_{bal}. The rate of energy consumption of the heating system is

$$q_h = \frac{K_{tot}}{\eta_h}[t_{bal} - t_o(\theta)]^+ \tag{52}$$

where η_h is the efficiency of the heating system, also designated on an annual basis as the annual fuel use efficiency (AFUE), θ is time, and the plus sign above the bracket indicates that only positive values are counted. If t_{bal}, K_{tot}, and η_h are constant, the annual heating consumption can be written as an integral:

$$Q_{h,yr} = \frac{K_{tot}}{\eta_h}\int[t_{bal} - t_o(\theta)]^+ d\theta \tag{53}$$

This integral of the temperature difference conveniently summarizes the effect of outdoor temperatures on a building. In practice, it is approximated by summing averages over short time intervals (daily or hourly); the results are called **degree-days** or **degree-hours.**

Annual Degree-Day Method

Annual Degree-Days. If daily average values of outdoor temperature are used for evaluating the integral, the degree-days for heating $DD_h(t_{bal})$ are obtained as

$$DD_h(t_{bal}) = (1\ \text{day})\sum_{\text{days}}(t_{bal} - t_o)^+ \tag{54}$$

with dimensions of kelvin · days. Here the summation is to extend over the entire year or over the heating season. It is a function of t_{bal}, reflecting the roles of t_i, heat gain, and loss coefficient. The balance point temperature t_{bal} is also known as the base of the degree-days. In terms of degree-days, the annual heating consumption is

$$Q_{h,yr} = \frac{K_{tot}}{\eta_h}DD_h(t_{bal}) \tag{55}$$

Heating degree-days or degree-hours for a balance point temperature of 18.3°C have been widely tabulated (this temperature represents average conditions in typical buildings in the past). The 18.3°C base is assumed whenever t_{bal} is not indicated explicitly. The extension of degree-day data to different bases is discussed later.

Cooling degree-days can be calculated using an equation analogous to Equation (54) for heating degree-days as

$$DD_c(t_{bal}) = (1\ \text{day})\sum_{\text{days}}(t_o - t_{bal})^+ \tag{56}$$

Although the definition of the balance point temperature is the same as that for heating, in a given building its numerical value for cooling is generally different from that for heating because q_i, K_{tot}, and t_i can be different. According to Claridge et al. (1987), t_{bal} can include both solar and internal gains as well as losses to the ground.

Calculating cooling energy consumption using degree-days is more difficult than heating. For cooling, the equation analogous to Equation (55) is

$$Q_{c,yr} = \frac{K_{tot}}{\eta_h}DD_c(t_{bal}) \tag{57}$$

for a building with static K_{tot}. That assumption is generally acceptable during the heating season, when windows are closed and the air exchange rate is fairly constant. However, during the intermediate or cooling season, heat gains can be eliminated, and the onset of mechanical cooling can be postponed by opening windows or increasing the ventilation. (In buildings with mechanical ventilation, this is called the **economizer** mode.) Mechanical air conditioning is needed only when the outdoor temperature exceeds the threshold t_{max}. This threshold is given by an equation analogous to Equation (51), replacing the closed-window heat transmission coefficient K_{tot} with K_{max} for open windows:

$$t_{max} = t_i - \frac{q_{gain}}{K_{max}} \tag{58}$$

K_{max} varies considerably with wind speed, but a constant value can be assumed for simple cases. The resulting sensible cooling load is shown schematically in Figure 12 as a function of t_o. The solid line is the load with open windows or increased ventilation; the dashed line shows the load if K_{max} were kept constant. The annual cooling load for this mode can be calculated by breaking the area under the solid line into a rectangle and a triangle, or

$$Q_c = K_{tot}[DD_c(t_{max}) + (t_{max} - t_{bal})N_{max}] \tag{59}$$

where $DD_c(t_{max})$ are the cooling degree-days for base t_{max}, and N_{max} is the number of days during the season when t_o rises above t_{max}. This is merely a schematic model of air conditioning. In practice, heat gains and ventilation rates vary, as does occupant behavior in using the windows and air conditioner. Also, in commercial buildings with economizers, the extra fan energy for increased ventilation must be added to the calculations. Finally, air-conditioning

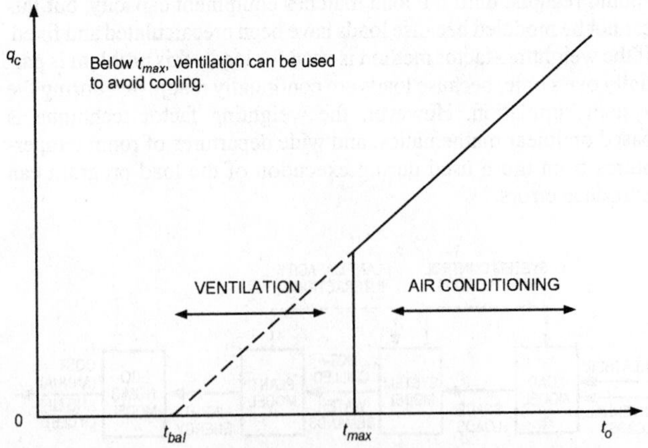

Fig. 12 Cooling Load as Function of Outdoor Temperature t_o

systems are often turned off during unoccupied periods. Therefore, cooling degree-hours better represent the period when equipment is operating than cooling degree-days because degree-days assume uninterrupted equipment operation as long as there is a cooling load.

Latent loads can form an appreciable part of a building's cooling load. The degree-day method can be used to estimate the latent load during the cooling season on a monthly basis by adding the following term to Equation (59):

$$q_{latent} = \dot{m} h_{fg}(W_o - W_i) \qquad (60)$$

where

q_{latent} = monthly latent cooling load, kW
$\dot{m}$ = monthly infiltration (total airflow), kg/s
h_{fg} = heat of vaporization of water, kJ/kg
W_o = outdoor humidity ratio (monthly averaged)
W_i = indoor humidity ratio (monthly averaged)

The degree-day method assumes that t_{bal} is constant, which is not well satisfied in practice. Solar gains are zero at night, and internal gains tend to be highest during the evening. The pattern for a typical house is shown in Figure 13. As long as t_o always stays below t_{bal}, variations average out without changing consumption. But for the situation in Figure 13, t_o rises above t_{bal} from shortly after 1000 h to 2200 h; the consequences for energy consumption depend on thermal inertia and HVAC system control. If this building had low inertia and temperature control were critical, heating would be needed at night and cooling during the day. In practice, this effect is reduced by thermal inertia and by the dead band of the thermostat, which allows t_i to float.

The closer t_o is to t_{bal}, the greater the uncertainty. If occupants keep windows closed during mild weather, t_i will rise above the set point. If they open windows, the potential benefit of heat gains is reduced. In either case, the true values of t_{bal} become uncertain. Therefore, the degree-day method, like any steady-state method, is unreliable for estimating consumption during mild weather. In fact, consumption becomes most sensitive to occupant behavior and cannot be predicted with certainty.

Despite these problems, the degree-day method (using an appropriate base temperature) can give remarkably accurate results for the annual heating energy of single-zone buildings dominated by losses through the walls and roof and/or ventilation. Typical buildings have time constants that are about 1 day, and a building's thermal inertia essentially averages over the diurnal variations, especially if t_i is allowed to float. Furthermore, energy consumption in mild

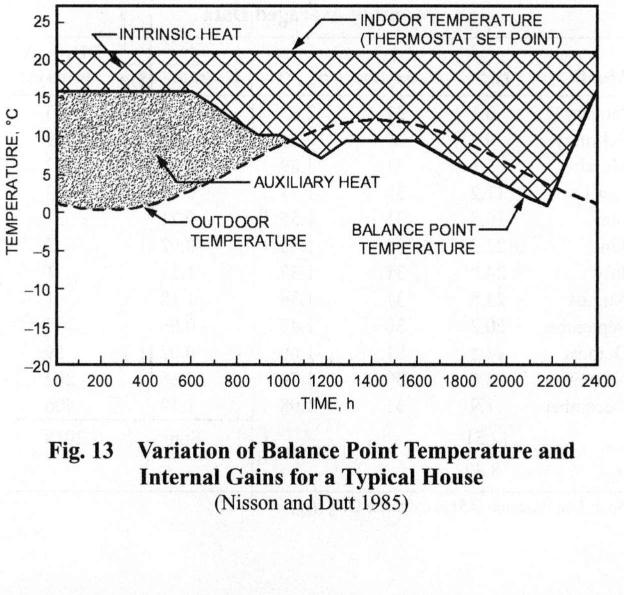

Fig. 13 Variation of Balance Point Temperature and Internal Gains for a Typical House
(Nisson and Dutt 1985)

weather is small; hence, a relatively large error here has only a small effect on the total for the season.

Variable-Base Annual Degree-Days. Calculating Q_h from degree-days $DD_h(t_{bal})$ depends on the value of t_{bal}. This value varies widely from one building to another because of widely differing personal preferences for thermostat settings and setbacks and because of different building characteristics. In response to the fuel crises of the 1970s, heat transmission coefficients have been reduced, and thermostat setback has become common. At the same time, energy use by appliances has increased. These trends all reduce t_{bal} (Fels and Goldberg 1986). Hence, in general, degree-days with the traditional base 18.3°C are not to be used.

Figure 14A shows how heating degree-days vary with t_{bal} for a particular site (New York). The plot is obtained by evaluating Equation (54) with data for the number of hours per year during which t_o is within 2.8 K temperature intervals centered at 25°C, 22.2°C, 19.4°C, 16.6°C, ..., −13.9°C. Data for the number of hours in each interval, or **bin**, are included as labels in this plot. Analogous curves, without these labels, are shown in Figure 14B for Houston, Washington, D.C., and Denver. If the annual average of t_o is known, the cooling degree-days to any base below 22°C ± 1.4 K can also be found.

Seasonal Efficiency. The seasonal efficiency η_h of heating equipment depends on factors such as steady-state efficiency, sizing, cycling effects, and energy conservation devices. It can be much lower than or comparable to steady-state efficiency. Alereza and Kusuda (1982) developed expressions to estimate seasonal efficiency for a variety of furnaces, if information on rated input and output is available. These expressions correlate seasonal efficiency with variables determined by using the equipment simulation capabilities of a large hourly simulation program and typical equipment performance curves supplied by the National Institute of Standards and Technology (NIST):

$$\eta = \frac{\eta_{ss} CF_{pl}}{1 + \alpha_D} \qquad (61)$$

where

η_{ss} = steady-state efficiency (rated output/input)
CF_{pl} = part-load correction factor
α_D = fraction of heat loss from ducts

The dimensionless term CF_{pl} is a characteristic of the part-load efficiency of the heating equipment, which may be calculated as follows:

Gas Forced-Air Furnaces

With pilot

$$CF_{pl} = 0.6328 + 0.5738(RLC) - 0.3323(RLC)^2$$

With intermittent ignition

$$CF_{pl} = 0.7791 + 0.1983(RLC) - 0.0711(RLC)^2$$

With intermittent ignition and loose stack damper

$$CF_{pl} = 0.9276 + 0.0732(RLC) - 0.0284(RLC)^2$$

Oil Furnaces Without Stack Damper

$$CF_{pl} = 0.7092 + 0.6515(RLC) - 0.4711(RLC)^2$$

Resistance Electric Furnaces

$$CF_{pl} = 1.0$$

These equations are based on many annual simulations for the equipment. The dimensionless ratio RLC of building design load to the capacity (rated output) of the equipment is defined as follows:

$$RLC = \frac{BLC}{CHT}(t_{bal} - t_{od})(1 + \alpha_D)$$

where

BLC = building loss coefficient, W/K
t_{od} = outside design temperature, °C
CHT = capacity (rated output) of heating equipment, W

BLC can be defined as design-day heat loss/($t_{bal} - t_{od}$). The design-day heat loss includes both infiltration and ground losses. Duct losses as a percentage of the design-day heat loss are added using the factor $(1 + \alpha_D)$. RLC assumes values in the range 0 to 1.0, appropriate for typical cases when heating equipment is oversized. Seasonal efficiency is also discussed by Chi and Kelly (1978), Mitchell (1983), and Parker et al. (1980).

Monthly Degree-Days

Many formulas have been proposed for estimating degree-days relative to an arbitrary base when detailed data are not available. The basic idea is to assume a typical probability distribution of temperature data, characterized by its average $\bar{t}_o$ and by its standard deviation σ. Erbs et al. (1983) developed a model that needs as input only the average $\bar{t}_o$ for each month of the year. The standard deviations σ_m for each month are then estimated from the correlation

$$\sigma_m = 1.45 - 0.0290\,\bar{t}_o + 0.0664\,\sigma_{yr} \tag{62}$$

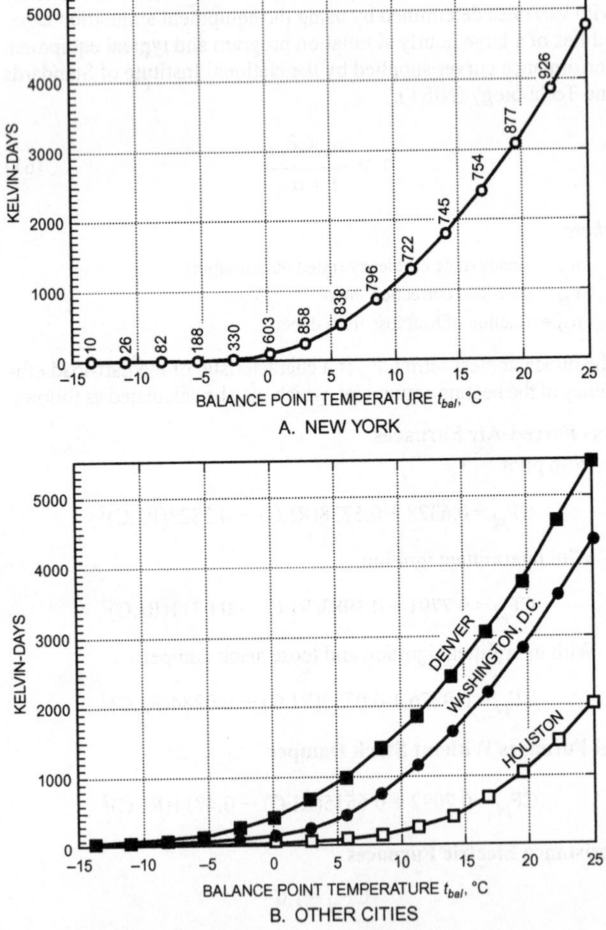

Fig. 14 Annual Heating Days $DD_h(t_{bal})$ as Function of Balance Temperature t_{bal}

This is a dimensional equation with t and σ in °C; σ_{yr} is the standard deviation of the monthly average temperatures about the annual average $\bar{t}_{o,yr}$:

$$\sigma_{yr} = \sqrt{\frac{1}{12}\sum_{1}^{12}(\bar{t}_o - \bar{t}_{o,yr})^2} \tag{63}$$

To obtain a simple expression for degree-days, a normalized temperature variable φ is defined as

$$\phi = \frac{\bar{t}_{bal} - \bar{t}_o}{\sigma_m\sqrt{N}} \tag{64}$$

where N = number of days in the month (N has units of day/month and φ has units of $\sqrt{\text{month/day}}$). Although temperature distributions can be different from month to month and location to location, most of this variability can be accounted for by the average and standard deviation of $\bar{t}_o$. Being centered around $\bar{t}_o$ and scaled by σ_m, φ eliminates these effects. In terms of φ, the monthly heating degree-days for any location are well approximated by

$$DD_h(t_{bal}) = \sigma_m N^{1.5}\left[\frac{\phi}{2} + \frac{\ln(e^{-a\phi} + e^{a\phi})}{2a}\right] \tag{65}$$

where $a = 1.698\sqrt{\text{day/month}}$.

For nine locations spanning most climatic zones of the United States, Erbs et al. (1983) verified that the annual heating degree-days can be estimated with a maximum error of 175 kelvin-days if Equation (65) is used for each month. For cooling degree-days, the largest error is 150 kelvin-days. Such errors are quite acceptable, representing less than 5% of the total.

Table 5 lists monthly heating degree-days for New York City, using the model of Erbs et al. (1983), given monthly averages of t_o as reproduced in column 2 of Table 5. The degree-days are based on a balance temperature of 15.6°C.

Table 6 contains degree-day data for several sites and monthly averaged outdoor temperatures needed for the algorithm. More complete tabulations of the latter are contained in Cinquemani et al. (1978) and in local climatological data summaries available from the National Climatic Data Center, Asheville, NC (NOAA 1973; www.ncdc.noaa.gov). Monthly degree-day data at various bases, as well as other climatic information for 209 U.S. and 14 Canadian cities, may be found in Appendix 3 to Balcomb et al. (1982).

Table 5 Degree-Day Calculation for New York City from Monthly Averaged Data

Month	$\bar{t}_o$, °C	N, day/mo.	σ_m, °C	φ, $\sqrt{\text{mo./day}}$	$DD_h(t_{bal})$, K·days
January	0.1	31	2.03	1.32	463
February	0.8	28	2.01	1.34	399
March	5.1	31	1.89	0.95	312
April	11.2	30	1.71	0.41	133
May	16.8	31	1.55	–0.21	31
June	22.0	30	1.40	–0.92	3
July	24.8	31	1.32	–1.33	1
August	23.8	31	1.34	–1.18	1
September	20.2	30	1.45	–0.66	7
October	14.8	31	1.60	0.02	59
November	8.6	30	1.79	0.66	202
December	1.9	31	1.98	1.19	406
$t_{o,yr}$	12.51			Sum	2018
σ_{yr}	8.80				

Note: Use Equation (65) to calculate $DD_h(t_{bal})$

Table 6 Degree-Day and Monthly Average Temperatures for Various Locations

Site	Variable-Base Heating Degree-Day, K·days[a]					Monthly Average Outdoor Temperature $\bar{t}_o$, °C[b]											
	18.3	15.6	12.8	10.0	7.2	Jan	Feb	Mar	Apr	May	Jun	Jul	Aug	Sep	Oct	Nov	Dec
Los Angeles, CA	692	290	88	14	0	12.5	13.1	13.6	14.9	16.6	18.1	20.3	20.8	20.4	18.4	15.8	13.8
Denver, CO	3342	2624	2001	1474	1029	−1.2	0.4	2.8	8.6	13.9	18.9	22.8	22.0	17.1	11.1	4.1	0.3
Miami, FL	114	30	4	0	0	19.6	19.9	21.8	23.9	25.6	27.2	27.9	28.3	27.6	25.4	22.3	20.2
Chicago, IL	3404	2751	2173	1666	1233	−4.3	−2.6	2.7	9.9	15.6	21.4	23.7	23.2	18.8	13.0	4.7	−1.9
Albuquerque, NM	2384	1797	1294	865	535	1.8	4.4	7.7	13.2	18.5	23.7	25.9	24.8	21.2	14.6	6.9	2.3
New York, NY	2727	2104	1559	1100	728	0.1	0.8	5.1	11.2	16.8	22.0	24.8	23.8	20.2	14.8	8.6	1.9
Bismarck, ND	5024	4253	3569	2959	2430	−13.2	−10.3	−3.8	6.1	12.4	17.7	21.6	20.7	14.2	8.2	−1.7	−9.1
Nashville, TN	2053	1532	1091	743	473	3.5	5.0	9.3	15.6	20.3	24.8	26.4	25.8	22.2	16.1	9.1	4.7
Dallas/Ft. Worth, TX	1272	858	527	292	139	7.4	9.7	13.2	19.1	23.2	27.6	29.8	29.9	25.7	20.0	13.3	9.0
Seattle, WA	2626	1816	1162	663	334	3.4	5.7	6.7	9.3	12.7	15.4	18.1	17.7	15.3	11.2	7.0	4.7

[a]*Source*: NOAA (1973). [b]*Source*: Cinquemani et al. (1978).

Table 7 Sample Annual Bin Data

Site	Bin																			
	39/ 41	36/ 38	33/ 35	30/ 32	27/ 29	24/ 26	21/ 23	18/ 20	15/ 17	12/ 14	9/ 11	6/ 8	3/ 5	0/ 2	−3/ −1	−6/ −4	−9/ −7	−12/ −10	−15/ −13	−18/ −16	−21/ −19
Chicago, IL			74	176	431	512	960	660	591	780	510	770	686	1671	380	304	125	66	49	11	4
Dallas/Ft. Worth, TX	4	170	322	511	922	1100	1077	750	803	870	581	728	418	464	37	3					
Denver, CO			81	217	406	390	570	726	712	902	809	783	750	1467	446	216	106	85	52	44	8
Los Angeles, CA	4	10	9	16	56	194	1016	1874	2280	2208	843	227	23								
Miami, FL			14	648	2147	2581	1852	734	390	202	100	76	14	2							
Nashville, TN		4	82	366	717	756	1291	831	693	801	670	858	639	793	141	89	29				
Seattle, WA				10	88	139	330	497	898	1653	1392	1844	1127	715	40	26	1				

Bin Method

For many applications, the degree-day method should not be used, even with the variable-base method, because the heat loss coefficient K_{tot}, the efficiency η_h of the HVAC system, or the balance point temperature t_{bal} may not be sufficiently constant. Heat pump efficiency, for example, varies strongly with outdoor temperature; efficiency of HVAC equipment may be affected indirectly by t_o when efficiency varies with load (common for boilers and chillers). Furthermore, in most commercial buildings, occupancy has a pronounced pattern, which affects heat gain, indoor temperature, and ventilation rate.

In such cases, steady-state calculation can yield good results for annual energy consumption if different temperature intervals and time periods are evaluated separately. This approach is known as the *bin method* because consumption is calculated for several values of the outdoor temperature t_o and multiplied by the number of hours N_{bin} in the temperature interval (bin) centered around that temperature:

$$Q_{bin} = N_{bin} \frac{K_{tot}}{\eta_h} [t_{bal} - t_o]^+ \qquad (66)$$

The superscript plus sign indicates that only positive values are counted; no heating is needed when t_o is above t_{bal}. Equation (66) is evaluated for each bin, and the total consumption is the sum of the Q_{bin} over all bins.

In the United States, the necessary weather data are available in ASHRAE (1995) and USAF (1978). Bins are usually in 2.8 K increments (when derived from 5°F bins) and are often collected in three daily 8 h shifts. Mean coincident wet-bulb temperature data (for each dry-bulb bin) are used to calculate latent cooling loads from infiltration and ventilation. The bin method considers both occupied and unoccupied building conditions and gives credit for internal loads by adjusting the balance point. For example, a calculation could be performed for 5°C outdoors (representing all occurrences from 3.6 to 6.4°C) and with building operation during the midnight to 0800 shift (5°C outdoors, representing all occurrences from 4°C). Because there are 23 2.8 K bins between −23 and 40.4°C and 3 8 h shifts, 69 separate operating points are calculated. For many applications, the number of calculations can be reduced. A residential heat pump (heating mode), for example, could be calculated for just the bins below 18.3°C without the three-shift breakdown. The data in Table 7 are samples of annual totals for a few sites, but ASHRAE (1995) and USAF (1978) include monthly data and data further separated into time intervals during the day.

Equipment performance may vary with load. For heat pumps, the U.S. Department of Energy adopted test procedures to determine the effect of dynamic operations. The bin method uses these results for a specific heat pump to adjust the integrated capacity for the effect of part-load operation. Figure 15 compares adjusted heat pump capacity to building heat loss in Example 4. This type of curve must be developed for each model heat pump as applied to an individual profile. The heat pump cycles on and off above the balance point temperature to meet the house load; supplemental heat is required at lower temperatures. This cycling can reduce performance, depending on the part-load factor at a given temperature. The cycling capacity adjustment factors used in this example to account for cycling degradation can be calculated from the equation in footnote a of Table 8.

Frosting and the necessary defrost cycle can reduce performance over steady-state conditions that do not include frosting. The effects of frosting and defrosting are already integrated into many (but not all) manufacturer's published performance data. Example 4 assumes that the manufacturer's data already account for frosting/defrosting losses (as indicated by the characteristic notch of the capacity curve in Figure 15) and shows how to adjust an integrated performance curve for cycling losses.

Example 4. Estimate the energy requirements for a residence with a design heat loss of 11 700 W at 30°C design temperature difference. The inside design temperature is 21°C. Average internal heat gains are estimated to be 1250 W. Assume a 10.5 kW heat pump with the characteristics given in Columns E and H of Table 8 and in Figure 15.

Table 8 Calculation of Annual Heating Energy Consumption for Example 4

Climate		House		Heat Pump						Supplemental			
A	B	C	D	E	F	G	H	I	J	K	L	M	N
Temp. Bin, °C	Temp. Diff., $t_{bal} - t_{bin}$	Weather Data Bin, h	Heat Loss Rate, kW	Heat Pump Integrated Heating Capacity, kW	Cycling Capacity Adjustment Factor[a]	Adjusted Heat Pump Capacity, kW[b]	Rated Electric Input, kW	Operating Time Fraction[c]	Heat Pump Supplied Heating, kWh[d]	Seasonal Heat Pump Electric Consumption, KWh[e]	Space Load, kWh[f]	Supplemental Heating Required, kWh[g]	Total Electric Energy Consumption, kWh[h]
16	1.8	693	0.70	12.80	0.764	9.78	3.74	0.072	488	187	485	—	187
13	4.8	801	1.87	12.01	0.789	9.48	3.63	0.197	1 496	573	1 497	—	573
10	7.8	670	3.04	11.22	0.818	9.18	3.52	0.331	2 036	781	2 037	—	781
7	10.8	858	4.21	9.80	0.857	8.40	3.40	0.501	3 611	1 462	3 612	—	1 462
4	13.8	639	5.38	8.49	0.908	7.71	3.18	0.698	3 439	1 418	3 438	—	1 418
1	16.8	793	6.55	7.98	0.955	7.62	3.10	0.860	5 196	2 114	5 195	—	2 114
−2	19.8	141	7.72	7.47	1.000	7.47	3.02	1.000	1 053	426	1 089	36	462
−5	22.8	89	8.89	6.95	1.000	6.95	2.93	1.000	618	261	791	173	434
−8	25.8	29	10.06	6.48	1.000	6.48	2.85	1.000	188	83	292	104	187
−11	28.8	0	11.23	5.69	1.000	—	—	—	—	—	—	—	—
								Totals:	18 125	7 305	18 436	313	7 618

[a]Cycling Capacity Adjustment Factor = $1 - C_d(1 - x)$, where C_d = degradation coefficient (default = 0.25 unless part load factor is known) and x = building heat loss per unit capacity at temperature bin. Cycling capacity = 1 at the balance point and below. The cycling capacity adjustment factor should be 1.0 at all temperature bins if the manufacturer includes cycling effects in the heat pump capacity (Column E) and associated electrical input (Column H).
[b]Column G = Column E × Column F
[c]Operating Time Factor equals smaller of 1 or Column D/Column G
[d]Column J = Column I × Column G × Column C
[e]Column K = Column I × Column H × Column C
[f]Column L = Column C × Column D
[g]Column M = Column L – Column J
[h]Column N = Column K + Column M

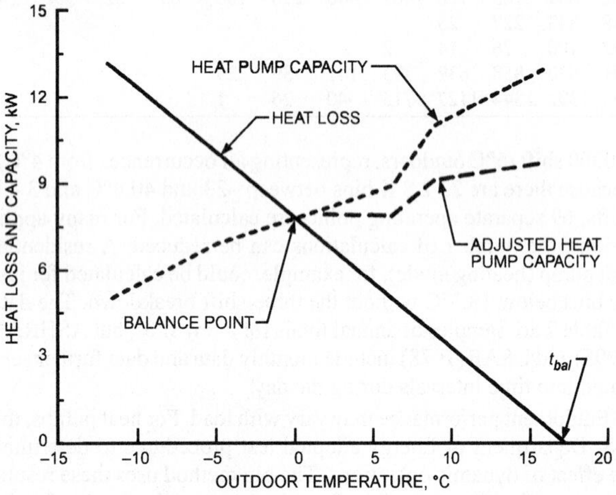

Fig. 15 Heat Pump Capacity and Building Load

Solution: The design heat loss is based on no internal heat generation. The heat pump system energy input is the net heat requirement of the space (i.e., envelope loss minus internal heat generation). The net heat loss per degree and the heating/cooling balance temperature may be computed:

$$HL/\Delta t = 11\ 700/30 = 390 \text{ W/K}$$

From Equation (51),

$$t_{bal} = 21 - (1250/390) = 17.8°\text{C}$$

Table 8 is then computed, resulting in 7618 kWh.

The **modified bin method** (Knebel 1983) extends the basic bin method to account for weekday/weekend and partial-day occupancy effects, to calculate net building loads (conduction, infiltration, internal loads, and solar loads) at four temperatures, rather than interpolate from design values, and to better describe secondary and primary equipment performance.

CORRELATION METHODS

One way to simplify energy analyses is to correlate energy requirements to various inputs. Typically, the result of a correlation is a simple equation that may be used in a calculator or small computer program, or to develop a graph that provides quick insight into the energy requirements. Examples are in ASHRAE *Standard* 90.1, which includes several empirical equations that may be used to predict energy consumption by many types of buildings.

The accuracy of correlation methods depends on the size and accuracy of the database and the statistical means used to develop the correlation. A database generated from measured data can lead to accurate correlations (Lachal et al. 1992). The key to proper use of a correlation is ensuring that the case being studied matches the cases used in developing the database. Inputs to the correlation (independent variables) indicate factors that are considered to significantly affect energy consumption. A correlation is invalid either when an input parameter is used beyond its valid range (corresponding to extrapolation rather than interpolation) or when some important feature of the building/system is not included in the available inputs to the correlation.

SIMULATING SECONDARY AND PRIMARY SYSTEMS

Traditionally, most energy analysis programs include a set of preprogrammed models that represent various systems (e.g., variable-air-volume, terminal reheat, multizone). In this scheme, the equations for each system are arranged so they can be solved sequentially. If this is not possible, then the smallest number of equations that must be solved simultaneously is solved using an appropriate technique. Furthermore, individual equations may vary from hour to hour in the simulation, depending on controls and operating conditions. For example, a dry coil uses different equations than a wet coil.

The primary disadvantage of this scheme is that it is relatively inflexible: to modify a system, the program source code may have to be modified and recompiled. Alternative strategies (Klein et al. 1994; Park et al. 1985) view the system as a series of components (e.g., fan, coil, pump, duct, pipe, damper, thermostat) that may be organized in a component library. Users of the program specify the connections between the components. The program then resolves the specification of components and connections into a set of simultaneous equations.

A refinement of component-based modeling is known as **equation-based modeling** (Buhl et al. 1993; Sowell and Moshier

1995). These models do not follow predetermined rules for a solution, and the user can specify which variables are inputs and which are outputs.

MODELING OF SYSTEM CONTROLS

Building control systems are typically hierarchical: higher-level, supervisory controls generate set points for lower-level, local loop controls. Supervisory-level controls, which include reset and optimal control, directly influence energy consumption. Local loop controllers may also affect energy performance; for example, proportional-only room temperature control results in a tradeoff between energy use and comfort. Faults in control systems and devices can also affect energy consumption (e.g., leaking valves and dampers can significantly increase energy use). It is particularly important to account for these departures from ideal behavior when simulating performance of real buildings using calibrated models. Modeling and simulation of supervisory control are increasingly handled by whole-building simulation programs. Simulation of local loop controls requires more specialized, component- or equation-based modeling environments.

Modern control systems, particularly direct digital controls (DDC), typically use integral action to drive the controlled variable to its set point. For energy modeling purposes, the controlled variable (e.g., supply air temperature) can be treated as being at the set point unless system capacity is insufficient. The simulation must determine whether the capacity required to meet set point exceeds available capacity. If it does, the available capacity is used to determine the actual value of the controlled variable. Where there is only proportional action, the resulting relationship between the controlled variable and the output of the system can be used to determine both values. For example, the action of a conventional pneumatic room temperature controller can be represented by a function relating heating and cooling delivery to space temperature. Similarly, supply air temperature reset control can be modeled as a relationship between outside or zone temperature and coil or fan discharge temperature. An accurate secondary system model must ensure that all controls are properly represented and that the governing equations are satisfied at each simulation time step. This often creates a need for iteration or for use of values from an earlier solution point.

Controls on space temperature affect the interaction between loads calculations and the secondary system simulation. A realistic model might require a dead band in space temperature in which no heating or cooling is called for; within this range, the true space sensible load is zero, and the true space temperature must be adjusted accordingly. If the thermostat has proportional control between zero and full capacity, the space temperature rises in proportion to the load during cooling and falls similarly during heating. Capacity to heat or cool also varies with space temperature after the control device has reached its maximum because capacity is proportional to the difference between supply and space temperatures. Failure to properly model these phenomena results in overestimating required energy.

INTEGRATION OF SYSTEM MODELS

Energy calculations for secondary systems involve construction of the complete system from the set of HVAC components. For example, a variable-air-volume (VAV) system is a single-path system that controls zone temperature by modulating airflow while maintaining constant supply air temperature. VAV terminal units, located at each zone, adjust the quantity of air reaching each zone depending on its load requirements. Reheat coils may be included to provide required heating for perimeter zones.

This VAV system simulation consists of a central air-handling unit and a VAV terminal unit with reheat coil located at each zone, as shown in Figure 16. The central air-handling unit includes a fan, cooling coil, preheat coil, and outside air economizer. Supply air leaving the air-handling unit is controlled to a fixed set point. The VAV terminal unit at each zone varies airflow to meet the cooling load. As zone cooling load decreases, the VAV terminal unit decreases zone airflow until the unit reaches its minimum position. If the cooling load continues to decrease, the reheat coil is activated to meet the zone load. As supply air volume leaving the unit decreases, fan power consumption also reduces. A variable-speed drive is used to control the supply fan.

The simulation is based on system characteristics and zone design requirements. For each zone, the inputs include sensible and latent loads, zone set-point temperature, and minimum zone supply-air mass flow. System characteristics include supply air temperature set point; entering water temperature of reheat, preheat, and cooling coils; minimum mass flow of outside air; and economizer temperature/enthalpy set point for minimum airflow.

The algorithm for performing calculations for this VAV system is shown in Figure 17. The algorithm directs sequential calculations of system performance. Calculations proceed from the zones along the return air path to the cooling coil inlet and back through the supply air path to the cooling coil discharge.

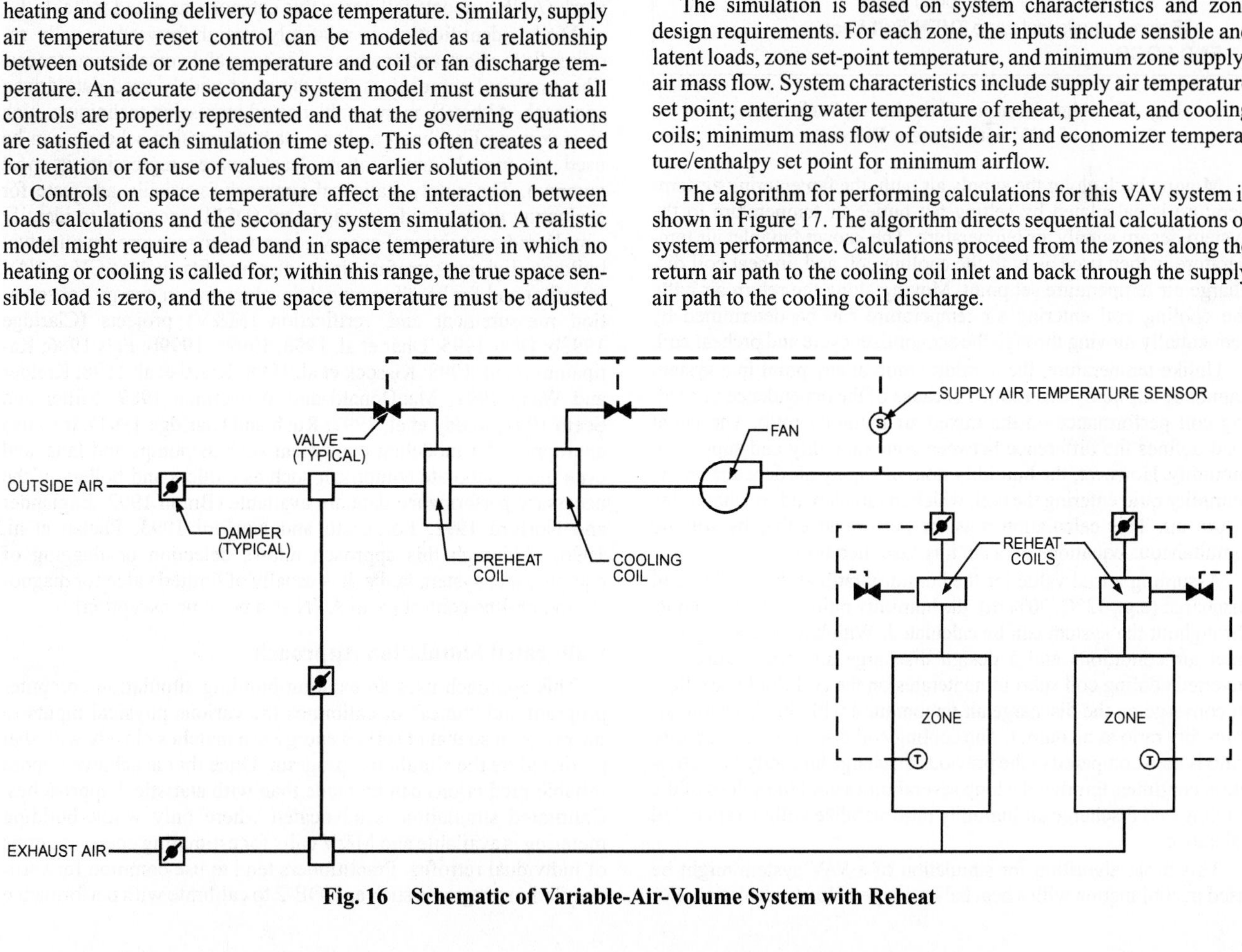

Fig. 16 Schematic of Variable-Air-Volume System with Reheat

```
BEGIN LOOP Calculate zone related design requirements
    • Calculate required supply airflow to meet zone load
    • Sum actual zone mass airflow rate
    • Sum zone latent loads
  IF zone equals last zone THEN Exit Loop
END LOOP
• Calculate system return air temperature from zone temps
• Assume an initial cooling coil leaving air humidity ratio

BEGIN LOOP Iterate on cooling coil leaving air humidity ratio
    • Calculate return air humidity ratio from latent loads
    • Calculate supply fan power consumption and
      entering fan air temperature
    • Calculate mixed air temperature and humidity
      ratio using an economizer cycle
  IF mixed air temperature is less than design
      supply air temperature THEN
        • Calculate preheat coil load
  ELSE
        • Calculate cooling coil load and leaving air
          humidity ratio
  ENDIF
  IF cooling coil leaving air humidity ratio converged
  THEN Exit Loop
END LOOP

BEGIN LOOP Calculate the zone reheat coil loads
  IF zone supply air temperature is greater than system
  design supply air temperature THEN
        • Calculate reheat coil load
          (Subroutine: COILINV/HCDET)
  ENDIF
    • Sum reheat coil loads for all zones
  IF zone equals last zone THEN Exit Loop
END LOOP
```

Fig. 17 Algorithm for Calculating Performance of VAV with System Reheat

Moving back along the supply air path, the fan entering air temperature is calculated by setting fan outlet air temperature to the system design supply air temperature. The known fan inlet air temperature is then used as both the cooling coil and preheat coil discharge air temperature set point. Moving along the return air path, the cooling coil entering air temperature can be determined by sequentially moving through the economizer cycle and preheat coil.

Unlike temperature, the humidity ratio at any point in a system cannot be explicitly determined because of the dependence of cooling coil performance on the mixed air humidity ratio. The latent load defines the difference between zone humidity and supply air humidity. However, the humidity ratio of supply air depends on the humidity ratio entering the coil, which in turn depends on that of the return air. This calculation must be performed either by solving simultaneous equations or, as in this case, iteration.

Assuming a trial value for the humidity ratio at the cooling coil discharge (e.g., 13°C, 90% rh), the humidity ratio at all other points throughout the system can be calculated. With known cooling coil inlet air conditions and a design discharge air temperature, the inverted cooling coil subroutine iterates on the coil fluid mass flow to converge on the discharge air temperature with the discharge air humidity ratio as an output. The cooling coil discharge air humidity ratio is then compared to the previous discharge humidity ratio. Iteration continues through the loop several times until the values of the cooling coil discharge air humidity ratio stabilize within a specified tolerance.

This basic algorithm for simulation of a VAV system might be used in conjunction with a heat balance type of load calculation. For a weighting factor approach, it would have to be modified to allow zone temperatures to vary and consequently zone loads to be readjusted. It should also be enhanced to allow possible limits on reheat temperature and/or cooling coil limits, zone humidity limits, outside air control (economizers), and/or heat-recovery devices, zone exhaust, return air fan, heat gain in the return air path because of lights, the presence of baseboard heaters, and more realistic control profiles. Most current building energy programs incorporate these and other features as user options, as well as algorithms for other types of systems.

DATA-DRIVEN MODELING

CATEGORIES OF DATA-DRIVEN METHODS

Data-driven methods for energy-use estimation in buildings and related HVAC&R equipment can be classified into three broad categories. These approaches differ widely in data requirements, time and effort needed to develop the associated models, user skill demands, and sophistication and reliability provided.

Empirical or "Black-Box" Approach

With this approach, a simple or multivariate regression model is identified between measured energy use and the various influential parameters (e.g., climatic variables, building occupancy). The form of the regression models can be either purely statistical or loosely based on some basic engineering formulation of energy use in the building. In any case, the identified model coefficients are such that no (or very little) physical meaning can be assigned to them. This approach can be used with any time scale (monthly, daily, hourly or subhourly) if appropriate data are available. Single-variate, multivariate, change point, Fourier series, and artificial neural network (ANN) models fall under this category, as noted in Table 1.

Model identification is relatively straightforward, usually requires little effort, and can be used in several diverse circumstances. The empirical approach is thus the most widely used data-driven approach. Although more sophisticated regression techniques such as maximum likelihood and two-stage regression schemes can be used for model identification, least-squares regression is most common. The purely statistical approach is usually adequate for evaluating demand-side management (DSM) programs to identify simple and conventional energy conservation measures in an actual building (lighting retrofits, air handler retrofits such as CV to VAV retrofits) and for baseline model development in energy conservation measurement and verification (M&V) projects (Claridge 1998b; Dhar 1995; Dhar et al. 1998, 1999a, 1999b; Fels 1986; Katipamula et al. 1998; Kissock et al. 1998; Krarti et al. 1998; Kreider and Wang 1991; MacDonald and Wasserman 1989; Miller and Seem 1991; Reddy et al. 1997; Ruch and Claridge 1991). It is also appropriate for modeling equipment such as pumps and fans, and even more elaborate equipment such as chillers and boilers, if the necessary performance data are available (Braun 1992; Englander and Norford 1992; Lorenzetti and Norford 1993; Phelan et al. 1996). Although this approach allows detection or flagging of equipment or system faults, it is usually of limited value for diagnosis and on-line control (with ANN as a possible exception).

Calibrated Simulation Approach

This approach uses an existing building simulation computer program and "tunes" or calibrates the various physical inputs to the program so that observed energy use matches closely with that predicted by the simulation program. Once that is achieved, more reliable predictions can be made than with statistical approaches. Calibrated simulation is advocated where only whole-building metering is available and M&V calls for estimating energy savings of individual retrofits. Practitioners tend to use common forward-simulation programs such as DOE-2 to calibrate with performance data. Hourly subaggregated monitored energy data (most compatible with the time step adopted by most building energy simulation programs) allow development of the most accurate calibrated model, but analysts usually must work with less data. Tuning can be done with monthly data or data that span only a few weeks or months over the year, but the resulting model is very likely to be increasingly less accurate with decrease in performance data.

The main challenges of calibrated simulation are that it is labor-intensive, requires a high level of user skill and knowledge in both simulation and practical building operation, is time-consuming, and often depends on the person doing the calibration. Several practical difficulties prevent achieving a calibrated simulation or a simulation that closely reflects actual building performance, including (1) measurement and adaptation of weather data for use by simulation programs (e.g., converting global horizontal solar into beam and diffuse solar radiation), (2) choice of methods used to calibrate the model, and (3) choice of methods used to measure required input parameters for the simulation (i.e., building mass, infiltration coefficients, and shading coefficients). Truly "calibrated" models have been achieved in only a few applications because they require a very large number of input parameters, a high degree of expertise, and enormous amounts of computing time, patience, and financial resources. Bou-Saada and Haberl (1995a, 1995b), Bronson et al. (1992), Corson (1992), Haberl and Bou-Saada (1998), Kaplan et al. (1990) Manke et al. (1996), and Norford et al. (1994) provide examples of different methods used to calibrate simulation models.

Katipamula and Claridge (1993) and Liu and Claridge (1998) suggested that simpler models could also work, and allow model calibration to be done much faster. Typically, the building is divided into two zones: an exterior or perimeter zone and an interior or a core zone. The core zone is assumed to be insulated from envelope heat losses/gains, and solar heat gains, infiltration heat loss/gain, and conduction gains/losses from the roof are taken as loads on the external zone only. Given the internal load schedule, building description, type of HVAC system, and climatic parameters, HVAC system loads can be estimated for each hour of the day and for as many days of the year as needed by the simplified systems model. Because there are fewer parameters to vary, calibration is much faster. Therefore, these models have a significant advantage over general-purpose models in buildings where the HVAC systems can be adequately modeled. These studies, based on the ASHRAE Simplified Energy Analysis Procedure (Knebel 1983), illustrate the applicability of this method both to baseline model development for M&V purposes and as a diagnostic tool for identifying potential operational problems and for estimating potential savings from optimized operating parameters.

Gray-Box Approach

This approach first formulates a physical model to represent the structure or physical configuration of the building or HVAC&R equipment or system, and then identifies important parameters representative of certain key and aggregated physical parameters and characteristics by statistical analysis (Rabl and Riahle 1992). This requires a high level of user expertise both in setting up the appropriate modeling equations and in estimating these parameters. Often an intrusive experimental protocol is necessary for proper parameter estimation, which also requires skill. This approach has great potential, especially for fault detection and diagnosis (FDD) and online control, but its applicability to whole-building energy use is limited. Examples of parameter estimation studies applied to building energy use are Andersen and Brandemuehl (1992), Braun (1990), Gordon and Ng (1995), Guyon and Palomo (1999a), Hammersten (1984), Rabl (1988), Reddy (1989), Reddy et al. (1999), Sonderegger (1977), and Subbarao (1988).

TYPES OF DATA-DRIVEN MODELS

Steady-state models do not consider effects such as thermal mass or capacitance that cause short-term temperature transients. Generally, these models are appropriate for monthly, weekly, or daily data and are often used for baseline model development. **Dynamic models** capture effects such as building warm-up or cooldown periods and peak loads, and are appropriate for building load control, FDD, and equipment control. A simple criterion to determine whether a model is steady-state or dynamic is to look for the presence of time-lagged variables, either in the response or regressor variables. Steady-state models do not contain time-lagged variables.

Steady-State Models

Several types of steady-state models are used for both building and equipment energy use: single-variate, multivariate, polynomial, and physical.

Single-Variate Models. Single-variate models (i.e., models with one regressor variable only) are perhaps the most widely used. They formulate energy use in a building as a function of one driving force that affects building energy use. An important aspect in identifying statistical models of baseline energy use is the choice of the functional form and the independent (or regressor) variables. Extensive studies (Fels 1986; Katipamula et al. 1994; Kissock et al. 1993; Reddy et al. 1997) have clearly indicated that the outdoor dry-bulb temperature is the most important regressor variable, especially at monthly time scales but also at daily time scales.

The simplest steady-state data-driven model is one developed by regressing monthly utility consumption data against average billing-period temperatures. The model must identify the balance-point temperatures (or change points) at which energy use switches from weather-dependent to weather-independent behavior. In its simplest form, the 18.3°C degree-day model is a change-point model that has a fixed change point at 18.3°C. Other examples include three- and five-parameter Princeton Scorekeeping Methods (PRISM) based on the variable-base degree-day concept (Fels 1986). An allied modeling approach for commercial buildings is the four-parameter (4-P) model developed by Ruch and Claridge (1991), which is based on the monthly mean temperature (and not degree-days). Table 9 shows the appropriate model functional forms. The three parameters are a weather-independent base-level use, a change point, and a temperature-dependent energy use, characterized as a slope of a line that is determined by regression. The four parameters include a change point, a slope above the change point, a slope below the change point, and the energy use associated with the change point. An data-driven bin method has also been proposed to handle more than four change points (Thamilseran and Haberl 1995).

Figure 18 shows several types of steady-state, single-variate data-driven models. Figure 18A shows a simple one-parameter, or constant, model, and Table 9 gives the equivalent notation for calculating the constant energy use using this model. Figure 18B shows a steady-state two-parameter (2-P) model where b_0 is the y-axis intercept and b_1 is the slope of the regression line for positive values of x, where x represents the ambient air temperature. The 2-P model represents cases when either heating or cooling is always required.

Figure 18C shows a three-parameter change-point model, typical of natural gas energy use in a single-family residence that uses gas for space heating and domestic water heating. In the notation of Table 9 for the three-parameter model, b_0 represents the baseline energy use and b_1 is the slope of the regression line for values of ambient temperature less than the change point b_2. In this type of notation, the superscripted plus sign indicates that only positive values of the parenthetical expression are considered. Figure 18D shows a three-parameter model for cooling energy use, and Table 9 provides the appropriate analytic expression.

Figures 18E and 18F illustrate four-parameter models for heating and cooling, respectively. The appropriate expressions for

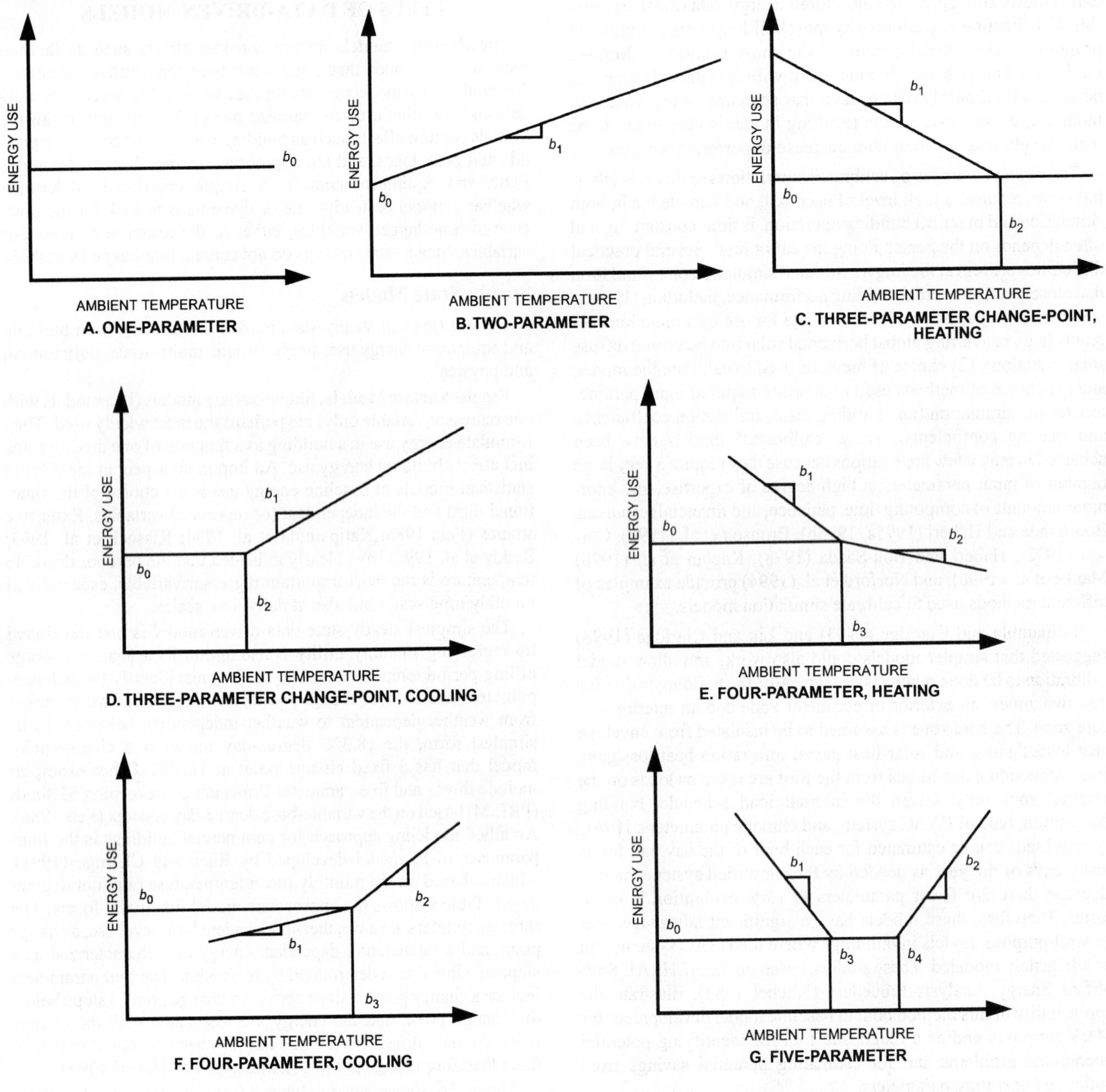

Fig. 18 Steady-State, Single-Variate Models for Modeling Energy Use in Residential and Commercial Buildings

Table 9 Single-Variate Models Applied to Utility Billing Data

Model Type	Independent Variable(s)	Form	Examples
One-parameter or constant (1-P)	None	$E = b_0$	Non-weather-sensitive demand
Two-parameter (2-P)	Temperature	$E = b_0 + b_1(T)$	
Three-parameter (3-P)	Degree-days/ Temperature	$E = b_0 + b_1(\mathrm{DD}_{BT})$ $E = b_0 + b_1(b_2 - T)^+$ $E = b_0 + b_1(T - b_2)^+$	Seasonal weather-sensitive use (fuel in winter, electricity in summer for cooling)
Four-parameter change point (4-P)	Temperature	$E = b_0 + b_1(b_3 - T)^+ - b_2(T - b_3)^+$ $E = b_0 - b_1(b_3 - T)^+ + b_2(T - b_3)^+$	Energy use in commercial buildings
Five-parameter (5-P)	Degree-days/ Monthly mean temperature	$E = b_0 - b_1(\mathrm{DD}_{TH}) + b_2(\mathrm{DD}_{TC})$ $E = b_0 + b_1(b_3 - T)^+ + b_2(T - b_4)^+$	Heating and cooling supplied by same meter

Note: DD denotes degree-days and T is monthly mean daily outdoor dry-bulb temperature.

calculating the heating and cooling energy consumption are found in Table 9: b_0 represents the baseline energy exactly at the change point b_3, and b_1 and b_2 are the lower and upper region regression slopes for ambient air temperature below and above the change point b_3. Figure 18G illustrates a 5-P model (Fels 1986), which is useful for modeling buildings that are electrically heated and cooled. The 5-P model has two change points and a base level consumption value.

The advantage of these steady-state data-driven models is that their use can be easily automated and applied to large numbers of buildings where monthly utility billing data and average daily temperatures for the billing period are available. Steady-state single-variate data-driven models have also been applied with success to daily data (Kissock et al. 1998). In such a case, the variable-base degree-day method and monthly mean temperature models described earlier for utility billing data analysis become identical in their functional form. Single-variate models can also be applied to daily data to compensate for differences such as weekday and weekend use by separating the data accordingly and identifying models for each period separately.

Disadvantages of steady-state single-variate data-driven models include insensitivity to dynamic effects (e.g., thermal mass) and to variables other than temperature (e.g., humidity and solar gain), and inappropriateness for some buildings (e.g., buildings with strong on/off schedule-dependent loads or buildings with multiple change points). Moreover, a single-variable, 3-P model such as the PRISM model (Fels 1986) has a physical basis only when energy use above a base level is linearly proportional to degree-days. This is a good approximation in the case of heating energy use in residential buildings where heating load never exceeds the heating system's capacity. However, commercial buildings generally have higher internal heat generation with simultaneous heating and cooling energy use and are strongly influenced by HVAC system type and control strategy. This makes energy use in commercial buildings less strongly influenced by outdoor air temperature alone. Therefore, it is not surprising that blind use of single-variate models has had mixed success at modeling energy use in commercial buildings (MacDonald and Wasserman 1989).

Change-point regression models work best with heating data from buildings with systems that have few or no part-load nonlinearities (i.e., systems that become less efficient as they begin to cycle on/off with part loads). In general, change-point regression models do not predict cooling loads as well because outdoor humidity has a large influence on latent loads on the cooling coil. Other factors that decrease the accuracy of change-point models include solar effects, thermal lags, and on/off HVAC schedules. Four-parameter models are a better statistical fit than three-parameter models in buildings with continuous, year-round cooling or heating (e.g., grocery stores and office buildings with high internal loads). However, every model should be checked to ensure that the regression does not falsely indicate an unreasonable relationship.

A major advantage of using a steady-state data-driven model to evaluate the effectiveness of energy conservation retrofits is its ability to factor out year-to-year weather variations by using a normalized annual consumption (NAC) (Fels 1986). Basically, annual energy conservation savings can be calculated by comparing the difference obtained by multiplying the pre- and postretrofit parameters by the weather conditions for the average year. Typically, 10 to 20 years of average daily weather data from a nearby weather service site are used to calculate 365 days of average weather conditions, which are then used to calculate the average pre- and postretrofit conditions.

Utilities and government agencies have found it advantageous to prescreen many buildings against test regression models. These data-driven models can be used to develop comparative figures of merit for buildings in a similar standard industrial code (SIC) classification. A minimum goodness of fit is usually established that determines whether the monthly utility billing data are well fitted by the one-, two-, three-, four-, or five-parameter model being tested. Comparative figures of merit can then be determined by dividing the parameters by the conditioned floor area to yield average daily energy use per unit area of conditioned space. For example, an area-normalized comparison of base-level parameters across residential buildings would be used to analyze weather-independent energy use. This information can be used by energy auditors to focus their efforts on those systems needing assistance (Haberl and Komor 1990a, 1990b).

Multivariate Models. Two types of steady-state, multivariate models have been reported:

- **Standard multiple-linear** or **change-point regression models**, where the set of data observations is treated without retaining the time-series nature of the data (Katipamula et al. 1998).
- **Fourier series models** that retain the time-series nature of building energy use data and capture the diurnal and seasonal cycles according to which buildings are operated (Dhar 1995; Dhar et al. 1998, 1999a, 1999b; Seem and Braun 1991).

These models are a logical extension of single-variate models, provided that the choice of variables to be included and their functional forms are based on the engineering principles on which HVAC systems and other systems in commercial buildings operate. The goal of modeling energy use by the multivariate approach is to characterize building energy use with a few readily available and reliable input variables. These input variables should be selected with care. The model should contain variables not affected by the retrofit and likely to change (for example, climatic variables) from preretrofit to postretrofit periods. Other less obvious variables, such as changes in operating hours, base load, and occupancy levels, should be included in the model if these are not energy conservation measures (ECMs) but variables that may change during the postretrofit period.

Environmental variables that meet these criteria for modeling heating and cooling energy use include outdoor air dry-bulb temperature, solar radiation, and outdoor specific humidity. Some of these are difficult to estimate or measure in an actual building and hence are not good candidates for regressor variables. Further, some of the variables vary little. Although their effect on energy use may be important, a data-driven model will implicitly lump their effect into the parameter that represents constant load. In commercial buildings, internally generated loads, such as the heat given off by people, lights, and electrical equipment, also affect heating and cooling energy use. These internal loads are difficult to measure in their entirety given the ambiguous nature of occupant and latent loads. However, monitored electricity used by internal lights and equipment is a good surrogate for total internal sensible loads (Reddy et al. 1999). For example, when the building is fully occupied, it is also likely to be experiencing high internal electric loads, and vice versa.

The effect of environmental variables is important for buildings such as offices but may be less so for mixed-use buildings (e.g., hotels and hospitals) and buildings such as retail buildings, schools, and assembly buildings. Differences in HVAC system behavior during occupied and unoccupied periods can be modeled by a dummy or indicator variable (Draper and Smith 1981). For some office buildings, there seems to be little need to include a dummy variable, but its inclusion in the general functional form adds flexibility.

Several standard statistical tests evaluate the goodness-of-fit of the model and the degree of influence that each independent variable exerts on the response variable (Draper and Smith 1981; Neter et al. 1989). Although energy use in fact depends on several variables, there are strong practical incentives for identifying the simplest model that results in acceptable accuracy. Multivariate models require more metering and are unusable if even one of the variables becomes unavailable. In addition, some regressor variables may be linearly correlated. This condition, called **multicollinearity**, can result in large uncertainty in the estimates of the regression coefficients (i.e., unintended error) and can also lead to poorer model prediction accuracy compared to a model where the regressors are not linearly correlated.

Several authors recommend using **principal component analysis (PCA)** to overcome multicollinearity effects. PCA was one of the strongest analysis methods in the ASHRAE Predictor Shootout I and II contests (Haberl and Thamilseran 1996; Kreider and Haberl 1994). Analysis of multiyear monitored daily energy use in a grocery store found a clear superiority of PCA over multivariate regression models (Ruch et al. 1993), but this conclusion is unproven for commercial building energy use in general. A more general evaluation by Reddy and Claridge (1994) of both analysis techniques using synthetic data from four different U.S. locations found that injudicious use of PCA may exacerbate rather than overcome problems associated with multicollinearity. Draper and Smith (1981) also caution against indiscriminate use of PCA.

The functional basis of air-side heating and cooling use in various HVAC system types has been addressed by Reddy et al. (1995) and subsequently applied to monitored data in commercial buildings (Katipamula et al. 1994, 1998). Because quadratic and cross-product terms of engineering equations are not usually picked up by multivariate models, strictly linear energy use models are often the only option.

In addition to T_o, internal electric equipment and lighting load E_{int}, solar loads q_{sol}, and latent effects via the outdoor dew-point temperature T_{dp} are candidate regressor variables. In commercial buildings, a major portion of the latent load derives from fresh air ventilation. However, this load appears only when the outdoor air dew-point temperature exceeds the cooling coil temperature. Hence, the term $(T_{dp} - T_s)^+$ (where the + sign indicates that the term is to be set to zero if negative, and T_s is the mean surface temperature of the cooling coil, typically about 11 to 13°C) is a more realistic descriptor of the latent loads than is T_{dp} alone. Using $(T_{dp} - T_s)^+$ as a regressor in the model is a simplification that seems to yield good accuracy.

Therefore, a multivariate linear regression model with an engineering basis has the following structure:

$$Q_{bldg} = \beta_0 + \beta_1(T_o - \beta_3)^- + \beta_2(T_o - \beta_3)^+ + \beta_4(T_{dp} - \beta_6)^- + \beta_5(T_{dp} - \beta_6)^+ + \beta_7 q_{sol} + \beta_8 E_{int} \quad (67)$$

Based on the preceding discussion, $\beta_4 = 0$. Introducing indicator variable terminology (Draper and Smith 1981), Equation (67) becomes

$$Q_{bldg} = a + bT_o + cI + dIT_o + eT_{dp}^+ + fq_{sol} + gE_{int} \quad (68)$$

where the indicator variable I is introduced to handle the change in slope of the energy use due to T_o. The variable I is set equal to 1 for T_o values to the right of the change point (i.e., for high T_o range) and set equal to 0 for low T_o values. As with the single-variate segmented models (i.e., 3-P and 4-P models), a search method is used to determine the change point that minimizes the total sum of squares of residuals (Fels 1986; Kissock et al. 1993).

Katipamula et al. (1994) found that Equation (68), appropriate for VAV systems, could be simplified for constant-volume HVAC systems:

$$Q_{bldg} = a + bT_o + eT_{dp}^+ + fq_{sol} + gE_{int} \quad (69)$$

Note that instead of using $(T_{dp} - T_s)^+$, the absolute humidity potential $(W_0 - W_s)^+$ could also be used, where W_0 is the outdoor absolute humidity, and W_s is the absolute humidity level at the dew point of the cooling coil (typically about 0.009 kg/kg). A final aspect to keep in mind is that the term T_{dp}^+ should be omitted from the regressor variable set when regressing heating energy use, because there are no latent loads on a heating coil.

These multivariate models are very accurate for daily time scales and slightly less so for hourly time scales. This is because changes in the way the building is operated during the day and the night lead to different relative effects of the various regressors on energy use, which cannot be accurately modeled by one single hourly model. Breaking up energy use data into hourly bins corresponding to each hour of the day and then identifying 24 individual hourly models leads to appreciably greater accuracy (Katipamula et al. 1994).

Polynomial Models. Historically, polynomial models have been widely used as pure statistical models to model the behavior of equipment such as pumps, fans, and chillers (Stoecker and Jones 1982). The theoretical aspects of calculating pump performance are well understood and documented. Pump capacity and efficiency are calculated from measurements of pump pressure, flow rate, and pump electrical power input. Phelan et al. (1996) studied the predictive ability of linear and quadratic models for electricity consumed by pumps and water mass flow rate, and concluded that quadratic models are superior to linear models. For fans, Phelan et al. (1996) studied the predictive ability of linear and quadratic polynomial single-variate models of fan electricity consumption as a function of supply air mass flow rate, and concluded that, although quadratic models are superior in terms of predicting energy use, the linear model seems to be the better overall predictor of both energy use and demand (i.e., maximum monthly power consumed by the fan). This is a noteworthy conclusion given that a third-order polynomial is warranted analytically as well as from monitored field data presented by previous authors (e.g., Englander and Norford 1992; Lorenzetti and Norford 1993).

Polynomial models have been used to correlate chiller (or evaporator) thermal cooling capacity or load Q_{evap} and the electrical power consumed by the chiller (or compressor) E_{comp} with the relevant number of influential physical parameters. For example, based on the functional form of the DOE-2 building simulation software (York and Cappiello 1982), models for part-load performance of energy equipment and plant, E_{comp}, can be modeled as the following triquadratic polynomial:

$$E_{comp} = a + bQ_{evap} + cT_{cond}^{in} + dT_{evap}^{out} + eQ_{evap}^2 + fT_{cond}^{in\,2} + gT_{evap}^{out\,2} + hQ_{evap}T_{cond}^{in} + iT_{evap}^{out}Q_{evap} + jT_{cond}^{in}T_{evap}^{out} + kQ_{evap}T_{cond}^{in}T_{evap}^{out} \quad (70)$$

In this model, there are 11 model parameters to identify. However, because all of them are unlikely to be statistically significant, a step-wise regression to the sample data set yields the optimal set of parameters to retain in a given model. Other authors, such as Braun (1992), have used slightly different polynomial forms.

Physical Models. In contrast to polynomial models, which have no physical basis (merely a convenient statistical one), physical models are based on fundamental thermodynamic or heat transfer considerations. These types of models are usually associated with the parameter estimation approach. Often, physical models are preferred because they generally have fewer parameters, and their mathematical formulation can be traced to actual physical principles that govern the performance of the building or equipment. Hence, model coefficients tend to be more robust, leading to sounder model predictions. Only a few studies have used steady-state physical models for parameter estimation relating to commercial building energy use [e.g., Reddy et al. (1999)]. Unlike in single-family residences, it is difficult to perform elaborately planned experiments in large buildings and obtain representative values of indoor fluctuations.

The generalized Gordon and Ng (GN) model (Gordon and Ng 2000) is a simple, analytical, universal model for chiller performance based on first principles of thermodynamics and linearized heat losses. The model predicts the dependent chiller coefficient of performance (COP) [the ratio of chiller (or evaporator) thermal cooling capacity Q_{ch} to electrical power E consumed by the chiller] with specially chosen independent, easily measurable parameters such as the fluid (water or air) temperature entering the condenser T_{cdi}, fluid temperature entering the evaporator T_{cdi}, and the thermal cooling capacity of the evaporator. The GN model is a three-parameter model in the following form:

$$\left(\frac{1}{COP}+1\right)\frac{T_{chi}}{T_{cdi}}-1 = a_1\frac{T_{chi}}{Q_{ch}}+a_2\frac{(T_{cdi}-T_{chi})}{T_{cdi}Q_{ch}} + a_3\frac{(1/COP+1)Q_{ch}}{T_{cdi}} \tag{71a}$$

where temperatures are in absolute units.

Substituting the following,

$$x_1=\frac{T_{chi}}{Q_{ch}},\quad x_2=\frac{(T_{cdi}-T_{chi})}{T_{cdi}Q_{ch}},\quad x_3=\frac{(1/COP+1)Q_{ch}}{T_{cdi}} \tag{71b}$$

and $$y=\left(\frac{1}{COP}+1\right)\frac{T_{chi}}{T_{cdi}}-1$$

the model given by Equation (71a) becomes

$$y=a_1x_1+a_2x_2+a_3x_3 \tag{71c}$$

which is a three-parameter linear model with no intercept term. The parameters of the model in Equation (71c) have the following physical meaning:

$a_1 = \Delta S$ = total internal entropy production in chiller

$a_2 = Q_{leak}$ = heat losses (or gains) from (or into) chiller

$a_3 = R$ = total heat exchanger thermal resistance = $1/C_{cd} + 1/C_{ch}$, where C is effective thermal conductance

Gordon and Ng (2000) point out that Q_{leak} is typically an order of magnitude smaller than the other terms, but it is not negligible for accurate modeling, and should be retained in the model if the other two parameters identified are to be used for chiller diagnostics. The same linear model structure as Equation (71c) can be used if the fluid temperature leaving the evaporator T_{cho} is used instead of T_{chi}. However, the physical interpretation of the term a_3 is modified accordingly.

Reddy and Anderson (2002) and Sreedharan and Haves (2001) found that the GN and multivariate polynomial (MP) models were comparable in their predictive abilities. The GN model requires much less data if selected judiciously [even four well-chosen data points can yield accurate models, as demonstrated by Corcoran and Reddy (2003)]. Jiang and Reddy (2003) tested the GN model against more than 50 data sets covering various generic types and sizes of water-cooled chillers (single- and double-stage centrifugal chillers with inlet guide vanes and variable-speed drives, screw, scroll), and found excellent predictive ability (coefficient of variation of RMSE in the range of 2 to 5%).

Dynamic Models

In general, steady-state data-driven models are used with monthly and daily data containing one or more independent variables. Dynamic data-driven models are usually used with hourly or subhourly data in cases where the building's thermal mass is significant enough to delay heat gains or losses. Dynamic models traditionally required solving a set of differential equations. Disadvantages of dynamic data-driven models include their complexity and the need for more detailed measurements to tune the model. More information on measurements, including whole-building metering, retrofit isolation metering, and whole-building calibrated simulation, can be found in ASHRAE *Guideline* 14, Measurement of Energy and Demand Savings, and the International Performance Measurement and Verification Protocol (IPMVP) (U.S. Department of Energy 2001a, 2001b, 2003). Unlike steady-state data-driven models, dynamic data-driven models usually require a high degree of user interaction and knowledge of the building or system being modeled.

Several residential energy studies have used dynamic data-driven models based on parameter estimation approaches, usually involving intrusive data gathering. Rabl (1988) classified the various types of dynamic data-driven models used for whole-building energy use identified the common underlying features of these models. There are essentially four different types of model formulations: thermal-network, time series, differential equation, and modal, all of which qualify as parameter-estimation approaches. Table 1 lists several pertinent studies in each category. A few studies (Hammersten 1984; Rabl 1988; Reddy 1989) evaluated these different approaches with the same data set. A number of papers reported results of applying different techniques, such as thermal-network and ARMA models, to residential and commercial building energy use (see Table 1). Examples of dynamic data-driven models for commercial building are found in Andersen and Brandemuehl (1992), Braun (1990), and Rabl (1988).

Dynamic data-driven models based on pure statistical approaches have also been reported. Two examples are machine learning (Miller and Seem 1991) and artificial neural networks (Kreider and Haberl 1994; Kreider and Wang 1991; Miller and Seem 1991).

Neural networks are considered to be intuitive because they learn by example rather than by following programmed rules. The ability to "learn" is one of their key aspects. A neural network consists of one input layer (which can contain one or more inputs), one or more hidden layers, and an output or target layer. One challenge of this technology is to construct a net with sufficient complexity to learn accurately without imposing excessive computational time.

The weights of a net are initiated with small random numbers. Then, the weights are adjusted iteratively or "trained" so that applying a set of inputs produces the desired set of outputs. Usually, a network is trained with a training data set that consists of many input/output pairs. Artificial neural networks have been trained by a wide variety of methods (McClelland and Rumelhart 1988, Wasserman 1989), including back propagation.

Neural networks have been useful in modeling energy use in commercial buildings for

- Predicting what a properly operating building should be doing compared to actual operation. If there is a difference, it can be used in an expert system to produce early diagnoses of building operation problems.
- Predicting what a building, before an energy retrofit, would have consumed under present conditions. When compared to the measured consumption of the retrofitted building, the difference represents a good estimate of the energy savings due to the retrofit. This represents one of the few ways that actual energy savings can be determined after the preretrofit building configuration has ceased to exist.

EXAMPLES USING DATA-DRIVEN METHODS

Modeling Utility Bill Data

The following example (taken from Sonderegger 1998) illustrates a utility bill analysis. Assume that values of utility bills over an entire year have been measured. To obtain the equation coefficients through regression, the utility bills must be normalized by the length of the time interval between utility bills. This is equivalent to expressing all utility bills, degree-days, and other independent variables by their daily averages.

Appropriate modeling software is used in which values are assumed for heating and cooling balance points; from these, the corresponding heating and cooling degree-days for each utility bill period are determined. Repeated regression is done till the regression equation represents the best fit to the meter data. The model coefficients are then assumed to be tuned. Some programs allow direct determination of these optimal model parameters without the user's manual tuning of the parameters.

A widely used statistic to gage the goodness-of-fit of the model is the **coefficient of determination R^2**. A value of $R^2 = 1$ indicates a perfect correlation between actual data and the regression equation; a value of $R^2 = 0$ indicates no correlation. For tuning for a performance contract, as a rule of thumb the value of R^2 should never be less than 0.75.

When more than one independent variable is included in the regression, R^2 is no longer sufficient to determine the goodness-of-fit. The standard error of the estimate of the coefficients becomes the more important determinant. The smaller the standard error compared to the coefficient's magnitude, the more reliable the coefficient estimate. To identify the significance of individual coefficients, ***t*-statistics** (or ***t*-values**) are used. These are simply the ratio of the coefficient estimate divided by the standard error of the estimate.

The coefficient of each variable included in the regression has a *t*-statistic. For a coefficient to be statistically meaningful, the absolute value of its *t*-statistic must be at least 2.0. In other words, under no circumstances should a variable be included in a regression if the standard error of its coefficient estimate is greater than half the magnitude of the coefficient (even when including a variable that increases the R^2). Generally, including more variables in a regression results in a higher R^2, but the significance of most individual coefficients is likely to decrease.

Figure 19 illustrates how well a regression fit captures measured baseline energy use in a hospital building. Cooling degree-days are found to be a significant variable, with the best fit for a base temperature of 12.2°C.

Individual utility bills may be unsuitable to develop a baseline and should be excluded from the regression. For example, a bill may be atypically high because of a one-time equipment malfunction that was subsequently repaired. However, it is often tempting to look for reasons to exclude bills that fall far from "the line" and not question those that are close to it. For example, bills for periods containing vacations or production shutdowns may look anomalously low, but excluding them from the regression would result in a chronic overestimate of the future baseline during the same period.

Neural Network Models

Figure 20 shows results for a single neural network typical of several hundred networks constructed for an academic engineering center located in central Texas. The cooling load is created by solar gains, internal gains, outdoor air sensible heat, and outdoor air humidity loads. The neural network is used to predict the preretrofit energy consumption for comparison with measured consumption of the retrofitted building. Six months of preretrofit data were available to train the network. Solid lines show the known building consumption data, and dashed lines show the neural network predictions. This figure shows that a neural network trained for one period (September 1989) can predict energy consumption well into the future (in this case, January 1990).

The network used for this prediction had two hidden layers. The input layer contained eight neurons that receive eight different types of input data as listed below. The output layer consisted of one neuron that gave the output datum (chilled-water consumption). Each training fact (i.e., training data set), therefore, contained eight input data (independent variables) and one pattern datum (dependent variable). The eight hourly input data used in each hour's data vector were selected on physical bases (Kreider and Rabl 1994) and were as follows:

- Hour number (0 to 2300)
- Ambient dry-bulb temperature
- Horizontal insolation
- Humidity ratio
- Wind speed
- Weekday/weekend binary flag (0, 1)

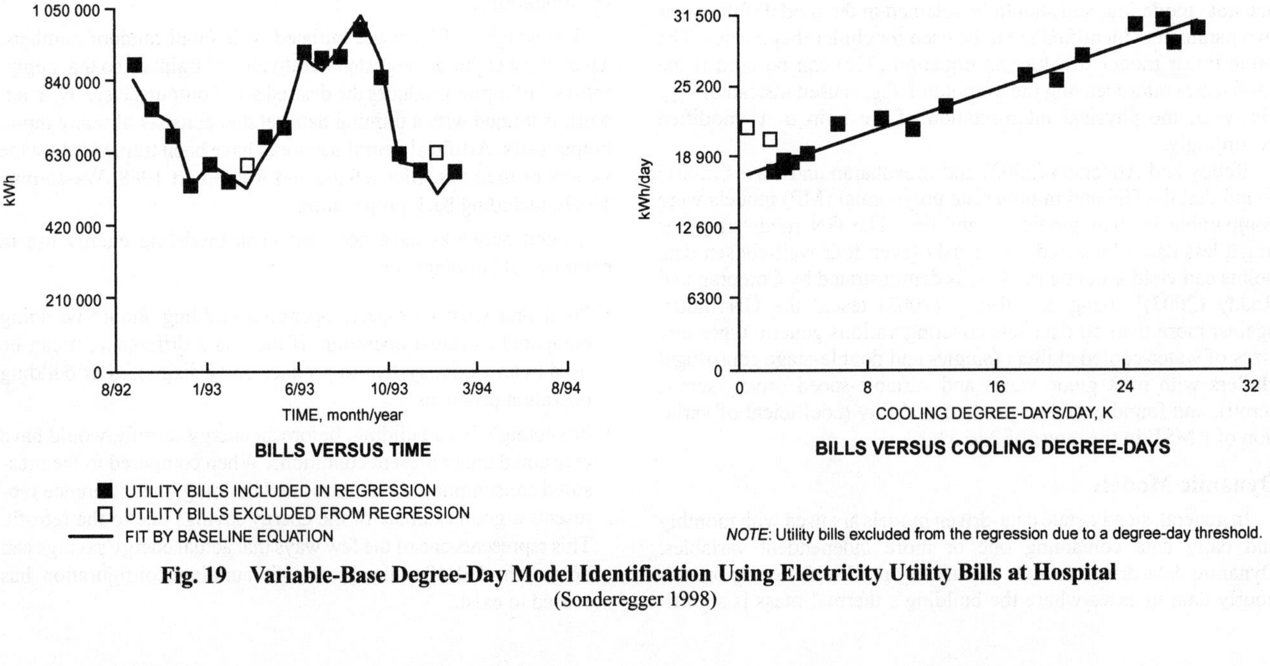

Fig. 19 Variable-Base Degree-Day Model Identification Using Electricity Utility Bills at Hospital
(Sonderegger 1998)

- Past hour's chilled-water consumption
- Second past hour's chilled-water consumption

These measured independent variables were able to predict chilled-water use to an RMS error of less than 4% (JCEM 1992).

Choosing an optimal network's configuration for a given problem remains an art. The number of hidden neurons and layers must be sufficient to meet the requirement of the given application. However, if too many neurons and layers are used, the network tends to memorize data rather than learning (i.e., finding the underlying patterns in the data). Further, choosing an excessively large number of hidden layers significantly increases the required training time for certain learning algorithms. Anstett and Kreider (1993), Krarti et al. (1998), Kreider and Wang (1991), and Wang and Kreider (1992) report additional case studies for commercial buildings.

MODEL SELECTION

Steady-state and dynamic data-driven models can be used with energy management and control systems to predict energy use (Kreider and Haberl 1994). Hourly or daily comparisons of measured versus predicted energy use can be used to determine whether systems are being left on unnecessarily or are in need of maintenance. Combinations of predicted energy use and a knowledge-based system can indicate above-normal energy use and diagnose the possible cause of the malfunction if sufficient historical information has been previously gathered (Haberl and Claridge 1987). Hourly systems that use artificial neural networks have also been constructed (Kreider and Wang 1991).

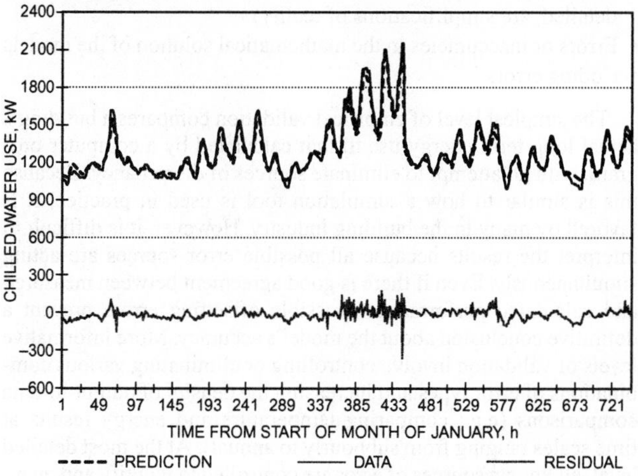

Fig. 20 Neural Network Prediction of Whole-Building, Hourly Chilled-Water Consumption for Commercial Building

More information on data-driven models can be found in the ASHRAE *Inverse Modeling Toolkit* (Haberl et al. 2003; Kissock et al. 2003). This toolkit contains FORTRAN 90 and executable code for performing linear and change-point linear regressions, variable-based degree-days, multilinear regression, and combined regressions. It also includes a complete test suite of data sets for testing all models.

Table 10 presents a decision diagram for selecting a forward or data-driven model where use of the model, degree of difficulty in understanding and applying the model, time scale for data used by the model, calculation time, and input variables used by the models are the criteria used to choose a particular model.

MODEL VALIDATION AND TESTING

ANSI/ASHRAE *Standard* 140, Method of Test for the Evaluation of Building Energy Analysis Computer Programs, was developed to identify and diagnose differences in predictions that may be caused by algorithmic differences, modeling limitations, or coding or input errors. *Standard* 140 allows all elements of a complete validation approach to be added as they become available. This structure corresponds to the following validation methodology, with subdivisions creating a matrix of six areas for testing:

1. Comparative tests—building envelope
2. Comparative tests—mechanical equipment
3. Analytical verification—building envelope
4. Analytical verification—mechanical equipment
5. Empirical validation—building envelope
6. Empirical validation—mechanical equipment

The current set of tests focus on categories 1 and 4. These tests are based on procedures developed by the National Renewable Energy Laboratory and field-tested by the International Energy Agency (IEA) over three IEA research tasks (Judkoff and Neymark 1995a; Neymark and Judkoff 2002). Additional tests are being developed under ASHRAE research projects (Spitler et al. 2001; Yuill and Haberl 2002) and under joint IEA Solar Heating and Cooling Programme/Energy Conservation in Buildings and Community Systems Task 34/Annex 43 (Judkoff and Neymark 2004) that are intended to fill in other categories of the validation matrix.

Table 10 Capabilities of Different Forward and Data-Driven Modeling Methods

Methods	Use[a]	Difficulty	Time Scale[b]	Calc. Time	Variables[c]	Accuracy
Simple linear regression	ES	Simple	D, M	Very fast	*T*	Low
Multiple linear regression	D, ES	Simple	D, M	Fast	*T, H, S, W, t*	Medium
ASHRAE bin method and data-driven bin method	ES	Moderate	H	Fast	*T*	Medium
Change-point models	D, ES	Simple	H, D, M	Fast	*T*	Medium
ASHRAE TC 4.7 modified bin method	ES, DE	Moderate	H	Medium	*T, S, tm*	Medium
Artificial neural networks	D, ES, C	Complex	S, H	Fast	*T, H, S, W, t, tm*	High
Thermal network	D, ES, C	Complex	S, H	Fast	*T, S, tm*	High
Fourier series analysis	D, ES, C	Moderate	S, H	Medium	*T, H, S, W, t, tm*	High
ARMA model	D, ES, C	Moderate	S, H	Medium	*T, H, S, W, t, tm*	High
Modal analysis	D, ES, C	Complex	S, H	Medium	*T, H, S, W, t, tm*	High
Differential equation	D, ES, C	Complex	S, H	Fast	*T, H, S, W, t, tm*	High
Computer simulation (component-based)	D, ES, C, DE	Very complex	S, H	Slow	*T, H, S, W, t, tm*	Medium
(fixed schematic)	D, ES, DE	Very complex	H	Slow	*T, H, S, W, t, tm*	Medium
Computer emulation	D, C	Very complex	S, H	Very slow	*T, H, S, W, t, tm*	High

Notes:
[a]Use shown includes diagnostics (D), energy savings calculations (ES), design (DE), and control (C).
[b]Time scales shown are hourly (H), daily (D), monthly (M), and subhourly (S).
[c]Variables include temperature (*T*), humidity (*H*), solar (*S*), wind (*W*), time (*t*), and thermal mass (*tm*).

METHODOLOGICAL BASIS

There are three ways to evaluate a whole-building energy simulation program's accuracy (Judkoff et al. 1983; Neymark and Judkoff 2002):

- *Empirical validation*, which compares calculated results from a program, subroutine, algorithm, or software object to monitored data from a real building, test cell, or laboratory experiment
- *Analytical verification*, which compares outputs from a program, subroutine, algorithm, or software object to results from a known analytical solution or a generally accepted numerical method calculation for isolated heat transfer under very simple, highly constrained boundary conditions
- *Comparative testing*, which compares a program to itself or to other programs

Table 11 compares these techniques (Judkoff 1988). In this table, the term "model" is the representation of reality for a given physical behavior. For example, heat transfer may be simulated with one-, two-, or three-dimensional thermal conduction models. The term "solution process" encompasses the mathematics and computer coding to solve a given model. The solution process for a model can be perfect, while the model remains inappropriate for a given physical situation, such as using a one-dimensional conduction model where two-dimensional conduction dominates. The term "truth standard" represents the standard of accuracy for predicting real behavior. An analytical solution is a "mathematical truth standard," but only tests the solution process for a model, not the appropriateness of the model. An approximate truth standard from an experiment tests both the solution process and appropriateness of the model within experimental uncertainty. The ultimate (or "absolute") validation truth standard would be comparison of simulation results with a perfectly performed empirical experiment, with all simulation inputs perfectly defined.

Establishing an absolute truth standard for evaluating a program's ability to analyze physical behavior requires empirical validation, but this is only possible within the range of measurement uncertainty, including that related to instruments, spatial and temporal discretization, and the overall experimental design. Test cells and buildings are large, relatively complex experimental objects. The exact design details, material properties, and construction in the field may not be known, so there is some uncertainty about the simulation model inputs that accurately represent the experimental object. Meticulous care is required to describe the experimental apparatus as clearly as possible to modelers to minimize this uncertainty. This includes experimental determination of as many material properties as possible, including overall building parameters such as overall steady-state heat transmission coefficient, infiltration rate, and thermal capacitance. Also required are detailed meteorological measurements. For example, many experiments measure global horizontal solar radiation, but very few experiments measure the splits between direct, diffuse, and ground reflected radiation, all of which are inputs to many whole-building energy simulation programs.

The National Renewable Energy Laboratory (NREL) divides empirical validation into different levels, because many validation studies produced inconclusive results. The levels of validation depend on the degree of control over possible sources of error in a simulation. These error sources consist of seven types, divided into two groups:

External Error Types

- Differences between actual building microclimate versus weather input used by the program
- Differences between actual schedules, control strategies, effects of occupant behavior, and other effects from the real building versus those assumed by the program user
- User error deriving building input files
- Differences between actual physical properties of the building (including HVAC systems) versus those input by the user

Internal Error Types

- Differences between actual thermal transfer mechanisms in the real building and its HVAC systems versus the simplified model of those processes in the simulation (all models, no matter how detailed, are simplifications of reality)
- Errors or inaccuracies in the mathematical solution of the models
- Coding errors

The simplest level of empirical validation compares a building's actual long-term energy use to that calculated by a computer program, with no attempt to eliminate sources of discrepancy. Because this is similar to how a simulation tool is used in practice, it is favored by many in the building industry. However, it is difficult to interpret the results because all possible error sources are acting simultaneously. Even if there is good agreement between measured and calculated performance, possible offsetting errors prevent a definitive conclusion about the model's accuracy. More informative levels of validation involve controlling or eliminating various combinations of error types and increasing the density of output-to-data comparisons (e.g., comparing temperature and energy results at time scales ranging from subhourly to annual). At the most detailed level, all known sources of error are controlled to identify and quantify unknown error sources and to reveal causal relationships associated with error sources.

This principle also applies to intermodel comparative testing and analytical verification. The more realistic the test case, the more difficult it is to establish causality and diagnose problems; the simpler

Table 11 Validation Techniques

Technique	Advantages	Disadvantages

Empirical (test of model and solution process)	• Approximate truth standard within experimental accuracy
	• Any level of complexity
		• Experimental uncertainties:
		  • Instrument calibration, spatial/temporal discretization
		  • Imperfect knowledge/specification of experimental object (building) being simulated
		• High-quality, detailed measurements are expensive and time-consuming
		• Only a limited number of test conditions are practical

Analytical (test of solution process)	• No input uncertainty • Exact mathematical truth standard for given model • Inexpensive	• No test of model validity • Limited to highly constrained cases for which analytical solutions can be derived
Comparative (relative test of model and solution process)	• No input uncertainty • Any level of complexity • Many diagnostic comparisons possible • Inexpensive and quick	• No absolute truth standard (only statistically based acceptance ranges are possible)

Source: Neymark and Judkoff (2002).

Table 12 Types of Extrapolation

Obtainable Data Points	Extrapolation
A few climates	Many climates
Short-term total energy use	Long-term total energy use, or vice versa
Short-term (hourly) temperatures and/or fluxes	Long-term total energy use, or vice versa
A few equipment performance points	Many equipment performance points
A few buildings representing a few sets of variable and parameter combinations	Many buildings representing many sets of variable and parameter combinations, or vice versa
Small-scale: simple test cells, buildings, and mechanical systems; laboratory experiments	Large-scale complex buildings with complex HVAC systems, or vice versa

Source: Neymark and Judkoff (2002).

and more controlled the test case, the easier it is to pinpoint sources of error or inaccuracy. Methodically building up to realistic cases is useful for testing interactions between algorithms modeling linked mechanisms.

A comparison between measured and calculated performance represents a small region in an immense *N*-dimensional parameter space. Investigators are constrained to exploring relatively few regions in this space, yet would like to be assured that the results are not coincidental (e.g., not a result of offsetting errors) and do represent the validity of the simulation elsewhere in the parameter space. Analytical and comparative techniques minimize the uncertainty of extrapolations around the limited number of sampled empirical domains. Table 12 classifies these extrapolations. Use of the term "vice versa" in Table 12 is intended to mean that the extrapolation can go both ways (e.g., from short-term to long-term data and from long-term to short-term data). This does not mean that such extrapolations are correct, but only that researchers and practitioners have either explicitly or implicitly made such inferences in the past.

Figure 21 shows one process to combine analytical, empirical, and comparative techniques. These three techniques may also be used together in other ways; for example, intermodel comparisons may be done before an empirical validation exercise, to better define the experiment and to help estimate experimental uncertainty by propagating all known error sources through one or more whole-building energy simulation programs (Hunn et al. 1982; Lomas et al. 1994).

For the path shown in Figure 21, the first step is running the code against analytical verification test cases to check its mathematical solution. Discrepancies must be corrected before proceeding further.

Second, the code is run against high-quality empirical validation data, and errors are corrected. Diagnosing error sources can be quite difficult and is an area of research in itself. Comparative techniques can be used to create diagnostics procedures (Judkoff 1988; Judkoff and Neymark 1995a, 1995b; Judkoff et al. 1980, 1983; Morck 1986; Neymark and Judkoff 2002; Spitler et al. 2001) and better define the experiments.

The third step is to check agreement of several different thermal solution and modeling approaches (that have passed through steps 1 and 2) in a variety of representative cases. This uses the comparative technique as an extrapolation tool. Deviations in the program predictions indicate areas for further investigation.

When programs successfully complete these three stages, they are considered validated for cases where acceptable agreement was achieved (i.e., for the range of building, climate, and mechanical system types represented by the test cases). Once several detailed simulation programs have satisfactorily completed the procedure, other programs and simplified design tools can be tested against them. A validation code does not necessarily represent truth. It does represent a set of algorithms that have been shown, through a repeatable procedure, to perform according to the current state of the art.

NREL methodology for validating building energy simulation programs has been generally accepted by the International Energy

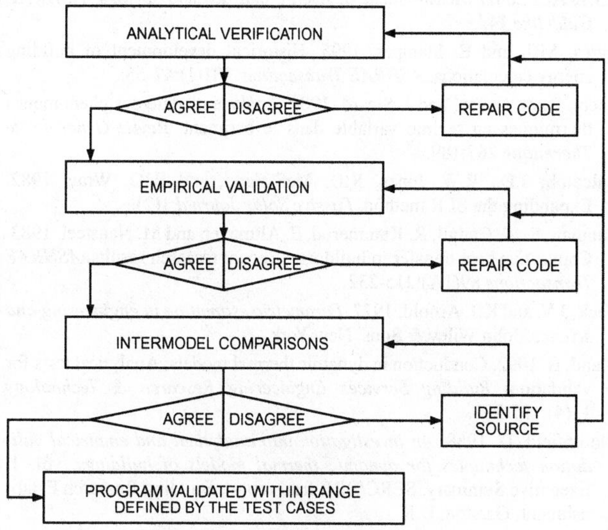

Fig. 21 Validation Method
(Neymark and Judkoff 2002)

Agency (Irving 1988), ASHRAE *Standard* 140 and Addendum p to ASHRAE *Standard* 90.1, and elsewhere, with refinements suggested by other researchers (Bland 1992; Bloomfield 1988, 1999; Guyon and Palomo 1999b; Irving 1988; Lomas 1991; Lomas and Bowman 1987; Lomas and Eppel 1992). Additionally, the Commission of European Communities has conducted considerable work under the PASSYS program (Jensen 1989; Jensen and van de Perre 1991).

SUMMARY OF PREVIOUS TESTING AND VALIDATION WORK

Neymark and Judkoff (2002) summarize approximately 100 articles and research papers on analytical, empirical, and comparative testing, from 1980 to 2004. Some of these works are listed by subject in the Bibliography.

REFERENCES

Alamdari, F. and G.P. Hammond. 1982. Time-dependent convective heat transfer in warm-air heated rooms. *Energy Conservation in the Built Environment: Proceedings of the CIB W67 Third International Symposium*, Dublin, pp. 209-220.

Alamdari, F. and G.P. Hammond. 1983. Improved data correlations for buoyancy-driven convection in rooms. *Building Services Engineering Research and Technology* 4(3):106-112.

Alereza, T. and T. Kusuda. 1982. Development of equipment seasonal performance models for simplified energy analysis methods. *ASHRAE Transactions* 88(2):249-262.

Altmayer, E.F., A.J. Gadgil, F.S. Bauman, and R.C. Kammerud. 1983. Correlations for convective heat transfer from room surfaces. *ASHRAE Transactions* 89(2A):61-77.

Andersen, I. and M.J. Brandemuehl. 1992. Heat storage in building thermal mass: A parametric study. *ASHRAE Transactions* 98(1):910-918.

Anstett, M. and J.F. Kreider. 1993. Application of artificial neural networks to commercial building energy use prediction. *ASHRAE Transactions* 99(1):505-517.

ASHRAE. 1995. *Bin and degree hour weather data for simplified energy calculations.*

ASHRAE. 2004. Energy standard for buildings except low-rise residential buildings. ANSI/ASHRAE/IESNA Addendum p to ANSI/ASHRAE/IESNA *Standard* 90.1-2004.

ASHRAE. 2004. Energy standard for buildings except low-rise residential buildings. ANSI/ASHRAE/IESNA *Standard* 90.1-2004.

ASHRAE. 2004. Standard method of test for the evaluation of building energy analysis computer programs. ANSI/ASHRAE *Standard* 140-2004.

ASHRAE. 2002. Measurement of energy and demand savings. ASHRAE *Guideline* 14.

Ayres, M.J. and E. Stamper. 1995. Historical development of building energy calculations. *ASHRAE Transactions* 101(1):47-55.

Bacot, P., A. Neveu, and J. Sicard. 1984. Analyse modale des phenomenes thermiques en regime variable dans le batiment. *Revue Generale de Thermique* 267:189.

Balcomb, J.D., R.W. Jones, R.D. McFarland, and W.O. Wray. 1982. Expanding the SLR method. *Passive Solar Journal* 1(2).

Bauman, F., A. Gadgil, R. Kammerud, E. Altmayer, and M. Nansteel. 1983. Convective heat transfer in buildings: Recent research results. *ASHRAE Transactions* 89(1A):215-232.

Beck, J.V. and K.J. Arnold, 1977. *Parametric estimation in engineering and science.* John Wiley & Sons, New York.

Bland, B. 1992. Conduction in dynamic thermal models: Analytical tests for validation. *Building Services Engineering Research & Technology* 13(4):197-208.

Bloomfield, D. 1988. *An investigation into analytical and empirical validation techniques for dynamic thermal models of buildings*, vol. 1, Executive Summary. SERC/BRE final report, Building Research Establishment, Garston, U.K.

Bloomfield. D. 1999. An overview of validation methods for energy and environmental software. *ASHRAE Transactions* 105(2).

Bohn, M.S., A.T. Kirkpatrick, and D.A. Olson. 1984. Experimental study of three-dimensional natural convection high-Rayleigh number. *Journal of Heat Transfer* 106:339-345.

Bonne, U. and J.E. Janssen. 1989. Efficiency and relative operating cost of central combustion heating system: IV, oil fired residential systems. *ASHRAE Transactions* 83(1):893-904.

Bourdouxhe, J.P., M. Grodent, J. Lebrun, and C. Saavedra. 1994a. A toolkit for primary HVAC system energy calculation—Part 1: Boiler model. *ASHRAE Transactions* 100(2):759-773.

Bourdouxhe, J.P., M. Grodent, J. Lebrun, C. Saavedra, and K. Silva. 1994b. A toolkit for primary HVAC system energy calculation—Part 2: Reciprocating chiller models. *ASHRAE Transactions* 100(2):774-786.

Bourdouxhe, J.P., M. Grodent, and C. Silva. 1994c. Cooling tower model developed in a toolkit for primary HVAC system energy calculation—Part 1: Model description and validation using catalog data. *Proceedings of the Fourth International Conference on System Simulation in Buildings*.

Bou-Saada, T. and J. Haberl. 1995a. A weather-day typing procedure for disaggregating hourly end-use loads in an electrically heated and cooled building from whole-building hourly data. *Proceedings of the 30th IECEC*, pp. 349-356.

Bou-Saada, T. and J. Haberl. 1995b. An improved procedure for developing calibrated hourly simulation models. *Proceedings of Building Simulation '95*. International Building Performance Simulation Association, Madison, WI.

Brandemuehl, M.J. 1993. *HVAC2 toolkit: Algorithms and subroutines for secondary HVAC systems energy calculations.* ASHRAE.

Brandemuehl, M.J. and S. Gabel. 1994. Development of a toolkit for secondary HVAC system energy calculations. *ASHRAE Transactions* 100(1):21-32.

Brandemuehl, M.J. and J.D. Bradford. 1999. Optimal supervisory control of cooling plants without storage. *Final Report* RP-823. ASHRAE.

Braun, J.E. 1988. *Methodologies for the design and control of chilled water systems.* Ph.D. dissertation, University of Wisconsin-Madison.

Braun, J.E. 1990. Reducing energy costs and peak electrical demand through optimal control of building thermal mass. *ASHRAE Transactions* 96(2):876-888.

Braun, J.E. 1992. A comparison of chiller-priority, storage-priority, and optimal control of an ice-storage system. *ASHRAE Transactions* 98(1): 893-902.

Bronson, D., S. Hinchey, J. Haberl, and D. O'Neal. 1992. A procedure for calibrating the DOE-2 simulation program to non-weather dependent loads. *ASHRAE Transactions* 98(1):636-652.

Buhl, W.F., A.E. Erdem, J.M. Nataf, F.C. Winkelmann, M.A. Moshier, and E.F. Sowell. 1990. The US EKS: Advances in the SPANK-based energy kernel system. *Proceedings of the Third International Conference on System Simulation in Buildings*, pp. 107-150.

Buhl, W.F., A.E. Erdem, F.C. Winkelmann, and E.F. Sowell. 1993. Recent improvements in SPARK: Strong component decomposition, multivalued objects and graphical interface. *Proceedings of Building Simulation '93*, pp. 283-390. International Building Performance Simulation Association.

Carroll, J.A. 1980. An "MRT method" of computing radiant energy exchange in rooms. *Systems Simulation and Economic Analysis*, San Diego, pp. 343-348.

Chandra, S. and A.A. Kerestecioglu. 1984. Heat transfer in naturally ventilated rooms: Data from full-scale measurements. *ASHRAE Transactions* 90(1B):211-224.

Chi, J. and G.E. Kelly. 1978. A method for estimating the seasonal performance of residential gas and oil-fired heating systems. *ASHRAE Transactions* 84(1):405.

Cinquemani, V., J.R. Owenby, and R.G. Baldwin. 1978. Input data for solar systems. U.S. Department of Energy *Report* No. E(49-26)1041.

Clark, D.R. 1985. *HVACSIM+ building systems and equipment simulation program: Reference manual.* NBSIR 84-2996, U.S. Department of Commerce, Washington, D.C.

Clarke, J.A. 2001. *Energy simulation in building design*, 2nd ed. Butterworth-Heinemann, Oxford.

Claridge, D. 1988a. Design methods for earth-contact heat transfer. *Progress in Solar Energy*, K. Boer, ed. American Solar Energy Society, Boulder, CO.

Claridge, D. 1998b. A perspective on methods for analysis of measured energy data from commercial buildings. *ASME Journal of Solar Energy Engineering* 120:150.

Claridge, D.E., M. Krarti, and M. Bida. 1987. A validation study of variable-base degree-day cooling calculations. *ASHRAE Transactions* 93(2):90-104.

Cole, R.J. 1976. The longwave radiation incident upon the external surface of buildings. *The Building Services Engineer* 44:195-206.

Cooper, K.W. and D.R. Tree. 1973. A re-evaluation of the average convection coefficient for flow past a wall. *ASHRAE Transactions* 79:48-51.

Corcoran, J.P. and T.A. Reddy. 2003. Improving the process of certified and witnessed factory testing for chiller procurement. *ASHRAE Transactions* 109(1).

Corson, G.C. 1992. Input-output sensitivity of building energy simulations. *ASHRAE Transactions* 98(1):618.

Crawley, D.B., L.K. Lawrie, F.C. Winkelmann, W.F. Buhl, Y. Joe Huang, C.O. Pedersen, R.K. Strand, R.J. Liesen, D.E. Fisher, M.J. Witte, and J. Glazer. 2001. EnergyPlus: Creating a new-generation building energy simulation program. *Energy and Buildings* 33(4):319-331.

Cumali, Z., A.O. Sezgen, R. Sullivan, R.C. Kammerud, E. Bales, and L.B. Bass. 1979. Extensions of methods used in analyzing building thermal loads. *Proceedings of the Thermal Performance of the Exterior Envelopes of Buildings*, pp. 411-420.

Davies, M.G. 1988. Design models to handle radiative and convective exchange in a room. *ASHRAE Transactions* 94(2):173-195.

DeCicco, J.M. 1990. Applying a linear model to diagnose boiler fuel consumption. *ASHRAE Transactions* 96(1):296-304.

Dhar, A. 1995. *Development of Fourier series and artificial neural network approaches to model hourly energy use in commercial buildings.* Ph.D. dissertation, ME Department, Texas A&M University.

Dhar, A., T.A. Reddy, and D.E. Claridge. 1998. Modeling hourly energy use in commercial buildings with Fourier series functional forms. *Journal of Solar Energy Engineering* 120:217.

Dhar, A., T.A. Reddy, and D.E. Claridge. 1999a. A Fourier series model to predict hourly heating and cooling energy use in commercial buildings with outdoor temperature as the only weather variable. *Journal of Solar Energy Engineering* 121:47-53.

Dhar, A., T.A. Reddy, and D.E. Claridge. 1999b. Generalization of the Fourier series approach to model hourly energy use in commercial buildings. *Journal of Solar Energy Engineering* 121:54-62.

Draper, N. and H. Smith. 1981. *Applied regression analysis*, 2nd ed. John Wiley & Sons, New York.

Elmahdy, A.H. and G.P. Mitalas. 1977. A simple model for cooling and dehumidifying coils for use in calculating energy requirements for buildings. *ASHRAE Transactions* 83(2):103-117.

Englander, S.L. and L.K. Norford. 1992. Saving fan energy in VAV systems—Part 1: Analysis of a variable-speed-drive retrofit. *ASHRAE Transactions* 98(1):3-18.

Erbs, D.G., S.A. Klein, and W.A. Beckman. 1983. Estimation of degree-days and ambient temperature bin data from monthly-average temperatures. *ASHRAE Journal* 25(6):60.

Fels, M., ed. 1986. Measuring energy savings: The scorekeeping approach. *Energy and Buildings* 9.

Fels, M. and M. Goldberg. 1986. Refraction of PRISM results in components of saved energy. *Energy and Buildings* 9:169.

Fracastoro, G., M. Masoero, and M. Cali. 1982. Surface heat transfer in building components. *Proceedings of the Thermal Performance of the Exterior Envelopes of Buildings II*, pp. 180-203.

Gordon, J.M. and K.C. Ng. 1994. Thermodynamic modeling of reciprocating chillers. *Journal of Applied Physics* 75(6):2769-2774.

Gordon, J.M and K.C. Ng. 1995. Predictive and diagnostic aspects of a universal thermodynamic model for chillers. *International Journal of Heat and Mass Transfer* 38(5):807-818.

Gordon, J.M. and K.C. Ng. 2000. *Cool thermodynamics*. Cambridge Press.

Gordon, J.M., K.C. Ng, and H.T. Chua. 1995. Centrifugal chillers: Thermodynamic modeling and a case study. *International Journal of Refrigeration* 18(4):253-257.

Guyon, G. and E. Palomo. 1999a. Validation of two French building energy programs—Part 2: Parameter estimation method applied to empirical validation. *ASHRAE Transactions* 105(2):709-720.

Guyon, G. and E. Palomo. 1999b. Validation of two French building energy analysis programs—Part 1: Analytical verification. *ASHRAE Transactions* 105(2).

Haberl, J.S. and T.E. Bou-Saada. 1998. Procedures for calibrating hourly simulation models to measured building energy and environmental data. *ASME Journal of Solar Energy Engineering* 120(August):193.

Haberl, J.S. and D.E. Claridge. 1987. An expert system for building energy consumption analysis: Prototype results. *ASHRAE Transactions* 93(1):979-998.

Haberl, J. and P. Komor. 1990a. Improving commercial building energy audits: How annual and monthly consumption data can help. *ASHRAE Journal* 32(8):26-33.

Haberl, J. and P. Komor. 1990b. Improving commercial building energy audits: How daily and hourly data can help. *ASHRAE Journal* 32(9):26-36.

Haberl, J.S. and S. Thamilseran. 1996. The great energy predictor shootout II: Measuring retrofit savings and overview and discussion of results. *ASHRAE Transactions* 102(2):419-435.

Haberl, J., D. Claridge, and K. Kissock. 2003. Inverse model toolkit (RP-1050): Application and testing. *ASHRAE Transactions* 109(2):435-448.

Haberl, J.S., T.A. Reddy, I.E. Figuero, and M. Medina. 1997. Overview of LoanSTAR chiller monitoring—Analysis of in-situ chiller diagnostics using ASHRAE RP-827 test method. Paper presented at Cool Sense National Integrated Chiller Retrofit Forum, Presidio, San Francisco, September.

Hammersten, S. 1984. *Estimation of energy balances for houses*. National Swedish Institute for Building Research.

Howell, R.H. and S. Suryanarayana. 1990. Sizing of radiant heating systems: Part I and Part II. *ASHRAE Transactions* 96(1):652-665.

Hunn, B.D., W.V. Turk, and W.O. Wray. 1982. *Validation of passive solar analysis/design tools using Class A performance evaluation data*. LA-UR-82-1732, Los Alamos National Laboratory, NM.

Irving, A. 1988. *Validation of dynamic thermal models, energy, and buildings*. Elsevier Sequoia, Lausanne, Switzerland.

JCEM. 1992. *Final report: Artificial neural networks applied to LoanSTAR data*. Joint Center for Energy Management *Report* TR/92/15.

Jensen, S., ed. 1989. *The PASSYS project phase 1–Subgroup model validation and development, Final report—1986-1989.* Commission of the European Communities, Directorate General XII.

Jensen, S. and R. van de Perre. 1991. Tools for whole model validation of building simulation programs: Experience from the CEC concerted action PASSYS. *Proceedings of Building Simulation '91*, Nice, France. International Building Performance Simulation Association.

Jiang, W. and T.A. Reddy. 2003. Re-evaluation of the Gordon-Ng performance models for water-cooled chillers. *ASHRAE Transactions* (109).

Judkoff, R. 1988. Validation of building energy analysis simulation programs at the Solar Energy Research Institute. *Energy and Buildings* 10(3):235.

Judkoff, R. and J. Neymark. 1995a. *International Energy Agency Building Energy Simulation Test (BESTEST) and diagnostic method.* NREL/TP-472-6231. National Renewable Energy Laboratory, Golden, CO. http://www.nrel.gov/docs/legosti/old/6231.pdf.

Judkoff, R. and J. Neymark. 1995b. *Home Energy Rating System Building Energy Simulation Test (HERS BESTEST).* NREL/TP-472-7332.: National Renewable Energy Laboratory, Golden, CO. http://www.nrel.gov/docs/legosti/fy96/7332a.pdf and http://www.nrel.gov/docs/legosti/fy96/7332b.pdf.

Judkoff, R. and J. Neymark. 2004. Testing and validation of building energy simulation tools. *Annex Document*, IEA SHC Task 34/ECBCS Annex 43. International Energy Agency, Solar Heating and Cooling Programme, and Energy Conservation in Buildings and Community Systems, Paris.

Judkoff, R., D. Wortman, C. Christensen, B. O'Doherty, D. Simms, and M. Hannifan. 1980. *A comparative study of four passive building energy simulations: DOE-2.1, BLAST, SUNCAT-2.4, DEROB-III*. SERI/TP-721-837. UC-59c. Solar Energy Research Institute (now National Renewable Energy Laboratory), Golden, CO.

Judkoff, R., D. Wortman, B. O'Doherty, and J. Burch. 1983. *A methodology for validating building energy analysis simulations*. SERI/TR-254-1508. Solar Energy Research Institute (now National Renewable Energy Laboratory), Golden, CO.

Kamal, S. and P. Novak. 1991. Dynamic analysis of heat transfer in buildings with special emphasis on radiation. *Energy and Buildings* 17(3):231-241.

Kaplan, M., J. McFerran, J. Jansen, and R. Pratt. 1990. Reconciliation of a DOE2.1C model with monitored end-use data from a small office building. *ASHRAE Transactions* 96(1):981.

Katipamula, S. and D.E. Claridge. 1993. Use of simplified systems model to measure retrofit energy savings. *Transactions of the ASME Journal of Solar Energy Engineering* 115(May):57-68.

Katipamula, S., T.A. Reddy, and D.E. Claridge. 1994. Development and application of regression models to predict cooling energy consumption in large commercial buildings. *Proceedings of the 1994 ASME/JSME/JSES International Solar Energy Conference*, San Francisco, p. 307.

Katipamula, S., T.A. Reddy, and D.E. Claridge. 1998. Multivariate regression modeling. *ASME Journal of Solar Energy Engineering* 120 (August):176.

Kays, W.M. and A.L. London. 1984. *Compact heat exchangers*, 3rd ed. McGraw-Hill, New York.

Kerrisk, J.F., N.M. Schnurr, J.E. Moore, and B.D. Hunn. 1981. The custom weighting-factor method for thermal load calculation in the DOE-2 computer program. *ASHRAE Transactions* 87(2):569-584.

Khalifa, A.J.N. and R.H. Marshall. 1990. Validation of heat transfer coefficients on interior building surfaces using a real-sized indoor test cell. *International Journal of Heat and Mass Transfer* 33(10):2219-2236.

Kissock, K., J. Haberl, and D. Claridge. 2003. Inverse model toolkit (RP-1050): Numerical algorithms for best-fit variable-base degree-day and change-point models. *ASHRAE Transactions* 109(2):425-434.

Kissock, J.K., T.A. Reddy, J.S. Haberl, and D.E. Claridge. 1993. E-model: A new tool for analyzing building energy use data. *Proceedings of the Industrial Energy Technology Conference*, Texas A&M University.

Kissock, J.K., T.A. Reddy, and D.E. Claridge. 1998. Ambient temperature regression analysis for estimating retrofit savings in commercial buildings. *ASME Journal of Solar Energy Engineering* 120:168.

Klein, S.A., W.A. Beckman, and J.A. Duffie. 1994. *TRNSYS: A transient simulation program.* Engineering Experiment Station *Report* 38-14, University of Wisconsin-Madison.

Knebel, D.E. 1983. *Simplified energy analysis using the modified bin method.* ASHRAE.

Krarti, M. 1994a. Time varying heat transfer from slab-on-grade floors with vertical insulation. *Building and Environment* 29(1):55-61.

Krarti, M. 1994b. Time varying heat transfer from horizontally insulated slab-on-grade floors. *Building and Environment* 29(1):63-71.

Krarti, M. and P. Chuangchid. 1999. *Cooler floor heat gain for refrigerated structures*. Final Report, ASHRAE Research Project TRP-953.

Krarti, M., D.E. Claridge, and J. Kreider. 1988a. The ITPE technique applied to steady-state ground-coupling problems. *International Journal of Heat and Mass Transfer* 31:1885-1898.

Krarti, M., D.E. Claridge, and J. Kreider. 1988b. ITPE method applications to time-varying two-dimensional ground-coupling problems. *International Journal of Heat and Mass Transfer* 31:1899-1911.

Krarti, M., J.F. Kreider, D. Cohen, and P. Curtiss. 1998. Estimation of energy savings for building retrofits using neural networks. *ASME Journal of Solar Energy Engineering* 120:211.

Kreider, J.F. and J. Haberl. 1994. Predicting hourly building energy usage: The great predictor shootout—Overview and discussion of results. *ASHRAE Transactions* 100(2):1104-1118.

Kreider, J.F. and A. Rabl. 1994. *Heating and cooling of buildings*. McGraw-Hill, New York.

Kreider, J.F. and X.A. Wang. 1991. Artificial neural networks demonstration for automated generation of energy use predictors for commercial buildings. *ASHRAE Transactions* 97(1):775-779.

Kusuda, T. 1969. Thermal response factors for multi-layer structures of various heat conduction systems. *ASHRAE Transactions* 75(1):246-271.

Labs, K., J. Carmody, R. Sterling, L. Shen, Y. Huang, and D. Parker. 1988. Building foundation design handbook. ORNL *Report* Sub/86-72143/1. Oak Ridge National Laboratory, Oak Ridge, TN.

Lachal, B., W.U. Weber, and O. Guisan. 1992. Simplified methods for the thermal analysis of multifamily and administrative buildings. *ASHRAE Transactions* 98.

Laret, L. 1991. Simplified performance models for cycling operation of boilers. *ASHRAE Transactions* 97(2):212-218.

Lebrun, J. 1993. Testing and modeling of fuel oil space-heating boilers—Synthesis of available results. *ASHRAE Transactions* 99(2).

Lebrun, J.J., J. Hannay, J.M. Dols, and M.A. Morant. 1985. Research of a good boiler model for HVAC energy simulation. *ASHRAE Transactions* 91(1B):60-83.

Lebrun, J., J.-P. Bourdouxhe, and M. Grodent. 1999. *HVAC 1 toolkit: A toolkit for primary HVAC system energy calculation*. ASHRAE.

Lewis, P.T. and D.K. Alexander. 1990. HTB2: A flexible model for dynamic building simulation. *Building and Environment*, pp. 7-16.

Liu, M. and D.E. Claridge. 1998. Use of calibrated HVAC system models to optimize system operation. *ASME Journal of Solar Energy Engineering* 120:131.

Lomas, K. 1991. Dynamic thermal simulation models of buildings: New method of empirical validation. *Building Services Engineering Research & Technology* 12(1):25-37.

Lomas, K. and N. Bowman. 1987. Developing and testing tools for empirical validation. Ch. 14, vol. IV of SERC/BRE final report, *An investigation in analytical and empirical validation techniques for dynamic thermal models of buildings*. Building Research Establishment, Garston, U.K.

Lomas, K. and H. Eppel. 1992. Sensitivity analysis techniques for building thermal simulation programs. *Energy and Buildings* (19)1:21-44.

Lomas, K., H. Eppel, C. Martin, and D. Bloomfield. 1994. *Empirical validation of thermal building simulation programs using test room data*. Vol. 1, Final Report. International Energy Agency Report #IEA21RN399/94. Vol. 2, Empirical Validation Package (1993), IEA21RR5/93. Vol. 3, Working Reports (1993), IEA21RN375/93. De Montfort University, Leicester, U.K.

Lorenzetti, D.M. and L.K. Norford. 1993. Pressure reset control of variable air volume ventilation systems. *Proceedings of the ASME International Solar Energy Conference*, Washington, D.C., p. 445.

MacDonald, J.M. and D.M. Wasserman. 1989. Investigation of metered data analysis methods for commercial and related buildings. Oak Ridge National Laboratory *Report* ORNL/CON-279.

Malmström, T.G., B. Mundt, and A.G. Bring. 1985. A simple boiler model. *ASHRAE Transactions* 91(1B):87-108

Manke, J.M., D.C. Hittle, and C.E. Hancock. 1996. Calibrating building energy analysis models using short-term data. *Proceedings of the ASME International Solar Energy Conference*, San Antonio, p. 369.

McClelland, J.L. and D.E. Rumelhart. 1988. *Exploration in parallel distributed processing*. MIT, Cambridge.

McQuiston, F.C. and J.D. Spitler. 1992. *Cooling and heating load calculation manual*. ASHRAE.

Melo, C. and G.P. Hammond. 1991. Modeling and assessing the sensitivity of external convection from building facades. In *Heat and mass transfer in building materials and structures*, pp. 683-695. J.B. Chaddock and B. Todorovic, eds. Hemisphere, New York.

Miller, D.E. 1980. The impact of HVAC process dynamics on energy use. *ASHRAE Transactions* 86(2):535-556.

Miller, R. and J. Seem. 1991. Comparison of artificial neural networks with traditional methods of predicting return from night setback. *ASHRAE Transactions* 97(2):500-508.

Mitalas, G.P. 1968. Calculations of transient heat flow through walls and roofs. *ASHRAE Transactions* 74(2):182-188.

Mitalas, G.P. and D.G. Stephenson. 1967. Room thermal response factors. *ASHRAE Transactions* 73(1):III.2.1-III.2.10.

Mitchell, J.W. 1983. *Energy engineering*. John Wiley & Sons, New York.

Morck, O. 1986. *Simulation model validation using test cell data*. IEA SHC Task VIII, Report #176, Thermal Insulation Laboratory, Technical University of Denmark, Lyngby.

Neter, J., W. Wasseran, and M. Kutner. 1989. *Applied linear regression models*, 2nd ed. Richard C. Irwin, Homewood, IL.

Neymark, J. and R. Judkoff. 2002. *International Energy Agency Building Energy Simulation Test and diagnostic method for heating, ventilating, and air-conditioning equipment models (HVAC BESTEST)*, vol. 1: Cases E100-E200. NREL/TP-550-30152. National Renewable Energy Laboratory, Golden, CO. http://www.nrel.gov/docs/fy02osti/30152.pdf.

Nisson, J.D.N. and G. Dutt. 1985. *The superinsulated home book*. John Wiley & Sons, New York.

NOAA. 1973. *Degree-days to selected bases*. U.S. National Climatic Data Center, Asheville, NC.

Norford, L.K., R.H. Socolow, E.S. Hsieh, and G.V. Spadaro. 1994. Two-to-one discrepancy between measured and predicted performance of a low-energy office building: Insights from a reconciliation based on the DOE-2 model. *Energy and Buildings* 21:121.

Park, C., D.R. Clark, and G.E. Kelly. 1985. An overview of HVACSIM+, a dynamic building/HVAC control systems simulation program. *Proceedings of the First Building Energy Simulation Conference*.

Parker, W.H., G.E. Kelly, and D. Didion. 1980. *A method for testing, rating, and estimating the heating seasonal performance of heat pumps*. National Bureau of Standards, NBSIR 80-2002.

Pedersen, C.O., R.J. Liesen, R.K. Strand, D.E. Fisher, L. Dong, and P.G. Ellis. 2001. *ASHRAE toolkit for building load calculations*. ASHRAE.

Pedersen, C.O., D.E. Fisher, R.J. Liesen, and R.K. Strand. 2003. ASHRAE toolkit for building load calculations. *ASHRAE Transactions* 109(1): 583-589.

Phelan, J., M.J. Brandemuehl, and M. Krarti. 1996. Final Report ASHRAE Project RP-827: Methodology development to measure in-situ chiller, fan, and pump performance. JCEM *Report* No. JCEM/TR/96-3, University of Colorado at Boulder.

Rabl, A. 1988. Parameter estimation in buildings: Methods for dynamic analysis of measured energy use. *Journal of Solar Energy Engineering* 110:52-66.

Rabl, A. and A. Riahle. 1992. Energy signature model for commercial buildings: Test with measured data and interpretation. *Energy and Buildings* 19:143-154.

Reddy, T. 1989. Application of dynamic building inverse models to three occupied residences monitored non-intrusively. *Proceedings of the Thermal Performance of Exterior Envelopes of Buildings IV*, ASHRAE/DOE/BTECC/CIBSE.

Reddy, T. and D. Claridge. 1994. Using synthetic data to evaluate multiple regression and principle component analyses for statistical modeling of daily building energy consumption. *Energy and Buildings* 24:35-44.

Reddy, T.A., S. Katipamula, J.K. Kissock, and D.E. Claridge. 1995. The functional basis of steady-state thermal energy use in air-side HVAC equipment. *Journal of Solar Energy Engineering* 117:31-39.

Reddy, T.A., N.F. Saman, D.E. Claridge, J.S. Haberl, W.D. Turner, and A. Chalifoux. 1997. Baselining methodology for facility level monthly energy use—Part 1: Theoretical aspects. *ASHRAE Transactions* 103(2): 336-347.

Reddy, T.A., S. Deng, and D.E. Claridge. 1999. Development of an inverse method to estimate overall building and ventilation parameters of large commercial buildings. *Journal of Solar Energy Engineering* 121:47.

Reddy, T.A. and K.K. Andersen. 2002. An evaluation of classical steady-state off-line linear parameter estimation methods applied to chiller performance data. *International Journal of HVAC&R Research* 8(1): 101-124.

Reddy, T.A., K.K. Andersen, and D. Niebur. 2003. Information content of incoming data during field monitoring: Application to chiller modeling. *International Journal of HVAC&R Research* 9(4).

Ruch, D. and D. Claridge. 1991. A four parameter change-point model for predicting energy consumption in commercial buildings. *Proceedings of the ASME International Solar Energy Conference*, pp. 433-440.

Ruch, D., L. Chen, J. Haberl, and D. Claridge. 1993. A change-point principle component analysis (CP/CAP) method for predicting energy use in commercial buildings: The PCA model. *Journal of Solar Energy Engineering* 115:77-84.

Seem, J.E. and J.E. Braun. 1991. Adaptive methods for real-time forecasting of building electricity demand. *ASHRAE Transactions* 97(1):710.

Shipp, P.H. and T.B. Broderick. 1983. Analysis and comparison of annual heating loads for various basement wall insulation strategies using transient and steady-state models. *Thermal Insulation, Materials, and*

Systems for Energy Conservation in the 80's. ASTM STP 789, F.A. Govan, D.M. Greason, and J.D. McAllister, eds. American Society for Testing and Materials, West Conshohocken, PA.

Shurcliff, W.A. 1984. *Frequency method of analyzing a building's dynamic thermal performance*. Cambridge, MA.

Sonderegger, R.C. 1977. *Dynamic models of house heating based on equivalent thermal parameters*. Ph.D. dissertation, Center for Energy and Environmental Studies *Report* No. 57. Princeton University, Princeton, NJ.

Sonderegger, R.C. 1985. Thermal modeling of buildings as a design tool. *Proceedings of CHMA 2000*, vol. 1.

Sonderegger, R.C. 1998. Baseline equation for utility bill analysis using both weather and non-weather related variables. *ASHRAE Transactions* 104(2):859-870.

Sowell, E.F. 1988. Classification of 200,640 parametric zones for cooling load calculations. *ASHRAE Transactions* 94(2):716-736.

Sowell, E.F. 1990. Lights: A numerical lighting/HVAC test cell. *ASHRAE Transactions* 96(2):780-786.

Sowell, E.F. and M.A. Moshier. 1995. HVAC component model libraries for equation-based solvers. *Proceedings of Building Simulation '95*, Madison, WI.

Spitler, J.D., C.O. Pedersen, and D.E. Fisher. 1991. Interior convective heat transfer in buildings with large ventilative flow rates. *ASHRAE Transactions* 97(1):505-515.

Spitler, J., S. Rees, and D. Xiao. 2001. *Development of an analytical verification test suite for whole building energy simulation programs—Building fabric*. Final Report for ASHRAE RP-1052. Oklahoma State University School of Mechanical and Aerospace Engineering, Stillwater.

Sreedharan, P. and P. Haves. 2001. Comparison of chiller models for use in model-based fault detection. *International Conference for Enhanced Building Operations* (ICEBO), Texas A&M University, Austin.

Steinman, M., L.N. Kalisperis, and L.H. Summers. 1989. The MRT-correction method: A new method of radiant heat exchange. *ASHRAE Transactions* 95(1):1015-1027.

Stephenson, D.G. and G.P. Mitalas. 1967. Cooling load calculations by thermal response factor method. *ASHRAE Transactions* 73(1):III.1.1-III.1.7.

Stoecker, W.F. and J.W. Jones. 1982. *Refrigeration and air conditioning*, 2nd ed. McGraw-Hill, New York.

Strand, R.K. and C.O. Pedersen. 1997. Implementation of a radiant heating and cooling model into an integrated building energy analysis program. *ASHRAE Transactions* 103(1):949-958.

Subbarao, K. 1986. Thermal parameters for single and multi-zone buildings and their determination from performance data. SERI *Report* SERI/TR-253-2617. Solar Energy Research Institute (now National Renewable Energy Laboratory), Golden, CO.

Subbarao, K. 1988. *PSTAR—Primary and secondary terms analysis and renormalization: A unified approach to building energy simulations and short-term monitoring*. SERI/TR-253-3175.

Taylor, R.D., C.O. Pedersen, and L. Lawrie. 1990. Simultaneous simulation of buildings and mechanical systems in heat balance based energy analysis programs. *Proceedings of the Third International Conference on System Simulation in Buildings*, Liege, Belgium.

Taylor, R.D., C.O. Pedersen, D. Fisher, R. Liesen, and L. Lawrie. 1991. Impact of simultaneous simulation of buildings and mechanical systems in heat balance based energy analysis programs on system response and control. *Proceedings of Building Simulation '91*. Sophia Antipolis, International Building Performance Simulation Association, Nice, France.

Thamilseran, S. and J. Haberl. 1995. A bin method for calculating energy conservation retrofit savings in commercial buildings. *Proceedings of the 1995 ASME/JSME/JSES International Solar Energy Conference*, pp. 111-124.

Threlkeld, J.L. 1970. *Thermal environmental engineering*, 2nd ed. Prentice-Hall, Englewood Cliffs, NJ.

USAF. 1978. Engineering weather data. Department of the Air Force *Manual* AFM 88-29. U.S. Government Printing Office, Washington, D.C.

U.S. Department of Energy. 2001a. *International Performance Measurement and Verification Protocol (IPMVP): Vol. I: Concepts and options for determining energy and water savings*. DOE/GO-102001-1187.

U.S. Department of Energy. 2001b. *International Performance Measurement and Verification Protocol (IPMVP): Vol. II: Concepts and practices for improved indoor environmental quality*. DOE/GO-102001-1188.

U.S. Department of Energy. 2003. *International Performance Measurement and Verification Protocol (IPMVP): Vol. III: Concepts and practices for determining energy savings in new construction*.

U.S. Department of Energy. 2004. *Building energy tools directory*. http://www.energytoolsdirectory.gov.

Walton, G.N. 1980. A new algorithm for radiant interchange in room loads calculations. *ASHRAE Transactions* 86(2):190-208.

Walton, G.N. 1983. *Thermal analysis research program reference manual*. NBSIR 83-2655. National Institute of Standards and Technology, Gaithersburg, MD.

Walton, G.N. 1993. *Computer programs for simulation of lighting/HVAC interactions*. NISTIR 5322. NIST.

Waltz, J.P. 1992. Practical experience in achieving high levels of accuracy in energy simulations of existing buildings. *ASHRAE Transactions* 98(1): 606-617.

Wang, X.A. and J.F. Kreider. 1992. Improved artificial neural networks for commercial building energy use prediction. *Journal of Solar Energy Engineering*.

Wasserman, P.D. 1989. *Neural computing, theory and practice*. Van Nostrand Reinhold, New York.

Yazdanian, M. and J. Klems. 1994. Measurement of the exterior convective film coefficient for windows in low-rise buildings. *ASHRAE Transactions* 100(1):1087-1096.

York, D.A. and C.C. Cappiello, eds. 1982. *DOE-2 engineers manual*. Lawrence Berkeley Laboratory *Report* LBL-11353 (LA-8520-M, DE83004575). National Technical Information Services, Springfield, VA.

Yuill, G. and J. Haberl. 2002. *Development of accuracy tests for mechanical system simulation*. Final Report, ASHRAE Research Project RP-865. University of Nebraska, Omaha.

BIBLIOGRAPHY

ASHRAE 1999. *A toolkit for primary HVAC system energy calculation*. ASHRAE Research Project TRP-665.

Adam, E.J. and J.L. Marchetti. 1999, Dynamic simulation of large boilers with natural recirculation. *Computer and Chemical Engineering* 23 (1999):1031-1040

Andrews, J.W. 1986. Impact of reduced firing rate on furnace and boiler efficiency. *ASHRAE Transactions* 92(1A):246-262.

Bonne, U. and A. Patani. 1980. *Performance* simulation of residential heating systems with HFLAME. *ASHRAE Transactions* 86(1):351.

Bonne, U. 1985. Furnace and boiler system efficiency and operating cost versus increased cycling frequency. *ASHRAE Transactions* 91(1B): 109-130.

Chi, J. and G.E. Kelly. 1978. A method for estimating the seasonal performance of residential gas and oil-fired heating system. *ASHRAE Transactions* 84(1):405-421.

Claus, G. and W. Stephan. 1985. A general computer simulation model for furnaces and boilers. *ASHRAE Transactions* 91(1B):47-59.

Kusuda, T. and T. Alereza. 1982. Development of equipment seasonal performance models for simplified energy analysis methods. *ASHRAE Transactions* 88(2).

Laret, L. 1988. Boiler physical models for use in large scale building simulation. SCS User 1 conference, Ostend.

Landry, R.W. and D.E. Maddox. 1993a. Seasonal efficiency and off-cycle flue loss measurements of two boilers. *ASHRAE Transactions* 99(2).

Landry, R.W., D.E. Maddox, and D.L. Bohac. 1994. Field validation of diagnostic techniques for estimating boiler part-load efficiency. *ASHRAE Transactions* 100(1):859-875.

Lee, W.D., M.M. Delichatsios, T.M. Hrycaj, and R.N. Caron. 1983. Review of furnace/boiler field test analysis techniques. *ASHRAE Transactions* 89(1B):700-705.

Lobenstein, M.S. 1994. Application of short-term diagnostic methods for measuring commercial boiler losses. *ASHRAE Transactions* 100(1): 876-890.

Niu, Z. and K.V. Wong. 1998. Adaptive simulation of boiler unit performance. *Energy Conversion Management* 39(13):1383-1394.

Shavit, G. 1995. Short-time-step analysis and simulation of homes and buildings during the last 100 years. *ASHRAE Transactions* 101(1): 856-868.

Sowell, E.F. and G.N. Walton. 1980. Efficient computation of zone loads. *ASHRAE Transactions* 86(1):49-72.

Sowell, E.F. and D.C. Hittle. 1995. Evolution of building energy simulation methodology. *ASHRAE Transactions* 101(1):850-855.

Spitler, J.D. 1996. *Annotated guide to load calculation models and algorithms*. ASHRAE.

Subbarao, K., J. Burch, and C.E. Hancock. 1990. How to accurately measure the load coefficient of a residential building. *Journal of Solar Energy Engineering*.

Tierney, T.M. and C.J. Fishman. 1994. Filed study of "real world" gas steam boiler seasonal efficiency *ASHRAE Transactions* 100(1):891-897.

U.S. Department of Energy. 2001. *International performance measurement & verification protocol, concepts and options for determining energy and water savings*, vol. I. U.S. Department of Energy, Washington, D.C.

U.S. Army. 1979. BLAST, the building loads analysis and system thermodynamics program—Users manual. U.S. Army Construction Engineering Research Laboratory *Report* E-153.l

Yuill, G.K. 1990. *An annotated guide to models and algorithms for energy calculations relating to HVAC equipment*. ASHRAE.

Analytical Verification

Bland, B. 1993. *Conduction tests for the validation of dynamic thermal models of buildings*. Building Research Establishment, Garston, U.K.

Bland, B.H. and D.P. Bloomfield. 1986. Validation of conduction algorithms in dynamic thermal models. *Proceedings of the CIBSE 5th International Symposium on the Use of Computers for Environmental Engineering Related to Buildings*, Bath, U.K.

CEN. 2004. PrEN ISO 13791. *Thermal performance of buildings—Calculation of internal temperatures of a room in summer without mechanical cooling—General criteria and validation procedures*. Final draft. Comité Européen de la Normalisation, Brussels.

Judkoff, R., D. Wortman, and B. O'Doherty. 1981. *A comparative study of four building energy simulations, Phase II: DOE-2.1, BLAST-3.0, SUNCAT-2.4, and DEROB-4*. Solar Energy Research Institute (now National Renewable Energy Laboratory), Golden, CO.

Pinney, A. and M. Bean. 1988. *A set of analytical tests for internal longwave radiation and view factor calculations*. Final Report of the BRE/SERC Collaboration, vol. II, Appendix II.2. Building Research Establishment, Garston, U.K.

Purdy, J. and I. Beausoleil-Morrison. 2003. *Building Energy Simulation Test and diagnostic method for heating, ventilating, and air-conditioning equipment models (HVAC BESTEST), fuel-fired furnace*. Natural Resources Canada CANMET Energy Technology Centre, Ottawa. http://www.iea-shc.org/task22/deliverables.htm.

Rodriguez, E. and S. Alvarez. 1991. *Solar shading analytical tests (I)*. Universidad de Savilla, Seville.

San Isidro, M. 2000. *Validating the solar shading test of IEA*. Centro de Investigaciones Energeticas Medioambientales y Tecnologicas, Madrid.

Stefanizzi, P., A. Wilson, and A. Pinney. 1988. *The internal longwave radiation exchange in thermal models*, vol. II, Chapter 9. Final Report of the BRE/SERC Collaboration. Building Research Establishment, Garston, U.K.

Tuomaala, P., ed. 1999. *IEA task 22: A working document of subtask A.1, analytical tests*. VTT Building Technology, Espoo, Finland.

Tuomaala, P., K. Piira, J. Piippo, and C. Simonson. 1999. *A validation test set for building energy simulation tools results obtained by BUS++*. VTT Building Technology, Espoo, Finland.

Walton, G. 1989. *AIRNET—A computer program for building airflow network modeling*. Appendix B: AIRNET Validation Tests. NISTIR 89-4072. National Institute of Standards and Technology, Gaithersburg, MD

Wortman, D., B. O'Doherty, and R. Judkoff. 1981. *The implementation of an analytical verification technique on three building energy analysis codes: SUNCAT 2.4, DOE 2.1, and DEROB III*. SERI/TP-721-1008, UL-59c. Solar Energy Research Institute (now National Renewable Energy Laboratory), Golden, CO.

Empirical Validation

Ahmad, Q. and S. Szokolay. 1993. Thermal design tools in Australia: A comparative study of TEMPER, CHEETAH, ARCHIPAK and QUICK. *Building Simulation '93*, Adelaide, Australia. International Building Performance Simulation Association.

Barakat, S. 1983. Passive solar heating studies at the Division of Building Research. *Building Research Note* 181. Division of Building Research, Ottawa.

Beausoleil-Morrison, I. and P. Strachan. 1999. On the significance of modeling internal surface convection in dynamic whole-building simulation programs. *ASHRAE Transactions* 105(2).

Bloomfield, D., Y. Candau, P. Dalicieux, S. DeLille, S. Hammond, K. Lomas, C. Martin, F. Parand, J. Patronis, and N. Ramdani. 1995. New techniques for validating building energy simulation programs. *Proceedings of Building Simulation '95*, Madison, WI. International Building Performance Simulation Association.

Boulkroune, K., Y. Candau, G. Piar, and A. Jeandel. 1993. Modeling and simulation of the thermal behavior of a dwelling under ALLAN. *Building Simulation '93*, Adelaide, Australia. International Building Performance Simulation Association.

Bowman, N. and K. Lomas. 1985. Empirical validation of dynamic thermal computer models of buildings. *Building Service Engineering Research and Technology* 6(4):153-162.

Bowman, N. and K. Lomas. 1985. Building energy evaluation. *Proceedings of the CICA Conference on Computers in Building Services Design*, Nottingham, pp. 99-110. Construction Industry Computer Association.

Burch, J., D. Wortman, R. Judkoff, and B. Hunn. 1985. *Solar Energy Research Institute validation test house site handbook*. LA-10333-MS and SERI/PR-254-2028. Solar Energy Research Institute (now National Renewable Energy Laboratory), Golden, CO, and Los Alamos National Laboratory, NM.

David, G. 1991. Sensitivity analysis and empirical validation of HLITE using data from the NIST indoor test cell. *Proceedings of Building Simulation '91*, Nice, France. International Building Performance Simulation Association.

Eppel, H. and K. Lomas. 1995. Empirical validation of three thermal simulation programs using data from a passive solar building. *Proceedings of Building Simulation '95*, Madison, WI. International Building Performance Simulation Association.

Fisher, D.E. and C.O. Pedersen. 1997. Convective heat transfer in building energy and thermal load calculations. *ASHRAE Transactions* 103(2): 137-148.

Guyon, G., and N. Rahni. 1997. Validation of a building thermal model in CLIM2000 simulation software using full-scale experimental data, sensitivity analysis and uncertainty analysis. *Proceedings of Building Simulation '97*, Prague. International Building Performance Simulation Association.

Guyon, G., S. Moinard, and N. Ramdani. 1999. Empirical validation of building energy analysis tools by using tests carried out in small cells. *Proceedings of Building Simulation '99*, Kyoto. International Building Performance Simulation Association.

Izquierdo, M., G. LeFebvre, E. Palomo, F. Boudaud, and A. Jeandel. 1995. A statistical methodology for model validation in the ALLAN™ simulation environment. *Proceedings of Building Simulation '95*, Madison, WI. International Building Performance Simulation Association.

Jensen, S. 1993. Empirical whole model validation case study: The PASSYS reference wall. *Proceedings of Building Simulation '93*, Adelaide, Australia. International Building Performance Simulation Association.

Judkoff, R. and D. Wortman. 1984. *Validation of building energy analysis simulations using 1983 data from the SERI Class A test house* (draft). SERI/TR-253-2806. Solar Energy Research Institute (now National Renewable Energy Laboratory), Golden, CO.

Judkoff, R., D. Wortman, and J. Burch. 1983. *Measured versus predicted performance of the SERI test house: A validation study*. SERI/TP-254-1953. Solar Energy Research Institute (now National Renewable Energy Laboratory), Golden, CO.

LeRoy, J., E. Groll, and J. Braun. 1997. *Capacity and power demand of unitary air conditioners and heat pumps under extreme temperature and humidity conditions*. Final Report, ASHRAE Research Project RP-859.

LeRoy, J., E. Groll, and J. Braun. 1998. Computer model predictions of dehumidification performance of unitary air conditioners and heat pumps under extreme operating conditions. *ASHRAE Transactions* 104(2).

Lomas, K. and N. Bowman. 1986. The evaluation and use of existing data sets for validating dynamic thermal models of buildings. *Proceedings of the CIBSE 5th International Symposium on the Use of Computers for Environmental Engineering Related to Buildings*, Bath, U.K.

Martin, C. 1991. *Detailed model comparisons: An empirical validation exercise using SERI-RES*. Contractor Report to U.K. Department of Energy, ETSU S 1197-p9.

Maxwell, G., P. Loutzenhiser, and C. Klaassen. 2003. *Daylighting—HVAC interaction tests for the empirical validation of building energy analysis tools*. Iowa State University, Department of Mechanical Engineering, Ames. http://www.iea-shc.org/task22/deliverables.htm.

McFarland, R. 1982. *Passive test cell data for the solar laboratory winter 1980-81*. LA-9300-MS. Los Alamos National Laboratory, NM.

Moinard, S. and G. Guyon. 1999. *Empirical validation of EDF ETNA and GENEC test-cell models*. Final Report, IEA SHC Task 22, Building Energy Analysis Tools, Project A.3. Electricité de France, Moret sur Loing. http://www.iea-shc.org/task22/deliverables.htm.

Nishitani, Y., M. Zheng, H. Niwa, and N. Nakahara. 1999. A comparative study of HVAC dynamic behavior between actual measurements and simulated results by HVACSIM+(J). *Proceedings of Building Simulation '99*, Kyoto. International Building Performance Simulation Association.

Rahni, N., N. Ramdani, Y. Candau, and G. Guyon. 1999. New experimental validation and model improvement tools for the CLIM2000 energy simulation software program. *Proceedings of Building Simulation '99*, Kyoto. International Building Performance Simulation Association.

Sullivan, R. 1998. *Validation studies of the DOE-2 building energy simulation program.* Final Report. LBNL-42241. Lawrence Berkeley National Laboratory, CA.

Travesi, J., G. Maxwell, C. Klaassen, M. Holtz, G. Knabe, C. Felsmann, M. Achermann, and M. Behne. 2001. *Empirical validation of Iowa Energy Resource Station building energy analysis simulation models.* Report, IEA SHC Task 22, Subtask A, Building Energy Analysis Tools, Project A.1 Empirical Validation. Centro de Investigaciones Energeticas, Medioambientales y Technologicas, Madrid. http://www.iea-shc.org/task22/reports/Iowa_Energy_Report.pdf.

Trombe, A., L. Serres, and A. Mavroulakis. 1993. Simulation study of coupled energy saving systems included in real site building. *Proceedings of Building Simulation '93*, Adelaide, Australia. International Building Performance Simulation Association.

Walker, I., J. Siegel, and G. Degenetais. 2001. Simulation of residential HVAC system performance. *Proceedings of eSim 2001*, Natural Resources Canada, Ottawa.

Yazdanian, M. and J. Klems. 1994. Measurement of the exterior convective film coefficient for windows in low-rise buildings. *ASHRAE Transactions* 100(1):1087-1096.

Zheng, M., Y. Nishitani, S. Hayashi, and N. Nakahara. 1999. Comparison of reproducibility of a real CAV system by dynamic simulation HVACSIM+ and TRNSYS. *Proceedings of Building Simulation '99*, Kyoto. International Building Performance Simulation Association.

See also Guyon and Palomo (1999a), Spitler et al. (1991), and U.S. Department of Energy (2004) in the References.

Intermodel Comparative Testing

Achermann, M. and G. Zweifel. 2003. *RADTEST—Radiant heating and cooling test cases.* University of Applied Sciences of Central Switzerland, Lucerne School of Engineering and Architecture. http://www.iea-shc.org/task22/deliverables.htm.

Deru, M., R. Judkoff, and J. Neymark. 2003. *Proposed IEA BESTEST ground-coupled cases.* International Energy Agency, Solar Heating and Cooling Programme Task 22, Working Document.

Fairey, P., M. Anello, L. Gu, D. Parker, M. Swami, and R. Vieira. 1998. *Comparison of EnGauge 2.0 heating and cooling load predictions with the HERS BESTEST criteria.* FSEC-CR-983-98. Florida Solar Energy Center, Cocoa.

Haddad, K. and I. Beausoleil-Morrison. 2001. Results of the HERS BESTEST on an energy simulation computer program. *ASHRAE Transactions* 107(2).

Haltrecht, D. and K. Fraser. 1997. Validation of HOT2000™ using HERS BESTEST. *Proceedings of Building Simulation '97*, Prague. International Building Performance Simulation Association.

ISSO. 2003. *Energie Diagnose Referentie Versie 3.0.* Institut voor Studie en Stimulering van Onderzoekop Het Gebied van Gebouwinstallaties, Rotterdam, The Netherlands.

Judkoff, R. 1985. *A comparative validation study of the BLAST-3.0, SERIRES-1.0, and DOE-2.1 A computer programs using the Canadian direct gain test building* (draft). SERI/TR-253-2652. Solar Energy Research Institute (now National Renewable Energy Laboratory), Golden, CO.

Judkoff, R. 1985. International Energy Agency building simulation comparison and validation study. *Proceedings of the Building Energy Simulation Conference*, Seattle.

Judkoff, R. 1986. *International Energy Agency sunspace intermodel comparison* (draft). SERI/TR-254-2977. Solar Energy Research Institute (now National Renewable Energy Laboratory), Golden, CO.

Judkoff, R. and J. Neymark. 1997. *Home Energy Rating System Building Energy Simulation Test for Florida (Florida-HERS BESTEST).* NREL/TP-550-23124. National Renewable Energy Laboratory, Golden, CO. http://www.nrel.gov/docs/legosti/fy97/23124a.pdf and http://www.nrel.gov/docs/legosti/fy97/23124b.pdf.

Judkoff, R. and J. Neymark. 1998. The BESTEST method for evaluating and diagnosing building energy software. *Proceedings of the ACEEE Summer Study 1998*, Washington, D.C. American Council for an Energy-Efficient Economy.

Judkoff, R. and J. Neymark. 1999. Adaptation of the BESTEST intermodel comparison method for proposed ASHRAE *Standard* 140P: Method of test for building energy simulation programs. *ASHRAE Transactions* 105(2).

Mathew, P. and A. Mahdavi. 1998. High-resolution thermal modeling for computational building design assistance. *Proceedings of the International Computing Congress, Computing in Civil Engineering*, Boston.

Natural Resources Canada. 2000. *Benchmark test for the evaluation of building energy analysis computer programs.* Natural Resources Canada, Ottawa. (Translation of original Japanese version, approved by the Japanese Ministry of Construction.)

Neymark, J. and R. Judkoff. 1997. A comparative validation based certification test for home energy rating system software. *Proceedings of Building Simulation '97*, Prague. International Building Performance Simulation Association.

Neymark, J. and R. Judkoff. 2004. *International Energy Agency Building Energy Simulation Test and diagnostic method for heating, ventilating, and air-conditioning equipment models (HVAC BESTEST)*, vol. 2: Cases E300-E545. NREL/TP-550-36754. National Renewable Energy Laboratory, Golden, CO. http://www.nrel.gov/docs/fy05osti/36754.pdf.

Sakamoto, Y. 2000. *Determination of standard values of benchmark test to evaluate annual heating and cooling load computer program.* Natural Resources Canada, Ottawa.

Soubdhan, T., T. Mara, H. Boyer, and A. Younes. 1999. *Use of BESTEST procedure to improve a building thermal simulation program.* Université de la Réunion, St Denis, La Reunion, France.

General Testing and Validation

Allen, E., D. Bloomfield, N. Bowman, K. Lomas, J. Allen, J. Whittle, and A. Irving. 1985. Analytical and empirical validation of dynamic thermal building models. *Proceedings of the First Building Energy Simulation Conference,* Seattle, pp. 274-280.

Beausoleil-Morrison, I. 2000. *The adaptive coupling of heat and air flow modelling within dynamic whole-building simulation.* Ph.D. dissertation. Energy Systems Research Unit, Department of Mechanical Engineering, University of Strathclyde, Glasgow.

Bloomfield, D. 1985. Appraisal techniques for methods of calculating the thermal performance of buildings. *Building Services Engineering Research & Technology.* 6(1):13-20.

Bloomfield, D., ed. 1989. *Design tool evaluation: Benchmark cases.* IEA T8B4. Solar Heating and Cooling Program, Task VIII: Passive and Hybrid Solar Low-Energy Buildings. Building Research Establishment, Garston, U.K.

Bloomfield, D., K. Lomas, and C. Martin. 1992. *Assessing programs which predict the thermal performance of buildings.* BRE Information Paper, IP7/92. Building Research Establishment, Garston, U.K.

Gough, M. 1999. *A review of new techniques in building energy and environmental modelling.* Final Report. BRE Contract No. BREA-42. Building Research Establishment, Garston, U.K.

Judkoff, R., S. Barakat, D. Bloomfield, B. Poel, R. Stricker, P. van Haaster, and D. Wortman. 1988. *International Energy Agency design tool evaluation procedure.* SERI/TP-254-3371. Solar Energy Research Institute (now National Renewable Energy Laboratory), Golden, CO.

Palomo, E. and G. Guyon. 2002. *Using parameters space analysis techniques for diagnostic purposes in the framework of empirical model validation.* LEPT-ENSAM, Talance, France. Electricité de France, Moret sur Loing.

CHAPTER 20

SPACE AIR DIFFUSION

ROOM air distribution systems are intended to provide thermal comfort and ventilation for space occupants and processes. Although air terminals (inlets and outlets), terminal units, local ducts, and rooms themselves may affect room air diffusion, this chapter addresses only air terminals and their direct effect on occupant comfort. This chapter is intended to present HVAC designers the fundamental characteristics of air distribution devices. For information on naturally ventilated spaces, see Chapter 16. For a discussion of various air distribution strategies, tools, and guidelines for design and application, see Chapter 56 in the 2007 *ASHRAE Handbook—HVAC Applications*. Chapter 19 in the 2008 *ASHRAE Handbook—HVAC Systems and Equipment* provides descriptions of the characteristics of various air terminals (inlets and outlets) and terminal units, as well as selection tools and guidelines. Other fundamental references include Bauman and Daly (2003), Chen and Glicksman (2003), Kirkpatrick and Elleson (1996), Rock and Zhu (2002), and Skistad et al. (2002).

Room air diffusion methods can be classified as one of the following:

- **Mixed systems** produce little or no thermal stratification of air within the space. Overhead air distribution is an example of this type of system.
- **Fully (thermally) stratified systems** produce little or no mixing of air within the occupied space. Thermal displacement ventilation is an example of this type of system.
- **Partially mixed systems** provide some mixing within the occupied and/or process space while creating stratified conditions in the volume above. Most underfloor air distribution designs are examples of this type of system.
- **Task/ambient conditioning systems** focus on conditioning only a certain portion of the space for thermal comfort and/or process control. Examples of task/ambient systems are personally controlled desk outlets (sometimes referred to as personal ventilation systems) and spot-conditioning systems.

Air distribution systems, such as displacement ventilation (DV) and underfloor air distribution (UFAD), that deliver air in cooling mode at or near floor level and return air at or near ceiling level produce varying amounts of room air stratification. Figure 1 presents a series of simplified vertical profiles of temperature and pollutant concentration representing the spectrum of stratified conditions that may exist under cooling operation, from fully stratified (e.g., DV systems) to fully mixed (e.g., conventional overhead systems). For floor-level supply, thermal plumes that develop over heat sources in the room play a major role in driving overall floor-to-ceiling air motion. The amount of stratification in the room is primarily determined by the balance between total room airflow and heat load. In practice, the actual temperature (or concentration) profile depends on the combined effects of various factors, but is largely driven by the characteristics of the room supply airflow and heat load configuration.

For room supply airflow, the major factors are

- Total room supply airflow quantity
- Room supply air temperature
- Diffuser type
- Diffuser throw height (or outlet velocity); this is associated with the amount of mixing provided by a floor diffuser (or room conditions near a low-sidewall DV diffuser)

For room heat loads, the major factors are

- Magnitude and number of loads in space
- Load type (point or distributed source)
- Elevation of load (e.g., overhead lighting, person standing on floor, floor-to-ceiling glazing)
- Radiative/convective split
- For pollutant concentration profiles, whether pollutants are associated with heat sources

INDOOR AIR QUALITY AND SUSTAINABILITY

Air diffusion methods affect not only indoor air quality (IAQ) and thermal comfort, but also energy consumption over the building's life. Choices made early in the design process are important. The U.S. Green Building Council's (USGBC 2005) Leadership in Energy and Environmental Design (LEED®) rating system, which was originally created in response to indoor air quality concerns, now includes prerequisites and credits for increasing ventilation effectiveness and improving thermal comfort. These requirements and optional points are relatively easy to achieve if good room air diffusion design principles, methods, and standards are followed.

Environmental tobacco smoke (ETS) control is a LEED prerequisite. Banning indoor smoking is a common approach, but if indoor smoking is to be allowed, ANSI/ASHRAE *Standard* 62.1 requires that more than the base non-ETS ventilation air be provided where ETS is present in all or part of a building. Rock (2006) provides additional guidance on dealing with ETS.

The **air change effectiveness** is affected directly by the room air distribution system's design, construction, and operation, but is very difficult to predict. Many attempts have been made to quantify air change effectiveness, including ASHRAE *Standard* 129. However, this standard is only for experimental tests in well-controlled laboratories, and should not be applied directly to real buildings.

ANSI/ASHRAE *Standard* 62.1-2007 provides a table of typical values to help predict ventilation effectiveness. For example, well-designed ceiling-based air distribution systems produce near-perfect air mixing in cooling mode, and yield an air change effectiveness of almost 1.0.

Displacement and underfloor air distribution (UFAD) systems have the potential for values greater than 1.0. More information on ceiling- and wall-mounted air inlets and outlets can be found in Rock and Zhu (2002). Displacement system performance is described in Chen and Glicksman (2003). Bauman and Daly (2003)

The preparation of this chapter is assigned to TC 5.3, Room Air Distribution.

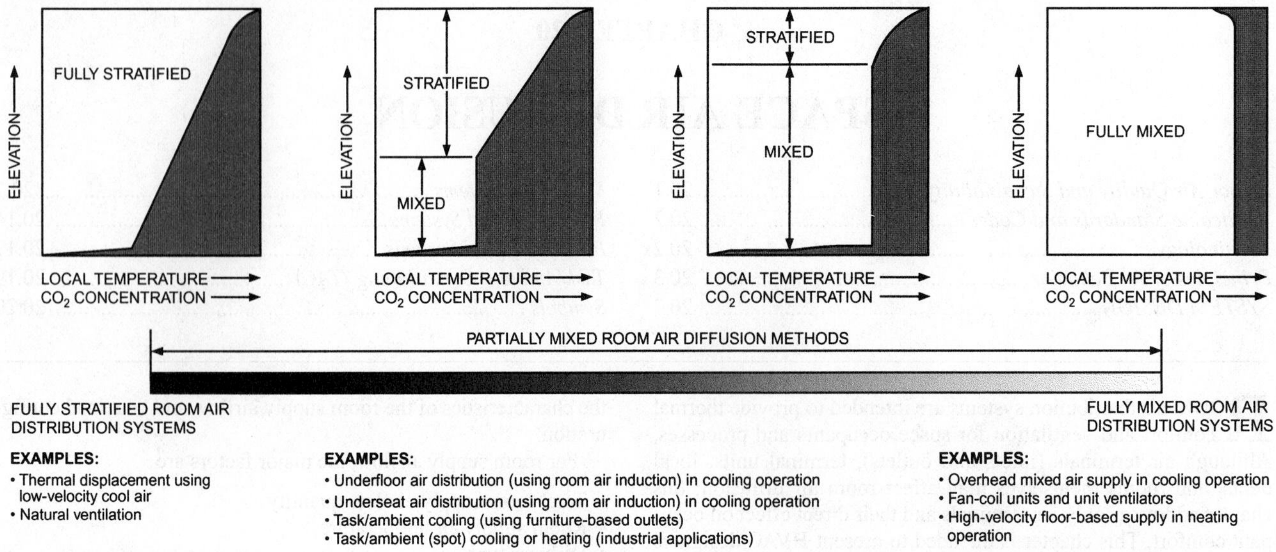

Fig. 1 Classification of Air Diffusion Methods

discuss UFAD in detail. (These three ASHRAE books were produced by research projects for Technical Committee 5.3.) More information on ANSI/ASHRAE *Standard* 62.1-2007 is available in its user's manual (ASHRAE 2007).

APPLICABLE STANDARDS AND CODES

The following standards and codes should be reviewed when applying various room air diffusion methods:

- ASHRAE *Standard* 55 specifies the combination of indoor thermal environmental factors and personal factors that will produce thermal acceptability to a majority of space occupants.
- ASHRAE *Standard* 62.1 establishes the ventilation requirements for acceptable indoor environmental quality. This standard is adopted as part of many building codes.
- ASHRAE/IESNA *Standard* 90.1 provides energy efficiency requirements that affect supply air characteristics.
- ASHRAE *Standard* 113 describes a method for evaluating the effectiveness of various room air distribution systems in achieving thermal comfort.
- ASHRAE *Standard* 129 specifies a method for measuring air-change effectiveness in mechanically ventilated spaces.

Local codes should also be checked to see how they apply to each of these subjects.

TERMINOLOGY

Adjacent zone. Area adjacent to an outlet in which long term occupancy is not recommended because of potential discomfort. Also called **clear** or **near zone**.

Aspect ratio. Ratio of length to width of opening or core of a grille.

Axial flow jet. Stream of air with motion approximately symmetrical along a line, although some spreading and drop or rise can occur from diffusion and buoyancy effects.

CAV. Constant air volume.

Coanda effect. Effect of a moving jet attaching to a parallel surface because of negative pressure developed between jet and surface.

Coefficient of discharge. Ratio of area at vena contracta to area of opening.

Cold air. General term for supply air, typically between 1.5 to 7°C.

Core area. Area of a register, grille, or linear slot pertaining to the frame or border, whichever is less.

Damper. Device used to vary the volume flow rate of air passing through a confined cross section by varying the cross-sectional area.

Diffuser. Outlet discharging supply air in various directions and planes.

Diffusion. Dispersion of air within a space.

Distribution. Moving air to or in a space by an outlet discharging supply air.

Draft. Undesired or excessive local cooling of a person caused by low temperature and air movement.

Drop. Vertical distance that the lower edge of a horizontally projected airstream descends between the outlet and the end of its throw.

Effective area. Net area of an outlet or inlet device through which air can pass; equal to the free area times the coefficient of discharge.

Entrainment. Movement of space air into the jet caused by the airstream discharged from the outlet (also known as secondary air motion).

Entrainment (or induction) ratio. Volume flow rate of total air (primary plus entrained air) divided by the volume flow rate of primary air at a given distance from the outlet.

Envelope. Outer boundary of an airstream moving at a perceptible velocity.

Exhaust opening or inlet. Any opening through which air is removed from a space.

Free area. Total minimum area of openings in an air outlet or inlet through which air can pass.

Grille. Functional or decorative device covering any area through which air passes.

Induction. See Entrainment.

Isothermal jet. Air jet with same temperature as surrounding air.

Lower (mixed) zone. In partially mixed systems, zone directly adjacent to floor, in which air is relatively well mixed.

Neck area. Nominal area of duct connection to air outlet or inlet.

Nonisothermal jet. Air jet with a discharge temperature different from surrounding air.

Occupied zone. Room volume where occupants are located (typically 1.8 m above floor level and 0.3 m from walls).

Outlet velocity. Average velocity of air emerging from outlet, measured in plane of opening.

Primary air. Air delivered to an outlet by a supply duct.

Radius of diffusion. Horizontal axial distance an airstream travels after leaving an air outlet before the maximum stream velocity is reduced to a specified terminal level (e.g., 0.25, 0.5, 0.75, or 1.0 m/s).

Register. Grille equipped with a flow control damper.

Spread. Divergence of airstream in horizontal and/or vertical plane after it leaves an outlet.

Stagnant zone. Area characterized by stratification and little air motion. This term does not necessarily imply poor air quality.

Stratification height. Vertical distance from floor to horizontal plane that defines lower boundary of upper mixed zone (in a fully stratified or partially mixed system).

Stratified zone. Zone in which air movement is entirely driven by buoyancy caused by convective heat sources. Typically found in fully stratified or partially mixed systems

Supply opening or outlet. Any opening or device through which supply air is delivered into a ventilated space being heated, cooled, humidified, or dehumidified. Supply outlets are classified according to their location in a room as sidewall, ceiling, baseboard, or floor outlets. However, because numerous designs exist, they are more accurately described by their construction features. (See Chapter 19 of the 2008 *ASHRAE Handbook—HVAC Systems and Equipment.*)

Terminal velocity. Maximum airstream velocity at end of throw.

Throw. Horizontal or vertical axial distance an airstream travels after leaving an air outlet before maximum stream velocity is reduced to a specified terminal velocity (e.g., 0.25, 0.5, 0.75, or 1.0 m/s), defined by ASHRAE *Standard* 70.

Total air. Mixture of discharged and entrained air.

Upper (mixed) zone. Zone in which air is relatively well mixed, with generally low average air velocities caused by the momentum of thermal plumes penetrating its lower boundary. Typically found in fully stratified or partially mixed systems.

Vane. Component of supply air outlet that imparts direction to the discharge jet.

Vane ratio. Ratio of depth of a vane to the space between two adjacent vanes.

VAV. Variable air volume.

Vena contracta. Smallest cross-sectional area of a fluid stream leaving an orifice.

PRINCIPLES OF JET BEHAVIOR

Air Jet Fundamentals

Air supplied to rooms through various types of outlets (e.g., grilles, ceiling diffusers, perforated panels) can be distributed by turbulent air jets (mixed and partially mixed systems) or in a low-velocity, unidirectional manner (stratified systems). The air jet discharged from an outlet is the primary factor affecting room air motion. Baturin (1972), Christianson (1989), and Murakami (1992) have further information on the relationship between the air jet and occupied zone.

If an air jet is not obstructed or affected by walls, ceiling, or other surfaces, it is considered a **free jet**.

Characteristics of the air jet in a room might be influenced by reverse flows created by the same jet entraining ambient air. If the supply air temperature is equal to the ambient room air temperature, the air jet is called an **isothermal jet**. A jet with an initial temperature different from the ambient air temperature is called a **nonisothermal jet**. The air temperature differential between supplied and ambient room air generates thermal forces (buoyancy) in jets, affecting the jet's (1) trajectory, (2) location at which it attaches to and separates from the ceiling/floor, and (3) throw. The significance of these effects depends on the ratio between the thermal buoyancy of the air and inertial forces.

Angle of Divergence. The angle of divergence is well defined near the outlet face, but the boundary contours are billowy and easily affected by external influences. Near the outlet, as in the room, air movement has local eddies, vortices, and surges. Internal forces governing this air motion are extremely delicate (Nottage et al. 1952a).

Measured angles of divergence (spread) for discharge into large open spaces usually range from 20 to 24°, with an average of 22°. Coalescing jets for closely spaced multiple outlets expand at smaller angles, averaging 18°, and jets discharging into relatively small spaces show even smaller angles of expansion (McElroy 1943). When outlet area is small compared to the dimensions of the space normal to the jet, the jet may be considered free as long as

$$X \leq 1.5\sqrt{A_R} \tag{1}$$

where

X = distance from face of outlet, m
A_R = cross-sectional area of confined space normal to jet, m^2

Jet Expansion Zones. The full length of an air jet, in terms of the maximum or centerline velocity and temperature differential at the cross section, can be divided into four zones:

- **Zone 1**, a short core zone extending about four diameters or widths from the outlet face, in which the maximum velocity (temperature) of the airstream remains practically unchanged.
- **Zone 2**, a transition zone, with its length determined by the type of outlet, aspect ratio of the outlet, initial airflow turbulence, etc.
- **Zone 3**, a zone of fully established turbulent flow that may be 25 to 100 equivalent air outlet diameters (widths for slot air diffusers) long.
- **Zone 4**, a zone of diffuser jet degradation, where maximum air velocity and temperature decrease rapidly. Distance to this zone and its length depend on the velocities and turbulence characteristics of ambient air. In a few diameters or widths, air velocity becomes less than 0.25 m/s. Characteristics of this zone are still not well understood.

Zone 3 is of major engineering importance because, in most cases, the diffuser jet enters the occupied area within this zone.

Centerline Velocities in Zones 1 and 2. In zone 1, the ratio V_x/V_o is constant and equal to the ratio of the center velocity of the jet at the start of expansion to the average velocity. The ratio V_x/V_o varies from approximately 1.0 for rounded entrance nozzles to about 1.2 for straight pipe discharges; it has much higher values for diverging discharge outlets.

Experimental evidence indicates that, in zone 2,

$$\frac{V_x}{V_o} = \sqrt{\frac{K_c H_o}{X}} \tag{2}$$

where

V_x = centerline velocity at distance X from outlet, m/s
V_o = $V_c/C_d R_{fa}$ = average initial velocity at discharge from open-ended duct or across contracted stream at vena contracta of orifice or multiple-opening outlet, m/s
V_c = nominal velocity of discharge based on core area, m/s
C_d = discharge coefficient (usually between 0.65 and 0.90)
R_{fa} = ratio of free area to gross (core) area
H_o = width of jet at outlet or at vena contracta, m
K_c = centerline velocity constant, depending on outlet type and discharge pattern (see Table 1)
X = distance from outlet to measurement of centerline velocity V_x, m

The aspect ratio (Tuve 1953) and turbulence (Nottage et al. 1952a) primarily affect centerline velocities in zones 1 and 2. Aspect ratio has little effect on the terminal zone of the jet when H_o is greater than 100 mm. This is particularly true of nonisothermal jets. When H_o is very small, induced air can penetrate the core of the jet, thus reducing centerline velocities. The difference in performance between a radial outlet with small H_o and an axial outlet with large H_o shows the importance of jet thickness.

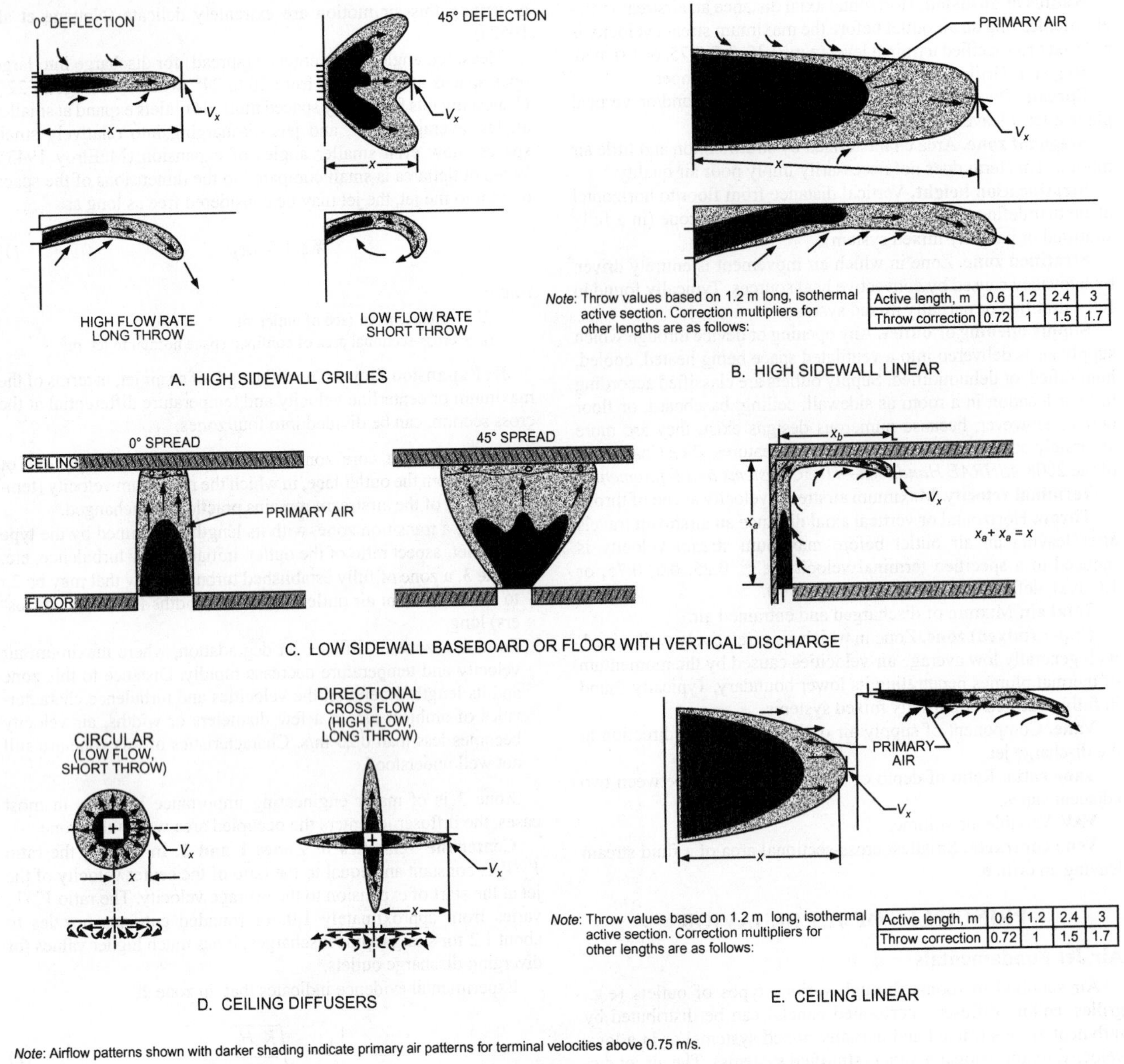

Fig. 2 Airflow Patterns of Different Diffusers

Table 1 Recommended Values for Centerline Velocity Constant K for Commercial Supply Outlets

Outlet Type	Discharge Pattern	A_0	K_c
High sidewall grilles	0° deflection[a]	Free	5.7
(Figure 2A)	Wide deflection	Free	4.2
High sidewall linear	Core less than 100 mm high[b]	Free	4.4
(Figure 2B)	Core more than 100 mm high	Free	5.0
Low sidewall	Up and on wall, no spread	Free	4.5
(Figure 2C)	Wide spread[b]	Free	3.0
Baseboard	Up and on wall, no spread	Core	4.0
(Figure 2C)	Wide spread	Core	2.0
Floor grille	No spread[b]	Free	4.7
(Figure 2C)	Wide spread	Free	1.6
Ceiling (Figure 2D)	360° horizontal[c]	Neck	1.1
	Four-way; little spread	Neck	3.8
Ceiling linear slot	One-way; horizontal along ceiling[b]	Free	5.5
(Figure 2E)			

[b]Free area is about 80% of core area.
[c]Free area is about 50% of core area.
[d]Cone free area is greater than duct area.

When air is discharged from relatively large perforated panels, the constant-velocity core formed by coalescence of individual jets extends a considerable distance from the panel face. In zone 1, when the ratio is less than 5, use the following equation for estimating centerline velocities (Koestel et al. 1949):

$$V_x = 1.2 V_o \sqrt{C_d R_{fa}} \tag{3}$$

Centerline Velocity in Zone 3. In zone 3, maximum or centerline velocities of straight-flow isothermal jets can be determined accurately from the following equations:

$$\frac{V_x}{V_o} = \frac{KH_o}{X} = \frac{K_c\sqrt{A_o}}{X} \tag{4}$$

$$V_x = \frac{K_c V_o \sqrt{A_o}}{X} = \frac{K_c Q_o}{X\sqrt{A_o}} \tag{5}$$

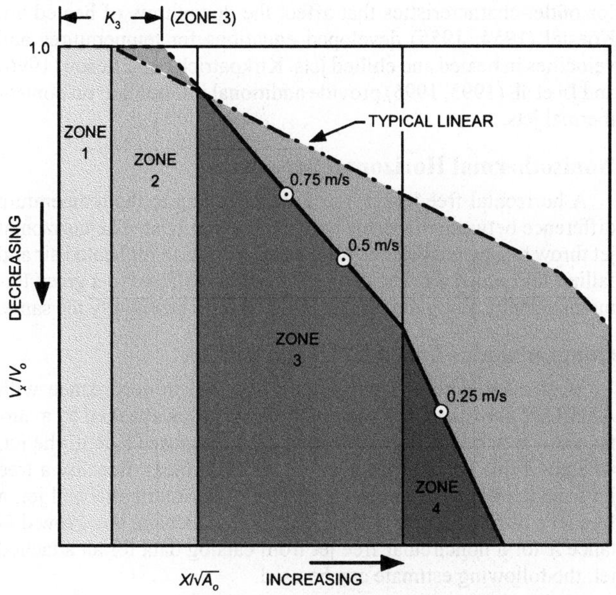

Fig. 3 Chart for Determining Centerline Velocities of Axial and Radial Jets

where

K = centerline velocity constant
H_o = effective or equivalent diameter of stream at discharge from open-ended duct or at contracted section, m
A_o = core area or neck area as shown in Table 1, m^2
A_c = measured gross (core) area of outlet, m^2
Q_o = discharge from outlet, m^3/s

Because A_o equals the effective area of the stream, the flow area for commercial registers and diffusers, according to ASHRAE *Standard* 70, can be used in Equation (4) with the appropriate value of K.

Determining Centerline Velocities. To correlate data from all four zones, centerline velocity ratios are plotted against distance from the outlet in Figure 3.

Airflow patterns of diffusers are related to the throw K-factors and throw distance. In general, diffusers with a circular airflow pattern have a shorter throw than those with a directional or cross-flow pattern. During cooling, the circular pattern tends to curl back from the end of the throw toward the diffuser, reducing the drop and ensuring that the cool air remains near the ceiling.

Cross-flow airflow patterns have a longer throw, and the individual side jets react similarly to jets from sidewall grilles. Jets with this pattern have a longer throw, and airflow does not roll back to the diffuser at the end of the throw, but continues to move away from the diffuser at low velocities.

Throw. Equation (5) can be transposed to determine the throw X of an outlet if the discharge volume and the centerline velocity are known:

$$X = \frac{KQ}{V_x\sqrt{A_0}} \tag{6}$$

The following example illustrates the use of Table 1 and Figure 3.

Example 1. A 300 by 450 mm high sidewall grille with an 280 by 430 mm core area is selected. From Table 1, K_c = 5 for zone 3. If the airflow is 0.3 m^3/s, what is the throw to 0.25, 0.5, and 0.75 m/s?

Solution:

From Equation (7),

$$X = \frac{1.13KQ}{V_x\sqrt{A_o}} = \frac{1.13 \times 5 \times 0.3}{V_x\sqrt{280 \times 430/10^6}} = \frac{4.885}{V_x}$$

Solving for 0.25 m/s throw,

$$X = 4.885/0.25 = 19.5 \text{ m}$$

But, according to Figure 3, 0.25 m/s is in zone 4, which is typically 20% less than calculated in Equation (4), or

$$X = 19.5 \times 0.80 = 15.6 \text{ m}$$

Solving for 0.5 m/s throw,

$$X = 4.885/0.50 = 9.8 \text{ m}$$

Solving for 0.75 m/s throw,

$$X = 4.885/0.75 = 6.5 \text{ m}$$

Velocity Profiles of Jets. In zone 3 of both axial and radial jets, the velocity distribution may be expressed by a single curve (Figure 3) in terms of dimensionless coordinates; this same curve can be used as a good approximation for adjacent portions of zones 2 and 4. Temperature and density differences have little effect on cross-sectional velocity profiles.

Velocity distribution in zone 3 can be expressed by the Gauss error function or probability curve, which is approximated by the following equation:

$$\left(\frac{r}{r_{0.5V}}\right)^2 = 3.3 \log\frac{V_x}{V} \tag{7}$$

where

r = radial distance of point under consideration from centerline of jet
$r_{0.5V}$ = radial distance in same cross-sectional plane from axis to point where velocity is one-half centerline velocity (i.e., $V = 0.5V_x$)
V_x = centerline velocity in same cross-sectional plane
V = actual velocity at point being considered

Experiments show that the conical angle for $r_{0.5V}$ is approximately one-half the total angle of divergence of a jet. The velocity profile curve for one-half of a straight-flow turbulent jet (the other half being a symmetrical duplicate) is shown in Figure 4. For multiple-opening outlets, such as grilles or perforated panels, the velocity profiles are similar, but the angles of divergence are smaller.

Entrainment Ratios. The following equations are for entrainment of circular jets and of jets from long slots. For third-zone expansion of circular jets,

$$\frac{Q_x}{Q_o} = \frac{2X}{K_c\sqrt{A_o}} \tag{8}$$

By substituting from Equation (4),

$$\frac{Q_x}{Q_o} = 2\frac{V_o}{V_x} \tag{9}$$

For a continuous slot with active sections up to 3 m and separated by 0.6 m,

$$\frac{Q_x}{Q_o} = \sqrt{\frac{2}{K_c}}\sqrt{\frac{X}{H_s}} \tag{10}$$

or, substituting from Equation (2),

$$\frac{Q_x}{Q_o} = \sqrt{2}\frac{V_o}{V_x} \tag{11}$$

where

Q_x = total volumetric flow rate at distance X from face of outlet, m^3/s
Q_o = discharge from outlet, m^3/s
X = distance from face of outlet, m
K_c = centerline velocity constant

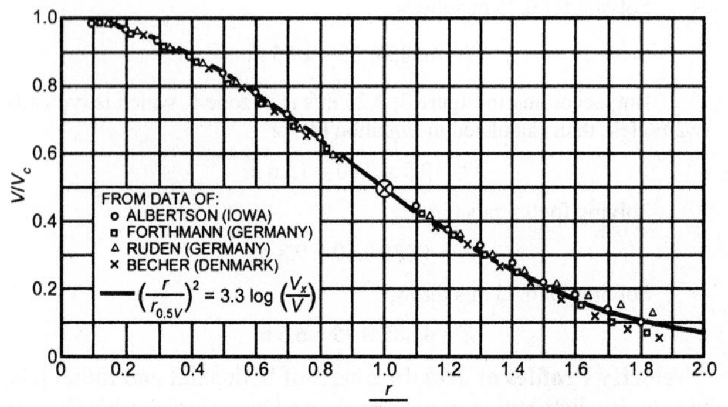

Fig. 4 Cross-Sectional Velocity Profiles for Straight-Flow Turbulent Jets

A_o = core area or neck area free (see Table 1), m²
H_s = width of slot, m

The entrainment ratio Q_x/Q_o is important in determining total air movement at a given distance from an outlet. For a given outlet, the entrainment ratio is proportional to the distance X [Equation (8)] or to the square root of the distance X [Equation (10)] from the outlet. Equations (9) and (11) show that, for a fixed centerline velocity V_x, the entrainment ratio is proportional to outlet velocity. Equations (9) and (11) also show that, at a given centerline and outlet velocity, a circular jet has greater entrainment and total air movement than a long slot. Comparing Equations (8) and (10), the long slot should have a greater rate of entrainment. The entrainment ratio at a given distance is less with a large K than with a small K.

Isothermal Radial Flow Jets

In a radial jet, as with an axial jet, the cross-sectional area at any distance from the outlet varies as the square of this distance. Centerline velocity gradients and cross-sectional velocity profiles are similar to those of zone 3 of axial jets, and the angles of divergence are about the same.

A jet from a ceiling plaque has the same form as half of a free radial jet. The jet is wider and longer than a free jet, with maximum velocity close to the surface. Koestel (1957) provides an equation for radial flow outlets.

Nonisothermal Jets

When the temperature of introduced air is different from the room air temperature, the diffuser air jet is affected by thermal buoyancy caused by air density difference. The trajectory of a non-isothermal jet introduced horizontally is determined by the Archimedes number (Baturin 1972):

$$\mathrm{Ar} = \frac{g L_o (T_o - T_A)}{V_o^2 T_A} \qquad (12)$$

where

g = gravitational acceleration rate, m/s²
L_o = length scale of diffuser outlet equal to hydraulic diameter of outlet, m
$(T_o - T_s)$ = initial temperature of jet – temperature of ambient air, °C
V_o = initial air velocity of jet, m/s
T_A = room air temperature, K

The influence of buoyant forces on horizontally projected heated and chilled jets is significant in heating and cooling with wall outlets. Koestel's (1955) equation describes the behavior of these jets.

Helander and Jakowatz (1948), Helander et al. (1953, 1954, 1957), Knaak (1957), and Yen et al. (1956) developed equations for outlet characteristics that affect the downthrow of heated air. Koestel (1954, 1955) developed equations for temperatures and velocities in heated and chilled jets. Kirkpatrick and Elleson (1996) and Li et al. (1993, 1995) provide additional information on nonisothermal jets.

Nonisothermal Horizontal Free Jet

A horizontal free jet rises or falls according to the temperature difference between it and the ambient environment. The horizontal jet throw to a given distance follows an arc, rising for heated air and falling for cooled air. The distance from the diffuser to a given terminal velocity along the discharge jet remains essentially the same.

Comparison of Free Jet to Attached Jet

Most manufacturers' throw data obtained in accordance with ASHRAE *Standard* 70 assume the discharge is attached to a surface. An attached jet induces air along the exposed side of the jet, whereas a free jet can induce air on all its surfaces. Because a free jet's induction rate is larger compared to that of an attached jet, a free jet's throw distance will be shorter. To calculate the throw distance X for a noncircular free jet from catalog data for an attached jet, the following estimate can be used.

$$X_{free} = X_{attached} \times 0.707 \qquad (13)$$

Circular free jets generally have longer throws compared to noncircular jets.

Jets from ceiling diffusers initially tend to attach to the ceiling surface, because of the force exerted by the Coanda effect. However, cold air jets will detach from the ceiling if the airstream's buoyancy forces are greater than the inertia of the moving air stream.

With separation, a cold draft may enter the occupied space, resulting in thermal discomfort. The thermal discomfort is caused by two factors: the cold draft of the separated jet in the occupied space, and the lack of adequate mixing in areas of the room not reached by the separated jet. The separation distance parameter x_s is the distance from the diffuser at which a jet separates from the ceiling.

Separation distance correlates with outlet jet conditions. Separation distance depends on the velocity constant K, outlet temperature, flow rate, and static pressure drop. For slot and round diffusers,

$$x_s = (48.04)(1.2)K^{1/2}(\Delta T/T)^{-1/2} Q_o^{1/4} \Delta P^{3/8} \qquad (14)$$

where

x_s = jet separation distance, m
K = centerline velocity constant
ΔT = room-jet temperature difference, K
T = average absolute room temperature, K
Q_o = outlet flow rate, m/s
ΔP = diffuser static pressure drop, Pa

A representative value of C_s that has been found to best match the results of analyses and experiments of a wide variety of diffusers is 1.2.

Surface Jets (Wall and Ceiling)

Attached jets travel at a higher velocity and entrain less air than a free jet. Values of centerline velocity constant K are approximately those for a free jet multiplied by $\sqrt{2}$; that is, the normal maximum of 6.2 for K for free jets becomes 8.8 for a similar jet discharged parallel to an adjacent surface.

When a jet is discharged parallel to but at some distance from a solid surface (wall, ceiling, or floor), its expansion in the direction of the surface is reduced, and entrained air must be obtained by recirculation from the jet instead of from ambient air (McElroy 1943; Nottage et al. 1952b; Zhang et al. 1990). The restriction to entrainment caused by the solid surface induces the **Coanda effect**, which makes the jet attach to a surface a short distance after it leaves the diffuser outlet. The jet then remains attached to the surface for some distance before separating again.

In nonisothermal cases, the jet's trajectory is determined by the balance between thermal buoyancy and the Coanda effect, which depends on jet momentum and distance between the jet exit and solid surface. The behavior of such nonisothermal surface jets has been studied by Kirkpatrick et al. (1991), Oakes (1987), Wilson et al. (1970), and Zhang et al. (1990), each addressing different factors. More systematic study of these jets in room ventilation flows is needed to provide reliable guidelines for designing air distribution systems.

Multiple Jets

Twin parallel air jets act independently until they interfere. The point of interference and its distance from outlets vary with the distance between outlets. From outlets to the point of interference, maximum velocity, as for a single jet, is on the centerline of each jet. After interference, velocity on a line midway between and parallel to the two jet centerlines increases until it equals jet centerline velocity. From this point, maximum velocity of the combined jet stream is on the midway line, and the profile seems to emanate from a single outlet of twice the area of one of the two outlets.

Airflow in Occupied Zone

Mixing Systems. Laboratory experiments on jets usually involve recirculated air with negligible resistance to flow on the return path. Experiments in small-cross-sectional mine tunnels, where return flow meets considerable resistance, show that jet expansion terminates abruptly at a distance that is independent of discharge velocity and is only slightly affected by outlet size. These distances are determined primarily by the return path's size and length. In a long tunnel with a cross section of 1.5 by 1.8 m, a jet may not travel more than 7.5 m; in a tunnel with a relatively large section (7.5 by 18 m), the jet may travel more than 75 m. McElroy (1943) provides data on this phase of jet expansion.

Zhang et al. (1990) found that, for a given heat load and room air supply rate, air velocity in the occupied zone increases when outlet discharge velocity increases. Therefore, the design supply air velocity should be high enough to maintain the jet traveling in the desired direction, to ensure good mixing before it reaches the occupied zone. Excessively high outlet air velocity induces high air velocity in the occupied zone and results in thermal discomfort.

Turbulence Production and Transport. Air turbulence in a room is mainly produced at the diffuser jet region by interaction of supply air with room air and with solid surfaces (walls or ceiling) in the vicinity. It is then transported to other parts of the room, including the occupied zone (Zhang et al. 1992). Turbulence is also damped by viscous effect. Air in the occupied zone usually contains very small amounts of turbulent kinetic energy compared to the jet region. Because turbulence may cause thermal discomfort (Fanger et al. 1989), air distribution systems should be designed so that stationary occupants are not subjected to the region where primary mixing between supply and room air occurs (except in specialized applications such as task ambient or spot-conditioning systems).

SYSTEM DESIGN

MIXED-AIR SYSTEMS

In mixed-air systems, high-velocity supply jets from air outlets maintain comfort by mixing room air with supply air. This air mixing, heat transfer, and resultant velocity reduction should occur outside the occupied zone. Occupant comfort is maintained not directly by motion of air from the outlets, but from secondary air motion that results from mixing in the unoccupied zone. Comfort is maximized when uniform temperature distribution and room air velocities of less than 0.25 m/s are maintained in the occupied zone.

Outlet Types

Straub and Chen (1957) and Straub et al. (1956) classified outlets into five groups:

Group A. Outlets mounted in or near the ceiling that discharge air horizontally.

Group B. Outlets mounted in or near the floor that discharge air vertically in a nonspreading jet.

Group C. Outlets mounted in or near the floor that discharge air vertically in a spreading jet.

Group D. Outlets mounted in or near the floor that discharge air horizontally.

Group E. Outlets mounted in or near the ceiling that project primary air vertically.

Analysis of outlet performance was based on primary air pattern, total air pattern, stagnant air layer, natural convection currents, return air pattern, and room air motion. Figures 5 to 9 show room air motion characteristics of the five outlet groups; exterior walls are depicted by heavy lines. The principles of air diffusion emphasized by these figures are as follows:

- Primary air (shown by dark envelopes in Figures 5 to 9) from the outlet down to a velocity of about 0.75 m/s can be treated analytically. Heating or cooling load has a strong effect on the characteristics of primary air.
- Total air, shown by light gray envelopes in Figures 5 to 9, is influenced by primary air and is of relatively high velocity (but less than 0.75 m/s). Total air is also influenced by the environment and drops during cooling or rises during heating; it is not subject to precise analytical treatment.
- Natural convection currents form a stagnant zone from the ceiling down during cooling, and from the floor up during heating. This zone forms below the terminal point of the total air during heating and above the terminal point during cooling. Because this zone results from natural convection currents, its air velocities are usually low (approximately 0.1 m/s), and the air stratifies in layers of increasing temperatures. The concept of a stagnant zone is important in properly applying and selecting outlets because it considers the natural convection currents from warm and cold surfaces and internal loads.
- A return inlet affects room air motion only in its immediate vicinity. The intake should be located in the stagnant zone to return the warmest room air during cooling or the coolest room air during heating. The importance of the location depends on the relative size of the stagnant zone, which depends on the type of outlet.
- The general room air motion (shown by arrows in white areas in Figures 5 to 9) is a gentle drift toward the total air. Room conditions are maintained by entraining room air into the total airstream. The room air motion between the stagnant zone and the total air is relatively slow and uniform. The highest air motion occurs in and near the total airstreams.

Group A Outlets. This group includes high sidewall grilles, sidewall diffusers, ceiling diffusers, linear ceiling diffusers, and similar outlets. High sidewall grilles and ceiling diffusers are illustrated in Figure 5.

Primary air envelopes (**isovels**) show a horizontal, two-jet pattern for the high sidewall and a 360° diffusion pattern for the ceiling outlet. Although variation of vane settings might cause a discharge in one, two, or three jets in the case of the sidewall outlet, or have a smaller diffusion angle for the ceiling outlet, the general effect in each is the same.

During cooling, the total air drops into the occupied zone at a distance from the outlet that depends on air quantity, supply velocity, temperature differential between supply and room air, deflection setting, ceiling effect, and type of loading within the space. Analytical

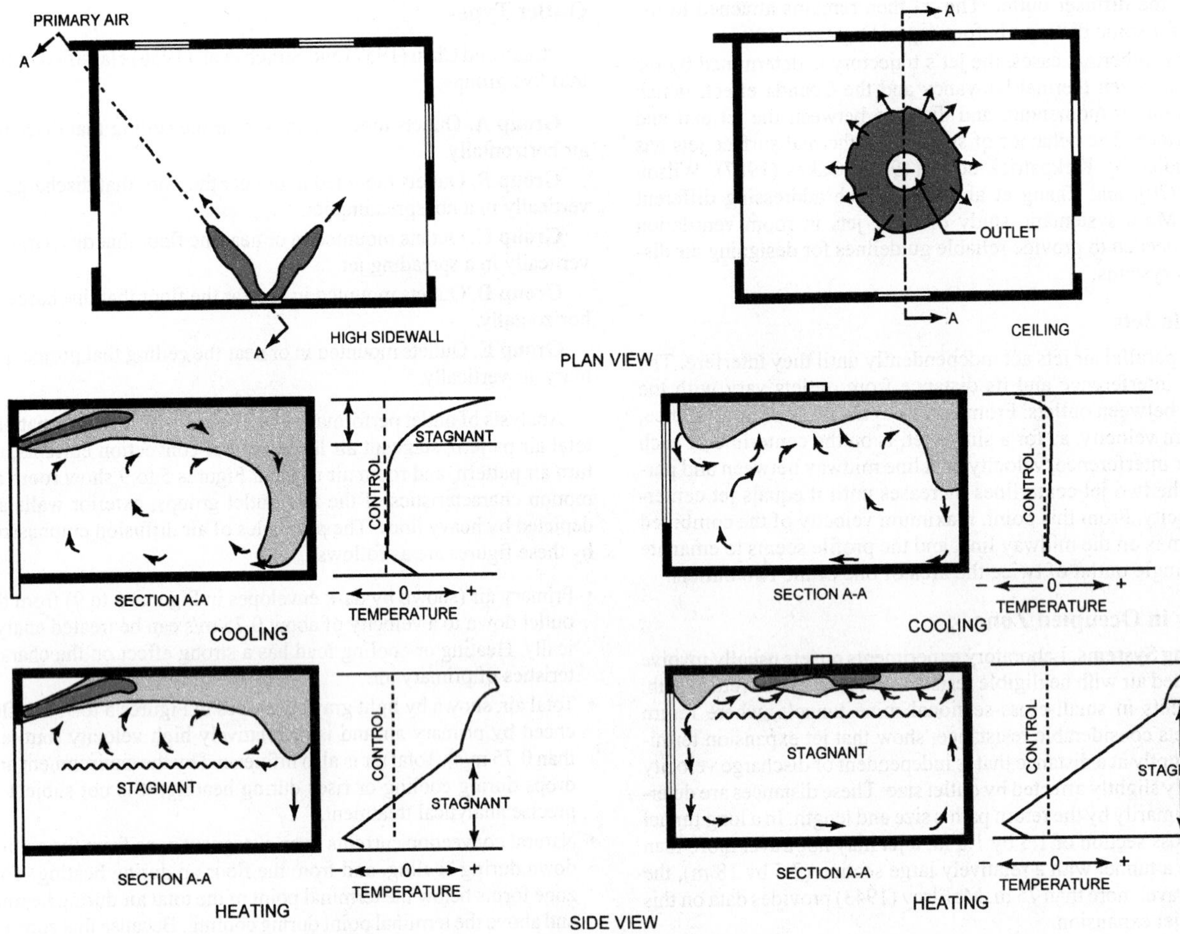

Fig. 5 Air Motion Characteristics of Group A Outlets
(Straub et al. 1956)

methods of relating some of these factors are presented in the section on Principles of Jet Behavior.

The cooling diagram for the high sidewall outlet shows an overthrow condition, which causes the total air to drop along the opposite wall and flow slowly for some distance across the floor. Velocities of about 0.5 to 0.75 m/s may be found near the wall but dissipate within about 100 mm of the wall.

The cooling diagram for the ceiling outlet shows that total air movement is counteracted by rising natural convection currents on the heated wall, and, therefore, drops before reaching the wall. On the other hand, the total air reaches the inside wall and descends for some distance along it. With this type of outlet, temperature variations in the room are minimized, with minimal stagnant volume. The maximum velocity and maximum temperature variation occur in and near the total air envelope; therefore, the drop region becomes important because it is an area with high effective draft temperature T_{ed} [see Equation (18)]. Consequently, how far the air drops before velocities and temperatures reach acceptable limits must be known.

Because these outlets discharge horizontally near the ceiling, the warmest air in the room is mixed immediately with cool primary air far above the occupied zone. Therefore, the outlets are capable of handling relatively large quantities of air at large temperature differentials.

During heating, warm supply air introduced at the ceiling can cause stratification in the space if there is insufficient induction of room air at the outlet. Selecting diffusers properly, limiting the room supply temperature differential, and maintaining air supply rates at a level high enough to ensure air mixing by induction provide adequate air diffusion and minimize stratification.

Several building codes and ASHRAE *Standard* 90.1 require sufficient insulation in exterior walls, so most perimeter spaces can be heated effectively by ceiling air distribution systems. Interior spaces, which generally have only cooling demand conditions, seldom require long-term heating and are seldom a design problem.

Flow rate and velocity for both heating and cooling are the same for the outlets shown in Figure 5. The heating diagram for the sidewall unit shows that, under these conditions, total air does not descend along the wall. Consequently, higher velocities might be beneficial in eliminating the stagnant zone, because high velocity causes some warm air to reach floor level and counteract stratification of the stagnant region.

The heating diagram for the ceiling outlet shows the effect of natural convection currents that produce a larger throw toward the cold exposed wall. The velocity of total air toward the exposed wall complements natural convection currents. However, the warm total air loses its downward momentum at its terminal point, and buoyancy forces cause it to rise toward the primary air. Although these forces are complementary, the heating effect of total air replaces cool natural convection currents with warm total air.

Group B Outlets. This group includes floor registers, baseboard units, low sidewall units, linear-type grilles in the floor or windowsill, and similar outlets. Figure 6 illustrates a floor outlet adjacent to an inside wall.

Because these outlets have no deflecting vanes, primary air is discharged in a single, vertical jet. When total air strikes the ceiling,

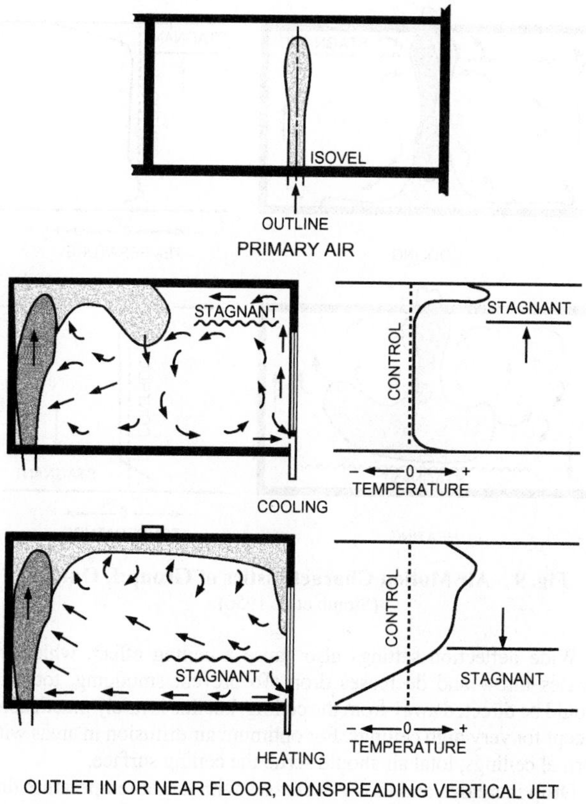

Fig. 6 Air Motion Characteristics of Group B Outlets
(Straub et al. 1956)

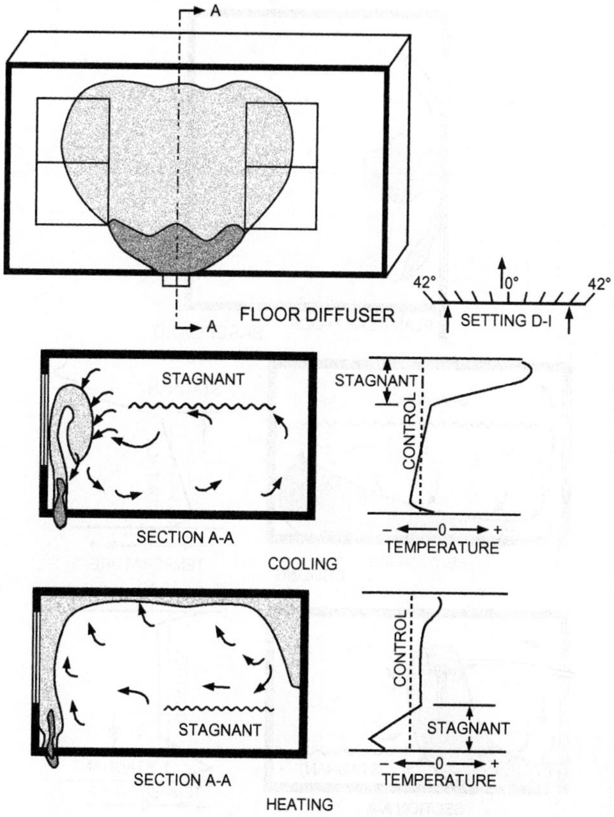

Fig. 7 Air Motion Characteristics of Group C Outlets
(Straub et al. 1956)

it fans out in all directions and, during cooling, follows the ceiling for some distance before dropping toward the occupied zone. During heating, the total airflow follows the ceiling across the room, then descends partway down the exterior wall.

The cooling diagram shows that a stagnant zone forms outside the total air region above its terminal point. Below the stagnant zone, air temperature is uniform, effecting complete cooling. Also, the space below the terminal point of total air is cooled satisfactorily. For example, if total airflow is projected upward for 2.4 m, the region from this level down to the floor will be cooled satisfactorily. However, this does not apply to an extremely large space. Judgment is needed to determine the acceptable size of the space outside the total air. A distance of 4.5 to 6 m between the drop region and the exposed wall is a conservative design value.

Comparison of Figures 5 and 6 for heating shows that the stagnant region is smaller for group B outlets than for group A outlets because air entrained close to the outlet is taken mainly from the stagnant region, which is the coolest air in the room. This results in greater temperature equalization and less buoyancy in the total air than occurs with group A outlets.

Although temperature gradients for both outlet groups are about the same, the stagnant layer is lower for group B than for group A.

Group C Outlets. This group includes floor diffusers, sidewall diffusers, linear-type diffusers, and other outlets installed in the floor or windowsill (Figure 7).

Although group C outlets are related to group B outlets, they are characterized by wide-spreading jets and diffusing action. Total air and room air characteristics are similar to those of group B, although the stagnant zone is larger during cooling and smaller during heating. Primary air diffusion usually causes the total air to fold back on the primary and total air during cooling, instead of following the ceiling. This makes it more difficult to project cool air, but it also provides a greater area for induction of room air. This is beneficial during heating because induced air comes from the lower regions of the room.

Group D Outlets. This group includes baseboard and low sidewall registers and similar outlets (Figure 8) that discharge primary air in single or multiple jets. During cooling, because air is discharged horizontally across the floor, the total air remains near the floor, and a large stagnant zone forms in the entire upper region of the room.

During heating, the total air rises toward the ceiling because of the buoyant effect. Temperature variations are uniform, except in the total air region.

Group E Outlets. This group includes ceiling diffusers, linear grilles, sidewall diffusers and grilles, and similar outlets mounted or designed for vertical downward air projection. Figure 9 shows the heating and cooling diagrams for such a ceiling diffuser.

During cooling, the total air projects to and follows the floor, producing a stagnant region near the ceiling. During heating, the total airflow reaches the floor and folds back toward the ceiling. If projected air does not reach the floor, a stagnant zone results.

Outlet Selection and Location

The design of a mixed-air distribution system is influenced by the same factors that affect design of an air-conditioning plant: building use, size, and construction type. Location and selection of supply outlets is further influenced by the interior design of the building, local sources of heat gain or loss, and outlet performance and design.

Local sources of heat gain or loss promote convection currents or cause stratification; they may, therefore, determine both the type and location of supply outlets. Outlets should be located to neutralize any undesirable convection currents set up by a concentrated load. If a concentrated heat source is located in the occupied zone, the heating effect can be counteracted by (1) directing cool air toward the source

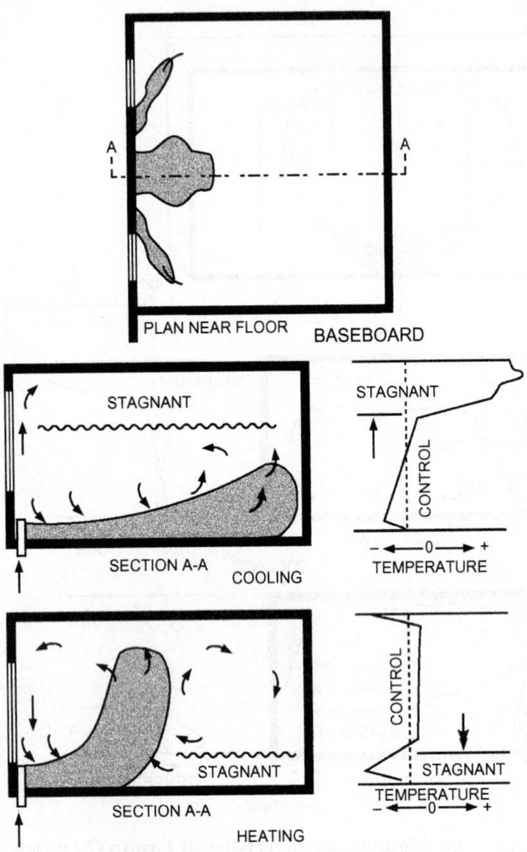

Fig. 8 Air Motion Characteristics of Group D Outlets
(Straub et al. 1956)

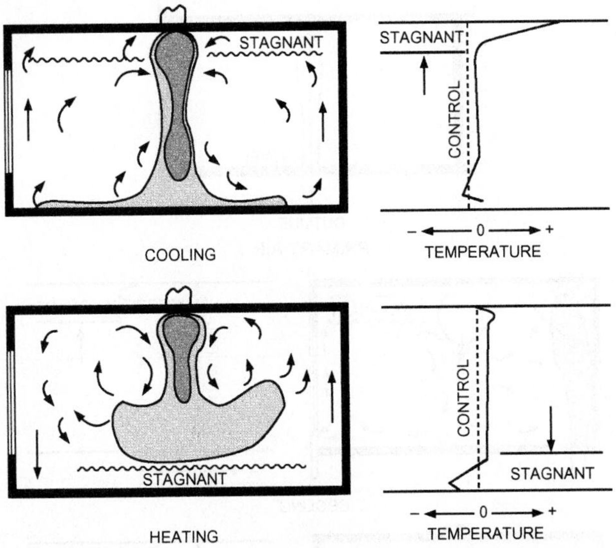

Fig. 9 Air Motion Characteristics of Group E Outlets
(Straub et al. 1956)

or (2) locating an exhaust or return grille adjacent to the source (more economical for cooling applications, because heat is withdrawn at its source rather than dissipated into the space). Where lighting loads are heavy (50 W/m^2) and ceilings relatively high (above 4.5 m), outlets should be located below the lighting load, and the stratified warm air should be removed by an exhaust or return fan. An exhaust fan is recommended if the wet-bulb air temperature is above that of the outdoors; a return fan is recommended if the wet-bulb temperature is below this temperature. These methods reduce the requirements for supply air.

The following selection considerations for outlets in groups A through E are based on analysis of outlet performance tests conducted by Straub and Chen (1957) and Straub et al. (1956).

Group A Outlets. Outlets mounted in or near the ceiling with horizontal air discharge should not be used with temperature differentials exceeding 15 K during heating. Hart and Int-Hout (1980) and Lorch and Straub (1983) recommended that temperature differentials not exceed 8 K during heating. Consequently, these outlets should be used for heating buildings in regions where winter heating is only a minor problem and, in northern latitudes, solely for interior spaces. However, these outlets are particularly suited for cooling and can be used with high airflow rates and large temperature differentials. They are usually selected for their cooling characteristics.

Performance is affected by various factors. Vane deflection settings reduce throw and drop by changing air from a single straight jet to a wide-spreading or fanned-out jet. Accordingly, a sidewall outlet with 0° deflection has a longer throw and a greater drop than a ceiling diffuser with a single 360° angle of deflection. Sidewall grilles and similar outlets with other deflection settings may have performance characteristics between these two extremes.

Wide deflection settings also cause a ceiling effect, which increases throw and decreases drop. To prevent smudging, total air should be directed away from the ceiling, but this is rarely practicable, except for very high ceilings. For optimum air diffusion in areas with normal ceilings, total air should scrub the ceiling surface.

Drop increases and throw decreases with larger temperature differentials. For constant temperature differential, airflow rate affects drop more than velocity. Therefore, to avoid drop, several small outlets in a room may be better than one large outlet.

With the data in the section on Principles of Jet Behavior, throw may be selected for part of the distance between outlet and wall or, preferably, for the entire distance. For outlets in opposite walls, throw should be one-half the distance between the walls. Following these recommendations, the air drops before striking the opposite wall or the opposing airstream. To counteract specific sources of heat gain or to provide higher air motion in rooms with high ceilings, a longer throw may be necessary. In no case should the drop exceed the distance from the outlet to the 1.8 m level.

To maintain maximum ventilation effectiveness with ceiling diffusers, throws should be kept as long as possible. With VAV designs, some overthrow at maximum design volumes is desirable; the highest induction can be maintained at reduced flows. Adequate induction by a ceiling-mounted diffuser prevents short-circuiting unmixed supply air between supply outlet and ceiling-mounted returns.

Group B Outlets. In selecting these outlets, it is important to provide enough throw to project air high enough for proper cooling in the occupied zone. Increased supply air velocity improves air diffusion during both heating and cooling. Also, a terminal velocity of about 0.75 m/s is found at the same distance from the floor during both heating and cooling. Therefore, outlets should be selected from data given in the section on Principles of Jet Behavior, with throw based on a terminal velocity of 0.75 m/s.

With outlets installed near the exposed wall, primary air is drawn toward the wall, resulting in a wall effect similar to the ceiling effect for ceiling outlets. This scrubbing of the wall increases heat gain or loss. To reduce scrubbing, outlets should be installed some distance from the wall, or supply air should be deflected away from the wall. However, to prevent air from dropping into the occupied zone before it reaches maximum projection, the distance should not be too large nor the angle too wide. A distance of 150 mm and an angle of 15° is satisfactory.

These outlets do not counteract natural convection currents unless they are installed in sufficient numbers around the space perimeter, preferably in locations of greatest heat gain or loss (under windows). The effect of drapes and blinds must be considered with outlets installed near windows. Correctly installed, these outlets handle large airflow rates with uniform air motion and temperatures.

Group C Outlets. These outlets can be used for heating, even with severe heat load conditions. Higher supply velocities produce better room air diffusion than lower velocities, but velocity is not critical in selecting these units for heating.

To achieve required projection for cooling, use temperature differentials of less than 8 K. With higher temperature differentials, supply air velocity is not sufficient to project the total air up to the desired level.

These outlets have been used successfully for residential heating, but they may also offer a solution for applications where heating requirements are severe and cooling requirements are moderate. For throw, refer to the section on Principles of Jet Behavior.

Group D Outlets. These outlets direct high-velocity total air into the occupied zone, and, therefore, are not recommended for comfort, particularly for summer cooling. For heating, outlet velocities should not be higher than 1.5 m/s, so that air velocities in the occupied zone will not be excessive. These outlets have been applied successfully to process installations where controlled air velocities are desired.

Group E Outlets. The different throws shown in the heating and cooling diagrams for these outlets become critical in selecting and applying the outlets. Because the total air enters the occupied zone for both cooling and heating, outlets are used for either cooling or heating, but seldom for both.

During cooling, temperature differential, supply air velocity, and airflow rate strongly influence projection. Therefore, low values of each should be selected.

During heating, it is important to select the correct supply air velocity to project warm air into the occupied zone. Temperature differential is also critical because a small temperature differential reduces variation of throw during cyclic fluctuation of the supply air temperature. Vane setting for deflection is as important here as it is for group B and C outlets.

Investigations by Miller and Nevins (1969) and Nevins and Ward (1968) in full-scale interior test rooms indicate that air temperatures and velocities throughout a room cooled by a ventilating ceiling are a linear function of room load (heat load per unit area), and are not affected significantly by variations in ceiling type, total air temperature differential, or air volumetric flow rate. Higher room loading produces wider room air temperature variations and higher velocities, which decrease performance.

These studies also found no appreciable difference in the performance of air-diffusing ceilings and circular ceiling diffusers for lower room loads (65 W/m^2). For higher room loads (250 W/m^2), an air-diffusing ceiling system has only slightly larger vertical temperature variations and slightly lower room air velocities than a ceiling diffuser system.

When the ventilating ceiling is used at exterior exposures, the additional load at the perimeter must be considered. During heating, the designer must provide for the cold-wall effect (radiation, convection, and conduction loads), as with any ceiling supply distribution system. Sound generated by the air supply device must also be considered in total system analysis to ensure that room sound levels do not exceed the design criteria.

Noise. Noise generated by diffusers transmits to the occupied space directly and cannot be attenuated. Therefore, the distribution system design should meet the sound level criteria specified in Chapter 47 of the 2007 *ASHRAE Handbook—HVAC Applications*.

Inlet Selection and Location

Selection. Selection of return and exhaust inlets depends on (1) velocity in the occupied zone near the inlets, (2) permissible pressure drop through the inlets, and (3) noise.

Velocity. Airflow patterns and room air movement are not influenced by the location of return and exhaust inlets beyond a distance of one characteristic length of the return or exhaust inlet (e.g., square root of the inlet area). Air handled by the inlet approaches from all directions, and its velocity decreases rapidly as distance from the inlet increases. Therefore, drafty conditions rarely occur near return inlets.

Permissible pressure drop. Permissible pressure drop depends on the designer's choice. Proper pressure drop allowances should be made for control or directive devices.

Noise. Noise generation and transmission through return inlets should also be taken into account in space acoustical space calculations.

Location. Inlets should be located to minimize short-circuiting of supply air, although tests conducted under ASHRAE *Standard* 129 show little short circuiting with cold ceiling supply and return air. If air is supplied by jets attached to the ceiling, exhaust inlets should be located between the jets or at the side of the room, away from supply air jets. In rooms with vertical temperature stratification, such as foundries, computer rooms, theaters, bars, kitchens, dining rooms, and club rooms, exhaust inlets should be located near the ceiling to collect warm air, odors, and fumes.

For industrial rooms with gas release, selection of exhaust inlet locations depends on the density of released gases and their temperature; locations should be specified for each application.

Exhaust inlets located in walls and doors, depending on their elevation, have the characteristics of either floor or ceiling returns. In large buildings with many small rooms, return air may be brought through door grilles or door undercuts into the corridors and then to a common return or exhaust. If pressure drop through door returns is excessive, air diffusion to the room may be seriously unbalanced by opening or closing doors. Outward leakage through doors or windows cannot be counted on for dependable results.

Ceiling-Based Air Diffusion

For the best thermal comfort conditions and highest ventilation effectiveness in an occupied space (e.g., office or retail store), the entire system performance of air diffusers should be considered. This is particularly true for open spaces, where airstreams from diffusers may interact with each other, and for perimeter spaces, where airstreams from diffusers interact with hot or cold perimeter walls. Although throw data for individual diffusers are used in system design, a mixed-air distribution system should maintain a high quality of air diffusion in the occupied space with low temperature variation, good air mixing, and no objectionable drafts in the occupied space (typically 150 mm to 1.8 m above the floor).

Adequate ventilation requires that the selected diffusers effectively mix (by entrainment) the total air in the room with the conditioned supply air, which is assumed to contain adequate ventilation air.

Interior Spaces. An interior space is conditioned exclusively for cooling loads, except after unoccupied periods when the space may have cooled to below a comfortable temperature. Tests by Hart and Int-Hout (1981), Miller (1979), Miller and Nash (1971), and Miller and Nevins (1970) suggest that the air diffusion performance index (ADPI) (see the section on ADPI under System Performance Evaluation) can be improved by moving diffusers closer together (i.e., specifying more diffusers for a given space and air quantity) and by limiting the supply air/room air temperature difference. In a given system of diffusers, these studies found an optimum operating range of air volumetric flow rates at a given thermal load. Operating load varies with diffuser design, ceiling height, thermal load, and diffuser orientation. This information can be obtained by constructing a mock-up representing the proposed building space, with several alternatives tested for ADPI values, in accordance with ASHRAE *Standard* 113. Usually, the diffuser manufacturer performs these tests and can provide the best choice of design options for a particular building. For a VAV system, diffuser spacing selection should not be based on maximum or design air volumes, but rather on the air volume range in which the system is expected to operate most of the time. For VAV applications, Miller (1979) recommends that the designer consider the expected variation in outlet air volume to ensure that ADPI values remain above a specified minimum. An ADPI of 80% or greater ensures that the space complies with the ASHRAE *Standard* 55 limit of 3 K in the occupied zone.

For an office environment in cooling mode, the design goal should be an ADPI greater than 80. The ADPI should not be used as a measure of performance for heating conditions. In both cases, ASHRAE *Standard* 55 recommends that the maximum temperature gradient (the difference in temperature between any two points) should not exceed 3 K.

Perimeter Spaces. Modern office buildings commonly use all-air mechanical systems to handle both heating and cooling thermal loads, instead of baseboards for heating and forced air for cooling. State energy codes (most based on the ASHRAE *Standard* 90 series) require that commercial buildings have exterior walls that meet minimum thermal performance criteria for a particular location. Typically, walls of new buildings have design heat losses as low as 100 to 300 W per linear metre of wall.

A successful all-air heating/cooling mechanical system requires the designer to consider several design variables (Hart and Int-Hout 1980; Lorch and Straub 1983; Rousseau 1983). The most important design variables include

- Supply air/room air temperature difference
- Diffuser type and design
- Design heating and cooling loads
- Supply air volumetric flow rates
- Distance between diffusers and perimeter wall
- Direction of air throw (toward wall, away from wall, or both)
- Ceiling height
- Desired air diffusion performance criteria

Linear diffusers placed parallel to the perimeter wall perform well. For year-round operation, linear diffusers with two-way throw (i.e., both toward and away from the perimeter wall) work best. Lorch and Straub (1983) reported optimum performance with a diffuser that throws warm air toward the perimeter wall during heating and chilled air in both directions during cooling. Performance was less than optimum with high discharge temperatures (greater than 8 K above ambient), both with one-way throw of air away from a cold wall and with one-way throw of chilled air toward the perimeter wall. During heating, the supply air temperature must be limited to avoid excessive thermal stratification. Diffusers should be located such that the published 0.8 m/s isothermal throw (which is typically unaffected by Δt) extends to within 1.4 m of the floor. According to ASHRAE *Standard* 62.1, if throw does not meet this requirement, and the discharge-to-room temperature differential exceeds 8 K, the ventilation rate must be increased by 25%. Furthermore, when the room-to-discharge differential exceeds 8 K, it is unlikely that the vertical temperature limitation of ASHRAE *Standard* 55 will be met. Figure 10 can be used to predict vertical projection on heated and cooled jets.

To resolve any uncertainty about performance, construct a mock-up with provisions for a cold wall; several variations of the design should be tested so that the best diffuser wall spacing and supply air volumes can be selected. The ADPI, room temperature gradients, or both, measured in accordance with ASHRAE *Standard* 113, can help gage system performance.

The following principles provide the best air diffusion quality and minimum energy use:

- For cooling, return air should exhaust from a location that takes advantage of any thermal stratification design. Often, this should be a high point, to take advantage of rising warm air. Cooling supply air should be introduced as close to the heat sources as possible. Alternatively, stratification designs may condition only part of the total space. In these cases, conditioned air is supplied and exhausted as close to the occupants as possible. In either case, comfort zone temperature gradients should be maintained within 3 K.
- For heating, thermal stratification should be discouraged. Heat should be introduced at points low in the large space. Ceiling-mounted fans may reduce stratification.

System Performance Evaluation

The object of air diffusion in warm-air heating, ventilating, and air-conditioning is to create the proper combination of temperature, humidity, and air motion in the occupied zone of the conditioned room (from the floor to 1.8 m above floor level) (Miller 1989). The effective draft temperature considers the physiological effects on a human body of air temperature, air motion, and relative humidity. Variation from accepted standard limits (see ASHRAE *Standard* 55) may cause occupant discomfort. Lack of uniform conditions in the space or excessive fluctuation of conditions in the same part of the space also produces discomfort. Discomfort can be caused by any of the following conditions:

- Excessive air motion (draft)
- Excessive room air temperature variations (horizontal, vertical, or both)
- Failure to deliver or distribute air according to load requirements at different locations
- Overly rapid fluctuation of room temperature

Draft. Koestel and Tuve (1955) and Reinmann et al. (1959) defined draft as any localized feeling of coolness or warmth of any portion of the body caused by both air movement and air temperature, with humidity and radiation considered constant. The warmth or coolness of a draft was measured above or below a controlled room condition of 24°C db at the center of the room, 0.75 m above the floor, with air moving at about 0.15 m/s.

To define the **effective draft temperature** T_{ed} (difference in temperature between any point in the occupied zone and the control condition), the investigators used the following equation proposed

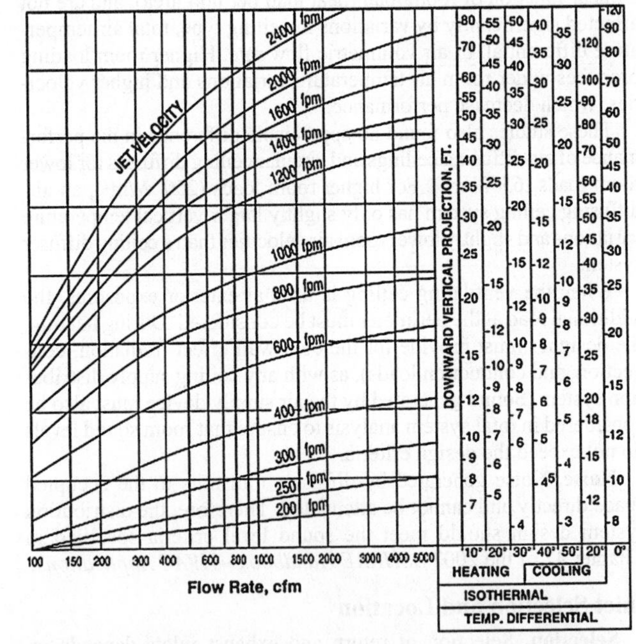

Fig. 10 Downward Vertical Projection of Heated and Cooled Jets Along Perimeter Spaces

by Rydberg and Norback (1949) and modified by Straub (Straub and Chen 1957; Straub et al. 1956) in discussion of a paper by Koestel and Tuve (1955):

$$\theta_{ed} = (T_x - T_c) - 8(V_x - 0.15) \quad (15)$$

where

T_{ed} = effective draft temperature, K
T_x = local airstream dry-bulb temperature, °C
T_c = average (control) room dry-bulb temperature, °C
V_x = local airstream centerline velocity, m/s

Equation (15) accounts for the feeling of coolness produced by air motion and is used to establish the neutral line in Figure 11. In summer, the local airstream temperature T_x is below the control temperature T_c. Hence, both temperature and velocity terms are negative when velocity V_x is greater than 0.15 m/s, and they both add to the feeling of coolness. In winter, if T_x is above T_c, any air velocity above 0.15 m/s subtracts from the feeling of warmth produced by T_x. Therefore, it is usually possible to have zero difference in effective temperature between location *x* and the control point in winter, but not in summer.

Houghten et al. (1938) presented data to statistically interpret the percentage of room occupants that will object to a given draft condition. Figure 11 presents the data in the form used by Koestel and Tuve (1955), showing that a person tolerates higher velocities and lower temperatures at ankle level than at neck level. Because of this, conditions in the zone approximately 0.75 to 1.5 m above the floor are more critical than conditions nearer the floor.

Air Velocity. Room air velocities less than 0.25 m/s are generally preferred, but even higher velocities may be acceptable to some occupants (Figure 11). ASHRAE *Standard* 55 recommends elevated air speeds at elevated air temperatures. No minimum air speeds are recommended for comfort, although air speeds below 0.1 m/s are usually imperceptible.

Air Diffusion Performance Index (ADPI). A high percentage of people are comfortable in sedentary (office) occupations when the effective draft temperature θ_{ed}, as defined in Equation (18), is between –1.5 and +1 K and the air velocity is less than 0.35 m/s. If several measurements of air velocity and air temperature are made throughout the occupied zone of an office, the ADPI is the percentage of measurement locations where these specifications for effective draft temperature and air velocity were met. An ADPI approaching 100% indicates the most desirable conditions (Miller 1971; Miller and Nash 1971; Miller and Nevins 1969, 1970, 1972; Nevins and Miller 1972; Nevins and Ward 1968).

The ADPI is based only on air velocity and effective draft temperature (a combination of local temperature variations from the room average) and is not directly related to dry-bulb temperature or relative humidity. These and similar effects, such as mean radiant temperature, must be accounted for separately according to ASHRAE *Standard* 55.

ADPI is applicable only for cooling-mode conditions; a measurement technique is specified in ASHRAE *Standard* 113. Heating conditions can be evaluated using ASHRAE *Standard* 55 guidelines or ISO *Standard* 7730, and can also be measured using ASHRAE *Standard* 113. The ADPI can be predicted from isothermal throw data determined under ASHRAE *Standard* 70 (see Table 3) to predict what will happen under cooling conditions, within the maximum range of room loads presented. These data were obtained, and are therefore most usable, in spaces with ceiling heights between 2.4 and 3 m. In a room with a single diffuser, ADPI may be overly sensitive to high airflow rates, because diffuser throws wash the room's walls.

Jet Throw. The throw of a jet is the distance from the outlet to a point where the maximum velocity in the stream cross section has been reduced to a selected terminal velocity. To estimate ADPI, terminal velocity V_T was selected for all diffusers as 0.25 m/s, except for ceiling slot diffusers, for which it was selected as 0.5 m/s. Manufacturers give data for jet throw from various diffusers for

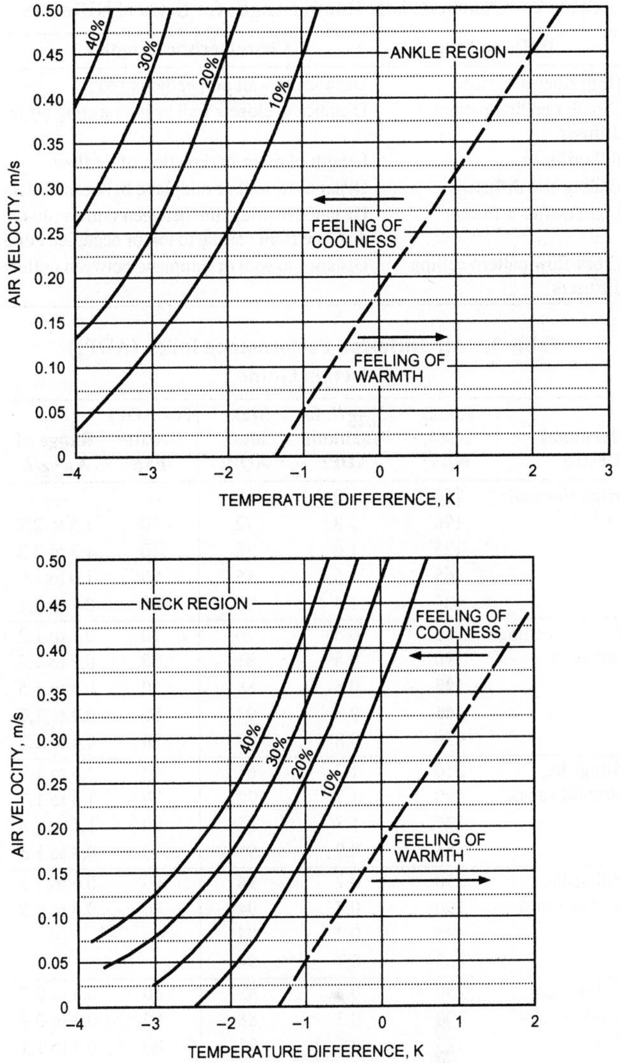

Fig. 11 Percentage of Occupants Objecting to Drafts in Air-Conditioned Room

isothermal conditions and without a boundary wall interfering with the jet.

The throw distance of a jet is denoted by X_{VT}, where subscript *VT* indicates the terminal velocity for which the throw is given. Characteristic room length *L* is the distance from the diffuser to the nearest boundary wall in the principle horizontal direction of the airflow. However, where air injected into the room does not impinge on a wall surface but collides with air from a neighboring diffuser, *L* is one-half the distance between diffusers plus the distance the mixed jet travels downward to reach the occupied zone. Table 2 defines characteristic length for various diffusers.

The midplane between diffusers also can be considered the module line when diffusers serve equal modules throughout a space, and a characteristic length consideration can be based on module dimension.

Load Considerations. Recommendations in Table 3 cover cooling loads of up to 250 W per square metre of floor surface. The loading is distributed uniformly over the floor up to about 22 W/m^2, lighting contributes about 30 W/m^2, and the remainder is supplied by a concentrated load against one wall that simulates a business machine or a large sun-loaded window. Over this range of data, the maximum ADPI condition is lower for the highest loads;

Table 2 Characteristic Room Length for Several Diffusers

Diffuser Type	Characteristic Length L
High sidewall grille	Distance to wall perpendicular to jet
Circular ceiling pattern diffuser	Distance to closest wall or intersecting air jet
Sill grille	Length of room in direction of jet flow
Ceiling slot diffuser	Distance to wall or midplane between outlets
Light troffer diffusers	Distance to midplane between outlets plus distance from ceiling to top of occupied zone
Cross-flow pattern ceiling diffusers	Distance to wall or midplane between outlets

Table 3 Air Diffusion Performance Index (ADPI) Selection Guide

Terminal Device	Room Load, W/m²	$X_{0.25}/L$ for Maximum ADPI	Maximum ADPI	For ADPI Greater than	Range of $X_{0.25}/L$
High sidewall grilles	250	1.8	68	—	—
	190	1.8	72	70	1.5 to 2.2
	125	1.6	78	70	1.2 to 2.3
	65	1.5	85	80	1.0 to 1.9
	<30	1.4	90	80	0.7 to 2.1
Circular ceiling diffusers	250	0.8	76	70	0.7 to 1.3
	190	0.8	83	80	0.7 to 1.2
	125	0.8	88	80	0.5 to 1.5
	65	0.8	93	80	0.4 to 1.7
	<30	0.8	99	80	0.4 to 1.7
Sill grille, straight vanes	250	1.7	61	60	1.5 to 1.7
	190	1.7	72	70	1.4 to 1.7
	125	1.3	86	80	1.2 to 1.8
	65	0.9	95	90	0.8 to 1.3
Sill grille, spread vanes	250	0.7	94	90	0.6 to 1.5
	190	0.7	94	80	0.6 to 1.7
	125	0.7	94	—	—
	65	0.7	94	—	—
Ceiling slot diffusers (for $T_{0.5}/L$)	250	0.3	85	80	0.3 to 0.7
	190	0.3	88	80	0.3 to 0.8
	125	0.3	91	80	0.3 to 1.1
	65	0.3	92	80	0.3 to 1.5
Light troffer diffusers	190	2.5	86	80	<3.8
	125	1.0	92	90	<3.0
	65	1.0	95	90	<4.5
Cross-flow pattern diffusers	35 to 160	2.0	96	90	1.4 to 2.7
	35 to 160	2.0	96	80	1.0 to 3.4

however, the optimum design condition changes only slightly with load.

Design Conditions. The quantity of air must be known from other design specifications. If it is not known, the solution must be obtained by trial and error.

The devices for which data were obtained are (1) high sidewall grilles; (2) circular pattern ceiling diffusers; (3) sill grilles; (4) two- and four-slot ceiling diffusers; (5) light troffer diffusers; and (6) square-faced one-, two-, three-, and four-jet pattern (cross-flow) ceiling diffusers. Table 3 summarizes recommendations on X_{VT}/L by giving the value of X_{50}/L at which ADPI is maximized for various loads, as well as a range of values of X_{50}/L for which ADPI is above a minimum specified value.

FULLY STRATIFIED SYSTEMS

Fully stratified air distribution systems have been used in industrial applications for many years. In the 1980s, they became a popular alternative for office and classroom HVAC in Europe, and their popularity has recently spread to North America because of their high contaminant removal efficiencies and their possible energy savings, especially in relatively mild climates. **Thermal displacement ventilation (TDV) systems** are the most widely used variant of these systems.

The main objective of a mixed-air system is to create a homogenous mixture of supply and room air throughout the space. Contaminants and heat are diluted and then extracted through the return inlet. TDV systems (Figure 12) do not attempt to mix heat and contaminants; instead, they allow them to escape into the upper uninhabited zone, from which they are extracted. With a TDV system, supply air is introduced directly into the occupied zone at low velocity and a temperature lower than that of room air. Contaminants and heat in the space are carried by convective flows (created by space heat sources) into the upper part of the room. Warm air in the upper zone does not recirculate into the occupied zone, so the temperature and concentration of most impurities at the exhaust inlet exceed those in the occupied zone and at the breathing level.

TDV systems offer increased ventilation effectiveness and may reduce HVAC energy consumption. Applications include classrooms, conference rooms, theaters, restaurants, supermarkets, and spaces with high ceilings (3 m and above) (Skistad et al. 2002).

Sandberg and Blomqvist (1989) suggest that the maximum convective cooling load in office buildings with TDV not exceed about 25 W/m², so that the maximum vertical temperature gradient in the occupied zone is not larger than 3 K. Kegel and Schulz (1989) and Svensson (1989) suggested higher cooling load limits of 30 to 40 W/m². However, Chen and Glicksman (1999) demonstrated that cooling loads up to 120 W/m² can be handled in the office environment if the ventilation rate is increased. Howe et al. (2003) reported successful application of TDV in a telecommunication equipment room with cooling loads up to 340 W/m², although thermal comfort was not the primary objective of this application.

Convective Flows Associated with Space Heat Sources

Convective heat flows in the space are the driving forces behind TDV systems. When the surface temperature of a heat source exceeds that of the air surrounding it, heat is transferred to ambient air by convection. This transfer warms the air and causes it to rise because of buoyancy. These rising plumes grow as they entrain room air. Radiant heat transfer does not directly affect heat plume formation, but may indirectly influence development of other heat source plumes by raising the surface temperature of the source.

Each space heat source forms its own thermal plume. Formation of the plume and its vertical travel are determined by several factors:

- Shape and surface area of heat source
- Intensity of heat source
- Air turbulence around heat source (turbulence discourages plume formation)
- Temperature gradient in the space (affects plume volume)

The heat plume rises until it encounters ambient air of similar temperature.

The Archimedes number [Equation (15)] relates the ratio between buoyancy forces and velocity forces of the air surrounding the heat source. Larger Archimedes numbers indicate that buoyancy dominates the air behavior, whereas smaller numbers indicate that inertia (velocity) dominates. Lower Archimedes numbers in mixed-air systems usually inhibit plume formation.

Characteristics of Thermal Plumes

As a thermal plume rises because of natural convection above a heat source, it entrains surrounding air and therefore increases in size and volume, and decreases in velocity (Figure 13). The maximum height to which a plume rises depends primarily on the heat source's strength, and secondarily on stratification in the room (which decreases the rising plume's buoyancy). The **stratified zone**

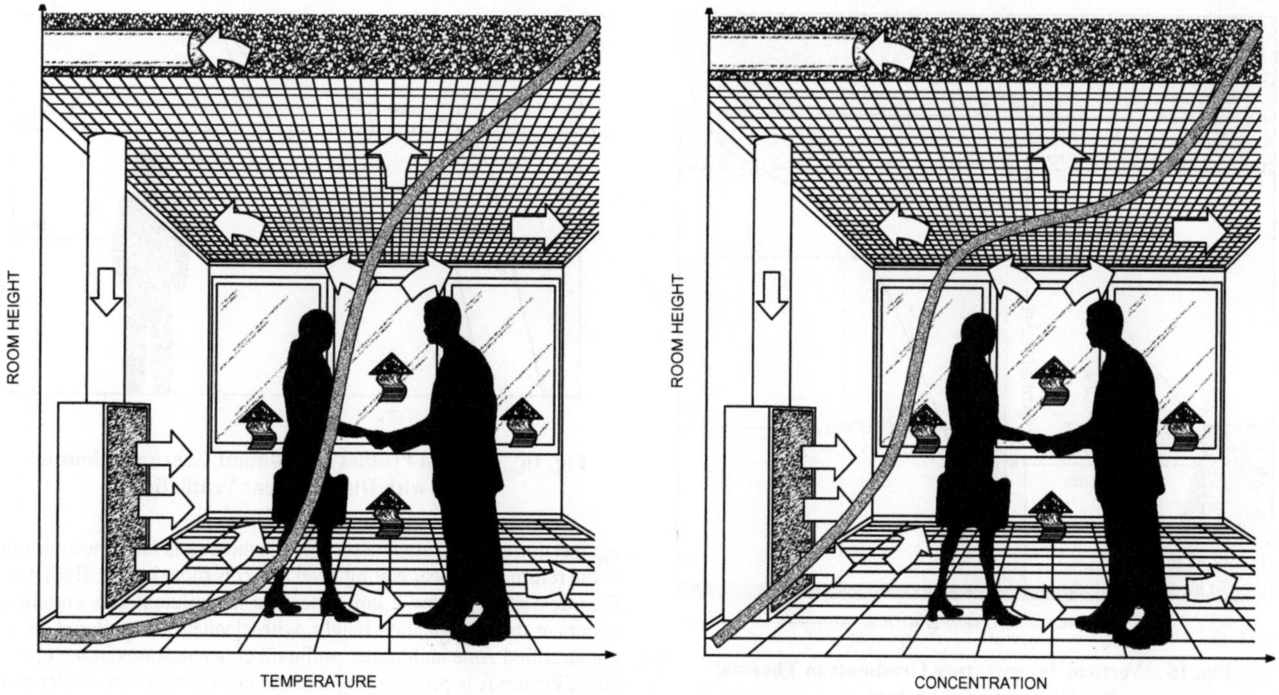

Fig. 12 Displacement Ventilation

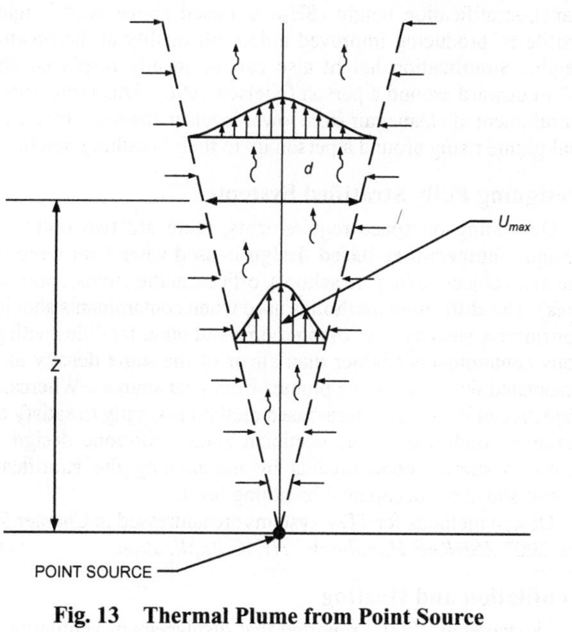

Fig. 13 Thermal Plume from Point Source

has little or no recirculation. In this region, cool supply air gradually flows across the room in a thin layer, typically 100 to 150 mm thick. It is drawn horizontally toward the heat sources, where it joins rising air in the plumes and is entrained upward. These plumes expand and rise until they encounter equally warm air in the upper regions of the space. The **upper zone** above the stratification height is characterized by low-velocity recirculation, which produces a fairly well-mixed layer of warm air with greater contaminant concentration than that in the lower levels of the space.

Typically, warmer, more polluted air will not reenter the stratified zone. This principle is the basis for the improved ventilation effectiveness and heat removal efficiency of TDV systems. In some situations (e.g., morning start-up, winter), there are also sources of cooling in the space, such as cold perimeter windows. The resulting

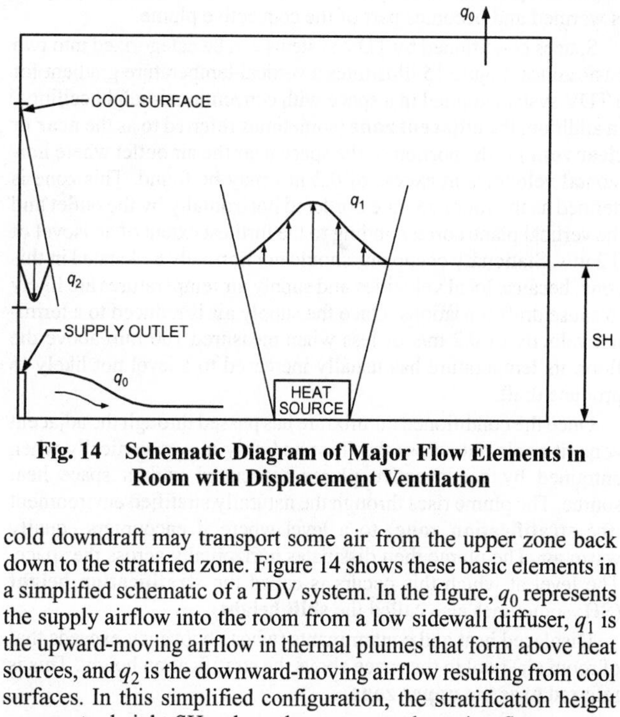

Fig. 14 Schematic Diagram of Major Flow Elements in Room with Displacement Ventilation

cold downdraft may transport some air from the upper zone back down to the stratified zone. Figure 14 shows these basic elements in a simplified schematic of a TDV system. In the figure, q_0 represents the supply airflow into the room from a low sidewall diffuser, q_1 is the upward-moving airflow in thermal plumes that form above heat sources, and q_2 is the downward-moving airflow resulting from cool surfaces. In this simplified configuration, the stratification height occurs at a height SH, where the net upward moving flow $q_1 - q_2$ equals q_0. An important objective in designing and operating a TDV system is to maintain stratification above the occupied zone.

Vertical Temperature Distribution

Thermal displacement ventilation (TDV) outlets discharge conditioned (typically 15.5 to 18°C) air at very low outlet velocities (less than 0.35 m/s). Cool air drops almost immediately to the floor, because of its negative buoyancy. The buoyancy of the supply causes it to remain near the floor until it comes into close contact with a convective heat source. The ascending plume associated with the source creates a stack effect that entrains supply air from the

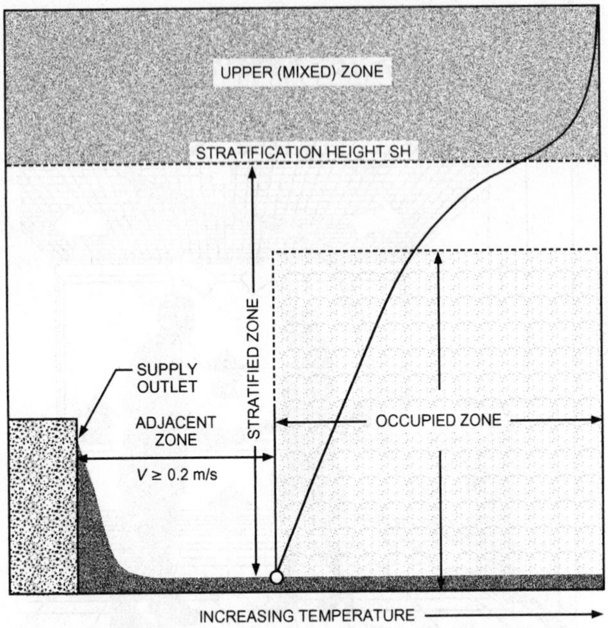

Fig. 15 Vertical Temperature Gradients in Thermal Displacement System

floor. As it passes vertically over the source, the displaced supply air is warmed and becomes part of the convective plume.

Spaces conditioned by TDV systems can be categorized into two basic zones. Figure 15 illustrates a vertical temperature gradient for a TDV system applied in a space with conventional-height ceilings. In addition, the **adjacent zone** (sometimes referred to as the **near** or **clear zone**) is the portion of the space near the air outlet where horizontal velocities in excess of 0.2 m/s may be found. This zone is defined as the room volume bordered horizontally by the outlet and the vertical plane corresponding to the furthest extent of an isovel of 0.2 m/s. Stationary occupants should not normally be located in this zone, because local velocities and supply air temperatures are likely to cause draft sensations. Once the supply air is reduced to a terminal velocity of 0.2 m/s or less when measured 100 mm above the floor, its temperature has usually increased to a level not likely to produce draft.

Once the conditioned air mixture has passed through the adjacent zone, it pools out across the floor and only moves vertically when entrained by a convective plume associated with a space heat source. The plume rises through the naturally stratified environment (the **stratification zone**) to a level where it encounters equally warm air. The plume then dissipates horizontally across the space. The level at which this occurs is called the **stratification height** (**SH**; sometimes also called the **shift height**).

Displaced heat and contaminants (whose buoyancy exceeds that of room air) pool in the space above the stratification height. This is referred to as the **upper zone**.

Contaminant Distribution

One of the key benefits of fully stratified systems is increased removal efficiency of contaminants associated with space heat sources. These contaminants are directly conveyed to the upper zone by thermal plumes associated with the heat sources.

Figure 16 illustrates how stratification height influences indoor air quality in the occupied zone for the idealized case of a TDV system serving a space with a single heat source (person) and its associated contaminant (person's breathing) (Skistad 1994). The figure shows two typical vertical profiles of pollutants from a person's breathing. Normalized pollutant concentrations (c/c_R) are plotted

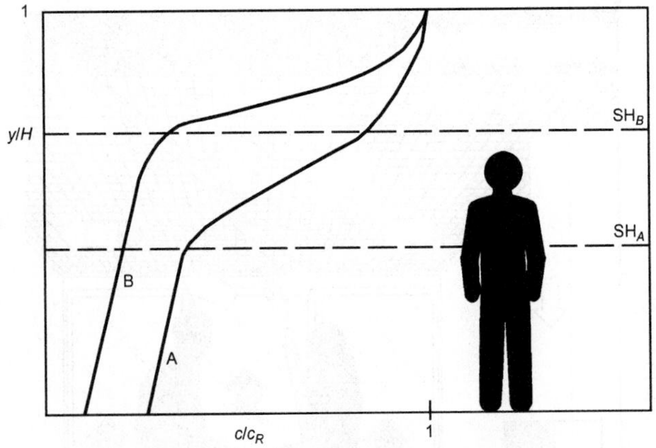

Fig. 16 Vertical Profiles of Pollutant Concentrations in Room with Displacement Ventilation

against normalized room height (y/H), where c_R is the concentration at the return grille near ceiling level and H is room height. Both profiles demonstrate how a large increase in pollutant concentration occurs at the stratification height, with cleaner, less polluted air in the stratified zone and higher pollutant concentrations in the upper zone. Profile A is produced by a lower airflow rate that results in a stratification height (SH_A) somewhat below head height of a standing occupant. By increasing the airflow rate (loads remain constant), stratification height (SH_B) is raised above head height in profile B, producing improved indoor air quality at the breathing height. Stratification height also can be locally displaced about 0.2 m upward around a person (Nielsen 1996). This represents the entrainment of cleaner air from lower levels in the room by the thermal plume rising around a person up to their breathing height.

Designing Fully Stratified Systems

Depending on space requirements, there are two options for design. **Temperature-based design** is used when heat removal is the main objective (e.g., in schools, offices, auditoriums, sport facilities). The **shift-zone method** is used when contaminants should be considered, such as in smoking rooms and other facilities with gaseous contaminants (lighter than air or of the same density as air) associated with convective plumes from heat sources. Whereas the objective of the temperature-based method is simply to satisfy temperature conditions in the occupied zone, shift-zone design also seeks to stratify contaminants by maintaining the stratification height above the occupants' breathing level.

Design methods for TDV systems are addressed in Chapter 56 of the 2007 *ASHRAE Handbook—HVAC Applications*.

Ventilation and Heating

Skistad et al. (2002) reported that displacement ventilation can be combined successfully with radiators and convectors at exterior walls to offset space heat losses. Radiant heating panels and heated floors also can be used with displacement ventilation. When the secondary heating system is used, displacement diffusers supply air at 2 K lower than room air temperature. In that case, displacement ventilation performs the same way as in cooling mode and all the benefits associated with better indoor air quality are preserved.

When warm air is supplied through displacement outlets, the system's performance is similar to that of a mixed-air system in heating mode.

Outlet Types

Outlets in TDV systems are designed to limit outlet velocities to about 0.35 m/s or less. This results in supply airflow capacities of typically 0.25 to 0.35 m³/s per square metre of discharge area.

Therefore, outlets used in TDV systems tend to be large compared to those used for mixed-air systems. Properly designed TDV outlets also incorporate provisions that create an equal distribution of supply air across their face to minimize discharge velocity variations. Equally distributing flow across the discharge area reduces the length of the outlet's adjacent zone.

TDV system outlets are available in various geometries and capacities. They may be mounted flush in a partition wall, either contained within the wall or extending into a mechanical space behind it. They are also often mounted adjacent to the partition wall (with either a 90 or 180° discharge pattern) or in a corner (with a quarter round discharge pattern). Others are free-standing and column-shaped, with a full radial discharge pattern.

Because TDV outlets discharge the air at such low velocities, they impart very little directional guidance to the supply airstream. This allows them to be mounted behind architectural elements such as louvers or screens and remain visually unobtrusive.

Floor diffusers that discharge supply air horizontally at low airflow rates can be used to create a fully stratified room environment. Floor diffusers with vertical discharge of turbulent air jets do not create such conditions, and are covered in the section on Partially Mixed Systems.

Much smaller versions of TDV outlets are used for underseat supply in public assembly (theaters, lecture halls, sports arenas, etc.) HVAC applications. These outlets are generally designed for much lower individual supply airflow capacities, and typically use warmer supply air. They may have internal mixing devices to help reduce their adjacent zone length.

Outlet Selection and Location

TDV outlets should be selected and located so that stationary space occupants are not located within their adjacent zone where draft risks are high. The low discharge velocities of TDV terminals create very little noise and thus are only of concern in very sensitive acoustical applications. System noise (noise from fans, dampers, ductwork, etc.) should be considered, however, because it is transmitted with the supply airflow.

Return Inlet Selection and Location

TDV return air inlets used should conform to the same requirements as those for mixed-air systems. They should always be located above the occupied zone, and should be provided within any confined space served by a TDV supply air terminal.

System Performance Evaluation

The primary comfort criterion of TDV systems is maintaining the design room air temperature (usually specified at the head level of the predominant space occupants) while limiting the vertical temperature difference between occupants' ankle and head levels to no more than 3 K. Because velocities in the occupied zone are very low, they are of minimal concern. Additional information may be found in ASHRAE *Standard* 113.

ADPI should not be used to evaluate fully stratified systems, because it essentially measures the degree of mixing achieved by the room air distribution system. A fully mixed environment would have the highest ADPI rating.

PARTIALLY MIXED SYSTEMS

Partially mixed room air distribution systems used for space cooling generally discharge conditioned air from a low sidewall or floor location, and the diffuser discharge turbulence is considerably greater than in fully stratified (TDV) systems. This creates a zone of high entrainment near the plane of discharge. A common example of partially mixed systems is **underfloor air distribution (UFAD) systems.**

UFAD systems differ from TDV systems primarily in the way air is delivered to the space: (1) air is supplied at higher velocities through smaller supply outlets, and (2) local air supply conditions are generally under the control of occupants, allowing comfort conditions to be optimized. By introducing supply air with greater momentum, UFAD systems alter conditions in the lower region of the space by increasing the amount of mixing and reducing the temperature gradient. At higher elevations in the room, above the influence of supply outlets, overall airflow performance is similar to that of TDV systems. Based on recent experimental results (Webster et al. 2002a, 2002b; Yamanaka et al. 2002) and an extension of displacement theory, three distinct zones in the room can be used to describe the room air diffusion for UFAD systems.

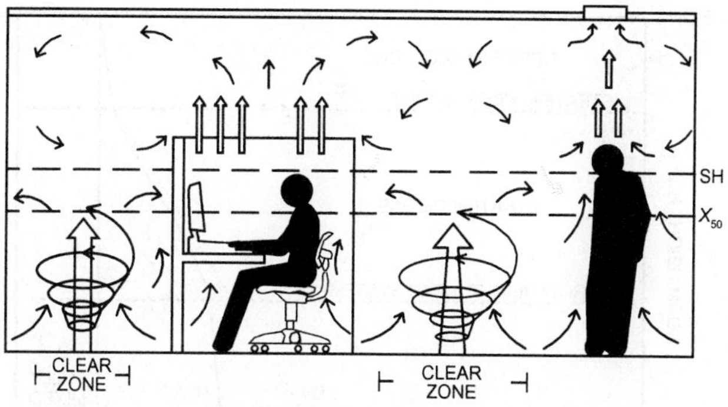

Fig. 17 Underfloor Air Distribution System with Diffuser Throw below Stratification Height

Figure 17 shows a schematic of typical airflow patterns in an UFAD system in an office environment. The diagram identifies two characteristic heights in the room that define the three zones in the room: (1) the throw height (X_{50}) of the floor diffusers, and (2) the stratification height (SH), similar to that found in TDV systems. As shown, UFAD diffusers typically create adjacent zones that have excessive draft and cool temperatures, making long-term occupancy not recommended. When under direct individual control by the occupant, however, these local thermal conditions may be acceptable, and even desirable. Increased mixing in the occupied zone diminishes ventilation effectiveness, compared to TDV systems. In any case, control and optimization of stratification is crucial to system design and sizing, energy-efficient operation, and comfort performance of UFAD systems.

Figure 18 compares typical vertical temperature profiles for UFAD, TDV, and conventional overhead mixing systems. The profiles shown are representative of normal operating conditions and are intended to demonstrate key differences and similarities between the three air distribution systems. The UFAD profile is based on temperatures in a space outside the direct influence of supply outlets (outside adjacent zones), and can vary significantly depending on several control factors (see the section on Controlling Stratification) (Webster et al. 2002a). In Figure 18, the nondimensional temperature (temperature ratio) is plotted versus room height, where T_H is room air temperature as a function of height, T_S is supply temperature, and T_E is temperature at the ceiling. The linear profile for TDV systems is based on the 50% rule of thumb that applies to rooms of conventional height and normal heating loads (Skistad 1994); the temperature near the floor is assumed to be halfway between the supply and exhaust temperatures. The TDV profile is assumed to join the UFAD profile at the stratification height. As long as the throw heights of the UFAD diffusers are below the stratification height, the upper zone is assumed to perform in a similar manner for both systems (for the same room-load-to-supply-volume ratio). The fully mixed system profile represents a uniformly mixed room with the temperature equal to the exhaust temperature.

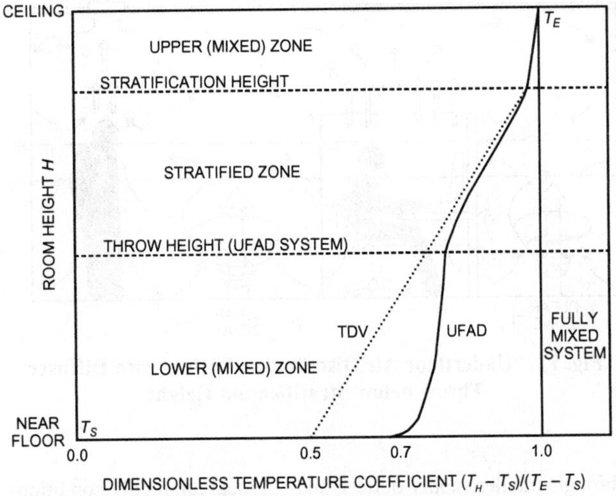

Fig. 18 Comparison of Typical Vertical Temperature Profiles for Underfloor Air Distribution, Displacement Ventilation, and Mixing Systems

Lower (Mixed) Zone

The lower zone is directly adjacent to the floor and varies in depth according to the vertical projection of the floor-based supply outlets used. The air in this layer is relatively well mixed because of the influence of high-velocity jets near the supply air outlets. The upper boundary of the lower zone coincides with the elevation at which supply air reaches a terminal velocity of around 0.25 m/s. The greater mixing in this zone increases the temperature ratio near floor to about 0.7, and reduces the gradient in comparison to TDV systems. The lower zone always exists, although its height may vary greatly depending on the vertical projection of supply outlets and the ratio of space heat load to supply airflow.

Stratified Zone

The stratified zone is a transition region between the lower and upper zones. Air movement in this zone is entirely buoyant, driven by rising thermal plumes around convective space heat sources. Formation of these plumes is uninhibited in this region, because air movement is not affected by supply air jets. Therefore, the vertical temperature gradient in this zone tends to be greatest, approaching that for TDV systems. The stratified zone only exists when the throw height of supply outlets is below the stratification height.

Upper (Mixed) Zone

The upper zone comprises warm (contaminated) air deposited by rising heat plumes within the space. Although its average air velocities are generally quite low, air in this zone is relatively well mixed as a result of the momentum of thermal plumes penetrating its lower boundary. This zone is analogous to the upper zone found in spaces served by TDV systems. Its bottom boundary, coincident with the stratification height, is primarily a function of the ratio of space heat load to supply airflow rate. If jets from supply outlets penetrate this zone, its depth (or even existence) may be affected, though, if properly controlled, this may be a secondary effect (Figure 19).

Temperature Near Floor

As shown in Figure 18, the greater mixing provided by turbulent supply outlets used in UFAD systems increases the temperature near the floor compared to TDV systems (for the same supply air temperature and volume). This effect is shown more clearly in Figure 20, which plots the nondimensional temperature near the floor as a function of overall room airflow rate, where T_F is the temperature near the floor, T_s is the supply temperature at the floor, and T_e is the temperature at the ceiling. Measurement heights for T_F are in the range of 75 to 100 mm. Experimental data for both swirl and variable-area floor diffusers are taken from Webster et al. (2002a). The curve for TDV systems is based on numerous measurements in different rooms (Mundt 1990).

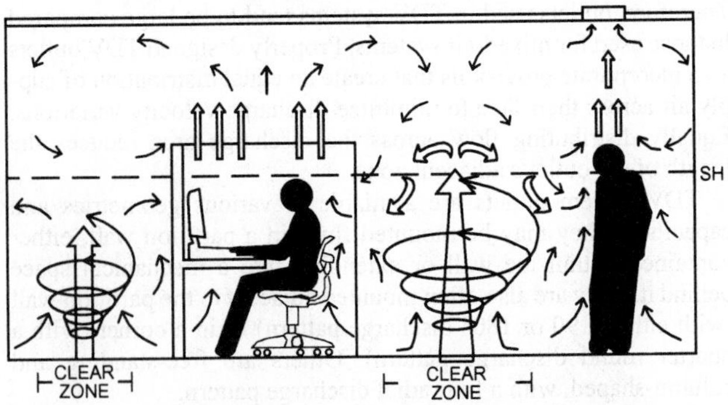

Fig. 19 Underfloor Air Distribution System with Diffuser Throw above Stratification Height

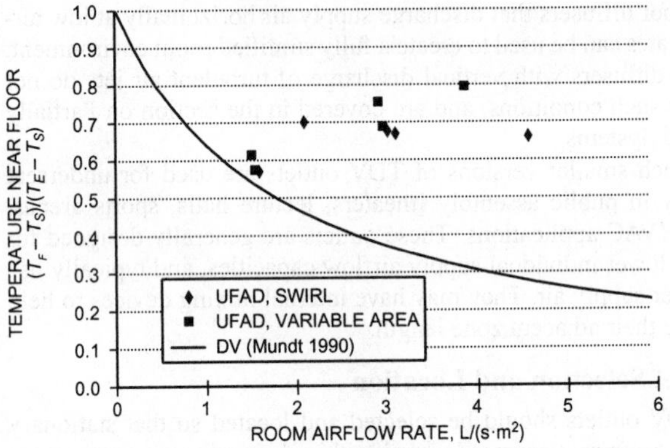

Fig. 20 Nondimensional Temperature near Floor Versus Room Airflow Rate

Experimental UFAD data taken from Webster et al. (2002a); TDV results from Mundt (1990).

Stratification Height

If vertical throw is equal to or less than the stratification height (see Figure 17), the only airflow crossing it will be from buoyancy effects, similar to TDV systems. As throw and mixing are reduced, UFAD systems tend to approach the operation of TDV systems. If throw height is close to or greater than the stratification height, cooler supply air penetrates the warmer upper layer before dropping back down into the lower region, bringing warm air with it (see Figure 19). Although a subject of ongoing research, recent results indicate that, as long as diffuser throw does not penetrate too far into the upper zone (up to 2.1 m in a 3 m high room), relatively similar comfort conditions are produced in the occupied zone, compared to diffusers with lower throws (Webster et al. 2002a).

The amount of air brought down influences temperatures in the lower region, and can also increase stratification height, but this is a secondary effect. Higher throws that penetrate the stratification height result in slightly warmer temperatures and a smaller gradient in the lower region.

When a very strong supply air jet penetrates far into the upper zone, it is possible to disrupt the stratified airflow pattern. For example, laboratory experiments (Bauman et al. 1991; Fisk et al. 1991) demonstrated that, when a fan-driven floor supply module was operated at higher air supply volumes, cool supply jets were

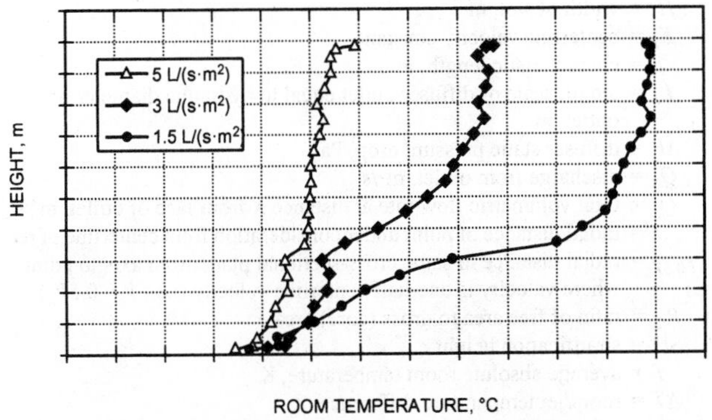

Fig. 21 Effect of Room Airflow Variation at Constant Heat Input, Swirl Diffusers, Interior Zone

able to reach the ceiling, thereby minimizing stratification and producing close to uniform ventilation conditions. This operating strategy of providing a well-mixed space reduces or eliminates the potential improvements in energy and ventilation performance described. To avoid eliminating a stratified space with UFAD systems, maximum vertical throws of diffusers should be limited to no closer than 0.6 to 0.9 m from the ceiling.

Controlling Stratification

Laboratory experiments have investigated the thermal stratification performance of UFAD systems using floor diffusers (Webster et al. 2002a, 2002b). Figure 21 shows the effect of variations in total room airflow on stratification for swirl diffusers operating in a simulated interior space with total heat input of 57 W/m^2 and a supply air temperature of 17.8°C. For constant heat input, stratification increases when room airflow is reduced. Figure 21 also demonstrates how a control strategy might optimize stratification performance. At the highest flow rate of 5 L/(s·m^2), the temperature profile exhibits only a small amount of stratification, with a head/foot temperature difference of 0.7 K. This represents a case where the space is overventilated. On the other hand, at the lowest flow rate of 1.5 L/(s·m^2), the head/foot temperature difference increases to 3.8 K, exceeding the limit of 3 K specified in ASHRAE *Standard* 55. This temperature profile demonstrates the sensitivity to changes in airflow rate, although it is highly unlikely that a system with cooling loads of this magnitude would be operated at such a low airflow rate. To improve energy performance (reduce airflow) while maintaining thermal comfort (avoiding excessive stratification), the middle profile at a flow rate of 3 L/(s·m^2) may be a reasonable target, because it has a head/foot temperature difference of 1.8 K. The difference between the middle and first profiles also demonstrates that, despite a 40% reduction in airflow rate, the temperature in the space only increases by about 0.6 K up to a height of nearly 1.2 m.

Heating Systems

In most applications, heating is primarily needed only near the building envelope, where heat loss to the outdoors can cool spaces and may cause discomfort. Heating may also be needed in some top-floor interior zones and during periods of low occupancy (e.g., nights and weekends).

In operation, delivering warm air from rapidly mixing diffusers near floor level is very effective at providing heat to the conditioned space. Because of buoyancy, the characteristic thermal stratification obtained in cooling operation is replaced with a well-mixed, uniform temperature distribution. Heating load calculation can therefore use the same methods as for conventional overhead air distribution systems.

Effective heating systems isolate the source of warm air from the thermal lag effect of the concrete slab (which is usually slightly cooler than room temperature). This can be done, for example, by ducting from an underfloor fan-coil unit, or by using baseboard radiation or convection units. Quick response on heating can be very important during morning start-up, particularly if night setback is used.

Outlets Types

Partially mixed systems use a wide variety of outlet types, because they are designed to promote mixing in a designated portion of the space. Most partially mixed systems are floor based, however, and those are the types discussed here.

Floor-based outlets used in partially mixed air distribution systems may be classified as passive or active. **Passive** diffusers are installed in the plenum under the raised access floor in UFAD systems. They are not directly ducted to either the conditioned air source or a fan-assisted terminal in the floor plenum. Instead, their supply airflow rate depends on the pressure in the raised-floor plenum that delivers the HVAC service. **Active** diffusers are connected to either a supply air duct or a fan-assisted terminal.

Both passive and active diffusers can be operated with constant or variable air volume. The supply airflow rate in variable-air-volume diffusers can be either automatically reset in response to a control signal, or manually adjusted by space occupants.

High-induction swirl diffusers are the most common type of UFAD supply air outlet. The swirling air pattern provides rapid mixing of supply air with room air up to the height of the diffuser's vertical throw. Although the discharge pattern for most swirl diffusers is not adjustable, occupants have limited control of the delivered air volume by rotating the face of the diffuser or opening the diffuser and adjusting a volume control damper. The maximum flow rate for most passive swirl diffusers operated at typical UFAD plenum pressures is about 0.05 m^3/s at 20 Pa. Most are equipped with a catch basin for dirt and liquid spills.

Linear bar diffusers are also commonly used in UFAD systems. They are often used as active diffusers (supplied by fan-assisted terminals with reheat provisions) for heating and/or cooling perimeter zones adjacent to exterior windows. They may also be used as passive diffusers to supply cooling directly from the pressurized floor plenum. In the latter case, their cooling delivery is usually variable volume and is automatically modulated in accordance with the space thermostat demand.

Passive floor diffusers may also be configured as variable-air-volume diffusers, requiring control and power connections to automatically adjust an integral volume control damper. These terminals may either deliver supply airflow in proportion to a space thermostat signal or use pulse-width modulation to constantly reset an inlet damper from fully open to fully closed (two-position operation). In the latter case, air is supplied through a slotted square floor grill in a jet-type airflow pattern. Occupants can adjust supply jet direction by changing the grille's orientation.

Plenum boxes with integral airflow dampers can also be used to provide automatic variable volume through UFAD floor diffusers. These can be either passive or active in operation, depending on whether they are fan assisted or directly supplied by the pressurized floor plenum.

Outlet Selection and Location

Outlets used in partially mixed air distribution systems should be located such that stationary occupants are not within their prescribed adjacent zone. Outlets that are intended to be manually adjustable by space occupants should be located within about a metre of the occupants.

Return Inlet Selection and Location

As in fully stratified systems, return inlets in partially mixed systems should be located above the occupied zone. These inlets should be of sufficient size to result in inlet velocities no greater than

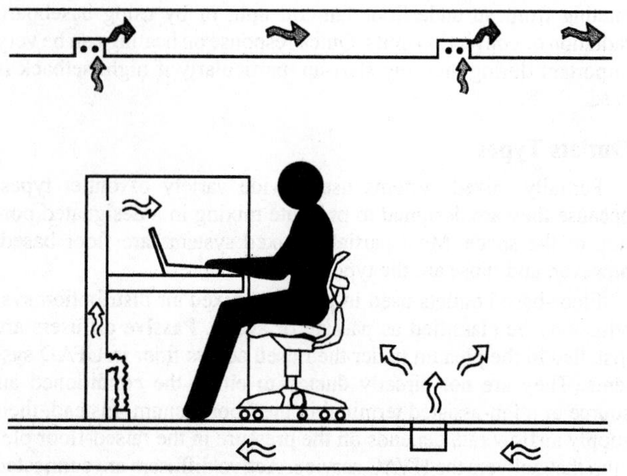

Fig. 22 Underfloor TAC and Personal HVAC System
(Matsunawa et al. 1995)

2.5 m/s, and should be located in every confined space with a supply air outlet.

System Performance Evaluation

The primary comfort criterion of UFAD systems is maintenance of the design room air temperature (usually specified at the head level of the predominant space occupants) while limiting the vertical temperature difference between occupants' ankle and head levels to no more than 3 K. Because velocities in the occupied zone are very low, they are of minimal concern. Additional information may be found in ASHRAE *Standard* 113.

ADPI should not be used to evaluate partially mixed systems, because it essentially measures the degree of mixing achieved by the room air distribution system. A fully mixed environment would have the highest ADPI rating.

TASK/AMBIENT CONDITIONING (TAC)

Task/ambient conditioning (TAC) is most commonly installed with underfloor air distribution (Arens et al. 1991; Bauman and Arens 1996; Bauman et al. 1991, 1993, 1995, 1998; Faulkner et al. 1993, 1999; Fisk et al. 1991; Matsunawa et al. 1995; Tsuzuki et al. 1999). TAC gives individuals some control over their local environment without adversely affecting that of nearby occupants. Typically, the occupant can control the speed, direction, and, in some cases, temperature of supply air. TAC systems are most frequently installed in open-plan offices to provide supply air and, in some cases, radiant heating directly into workstations. Figure 22 shows an underfloor TAC system with a local (personal HVAC) diffuser located in the partition in front of the office worker (Matsunawa et al. 1995).

Bauman et al. (1998) and de Dear and Brager (1999) found that building occupants who have no individual control capabilities are twice as sensitive to changes in temperature as occupants who do have individual thermal control.

SYMBOLS

A_c = measured gross (core) area of outlet, m^2
A_o = core area or neck area, m^2
A_R = cross-sectional area of confined space normal to jet, m^2
Ar = Archimedes number [Equation (12)]
c = pollutant concentration
C_d = discharge coefficient (usually between 0.65 and 0.90)
c_R = concentration of pollutant at return grille near ceiling level
g = gravitational acceleration rate, m/s^2
H = height or width of slot (Table 2), or of room
H_o = width of jet at outlet or at vena contracta, m
H_s = width of slot, m
K_c = centerline velocity constant
L = characteristic length, m
L_o = length scale of diffuser outlet equal to hydraulic diameter of outlet, m
ΔP = diffuser static pressure drop, Pa
Q_o = discharge from outlet, m^3/s
Q_x = total volumetric flow rate at distance X from face of outlet, m^3/s
r = radial distance of point under consideration from centerline of jet
$r_{0.5V}$ = radial distance in same cross-sectional plane from axis to point where velocity is one-half centerline velocity (i.e., $V = 0.5V_x$)
R_{fa} = ratio of free area to gross (core) area
SH = stratification height
T = average absolute room temperature, K
ΔT = room/jet temperature difference, K
T_A = temperature of ambient air, °C
T_c = average (control) room dry-bulb temperature, °C
T_E = temperature at ceiling, °C
T_F = temperature near floor, °C
T_H = temperature at given height, °C
T_O = initial temperature of jet, °C
T_S = supply temperature, °C
T_x = local airstream dry-bulb temperature, °C
V = actual velocity at point being considered
V_c = nominal velocity of discharge based on core area, m/s
V_o = initial air velocity of jet, m/s
V_T = terminal velocity, m/s
V_x = centerline velocity, m/s
X = distance from face of outlet to location of centerline velocity V_X, m
$X_{attached}$ = throw distance of attached jet, m
X_{free} = throw distance of free jet, m
X_H = throw height from floor outlet, m
X_{VT} = distance to given terminal velocity, m
θ_{ed} = effective draft temperature, °C

REFERENCES

Arens, E.A., F. Bauman, L. Johnston, and H. Zhang. 1991. Testing of localized ventilation systems in a new controlled environment chamber. *Indoor Air* 3:263-281.

ASHRAE. 2004. Thermal environmental conditions for human occupancy. ANSI/ASHRAE *Standard* 55-2004.

ASHRAE. 2007. Ventilation for acceptable indoor air quality. ANSI/ASHRAE *Standard* 62.1-2007.

ASHRAE. 1991. Method of testing for rating the performance of air outlets and inlets. ANSI/ASHRAE *Standard* 70-1991.

ASHRAE. 2001. Energy standard for buildings except low-rise residential buildings. ANSI/ASHRAE *Standard* 90.1-2001.

ASHRAE. 1990. Method of testing for room air diffusion. ANSI/ASHRAE *Standard* 113-1990.

ASHRAE. 2002. Measuring air-change effectiveness. ANSI/ASHRAE *Standard* 129-1997 (RA 2002).

ASHRAE. 2007. Standard *62.1 user's manual.*

Baturin, V.V. 1972. *Fundamentals of industrial ventilation*, 3rd ed. Translated by O.M. Blunn. Pergamon Press, New York.

Bauman, F. and E. Arens. 1996. *Task/ambient conditioning systems: Engineering and application guidelines.* Center for Environmental Design Research, University of California, Berkeley.

Bauman, F.S. and A. Daly. 2003. *Underfloor air distribution design guide.* ASHRAE.

Bauman, F.S., L.P. Johnston, H. Zhang, and E.A. Arens. 1991. Performance testing of a floor-based, occupant-controlled office ventilation system. *ASHRAE Transactions* 97(1):553-565.

Bauman, F.S., H. Zhang, E. Arens, and C. Benton. 1993. Localized comfort control with a desktop task conditioning system: Laboratory and field measurements. *ASHRAE Transactions* 99(2):733-749.

Bauman, F.S., E.A. Arens, S. Tanabe, H. Zhang, and A. Baharlo. 1995. Testing and optimizing the performance of a floor-based task conditioning system. *Energy and Buildings* 22(3):173-186.

Bauman, F.S., T.G. Carter, A.V. Baughman, and E.A. Arens. 1998. Field study of the impact of a desktop task/ambient conditioning system in office buildings. *ASHRAE Transactions* 104(1):1153-1171.

Chen, Q. and L. Glicksman. 1999. Performance evaluation and development of design guidelines for displacement ventilation. ASHRAE Research Project RP-949, *Final Report.*

Chen, Q. and L. Glicksman. 2003. *System performance evaluation and design guidelines for displacement ventilation*. ASHRAE.

Christianson, L.L., ed. 1989. *Building systems: Room air and air contaminant distribution*. ASHRAE.

de Dear, R.J. and G.S. Brager. 1999. Developing an adaptive model of thermal comfort and preference. *ASHRAE Transactions* 104(1A):145-167.

Fanger, P.O., A.K. Melikov, H. Hanzawa, and J. Ring. 1988. Air turbulence and sensation of draft. *Energy and Buildings* 12:21-39.

Faulkner, D., W.J. Fisk, and D.P. Sullivan. 1993. Indoor air flow and pollutant removal in a room with desktop ventilation. *ASHRAE Transactions* 99(2):750-758.

Faulkner, D., W.J. Fisk, D.P. Sullivan, and D.P. Wyon. 1999. Ventilation efficiencies of task/ambient conditioning systems with desk-mounted air supplies. *Proceedings of Indoor Air '99*, Edinburgh, Scotland, 8-13 August.

Fisk, W.J., D. Faulkner, D. Pih, P. McNeel, F. Bauman, and E. Arens. 1991. Indoor air flow and pollutant removal in a room with task ventilation. *Indoor Air* 3:247-262.

Hart, G.H. and D. Int-Hout. 1980. The performance of a continuous linear diffuser in the perimeter zone of an office environment. *ASHRAE Transactions* 86(2).

Hart, G.H. and D. Int-Hout. 1981. The performance of a continuous linear diffuser in the interior zone of an open office environment. *ASHRAE Transactions* 87(2).

Helander, L. and C.V. Jakowatz. 1948. Downward projection of heated air. *ASHVE Transactions* 54:71.

Helander, L., S.M. Yen, and R.E. Crank. 1953. Maximum downward travel of heated jets from standard long radius ASME nozzles. *ASHVE Transactions* 59:241.

Helander, L., S.M. Yen, and L.B. Knee. 1954. Characteristics of downward jets of heated air from a vertical delivery discharge unit heater. *ASHVE Transactions* 60:359.

Helander, L., S.M. Yen, and W. Tripp. 1957. Outlet characteristics that affect the downthrow of heated air jets. *ASHAE Transactions* 63:255.

Houghten, F.C., C. Gutberlet, and E. Witkowski. 1938. Draft temperatures and velocities in relation to skin temperatures and feelings of warmth. *ASHVE Transactions* 44:289.

Howe, M., D. Holland, and A. Livchak. 2003. Displacement ventilation—Smart way to deal with increased heat gains in the telecommunication equipment room. *ASHRAE Transactions* 109(1):323-327.

ISO. 1994. Moderate thermal environments—Determination of the PMV and PPD indices and specification of the conditions for thermal comfort. *Standard* 7730-1994. International Organization for Standardization, Geneva.

Kegel, B. and U.W. Schulz. 1989. Displacement ventilation for office buildings. *Proceedings of the 10th AIVC Conference*, Helsinki.

Kirkpatrick, A. and J. Elleson. 1996. *Design guide for cold air distribution systems*. ASHRAE.

Kirkpatrick, A., T. Malmstrom, P. Miller, and V. Hassani. 1991. Use of low temperature air for cooling of buildings. *Proceedings of Building Simulation*.

Knaak, R. 1957. Velocities and temperatures on axis of downward heated jet from 4-inch long-radius ASME nozzle. *ASHAE Transactions* 63:527.

Koestel, A. 1954. Computing temperatures and velocities in vertical jets of hot or cold air. *ASHVE Transactions* 60:385.

Koestel, A. 1955. Paths of horizontally projected heated and chilled air jets. *ASHAE Transactions* 61:213.

Koestel, A. 1957. Jet velocities from radial flow outlets. *ASHAE Transactions* 63:505.

Koestel, A. and J.B. Austin, Jr. 1956. Air velocities in two parallel ventilating jets. *ASHAE Transactions* 62:425.

Koestel, A. and G.L. Tuve. 1955. Performance and evaluation of room air distribution systems. *ASHAE Transactions* 61:533.

Koestel, A., P. Hermann, and G.L. Tuve. 1949. Air streams from perforated panels. *ASHVE Transactions* 55:283.

Koestel, A., P. Hermann, and G.L. Tuve. 1950. Comparative study of ventilating jets from various types of outlets. *ASHVE Transactions* 56:459.

Li, Z., J.S. Zhang, A.M. Zhivov, and L.L. Christianson. 1993. Characteristics of diffuser air jets and airflow in the occupied regions of mechanically ventilated rooms: A literature review. *ASHRAE Transactions* 99(1): 1119-1127.

Li, Z., L.L. Christianson, and J.S. Zhang. 1995. *Separation distances of nonisothermal air jets*. Research Triangle Park, NC.

Lorch, F.A. and H.E. Straub. 1983. Performance of overhead slot diffusers with simulated heating and cooling conditions. *ASHRAE Transactions* 89(1).

Matsunawa, K., H. Iizuka, and S. Tanabe. 1995. Development and application of an underfloor air-conditioning system with improved outlets for a "smart" building in Tokyo. *ASHRAE Transactions* 101(2):887-901.

McElroy, G.E. 1943. Air flow at discharge of fan-pipe lines in mines. U.S. Bureau of Mines *Report of Investigations* 19.

Miller, P.L. 1971. Room air distribution performance of four selected outlets. *ASHRAE Transactions* 77(2):194.

Miller, P.L. 1979. Design of room air diffusion systems using the air diffusion performance index (ADPI). *ASHRAE Journal* 10:85.

Miller, P.L. 1989. Descriptive methods. In *Building systems: Room air and air contaminant distribution*, L.L. Christianson, ed. ASHRAE.

Miller, P.L. and R.T. Nash. 1971. A further analysis of room air distribution performance. *ASHRAE Transactions* 77(2):205.

Miller, P.L. and R.G. Nevins. 1969. Room air distribution with an air distributing ceiling—Part II. *ASHRAE Transactions* 75:118.

Miller, P.L. and R.G. Nevins. 1970. Room air distribution performance of ventilating ceilings and cone-type circular ceiling diffusers. *ASHRAE Transactions* 76(1):186.

Miller, P.L. and R.G. Nevins. 1972. An analysis of the performance of room air distribution systems. *ASHRAE Transactions* 78(2):191.

Murakami, S. 1992. New scales for ventilation efficiency and their application based on numerical simulation of room airflow. International Symposium on Room Air Convection and Ventilation Effectiveness.

Nielsen, P.V. 1996. Temperature distribution in a displacement ventilated room. *ROOMVENT 1996, Proceedings of the 5th International Conference on Air Distribution in Rooms*, Yokohama.

Nevins, R.G. and P.L. Miller. 1972. Analysis, evaluation and comparison of room air distribution performance. *ASHRAE Transactions* 78(2):235.

Nevins, R.G. and E.D. Ward. 1968. Room air distribution with an air distributing ceiling. *ASHRAE Transactions* 74:VI.2.1.

Nottage, H.B., J.G. Slaby, and W.P. Gojsza. 1952a. Outlet turbulence intensity as a factor in isothermal-jet flow. *ASHVE Transactions* 58:343.

Nottage, H.B., J.G. Slaby, and W.P. Gojsza. 1952b. Isothermal ventilation jet fundamentals. *ASHVE Transactions* 58:107.

Oakes, W.C. 1987. *Experimental investigation of Coanda jet*. M.S. thesis, Michigan State University, East Lansing.

Reinmann, J.J., A. Koestel, and G.L. Tuve. 1959. Evaluation of three room air distribution systems for summer cooling. *ASHRAE Transactions* 65:717.

Rock, B.A. 2006. *Ventilation for environmental tobacco smoke—Controlling ETS irritants where smoking is allowed*. ASHRAE and Elsevier.

Rock, B.A. and D. Zhou. 2002. *Designer's guide to ceiling-based air diffusion* (RP-1065). ASHRAE.

Rousseau, W.H. 1983. Perimeter air diffusion performance index tests for heating with a ceiling slot diffuser. *ASHRAE Transactions* 89(1).

Rydberg, J. and P. Norback. 1949. Air distribution and draft. *ASHVE Transactions* 55:225.

Sandberg, M. and C. Blomqvist. 1989. Displacement ventilation in office rooms. *ASHRAE Transactions* 95(2):1041-1049.

Skistad, H. 1994. *Displacement ventilation*. Research Studies Press, John Wiley & Sons, West Sussex, U.K.

Skistad, H., E. Mundt, P. Nielsen, K. Hagstrom, and J. Railio. 2002. Displacement ventilation in non-industrial premises. *REHVA Guidebook* 1.

Straub, H.E. and M.M. Chen. 1957. Distribution of air within a room for year-round air conditioning—Part II. University of Illinois Engineering Experiment Station *Bulletin* 442.

Straub, H.E., S.F. Gilman, and S. Konzo. 1956. Distribution of air within a room for year-round air conditioning—Part I. University of Illinois Engineering Experiment Station *Bulletin* 435.

Svensson, A.G.L. 1989. Nordic experiences of displacement ventilation systems. *ASHRAE Transactions* 95(2):1013-1017.

Tsuzuki, K., E.A. Arens, F.S. Bauman, and D.P. Wyon. 1999. Individual thermal comfort control with desk-mounted and floor-mounted task/ambient conditioning (TAC) systems. *Proceedings of Indoor Air '99*, Edinburgh, vol. 2, pp. 368-373.

Tuve, G.L. 1953. Air velocities in ventilating jets. *ASHVE Transactions* 59:261.

USGBC. 2005. *LEED® for new construction & major renovations*, v. 2.2. U.S. Green Building Council, Washington, D.C. Available from http://www.usgbc.org/ShowFile.aspx?DocumentID=1095.

Webster, T., F. Bauman, and J. Reese. 2002a. Underfloor air distribution: Thermal stratification. *ASHRAE Journal* 44(5):28-36.

Webster, T., F. Bauman, J. Reese, and M. Shi. 2002b. Thermal stratification performance of underfloor air distribution (UFAD) systems. *Proceedings of Indoor Air 2002*, Monterey, CA.

Wilson, J.D., M.L. Esmay, and S. Persson. 1970. Wall-jet velocity and temperature profiles resulting from a ventilation inlet. *ASAE Transactions*.

Yen, S.M., L. Helander, and L.B. Knee. 1956. Characteristics of downward jets from a vertical discharge unit heater. *ASHAE Transactions* 62:123.

Zhang, J.S., L.L. Christianson, and G.L. Riskowski. 1990. Regional airflow characteristics in a mechanically ventilated room under nonisothermal conditions. *ASHRAE Transactions* 96(1):751-759.

Zhang, J.S., L.L. Christianson, G.J. Wu, and G.L. Riskowski. 1992. Detailed measurements of room air distribution for evaluating numerical simulation models. *ASHRAE Transactions* 98(1):58-65.

BIBLIOGRAPHY

Ball, H.D., R.G. Nevins, and H.E. Straub. 1971. Thermal analysis of heat removal troffers. *ASHRAE Transactions* 77(2).

Bauman, F., P. Pecora, and T. Webster. 1999. *How low can you go? Air flow performance of low-height underfloor plenums*. Center for the Built Environment, University of California, Berkeley.

Hanzawa, H., and Y. Nagasawa. 1990. Thermal comfort with underfloor air-conditioning systems. *ASHRAE Transactions* 96(2).

Heiselberg, P. and M. Sandberg. 1990. Convection from a slender cylinder in a ventilated room. *Proceedings of ROOMVENT '90*, Oslo.

Houghton, D. 1995. *Turning air conditioning on its head: Underfloor air distribution offers flexibility, comfort, and efficiency*. E Source TU-95-8. E Source, Inc., Boulder, CO.

Int-Hout, D. 1981. Measurement of room air diffusion in actual office environments to predict occupant thermal comfort. *ASHRAE Transactions* 87(2).

Jackman, P.J. 1991. Displacement ventilation. CIBSE National Conference. Chartered Institution of Building Services Engineers, London.

Jackman, P.J. and P.A. Appleby. 1990. Displacement flow ventilation. BSRIA *Project Report*. Building Services Research and Information Association, Berkshire, U.K.

Livchak, A. and D. Nall. 2001. Displacement ventilation—Application for hot and humid climate. *Proceedings of CLIMA 2000*, Napoli.

Loudermilk, K. 1999. Underfloor air distribution solutions for open office applications. *ASHRAE Transactions* 105(1):605-613.

Mattsson, M. 2000. A note on the thermal comfort in displacement ventilated classrooms. *ROOMVENT 2000, Proceedings of the 7th International Conference on Air Distribution in Rooms*.

McCarry, B.T. 1995. Underfloor air distribution systems: Benefits and when to use the system in building design. *ASHRAE Transactions* 101(2):902-911.

McCarry, B.T. 1998. Innovative underfloor system. *ASHRAE Journal* 40(3).

Melikov, A.K. and J.B. Nielsen. 1989. Local thermal discomfort due to draft and vertical temperature difference in rooms with displacement ventilation. *ASHRAE Transactions* 95(2):1050-1057.

Nelson, D.W. and G.E. Smedberg. 1943. Performance of side outlets on horizontal ducts. *ASHVE Transactions* 49:58.

Nelson, D.W., H. Krans, and A.F. Tuthill. 1940. The performance of stack heads. *ASHVE Transactions* 46:205.

Nelson, D.W., D.H. Lamb, and G.E. Smedberg. 1942. Performance of stack heads equipped with grilles. *ASHVE Transactions* 48:279.

Poz, M.Y. 1991. Theoretical investigation and practical applications of nonisothermal jets for the rooms ventilating. Current East/West HVAC Developments. IEI/CIBSE/ABOK Joint Conference.

Scaret, E. 1985. *Ventilation by displacement: Characterization and design implications*. Elsevier Science, New York.

Seppanen, O.A., W.J. Fisk, J. Eto, and D.T. Grimsrud. 1989. Comparison of conventional mixing and displacement air-conditioning and ventilating systems in U.S. commercial buildings. *ASHRAE Transactions* 95(2): 1028-1040.

Shilkrot, E. and A. Zhivov. 1992. Room ventilation with designed vertical air temperature stratification. *ROOMVENT '92, Proceedings of the 3rd International Conference on Engineering Aero- and Thermodynamics of Ventilated Rooms*.

Shute, R.W. 1992. Integrating access floor plenums for HVAC air distribution. *ASHRAE Journal* 34(10).

Shute, R.W. 1995. Integrated access floor HVAC: Lessons learned. *ASHRAE Transactions* 101(2):877-886.

Sodec, F. and R. Craig. 1990. The underfloor air supply system—The European experience. *ASHRAE Transactions* 96(2).

Spoormaker, H.J. 1990. Low-pressure underfloor HVAC system. *ASHRAE Transactions* 96(2).

Stymne, H., M. Sandberg, and M. Mattsson. 1991. Dispersion pattern of contaminants in a displacement ventilation room—Implications for demand control. *Proceedings of the 12th Air Movement and Ventilation Control Within Buildings*, Ottawa.

Tan, H., T. Murata, K. Aoki, and T. Kurabuchi. 1998. Cooled ceilings/displacement ventilation hybrid air conditioning system—Design criteria. *Proceedings of ROOMVENT '98*, Stockholm.

Tanabe, S. and K. Kimura. 1996. Comparisons of ventilation performance and thermal comfort among displacement, underfloor and ceiling based air distribution systems by experiments in a real sized office chamber. *ROOMVENT '96, Proceedings of the 5th International Conference on Air Distribution in Rooms*.

Wyon, D.P. and M. Sandberg. 1996. Discomfort due to vertical temperature gradients. *Indoor Air* 6:48-54.

Zhivov, A. 1990. Variable-air-volume ventilation systems for industrial buildings. *ASHRAE Transactions* 96(2):367-372.

CHAPTER 21

DUCT DESIGN

COMMERCIAL, industrial, and residential air duct system design must consider (1) space availability, (2) space air diffusion, (3) noise levels, (4) air distribution system (duct and equipment), (5) duct heat gains and losses, (6) balancing, (7) fire and smoke control, (8) initial investment cost, and (9) system operating cost.

Deficiencies in duct design can result in systems that operate incorrectly or are expensive to own and operate. Poor design or lack of system sealing can produce inadequate airflow rates at the terminals, leading to discomfort, loss of productivity, and even adverse health effects. Lack of sound attenuation may lead to objectionable noise levels. Proper duct insulation eliminates excessive heat gain or loss.

In this chapter, system design and calculation of a system's frictional and dynamic resistance to airflow are considered. Chapter 18 of the 2008 *ASHRAE Handbook—HVAC Systems and Equipment* examines duct construction and presents construction standards for residential, commercial, and industrial HVAC and exhaust systems.

BERNOULLI EQUATION

The Bernoulli equation can be developed by equating the forces on an element of a stream tube in a frictionless fluid flow to the rate of momentum change. On integrating this relationship for steady flow, the following expression (Osborne 1966) results:

$$\frac{v^2}{2} + \int\frac{dP}{\rho} + gz = \text{constant, N·m/kg} \tag{1}$$

where

v = streamline (local) velocity, m/s
P = absolute pressure, Pa (N/m²)
ρ = density, kg/m³
g = acceleration caused by gravity, m/s²
z = elevation, m

Assuming constant fluid density in the system, Equation (1) reduces to

$$\frac{v^2}{2} + \frac{P}{\rho} + gz = \text{constant, N·m/kg} \tag{2}$$

Although Equation (2) was derived for steady, ideal frictionless flow along a stream tube, it can be extended to analyze flow through ducts in real systems. In terms of pressure, the relationship for fluid resistance between two sections is

$$\frac{\rho_1 V_1^2}{2} + P_1 + g\rho_1 z_1 = \frac{\rho_2 V_2^2}{2} + P_2 + g\rho_2 z_2 + \Delta p_{t,1-2} \tag{3}$$

where

V = average duct velocity, m/s
$\Delta p_{t,1-2}$ = total pressure loss caused by friction and dynamic losses between sections 1 and 2, Pa

In Equation (3), V (section average velocity) replaces v (streamline velocity) because experimentally determined loss coefficients allow for errors in calculating $v^2/2$ (velocity pressure) across streamlines.

On the left side of Equation (3), add and subtract p_{z1}; on the right side, add and subtract p_{z2}, where p_{z1} and p_{z2} are the values of atmospheric air at heights z_1 and z_2. Thus,

$$\frac{\rho_1 V_1^2}{2} + P_1 + (p_{z1} - p_{z1}) + g\rho_1 z_1 = \frac{\rho_2 V_2^2}{2} + P_2 + (p_{z2} - p_{z2}) + g\rho_2 z_2 + \Delta p_{t,1-2} \tag{4}$$

Atmospheric pressure at any elevation (p_{z1} and p_{z2}) expressed in terms of the atmospheric pressure p_a at the same datum elevation is given by

$$p_{z1} = p_a - g\rho_a z_1 \tag{5}$$

$$p_{z2} = p_a - g\rho_a z_2 \tag{6}$$

Substituting Equations (5) and (6) into Equation (4) and simplifying yields the total pressure change between sections 1 and 2. Assume no temperature change between sections 1 and 2 (no heat exchanger within the section); therefore, $\rho_1 = \rho_2$. When a heat exchanger is located in the section, the average of the inlet and outlet temperatures is generally used. Let $\rho = \rho_1 = \rho_2$. $(P_1 - p_{z1})$ and $(P_2 - p_{z2})$ are gage pressures at elevations z_1 and z_2.

$$\Delta p_{t,1-2} = \left(p_{s,1} + \frac{\rho V_1^2}{2}\right) - \left(p_{s,2} + \frac{\rho V_2^2}{2}\right) + g(\rho_a - \rho)(z_2 - z_1) \tag{7a}$$

$$\Delta p_{t,1-2} = \Delta p_t + \Delta p_{se} \tag{7b}$$

$$\Delta p_t = \Delta p_{t,1\text{-}2} + \Delta p_{se} \tag{7c}$$

where

$p_{s,1}$ = static pressure, gage at elevation z_1, Pa

The preparation of this chapter is assigned to TC 5.2, Duct Design.

$p_{s,2}$ = static pressure, gage at elevation z_2, Pa
V_1 = average velocity at section 1, m/s
V_2 = average velocity at section 2, m/s
ρ_a = density of ambient air, kg/m^3
ρ = density of air or gas in duct, kg/m^3
Δp_{se} = thermal gravity effect, Pa
Δp_t = total pressure change between sections 1 and 2, Pa
$\Delta p_{t,1\text{-}2}$ = total pressure loss caused by friction and dynamic losses between sections 1 and 2, Pa

HEAD AND PRESSURE

The terms **head** and **pressure** are often used interchangeably; however, head is the height of a fluid column supported by fluid flow, whereas pressure is the normal force per unit area. For liquids, it is convenient to measure head in terms of the flowing fluid. With a gas or air, however, it is customary to measure pressure on a column of liquid.

Static Pressure

The term $p/\rho g$ is static head; p is static pressure.

Velocity Pressure

The term $V^2/2g$ refers to velocity head, and $\rho V^2/2$ refers to velocity pressure. Although velocity head is independent of fluid density, velocity pressure [Equation (8)] is not.

$$p_v = \rho V^2/2 \tag{8}$$

where

p_v = velocity pressure, Pa
V = fluid mean velocity, m/s

For air at standard conditions (1.204 kg/m^3), Equation (8) becomes

$$p_v = 0.602\,V^2 \tag{9}$$

Velocity is calculated by

$$V = Q/A \tag{10}$$

where

Q = airflow rate, L/s
A = cross-sectional area of duct, m^2

Total Pressure

Total pressure is the sum of static pressure and velocity pressure:

$$p_t = p_s + \rho V^2/2 \tag{11}$$

or

$$p_t = p_s + p_v \tag{12}$$

where

p_t = total pressure, Pa
p_s = static pressure, Pa

Pressure Measurement

The range, precision, and limitations of instruments for measuring pressure and velocity are discussed in Chapter 36. The manometer is a simple and useful means for measuring partial vacuum and low pressure. Static, velocity, and total pressures in a duct system relative to atmospheric pressure can be measured with a pitot tube connected to a manometer. Pitot tube construction and locations for traversing round and rectangular ducts are presented in Chapter 36.

SYSTEM ANALYSIS

The total pressure change caused by friction, fittings, equipment, and net **thermal gravity effect (stack effect)** for each section of a duct system is calculated by the following equation:

$$\Delta p_{t_i} = \Delta p_{f_i} + \sum_{j=1}^{m} \Delta p_{ij} + \sum_{k=1}^{n} \Delta p_{ik} - \sum_{r=1}^{\lambda} \Delta p_{se_{ir}} \tag{13}$$

$$\text{for } i = 1, 2, \ldots, n_{up} + n_{dn}$$

where

Δp_{t_i} = net total pressure change for i-section, Pa
Δp_{f_i} = pressure loss due to friction for i-section, Pa
Δp_{ij} = total pressure loss due to j-fittings, including fan system effect (FSE), for i-section, Pa
Δp_{ik} = pressure loss due to k-equipment for i-section, Pa
$\Delta p_{se_{ir}}$ = thermal gravity effect due to r-stacks for i-section, Pa
m = number of fittings within i-section
n = number of equipment within i-section
λ = number of stacks within i-section
n_{up} = number of duct sections upstream of fan (exhaust/return air subsystems)
n_{dn} = number of duct sections downstream of fan (supply air subsystems)

From Equation (7), the thermal gravity effect for each nonhorizontal duct with a density other than that of ambient air is determined by the following equation:

$$\Delta p_{se} = g(\rho_a - \rho)(z_2 - z_1) \tag{14}$$

where

Δp_{se} = thermal gravity effect, Pa
z_1 and z_2 = elevation from datum in direction of airflow (Figure 1), m
ρ_a = density of ambient air, kg/m^3
ρ = density of air or gas within duct, kg/m^3
g = 9.81 = gravitational acceleration, m/s^2

Example 1. For Figure 1, calculate the thermal gravity effect for two cases: (a) air cooled to –34°C, and (b) air heated to 540°C. Density of air at 34°C is 1.477 kg/m^3 and at 540°C is 434 kg/m^3. Density of ambient air is 1.204 kg/m^3. Stack height is 15 m.

Solution:

$$\Delta p_{se} = 9.81(\rho_a - \rho)z$$

(a) For $\rho > \rho_a$ (Figure 1A),

$$\Delta p_{se} = 9.81(1.204 - 1.477)15 = -40 \text{ Pa}$$

(b) For $\rho < \rho_a$ (Figure 1B),

$$\Delta p_{se} = 9.81(1.204 - 0.434)15 = +113 \text{ Pa}$$

Example 2. Calculate the thermal gravity effect for the two-stack system shown in Figure 2, where the air is 120°C and stack heights are 15 and 30 m. Density of 120°C air is 0.898 kg/m^3; ambient air is 1.204 kg/m^3.

Solution:

$$\Delta p_{se} = 9.81(\rho_a - \rho)(z_2 - z_1) = 9.81(1.204 - 0.898)(30 - 15) = 45 \text{ Pa}$$

For the system shown in Figure 3, the direction of air movement created by the thermal gravity effect depends on the initiating force (e.g., fans, wind, opening and closing doors, turning equipment on and off). If for any reason air starts to enter the left stack (Figure 3A), it creates a buoyancy effect in the right stack. On the other hand, if flow starts to enter the right stack (Figure 3B), it creates a buoyancy effect in the left stack. In both cases, the produced thermal gravity effect is stable and depends on stack height and magnitude

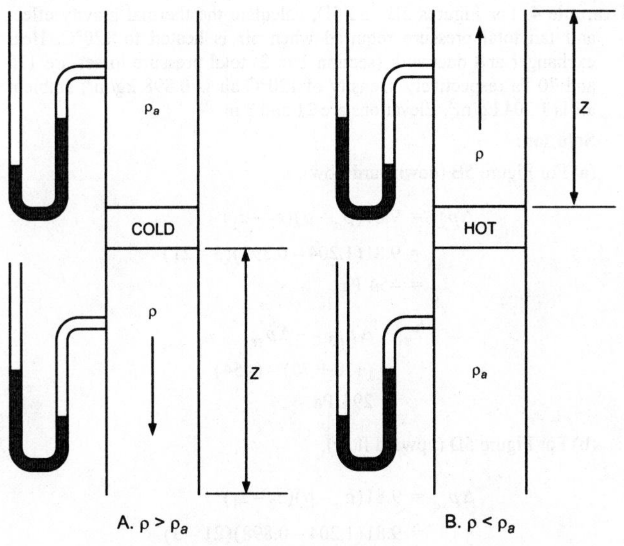

Fig. 1 Thermal Gravity Effect for Example 1

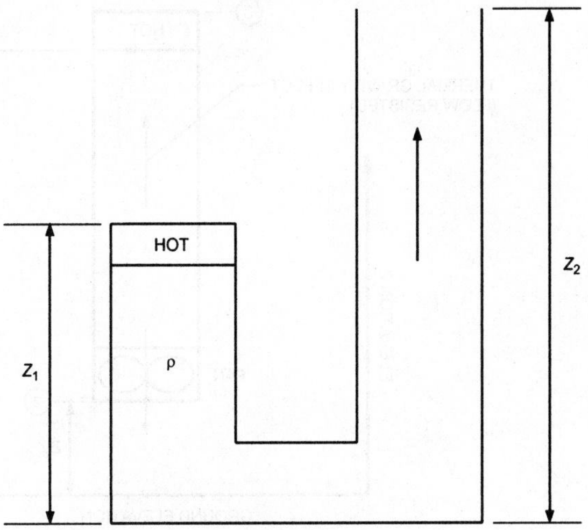

Fig. 2 Multiple Stacks for Example 2

of heating. The starting direction of flow is important when using natural convection for ventilation.

To determine the fan total pressure requirement for a system, use the following equation:

$$P_t = \sum_{i \varepsilon F_{up}} \Delta p_{t_i} + \sum_{i \varepsilon F_{dn}} \Delta p_{t_i} \qquad \text{for } i = 1, 2, \ldots, n_{up} + n_{dn} \tag{15}$$

where

F_{up} and F_{dn} = sets of duct sections upstream and downstream of fan
P_t = fan total pressure, Pa
ε = symbol that ties duct sections into system paths from exhaust/return air terminals to supply terminals

Figure 4 illustrates the use of Equation (15). This system has three supply and two return terminals consisting of nine sections connected in six paths: 1-3-4-9-7-5, 1-3-4-9-7-6, 1-3-4-9-8, 2-4-9-7-5, 2-4-9-7-6, and 2-4-9-8. Sections 1 and 3 are unequal area; thus, they are assigned separate numbers in accordance with the rules for identifying sections (see step 4 in the section on HVAC Duct Design Procedures). To determine the fan pressure requirement, apply the following six equations, derived from Equation (15). These equations must be satisfied to attain pressure balancing for

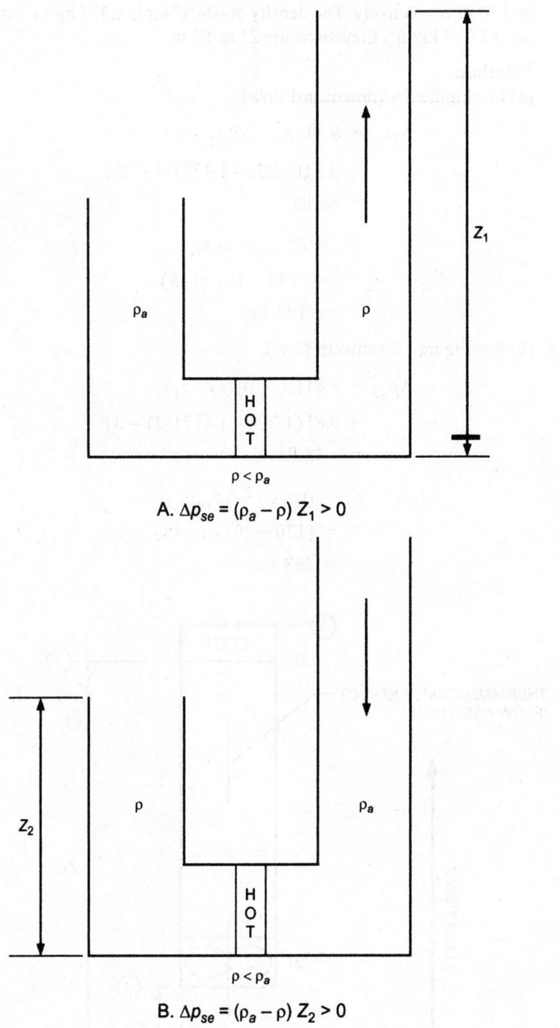

Fig. 3 Multiple Stack Analysis

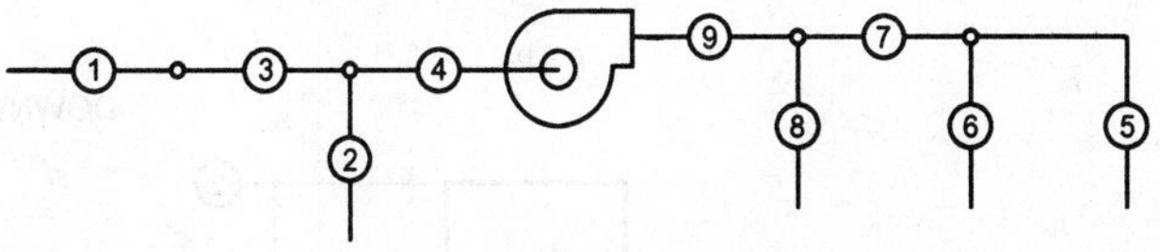

Fig. 4 Illustrative 6-Path, 9-Section System

design airflow. Relying entirely on dampers is not economical and may create objectionable flow-generated noise.

$$\left\{\begin{aligned}
P_t &= \Delta p_1 + \Delta p_3 + \Delta p_4 + \Delta p_9 + \Delta p_7 + \Delta p_5 \\
P_t &= \Delta p_1 + \Delta p_3 + \Delta p_4 + \Delta p_9 + \Delta p_7 + \Delta p_6 \\
P_t &= \Delta p_1 + \Delta p_3 + \Delta p_4 + \Delta p_9 + \Delta p_8 \\
P_t &= \Delta p_2 + \Delta p_4 + \Delta p_9 + \Delta p_7 + \Delta p_5 \\
P_t &= \Delta p_2 + \Delta p_4 + \Delta p_9 + \Delta p_7 + \Delta p_6 \\
P_t &= \Delta p_2 + \Delta p_4 + \Delta p_9 + \Delta p_8
\end{aligned}\right. \tag{16}$$

Example 3. For Figures 5A and 5C, calculate the thermal gravity effect and fan total pressure required when the air is cooled to –34°C. The heat exchanger and ductwork (section 1 to 2) total pressure losses are 170 and 70 Pa respectively. The density of −34°C air is 1.477 kg/m³; ambient air is 1.204 kg/m³. Elevations are 21 and 3 m.

Solution:

(a) For Figure 5A (downward flow),

$$\Delta p_{se} = 9.81(\rho_a - \rho)(z_2 - z_1) = 9.81(1.204 - 1.477)(3 - 21) = 48 \text{ Pa}$$

$$P_t = \Delta p_{t,3\text{-}2} - \Delta p_{se} = (170 + 70) - (48) = 192 \text{ Pa}$$

(b) For Figure 5C (upward flow),

$$\Delta p_{se} = 9.81(\rho_a - \rho)(z_2 - z_1) = 9.81(1.204 - 1.477)(21 - 3) = -48 \text{ Pa}$$

$$P_t = \Delta p_{t,3\text{-}2} - \Delta p_{se} = (170 + 70) - (-48) = 288 \text{ Pa}$$

Example 4. For Figures 5B and 5D, calculate the thermal gravity effect and fan total pressure required when air is heated to 120°C. Heat exchanger and ductwork (section 1 to 2) total pressure losses are 170 and 70 Pa respectively. Density of 120°C air is 0.898 kg/m³; ambient air is 1.204 kg/m³. Elevations are 21 and 3 m.

Solution:

(a) For Figure 5B (downward flow),

$$\Delta p_{se} = 9.81(\rho_a - \rho)(z_2 - z_1) = 9.81(1.204 - 0.898)(3 - 21) = -54 \text{ Pa}$$

$$P_t = \Delta p_{t,3\text{-}2} - \Delta p_{se} = (170 + 70) - (-54) = 294 \text{ Pa}$$

(b) For Figure 5D (upward flow),

$$\Delta p_{se} = 9.81(\rho_a - \rho)(z_2 - z_1) = 9.81(1.204 - 0.898)(21 - 3) = 54 \text{ Pa}$$

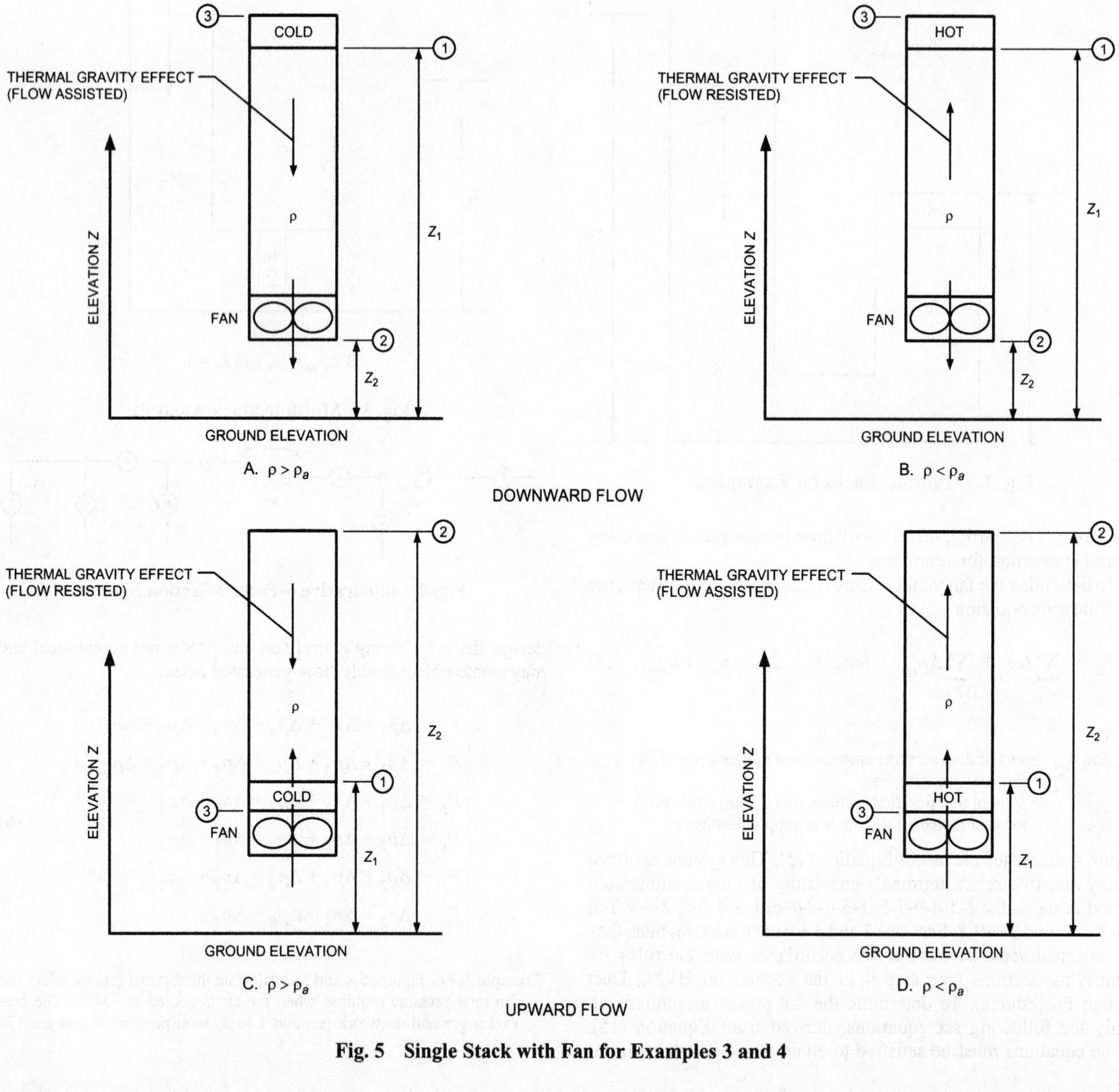

Fig. 5 Single Stack with Fan for Examples 3 and 4

$$P_t = \Delta p_{t,3\text{-}2} - \Delta p_{se}$$
$$= (170 + 70) - (54)$$
$$= 186 \text{ Pa}$$

Example 5. Calculate the thermal gravity effect for each section of the system shown in Figure 6, and the systems' net thermal gravity effect. Density of ambient air is 1.204 kg/m³, and the lengths are as follows: z_1 = 15 m, z_2 = 27 m, z_4 = 30 m, z_5 = 8 m, and z_9 = 60 m. Pressure required at section 3 is –25 Pa. Write the equation to determine the fan total pressure requirement.

Solution: The following table summarizes the thermal gravity effect for each section of the system as calculated by Equation (14). The net thermal gravity effect for the system is 118 Pa. To select a fan, use the following equation:

$$P_t = 25 + \Delta p_{t,1\text{-}7} + \Delta p_{t,8\text{-}9} - \Delta p_{se} = 25 + \Delta p_{t,1\text{-}7}$$
$$+ \Delta p_{t,8\text{-}9} - 118 = \Delta p_{t,1\text{-}7} + \Delta p_{t,8\text{-}9} - 93$$

Path (x–x′)	Temp., °C	ρ, kg/m³	Δz ($z_{x'} - z_x$), m	Δρ ($\rho_a - \rho_{x\text{-}x'}$), kg/m³	Δp_{se}, Pa [Eq. (14)]
1-2	815	0.324	(27 – 15)	+0.880	+104
3-4	540	0.434	0	+0.770	0
4-5	540	0.434	(8 – 30)	+0.770	–166
6-7	120	0.898	0	+0.306	0
8-9	120	0.898	(60 – 0)	+0.306	+180
Net Thermal Gravity Effect					118

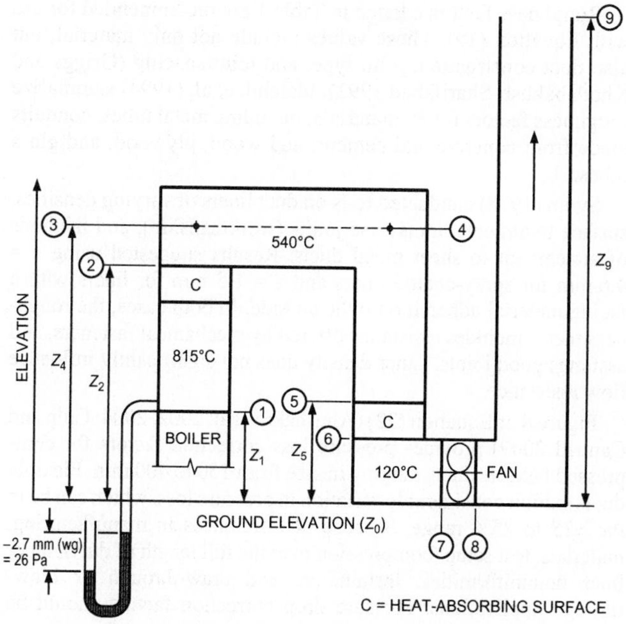

Fig. 6 Triple Stack System for Example 5

PRESSURE CHANGES IN SYSTEM

Figure 7 shows total and static pressure changes in a fan/duct system consisting of a fan with both supply and return air ductwork. Also shown are total and static pressure gradients referenced to atmospheric pressure.

For all constant-area sections, total and static pressure losses are equal. At diverging transitions, velocity pressure decreases, absolute total pressure decreases, and absolute static pressure can increase. The static pressure increase at these sections is known as **static regain.**

At converging transitions, velocity pressure increases in the direction of airflow, and absolute total and absolute static pressures decrease.

At the exit, total pressure loss depends on the shape of the fitting and the flow characteristics. Exit loss coefficients C_o can be greater than, less than, or equal to one. Total and static pressure grade lines for the various coefficients are shown in Figure 7. Note that, for a loss coefficient less than one, static pressure upstream of the exit is less than atmospheric pressure (negative). Static pressure just upstream of the discharge fitting can be calculated by subtracting the upstream velocity pressure from the upstream total pressure.

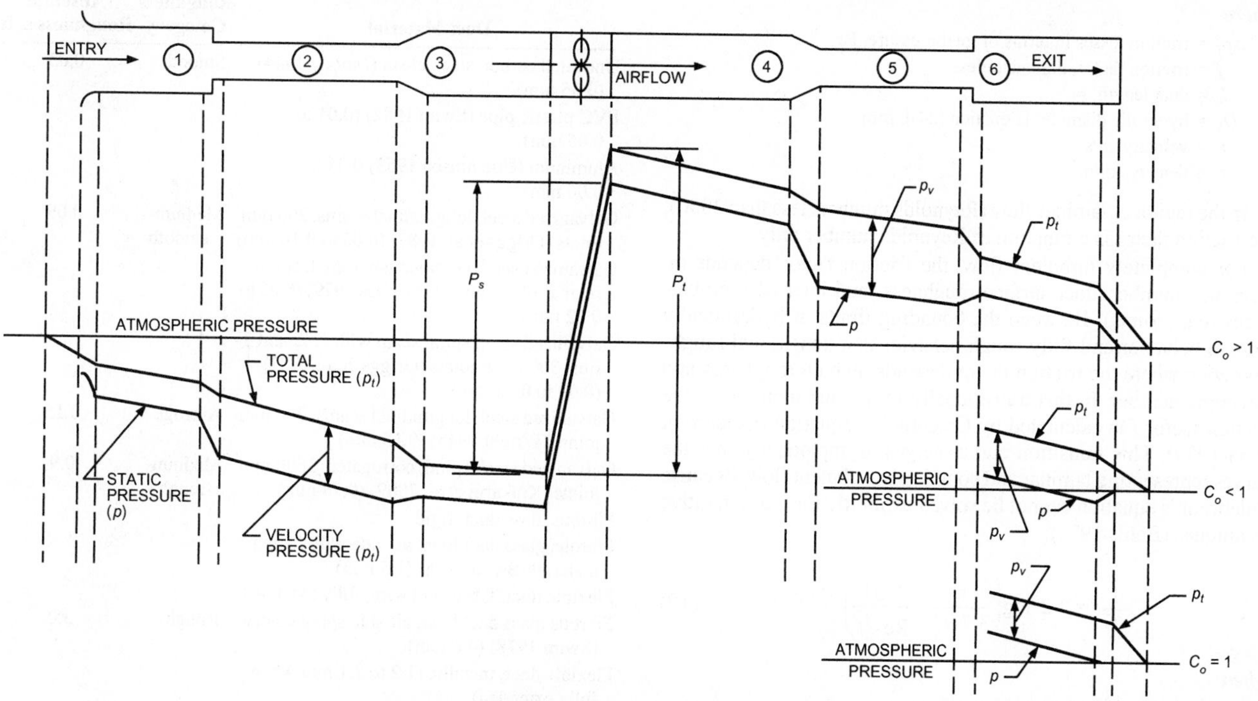

Fig. 7 Pressure Changes During Flow in Ducts

At section 1, total pressure loss depends on the shape of the entry. Total pressure immediately downstream of the entrance equals the difference between the upstream pressure, which is zero (atmospheric pressure), and loss through the fitting. Static pressure of ambient air is zero; several diameters downstream, static pressure is negative, equal to the sum of the total pressure (negative) and the velocity pressure (always positive).

System resistance to airflow is noted by the total pressure grade line in Figure 7. Sections 3 and 4 include fan system effect pressure losses. To obtain the fan static pressure requirement for fan selection where fan total pressure is known, use

$$P_s = P_t - p_{v,o} \tag{17}$$

where

P_s = fan static pressure, Pa
P_t = fan total pressure, Pa
$p_{v,o}$ = fan outlet velocity pressure, Pa

FLUID RESISTANCE

Duct system losses are the irreversible transformation of mechanical energy into heat. The two types of losses are (1) friction losses and (2) dynamic losses.

FRICTION LOSSES

Friction losses are due to fluid viscosity and result from momentum exchange between molecules (in laminar flow) or between individual particles of adjacent fluid layers moving at different velocities (in turbulent flow). Friction losses occur along the entire duct length.

Darcy and Colebrook Equations

For fluid flow in conduits, friction loss can be calculated by the Darcy equation:

$$\Delta p_f = \frac{1000 fL}{D_h} \times \frac{\rho V^2}{2} \tag{18}$$

where

Δp_f = friction losses in terms of total pressure, Pa
f = friction factor, dimensionless
L = duct length, m
D_h = hydraulic diameter [Equation (24)], mm
V = velocity, m/s
ρ = density, kg/m^3

In the region of laminar flow (Reynolds numbers less than 2000), the friction factor is a function of Reynolds number only.

For completely turbulent flow, the friction factor depends on Reynolds number, duct surface roughness, and internal protuberances (e.g., joints). Between the bounding limits of hydraulically smooth behavior and fully rough behavior is a transitional roughness zone where the friction factor depends on both roughness and Reynolds number. In this transitionally rough, turbulent zone, the friction factor f is calculated by Colebrook's equation (Colebrook 1938-1939). This transition curve merges asymptotically into the curves representing laminar and completely turbulent flow. Because Colebrook's equation cannot be solved explicitly for f, use iterative techniques (Behls 1971).

$$\frac{1}{\sqrt{f}} = -2\log\left(\frac{\varepsilon}{3.7D_h} + \frac{2.51}{\text{Re}\sqrt{f}}\right) \tag{19}$$

where

ε = material absolute roughness factor, mm
Re = Reynolds number

Reynolds number (Re) may be calculated by using the following equation.

$$\text{Re} = \frac{D_h V}{1000\nu} \tag{20}$$

where ν = kinematic viscosity, m^2/s.

For standard air and temperature between 4 and 38°C, Re can be calculated by

$$\text{Re} = 66.4\, D_h V \tag{21}$$

Roughness Factors

Roughness factors ε listed in Table 1 are recommended for use with Equation (19). These values include not only material, but also duct construction, joint type, and joint spacing (Griggs and Khodabakhsh-Sharifabad 1992). Idelchik et al. (1994) summarize roughness factors for 80 materials, including metal tubes; conduits made from concrete and cement; and wood, plywood, and glass tubes.

Swim (1978) conducted tests on duct liners of varying densities, surface treatments, transverse joints (workmanship), and methods of attachment to sheet metal ducts. Results suggested using ε = 4.6 mm for spray-coated liners and ε = 1.5 mm for liners with a facing material adhered onto the air side. In both cases, the roughness factor includes resistance offered by mechanical fasteners, and assumes good joints. Liner density does not significantly influence flow resistance.

Figure 8 or Equation (22) (Abushakra et al. 2002, 2004; Culp and Cantrill 2009) provides pressure loss correction factors for compressed flexible ducts ranging in size from 150 to 400 mm. Flexible ducts exhibit considerable variation in pressure loss, which can be in the ±15 to 25% range, because of differences in manufacturing, materials, test setup (compression over the full length of duct), inner liner nonuniformities, installation, and draw-through or blow-through applications. Pressure drop correction factors should be

Table 1 Duct Roughness Factors

Duct Material	Roughness Category	Absolute Roughness ε, ft
Uncoated carbon steel, clean (Moody 1944) (0.05 mm) PVC plastic pipe (Swim 1982) (0.01 to 0.05 mm) Aluminum (Hutchinson 1953) 0.04 to 0.06 mm)	Smooth	0.03
Galvanized steel, longitudinal seams, 200 mm joints (Griggs et al. 1987) (0.05 to 0.10 mm) Galvanized steel, continuously rolled, spiral seams, 3000 mm joints (Jones 1979) (0.06 to 0.12 mm) Galvanized steel, spiral seam with 1, 2, and 3 ribs, 3600 mm joints (Griggs et al. 1987) (0.09 to 0.12 mm)	Medium-smooth	0.09
Galvanized steel, longitudinal seams, 760 mm joints (Wright 1945) (0.15 mm)	Average	0.15
Galvanized steel, spiral, corrugated, 3600 mm joints (Kulkarni et al. 2009) (0.74 mm) Fibrous glass duct, rigid Fibrous glass duct liner, air side with facing material (Swim 1978) (1.5 mm)	Medium-rough	0.9
Flexible duct, fabric and wire, fully extended Fibrous glass duct liner, air side spray coated (Swim 1978) (4.6 mm) Flexible duct, metallic (1.2 to 2.1 mm when fully extended) Concrete (Moody 1944) (1.3 to 3.0 mm)	Rough	3.0

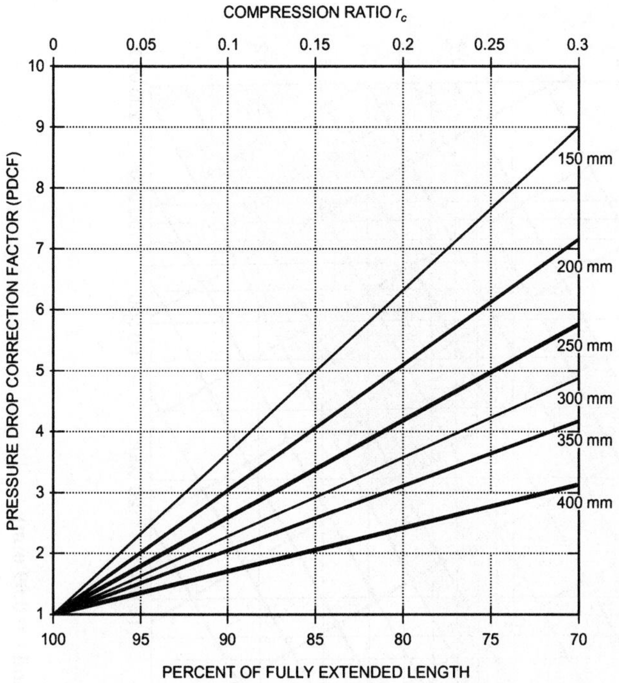

Fig. 8 Pressure Loss Correction Factor for Flexible Duct Not Fully Extended

applied to medium-rough ducts (ε = 0.9 mm); they can be obtained by multiplying the values from the friction chart for galvanized ducts (Figure 9) by 1.55, where (ε = 0.09 mm).

For commercial systems, flexible ducts should be

- Limited to connections between duct branches and diffusers or variable-air-volume (VAV) terminal units
- No more than 1.5 m in length, fully stretched
- Installed without any radial compression (kinks)
- Not used in lieu of fittings

For 150 to 400 mm ducts that are 70% extended, pressure losses can be three to nine times greater than those for a fully extended flexible duct of the same diameter.

$$PDCF = 1 + 58 r_c e^{-0.00496D} \tag{22}$$

with

$$r_c = 1 - (L/L_{FE}) \tag{23}$$

where

PDCF = pressure drop correction factor
r_c = compression ratio, dimensionless
D = flexible duct diameter, mm
L = installed duct length, m
L_{FE} = duct length fully extended, m

Friction Chart

Fluid resistance caused by friction in round ducts can be determined by the friction chart (Figure 9). This chart is based on standard air flowing through round galvanized ducts with beaded slip couplings on 1220 mm centers, equivalent to an absolute roughness of 0.09 mm.

Changes in barometric pressure, temperature, and humidity affect air density, air viscosity, and Reynolds number. No corrections to Figure 9 are needed for (1) duct materials with a medium-smooth roughness factor, (2) temperature variations of ±15 K from 20°C, (3) elevations to 500 m, and (4) duct pressures from –5 to +5 kPa relative to ambient pressure. These individual variations in temperature, elevation, and duct pressure result in duct losses within ±5% of the standard air friction chart.

For duct materials not categorized as medium-smooth in Table 1, and for variations in temperature, barometric pressure (elevation), and duct pressures (outside the range listed), calculate friction loss in a duct by the Colebrook and Darcy equations [Equations (19) and (18), respectively].

Noncircular Ducts

A momentum analysis can relate average wall shear stress to pressure drop per unit length for fully developed turbulent flow in a passage of arbitrary shape but uniform longitudinal cross-sectional area. This analysis leads to the definition of **hydraulic diameter**:

$$D_h = 4A/P \tag{24}$$

where

D_h = hydraulic diameter, mm
A = duct area, mm^2
P = perimeter of cross section, mm

Although hydraulic diameter is often used to correlate noncircular data, exact solutions for laminar flow in noncircular passages show that this causes some inconsistencies. No exact solutions exist for turbulent flow. Tests over a limited range of turbulent flow indicated that fluid resistance is the same for equal lengths of duct for equal mean velocities of flow if the ducts have the same ratio of cross-sectional area to perimeter. From experiments using round, square, and rectangular ducts having essentially the same hydraulic diameter, Huebscher (1948) found that each, for most purposes, had the same flow resistance at equal mean velocities. Tests by Griggs and Khodabakhsh-Sharifabad (1992) also indicated that experimental rectangular duct data for airflow over the range typical of HVAC systems can be correlated satisfactorily using Equation (19) together with hydraulic diameter, particularly when a realistic experimental uncertainty is accepted. These tests support using hydraulic diameter to correlate noncircular duct data.

Rectangular Ducts. Huebscher (1948) developed the relationship between rectangular and round ducts that is used to determine size equivalency based on equal flow, resistance, and length. This relationship, Equation (25), is the basis for Table 2.

$$D_e = \frac{1.30(ab)^{0.625}}{(a+b)^{0.250}} \tag{25}$$

where

D_e = circular equivalent of rectangular duct for equal length, fluid resistance, and airflow, mm
a = length one side of duct, mm
b = length adjacent side of duct, mm

To determine equivalent round duct diameter, use Table 2. Equations (18) and (19) must be used to determine pressure loss.

Flat Oval Ducts. To convert round ducts to flat oval sizes, use Table 3, which is based on Equation (26) (Heyt and Diaz 1975), the circular equivalent of a flat oval duct for equal airflow, resistance, and length. Equations (18) and (19) must be used to determine friction loss.

$$D_e = \frac{1.55 AR^{0.625}}{P^{0.250}} \tag{26}$$

where AR is the cross-sectional area of flat oval duct defined as

$$AR = (\pi a^2/4) + a(A - a) \tag{27}$$

and the perimeter P is calculated by

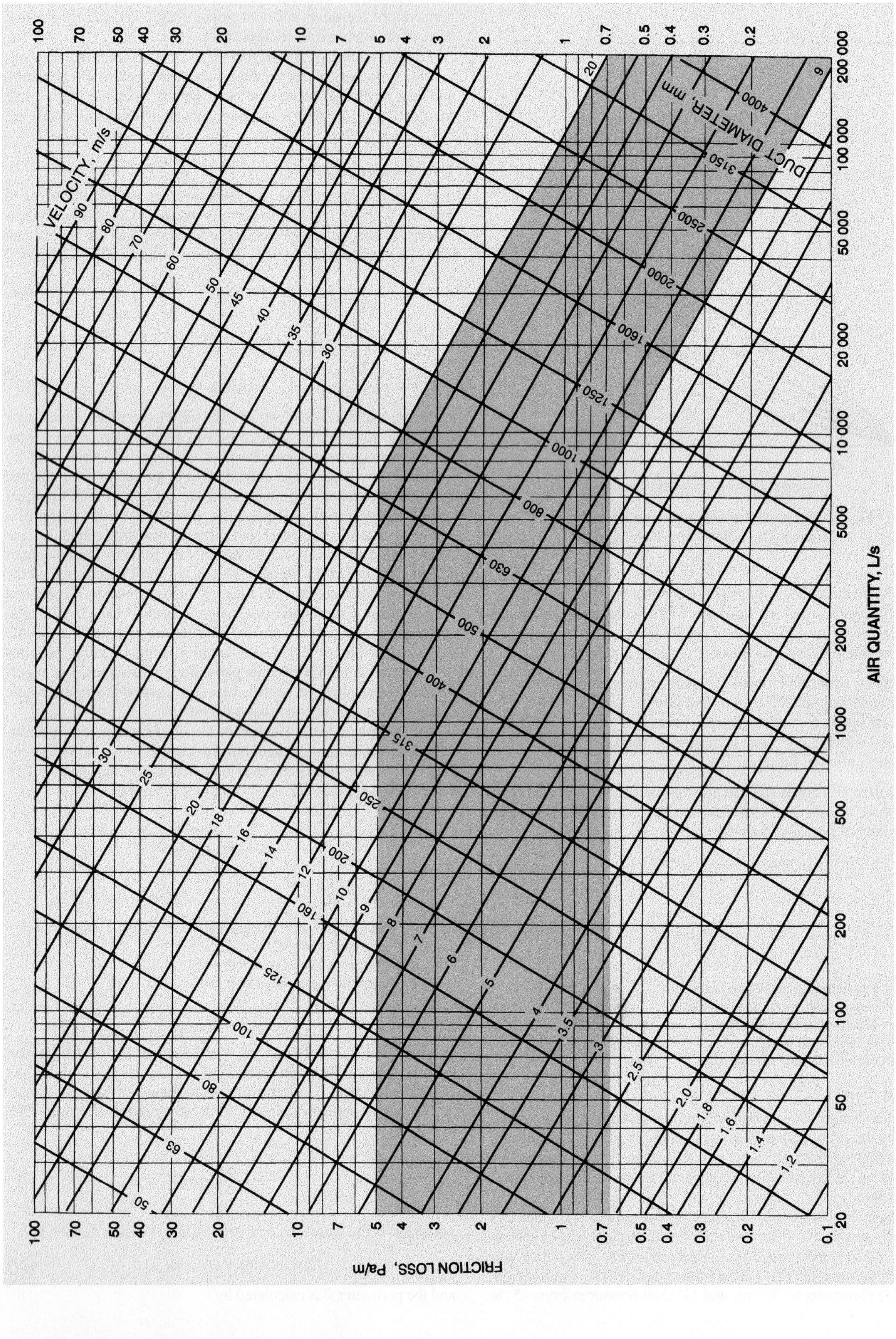

Fig. 9 Friction Chart for Round Duct (ρ = 1.20 kg/m^3 and ε = 0.09 mm)

$$P = \pi a + 2(A - a) \tag{28}$$

where

P = perimeter of flat oval duct, mm
A = major axis of flat oval duct, mm
a = minor axis of flat oval duct, mm

DYNAMIC LOSSES

Dynamic losses result from flow disturbances caused by duct-mounted equipment and fittings (e.g., entries, exits, elbows, transitions, and junctions) that change the airflow path's direction and/or area. Idelchik et al. (1994) discuss parameters affecting fluid resistance of fittings and presents local loss coefficients in three forms: tables, curves, and equations.

Local Loss Coefficients

The dimensionless coefficient C is used for fluid resistance, because this coefficient has the same value in dynamically similar streams (i.e., streams with geometrically similar stretches, equal Reynolds numbers, and equal values of other criteria necessary for dynamic similarity). The fluid resistance coefficient represents the ratio of total pressure loss to velocity pressure at the referenced cross section:

$$C = \frac{\Delta p_j}{\rho(V^2/2)} = \frac{\Delta p_j}{p_v} \tag{29}$$

where

C = local loss coefficient, dimensionless
Δp_j = total pressure loss, Pa
ρ = density, kg/m^3
V = velocity, m/s
p_v = velocity pressure, Pa

Dynamic losses occur along a duct length and cannot be separated from friction losses. For ease of calculation, dynamic losses are assumed to be concentrated at a section (local) and exclude friction. Frictional losses must be considered only for relatively long fittings. Generally, fitting friction losses are accounted for by measuring duct lengths from the centerline of one fitting to that of the next fitting. For fittings closely coupled (less than six hydraulic diameters apart), the flow pattern entering subsequent fittings differs from the flow pattern used to determine loss coefficients. Adequate data for these situations are unavailable.

For all fittings, except junctions, calculate the total pressure loss Δp_j at a section by

$$\Delta p_j = C_o p_{v,o} \tag{30}$$

where the subscript o is the cross section at which the velocity pressure is referenced. Dynamic loss is based on the actual velocity in the duct, not the velocity in an equivalent circular duct. For the cross section to reference a fitting loss coefficient, see step 4 in the section on HVAC Duct Design Procedures. Where necessary (e.g., unequal-area fittings), convert a loss coefficient from section o to section i using Equation (31), where V is the velocity at the respective sections.

$$C_i = \frac{C_o}{(V_i/V_o)^2} \tag{31}$$

For converging and diverging flow junctions, total pressure losses through the straight (main) section are calculated as

$$\Delta p_j = C_{c,s} p_{v,c} \tag{32}$$

For total pressure losses through the branch section,

$$\Delta p_j = C_{c,b} p_{v,c} \tag{33}$$

where $p_{v,c}$ is the velocity pressure at the common section c, and $C_{c,s}$ and $C_{c,b}$ are loss coefficients for the straight (main) and branch flow paths, respectively, each referenced to the velocity pressure at section c. To convert junction local loss coefficients referenced to straight and branch velocity pressures, use the following equation:

$$C_i = \frac{C_{c,i}}{(V_i/V_c)^2} \tag{34}$$

where

C_i = local loss coefficient referenced to section being calculated (see subscripts), dimensionless
$C_{c,i}$ = straight ($C_{c,s}$) or branch ($C_{c,b}$) local loss coefficient referenced to dynamic pressure at common section, dimensionless
V_i = velocity at section to which C_i is being referenced, m/s
V_c = velocity at common section, m/s

Subscripts:

b = branch
s = straight (main) section
c = common section

The junction of two parallel streams moving at different velocities is characterized by turbulent mixing of the streams, accompanied by pressure losses. In the course of this mixing, momentum is exchanged between particles moving at different velocities, resulting in equalization of the velocity distributions in the common stream. The jet with higher velocity loses part of its kinetic energy by transmitting it to the slower jet. The loss in total pressure before and after mixing is always large and positive for the higher-velocity jet, and increases with an increase in the amount of energy transmitted to the lower-velocity jet. Consequently, the local loss coefficient [Equation (29)] is always positive. Energy stored in the lower-velocity jet increases because of mixing. The loss in total pressure and the local loss coefficient can, therefore, also have negative values for the lower velocity jet (Idelchik et al. 1994).

Duct Fitting Database

A duct fitting database that includes more than 220 round, flat oval, and rectangular fittings is available from ASHRAE (2009).

The fittings are numbered (coded) as shown in Table 4. Entries and converging junctions are only in the exhaust/return portion of systems. Exits and diverging junctions are only in supply systems. Equal-area elbows, obstructions, and duct-mounted equipment are common to both supply and exhaust systems. Transitions and unequal-area elbows can be either supply or exhaust fittings. Fitting ED5-1 (see the section on Fitting Loss Coefficients) is an **E**xhaust fitting with a round shape (**D**iameter). The number 5 indicates that the fitting is a junction, and 1 is its sequential number. Fittings SR31 and ER3-1 are **S**upply and **E**xhaust fittings, respectively. The R indicates that the fitting is **R**ectangular, and the 3 identifies the fitting as an elbow. Note that the cross-sectional areas at sections 0 and 1 are not equal (see the section on Fitting Loss Coefficients). Otherwise, the elbow would be a **C**ommon fitting such as CR3-6. Additional fittings are reproduced in the section on Fitting Loss Coefficients to support the example design problems (see Table 10 for Example 6; see Table 12 for Example 7).

Bends in Flexible Duct

Abushakra et al. (2002) show that loss coefficients for bends in flexible ductwork vary widely from condition to condition, with no uniform or consistent trends. Loss coefficients range from a low of 0.87 to a high of 3.27. Flexible duct elbows should not be used in lieu of rigid elbows.

Table 2 Circular Equivalents of Rectangular Duct for Equal Friction and Capacity[a]

Lgth Adj.[b]	Length of One Side of Rectangular Duct *a*, mm																			
	100	125	150	175	200	225	250	275	300	350	400	450	500	550	600	650	700	750	800	900
	Circular Duct Diameter, mm																			
100	109																			
125	122	137																		
150	133	150	164																	
175	143	161	177	191																
200	152	172	189	204	219															
225	161	181	200	216	232	246														
250	169	190	210	228	244	259	273													
275	176	199	220	238	256	272	287	301												
300	183	207	229	248	266	283	299	314	328											
350	195	222	245	267	286	305	322	339	354	383										
400	207	235	260	283	305	325	343	361	378	409	437									
450	217	247	274	299	321	343	363	382	400	433	464	492								
500	227	258	287	313	337	360	381	401	420	455	488	518	547							
550	236	269	299	326	352	375	398	419	439	477	511	543	573	601						
600	245	279	310	339	365	390	414	436	457	496	533	567	598	628	656					
650	253	289	321	351	378	404	429	452	474	515	553	589	622	653	683	711				
700	261	298	331	362	391	418	443	467	490	533	573	610	644	677	708	737	765			
750	268	306	341	373	402	430	457	482	506	550	592	630	666	700	732	763	792	820		
800	275	314	350	383	414	442	470	496	520	567	609	649	687	722	755	787	818	847	875	
900	289	330	367	402	435	465	494	522	548	597	643	686	726	763	799	833	866	897	927	984
1000	301	344	384	420	454	486	517	546	574	626	674	719	762	802	840	876	911	944	976	1037
1100	313	358	399	437	473	506	538	569	598	652	703	751	795	838	878	916	953	988	1022	1086
1200	324	370	413	453	490	525	558	590	620	677	731	780	827	872	914	954	993	1030	1066	1133
1300	334	382	426	468	506	543	577	610	642	701	757	808	857	904	948	990	1031	1069	1107	1177
1400	344	394	439	482	522	559	595	629	662	724	781	835	886	934	980	1024	1066	1107	1146	1220
1500	353	404	452	495	536	575	612	648	681	745	805	860	913	963	1011	1057	1100	1143	1183	1260
1600	362	415	463	508	551	591	629	665	700	766	827	885	939	991	1041	1088	1133	1177	1219	1298
1700	371	425	475	521	564	605	644	682	718	785	849	908	964	1018	1069	1118	1164	1209	1253	1335
1800	379	434	485	533	577	619	660	698	735	804	869	930	988	1043	1096	1146	1195	1241	1286	1371
1900	387	444	496	544	590	663	674	713	751	823	889	952	1012	1068	1122	1174	1224	1271	1318	1405
2000	395	453	506	555	602	646	688	728	767	840	908	973	1034	1092	1147	1200	1252	1301	1348	1438
2100	402	461	516	566	614	659	702	743	782	857	927	993	1055	1115	1172	1226	1279	1329	1378	1470
2200	410	470	525	577	625	671	715	757	797	874	945	1013	1076	1137	1195	1251	1305	1356	1406	1501
2300	417	478	534	587	636	683	728	771	812	890	963	1031	1097	1159	1218	1275	1330	1383	1434	1532
2400	424	486	543	597	647	695	740	784	826	905	980	1050	1116	1180	1241	1299	1355	1409	1461	1561
2500	430	494	552	606	658	706	753	797	840	920	996	1068	1136	1200	1262	1322	1379	1434	1488	1589
2600	437	501	560	616	668	717	764	810	853	935	1012	1085	1154	1220	1283	1344	1402	1459	1513	1617
2700	443	509	569	625	678	728	776	822	866	950	1028	1102	1173	1240	1304	1366	1425	1483	1538	1644
2800	450	516	577	634	688	738	787	834	879	964	1043	1119	1190	1259	1324	1387	1447	1506	1562	1670
2900	456	523	585	643	697	749	798	845	891	977	1058	1135	1208	1277	1344	1408	1469	1529	1586	1696

Lgth Adj.[b]	Length of One Side of Rectangular Duct *a*, mm																			
	1000	1100	1200	1300	1400	1500	1600	1700	1800	1900	2000	2100	2200	2300	2400	2500	2600	2700	2800	2900
	Circular Duct Diameter, mm																			
1000	1093																			
1100	1146	1202																		
1200	1196	1256	1312																	
1300	1244	1306	1365	1421																
1400	1289	1354	1416	1475	1530															
1500	1332	1400	1464	1526	1584	1640														
1600	1373	1444	1511	1574	1635	1693	1749													
1700	1413	1486	1555	1621	1684	1745	1803	1858												
1800	1451	1527	1598	1667	1732	1794	1854	1912	1968											
1900	1488	1566	1640	1710	1778	1842	1904	1964	2021	2077										
2000	1523	1604	1680	1753	1822	1889	1952	2014	2073	2131	2186									
2100	1558	1640	1719	1793	1865	1933	1999	2063	2124	2183	2240	2296								
2200	1591	1676	1756	1833	1906	1977	2044	2110	2173	2233	2292	2350	2405							
2300	1623	1710	1793	1871	1947	2019	2088	2155	2220	2283	2343	2402	2459	2514						
2400	1655	1744	1828	1909	1986	2060	2131	2200	2266	2330	2393	2453	2511	2568	2624					
2500	1685	1776	1862	1945	2024	2100	2173	2243	2311	2377	2441	2502	2562	2621	2678	2733				
2600	1715	1808	1896	1980	2061	2139	2213	2285	2355	2422	2487	2551	2612	2672	2730	2787	2842			
2700	1744	1839	1929	2015	2097	2177	2253	2327	2398	2466	2533	2598	2661	2722	2782	2840	2896	2952		
2800	1772	1869	1961	2048	2133	2214	2292	2367	2439	2510	2578	2644	2708	2771	2832	2891	2949	3006	3061	
2900	1800	1898	1992	2081	2167	2250	2329	2406	2480	2552	2621	2689	2755	2819	2881	2941	3001	3058	3115	3170

[a]Table based on $D_e = 1.30(ab)^{0.625}/(a + b)^{0.25}$.

[b]Length adjacent side of rectangular duct *b*, mm.

Table 3 Equivalent Flat Oval Duct Dimensions

Circular Duct Diameter, mm	Minor Axis *a*, mm																
	70	100	125	150	175	200	250	275	300	325	350	375	400	450	500	550	600
	Major Axis *A*, mm																
125	205																
140	265	180															
160	360	235	190														
180	475	300	235	200													
200		380	290	245	215												
224		490	375	305	—	240											
250			475	385	325	290											
280				485	410	360	—	285									
315				635	525	—	—	345	325								
355				840	—	580	460	425	395	375							
400				1115	—	760	—	530	490	460	435						
450				1490	—	995	—	675	—	570	535	505					
500						1275	—	845	—	700	655	615	580				
560						1680	—	1085	—	890	820	765	720				
630								1425	—	1150	1050	970	905	810			
710										1505	1370	1260	1165	1025			
800											1800	1645	1515	1315	1170	1065	
900												2165	1985	1705	1500	1350	
1000														2170	1895	1690	
1120															2455	2170	1950
1250																2795	2495

Table 4 Duct Fitting Codes

Fitting Function	Geometry	Category	Sequential Number
S: Supply	D: round (Diameter)	1. Entries	1,2,3...*n*
		2. Exits	
E: Exhaust/Return	R: Rectangular	3. Elbows	
		4. Transitions	
C: Common (supply and return)	F: Flat oval	5. Junctions	
		6. Obstructions	
		7. Fan and system interactions	
		8. Duct-mounted equipment	
		9. Dampers	
		10. Hoods	

DUCTWORK SECTIONAL LOSSES

Darcy-Weisbach Equation

Total pressure loss in a duct section is calculated by combining Equations (18) and (29) in terms of Δp, where ΣC is the summation of local loss coefficients in the duct section. Each fitting loss coefficient must be referenced to that section's velocity pressure.

$$\Delta p = \left(\frac{1000 f L}{D_h} + \Sigma C\right)\left(\frac{\rho V^2}{2}\right) \tag{35}$$

FAN/SYSTEM INTERFACE

Fan Inlet and Outlet Conditions

Fan performance data measured in the field may show lower performance capacity than manufacturers' ratings. The most common causes of deficient performance of the fan/system combination are improper outlet connections, nonuniform inlet flow, and swirl at the fan inlet. These conditions alter the fan's aerodynamic characteristics so that its full flow potential is not realized. One bad connection can reduce fan performance far below its rating. No data have been published that account for the effects of fan inlet and outlet flexible vibration connectors.

Normally, a fan is tested with open inlets and a section of straight duct attached to the outlet (ASHRAE *Standard* 51). This setup results in uniform flow into the fan and efficient static pressure recovery on the fan outlet. If good inlet and outlet conditions are not provided in the actual installation, the performance of the fan suffers. To select and apply the fan properly, these effects must be considered, and the pressure requirements of the fan, as calculated by standard duct design procedures, must be increased.

Figure 10 illustrates deficient fan/system performance. System pressure losses have been determined accurately, and a fan has been selected for operation at point 1. However, no allowance has been made for the effect of system connections to the fan on fan performance. To compensate, a fan system effect must be added to the calculated system pressure losses to determine the actual system curve. The point of intersection between the fan performance curve and the actual system curve is point 4. The actual flow volume is, therefore, deficient by the difference from 1 to 4. To achieve design flow volume, a fan system effect pressure loss equal to the pressure difference between points 1 and 2 should be added to the calculated system pressure losses, and the fan should be selected to operate at point 2.

Fan System Effect Coefficients

The system effect concept was formulated by Farquhar (1973) and Meyer (1973); the magnitudes of the system effect, called **system effect factors**, were determined experimentally by the Air Movement and Control Association (AMCA 2007a; Brown 1973; Clarke et al. 1978). The system effect factors, converted to local loss coefficients, are in the *ASHRAE Duct Fitting Database* (2009) for both centrifugal and axial fans. Fan system effect coefficients are only an approximation. Fans of different types and even fans of the same type, but supplied by different manufacturers, do not necessarily react to a system in the same way. Therefore, judgment based on experience must be applied to any design.

Fan Outlet Conditions. Fans intended primarily for duct systems are usually tested with an outlet duct in place (ASHRAE *Standard* 51). Figure 11 shows the changes in velocity profiles at various distances from the fan outlet. For 100% recovery, the duct, including transition, must meet the requirements for 100% effective duct length [L_e (Figure 11)], which is calculated as follows:

For $V_o > 13$ m/s,

$$L_e = \frac{V_o \sqrt{A_o}}{4500} \quad (36)$$

For $V_o \le 13$ m/s,

$$L_e = \frac{\sqrt{A_o}}{350} \quad (37)$$

where

V_o = duct velocity, m/s
L_e = effective duct length, m
A_o = duct area, mm^2

As illustrated by Fitting SR7-1 in the section on Fitting Loss Coefficients, centrifugal fans should not abruptly discharge to the atmosphere. A diffuser design should be selected from Fitting SR7-2 (see the section on Fitting Loss Coefficients) or SR7-3 [see ASHRAE (2009)].

Fan Inlet Conditions. For rated performance, air must enter the fan uniformly over the inlet area in an axial direction without prerotation. Nonuniform flow into the inlet is the most common cause of reduced fan performance. Such inlet conditions are not equivalent to a simple increase in system resistance; therefore, they cannot be treated as a percentage decrease in the flow and pressure from the fan. A poor inlet condition results in an entirely new fan performance. An elbow at the fan inlet, for example Fitting ED7-2 (see the

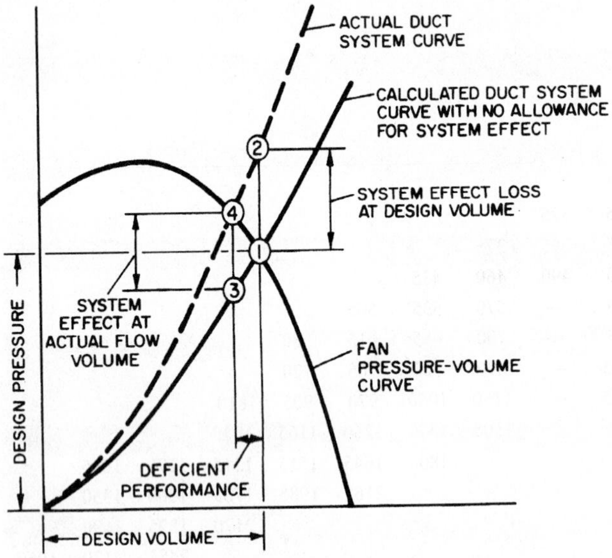

Fig. 10 Deficient System Performance with System Effect Ignored

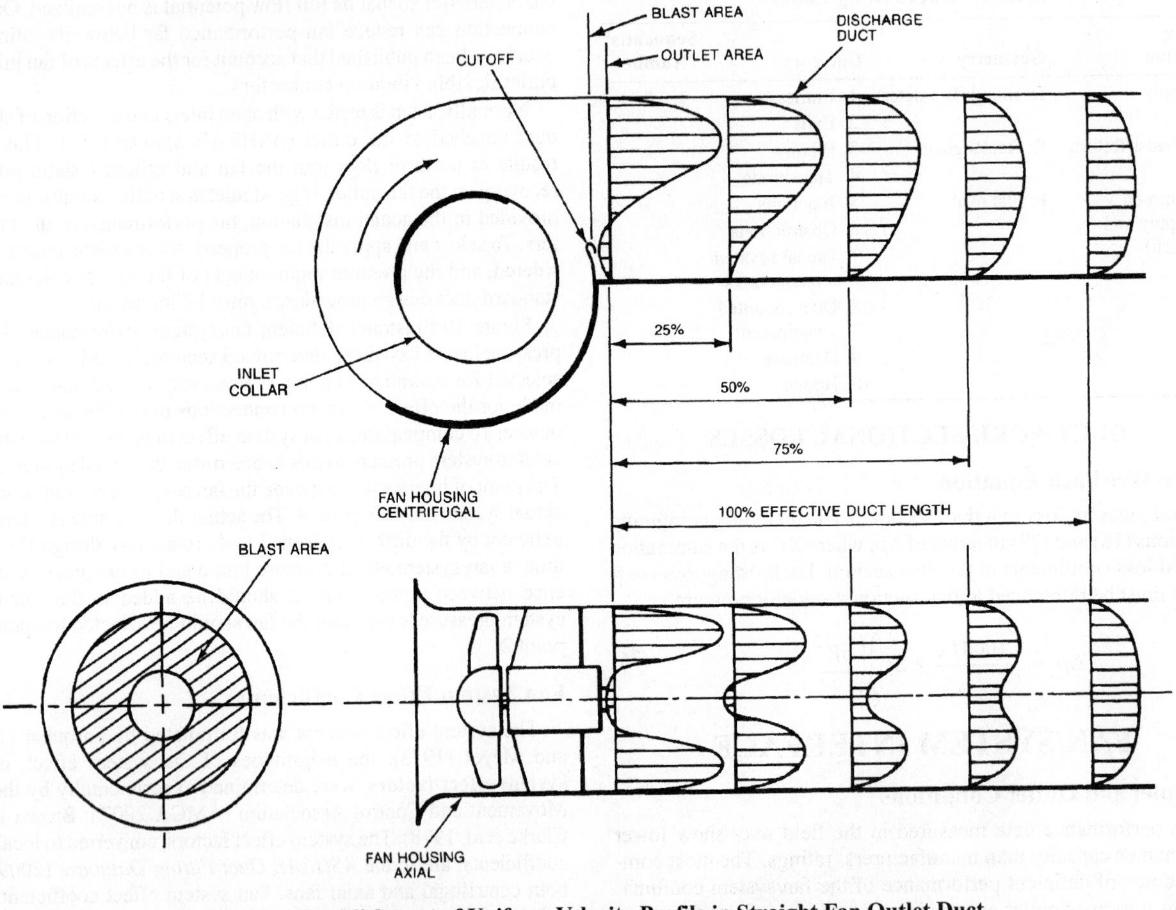

Fig. 11 Establishment of Uniform Velocity Profile in Straight Fan Outlet Duct
(Adapted by permission from AMCA *Publication* 201)

section on Fitting Loss Coefficients), causes turbulence and uneven flow into the fan impeller. Losses from the fan system effect can be eliminated by including an adequate length of straight duct between the elbow and the fan inlet.

The ideal inlet condition allows air to enter axially and uniformly without spin. A spin in the same direction as the impeller rotation reduces the pressure/volume curve by an amount dependent on the vortex's intensity. A counterrotating vortex at the inlet slightly increases the pressure/volume curve, but the power is increased substantially.

Inlet spin may arise from many different approach conditions, and sometimes the cause is not obvious. Inlet spin can be avoided by providing an adequate length of straight duct between the elbow and the fan inlet. Figure 12 illustrates some common duct connections that cause inlet spin and includes recommendations for correcting spin.

Fans within plenums and cabinets or next to walls should be located so that air may flow unobstructed into the inlets. Fan performance is reduced if the space between the fan inlet and the enclosure is too restrictive. System effect coefficients for fans in an enclosure or adjacent to walls are listed under Fitting ED7-1 (see the section on Fitting Loss Coefficients). How the airstream enters an enclosure in relation to the fan inlets also affects fan performance. Plenum or enclosure inlets or walls that are not symmetrical with the fan inlets cause uneven flow and/or inlet spin.

Testing, Adjusting, and Balancing Considerations

Fan system effects (FSEs) are not only to be used in conjunction with the system resistance characteristics in the fan selection process, but are also applied in the calculations of the results of testing, adjusting, and balancing (TAB) field tests to allow direct comparison to design calculations and/or fan performance data. Fan inlet swirl and the effect on system performance of poor fan inlet and outlet ductwork connections cannot be measured directly. Poor inlet flow patterns affect fan performance within the impeller wheel (centrifugal fan) or wheel rotor impeller (axial fan), while the fan outlet system effect is flow instability and turbulence within the fan discharge ductwork.

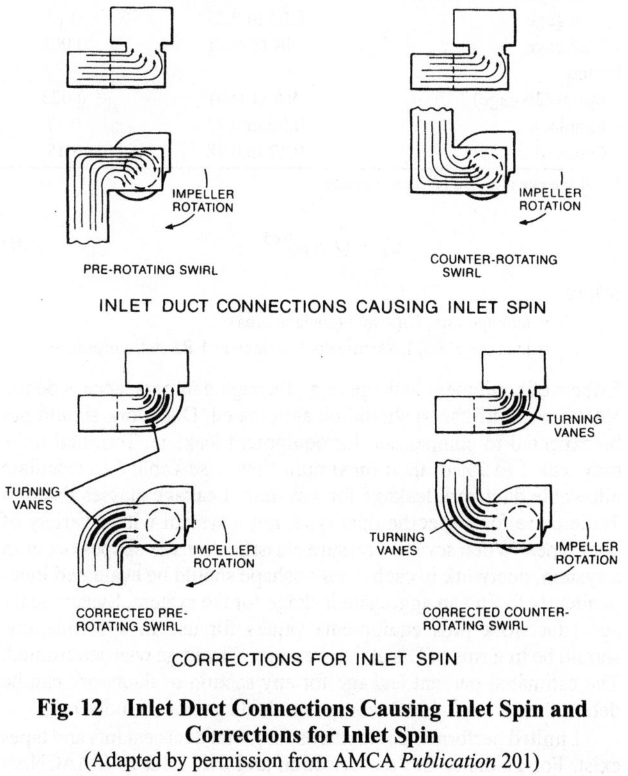

Fig. 12 Inlet Duct Connections Causing Inlet Spin and Corrections for Inlet Spin
(Adapted by permission from AMCA *Publication* 201)

The static pressure at the fan inlet and the static pressure at the fan outlet may be measured directly in some systems. In most cases, static pressure measurements for use in determining fan total (or static) pressure will not be made directly at the fan inlet and outlet, but at locations a relatively short distance from the fan inlet and downstream from the fan outlet. To calculate fan total pressure for this case from field measurements, use Equation (38), where Δp_{x-y} is the summation of calculated total pressure losses between the fan inlet and outlet sections noted. Plane 3 is used to determine airflow rate. If necessary, use Equation (17) to calculate fan static pressure knowing fan total pressure. For locating measurement planes and calculation procedures, consult AMCA *Publication* 203 (AMCA 2007b).

$$P_t = (p_{s,5} + p_{v,5}) + \Delta p_{2\text{-}5} + \mathrm{FSE}_2 + (p_{s,4} + p_{v,4}) + \Delta p_{4\text{-}1} + \mathrm{FSE}_1 + \mathrm{FSE}_{1,sw} \qquad (38)$$

where

P_t = fan total pressure, Pa
p_s = static pressure, Pa
p_v = velocity pressure, Pa
FSE = fan system effect, Pa
$\Delta p_{x\text{-}y}$ = summarization of total pressure losses between planes *x* and *y*, Pa

Subscripts [numerical subscripts same as used by AMCA (2007b)]:
1 = fan inlet
2 = fan outlet
3 = plane of airflow measurement
4 = plane of static pressure measurement upstream of fan
5 = plane of static pressure measurement downstream of fan
sw = swirl

DUCT SYSTEM DESIGN

DESIGN CONSIDERATIONS

Space Pressure Relationships

Space pressure is determined by fan location and duct system arrangement. For example, a supply fan that pumps air into a space increases space pressure; an exhaust fan reduces space pressure. If both supply and exhaust fans are used, space pressure depends on the relative capacity of the fans. Space pressure is positive if supply exceeds exhaust and negative if exhaust exceeds supply (Osborne 1966). System pressure variations caused by wind can be minimized or eliminated by careful selection of intake air and exhaust vent locations (see Chapter 24).

Fire and Smoke Management

Because duct systems can convey smoke, hot gases, and fire from one area to another and can accelerate a fire within the system, fire protection is an essential part of air-conditioning and ventilation system design. Generally, fire safety codes require compliance with the standards of national organizations. NFPA *Standard* 90A examines fire safety requirements for (1) ducts, connectors, and appurtenances; (2) plenums and corridors; (3) air outlets, air inlets, and fresh air intakes; (4) air filters; (5) fans; (6) electric wiring and equipment; (7) air-cooling and -heating equipment; (8) building construction, including protection of penetrations; and (9) controls, including smoke control.

Fire safety codes often refer to the testing and labeling practices of nationally recognized laboratories, such as Factory Mutual and Underwriters Laboratories (UL). UL's annual *Building Materials Directory* lists fire and smoke dampers that have been tested and meet the requirements of UL *Standards* 555 and 555S. This directory also summarizes maximum allowable sizes for individual dampers and assemblies of these dampers. Fire dampers are 1.5 h or 3 h fire-rated. Smoke dampers are classified by (1) temperature degradation [ambient air or high temperature (120°C minimum)] and

(2) leakage at 250 and 1000 Pa pressure difference (2 and 3 kPa classification optional). Smoke dampers are tested under conditions of maximum airflow. UL's annual *Fire Resistance Directory* lists fire resistances of floor/roof and ceiling assemblies with and without ceiling fire dampers.

For a more detailed presentation of fire protection, see the NFPA (2008) *Fire Protection Handbook*, Chapter 52 of the 2007 *ASHRAE Handbook—HVAC Applications*, and Klote and Milke (2002).

Duct Insulation

In all new construction (except low-rise residential buildings), air-handling ducts and plenums that are part of an HVAC air distribution system should be thermally insulated in accordance with ASHRAE *Standard* 90.1. Duct insulation for new low-rise residential buildings should comply with ASHRAE *Standard* 90.2. Existing buildings should meet requirements of ASHRAE *Standard* 100. In all cases, thermal insulation should meet local code requirements. Insulation thicknesses in these standards are minimum values; economic and thermal considerations may justify higher insulation levels. Additional insulation, vapor retarders, or both may be required to limit vapor transmission and condensation.

Duct heat gains or losses must be known to calculate supply air quantities, supply air temperatures, and coil loads. To estimate duct heat transfer and entering or leaving air temperatures, refer to Chapter 23.

Duct System Leakage

It is recommended that all transverse joints, longitudinal seams, and ductwork penetrations be sealed. **Longitudinal seams** are joints oriented in the direction of airflow. **Duct wall penetrations** are openings made by screws, non-self-sealing fasteners, pipe, tubing, rods, and wire. All other connections are considered **transverse joints**, which are connections of two duct or fitting elements oriented perpendicular to flow (e.g., spin-ins, taps, branch connections, duct connections to equipment). System (ductwork and equipment) leakage should be tested to verify the installing contractor's workmanship and sealing practices.

Leakage in all unsealed ducts varies considerably with the fabricating machinery used, material thickness, assembly methods, and installation workmanship. For sealed ducts, a wide variety of sealing methods and products exists. Sealed and unsealed duct leakage tests (AISI/SMACNA 1972; ASHRAE/SMACNA/TIMA 1985; Swim and Griggs 1995) confirmed that longitudinal seam, transverse joint, and assembled duct leakage can be represented by Equation (39) and that, for the same construction, leakage is not significantly different in negative and positive modes. Table 5 presents a range of leakage rates for longitudinal seams commonly used in metal duct construction. Longitudinal seam leakage for unsealed or unwelded metal ducts is about 10 to 15% of total duct leakage.

$$Q = C\Delta p_n^N \tag{39}$$

where

Q = duct leakage rate, L/(s·m²)
C = constant reflecting area characteristics of leakage path
Δp_s = static pressure differential from duct interior to exterior, Pa
N = exponent relating turbulent or laminar flow in leakage path

The AISI/ASHRAE/SMACNA/TIMA data showed that duct leakage (equipment not included) is best predicted by duct surface area and pressure, because surface area highlights the effect of system size. Duct leakage were grouped into a geometric series of **leakage classes C_L** (Figure 13) based on Equation (40), where the exponent N is assumed to be 0.65. Table 6 shows leakage classes for commonly used duct construction and sealing practices (equipment leakage excluded).

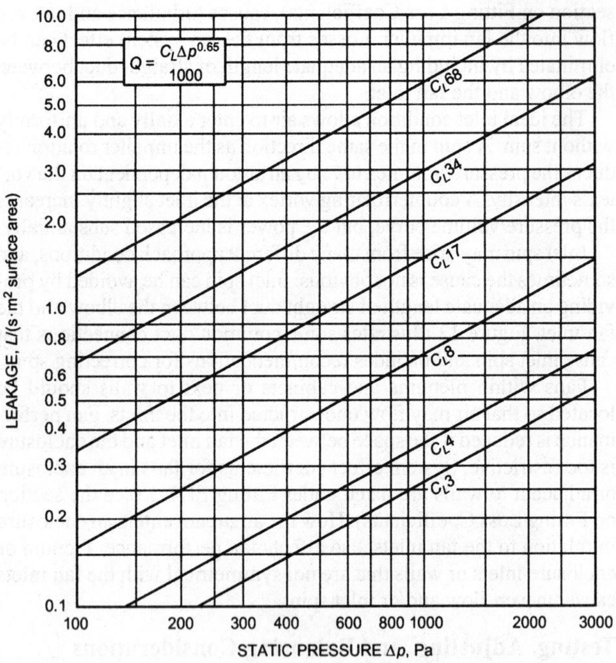

Fig. 13 Duct Leakage Classifications

Table 5 Unsealed Longitudinal Seam Leakage, Metal Ducts

	Leakage, L per metre Seam Length*	
Type of Duct/Seam	**Range**	**Average**
Rectangular		
Pittsburgh lock		
26 gage	0.015 to 0.03	0.025
22 gage	0.0015 to 0.003	0.0025
Button punch snaplock		
26 gage	0.05 to 0.23	0.12
22 gage	NA (1 test)	0.005
Round		
Spiral (26 gage)	NA (1 test)	0.023
Snaplock	0.06 to 0.22	0.17
Grooved	0.17 to 0.28	0.19

*Leakage rate is at 250 Pa static pressure.

$$C_L = Q/\Delta p_n^{0.65} \tag{40}$$

where

Q = leakage rate, L/(s·m²) (surface area)
C_L = leakage class, L/(s·m²) duct surface at 1 Pa static pressure

Effects of equipment leakage (e.g., through dampers, access doors, VAV boxes, diffusers) should be anticipated. Ductwork should not be expected to compensate for equipment leakage. Terminal units may leak 1 to 2% of their maximum flow. Use Table 6 to calculate allowable ductwork leakage for a system. Leakage classes listed in Table 6 are for a specific duct type, not a system with a variety of duct types. When several pressure classifications or shapes occur in a system, ductwork in each class or shape should be evaluated independently to find an aggregate leakage for the system. System leakage (ductwork plus equipment) values for use in specifications should be in terms of L/s at the pressure(s) leakage was determined. The estimated percent leakage for any section of ductwork can be determined from Table 7 (equipment leakage not included).

Limited performance standards for metal duct sealants and tapes exist. For guidance in their selection and use, refer to SMACNA's

Table 6 Duct Leakage Classification[a]

Duct Type	Sealed[b,c] Predicted Leakage Class C_L	Sealed[b,c] Leakage Rate, L/(s·m²) at 250 Pa	Unsealed[c] Predicted Leakage Class C_L	Unsealed[c] Leakage Rate, L/(s·m²) at 250 Pa
Metal (flexible excluded)				
Round and flat oval	4	0.14	42 (8 to 99)	1.5 (0.3 to 3.6)
Rectangular	17	0.62	68 (17 to 155)	2.5 (0.6 to 5.6)
Flexible				
Metal, aluminum	11	0.40	42 (17 to 76)	1.5 (0.6 to 2.8)
Nonmetal	17	0.62	30 (6 to 76)	1.5 (0.2 to 2.8)
Fibrous glass				
Round	4	0.14	NA	NA
Rectangular	8	0.29	NA	NA

[a]Leakage classes here are averages based on tests conducted by AISI/SMACNA (1972), ASHRAE/SMACNA/TIMA (1985), and Swim and Griggs (1995).
[b]"Sealed" leakage classes assume that, for metal ducts, all transverse joints, seams, and openings in duct wall are sealed.
[c]Leakage classes anticipate about 0.82 joints per metre of duct. For systems with a high fitting-to-straight-duct ratio, greater leakage occurs in both sealed and unsealed conditions.

Table 7 Leakage as Percentage of Airflow[a,b]

Leakage Class	System L/s per m² Duct Surface[c]	Static Pressure, Pa 125	250	500	750	1000	1500
68	10	15	24	38	49	59	77
	12.7	12	19	30	39	47	62
	15	10	16	25	33	39	51
	20	7.7	12	19	25	30	38
	25	6.1	9.6	15	20	24	31
34	10	7.7	12	19	25	30	38
	12.7	6.1	9.6	15	20	24	31
	15	5.1	8.0	13	16	20	26
	20	3.8	6.0	9.4	12	15	19
	25	3.1	4.8	7.5	9.8	12	15
17	10	3.8	6	9.4	12	15	19
	12.7	3.1	4.8	7.5	9.8	12	15
	15	2.6	4.0	6.3	8.2	9.8	13
	20	1.9	3.0	4.7	6.1	7.4	9.6
	25	1.5	2.4	3.8	4.9	5.9	7.7
8	10	1.9	3	4.7	6.1	7.4	9.6
	12.7	1.5	2.4	3.8	4.9	5.9	7.7
	15	1.3	2.0	3.1	4.1	4.9	6.4
	20	1.0	1.5	2.4	3.1	3.7	4.8
	25	0.8	1.2	1.9	2.4	3.0	3.8
4	10	1.0	1.5	2.4	3.1	3.7	4.8
	12.7	0.8	1.2	1.9	2.4	3.0	3.8
	15	0.6	1.0	1.6	2.0	2.5	3.2
	20	0.5	0.8	1.3	1.6	2.0	2.6
	25	0.4	0.6	0.9	1.2	1.5	1.9

[a]Adapted with permission from *HVAC Air Duct Leakage Test Manual* (SMACNA 1985, Appendix A).
[b]Percentage applies to airflow entering a section of duct operating at an assumed pressure equal to average of upstream and downstream pressures.
[c]Ratios in this column are typical of fan volumetric flow rate divided by total system surface. Portions of systems may vary from these averages.

HVAC Duct Construction Standards (2005). Fibrous glass ducts and their closure systems are covered by UL *Standards* 181 and 181A. For fibrous glass duct construction standards, consult NAIMA (2002) and SMACNA (2003). Flexible duct performance and installation standards are covered by UL *Standards* 181 and 181B and ADC (2003). Soldered or welded duct construction is necessary where sealants are not suitable. Sealants used on exterior ducts must be resistant to weather, temperature cycles, sunlight, and ozone.

Shaft and compartment pressure changes affect duct leakage and are important to health and safety in the design and operation of contaminant and smoke control systems. Shafts should not be used for supply, return, and/or exhaust air without accounting for their leakage rates. Airflow around buildings, building component leakage, and the distribution of inside and outside pressures over the height of a building, including shafts, are discussed in Chapters 16 and 24.

Table 8 Typical Design Velocities for HVAC Components

Duct Element	Face Velocity, m/s
Louvers[a]	
Intake	
3300 L/s and greater	2
Less than 3300 L/s	See Figure 14
Exhaust	
2400 L/s and greater	2.5
Less than2400 L/s	See Figure 14
Filters[b]	
Panel filters	
Viscous impingement	1 to 4
Dry-type, extended-surface	
Flat (low efficiency)	Duct velocity
Pleated media (intermediate efficiency)	Up to 3.8
HEPA	1.3
Renewable media filters	
Moving-curtain viscous impingement	2.5
Moving-curtain dry media	1
Electronic air cleaners	
Ionizing type	0.8 to 1.8
Heating Coils[c]	
Steam and hot water	2.5 to 5 1 min., 8 max.
Electric	
Open wire	Refer to mfg. data
Finned tubular	Refer to mfg. data
Dehumidifying Coils[d]	2 to 3
Air Washers[e]	
Spray type	Refer to mfg. data
Cell type	Refer to mfg. data
High-velocity spray type	6 to 9

[a]Based on assumptions presented in text.
[b]Abstracted from Ch. 28, 2008 *ASHRAE Handbook—HVAC Systems and Equipment.*
[c]Abstracted from Ch. 26, 2008 *ASHRAE Handbook—HVAC Systems and Equipment.*
[d]Abstracted from Ch. 22, 2008 *ASHRAE Handbook—HVAC Systems and Equipment.*
[e]Abstracted from Ch. 40, 2008 *ASHRAE Handbook—HVAC Systems and Equipment.*

System Component Design Velocities

Table 8 summarizes face velocities for HVAC components in built-up systems. In most cases, the values are abstracted from pertinent chapters in the 2008 *ASHRAE Handbook—HVAC Systems and Equipment*; final selection of components should be based on data in these chapters or, preferably, from manufacturers.

Use Figure 14 for preliminary sizing of air intake and exhaust louvers. For air quantities greater than 3300 L/s per louver, the air intake gross louver openings are based on 2 m/s; for exhaust louvers, 2.5 m/s is used for air quantities of 2400 L/s per louver and greater. For smaller air quantities, refer to Figure 14. These criteria are presented on a per-louver basis (i.e., each louver in a bank of louvers) to include each louver frame. Representative production-run louvers were used in establishing Figure 14, and all data used were based on AMCA *Standard* 500-L tests. For louvers larger than

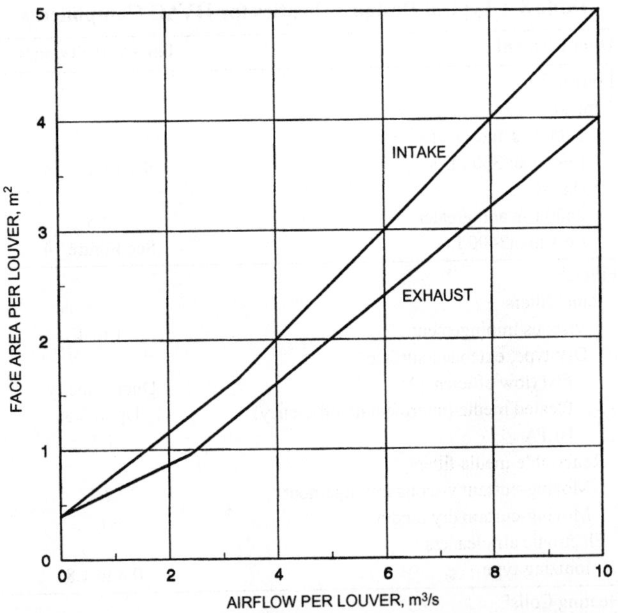

Parameters Used to Establish Figure	Intake Louver	Exhaust Louver
Minimum free area (1220 mm square test section), %	45	45
Water penetration, mL/(m²·0.25 h)	Negligible (less than 0.3)	N/A
Maximum static pressure drop, Pa	35	60

Fig. 14 Criteria for Louver Sizing

1.5 m^2, the free areas are greater than 45%; for louvers less than 1.5 m^2, free areas are less than 45%. Unless specific louver data are analyzed, no louver should have a face area less than 0.4 m^2. If debris can collect on the screen of an intake louver, or if louvers are located at grade with adjacent pedestrian traffic, louver face velocity should not exceed 0.5 m/s.

Louvers require special treatment because the blade shapes, angles, and spacing cause significant variations in louver-free area and performance (pressure drop and water penetration). Selection and analysis should be based on test data obtained from the manufacturer in accordance with AMCA *Standard* 500-L, which presents both pressure drop and water penetration test procedures and a uniform method for calculating the free area of a louver. Tests are conducted on a 1220 mm square louver with the frame mounted flush in the wall. For water penetration tests, rainfall is 100 mm/h, no wind, and the water flow down the wall is 0.05 L/s per linear metre of louver width.

AMCA *Standard* 500-L also includes a method for measuring water rejection performance of louvers subjected to simulated rain and wind pressures. These louvers are tested at a rainfall of 76 mm/h falling on the louver's face with a predetermined wind velocity directed at the face of the louver (typically 13 or 20 m/s). Effectiveness ratings are assigned at various airflow rates through the louver.

System and Duct Noise

The major sources of noise from air-conditioning systems are diffusers, grilles, fans, ducts, fittings, and vibrations. Chapter 47 of the 2007 *ASHRAE Handbook—HVAC Applications* discusses sound control for each of these sources, as well as methods for calculating required sound attenuation. Sound control for terminal devices consists of selecting devices that meet the design goal under all operating conditions and installing them properly so that no additional sound is generated. The sound power output of a fan is determined by the type of fan, airflow, and pressure. Sound control in the duct system requires proper duct layout, sizing, and provision for installing duct attenuators, if required. Noise generated by a system increases with both duct velocity and system pressure.

Testing and Balancing

Each air duct system should be tested, adjusted, and balanced. Detailed procedures are given in Chapter 37 of the 2007 *ASHRAE Handbook—HVAC Applications*. To properly determine fan total (or static) pressure from field measurements taking into account fan system effect, see the section on Fan/System Interface. Equation (38) allows direct comparison of system resistance to design calculations and/or fan performance data. It is important that system effect magnitudes be known prior to testing. If necessary, use Equation (17) to calculate fan static pressure knowing fan total pressure [Equation (38)]. For TAB calculation procedures of numerous fan/ system configurations encountered in the field, refer to AMCA (2007b).

DUCT DESIGN METHODS

Duct design methods for HVAC systems and for exhaust systems conveying vapors, gases, and smoke are the equal-friction method, the static regain method, and the T-method. The section on Industrial Exhaust System Duct Design presents the design criteria and procedures for exhaust systems conveying particulates. Equal friction and static regain are nonoptimizing methods, and the T-method is a practical optimization method introduced by Tsal et al. (1988).

To ensure that system designs are acoustically acceptable, noise generation should be analyzed and sound attenuators and/or acoustically lined duct provided where necessary.

Equal-Friction Method

In the equal-friction method, ducts are sized for a constant pressure loss per unit length. The shaded area of the friction chart (see Figure 9) is the suggested range of friction rate and air velocity. When energy cost is high and installed ductwork cost is low, a low-friction-rate design is more economical. For low energy cost and high duct cost, a higher friction rate is more economical. After initial sizing, calculate total pressure loss for all duct sections, and then resize sections to balance pressure losses at each junction.

Static Regain Method

This design method is only applicable to supply air systems. The objective is to obtain the same static pressure at diverging flow junctions by changing downstream duct sizes. This design objective can be developed by rearranging Equation (7a) and setting $p_{s,2}$ equal to $p_{s,1}$ (neglecting thermal gravity effect term). This means that the change in static pressure from one section to another is zero, which is satisfied when the change in total pressure is equal to the change in velocity pressure. Thus,

$$p_{s,1} - p_{s,2} = \Delta p_{t,1\text{-}2} - \left[\frac{\rho V_1^2}{2} - \frac{\rho V_2^2}{2}\right] \quad (41)$$

and

$$\Delta p_{t,1\text{-}2} = \frac{\rho V_1^2}{2} - \frac{\rho V_2^2}{2} \quad (42)$$

where $\Delta p_{t,1\text{-}2}$ is total pressure loss from upstream of junction 1 to upstream of junction 2. Junction 2 can be a terminal section, where the total pressure is zero. For each main section, the straight-through and branch sections immediately downstream of the main duct section are determined by iteration of that section's size until Equation (42) is satisfied. However, there could be cases when the straight or branch sections need to be larger than the upstream section to satisfy Equation (42). Fittings in the 2009 *ASHRAE Duct Fitting Database* have not been tested under these conditions, and making downstream sections larger than upstream sections is not practical. The largest straight-through or branch size should be limited to that of the upstream section. The imbalance that occurs is resolved during total-pressure balancing of the system.

To start system design, a maximum velocity is selected for the root section (duct section downstream of a fan). In Figure 16, section 19 is the root for the supply air subsystem. The shaded area on the friction chart (see Figure 9) is the suggested range of air velocity. When energy cost is high and installed ductwork cost is low, a lower initial velocity is more economical. For low energy cost and high duct cost, a higher velocity is more economical.

Because terminal sections often require additional static pressure to operate VAV terminal boxes properly, that static pressure requirement is added into the section after it is sized using static regain. Otherwise, the downstream section could be larger than the upstream section. For calculating duct sizes, the total pressure losses of grilles, registers, diffusers, or constant-volume (CV) terminal boxes should be included in the sizing iterations.

Total Pressure Balancing. After completing duct sizing by the static regain method, any residual unbalance can be reduced or eliminated by calculating the system's total pressure (pressure required in the critical paths) and changing duct sizes or fittings in other paths to increase the paths' total pressure to approximate what is needed in the critical paths.

T-Method

T-method optimization (Tsal et al. 1988) is a dynamic programming procedure based on Bellman's (1957) tee-staging idea, except that phase-level vector tracing is eliminated by optimizing locally at each stage. This modification reduces the number of calculations, but requires iteration.

Ductwork sizes are determined by minimizing the objective function:

$$E = E_p(\text{PWEF}) + E_s \quad (43)$$

where

E = present-worth owning and operating cost
E_p = first-year energy cost
E_s = initial cost
PWEF = present worth escalation factor (Smith 1968), dimensionless

The objective function includes both initial system cost and present worth of energy. Hours of operation, annual escalation and interest rates, and amortization period are also required for optimization.

The following constraints are necessary for duct optimization (Tsal and Adler 1987):

- *Continuity.* For each node, flow in equals flow out.
- *Pressure balancing.* Total pressure loss in each path must equal fan total pressure; or, in effect, at any junction, total pressure loss for all paths is the same.
- *Nominal duct size.* Ducts are constructed in discrete, nominal sizes. Each diameter of a round duct or height and width of a rectangular duct is rounded to the nearest increment, usually 25 or 50 mm, or according to ISO standards where applicable. If a lower nominal size is selected, initial cost decreases, but pressure loss increases and may exceed the fan pressure. If a higher nominal size is selected, the opposite is true: initial cost increases, but section pressure loss decreases. However, this lower pressure at one section may allow smaller ducts to be selected for sections that follow. Therefore, optimization must consider size rounding.
- *Air velocity restriction.* Maximum allowable velocity is an acoustic limitation (ductwork regenerated noise).
- *Construction restriction.* Architectural limits may restrict duct sizes. If air velocity or construction constraints are violated during an iteration, a duct size must be calculated. Pressure loss calculated for this preselected duct size is considered a fixed loss.

T-method simulation, developed by Tsal et al. (1990), determines the flow in each duct section of an existing system with a known operating fan performance curve. The simulation version of the T-method converges very efficiently. Usually three iterations are sufficient to obtain a solution with a high degree of accuracy.

Many HVAC problems require duct system simulation. In addition to the following concerns that can be clarified by simulation, the T-method is an excellent design tool for simulating flow distribution within a system with various modes of operation.

- Flow distribution in a VAV system caused by terminal box flow diversity
- Airflow redistribution caused by HVAC system additions and/or modifications
- System airflow analysis for partially occupied buildings
- Necessity to replace fans and/or motors when retrofitting an air distribution system
- Multiple-fan system operating condition when one or more fans shut down
- Pressure differences between adjacent confined spaces in a nuclear facility when a design basis accident (DBA) occurs (Farajian et al. 1992)
- Smoke management system performance during a fire, when some fire/smoke dampers close and others remain open

Availability. Software for T-method optimization is under development to identify optimum duct design, considering energy, operation, and construction costs.

BALANCING DAMPERS

Constant-Volume (CV) Systems

Dampers should be provided throughout CV systems. Systems designed using the inherently non-self-balancing equal-friction method should have balancing dampers at each branch throughout the system, unless sections are resized to balance pressure losses at each junction. Self-balancing design methods, such as static regain and the T-method, produce fairly well-balanced systems and theoretically do not need balancing dampers; however, because of the accuracy limitations of fitting data (loss coefficients), use of fittings for which no data are available, and effects of close-coupled fittings, dampers should be provided.

Variable-Air-Volume (VAV) Systems

VAV systems in balance at design loads will not be in balance at part-load conditions, because there is no single critical path in VAV systems. The critical path is dynamic and continually changing as loads on a building change. In general, balancing dampers are not needed for systems designed by the static regain or T-method, because these design methods are self-balancing at design loads and VAV boxes compensate for inaccuracy in fitting data or data inaccuracy caused by close-coupled fittings (at design loads) and system pressure variation (at part loads). Balancing dampers, however, are required for systems designed using the non-self-balancing equal-friction method. For systems designed using any method, dampers should not be installed in the inlets to VAV boxes.

For any design method, VAV terminal units may have upstream static pressures higher than for which the box is rated, thus possibly introducing noise into occupied spaces. In these cases, control algorithms can poll the VAV boxes and drive the duct static pressure to the minimum set point required to keep at least one unit at starvation (open) at any given time. Upstream static pressure should always be kept at a minimum that is easy for the VAV box to control. Because there may be large differences in static pressure at riser takeoffs serving many floors from a single air handler, manual dampers should be provided at each floor takeoff so that testing, adjusting, and balancing (TAB) contractors can field-adjust them after construction. Alternatively, these takeoff dampers could also be dynamically controlled to adjust the downstream static pressure applied to the VAV boxes, while simultaneously driving the air handler to the lowest possible static pressure set point.

Silencers downstream of VAV terminal units should not be necessary if the VAV box damper is operating at nearly open conditions. Their use in this location should be based on careful acoustical analysis, because silencers add total pressure to the system and therefore create more system noise by causing air handlers to operate at higher speeds for a given airflow.

HVAC DUCT DESIGN PROCEDURES

The general procedure for HVAC system duct design is as follows:

1. Study the building plans, and arrange supply and return outlets to provide proper distribution of air in each space. Adjust calculated air quantities for duct heat gains or losses and duct leakage. Also, adjust supply, return, and/or exhaust air quantities to meet space pressurization requirements.
2. Select outlet sizes from manufacturers' data (see Chapter 20).
3. Sketch the duct system, connecting supply outlets and return intakes with the air-handling units/air conditioners. Use rigid round ducts, minimize the number of fittings, and avoid close-coupled fittings because little is known about the resulting loss coefficients. If space is restricted and a properly designed round duct is too large, the next best option to minimize leakage and pressure losses is to use flat oval ductwork. Multiple runs of round duct should also be considered. Limit flexible duct to the final 1.5 m of connections to diffusers and terminal boxes, with no more than 5% compression. They should be installed without kinks or crimps, and no more offset between the diffuser and rigid duct than 1/8th the diffuser neck diameter to prevent a significant increase in noise level (see Figure 11 in Chapter 47 of the 2007 *ASHRAE Handbook—HVAC Applications*).
4. Divide the system into sections and number each section. A duct system should be divided at all points where flow, size, or shape changes. Assign fittings to the section toward the supply and return (or exhaust) terminals. The following examples are for the fittings identified for Example 6 (Figure 15), and system section numbers assigned (Figure 16). For converging flow fitting 3, assign the straight-through flow to section 1 (toward terminal 1), and the branch to section 2 (toward terminal 4). For diverging flow fitting 24, assign the straight-through flow to section 13 (toward terminals 26 and 29) and the branch to section 10

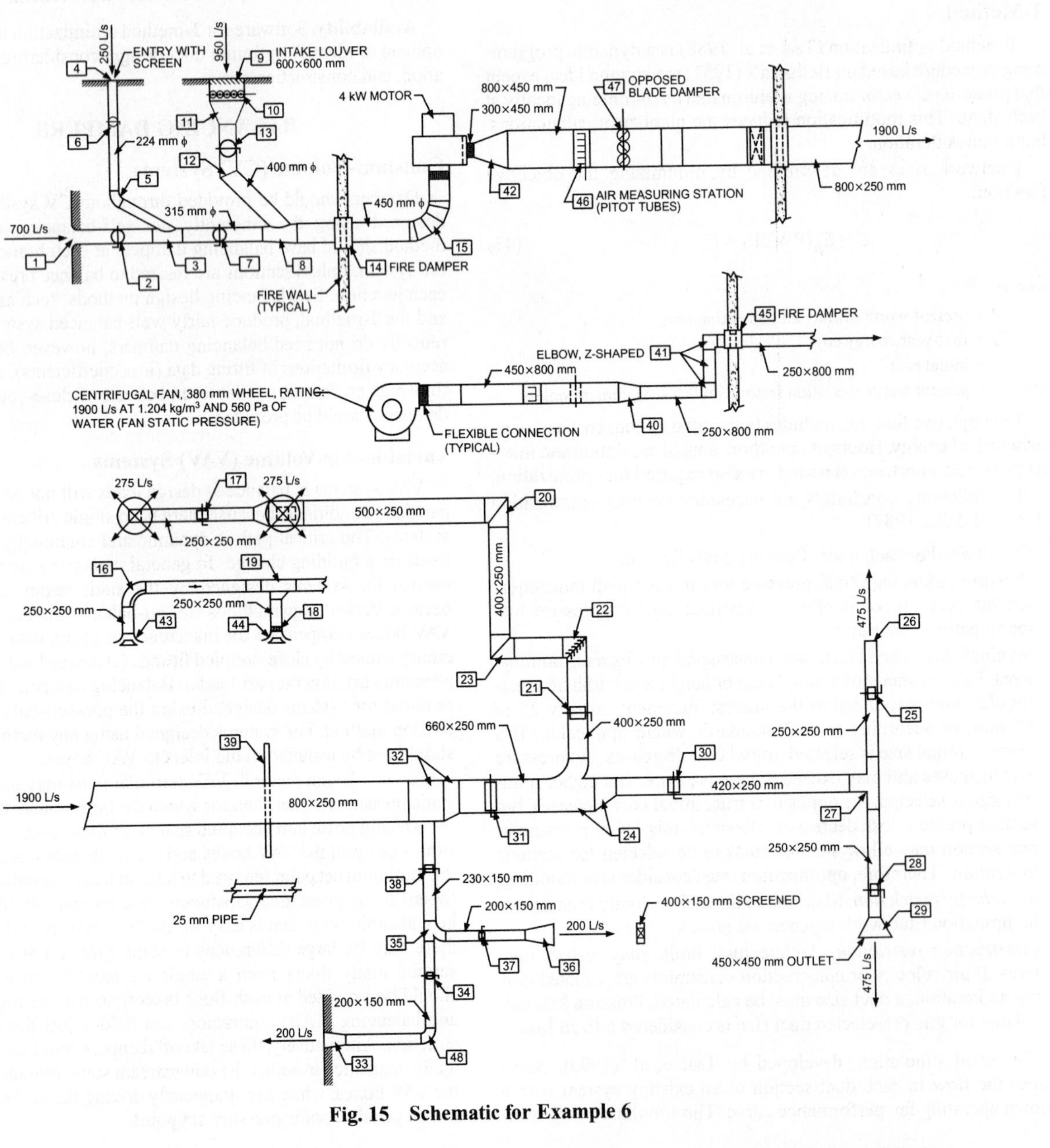

Fig. 15 Schematic for Example 6

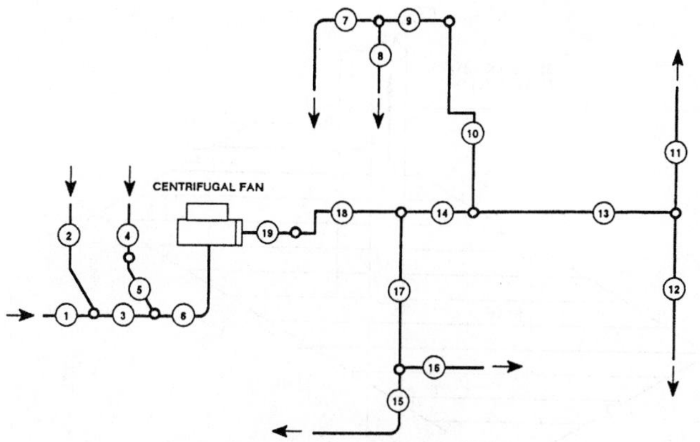

Fig. 16 System Schematic with Section Numbers for Example 6

(toward terminals 43 and 44). For transition fitting 11, assign the fitting to upstream section 4 [toward terminal 9 (intake louver)]. For fitting 20, assign the unequal area elbow to downstream section 9 (toward diffusers 43 and 44). The fan outlet diffuser, fitting 42, is assigned to section 19 (again, toward the supply duct terminals).

5. Size ducts by the selected design method. Calculate system total pressure loss; then select the fan (refer to Chapter 20 of the 2008 *ASHRAE Handbook—HVAC Systems and Equipment*).
6. Lay out the system in detail. If duct routing and fittings vary significantly from the original design, recalculate pressure losses. Reselect the fan if necessary.
7. Resize duct sections to approximately balance pressures at each junction.
8. Analyze the design for objectionable noise levels, and specify lined duct, double-wall duct, and sound attenuators as necessary. Refer to the section on System and Duct Noise.

Example 6. For the system illustrated by Figures 15 and 16, size the ductwork by the equal-friction method, and pressure-balance the system by changing duct sizes (use 10 mm increments for rectangular, and available spiral duct forming heads: 80, 100, 125, 140, 150, 160, 180, 200, 224, 250, 280, 300, 315, 355, 400, 450, 500, 560, 600, 630, 710, 800, 900, 1000, 1120, 1250, 1300, 1400, 1500, 1600, 1800, 2000, 2100, 2200, 2300, 2400, and 2500 mm). Determine system resistance and total pressure unbalance at junctions. Airflow quantities are actual values adjusted for heat gains or losses, and ductwork is sealed (assume no leakage), galvanized steel ducts with transverse joints on 1200 mm centers (ε = 0.09 mm). Air is at standard conditions (1.204 kg/m^3 density).

Because Figure 15 is intended to illustrate calculation procedures, its duct layout is not typical of any real duct system. The layout includes fittings from the local loss coefficient tables, with emphasis on converging and diverging tees and various types of entries and discharges. The supply system is constructed of rectangular ductwork; the return system, round ductwork.

Solution: See Figure 16 for section numbers assigned to the system. Duct sections are sized within the suggested range of friction rate shown on the friction chart (see Figure 9). Tables 9 and 10 give total pressure loss calculations and the supporting summary of loss coefficients by sections. Straight-duct friction factor and pressure loss were calculated by Equations (18) and (19). Fitting loss coefficients are from the 2009 *ASHRAE Duct Fitting Database*. Loss coefficients were calculated automatically by the database program (not by manual interpolation). Pressure loss values in Table 9 for diffusers (fittings 43 and 44), louver (fitting 9), and air-measuring station (fitting 46) are manufacturers' data.

Pressure unbalance at junctions is shown in Figure 17, the total pressure grade line for the system. System resistance P_t is 704 Pa. Noise levels and the need for sound attenuation were not evaluated. To calculate the fan static pressure, use Equation (17):

$$P_s = 704 - 119 = 585 \text{ Pa}$$

where 119 Pa is the fan outlet velocity pressure.

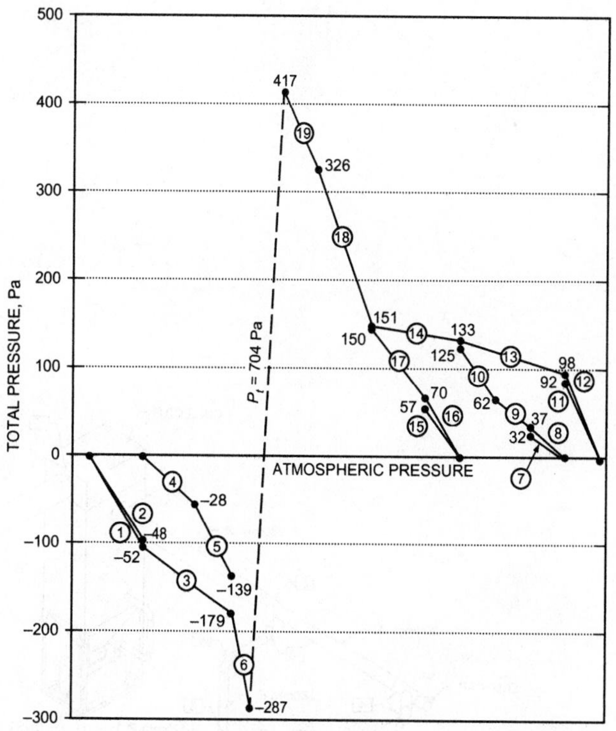

Fig. 17 Total Pressure Grade Line for Example 6

INDUSTRIAL EXHAUST SYSTEM DUCT DESIGN

Chapter 30 of the 2007 *ASHRAE Handbook—HVAC Applications* discusses design criteria, including hood design, for industrial exhaust systems. Exhaust systems conveying vapors, gases, and smoke can be designed by the equal-friction or T-method. Systems conveying particulates are designed by the constant velocity method at duct velocities adequate to convey particles to the system air cleaner. For contaminant transport velocities, see Table 2 in Chapter 30 of the 2007 *ASHRAE Handbook—HVAC Applications*.

Two pressure-balancing methods can be considered when designing industrial exhaust systems. One method uses balancing devices (e.g., dampers, blast gates) to obtain design airflow through each hood. The other approach balances systems by adding resistance to ductwork sections (i.e., changing duct size, selecting different fittings, and increasing airflow). This self-balancing method is preferred, especially for systems conveying abrasive materials. Where potentially explosive or radioactive materials are conveyed, the prebalanced system is mandatory because contaminants could accumulate at the balancing devices. To balance systems by increasing airflow, use Equation (44) which assumes that all ductwork has the same diameter and that fitting loss coefficients, including main and branch tee coefficients, are constant.

$$Q_c = Q_d (P_h / P_l)^{0.5} \tag{44}$$

where

Q_c = airflow rate required to increase P_l to P_h, L/s
Q_d = total airflow rate through low-resistance duct run, L/s
P_h = absolute value of pressure loss in high-resistance ductwork section(s), Pa
P_l = absolute value of pressure loss in low-resistance ductwork section(s), Pa

For systems conveying particulates, use elbows with a large centerline radius-to-diameter ratio (r/D), greater than 1.5 whenever possible. If r/D is 1.5 or less, abrasion in dust-handling systems can

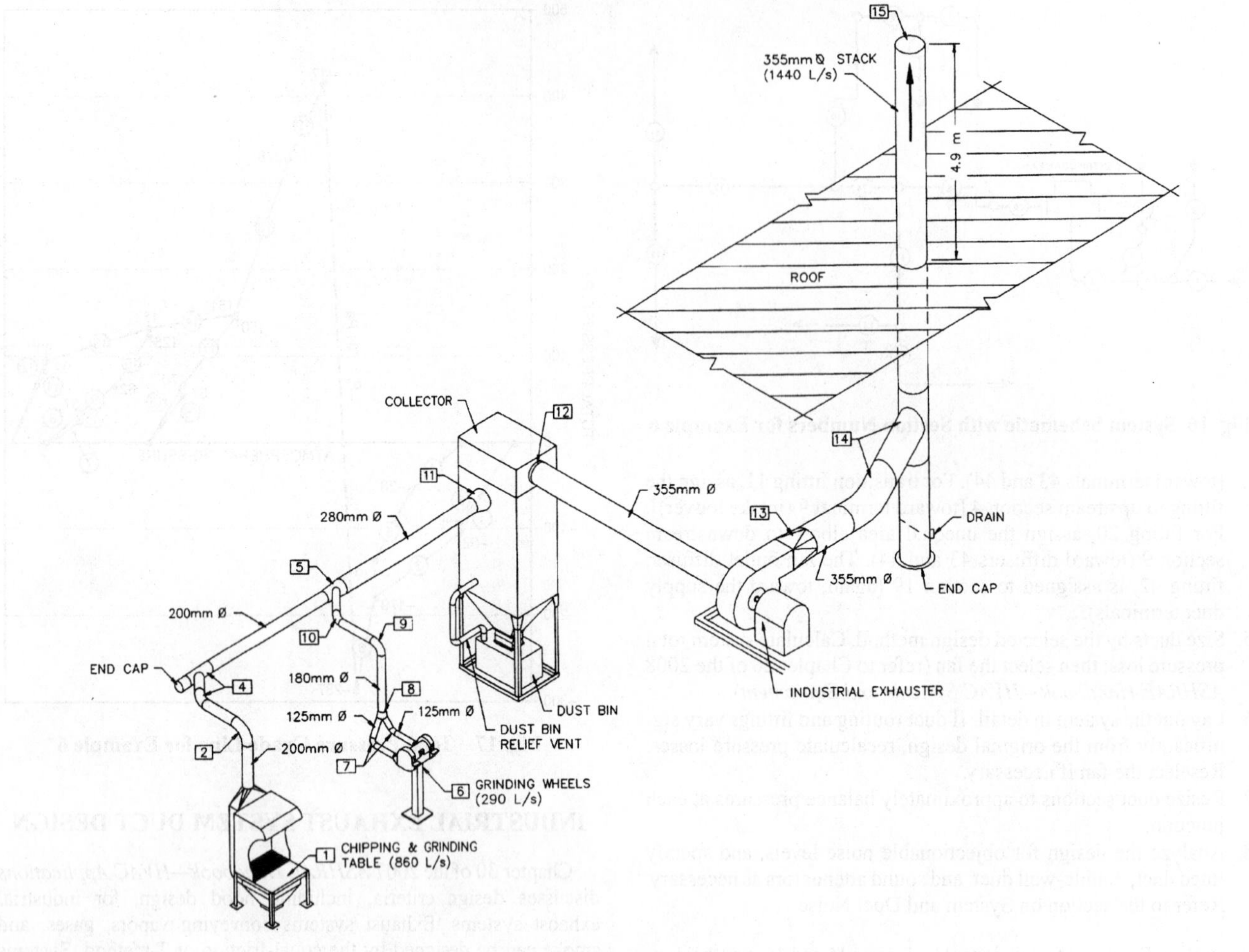

Fig. 18 Metalworking Exhaust System for Example 7

reduce the life of elbows. Elbows are often made of seven or more gores, especially in large diameters. For converging flow fittings, a 30° entry angle is recommended to minimize energy losses and abrasion in dust-handling systems. For the entry loss coefficients of hoods and equipment for specific operations, see Chapter 30 of the 2007 *ASHRAE Handbook—HVAC Applications* and ACGIH (2007).

Example 7. For the metalworking exhaust system in Figures 18 and 19, size the ductwork and calculate fan static pressure requirement for an industrial exhaust designed to convey granular materials. Pressure-balance the system by changing duct sizes and adjusting airflow rates. Minimum particulate transport velocity for the chipping and grinding table ducts (sections 1 and 5, Figure 19) is 20 m/s. For ducts associated with the grinder wheels (sections 2, 3, 4, and 5), minimum duct velocity is 23 m/s. Ductwork is galvanized steel, with absolute roughness of 0.09 mm. Use sizes for which spiral duct is available (80, 100, 125, 140, 150, 160, 180, 200, 224, 250, 280, 300, 315, 355, 400, 450, 500, 560, 600, 630, 710, 800, 900, 1000, 1120, 1250, 1300, 1400, 1500, 1600, 1800, 2000, 2100, 2200, 2300, 2400, and 2500 mm).

The building is one story, and the design wind velocity is 9 m/s. For the stack, use design J shown in Figure 2 in Chapter 44 of the 2007 *ASHRAE Handbook—HVAC Applications* for complete rain protection; stack height, determined by calculations from Chapter 44, is 4.9 m above the roof. This height is based on minimized stack downwash; therefore, the stack discharge velocity must exceed 1.5 times the design wind velocity.

Solution: The following table summarizes initial duct sizes and transport velocities for contaminated ducts upstream of the collector. The 22.8 m/s velocity in sections 2 and 3 is acceptable because the transport velocity is not significantly lower than 23 m/s. For the next available

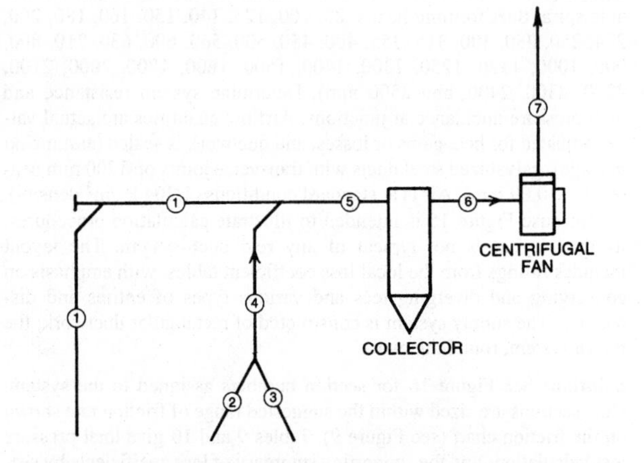

Fig. 19 System Schematic with Section Numbers for Example 7

duct size (160 mm diameter), duct velocity is 28.8 m/s, significantly higher than 23 m/s.

Duct Section	Design Airflow, L/s	Transport Velocity, m/s	Duct Diameter, mm	Duct Velocity, m/s
1	850	20	224	21.6
2, 3	290 each	23	125	23.6
4	580	23	180	22.8
5	1430	23	180	23.2

Design calculations up through the junction after sections 1 and 4 are summarized as follows:

Design No.	D_1, mm	Δp_1, Pa	Δp_{2+4}, Pa	Imbalance, $\Delta p_1 - \Delta p_{2+4}$
1	224	411	794	−383
2	200	762	850	−88
3	180	1320	712	+609

$Q_1 = 850$ L/s $Q_3 = 290$ L/s; $D_3 = 125$ mm dia.
$Q_2 = 290$ L/s; $D_2 = 125$ mm dia. $Q_4 = 850$ L/s; $D_4 = 180$ mm dia.

For (initial) design 1, the imbalance between section 1 and section 2 (or 3) is 383 Pa, with section 1 requiring additional resistance. Decreasing section 1 duct diameter by manufactured spiral duct sizes results in the least imbalance, 88 Pa, when the duct diameter is 200 mm (design 2). Because section 1 requires additional resistance, estimate the new airflow rate using Equation (44):

$$Q_{c,1} = 850(850/762)^{0.5} = 900 \text{ L/s}$$

At 900 L/s flow in section 1, 130 Pa imbalance remains at the junction of sections 1 and 4. By trial-and-error solution, balance is attained when the flow in section 1 is 860 L/s. The duct between the collector and fan inlet is 355 mm round to match the fan inlet (340 mm diameter). To minimize downwash, the stack discharge velocity must exceed 13.5 m/s, 1.5 times the design wind velocity (9 m/s) as stated in the problem definition. Therefore, the stack is 355 mm round, and the stack discharge velocity is 14.5 m/s.

Table 11 summarizes the system losses by sections. The straight duct friction factor and pressure loss were calculated by Equations (18) and (19). Table 12 lists fitting loss coefficients and input parameters necessary to determine the loss coefficients. The fitting loss coefficients are from the 2009 *ASHRAE Duct Fitting Database*. The fitting loss coefficient tables are included in the section on Fitting Loss Coefficients for illustration but cannot be obtained exactly by manual interpolation because the coefficients were calculated by the duct fitting database algorithms (more significant figures). Figure 20 shows a pressure grade line of the system. Fan total pressure, calculated by Equation (15), is 1992 Pa. To calculate the fan static pressure, use Equation (17):

$$P_s = 1992 - 192 = 1800 \text{ Pa}$$

where 192 Pa is the fan outlet velocity pressure. The fan airflow rate is 1440 L/s, and its outlet area is 0.081 m^3 (260 by 310 mm). Therefore, the fan outlet velocity is 17.9 m/s.

Hood suction for the chipping and grinding table hood is 560 Pa, calculated by Equation (5) from Chapter 30 of the 2007 *ASHRAE Handbook—HVAC Applications* [$P_{s,h}$ = (1 + 0.25)(451) = 560 Pa, where 0.25 is hood entry loss coefficient C_o, and 451 is duct velocity pressure P_v a few diameters downstream from the hood]. Similarly, hood suction for each grinder wheel is 170 Pa:

$$P_{2,3} = (1 + 0.4)(336) = 470 \text{ Pa}$$

where 0.4 is the hood entry loss coefficient, and 336 Pa is the duct velocity pressure.

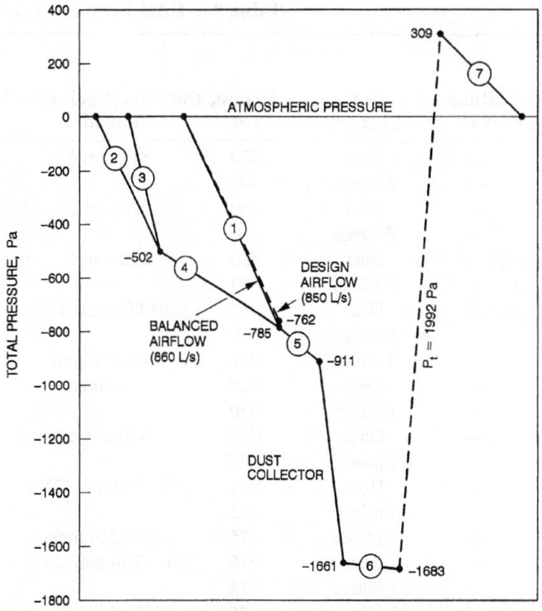

Fig. 20 Total Pressure Grade Line for Example 7

REFERENCES

Abushakra, B., I.S. Walker, and M.H. Sherman. 2002. A study of pressure losses in residential air distribution systems. *Proceedings of the ACEEE Summer Study 2002*, American Council for an Energy Efficient Economy, Washington, D.C. LBNL *Report* 49700. Lawrence Berkeley National Laboratory, CA.

Abushakra, B., I.S. Walker, and M.H. Sherman. 2004. Compression effects on pressure loss in flexible HVAC ducts. *International Journal of HVAC&R Research* (now *HVAC&R Research*)10(3):275-289.

ACGIH. 2007. *Industrial ventilation: A manual of recommended practice for design*, 26th ed. American Conference of Governmental Industrial Hygienists, Lansing, MI.

ADC. 2003. *Flexible duct performance and installation standards*, 4th ed. Air Diffusion Council, Schaumburg, IL.

AISI/SMACNA. 1972. *Measurement and analysis of leakage rates from seams and joints of air handling systems*. American Iron and Steel Institute, Washington, D.C., and Sheet Metal and Air Conditioning Contractors' National Association, Chantilly, VA.

AMCA. 2007. Laboratory method of testing louvers for rating. ANSI/AMCA *Standard* 500-L-07. Air Movement and Control Association International, Arlington Heights, IL.

AMCA. 2007a. Fans and systems. AMCA *Publication* 201-02 (R2007). Air Movement and Control Association International, Arlington Heights, IL.

AMCA. 2007b. Field performance measurement of fan systems. AMCA *Publication* 203-90 (R2007). Air Movement and Control Association International, Arlington Heights, IL.

ASHRAE. 2007. Laboratory methods for testing fans for certified aerodynamic performance rating. ANSI/ASHRAE *Standard* 51-07. Also ANSI/AMCA *Standard* 210-07.

ASHRAE. 2007. Energy standard for buildings except low-rise residential buildings. ANSI/ASHRAE/IESNA *Standard* 90.1-2007.

ASHRAE. 2007. Energy-efficient design of low-rise residential buildings. ANSI/ASHRAE *Standard* 90.2-2007.

ASHRAE. 2006. Energy conversation in existing buildings. ANSI/ASHRAE/IESNA *Standard* 100-2006.

ASHRAE. 2009. *ASHRAE duct fitting database*.

ASHRAE/SMACNA/TIMA. 1985. Investigation of duct leakage (RP-308). ASHRAE Research Project, *Final Report*.

Behls, H.F. 1971. Computerized calculation of duct friction. *Building Science Series* 39, p. 363. National Institute of Standards and Technology, Gaithersburg, MD.

Bellman, R.E. 1957. *Dynamic programming*. Princeton University, New York.

Brown, R.B. 1973. Experimental determinations of fan system effect factors. In *Fans and systems*, ASHRAE *Symposium Bulletin* LO-73-1, Louisville, KY (June).

Clarke, M.S., J.T. Barnhart, F.J. Bubsey, and E. Neitzel. 1978. The effects of system connections on fan performance. *ASHRAE Transactions* 84(2):227-263.

Colebrook, C.F. 1938-1939. Turbulent flow in pipes, with particular reference to the transition region between the smooth and rough pipe laws. *Journal of the Institution of Civil Engineers* 11:133.

Culp, C. and D. Cantrill. 2009. Static pressure losses in 12", 14", and 16" nonmetallic flexible ducts with compression and sag (RP-1333). *ASHRAE Transactions* 115(1).

Table 9 Total Pressure Loss Calculations by Sections for Example 6

Duct Section[a]	Fitting No.[b]	Duct Element	Airflow, L/s	Duct Size (Equivalent Round)	Velocity, m/s	Velocity Pressure, Pa	Duct Length,[c] m	Summary of Fitting Loss Coefficients[d]	Duct Pressure Loss,[e] Pa/m	Total Pressure Loss, Pa	Section Pressure Loss, Pa
1	—	Duct	700	315 mm ϕ	9.0	—	4.6	—	2.7	13	
	—	Fittings	700		9.0	49	—	0.80	—	39	52
2	—	Duct	250	224 mm ϕ	6.3	—	18.3	—	2.2	40	
	—	Fittings	250	—	6.3	24	—	–0.36	—	–9	31
3	—	Duct	950	315 mm ϕ	12.2	—	6.1	—	4.9	30	
	—	Fittings	950	—	12.2	89	—	1.09	—	97	127
4	—	Duct	950	600×600 mm (656)	2.6	—	1.5	—	0.1	0	
	—	Fittings	950	—	2.6	4	—	0.68	—	3	
	9	Louver	950	600×600 mm	—	—	—	—	—	25[f]	28
5	—	Duct	950	400 mm ϕ	7.6	—	18.3	—	1.5	27	
	—	Fittings	950	—	7.6	34	—	2.47	—	84	111
6	—	Duct	1900	450 mm ϕ	11.9	—	9.1	—	3.0	27	
	—	Fittings	1900	—	11.9	86	—	0.94	—	81	108
7	—	Duct	275	250×250 mm (273)	4.4	—	4.3	—	1.0	4	
	—	Fittings	275	—	4.4	12	—	0.26	—	3	
	43	Diffuser	275	250×250 mm	—	—	—	—	—	25[f]	32
8	—	Duct	275	250·×250 mm (273)	4.4	—	1.2	—	1.0	1	
	—	Fittings	275	—	4.4	12	—	0.91	—	11	
	44	Diffuser	275	250×250 mm	—	—	—	—	—	25[f]	37
9	—	Duct	550	500×250 mm (381)	4.4	—	7.6	—	0.7	5	
	—	Fittings	550	—	4.4	12	—	1.67	—	20	25
10	—	Duct	550	400×250 mm (343)	5.5	—	13.7	—	1.1	15	
	—	Fittings	550	—	5.5	18	—	2.69	—	48	63
11	—	Duct	475	250×250 mm (273)	7.6	—	3.0	—	2.7	8	
	—	Fittings	475	—	7.6	35	—	2.41	—	84	92
12	—	Duct	475	250×250 mm (273)	7.6	—	6.7	—	2.7	18	
	—	Fittings	475	—	7.6	35	—	2.30	—	80	98
13	—	Duct	950	420×250 mm (351)	9.0	—	10.7	—	2.8	30	
	—	Fittings	950	—	9.0	49	—	0.10	—	5	35
14	—	Duct	1500	660×250 mm (414)	9.1	—	4.6	—	2.4	11	
	—	Fittings	1500	—	9.1	50	—	0.13	—	7	18
15	—	Duct	200	200×150 mm (189)	6.7	—	12.2	—	3.3	40	
	—	Fittings	200	—	6.7	27	—	0.62	—	17	57
16	—	Duct	200	200×150 mm (189)	6.7	—	6.1	—	3.3	20	
	—	Fittings	200	—	6.7	27	—	1.87	—	50	70
17	—	Duct	400	230×150 mm (202)	11.6	—	4.2	—	8.7	36	
	—	Fittings	400	—	11.6	81	—	0.54	—	44	80
18	—	Duct	1900	800×250 mm (470)	9.5	—	7.0	—	2.4	17	
	—	Fittings	1900	—	9.5	54	—	2.93	—	158	175
19	—	Duct	1900	800×450 mm (649)	5.3	—	3.7	—	0.5	2	
	—	Fittings	1900	—	5.3	17	—	4.37	—	74	
	46	Air-meas. station	1900	—	—	—	—	—	—	15[f]	91

[a]See Figure 16.
[b]See Figure 15.
[c]Duct lengths are to fitting centerlines.
[d]See Table 10.
[e]Duct pressure based on 0.09 mm absolute roughness factor.
[f]Pressure drop based on manufacturers' data.

Table 10 Loss Coefficient Summary by Sections for Example 6

Duct Section	Fitting Number	Type of Fitting	ASHRAE Fitting No.*	Parameters	Loss Coefficient
1	1	Entry	ED1-3		0.03
	2	Damper	CD9-1	$\theta = 0°$	0.60
	3	Wye (30°), main	ED5-1	$A_s/A_c = 1.0$, $A_b/A_c = 0.506$, $Q_s/Q_c = 0.74$	0.17 (C_s)
	Summation of Section 1 loss coefficients				0.80
2	4	Entry	ED1-1	$L = 0$, $t = 1.61$ mm (16 gage)	0.50
	4	Screen	CD6-1	$n = 0.60$, $A_1/A_o = 1$	0.97
	5	Elbow	CD3-7	45°, $r/D = 1.5$, pleated	0.19
	6	Damper	CD9-1	$\theta = 0°$	0.60
	3	Wye (30°), branch	ED5-1	$A_s/A_c = 1.0$, $A_b/A_c = 0.506$, $Q_b/Q_c = 0.26$	–2.62 (C_b)
	Summation of Section 2 loss coefficients				0.03
3	7	Damper	CD9-1	$\theta = 0°$	0.60
	8	Wye (45°), main	ED5-2	$A_s/A_c = 0.498$, $A_b/A_c = 0.490$, $Q_s/Q_c = 0.5$	0.49 (C_s)
	Summation of Section 3 loss coefficients				1.09

*2009 *ASHRAE Duct Fitting Database* data for fittings reprinted in section on Fitting Loss Coefficients.

Table 10 Loss Coefficient Summary by Sections for Example 6 (*Concluded*)

Duct Section	Fitting Number	Type of Fitting	ASHRAE Fitting No.*	Parameters	Loss Coefficient
4	10	Damper	CR9-4	$\theta = 0°$	0.18
	11	Transition	ER4-3	L = 750 mm, $A_o/A_1 = 2.86$, $\theta = 15°$	0.50
Summation of Section 4 loss coefficients					0.90
5	12	Elbow	CD3-17	45°, mitered	0.71
	13	Damper	CD9-1	$\theta = 0°$	0.60
	8	Wye (45°), branch	ED5-2	$Q_b/Q_c = 0.5$, $A_s/A_c = 0.490$, $A_b/A_c = 0.790$	1.16 (C_b)
Summation of Section 5 loss coefficients					2.47
6	14	Fire damper	CD9-3	Curtain type, Type C	0.12
	15	Elbow	CD3-9	90°, 5 gore, r/D =1.5	0.15
	—	Fan and system interaction	ED7-2	90° elbow, 4 gore, r/D = 1.5, L = 900 mm	0.67
Summation of Section 6 loss coefficients					0.87
7	16	Elbow	CR3-3	90°, r/W = 0.70, 1 splitter vane	0.14
	17	Damper	CR9-1	$\theta = 0°$, $H/W = 1.0$	0.08
	19	Tee, main	SR5-13	$Q_s/Q_c = 0.5$, $A_s/A_c = 0.50$	0.04 (C_s)
Summation of Section 7 loss coefficients					0.26
8	19	Tee, branch	SR5-13	$Q_b/Q_c = 0.5$, $A_b/A_c = 0.50$	0.73 (C_b)
	18	Damper	CR9-3	$\theta = 0°$	0.18
Summation of Section 8 loss coefficients					0.91
9	20	Elbow	SR3-1	90°, mitered, $H/W_1 = 0.625$, $W_o/W_1 = 1.25$	1.67
Summation of Section 9 loss coefficients					1.67
10	21	Damper	CR9-1	$\theta = 0°$, $H/W = 0.625$	0.08
	22	Elbow	CR3-9	90°, single-thickness vanes, 40 mm vane spacing	0.11
	23	Elbow	CR3-6	$\theta = 90°$, mitered, $H/W = 0.625$	1.25
	24	Tee, branch	SR5-1	$r/W_b = 1.0$, $Q_b/Q_c = 0.367$, $A_s/A_c = 0.636$, $A_b/A_c = 0.606$	1.25 (C_b)
Summation of Section 10 loss coefficients					2.69
11	25	Damper	CR9-1	$\theta = 0°$, $H/W = 1.0$	0.08
	26	Exit	SR2-1	$H/W = 1.0$, Re = 125 800	1.00
	27	Bullhead tee w/o vanes	SR5-15	$Q_{b1}/Q_c = 0.5$, $A_{b1}/A_c = 0.595$	1.33 (C_b)
Summation of Section 11 loss coefficients					2.41
12	28	Damper	CR9-1	$\theta = 0°$, $H/W = 1.0$	0.08
	29	Exit	SR2-5	$\theta = 30°$, $A_1/A_o = 3.86$, Re = 126 000, L = 450 mm	0.89
	27	Bullhead tee w/o vanes	SR5-15	$Q_{b2}/Q_c = 0.5$, $A_{b2}/A_c = 0.595$	1.33 (C_b)
Summation of Section 12 loss coefficients					2.30
13	30	Damper	CR9-1	$\theta = 0°$, $H/W = 0.595$	0.08
	24	Tee, main	SR5-1	$r/W_b = 1.0$, $Q_s/Q_c = 0.63$, $A_s/A_c = 0.633$, $A_b/A_c = 0.606$	0.02 (C_s)
Summation of Section 13 loss coefficients					0.10
14	31	Damper	CR9-1	$\theta = 0°$, $H/W = 0.38$	0.08
	32	Tee, main	SR5-13	$Q_s/Q_c = 0.79$, $A_s/A_c = 0.825$	0.05 (C_s)
Summation of Section 14 loss coefficients					0.13
15	48	Elbow	CR3-1	$\theta = 90°$, $r/W = 1.5$, $H/W = 0.75$	0.19
	33	Exit	SR2-6	L = 500 mm, $D_h = 171$	0.26
	34	Damper	CR9-1	$\theta = 0°$, $H/W = 0.75$	0.08
	35	Tee, main	SR5-1	$r/W_b = 1.0$, $Q_s/Q_c = 0.5$, $A_s/A_c = 0.870$, $A_b/A_c = 0.870$	0.09 (C_s)
Summation of Section 15 loss coefficients					0.62
16	36	Exit	SR2-3	$\theta = 20°$, L = 500 mm, $A_1/A_o = 2.0$, Re = 76 000	0.63
	36	Screen	CR6-1	$n = 0.8$, $A_1/A_o = 2.06$	0.08
	37	Damper	CR9-1	$\theta = 0°$, $H/W = 0.75$	0.08
	35	Tee, branch	SR5-1	$r/W_b = 1.0$, $Q_b/Q_c = 0.5$, $A_s/A_c = 0.870$, $A_b/A_c = 0.870$	1.08 (C_b)
Summation of Section 16 loss coefficients					1.87
17	38	Damper	CR9-1	$\theta = 0°$, $H/W = 0.65$	0.08
	32	Tee, branch	SR5-13	$Q_b/Q_c = 0.21$, $A_b/A_c = 0.187$	0.46 (C_b)
Summation of Section 17 loss coefficients					0.54
18	39	Obstruction, pipe	CR6-4	Re = 16 000, $y = 0$, d = 25 mm, $S_m/A_o = 0.10$, $y/H = 0$	0.17
	40	Transition	SR4-1	$\theta = 25°$, $A_o/A_1 = 0.556$, L = 450 mm	0.04
	41	Elbows, Z-shaped	CR3-17	L = 1000 mm, L/W = 4.2 4.0, $H/W = 3.2$, Re = 240 000	2.53
	45	Fire damper	CR9-6	Curtain type, Type B	0.19
Summation of Section 18 loss coefficients					2.93
19	42	Diffuser, fan	SR7-17	$\theta_1 = 28°$, L = 1000 mm, $A_o/A_1 = 2.67$, $C_1 = 0.59$	4.19 (C_o)
	47	Damper	CR9-4	$\theta = 0°$	0.18
Summation of Section 19 loss coefficients					4.37

*2009 *ASHRAE Duct Fitting Database* data for fittings reprinted in section on Fitting Loss Coefficients

Table 11 Total Pressure Loss Calculations by Sections for Example 7

Duct Section[a]	Duct Element	Airflow, L/s	Duct Size	Velocity, m/s	Velocity Pressure, Pa	Duct Length,[b] m	Summary of Fitting Loss Coefficients[c]	Duct Pressure Loss, Pa/m[d]	Total Pressure Loss, Pa	Section Pressure Loss, Pa
1	Duct	860	200 mm ϕ	27.4	—	7.32	—	40	293	
	Fittings	860	—	27.4	451	—	1.09	—	492	785
2, 3	Duct	290	125 mm ϕ	23.6	—	2.7	—	54	146	
	Fittings	290	—	23.6	336	—	1.06	—	356	502
4	Duct	580	180 mm ϕ	22.8	—	3.84	—	32	123	
	Fittings	580	—	22.8	313	—	0.51	—	160	283
5	Duct	1440	280 mm ϕ	23.4	—	2.7	—	18.5	50	
	Fittings	1440	—	23.4	329	—	0.23	—	76	126
—	Collector,[e] fabric	1440	—	—	—	—	—	—	750	750
6	Duct	1440	355 mm ϕ	14.5	—	3.0	—	6	18	
	Fittings	1440	—	14.5	127	—	0.03	—	4	22
7	Duct	1440	355 mm ϕ	14.5	—	14.0	—	6	84	
	Fittings	1440	—	14.5	127	—	1.77	—	225	309

[a]See Figure 15.
[b]Duct lengths are to fitting centerlines.
[c]See Table 12.
[d]Duct pressure based on a 0.09 mm absolute roughness factor.
[e]Collector manufacturers set fabric bag cleaning mechanism to actuate at a pressure difference of 750 Pa between inlet and outlet plenums. Pressure difference across clean media is approximately 400 Pa.

Table 12 Loss Coefficient Summary by Sections for Example 7

Duct Section	Fitting Number	Type of Fitting	ASHRAE Fitting No.[a]	Parameters	Loss Coefficient
1	1	Hood[b]	—	Hood face area: 0.9 by 1.2 m	0.25
	2	Elbow	CD3-10	90°, 7 gore, $r/D = 2.5$	0.11
	4	Capped wye (45°), with 45° elbow	ED5-6	$A_b/A_c = 1$	0.61 (C_b)
	5	Wye (30°), main	ED5-1	$Q_s/Q_c = 0.60$, $A_s/A_c = 0.510$, $A_b/A_c = 0.413$	0.12 (C_s)
Summation of Section 1 loss coefficients					1.09
2,3	6	Hood[c]	—	Type hood: For double wheels, dia. = 560 mm each, wheel width = 100 mm each; type takeoff: tapered	0.40
	7	Elbow	CD3-12	90°, 3 gore, $r/D = 1.5$	0.34
	8	Symmetrical wye (60°)	ED5-9	$Q_b/Q_c = 0.5$, $A_{b1}/A_c = 0.482$, $A_{b2}/A_c = 0.482$	0.32 (C_b)
Summation of Sections 2 and 3 loss coefficients					1.06
4	9	Elbow	CD3-10	90°, 7 gore, $r/D = 2.5$	0.11
	10	Elbow	CD3-13	60°, 3 gore, $r/D = 1.5$	0.19
	5	Wye (30°), branch	ED5-1	$Q_b/Q_c = 0.40$, $A_s/A_c = 0.510$, $A_b/A_c = 0.413$	0.21 (C_b)
Summation of Section 4 loss coefficients					0.51
5	11	Exit, conical diffuser to collector	ED2-1	$L = 600$ mm, $L/D_o = 2.14$, $A_1/A_o \approx 21$	0.23
Summation of Section 5 loss coefficients					0.23
6	12	Entry, bellmouth from collector	ER2-1	$r/D_1 = 0.21$, $r = 75$ mm, $C_o = 4.69$	0.03 (C_1)
Summation of Section 6 loss coefficients					0.03
7	13	Diffuser, fan outlet[d]	SD4-2	Fan outlet size: 260 by 310 mm; $L = 460$ mm	0.16
	14	Capped wye (45°), with 45° elbow	ED5-6	$A_b/A_c = 1$	0.61 (C_b)
	15	Stackhead	SD2-6	$D_e/D = 1$	1.0
Summation of Section 7 loss coefficients					1.77

[a]*ASHRAE Duct Fitting Database* (2009) data for fittings reprinted in the section on Fitting Loss Coefficients.
[b]From *Industrial Ventilation* (ACGIH 2007, Figure VS-80-19).
[c]From *Industrial Ventilation* (ACGIH 2007, Figure VS-80-11).
[d]Fan specified: Industrial exhauster for granular materials: 530 mm wheel diameter, 340 mm inlet diameter, 260 by 310 mm outlet, 6 kW motor.

Farajian, T., G. Grewal, and R.J. Tsal. 1992. Post-accident air leakage analysis in a nuclear facility via T-method airflow simulation. *Proceedings of the 22nd DOE/NRC Nuclear Air Cleaning and Treatment Conference*, Denver, CO, vol. 1, pp. 374-392. (Available at www.hss.energy.gov/CSA/CSP/hepa/Nureg_22nd/session8.pdf.)

Farquhar, H.F. 1973. System effect values for fans. In *Fans and systems*, ASHRAE *Symposium Bulletin* LO-73-1, Louisville, KY (June).

Griggs, E.I. and F. Khodabakhsh-Sharifabad. 1992. Flow characteristics in rectangular ducts (RP-549). *ASHRAE Transactions* 98(1):116-127.

Griggs, E.I., W.B. Swim, and G.H. Henderson. 1987. Resistance to flow of round galvanized ducts. *ASHRAE Transactions* 93(1):3-16.

Heyt, J.W. and M.J. Diaz. 1975. Pressure drop in flat-oval spiral air duct. *ASHRAE Transactions* 81(2):221-232.

Huebscher, R.G. 1948. Friction equivalents for round, square and rectangular ducts. *ASHVE Transactions* 54:101-118.

Hutchinson, F.W. 1953. Friction losses in round aluminum ducts. *ASHVE Transactions* 59:127-138.

Idelchik, I.E., M.O. Steinberg, G.R. Malyavskaya, and O.G. Martynenko. 1994. *Handbook of hydraulic resistance*, 3rd ed. CRC Press/Begell House, Boca Raton.

Jones, C.D. 1979. *Friction factor and roughness of United Sheet Metal Company spiral duct.* United Sheet Metal, Division of United McGill Corp., Westerville, OH (August). Based on data in *Friction loss tests*, United Sheet Metal Company Spiral Duct, Ohio State University Engineering Experiment Station, File No. T-1011, September 1958.

Klote, J.H. and J.A. Milke. 2002. *Principles of smoke management.* ASHRAE.

Kulkarni, D., S. Khaire, and S. Idem. 2009. Pressure loss of corrugated spiral duct. *ASHRAE Transactions* 115(1).

Meyer, M.L. 1973. A new concept: The fan system effect factor. In *Fans and systems*, ASHRAE *Symposium Bulletin* LO-73-1, Louisville, KY (June).

Moody, L.F. 1944. Friction factors for pipe flow. *ASME Transactions* 66:671.

NAIMA. 2002. *Fibrous glass duct construction standards*, 5th ed. North American Insulation Manufacturers Association.

NFPA. 2002. Installation of air-conditioning and ventilating systems. ANSI/NFPA *Standard* 90A. National Fire Protection Association, Quincy, MA.

NFPA. 2008. *Fire protection handbook*. National Fire Protection Association. Quincy, MA.

Osborne, W.C. 1966. *Fans*. Pergamon, London.

SMACNA. 1985. *HVAC air duct leakage test manual*. Sheet Metal and Air Conditioning Contractors' National Association, Chantilly, VA.

SMACNA. 2003. *Fibrous glass duct construction standards*, 7th ed. Sheet Metal and Air Conditioning Contractors' National Association, Chantilly, VA.

SMACNA. 2005. *HVAC duct construction standards—Metal and flexible*, 3rd ed. ANSI. Sheet Metal and Air Conditioning Contractors' National Association, Chantilly, VA.

Smith, G.W. 1968. *Engineering economy: Analysis of capital expenditures*. Iowa State University, Ames.

Swim, W.B. 1978. Flow losses in rectangular ducts lined with fiberglass. *ASHRAE Transactions* 84(2):216.

Swim, W.B. 1982. Friction factor and roughness for airflow in plastic pipe. *ASHRAE Transactions* 88(1):269.

Swim, W.B. and E.I. Griggs. 1995. Duct leakage measurement and analysis. *ASHRAE Transactions* 101(1):274-291.

Tsal, R.J. and M.S. Adler. 1987. Evaluation of numerical methods for ductwork and pipeline optimization. *ASHRAE Transactions* 93(1):17-34.

Tsal, R.J., H.F. Behls, and R. Mangel. 1988. T-method duct design, Part I: Optimization theory; Part II: Calculation procedure and economic analysis. *ASHRAE Transactions* 94(2):90-111.

Tsal, R.J., H.F. Behls, and R. Mangel. 1990. T-method duct design, Part III: Simulation. *ASHRAE Transactions* 96(2).

UL. Published annually. *Building materials directory*. Underwriters Laboratories, Northbrook, IL.

UL. Published annually. *Fire resistance directory*. Underwriters Laboratories, Northbrook, IL.

UL. 2005. Factory-made air ducts and air connectors, 10th ed. ANSI/UL *Standard* 181. Underwriters Laboratories, Northbrook, IL.

UL. 2005. Closure systems for use with rigid air ducts and air connectors, 3rd ed. ANSI/UL *Standard* 181A. Underwriters Laboratories, Northbrook, IL.

UL. 2005. Closure systems for use with rigid air ducts and air connectors, 2nd ed. ANSI/UL *Standard* 181B. Underwriters Laboratories, Northbrook, IL.

UL. 1999. Fire dampers, 6th ed. *Standard* UL 555. Underwriters Laboratories, Northbrook, IL.

UL. 1999. Smoke dampers. UL Standard 555S. Underwriters Laboratories, Northbrook, IL.

Wright, D.K., Jr. 1945. A new friction chart for round ducts. *ASHVE Transactions* 51:303-316.

FITTING LOSS COEFFICIENTS

Fittings to support Examples 6 and 7 and some of the more common fittings are reprinted here.

For the complete fitting database see the *ASHRAE Duct Fitting Database* (ASHRAE 2009).

ROUND FITTINGS

CD3-1 Elbow, Die Stamped, 90 Degree, r/D = 1.5

D, mm	75	100	125	150	180	200	230	250
C_o	0.30	0.21	0.16	0.14	0.12	0.11	0.11	0.11

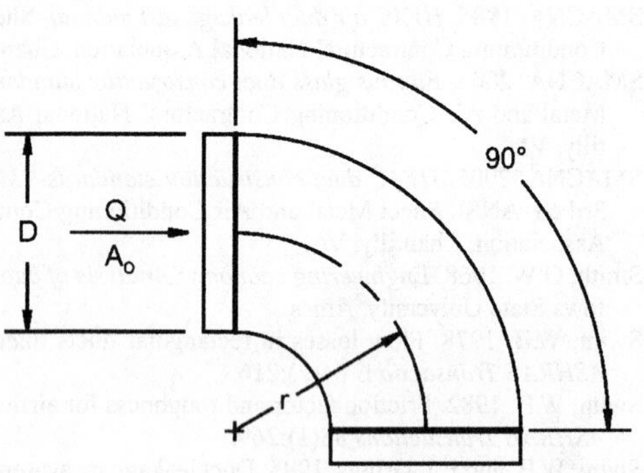

CD3-3 Elbow, Die Stamped, 45 Degree, r/D = 1.5

D, mm	75	100	125	150	180	200	230	250
C_o	0.18	0.13	0.10	0.08	0.07	0.07	0.07	0.07

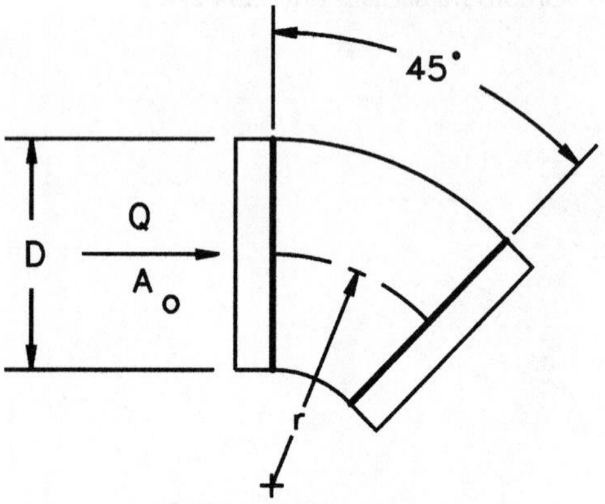

CD3-5 Elbow, Pleated, 90 Degree, r/D = 1.5

D, mm	100	150	200	250	300	350	400
C_o	0.57	0.43	0.34	0.28	0.26	0.25	0.25

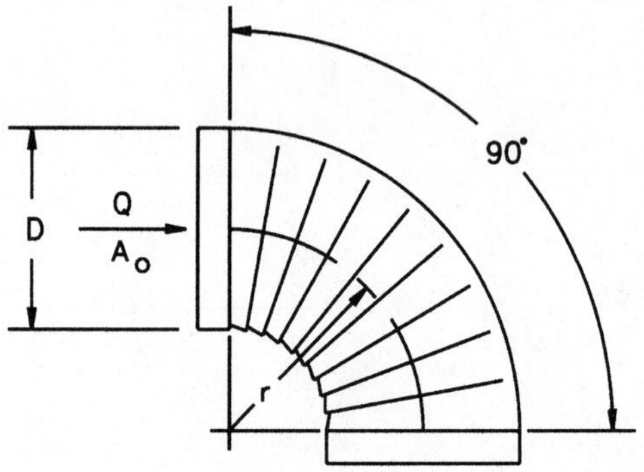

CD3-7 Elbow, Pleated, 45 Degree, r/D = 1.5

D, mm	100	150	200	250	300	350	400
C_o	0.34	0.26	0.21	0.17	0.16	0.15	0.15

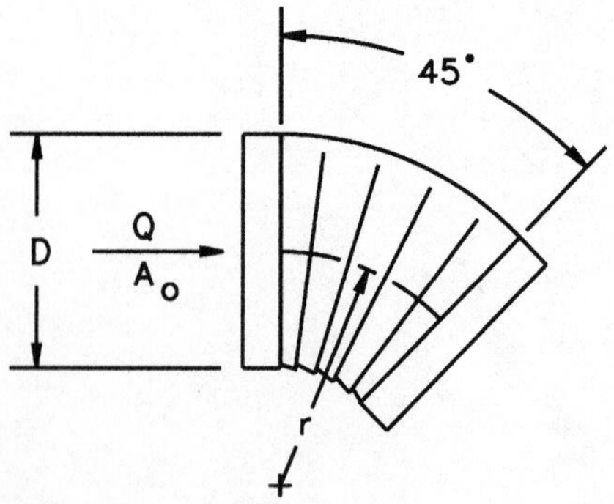

CD3-9 Elbow, 5 Gore, 90 Degree, $r/D = 1.5$

D, mm	75	150	230	300	380	450	530	600	690	750	1500
C_o	0.51	0.28	0.21	0.18	0.16	0.15	0.14	0.13	0.12	0.12	0.12

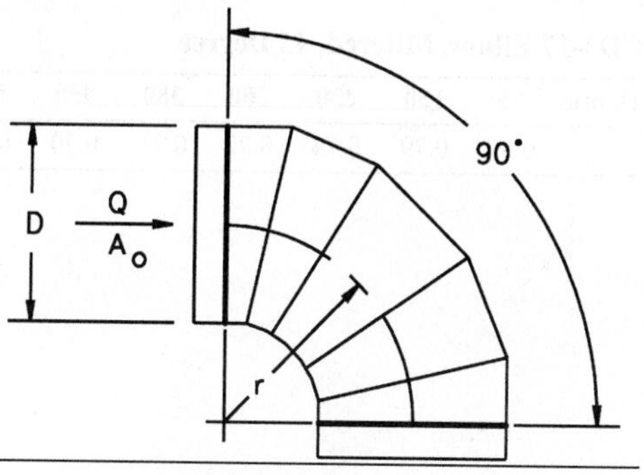

CD3-10 Elbow, 7 Gore, 90 Degree, $r/D = 2.5$

D, mm	75	150	230	300	380	450	690	1500
C_o	0.16	0.12	0.10	0.08	0.07	0.06	0.05	0.03

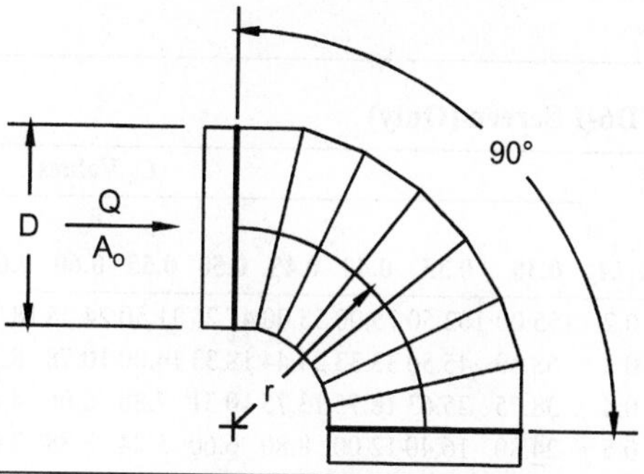

CD3-12 Elbow, 3 Gore, 90 Degree, $r/D = 0.75$ to 2.0

r/D	0.75	1.00	1.50	2.00
C_o	0.54	0.42	0.34	0.33

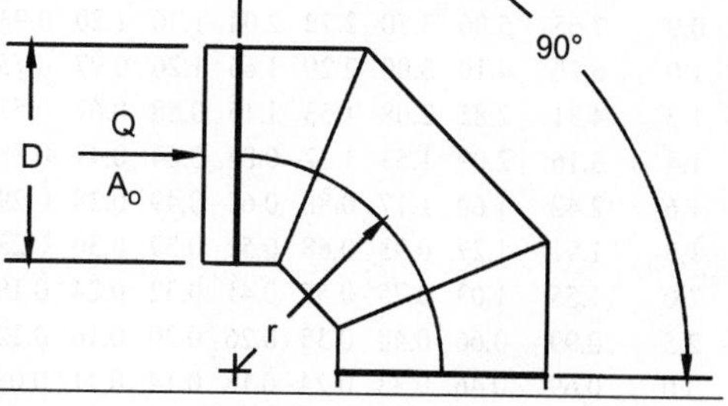

CD3-13 Elbow, 3 Gore, 60 Degree, $r/D = 1.5$

D, mm	75	150	230	300	380	450	530	600	690	750	1500
C_o	0.40	0.21	0.16	0.14	0.12	0.12	0.11	0.10	0.09	0.09	0.09

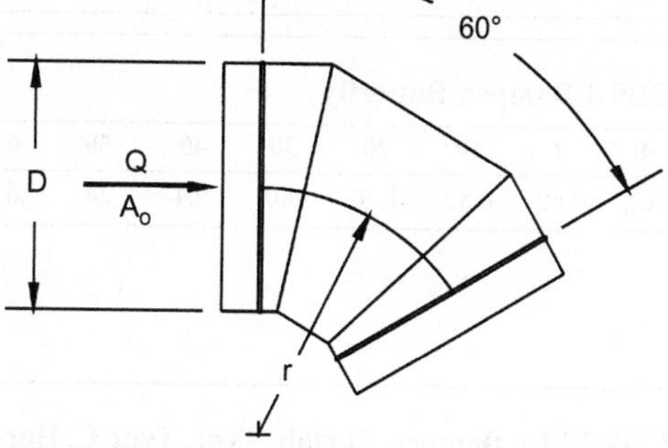

CD3-14 Elbow, 3 Gore, 45 Degree, $r/D = 1.5$

D, mm	75	150	230	300	380	450	530	600	690	750	1500
C_o	0.31	0.17	0.13	0.11	0.11	0.09	0.08	0.08	0.07	0.07	0.07

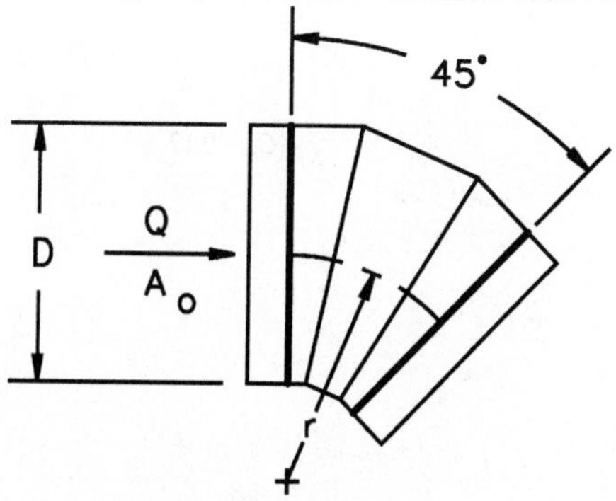

CD3-17 Elbow, Mitered, 45 Degree

D, mm	75	150	230	300	380	450	530	600	690	1500
C_o	0.87	0.79	0.74	0.72	0.71	0.70	0.69	0.68	0.68	0.67

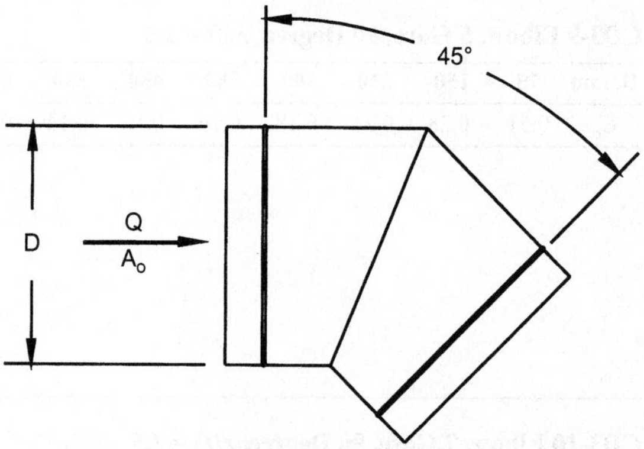

CD6-1 Screen (Only)

	C_o Values												
	n												
A_1/A_o	0.30	0.35	0.40	0.45	0.50	0.55	0.60	0.65	0.70	0.75	0.80	0.90	1.00
0.2	155.00	102.50	75.00	55.00	41.25	31.50	24.25	18.75	14.50	11.00	8.00	3.50	0.0
0.3	68.89	45.56	33.33	24.44	18.33	14.00	10.78	8.33	6.44	4.89	3.56	1.56	0.0
0.4	38.75	25.63	18.75	13.75	10.31	7.88	6.06	4.69	3.63	2.75	2.00	0.88	0.0
0.5	24.80	16.40	12.00	8.80	6.60	5.04	3.88	3.00	2.32	1.76	1.28	0.56	0.0
0.6	17.22	11.39	8.33	6.11	4.58	3.50	2.69	2.08	1.61	1.22	0.89	0.39	0.0
0.7	12.65	8.37	6.12	4.49	3.37	2.57	1.98	1.53	1.18	0.90	0.65	0.29	0.0
0.8	9.69	6.40	4.69	3.44	2.58	1.97	1.52	1.17	0.91	0.69	0.50	0.22	0.0
0.9	7.65	5.06	3.70	2.72	2.04	1.56	1.20	0.93	0.72	0.54	0.40	0.17	0.0
1.0	6.20	4.10	3.00	2.20	1.65	1.26	0.97	0.75	0.58	0.44	0.32	0.14	0.0
1.2	4.31	2.85	2.08	1.53	1.15	0.88	0.67	0.52	0.40	0.31	0.22	0.10	0.0
1.4	3.16	2.09	1.53	1.12	0.84	0.64	0.49	0.38	0.30	0.22	0.16	0.07	0.0
1.6	2.42	1.60	1.17	0.86	0.64	0.49	0.38	0.29	0.23	0.17	0.13	0.05	0.0
1.8	1.91	1.27	0.93	0.68	0.51	0.39	0.30	0.23	0.18	0.14	0.10	0.04	0.0
2.0	1.55	1.03	0.75	0.55	0.41	0.32	0.24	0.19	0.15	0.11	0.08	0.04	0.0
2.5	0.99	0.66	0.48	0.35	0.26	0.20	0.16	0.12	0.09	0.07	0.05	0.02	0.0
3.0	0.69	0.46	0.33	0.24	0.18	0.14	0.11	0.08	0.06	0.05	0.04	0.02	0.0
4.0	0.39	0.26	0.19	0.14	0.10	0.08	0.06	0.05	0.04	0.03	0.02	0.01	0.0
6.0	0.17	0.11	0.08	0.06	0.05	0.04	0.03	0.02	0.02	0.01	0.01	0.00	0.0

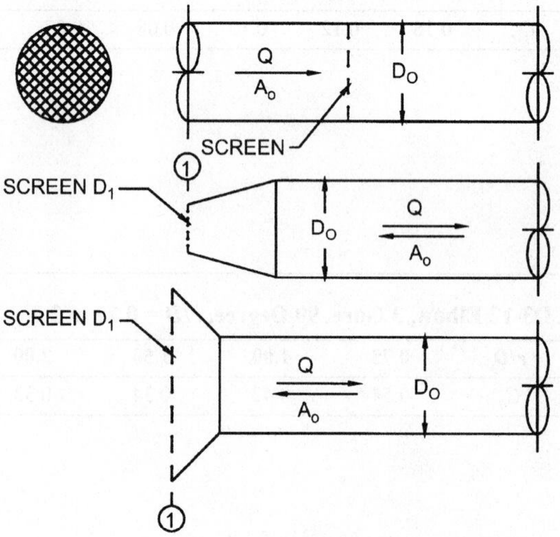

n = free area ratio of screen
A_o = area of duct
A_1 = cross-sectional area of duct or fitting where screen is located

CD9-1 Damper, Butterfly

θ	0	10	20	30	40	50	60	70	75	90
C_o	0.60	0.85	1.70	4.0	9.4	24	67	215	400	9999

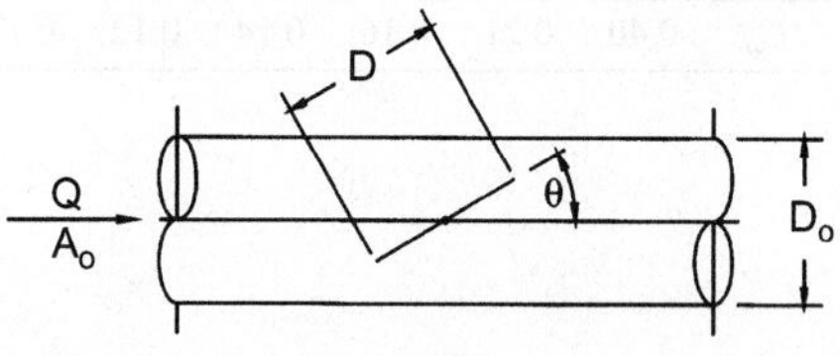

$$\frac{D}{D_o} = 0.98$$

CD9-3 Fire Damper, Curtain Type, Type C, Horizontal Duct

$C_o = 0.12$

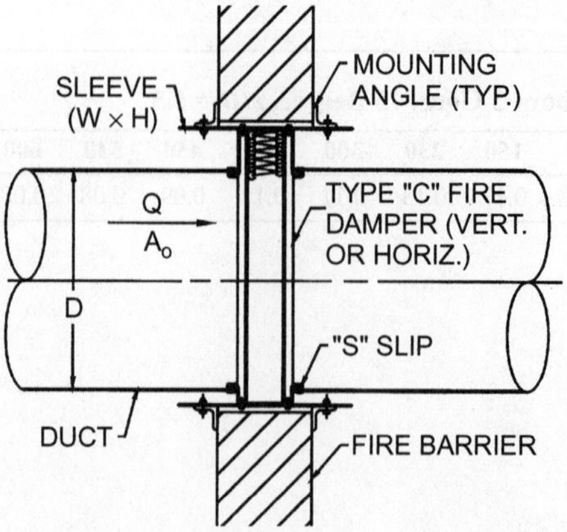

ED1-1 Duct Mounted in Wall

	C_o Values								
	L/D								
t/D	0.0	0.002	0.01	0.05	0.10	0.20	0.30	0.50	10.0
0.00	0.50	0.57	0.68	0.80	0.86	0.92	0.97	1.00	1.00
0.02	0.50	0.51	0.52	0.55	0.60	0.66	0.69	0.72	0.72
0.05	0.50	0.50	0.50	0.50	0.50	0.50	0.50	0.50	0.50
10.00	0.50	0.50	0.50	0.50	0.50	0.50	0.50	0.50	0.50

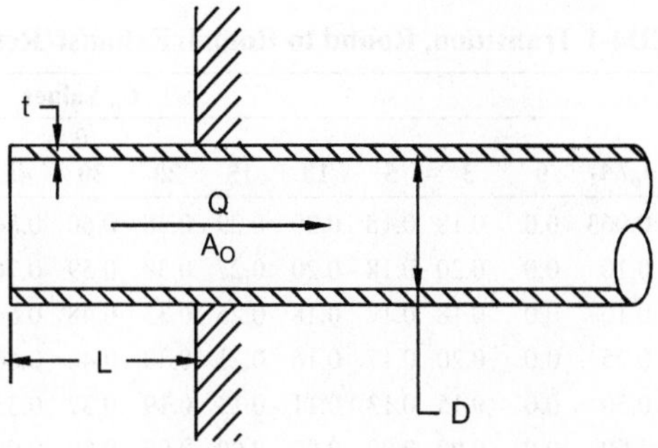

ED1-3 Bellmouth, with Wall

r/D	0.0	0.01	0.02	0.03	0.04	0.05	0.06	0.08	0.10	0.12	0.16	0.20	10.0
C_o	0.50	0.44	0.37	0.31	0.26	0.22	0.20	0.15	0.12	0.09	0.06	0.03	0.03

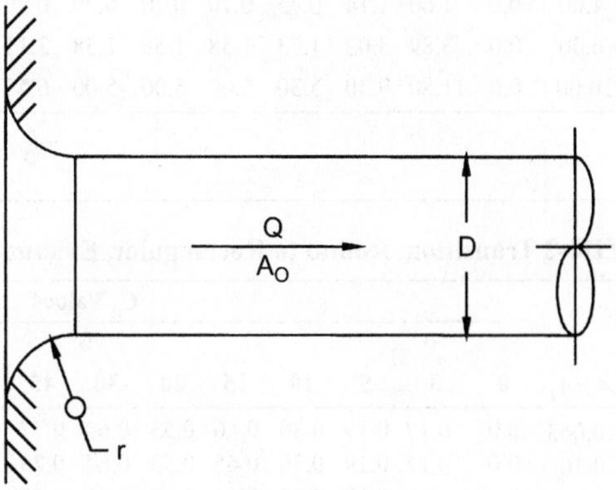

ED2-1 Conical Diffuser, Round to Plenum, Exhaust/Return Systems

	C_o Values										
	L/D_o										
A_1/A_o	0.5	1.0	2.0	3.0	4.0	5.0	6.0	8.0	10.0	12.0	14.0
1.0	0.00	0.00	0.00	0.00	0.00	0.00	0.00	0.00	0.00	0.00	0.00
1.5	0.03	0.02	0.03	0.03	0.04	0.05	0.06	0.08	0.10	0.11	0.13
2.0	0.08	0.06	0.04	0.04	0.04	0.05	0.05	0.06	0.08	0.09	0.10
2.5	0.13	0.09	0.06	0.06	0.06	0.06	0.06	0.06	0.07	0.08	0.09
3.0	0.17	0.12	0.09	0.07	0.07	0.06	0.06	0.07	0.07	0.08	0.08
4.0	0.23	0.17	0.12	0.10	0.09	0.08	0.08	0.08	0.08	0.08	0.08
6.0	0.30	0.22	0.16	0.13	0.12	0.10	0.10	0.09	0.09	0.09	0.08
8.0	0.34	0.26	0.18	0.15	0.13	0.12	0.11	0.10	0.09	0.09	0.09
10.0	0.36	0.28	0.20	0.16	0.14	0.13	0.12	0.11	0.10	0.09	0.09
14.0	0.39	0.30	0.22	0.18	0.16	0.14	0.13	0.12	0.10	0.10	0.10
20.0	0.41	0.32	0.24	0.20	0.17	0.15	0.14	0.12	0.11	0.11	0.10
1000.0	0.41	0.32	0.24	0.20	0.17	0.15	0.14	0.12	0.11	0.11	0.10

	Optimum Angle θ, degrees										
A_1/A_o	0.5	1.0	2.0	3.0	4.0	5.0	6.0	8.0	10.0	12.0	14.0
1.0	0	0	0	0	0	0	0	0	0	0	0
1.5	17	10	6.5	4.5	3.5	2.8	2.2	1.7	1.2	1.0	0.8
2.0	21	14	8.5	6.2	5.0	4.3	3.8	3.0	2.3	2.0	1.6
2.5	25	16	10	7.4	6.0	5.4	4.8	4.0	3.5	3.0	2.5
3.0	27	17	11	8.5	7.0	6.1	5.6	4.8	4.2	3.8	3.2
4.0	29	20	13	9.8	8.0	7.2	6.6	5.8	5.2	4.8	4.4
6.0	31	21	14	11	9.4	8.2	7.4	6.2	5.6	5.2	4.7
8.0	32	22	15	12	10	8.8	8.0	6.6	5.8	5.4	5.0
33	33	23	15	12	11	9.4	8.4	7.0	6.2	5.5	5.2
14.0	33	24	16	13	11	9.6	8.7	7.3	6.3	5.6	5.4
20.0	34	24	16	13	11	9.8	9.0	7.5	6.5	6.0	5.6
1000.0	34	24	16	13	11	9.8	9.0	7.5	6.5	6.0	5.6

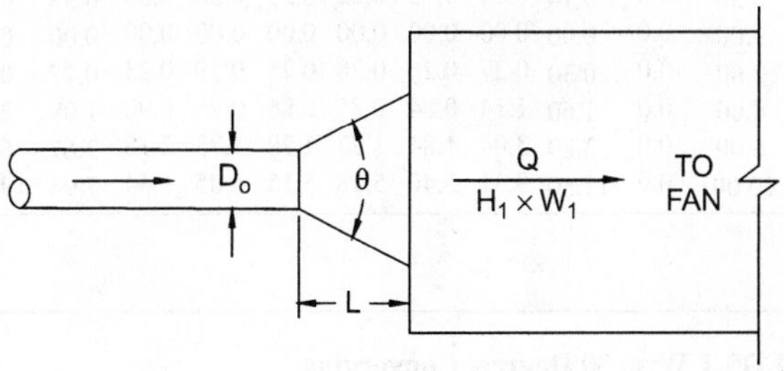

ED4-1 Transition, Round to Round, Exhaust/Return Systems

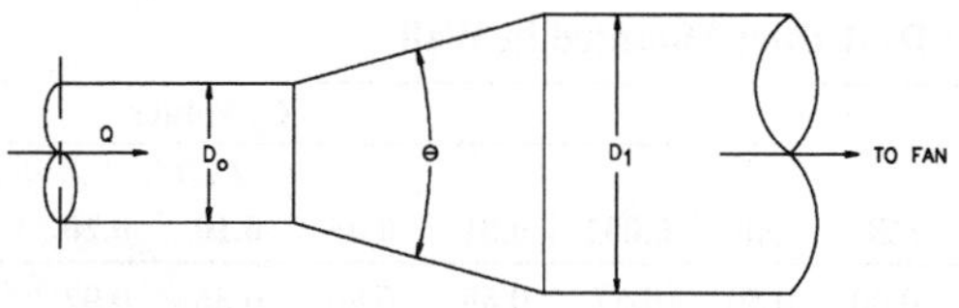

	C_o Values												
	θ												
A_o/A_1	0	3	5	10	15	20	30	45	60	90	120	150	180
0.063	0.0	0.18	0.18	0.20	0.29	0.38	0.60	0.84	0.88	0.88	0.88	0.88	0.88
0.10	0.0	0.20	0.18	0.20	0.27	0.38	0.59	0.76	0.80	0.83	0.84	0.83	0.83
0.167	0.0	0.18	0.17	0.18	0.25	0.33	0.48	0.66	0.77	0.74	0.73	0.73	0.72
0.25	0.0	0.20	0.17	0.16	0.21	0.30	0.46	0.61	0.68	0.64	0.63	0.62	0.62
0.50	0.0	0.15	0.13	0.11	0.13	0.19	0.32	0.33	0.33	0.32	0.31	0.30	0.30
1.00	0.0	0.00	0.00	0.00	0.00	0.00	0.00	0.00	0.00	0.00	0.00	0.00	0.00
2.00	0.0	0.30	0.26	0.21	0.19	0.19	0.19	0.23	0.27	0.51	0.73	0.90	0.95
4.00	0.0	1.60	1.14	0.75	0.70	0.70	0.70	0.90	1.09	2.78	4.29	5.63	6.53
6.00	0.0	3.89	3.02	1.73	1.58	1.58	1.58	2.12	2.66	6.62	10.01	13.03	15.12
10.00	0.0	11.80	9.30	5.30	5.00	5.00	5.00	6.45	7.90	19.00	28.50	36.70	42.70

ED4-2 Transition, Round to Rectangular, Exhaust/Return Systems

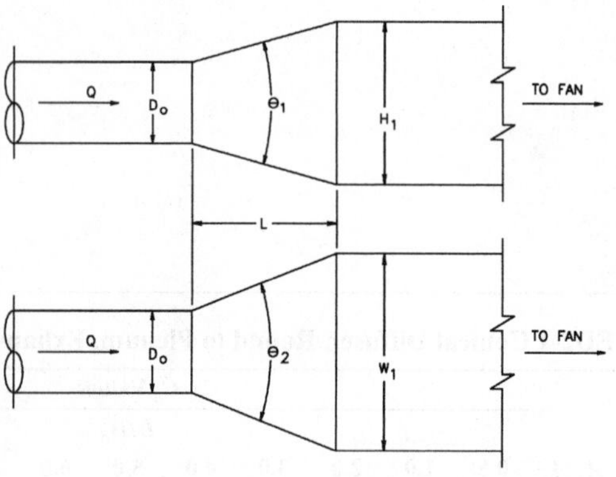

	C_o Values												
	θ												
A_o/A_1	0	3	5	10	15	20	30	45	60	90	120	150	180
0.063	0.0	0.17	0.19	0.30	0.46	0.53	0.64	0.77	0.88	0.95	0.95	0.94	0.93
0.10	0.0	0.17	0.19	0.30	0.45	0.53	0.64	0.75	0.84	0.89	0.89	0.89	0.88
0.167	0.0	0.18	0.19	0.30	0.44	0.53	0.63	0.72	0.78	0.79	0.79	0.79	0.79
0.25	0.0	0.16	0.18	0.25	0.36	0.45	0.52	0.58	0.62	0.64	0.64	0.64	0.64
0.50	0.0	0.14	0.14	0.15	0.22	0.25	0.30	0.33	0.33	0.33	0.32	0.31	0.30
1.00	0.0	0.00	0.00	0.00	0.00	0.00	0.00	0.00	0.00	0.00	0.00	0.00	0.00
2.00	0.0	0.30	0.27	0.26	0.28	0.25	0.19	0.23	0.27	0.52	0.75	0.91	0.95
4.00	0.0	1.60	1.14	0.84	0.85	0.86	0.76	0.90	1.09	2.78	4.30	5.65	6.55
6.00	0.0	3.89	3.04	1.84	1.77	1.78	1.73	2.18	2.67	6.67	10.07	13.09	15.18
10.00	0.0	11.80	9.31	5.40	5.18	5.15	5.05	6.44	7.94	19.06	28.55	36.75	42.75

ED5-1 Wye, 30 Degree, Converging

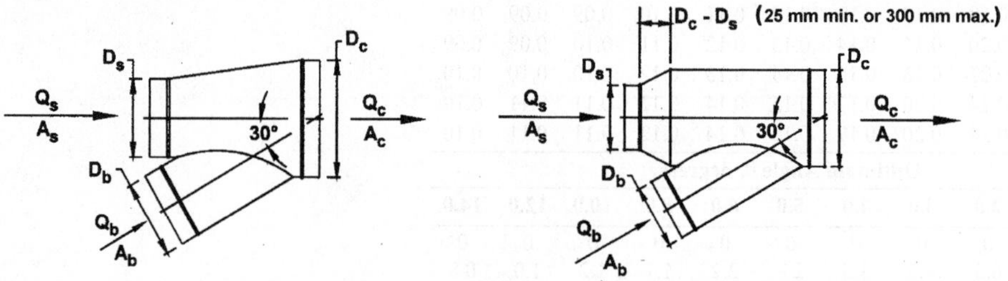

		C_b Values								
		Q_b/Q_c								
A_s/A_c	A_b/A_c	0.1	0.2	0.3	0.4	0.5	0.6	0.7	0.8	0.9
0.1	0.1	−13.25	−1.80	0.01	0.55	0.75	0.84	0.88	0.91	0.97
	0.2	−56.10	−10.12	−2.80	−0.63	0.19	0.53	0.69	0.75	0.78
	0.3	−127.28	−23.81	−7.31	−2.44	−0.59	0.19	0.52	0.66	0.70
	0.4	−226.84	−42.88	−13.55	−4.89	−1.61	−0.22	0.38	0.62	0.68
	0.5	−354.79	−67.34	−21.52	−7.98	−2.86	−0.69	0.24	0.61	0.70
	0.6	−511.13	−97.21	−31.22	−11.73	−4.35	−1.23	0.11	0.64	0.77
	0.7	−695.87	−132.47	−42.66	−16.13	−6.08	−1.84	0.00	0.71	0.89
	0.8	−909.01	−173.14	−55.83	−21.17	−8.05	−2.51	−0.12	0.82	1.05
	0.9	−1151.	−219.20	−70.73	−26.87	−10.27	−3.25	−0.22	0.97	1.26
	1.0	−1420.	−270.66	−87.36	−33.21	−12.72	−4.05	−0.31	1.15	1.51

ED5-1 Wye, 30 Degree, Converging (*Continued*)

		C_b Values (*Continued*)								
		Q_b/Q_c								
A_s/A_c	A_b/A_c	0.1	0.2	0.3	0.4	0.5	0.6	0.7	0.8	0.9
0.2	0.1	−5.30	−0.24	0.54	0.77	0.85	0.88	0.90	0.93	0.98
	0.2	−24.17	−3.78	−0.60	0.30	0.64	0.77	0.83	0.88	0.98
	0.3	−55.88	−9.77	−2.57	−0.50	0.25	0.55	0.67	0.70	0.71
	0.4	−99.93	−17.94	−5.13	−1.45	−0.11	0.42	0.62	0.68	0.68
	0.5	−156.51	−28.40	−8.37	−2.62	−0.52	0.30	0.62	0.71	0.69
	0.6	−225.62	−41.13	−12.30	−4.01	−0.99	0.20	0.66	0.78	0.75
	0.7	−307.26	−56.14	−16.90	−5.61	−1.51	0.11	0.73	0.90	0.86
	0.8	−401.44	−73.44	−22.18	−7.44	−2.08	0.04	0.84	1.06	1.01
	0.9	−508.15	−93.02	−28.15	−9.49	−2.71	−0.03	0.99	1.27	1.20
	1.0	−627.39	−114.89	−34.80	−11.77	−3.39	−0.08	1.18	1.52	1.43
0.3	0.1	−2.77	0.26	0.71	0.83	0.88	0.90	0.91	0.93	0.99
	0.2	−13.97	−1.77	0.08	0.59	0.77	0.84	0.88	0.92	1.06
	0.3	−33.06	−5.33	−1.09	0.10	0.51	0.66	0.71	0.72	0.74
	0.4	−59.43	−10.08	−2.52	−0.41	0.32	0.59	0.67	0.68	0.66
	0.5	−93.24	−16.11	−4.30	−1.00	0.14	0.56	0.69	0.70	0.66
	0.6	−134.51	−23.45	−6.44	−1.68	−0.03	0.57	0.76	0.77	0.70
	0.7	−183.25	−32.08	−8.93	−2.45	−0.21	0.61	0.87	0.88	0.79
	0.8	−239.47	−42.01	−11.77	−3.32	−0.38	0.69	1.02	1.03	0.91
	0.9	−303.16	−53.25	−14.97	−4.27	−0.56	0.80	1.21	1.23	1.07
	1.0	−374.32	−65.79	−18.53	−5.32	−0.73	0.94	1.45	1.47	1.27
0.4	0.1	−1.58	0.48	0.78	0.86	0.89	0.90	0.91	0.93	0.99
	0.2	−9.20	−0.85	0.39	0.71	0.82	0.87	0.90	0.94	1.09
	0.3	−22.31	−3.24	−0.38	0.39	0.64	0.73	0.76	0.78	0.85
	0.4	−40.52	−6.48	−1.37	0.02	0.48	0.64	0.67	0.66	0.65
	0.5	−63.71	−10.50	−2.50	−0.33	0.40	0.63	0.69	0.67	0.63
	0.6	−92.00	−15.37	−3.84	−0.71	0.33	0.67	0.75	0.71	0.65
	0.7	−125.40	−21.08	−5.40	−1.13	0.28	0.75	0.85	0.80	0.70
	0.8	−163.90	−27.65	−7.16	−1.59	0.25	0.86	1.00	0.93	0.80
	0.9	−207.52	−35.07	−9.14	−2.09	0.25	1.02	1.18	1.10	0.93
	1.0	−256.25	−43.35	−11.33	−2.63	0.26	1.21	1.42	1.31	1.09
0.5	0.1	−0.94	0.60	0.82	0.87	0.89	0.90	0.91	0.93	0.99
	0.2	−6.62	−0.36	0.54	0.77	0.85	0.88	0.90	0.95	1.11
	0.3	−16.42	−2.11	−0.01	0.54	0.72	0.78	0.80	0.83	0.96
	0.4	−30.26	−4.59	−0.79	0.22	0.54	0.64	0.66	0.64	0.64
	0.5	−47.68	−7.55	−1.61	−0.02	0.48	0.63	0.65	0.62	0.59
	0.6	−68.93	−11.13	−2.56	−0.28	0.45	0.67	0.69	0.65	0.58
	0.7	−94.00	−15.31	−3.65	−0.55	0.44	0.74	0.77	0.71	0.61
	0.8	−122.90	−20.12	−4.88	−0.83	0.46	0.85	0.90	0.81	0.68
	0.9	−155.63	−25.54	−6.25	−1.12	0.51	1.00	1.06	0.94	0.77
	1.0	−192.18	−31.58	−7.77	−1.43	0.59	1.19	1.26	1.12	0.90
0.6	0.1	−0.57	0.66	0.84	0.88	0.89	0.90	0.91	0.93	0.99
	0.2	−5.12	−0.10	0.62	0.79	0.85	0.87	0.90	0.95	1.11
	0.3	−13.00	−1.49	0.18	0.61	0.75	0.79	0.82	0.86	1.02
	0.4	−24.31	−3.55	−0.50	0.30	0.55	0.62	0.63	0.62	0.63
	0.5	−38.41	−5.94	−1.16	0.09	0.48	0.59	0.60	0.57	0.55
	0.6	−55.58	−8.80	−1.92	−0.12	0.45	0.61	0.62	0.57	0.52
	0.7	−75.83	−12.16	−2.79	−0.33	0.44	0.66	0.67	0.60	0.52
	0.8	−99.17	−16.00	−3.76	−0.54	0.46	0.74	0.76	0.67	0.56
	0.9	−125.60	−20.33	−4.83	−0.76	0.51	0.86	0.88	0.77	0.62
	1.0	−155.12	−25.14	−6.02	−0.99	0.58	1.02	1.04	0.90	0.71
0.7	0.1	−0.35	0.70	0.84	0.88	0.89	0.90	0.90	0.92	0.99
	0.2	−4.24	0.05	0.65	0.80	0.85	0.87	0.89	0.94	1.12
	0.3	−11.00	−1.15	0.27	0.63	0.75	0.79	0.82	0.87	1.06
	0.4	−20.82	−3.00	−0.38	0.31	0.52	0.59	0.60	0.59	0.61
	0.5	−32.99	−5.09	−0.98	0.10	0.43	0.53	0.54	0.52	0.51
	0.6	−47.78	−7.58	−1.67	−0.11	0.38	0.52	0.53	0.49	0.45
	0.7	−65.22	−10.50	−2.44	−0.32	0.34	0.53	0.54	0.49	0.43
	0.8	−85.32	−13.83	−3.30	−0.53	0.33	0.58	0.59	0.52	0.43
	0.9	−108.07	−17.58	−4.26	−0.75	0.34	0.66	0.67	0.58	0.46
	1.0	−133.48	−21.76	−5.30	−0.97	0.38	0.76	0.78	0.67	0.51
0.8	0.1	−0.23	0.71	0.84	0.88	0.89	0.89	0.90	0.92	0.98
	0.2	−3.75	0.11	0.65	0.79	0.84	0.86	0.88	0.94	1.12
	0.3	−9.88	−0.99	0.29	0.63	0.74	0.78	0.81	0.87	1.09
	0.4	−18.88	−2.75	−0.36	0.28	0.48	0.55	0.56	0.57	0.61
	0.5	−29.98	−4.71	−0.96	0.04	0.36	0.46	0.47	0.46	0.47
	0.6	−43.46	−7.05	−1.64	−0.20	0.26	0.41	0.43	0.41	0.39
	0.7	−59.34	−9.77	−2.40	−0.44	0.19	0.38	0.41	0.38	0.34
	0.8	−77.64	−12.88	−3.26	−0.69	0.13	0.38	0.42	0.37	0.31
	0.9	−98.35	−16.38	−4.20	−0.95	0.09	0.40	0.45	0.39	0.30
	1.0	−121.48	−20.27	−5.24	−1.23	0.06	0.45	0.51	0.43	0.31

ED5-1 Wye, 30 Degree, Converging (*Continued*)

C_b Values (*Concluded*)

		Q_b/Q_c								
A_s/A_c	A_b/A_c	0.1	0.2	0.3	0.4	0.5	0.6	0.7	0.8	0.9
0.9	0.1	–0.18	0.72	0.84	0.87	0.88	0.89	0.90	0.92	0.98
	0.2	–3.52	0.12	0.64	0.78	0.82	0.85	0.88	0.93	1.12
	0.3	–9.34	–0.95	0.28	0.60	0.71	0.76	0.80	0.87	1.10
	0.4	–17.96	–2.70	–0.40	0.22	0.43	0.50	0.53	0.54	0.60
	0.5	–28.58	–4.65	–1.05	–0.07	0.26	0.37	0.40	0.41	0.42
	0.6	–41.45	–6.97	–1.77	–0.35	0.12	0.28	0.32	0.32	0.32
	0.7	–56.61	–9.66	–2.58	–0.65	0.00	0.21	0.27	0.26	0.24
	0.8	–74.08	–12.74	–3.49	–0.97	–0.12	0.16	0.23	0.22	0.18
	0.9	–93.84	–16.21	–4.50	–1.30	–0.23	0.13	0.21	0.19	0.14
	1.0	–115.92	–20.06	–5.61	–1.66	–0.34	0.11	0.21	0.18	0.11
1.0	0.1	–0.17	0.71	0.83	0.87	0.88	0.89	0.90	0.92	0.98
	0.2	–3.48	0.10	0.62	0.76	0.81	0.84	0.87	0.92	1.11
	0.3	–9.22	–1.00	0.23	0.56	0.68	0.74	0.78	0.86	1.11
	0.4	–17.76	–2.79	–0.50	0.14	0.37	0.45	0.49	0.52	0.60
	0.5	–28.31	–4.82	–1.21	–0.20	0.15	0.28	0.33	0.35	0.38
	0.6	–41.06	–7.21	–2.01	–0.55	–0.04	0.15	0.22	0.23	0.25
	0.7	–56.09	–9.99	–2.91	–0.92	–0.23	0.03	0.12	0.14	0.15
	0.8	–73.39	–13.17	–3.92	–1.32	–0.41	–0.07	0.04	0.06	0.06
	0.9	–92.98	–16.75	–5.04	–1.75	–0.60	–0.17	–0.03	–0.01	–0.02
	1.0	–114.85	–20.74	–6.28	–2.21	–0.79	–0.26	–0.09	–0.07	–0.09

C_s Values

		Q_s/Q_c								
A_s/A_c	A_b/A_c	0.1	0.2	0.3	0.4	0.5	0.6	0.7	0.8	0.9
0.1	0.1	–3.90	–1.07	–0.04	0.66	1.27	1.87	2.47	3.10	3.76
	0.2	–3.76	–0.34	0.52	1.05	1.53	2.02	2.56	3.14	3.77
	0.3	–2.50	0.10	0.76	1.20	1.62	2.08	2.59	3.15	3.77
	0.4	–1.64	0.35	0.88	1.27	1.67	2.11	2.60	3.15	3.77
	0.5	–1.05	0.52	0.96	1.32	1.69	2.12	2.61	3.16	3.77
	0.6	–0.63	0.63	1.02	1.35	1.71	2.13	2.61	3.16	3.77
	0.7	–0.32	0.71	1.06	1.37	1.73	2.14	2.62	3.16	3.77
	0.8	–0.07	0.78	1.09	1.39	1.74	2.15	2.62	3.16	3.77
	0.9	0.13	0.83	1.11	1.40	1.74	2.15	2.62	3.16	3.77
	1.0	0.29	0.87	1.13	1.41	1.75	2.15	2.63	3.17	3.77
0.2	0.1	–14.54	–4.50	–1.82	–0.62	0.05	0.47	0.75	0.95	1.09
	0.2	–16.02	–3.15	–0.80	0.04	0.45	0.69	0.86	0.99	1.10
	0.3	–11.65	–1.94	–0.26	0.32	0.60	0.77	0.90	1.01	1.10
	0.4	–8.56	–1.20	0.05	0.47	0.68	0.82	0.92	1.02	1.11
	0.5	–6.41	–0.71	0.25	0.57	0.73	0.84	0.93	1.02	1.11
	0.6	–4.85	–0.36	0.38	0.63	0.76	0.86	0.94	1.02	1.11
	0.7	–3.68	–0.10	0.48	0.68	0.79	0.87	0.95	1.03	1.11
	0.8	–2.77	0.10	0.56	0.71	0.81	0.88	0.95	1.03	1.11
	0.9	–2.04	0.26	0.62	0.74	0.82	0.89	0.95	1.03	1.11
	1.0	–1.45	0.38	0.66	0.76	0.83	0.89	0.96	1.03	1.11
0.3	0.1	–32.30	–10.04	–4.34	–1.94	–0.73	–0.07	0.30	0.50	0.59
	0.2	–36.37	–7.59	–2.48	–0.79	–0.06	0.29	0.47	0.57	0.61
	0.3	–26.79	–5.07	–1.42	–0.27	0.21	0.42	0.53	0.59	0.61
	0.4	–19.94	–3.49	–0.80	0.02	0.35	0.49	0.56	0.60	0.62
	0.5	–15.18	–2.44	–0.41	0.20	0.43	0.54	0.58	0.61	0.62
	0.6	–11.73	–1.70	–0.13	0.32	0.49	0.56	0.60	0.61	0.62
	0.7	–9.13	–1.14	0.07	0.41	0.53	0.58	0.60	0.61	0.62
	0.8	–7.11	–0.72	0.23	0.48	0.57	0.60	0.61	0.62	0.62
	0.9	–5.49	–0.38	0.35	0.53	0.59	0.61	0.62	0.62	0.62
	1.0	–4.17	–0.11	0.45	0.58	0.61	0.62	0.62	0.62	0.62
0.4	0.1	–57.18	–17.78	–7.80	–3.69	–1.66	–0.59	–0.02	0.26	0.37
	0.2	–64.82	–13.76	–4.74	–1.81	–0.59	–0.02	0.24	0.36	0.39
	0.3	–47.92	–9.38	–2.93	–0.94	–0.16	0.19	0.34	0.39	0.40
	0.4	–35.81	–6.62	–1.88	–0.46	0.07	0.30	0.38	0.41	0.40
	0.5	–27.39	–4.78	–1.20	–0.16	0.22	0.36	0.41	0.42	0.41
	0.6	–21.28	–3.48	–0.73	0.04	0.31	0.41	0.43	0.43	0.41
	0.7	–16.68	–2.51	–0.38	0.20	0.38	0.44	0.45	0.43	0.41
	0.8	–13.10	–1.77	–0.12	0.31	0.44	0.46	0.46	0.44	0.41
	0.9	–10.24	–1.18	0.09	0.40	0.48	0.48	0.46	0.44	0.41
	1.0	–7.90	–0.69	0.26	0.47	0.51	0.50	0.47	0.44	0.41

ED5-1 Wye, 30 Degree, Converging (*Continued*)

		C_s Values (*Concluded*)								
		Q_b/Q_c								
A_s/A_c	A_b/A_c	0.1	0.2	0.3	0.4	0.5	0.6	0.7	0.8	0.9
0.5	0.1	−89.21	−27.74	−12.24	−5.89	−2.79	−1.18	−0.33	0.08	0.23
	0.2	−101.39	−21.64	−7.61	−3.07	−1.19	−0.34	0.05	0.22	0.26
	0.3	−75.05	−14.87	−4.83	−1.75	−0.54	−0.03	0.19	0.26	0.27
	0.4	−56.18	−10.59	−3.21	−1.02	−0.20	0.13	0.26	0.29	0.27
	0.5	−43.04	−7.74	−2.16	−0.56	0.02	0.23	0.30	0.30	0.27
	0.6	−33.51	−5.72	−1.43	−0.24	0.16	0.30	0.33	0.31	0.28
	0.7	−26.34	−4.22	−0.90	−0.01	0.27	0.35	0.35	0.32	0.28
	0.8	−20.75	−3.06	−0.49	0.16	0.35	0.39	0.37	0.33	0.28
	0.9	−16.29	−2.14	−0.17	0.30	0.41	0.41	0.38	0.33	0.28
	1.0	−12.64	−1.39	0.10	0.41	0.46	0.44	0.39	0.33	0.28
0.6	0.1	−128.36	−39.93	−17.66	−8.57	−4.15	−1.85	−0.66	−0.09	0.12
	0.2	−146.06	−31.26	−11.09	−4.56	−1.89	−0.68	−0.12	0.10	0.16
	0.3	−108.19	−21.55	−7.12	−2.69	−0.97	−0.24	0.07	0.17	0.17
	0.4	−81.04	−15.40	−4.80	−1.65	−0.48	−0.01	0.17	0.20	0.18
	0.5	−62.13	−11.31	−3.30	−0.99	−0.17	0.13	0.22	0.22	0.18
	0.6	−48.43	−8.41	−2.25	−0.54	0.03	0.22	0.26	0.24	0.18
	0.7	−38.10	−6.25	−1.49	−0.22	0.18	0.29	0.29	0.25	0.19
	0.8	−30.07	−4.59	−0.90	0.03	0.30	0.34	0.31	0.25	0.19
	0.9	−23.64	−3.27	−0.44	0.23	0.39	0.38	0.33	0.26	0.19
	1.0	−18.39	−2.20	−0.06	0.39	0.46	0.42	0.34	0.27	0.19
0.7	0.1	−174.66	−54.33	−24.05	−11.71	−5.72	−2.62	−1.01	−0.25	0.03
	0.2	−198.85	−42.62	−15.17	−6.31	−2.68	−1.04	−0.29	0.01	0.08
	0.3	−147.33	−29.41	−9.78	−3.77	−1.44	−0.45	−0.04	0.10	0.10
	0.4	−110.40	−21.07	−6.64	−2.36	−0.77	−0.14	0.09	0.15	0.11
	0.5	−84.67	−15.50	−4.60	−1.48	−0.36	0.05	0.17	0.17	0.11
	0.6	−66.02	−11.56	−3.19	−0.86	−0.08	0.18	0.23	0.19	0.12
	0.7	−51.97	−8.63	−2.15	−0.42	0.12	0.27	0.27	0.20	0.12
	0.8	−41.04	−6.37	−1.35	−0.08	0.27	0.34	0.29	0.21	0.12
	0.9	−32.30	−4.58	−0.72	0.19	0.39	0.39	0.32	0.22	0.12
	1.0	−25.16	−3.12	−0.21	0.40	0.49	0.43	0.33	0.23	0.13
0.8	0.1	−228.09	−70.95	−31.43	−15.33	−7.52	−3.48	−1.39	−0.40	−0.04
	0.2	−259.75	−55.70	−19.86	−8.29	−3.56	−1.43	−0.46	−0.06	−0.03
	0.3	−192.48	−38.47	−12.84	−4.99	−1.95	−0.66	−0.12	0.05	0.05
	0.4	−144.25	−27.58	−8.74	−3.16	−1.09	−0.26	0.05	0.11	0.06
	0.5	−110.65	−20.32	−6.08	−2.00	−0.55	−0.01	0.15	0.15	0.07
	0.6	−86.30	−15.17	−4.24	−1.20	−0.19	0.15	0.22	0.17	0.08
	0.7	−67.95	−11.34	−2.88	−0.62	0.08	0.27	0.27	0.19	0.08
	0.8	−53.67	−8.40	−1.84	−0.18	0.28	0.36	0.30	0.20	0.08
	0.9	−42.26	−6.05	−1.02	0.16	0.44	0.43	0.33	0.21	0.08
	1.0	−32.93	−4.15	−0.35	0.44	0.56	0.49	0.36	0.22	0.09
0.9	0.1	−288.66	−89.79	−39.78	−19.41	−9.54	−4.43	−1.80	−0.55	−0.09
	0.2	−328.76	−70.51	−25.16	−10.53	−4.54	−1.84	−0.62	−0.12	0.00
	0.3	−243.63	−48.72	−16.28	−6.35	−2.50	−0.87	−0.20	0.03	0.03
	0.4	−182.60	−34.94	−11.09	−4.03	−1.41	−0.37	0.02	0.10	0.04
	0.5	−140.07	−25.75	−7.74	−2.57	−0.74	−0.06	0.15	0.14	0.05
	0.6	−109.25	−19.24	−5.40	−1.56	−0.28	0.15	0.23	0.17	0.05
	0.7	−86.04	−14.40	−3.68	−0.83	0.06	0.30	0.30	0.20	0.06
	0.8	−67.96	−10.66	−2.37	−0.27	0.31	0.41	0.34	0.21	0.06
	0.9	−53.52	−7.70	−1.33	0.17	0.51	0.50	0.38	0.22	0.06
	1.0	−41.71	−5.29	−0.49	0.52	0.67	0.57	0.41	0.23	0.07
1.0	0.1	−356.36	−110.84	−49.12	−23.97	−11.78	−5.48	−2.23	−0.69	−0.12
	0.2	−405.88	−87.06	−31.07	−13.01	−5.62	−2.29	−0.77	−0.16	−0.02
	0.3	−300.78	−60.15	−20.11	−7.85	−3.10	−1.09	−0.26	0.02	0.02
	0.4	−225.44	−43.14	−13.70	−4.99	−1.76	−0.47	0.01	0.11	0.04
	0.5	−172.93	−31.80	−9.56	−3.18	−0.92	−0.09	0.17	0.17	0.05
	0.6	−134.89	−23.76	−6.68	−1.94	−0.35	0.17	0.28	0.20	0.06
	0.7	−106.23	−17.78	−4.56	−1.04	0.06	0.36	0.35	0.23	0.06
	0.8	−83.92	−13.18	−2.93	−0.35	0.37	0.50	0.41	0.25	0.06
	0.9	−66.08	−9.52	−1.65	0.19	0.62	0.61	0.46	0.26	0.07
	1.0	−51.51	−6.54	−0.61	0.63	0.81	0.70	0.49	0.28	0.07

ED5-2 Wye, 45 Degree, Converging

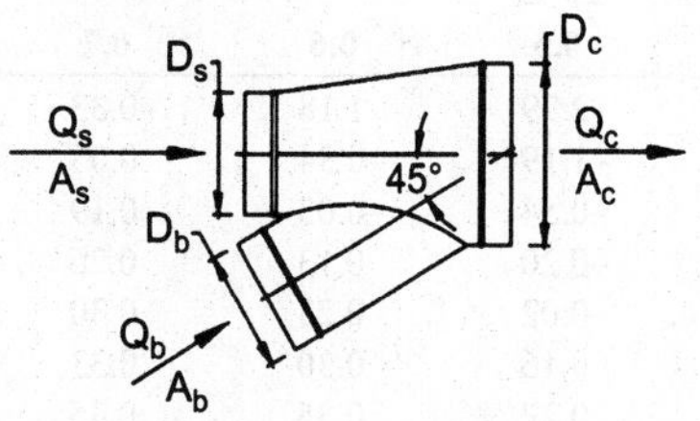

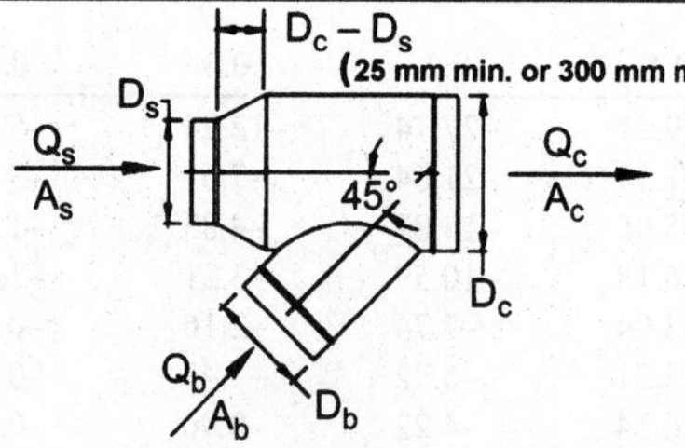

		C_b Values								
		Q_b/Q_c								
A_s/A_c	A_b/A_c	0.1	0.2	0.3	0.4	0.5	0.6	0.7	0.8	0.9
0.1	0.1	−13.70	−1.90	−0.02	0.54	0.75	0.85	0.89	0.92	0.96
	0.2	−57.73	−10.44	−2.88	−0.64	0.22	0.59	0.76	0.85	0.94
	0.3	−131.08	−24.63	−7.59	−2.53	−0.60	0.24	0.61	0.79	0.92
	0.4	−233.78	−44.46	−14.15	−5.15	−1.71	−0.23	0.43	0.72	0.88
	0.5	−365.85	−69.96	−22.58	−8.50	−3.12	−0.81	0.21	0.65	0.82
	0.6	−527.21	−101.08	−32.83	−12.55	−4.80	−1.49	−0.02	0.59	0.79
	0.7	−717.81	−137.79	−44.90	−17.28	−6.74	−2.23	−0.23	0.60	0.85
	0.8	−937.72	−180.12	−58.79	−22.73	−8.96	−3.06	−0.45	0.63	0.95
	0.9	−1187.	−228.09	−74.53	−28.88	−11.45	−3.99	−0.69	0.67	1.07
	1.0	−1465.	−281.68	−92.10	−35.74	−14.23	−5.01	−0.94	0.74	1.22
0.2	0.1	−5.52	−0.26	0.56	0.79	0.88	0.92	0.95	0.97	1.05
	0.2	−25.19	−3.97	−0.64	0.32	0.67	0.82	0.90	0.96	1.08
	0.3	−58.03	−10.14	−2.63	−0.45	0.36	0.69	0.84	0.93	1.08
	0.4	−104.08	−18.80	−5.40	−1.51	−0.07	0.52	0.77	0.88	1.01
	0.5	−163.36	−29.97	−8.97	−2.87	−0.62	0.29	0.67	0.80	0.84
	0.6	−235.59	−43.47	−13.22	−4.44	−1.20	0.12	0.65	0.83	0.85
	0.7	−320.90	−59.38	−18.21	−6.25	−1.84	−0.04	0.68	0.91	0.93
	0.8	−419.32	−77.73	−23.95	−8.33	−2.56	−0.22	0.72	1.02	1.02
	0.9	−530.86	−98.50	−30.44	−10.66	−3.36	−0.40	0.79	1.16	1.14
	1.0	−655.51	−121.72	−37.68	−13.26	−4.25	−0.59	0.87	1.33	1.28
0.3	0.1	−2.74	0.32	0.78	0.90	0.94	0.97	0.99	1.02	1.13
	0.2	−14.27	−1.77	0.13	0.66	0.85	0.93	0.97	1.03	1.21
	0.3	−33.62	−5.28	−0.95	0.27	0.70	0.87	0.94	1.01	1.19
	0.4	−60.85	−10.26	−2.48	−0.30	0.47	0.77	0.88	0.93	1.04
	0.5	−95.87	−16.64	−4.44	−1.00	0.21	0.66	0.82	0.84	0.84
	0.6	−138.38	−24.26	−6.68	−1.73	0.01	0.66	0.88	0.91	0.88
	0.7	−188.60	−33.25	−9.32	−2.58	−0.20	0.68	0.98	1.02	0.95
	0.8	−246.54	−43.60	−12.34	−3.54	−0.43	0.72	1.11	1.15	1.03
	0.9	−312.21	−55.33	−15.76	−4.61	−0.68	0.78	1.26	1.31	1.13
	1.0	−385.59	−68.43	−19.56	−5.79	−0.94	0.86	1.45	1.49	1.24
0.4	0.1	−1.32	0.63	0.90	0.96	0.99	1.00	1.02	1.06	1.20
	0.2	−8.77	−0.64	0.54	0.85	0.95	0.99	1.03	1.09	1.31
	0.3	−21.41	−2.85	−0.10	0.63	0.87	0.96	1.00	1.06	1.26
	0.4	−39.30	−6.02	−1.05	0.28	0.72	0.87	0.91	0.92	1.00
	0.5	−62.10	−9.96	−2.16	−0.06	0.63	0.85	0.90	0.88	0.86
	0.6	−89.77	−14.65	−3.42	−0.38	0.61	0.93	0.99	0.95	0.90
	0.7	−122.46	−20.19	−4.88	−0.74	0.61	1.04	1.12	1.06	0.95
	0.8	−160.18	−26.56	−6.55	−1.15	0.62	1.18	1.29	1.19	1.01
	0.9	−202.93	−33.77	−8.44	−1.60	0.64	1.36	1.48	1.35	1.07
	1.0	−250.70	−41.83	−10.54	−2.09	0.68	1.56	1.71	1.53	1.15
0.5	0.1	−0.44	0.83	0.98	1.01	1.02	1.03	1.05	1.10	1.27
	0.2	−5.45	0.04	0.79	0.97	1.02	1.04	1.07	1.14	1.39
	0.3	−14.10	−1.39	0.40	0.84	0.97	1.00	1.02	1.07	1.28
	0.4	−26.48	−3.53	−0.24	0.59	0.83	0.89	0.88	0.85	0.86
	0.5	−41.84	−5.96	−0.80	0.51	0.88	0.97	0.95	0.90	0.87
	0.6	−60.61	−8.90	−1.46	0.43	0.97	1.09	1.06	0.97	0.90
	0.7	−82.80	−12.36	−2.22	0.35	1.09	1.25	1.20	1.08	0.93
	0.8	−108.39	−16.35	−3.09	0.27	1.24	1.45	1.38	1.20	0.96
	0.9	−137.41	−20.86	−4.07	0.19	1.42	1.68	1.59	1.35	0.99
	1.0	−169.84	−25.90	−5.15	0.11	1.63	1.95	1.83	1.52	1.02
0.6	0.1	−0.41	0.83	0.98	1.02	1.03	1.04	1.07	1.13	1.33
	0.2	−5.54	−0.08	0.70	0.91	0.98	1.01	1.05	1.14	1.42
	0.3	−14.48	−1.75	0.13	0.64	0.81	0.88	0.92	0.98	1.19
	0.4	−27.10	−4.14	−0.68	0.26	0.57	0.68	0.71	0.72	0.76
	0.5	−42.84	−6.91	−1.50	−0.02	0.47	0.64	0.68	0.69	0.70
	0.6	−62.07	−10.28	−2.48	−0.34	0.37	0.61	0.67	0.66	0.63
	0.7	−84.79	−14.26	−3.62	−0.71	0.27	0.59	0.67	0.63	0.54
	0.8	−111.02	−18.84	−4.92	−1.12	0.16	0.58	0.67	0.61	0.44
	0.9	−140.76	−24.03	−6.40	−1.57	0.04	0.58	0.68	0.59	0.31
	1.0	−174.01	−29.83	−8.04	−2.07	−0.08	0.58	0.70	0.56	0.15

ED5-2 Wye, 45 Degree, Converging (*Continued*)

		C_b Values (*Concluded*)								
		Q_b/Q_c								
A_s/A_c	A_b/A_c	0.1	0.2	0.3	0.4	0.5	0.6	0.7	0.8	0.9
0.7	0.1	0.03	0.94	1.03	1.05	1.06	1.07	1.10	1.16	1.39
	0.2	−3.96	0.25	0.83	0.97	1.01	1.04	1.08	1.17	1.47
	0.3	−11.07	−1.10	0.34	0.71	0.83	0.87	0.90	0.95	1.13
	0.4	−20.92	−2.92	−0.27	0.43	0.65	0.72	0.73	0.73	0.77
	0.5	−33.20	−5.01	−0.85	0.24	0.59	0.69	0.71	0.69	0.70
	0.6	−48.21	−7.55	−1.55	0.03	0.53	0.68	0.69	0.65	0.61
	0.7	−65.95	−10.56	−2.37	−0.20	0.48	0.68	0.69	0.62	0.49
	0.8	−86.42	−14.01	−3.30	−0.46	0.43	0.68	0.69	0.58	0.35
	0.9	−109.65	−17.93	−4.35	−0.75	0.38	0.70	0.70	0.53	0.18
	1.0	−135.63	−22.32	−5.53	−1.07	0.33	0.72	0.71	0.48	−0.03
0.8	0.1	0.38	1.02	1.08	1.08	1.08	1.09	1.12	1.19	1.44
	0.2	−2.78	0.50	0.91	1.01	1.03	1.05	1.09	1.18	1.49
	0.3	−8.58	−0.65	0.47	0.74	0.82	0.85	0.86	0.89	1.02
	0.4	−16.29	−2.00	0.05	0.56	0.71	0.75	0.74	0.74	0.78
	0.5	−25.98	−3.59	−0.37	0.44	0.68	0.73	0.72	0.69	0.69
	0.6	−37.82	−5.52	−0.87	0.31	0.65	0.72	0.70	0.64	0.58
	0.7	−51.83	−7.79	−1.44	0.17	0.63	0.73	0.69	0.59	0.43
	0.8	−68.01	−10.42	−2.10	0.01	0.62	0.75	0.69	0.53	0.25
	0.9	−86.37	−13.39	−2.84	−0.16	0.61	0.77	0.68	0.47	0.03
	1.0	−106.91	−16.73	−3.68	−0.35	0.61	0.79	0.68	0.38	−0.25
0.9	0.1	0.65	1.10	1.11	1.10	1.10	1.11	1.14	1.22	1.49
	0.2	−1.87	0.68	0.98	1.03	1.05	1.06	1.09	1.18	1.49
	0.3	−6.70	−0.33	0.54	0.74	0.79	0.80	0.80	0.81	0.87
	0.4	−12.69	−1.29	0.29	0.66	0.76	0.77	0.75	0.74	0.78
	0.5	−20.37	−2.48	0.00	0.59	0.74	0.75	0.72	0.69	0.67
	0.6	−29.77	−3.94	−0.34	0.52	0.73	0.75	0.70	0.63	0.54
	0.7	−40.89	−5.66	−0.73	0.45	0.74	0.76	0.68	0.56	0.36
	0.8	−53.74	−7.64	−1.18	0.37	0.76	0.78	0.67	0.48	0.13
	0.9	−68.32	−9.89	−1.69	0.28	0.77	0.80	0.65	0.38	−0.15
	1.0	−84.66	−12.42	−2.27	0.18	0.80	0.83	0.62	0.26	−0.49
1.0	0.1	0.88	1.16	1.14	1.12	1.12	1.13	1.16	1.25	1.54
	0.2	−1.17	0.81	1.02	1.05	1.05	1.06	1.09	1.18	1.48
	0.3	−5.09	−0.02	0.64	0.78	0.81	0.81	0.80	0.80	0.86
	0.4	−9.81	−0.72	0.48	0.74	0.79	0.78	0.76	0.74	0.77
	0.5	−15.89	−1.61	0.29	0.71	0.79	0.77	0.72	0.68	0.65
	0.6	−23.34	−2.69	0.07	0.68	0.80	0.77	0.69	0.60	0.49
	0.7	−32.15	−3.96	−0.18	0.66	0.82	0.78	0.67	0.51	0.27
	0.8	−42.35	−5.44	−0.47	0.64	0.85	0.79	0.63	0.41	0.00
	0.9	−53.94	−7.12	−0.80	0.61	0.88	0.81	0.60	0.28	−0.34
	1.0	−66.93	−9.01	−1.17	0.58	0.92	0.82	0.55	0.13	−0.75

		C_s Values								
		Q_s/Q_c								
A_s/A_c	A_b/A_c	0.1	0.2	0.3	0.4	0.5	0.6	0.7	0.8	0.9
0.1	0.1	−0.64	−0.63	0.17	1.00	1.87	2.79	3.76	4.81	5.92
	0.2	−2.38	−0.06	0.77	1.47	2.19	2.99	3.88	4.86	5.93
	0.3	−1.56	0.35	1.03	1.64	2.30	3.06	3.91	4.87	5.94
	0.4	−0.89	0.59	1.17	1.73	2.36	3.09	3.93	4.88	5.94
	0.5	−0.40	0.75	1.26	1.78	2.40	3.11	3.94	4.88	5.94
	0.6	−0.04	0.86	1.32	1.82	2.42	3.13	3.95	4.89	5.94
	0.7	0.23	0.95	1.36	1.85	2.44	3.14	3.96	4.89	5.94
	0.8	0.45	1.01	1.40	1.87	2.45	3.15	3.96	4.89	5.94
	0.9	0.62	1.06	1.42	1.88	2.46	3.15	3.96	4.89	5.94
	1.0	0.76	1.10	1.44	1.89	2.47	3.16	3.97	4.89	5.94
0.2	0.1	−0.33	−2.09	−1.13	−0.35	0.22	0.65	0.97	1.23	1.45
	0.2	−10.16	−2.08	−0.43	0.24	0.62	0.88	1.10	1.29	1.46
	0.3	−7.83	−1.20	0.03	0.50	0.77	0.97	1.14	1.30	1.46
	0.4	−5.62	−0.59	0.30	0.65	0.85	1.01	1.16	1.31	1.46
	0.5	−3.96	−0.18	0.48	0.74	0.90	1.04	1.18	1.32	1.47
	0.6	−2.71	0.12	0.60	0.80	0.94	1.06	1.19	1.32	1.47
	0.7	−1.75	0.34	0.70	0.85	0.96	1.07	1.19	1.32	1.47
	0.8	−0.99	0.52	0.77	0.88	0.98	1.08	1.20	1.32	1.47
	0.9	−0.38	0.66	0.82	0.91	0.99	1.09	1.20	1.33	1.47
	1.0	0.13	0.77	0.87	0.93	1.00	1.10	1.20	1.33	1.47

ED5-2 Wye, 45 Degree, Converging (*Continued*)

		C_s Values (*Continued*)								
		Q_s/Q_c								
A_s/A_c	A_b/A_c	0.1	0.2	0.3	0.4	0.5	0.6	0.7	0.8	0.9
0.3	0.1	−0.18	−4.36	−2.61	−1.29	−0.45	0.08	0.41	0.60	0.71
	0.2	−23.33	−5.14	−1.67	−0.44	0.12	0.42	0.58	0.67	0.72
	0.3	−18.44	−3.44	−0.84	0.00	0.36	0.54	0.64	0.69	0.73
	0.4	−13.64	−2.22	−0.34	0.25	0.49	0.60	0.67	0.70	0.73
	0.5	−10.00	−1.37	0.00	0.41	0.57	0.64	0.69	0.71	0.73
	0.6	−7.26	−0.75	0.24	0.52	0.62	0.67	0.70	0.72	0.73
	0.7	−5.15	−0.29	0.41	0.60	0.66	0.69	0.71	0.72	0.73
	0.8	−3.48	0.07	0.55	0.66	0.69	0.70	0.71	0.72	0.73
	0.9	−2.14	0.36	0.65	0.71	0.72	0.72	0.72	0.72	0.73
	1.0	−1.03	0.60	0.74	0.75	0.73	0.73	0.72	0.72	0.73
0.4	0.1	−0.46	−7.64	−4.66	−2.49	−1.15	−0.36	0.10	0.33	0.43
	0.2	−42.17	−9.48	−3.34	−1.23	−0.31	0.12	0.33	0.42	0.44
	0.3	−33.68	−6.60	−1.98	−0.53	0.05	0.31	0.41	0.45	0.45
	0.4	−25.24	−4.51	−1.13	−0.13	0.25	0.40	0.46	0.47	0.45
	0.5	−18.83	−3.04	−0.57	0.13	0.37	0.46	0.48	0.48	0.46
	0.6	−13.99	−1.97	−0.17	0.31	0.46	0.50	0.50	0.48	0.46
	0.7	−10.27	−1.17	0.12	0.44	0.52	0.53	0.51	0.49	0.46
	0.8	−7.32	−0.54	0.35	0.54	0.57	0.55	0.52	0.49	0.46
	0.9	−4.94	−0.04	0.53	0.62	0.61	0.57	0.53	0.49	0.46
	1.0	−2.98	0.37	0.68	0.68	0.64	0.58	0.54	0.50	0.46
0.5	0.1	−1.43	−12.03	−7.36	−4.03	−2.01	−0.84	−0.18	0.14	0.26
	0.2	−66.95	−15.18	−5.49	−2.21	−0.81	−0.16	0.14	0.26	0.28
	0.3	−53.80	−10.77	−3.45	−1.17	−0.27	0.11	0.26	0.30	0.29
	0.4	−40.66	−7.54	−2.16	−0.57	0.02	0.25	0.32	0.33	0.30
	0.5	−30.68	−5.27	−1.30	−0.18	0.21	0.33	0.36	0.34	0.30
	0.6	−23.15	−3.62	−0.69	0.09	0.33	0.39	0.38	0.35	0.30
	0.7	−17.34	−2.38	−0.24	0.29	0.42	0.43	0.40	0.35	0.30
	0.8	−12.75	−1.41	0.11	0.44	0.49	0.47	0.41	0.36	0.30
	0.9	−9.04	−0.64	0.39	0.56	0.55	0.49	0.43	0.36	0.30
	1.0	−5.99	0.00	0.61	0.65	0.59	0.51	0.43	0.36	0.30
0.6	0.1	−3.34	−17.58	−10.74	−5.94	−3.06	−1.39	−0.48	−0.03	0.13
	0.2	−97.90	−22.29	−8.18	−3.41	−1.39	−0.46	−0.03	0.13	0.16
	0.3	−79.03	−15.99	−5.28	−1.94	−0.64	−0.09	0.13	0.19	0.17
	0.4	−60.15	−11.37	−3.44	−1.09	−0.23	0.10	0.21	0.22	0.18
	0.5	−45.80	−8.13	−2.22	−0.55	0.03	0.22	0.26	0.24	0.18
	0.6	−34.97	−5.77	−1.35	−0.17	0.20	0.30	0.30	0.25	0.18
	0.7	−26.62	−3.98	−0.71	0.11	0.33	0.36	0.32	0.26	0.19
	0.8	−20.02	−2.59	−0.21	0.33	0.43	0.41	0.34	0.26	0.19
	0.9	−14.68	−1.48	0.18	0.49	0.51	0.44	0.35	0.27	0.19
	1.0	−10.29	−0.57	0.51	0.63	0.57	0.47	0.37	0.27	0.19
0.7	0.1	−6.43	−24.36	−14.82	−8.23	−4.31	−2.04	−0.81	−0.20	0.01
	0.2	−135.28	−30.88	−11.42	−4.85	−2.08	−0.80	−0.21	0.02	0.06
	0.3	−109.64	−22.35	−7.50	−2.88	−1.07	−0.31	0.00	0.09	0.07
	0.4	−83.96	−16.08	−5.02	−1.73	−0.52	−0.05	0.11	0.13	0.08
	0.5	−64.44	−11.67	−3.36	−0.99	−0.17	0.11	0.18	0.15	0.09
	0.6	−49.71	−8.47	−2.19	−0.48	0.06	0.22	0.22	0.17	0.09
	0.7	−38.35	−6.04	−1.31	−0.10	0.24	0.30	0.26	0.18	0.09
	0.8	−29.37	−4.16	−0.64	0.18	0.37	0.36	0.28	0.19	0.09
	0.9	−22.12	−2.65	−0.10	0.41	0.47	0.40	0.30	0.19	0.09
	1.0	−16.14	−1.41	0.33	0.60	0.55	0.44	0.32	0.20	0.09
0.8	0.1	−10.94	−32.43	−19.63	−10.93	−5.77	−2.80	−1.18	−0.38	−0.09
	0.2	−179.32	−41.01	−15.25	−6.55	−2.88	−1.19	−0.41	−0.10	−0.04
	0.3	−145.86	−29.89	−10.14	−3.99	−1.58	−0.55	−0.13	0.00	−0.02
	0.4	−112.34	−21.71	−6.91	−2.50	−0.86	−0.22	0.01	0.05	−0.01
	0.5	−86.85	−15.96	−4.75	−1.54	−0.41	−0.01	0.10	0.08	0.00
	0.6	−67.62	−11.78	−3.22	−0.87	−0.10	0.13	0.16	0.10	0.00
	0.7	−52.79	−8.62	−2.08	−0.38	0.12	0.23	0.20	0.11	0.00
	0.8	−41.06	−6.16	−1.20	0.00	0.29	0.31	0.23	0.12	0.01
	0.9	−31.59	−4.19	−0.51	0.29	0.43	0.37	0.26	0.13	0.01
	1.0	−23.78	−2.58	0.06	0.53	0.54	0.42	0.28	0.14	0.01

ED5-2 Wye, 45 Degree, Converging (*Continued*)

		C_s Values (*Concluded*)								
		Q_s/Q_c								
A_s/A_c	A_b/A_c	0.1	0.2	0.3	0.4	0.5	0.6	0.7	0.8	0.9
0.9	0.1	–17.13	–41.85	–25.21	–14.05	–7.45	–3.66	–1.59	–0.57	–0.20
	0.2	–230.27	–52.75	–19.69	–8.53	–3.81	–1.63	–0.63	–0.22	–0.13
	0.3	–187.95	–38.69	–13.24	–5.29	–2.16	–0.83	–0.28	–0.10	–0.10
	0.4	–145.53	–28.34	–9.15	–3.41	–1.26	–0.41	–0.10	–0.04	–0.09
	0.5	–113.27	–21.07	–6.42	–2.19	–0.69	–0.15	0.01	0.00	–0.09
	0.6	–88.94	–15.78	–4.48	–1.35	–0.30	0.03	0.09	0.03	–0.08
	0.7	–70.16	–11.78	–3.04	–0.73	–0.02	0.16	0.14	0.04	–0.08
	0.8	–55.33	–8.67	–1.93	–0.25	0.20	0.26	0.18	0.06	–0.07
	0.9	–43.33	–6.18	–1.05	0.12	0.37	0.33	0.21	0.07	–0.07
	1.0	–33.46	–4.14	–0.34	0.42	0.50	0.39	0.24	0.08	–0.07
1.0	0.1	–25.23	–52.69	–31.58	–17.61	–9.37	–4.64	–2.06	–0.79	–0.31
	0.2	–288.39	–66.15	–24.77	–10.80	–4.88	–2.14	–0.87	–0.35	–0.22
	0.3	–236.14	–48.79	–16.81	–6.80	–2.85	–1.15	–0.44	–0.20	–0.19
	0.4	–183.77	–36.02	–11.76	–4.47	–1.73	–0.63	–0.22	–0.12	–0.18
	0.5	–143.95	–27.05	–8.39	–2.98	–1.03	–0.31	–0.08	–0.08	–0.17
	0.6	–113.91	–20.52	–6.00	–1.93	–0.55	–0.09	0.01	–0.04	–0.16
	0.7	–90.73	–15.58	–4.23	–1.17	–0.20	0.07	0.08	–0.02	–0.16
	0.8	–72.41	–11.74	–2.86	–0.58	0.06	0.19	0.13	–0.01	–0.16
	0.9	–57.61	–8.66	–1.77	–0.12	0.27	0.28	0.16	0.01	–0.15
	1.0	–45.42	–6.15	–0.88	0.25	0.44	0.36	0.20	0.02	–0.15

ED5-3 Tee, D_c < or = 250 mm, Converging

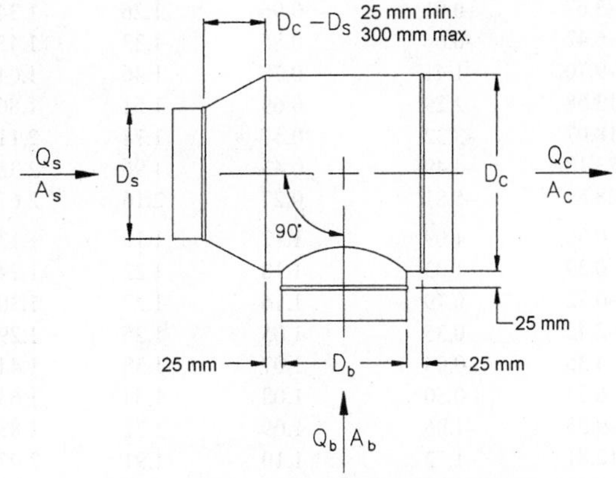

		C_b Values								
		Q_b/Q_c								
A_s/A_c	A_b/A_c	0.1	0.2	0.3	0.4	0.5	0.6	0.7	0.8	0.9
0.1	0.1	–13.39	–1.73	0.13	0.68	0.89	0.98	1.02	1.05	1.08
	0.2	–56.68	–9.99	–2.53	–0.32	0.52	0.88	1.04	1.12	1.18
	0.3	–128.89	–23.79	–6.99	–2.02	–0.12	0.68	1.04	1.20	1.29
	0.4	–230.03	–43.12	–13.26	–4.40	–1.04	0.40	1.03	1.30	1.42
	0.5	–360.10	–68.01	–21.33	–7.49	–2.23	0.02	1.00	1.40	1.53
	0.6	–519.10	–98.44	–31.20	–11.27	–3.69	–0.46	0.95	1.52	1.66
	0.7	–706.92	–134.35	–42.83	–15.70	–5.38	–0.99	0.93	1.70	1.88
	0.8	–923.64	–175.79	–56.25	–20.82	–7.34	–1.60	0.90	1.91	2.15
	0.9	–1169.	–222.75	–71.47	–26.62	–9.56	–2.30	0.87	2.14	2.44
	1.0	–1444.	–275.24	–88.47	–33.10	–12.04	–3.08	0.84	2.40	2.76
0.2	0.1	–5.33	–0.12	0.69	0.92	1.01	1.04	1.06	1.08	1.13
	0.2	–24.56	–3.63	–0.36	0.59	0.93	1.08	1.14	1.19	1.27
	0.3	–56.72	–9.54	–2.15	–0.01	0.78	1.10	1.23	1.30	1.39
	0.4	–101.83	–17.86	–4.68	–0.87	0.52	1.09	1.32	1.41	1.48
	0.5	–159.91	–28.59	–7.98	–2.02	0.17	1.05	1.40	1.51	1.51
	0.6	–230.83	–41.68	–11.98	–3.39	–0.24	1.03	1.53	1.66	1.61
	0.7	–314.56	–57.10	–16.68	–4.98	–0.69	1.04	1.71	1.90	1.82
	0.8	–411.18	–74.90	–22.10	–6.82	–1.21	1.04	1.92	2.16	2.05
	0.9	–520.69	–95.08	–28.25	–8.90	–1.81	1.04	2.15	2.45	2.31
	1.0	–643.09	–117.63	–35.12	–11.24	–2.47	1.04	2.41	2.78	2.58

ED5-3 Tee, D_c < or = 250 mm, Converging (*Continued*)

		C_b Values (*Continued*)								
		Q_b/Q_c								
A_s/A_c	A_b/A_c	0.1	0.2	0.3	0.4	0.5	0.6	0.7	0.8	0.9
0.3	0.1	−2.67	0.42	0.88	1.01	1.05	1.07	1.09	1.11	1.18
	0.2	−14.05	−1.55	0.36	0.89	1.08	1.16	1.19	1.23	1.34
	0.3	−33.18	−4.91	−0.58	0.64	1.07	1.23	1.30	1.34	1.44
	0.4	−60.09	−9.68	−1.94	0.24	1.00	1.29	1.39	1.42	1.47
	0.5	−94.80	−15.89	−3.74	−0.33	0.87	1.32	1.46	1.46	1.38
	0.6	−136.97	−23.33	−5.84	−0.92	0.81	1.45	1.65	1.66	1.53
	0.7	−186.81	−32.14	−8.32	−1.62	0.74	1.61	1.88	1.88	1.70
	0.8	−244.33	−42.30	−11.19	−2.43	0.65	1.78	2.14	2.13	1.88
	0.9	−309.54	−53.82	−14.44	−3.35	0.54	1.98	2.42	2.41	2.08
	1.0	−382.43	−66.70	−18.08	−4.39	0.42	2.19	2.74	2.72	2.29
0.4	0.1	−1.36	0.69	0.98	1.06	1.08	1.10	1.11	1.14	1.23
	0.2	−8.95	−0.54	0.71	1.04	1.15	1.20	1.22	1.26	1.40
	0.3	−21.82	−2.70	0.16	0.94	1.19	1.29	1.32	1.35	1.47
	0.4	−39.99	−5.81	−0.67	0.73	1.19	1.35	1.39	1.39	1.41
	0.5	−63.37	−9.82	−1.75	0.45	1.18	1.42	1.47	1.43	1.32
	0.6	−91.72	−14.59	−2.97	0.20	1.26	1.60	1.67	1.60	1.43
	0.7	−125.23	−20.24	−4.41	−0.10	1.34	1.81	1.90	1.81	1.56
	0.8	−163.91	−26.77	−6.09	−0.45	1.43	2.04	2.16	2.03	1.69
	0.9	−207.76	−34.17	−7.99	−0.85	1.53	2.30	2.44	2.28	1.82
	1.0	−256.79	−42.45	−10.12	−1.30	1.63	2.58	2.75	2.54	1.95
0.5	0.1	−0.60	0.85	1.04	1.09	1.11	1.12	1.13	1.16	1.27
	0.2	−6.03	0.04	0.91	1.13	1.20	1.22	1.24	1.29	1.44
	0.3	−15.35	−1.46	0.56	1.09	1.25	1.30	1.32	1.35	1.46
	0.4	−28.59	−3.67	−0.01	0.96	1.26	1.34	1.35	1.32	1.29
	0.5	−45.45	−6.42	−0.66	0.85	1.33	1.45	1.45	1.38	1.24
	0.6	−65.92	−9.70	−1.41	0.78	1.46	1.64	1.63	1.53	1.32
	0.7	−90.12	−13.58	−2.29	0.69	1.61	1.86	1.85	1.70	1.39
	0.8	−118.07	−18.07	−3.32	0.57	1.78	2.11	2.09	1.89	1.46
	0.9	−149.75	−23.18	−4.49	0.43	1.96	2.38	2.35	2.09	1.53
	1.0	−185.19	−28.89	−5.81	0.27	2.16	2.67	2.63	2.31	1.57
0.6	0.1	−0.11	0.96	1.09	1.12	1.12	1.13	1.15	1.18	1.31
	0.2	−4.20	0.39	1.03	1.18	1.22	1.24	1.26	1.30	1.47
	0.3	−11.33	−0.72	0.79	1.16	1.27	1.30	1.31	1.33	1.43
	0.4	−21.57	−2.42	0.35	1.05	1.25	1.29	1.27	1.22	1.12
	0.5	−34.29	−4.35	−0.03	1.07	1.38	1.44	1.41	1.32	1.16
	0.6	−49.85	−6.73	−0.50	1.08	1.54	1.63	1.57	1.45	1.19
	0.7	−68.26	−9.55	−1.06	1.09	1.71	1.83	1.76	1.58	1.21
	0.8	−89.52	−12.81	−1.72	1.10	1.91	2.07	1.97	1.73	1.22
	0.9	−113.64	−16.52	−2.47	1.10	2.12	2.32	2.20	1.88	1.21
	1.0	−140.62	−20.68	−3.33	1.09	2.35	2.60	2.44	2.03	1.16
0.7	0.1	0.22	1.03	1.12	1.14	1.14	1.14	1.16	1.20	1.35
	0.2	−3.00	0.62	1.10	1.21	1.23	1.24	1.26	1.31	1.49
	0.3	−8.74	−0.27	0.91	1.19	1.26	1.27	1.27	1.28	1.36
	0.4	−16.90	−1.59	0.58	1.11	1.25	1.27	1.24	1.18	1.06
	0.5	−26.99	−3.06	0.33	1.17	1.38	1.41	1.36	1.26	1.06
	0.6	−39.35	−4.86	0.02	1.22	1.54	1.57	1.50	1.35	1.05
	0.7	−53.97	−7.01	−0.35	1.29	1.72	1.76	1.65	1.45	1.02
	0.8	−70.87	−9.50	−0.79	1.35	1.91	1.97	1.82	1.54	0.96
	0.9	−90.04	−12.34	−1.31	1.41	2.12	2.19	2.00	1.64	0.86
	1.0	−111.50	−15.53	−1.89	1.46	2.34	2.43	2.19	1.73	0.72
0.8	0.1	0.46	1.08	1.14	1.15	1.15	1.16	1.17	1.22	1.38
	0.2	−2.20	0.76	1.14	1.22	1.24	1.24	1.26	1.31	1.49
	0.3	−7.04	−0.01	0.95	1.18	1.23	1.23	1.23	1.22	1.27
	0.4	−13.77	−1.06	0.71	1.13	1.24	1.24	1.20	1.13	1.00
	0.5	−22.11	−2.24	0.54	1.20	1.36	1.36	1.30	1.19	0.97
	0.6	−32.33	−3.69	0.31	1.27	1.50	1.50	1.41	1.25	0.90
	0.7	−44.42	−5.41	0.04	1.34	1.66	1.65	1.53	1.30	0.81
	0.8	−58.40	−7.42	−0.29	1.42	1.83	1.83	1.65	1.35	0.67
	0.9	−74.28	−9.72	−0.67	1.49	2.01	2.01	1.78	1.38	0.49
	1.0	−92.06	−12.30	−1.12	1.56	2.21	2.20	1.92	1.40	0.24

ED5-3 Tee, D_c < or = 250 mm, Converging (*Continued*)

		C_b Values (*Concluded*)								
		Q_b/Q_c								
A_s/A_c	A_b/A_c	0.1	0.2	0.3	0.4	0.5	0.6	0.7	0.8	0.9
0.9	0.1	0.62	1.12	1.16	1.16	1.16	1.17	1.19	1.24	1.41
	0.2	−1.67	0.85	1.16	1.22	1.23	1.24	1.25	1.30	1.48
	0.3	−5.95	0.12	0.95	1.14	1.18	1.18	1.16	1.15	1.14
	0.4	−11.68	−0.74	0.77	1.12	1.20	1.20	1.16	1.08	0.93
	0.5	−18.85	−1.74	0.63	1.18	1.31	1.30	1.23	1.11	0.86
	0.6	−27.63	−2.98	0.44	1.24	1.42	1.41	1.31	1.13	0.75
	0.7	−38.04	−4.45	0.21	1.30	1.55	1.53	1.39	1.14	0.58
	0.8	−50.07	−6.17	−0.07	1.36	1.69	1.66	1.47	1.13	0.37
	0.9	−63.75	−8.14	−0.40	1.42	1.83	1.79	1.54	1.11	0.09
	1.0	−79.08	−10.36	−0.79	1.46	1.98	1.92	1.61	1.06	−0.26
1.0	0.1	0.74	1.15	1.18	1.17	1.17	1.18	1.20	1.25	1.43
	0.2	−1.33	0.89	1.16	1.21	1.22	1.22	1.24	1.29	1.46
	0.3	−5.30	0.15	0.90	1.08	1.11	1.11	1.09	1.06	0.99
	0.4	−10.31	−0.57	0.78	1.09	1.16	1.15	1.11	1.03	0.86
	0.5	−16.71	−1.47	0.64	1.13	1.24	1.22	1.15	1.03	0.74
	0.6	−24.56	−2.59	0.46	1.17	1.32	1.30	1.20	1.01	0.57
	0.7	−33.87	−3.93	0.23	1.20	1.41	1.38	1.24	0.97	0.34
	0.8	−44.64	−5.49	−0.05	1.22	1.51	1.46	1.27	0.91	0.05
	0.9	−56.89	−7.29	−0.38	1.24	1.59	1.54	1.28	0.82	−0.33
	1.0	−70.62	−9.32	−0.77	1.24	1.68	1.61	1.28	0.69	−0.80

		C_s Values								
		Q_s/Q_c								
A_s/A_c	A_b/A_c	0.1	0.2	0.3	0.4	0.5	0.6	0.7	0.8	0.9
0.1	0.1	6.57	1.67	1.10	0.95	0.88	0.85	0.84	0.83	0.82
	0.2	4.13	1.39	1.03	0.92	0.87	0.85	0.83	0.83	0.82
	0.3	3.30	1.30	1.00	0.91	0.87	0.85	0.83	0.82	0.82
	0.4	2.89	1.24	0.99	0.90	0.86	0.84	0.83	0.82	0.82
	0.5	2.63	1.21	0.97	0.90	0.86	0.84	0.83	0.82	0.82
	0.6	2.45	1.18	0.97	0.89	0.86	0.84	0.83	0.82	0.82
	0.7	2.32	1.16	0.96	0.89	0.86	0.84	0.83	0.82	0.82
	0.8	2.22	1.15	0.95	0.89	0.85	0.84	0.83	0.82	0.82
	0.9	2.14	1.13	0.95	0.88	0.85	0.84	0.83	0.82	0.82
	1.0	2.07	1.12	0.94	0.88	0.85	0.84	0.83	0.82	0.82
0.2	0.1	34.53	5.26	2.11	1.29	0.98	0.84	0.76	0.71	0.68
	0.2	18.11	3.42	1.62	1.11	0.90	0.80	0.74	0.70	0.68
	0.3	12.67	2.79	1.45	1.04	0.87	0.78	0.73	0.70	0.68
	0.4	9.98	2.47	1.36	1.01	0.85	0.77	0.72	0.69	0.67
	0.5	8.39	2.27	1.30	0.98	0.84	0.76	0.72	0.69	0.67
	0.6	7.34	2.13	1.26	0.96	0.83	0.76	0.72	0.69	0.67
	0.7	6.61	2.02	1.22	0.95	0.82	0.75	0.71	0.69	0.67
	0.8	6.08	1.94	1.19	0.93	0.81	0.75	0.71	0.68	0.67
	0.9	5.68	1.87	1.17	0.92	0.80	0.74	0.70	0.68	0.66
	1.0	4.55	1.61	1.05	0.86	0.76	0.71	0.68	0.66	0.65
0.3	0.1	90.35	12.35	4.15	2.07	1.30	0.95	0.76	0.65	0.59
	0.2	44.33	7.19	2.80	1.57	1.08	0.84	0.71	0.63	0.57
	0.3	29.24	5.46	2.33	1.40	1.00	0.80	0.69	0.62	0.57
	0.4	21.88	4.59	2.09	1.30	0.96	0.78	0.67	0.61	0.56
	0.5	17.62	4.06	1.93	1.24	0.92	0.76	0.66	0.60	0.56
	0.6	14.90	3.71	1.82	1.19	0.90	0.74	0.65	0.59	0.55
	0.7	13.06	3.45	1.74	1.15	0.88	0.73	0.64	0.59	0.55
	0.8	11.78	3.26	1.67	1.12	0.86	0.72	0.63	0.58	0.54
	0.9	9.02	2.64	1.41	0.97	0.77	0.66	0.59	0.54	0.51
	1.0	8.36	2.52	1.36	0.95	0.75	0.65	0.58	0.54	0.51
0.4	0.1	167.76	22.21	7.04	3.22	1.81	1.17	0.84	0.64	0.52
	0.2	78.99	12.25	4.42	2.26	1.39	0.97	0.74	0.60	0.50
	0.3	50.14	8.96	3.54	1.92	1.24	0.90	0.70	0.57	0.49
	0.4	36.26	7.32	3.08	1.74	1.16	0.85	0.67	0.56	0.48
	0.5	28.38	6.35	2.80	1.63	1.10	0.82	0.65	0.54	0.47
	0.6	23.50	5.72	2.61	1.54	1.05	0.79	0.63	0.53	0.46
	0.7	20.32	5.27	2.46	1.47	1.02	0.77	0.62	0.52	0.45
	0.8	14.94	4.13	1.98	1.21	0.85	0.65	0.53	0.46	0.40
	0.9	13.55	3.88	1.89	1.16	0.82	0.63	0.52	0.45	0.39
	1.0	12.66	3.69	1.80	1.12	0.79	0.62	0.51	0.44	0.39

ED5-3 Tee, D_c < or = 250 mm, Converging (*Continued*)

		C_s Values (*Concluded*)								
		Q_s/Q_c								
A_s/A_c	A_b/A_c	0.1	0.2	0.3	0.4	0.5	0.6	0.7	0.8	0.9
0.5	0.1	252.09	33.17	10.32	4.56	2.44	1.47	0.97	0.67	0.49
	0.2	114.73	17.76	6.27	3.07	1.79	1.16	0.81	0.60	0.46
	0.3	70.56	12.71	4.92	2.56	1.56	1.05	0.75	0.56	0.44
	0.4	49.68	10.24	4.23	2.29	1.43	0.98	0.71	0.54	0.42
	0.5	38.12	8.81	3.81	2.11	1.34	0.93	0.68	0.52	0.41
	0.6	31.23	7.90	3.53	1.99	1.27	0.88	0.65	0.50	0.39
	0.7	21.87	6.00	2.75	1.57	1.01	0.71	0.52	0.40	0.32
	0.8	19.30	5.57	2.59	1.49	0.96	0.67	0.50	0.38	0.30
	0.9	17.84	5.27	2.46	1.42	0.92	0.65	0.48	0.37	0.29
	1.0	17.16	5.05	2.36	1.36	0.88	0.62	0.46	0.35	0.28
0.6	0.1	323.56	42.99	13.40	5.88	3.09	1.80	1.12	0.73	0.48
	0.2	142.32	22.64	8.06	3.91	2.23	1.39	0.92	0.63	0.44
	0.3	84.89	16.05	6.28	3.24	1.92	1.23	0.83	0.58	0.41
	0.4	58.43	12.90	5.39	2.88	1.75	1.14	0.78	0.55	0.39
	0.5	44.34	11.13	4.86	2.66	1.63	1.07	0.74	0.52	0.37
	0.6	29.06	8.20	3.69	2.04	1.25	0.81	0.55	0.38	0.26
	0.7	24.71	7.51	3.44	1.91	1.18	0.77	0.52	0.35	0.24
	0.8	22.56	7.06	3.26	1.81	1.11	0.72	0.48	0.33	0.22
	0.9	21.89	6.78	3.12	1.73	1.06	0.68	0.45	0.30	0.20
	1.0	22.24	6.61	3.00	1.65	1.00	0.65	0.43	0.28	0.18
0.7	0.1	360.67	49.26	15.65	6.94	3.65	2.11	1.29	0.80	0.49
	0.2	152.32	25.82	9.48	4.66	2.65	1.63	1.04	0.68	0.44
	0.3	87.85	18.38	7.46	3.88	2.29	1.44	0.94	0.62	0.40
	0.4	59.34	14.92	6.47	3.48	2.09	1.33	0.87	0.58	0.37
	0.5	35.18	10.56	4.78	2.60	1.55	0.97	0.62	0.38	0.22
	0.6	28.26	9.51	4.41	2.42	1.45	0.90	0.57	0.35	0.19
	0.7	25.45	8.91	4.16	2.28	1.36	0.85	0.53	0.32	0.17
	0.8	25.21	8.60	3.99	2.18	1.29	0.79	0.49	0.28	0.14
	0.9	26.68	8.48	3.86	2.08	1.22	0.74	0.45	0.25	0.12
	1.0	29.34	8.49	3.77	2.01	1.16	0.70	0.41	0.22	0.10
0.8	0.1	343.46	49.71	16.47	7.52	4.02	2.35	1.43	0.87	0.51
	0.2	136.74	26.38	10.30	5.22	3.01	1.85	1.17	0.74	0.45
	0.3	75.52	19.20	8.32	4.45	2.64	1.66	1.06	0.67	0.41
	0.4	37.55	12.79	5.92	3.23	1.91	1.17	0.72	0.42	0.21
	0.5	27.25	11.28	5.41	2.98	1.77	1.08	0.66	0.37	0.18
	0.6	24.23	10.57	5.10	2.81	1.66	1.01	0.60	0.33	0.14
	0.7	25.36	10.32	4.91	2.69	1.57	0.94	0.55	0.29	0.11
	0.8	29.09	10.37	4.80	2.59	1.50	0.88	0.50	0.25	0.08
	0.9	34.55	10.60	4.74	2.50	1.42	0.82	0.46	0.21	0.05
	1.0	41.23	10.98	4.71	2.43	1.36	0.77	0.41	0.18	0.01
0.9	0.1	256.86	42.66	15.41	7.44	4.14	2.48	1.53	0.93	0.54
	0.2	90.70	23.73	10.34	5.54	3.28	2.05	1.30	0.81	0.47
	0.3	29.93	14.20	6.95	3.86	2.30	1.41	0.85	0.48	0.22
	0.4	16.27	12.21	6.28	3.55	2.12	1.29	0.77	0.42	0.18
	0.5	14.80	11.58	5.96	3.35	1.99	1.20	0.70	0.37	0.14
	0.6	19.43	11.62	5.81	3.23	1.89	1.13	0.64	0.32	0.10
	0.7	27.55	12.06	5.77	3.14	1.81	1.06	0.59	0.27	0.06
	0.8	37.84	12.73	5.79	3.07	1.74	0.99	0.53	0.23	0.02
	0.9	49.59	13.57	5.85	3.01	1.67	0.93	0.48	0.18	−0.02
	1.0	62.35	14.52	5.94	2.97	1.61	0.87	0.42	0.14	−0.06
1.0	0.1	94.95	27.29	12.24	6.64	3.96	2.48	1.57	0.98	0.57
	0.2	−6.40	12.70	7.32	4.31	2.64	1.64	1.00	0.56	0.25
	0.3	−17.35	10.90	6.66	3.97	2.44	1.51	0.90	0.49	0.20
	0.4	−11.05	11.02	6.50	3.82	2.32	1.41	0.83	0.43	0.15
	0.5	2.15	11.91	6.54	3.74	2.23	1.33	0.76	0.38	0.10
	0.6	18.80	13.18	6.67	3.70	2.16	1.26	0.70	0.32	0.06
	0.7	37.42	14.67	6.86	3.68	2.09	1.19	0.63	0.26	0.01
	0.8	57.27	16.30	7.09	3.67	2.03	1.12	0.57	0.21	−0.04
	0.9	77.95	18.02	7.35	3.66	1.97	1.06	0.51	0.15	−0.09
	1.0	99.20	19.80	7.61	3.67	1.92	1.00	0.45	0.10	−0.14

D5-3, D_c > 250 mm, Converging

		C_b Values								
		Q_b/Q_c								
A_s/A_c	A_b/A_c	0.1	0.2	0.3	0.4	0.5	0.6	0.7	0.8	0.9
0.1	0.1	−13.86	−1.90	0.03	0.61	0.83	0.92	0.96	0.98	0.98
	0.2	−58.25	−10.48	−2.80	−0.51	0.36	0.74	0.90	0.96	0.96
	0.3	−132.23	−24.75	−7.50	−2.36	−0.39	0.45	0.82	0.96	0.96
	0.4	−235.84	−44.74	−14.07	−4.93	−1.43	0.07	0.73	0.98	0.99
	0.5	−369.15	−70.45	−22.51	−8.23	−2.76	−0.42	0.61	1.01	1.05
	0.6	−532.21	−101.89	−32.83	−12.26	−4.38	−1.00	0.48	1.06	1.13
	0.7	−725.06	−139.08	−45.04	−17.02	−6.30	−1.70	0.33	1.13	1.24
	0.8	−947.77	−182.03	−59.15	−22.53	−8.52	−2.50	0.16	1.22	1.38
	0.9	−1200.	−230.76	−75.15	−28.78	−11.03	−3.40	−0.03	1.32	1.55
	1.0	−1483.	−285.27	−93.06	−35.78	−13.84	−4.41	−0.25	1.43	1.75
0.2	0.1	−5.86	−0.35	0.54	0.81	0.91	0.95	0.97	0.97	0.96
	0.2	−26.08	−4.19	−0.70	0.33	0.71	0.87	0.93	0.95	0.93
	0.3	−59.71	−10.53	−2.72	−0.43	0.43	0.78	0.91	0.95	0.91
	0.4	−106.78	−19.39	−5.53	−1.46	0.05	0.67	0.91	0.97	0.91
	0.5	−167.36	−30.77	−9.12	−2.78	−0.42	0.55	0.93	1.02	0.93
	0.6	−241.50	−44.68	−13.50	−4.37	−0.97	0.42	0.96	1.10	0.98
	0.7	−329.25	−61.15	−18.68	−6.25	−1.62	0.27	1.02	1.21	1.06
	0.8	−430.67	−80.18	−24.67	−8.42	−2.37	0.10	1.09	1.35	1.17
	0.9	−545.81	−101.78	−31.47	−10.89	−3.22	−0.08	1.17	1.52	1.31
	1.0	−674.72	−125.98	−39.08	−13.64	−4.17	−0.28	1.28	1.72	1.48
0.3	0.1	−3.26	0.15	0.70	0.86	0.93	0.96	0.97	0.97	0.95
	0.2	−15.50	−2.16	−0.04	0.58	0.81	0.90	0.93	0.94	0.91
	0.3	−35.76	−5.90	−1.20	0.16	0.66	0.85	0.92	0.92	0.88
	0.4	−64.09	−11.09	−2.78	−0.38	0.48	0.82	0.93	0.94	0.86
	0.5	−100.54	−17.73	−4.78	−1.06	0.29	0.80	0.97	0.98	0.87
	0.6	−145.16	−25.85	−7.21	−1.86	0.06	0.80	1.05	1.05	0.90
	0.7	−198.01	−35.46	−10.08	−2.81	−0.19	0.82	1.15	1.16	0.96
	0.8	−259.13	−46.56	−13.39	−3.89	−0.47	0.85	1.28	1.30	1.05
	0.9	−328.59	−59.18	−17.15	−5.11	−0.78	0.89	1.44	1.47	1.17
	1.0	−406.44	−73.33	−21.37	−6.48	−1.12	0.94	1.63	1.68	1.32
0.4	0.1	−1.99	0.38	0.77	0.89	0.94	0.96	0.97	0.97	0.95
	0.2	−10.31	−1.18	0.26	0.69	0.84	0.91	0.93	0.93	0.90
	0.3	−23.96	−3.65	−0.48	0.43	0.75	0.88	0.91	0.91	0.86
	0.4	−42.98	−7.03	−1.46	0.11	0.67	0.87	0.93	0.91	0.84
	0.5	−67.44	−11.35	−2.69	−0.26	0.59	0.90	0.97	0.94	0.84
	0.6	−97.39	−16.60	−4.17	−0.69	0.52	0.95	1.06	1.01	0.87
	0.7	−132.88	−22.81	−5.91	−1.17	0.46	1.03	1.17	1.11	0.92
	0.8	−173.96	−29.99	−7.90	−1.73	0.40	1.15	1.33	1.24	1.00
	0.9	−220.69	−38.15	−10.16	−2.35	0.35	1.29	1.51	1.40	1.11
	1.0	−273.12	−47.31	−12.70	−3.04	0.29	1.45	1.74	1.61	1.26
0.5	0.1	−1.26	0.51	0.81	0.90	0.94	0.96	0.97	0.96	0.95
	0.2	−7.26	−0.62	0.43	0.75	0.86	0.91	0.93	0.93	0.90
	0.3	−16.99	−2.35	−0.07	0.57	0.80	0.89	0.91	0.90	0.87
	0.4	−30.49	−4.67	−0.72	0.38	0.76	0.89	0.92	0.90	0.85
	0.5	−47.82	−7.61	−1.50	0.19	0.75	0.93	0.97	0.93	0.85
	0.6	−69.03	−11.17	−2.42	−0.03	0.76	1.01	1.05	0.98	0.88
	0.7	−94.17	−15.37	−3.49	−0.26	0.80	1.13	1.17	1.07	0.93
	0.8	−123.30	−20.22	−4.71	−0.50	0.87	1.29	1.33	1.20	1.02
	0.9	−156.48	−25.73	−6.09	−0.77	0.96	1.48	1.53	1.36	1.13
	1.0	−193.74	−31.92	−7.63	−1.07	1.06	1.71	1.77	1.56	1.28
0.6	0.1	−0.79	0.59	0.83	0.91	0.95	0.96	0.97	0.97	0.95
	0.2	−5.28	−0.27	0.54	0.78	0.88	0.91	0.93	0.93	0.91
	0.3	−12.43	−1.51	0.18	0.66	0.83	0.89	0.91	0.91	0.89
	0.4	−22.29	−3.15	−0.25	0.55	0.82	0.90	0.92	0.91	0.88
	0.5	−34.92	−5.19	−0.74	0.46	0.84	0.95	0.96	0.93	0.89
	0.6	−50.35	−7.64	−1.30	0.38	0.91	1.05	1.04	0.98	0.93
	0.7	−68.66	−10.52	−1.94	0.32	1.01	1.18	1.16	1.07	0.99
	0.8	−89.89	−13.83	−2.65	0.26	1.15	1.36	1.33	1.19	1.08
	0.9	−114.09	−17.61	−3.46	0.22	1.32	1.59	1.53	1.35	1.21
	1.0	−141.33	−21.84	−4.35	0.18	1.54	1.85	1.77	1.54	1.37

D5-3, D_c > 250 mm, Converging (*Continued*)

		C_b Values (*Continued*)								
		Q_b/Q_c								
A_s/A_c	A_b/A_c	0.1	0.2	0.3	0.4	0.5	0.6	0.7	0.8	0.9
0.7	0.1	−0.47	0.65	0.85	0.92	0.95	0.96	0.97	0.97	0.96
	0.2	−3.90	−0.03	0.61	0.81	0.89	0.92	0.94	0.94	0.93
	0.3	−9.25	−0.94	0.35	0.72	0.85	0.90	0.92	0.92	0.92
	0.4	−16.54	−2.10	0.07	0.66	0.85	0.91	0.93	0.92	0.92
	0.5	−25.85	−3.51	−0.22	0.64	0.90	0.97	0.97	0.94	0.95
	0.6	−37.21	−5.18	−0.54	0.65	1.00	1.07	1.05	1.00	1.00
	0.7	−50.68	−7.13	−0.87	0.70	1.14	1.22	1.17	1.08	1.08
	0.8	−66.31	−9.37	−1.24	0.78	1.33	1.41	1.33	1.21	1.20
	0.9	−84.17	−11.92	−1.64	0.89	1.56	1.65	1.53	1.36	1.34
	1.0	−104.29	−14.78	−2.09	1.03	1.84	1.94	1.78	1.56	1.52
0.8	0.1	−0.23	0.69	0.87	0.93	0.95	0.97	0.97	0.98	0.97
	0.2	−2.90	0.15	0.67	0.83	0.90	0.93	0.94	0.95	0.96
	0.3	−6.91	−0.53	0.47	0.76	0.87	0.91	0.93	0.94	0.96
	0.4	−12.31	−1.34	0.30	0.74	0.88	0.93	0.94	0.95	0.98
	0.5	−19.16	−2.29	0.15	0.77	0.94	0.99	0.98	0.98	1.03
	0.6	−27.50	−3.39	0.01	0.84	1.06	1.09	1.06	1.03	1.11
	0.7	−37.38	−4.66	−0.11	0.97	1.23	1.24	1.18	1.12	1.21
	0.8	−48.87	−6.11	−0.22	1.15	1.46	1.45	1.35	1.25	1.35
	0.9	−62.01	−7.75	−0.33	1.37	1.73	1.70	1.55	1.41	1.52
	1.0	−76.85	−9.59	−0.44	1.63	2.06	2.00	1.80	1.61	1.73
0.9	0.1	−0.05	0.72	0.88	0.93	0.96	0.97	0.98	0.99	0.99
	0.2	−2.14	0.28	0.71	0.85	0.91	0.94	0.96	0.97	0.99
	0.3	−5.14	−0.21	0.57	0.80	0.88	0.92	0.95	0.97	1.02
	0.4	−9.09	−0.76	0.47	0.80	0.91	0.94	0.96	0.98	1.06
	0.5	−14.06	−1.36	0.42	0.86	0.98	1.01	1.01	1.02	1.14
	0.6	−20.08	−2.04	0.42	0.99	1.11	1.12	1.09	1.09	1.24
	0.7	−27.21	−2.79	0.47	1.17	1.30	1.27	1.21	1.19	1.38
	0.8	−35.50	−3.63	0.55	1.42	1.55	1.49	1.38	1.32	1.55
	0.9	−45.01	−4.57	0.66	1.72	1.86	1.75	1.59	1.49	1.75
	1.0	−55.79	−5.64	0.80	2.08	2.22	2.06	1.84	1.69	1.99
1.0	0.1	0.09	0.75	0.89	0.94	0.97	0.98	0.99	1.00	1.01
	0.2	−1.54	0.39	0.74	0.87	0.92	0.95	0.97	0.99	1.03
	0.3	−3.75	0.03	0.64	0.83	0.90	0.94	0.97	1.00	1.08
	0.4	−6.57	−0.32	0.61	0.85	0.93	0.97	0.99	1.03	1.16
	0.5	−10.05	−0.65	0.64	0.94	1.02	1.03	1.04	1.08	1.26
	0.6	−14.24	−0.98	0.74	1.10	1.16	1.15	1.13	1.16	1.40
	0.7	−19.20	−1.32	0.91	1.33	1.37	1.31	1.26	1.27	1.57
	0.8	−24.98	−1.69	1.14	1.63	1.63	1.53	1.43	1.41	1.78
	0.9	−31.62	−2.10	1.42	2.00	1.96	1.80	1.64	1.59	2.02
	1.0	−39.19	−2.55	1.76	2.43	2.35	2.12	1.90	1.81	2.30

		C_s Values								
		Q_b/Q_c								
A_s/A_c	A_b/A_c	0.1	0.2	0.3	0.4	0.5	0.6	0.7	0.8	0.9
0.1	0.1	7.87	1.70	1.07	0.92	0.86	0.84	0.82	0.82	0.81
	0.2	4.21	1.30	0.97	0.88	0.85	0.83	0.82	0.81	0.81
	0.3	3.02	1.16	0.93	0.87	0.84	0.83	0.82	0.81	0.81
	0.4	2.45	1.10	0.92	0.86	0.84	0.83	0.82	0.81	0.81
	0.5	2.13	1.07	0.91	0.86	0.84	0.82	0.82	0.81	0.81
	0.6	1.93	1.04	0.90	0.86	0.84	0.82	0.82	0.81	0.81
	0.7	1.80	1.03	0.90	0.85	0.83	0.82	0.82	0.81	0.81
	0.8	1.72	1.02	0.90	0.85	0.83	0.82	0.82	0.81	0.81
	0.9	1.67	1.01	0.89	0.85	0.83	0.82	0.82	0.81	0.81
	1.0	1.63	1.01	0.89	0.85	0.83	0.82	0.82	0.81	0.81
0.2	0.1	44.93	6.00	2.16	1.24	0.92	0.78	0.71	0.67	0.65
	0.2	20.43	3.28	1.45	0.98	0.81	0.73	0.69	0.66	0.64
	0.3	12.53	2.40	1.22	0.90	0.77	0.71	0.68	0.66	0.64
	0.4	8.78	1.98	1.12	0.86	0.76	0.70	0.67	0.66	0.64
	0.5	6.69	1.75	1.06	0.84	0.75	0.70	0.67	0.65	0.64
	0.6	5.43	1.61	1.02	0.83	0.74	0.70	0.67	0.65	0.64
	0.7	4.64	1.52	1.00	0.82	0.74	0.70	0.67	0.65	0.64
	0.8	4.15	1.47	0.98	0.81	0.74	0.69	0.67	0.65	0.64
	0.9	3.86	1.43	0.97	0.81	0.74	0.69	0.67	0.65	0.64
	1.0	3.71	1.42	0.97	0.81	0.73	0.69	0.67	0.65	0.64

D5-3, D_c > 250 mm, Converging (*Continued*)

		C_s Values (*Continued*)								
		Q_b/Q_c								
A_s/A_c	A_b/A_c	0.1	0.2	0.3	0.4	0.5	0.6	0.7	0.8	0.9
0.3	0.1	118.96	14.64	4.45	2.03	1.20	0.84	0.66	0.57	0.51
	0.2	51.24	7.11	2.49	1.33	0.90	0.70	0.60	0.54	0.50
	0.3	29.57	4.70	1.87	1.10	0.80	0.66	0.58	0.53	0.50
	0.4	19.40	3.57	1.58	1.00	0.76	0.64	0.57	0.52	0.50
	0.5	13.84	2.96	1.42	0.94	0.73	0.62	0.56	0.52	0.50
	0.6	10.58	2.59	1.32	0.90	0.72	0.62	0.56	0.52	0.49
	0.7	8.64	2.38	1.27	0.88	0.71	0.61	0.56	0.52	0.49
	0.8	7.52	2.25	1.23	0.87	0.70	0.61	0.56	0.52	0.49
	0.9	6.95	2.19	1.22	0.87	0.70	0.61	0.56	0.52	0.49
	1.0	6.76	2.17	1.21	0.86	0.70	0.61	0.55	0.52	0.49
0.4	0.1	218.57	26.35	7.61	3.18	1.65	1.00	0.68	0.50	0.40
	0.2	90.30	12.10	3.91	1.85	1.08	0.74	0.55	0.45	0.38
	0.3	49.68	7.59	2.74	1.42	0.90	0.65	0.51	0.43	0.37
	0.4	30.96	5.51	2.21	1.23	0.82	0.61	0.49	0.42	0.37
	0.5	21.00	4.40	1.92	1.13	0.78	0.59	0.48	0.42	0.37
	0.6	15.43	3.78	1.76	1.07	0.75	0.58	0.48	0.41	0.37
	0.7	12.36	3.44	1.67	1.04	0.74	0.57	0.48	0.41	0.37
	0.8	10.86	3.27	1.63	1.02	0.73	0.57	0.47	0.41	0.37
	0.9	10.40	3.22	1.61	1.01	0.73	0.57	0.47	0.41	0.37
	1.0	10.67	3.25	1.62	1.02	0.73	0.57	0.47	0.41	0.37
0.5	0.1	320.10	38.52	10.97	4.44	2.18	1.21	0.72	0.46	0.31
	0.2	126.36	16.99	5.39	2.42	1.32	0.81	0.54	0.38	0.28
	0.3	65.94	10.28	3.65	1.79	1.05	0.68	0.48	0.35	0.27
	0.4	38.84	7.27	2.87	1.51	0.93	0.63	0.45	0.34	0.27
	0.5	25.07	5.74	2.47	1.37	0.87	0.60	0.44	0.33	0.26
	0.6	17.98	4.95	2.27	1.29	0.84	0.58	0.43	0.33	0.26
	0.7	14.69	4.58	2.17	1.26	0.82	0.58	0.43	0.33	0.26
	0.8	13.78	4.48	2.15	1.25	0.82	0.57	0.43	0.33	0.26
	0.9	14.45	4.56	2.17	1.26	0.82	0.58	0.43	0.33	0.26
	1.0	16.24	4.76	2.22	1.28	0.83	0.58	0.43	0.33	0.26
0.6	0.1	393.66	47.81	13.66	5.50	2.64	1.40	0.78	0.44	0.23
	0.2	146.22	20.32	6.54	2.92	1.54	0.89	0.54	0.33	0.20
	0.3	70.93	11.95	4.37	2.13	1.20	0.73	0.46	0.30	0.18
	0.4	38.66	8.37	3.44	1.80	1.06	0.67	0.43	0.28	0.18
	0.5	23.61	6.70	3.00	1.64	0.99	0.64	0.42	0.28	0.18
	0.6	17.17	5.98	2.82	1.57	0.97	0.62	0.41	0.27	0.18
	0.7	15.64	5.81	2.77	1.56	0.96	0.62	0.41	0.27	0.18
	0.8	17.19	5.98	2.82	1.57	0.97	0.62	0.41	0.27	0.18
	0.9	20.79	6.38	2.92	1.61	0.98	0.63	0.42	0.27	0.18
	1.0	25.82	6.94	3.07	1.66	1.00	0.64	0.42	0.28	0.18
0.7	0.1	409.10	50.88	14.82	6.03	2.90	1.51	0.81	0.41	0.17
	0.2	137.78	20.74	7.01	3.21	1.70	0.96	0.54	0.29	0.13
	0.3	58.74	11.96	4.73	2.39	1.34	0.79	0.47	0.26	0.12
	0.4	27.78	8.52	3.84	2.06	1.21	0.73	0.44	0.24	0.11
	0.5	16.04	7.21	3.50	1.94	1.15	0.71	0.43	0.24	0.11
	0.6	13.91	6.97	3.44	1.92	1.14	0.70	0.42	0.24	0.11
	0.7	17.28	7.35	3.54	1.95	1.16	0.71	0.43	0.24	0.11
	0.8	24.08	8.10	3.73	2.02	1.19	0.72	0.43	0.24	0.11
	0.9	33.17	9.11	3.99	2.12	1.23	0.74	0.44	0.25	0.11
	1.0	43.86	10.30	4.30	2.23	1.28	0.76	0.45	0.25	0.11
0.8	0.1	341.98	45.02	13.75	5.80	2.86	1.50	0.79	0.38	0.12
	0.2	92.97	17.35	6.57	3.21	1.75	0.99	0.55	0.27	0.08
	0.3	26.98	10.02	4.67	2.52	1.46	0.86	0.48	0.24	0.07
	0.4	6.75	7.77	4.09	2.31	1.37	0.81	0.46	0.23	0.06
	0.5	4.83	7.56	4.03	2.29	1.36	0.81	0.46	0.23	0.06
	0.6	12.05	8.36	4.24	2.37	1.39	0.83	0.47	0.23	0.07
	0.7	24.51	9.75	4.60	2.49	1.45	0.85	0.48	0.24	0.07
	0.8	40.23	11.49	5.05	2.66	1.52	0.88	0.50	0.24	0.07
	0.9	58.13	13.48	5.57	2.85	1.60	0.92	0.51	0.25	0.07
	1.0	77.56	15.64	6.13	3.05	1.68	0.96	0.53	0.26	0.08

D5-3, D_c > 250 mm, Converging (*Continued*)

		C_s Values (*Concluded*)								
		Q_b/Q_c								
A_s/A_c	A_b/A_c	0.1	0.2	0.3	0.4	0.5	0.6	0.7	0.8	0.9
0.9	0.1	179.59	28.81	10.06	4.66	2.45	1.34	0.71	0.32	0.07
	0.2	10.77	10.05	5.20	2.91	1.70	0.99	0.55	0.25	0.04
	0.3	−21.27	6.49	4.28	2.57	1.56	0.93	0.52	0.24	0.04
	0.4	−19.11	6.73	4.34	2.60	1.57	0.93	0.52	0.24	0.04
	0.5	−3.28	8.49	4.80	2.76	1.64	0.97	0.54	0.24	0.04
	0.6	19.39	11.01	5.45	3.00	1.74	1.01	0.56	0.25	0.04
	0.7	45.97	13.96	6.21	3.27	1.86	1.07	0.58	0.27	0.05
	0.8	74.99	17.18	7.05	3.58	1.98	1.13	0.61	0.28	0.05
	0.9	105.64	20.59	7.93	3.89	2.12	1.19	0.64	0.29	0.06
	1.0	137.43	24.12	8.85	4.23	2.26	1.26	0.67	0.31	0.06
1.0	0.1	−73.14	2.79	3.92	2.68	1.70	1.04	0.58	0.26	0.03
	0.2	−99.78	−0.17	3.15	2.40	1.58	0.98	0.56	0.25	0.02
	0.3	−75.42	2.54	3.85	2.65	1.69	1.03	0.58	0.26	0.03
	0.4	−38.31	6.66	4.92	3.04	1.86	1.11	0.62	0.28	0.03
	0.5	3.90	11.35	6.14	3.48	2.04	1.20	0.66	0.29	0.04
	0.6	48.66	16.32	7.43	3.94	2.24	1.29	0.70	0.31	0.04
	0.7	94.88	21.46	8.76	4.43	2.45	1.38	0.75	0.33	0.05
	0.8	142.01	26.70	10.12	4.92	2.66	1.48	0.79	0.35	0.06
	0.9	189.74	32.00	11.49	5.41	2.87	1.58	0.84	0.37	0.07
	1.0	237.90	37.35	12.88	5.92	3.08	1.68	0.88	0.39	0.07

ED5-6 Capped Wye, Branch with 45-Degree Elbow, Branch 90 Degrees to Main, Converging, r/D_b = 1.5

A_b/A_c	0.1	0.2	0.3	0.4	0.5	0.6	0.7	0.8	0.9	1.0
C_b	1.02	0.97	0.93	0.88	0.84	0.79	0.75	0.70	0.66	0.61

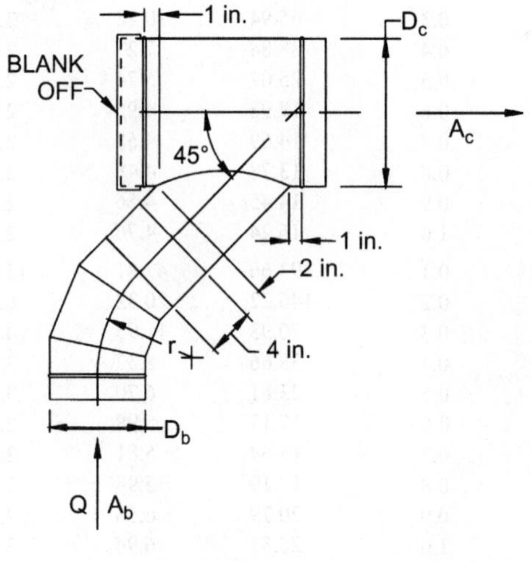

ED5-9 Symmetrical Wye, 60 Degree, $D_{b1} \geq D_{b2}$, Converging

		C_{b1} Values								
		Q_{b1}/Q_c								
A_{b1}/A_c	A_{b2}/A_c	0.1	0.2	0.3	0.4	0.5	0.6	0.7	0.8	0.9
0.1	0.1	−3.00	−0.50	−0.11	0.06	0.12	0.14	0.14	0.13	0.11
0.2	0.1	−16.00	−3.00	−1.01	0.01	0.32	0.44	0.49	0.56	0.49
	0.2	−11.95	−1.89	−0.09	0.41	0.62	0.74	0.80	0.80	0.79
0.3	0.1	−54.00	−11.25	−3.57	−0.43	−0.22	0.38	0.55	1.41	1.22
	0.2	−45.45	−9.39	−2.44	−0.41	0.33	0.68	0.89	1.03	1.13
	0.3	−16.88	−2.92	−0.09	0.59	0.85	1.02	1.12	1.12	1.22
0.4	0.1	−97.28	−18.48	−6.35	−1.58	−0.57	−0.15	0.23	0.35	0.50
	0.2	−72.04	−14.00	−4.26	−1.24	−0.32	0.09	0.40	0.50	0.62
	0.3	−52.95	−9.91	−2.86	−0.91	−0.06	0.32	0.56	0.64	0.73
	0.4	−40.00	−6.22	−2.15	−0.57	0.19	0.56	0.72	0.79	0.85
0.5	0.1	−167.71	−32.20	−10.05	−2.52	−1.25	−0.26	0.17	0.34	0.36
	0.2	−126.04	−23.80	−7.44	−2.64	−0.85	−0.13	0.16	0.26	0.28
	0.3	−91.07	−16.91	−5.16	−1.73	−0.46	0.04	0.23	0.29	0.28
	0.4	−56.41	−10.07	−2.90	−0.82	−0.07	0.21	0.30	0.31	0.29
	0.5	−30.58	−5.23	−1.06	0.00	0.32	0.43	0.47	0.47	0.41

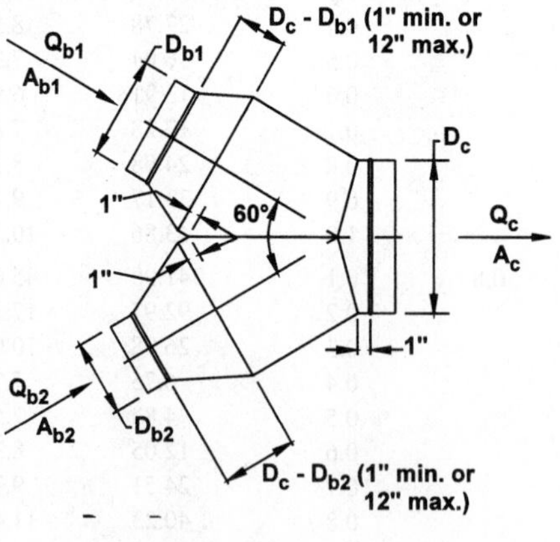

ED5-9 Symmetrical Wye, 60 Degree, $D_{b1} \geq D_{b2}$, Converging (*Continued*)

C_{b1} Values (*Concluded*)

		Q_{b1}/Q_c								
A_{b1}/A_c	A_{b2}/A_c	0.1	0.2	0.3	0.4	0.5	0.6	0.7	0.8	0.9
0.6	0.1	−299.02	−55.99	−16.77	−5.89	−2.09	−0.54	0.11	0.25	0.23
	0.2	−209.81	−39.31	−12.13	−4.35	−1.54	−0.40	0.06	0.25	0.23
	0.3	−147.43	−27.69	−8.75	−3.20	−1.13	−0.29	0.07	0.23	0.22
	0.4	−85.06	−16.07	−5.38	−2.04	−0.71	−0.17	0.08	0.23	0.22
	0.5	−58.22	−11.03	−3.84	−1.49	−0.50	−0.09	0.11	0.23	0.22
	0.6	−40.57	−7.86	−2.60	−0.99	−0.32	0.00	0.14	0.23	0.22
0.7	0.1	−420.02	−77.23	−23.37	−8.01	−3.30	−1.46	−0.71	−0.10	0.03
	0.2	−285.70	−53.45	−16.65	−6.05	−2.52	−1.02	−0.46	−0.02	0.06
	0.3	−195.01	−37.35	−12.21	−4.72	−1.87	−0.77	−0.14	0.04	0.09
	0.4	−104.16	−21.18	−7.20	−3.23	−1.37	−0.39	−0.10	0.08	0.12
	0.5	−67.21	−13.02	−4.52	−1.78	−0.73	−0.26	−0.03	0.12	0.15
	0.6	−49.01	−9.63	−3.13	−1.28	−0.51	−0.14	−0.02	0.16	0.17
	0.7	−59.33	−10.05	−2.53	−0.54	−0.21	−0.09	−0.01	0.23	0.24
0.8	0.1	−518.26	−95.93	−30.34	−11.09	−4.30	−2.51	−1.58	−0.63	−0.31
	0.2	−373.33	−69.73	−21.93	−8.08	−3.84	−1.96	−1.31	−0.50	−0.24
	0.3	−247.31	−48.35	−16.32	−6.65	−2.89	−1.51	−0.49	−0.30	−0.16
	0.4	−120.88	−26.76	−9.24	−4.80	−2.30	−0.71	−0.39	−0.20	−0.08
	0.5	−72.08	−14.20	−4.98	−2.00	−1.02	−0.53	−0.26	−0.10	0.01
	0.6	−55.91	−11.20	−3.56	−1.60	−0.77	−0.36	−0.13	0.01	0.05
	0.7	−35.96	−7.20	−2.31	−1.08	−0.45	−0.09	0.03	0.11	0.13
	0.8	−16.00	−3.20	−1.07	−0.56	−0.13	0.18	0.20	0.20	0.21
0.9	0.1	−629.39	−114.67	−35.12	−13.73	−6.55	−3.65	−2.25	−1.20	−0.70
	0.2	−473.23	−88.43	−27.99	−11.44	−5.67	−3.21	−2.07	−1.11	−0.65
	0.3	−303.64	−60.65	−21.13	−9.65	−4.91	−2.87	−1.51	−0.95	−0.58
	0.4	−216.44	−44.78	−16.20	−8.35	−4.46	−2.31	−1.43	−0.87	−0.52
	0.5	−116.49	−28.35	−12.15	−6.45	−3.65	−2.19	−1.35	−0.81	−0.47
	0.6	−98.16	−25.31	−10.76	−5.82	−3.48	−2.16	−1.35	−0.81	−0.49
	0.7	−78.15	−21.31	−9.54	−5.37	−3.28	−1.99	−1.25	−0.75	−0.44
	0.8	−58.15	−17.32	−8.33	−4.93	−3.08	−1.82	−1.15	−0.69	−0.39
	0.9	−72.90	−18.23	−8.10	−4.56	−2.92	−1.92	−1.29	−0.66	−0.39
1.0	0.1	−677.01	−124.30	−37.45	−16.24	−8.10	−4.89	−3.06	−1.95	−1.23
	0.2	−585.16	−109.39	−34.85	−15.63	−8.00	−4.86	−3.06	−1.95	−1.23
	0.3	−363.31	−74.20	−26.68	−13.44	−7.60	−4.72	−2.96	−1.88	−1.17
	0.4	−345.54	−68.75	−25.56	−13.13	−7.40	−4.58	−2.92	−1.84	−1.16
	0.5	−175.00	−47.50	−22.22	−12.81	−7.40	−4.58	−2.92	−1.84	−1.16
	0.6	−155.00	−45.00	−21.00	−11.88	−7.40	−4.77	−3.13	−2.02	−1.28
	0.7	−136.79	−41.38	−19.95	−11.58	−7.40	−4.77	−3.13	−2.02	−1.28
	0.8	−118.58	−37.76	−18.91	−11.29	−7.40	−4.77	−3.13	−2.02	−1.28
	0.9	−100.29	−34.13	−17.90	−10.99	−7.39	−4.77	−3.13	−2.02	−1.28
	1.0	−82.00	−30.50	−16.89	−10.69	−7.39	−4.77	−3.13	−2.02	−1.28

C_{b1} Values

		Q_{b2}/Q_c								
A_{b1}/A_c	A_{b2}/A_c	0.1	0.2	0.3	0.4	0.5	0.6	0.7	0.8	0.9
0.1	0.1	−3.00	−0.50	−0.11	0.06	0.12	0.14	0.14	0.13	0.11
0.2	0.1	−2.70	−0.04	0.23	0.15	0.16	0.18	0.20	0.17	0.16
	0.2	−11.95	−1.89	−0.09	0.41	0.62	0.74	0.80	0.80	0.79
0.3	0.1	−2.12	0.12	0.33	0.22	0.22	0.23	0.26	0.22	0.22
	0.2	−2.00	−0.30	0.22	0.42	0.61	0.73	0.78	0.77	0.76
	0.3	−16.88	−2.92	−0.09	0.59	0.85	1.02	1.12	1.12	1.22
0.4	0.1	−2.38	−0.17	0.13	0.23	0.25	0.24	0.23	0.24	0.24
	0.2	−6.95	−1.00	0.16	0.53	0.67	0.71	0.72	0.72	0.71
	0.3	−16.21	−2.90	−0.44	0.40	0.79	0.98	1.05	1.06	1.05
	0.4	−40.00	−6.22	−2.15	−0.57	0.19	0.56	0.72	0.79	0.85
0.5	0.1	−1.58	0.11	0.33	0.31	0.32	0.33	0.34	0.32	0.32
	0.2	−4.82	−0.01	0.56	0.71	0.82	0.89	0.92	0.90	0.89
	0.3	−12.27	−1.17	0.44	0.88	1.11	1.25	1.29	1.25	1.23
	0.4	−22.40	−2.93	−0.21	0.48	0.73	0.84	0.88	0.87	0.82
	0.5	−30.58	−5.23	−1.06	0.00	0.32	0.43	0.47	0.46	0.41

ED5-9 Symmetrical Wye, 60 Degree, $D_{b1} \geq D_{b2}$, Converging (*Continued*)

C_{b1} Values (*Concluded*)

		Q_{b2}/Q_c								
A_{b1}/A_c	A_{b2}/A_c	0.1	0.2	0.3	0.4	0.5	0.6	0.7	0.8	0.9
0.6	0.1	−0.78	0.11	0.32	0.40	0.42	0.43	0.43	0.42	0.42
	0.2	−3.68	0.07	0.77	0.98	1.06	1.08	1.08	1.06	1.04
	0.3	−9.06	−0.55	0.86	1.27	1.42	1.48	1.49	1.46	1.42
	0.4	−17.62	−2.12	0.06	0.60	0.83	0.95	0.98	0.95	0.91
	0.5	−28.00	−4.26	−0.99	−0.16	0.20	0.39	0.45	0.41	0.38
	0.6	−40.57	−7.86	−2.60	−0.99	−0.32	0.00	0.14	0.23	0.22
0.7	0.1	−0.12	0.17	0.22	0.34	0.39	0.40	0.40	0.39	0.39
	0.2	−1.24	0.33	0.55	0.86	0.98	1.02	1.04	1.03	1.02
	0.3	−4.03	0.06	0.73	1.20	1.39	1.47	1.49	1.47	1.44
	0.4	−9.77	−0.84	0.30	0.36	0.71	0.89	0.97	0.98	0.97
	0.5	−15.88	−2.51	−0.34	−0.06	0.21	0.51	0.65	0.68	0.70
	0.6	−23.89	−4.60	−1.54	−0.55	−0.51	−0.04	0.21	0.37	0.44
	0.7	−59.33	−10.05	−2.53	−0.54	−0.21	−0.09	−0.01	0.23	0.24
0.8	0.1	0.53	0.24	0.12	0.29	0.36	0.37	0.37	0.36	0.35
	0.2	1.20	0.60	0.33	0.73	0.90	0.97	1.00	1.00	0.99
	0.3	0.99	0.68	0.60	1.13	1.36	1.45	1.49	1.48	1.46
	0.4	−1.92	0.44	0.53	0.11	0.59	0.83	0.96	1.01	1.03
	0.5	−3.75	−0.75	0.31	0.05	0.22	0.62	0.84	0.96	1.03
	0.6	−7.20	−1.35	−0.48	−0.11	−0.70	−0.09	0.28	0.51	0.65
	0.7	−11.03	−2.14	−0.74	−0.29	−2.11	0.01	0.26	0.42	0.52
	0.8	−16.00	−3.20	−1.07	−0.56	−0.13	0.18	0.20	0.20	0.21
0.9	0.1	−0.13	0.32	0.23	0.32	0.36	0.36	0.36	0.35	0.34
	0.2	−0.98	0.80	0.61	0.85	0.97	1.03	1.04	1.03	1.01
	0.3	−3.06	0.35	0.55	1.06	1.32	1.44	1.49	1.49	1.48
	0.4	−7.36	−2.06	−1.01	−0.12	0.47	0.78	0.95	1.04	1.09
	0.5	−11.88	−4.00	−1.88	−0.98	−0.30	0.24	0.56	0.75	0.87
	0.6	−18.18	−5.99	−3.20	−1.67	−1.08	−0.30	0.18	0.49	0.70
	0.7	−25.36	−8.36	−4.42	−2.45	−2.82	−0.55	−0.01	0.34	0.56
	0.8	−33.92	−11.20	−5.87	−3.43	−1.94	−0.90	−0.35	0.00	0.24
	0.9	−72.90	−18.23	−8.10	−4.56	−2.92	−1.92	−1.29	−0.66	−0.39
1.0	0.1	−0.78	0.40	0.33	0.35	0.36	0.36	0.35	0.34	0.33
	0.2	−3.16	1.00	0.89	0.96	1.05	1.08	1.08	1.06	1.04
	0.3	−7.11	0.02	0.50	0.99	1.29	1.43	1.49	1.50	1.50
	0.4	−12.80	−4.56	−2.56	−0.36	0.35	0.72	0.93	1.07	1.15
	0.5	−20.00	−7.25	−4.06	−2.02	−0.81	−0.14	0.27	0.54	0.72
	0.6	−29.16	−10.62	−5.92	−3.24	−1.47	−0.50	0.09	0.48	0.74
	0.7	−39.69	−14.58	−8.11	−4.61	−3.53	−1.10	−0.28	0.25	0.60
	0.8	−51.84	−19.20	−10.67	−6.30	−3.75	−1.97	−0.89	−0.20	0.27
	0.9	−66.02	−24.50	−13.59	−8.31	−5.93	−3.18	−1.83	−0.95	−0.35
	1.0	−82.00	−30.50	−16.89	−10.69	−7.39	−4.77	−3.13	−2.02	−1.28

ED7-1 Centrifugal Fan Located in Plenum or Cabinet

L/D_o	0.30	0.40	0.50	0.75
C_o	0.80	0.53	0.40	0.22

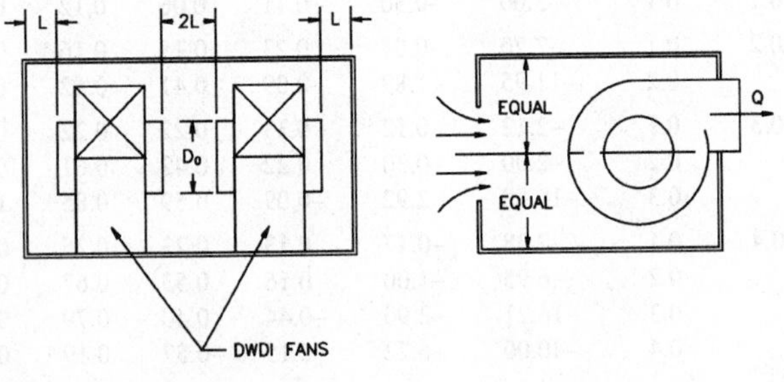

ED7-2 Fan Inlet, Centrifugal, SWSI, with 4 Gore Elbow

	C_o Values			
	L/D_o			
r/D_o	0.0	2.0	5.0	10.0
0.50	1.80	1.00	0.53	0.53
0.75	1.40	0.80	0.40	0.40
1.00	1.20	0.67	0.33	0.33
1.50	1.10	0.60	0.33	0.33
2.00	1.00	0.53	0.33	0.33
3.00	0.67	0.40	0.22	0.22

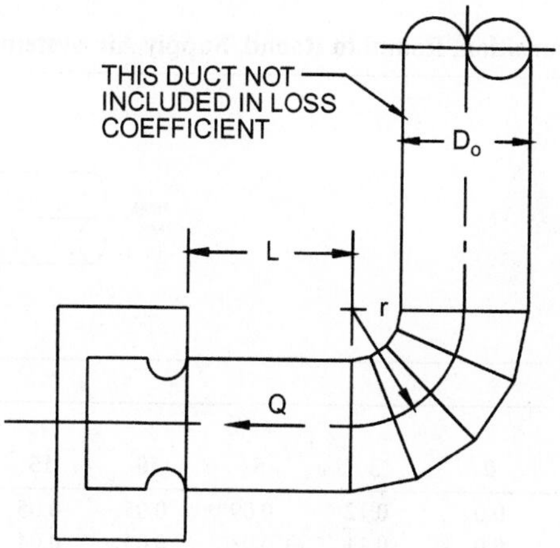

SD1-1 Bellmouth, Plenum to Round, Supply Air Systems

r/D_o	0.0	0.01	0.02	0.03	0.04	0.05	0.06	0.08	0.10	0.12	0.16	0.20	10.0
C_o	0.50	0.44	0.37	0.31	0.26	0.22	0.20	0.15	0.12	0.09	0.06	0.03	0.03

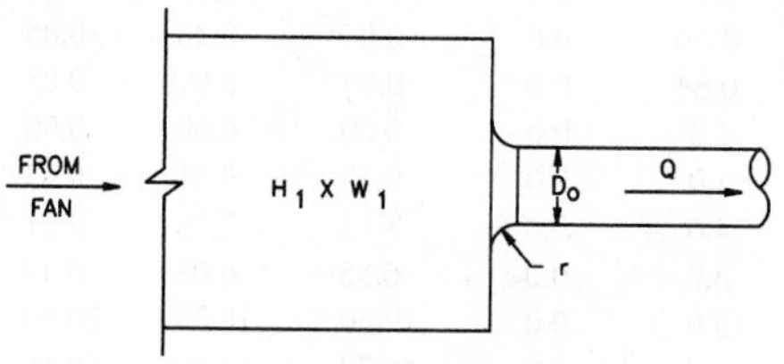

SD1-2 Conical Bellmouth/Sudden Contraction, Plenum to Round, Supply Air Systems

	C_o Values								
	θ								
L/D_o	0	10	20	30	45	60	100	140	180
0.00	0.50	0.50	0.50	0.50	0.50	0.50	0.50	0.50	0.50
0.025	0.50	0.47	0.45	0.43	0.41	0.40	0.42	0.45	0.50
0.05	0.50	0.45	0.41	0.36	0.33	0.30	0.35	0.42	0.50
0.075	0.50	0.42	0.35	0.30	0.26	0.23	0.30	0.40	0.50
0.10	0.50	0.39	0.32	0.25	0.22	0.18	0.27	0.38	0.50
0.15	0.50	0.37	0.27	0.20	0.16	0.15	0.25	0.37	0.50
0.60	0.50	0.27	0.18	0.13	0.11	0.12	0.23	0.36	0.50

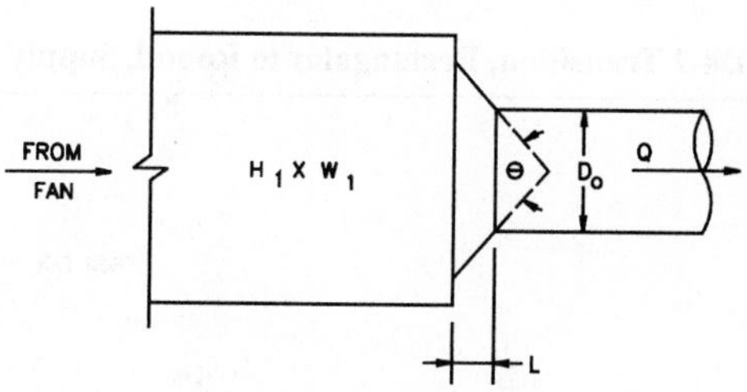

SD2-6 and SD2-7 Stackheads

D_e/D	0.3	0.4	0.5	0.6	0.7	0.8	0.9	1.0
C_o	130.	41.02	16.80	8.10	4.37	2.56	1.60	1.00

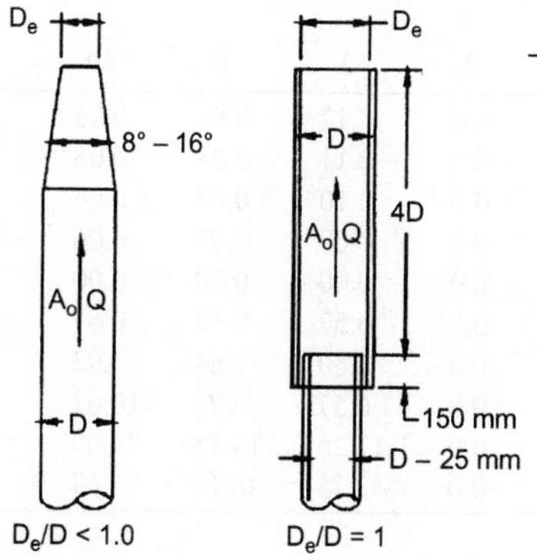

SD2-7 SD2-6

SD4-1 Transition, Round to Round, Supply Air Systems

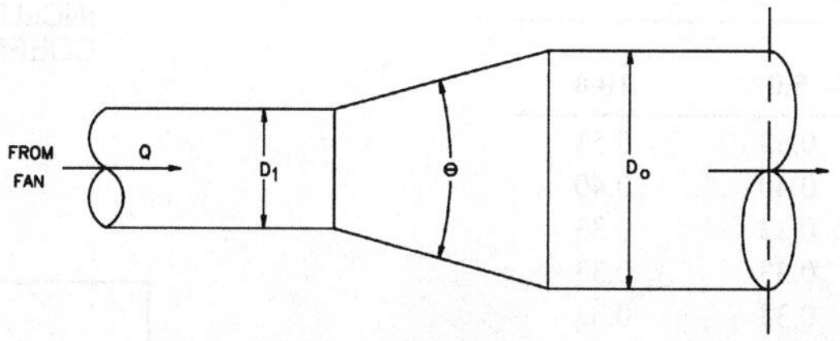

	C_o Values												
	θ												
A_o/A_1	0	3	5	10	15	20	30	45	60	90	120	150	180
0.10	0.0	0.12	0.09	0.05	0.05	0.05	0.05	0.06	0.08	0.19	0.29	0.37	0.43
0.167	0.0	0.11	0.08	0.05	0.04	0.04	0.04	0.06	0.07	0.18	0.28	0.36	0.42
0.25	0.0	0.10	0.07	0.05	0.04	0.04	0.04	0.06	0.07	0.17	0.27	0.35	0.41
0.39	0.0	0.10	0.07	0.05	0.05	0.05	0.05	0.06	0.06	0.16	0.25	0.32	0.36
0.50	0.0	0.07	0.06	0.05	0.05	0.05	0.05	0.06	0.07	0.13	0.18	0.23	0.24
0.64	0.0	0.07	0.07	0.05	0.04	0.04	0.04	0.05	0.06	0.09	0.13	0.17	0.19
1.0	0.0	0.00	0.00	0.00	0.00	0.00	0.00	0.00	0.00	0.00	0.00	0.00	0.00
2.0	0.0	0.59	0.51	0.43	0.52	0.76	1.26	1.32	1.30	1.26	1.23	1.21	1.19
4.0	0.0	3.15	2.78	2.51	3.38	4.77	7.38	9.70	10.88	10.29	10.08	9.96	9.84
6.0	0.0	6.55	6.08	6.44	9.14	11.92	17.35	23.58	27.58	26.71	26.32	26.15	25.99
10.0	0.0	19.50	18.25	20.00	27.30	38.00	58.50	76.00	80.00	83.40	84.00	83.35	82.70
16.0	0.0	45.82	44.80	50.18	73.73	96.77	153.60	215.04	225.28	225.28	225.28	225.28	225.28

SD4-2 Transition, Rectangular to Round, Supply Air Systems

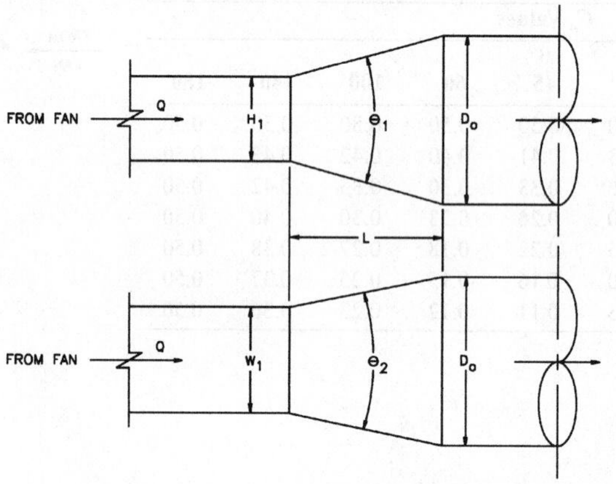

	C_o Values												
	θ												
A_o/A_1	0	3	5	10	15	20	30	45	60	90	120	150	180
0.10	0.0	0.12	0.09	0.05	0.05	0.05	0.05	0.06	0.08	0.19	0.29	0.37	0.43
0.167	0.0	0.11	0.08	0.05	0.05	0.05	0.05	0.06	0.07	0.19	0.28	0.37	0.42
0.25	0.0	0.10	0.07	0.05	0.05	0.05	0.05	0.06	0.07	0.17	0.27	0.35	0.41
0.50	0.0	0.08	0.07	0.06	0.07	0.06	0.05	0.06	0.07	0.13	0.19	0.23	0.24
1.0	0.0	0.00	0.00	0.00	0.00	0.00	0.00	0.00	0.00	0.00	0.00	0.00	0.00
2.0	0.0	0.57	0.55	0.61	0.87	1.00	1.20	1.30	1.30	1.30	1.28	1.24	1.20
4.0	0.0	2.60	2.84	3.92	5.72	7.20	8.32	9.28	9.92	10.24	10.24	10.24	10.24
6.0	0.0	6.57	6.75	10.62	15.84	18.90	22.50	25.74	27.90	28.44	28.44	28.35	28.26
10.0	0.0	17.25	18.75	30.00	45.00	53.00	63.50	75.00	84.00	89.00	89.00	88.50	88.00
16.0	0.0	42.75	48.13	77.57	116.74	136.45	164.10	196.86	224.26	241.92	241.92	240.38	238.59

SD5-1 Wye, 45 Degree, Diverging

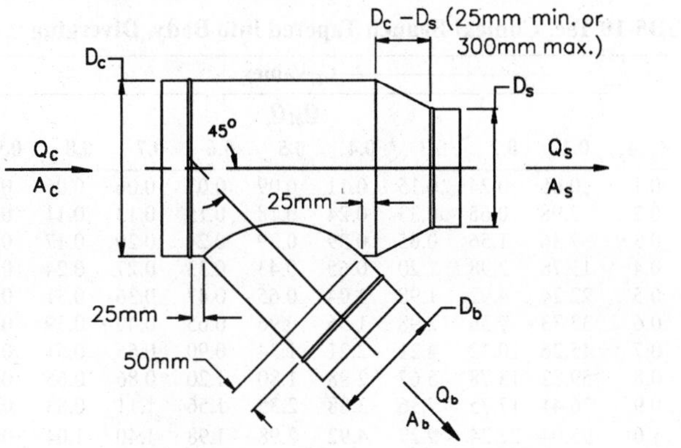

	C_b Values								
	Q_b/Q_c								
A_b/A_c	0.1	0.2	0.3	0.4	0.5	0.6	0.7	0.8	0.9
0.1	0.38	0.38	0.48	0.45	0.40	0.36	0.32	0.29	0.26
0.2	2.25	0.38	0.31	0.38	0.47	0.48	0.47	0.45	0.42
0.3	6.29	1.02	0.38	0.30	0.33	0.38	0.45	0.48	0.48
0.4	12.41	2.25	0.74	0.38	0.30	0.31	0.35	0.38	0.44
0.5	20.58	4.01	1.37	0.62	0.38	0.30	0.30	0.32	0.36
0.6	30.78	6.29	2.25	1.02	0.56	0.38	0.31	0.30	0.31
0.7	43.02	9.10	3.36	1.57	0.85	0.52	0.38	0.31	0.30
0.8	57.29	12.41	4.71	2.25	1.22	0.74	0.50	0.38	0.32
0.9	73.59	16.24	6.29	3.06	1.69	1.02	0.67	0.48	0.38
1.0	91.92	20.58	8.11	4.01	2.25	1.37	0.90	0.62	0.47
	C_s Values								
	Q_s/Q_c								
A_s/A_c	0.1	0.2	0.3	0.4	0.5	0.6	0.7	0.8	0.9
0.1	0.13	0.24	0.57	0.74	0.74	0.70	0.65	0.60	0.56
0.2	0.20	0.13	0.15	0.16	0.28	0.57	0.69	0.74	0.75
0.3	0.90	0.14	0.13	0.14	0.15	0.16	0.20	0.42	0.57
0.4	2.88	0.20	0.14	0.13	0.14	0.15	0.15	0.16	0.34
0.5	6.25	0.38	0.17	0.14	0.13	0.14	0.14	0.15	0.15
0.6	11.88	0.90	0.20	0.14	0.14	0.13	0.14	0.14	0.15
0.7	18.62	1.72	0.33	0.18	0.16	0.14	0.13	0.15	0.14
0.8	26.88	2.88	0.50	0.20	0.15	0.14	0.13	0.13	0.14
0.9	36.45	4.46	0.90	0.30	0.19	0.16	0.15	0.14	0.13
1.0	45.00	6.25	1.44	0.38	0.20	0.17	0.12	0.13	0.14

SD5-9 Tee, Diverging

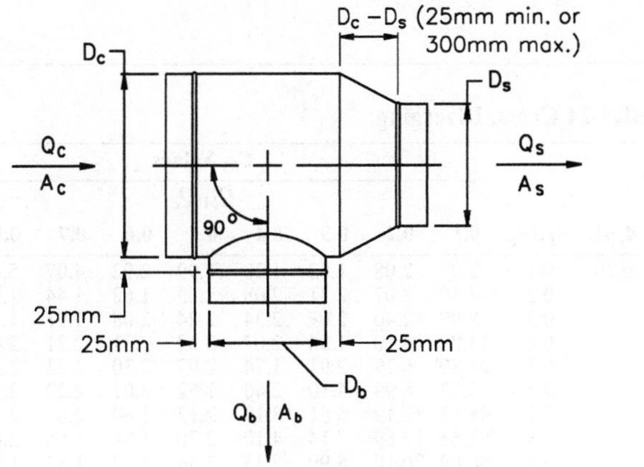

	C_b Values								
	Q_b/Q_c								
A_b/A_c	0.1	0.2	0.3	0.4	0.5	0.6	0.7	0.8	0.9
0.1	1.20	0.62	0.80	1.28	1.99	2.92	4.07	5.44	7.02
0.2	4.10	1.20	0.72	0.62	0.66	0.80	1.01	1.28	1.60
0.3	8.99	2.40	1.20	0.81	0.66	0.62	0.64	0.70	0.80
0.4	15.89	4.10	1.94	1.20	0.88	0.72	0.64	0.62	0.63
0.5	24.80	6.29	2.91	1.74	1.20	0.92	0.77	0.68	0.63
0.6	35.73	8.99	4.10	2.40	1.62	1.20	0.96	0.81	0.72
0.7	48.67	12.19	5.51	3.19	2.12	1.55	1.20	0.99	0.85
0.8	63.63	15.89	7.14	4.10	2.70	1.94	1.49	1.20	1.01
0.9	80.60	20.10	8.99	5.13	3.36	2.40	1.83	1.46	1.20
1.0	99.60	24.80	11.07	6.29	4.10	2.91	2. 20	1.74	1.43
	C_s Values								
	Q_s/Q_c								
A_s/A_c	0.1	0.2	0.3	0.4	0.5	0.6	0.7	0.8	0.9
0.1	0.13	0.24	0.57	0.74	0.74	0.70	0.65	0.60	0.56
0.2	0.20	0.13	0.15	0.16	0.28	0.57	0.69	0.74	0.75
0.3	0.90	0.14	0.13	0.14	0.15	0.16	0.20	0.42	0.57
0.4	2.88	0.20	0.14	0.13	0.14	0.15	0.15	0.16	0.34
0.5	6.25	0.38	0.17	0.14	0.13	0.14	0.14	0.15	0.15
0.6	11.88	0.90	0.20	0.14	0.14	0.13	0.14	0.14	0.15
0.7	18.62	1.72	0.33	0.18	0.16	0.14	0.13	0.15	0.14
0.8	26.88	2.88	0.50	0.20	0.15	0.14	0.13	0.13	0.14
0.9	36.45	4.46	0.90	0.30	0.19	0.16	0.15	0.14	0.13
1.0	45.00	6.25	1.44	0.38	0.20	0.17	0.12	0.13	0.14

SD5-10 Tee, Conical Branch Tapered into Body, Diverging

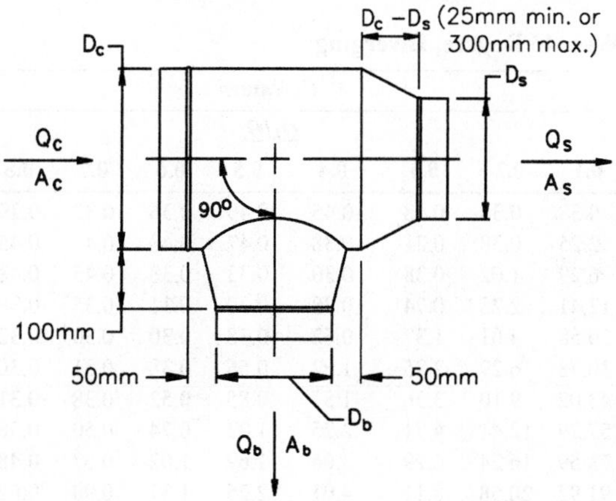

C_b Values

A_b/A_c	Q_b/Q_c 0.1	0.2	0.3	0.4	0.5	0.6	0.7	0.8	0.9
0.1	0.65	0.24	0.15	0.11	0.09	0.07	0.06	0.05	0.05
0.2	2.98	0.65	0.33	0.24	0.18	0.15	0.13	0.11	0.10
0.3	7.36	1.56	0.65	0.39	0.29	0.24	0.20	0.17	0.15
0.4	13.78	2.98	1.20	0.65	0.43	0.33	0.27	0.24	0.21
0.5	22.24	4.92	1.98	1.04	0.65	0.47	0.36	0.31	0.27
0.6	32.73	7.36	2.98	1.56	0.96	0.65	0.49	0.39	0.33
0.7	45.26	10.32	4.21	2.21	1.34	0.90	0.65	0.51	0.42
0.8	59.82	13.78	5.67	2.98	1.80	1.20	0.86	0.65	0.52
0.9	76.41	17.75	7.36	3.88	2.35	1.56	1.11	0.83	0.65
1.0	95.04	22.24	9.27	4.92	2.98	1.98	1.40	1.04	0.81

C_s Values

A_s/A_c	Q_s/Q_c 0.1	0.2	0.3	0.4	0.5	0.6	0.7	0.8	0.9
0.1	0.13	0.24	0.57	0.74	0.74	0.70	0.65	0.60	0.56
0.2	0.20	0.13	0.15	0.16	0.28	0.57	0.69	0.74	0.75
0.3	0.90	0.14	0.13	0.14	0.15	0.16	0.20	0.42	0.57
0.4	2.88	0.20	0.14	0.13	0.14	0.15	0.15	0.16	0.34
0.5	6.25	0.38	0.17	0.14	0.13	0.14	0.14	0.15	0.15
0.6	11.88	0.90	0.20	0.14	0.14	0.13	0.14	0.14	0.15
0.7	18.62	1.72	0.33	0.18	0.16	0.14	0.13	0.15	0.14
0.8	26.88	2.88	0.50	0.20	0.15	0.14	0.13	0.13	0.14
0.9	36.45	4.46	0.90	0.30	0.19	0.16	0.15	0.14	0.13
1.0	45.00	6.25	1.44	0.38	0.20	0.17	0.12	0.13	0.14

SD5-24 Cross, Diverging

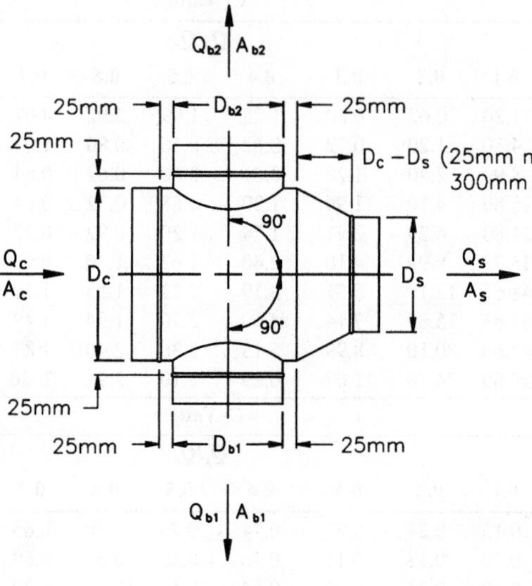

C_{b1} Values

A_s/A_c	A_{b1}/A_c	Q_{b1}/Q_c 0.1	0.2	0.3	0.4	0.5	0.6	0.7	0.8	0.9
0.20	0.1	2.07	2.08	1.62	1.30	1.99	2.92	4.07	5.44	7.02
	0.2	4.10	2.07	2.31	2.08	1.83	1.62	1.44	1.30	1.60
	0.3	8.99	2.40	2.07	2.34	2.24	2.08	1.91	1.76	1.62
	0.4	15.89	4.10	1.94	2.07	2.32	2.31	2.21	2.08	1.95
	0.5	24.80	6.29	2.91	1.74	2.07	2.30	2.33	2.27	2.18
	0.6	35.73	8.99	4.10	2.40	1.62	2.07	2.29	2.34	2.31
	0.7	48.67	12.19	5.51	3.19	2.12	1.60	2.07	2.27	2.33
	0.8	63.63	15.89	7.14	4.10	2.70	1.94	1.68	2.07	2.25
	0.9	80.60	20.10	8.99	5.13	3.36	2.40	1.83	1.74	2.07
	1.0	99.60	24.80	11.07	6.29	4.10	2.91	2.20	1.74	1.78
0.35	0.1	1.20	3.25	3.11	2.69	2.32	2.92	4.07	5.44	7.02
	0.2	4.10	1.20	2.44	3.25	3.28	3.11	2.90	2.69	2.49
	0.3	8.99	2.40	1.20	1.69	2.88	3.25	3.31	3.23	3.11
	0.4	15.89	4.10	1.94	1.20	1.12	2.44	3.02	3.25	3.31
	0.5	24.80	6.29	2.91	1.74	1.20	0.92	2.04	2.73	3.09
	0.6	35.73	8.99	4.10	2.40	1.62	1.20	0.96	1.69	2.44
	0.7	48.67	12.19	5.51	3.19	2.12	1.55	1.20	0.99	1.38
	0.8	63.63	15.89	7.14	4.10	2.70	1.94	1.49	1.20	1.01
	0.9	80.60	20.10	8.99	5.13	3.36	2.40	1.83	1.46	1.20
	1.0	99.60	24.80	11.07	6.29	4.10	2.91	2.20	1.74	1.43
0.55	0.1	1.20	0.62	0.80	1.28	1.99	2.92	4.07	5.44	7.02
	0.2	4.10	1.20	0.72	0.62	0.66	0.80	1.01	1.28	1.60
	0.3	8.99	2.40	1.20	0.81	0.66	0.62	0.64	0.70	0.80
	0.4	15.89	4.10	1.94	1.20	0.88	0.72	0.64	0.62	0.63
	0.5	24.80	6.29	2.91	1.74	1.20	0.92	0.77	0.68	0.63
	0.6	35.73	8.99	4.10	2.40	1.62	1.20	0.96	0.81	0.72
	0.7	48.67	12.19	5.51	3.19	2.12	1.55	1.20	0.99	0.85
	0.8	63.63	15.89	7.14	4.10	2.70	1.94	1.49	1.20	1.01
	0.9	80.60	20.10	8.99	5.13	3.36	2.40	1.83	1.46	1.20
	1.0	99.60	24.80	11.07	6.29	4.10	2.91	2.20	1.74	1.43

SD5-24 Cross, Diverging (*Continued*)

		C_{b1} Values (*Concluded*)								
		Q_{b1}/Q_c								
A_s/A_c	A_{b1}/A_c	0.1	0.2	0.3	0.4	0.5	0.6	0.7	0.8	0.9
0.80	0.1	1.20	0.62	0.80	1.28	1.99	2.92	4.07	5.44	7.02
	0.2	4.10	1.20	0.72	0.62	0.66	0.80	1.01	1.28	1.60
	0.3	8.99	2.40	1.20	0.81	0.66	0.62	0.64	0.70	0.80
	0.4	15.89	4.10	1.94	1.20	0.88	0.72	0.64	0.62	0.63
	0.5	24.80	6.29	2.91	1.74	1.20	0.92	0.77	0.68	0.63
	0.6	35.73	8.99	4.10	2.40	1.62	1.20	0.96	0.81	0.72
	0.7	48.67	12.19	5.51	3.19	2.12	1.55	1.20	0.99	0.85
	0.8	63.63	15.89	7.14	4.10	2.70	1.94	1.49	1.20	1.01
	0.9	80.60	20.10	8.99	5.13	3.36	2.40	1.83	1.46	1.20
	1.0	99.60	24.80	11.07	6.29	4.10	2.91	2.20	1.74	1.43
1.00	0.1	1.20	0.62	0.80	1.28	1.99	2.92	4.07	5.44	7.02
	0.2	4.10	1.20	0.72	0.62	0.66	0.80	1.01	1.28	1.60
	0.3	8.99	2.40	1.20	0.81	0.66	0.62	0.64	0.70	0.80
	0.4	15.89	4.10	1.94	1.20	0.88	0.72	0.64	0.62	0.63
	0.5	24.80	6.29	2.91	1.74	1.20	0.92	0.77	0.68	0.63
	0.6	35.73	8.99	4.10	2.40	1.62	1.20	0.96	0.81	0.72
	0.7	48.67	12.19	5.51	3.19	2.12	1.55	1.20	0.99	0.85
	0.8	63.63	15.89	7.14	4.10	2.70	1.94	1.49	1.20	1.01
	0.9	80.60	20.10	8.99	5.13	3.36	2.40	1.83	1.46	1.20
	1.0	99.60	24.80	11.07	6.29	4.10	2.91	2.20	1.74	1.43

	C_s Values								
	Q_s/Q_c								
A_s/A_c	0.1	0.2	0.3	0.4	0.5	0.6	0.7	0.8	0.9
0.1	0.13	0.24	0.57	0.74	0.74	0.70	0.65	0.60	0.56
0.2	0.20	0.13	0.15	0.16	0.28	0.57	0.69	0.74	0.75
0.3	0.90	0.14	0.13	0.14	0.15	0.16	0.20	0.42	0.57
0.4	2.88	0.20	0.14	0.13	0.14	0.15	0.15	0.16	0.34
0.5	6.25	0.38	0.17	0.14	0.13	0.14	0.14	0.15	0.15
0.6	11.88	0.90	0.20	0.14	0.14	0.13	0.14	0.14	0.15
0.7	18.62	1.72	0.33	0.18	0.16	0.14	0.13	0.15	0.14
0.8	26.88	2.88	0.50	0.20	0.15	0.14	0.13	0.13	0.14
0.9	36.45	4.46	0.90	0.30	0.19	0.16	0.15	0.14	0.13
1.0	45.00	6.25	1.44	0.38	0.20	0.17	0.12	0.13	0.14

For the other branch, subscripts 1 and 2 change places.

SD5-25 Cross, Conical Branches Tapered into Body, Diverging

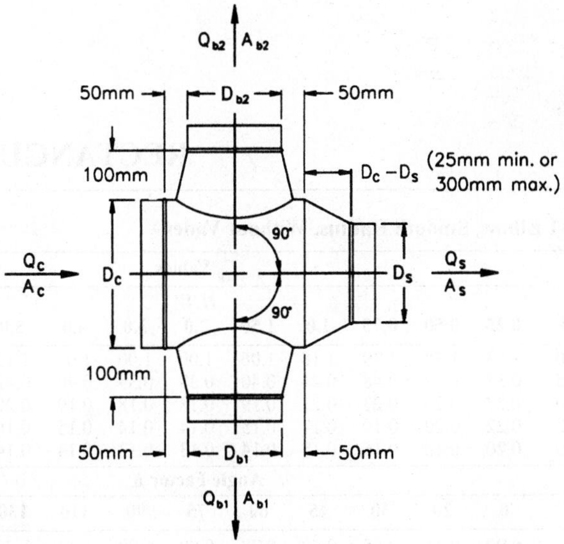

		C_{b1} Values								
		Q_{b1}/Q_c								
A_s/A_c	A_{b1}/A_c	0.1	0.2	0.3	0.4	0.5	0.6	0.7	0.8	0.9
0.20	0.1	2.07	2.08	1.62	1.30	1.08	0.93	0.81	0.72	0.64
	0.2	2.98	2.07	2.31	2.08	1.83	1.62	1.44	1.30	1.18
	0.3	7.36	1.56	2.07	2.34	2.24	2.08	1.91	1.76	1.62
	0.4	13.78	2.98	1.20	2.07	2.32	2.31	2.21	2.08	1.95
	0.5	22.24	4.92	1.98	1.28	2.07	2.30	2.33	2.27	2.18
	0.6	32.73	7.36	2.98	1.56	1.48	2.07	2.29	2.34	2.31
	0.7	45.26	10.32	4.21	2.21	1.34	1.60	2.07	2.27	2.33
	0.8	59.82	13.78	5.67	2.98	1.80	1.20	1.68	2.07	2.25
	0.9	76.41	17.75	7.36	3.88	2.35	1.56	1.12	1.74	2.07
	1.0	95.04	22.24	9.27	4.92	2.98	1.98	1.40	1.28	1.78
0.35	0.1	0.65	3.25	3.11	2.69	2.32	2.03	1.80	1.61	1.46
	0.2	2.98	0.65	2.44	3.25	3.28	3.11	2.90	2.69	2.49
	0.3	7.36	1.56	0.65	1.69	2.88	3.25	3.31	3.23	3.11
	0.4	13.78	2.98	1.20	0.65	1.12	2.44	3.02	3.25	3.31
	0.5	22.24	4.92	1.98	1.04	0.65	0.69	2.04	2.73	3.09
	0.6	32.73	7.36	2.98	1.56	0.96	0.65	0.49	1.69	2.44
	0.7	45.26	10.32	4.21	2.21	1.34	0.90	0.65	0.51	1.38
	0.8	59.82	13.78	5.67	2.98	1.80	1.20	0.86	0.65	0.52
	0.9	76.41	17.75	7.36	3.88	2.35	1.56	1.11	0.83	0.65
	1.0	95.04	22.24	9.27	4.92	2.98	1.98	1.40	1.04	0.81
0.55	0.1	0.65	1.50	1.56	1.38	1.20	1.06	0.94	0.84	0.77
	0.2	2.98	0.65	0.89	1.50	1.60	1.56	1.47	1.38	1.28
	0.3	7.36	1.56	0.65	0.39	1.20	1.50	1.59	1.59	1.56
	0.4	13.78	2.98	1.20	0.65	0.43	0.89	1.31	1.50	1.58
	0.5	22.24	4.92	1.98	1.04	0.65	0.47	0.61	1.09	1.36
	0.6	32.73	7.36	2.98	1.56	0.96	0.65	0.49	0.39	0.89
	0.7	45.26	10.32	4.21	2.21	1.34	0.90	0.65	0.51	0.42
	0.8	59.82	13.78	5.67	2.98	1.80	1.20	0.86	0.65	0.52
	0.9	76.41	17.75	7.36	3.88	2.35	1.56	1.11	0.83	0.65
	1.0	95.04	22.24	9.27	4.92	2.98	1.98	1.40	1.04	0.81

SD5-25 Cross, Conical Branches Tapered into Body, Diverging (*Continued*)

		C_{b1} Values (*Concluded*)								
		Q_{b1}/Q_c								
A_s/A_c	A_{b1}/A_c	0.1	0.2	0.3	0.4	0.5	0.6	0.7	0.8	0.9
0.80	0.1	0.65	0.24	0.15	0.11	0.09	0.07	0.06	0.05	0.05
	0.2	2.98	0.65	0.33	0.24	0.18	0.15	0.13	0.11	0.10
	0.3	7.36	1.56	0.65	0.39	0.29	0.24	0.20	0.17	0.15
	0.4	13.78	2.98	1.20	0.65	0.43	0.33	0.27	0.24	0.21
	0.5	22.24	4.92	1.98	1.04	0.65	0.47	0.36	0.31	0.27
	0.6	32.73	7.36	2.98	1.56	0.96	0.65	0.49	0.39	0.33
	0.7	45.26	10.32	4.21	2.21	1.34	0.90	0.65	0.51	0.42
	0.8	59.82	13.78	5.67	2.98	1.80	1.20	0.86	0.65	0.52
	0.9	76.41	17.75	7.36	3.88	2.35	1.56	1.11	0.83	0.65
	1.0	95.04	22.24	9.27	4.92	2.98	1.98	1.40	1.04	0.81
1.00	0.1	0.65	0.24	0.15	0.11	0.09	0.07	0.06	0.05	0.05
	0.2	2.98	0.65	0.33	0.24	0.18	0.15	0.13	0.11	0.10
	0.3	7.36	1.56	0.65	0.39	0.29	0.24	0.20	0.17	0.15
	0.4	13.78	2.98	1.20	0.65	0.43	0.33	0.27	0.24	0.21
	0.5	22.24	4.92	1.98	1.04	0.65	0.47	0.36	0.31	0.27
	0.6	32.73	7.36	2.98	1.56	0.96	0.65	0.49	0.39	0.33
	0.7	45.26	10.32	4.21	2.21	1.34	0.90	0.65	0.51	0.42
	0.8	59.82	13.78	5.67	2.98	1.80	1.20	0.86	0.65	0.52
	0.9	76.41	17.75	7.36	3.88	2.35	1.56	1.11	0.83	0.65
	1.0	95.04	22.24	9.27	4.92	2.98	1.98	1.40	1.04	0.81

	C_s Values								
	Q_s/Q_c								
A_s/A_c	0.1	0.2	0.3	0.4	0.5	0.6	0.7	0.8	0.9
0.1	0.13	0.24	0.57	0.74	0.74	0.70	0.65	0.60	0.56
0.2	0.20	0.13	0.15	0.16	0.28	0.57	0.69	0.74	0.75
0.3	0.90	0.14	0.13	0.14	0.15	0.16	0.20	0.42	0.57
0.4	2.88	0.20	0.14	0.13	0.14	0.15	0.15	0.16	0.34
0.5	6.25	0.38	0.17	0.14	0.13	0.14	0.14	0.15	0.15
0.6	11.88	0.90	0.20	0.14	0.14	0.13	0.14	0.14	0.15
0.7	18.62	1.72	0.33	0.18	0.16	0.14	0.13	0.15	0.14
0.8	26.88	2.88	0.50	0.20	0.15	0.14	0.13	0.13	0.14
0.9	36.45	4.46	0.90	0.30	0.19	0.16	0.15	0.14	0.13
1.0	45.00	6.25	1.44	0.38	0.20	0.17	0.12	0.13	0.14

For the other branch, subscripts 1 and 2 change places

RECTANGULAR FITTINGS

CR3-1 Elbow, Smooth Radius, Without Vanes

$C_o = KC_p$ where K = angle factor

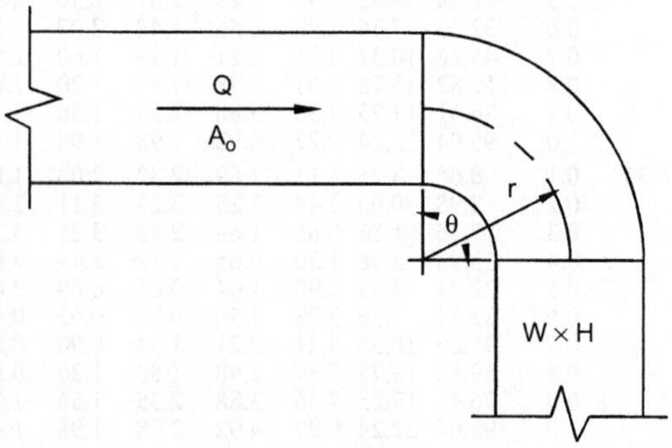

	C_p Values										
	H/W										
r/W	0.25	0.50	0.75	1.0	1.50	2.0	3.0	4.0	5.0	6.0	8.0
0.50	1.53	1.38	1.29	1.18	1.06	1.00	1.00	1.06	1.12	1.16	1.18
0.75	0.57	0.52	0.48	0.44	0.40	0.39	0.39	0.40	0.42	0.43	0.44
1.00	0.27	0.25	0.23	0.21	0.19	0.18	0.18	0.19	0.20	0.21	0.21
1.50	0.22	0.20	0.19	0.17	0.15	0.14	0.14	0.15	0.16	0.17	0.17
2.00	0.20	0.18	0.16	0.15	0.14	0.13	0.13	0.14	0.14	0.15	0.15

	Angle Factor K										
θ	0	20	30	45	60	75	90	110	130	150	180
K	0.00	0.31	0.45	0.60	0.78	0.90	1.00	1.13	1.20	1.28	1.40

CR3-3 Elbow, Smooth Radius, One Splitter Vane

C_p Values

r/W	H/W 0.25	0.50	1.0	1.50	2.0	3.0	4.0	5.0	6.0	7.0	8.0
0.55	0.52	0.40	0.43	0.49	0.55	0.66	0.75	0.84	0.93	1.01	1.09
0.60	0.36	0.27	0.25	0.28	0.30	0.35	0.39	0.42	0.46	0.49	0.52
0.65	0.28	0.21	0.18	0.19	0.20	0.22	0.25	0.26	0.28	0.30	0.32
0.70	0.22	0.16	0.14	0.14	0.15	0.16	0.17	0.18	0.19	0.20	0.21
0.75	0.18	0.13	0.11	0.11	0.11	0.12	0.13	0.14	0.14	0.15	0.15
0.80	0.15	0.11	0.09	0.09	0.09	0.09	0.10	0.10	0.11	0.11	0.12
0.85	0.13	0.09	0.08	0.07	0.07	0.08	0.08	0.08	0.08	0.09	0.09
0.90	0.11	0.08	0.07	0.06	0.06	0.06	0.06	0.07	0.07	0.07	0.07
0.95	0.10	0.07	0.06	0.05	0.05	0.05	0.05	0.05	0.06	0.06	0.06
1.00	0.09	0.06	0.05	0.05	0.04	0.04	0.04	0.05	0.05	0.05	0.05

Angle Factor K

θ	0	30	45	60	90
K	0.00	0.45	0.60	0.78	1.00

Curve Ratio CR

r/W	0.55	0.60	0.65	0.70	0.75	0.80	0.85	0.90	0.95	1.0
CR	0.218	0.302	0.361	0.408	0.447	0.480	0.509	0.535	0.557	0.577

Throat Radius/Width Ratio (R/W)

r/W	0.55	0.60	0.65	0.70	0.75	0.80	0.85	0.90	0.95	1.0
R/W	0.05	0.10	0.15	0.20	0.25	0.30	0.35	0.40	0.45	0.50

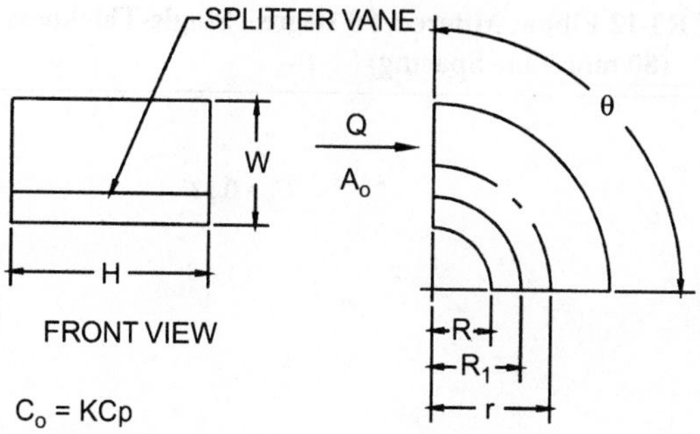

$C_o = KC_p$

$R_1 = R/CR$

where

R = throat radius

R_1 = splitter vane radius

CR = curve ratio

K = angle factor

CR3-6 Elbow, Mitered

C_o Values

θ	H/W 0.25	0.50	0.75	1.00	1.50	2.0	3.0	4.0	5.0	6.0	8.0
20	0.08	0.08	0.08	0.07	0.07	0.07	0.06	0.06	0.05	0.05	0.05
30	0.18	0.17	0.17	0.16	0.15	0.15	0.13	0.13	0.12	0.12	0.11
45	0.38	0.37	0.36	0.34	0.33	0.31	0.28	0.27	0.26	0.25	0.24
60	0.60	0.59	0.57	0.55	0.52	0.49	0.46	0.43	0.41	0.39	0.38
75	0.89	0.87	0.84	0.81	0.77	0.73	0.67	0.63	0.61	0.58	0.57
90	1.30	1.27	1.23	1.18	1.13	1.07	0.98	0.92	0.89	0.85	0.83

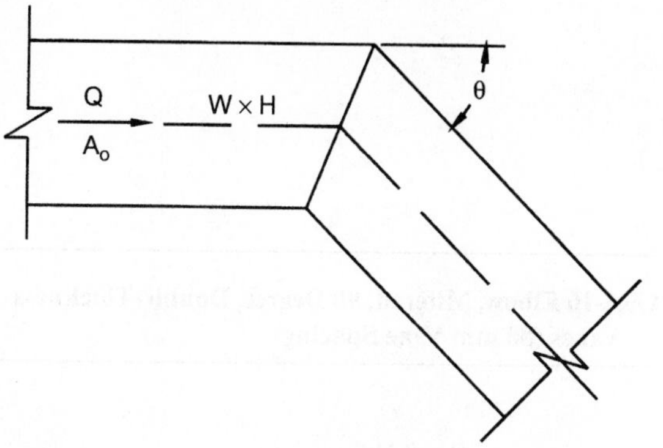

CR3-9 Elbow, Mitered, 90 Degree, Single-Thickness Vanes (40 mm Vane Spacing)

$C_o = 0.11$

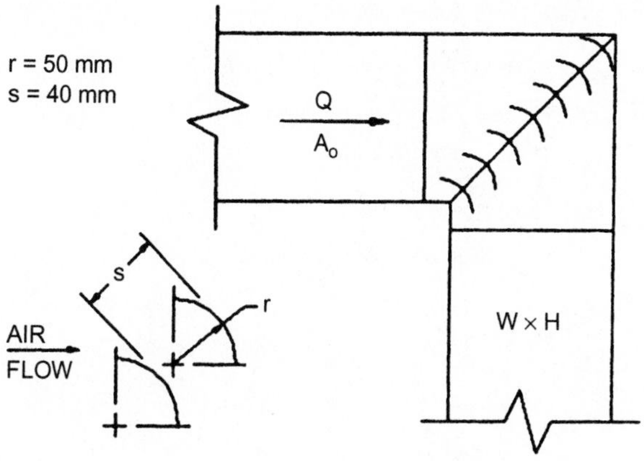

CR3-12 Elbow, Mitered, 90 Degree, Single-Thickness Vanes (80 mm Vane Spacing)

$C_o = 0.33$

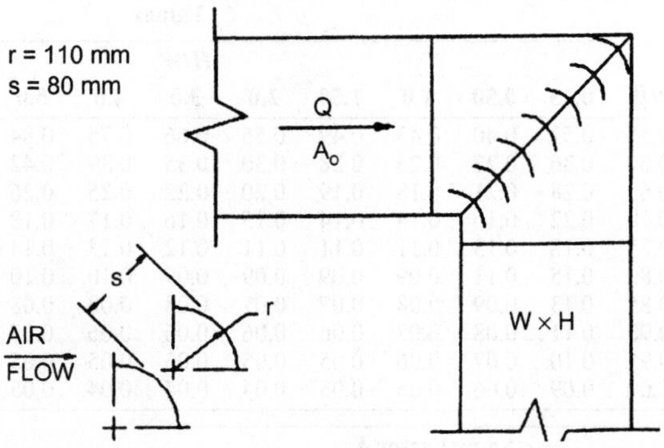

CR3-15 Elbow, Mitered, 90 Degree, Double-Thickness Vanes (60 mm Vane Spacing)

$C_o = 0.25$

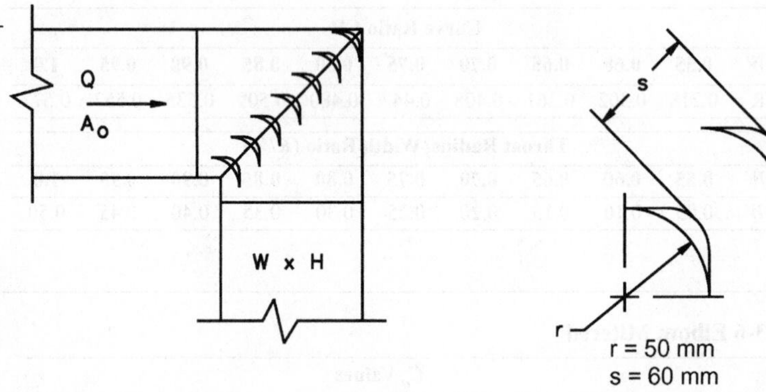

CR3-16 Elbow, Mitered, 90 Degree, Double-Thickness Vanes (80 mm Vane Spacing)

$C_o = 0.41$

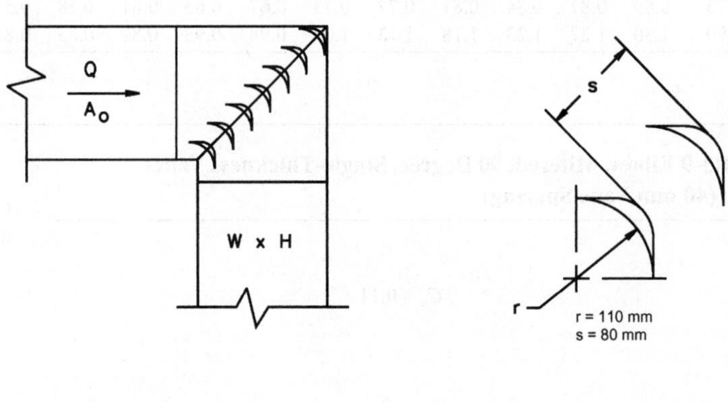

CR3-17 Elbow, Z-Shaped

	C_p Values												
	L/W												
H/W	**0.0**	**0.4**	**0.6**	**0.8**	**1.0**	**1.2**	**1.4**	**1.6**	**1.8**	**2.0**	**4.0**	**8.0**	**10.0**
0.25	0.0	0. 68	0.99	1.77	2.89	3.97	4.41	4.60	4.64	4.60	3.39	3.03	2.70
0.50	0.0	0.66	0.96	1.72	2.81	3.86	4.29	4.47	4.52	4.47	3.30	2.94	2.62
0.75	0.0	0.64	0.94	1.67	2.74	3.75	4.17	4.35	4.39	4.35	3.20	2.86	2.55
1.0	0.0	0.62	0.90	1.61	2.63	3.61	4.01	4.18	4.22	4.18	3.08	2.75	2.45
1.5	0.0	0.59	0.86	1.53	2.50	3.43	3.81	3.97	4.01	3.97	2.93	2.61	2.33
2.0	0.0	0.56	0.81	1.45	2.37	3.25	3.61	3.76	3.80	3.76	2.77	2.48	2.21
3.0	0.0	0.51	0.75	1.34	2.18	3.00	3.33	3.47	3.50	3.47	2.56	2.28	2.03
4.0	0.0	0.48	0.70	1.26	2.05	2.82	3.13	3.26	3.29	3.26	2.40	2.15	1.91
6.0	0.0	0.45	0.65	1.16	1.89	2.60	2.89	3.01	3.04	3.01	2.22	1.98	1.76
8.0	0.0	0.43	0.63	1.13	1.84	2.53	2.81	2.93	2.95	2.93	2.16	1.93	1.72

Reynolds Number Correction Factor K_r

Re/1000	10	20	30	40	60	80	100	140	500
K_r	1.40	1.26	1.19	1.14	1.09	1.06	1.04	1.00	1.00

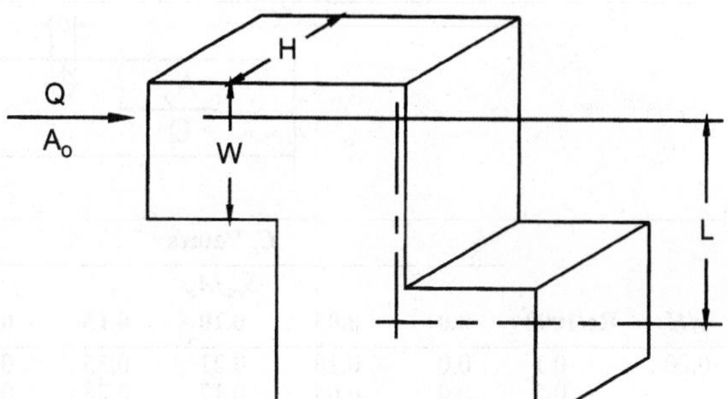

$C_o = K_r C_p$
where K_r = Reynolds number correction factor

CR6-1 Screen (Only)

	C_o Values												
	n												
A_1/A_o	**0.30**	**0.35**	**0.40**	**0.45**	**0.50**	**0.55**	**0.60**	**0.65**	**0.70**	**0.75**	**0.80**	**0.90**	**1.0**
0.2	155.0	103.0	75.00	55.00	41.25	31.50	24.25	18.75	14.50	11.00	8.00	3.50	0.0
0.3	68.89	45.56	33.33	24.44	18.33	14.00	10.78	8.33	6.44	4.89	3.56	1.56	0.0
0.4	38.75	25.63	18.75	13.75	10.31	7.88	6.06	4.69	3.63	2.75	2.00	0.88	0.0
0.5	24.80	16.40	12.00	8.80	6.60	5.04	3.88	3.00	2.32	1.76	1.28	0.56	0.0
0.6	17.22	11.39	8.33	6.11	4.58	3.50	2.69	2.08	1.61	1.22	0.89	0.39	0.0
0.7	12.65	8.37	6.12	4.49	3.37	2.57	1.98	1.53	1.18	0.90	0.65	0.29	0.0
0.8	9.69	6.40	4.69	3.44	2.58	1.97	1.52	1.17	0.91	0.69	0.50	0.22	0.0
0.9	7.65	5.06	3.70	2.72	2.04	1.56	1.20	0.93	0.72	0.54	0.40	0.17	0.0
1.0	6.20	4.10	3.00	2.20	1.65	1.26	0.97	0.75	0.58	0.44	0.32	0.14	0.0
1.2	4.31	2.85	2.08	1.53	1.15	0.88	0.67	0.52	0.40	0.31	0.22	0.10	0.0
1.4	3.16	2.09	1.53	1.12	0.84	0.64	0.49	0.38	0.30	0.22	0.16	0.07	0.0
1.6	2.42	1.60	1.17	0.86	0.64	0.49	0.38	0.29	0.23	0.17	0.13	0.05	0.0
1.8	1.91	1.27	0.93	0.68	0.51	0.39	0.30	0.23	0.18	0.14	0.10	0.04	0.0
2.0	1.55	1.03	0.75	0.55	0.41	0.32	0.24	0.19	0.15	0.11	0.08	0.04	0.0
2.5	0.99	0.66	0.48	0.35	0.26	0.20	0.16	0.12	0.09	0.07	0.05	0.02	0.0
3.0	0.69	0.46	0.33	0.24	0.18	0.14	0.11	0.08	0.06	0.05	0.04	0.02	0.0
4.0	0.39	0.26	0.19	0.14	0.10	0.08	0.06	0.05	0.04	0.03	0.02	0.01	0.0
6.0	0.17	0.11	0.08	0.06	0.05	0.04	0.03	0.02	0.02	0.01	0.01	0.00	0.0

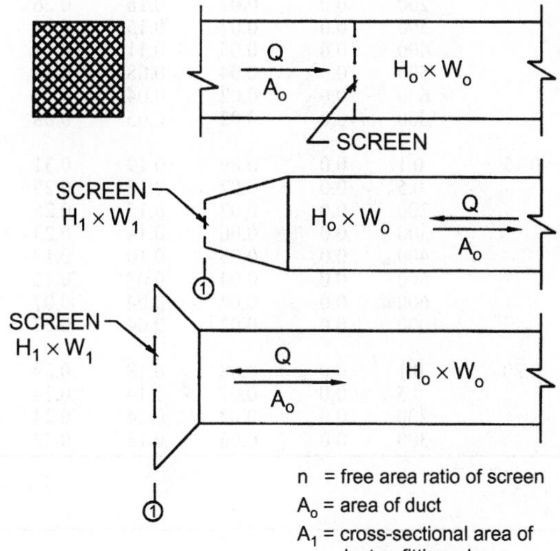

n = free area ratio of screen
A_o = area of duct
A_1 = cross-sectional area of duct or fitting where screen is located

CR6-4 Obstruction, Smooth Cylinder in Rectangular Duct

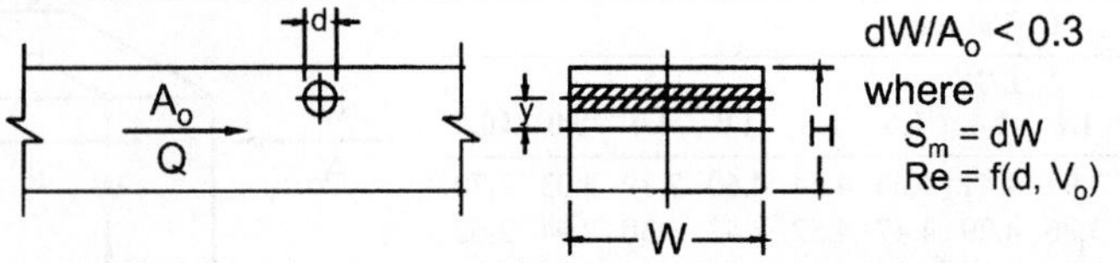

		C_o Values				
		S_m/A_o				
y/H	Re/1000	0.0	0.05	0.10	0.15	0.20
0.00	0.1	0.0	0.10	0.21	0.35	0.47
	0.5	0.0	0.08	0.17	0.28	0.38
	200	0.0	0.08	0.17	0.28	0.38
	300	0.0	0.07	0.16	0.26	0.35
	400	0.0	0.05	0.11	0.19	0.25
	500	0.0	0.04	0.09	0.14	0.19
	600	0.0	0.02	0.05	0.07	0.10
	1000	0.0	0.02	0.05	0.08	0.11
0.05	0.1	0.0	0.10	0.21	0.34	0.46
	0.5	0.0	0.08	0.17	0.27	0.37
	200	0.0	0.08	0.17	0.27	0.37
	300	0.0	0.07	0.15	0.25	0.34
	400	0.0	0.05	0.11	0.18	0.24
	500	0.0	0.04	0.08	0.13	0.18
	600	0.0	0.02	0.04	0.07	0.10
	1000	0.0	0.02	0.05	0.08	0.11
0.10	0.1	0.0	0.09	0.20	0.32	0.44
	0.5	0.0	0.07	0.16	0.26	0.35
	200	0.0	0.07	0.16	0.26	0.35
	300	0.0	0.07	0.15	0.24	0.32
	400	0.0	0.05	0.11	0.17	0.23
	500	0.0	0.04	0.08	0.13	0.18
	600	0.0	0.02	0.04	0.07	0.09
	1000	0.0	0.02	0.05	0.08	0.10
0.15	0.1	0.0	0.09	0.19	0.31	0.42
	0.5	0.0	0.07	0.15	0.25	0.34
	200	0.0	0.07	0.15	0.25	0.34
	300	0.0	0.06	0.14	0.23	0.31
	400	0.0	0.05	0.10	0.17	0.22
	500	0.0	0.04	0.08	0.12	0.17
	600	0.0	0.02	0.04	0.07	0.09
	1000	0.0	0.02	0.04	0.07	0.10
0.20	0.1	0.0	0.08	0.18	0.29	0.40
	0.5	0.0	0.07	0.14	0.24	0.32
	200	0.0	0.07	0.14	0.24	0.32
	300	0.0	0.06	0.13	0.22	0.29
	400	0.0	0.04	0.10	0.16	0.21
	500	0.0	0.03	0.07	0.12	0.16
	600	0.0	0.02	0.04	0.06	0.09
	1000	0.0	0.02	0.04	0.07	0.09
0.25	0.1	0.0	0.08	0.17	0.28	0.38
	0.5	0.0	0.06	0.14	0.22	0.30
	200	0.0	0.06	0.14	0.22	0.30
	300	0.0	0.06	0.12	0.20	0.28
	400	0.0	0.04	0.09	0.15	0.20
	500	0.0	0.03	0.07	0.11	0.15
	600	0.0	0.02	0.04	0.06	0.08
	1000	0.0	0.02	0.04	0.06	0.09
0.30	0.1	0.0	0.07	0.16	0.26	0.35
	0.5	0.0	0.06	0.13	0.21	0.28
	200	0.0	0.06	0.13	0.21	0.28
	300	0.0	0.05	0.12	0.19	0.26
	400	0.0	0.04	0.08	0.14	0.19
	500	0.0	0.03	0.06	0.10	0.14
	600	0.0	0.02	0.03	0.05	0.07
	1000	0.0	0.02	0.04	0.06	0.08
0.35	0.1	0.0	0.07	0.14	0.23	0.32
	0.5	0.0	0.05	0.11	0.19	0.25
	200	0.0	0.05	0.11	0.19	0.25
	300	0.0	0.05	0.11	0.17	0.23
	400	0.0	0.04	0.08	0.12	0.17
	500	0.0	0.03	0.06	0.09	0.13
	600	0.0	0.01	0.03	0.05	0.07
	1000	0.0	0.02	0.03	0.05	0.07
0.40	0.1	0.0	0.06	0.13	0.20	0.28
	0.5	0.0	0.05	0.10	0.16	0.22
	200	0.0	0.05	0.10	0.16	0.22
	300	0.0	0.04	0.09	0.15	0.20
	400	0.0	0.03	0.07	0.11	0.15
	500	0.0	0.02	0.05	0.08	0.11
	600	0.0	0.01	0.03	0.04	0.06
	1000	0.0	0.01	0.03	0.05	0.06

CR9-1 Damper, Butterfly

	C_o Values									
	θ									
H/W	0	10	20	30	40	50	60	65	70	90
0.10	0.04	0.30	1.10	3.0	8.0	23.0	60.	100.	190.	9999
0.50	0.04	0.30	1.10	3.0	8.0	23.0	60.	100.	190.	9999
1.0	0.04	0.30	1.10	3.0	8.0	23.0	60.	100.	190.	9999
1.5	0.04	0.35	1.25	3.6	10.0	29.0	80.	155.	230.	9999
2.0	0.04	0.35	1.25	3.6	10.0	29.0	80.	155.	230.	9999

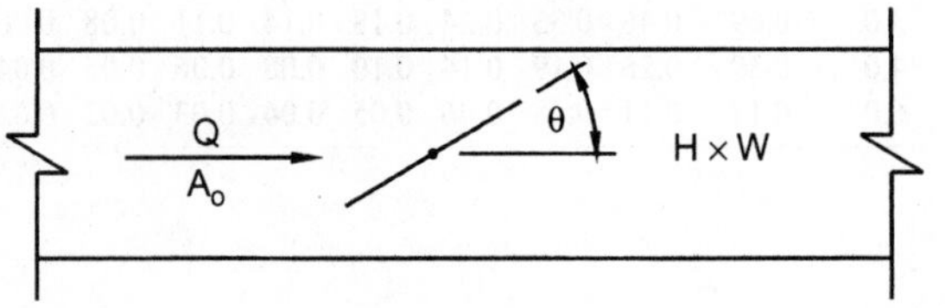

CR9-3 Damper, Parallel and Opposed 3V Blades, Open

$C_o = 0.37$

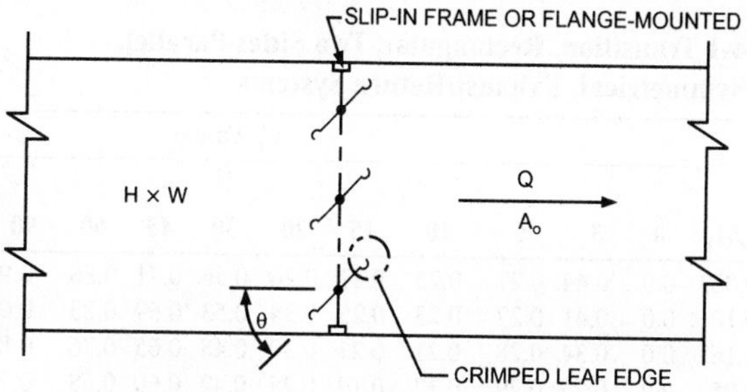

CR9-4 Damper, Parallel and Opposed Airfoil Blades, Open

$C_o = 0.18$

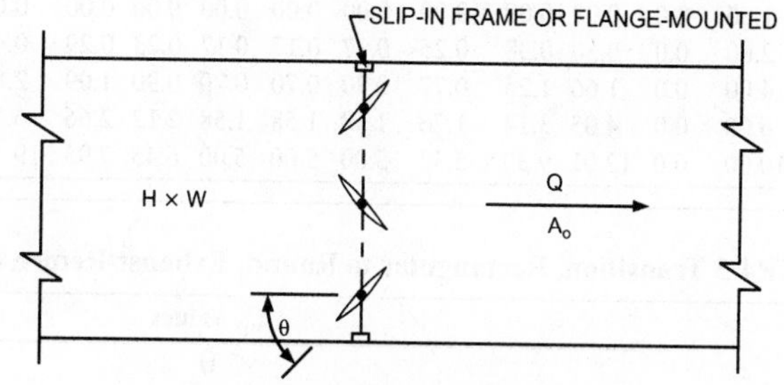

CR9-6 Fire Damper, Curtain Type, Type B, Horizontal Duct

$C_o = 0.19$

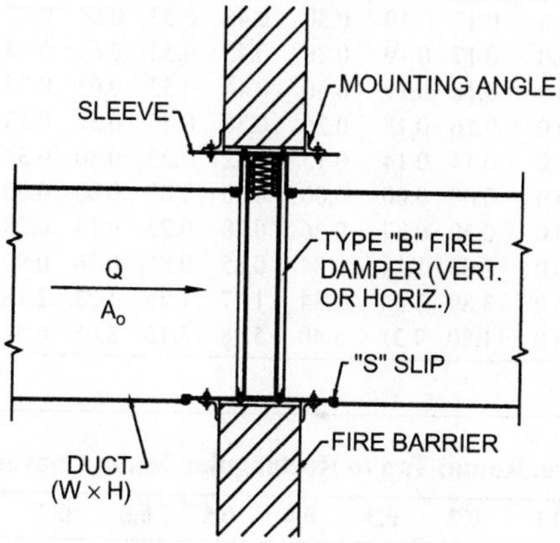

ER2-1 Bellmouth, Plenum to Round, Exhaust/Return Systems

r/D_1	0.0	0.01	0.02	0.03	0.04	0.05	0.06	0.08	0.10	0.12	0.16	0.20	10.0
C_1	0.50	0.44	0.37	0.31	0.26	0.22	0.20	0.15	0.12	0.09	0.06	0.03	0.03

$$C_o = C_1\left(\frac{A_o}{A_1}\right)^2$$

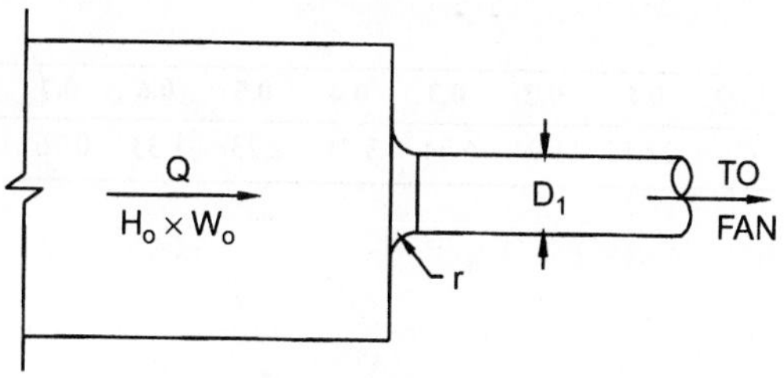

ER3-1 Elbow, 90 Degree, Variable Inlet/Outlet Areas, Exhaust/Return Systems

	C_o Values						
	W_1/W_o						
H/W_o	0.6	0.8	1.0	1.2	1.4	1.6	2.0
0.25	1.76	1.43	1.24	1.14	1.09	1.06	1.06
1.00	1.70	1.36	1.15	1.02	0.95	0.90	0.84
4.00	1.46	1.10	0.90	0.81	0.76	0.72	0.66
100.00	1.50	1.04	0.79	0.69	0.63	0.60	0.55

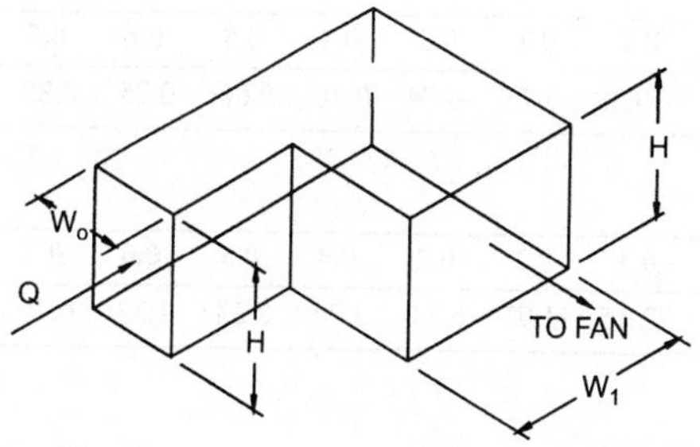

ER4-1 Transition, Rectangular, Two Sides Parallel, Symmetrical, Exhaust/Return Systems

	C_o Values												
	θ												
A_o/A_1	0	3	5	10	15	20	30	45	60	90	120	150	180
0.063	0.0	0.44	0.27	0.25	0.27	0.36	0.56	0.71	0.86	0.99	0.99	0.98	0.98
0.10	0.0	0.41	0.27	0.23	0.25	0.34	0.53	0.69	0.83	0.94	0.94	0.92	0.91
0.167	0.0	0.34	0.28	0.21	0.23	0.30	0.48	0.65	0.76	0.83	0.83	0.82	0.80
0.25	0.0	0.26	0.29	0.17	0.19	0.25	0.42	0.60	0.68	0.70	0.70	0.68	0.66
0.50	0.0	0.16	0.24	0.14	0.13	0.15	0.24	0.35	0.37	0.38	0.37	0.36	0.35
1.00	0.0	0.00	0.00	0.00	0.00	0.00	0.00	0.00	0.00	0.00	0.00	0.00	0.00
2.00	0.0	0.30	0.38	0.25	0.17	0.17	0.17	0.23	0.29	0.49	0.66	0.81	0.88
4.00	0.0	1.66	1.25	0.77	0.70	0.70	0.70	0.90	1.09	2.84	4.36	5.69	6.57
6.00	0.0	4.05	3.14	1.76	1.58	1.58	1.58	2.12	2.66	6.71	10.11	13.13	15.20
10.00	0.0	12.01	9.39	5.33	5.00	5.00	5.00	6.45	7.93	19.10	28.60	36.79	42.79

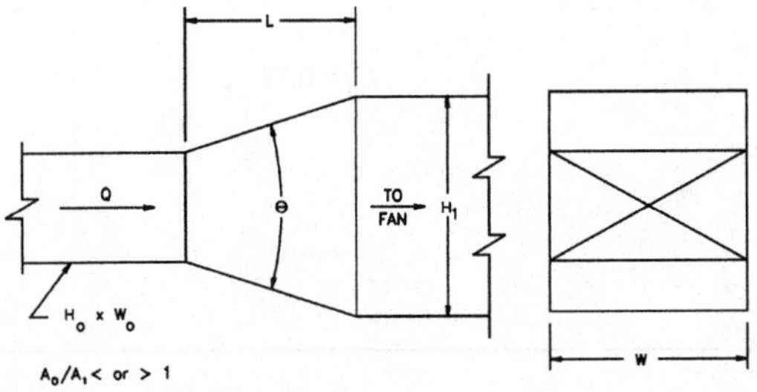

ER4-3 Transition, Rectangular to Round, Exhaust/Return Systems

	C_o Values												
	θ												
A_o/A_1	0	3	5	10	15	20	30	45	60	90	120	150	180
0.063	0.0	0.17	0.19	0.30	0.46	0.53	0.64	0.77	0.88	0.95	0.95	0.94	0.93
0.10	0.0	0.17	0.19	0.30	0.45	0.53	0.64	0.75	0.84	0.89	0.89	0.89	0.88
0.167	0.0	0.18	0.19	0.30	0.44	0.53	0.63	0.72	0.78	0.79	0.79	0.79	0.79
0.25	0.0	0.16	0.18	0.25	0.36	0.45	0.52	0.58	0.62	0.64	0.64	0.64	0.64
0.50	0.0	0.14	0.14	0.15	0.22	0.25	0.30	0.33	0.33	0.33	0.32	0.31	0.30
1.00	0.0	0.00	0.00	0.00	0.00	0.00	0.00	0.00	0.00	0.00	0.00	0.00	0.00
2.00	0.0	0.30	0.27	0.26	0.28	0.25	0.19	0.23	0.27	0.52	0.75	0.91	0.95
4.00	0.0	1.60	1.14	0.84	0.85	0.86	0.76	0.90	1.09	2.78	4.30	5.65	6.55
6.00	0.0	3.89	3.04	1.84	1.77	1.78	1.73	2.18	2.67	6.67	10.07	13.09	15.18
10.00	0.0	11.80	9.31	5.40	5.18	5.15	5.05	6.44	7.94	19.06	28.55	36.75	42.75

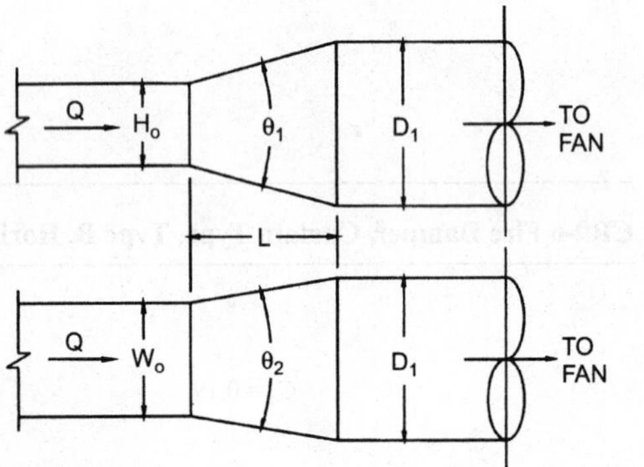

A_o/A_1 < or > 1
θ is larger of θ_1 and θ_2

ER5-2 Tee, Round Tap to Rectangular Main, Converging

Q_b/Q_c	0.1	0.2	0.3	0.4	0.5	0.6	0.7	0.8	0.9	1.0
C_b	−14.00	−2.38	0.50	0.65	1.03	1.17	1.19	1.33	1.51	1.44

Q_s/Q_c	0.1	0.2	0.3	0.4	0.5	0.6	0.7	0.8	0.9	1.0
C_s	22.15	11.91	6.54	3.74	2.23	1.33	0.76	0.38	0.10	0.0

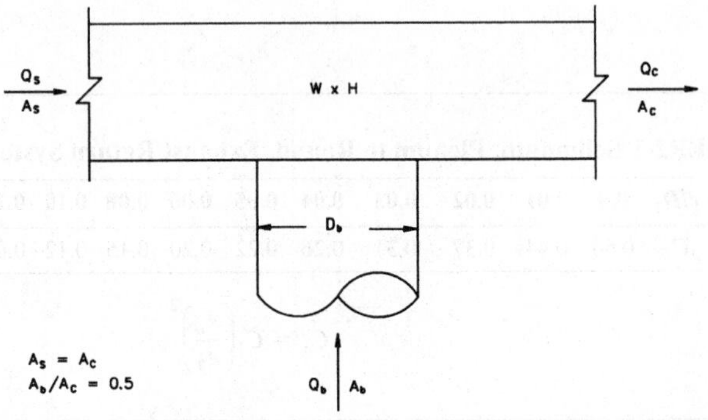

ER5-3 Tee, 45 Degree Entry Branch, Converging

Q_b/Q_c	0.1	0.2	0.3	0.4	0.5	0.6	0.7	0.8	0.9	1.0
C_b	−19.38	−3.75	−0.74	0.48	0.66	0.75	0.85	0.77	0.83	0.83

Q_s/Q_c	0.1	0.2	0.3	0.4	0.5	0.6	0.7	0.8	0.9	1.0
C_s	22.15	11.91	6.54	3.74	2.23	1.33	0.76	0.38	0.10	0.0

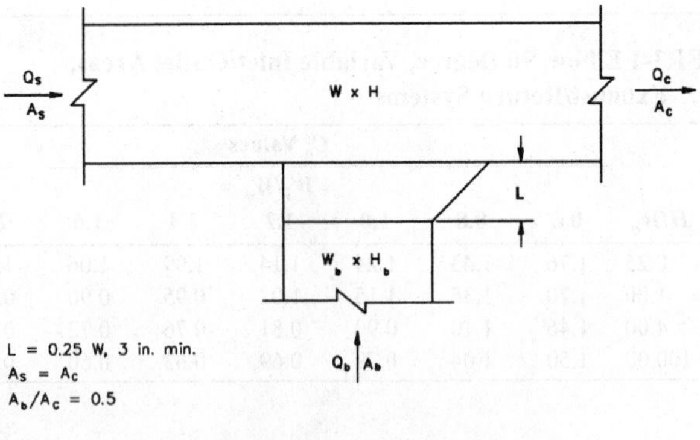

ER7-1 Fan Inlet, Centrifugal, SWSI, 90 Degree Smooth Radius Elbow (Square)

	C_o Values			
	L/H			
r/H	0.0	2.0	5.0	10.0
0.50	2.50	1.60	0.80	0.80
0.75	2.00	1.20	0.67	0.67
1.00	1.20	0.67	0.33	0.33
1.50	1.00	0.57	0.30	0.30
2.00	0.80	0.47	0.26	0.26

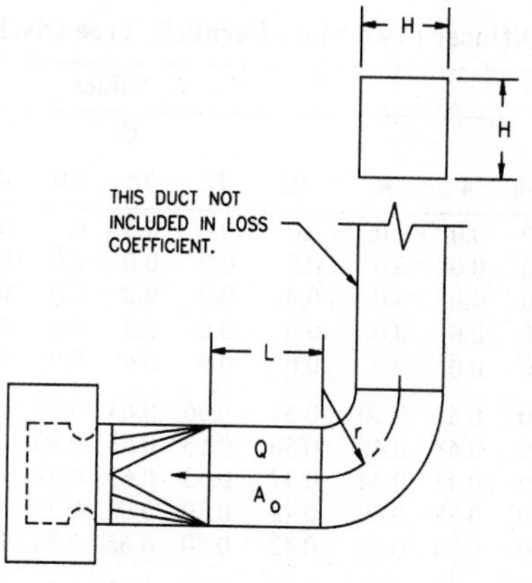

SR1-1 Conical Bellmouth/Sudden Contraction, Plenum to Rectangular, Supply Air Systems

	C_o Values								
	θ								
L/D_h	0	10	20	30	40	60	100	140	180
0.000	0.50	0.50	0.50	0.50	0.50	0.50	0.50	0.50	0.50
0.025	0.50	0.47	0.45	0.43	0.41	0.40	0.42	0.45	0.50
0.050	0.50	0.45	0.41	0.36	0.33	0.30	0.35	0.42	0.50
0.075	0.50	0.42	0.35	0.30	0.26	0.23	0.30	0.40	0.50
0.100	0.50	0.39	0.32	0.25	0.22	0.18	0.27	0.38	0.50
0.150	0.50	0.37	0.27	0.20	0.16	0.15	0.25	0.37	0.50
0.600	0.50	0.27	0.18	0.13	0.11	0.12	0.23	0.36	0.50

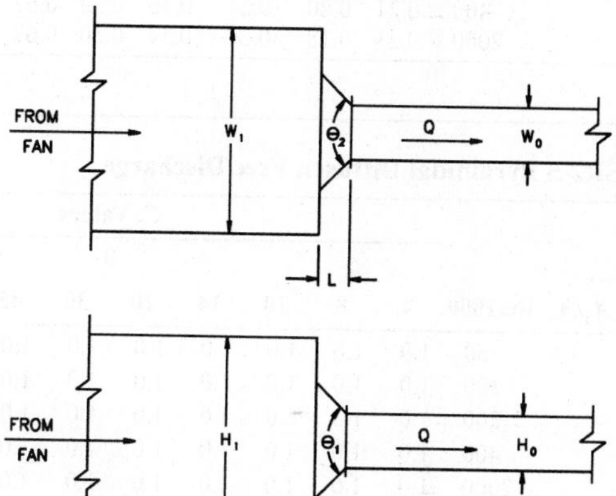

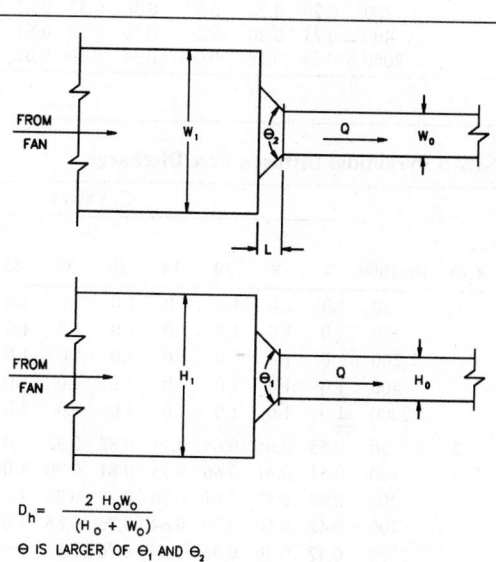

$$D_h = \frac{2\,H_oW_o}{(H_o + W_o)}$$

θ IS LARGER OF θ_1 AND θ_2

SR2-1 Abrupt Exit

	Laminar Flow									
H/W	0.1	0.2	0.9	0.999	1.0	1.001	1.1	4.0	5.0	10.0
C_o	1.55	1.55	1.55	1.55	2.00	1.555	1.55	1.55	1.55	1.55

Turbulent Flow

$C_o = 1.0$

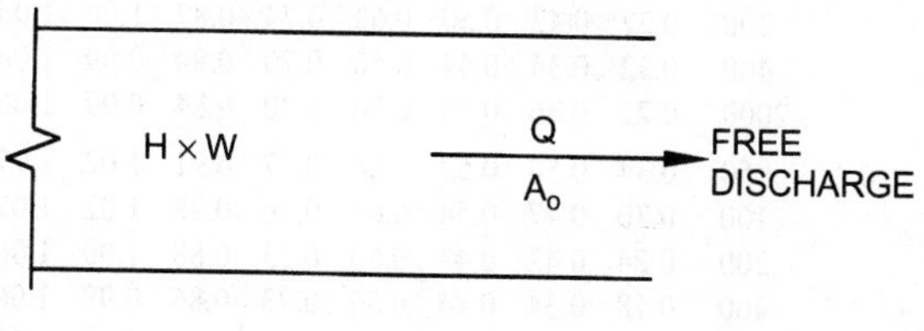

SR2-3 Plain Diffuser (Two Sides Parallel), Free Discharge

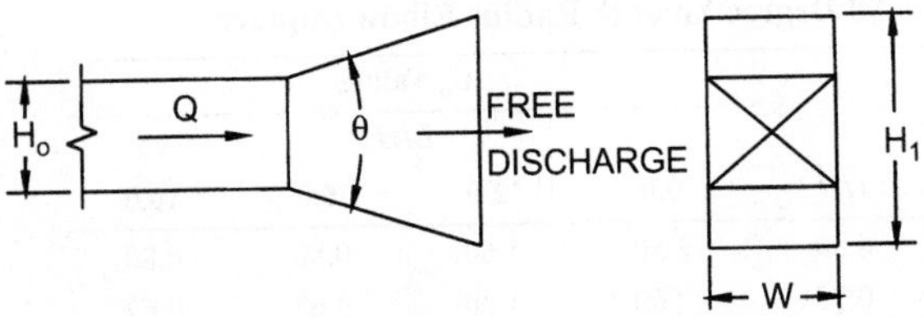

A_1/A_o	Re/1000	C_o Values θ = 4	8	10	14	20	30	45	60	90	120
1	50	0.0	0.0	0.0	0.0	0.0	0.0	0.0	0.0	0.0	0.0
	100	0.0	0.0	0.0	0.0	0.0	0.0	0.0	0.0	0.0	0.0
	200	0.0	0.0	0.0	0.0	0.0	0.0	0.0	0.0	0.0	0.0
	400	0.0	0.0	0.0	0.0	0.0	0.0	0.0	0.0	0.0	0.0
	2000	0.0	0.0	0.0	0.0	0.0	0.0	0.0	0.0	0.0	0.0
2	50	0.51	0.50	0.51	0.56	0.63	0.80	0.96	1.04	1.09	1.09
	100	0.48	0.48	0.50	0.56	0.63	0.80	0.96	1.04	1.09	1.09
	200	0.42	0.44	0.47	0.53	0.63	0.74	0.93	1.02	1.08	1.08
	400	0.38	0.40	0.42	0.50	0.62	0.74	0.93	1.02	1.08	1.08
	2000	0.38	0.40	0.42	0.50	0.62	0.74	0.93	1.02	1.08	1.08
4	50	0.35	0.34	0.38	0.48	0.63	0.76	0.91	1.03	1.07	1.07
	100	0.31	0.31	0.36	0.45	0.59	0.72	0.88	1.02	1.07	1.07
	200	0.27	0.26	0.31	0.41	0.53	0.67	0.83	0.96	1.06	1.06
	400	0.21	0.22	0.27	0.39	0.53	0.67	0.83	0.96	1.06	1.06
	2000	0.21	0.22	0.27	0.39	0.53	0.67	0.83	0.96	1.06	1.06
6	50	0.36	0.32	0.34	0.41	0.56	0.70	0.84	0.96	1.08	1.08
	100	0.32	0.27	0.30	0.41	0.56	0.70	0.84	0.96	1.08	1.08
	200	0.26	0.24	0.27	0.36	0.52	0.67	0.81	0.94	1.06	1.06
	400	0.21	0.20	0.24	0.36	0.52	0.67	0.81	0.94	1.06	1.06
	2000	9.21	0.18	0.24	0.34	0.50	0.67	0.81	0.94	1.05	1.05

SR2-5 Pyramidal Diffuser, Free Discharge

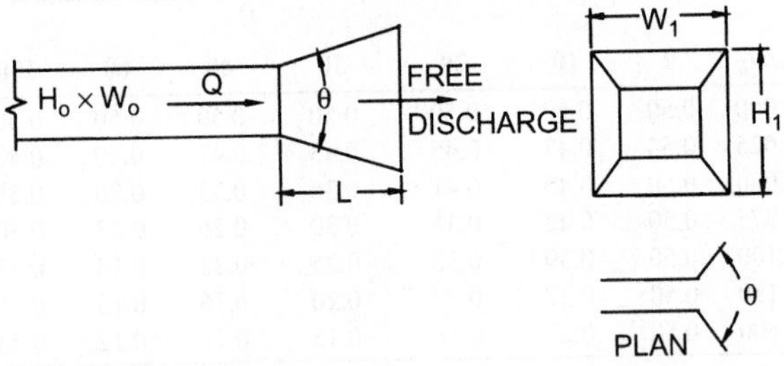

A_1/A_o	Re/1000	C_o Values θ = 4	8	10	14	20	30	45	60	90	120
1	50	1.0	1.0	1.0	1.0	1.0	1.0	1.0	1.0	1.0	1.0
	100	1.0	1.0	1.0	1.0	1.0	1.0	1.0	1.0	1.0	1.0
	200	1.0	1.0	1.0	1.0	1.0	1.0	1.0	1.0	1.0	1.0
	400	1.0	1.0	1.0	1.0	1.0	1.0	1.0	1.0	1.0	1.0
	2000	1.0	1.0	1.0	1.0	1.0	1.0	1.0	1.0	1.0	1.0
2	50	0.55	0.65	0.68	0.74	0.82	0.92	1.05	1.10	1.08	1.08
	100	0.51	0.61	0.66	0.73	0.81	0.90	1.04	1.09	1.08	1.08
	200	0.47	0.57	0.61	0.70	0.79	0.89	1.04	1.09	1.08	1.08
	400	0.42	0.50	0.56	0.64	0.76	0.88	1.02	1.07	1.08	1.08
	2000	0.42	0.50	0.56	0.64	0.76	0.88	1.02	1.07	1.08	1.08
4	50	0.38	0.53	0.60	0.69	0.78	0.90	1.02	1.07	1.09	1.09
	100	0.33	0.49	0.55	0.66	0.78	0.90	1.02	1.07	1.09	1.09
	200	0.27	0.42	0.50	0.62	0.74	0.87	1.00	1.06	1.08	1.08
	400	0.22	0.36	0.44	0.56	0.70	0.84	0.99	1.06	1.08	1.08
	2000	0.22	0.36	0.44	0.56	0.70	0.84	0.99	1.06	1.08	1.08
6	50	0.34	0.50	0.57	0.66	0.77	0.91	1.02	1.07	1.08	1.08
	100	0.30	0.47	0.54	0.63	0.76	0.98	1.02	1.07	1.08	1.08
	200	0.24	0.42	0.48	0.60	0.73	0.88	1.00	1.06	1.08	1.08
	400	0.18	0.34	0.44	0.56	0.73	0.86	0.98	1.06	1.08	1.08
	2000	0.18	0.34	0.44	0.56	0.73	0.86	0.98	1.06	1.08	1.08
10	50	0.30	0.45	0.53	0.64	0.74	0.85	0.97	1.10	1.12	1.12
	100	0.25	0.40	0.48	0.62	0.73	0.85	0.97	1.10	1.12	1.12
	200	0.20	0.34	0.44	0.56	0.69	0.82	0.95	1.10	1.11	1.11
	400	0.16	0.28	0.40	0.55	0.67	0.80	0.93	1.09	1.11	1.11
	2000	0.16	0.28	0.40	0.55	0.67	0.80	0.93	1.09	1.11	1.11

SR2-6 Pyramidal Diffuser, with Wall

L/D_h	0.5	1.0	2.0	3.0	4.0	5.0	6.0	8.0	10.0	12.0	14.0
C_o	0.49	0.40	0.30	0.26	0.23	0.21	0.19	0.17	0.16	0.15	0.14
θ	26	19	13	11	9	8	7	6	6	5	5

θ is the optimum angle.

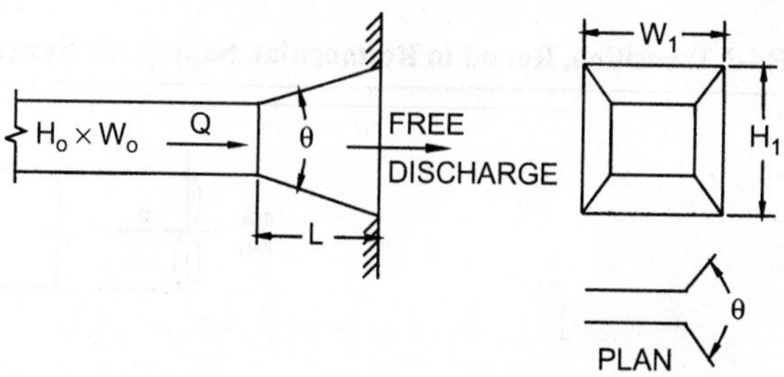

SR3-1 Elbow, 90 Degree, Variable Inlet/Outlet Areas, Supply Air Systems

	C_o Values						
	W_o/W_1						
H/W_1	0.6	0.8	1.0	1.2	1.4	1.6	2.0
0.25	0.63	0.92	1.24	1.64	2.14	2.71	4.24
1.00	0.61	0.87	1.15	1.47	1.86	2.30	3.36
4.00	0.53	0.70	0.90	1.17	1.49	1.84	2.64
100.	0.54	0.67	0.79	0.99	1.23	1.54	2.20

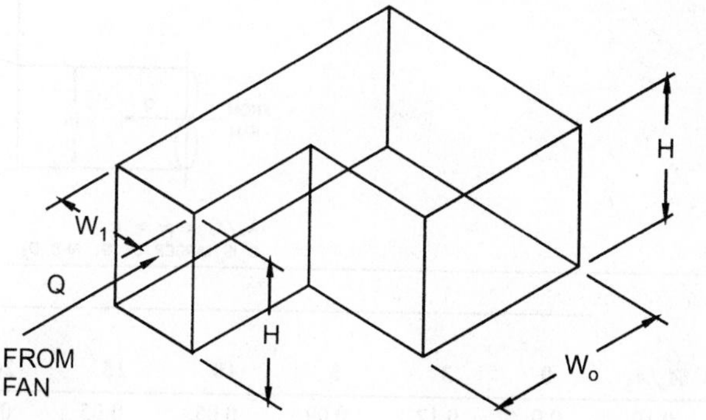

SR4-1 Transition, Rectangular, Two Sides Parallel, Symmetrical, Supply Air Systems

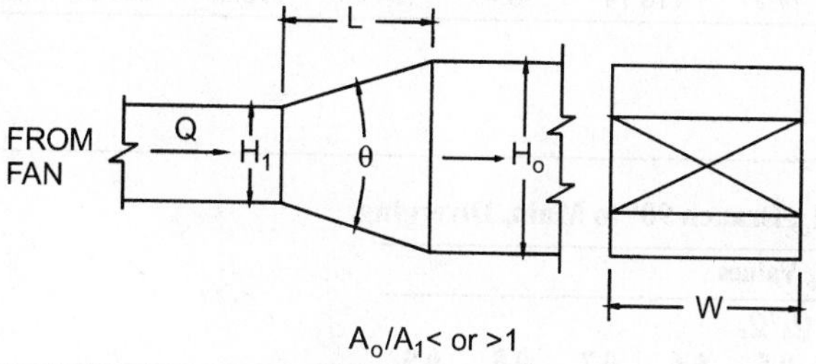

	C_o Values												
	θ												
A_o/A_1	0	3	5	10	15	20	30	45	60	90	120	150	180
0.10	0.0	0.12	0.09	0.05	0.05	0.05	0.05	0.06	0.08	0.19	0.29	0.37	0.43
0.167	0.0	0.11	0.09	0.05	0.04	0.04	0.04	0.06	0.07	0.19	0.28	0.36	0.42
0.25	0.0	0.10	0.08	0.05	0.04	0.04	0.04	0.06	0.07	0.18	0.27	0.36	0.41
0.50	0.0	0.08	0.09	0.06	0.04	0.04	0.04	0.06	0.07	0.12	0.17	0.20	0.27
1.00	0.0	0.00	0.00	0.00	0.00	0.00	0.00	0.00	0.00	0.00	0.00	0.00	1.00
2.00	0.0	0.64	0.96	0.54	0.52	0.62	0.94	1.40	1.48	1.52	1.48	1.44	1.40
4.00	0.0	4.16	4.64	2.72	3.09	4.00	6.72	9.60	10.88	11.20	11.20	10.88	10.56
6.00	0.0	12.24	10.08	7.38	8.10	10.80	17.28	23.40	27.36	29.88	29.88	29.34	28.80
10.00	0.0	40.50	27.20	23.30	25.10	34.00	52.84	69.00	82.50	93.50	93.50	92.40	91.30
16.00	0.0	112.64	68.35	63.74	67.84	92.93	142.13	182.53	220.16	254.21	254.21	251.90	249.60

SR4-3 Transition, Round to Rectangular, Supply Air Systems

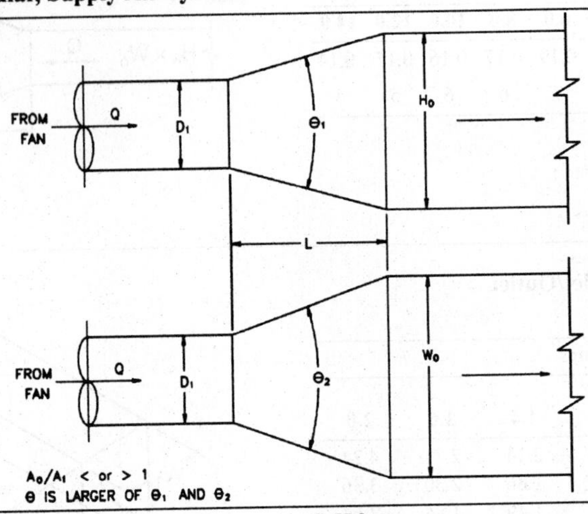

C_o Values

A_o/A_1	θ = 0	3	5	10	15	20	30	45	60	90	120	150	180
0.10	0.0	0.12	0.09	0.05	0.05	0.05	0.05	0.06	0.08	0.19	0.29	0.37	0.43
0.167	0.0	0.11	0.08	0.05	0.05	0.05	0.05	0.06	0.07	0.19	0.28	0.37	0.42
0.25	0.0	0.10	0.07	0.05	0.05	0.05	0.05	0.06	0.07	0.17	0.27	0.35	0.41
0.50	0.0	0.08	0.07	0.06	0.07	0.06	0.05	0.06	0.07	0.13	0.19	0.23	0.24
1.00	0.0	0.00	0.00	0.00	0.00	0.00	0.00	0.00	0.00	0.00	0.00	0.00	0.00
2.00	0.0	0.57	0.55	0.61	0.87	1.00	1.20	1.30	1.30	1.30	1.28	1.24	1.20
4.00	0.0	2.60	2.84	3.92	5.72	7.20	8.32	9.28	9.92	10.24	10.24	10.24	10.24
6.00	0.0	6.57	6.75	10.62	15.84	18.90	22.50	25.74	27.90	28.44	28.44	28.35	28.26
10.00	0.0	17.25	18.75	30.00	45.00	53.00	63.50	75.00	84.0	89.00	89.00	88.50	88.00
16.00	0.0	42.75	48.13	77.57	116.74	136.45	164.10	196.86	224.26	241.92	241.92	240.38	238.59

SR5-1 Smooth Wye of Type $A_s + A_b \geq A_c$, Branch 90° to Main, Diverging

C_b Values

A_s/A_c	A_b/A_c	Q_b/Q_c = 0.1	0.2	0.3	0.4	0.5	0.6	0.7	0.8	0.9
0.50	0.25	2.25	0.48	0.25	0.18	0.17	0.16	0.17	0.17	0.17
	0.50	11.00	2.38	1.06	0.64	0.52	0.47	0.47	0.47	0.48
	1.00	60.00	13.00	4.78	2.06	0.96	0.47	0.31	0.27	0.26
0.75	0.25	2.19	0.55	0.35	0.31	0.33	0.35	0.36	0.37	0.39
	0.50	13.00	2.50	0.89	0.47	0.34	0.31	0.32	0.36	0.43
	1.00	70.00	15.00	5.67	2.63	1.36	0.78	0.53	0.41	0.36
1.00	0.25	3.44	0.78	0.42	0.33	0.30	0.31	0.40	0.42	0.46
	0.50	15.50	3.00	1.11	0.63	0.48	0.42	0.40	0.42	0.46
	1.00	67.00	13.75	5.11	2.31	1.28	0.81	0.59	0.47	0.46

C_s Values

A_s/A_c	A_b/A_c	Q_s/Q_c = 0.1	0.2	0.3	0.4	0.5	0.6	0.7	0.8	0.9
0.50	0.25	8.65	1.12	0.21	0.05	0.06	0.10	0.15	0.19	0.24
	0.50	7.50	0.98	0.19	0.06	0.06	0.10	0.14	0.18	0.22
	1.00	5.21	0.68	0.15	0.06	0.07	0.10	0.13	0.16	0.19
0.75	0.25	19.62	3.25	0.86	0.23	0.05	0.02	0.00	0.00	0.05
	0.50	20.62	3.24	0.76	0.14	−0.03	−0.07	−0.05	−0.01	0.03
	1.00	17.01	2.55	0.55	0.07	−0.05	−0.05	−0.02	0.02	0.06
1.00	0.25	46.00	9.50	3.22	1.31	0.52	0.14	−0.02	−0.05	−0.01
	0.50	35.34	6.49	1.98	0.69	0.22	0.00	−0.04	−0.05	−0.05
	1.00	38.95	7.10	2.15	0.74	0.23	0.03	−0.04	−0.05	−0.04

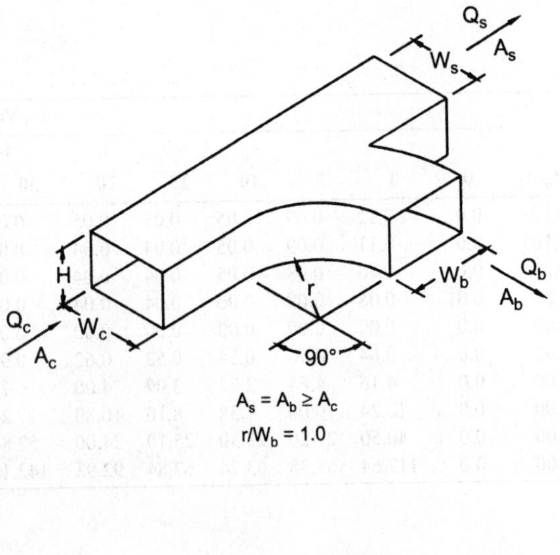

SR5-3 Wye of the Type $A_s + A_b > A_c$, $A_s = A_c$, 45 Degree, Diverging

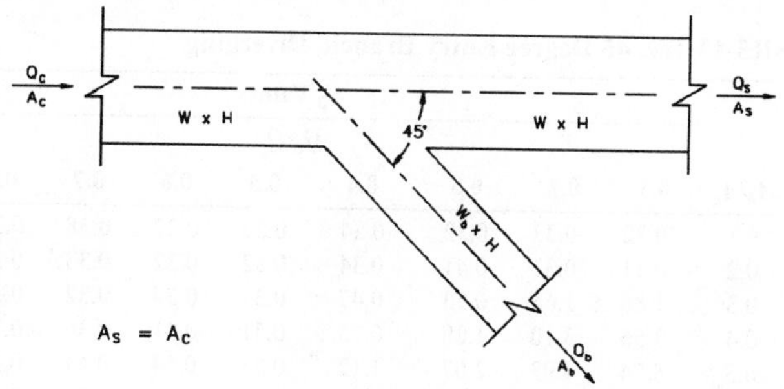

	C_b Values								
	Q_b/Q_c								
A_b/A_c	0.1	0.2	0.3	0.4	0.5	0.6	0.7	0.8	0.9
0.1	0.60	0.52	0.57	0.58	0.64	0.67	0.70	0.71	0.73
0.2	2.24	0.56	0.44	0.45	0.51	0.54	0.58	0.60	0.62
0.3	5.93	1.08	0.52	0.41	0.43	0.46	0.49	0.52	0.54
0.4	10.61	1.89	0.72	0.43	0.34	0.31	0.31	0.33	0.34
0.5	17.70	3.23	1.14	0.59	0.40	0.31	0.30	0.30	0.31
0.6	26.66	5.01	1.75	0.84	0.50	0.36	0.31	0.30	0.30
0.7	37.49	7.22	2.53	1.17	0.66	0.43	0.35	0.32	0.30
0.8	50.20	9.87	3.49	1.61	0.88	0.54	0.41	0.35	0.32
0.9	64.77	12.95	4.63	2.13	1.14	0.69	0.50	0.40	0.35

Q_s/Q_c	0.1	0.2	0.3	0.4	0.5	0.6	0.7	0.8	0.9
C_s	32.40	6.40	2.18	0.90	0.40	0.18	0.07	0.03	0.00

SR5-5 Tee of the Type $A_s + A_b > A_c$, $A_s = A_c$, Diverging

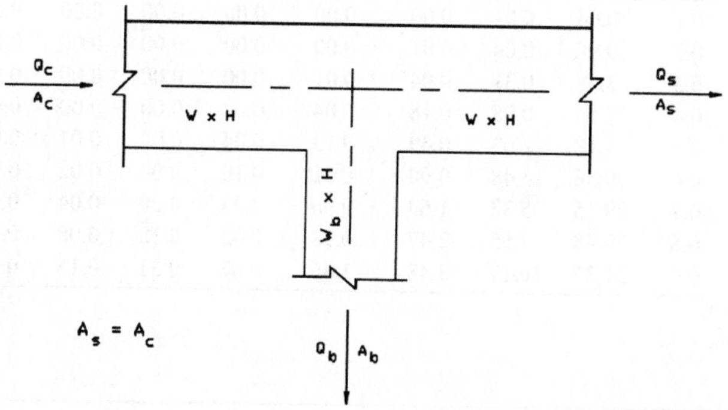

	C_b Values								
	Q_b/Q_c								
A_b/A_c	0.1	0.2	0.3	0.4	0.5	0.6	0.7	0.8	0.9
0.1	2.06	1.20	0.99	0.87	0.88	0.87	0.87	0.86	0.86
0.2	5.15	1.92	1.29	1.03	0.99	0.94	0.92	0.90	0.89
0.3	10.30	3.12	1.78	1.28	1.16	1.06	1.01	0.97	0.94
0.4	15.90	4.35	2.24	1.48	1.11	0.88	0.80	0.75	0.72
0.5	24.31	6.31	3.04	1.90	1.35	1.03	0.91	0.83	0.78
0.6	34.60	8.70	4.03	2.41	1.65	1.22	1.04	0.94	0.87
0.7	46.75	11.53	5.19	3.01	2.00	1.44	1.20	1.06	0.96
0.8	60.78	14.79	6.53	3.70	2.40	1.69	1.38	1.20	1.07
0.9	76.67	18.49	8.05	4.49	2.86	1.98	1.59	1.36	1.20

Q_s/Q_c	0.1	0.2	0.3	0.4	0.5	0.6	0.7	0.8	1.0
C_s	32.40	6.40	2.18	0.90	0.40	0.18	0.07	0.03	0.00

SR5-11 Tee, Rectangular Main to Round Tap, Diverging

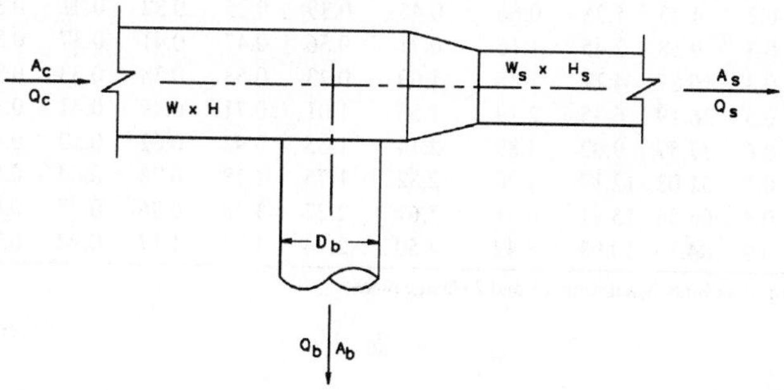

	C_b Values								
	Q_b/Q_c								
A_b/A_c	0.1	0.2	0.3	0.4	0.5	0.6	0.7	0.8	0.9
0.1	1.58	0.94	0.83	0.79	0.77	0.76	0.76	0.76	0.75
0.2	4.20	1.58	1.10	0.94	0.87	0.83	0.80	0.79	0.78
0.3	8.63	2.67	1.58	1.20	1.03	0.91	0.88	0.85	0.83
0.4	14.85	4.20	2.25	1.58	1.27	1.10	1.00	0.94	0.90
0.5	22.87	6.19	3.13	2.07	1.58	1.32	1.16	1.06	0.99
0.6	32.68	8.63	4.20	2.67	1.96	1.58	1.35	1.20	1.10
0.7	44.30	11.51	5.48	3.38	2.41	1.89	1.58	1.38	1.24
0.8	57.71	14.85	6.95	4.20	2.94	2.25	1.84	1.58	1.40
0.9	72.92	18.63	8.63	5.14	3.53	2.67	2.14	1.81	1.58

	C_s Values								
	Q_s/Q_c								
A_s/A_c	0.1	0.2	0.3	0.4	0.5	0.6	0.7	0.8	0.9
0.1	0.04	0.01	0.00	0.00	0.00	0.00	0.00	0.00	0.00
0.2	0.98	0.04	0.01	0.00	0.00	0.00	0.00	0.00	0.00
0.3	3.48	0.31	0.04	0.01	0.00	0.00	0.00	0.00	0.00
0.4	7.55	0.98	0.18	0.04	0.02	0.00	0.00	0.00	0.00
0.5	13.18	2.03	0.49	0.13	0.04	0.00	0.01	0.00	0.00
0.6	20.38	3.48	0.98	0.31	0.10	0.04	0.02	0.01	0.00
0.7	29.15	5.32	1.64	0.60	0.23	0.09	0.04	0.02	0.01
0.8	39.48	7.55	2.47	0.98	0.42	0.18	0.08	0.04	0.02
0.9	51.37	10.17	3.48	1.46	0.67	0.31	0.15	0.07	0.04

SR5-13 Tee, 45 Degree Entry Branch, Diverging

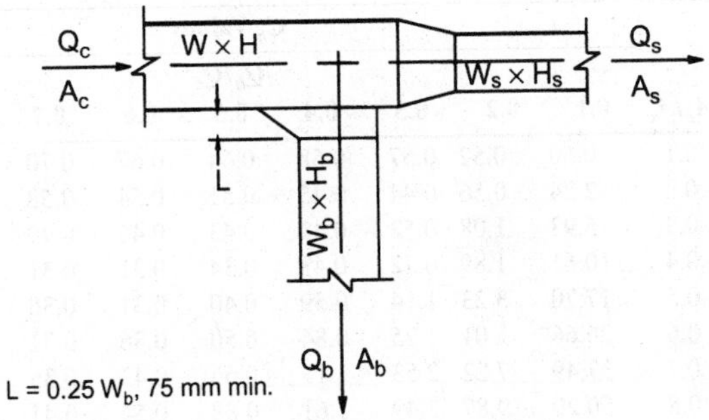

	C_b Values								
	Q_b/Q_c								
A_b/A_c	0.1	0.2	0.3	0.4	0.5	0.6	0.7	0.8	0.9
0.1	0.32	0.33	0.32	0.34	0.32	0.37	0.38	0.39	0.40
0.2	0.31	0.32	0.41	0.34	0.32	0.32	0.33	0.34	0.35
0.3	1.86	1.65	0.73	0.47	0.37	0.34	0.32	0.32	0.32
0.4	3.56	3.10	1.28	0.73	0.51	0.41	0.36	0.34	0.32
0.5	5.74	4.93	2.07	1.12	0.73	0.54	0.44	0.38	0.35
0.6	8.48	7.24	3.10	1.65	1.03	0.73	0.56	0.47	0.41
0.7	11.75	10.00	4.32	3.31	1.42	0.98	0.73	0.58	0.49
0.8	15.57	13.22	5.74	3.10	1.90	1.28	0.94	0.73	0.60
0.9	19.92	16.90	7.38	4.02	2.46	1.65	1.19	0.91	0.73

	C_s Values								
	Q_s/Q_c								
A_s/A_c	0.1	0.2	0.3	0.4	0.5	0.6	0.7	0.8	0.9
0.1	0.04	0.01	0.00	0.00	0.00	0.00	0.00	0.00	0.00
0.2	0.98	0.04	0.01	0.00	0.00	0.00	0.00	0.00	0.00
0.3	3.48	0.31	0.04	0.01	0.00	0.00	0.00	0.00	0.00
0.4	7.55	0.98	0.18	0.04	0.02	0.00	0.00	0.00	0.00
0.5	13.18	2.03	0.49	0.13	0.04	0.00	0.01	0.00	0.00
0.6	20.38	3.48	0.98	0.31	0.10	0.04	0.02	0.01	0.00
0.7	29.15	5.32	1.64	0.60	0.23	0.09	0.04	0.02	0.01
0.8	39.48	7.55	2.47	0.98	0.42	0.18	0.08	0.04	0.02
0.9	51.37	10.17	3.48	1.46	0.67	0.31	0.15	0.07	0.04

SR5-15 Bullhead Tee Without Vanes, Diverging

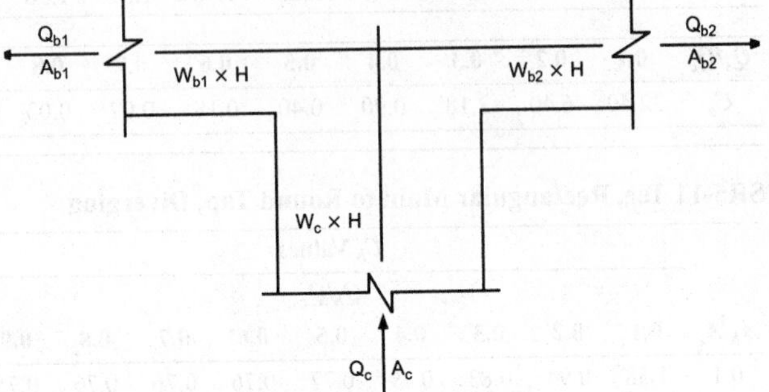

	C_{b1} Values								
	Q_{b1}/Q_c								
A_{b1}/A_c	0.1	0.2	0.3	0.4	0.5	0.6	0.7	0.8	0.9
0.1	1.34	0.53	0.37	0.30	0.29	0.28	0.27	0.27	0.27
0.2	4.43	1.25	0.66	0.45	0.39	0.35	0.32	0.31	0.30
0.3	9.58	2.45	1.16	0.71	0.56	0.47	0.41	0.37	0.35
0.4	16.87	4.17	1.88	1.09	0.73	0.53	0.38	0.33	0.30
0.5	26.19	6.35	2.79	1.56	1.01	0.71	0.49	0.41	0.37
0.6	37.57	9.02	3.89	2.14	1.35	0.92	0.62	0.52	0.45
0.7	51.03	12.17	5.20	2.82	1.75	1.18	0.78	0.64	0.54
0.8	66.55	15.81	6.71	3.61	2.22	1.48	0.96	0.78	0.65
0.9	84.15	19.93	8.42	4.50	2.74	1.81	1.17	0.94	0.78

For other branch, subscripts 1 and 2 change places.

SR7-1 Fan, Centrifugal, Without Outlet Diffuser, Free Discharge

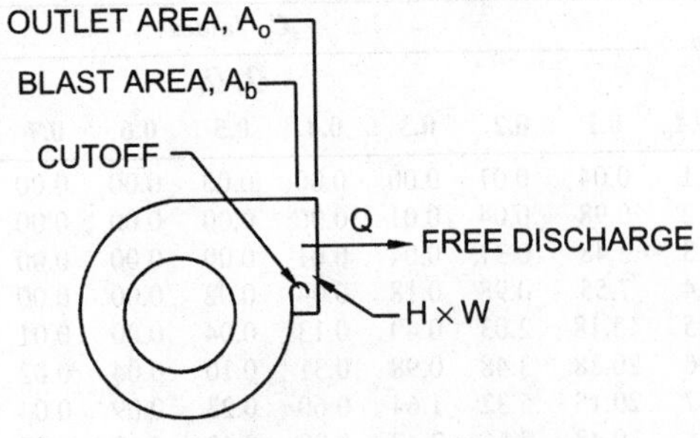

A_b/A_o	0.4	0.5	0.6	0.7	0.8	0.9	1.0
C_o	2.00	2.00	1.00	0.80	0.47	0.22	0.00

SR7-2 Plane Asymmetric Diffuser at Centrifugal Fan Outlet, Free Discharge

	C_o Values					
	A_1/A_o					
θ	1.5	2.0	2.5	3.0	3.5	4.0
10	0.51	0.34	0.25	0.21	0.18	0.17
15	0.54	0.36	0.27	0.24	0.22	0.20
20	0.55	0.38	0.31	0.27	0.25	0.24
25	0.59	0.43	0.37	0.35	0.33	0.33
30	0.63	0.50	0.46	0.44	0.43	0.42
35	0.65	0.56	0.53	0.52	0.51	0.50

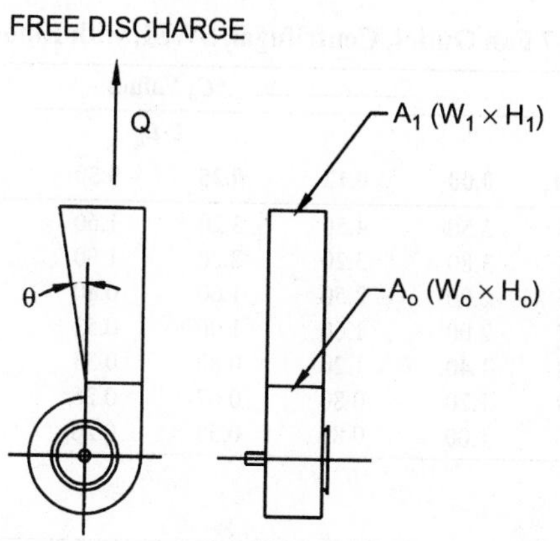

SR7-5 Fan Outlet, Centrifugal, SWSI, with Elbow (Position A)

	C_o Values					
	L/L_e					
A_b/A_o	0.00	0.12	0.25	0.50	1.0	10.0
0.4	3.20	2.50	1.80	0.80	0.0	0.0
0.5	2.20	1.80	1.20	0.53	0.0	0.0
0.6	1.60	1.40	0.80	0.40	0.0	0.0
0.7	1.00	0.80	0.53	0.26	0.0	0.0
0.8	0.80	0.67	0.47	0.18	0.0	0.0
0.9	0.53	0.47	0.33	0.18	0.0	0.0
1.0	0.53	0.47	0.33	0.18	0.0	0.0

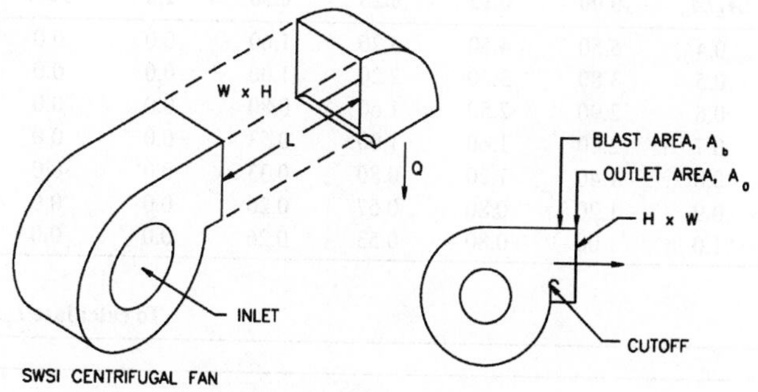

$$V_o > 13\text{ m/s:}\quad L_e = \frac{V_o\sqrt{A_o}}{4500}$$

$$V_o \le 13\text{ m/s:}\quad L_e = \frac{\sqrt{A_o}}{350}$$

where:

V_o = duct velocity, m/s
L_e = effective duct length, m
A_o = duct area, mm^2

SR7-6 Fan Outlet, Centrifugal, SWSI, with Elbow (Position B)

	C_o Values					
	L/L_e					
A_b/A_o	0.00	0.12	0.25	0.50	1.0	10.0
0.4	3.80	3.20	2.20	1.00	0.0	0.0
0.5	2.90	2.20	1.60	0.67	0.0	0.0
0.6	2.00	1.60	1.20	0.53	0.0	0.0
0.7	1.40	1.00	0.67	0.33	0.0	0.0
0.8	1.00	0.80	0.53	0.26	0.0	0.0
0.9	0.80	0.67	0.47	0.18	0.0	0.0
1.0	0.67	0.53	0.40	0.18	0.0	0.0

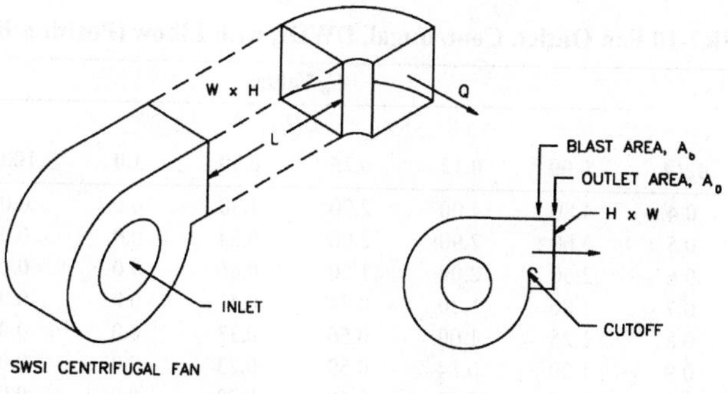

To calculate L_e, see Fitting SR7-5.

SR7-7 Fan Outlet, Centrifugal, SWSI, with Elbow (Position C)

A_b/A_o	C_o Values, L/L_e = 0.00	0.12	0.25	0.50	1.0	10.0
0.4	5.50	4.50	3.20	1.60	0.0	0.0
0.5	3.80	3.20	2.20	1.00	0.0	0.0
0.6	2.90	2.50	1.60	0.80	0.0	0.0
0.7	2.00	1.60	1.00	0.53	0.0	0.0
0.8	1.40	1.20	0.80	0.33	0.0	0.0
0.9	1.20	0.80	0.67	0.26	0.0	0.0
1.0	1.00	0.80	0.53	0.26	0.0	0.0

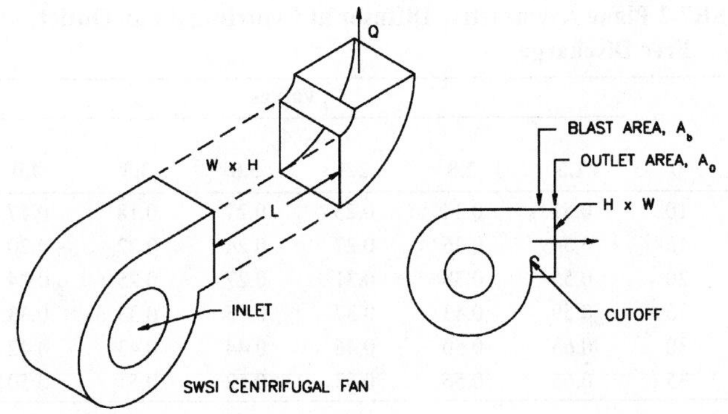

To calculate L_e, see Fitting SR7-5.

SR7-8 Fan Outlet, Centrifugal, SWSI, with Elbow (Position D)

A_b/A_o	C_o Values, L/L_e = 0.00	0.12	0.25	0.50	1.0	10.0
0.4	5.50	4.50	3.20	1.60	0.0	0.0
0.5	3.80	3.20	2.20	1.00	0.0	0.0
0.6	2.90	2.50	1.60	0.80	0.0	0.0
0.7	2.00	1.60	1.00	0.53	0.0	0.0
0.8	1.40	1.20	0.80	0.33	0.0	0.0
0.9	1.20	0.80	0.67	0.26	0.0	0.0
1.0	1.00	0.80	0.53	0.26	0.0	0.0

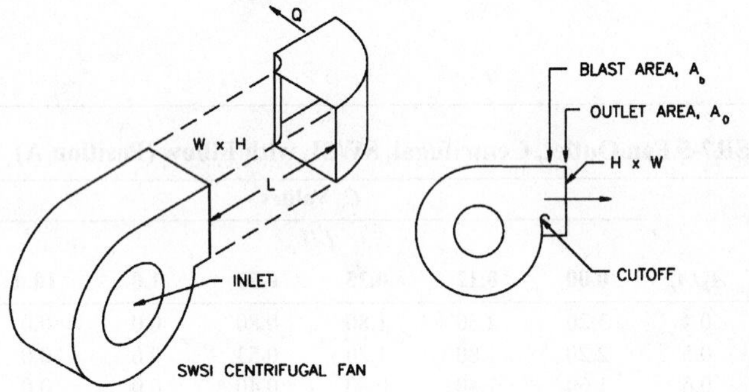

To calculate L_e, see Fitting SR7-5.

SR7-9 Fan Outlet, Centrifugal, DWDI, with Elbow (Position A)

A_b/A_o	C_o Values, L/L_e = 0.00	0.12	0.25	0.50	1.0	10.0
0.4	3.20	2.50	1.80	0.80	0.0	0.0
0.5	2.20	1.80	1.20	0.53	0.0	0.0
0.6	1.60	1.40	0.80	0.40	0.0	0.0
0.7	1.00	0.80	0.53	0.26	0.0	0.0
0.8	0.80	0.67	0.47	0.18	0.0	0.0
0.9	0.53	0.47	0.33	0.18	0.0	0.0
1.0	0.53	0.47	0.33	0.18	0.0	0.0

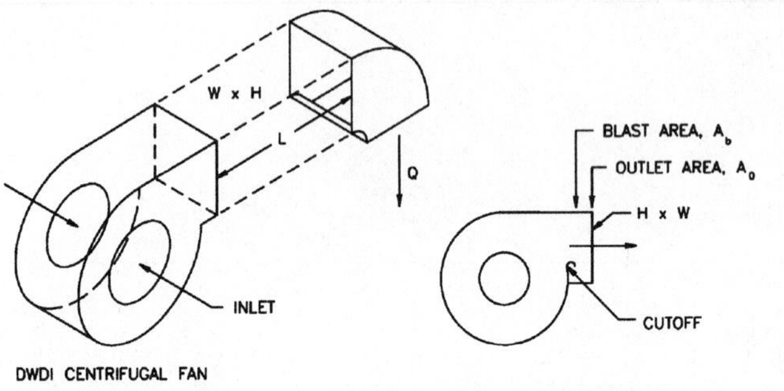

To calculate L_e, see Fitting SR7-5.

SR7-10 Fan Outlet, Centrifugal, DWDI, with Elbow (Position B)

A_b/A_o	C_o Values, L/L_e = 0.00	0.12	0.25	0.50	1.0	10.0
0.4	4.80	4.00	2.90	1.30	0.0	0.0
0.5	3.60	2.90	2.00	0.84	0.0	0.0
0.6	2.50	2.00	1.50	0.66	0.0	0.0
0.7	1.80	1.30	0.84	0.41	0.0	0.0
0.8	1.25	1.00	0.66	0.33	0.0	0.0
0.9	1.00	0.84	0.59	0.23	0.0	0.0
1.0	0.84	0.66	0.50	0.23	0.0	0.0

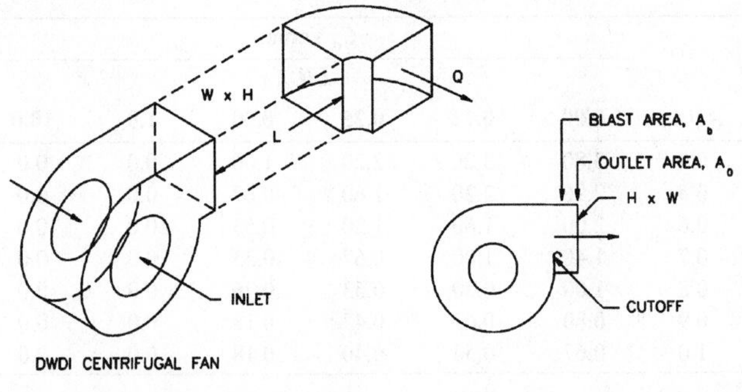

To calculate L_e, see Fitting SR7-5.

SR7-11 Fan Outlet, Centrifugal, DWDI, with Elbow (Position C)

	C_o Values					
	L/L_e					
A_b/A_o	0.00	0.12	0.25	0.50	1.0	10.0
0.4	5.50	4.50	3.20	1.60	0.0	0.0
0.5	3.80	3.20	2.20	1.00	0.0	0.0
0.6	2.90	2.50	1.60	0.80	0.0	0.0
0.7	2.00	1.60	1.00	0.53	0.0	0.0
0.8	1.40	1.20	0.80	0.33	0.0	0.0
0.9	1.20	0.80	0.67	0.26	0.0	0.0
1.0	1.00	0.80	0.53	0.26	0.0	0.0

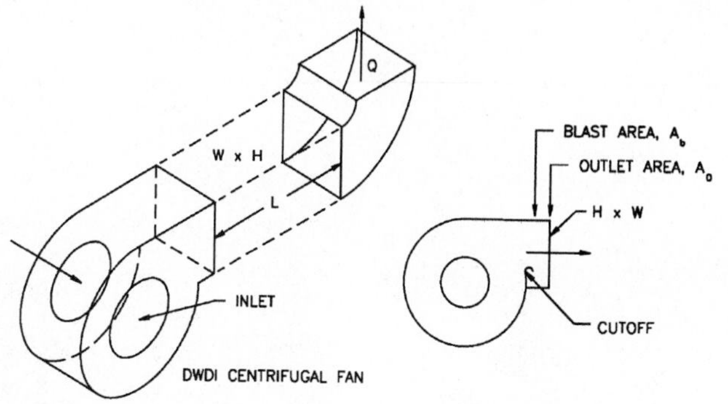

To calculate L_e, see Fitting SR7-5.

SR7-12 Fan Outlet, Centrifugal, DWDI, with Elbow (Position D)

	C_o Values					
	L/L_e					
A_b/A_o	0.00	0.12	0.25	0.50	1.0	10.0
0.4	4.70	3.80	2.70	1.40	0.0	0.0
0.5	3.20	2.70	1.90	0.85	0.0	0.0
0.6	2.50	2.10	1.40	0.68	0.0	0.0
0.7	1.70	1.40	0.85	0.45	0.0	0.0
0.8	1.20	1.00	0.68	0.26	0.0	0.0
0.9	1.00	0.68	0.57	0.22	0.0	0.0
1.0	0.85	0.68	0.45	0.22	0.0	0.0

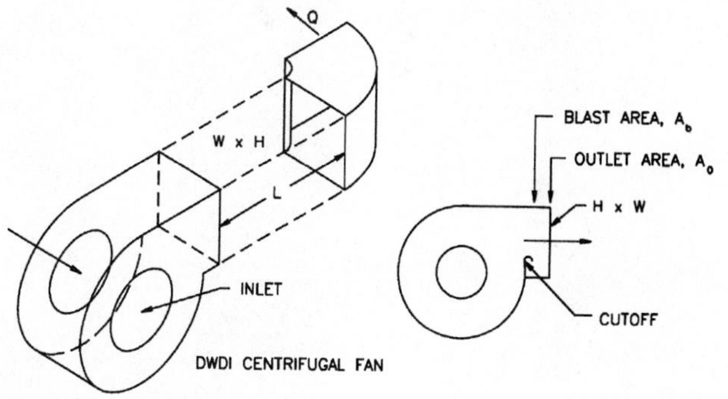

To calculate L_e, see Fitting SR7-5.

SR7-17 Pyramidal Diffuser at Centrifugal Fan Outlet with Ductwork

	C_1 Values						
	A_o/A_1						
θ	1.0	1.5	2.0	2.5	3.0	3.5	4.0
0	0.00	0.00	0.00	0.00	0.00	0.00	0.00
10	0.00	0.10	0.18	0.21	0.23	0.24	0.25
15	0.00	0.23	0.33	0.38	0.40	0.42	0.44
20	0.00	0.31	0.43	0.48	0.53	0.56	0.58
25	0.00	0.36	0.49	0.55	0.58	0.62	0.64
30	0.00	0.42	0.53	0.59	0.64	0.67	0.69

$$C_o = C_1\left(\frac{A_o}{A_1}\right)^2$$

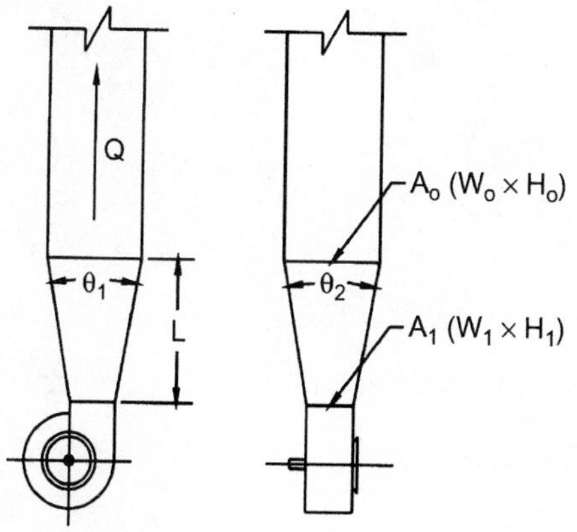

θ is larger of θ_1 and θ_2

CHAPTER 22

PIPE SIZING

THIS CHAPTER includes tables and charts to size piping for various fluid flow systems. Further details on specific piping systems can be found in appropriate chapters of the ASHRAE Handbook.

Two related but distinct concerns emerge when designing a fluid flow system: sizing the pipe and determining the flow-pressure relationship. The two are often confused because they can use the same equations and design tools. Nevertheless, they should be determined separately.

The emphasis in this chapter is on the problem of sizing the pipe, and to this end design charts and tables for specific fluids are presented in addition to the equations that describe the flow of fluids in pipes. Once a system has been sized, it should be analyzed with more detailed methods of calculation to determine the pump pressure required to achieve the desired flow. Computerized methods are well suited to handling the details of calculating losses around an extensive system.

PRESSURE DROP EQUATIONS

Darcy-Weisbach Equation

Pressure drop caused by fluid friction in fully developed flows of all "well-behaved" (Newtonian) fluids is described by the Darcy-Weisbach equation:

$$\Delta p = f\left(\frac{L}{D}\right)\left(\frac{\rho V^2}{2}\right) \qquad (1)$$

where

Δp = pressure drop, Pa
f = friction factor, dimensionless (from Moody chart, Figure 13 in Chapter 3)
L = length of pipe, m
D = internal diameter of pipe, m
ρ = fluid density at mean temperature, kg/m³
V = average velocity, m/s

This equation is often presented in specific energy form as

$$\Delta h = \frac{\Delta p}{\rho g} = f\left(\frac{L}{D}\right)\left(\frac{V^2}{2g}\right) \qquad (2)$$

where

Δh = energy loss, m
g = acceleration of gravity, m/s²

In this form, the density of the fluid does not appear explicitly (although it is in the Reynolds number, which influences f).

The preparation of this chapter is assigned to TC 6.1, Hydronic and Steam Equipment and Systems.

The friction factor f is a function of pipe roughness ε, inside diameter D, and parameter Re, the Reynolds number:

$$\mathrm{Re} = DV\rho/\mu \qquad (3)$$

where

Re = Reynolds number, dimensionless
ε = absolute roughness of pipe wall, m
μ = dynamic viscosity of fluid, Pa·s

The friction factor is frequently presented on a Moody chart (Figure 13 in Chapter 3) giving f as a function of Re with ε/D as a parameter.

A useful fit of smooth and rough pipe data for the usual turbulent flow regime is the **Colebrook equation**:

$$\frac{1}{\sqrt{f}} = 1.74 - 2\log\left(\frac{2\varepsilon}{D} + \frac{18.7}{\mathrm{Re}\sqrt{f}}\right) \qquad (4)$$

Another form of Equation (4) appears in Chapter 3, but the two are equivalent. Equation (4) is more useful in showing behavior at limiting cases—as ε/D approaches 0 (smooth limit), the $18.7/\mathrm{Re}\sqrt{f}$ term dominates; at high ε/D and Re (fully rough limit), the $2\varepsilon/D$ term dominates.

Equation (4) is implicit in f; that is, f appears on both sides, so a value for f is usually obtained iteratively.

Hazen-Williams Equation

A less widely used alternative to the Darcy-Weisbach formulation for calculating pressure drop is the Hazen-Williams equation, which is expressed as

$$\Delta p = 6.819L\left(\frac{V}{C}\right)^{1.852}\left(\frac{1}{D}\right)^{1.167}(\rho g) \qquad (5)$$

or

$$\Delta h = 6.819L\left(\frac{V}{C}\right)^{1.852}\left(\frac{1}{D}\right)^{1.167} \qquad (6)$$

where C = roughness factor.

Typical values of C are 150 for plastic pipe and copper tubing, 140 for new steel pipe, down to 100 and below for badly corroded or very rough pipe.

Valve and Fitting Losses

Valves and fittings cause pressure losses greater than those caused by the pipe alone. One formulation expresses losses as

$$\Delta p = K\rho\left(\frac{V^2}{2}\right) \quad \text{or} \quad \Delta h = K\left(\frac{V^2}{2g}\right) \qquad (7)$$

where K = geometry- and size-dependent loss coefficient (Tables 1 through 4).

Table 1 K Factors—Screwed Pipe Fittings

Nominal Pipe Dia., mm	90° Ell Reg.	90° Ell Long	45° Ell	Return Bend	Tee-Line	Tee-Branch	Globe Valve	Gate Valve	Angle Valve	Swing Check Valve	Bell Mouth Inlet	Square Inlet	Projected Inlet
10	2.5	—	0.38	2.5	0.90	2.7	20	0.40	—	8.0	0.05	0.5	1.0
15	2.1	—	0.37	2.1	0.90	2.4	14	0.33	—	5.5	0.05	0.5	1.0
20	1.7	0.92	0.35	1.7	0.90	2.1	10	0.28	6.1	3.7	0.05	0.5	1.0
25	1.5	0.78	0.34	1.5	0.90	1.8	9	0.24	4.6	3.0	0.05	0.5	1.0
32	1.3	0.65	0.33	1.3	0.90	1.7	8.5	0.22	3.6	2.7	0.05	0.5	1.0
40	1.2	0.54	0.32	1.2	0.90	1.6	8	0.19	2.9	2.5	0.05	0.5	1.0
50	1.0	0.42	0.31	1.0	0.90	1.4	7	0.17	2.1	2.3	0.05	0.5	1.0
65	0.85	0.35	0.30	0.85	0.90	1.3	6.5	0.16	1.6	2.2	0.05	0.5	1.0
80	0.80	0.31	0.29	0.80	0.90	1.2	6	0.14	1.3	2.1	0.05	0.5	1.0
100	0.70	0.24	0.28	0.70	0.90	1.1	5.7	0.12	1.0	2.0	0.05	0.5	1.0

Source: *Engineering Data Book* (HI 1979).

Table 2 K Factors—Flanged Welded Pipe Fittings

Nominal Pipe Dia., mm	90° Ell Reg.	90° Ell Long	45° Ell Long	Return Bend Standard	Return Bend Long-Radius	Tee-Line	Tee-Branch	Glove Valve	Gate Valve	Angle Valve	Swing Check Valve
25	0.43	0.41	0.22	0.43	0.43	0.26	1.0	13	—	4.8	2.0
32	0.41	0.37	0.22	0.41	0.38	0.25	0.95	12	—	3.7	2.0
40	0.40	0.35	0.21	0.40	0.35	0.23	0.90	10	—	3.0	2.0
50	0.38	0.30	0.20	0.38	0.30	0.20	0.84	9	0.34	2.5	2.0
65	0.35	0.28	0.19	0.35	0.27	0.18	0.79	8	0.27	2.3	2.0
80	0.34	0.25	0.18	0.34	0.25	0.17	0.76	7	0.22	2.2	2.0
100	0.31	0.22	0.18	0.31	0.22	0.15	0.70	6.5	0.16	2.1	2.0
150	0.29	0.18	0.17	0.29	0.18	0.12	0.62	6	0.10	2.1	2.0
200	0.27	0.16	0.17	0.27	0.15	0.10	0.58	5.7	0.08	2.1	2.0
250	0.25	0.14	0.16	0.25	0.14	0.09	0.53	5.7	0.06	2.1	2.0
300	0.24	0.13	0.16	0.24	0.13	0.08	0.50	5.7	0.05	2.1	2.0

Source: *Engineering Data Book* (HI 1979).

Table 3 Approximate Range of Variation for K Factors

90° Elbow	Regular screwed	±20% above 50 mm	Tee	Screwed, line or branch	±25%
		±40% below 50 mm		Flanged, line or branch	±35%
	Long-radius screwed	±25%	Globe valve	Screwed	±25%
	Regular flanged	±35%		Flanged	±25%
	Long-radius flanged	±30%	Gate valve	Screwed	±25%
45° Elbow	Regular screwed	±10%		Flanged	±50%
	Long-radius flanged	±10%	Angle valve	Screwed	±20%
Return bend (180°)	Regular screwed	±25%		Flanged	±50%
	Regular flanged	±35%	Check valve	Screwed	±50%
	Long-radius flanged	±30%		Flanged	+200% –80%

Source: *Engineering Data Book* (HI 1979).

Example 1. Determine the pressure drop for 15°C water flowing at 1 m/s through a nominal 25 mm, 90° threaded elbow.

Solution: From Table 1, the *K* for a 25 mm, 90° threaded elbow is 1.5.

$$\Delta p = 1.5 \times 1^2/2 = 750 \text{ Pa}$$

The loss coefficient for valves appears in another form as A_v, a dimensional coefficient expressing the flow through a valve at a specified pressure drop.

$$Q = A_v\sqrt{\Delta p/\rho} \quad (8)$$

where

Q = volumetric flow, m³/s
A_v = valve coefficient, m³/s at Δp = 1 Pa
Δp = pressure drop, Pa
ρ = density of fluid ≈ 1000 kg/m³ for water at temperatures below 120°C

See the section on Control Valve Sizing in Chapter 46 of the 2008 *ASHRAE Handbook—HVAC Systems and Equipment* for more information on valve coefficients.

Example 2. Determine the volumetric flow through a valve with A_v = 0.00024 for an allowable pressure drop of 35 kPa.

Solution: $Q = 0.00024\sqrt{35\,000/1000} = 0.0014$ **m³/s = 1.4 L/s**

Alternative formulations express fitting losses in terms of equivalent lengths of straight pipe (Table 8 and Figure 7). Pressure loss data for fittings are also presented in Idelchik (1986).

Equation (7) and data in Tables 1 and 2 are based on the assumption that separated flow in the fitting causes the *K* factors to be independent of Reynolds number. In reality, the *K* factor for most pipe fittings varies with Reynolds number. Tests by Rahmeyer (1999a, 1999b, 2002a, 2002b) (ASHRAE research projects RP-968 and RP-1034) on 50 mm threaded and 100, 300, 400, 500, and 600 mm welded steel fittings

Table 4 Summary of Test Data for Ells, Reducers, and Expansions

	Past[a]	Rahmeyer Data[b] 1.2 m/s	2.4 m/s	3.6 m/s
50 mm S.R.[c] ell (*R*/*D* = 1) thread	0.60 to 1.0 (1.0)[d]	0.60	0.68	0.736
100 mm S.R. ell (*R*/*D* = 1) weld	0.30 to 0.34	0.37	0.34	0.33
25 mm L.R. ell (*R*/*D* = 1.5) weld	to 1.0	—	—	—
50 mm L.R. ell (*R*/*D* = 1.5) weld	0.50 to 0.7	—	—	—
100 mm L.R. ell (*R*/*D* = 1.5) weld	0.22 to 0.33 (0.22)[d]	0.26	0.24	0.23
150 mm L.R. ell (*R*/*D* = 1.5) weld	0.25	—	—	—
200 mm L.R. ell (*R*/*D* = 1.5) weld	0.20 to 0.26	—	—	—
250 mm L.R. ell (*R*/*D* = 1.5) weld	0.17	—	—	—
300 mm L.R. ell (*R*/*D* = 1.5) weld	0.16	0.17	0.17	0.17
400 mm L.R. ell (*R*/*D* = 1.5) weld	0.12	0.12	0.12	0.11
500 mm L.R. ell (*R*/*D* = 1.5) weld	0.09	0.12	0.10	0.10
600 mm L.R. ell (*R*/*D* = 1.5) weld	0.07	0.098	0.089	0.089
Reducer (50 by 40 mm) thread	—	0.53	0.28	0.20
(100 by 80 mm) weld	0.22	0.23	0.14	0.10
(300 by 250 mm) weld	—	0.14	0.14	0.14
(400 by 300 mm) weld	—	0.17	0.16	0.17
(500 by 400 mm) weld	—	0.16	0.13	0.13
(600 by 500 mm) weld	—	0.053	0.053	0.055
Expansion (40 by 50 mm) thread	—	0.16	0.13	0.02
(80 by 100 mm) weld	—	0.11	0.11	0.11
(250 by 300 mm) weld	—	0.11	0.11	0.11
(300 by 400 mm) weld	—	0.073	0.076	0.073
(400 by 500 mm) weld	—	0.024	0.021	0.022
(500 by 600 mm) weld	—	0.020	0.023	0.020

Source: Rahmeyer (1999c).
[a]Published data by Crane (1988), Freeman (1941), and Hydraulic Institute (1979).
[b]Rahmeyer (1999a, 2002a).
[c]S.R.—short radius or regular ell; L.R.—long-radius ell.
[d]( ) Data published in 1993 *ASHRAE Handbook—Fundamentals*.

Table 5 Summary of Test Data for Pipe Tees

	Past[a]	Rahmeyer Data[b] 1.2 m/s	2.4 m/s	3.6 m/s
50 mm thread tee, 100% branch	1.20 to 1.80 (1.4)[c]	0.93	—	—
100% line (flow-through)	0.50 to 0.90 (0.90)[c]	0.19	—	—
100% mix	—	1.19	—	—
100 mm weld tee, 100% branch	0.70 to 1.02 (0.70)[c]	—	0.57	—
100% line (flow-through)	0.15 to 0.34 (0.15)[c]	—	0.06	—
100% mix	—	—	0.49	—
300 mm weld tee, 100% branch	0.52	0.70	0.63	0.62
100% line (flow-through)	0.09	0.062	0.091	0.096
100% mix	—	0.88	0.72	0.72
400 mm weld tee, 100% branch	0.47	0.54	0.55	0.54
100% line (flow-through)	0.07	0.032	0.028	0.028
100% mix	—	0.74	0.74	0.76

[a]Published data by Crane (1988), Freeman (1941), and the Hydraulic Institute (1979).
[b]Rahmeyer (199b, 2002b).
[c]Data published in 1993 *ASHRAE Handbook—Fundamentals*.

Table 6 Water Velocities Based on Type of Service

Type of Service	Velocity, m/s	Reference
General service	1.2 to 3.0	a, b, c
City water	0.9 to 2.1	a, b
	0.6 to 1.5	c
Boiler feed	1.8 to 4.6	a, c
Pump suction and drain lines	1.2 to 2.1	a, b

[a]Crane Co. (1976). [b]Carrier (1960). [c]Grinnell Company (1951).

Table 7 Maximum Water Velocity to Minimize Erosion

Normal Operation, h/yr	Water Velocity, m/s
1500	4.6
2000	4.4
3000	4.0
4000	3.7
6000	3.0

Source: Carrier (1960).

Table 8 Test Summary for Loss Coefficients *K* and Equivalent Loss Lengths

Schedule 80 PVC Fitting		*K*	*L*, m
Injected molded elbow,	50 mm	0.91 to 1.00	2.6 to 2.8
	100 mm	0.86 to 0.91	5.6 to 5.9
	150 mm	0.76 to 0.91	8.0 to 9.5
	200 mm	0.68 to 0.87	10.0 to 12.8
200 mm fabricated elbow, Type I, components		0.40 to 0.42	5.9 to 6.2
Type II, mitered		0.073 to 0.76	10.8 to 11.2
150 by 100 mm injected molded reducer		0.12 to 0.59	1.2 to 6.2
Bushing type		0.49 to 0.59	5.2 to 6.2
200 by 150 mm injected molded reducer		0.13 to 0.63	1.9 to 9.3
Bushing type		0.48 to 0.68	7.1 to 10.0
Gradual reducer type		0.21	3.1
100 by 150 mm injected molded expansion		0.069 to 1.19	0.46 to 7.7
Bushing type		0.069 to 1.14	0.46 to 7.4
150 by 200 mm injected molded expansion		0.95 to 0.96	10.0 to 10.1
Bushing type		0.94 to 0.95	9.9 to 10.0
Gradual reducer type		0.99	10.4

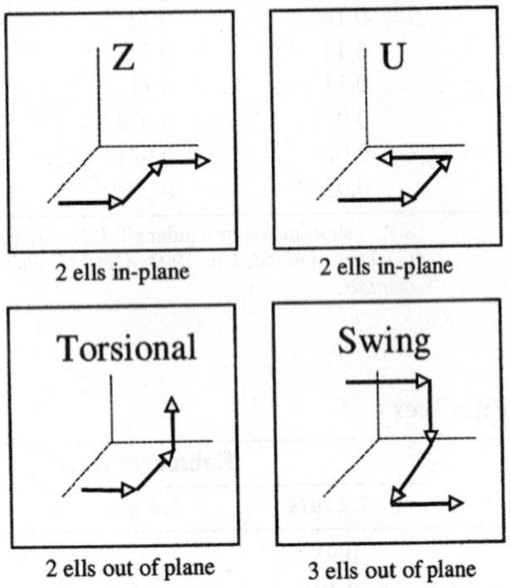

Fig. 1 Close-Coupled Test Configurations

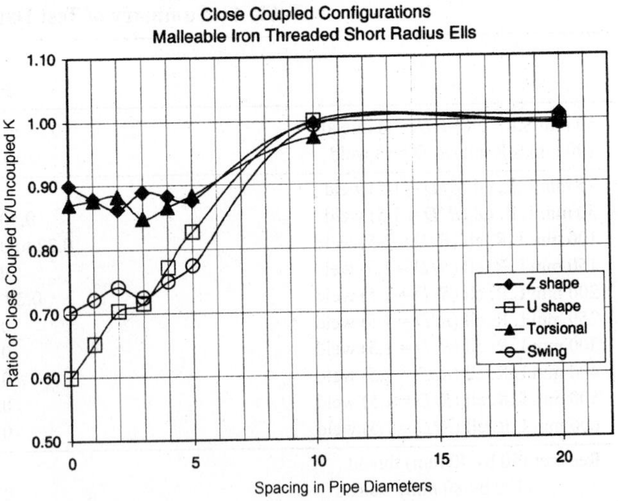

Fig. 2 Summary Plot of Effect of Close-Coupled Configurations for 50 mm Ells

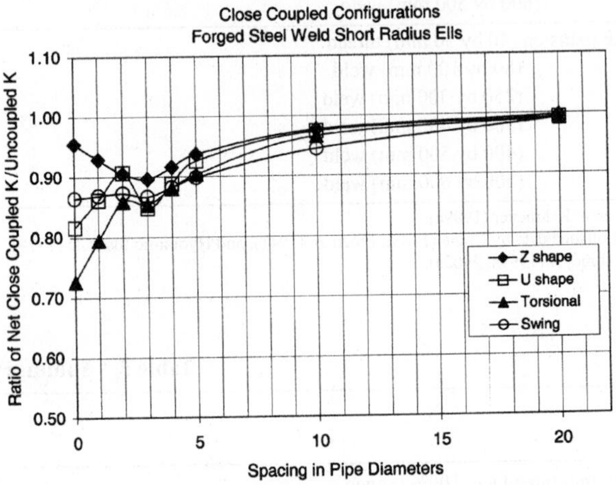

Fig. 3 Summary Plot of Effect of Close-Coupled Configurations for 100 mm Ells

demonstrate the variation and are shown in Tables 4 and 5. The studies also present *K* factors of diverting and mixing flows in tees, ranging from full through flow to full branch flow. They also examined the variation in *K* factors caused by variations in geometry among manufacturers and by surface defects in individual fittings.

Hegberg (1995) and Rahmeyer (1999a,b) discuss the origins of some of the data shown in Table 4 and Table 5. The Hydraulic Institute (1979) data appear to have come from Freeman (1941), work that was actually performed in 1895. The work of Giesecke (1926) and Giesecke and Badgett (1931, 1932a,b) may not be representative of present-day fittings.

Further extending the work on determination of fitting *K* factors to PVC piping systems, Rahmeyer (2003a, 2003b) (ASHRAE research project RP-1193) found the data in Tables 8 and 9 giving *K* factors for Schedule 80 PVC 50, 100, 150, and 200 mm ells, reducers, expansions, and tees. The results of these tests are also presented in the cited papers in terms of equivalent lengths. In general, PVC fitting geometry varied much more from one manufacturer to another than steel fittings did.

Losses in Multiple Fittings

Typical fitting loss calculations are done as if each fitting is isolated and has no interaction with any other. Rahmeyer (2002c) (ASHRAE research project RP-1035) tested 50 mm threaded ells and 100 mm ells in two and three fitting assemblies of several geometries, at varying spacings. Figure 1 shows the geometries, and Figures 2 and 3 show the ratio of coupled *K* values to uncoupled *K* values (i.e., fitting losses for the assembly compared with losses from the same number of isolated fittings). The most important conclusion is that the interaction between fittings always reduces the loss. Also, although geometry of the assembly has a definite effect, the effects are not the same for 50 mm threaded and 100 mm welded ells. Thus, the traditional practice of adding together losses from individual fittings gives a conservative (high-limit) estimate.

Calculating Pressure Losses

The most common engineering design flow loss calculation selects a pipe size for the desired total flow rate and available or allowable pressure drop.

Because either formulation of fitting losses requires a known diameter, pipe size must be selected before calculating the detailed influence of fittings. A frequently used rule of thumb assumes that the design length of pipe is 50 to 100% longer than actual to account for fitting losses. After a pipe diameter has been selected on this basis, the influence of each fitting can be evaluated.

Table 9 Test Summary for Loss Coefficients *K* of PVC Tees

Branching		
Schedule 80 PVC Fitting	$K_{1\text{-}2}$	$K_{1\text{-}3}$
50 mm injection molded branching tee, 100% line flow	0.13 to 0.26	—
50/50 flow	0.07 to 0.22	—
100% branch flow	—	0.98 to 1.39
100 mm injection molded branching tee, 100% line flow	0.07 to 0.22	—
50/50 flow	0.03 to 0.13	0.74 to 0.82
100% branch flow	—	0.95 to 1.15
150 mm injection molded branching tee, 100% line flow	0.01 to 0.14	—
50/50 flow	0.06 to 0.11	0.70 to 0.84
100% branch flow	—	0.95 to 1.15
150 mm fabricated branching tee, 100% line flow	0.21 to 0.22	—
50/50 flow	0.04 to 0.09	1.29 to 1.40
100% branch flow	—	1.74 to 1.88
200 mm injection molded branching tee, 100% line flow	0.04 to 0.09	—
50/50 flow	0.04 to 0.07	0.64 to 0.75
100% branch flow	—	0.85 to 0.96
200 mm fabricated branching tee, 100% line flow	0.09 to 0.16	—
50/50 flow	0.08 to 0.13	1.07 to 1.16
100% branch flow	—	1.40 to 1.62

Mixing		
PVC Fitting	$K_{1\text{-}2}$	$K_{3\text{-}2}$
50 mm injection molded mixing tee, 100% line flow	0.12 to 0.25	—
50/50 flow	1.22 to 1.19	0.89 to 1.88
100% mix flow	—	0.89 to 1.54
100 mm injection molded mixing tee, 100% line flow	0.07 to 0.18	—
50/50 flow	1.19 to 1.88	0.98 to 1.88
100% mix flow	—	0.88 to 1.02
150 mm injection molded mixing tee, 100% line flow	0.06 to 0.14	—
50/50 flow	1.26 to 1.80	1.02 to 1.60
100% mix flow	—	0.90 to 1.07
150 mm fabricated mixing tee, 100% line flow	0.19 to 0.21	—
50/50 flow	2.94 to 3.32	2.57 to 3.17
100% mix flow	—	1.72 to 1.98
200 mm injection molded mixing tee, 100% line flow	0.04 to 0.09	—
50/50 flow	1.10 to 1.60	0.96 to 1.32
100% mix flow	—	0.81 to 0.93
200 mm fabricated mixing tee, 100% line flow	0.13 to 0.70	—
50/50 flow	2.36 to 10.62	2.02 to 2.67
100% mix flow	—	1.34 to 1.53

Coefficients based on average velocity of 2.43 m/s. Range of values varies with fitting manufacturers. Line or straight flow is Q_2/Q_1 = 100%. Branch flow is Q_2/Q_1 = 0%.

WATER PIPING

FLOW RATE LIMITATIONS

Stewart and Dona (1987) surveyed the literature relating to water flow rate limitations. Noise, erosion, and installation and operating costs all limit the maximum and minimum velocities in piping systems. If piping sizes are too small, noise levels, erosion levels, and pumping costs can be unfavorable; if piping sizes are too large, installation costs are excessive. Therefore, pipe sizes are chosen to minimize initial cost while avoiding the undesirable effects of high velocities.

A variety of upper limits of water velocity and/or pressure drop in piping and piping systems is used. One recommendation places a velocity limit of 1.2 m/s for 50 mm pipe and smaller, and a pressure drop limit of 400 Pa/m for piping over 50 mm. Other guidelines are based on the type of service (Table 6) or the annual operating hours (Table 7). These limitations are imposed either to control the levels of pipe and valve noise, erosion, and water hammer pressure or for economic reasons. Carrier (1960) recommends that the velocity not exceed 4.6 m/s in any case.

Noise Generation

Velocity-dependent noise in piping and piping systems results from any or all of four sources: turbulence, cavitation, release of entrained air, and water hammer. In investigations of flow-related noise, Marseille (1965), Ball and Webster (1976), and Rogers (1953, 1954, 1956) reported that velocities on the order of 3 to 5 m/s lie within the range of allowable noise levels for residential and commercial buildings. The experiments showed considerable variation in the noise levels obtained for a specified velocity. Generally, systems with longer pipe and with more numerous fittings and valves were noisier. In addition, sound measurements were taken under widely differing conditions; for example, some tests used plastic-covered pipe, while others did not. Thus, no detailed correlations relating sound level to flow velocity in generalized systems are available.

The noise generated by fluid flow in a pipe increases sharply if cavitation or the release of entrained air occurs. Usually the combination of a high water velocity with a change in flow direction or a decrease in the cross section of a pipe causing a sudden pressure drop is necessary to cause cavitation. Ball and Webster (1976) found that at their maximum velocity of 13 m/s, cavitation did not occur in straight pipe; using the apparatus with two elbows, cold water velocities up to 6.5 m/s caused no cavitation. Cavitation did occur in orifices of 1:8 area ratio (orifice flow area is one-eighth of pipe flow area) at 1.5 m/s and in 1:4 area ratio orifices at 3 m/s (Rogers 1954).

Some data are available for predicting hydrodynamic (liquid) noise generated by control valves. The International Society for Measurement and Control compiled prediction correlations in an effort to develop control valves for reduced noise levels (ISA 1985). The correlation to predict hydrodynamic noise from control valves is

$$SL = 10 \log A_v + 20 \log \Delta p - 30 \log t + 76.6 \qquad (9)$$

where

SL = sound level, dB
A_v = valve coefficient, $m^3/(s \cdot \sqrt{Pa})$
Q = flow rate, m^3/s
Δp = pressure drop across valve, Pa
t = downstream pipe wall thickness, mm

Air entrained in water usually has a higher partial pressure than the water. Even when flow rates are small enough to avoid cavitation, the release of entrained air may create noise. Every effort should be made to vent the piping system or otherwise remove entrained air.

Erosion

Erosion in piping systems is caused by water bubbles, sand, or other solid matter impinging on the inner surface of the pipe. Generally, at velocities lower than 3 m/s, erosion is not significant as long as there is no cavitation. When solid matter is entrained in the fluid at high velocities, erosion occurs rapidly, especially in bends. Thus, high velocities should not be used in systems where sand or other solids are present or where slurries are transported.

Allowances for Aging

With age, the internal surfaces of pipes become increasingly rough, which reduces the available flow with a fixed pressure supply. However, designing with excessive age allowances may result in oversized piping. Age-related decreases in capacity depend on the type of water, type of pipe material, temperature of water, and type of system (open or closed) and include

- Sliming (biological growth or deposited soil on the pipe walls), which occurs mainly in unchlorinated, raw water systems.
- Caking of calcareous salts, which occurs in hard water (i.e., water bearing calcium salts) and increases with water temperature.
- Corrosion (incrustations of ferrous and ferric hydroxide on the pipe walls), which occurs in metal pipe in soft water. Because oxygen is necessary for corrosion to take place, significantly more corrosion takes place in open systems.

Allowances for expected decreases in capacity are sometimes treated as a specific amount (percentage). Dawson and Bowman (1933) added an allowance of 15% friction loss to new pipe (equivalent to an 8% decrease in capacity). The *HDR Design Guide* (1981) increased the friction loss by 15 to 20% for closed piping systems and 75 to 90% for open systems. Carrier (1960) indicates a factor of approximately 1.75 between friction factors for closed and open systems.

Obrecht and Pourbaix (1967) differentiated between the corrosive potential of different metals in potable water systems and concluded that iron is the most severely attacked, then galvanized steel, lead, copper, and finally copper alloys (i.e., brass). Hunter (1941) and Freeman (1941) showed the same trend. After four years of cold and hot water use, copper pipe had a capacity loss of 25 to 65%. Aged ferrous pipe has a capacity loss of 40 to 80%. Smith (1983) recommended increasing the design discharge by 1.55 for uncoated cast iron, 1.08 for iron and steel, and 1.06 for cement or concrete.

The Plastic Pipe Institute (1971) found that corrosion is not a problem in plastic pipe; the capacity of plastic pipe in Europe and the United States remains essentially the same after 30 years in use.

Extensive age-related flow data are available for use with the Hazen-Williams empirical equation. Difficulties arise in its application, however, because the original Hazen-Williams roughness coefficients are valid only for the specific pipe diameters, water velocities, and water viscosities used in the original experiments. Thus, when the *C*s are extended to different diameters, velocities, and/or water viscosities, errors of up to about 50% in pipe capacity can occur (Williams and Hazen 1933, Sanks 1978).

Water Hammer

When any moving fluid (not just water) is abruptly stopped, as when a valve closes suddenly, large pressures can develop. While detailed analysis requires knowledge of the elastic properties of the pipe and the flow-time history, the limiting case of rigid pipe and instantaneous closure is simple to calculate. Under these conditions,

$$\Delta p_h = \rho c_s V \tag{10}$$

where

Δp_h = pressure rise caused by water hammer, Pa
ρ = fluid density, kg/m^3
c_s = velocity of sound in fluid, m/s
V = fluid flow velocity, m/s

The c_s for water is 1439 m/s, although the elasticity of the pipe reduces the effective value.

Example 3. What is the maximum pressure rise if water flowing at 3 m/s is stopped instantaneously?

Solution:

$$\Delta p_h = 1000 \times 1439 \times 3 = 4.32 \text{ MPa}$$

Other Considerations

Not discussed in detail in this chapter, but of potentially great importance, are a number of physical and chemical considerations: pipe and fitting design, materials, and joining methods must be appropriate for working pressures and temperatures encountered, as well as being suitably resistant to chemical attack by the fluid.

Other Piping Materials and Fluids

For fluids not included in this chapter or for piping materials of different dimensions, manufacturers' literature frequently supplies pressure drop charts. The Darcy-Weisbach equation, with the Moody chart or the Colebrook equation, can be used as an alternative to pressure drop charts or tables.

HYDRONIC SYSTEM PIPING

The Darcy-Weisbach equation with friction factors from the Moody chart or Colebrook equation (or, alternatively, the Hazen-Williams equation) is fundamental to calculating pressure drop in hot and chilled water piping; however, charts calculated from these equations (such as Figures 4, 5, and 6) provide easy determination of pressure drops for specific fluids and pipe standards. In addition, tables of pressure drops can be found in Hydraulic Institute (1979) and Crane Co. (1976).

The Reynolds numbers represented on the charts in Figures 4, 5, and 6 are all in the turbulent flow regime. For smaller pipes and/or lower velocities, the Reynolds number may fall into the laminar regime, in which the Colebrook friction factors are no longer valid.

Most tables and charts for water are calculated for properties at 15°C. Using these for hot water introduces some error, although the answers are conservative (i.e., cold water calculations overstate the pressure drop for hot water). Using 15°C water charts for 90°C water should not result in errors in Δp exceeding 20%.

Range of Usage of Pressure Drop Charts

General Design Range. The general range of pipe friction loss used for design of hydronic systems is between 100 and 400 Pa/m of pipe. A value of 250 Pa/m represents the mean to which most systems are designed. Wider ranges may be used in specific designs if certain precautions are taken.

Piping Noise. Closed-loop hydronic system piping is generally sized below certain arbitrary upper limits, such as a velocity limit of 1.2 m/s for 50 mm pipe and under, and a pressure drop limit of 400 Pa/m for piping over 50 mm in diameter. Velocities in excess of 1.2 m/s can be used in piping of larger size. This limitation is generally accepted, although it is based on relatively inconclusive experience with noise in piping. **Water velocity noise** is not caused by water but by free air, sharp pressure drops, turbulence, or a combination of these, which in turn cause cavitation or flashing of water into steam. Therefore, higher velocities may be used if proper precautions are taken to eliminate air and turbulence.

Air Separation

Air in hydronic systems is usually undesirable because it causes flow noise, allows oxygen to react with piping materials, and sometimes even prevents flow in parts of a system. Air may enter a system at an air-water interface in an open system or in an expansion tank in a closed system, or it may be brought in dissolved in makeup water. Most hydronic systems use air separation devices to remove air. The solubility of air in water increases with pressure and decreases with temperature; thus, separation of air from water is best achieved at the point of lowest pressure and/or highest temperature in a system. For more information, see Chapter 12 of the 2008 *ASHRAE Handbook—HVAC Systems and Equipment.*

In the absence of venting, air can be entrained in the water and carried to separation units at flow velocities of 0.5 to 0.6 m/s or more in pipe 50 mm and under. Minimum velocities of 0.6 m/s are therefore recommended. For pipe sizes 50 mm and over, minimum velocities corresponding to a pressure loss of 75 Pa are normally used. Maintenance of minimum velocities is particularly important in the upper floors of high-rise buildings where the air tends to come out of solution because of reduced pressures. Higher velocities should be used in **downcomer** return mains feeding into air separation units located in the basement.

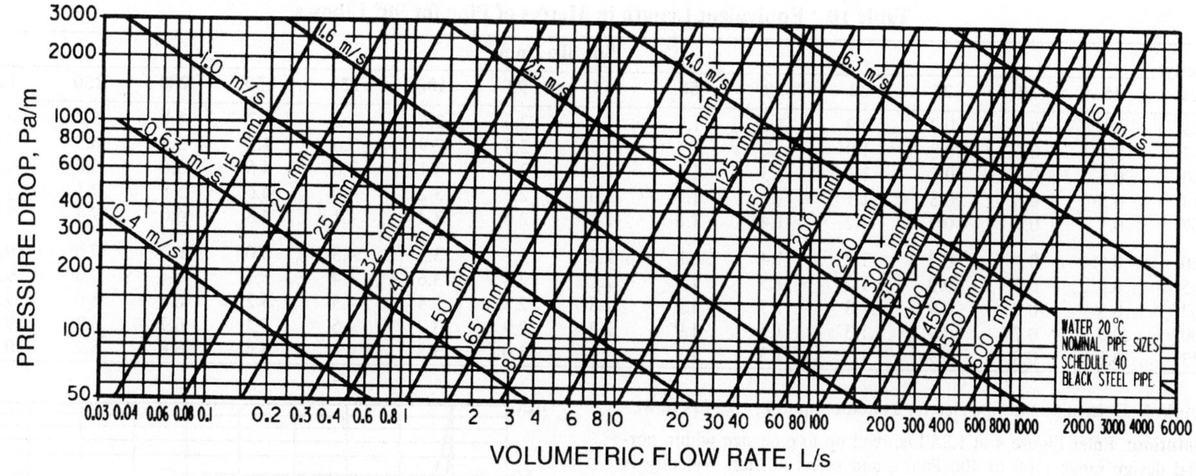

Fig. 4 Friction Loss for Water in Commercial Steel Pipe (Schedule 40)

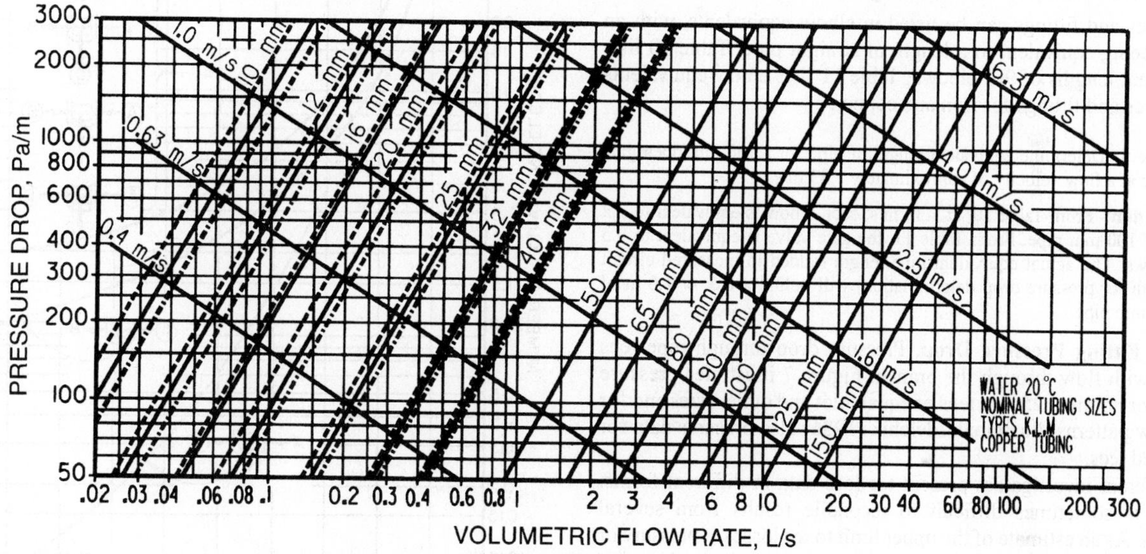

Fig. 5 Friction Loss for Water in Copper Tubing (Types K, L, M)

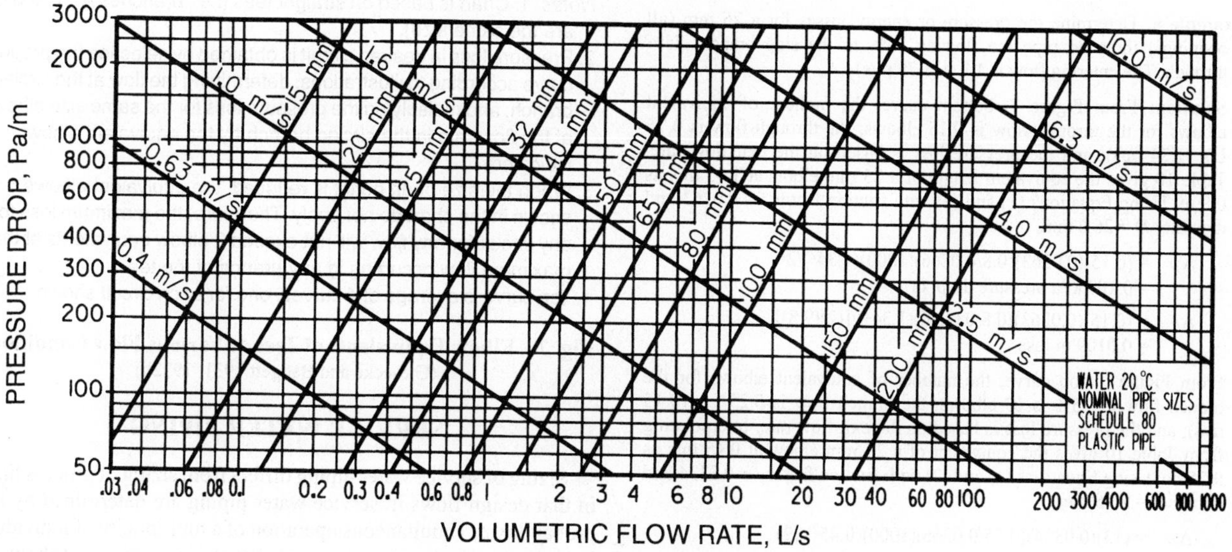

Fig. 6 Friction Loss for Water in Plastic Pipe (Schedule 80)

Table 10 Equivalent Length in Metres of Pipe for 90° Elbows

Velocity, m/s	Pipe Size, mm 15	20	25	32	40	50	65	90	100	125	150	200	250	300
0.33	0.4	0.5	0.7	0.9	1.1	1.4	1.6	2.0	2.6	3.2	3.7	4.7	5.7	6.8
0.67	0.4	0.6	0.8	1.0	1.2	1.5	1.8	2.3	2.9	3.6	4.2	5.3	6.3	7.6
1.00	0.5	0.6	0.8	1.1	1.3	1.6	1.9	2.5	3.1	3.8	4.5	5.6	6.8	8.0
1.33	0.5	0.6	0.8	1.1	1.3	1.7	2.0	2.5	3.2	4.0	4.6	5.8	7.1	8.4
1.67	0.5	0.7	0.9	1.2	1.4	1.8	2.1	2.6	3.4	4.1	4.8	6.0	7.4	8.8
2.00	0.5	0.7	0.9	1.2	1.4	1.8	2.2	2.7	3.5	4.3	5.0	6.2	7.6	9.0
2.35	0.5	0.7	0.9	1.2	1.5	1.9	2.2	2.8	3.6	4.4	5.1	6.4	7.8	9.2
2.67	0.5	0.7	0.9	1.3	1.5	1.9	2.3	2.8	3.6	4.5	5.2	6.5	8.0	9.4
3.00	0.5	0.7	0.9	1.3	1.5	1.9	2.3	2.9	3.7	4.5	5.3	6.7	8.1	9.6
3.33	0.5	0.8	0.9	1.3	1.5	1.9	2.4	3.0	3.8	4.6	5.4	6.8	8.2	9.8

Example 4. Determine the pipe size for a circuit requiring 1.25 L/s flow.

Solution: Enter Figure 4 at 1.25 L/s, read up to pipe size within normal design range (100 to 400 Pa/m), and select 40 mm. Velocity is 1 m/s and pressure loss is 300 Pa/m.

Valve and Fitting Pressure Drop

Valves and fittings can be listed in elbow equivalents, with an elbow being equivalent to a length of straight pipe. Table 10 lists equivalent lengths of 90° elbows; Table 11 lists elbow equivalents for valves and fittings for iron and copper.

Example 5. Determine equivalent length of pipe for a 100 mm open gate valve at a flow velocity of approximately 1.33 m/s.

Solution: From Table 10, at 1.33 m/s, each elbow is equivalent to 3.2 m of 100 mm pipe. From Table 11, the gate valve is equivalent to 0.5 elbows. The actual equivalent pipe length (added to measured circuit length for pressure drop determination) will be 3.2 × 0.5, or 1.6 m of 100 mm pipe.

Tee Fitting Pressure Drop. Pressure drop through pipe tees varies with flow through the branch. Figure 7 illustrates pressure drops for nominal 25 mm tees of equal inlet and outlet sizes and for the flow patterns illustrated. Idelchik (1986) also presents data for threaded tees.

Different investigators present tee loss data in different forms, and it is sometimes difficult to reconcile results from several sources. As an estimate of the upper limit to tee losses, a pressure or head loss coefficient of 1.0 may be assumed for entering and leaving flows (i.e., $\Delta p = 1.0\rho V_{in}^2/2 + 1.0\rho V_{out}^2/2$).

Example 6. Determine the pressure or energy losses for a 25 mm (all openings) threaded pipe tee flowing 25% to the side branch, 75% through. The entering flow is 1 L/s (1.79 m/s).

Solution: From Figure 7, bottom curve, the number of equivalent elbows for the through-flow is 0.15 elbows; the through-flow is 0.75 L/s (1.34 m/s); and the pressure loss is based on the exit flow rate. Table 10 gives the equivalent length of a 25 mm elbow at 1.33 m/s as 0.8 m. Using Equations (1) and (2) with friction factor $f = 0.0263$ and diameter $D = 26.6$ mm,

$$\Delta p = (0.15)(0.0263)(0.8/0.0266)(1000)(1.34^2)/2$$
$$= 0.107 \text{ kPa pressure drop, or}$$

$$\Delta h = (0.15)(0.0263)(0.8/0.0266)(1.34^2)/[(2)(9.8)]$$
$$= 0.0109 \text{ m loss}$$

From Figure 7, top curve, the number of equivalent elbows for the branch flow of 25% is 13 elbows; the branch flow is 0.25 L/s (0.45 m/s); and the pressure loss is based on the exit flow rate. Interpolating from Table 10 gives the equivalent of a 25 mm elbow at 0.45 m/s as 0.75 m. Using Equations (1) and (2) with friction factor $f = 0.0334$ and diameter = 26.6 mm,

$$\Delta p = (13)(0.0334)(0.75/0.0266)(1000)(0.45^2)/(2)$$
$$= 1.24 \text{ kPa pressure drop, or}$$

$$\Delta h = (13)(0.0334)(0.75/0.0266)(0.45^2)/[(2)(9.8)]$$
$$= 0.126 \text{ m loss}$$

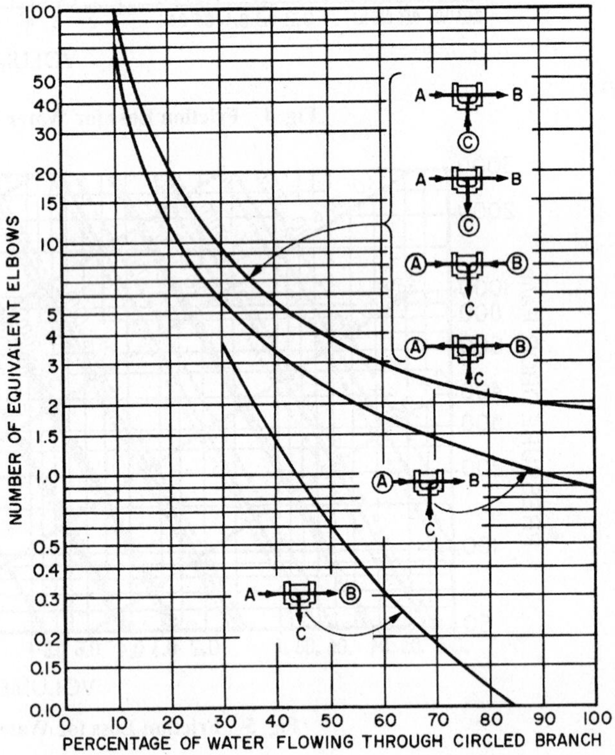

Notes: 1. Chart is based on straight tees (i.e., branches A, B, and C are the same size).
2. Pressure loss in desired circuit is obtained by selecting the proper curve according to illustrations, determining the flow at the circled branch, and multiplying the pressure loss for the same size elbow at the flow rate in the circled branch by the equivalent elbows indicated.
3. When the size of an outlet is reduced, the equivalent elbows shown in the chart do not apply. Therefore, the maximum loss for any circuit for any flow will not exceed 2 elbow equivalents at the maximum flow occurring in any branch of the tee.
4. Top curve is average of 4 curves, one for each circuit shown.

Fig. 7 Elbow Equivalents of Tees at Various Flow Conditions (Giesecke and Badgett 1931, 1932b)

SERVICE WATER PIPING

Sizing of service water piping differs from sizing of process lines in that design flows in service water piping are determined by the probability of simultaneous operation of a multiplicity of individual loads such as water closets, urinals, lavatories, sinks, and showers. The full flow characteristics of each load device are readily obtained from manufacturers; however, service water piping sized to handle

Table 11 Iron and Copper Elbow Equivalents[a]

Fitting	Iron Pipe	Copper Tubing
Elbow, 90°	1.0	1.0
Elbow, 45°	0.7	0.7
Elbow, 90° long-radius	0.5	0.5
Elbow, welded, 90°	0.5	0.5
Reduced coupling	0.4	0.4
Open return bend	1.0	1.0
Angle radiator valve	2.0	3.0
Radiator or convector	3.0	4.0
Boiler or heater	3.0	4.0
Open gate valve	0.5	0.7
Open globe valve	12.0	17.0

Source: Giesecke (1926) and Giesecke and Badgett (1931, 1932a).
[a]See Table 10 for equivalent length of one elbow.

Table 12 Proper Flow and Pressure Required During Flow for Different Fixtures

Fixture	Flow Pressure, kPa (gage)[a]	Flow, L/s
Ordinary basin faucet	55	0.2
Self-closing basin faucet	85	0.2
Sink faucet—10 mm	70	0.3
Sink faucet—15 mm	35	0.3
Dishwasher	105 to 175	—[b]
Bathtub faucet	35	0.4
Laundry tube cock—8 mm	35	0.3
Shower	85	0.2 to 0.6
Ball cock for closet	105	0.2
Flush valve for closet	70 to 140	1.0 to 2.5[c]
Flush valve for urinal	105	1.0
Garden hose, 15 m, and sill cock	210	0.3

[a]Flow pressure is the pressure in the pipe at the entrance to the particular fixture considered.
[b]Varies; see manufacturers' data.
[c]Wide range due to variation in design and type of flush valve closets.

all load devices simultaneously would be seriously oversized. Thus, a major issue in sizing service water piping is to determine the diversity of the loads.

The procedure shown in this chapter uses the work of R.B. Hunter for estimating diversity (Hunter 1940, 1941). The present-day plumbing designer is usually constrained by building or plumbing codes, which specify the individual and collective loads to be used for pipe sizing. Frequently used codes (including the BOCA *National Plumbing Code*, *Standard Plumbing Code*, *Uniform Plumbing Code*, and *National Standard Plumbing Code*) contain procedures quite similar to those shown here. The designer must be aware of the applicable code for the location being considered.

Federal mandates are forcing plumbing fixture manufacturers to reduce design flows to many types of fixtures, but these may not yet be included in locally adopted codes. Also, the designer must be aware of special considerations; for example, toilet usage at sports arenas will probably have much less diversity than the codes allow and thus may require larger supply piping than the minimum specified by the codes.

Table 12 gives the rate of flow desirable for many common fixtures and the average pressure necessary to give this rate of flow. The pressure varies with fixture design.

In estimating the load, the rate of flow is frequently computed in **fixture units**, which are relative indicators of flow. Table 13 gives the demand weights in terms of fixture units for different plumbing fixtures under several conditions of service, and Figure 8 gives the estimated demand corresponding to any total number of fixture units. Figures 9 and 10 provide more accurate estimates at the lower end of the scale.

The estimated demand load for fixtures used intermittently on any supply pipe can be obtained by multiplying the number of

Table 13 Demand Weights of Fixtures in Fixture Units[a]

Fixture or Group[b]	Occupancy	Type of Supply Control	Weight in Fixture Units[c]
Water closet	Public	Flush valve	10
Water closet	Public	Flush tank	5
Pedestal urinal	Public	Flush valve	10
Stall or wall urinal	Public	Flush valve	5
Stall or wall urinal	Public	Flush tank	3
Lavatory	Public	Faucet	2
Bathtub	Public	Faucet	4
Shower head	Public	Mixing valve	4
Service sink	Office, etc.	Faucet	3
Kitchen sink	Hotel or restaurant	Faucet	4
Water closet	Private	Flush valve	6
Water closet	Private	Flush tank	3
Lavatory	Private	Faucet	1
Bathtub	Private	Faucet	2
Shower head	Private	Mixing valve	2
Bathroom group	Private	Flush valve for closet	8
Bathroom group	Private	Flush tank for closet	6
Separate shower	Private	Mixing valve	2
Kitchen sink	Private	Faucet	2
Laundry trays (1 to 3)	Private	Faucet	3
Combination fixture	Private	Faucet	3

Source: Hunter (1941).
[a]For supply outlets likely to impose continuous demands, estimate continuous supply separately, and add to total demand for fixtures.
[b]For fixtures not listed, weights may be assumed by comparing the fixture to a listed one using water in similar quantities and at similar rates.
[c]The given weights are for total demand. For fixtures with both hot and cold water supplies, the weights for maximum separate demands can be assumed to be 75% of the listed demand for the supply.

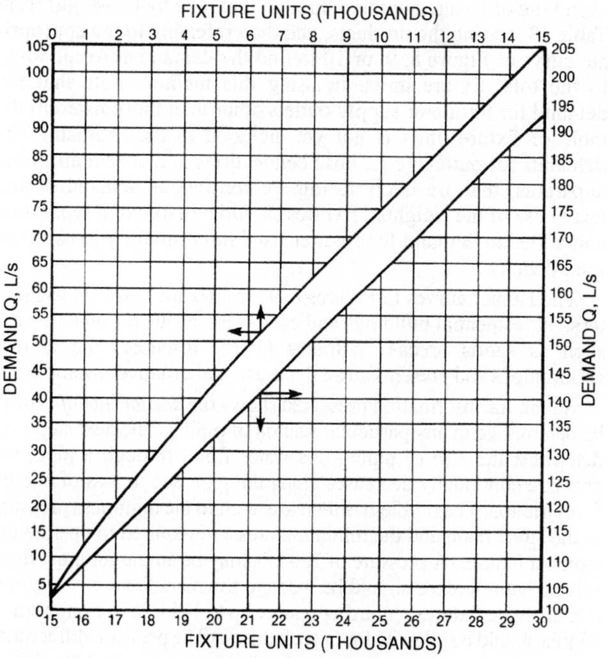

Fig. 8 Demand Versus Fixture Units, Mixed System, High Part of Curve
(Hunter 1941)

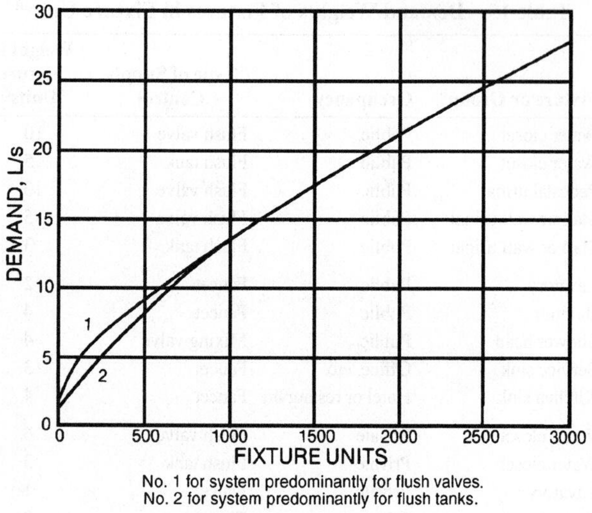

Fig. 9 Estimate Curves for Demand Load
(Hunter 1941)

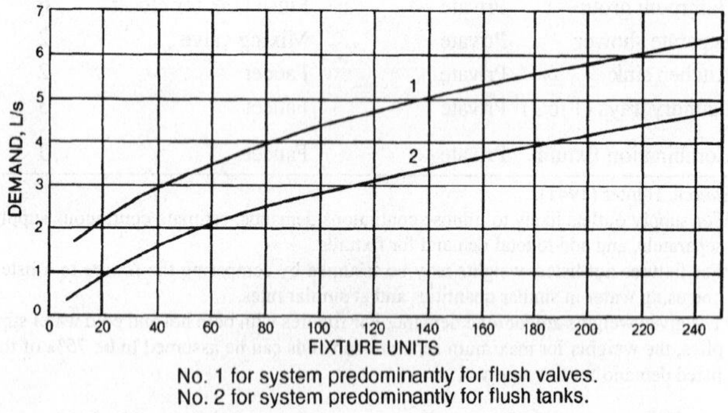

Fig. 10 Section of Figure 9 on Enlarged Scale

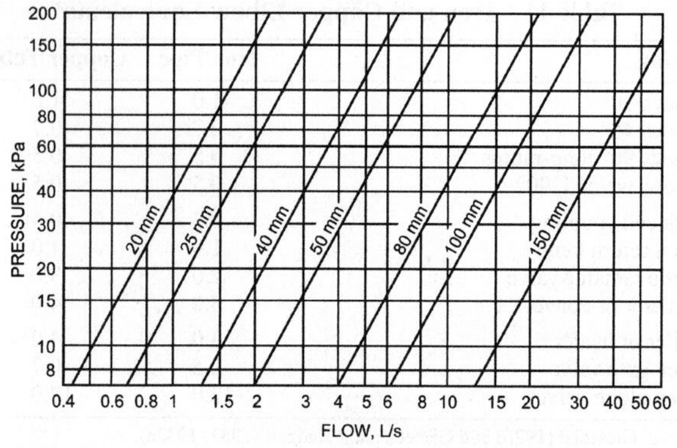

Fig. 11 Pressure Losses in Disk-Type Water Meters

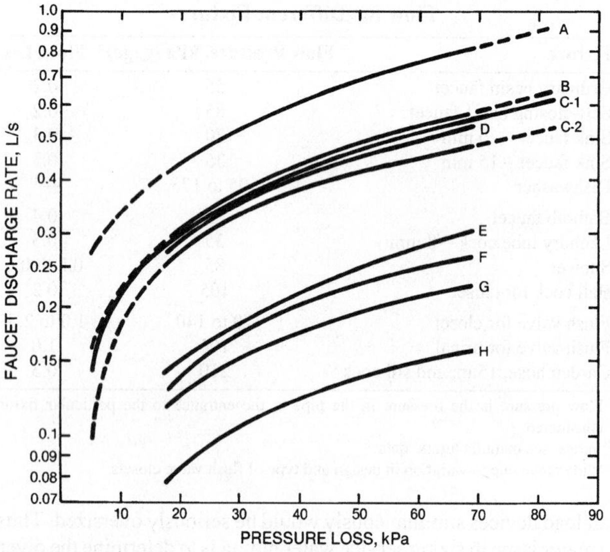

A. 12.7 mm laundry bibb (old style)
B. Laundry compression faucet
C-1. 12.7 mm compression sink faucet (mfr. 1)
C-2. 12.7 mm compression sink faucet (mfr. 2)
D. Combination compression bathtub faucets (both open)
E. Combination compression sink faucet
F. Basin faucet
G. Spring self-closing faucet
H. Slow self-closing faucet
(Dashed lines indicate recommended extrapolation)

Fig. 12 Variation of Pressure Loss with Flow Rate for Various Faucets and Cocks

each kind of fixture supplied through that pipe by its weight from Table 13, adding the products, and then referring to the appropriate curve of Figure 8, 9, or 10 to find the demand corresponding to the total fixture units. In using this method, note that the demand for fixture or supply outlets other than those listed in the table of fixture units is not yet included in the estimate. The demands for outlets (e.g., hose connections and air-conditioning apparatus) that are likely to impose continuous demand during heavy use of the weighted fixtures should be estimated separately and added to demand for fixtures used intermittently to estimate total demand.

The Hunter curves in Figures 8, 9, and 10 are based on use patterns in residential buildings and can be erroneous for other usages such as sports arenas. Williams (1976) discusses the Hunter assumptions and presents an analysis using alternative assumptions.

So far, the information presented shows the *design rate of flow* to be determined in any particular section of piping. The next step is to determine the *size* of piping. As water flows through a pipe, the pressure continually decreases along the pipe due to loss of energy from friction. The problem is then to ascertain the minimum pressure in the street main and the minimum pressure required to operate the topmost fixture. (A pressure of 100 kPa may be ample for most flush valves, but reference should be made to the manufacturers' requirements. Some fixtures require a pressure up to 175 kPa. A minimum of 55 kPa should be allowed for other fixtures.) The pressure differential overcomes pressure losses in the distributing system and the difference in elevation between the water main and the highest fixture.

The pressure loss (in kPa) resulting from the difference in elevation between the street main and the highest fixture can be obtained by multiplying the difference in elevation in metres by the conversion factor 9.8.

Pressure losses in the distributing system consist of pressure losses in the piping itself, plus the pressure losses in the pipe fittings, valves, and the water meter, if any. Approximate design pressure losses and flow limits for disk-type meters for various rates of flow are given in Figure 11. Water authorities in many localities require compound meters for greater accuracy with varying flow; consult the local utility. Design data for compound meters differ from the data in Figure 11. Manufacturers give data on exact pressure losses and capacities.

Figure 12 shows the variation of pressure loss with rate of flow for various faucets and cocks. The water demand for hose bibbs or other large-demand fixtures taken off the building main frequently results in inadequate water supply to the upper floor of a building. This condition can be prevented by sizing the distribution system so that the pressure drops from the street main to all fixtures are the same. An ample building main (not less than 25 mm where possible) should be maintained until all branches to hose bibbs have been connected. Where the street main pressure is excessive and a pressure reducing valve is used to prevent water hammer or excessive pressure at the fixtures, the hose bibbs should be connected ahead of the reducing valve.

The principles involved in sizing upfeed and downfeed systems are the same. In the downfeed system, however, the difference in elevation between the overhead supply mains and the fixtures provides the pressure required to overcome pipe friction. Because friction pressure loss and height pressure loss are not additive, as in an upfeed system, smaller pipes may be used with a downfeed system.

Plastic Pipe

The maximum safe water velocity in a thermoplastic piping system under most operating conditions is typically 1.5 m/s; however, higher velocities can be used in cases where the operating characteristics of valves and pumps are known so that sudden changes in flow velocity can be controlled. The total pressure in the system at any time (operating pressure plus surge of water hammer) should not exceed 150% of the pressure rating of the system.

Procedure for Sizing Cold Water Systems

The recommended procedure for sizing piping systems is outlined below.

1. Sketch the main lines, risers, and branches, and indicate the fixtures to be served. Indicate the rate of flow of each fixture.
2. Using Table 13, compute the demand weights of the fixtures in fixture units.
3. Determine the total demand in fixture units and, using Figure 8, 9, or 10, find the expected demand.
4. Determine the equivalent length of pipe in the main lines, risers, and branches. Because the sizes of the pipes are not known, the exact equivalent length of various fittings cannot be determined. Add the equivalent lengths, starting at the street main and proceeding along the service line, the main line of the building, and up the riser to the top fixture of the group served.
5. Determine the average minimum pressure in the street main and the minimum pressure required for the operation of the topmost fixture, which should be 50 to 175 kPa above atmospheric.
6. Calculate the approximate design value of the average pressure drop per unit length of pipe in equivalent length determined in step 4.

$$\Delta p = (p_s - 9.8H - p_f - p_m)/L \tag{11}$$

where

Δp = average pressure loss per metre of equivalent length of pipe, kPa
p_s = pressure in street main, kPa
p_f = minimum pressure required to operate topmost fixture, kPa
p_m = pressure drop through water meter, kPa
H = height of highest fixture above street main, m
L = equivalent length determined in step 4, m

If the system is downfeed supply from a gravity tank, height of water in the tank, converted to kPa by multiplying by 9.8, replaces the street main pressure, and the term $9.8H$ is added instead of subtracted in calculating Δp. In this case, H is the vertical distance of the fixture below the bottom of the tank.

7. From the expected rate of flow determined in step 3 and the value of Δp calculated in step 6, choose the sizes of pipe from Figure 4, 5, or 6.

Example 7. Assume a minimum street main pressure of 375 kPa; a height of topmost fixture (a urinal with flush valve) above street main of 15 m; an equivalent pipe length from water main to highest fixture of 30 m; a total load on the system of 50 fixture units; and that the water closets are flush valve operated. Find the required size of supply main.

Solution: From Figure 10, the estimated peak demand is 3.2 L/s. From Table 12, the minimum pressure required to operate the topmost fixture is 105 kPa. For a trial computation, choose the 40 mm meter. From Figure 11, the pressure drop through a 40 mm disk-type meter for a flow of 3.2 L/s is 45 kPa.

The pressure drop available for overcoming friction in pipes and fittings is 375 − 9.8 × 15 − 105 − 45 = 78 kPa.

At this point, estimate the equivalent pipe length of the fittings on the direct line from the street main to the highest fixture. The exact equivalent length of the various fittings cannot be determined since the pipe sizes of the building main, riser, and branch leading to the highest fixture are not yet known, but a first approximation is necessary to tentatively select pipe sizes. If the computed pipe sizes differ from those used in determining the equivalent length of pipe fittings, a recalculation using the computed pipe sizes for the fittings will be necessary. For this example, assume that the total equivalent length of the pipe fittings is 15 m.

The permissible pressure loss per metre of equivalent pipe is 78/(30 + 15) = 1.7 kPa/m. A 40 mm building main is adequate.

The sizing of the branches of the building main, the risers, and the fixture branches follows these principles. For example, assume that one of the branches of the building main carries the cold water supply for 3 water closets, 2 bathtubs, and 3 lavatories. Using the permissible pressure loss of 1.7 kPa/m, the size of branch (determined from Table 13 and Figures 4 and 10) is found to be 4 mm. Items included in the computation of pipe size are as follows:

Fixtures, No. and Type	Fixture Units (Table 13 and Note c)			Demand (Figure 10)	Pipe Size (Figure 4)
3 flush valves	3 × 6	=	18		
2 bathtubs	0.75 × 2 × 2	=	3		
3 lavatories	0.75 × 3 × 1	=	2.25		
Total		=	23.25	2.4 L/s	40 mm

Table 14 is a guide to minimum pipe sizing where flush valves are used.

Velocities exceeding 3 m/s cause undesirable noise in the piping system. This usually governs the size of larger pipes in the system, while in small pipe sizes, the friction loss usually governs the selection because the velocity is low compared to friction loss. Velocity is the governing factor in downfeed systems, where friction loss is usually neglected. Velocity in branches leading to pump suctions should not exceed 1.5 m/s.

If the street pressure is too low to adequately supply upper-floor fixtures, the pressure must be increased. Constant or variable speed booster pumps, alone or in conjunction with gravity supply tanks, or hydropneumatic systems may be used.

Flow control valves for individual fixtures under varying pressure conditions automatically adjust the flow at the fixture to a predetermined quantity. These valves allow the designer to (1) limit the flow at the individual outlet to the minimum suitable for the

Table 14 Allowable Number of 25 mm Flush Valves Served by Various Sizes of Water Pipe[a]

Pipe Size, mm	No. of 25 mm Flush Valves
32	1
40	2-4
50	5-12
65	13-25
75	26-40
100	41-100

[a]Two 20 mm flush valves are assumed equal to one 25 mm flush valve but can be served by a 25 mm pipe. Water pipe sizing must consider demand factor, available pressure, and length of run.

purpose, (2) hold the total demand for the system more closely to the required minimum, and (3) design the piping system as accurately as is practicable for the requirements.

STEAM PIPING

Pressure losses in steam piping for flows of dry or nearly dry steam are governed by Equations (1) through (7) in the section on Pressure Drop Equations. This section incorporates these principles with other information specific to steam systems.

Pipe Sizes

Required pipe sizes for a given load in steam heating depend on the following factors:

- The initial pressure and the total pressure drop that can be allowed between the source of supply and the end of the return system
- The maximum velocity of steam allowable for quiet and dependable operation of the system, taking into consideration the direction of condensate flow
- The equivalent length of the run from the boiler or source of steam supply to the farthest heating unit

Initial Pressure and Pressure Drop. Table 15 lists pressure drops commonly used with corresponding initial steam pressures for sizing steam piping.

Several factors, such as initial pressure and pressure required at the end of the line, should be considered, but it is most important that (1) the total pressure drop does not exceed the initial gage pressure of the system (and in practice it should never exceed one-half the initial gage pressure); (2) the pressure drop is not great enough to cause excessive velocities; (3) a constant initial pressure is maintained, except on systems specially designed for varying initial pressures (e.g., subatmospheric pressure), which normally operate under controlled partial vacuums; and (4) for gravity return systems, the pressure drop to the heating units does not exceed the water column available for removing condensate (i.e., the height above the boiler water line of the lowest point on the steam main, on the heating units, or on the dry return).

Maximum Velocity. For quiet operation, steam velocity should be 40 to 60 m/s, with a maximum of 75 m/s. The lower the velocity, the quieter the system. When the condensate must flow against the steam, even in limited quantity, the velocity of the steam must not exceed limits above which the disturbance between the steam and the counterflowing water may (1) produce objectionable sound, such as water hammer, or (2) result in the retention of water in certain parts of the system until the steam flow is reduced sufficiently to permit the water to pass. The velocity at which these disturbances take place is a function of (1) pipe size; (2) the pitch of the pipe if it runs horizontally; (3) the quantity of condensate flowing against the steam; and (4) the freedom of the piping from water pockets that, under certain conditions, act as a restriction in pipe size. Table 16 lists maximum capacities for various size steam lines.

Equivalent Length of Run. All tables for the flow of steam in pipes based on pressure drop must allow for pipe friction, as well as for the resistance of fittings and valves. These resistances are generally stated in terms of straight pipe; that is, a certain fitting produces a drop in pressure equivalent to the stated length of straight run of the same size of pipe. Table 17 gives the length of straight pipe usually allowed for the more common types of fittings and valves. In all pipe sizing tables in this chapter, the *length of run* refers to the *equivalent length of run* as distinguished from the *actual length* of pipe. A common sizing method is to assume the length of run and to check this assumption after pipes are sized. For this purpose, the length of run is usually assumed to be double the actual length of pipe.

Example 8. Using Table 17, determine the length of pipe for the run illustrated.

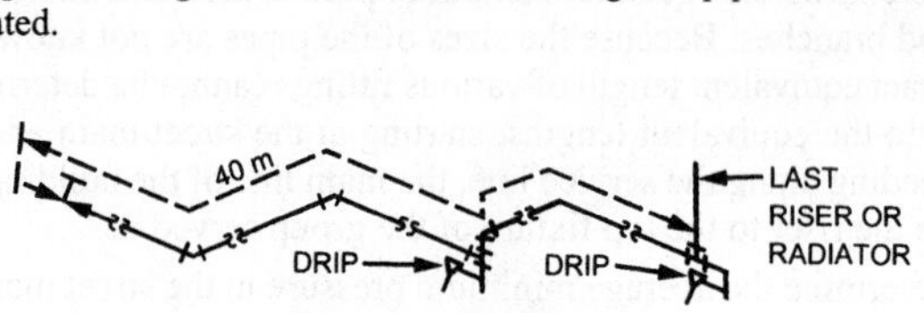

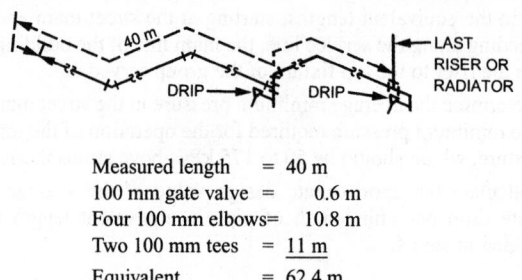

Measured length	= 40 m
100 mm gate valve	= 0.6 m
Four 100 mm elbows	= 10.8 m
Two 100 mm tees	= 11 m
Equivalent	= 62.4 m

Table 15 Pressure Drops Used for Sizing Steam Pipe[a]

Initial Steam Pressure, kPa[b]	Pressure Drop, Pa/m	Total Pressure Drop in Steam Supply Piping, kPa
Vacuum return	30 to 60	7 to 14
101	7	0.4
108	30	0.4 to 1.7
115	30	3.5
135	60	10
170	115	20
205	225	30
310	450	35 to 70
445	450 to 1100	70 to 105
790	450 to 1100	105 to 170
1140	450 to 2300	170 to 210

[a]Equipment, control valves, and so forth must be selected based on delivered pressures.
[b]Subtract 101 to convert to pressure above atmospheric.

Table 16 Comparative Capacity of Steam Lines at Various Pitches for Steam and Condensate Flowing in Opposite Directions

	Nominal Pipe Diameter, mm									
	20		25		32		40		50	
Pitch of Pipe, mm/m	Capacity	Maximum Velocity	Capacity	Maximum Velocity	Capacity	Maximum Velocity	Capacity	Maximum Velocity	Capacity	Maximum Velocity
20	0.4	2.4	0.9	2.7	1.5	3.4	2.5	3.7	5.4	4.6
40	0.5	3.4	1.1	3.7	2	4.3	3.3	4.9	6.8	5.5
80	0.7	4.0	1.5	4.6	2.5	5.2	4.2	5.8	8.7	7.3
120	0.8	4.3	1.6	5.2	3.1	6.1	4.7	6.7	10.5	8.2
170	0.9	4.9	1.9	5.8	3.4	6.7	5.3	7.3	11.7	9.1
250	1.0	5.2	2.2	6.7	3.9	7.6	5.9	7.9	12.5	9.8
350	1.2	6.7	2.4	7.3	4.2	7.9	6.4	8.5	12.9	9.8
420	1.3	6.7	2.6	7.6	4.9	9.4	7.5	10.1	14.5	10.1

Source: Laschober et al. (1966).

Capacity in g/s; velocity in m/s.

Table 17 Equivalent Length of Fittings to Be Added to Pipe Run

Nominal Pipe Diameter, mm	Length to Be Added to Run, m				
	Standard Elbow	Side Outside Tee[b]	Gate Valve[a]	Globe Valve[a]	Angle Valve[a]
15	0.4	0.9	0.1	4	2
20	0.5	1.2	0.1	5	3
25	0.7	1.5	0.1	7	4
32	0.9	1.8	0.2	9	5
40	1.1	2.1	0.2	10	6
50	1.3	2.4	0.3	14	7
65	1.5	3.4	0.3	16	8
80	1.9	4.0	0.4	20	10
100	2.7	5.5	0.6	28	14
125	3.3	6.7	0.7	34	17
150	4.0	8.2	0.9	41	20
200	5.2	11	1.1	55	28
250	6.4	14	1.4	70	34
300	8.2	16	1.7	82	40
350	9.1	19	1.9	94	46

[a]Valve in full-open position.
[b]Values apply only to a tee used to divert the flow in the main to the last riser.

Sizing Charts

Figure 13 is the basic chart for determining the flow rate and velocity of steam in Schedule 40 pipe for various values of pressure drop per unit length, based on saturated steam at standard pressure (101.325 kPa). Using the multiplier chart (Figure 14), Figure 13 can be used at all saturation pressures between 101 and 1500 kPa (see Example 10).

LOW-PRESSURE STEAM PIPING

Values in Table 18 (taken from Figure 13) provide a more rapid means of selecting pipe sizes for the various pressure drops listed and for systems operated at 25 and 85 kPa (gage). The flow rates shown for 25 kPa can be used for saturated pressures from 7 to 41 kPa, and those shown for 85 kPa can be used for saturated pressures from 55 to 110 kPa with an error not exceeding 8%.

Both Figure 13 and Table 18 can be used where the flow of condensate does not inhibit the flow of steam. Columns B and C of Table 19 are used in cases where steam and condensate flow in opposite directions, as in risers or runouts that are not dripped. Columns D, E, and F are for one-pipe systems and include risers, radiator valves and vertical connections, and radiator and riser runout sizes, all of which are based on the critical velocity of the steam to permit the counterflow of condensate without noise.

Return piping can be sized using Table 20, in which pipe capacities for wet, dry, and vacuum return lines are shown for several values of pressure drop per metre of equivalent length.

Example 9. What pressure drop should be used for the steam piping of a system if the measured length of the longest run is 150 m, and the initial pressure must not exceed 14 kPa above atmospheric?

Solution: It is assumed, if the measured length of the longest run is 150 m, that when the allowance for fittings is added, the equivalent length of run does not exceed 300 m. Then, with the pressure drop not over one-half of the initial pressure, the drop could be 7 kPa or less. With a pressure drop of 7 kPa and a length of run of 300 m, the drop would be 23 Pa/m; if the total drop were 3.5 kPa, the drop would be 12 Pa/m. In both cases, the pipe could be sized for a desired capacity according to Figure 13.

On completion of the sizing, the drop could be checked by taking the longest line and actually calculating the equivalent length of run from the pipe sizes determined. If the calculated drop is less than that assumed, the pipe size is adequate; if it is more, an unusual number of fittings is probably involved, and either the lines must be straightened, or the next larger pipe size must be tried.

HIGH-PRESSURE STEAM PIPING

Many heating systems for large industrial buildings use high-pressure steam [100 to 1000 kPa (gage)]. These systems usually have unit heaters or large built-up fan units with blast heating coils. Temperatures are controlled by a modulating or throttling thermostatic valve or by face or bypass dampers controlled by the room air temperature, fan inlet, or fan outlet.

Use of Basic and Velocity Multiplier Charts

Example 10. Given a flow rate of 0.85 kg/s, an initial steam pressure of 800 kPa, and a pressure drop of 2.5 kPa/m, find the size of Schedule 40 pipe required and the velocity of steam in the pipe.

Solution: The following steps are illustrated by the broken line on Figures 13 and 14.

1. Enter Figure 13 at a flow rate of 0.85 kg/s, and move vertically to the horizontal line at 800 kPa.
2. Follow along inclined multiplier line (upward and to the left) to horizontal 101 kPa line. The equivalent mass flow at 101 kPa is about 0.30 kg/s.
3. Follow the 0.30 kg/s line vertically until it intersects the horizontal line at 2500 Pa/m pressure drop. Nominal pipe size is 65 mm. The equivalent steam velocity at 101 kPa is about 165 m/s.
4. To find the steam velocity at 800 kPa, locate the value of 165 m/s on the ordinate of the velocity multiplier chart (Figure 14) at 101 kPa.
5. Move along the inclined multiplier line (downward and to the right) until it intersects the vertical 800 kPa pressure line. The velocity is about 65 m/s.

Note: Steps 1 through 5 would be rearranged or reversed if different data were given.

STEAM CONDENSATE SYSTEMS

The majority of steam systems used in heating applications are two-pipe systems, in which the two pipes are the "steam" pipe and the "condensate" pipe. This discussion is limited to the sizing of the condensate lines in two-pipe systems.

Two-Pipe Systems

When steam is used for heating a liquid to 102°C or less (e.g., in domestic water heat exchangers, domestic heating water converters, or air-heating coils), the devices are usually provided with a steam control valve. As the control valve throttles, the absolute pressure in the load device decreases, removing all pressure motivation for flow in the condensate return system. In order to ensure the flow of steam condensate from the load device through the trap and into the return system, it is necessary to provide a vacuum breaker on the device ahead of the trap. This ensures a minimum pressure at the trap inlet of atmospheric pressure plus whatever liquid leg the designer has provided. Then, to ensure flow through the trap, it is necessary to design the condensate system so that it will never have a pressure above atmospheric in the condensate return line.

Vented (Open) Return Systems. To achieve this pressure requirement, the condensate return line is usually vented to the atmosphere (1) near the point of entrance of the flow streams from the load traps, (2) in proximity to all connections from drip traps, and (3) at transfer pumps or feedwater receivers.

With this design, the only motivation for flow in the return system is gravity. Return lines that are below the liquid level in the

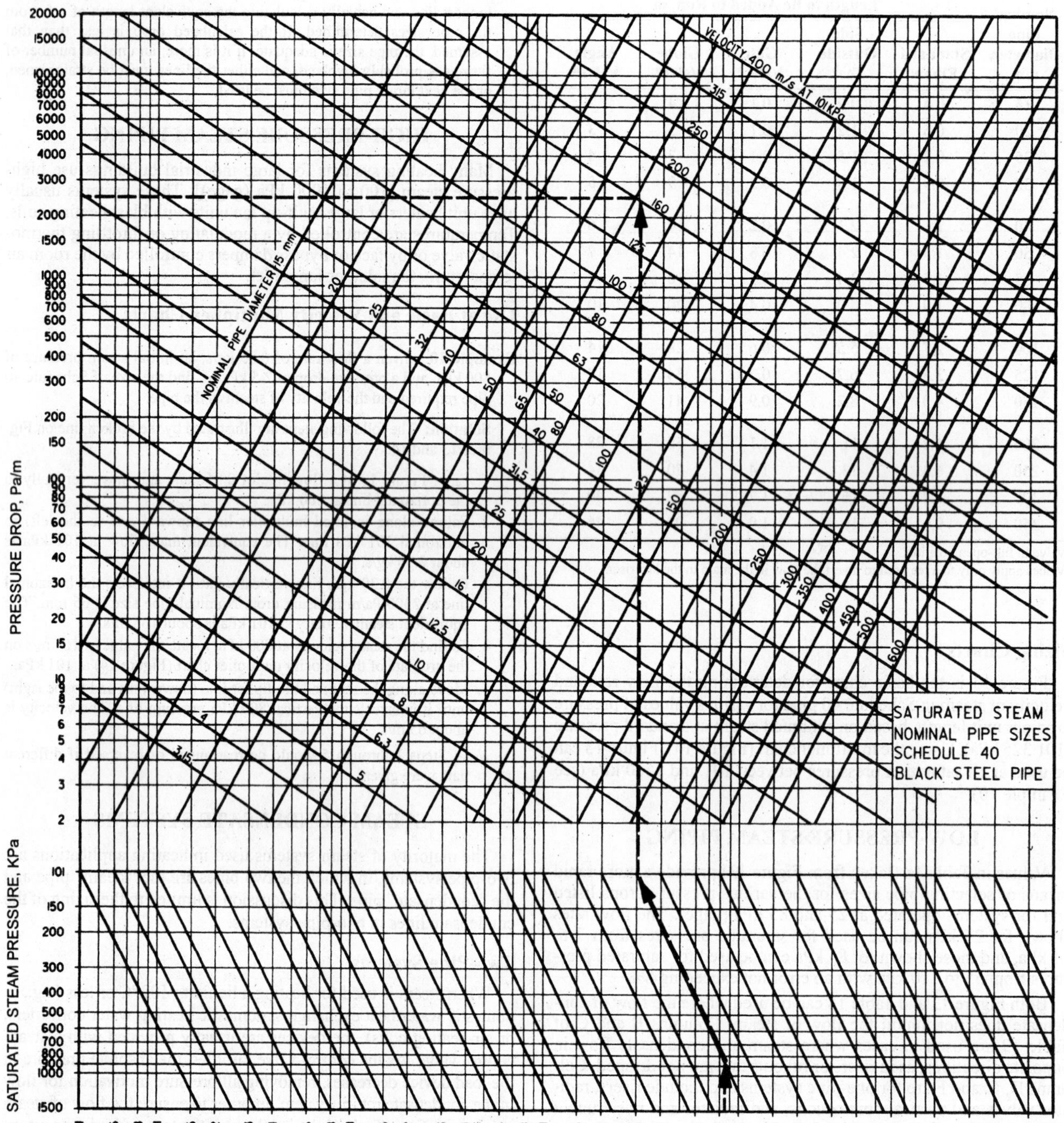

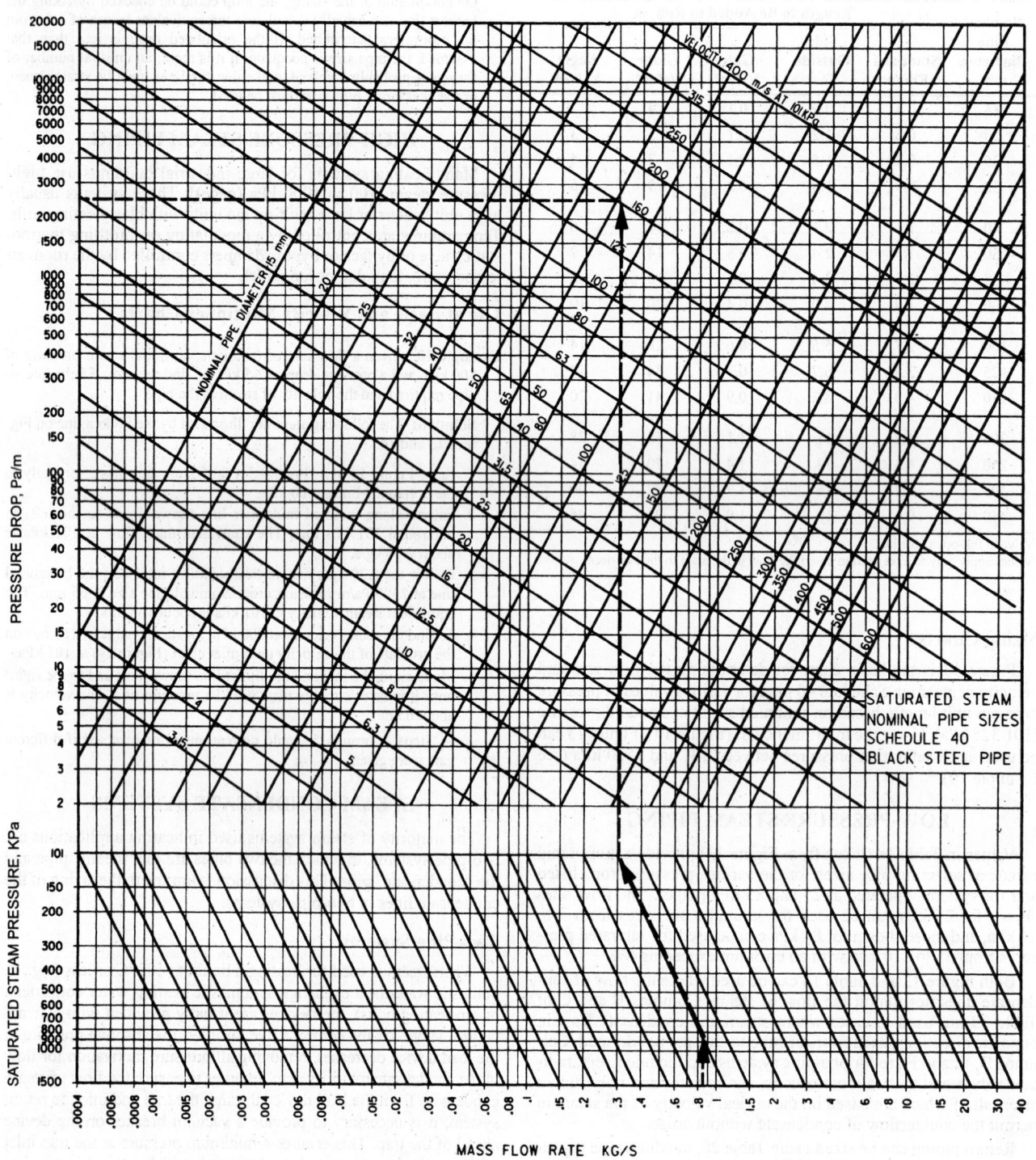

Notes: Based on Moody Friction Factor where flow of condensate does not inhibit the flow of steam. See Figure 14 for obtaining flow rates and velocities of all saturation pressures between 101 and 1500 kPa; see also Examples 9 and 10.

Fig. 13 Flow Rate and Velocity of Steam in Schedule 40 Pipe at Saturation Pressure of 101 kPa

Table 18 Flow Rate of Steam in Schedule 40 Pipe

Nominal Pipe Size, mm	Pressure Drop, Pa/m													
	14 Pa/m		28 Pa/m		58 Pa/m		113 Pa/m		170 Pa/m		225 Pa/m		450 Pa/m	
	Sat. Press., kPa		Sat. Press., kPa		Sat. Press., kPa		Sat. Press., kPa		Sat. Press., kPa		Sat. Press., kPa		Sat. Press., kPa	
	25	85	25	85	25	85	25	85	25	85	25	85	25	85
20	1.1	1.4	1.8	2.0	2.5	3.0	3.7	4.4	4.5	5.4	5.3	6.3	7.6	9.2
25	2.1	2.6	3.3	3.9	4.7	5.8	6.8	8.3	8.6	10	10	12	14	17
32	4.5	5.7	6.7	8.3	9.8	12	14	17	18	21	20	25	29	35
40	7.1	8.8	11	13	15	19	22	26	27	33	31	38	45	54
50	14	17	20	24	29	36	42	52	53	64	60	74	89	107
65	22	27	33	39	48	58	68	83	86	103	98	120	145	173
80	40	48	59	69	83	102	121	146	150	180	174	210	246	302
90	58	69	84	101	125	153	178	214	219	265	252	305	372	435
100	81	101	120	146	178	213	249	302	309	378	363	436	529	617
125	151	180	212	265	307	378	450	536	552	662	643	769	945	1 080
150	242	290	355	422	499	611	718	857	882	1 080	1 060	1 260	1 500	1 790
200	491	605	702	882	1 020	1 260	1 440	1 800	1 830	2 230	2 080	2 580	3 020	3 720
250	907	1 110	1 290	1 590	1 890	2 290	2 650	3 280	3 300	4 030	3 780	4 660	5 380	6 550
300	1 440	1 730	2 080	2 460	2 950	3 580	4 160	5 040	5 170	6 240	6 050	7 250	8 540	10 200

Notes:
1. Flow rate is in g/s at initial saturation pressures of 25 and 85 kPa (gage). Flow is based on Moody friction factor, where the flow of condensate does not inhibit the flow of steam.
2. The flow rates at 25 kPa cover saturated pressure from 7 to 41 kPa, and the rates at 85 kPa cover saturated pressure from 55 to 110 kPa with an error not exceeding 8%.
3. The steam velocities corresponding to the flow rates given in this table can be found from Figures 10 and 11.

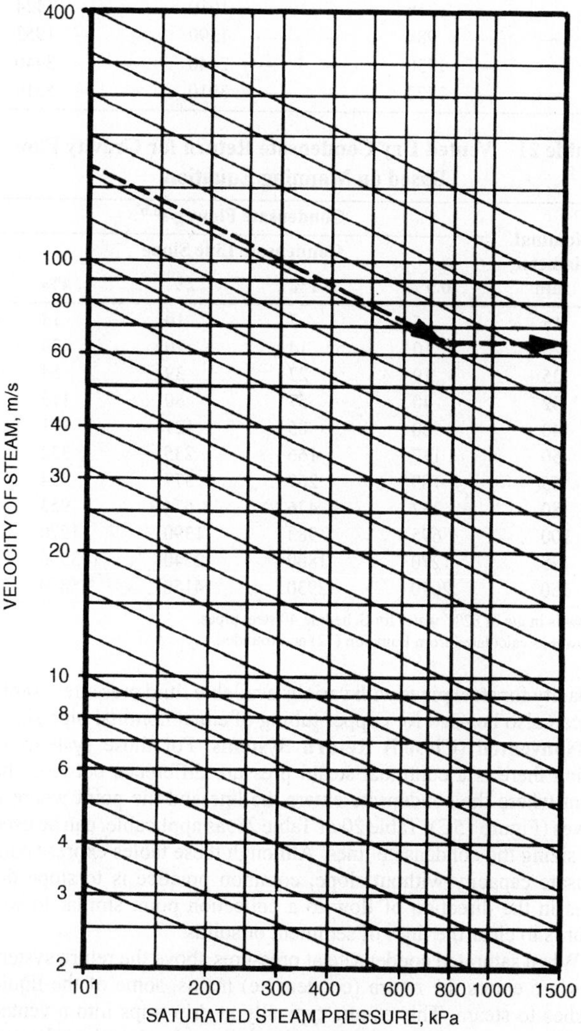

Fig. 14 Velocity Multiplier Chart for Figure 13

Table 19 Steam Pipe Capacities for Low-Pressure Systems

Nominal Pipe Size, mm	Capacity, g/s				
	Two-Pipe System		One-Pipe Systems		
	Condensate Flowing Against Steam		Supply Risers Upfeed	Radiator Valves and Vertical Connections	Radiator and Riser Runouts
	Vertical	Horizontal			
A	B[a]	C[b]	D[c]	E	F[b]
20	1.0	0.9	0.8	—	0.9
25	1.8	1.8	1.4	0.9	0.9
32	3.9	3.4	2.5	2.0	2.0
40	6.0	5.3	4.8	2.9	2.0
50	12	11	9.1	5.3	2.9
65	20	17	14	—	5.3
80	36	25	25	—	8.2
90	49	36	36	—	15
100	64	54	48	—	23
125	132	99	—	—	35
150	227	176	—	—	69
200	472	378	—	—	—
250	882	718	—	—	—
300	1450	1200	—	—	—
400	2770	2390	—	—	—

Notes:
1. For one- or two-pipe systems in which condensate flows against the steam flow.
2. Steam at average pressure of 7 kPa (gage) is used as a basis of calculating capacities.

[a]Do not use Column B for pressure drops of less than 13 Pa per metre of equivalent run. Use Figure 13 or Table 17 instead.
[b]Pitch of horizontal runouts to risers and radiators should be not less than 40 mm/m. Where this pitch cannot be obtained, runouts over 2.5 m in length should be one pipe size larger than that called for in this table.
[c]Do not use Column D for pressure drops of less than 9 Pa per metre of equivalent run, except on sizes 80 mm and over. Use Figure 13 or Table 17 instead.

Table 20 Return Main and Riser Capacities for Low-Pressure Systems, g/s

	Pipe Size, mm	7 Pa/m			9 Pa/m			14 Pa/m			28 Pa/m			57 Pa/m			113 Pa/m		
		Wet	Dry	Vac.	Wet	Dry	Vac.	Wet	Dry	Vac.	Wet	Dry	Vac.	Wet	Dry	Vac.	Wet	Dry	Vac.
	G	H	I	J	K	L	M	N	O	P	Q	R	S	T	U	V	W	X	Y
Return Main	20	—	—	—	—	—	5	—	—	13	—	—	18	—	—	25	—	—	36
	25	16	8	—	18	9	18	22	10	22	32	13	31	44	14	44	—	—	62
	32	27	16	—	31	19	31	38	21	38	54	27	54	76	30	76	—	—	107
	40	43	26	—	50	30	49	60	33	60	85	43	85	120	48	120	—	—	169
	50	88	59	—	102	67	103	126	72	126	176	93	179	252	104	252	—	—	357
	65	149	96	—	199	109	171	212	120	212	296	155	300	422	171	422	—	—	596
	80	237	184	—	268	197	275	338	221	338	473	284	479	674	315	674	—	—	953
	90	347	248	—	416	277	410	504	315	504	693	407	716	1010	451	1010	—	—	1424
	100	489	369	—	577	422	567	693	473	693	977	609	984	1390	678	1390	—	—	1953
	125	—	—	—	—	—	993	—	—	1220	—	—	1730	—	—	2440	—	—	3440
	150	—	—	—	—	—	1590	—	—	1950	—	—	2770	—	—	3910	—	—	5519
Riser	20	—	6	—	—	6	18	—	6	22	—	6	31	—	6	44	—	—	62
	25	—	14	—	—	14	31	—	14	38	—	14	54	—	14	76	—	—	107
	32	—	31	—	—	31	49	—	31	60	—	31	85	—	31	120	—	—	169
	40	—	47	—	—	47	103	—	47	126	—	47	179	—	47	252	—	—	357
	50	—	95	—	—	95	171	—	95	212	—	95	300	—	95	422	—	—	596
	65	—	—	—	—	—	275	—	—	338	—	—	479	—	—	674	—	—	953
	80	—	—	—	—	—	410	—	—	504	—	—	716	—	—	1010	—	—	1424
	90	—	—	—	—	—	564	—	—	693	—	—	984	—	—	1390	—	—	1953
	100	—	—	—	—	—	993	—	—	1220	—	—	1730	—	—	2440	—	—	3440
	125	—	—	—	—	—	1590	—	—	1950	—	—	2772	—	—	3910	—	—	5519

downstream receiver or boiler and are thus filled with liquid are called wet returns; those above the liquid level have both liquid and gas in the pipes and are called dry returns.

The dry return lines in a vented return system have flowing liquid in the bottom of the line and gas or vapor in the top (Figure 15A). The liquid is the condensate, and the gas may be steam, air, or a mixture of the two. The flow phenomenon for these dry return systems is open channel flow, which is best described by the **Manning equation**:

$$Q = \frac{1.00Ar^{2/3}S^{1/2}}{n} \tag{12}$$

where

Q = volumetric flow rate, m^3/s
A = cross-sectional area of conduit, m^2
r = hydraulic radius of conduit, m
n = coefficient of roughness (usually 0.012)
S = slope of conduit, m/m

Table 21 Vented Dry Condensate Return for Gravity Flow Based on Manning Equation

Nominal Diameter, mm	Condensate Flow, g/s[a,b] — Condensate Line Slope 0.5%	1%	2%	4%
15	5	7	10	13
20	10	14	20	29
25	19	27	39	54
32	40	57	80	113
40	60	85	121	171
50	117	166	235	332
65	189	267	377	534
80	337	476	674	953
100	695	983	1390	1970
125	1270	1800	2540	3590
150	2070	2930	4150	5860

[a] Flow is in g/s of 82°C water for Schedule 40 steel pipes.
[b] Flow was calculated from Equation (12) and rounded.

Table 21 is a solution to Equation (12) that shows pipe size capacities for steel pipes with various pitches. Recommended practice is to size vertical lines by the maximum pitch shown, although they would actually have a capacity far in excess of that shown. As the pitch increases, hydraulic jump that could fill the pipe and other transient effects that could cause water hammer should be avoided. Flow values in Table 21 are calculated for Schedule 40 steel pipe, with a factor of safety of 3.0, and can be used for copper pipes of the same nominal pipe size.

The flow characteristics of **wet return lines** (Figure 15B) are best described by the Darcy-Weisbach equation [Equation (1)]. The motivation for flow is the fluid pressure difference between the entering section of the flooded line and the leaving section. It is common practice, in addition to providing for the fluid pressure differential, to slope the return in the direction of flow to a collection point such as a dirt leg in order to clear the line of sediment or solids. Table 22 is a solution to Equation (1) that shows pipe size capacity for steel pipes with various available fluid pressures. Table 22 can also be used for copper tubing of equal nominal pipe size.

Nonvented (Closed) Return Systems. For those systems in which there is a continual steam pressure difference between the point where the condensate enters the line and the point where it leaves (Figure 15C), Table 20 or Table 23, as applicable, can be used for sizing the condensate lines. Although these tables express condensate capacity without slope, common practice is to slope the lines in the direction of flow to a collection point similar to wet returns to clear the lines of sediment or solids.

When saturated condensate at pressures above the return system pressure enters the return (condensate) mains, some of the liquid flashes to steam. This occurs typically at drip traps into a vented return system or at load traps leaving process load devices that are not valve-controlled and typically have no subcooling. If the return

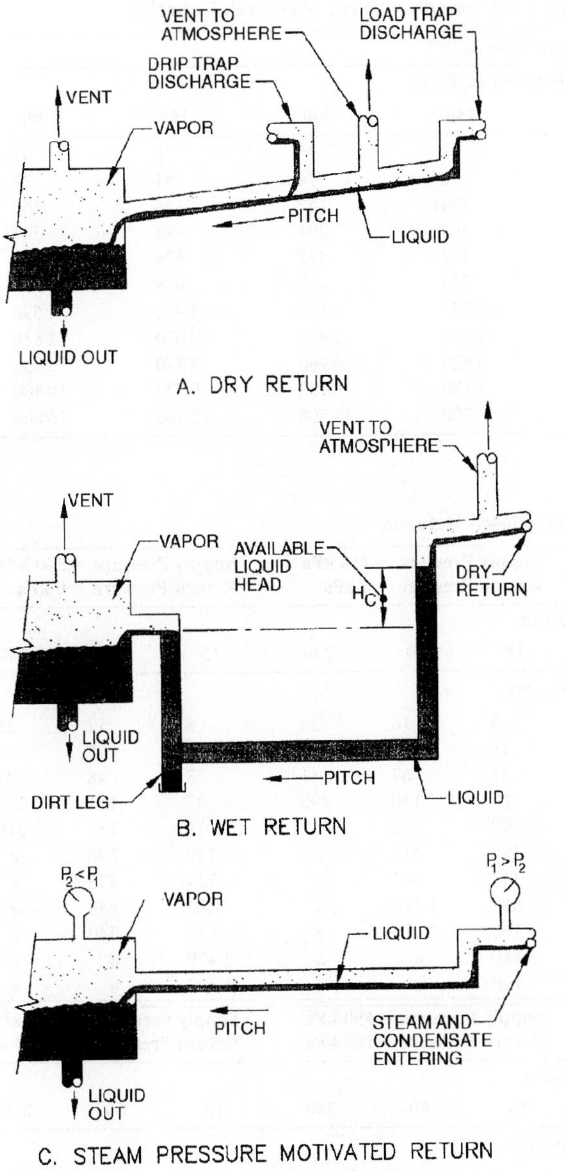

Fig. 15 Types of Condensate Return Systems

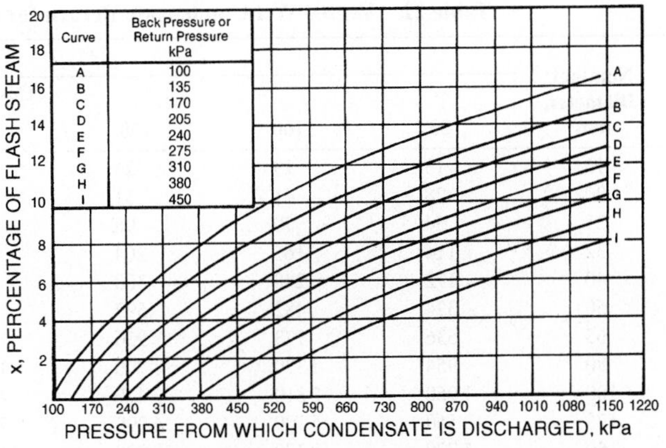

Fig. 16 Working Chart for Determining Percentage of Flash Steam (Quality)

main is vented, the vent lines will relieve any excessive pressure and prevent a back pressure phenomenon that could restrict the flow through traps from valved loads; the pipe sizing would be as described above for vented dry returns. If the return line is not vented, the flash steam results in a pressure rise at that point and the piping could be sized as described above for closed returns, and in accordance with Table 20 or Table 23, as applicable.

The passage of the fluid through the steam trap is a throttling or constant enthalpy process. The resulting fluid on the downstream side of the trap can be a mixture of saturated liquid and vapor. Thus, in nonvented returns, it is important to understand the condition of the fluid when it enters the return line from the trap.

The condition of the condensate downstream of the trap can be expressed by the quality x, defined as

$$x = \frac{m_v}{m_l + m_v} \qquad (13)$$

where

m_v = mass of saturated vapor in condensate
m_l = mass of saturated liquid in condensate

Likewise, the volume fraction V_c of the vapor in the condensate is expressed as

$$V_c = \frac{V_v}{V_l + V_v} \qquad (14)$$

where

V_v = volume of saturated vapor in condensate
V_l = volume of saturated liquid in condensate

The quality and the volume fraction of the condensate downstream of the trap can be estimated from Equations (13) and (14), respectively.

$$x = \frac{h_1 - h_{f_2}}{h_{g_2} - h_{f_2}} \qquad (15)$$

$$V_c = \frac{x v_{g_2}}{v_{f_2}(1 - x) + x v_{g_2}} \qquad (16)$$

where

h_1 = enthalpy of liquid condensate entering trap evaluated at supply pressure for saturated condensate or at saturation pressure corresponding to temperature of subcooled liquid condensate
h_{f_2} = enthalpy of saturated liquid at return or downstream pressure of trap
h_{g_2} = enthalpy of saturated vapor at return or downstream pressure of trap
v_{f_2} = specific volume of saturated liquid at return or downstream pressure of trap
v_{g_2} = specific volume of saturated vapor at return or downstream pressure of trap

Table 24 presents some values for quality and volume fraction for typical supply and return pressures in heating and ventilating systems. Note that the percent of vapor on a mass basis x is small, while the percent of vapor on a volume basis V_c is very large. This indicates that the return pipe cross section is predominantly occupied by vapor. Figure 16 is a working chart to determine the quality of the condensate entering the return line from the trap for various combinations of supply and return pressures. If the liquid is subcooled entering the trap, the saturation pressure corresponding to the liquid temperature should be used for the supply or upstream pressure. Typical pressures in the return line are given in Table 25.

One-Pipe Systems

Gravity one-pipe air vent systems in which steam and condensate flow in the same pipe, frequently in opposite directions, are considered obsolete and are no longer being installed. Chapter 33

Table 22 Vented Wet Condensate Return for Gravity Flow Based on Darcy-Weisbach Equation

Nominal Diameter, mm	Condensate Flow, g/s[a,b]							
	Condensate Pressure, Pa/m							
	50	100	150	200	250	300	350	400
15	13	19	24	28	32	35	38	41
20	28	41	51	60	68	74	81	87
25	54	79	98	114	129	142	154	165
32	114	165	204	238	267	294	318	341
40	172	248	308	358	402	442	479	513
50	334	482	597	694	779	857	928	994
65	536	773	956	1 110	1 250	1 370	1 480	1 590
80	954	1 370	1 700	1 970	2 210	2 430	2 630	2 810
100	1 960	2 810	3 470	4 030	4 520	4 960	5 370	5 750
125	3 560	5 100	6 290	7 290	8 180	8 980	9 720	10 400
150	5 770	8 270	10 200	11 800	13 200	14 500	15 700	16 800

[a] Flow is in g/s of 82°C water for Schedule 40 steel pipes.
[b] Flow was calculated from Equation (1) and rounded.

Table 23 Flow Rate for Dry-Closed Returns

Pipe Dia. D, mm	Supply Pressure = 35 kPa Return Pressure = 0 kPa			Supply Pressure = 100 kPa Return Pressure = 0 kPa			Supply Pressure = 210 kPa Return Pressure = 0 kPa			Supply Pressure = 340 kPa Return Pressure = 0 kPa		
	Δp/L, Pa/m											
	15	60	240	15	60	240	15	60	240	15	60	240
	Flow Rate, g/s											
15	30	66	139	12	26	57	8	16	35	5	12	25
20	64	141	302	26	57	120	16	35	74	11	25	53
25	126	271	572	50	108	229	32	67	141	23	48	101
32	265	567	1 200	106	227	479	66	140	295	47	101	212
40	399	854	1 790	160	343	718	98	210	442	71	151	318
50	786	1 680	a	315	670	a	194	412	a	140	296	a
65	1 260	2 680	a	508	1 070	a	312	662	a	224	476	a
80	2 270	4 790	a	907	1 920	a	559	1 180	a	402	848	a
100	4 690	9 830	a	1 880	3 940	a	1 160	2 420	a	839	1 740	a
150	13 900	a	a	5 580	a	a	3 440	a	a	2 470	a	a
200	28 800	a	a	11 600	a	a	7 110	a	a	5 100	a	a

Pipe Dia. D, mm	Supply Pressure = 690 kPa Return Pressure = 0 kPa			Supply Pressure = 1030 kPa Return Pressure = 0 kPa			Supply Pressure = 690 kPa Return Pressure = 100 kPa			Supply Pressure = 1030 kPa Return Pressure = 100 kPa		
	Δp/L, Pa/m											
	15	60	240	15	60	240	15	60	240	15	60	240
	Flow Rate, g/s											
15	4	8	17	3	6	14	7	15	33	5	12	25
20	8	17	37	6	14	29	15	33	71	12	25	53
25	15	33	69	13	26	57	30	63	134	23	49	101
32	32	68	142	25	55	117	63	134	277	48	101	212
40	48	102	214	39	83	176	95	202	418	72	152	315
50	95	200	a	77	164	a	185	391	813	141	296	617
65	151	321	a	123	265	a	299	630	1 300	227	476	983
80	272	573	a	222	467	a	533	1 120	a	403	845	a
100	562	1180	a	459	961	a	1 100	2 290	a	834	1 740	a
150	1 660	a	a	1 360	a	a	3 260	6 750	a	2 470	5 120	a
200	3 450	a	a	2 820	a	a	6 730	13 900	a	5 100	10 500	a

[a] For these sizes and pressure losses, the velocity is above 35 m/s. Select another combination of size and pressure loss.

of the 1993 *ASHRAE Handbook—Fundamentals* or earlier ASHRAE Handbook volumes include descriptions of and design information for one-pipe systems.

GAS PIPING

Piping for gas appliances should be of adequate size and installed so that it provides a supply of gas sufficient to meet the maximum demand without undue loss of pressure between the point of supply (the meter) and the appliance. The size of gas pipe required depends on (1) maximum gas consumption to be provided, (2) length of pipe and number of fittings, (3) allowable pressure loss from the outlet of the meter to the appliance, and (4) density of the gas.

Insufficient gas flow from excessive pressure losses in gas supply lines can cause inefficient operation of gas-fired appliances and sometimes create hazardous operations. Gas-fired appliances are normally equipped with a data plate giving information on maximum

Table 24 Flash Steam from Steam Trap on Pressure Drop

Supply Pressure, kPa (gage)	Return Pressure, kPa (gage)	x, Fraction Vapor, Mass Basis	V_c, Fraction Vapor, Volume Basis
35	0	0.016	0.962
103	0	0.040	0.985
207	0	0.065	0.991
345	0	0.090	0.994
690	0	0.133	0.996
1030	0	0.164	0.997
690	103	0.096	0.989
1030	103	0.128	0.992

Table 25 Estimated Return Line Pressures

Pressure Drop, Pa/m	Pressure in Return Line, Pa (gage)	
	200 kPa (gage) Supply	1000 kPa (gage) Supply
30	3.5	9
60	7	18
120	14	35
180	21	52
240	28	70
480	—	138

Table 26 Maximum Capacity of Gas Pipe in Litres per Second

Nominal Iron Pipe Size, mm	Internal Diameter, mm	Length of Pipe, m											
		5	10	15	20	25	30	35	40	45	50	55	60
8	9.25	0.19	0.13	0.11	0.09	0.08	0.07	0.07	0.06	0.06	0.06	0.05	0.05
10	12.52	0.43	0.29	0.24	0.20	0.18	0.16	0.15	0.14	0.13	0.12	0.12	0.11
15	15.80	0.79	0.54	0.44	0.37	0.33	0.30	0.28	0.26	0.24	0.23	0.22	0.21
20	20.93	1.65	1.13	0.91	0.78	0.69	0.63	0.58	0.54	0.50	0.47	0.45	0.43
25	26.14	2.95	2.03	1.63	1.40	1.24	1.12	1.03	0.96	0.90	0.85	0.81	0.77
32	35.05	6.4	4.4	3.5	3.0	2.7	2.4	2.2	2.1	1.9	1.8	1.7	1.7
40	40.89	9.6	6.6	5.3	4.5	4.0	3.6	3.3	3.1	2.9	2.8	2.6	2.5
50	52.50	18.4	12.7	10.2	8.7	7.7	7.0	6.4	6.0	5.6	5.3	5.0	4.8
65	62.71	29.3	20.2	16.2	13.9	12.3	11.1	10.2	9.5	8.9	8.4	8.0	7.7
80	77.93	51.9	35.7	28.6	24.5	21.7	19.7	18.1	16.8	15.8	14.9	14.2	13.5
100	102.26	105.8	72.7	58.4	50.0	44.3	40.1	36.9	34.4	32.2	30.4	28.9	27.6

Note: Capacity is in litres per second at gas pressures of 3.5 kPa (gage) or less and a pressure drop of 75 Pa; density = 0.735 kg/m³.

gas flow requirements or input as well as inlet gas pressure requirements. The gas utility in the area of installation can give the gas pressure available at the utility's gas meter. Using the information, the required size of gas piping can be calculated for satisfactory operation of the appliance(s).

Table 26 gives pipe capacities for gas flow for up to 60 m of pipe based on a gas density of 0.735 kg/m³. Capacities for pressures less than 10 kPa may also be determined by the following equation from NFPA/IAS *National Fuel Gas Code*:

$$Q = 0.0001d^{2.623}(\Delta p/CL)^{0.541} \quad (17)$$

where

Q = flow rate at 15°C and 101 kPa, L/s
d = inside diameter of pipe, mm
Δp = pressure drop, Pa
C = factor for viscosity, density, and temperature
= $0.00223(t + 273)s^{0.848}\mu^{0.152}$
t = temperature, °C
s = ratio of density of gas to density of air at 15°C and 101 kPa
μ = viscosity of gas, μPa·s (12 for natural gas, 8 for propane)
L = pipe length, m

Gas service in buildings is generally delivered in the "low-pressure" range of 1.7 kPa (gage). The maximum pressure drop allowable in piping systems at this pressure is generally 125 Pa but is subject to regulation by local building, plumbing, and gas appliance codes (see also the NFPA/IAS *National Fuel Gas Code*).

Where large quantities of gas are required or where long lengths of pipe are used (e.g., in industrial buildings), low-pressure limitations result in large pipe sizes. Local codes may allow and local gas companies may deliver gas at higher pressures [e.g., 15, 35, or 70 kPa (gage)]. Under these conditions, an allowable pressure drop of 10% of the initial pressure is used, and pipe sizes can be reduced significantly. Gas pressure regulators at the appliance must be specified to accommodate higher inlet pressures. NFPA/IAS (1992) provides information on pipe sizing for various inlet pressures and pressure drops at higher pressures.

More complete information on gas piping can be found in the *Gas Engineers' Handbook* (1970).

FUEL OIL PIPING

The pipe used to convey fuel oil to oil-fired appliances must be large enough to maintain low pump suction pressure and, in the case of circulating loop systems, to prevent overpressure at the burner oil pump inlet. Pipe materials must be compatible with the fuel and must be carefully assembled to eliminate all leaks. Leaks in suction lines cause pumping problems that result in unreliable burner operation. Leaks in pressurized lines create fire hazards. Cast-iron or aluminum fittings and pipe are unacceptable. Pipe joint compounds must be selected carefully.

Oil pump suction lines should be sized so that at maximum suction line flow conditions, the maximum vacuum will not exceed 34 kPa for distillate grade fuels and 50 kPa for residual oils. Oil supply lines to burner oil pumps should not be pressurized by circulating loop systems or aboveground oil storage tanks to more than 34 kPa, or pump shaft seals may fail. A typical oil circulating loop system is shown in Figure 17.

In assembling long fuel pipe lines, care should be taken to avoid air pockets. On overhead circulating loops, the line should vent air at all high points. Oil supply loops for one or more burners should be the continuous circulation type, with excess fuel returned to the storage tank. Dead-ended pressurized loops can be used, but air or vapor venting is more problematic.

Where valves are used, select ball or gate valves. Globe valves are not recommended because of their high pressure drop characteristics.

Oil lines should be tested after installation, particularly if they are buried, enclosed, or otherwise inaccessible. Failure to perform this test is a frequent cause of later operating difficulties. A suction

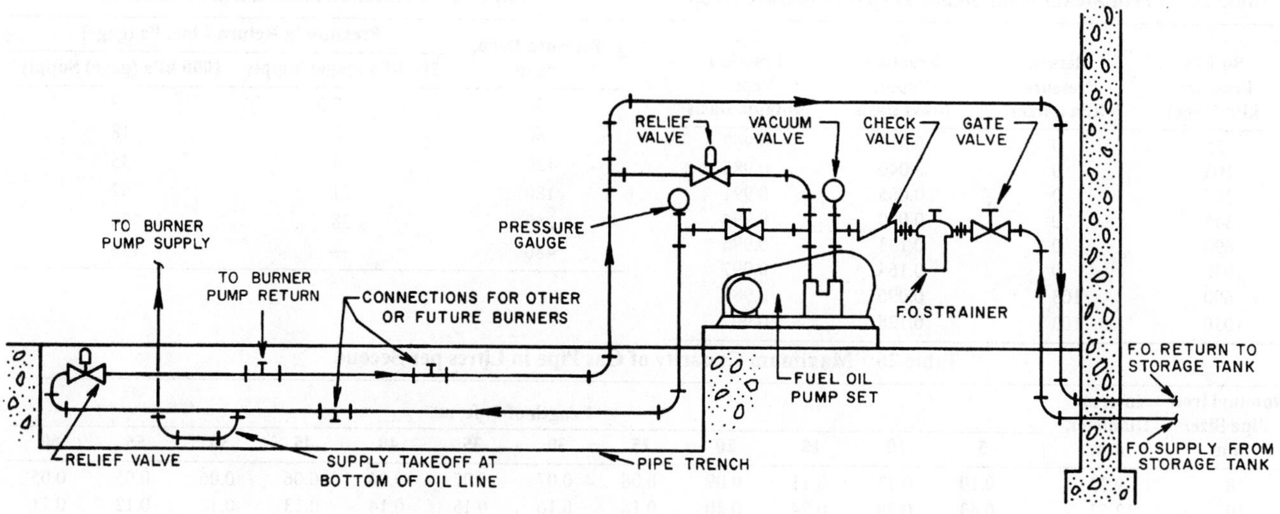

Fig. 17 Typical Oil Circulating Loop

Table 27 Recommended Nominal Size for Fuel Oil Suction Lines from Tank to Pump (Residual Grades No. 5 and No. 6)

Pumping Rate, L/h	Length of Run in Metres at Maximum Suction Lift of 4.5 kPa									
	10	20	30	40	50	60	70	80	90	100
50	40	40	40	50	50	50	65	65	65	80
100	40	40	50	50	65	65	65	65	80	80
200	40	50	50	50	65	65	65	80	80	80
300	50	50	65	65	65	80	80	80	80	80
400	50	50	65	65	80	80	80	80	80	100
500	50	65	65	65	80	80	80	80	100	100
600	65	65	65	80	80	80	100	100	100	100
700	65	65	65	80	80	100	100	100	100	100
800	65	65	80	80	100	100	100	100	100	100

Notes:
1. Sizes (in millimetres) are nominal.
2. Pipe sizes smaller than 25 mm ISO are not recommended for use with residual grade fuel oils.
3. Lines conveying fuel oil from pump discharge port to burners and tank return may be reduced by one or two sizes, depending on piping length and pressure losses.

Table 28 Recommended Nominal Size for Fuel Oil Suction Lines from Tank to Pump (Distillate Grades No. 1 and No. 2)

Pumping Rate, L/h	Length of Run in Metres at Maximum Suction Lift of 9.0 kPa									
	10	20	30	40	50	60	70	80	90	100
50	15	15	15	15	15	20	20	20	25	25
100	15	15	15	15	20	20	20	20	25	25
200	15	20	20	20	20	20	25	25	25	25
300	15	20	20	20	20	25	25	25	25	32
400	20	20	20	20	25	25	25	25	32	32
500	20	25	25	25	25	25	32	32	32	32
600	20	25	25	25	25	32	32	32	32	50
700	20	25	25	25	25	32	32	32	50	50
800	20	25	25	25	32	32	32	32	50	50

Note: Sizes (in millimetres) are nominal.

line can be hydrostatically tested at 1.5 times its maximum operating pressure or at a vacuum of not less than 70 kPa. Pressure or vacuum tests should continue for at least 60 min. If there is no noticeable drop in the initial test pressure, the lines can be considered tight.

Pipe Sizes for Heavy Oil

Tables 27 and 28 give recommended pipe sizes for handling No. 5 and No. 6 oils (residual grades) and No. 1 and No. 2 oils (distillate grades), respectively.

Storage tanks and piping and pumping facilities for delivering the oil from the tank to the burner are important considerations in the design of an industrial oil-burning system.

The construction and location of the tank and oil piping are usually subject to local regulations and National Fire Protection Association (NFPA) *Standards* 30 and 31.

REFERENCES

Ball, E.F. and C.J.D. Webster. 1976. Some measurements of water-flow noise in copper and ABS pipes with various flow velocities. *The Building Services Engineer* 44(2):33.

BOCA. 1992. *BOCA National plumbing code*, 9th ed. Building Officials and Code Administrators International, Country Club Hills, IL.

Carrier. 1960. Piping design. In *System design manual*. Carrier Air Conditioning Company, Syracuse, NY.

Crane Co. 1976. Flow of fluids through valves, fittings and pipe. *Technical Paper* 410. Crane Company, New York.

Crane Co. 1988. Flow of fluids through valves, fittings and pipe. *Technical Paper* 410. Crane Company, New York.

Dawson, F.M. and J.S. Bowman. 1933. Interior water supply piping for residential buildings. University of Wisconsin Experiment Station *Bulletin* 77.

Freeman, J.R. 1941. *Experiments upon the flow of water in pipes*. American Society of Mechanical Engineers, New York.

Gas engineers' handbook. 1970. Industrial Press, New York.

Giesecke, F.E. 1926. Friction of water elbows. *ASHVE Transactions* 32:303.

Giesecke, F.E. and W.H. Badgett. 1931. Friction heads in one-inch standard cast-iron tees. *ASHVE Transactions* 37:395.

Giesecke, F.E. and W.H. Badgett. 1932a. Loss of head in copper pipe and fittings. *ASHVE Transactions* 38:529.

Giesecke, F.E. and W.H. Badgett. 1932b. Supplementary friction heads in one-inch cast-iron tees. *ASHVE Transactions* 38:111.

Grinnell Company. 1951. *Piping design and engineering*. Grinnell Company, Cranston, RI.

HDR design guide. 1981. Hennington, Durham and Richardson, Omaha, NE.

Hegberg, R.A. 1995. Where did the k-factors for pressure loss in fittings come from? *ASHRAE Transactions* 101(1):1264-78.

Howell, R.H. 1985. Evaluation of sizing methods for steam condensate systems. *ASHRAE Transactions* 91(1).

Hunter, R.B. 1940. Methods of estimating loads in plumbing systems. NBS *Report* BMS 65. National Institute of Standards and Technology, Gaithersburg, MD.

Hunter, R.B. 1941. Water distributing systems for buildings. NBS *Report* BMS 79. National Institute of Standards and Technology, Gaithersburg, MD.

Hydraulic Institute. 1979. *Engineering data book*. Hydraulic Institute, Parsippany, NJ.

IAPMO. 1994. *Uniform plumbing code*. International Association of Plumbing and Mechanical Officials, Walnut, CA.

Idelchik, I.E. 1986. *Handbook of hydraulic resistance*. Hemisphere Publishing, New York.

ISA. 1985. Flow equations for sizing control valves. ANSI/ISA *Standard* S75.01-85. International Society for Measurement and Control, Research Triangle Park, NC.

Laschober, R.R., G.Y. Anderson, and D.G. Barbee. 1966. Counterflow of steam and condensate in slightly pitched pipes. *ASHRAE Transactions* 72(1):157.

Marseille, B. 1965. Noise transmission in piping. *Heating and Ventilating Engineering* (June):674.

NAPHCC. 1996. *National standard plumbing code*. National Association of Plumbing-Heating-Cooling Contractors, Falls Church, VA.

NFPA. 1992. Installation of oil burning equipment. ANSI/NFPA *Standard* 31-92. National Fire Protection Association, Quincy, MA.

NFPA. 1993. Flammable and combustible liquids code. ANSI/NFPA *Standard* 30-93. National Fire Protection Association, Quincy, MA.

NFPA/IAS. 1992. *National fuel gas code*. ANSI/NFPA *Standard* 54-92. National Fire Protection Association, Quincy, MA. ANSI/IAS *Standard* Z223.1-92. American Gas Association, Arlington, VA.

Obrecht, M.F. and M. Pourbaix. 1967. Corrosion of metals in potable water systems. *AWWA* 59:977. American Water Works Association, Denver, CO.

Plastic Pipe Institute. 1971. *Water flow characteristics of thermoplastic pipe*. Plastic Pipe Institute, New York.

Rahmeyer, W.J. 1999a. Pressure loss coefficients of threaded and forged weld pipe fittings for ells, reducing ells, and pipe reducers. *ASHRAE Transactions* 105(2):334-354.

Rahmeyer, W.J. 1999b. Pressure loss coefficients of pipe fittings for threaded and forged weld pipe tees. *ASHRAE Transactions* 105(2):355-385.

Rahmeyer, W.J. 2002a. Pressure loss data for large pipe ells, reducers, and expansions. *ASHRAE Transactions* 108(1):360-375.

Rahmeyer, W.J. 2002b. Pressure loss data for large pipe tees. *ASHRAE Transactions* 108(1):376-389.

Rahmeyer, W.J. 2002c. Pressure loss coefficients for close-coupled pipe ells. *ASHRAE Transactions* 108(1):390-406.

Rahmeyer, W.J. 2003a. Pressure loss data for PVC pipe elbows, reducers, and expansions. *ASHRAE Transactions* 109(2):230-251.

Rahmeyer, W.J. 2003b. Pressure loss data for PVC pipe tees. *ASHRAE Transactions* 109(2):252-271.

Rogers, W.L. 1953. Experimental approaches to the study of noise and noise transmission in piping systems. *ASHVE Transactions* 59:347-360.

Rogers, W.L. 1954. Sound-pressure levels and frequencies produced by flow of water through pipe and fittings. *ASHRAE Transactions* 60:411-430.

Rogers, W.L. 1956. Noise production and damping in water piping. *ASHAE Transactions* 62:39.

Sanks, R.L. 1978. *Water treatment plant design for the practicing engineer.* Ann Arbor Science, Ann Arbor, MI.

SBCCI. 1994. *Standard plumbing code.* Southern Building Code Congress International, Birmingham, AL.

Smith, T. 1983. Reducing corrosion in heating plants with special reference to design considerations. *Anti-Corrosion Methods and Materials* 30 (October):4.

Stewart, W.E. and C.L. Dona. 1987. Water flow rate limitations. *ASHRAE Transactions* 93(2):811-825.

Williams, G.J. 1976. The Hunter curves revisited. *Heating/Piping/Air Conditioning* (November):67.

Williams, G.S. and A. Hazen. 1933. *Hydraulic tables.* John Wiley & Sons, New York.

CHAPTER 23

INSULATION FOR MECHANICAL SYSTEMS

THIS chapter deals with applications of thermal and acoustical insulation for mechanical systems in residential, commercial, and industrial facilities. Applications include pipes, tanks, vessels and equipment, and ducts.

Thermal insulation is primarily used to limit heat gain or loss from surfaces operating at temperatures above or below ambient temperature. Insulation may be used to satisfy one or more of the following design objectives:

- **Energy conservation**: minimizing unwanted heat loss/gain from building HVAC systems, as well as preserving natural and financial resources
- **Personnel protection**: controlling surface temperatures to avoid contact burns (hot or cold)
- **Condensation control**: minimizing condensation by keeping surface temperature above the dew point of surrounding air
- **Process control**: minimizing temperature change in process fluids where close control is needed
- **Freeze protection**: minimizing energy required for heat tracing systems and/or extending the time to freezing in the event of system failure
- **Noise control**: reducing/controlling noise in mechanical systems
- **Fire safety**: protecting critical building elements and slowing the spread of fire in buildings

Fundamentals of thermal insulation are covered in Chapter 25; applications in insulated assemblies are discussed in Chapter 27; and data on thermal and water vapor transmission data are in Chapter 26.

DESIGN CONSIDERATIONS

Energy Conservation

Thermal insulation is commonly used to reduce energy consumption of HVAC systems and equipment. Minimum insulation levels for ductwork and piping are often dictated by energy codes, many of which are based on ASHRAE *Standards* 90.1 and 90.2. In many cases, it may be cost-effective to go beyond the minimum levels dictated by energy codes. Thicknesses greater than the optimum economic thickness may be required for other technical reasons such as condensation control, personnel protection, or noise control.

Tables 1 to 3 contain minimum insulation levels for ducts and pipes, excerpted from ANSI/ASHRAE *Standard* 90.1-2007, Energy Standard for Buildings Except Low-Rise Residential Buildings.

Interest in **green buildings** (i.e., those that are environmentally responsible and energy efficient, as well as healthier places to work) is increasing. The LEED® (Leadership in Energy and Environmental Design) Green Building Rating System™, created by the U.S. Green Building Council, is a voluntary rating system that sets out sustainable design and performance criteria for buildings. It evaluates environmental performance from a whole-building perspective and awards points based on satisfying performance criteria in several different categories. Different levels of green building certification are awarded based on the total points earned. The role of mechanical insulation in reducing energy usage, along with the associated greenhouse gas emissions, can help to contribute to LEED certification and should be considered when designing an insulation system.

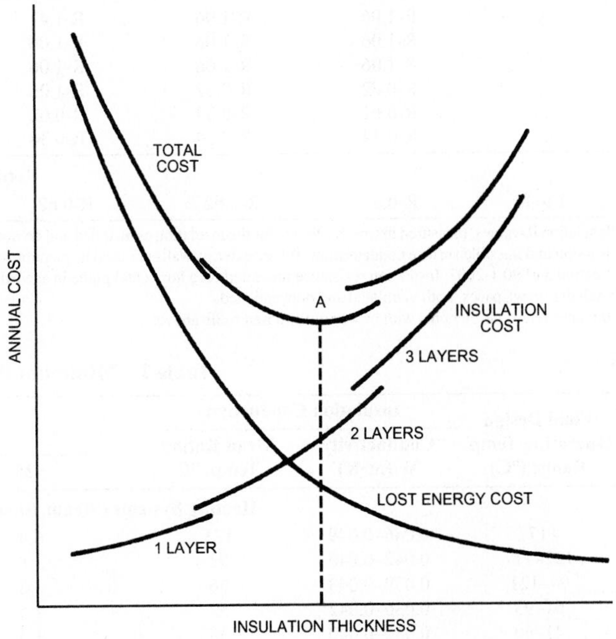

Fig. 1 Determination of Economic Thickness of Insulation

Economic Thickness

Economics can be used to (1) select the optimum insulation thickness for a specific insulation, or (2) evaluate two or more insulation materials for least cost for a given level of thermal performance. In either case, economic considerations determine the most cost-effective solution for insulating over a specific period.

Life-cycle costing considers the initial cost of the insulation system plus the ongoing value of energy savings over the expected service lifetime. The economic thickness is defined as the thickness that minimizes the total life-cycle cost.

Labor and material costs of installed insulation increase with thickness. Insulation is often applied in multiple layers (1) because materials are not manufactured in single layers of sufficient thickness and, (2) in many cases, to accommodate expansion and contraction of insulation and system components. Figure 1 shows installed costs for a multilayer application. The slope of the curves is discontinuous and increases with the number of layers because labor and material costs increase more rapidly as thickness increases. Figure 1 shows curves of total annual costs of operation, insulation costs, and lost energy costs. Point A on the total cost

The preparation of this chapter is assigned to TC 1.8, Mechanical Systems Insulation.

Table 1 Minimum Duct Insulation R-Value,[a] Cooling and Heating Only Supply Ducts and Return Ducts

	Duct Location						
Climate Zone	Exterior	Ventilated Attic	Unvented Attic Above Insulated Ceiling	Unvented Attic with Roof Insulation[a]	Unconditioned Space[b]	Indirectly Conditioned Space[c]	Buried
Heating-Only Ducts							
1, 2	none	none	none	none	none	none	none
3	R-0.62	none	none	none	none	none	none
4	R-0.62	none	none	none	none	none	none
5	R-1.06	R-0.62	none	none	none	none	R-0.62
6	R-1.06	R-1.06	R-0.62	none	none	none	R-0.62
7	R-1.41	R-1.06	R-1.06	none	R-0.62	none	R-0.62
8	R-1.41	R-1.41	R-1.06	none	R-1.06	none	R-1.06
Cooling-Only Ducts							
1	R-1.06	R-1.06	R-1.41	R-0.62	R-0.62	none	R-0.62
2	R-1.06	R-1.06	R-1.06	R-0.62	R-0.62	none	R-0.62
3	R-1.06	R-1.06	R-1.06	R-0.62	R-0.64	none	none
4	R-0.62	R-0.62	R-1.06	R-0.34	R-0.34	none	none
5, 6	R-0.62	R-0.34	R-0.62	R-0.34	R-0.34	none	none
7, 8	R-0.34	R-0.34	R-0.34	R-0.34	R-0.34	none	none
Return Ducts							
1 to 8	R-0.62	R-0.62	R-0.62	none	none	none	none

[a]Insulation R-values, measured in $(m^2 \cdot K)/W$, are for the insulation as installed and do not include film resistance. The required minimum thicknesses do not consider water vapor transmission and possible surface condensation. Where exterior walls are used as plenum walls, wall insulation shall be as required by the most restrictive condition of Section 6.4.4.2 or Section 5 of 90.1-2007. Insulation resistance measured on a horizontal plane in accordance with ASTM C518 at a mean temperature of 23.9°C at the installed thickness.
[b]Includes crawlspaces, both ventilated and nonventilated.
[c]Includes return air plenums with or without exposed roofs above.

Table 2 Minimum Pipe Insulation Thickness[a]

Fluid Design Operating Temp. Range (°C)	Insulation Conductivity		Nominal Pipe or Tube Size (cm)				
	Conductivity W/(m·K)	Mean Rating Temp. °C	<25	25 to <40	0 to <100	100 to <200	≥200
Heating Systems (Steam, Steam Condensate, and Hot Water)[b,c]							
>177	0.046–0.049	121	6.4	7.6	7.6	10.2	10.2
122–177	0.042–0.046	93	3.8	6.4	7.6	7.6	7.6
94–121	0.039–0.043	66	3.8	3.8	5.1	5.1	5.1
61–93	0.036–0.042	52	2.5	2.5	2.5	3.8	3.8
41–60	0.032–0.040	38	1.3	1.3	2.5	2.5	2.5
Domestic and Service Hot-Water Systems							
41+	0.032–0.040	38	1.3	1.3	2.5	2.5	2.5
Cooling Systems (Chilled Water, Brine, and Refrigerant)[d]							
4–16	0.032–0.040	38	1.3	1.3	2.5	2.5	2.5
<4	0.032–0.040	38	1.3	2.5	2.5	2.5	3.8

[a]For insulation outside the stated conductivity range, the minimum thickness (T) shall be determined as follows:

$$T = r\{(1 + t/r)K/k - 1\}$$

where T = minimum insulation thickness (cm), r = actual outside radius of pipe (cm), t = insulation thickness listed in this table for applicable fluid temperature and pipe size, K = conductivity of alternate material at mean rating temperature indicated for the applicable fluid temperature (W/m·K); and k = the upper value of the conductivity range listed in this table for the applicable fluid temperature.

[b]These thicknesses are based on energy *efficiency* considerations only. Additional insulation is sometimes required relative to safety issues/surface temperature.
[c]Piping insulation is not required between the control valve and coil on run-outs when the control valve is located within 1.2 m of the coil and the pipe size is 25 mm or less.
[d]These thicknesses are based on energy *efficiency* considerations only. Issues such as water vapor permeability or surface condensation sometimes require vapor retarders or additional insulation.

curve corresponds to the economic insulation thickness, which, in this example, is in the double-layer range. Viewing the calculated economic thickness as a minimum thickness provides a hedge against unforeseen fuel price increases and conserves energy.

Initially, as insulation is applied, the total life-cycle cost decreases because the value of incremental energy savings is greater than the incremental cost of insulation. Additional insulation reduces total cost up to a thickness where the change in total cost is equal to zero. At this point, no further reduction can be obtained; beyond it, incremental insulation costs exceed the additional energy savings derived by adding another increment of insulation.

Economic analysis should also consider the time value of money, which can be based on a desired rate of return for the insulation investment. Energy costs are volatile, and a fuel cost inflation factor is sometimes included to account for the possibility that fuel costs may increase more quickly than general inflation. Insulation system maintenance costs should also be included, along with cost savings associated with the ability to specify lower capacity equipment, resulting in lower first costs.

Chapter 36 of the 2007 *ASHRAE Handbook—HVAC Applications* has more information on economic analysis.

Personnel Protection

In many applications, insulation is provided to protect personnel from burns. The potential for burns to human skin is a complex function of surface temperature, surface material, and time of contact. ASTM *Standard* C1055 has a good discussion of these factors. Standard industry practice is to specify a maximum temperature of 60°C

Table 3 Minimum Duct Insulation R-Value,[a] Combined Heating and Cooling Supply Ducts and Return Ducts

	Duct Location						
Climate Zone	Exterior	Ventilated Attic	Unvented Attic Above Insulated Ceiling	Unvented Attic with Roof Insulation[a]	Unconditioned Space[b]	Indirectly Conditioned Space[c]	Buried
				Supply Ducts			
1	R-1.06	R-1.06	R-1.41	R-0.62	R-0.62	none	R-0.62
2	R-1.06	R-1.06	R-1.06	R-0.62	R-0.62	none	R-0.62
3	R-1.06	R-1.06	R-1.06	R-0.62	R-0.62	none	R-0.62
4	R-1.06	R-1.06	R-1.06	R-0.62	R-0.62	none	R-0.62
5	R-1.06	R-1.06	R-1.06	R-0.34	R-0.62	none	R-0.62
6	R-1.41	R-1.06	R-1.06	R-0.34	R-0.62	none	R-0.62
7	R-1.41	R-1.06	R-1.06	R-0.34	R-0.62	none	R-0.62
8	R-1.41	R-1.41	R-1.41	R-0.34	R-1.06	none	R-1.06
				Return Ducts			
1 to 8	R-0.62	R-0.62	R-0.62	none	none	none	none

[a]Insulation R-values, measured in $(m^2 \cdot K)/W$, are for the insulation as installed and do not include film resistance. The required minimum thicknesses do not consider water vapor transmission and possible surface condensation. Where exterior walls are used as plenum walls, wall insulation shall be as required by the most restrictive condition of Section 6.4.4.2 or Section 5 of 90.1-2007. Insulation resistance measured on a horizontal plane in accordance with ASTM C518 at a mean temperature of 23.9°C at the installed thickness.
[b]Includes crawlspaces, both ventilated and nonventilated.
[c]Includes return air plenums with or without exposed roofs above.

for surfaces that may be contacted by personnel. For indoor applications, maximum air temperatures depend on the facility and location, and are typically lower than design outdoor conditions. For outdoor installations, base calculations on summer design ambient temperatures with no wind (i.e., the worst case). Surface temperatures increase because of solar loading, but are usually neglected because of variability in orientation, solar intensity, and many other complicating factors. Engineering judgment must be used in selecting ambient and operating temperatures and wind conditions for these calculations.

Note that the choice of jacketing strongly affects a surface's relative safety. Higher-emittance jacketing materials (e.g., plastic, painted metals) can be selected to minimize the surface temperature. Jacketing material also affects the relative safety at a given surface temperature. For example, at 80°C, a stainless steel jacket blisters skin more severely than a nonmetallic jacket at equal contact time.

Condensation Control

For cold systems, avoiding surface condensation often guides insulation system design. The design goal is to keep the surface temperature above the surrounding air's dew-point temperature. Calculating surface temperature is relatively simple, but selection of design conditions is often confusing.

To illustrate, Table 4 shows insulation thickness required to prevent condensation on the exterior surface of an insulated tank containing a liquid held at 4°C located in a mechanical room with dry-bulb temperature of 27°C. Note that, at high relative humidities, the thickness required to prevent surface condensation increases dramatically, and becomes impractical above 90% rh.

For outdoor applications (or for unconditioned spaces vented to outdoor air), there are always some hours per year where the ambient air is saturated or nearly saturated. For these times, no amount of insulation will prevent surface condensation. Figure 2 shows the frequency distribution of outdoor relative humidity based on typical meteorological year weather data for Charlotte, NC (Marion and Urban 1995). There are over 1200 h per year when the relative humidity is equal to or greater than 90%, and nearly 600 h per year when the relative humidity is equal to or greater than 95%.

For outdoor applications and mechanical rooms vented to outdoor conditions, it is suggested to design for a relative humidity of 90% at the project's design dew-point temperature. (Design dew-point data may be found in Chapter 14.) For Charlotte, the 0.4% design dew-point temperature is 23°C. Using a psychrometric chart, the 23°C dew-point temperature line intersects the 90% rh curve at a dry-bulb temperature of approximately 25°C. The recommended design condition for outdoor installations in Charlotte is therefore

Table 4 Insulation Thickness Required to Prevent Surface Condensation

Relative Humidity, %	Thickness, mm
20	—
30	2.5
40	5.0
50	7.5
60	13
70	18
80	33
90	74
95	150

Note: Calculated using Equation (14), assuming surface conductance of 6.8 $W/(m^2 \cdot K)$ and insulation with thermal conductivity of 0.043 $W/(m \cdot K)$. Different assumed values yield different results.

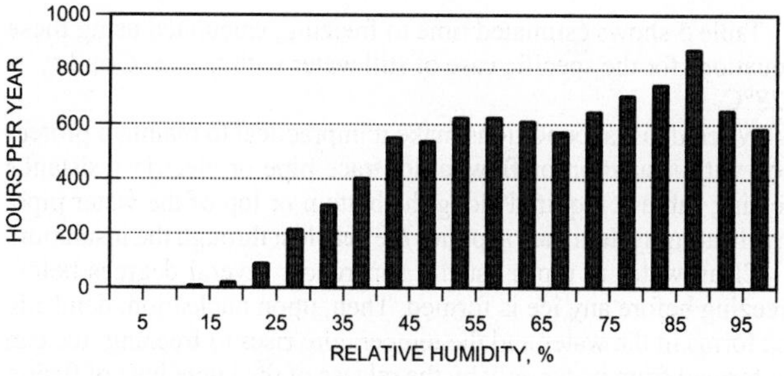

Fig. 2 Relative Humidity Histogram for Charlotte, NC

25°C db at 90% rh. Appropriate water-resistant vapor-retarder jacketing or mastics must then be specified to protect the system from the inevitable surface condensation.

Freeze Prevention

It is important to recognize that insulation retards heat flow; it does not stop it completely. If the surrounding air temperature remains low enough for an extended period, insulation cannot prevent freezing of still water or of water flowing at a rate insufficient for the available heat content to offset heat loss. Insulation can prolong the time required for freezing, or prevent freezing if flow is maintained at a sufficient rate. To calculate time θ (in hours) required for water to cool to 0°C with no flow, use the following equation:

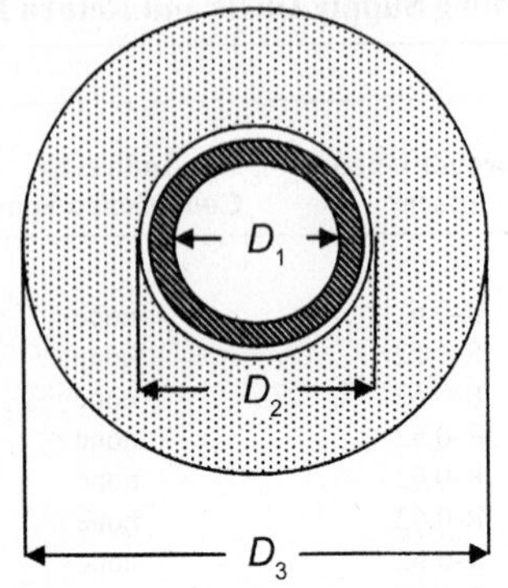

Fig. 3 Time to Freeze Nomenclature

$$\theta = (1/3600)\rho C_p \pi (D_1/2)^2 R_T \ln[(t_i - t_a)/(t_f - t_a)] \quad (1)$$

where

θ = time to freezing, h
ρ = density of water = 1000 kg/m^3
C_p = specific heat of water = 4200 J/(kg·K)
D_1 = inside diameter of pipe, m (see Figure 3)
R_T = combined thermal resistance of pipe wall, insulation, and exterior air film (for a unit length of pipe)
t_i = initial water temperature, °C
t_a = ambient air temperature, °C
t_f = freezing temperature, °C

As a conservative assumption for insulated pipes, thermal resistances of pipe walls and exterior air film are usually neglected. Resistance of the insulation layer for a unit length of pipe is calculated as

$$R_T = 12 \ln(D_3/D_2)/(2\pi k) \quad (2)$$

where

D_3 = outer diameter of insulation, m
D_2 = inner diameter of insulation, m
k = thermal conductivity of insulation material, W/(m·K)

Table 5 shows estimated time to freezing, calculated using these equations for the specific case of still water with t_i = 6°C and t_a = −28°C.

When unusual conditions make it impractical to maintain protection with insulation or flow, a hot trace pipe or electric resistance heating cable is required along the bottom or top of the water pipe. The heating system then supplies the heat lost through the insulation.

Clean water in pipes usually supercools several degrees below freezing before any ice is formed. Then, upon nucleation, dendritic ice forms in the water and the temperature rises to freezing. Ice can be formed from water only by the release of the latent heat of fusion (335 kJ/kg) through the pipe insulation. Well-insulated pipes may greatly retard this release of latent heat. Gordon (1996) showed that water pipes burst not because of ice crystal growth in the pipe, but because of elevated fluid pressure within a confined pipe section occluded by a growing ice blockage.

Table 5 Time to Cool Water to Freezing, h

Nominal Pipe Size, mm	Insulation Thickness, mm: 13	25	38	50	75	100
15	0.1	0.2	0.2	0.3	—	—
25	0.3	0.4	0.5	0.6	0.8	—
40	0.4	0.8	1.0	1.3	1.5	—
50	0.6	1.1	1.4	1.7	2.2	2.5
80	0.9	1.7	2.3	2.9	3.7	4.5
100	1.3	2.4	3.3	4.1	5.5	6.6
125	1.6	3.0	4.3	5.4	7.4	9.1
150	1.9	3.7	5.3	6.9	9.4	11.7
200	—	5.3	7.6	9.6	13.7	16.9
250	—	6.5	10.2	12.9	17.9	22.3
300	—	8.8	12.5	15.8	22.1	27.7

Note: Assumes initial temperature = 5.5°C, ambient air temperature = −28°C, and insulation thermal conductivity = 0.0432 W/(m·K). Thermal resistances of pipe and air film are neglected. Different assumed values will yield different results.

Noise Control

Duct Insulation. Without insulation, the acoustical environment of mechanically conditioned buildings can be greatly compromised, resulting in reduced productivity and a decrease in occupant comfort. HVAC ducts act as conduits for mechanical equipment noise, and also carry office noise between occupied spaces. Additionally, some ducts can create their own noise through duct wall vibrations or expansion and contraction. Lined sheet metal ducts and fibrous glass rigid ducts can greatly reduce transmission of HVAC noise through the duct system. The insulation also reduces cross-talk from one room to another through the ducts. A good discussion of duct acoustics is provided in Chapter 47 of the 2007 *ASHRAE Handbook—HVAC Applications*. Duct insulation can be used to provide both attenuation loss and breakout noise reduction.

Attenuation loss is noise absorbed within the duct. In uninsulated ducts, it is a function of duct geometry and dimensions as well as noise frequency. Internal insulation liners are generally available for most duct geometries. Chapter 47 in the 2007 *ASHRAE Handbook—HVAC Applications* provides attenuation losses for square, rectangular, and round ducts lined with fibrous glass, and also gives guidance on the use of insulation in plenums to absorb duct system noise. Internal linings can be very effective in fittings such as elbows, which can have 2 to 8 times more attenuation than an unlined elbow of the same size. For alternative lining materials, consult individual manufacturers.

It is difficult to write specifications for sound attenuation because it changes with every duct dimension and configuration. Thus, insulation materials are generally selected for attenuation based on sound absorption ratings. Sound absorption tests are run per ASTM *Standard* C423 in large reverberation rooms with random sound incidence. The test specimens are laid on the chamber floor per ASTM *Standard* E795, Type A mounting. This mode of sound exposure is quite different from the exposure of internal linings installed in an air duct. Therefore, sound absorption ratings for materials can only be used for general comparisons of effectiveness when used in air ducts of varying dimensions (Kuntz and Hoover 1987).

Breakout noise is from vibration of the duct wall caused by air pressure fluctuations in the duct. Absorptive insulation can be used in combination with mass-loaded jacketings or mastics on the duct exterior to reduce breakout noise. This technique is only minimally effective on rectangular ducts, which require the insulation and mass composite to be physically separated from the duct wall to be very effective. For round ducts, as with pipes, absorptive insulation and mass composite can be effective even when directly applied to the duct surface. Chapter 47 in the 2007 *ASHRAE Handbook—HVAC Applications* provides breakout noise guidance data.

Noise Radiating from Pipes. Noise from piping can be reduced by adding an absorptive insulation and jacketing material. By knowing the sound insertion loss of insulation and jacketing material combinations, the expected level of noise reduction in the field can be estimated. A range of jacket weights and insulation thicknesses can be used to reduce noise. Jackets used to reduce noise are typically referred to as being mass-filled. Some products for outdoor applications use mass-filled vinyl (MFV) in combination with aluminum.

Pipe insertion loss is a measurement (in dB) of the reduction in sound pressure level from a pipe as a result of application of insulation and jacketing. Measured at different frequencies, the noise level from

Table 6 Insertion Loss for Pipe Insulation Materials, dB

Pipe Size, mm	Insulation Material	Insulation Thickness, mm	Jacket	Frequency, Hz 500	1000	2000	4000
150	Fibrous glass	50	ASJ[a]	2	9	14	16
			0.5 mm aluminum	3	16	24	33
			5 kg/m² MFV[b] with Al	13	20	32	40
		100	ASJ	4	21	27	33
			0.5 mm aluminum	3	17	27	42
	Flexible elastomeric	13	None	0	2	5	10
		25		0	2	5	10
		13	5 kg/m² MFV with Al	0	14	18	20
		25		0	16	20	26
300	Fibrous glass	50	ASJ	0	12	19	23
			0.5 mm aluminum	4	19	25	26
		100	ASJ	8	16	22	26
			0.5 mm aluminum	12	22	30	32
			5 kg/m² MFV with Al	14	23	31	31
	Mineral wool	50	0.4mm aluminum	1	9	18	28
		75		0	14	19	30

[a]ASJ = all-service jacket, a typical factory-applied vapor retarder applied to many products.
[b]MFV = mass filled vinyl, a field-installed jacket, which has considerably more mass than ASJ.

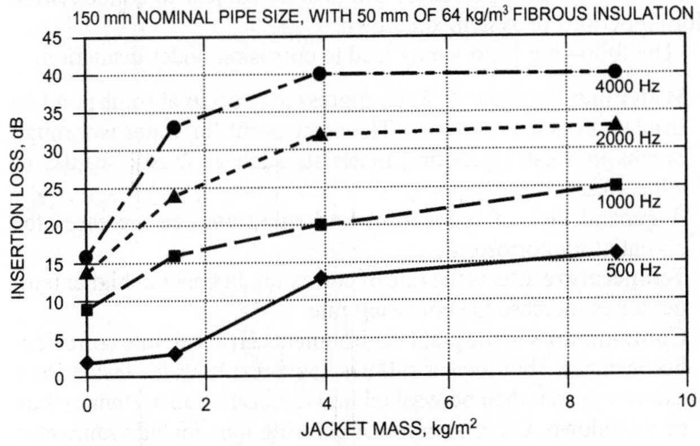

Fig. 4 Insertion Loss Versus Mass of Jacket

the jacketed pipe is subtracted from that of the bare pipe; the larger the insertion loss number, the larger the amount of noise reduction.

ASTM *Standard* E1222 describes how to determine insertion loss of pipe jacketing systems. A band-limited white noise test signal is produced inside a steel pipe located in a reverberation room, using a loudspeaker or acoustic driver at one end of the pipe to produce the noise. Average sound pressure levels are measured in the room for two conditions: with sound radiating from a bare pipe, and with the same pipe covered with a jacketing system. The insertion loss of the jacketing system is the difference in the sound pressure levels measured, adjusted for changes in room absorption caused by the jacketing system's presence. Results may be obtained in a series of 100 Hz wide bands or in one-third octave bands from 500 to 5000 Hz.

Table 6 gives measured insertion loss values for several pipe insulation and jacket combinations. The weight of the jacket material significantly affects insertion loss of pipe insulation systems. Figure 4 represents insertion loss of typical fibrous pipe insulations with various masses of jacketing (Miller 2001).

It is very important that sound sources be well identified in industrial settings. It is possible to treat a noisy pipe very effectively and have no significant influence on ambient sound measurement after treatment. Is it important that all sources of noise above desired levels receive acoustical treatment, beginning with the largest source, or no improvement will be observed.

Fire Safety

Materials used to insulate mechanical equipment generally must meet the requirements of local codes adopted by governmental entities having jurisdiction over the project. In the United States, most local codes incorporate or are patterned after model codes developed and maintained by organizations such as the National Fire Protection Association (NFPA) and the more recent International Code Council (International Codes). Refer to local codes to determine specific requirements.

Most codes related to insulation product fire safety refer to the surface burning characteristics as determined by the Steiner tunnel test (ASTM *Standard* E84, NFPA *Standard* 255, UL *Standard* 723, or CAN/ULC *Standard* S-102). These similar test methods evaluate the flame spread and smoke developed from samples mounted in a 7.62 m long tunnel and subsequently exposed to a controlled flame. Results are given in terms of *flame spread* and *smoke developed* indices, which are relative to a baseline index and calibration standards of inorganic reinforced cement board (0) and select grade red oak flooring (100). Samples are normally mounted with the exposed surface face down in the ceiling of the tunnel. Upon ignition, the progress of the flame front is timed while being tracked visually for distance down the tunnel, with the results used to calculate the flame spread index. Smoke index is determined by measuring smoke density with a light cell mounted in the exhaust stream.

Using supporting materials on the underside of the test specimen can lower the flame spread index. Materials that melt, drip, or delaminate to such a degree that the continuity of the flame front is destroyed give low flame spread indices that do not relate directly to indices obtained by testing materials that remain in place. Alternative means of testing may be necessary to fully evaluate some of these materials.

For pipe and duct insulation products, samples are prepared and mounted in the tunnel per ASTM *Standard* E2231, which directs that "the material, system, composite, or assembly tested shall be representative of the completed insulation system used in actual field installations, in terms of the components, including their respective thicknesses." Samples are constructed to mimic, as closely as possible, the products as they will be used, including any facings and adhesives as appropriate.

Duct insulation generally requires a flame spread index of not more than 25 and a smoke developed index of not more than 50, when tested in accordance with ASTM *Standard* E84. Codes often require factory-made duct insulations (e.g., insulated flexible ducts, rigid fibrous glass ducts) to be listed and labeled per UL *Standard* 181, Factory-Made Air Ducts and Air Connectors. This standard specifies a number of other fire tests (e.g., flame penetration and low-energy ignition) as part of the listing requirements.

Some building codes require that duct insulations meet the fire hazard requirements of NFPA *Standard* 90A or 90B, to restrict spread of smoke, heat, and fire through duct systems, and to minimize ignition sources. Local code authorities should also be consulted for specific requirements.

For pipe insulation, the requirement is generally a maximum flame spread index of 25 and a maximum smoke developed index of 450. For insulation materials exposed within supply and return ducts and plenums, the typical requirement is that the materials be noncombustible or have a maximum flame spread index of 25 and maximum smoke developed index of 50. Consult local code authorities for specific requirements.

The term *noncombustible*, as defined by building codes, refers to materials that pass the requirements of ASTM *Standard* E136. This test method involves introducing a small specimen of the material into a furnace initially maintained at a temperature of 750°C. The temperature rise of the furnace is monitored and the specimen is observed for any flaming. Criteria for passing include limits on temperature rise, flaming, and weight loss of the specimen. Some building codes accept as noncombustible a composite material having a structural base of noncombustible material and a surfacing not more than 3 mm thick that has a flame spread index not greater than 50. A related term sometimes referenced in building codes is *limited combustible*, which is an intermediate category that considers the potential heat content of materials determined per the testing requirements of NFPA *Standard* 259.

Mechanical insulation materials are often used as a component in systems or assemblies designed to protect buildings and equipment from the effects or spread of fire (i.e., **fire-resistance assemblies**). They can include walls, roofs, floors, columns, beams, partitions, joints, and through-penetration fire stops. Specific designs are tested and assigned hourly ratings based on performance in full-scale fire tests. Note that insulation materials alone are not assigned hourly fire resistance ratings; ratings are assigned to a system or assembly that may include specific insulation products, along with other elements such as framing members, fasteners, wallboard, etc.

Fire resistance ratings are often developed using ASTM *Standard* E119. This test exposes assemblies (walls, partitions, floor or roof assemblies, and through-penetration fire stops) to a standard fire exposure controlled to achieve specified temperatures throughout a specified time period. The time-temperature curve is intended to be representative of building fires where the primary fuel is solid, and specifies a temperature of 540°C at 5 min, 930°C at 1 h, and 1260°C at 8 h. In the hydrocarbon processing industry, liquid hydrocarbon-fueled pool fires are a concern; fire resistance ratings for these applications are tested per ASTM *Standard* E1529. This time-temperature curve rises rapidly to a temperature of 1090°C within 5 min, and remains there for the duration of the test.

Fire-resistant rated designs can be found in the directories of listing agencies. Examples of such not-for-profit agencies include Underwriters Laboratories, Factory Mutual, and UL Canada.

The following standard cross-references are provided for products to be tested in Canada. Although these are parallel Canadian standards, the requirements may differ from those of ASTM standards.

ASTM *Standard* E84	CAN/ULC *Standard* S102, Standard Method of Test for Surface Burning Characteristics of Building Materials and Assemblies
ASTM *Standard* E119	CAN/ULC *Standard* S101-M, Standard Methods of Fire Endurance Tests of Building Construction and Materials
ASTM *Standard* E136	CAN *Standard* 4-S114, Standard Method of Test for Determination of Noncombustibility in Building Materials
ASTM *Standard* E1529	There is no Canadian equivalent standard on this subject

Corrosion Under Insulation

Corrosion of metal pipe, vessels, and equipment under insulation, though not typically caused by the insulation, is still a significant issue that must be considered during the design of any mechanical insulation system. The propensity for corrosion depends on many factors, including the ambient environment and operating temperature of the metal.

Corrosion under insulation (CUI) is most prevalent in outdoor industrial environments such as refineries and chemical plants. Corrosion can be very costly because of forced downtime of processes and can be a health and safety hazard as well. Although insulation itself may not necessarily be the cause of corrosion, it can be a passive component because it is in direct contact with the pipe or equipment surface.

Very little information is published regarding commercial environments. It is not likely that corrosion is a major concern for most insulated surfaces located indoors. Corrosion under insulation could be a concern on indoor systems that are frequently washed down, such as in the food processing industry.

Water from condensation on cold surfaces can be present on both indoor and outdoor insulation systems if there is damage to the vapor retarder. Hot processes can also be subject to condensation during periods of system shutdown.

The following factors may lead to corrosion under insulation.

- **Water** must be present. Water ingress may occur at some point on insulated outdoor surfaces. The entry point for water is through breaks in weatherproofing materials such as mastic, caulk, or adhesives.
- A general lack of **inspection and maintenance** increases the potential for corrosion
- **Temperature** affects the rate of corrosion. In general, higher temperatures increase the corrosion rate.
- **Contaminants** in the plant environment can accelerate corrosion. For instance, chlorides or sulfates could reside on the insulation's exterior jacket, then be washed into the insulation system by rain or washdown. Other sources of chloride ions include rainwater, ocean mist, and cooling tower spray, each of which can provide a major and virtually inexhaustible supply of ions. Even if the level of chloride ions in the water is low, significant amounts of ions can accumulate at the pipe surface by a continuing cycle of water penetrations and evaporation. Chloride ions only contribute to stress corrosion cracking of stainless steel when water (liquid or vapor) and the ions are present at the surface of a pipe at temperatures above ambient, usually when the surface is above about 60°C and below about 150°C. Exposure of the insulation system to water from some outside source is inevitable, so the key to eliminating stress corrosion cracking lies in preventing moisture and ions, even in small amounts, from reaching the metal surface.
- **Insulation** can contain leachable corrosive agents.
- **Austenitic stainless steels** are particularly susceptible to attack from chlorides. Austenitic stainless steels are generally classified as "18-8s": austenitic alloys containing approximately 18% chromium, 8% nickel, and the balance iron. Besides the basic alloy UNS S30400, these stainless alloys include molybdenum (UNS S31600 and S31700), carbon-stabilized (UNS S321000 and S347000), and low-carbon grades (UNS S30403 and S31603) (NACE 2004).

For outdoor applications, no insulation material alone can prevent penetration of moisture and ions to the metal surface, so additional lines of defense, such as a properly designed, installed, and maintained protective jacket, are necessary. If process temperatures are lower than ambient (even for short periods of time such as during shutdowns), a vapor retarder is also required.

Even with a protective jacket and vapor retarder, it is likely that some moisture and ions will eventually enter the system because of abuse, wear, age, or improper installation. No installation is ideal in any real-world setting. Because most people only consider the chlorides arising from the insulation material, the crucial issue of water and ions infiltrating the insulation system from the environment and yielding metal corrosion remains unaddressed. Thus, painting the pipe is the second and most important line of defense, and is necessary if pipe temperature is in the 60 to 150°C range for significant periods of time. To minimize the potential for corrosion, metal pipe should be primed with, for example, an epoxy coating. This alternative offers superior protection against corrosion, because priming protects against ions arising from the insulation and, more importantly, from ions that enter the system from the environment.

To minimize corrosion,

- Design, install, and maintain insulation systems to minimize ponding water or penetration of water into the system. Flat sections should be designed with a pitch to shed water. Top sections should overlap the sides to provide a watershed effect, preventing water penetration in the seam. Design should always minimize penetrations; necessary protrusions (e.g., supports, valves, flanges) should be designed to shed rather than capture water. Water from external sources can enter at any discontinuity in the insulation system.
- Insulation should be appropriate for its intended application and service temperature. NACE *Standard* RP0198 states, "CUI of carbon steel is possible under all types of insulation. The insulation type may only be a contributing factor. The insulation characteristics with the most influence on CUI are (1) water-leachable salt content in insulation that may contribute to corrosion, such as chloride, sulfate, and acidic materials in fire retardants; (2) water retention, permeability, and wettability of the insulation; and (3) foams containing residual compounds that react with water to form hydrochloric or other acids. Because CUI is a product of wet metal exposure duration, the insulation system that holds the least amount of water and dries most quickly should result in the least amount of corrosion damage to equipment."
- Ancillary materials used for weatherproofing (e.g., sealants, caulks, weather stripping, adhesives, mastics) should be appropriate for the application, and be applied following the manufacturer's recommendations.
- Maintenance should monitor for and immediately repair compromises in the protective jacketing system. Because water may infiltrate the insulation system, inspection ports should be used to facilitate inspection without requiring insulation removal. This is particularly important on subambient systems.
- Because some water will eventually enter the system, a protective pipe coating is necessary for good design. The type of coating depends on temperature (see NACE *Standard* RP0198 for coating guidelines). In Europe, essentially all piping is coated for corrosion protection. This is not necessarily the case in the United States, but should be considered as part of good design practice.
- When using austenitic stainless steel, all insulation products and accessories should meet the requirements of ASTM *Standard* C795. Likewise, any ancillary weatherproofing materials should have low chloride content.

MATERIALS AND SYSTEMS

Categories of Insulation Materials

Turner and Malloy (1981) categorized insulation materials into four types:

- **Fibrous** insulations are composed of small-diameter fibers that finely divide the air space. The fibers may be organic or inorganic, and are normally (but not always) held together by a binder.
- **Granular** insulations are composed of small nodules that contain voids or hollow spaces. These materials are sometimes considered open-cell materials, because gases can transfer between the individual spaces.
- **Cellular** insulations are composed of small, individual cells, either interconnecting or sealed from each other, to form a cellular structure. Glass, plastics, and rubber may comprise the base material, and various foaming agents are used.

  Cellular insulations are often further classified as either open-cell (i.e., cells are interconnecting) or closed-cell (i.e., cells sealed from each other). Generally, materials with greater than 90% closed-cell content are considered to be closed-cell materials.
- **Reflective** insulations and treatments are added to surfaces to lower long-wave emittance, thereby reducing radiant heat transfer from the surface. Low-emittance jackets and facings are often used in combination with other insulation materials.

Another material sometimes called **thermal insulating paint** or **coating** is available for use on pipes ducts and tanks. These products' performance must be clearly understood before using them as thermal insulation. These paints and coatings have not been extensively tested and additional research is needed to verify their performance. Further discussion of these products can be found in Hart (2006).

Physical Properties of Insulation Materials

Selecting an insulation material for a particular application requires understanding the various physical properties associated with available materials.

Operating temperature is often the primary consideration. Maximum temperature capability is normally assessed using ASTM *Standard* C411 by exposing samples to hot surfaces for an extended time, and assessing the materials for any changes in properties. Evidence of warping, cracking, delamination, flaming, melting, or dripping are indications that the maximum use temperature of the material has been exceeded. There is currently no industry-accepted test method for determining the minimum operating temperature of an insulation material, but minimum temperatures are normally determined by evaluating the material's integrity and physical properties after exposure to low temperatures.

Thermal conductivity of insulation materials is a function of temperature. Many specifications call for insulation conductivity values evaluated at a mean temperature of 24°C. Most manufacturers provide conductivity data over a range of temperatures to allow evaluations closer to actual operating conditions. Conductivity of flat product is generally measured per ASTM *Standards* C177 or C518, whereas pipe insulation conductivity is generally determined using ASTM *Standard* C335.

Compressive resistance is important where the insulation must support a load without crushing (e.g., insulation inserts in pipe hangers and supports). When insulation is used in an expansion or contraction joint to take up a dimensional change, lower values of compressive resistance are desirable. ASTM *Standard* C165 is used to measure compressive resistance for fibrous materials, and ASTM *Standard* D1621 is used for foam plastic materials.

Water vapor permeability is the water vapor flux through a material induced by a unit vapor pressure gradient across the material. For insulating materials, it is commonly expressed in units of ng/(s·m·Pa). A related and often confused term is **water vapor permeance** [in ng/(s·m^2·Pa)], which measures water vapor flux through a material of specific thickness and is generally used to define vapor retarder performance. In below-ambient applications, it is important to minimize the rate of water vapor flow to the cold surface. This is normally accomplished by using vapor retarders with low permeance, insulation materials with low permeability, or both. ASTM *Standard* E96 is used to measure water vapor transmission properties of insulation materials.

Water absorption is generally measured by immersing a sample of material under a specified pressure of water for a specified time

Table 7 Performance Property Guide for Insulation Materials

	Calcium Silicate	Flexible Elastomeric	Mineral Fiber	Cellular Glass	Cellular Polystyrene	Cellular Polyiso-cyanurate	Cellular Phenolic	Cellular Polyolefin
ASTM *Standard*	C533	C534	C547, C553, C612	C552	C578	C591	C1126	C1427
Type/grade listed	Type I	Type I Grade 1	Type IVB Category 1	Type I Grade 1	Type XIII	Type IV Grade 2	Type III Grade 1	Type I Grade 1
Max. operating temperature, °C	649	104	649	427	74	150	125	93
Min. operating temperature, °C	60	–57	–18	–268	–183	–183	–40	–101
Min. compressive resistance, kPa	688 at 5%	NS	NS	45 at failure	138 at 10%	145 at 10%	124	NS
Max. thermal conductivity, W/(m·K)								
–18°C mean	NA	0.038	NA	0.039	0.032	0.026	0.019	0.048
–4°C	NA	NS	0.034	NS	0.034	NS	NS	NS
24°C	NA	0.040	0.035	0.045	0.037	0.026	0.019	0.050
93°C	0.065	NA	0.043	0.058	NA	0.035	NA	NA
204°C	0.079	NA	0.061	0.084	NA	NA	NA	NA
316°C	0.095	NA	0.091	NA	NA	NA	NA	NA
Maximum water vapor permeability, ng/(s·m·Pa)	NS	0.15	NA	0.007	2.2	5.8	0.22	0.07
Maximum liquid water absorption, % volume	NS	0.2	NS	0.5	0.5 (24 h)	0.5 (24 h)	3.0 to 8.0	0.2
Maximum water vapor sorption, % mass	NS	NS	5	NS	NS	NS	NS	NS
Maximum surface burning characteristics	0/0	25/50	25/50	5/0	NS	NS	25/50	NS

Note: NA = not applicable. NS = not stated (i.e., ASTM Standards do not include a value for this property). Properties not stated do not necessarily indicate that material is not appropriate for a given application depending on that property. See previous editions of *ASHRAE Handbook—Fundamentals* for data on historical insulation materials.

period. It is a useful measure of the amount of liquid water absorbed from water leaks in weather barriers or during construction.

Typical physical properties of interest are given in Table 7. Values in this table are taken from the relevant ASTM material specification with permission from ASTM International. Within each material category, a variety in types and grades of materials exist. A representative type and grade are listed in Table 7 for each material category; refer to ASTM standards or to manufacturers for specific data.

Weather Protection

The importance of weather barriers cannot be overstated. Premature failure can lead to insulation failure, with safety and economic consequences.

Safety consequences

- If insulation is installed for burn protection from a hot pipe or equipment, water entering the insulation system can vaporize into steam and cause a surface temperature well above the expected 60°C, the common design temperature for personnel protection.
- Pipe or equipment can corrode, rupture, and release a hazardous material.

Economic consequences

- Wet insulation has higher thermal conductivity and lower insulation values.
- On a hot system, 1 kg of water entering the system requires 1 kJ to revaporize. If this vapor cannot vent easily, it can condense, causing interior jacket corrosion; the weather barrier will begin consuming itself from the inside out. Consequently, the system cannot deliver the desired energy and will quickly require an expensive repair.
- On a very cold system, improper vapor retarder selection allows moisture to migrate to the cold surface because of the continuous drive of vapor pressure. A hole in the system allows direct water influx. Either of these entry mechanisms results in ice formation, which separates the insulation and weather protection barrier from the pipe or vessel surface.

Many more scenarios must be considered, especially when the broad range of features required of a weather barrier are considered. Turner and Malloy (1981) define a weather barrier as "a material or materials, which, when installed on the outer surface of thermal insulation, protects the insulation from . . . rain, snow, sleet, wind, solar radiation, atmospheric contamination and mechanical damage." With this definition in mind, several service requirements must be considered.

- **Internal mechanical forces**: Expansion and contraction of the pipe or vessel must be considered because the resulting forces are transferred to the external surface of the weather barrier. Ability to slide, elongate, or contract must be provided.
- **External mechanical forces**: Mechanical abuse (i.e., tools being dropped, abrasion from wind-driven sand, personnel walking on the system) inflicted on a pipe or vessel needs to be considered in design. This may affect insulation type, as well as the weather barrier jacketing type.
- **Dimensional stability**: Some cellular materials can show irreversible dimensional change after installation. The manufacturers of these materials provide installation guidelines to minimize the effects of dimensional change. If guidelines are not followed, failure of joint seals can occur, which can lead to system failure.
- **Chemical resistance**: Some industrial environments may have airborne or spilled corrosive agents that accumulate on the weather barrier and chemically attack the pipe or vessel jacketing. Elements that create corrosive issues must be well understood and accounted for. Insulation design of coastal facilities should account for chloride attack.
- **Galvanic corrosion**: Contacts between two different types of metal must be considered for galvanic corrosion potential. Similarly, water can act as an electrolyte, and galvanic corrosion can occur because of the different potential of the pipe and vessel and a metal jacketing.
- **Insulation corrosivity**: Some insulation materials can cause metal jacket corrosion or chemically attack some polymer films. Both of these situations shorten service life.
- **Thermal degradation**: Hot systems are typically designed so that the surface temperature of the insulation and jacketing material do not exceed 60°C. The long-term effect of 60°C on the jacketing material must be considered. Additionally, there may be solar radiation load and perhaps parallel heat loss from an adjacent pipe. Turner and Malloy (1981) suggest that 120°C should be considered as the long-term operating temperature of the jacketing material

selected. This is a critical design consideration, particularly for a nonmetal jacket.

- **Installation and application logistics**: Often, the insulation contractor installs more insulation in a day than can be protected with jacket. If it rains, the exposed insulation gets saturated and, the next day, the jacket is installed over the wet insulation. This creates an obvious potential corrosion issue before the installation is operational, and must be corrected immediately. It should also be understood that the size, shape, and adjacent space available for work may dictate the type of weather barrier used, even if it is a less desirable option. If this is the case, the maintenance schedule must recognize and accommodate for this.
- **Maintenance**: The importance of a maintenance and inspection plan cannot be overemphasized to achieve the service life expected of the design.

Materials Used as Weather Barriers for Insulation. Metal rolls or sheets of various thicknesses are available with embossing, corrugation, moisture barriers, and different banding and closure methods. Elbows and tees are also available for piping. Typical metal jacketing materials are

- Bare aluminum
- Coated aluminum
- Stainless steel
- Painted steel
- Galvanized steel
- Aluminum-zinc coated steel

Polymeric (plastic) rolls or sheets are available at various thicknesses. These materials are glued or solvent-welded, depending on the polymer. Elbows and tees are also available for piping for some type of polymers. Typical polymeric (plastic) jacketing materials include

- Polyvinyl chloride (PVC)
- Polyvinyliedene chloride (PVDC)
- Polyisobutylene
- Multiple-layer composite materials (e.g., polymeric/foil/mesh laminates)
- Fabrics (silicone-impregnated fiberglass)

Numerous mastics are available. Mastics are often used with fiberglass cloth or canvas to encapsulate pipes, tanks, or other vessels; they are also used at insulation terminations and at or around protrusions such as valves or supports. It is important to choose the correct mastic for the application, considering surface temperature, insulation type, fire hazard classification, water resistance, and vapor permeability requirements. Mastics are brushed, troweled, or sprayed on the surface at a thickness recommended by the manufacturer.

Importance of Workmanship and Knowledge. Workmanship and knowledge are key to successful insulation weather barrier design. The importance of working with the installing contractor and material manufacturers regarding fitness for use of each material is paramount. The Midwest Insulation Contractors Association (MICA 1999) publishes an excellent resource regarding materials used as weather barriers: the *National Commercial and Industrial Insulation Manual*, in print and CD-ROM, is available from http://www.micainsulation.org/standards/manual.html.

Vapor Retarders

Water vapor control is extremely important for piping and equipment operating below ambient temperatures. These systems are typically insulated to prevent surface condensation and control heat gain. Piping and equipment typically create an absolute barrier to passage of water vapor, so any vapor-pressure difference imposed across the insulation system results in the potential for condensation at the cold surface. A high-quality vapor retarder material or system is essential for these systems to perform adequately. Research (Mumaw 2001) has shown that the design, installation, and performance of the vapor retarder systems are key to an insulation system's ability to minimize water vapor ingress.

Moisture-related problems include thermal performance loss, health and safety issues, structural degradation, and aesthetic issues. Water may enter the insulation system through water vapor diffusion, air leakage carrying water vapor, and leakage of surface water. A vapor retarder is a material or system that will adequately reduce the transmission of water vapor through the insulation system. The vapor retarder system is seldom intended to resist the entry of surface water or prevent air leakage, but can occasionally be considered the second line of defense for these moisture sources.

The performance of the vapor retarder material or system is characterized by its water vapor permeance. Chapter 23 has a thorough description of the physics associated with water vapor transport. Water vapor permeance can be evaluated per ASTM *Standard* E96 by imposing a vapor pressure difference across vapor retarder material that has been sealed to a test cup, and gravimetrically measuring the moisture gain or loss.

Faulty application can impair vapor retarder performance. The effectiveness of installation and application techniques must be considered when selecting a vapor retarder system. Factors such as vapor retarder structure, number of joints, mastics and adhesives that are used, and inspection procedures affect performance and durability.

The insulation system should be dry before application of a vapor retarder to prevent trapping water vapor in the system. The system must be protected from undue weather exposure that could introduce moisture into the insulation before the system is sealed.

When selecting a vapor retarder, the vapor pressure difference across the insulation system should be considered. Higher vapor pressure differences typically require a lower-permeance vapor retarder to control the overall moisture pickup of the system. Service conditions affect the direction and magnitude of the vapor pressure difference. Unidirectional flow exists when the water vapor pressure is constantly higher on one side of insulation system. Reversible flow exists when vapor pressure may be higher on either side, typically caused by diurnal or seasonal changes on one side of the system. Properties of insulating materials used should be considered. All materials reduce water vapor flow, but low-permeance insulations can add to the overall water vapor transport resistance of the insulation system. Some low-permeability materials are considered to be vapor retarders without any additional jacket material.

Vapor Retarder Jackets. There is some inconsistency in the nomenclature used for materials used as vapor retarders for pipe, tank, and equipment insulation. Designations such as *jacket*, *jacketing*, *facing,* and *all-service jacket* (*ASJ*) are all applied to this component, sometimes interchangeably. On the other hand, the vapor retarder component of insulation for air-handling systems, such as duct wrap and duct board, is typically referred to only as *facing*. The term *vapor diffusion retarder* (*VDR*) is also used to generically describe these materials.

In this chapter, *vapor retarder* denotes the vapor-retarding membrane of the system, but the reader should be aware of the various terms that may be encountered. In addition, some insulation materials (e.g., closed-cell foam materials with low water vapor permeability) are considered vapor retarders in themselves without any additional retarding membrane.

Vapor Retarders for Pipe, Tank, and Equipment Insulation. Materials or combinations of materials used for vapor retarders can take many different forms. Necessarily, one component must be a material that offers significant resistance to vapor passage. A commonly used preformed material for pipe, tank, and equipment vapor retarder applications is the lamination of white paper, reinforcing fiberglass scrim, and aluminum foil or metallized polyester film for the foil component. These products are generally referred to as **all-service jackets (ASJs)**, and meet the requirements of ASTM

Standard C1136, the accepted industry material standard for pipe insulation applications. These facings are commonly used as the outer finish in low-abuse indoor areas; elsewhere, they are covered by a protective metal or plastic jacket. Many types of insulation are supplied with factory-applied ASJ vapor retarders.

Note that ASJs may have service limitations on below-ambient systems in wet environments. Condensation on the surface (possibly caused by inadequate insulation thickness), or moisture migration under the ASJ (through breaches or holes), or liquid or water (from an outside source) can degrade the ASJ by mold growth on the paper and/or corrosion of the aluminum vapor retarder component.

In addition to traditional ASJ vapor retarders, low-permeance monolayer plastic film and sheet, laminations using heavy-gage foil, and other types of sheet structures are used in very-low-temperature applications. These are not typically referred to as ASJ, and are often procured separately from the insulation and applied in fabrication shops or in the field. Examples include polyethylene terephthalate (PET), polyvinyl chloride (PVC), and polyvinyliedene chloride (PVDC). They are typically used in more demanding applications, and often are covered by protective jacket. These facings generally meet the requirements of ASTM *Standard* C1136, Type IV, or ASTM *Standard* C921.

The moisture-sensitive nature of paper and the relative frailty of aluminum foil can be problematic in the potentially high-moisture environment of below-ambient applications. Exposure to water, either from condensation caused by inadequate insulation thickness or from ambient sources, can cause degradation and distortion of the paper, higher likelihood of mold growth, and foil corrosion, leading to vapor retarder failure. The presence of leachable chloride in flame-retardant ASJ structures can promote corrosion of the foil or metallized film. The anticipated trend in vapor retarders for pipe insulation is toward nonpaper structures, metallized films, and better-protected foil laminates.

For most common vapor retarder jackets, matching pressure-sensitive tapes are available for making joint and puncture seals. Mastics are available and used where fittings, supports, and other obstructions make a proper vapor seal difficult to achieve. Highly conformable tapes are sometimes used for this purpose, as well. Applied mastic systems are a vapor-retarding layer; they are often called **vapor barriers** by manufacturers, but their vapor resistance is a function of the thickness and quality of the mastic application. Also, some mastic may not be compatible with certain insulation types. For this reason, always consult the insulation manufacturer for recommendations on the correct type of vapor retarder to use in the application.

Below-ambient piping and equipment in general, and below-freezing applications in particular, are the most demanding applications for an insulation vapor retarder. Even though extremely low-permeance (as low as zero) vapor retarder materials exist, a perfect barrier in a system that is field-installed and includes numerous joints and penetrations is extremely difficult to achieve. It follows that adequate system design, proper insulation and jacketing material selection, and careful workmanship are all equally important.

Air-Handling Systems. Vapor retarders for equipment and duct insulation take various forms. Probably because of the relatively less severe and demanding conditions in air-handling systems, current vapor retarder materials seem to adequately meet these performance requirements. In general, moisture problems are not often encountered if insulation design is adequate for the application, and some low-permeability insulation materials are used without separate vapor retarders. For fiberglass duct wrap and duct board, a lamination of aluminum **foil, scrim, and kraft paper (FSK)** has long been the material of choice, although flexible vinyl and other white or black-colored facings are occasionally used. All of these facings can be procured separately in roll form, and used on any type of insulation. ASTM *Standard* C1136, Type II, is a typical specification for factory-applied vapor retarder on duct insulation (except flexible duct). Flexible (flex) ducting typically incorporates a plastic film or film lamination that contains a metallized substrate as a vapor-retarding component.

Application-specific pressure-sensitive tapes or mastics are usually used to seal joints. As in any cold system where a vapor retarder is required, design, materials, and workmanship must be properly addressed. The insulation manufacturer's recommendations should be followed.

INSTALLATION

Pipe Insulation

Small pipes can be insulated with cylindrical half-sections of rigid insulation or with preformed flexible material. Larger pipes can be insulated with flexible material or with curved, flat segmented, or cylindrical half, third, or quarter sections of rigid insulation, particularly where removal for frequent servicing of the pipe is necessary. Fittings (valves, tees, crosses, and elbows) use preformed fitting insulation, fabricated fitting insulation, individual pieces cut from sectional straight-pipe insulation, or insulating cements. Fitting insulations should always be equal in thermal performance to the pipe insulation.

Securing Methods. The method of securing varies with the type of insulation, size of pipe, form and weight of insulation, and type of jacketing (i.e., field- or factory-applied). Insulation with factory-applied jacketing can be secured on small piping by securing the overlapping jacket, which usually includes an integral sealing tape. Large piping may require supplemental wiring or banding. Insulation on large piping requiring separate jacketing is wired or banded in place, and the jacket is cemented, wired, or banded, depending on the type. Insulation with factory-applied metal or PVC jacketing is secured by specific design of the jacket and its joint closure. Flexible closed-cell materials require no jacket for most applications and are applied using specially formulated contact adhesives.

Insulating Pipe Hangers. All piping is held in place by hangers and supports. Selection and treatment of pipe hangers and supports can significantly affect thermal performance of an insulation system. Thus, it is important that the piping engineer and insulation specifier coordinate during project design to ensure that correct hangers are used and sufficient physical space is maintained to allow for the required thickness of insulation.

A typical **ring** or **line size** hanger is illustrated in Figure 5A. This type of hanger is commonly used on above-ambient lines at moderate temperature. However, it provides a thermal short circuit through the insulation, and the penetration is difficult to seal effectively against water vapor, so it is not recommended for below-ambient applications.

Pipe shoes (Figure 5B) are used for hot piping of large diameter (heavy weight) and where significant pipe movement is expected. The design allows for pipe movement without damage to the insulation or the finish. The design is not recommended for below-ambient applications because of the thermal short circuit and difficulty in vapor sealing.

A better solution is to use **clevis** hangers (Figure 5C), which are sized to allow clearance for the specified thickness of insulation, and avoid the short circuit associated with ring hangers. Shields (or saddles) spread the load from the pipe, its contents, and the insulation material over an area sufficient to support the system without significantly compressing the insulation material. Table 8 provides guidance on saddle lengths for fiberglass pipe insulation. For pipe sizes above 80 mm, it is recommended that high-density inserts (foam, high-density fiberglass, or wood blocks) be used. Table 9 gives recommended saddle lengths for 32 kg/m^3 polyisocyanurate foam insulation. Preinsulated saddles are available.

Insulation Finish for Above-Ambient Temperatures. Requirements for pipe insulation finishes for above-ambient applications

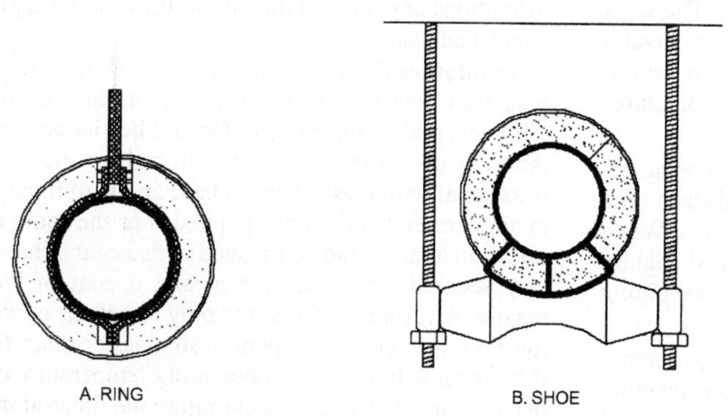

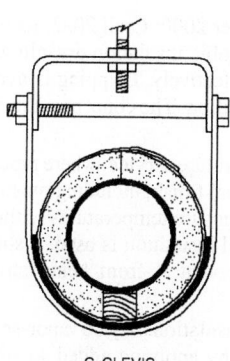

Fig. 5 Insulating Pipe Hangers

Table 8 Minimum Saddle Lengths for Use with Fibrous Glass Pipe Insulation*

Pipe Size, NPS	Insulation Thickness, mm	Minimum Saddle Length, mm — Hanger Spacing, m: 1.2	1.5	1.8	2.1	2.4	2.7	3.0	3.3	3.7
25	13	125	125	150	200					
	25	75	75	125	125					
	38	75	75	125	125					
	50	75	75	75	75					
	75	75	75	75	75					
50	13	150	200	200	275	275	300	350		
	25	125	125	150	200	225	275	275		
	38	125	125	150	200	200	225	225		
	50	125	125	125	150	150	200	200		
	75	125	125	125	150	150	150	200		
80	13			300	375	425	500	525	600	650
	25			275	300	375	425	450	500	575
	38			225	275	300	350	375	425	450
	50			225	225	275	300	350	350	375
	75			225	225	275	300	350	350	375

*For pipe sizes above 80 mm, use high-density inserts be used to support the pipe

Table 9 Minimum Saddle Lengths for Use with 32 kg/m³ Polyisocyanurate Foam Insulation (13 to 75 mm thick)

Pipe Size, NPS	Minimum Saddle Length,* mm, Hanger Spacing, m: 1.2	1.5	1.8	2.1	2.4	2.7	3.0	3.3	3.7
80	100	100	100	100	100	100	100	100	150
100	100	100	100	150	150	150	200	200	200
150	150	150	150	150	200	200	200	200	200
200	200	200	200	200	200	200	200	200	300
250	200	200	200	300	300	300	300	300	300
300	200	200	300	300	300	300	300	300	300
400	300	300	450	450	450	450	450	450	450

*22 gage hung; 20 gage setting.

are usually governed by location. Appearance and durability are the primary design considerations for indoor applications. For outdoor applications, finishes are provided primarily for weather protection. The finishes may be factory-applied jackets or field-applied metal or polymeric jackets.

Insulation Finish for Below-Ambient Temperatures. Piping at temperatures below ambient is insulated to limit heat gain and prevent condensation of moisture from the ambient air. Because metallic piping is an absolute barrier to water vapor, it becomes the condensing surface. Therefore, the outer surface of the insulation must be covered by an impervious membrane, or the insulation material itself must be highly resistant to water vapor diffusion.

Vapor retarders for straight pipe insulation are generally designed to meet operating temperature, fire safety, and appearance requirements. Flexible closed-cell materials are often installed without separate vapor retarders, relying on the low permeability of the insulation material to resist vapor flow, and must be carefully sealed or cemented to avoid gaps in insulation. Jacketing used as a vapor retarder may use various materials, alone or in combination, such as paper, aluminum foil, vacuum-metallized or low-permeance plastic films, and reinforcing. The most commonly used products have been ASJ (white), foil-reinforced kraft (FRK), metallized polyester film, or plastic sheeting. An important feature of such jacketing is very low permeance in a relatively thin layer, which provides flexibility for ease of cementing and sealing laps and end-joint strips. This type of jacketing is commonly used indoors without additional treatment. In some cases of operating temperatures below –18°C, multilayer insulation and jacketing may be used. With long lines of piping, insulation should be sealed off every 5 or 6 m with vapor stops to limit water penetration if vapor retarder damage occurs.

Insulation fittings are usually vapor-sealed by applying suitable materials in the field, and may vary with the type of insulation and operating temperature. For temperatures above –12°C, the vapor seal can be a lapped spiral wrap of plastic film adhesive tape or a relatively thin coat of vapor-seal mastic. For temperatures below –12°C, common practice is to double-wrap a very-low-permeance plastic film adhesive tape or apply two coats of vapor-seal mastic reinforced with open-weave glass or other fabric. Mastic thickness increases with decreasing temperature.

Insulated cold piping should receive special attention when exposed to ambient or unconditioned air. Because cold piping frequently operates year-round, a unidirectional vapor drive may exist. Even with vapor-retarding insulation, jackets, and vapor sealing of joints and fittings, moisture inevitably accumulates in permeable insulations. This not only reduces the thermal resistance of the insulation, it also accelerates condensation on the jacket surface with consequent dripping of water and possible growth of mold and mildew. Depending on local conditions, these problems can arise in less than 3 years, or as many as 30 years. Periodic insulation replacement should be considered, and the piping installation should be accessible for such replacement. Very-low-permeability insulating materials [e.g., materials not exceeding 0.15 ng/(s·m·Pa)] have been used to extend system life and reduce replacement frequency. The lower the insulation's permeability, the longer its life, given proper installation.

An alternative approach is to accept the inevitable water vapor ingress, and to provide a means of removing condensed water from the system. One means of accomplishing this is the use of a hydrophilic wicking material to remove condensed water from the surface of cold piping for transport (via the combination of capillary forces and gravity) outside the system where it can be evaporated to the ambient air (Brower 2000; Crall 2002; Korsgaard 1993). The wick keeps the hydrophobic insulation dry, allowing the thermal insulation to perform effectively. Dripping is avoided if ambient conditions allow evaporation. The concept is limited to pipe temperatures above freezing.

For dual-temperature service, where pipe operating temperatures cycle, the vapor-seal finish, including mastics, must withstand pipe movement and exposure temperatures without deterioration. When flexible closed-cell insulation is used, it should be applied slightly compressed to prevent it from being strained when the piping expands.

Outdoor pipe insulation may be vapor-sealed in the same manner as indoor piping, by applying added weather protection jacketing without damage to the vapor retarder and sealing it to keep out water. In some instances, heavy-duty weather and vapor-seal finish may be used. It is recommended that weather protection jackets installed over vapor retarders use bands or some other closure method that does not penetrate the weather protection jacketing.

Underground Pipe Insulation. Both heated and cooled underground piping systems are insulated. Protecting underground insulated piping is more difficult than protecting aboveground piping. Groundwater conditions, including chemical or electrolytic contributions by the soil and the existence of water pressure, require special design to protect insulated pipes from corrosion and maintain insulation thermal integrity. For optimal performance, walk-through tunnels, conduits, or integral protective coverings are generally provided to protect the pipe and insulation from water. Examples and general design features of conduits, tunnels, and direct burial systems can be found in Chapter 11 of the 2008 *ASHRAE Handbook—HVAC Systems and Equipment*.

Tanks, Vessels, and Equipment

Flat, curved, and irregular surfaces, such as tanks, vessels, boilers, and chimney connectors, are normally insulated with flexible or semirigid sheets or boards or rigid insulation blocks fabricated to fit the specific application. Tank and vessel head segments must be curved or flat cut to fit in single piece or segments per ASTM *Standard* C450. Head segments must be cut to eliminate voids at the head section, and in a minimum number of pieces to minimize joints. Prefabricated flat head sections should be installed in the same number of layers and thickness as the vessel walls, and void areas behind the flat head should be filled with packable insulation. Typically, the curved segments are fabricated to fit the contour of the vessel surface in equal pieces to go around the vessel with a minimum number of joints. Because no general procedure can apply to all materials and conditions, manufacturers' specifications and instructions must be followed for specific applications.

Securing Methods. Insulations are secured in various ways, depending on the form of insulation and contour of the surface to be insulated. Flexible insulations are adhered to tanks, vessels, and equipment using contact adhesive, pressure-sensitive adhesives, or other systems recommended by the manufacturers. The insulation's flexibility lends itself to curved surfaces. Rigid or semirigid insulations on small-diameter, cylindrical vessels can be prefabricated and adhered or mechanically attached, as appropriate. On larger cylindrical vessels, angle iron ledges to support the insulation against slippage can supplement banding. Where diameters exceed 3 to 4 m, slotted angle iron may be run lengthwise on the cylinder, at intervals around the circumference to secure and avoid an excessive length of banding.

Rigid and semirigid insulations can be secured on large flat and cylindrical surfaces by banding or wiring and can be supplemented by fastening with various welded studs at frequent intervals. On large flat, cylindrical, and spherical surfaces, it is often advantageous to secure the insulation by impaling it on welded studs or pins and fastening it with speed washers. Flexible closed-cell insulations are adhered directly to these surfaces, using a suitable contact adhesive.

Insulation Finish. Insulation finish is often required to protect insulation against mechanical damage and weather, consistent with acceptable appearance. On smaller indoor equipment, insulation is commonly covered with tightly stretched and secured hexagonal wire mesh. Then, a base and hard finish coat of cement is applied, and sometimes painted. For the same equipment outdoors, insulation can be finished with a coat of hard cement, properly secured hexagonal mesh, and a coat of weather-resistant mastic. A variation is to apply only two coats of weather-resistant mastic reinforced with open-mesh glass or other fabric; however, this finish is limited to an operating temperature of about 150°C, because metal expansion can rupture the finish at insulation joints. Larger equipment may be finished indoors and out with suitable sheet metal.

Outdoor finish is generally metal jacketing, properly flashed around penetrations (e.g., access openings, pipe connections, and structural supports) to maintain weathertightness. Various outdoor finishes are available for different types of insulations.

For below-ambient operating temperatures, insulation is finished, as required, to prevent condensation and protect against mechanical damage and weather, consistent with acceptable appearance. In accordance with the operating temperature, the finish must retard vapor to avoid moisture entry from surrounding air, which can increase the insulation's thermal conductivity or deterioration, or corrode the metal equipment surface.

Whenever a vapor retarder is required, all penetrations such as access openings, pipe connections, and structural supports must be properly treated with an appropriate vapor-retarder film, mastic, or other sealant. Equipment must be insulated from structural steel by isolating supports of high compressive strength and reasonably low thermal conductivity, such as a rigid insulation material or a hardwood block. The vapor retarder must carry over this insulation from the equipment to the supporting steel to ensure proper sealing.

If the equipment rests directly on steel supports, the supports must be insulated for some distance from the points of contact. Commonly, insulation and vapor retarder are extended 8 to 10 times the thickness of the insulation applied to the equipment.

For dual-temperature service, where vessels are alternately cold and hot, vapor retarder finish materials and design must withstand movement caused by temperature change.

Ducts

Ducts are used to convey air or process gases for several purposes. In general, their uses can be divided into process ducts and HVAC ducts. **Process ducts** can range from industrial hot exhaust to subambient process gases, and can be outdoors or inside. They can need insulation for various reasons, including thermal energy conservation, personnel protection, process control, condensation control and noise attenuation. Because of the wide range of possible operating temperatures and environmental conditions, selection of duct insulation and jacketings for industrial processes requires careful consideration of all operational, environmental, and human safety factors. Issues of energy conservation, personnel protection, condensation control, and process control can be solved by careful analysis of heat flow. Computer programs are available for calculating heat transfer, surface temperatures for personnel protection, condensation control, and economic thickness.

HVAC ducts carry air to conditioned spaces inhabited by people, animals, sensitive equipment, or a combination thereof. Thermal and acoustical duct insulation is one of the keys to a well-designed system that provides both occupant comfort and acceptable indoor air quality (IEQ). These insulation products help maintain a consistent air temperature throughout the system, reduce condensation, absorb system operation noise, and conserve energy.

Typical air temperatures for HVAC applications are 4 to 50°C. Because of the more moderate temperature ranges associated with HVAC applications, there is a wide range of insulation materials available. Where acoustical and thermal considerations are significant, sheet metal ducts are often internally insulated, or the ducts themselves are constructed of materials that form both the air-conveying duct and the insulation. Where acoustical concerns are not significant, sheet metal ducts can be externally insulated with rigid, semirigid, or flexible insulation materials. Again, another alternative is to use ducts that incorporate insulation as part of their construction. The determining factor in duct construction and insulation materials selection is often a combination of performance criteria and budgetary limitations.

The need for duct insulation is influenced by the

- Duct location (e.g., indoors or outdoors; conditioned, semiconditioned, or unconditioned space)
- Effect of heat loss or gain on equipment size and operating cost
- Need to prevent condensation on low-temperature ducts
- Need to control temperature change in long duct lengths
- Need to control noise transmitted within the duct or through the duct wall

All HVAC ducts exposed to outdoor conditions, as well as those passing through unconditioned or semiconditioned spaces, should be insulated. Analyses of temperature change, heat loss or gain and other factors affecting the economics of thermal insulation are essential for large commercial and industrial projects. ASHRAE *Standard* 90.1 and building codes set minimum standards for thermal efficiency, but economic thickness is often greater than the minimum. Additionally, the standards and codes do not address surface condensation issues. These considerations are often the primary driver of minimum thickness in unconditioned or semiconditioned locations subject to moderate or greater relative humidity.

Duct thermal efficiencies are generally regulated by local or national codes by specifying minimum thermal resistances, or R-values. These R-values are most often determined by testing per ASTM *Standards* C518 or C177, as required by the Federal Trade Commission (FTC) for reporting R-values of duct wrap insulations. Neither method allows for increased thermal resistance caused by convective or radiative surface effects. To comply with current code language, it is recommended that R-value requirements in specifications for duct insulation be based on *Standards* C177 or C518 testing at 24°C mean temperature and at the installed thickness of the insulation. Insulation products for ducts are available in a range of R-values, dependent predominantly on insulation thickness, but also somewhat on insulation density.

Temperature Control Calculations for Air Ducts. Duct heat gains or losses must be known for the calculation of supply air quantities, supply air temperatures, and coil loads (see Chapter 17 of this volume and Chapter 4 of the 2008 *ASHRAE Handbook—HVAC Systems and Equipment*). Heat loss programs based on ASTM *Standard* C680 may be used to calculate thermal energy transfer through the duct walls. Duct air exit temperatures can then be estimated using the following equations:

$$t_{drop} \text{ or } t_{gain} = 0.2\left(\frac{qPL}{VC_p\rho A}\right) \quad (3)$$

then, for warm air ducts,

$$t_{exit} = t_{enter} - t_{drop} \quad (4)$$

and for cold air ducts,

$$t_{exit} = t_{enter} - t_{gain} \quad (5)$$

where

t_{drop} = temperature loss for warm air ducts, K
t_{enter} = entering air temperature, K
t_{gain} = temperature rise for cool air ducts, K
t_{exit} = exit temperature for either warm or cool air ducts, °C
q = heat loss through duct wall, W/m²
P = duct perimeter, mm
L = length of duct run, m
V = air velocity in duct, m/s
C_p = specific heat of air, 1.006 kJ/(kg·K)
ρ = density of air, 1.20 kg/m³
A = area of duct, m²
0.2 = conversion factor for length, time units

Example 1. A 20 m length of 0.6 by 0.9 m uninsulated sheet metal duct, freely suspended, conveys heated air through a space maintained at 4°C. The ASTM *Standard* C680 heat loss calculation gives a heat transfer rate of 444 W/m². Based on heat loss calculations for the heated zone, 8.1 m³/s of standard air [c_p = 1006 J/(kg·K)] at a supply air temperature of 50°C is required. The duct is connected directly to the heated zone. Determine the temperature of the air entering the duct.

Solution: The area of the duct is 0.6 × 0.9 = 0.54 m².

Air velocity V is calculated as

$$\frac{\text{Volumetric flow}}{\text{Area}} = \frac{8.1}{0.54} = 15 \text{ m/s}$$

Duct perimeter P is

$$(0.6 + 0.9) \times 2 = 3 \text{ m}$$

Temperature drop t_{drop} is

$$\frac{444 \times 3 \times 20}{15 \times 1006 \times 1.20 \times 0.54} = 2.7 \text{ K}$$

Temperature of air entering the duct is thus

$$50 + 0.3 = 50.3°\text{C}$$

Example 2. Repeat Example 1, except the duct is insulated externally with 25 mm thick insulation material having a heat transfer rate of 44.7 W/m².

Solution: All values except q remain the same as in the previous example. Therefore, t_{drop} is

$$\frac{44.7 \times 3 \times 20}{15 \times 1006 \times 1.20 \times 0.54} = 0.27 \text{ K}$$

Temperature of air entering the duct is thus

$$50 + 0.3 = 50.3°\text{C}$$

Preventing Surface Condensation on Cool Air Ducts. Insulation also can prevent surface condensation on cool air ducts operating in warm and humid environments. This reduces the opportunity for microbial growth as well as other moisture-related building damage. Condensation forms on cold air-conditioning ducts anywhere the exterior surface temperature reaches the dew point. The moisture may remain in place or drip, causing moisture damage and creating a potential for microbial contamination.

Preventing surface condensation requires that sufficient thermal resistance be installed for the condensation design conditions. Figures 6 and 7 give installed R-value requirements to prevent surface condensation on insulated air ducts. The first chart (for emittance = 0.1) should be used for foil-faced insulation products. The second chart is based on materials with a surface emittance of 0.9. The

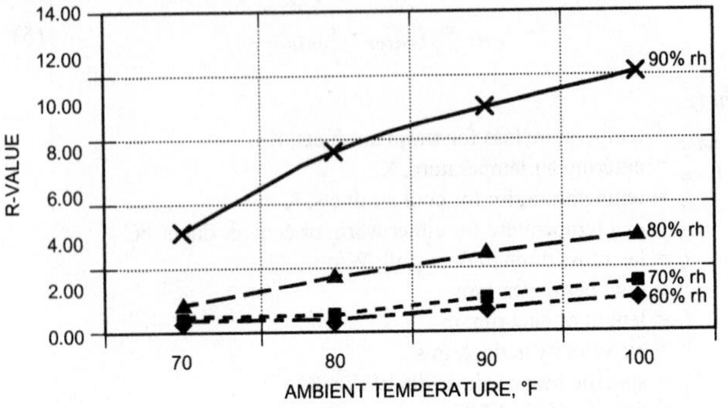

Fig. 6 R-Value Required to Prevent Condensation on Surface with Emittance ε = 0.1

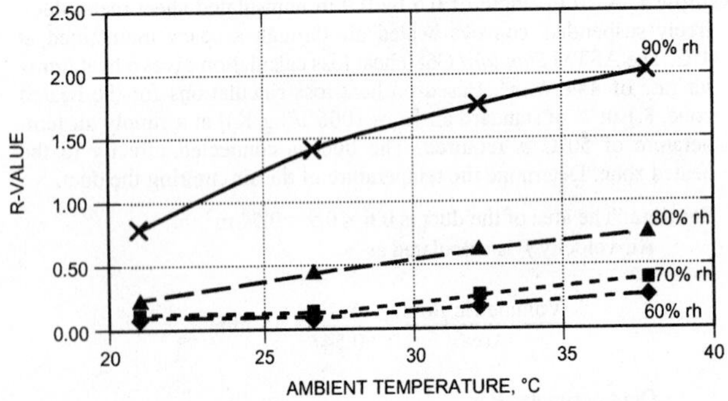

Fig. 7 R-Value Required to Prevent Condensation on Surface with Emittance ε = 0.9

designer must choose the appropriate environmental conditions for the location. It may be financially imprudent to design for the most extreme condition that could occur during a system's life, but it is also important to be aware that the worst-case condition for condensation control is not the maximum design load of coincident dry bulb and wet bulb. Rather, the worst case for condensation occurs when relative humidity is high, such as when the dry bulb is only very slightly above the wet bulb. This condition often occurs in the early morning in many climates.

For cold-duct applications, it is critical that water vapor not be allowed to enter the insulation system and condense on the cold duct surface. Once water begins to condense, loss of thermal efficiency is inevitable. This leads to further surface condensation on the surface of the insulation. To prevent this, exterior duct insulations must have a low vapor permeance. Permeance values of 0.1 perms or less are generally recommended for cold-duct applications. It is equally important that all exterior duct insulation joints are well sealed. Areas of special concern are often found around duct flanges, hangers, and other fittings.

Insulation Materials for HVAC Ducts. Insulated ducts in buildings can consist of insulated sheet metal, fibrous glass, or insulated flexible ducts, all of which provide combined air barrier, thermal insulation, and some degree of sound absorption. Ducts embedded in or below floor slabs may be of compressed fiber, ceramic tile, or other rigid materials. Depending on the insulation material, there are a number of standards that specify the material requirements.

Duct insulations include semirigid boards and flexible blanket types, composed of organic and inorganic materials in fibrous, cellular, or bonded particle forms. Insulations for exterior surfaces may have attached vapor retarders or facings, or vapor retarders may be applied separately. When applied to the duct interior as a liner, insulation both insulates thermally and absorbs sound. Duct liner insulations have sound-permeable surfaces on the side facing the airstream capable of withstanding duct design air velocities or duct cleaning without deterioration.

Abuse Resistance. One important consideration in the choice of external insulations for air ducts is abuse resistance. Some insulation materials have more abuse resistance than others, but most rigid insulations will not withstand high abuse such as foot traffic. In high-traffic locations, a combination of insulation and protective jacketings is required. In areas where the insulation is generally inaccessible to human contact, less rigid insulations are acceptable.

One important consideration for internal insulation abuse resistance is that, in large commercial units, it is common for maintenance personnel to enter and move around. In these instances, it is critical that structural elements be provided to keep foot traffic off the insulation.

Duct Airstream Surface Durability. One of the most important considerations in choosing internal duct insulations is resistance to air erosion. Each material has a maximum airflow velocity rating, which should be determined using an erosion test methodology in accordance with either UL *Standard* 181 or ASTM *Standard* C1071. Under these methods, the liner material is subjected to velocities that are two and one-half times the maximum rated air velocity. Air erosion testing should include evaluation of the insulation for evidence of erosion, cracking, or delamination.

Additionally, internal insulation must be resistant to aging effects in the air duct environment. Insulation materials have maximum temperatures for prolonged exposure, some codes impose temperature requirements. Ensure that the material selected will have no aging effects at either the anticipated maximum duct temperature or the temperature specified by the code bodies for the local jurisdiction.

Another durability concern is ultraviolet (UV) resistance. Ultraviolet-generating equipment is used to mitigate microbial activity. Determine, both from the UV equipment manufacturer as well as the insulation manufacturer, whether the anticipated UV exposure poses a threat to the insulation.

Duct Airflow Characteristics. Internal duct insulations and ducts that have insulation as part of their construction have increased frictional pressure loss characteristics compared to bare sheet metal. Generally, duct dimensions are oversized to compensate for the increased frictional pressure losses and the decrease in internal cross section caused by the insulation thickness. However, frictional losses are only part of the total static pressure loss in a duct; dynamic fitting losses should also be considered in any required resizing. Generally, internal linings conform to the shape of the fitting in which they are installed. For this reason, the insulated fitting is assumed to have the same dynamic pressure loss as the uninsulated fitting of the same dimension. See Chapter 21 for further details on frictional pressure loss characteristics of internal linings and how they affect pressure drop and duct-sizing requirements.

Securing Methods. Exterior rigid or flexible duct insulation can be attached with adhesive, with supplemental preattached pins and clips, or with wiring or banding. Individual manufacturers of these materials should be consulted for their installation requirements. Flexible duct wraps do not require attachment except on bottom duct panels more than 600 mm wide. For larger ducts, pins placed at a maximum spacing of 600 mm or less are sufficient. Internal liners are attached with adhesive and pins, in accordance with industry standards.

Leakage Considerations. To achieve the full thermal benefits of insulation, air ducts should be substantially sealed against leakage under operating pressure. The insulation material should not be counted on to provide leakage resistance, unless the insulation is part of the actual duct. Using the case in Example 1, 10% air leakage from an unsealed duct represents an energy loss of 1.66 times the energy lost through heat transfer through the entire 20 m of uninsulated duct. When that same 10% leakage is compared against an insulated duct, the energy lost through leakage is 15.3 times the losses through heat transfer through the insulation over the entire duct length.

Outdoor Applications. Insulated air ducts located outdoors generally require specific protection against the elements, including water, ice, hail, wind, ultraviolet exposure, vermin, birds, other animals, and mechanical abuse. Strategies for protecting externally insulated ducts located outdoors include protective metal jackets and glass fabric with weather barrier mastic. Note that most of these protective weather treatments do not replace the need for a vapor retarder for cold-duct applications.

Special Considerations.

Cooling-only ducts in cold climates. These applications generally occur in northern climates with ducts that run through unconditioned spaces such as attics. Warm air from the conditioned space enters through registers and into the unused ducts. This relatively moist air then condenses in the cold portions of the duct. Condensation encourages odor problems, mold growth, and degradation of the insulation. In the worst cases, water build-up becomes so excessive that water-soaked or frozen ducts can collapse and break through ceilings. The solution is to completely seal all entry points into the ducts, generally by sealing behind all registers, using a very good vapor retarder such as 0.2 mm polyethylene sheet.

Covering ducts with insulation in attics in hot and humid climates. In an effort to conserve energy, attic insulation levels have been increasing. Often, these attics are insulated with pneumatically applied loose fill insulation. If this insulation comes into contact with duct insulation, it could lower surface temperatures on the facing of the duct insulation below dew point during humid conditions. For this reason, it is important that the ducts be supported so that they are above the attic insulation. Many building codes in humid areas (e.g., Florida) require this, and it should be considered good practice in all humid climates.

DESIGN DATA

Estimating Heat Loss and Gain

Fundamentals of heat transfer are covered in Chapter 4, and the concepts are extended to insulation systems in Chapter 25. Steady-state, one-dimensional heat flow through insulation systems is governed by Fourier's law:

$$Q = -kA\,dT/dx \qquad (6)$$

where

Q = rate of heat flow, W
A = cross-sectional area normal to heat flow, m²
k = thermal conductivity of insulation material, W/(m·K)
dT/dx = temperature gradient, °C/m

For flat geometry of finite thickness, the equation reduces to

$$Q = kA(T_1 - T_2)/L \qquad (7)$$

where L is insulation thickness, in m

For radial geometry, the equation becomes:

$$Q = kA_2(T_1 - T_2)/[r_2 \ln(r_2/r_1)] \qquad (8)$$

where

r_1 = outer radius, m
r_2 = inner radius, m
A_2 = area of outer surface, m²

The term $r_2 \ln(r_2/r_1)$ is sometimes called the **equivalent thickness** of the insulation layer. Equivalent thickness is the thickness of insulation that, if installed on a flat surface, would equal the heat flux at the outer surface of the cylindrical geometry.

Heat transfer from surfaces is a combination of convection and radiation. Usually, these modes are assumed to be additive, and therefore a combined surface coefficient can be used to estimate the heat flow to and from a surface:

Table 10 Emittance Data of Commonly Used Materials

Material	Emittance ε at ~27°C
All-service jacket (ASJ)	0.9
Aluminum paint	0.5
Aluminum	
Anodized	0.8
Commercial sheet	0.1
Embossed	0.2
Oxidized	0.1 to 0.2
Polished	0.04
Aluminum-zinc coated steel	0.06
Canvas	0.7 to 0.9
Colored mastic	0.9
Copper	
Highly polished	0.03
Oxidized	0.8
Elastomeric or polyisobutylene	0.9
Galvanized steel	
Dipped or dull	0.3
New, bright	0.1
Iron or steel	0.8
Painted metal	0.8
Plastic pipe or jacket (PVC, PVDC, or PET)	0.9
Roofing felt and black mastic	0.9
Rubber	0.9
Silicon-impregnated fiberglass fabric	0.9
Stainless steel, new, cleaned	0.2

$$h_s = h_c + h_r \qquad (9)$$

where

h_s = combined surface coefficient, W/(m²·K)
h_c = convection coefficient, W/(m²·K)
h_r = radiation coefficient, W/(m²·K)

Assuming the radiant environment is equal to the ambient air temperature, the heat loss/gain at a surface can be calculated as

$$Q = h_s A(T_{surf} - T_{amb}) \qquad (10)$$

The radiation coefficient is usually estimated as

$$h_r = \varepsilon\sigma(T_{surf}^4 - T_{amb}^4)/(T_{surf} - T_{amb}) \qquad (11)$$

where

ε = surface emittance
σ = Stephen-Boltzmann constant, 5.67 × 10⁻⁸ W/(m²·K⁴)

Table 10 gives the approximate emittance of commonly used materials.

Controlling Surface Temperatures

A common calculation associated with mechanical insulation systems involves determining the thickness of insulation required to control the surface temperature to a certain value given the operating temperature of the process and the ambient temperature. For example, it may be desired to calculate the thickness of tank insulation required to keep the outside surface temperature at or below 60°C when the fluid in the tank is 232°C and the ambient temperature is 27°C.

At steady state, the heat flow through the insulation to the outside surface equals heat flow from the surface to the ambient air:

$$Q_{ins} = Q_{surf} \qquad (12)$$

or

$$(k/X)A(T_{hot} - T_{surf}) = hA(T_{surf} - T_{amb}) \qquad (13)$$

Rearranging this equation yields

$$X = (k/h)[(T_{hot} - T_{surf})/(T_{surf} - T_{amb})] \quad (14)$$

Because the ratio of temperature differences is known, the required thickness can be calculated by multiplying by the ratio of the insulation material conductivity to the surface coefficient.

For this example, assume the surface coefficient can be estimated as 5.7 W/(m²·K), and the conductivity of the insulation to be used is 0.036 W/(m·K). The required thickness can then be estimated as

$$X = \left(\frac{0.036}{5.7}\right)\left[\frac{(230-60)}{(60-27)}\right] = 0.032 \text{ m or } 32 \text{ mm} \quad (15)$$

This estimated thickness would be rounded up to the next available size, probably 38 mm.

For radial heat flow, the thickness calculated represents the equivalent thickness; the actual thickness ($r_2 - r_1$) is less, per Equation (8).

This simple procedure can be used as a first-order estimate. In reality, the surface coefficient is not constant, but varies as a function of surface temperature, air velocity, orientation, and surface emittance.

When performing these calculations, it is important to use the actual dimensions for the pipe and tubing insulation. Many (but not all) pipe and tubing insulation products conform to dimensional standards originally published by the U.S. Navy in *Military Standard* MIL-I-2781 and since adopted by other organizations, including ASTM. Standard pipe and insulation dimensions are given for reference in Table 11, and standard tubing and insulation dimensions in Table 12. Corresponding dimensional data for flexible closed-cell insulations are given in Tables 13 and 14.

For mechanical insulation systems, it is also important to realize that the thermal conductivity k of most insulation products varies significantly with temperature. Manufacturer's literature usually provides curves or tabulations of conductivity versus temperature. When performing heat transfer calculations, it is important to use the effective thermal conductivity, which can be obtained by integration of the conductivity versus temperature curve, or (as an approximation) using the conductivity evaluated at the meantemperature

Table 11 Inner and Outer Diameters of Standard Tubing Insulation

Tube Size, mm	Tube OD, mm	Insulation ID, mm	Insulation Nominal Thickness, mm: 25	38	50	63	75	88	100	113	125
10	12.7	13	60	89	114	141	168	—	—	—	—
15	15.9	16	73	89	114	141	168	—	—	—	—
20	22.2	23	73	102	127	168	194	219	244	273	298
25	28.6	29	73	102	127	168	194	219	244	273	298
32	34.9	35	89	114	141	168	194	219	244	273	298
40	41.3	42	89	114	141	168	194	219	244	273	298
50	54.0	55	102	127	168	194	219	244	273	298	324
65	66.7	68	114	141	168	194	219	244	273	298	324
80	79.4	80	127	168	194	219	244	273	298	324	356
90	92.1	93	141	168	194	219	244	273	298	324	356
100	105	106	168	194	219	244	273	298	324	356	381
125	130	131	194	219	244	273	298	324	356	381	406
150	156	157	219	244	273	298	324	356	381	406	432

Table 12 Inner and Outer Diameters of Standard Pipe Insulation

Pipe Size, mm	Pipe OD, mm.	Insulation ID, mm	Insulation Nominal Thickness, mm: 25	38	50	63	75	88	100	113	125
15	21.3	22	73	102	127	168	194	219	244	273	298
20	26.7	27	73	102	127	168	194	219	244	273	298
25	33.4	34	89	114	141	168	194	219	244	273	298
32	42.2	43	89	127	141	168	194	219	244	273	298
40	48.3	49	102	127	168	194	219	244	273	298	324
50	60.3	61	114	141	168	194	219	244	273	298	324
65	73.0	74	127	168	194	219	244	273	298	324	356
80	88.9	90	141	168	194	219	244	273	298	324	356
90	102	102	168	194	219	244	273	298	324	356	356
100	114	115	168	194	219	244	273	298	324	356	381
115	127	128	194	219	244	273	298	324	356	381	381
125	141	143	194	219	244	273	298	324	356	381	406
150	168	170	219	244	273	298	324	356	381	406	432
175	194	196	—	273	298	324	356	381	406	432	457
200	219	221	—	298	324	356	381	406	432	457	483
225	244	246	—	324	356	381	406	432	457	483	508
250	273	275	—	356	381	406	432	457	483	508	533
275	298	300	—	381	406	432	457	483	508	533	559
300	324	326	—	406	432	457	483	508	533	559	584
350	356	358	—	432	457	483	508	533	559	584	610

Table 13 Inner and Outer Diameters of Standard Flexible Closed-Cell Pipe Insulation

Pipe Size, mm	Pipe OD, mm	Insulation ID, mm	Insulation OD, mm Insulation Nominal Thickness, mm 13	19	25
15	21.3	24.6	47.5	62.7	75.4
20	26.7	28.7	51.6	66.8	79.5
25	33.4	36.6	62.0	74.7	87.4
32	42.2	45.2	70.6	85.9	96.0
40	48.3	51.6	77.0	92.2	102
50	60.3	63.5	88.9	104	114
65	73.0	76.2	102	117	127
80	88.9	94.0	118	134	146
90	102	107	135	150	163
100	114	119	149	163	175
125	141	146	174	189	202
150	168	173	201	217	229
200	219	224	252	267	—

Table 14 Inner and Outer Diameters of Standard Flexible Closed-Cell Tubing Insulation

Tube Nominal Size, mm	Tube OD, mm	Insulation ID, mm	Insulation OD, mm Insulation Nominal Thickness, mm 13	19	25
10	12.7	15.2	38.1	49.5	—
15	15.9	19.1	41.9	54.0	69.9
20	22.2	25.4	49.5	63.5	76.2
25	28.6	31.8	56.4	72.4	82.6
32	34.9	38.1	63.5	78.7	88.9
40	41.3	44.5	69.9	85.1	95.3
50	54.0	57.2	82.6	97.8	108
65	66.7	69.9	95.3	110	121
80	79.4	82.6	108	123	133
90	92.1	95.3	123	138	151
100	105	108	136	151	164

Table 15 Heat Loss from Bare Steel Pipe to Still Air at 27°C, W/m

Nominal Pipe Size, mm	Pipe Inside Temperature, °C 82	138	193	249	304
15	54.1	133	234	362	524
20	65.5	160	285	441	640
25	79.3	195	346	538	781
32	98.1	241	429	668	971
40	110	272	484	756	1100
50	135	336	599	936	1360
65	161	400	714	1120	1630
80	193	480	856	1350	1960
90	219	543	971	1520	2220
100	244	607	1090	1700	2490
115	270	670	1200	1880	2750
125	301	747	1340	2100	3070
150	354	880	1580	2480	3620
175	405	1000	1810	2840	4140
200	455	1130	2030	3190	4670
225	505	1260	2250	3540	5190
250	560	1390	2510	3940	5770
300	660	1640	2950	4640	6820
350	718	1790	3210	5060	7420
400	817	2040	3660	5770	8450
450	916	2290	4100	6470	9490
500	1020	2530	4550	7170	10 500
600	1210	3030	5440	8570	12 600

Table 16 Heat Loss from Bare Copper Tube to Still Air at 27°C, W/m

Nominal Pipe Size, mm	Pipe Inside Temperature, °C 49	66	82	99	116
10	10.2	19.8	30.7	42.5	55.3
15	12.2	23.7	36.7	51.0	66.5
20	16.1	31.4	48.7	67.7	88.3
25	19.9	38.9	60.5	84.1	110
32	23.6	46.4	72.0	100	131
40	27.4	53.7	83.5	116	152
50	34.7	68.3	106	148	193
65	42.0	82.7	129	180	235
80	49.2	97.1	151	210	276
90	56.4	112	173	241	316
100	63.5	125	195	272	357
125	77.8	153	238	334	436
150	91.9	181	283	394	517
200	120	237	368	515	676
250	148	291	455	635	833
300	176	346	540	756	991

across the insulation layer. ASTM *Standard* C680 provides the algorithms and calculation methodologies for incorporating these equations in computer programs.

These complications are readily handled for a variety of boundary conditions using available computer programs, such as the NAIMA 3E Plus® program [available as a download from the Web site of the North American Insulation Manufacturers Association (NAIMA), www.naima.org].

Estimates of the heat loss from bare pipe and tubing are given in Tables 15 and 16. These are useful for quickly estimating the cost of lost energy from uninsulated piping.

PROJECT SPECIFICATIONS

The importance of a well-prepared specification to meet energy conservation objectives is paramount. Specifications should

- Identify systems and equipment that must be insulated
- Identify precisely the materials selected, including thickness and jacketing, etc.
- Define the procedure for submitting alternative materials and systems
- Specify installation requirements
- Describe procedures to ensure the job is done correctly
- Comply with regional and national building codes

Although each of these steps is important, identifying systems that must be insulated is critical. When defining the materials to be used, it is important to specify them exactly, while allowing for submission of generic equivalents or value-engineered materials. Overspecifying materials limits potentially good options, and underspecifying may allow underperforming materials to be used. A proper balance is needed, and specifying key properties is required. Specifying installation requirements is as important as specifying the correct materials. Specifying procedures for submittals and quality control at the job will ensure correctness.

Reference standards from ASHRAE, ASTM, MICA, and others should be incorporated into the specifications; this practice saves time with respect to specification development, and shortens the specification considerably. Specifications that are not reviewed and updated periodically can perpetuate old technologies, obsolete materials, and fall out of code compliance.

Essentially all manufacturers of mechanical insulation products offer guide specifications for their products. These documents are insightful and offer credible information about specific products and the accessories commonly used with them. These documents are widely available on manufacturers' Web sites.

ASHRAE Learning Institute (ALI) offers training on mechanical insulation to assist in system design and specification construction. The program closely relates to this chapter and provides information on how to design and specify the insulation systems for mechanical equipment, piping, and ductwork. Specifically, the training is designed to familiarize students with

- The concept of insulation as a "system," one that requires careful design and specificity to perform to expectations.
- The multiple, detailed steps involved in insulation system design and product selection.
- Critical installation requirements to include in the specification.
- Using ASHRAE tools and other software programs to quantify economic, energy, and environmental benefits of well-designed and specified insulation systems.

More information on ALI training can be found at http://www.ashrae.org/education/page/554.

STANDARDS

ANSI/ASHRAE

Standard 90.2-2007	Energy-Efficient Design of Low-rise Residential Buildings

ANSI/ASHRAE/IESNA

Standard 90.1-2007	Energy Standard for Buildings Except Low-rise Residential Buildings

ASTM

Standard 165-00	Test Method for Measuring Compressive Properties of Thermal Insulations
C177-04	Test Method for Steady-State Heat Flux Measurements and Thermal Transmission Properties by Means of the Guarded-hot-plate Apparatus
C355-04	Test Method for Steady-State Heat Transfer Properties of Horizontal Pipe Insulation
C411-04	Test Method for Hot-Surface Performance of High-Temperature Thermal Insulation
C423-02a	Test Method for Sound Absorption and Sound Absorption Coefficients by the Reverberation Room Method
C450-02	Practice for Fabrication of Thermal Insulating Fitting Covers for NPS Piping, and Vessel Lagging
C518-04	Test Method for Steady-State Thermal Transmission Properties by Means of the Heat Flow Meter Apparatus
C533-04	Specification for Calcium Silicate Block and Pipe Thermal Insulation
C534-03	Specification for Preformed Flexible Elastomeric Cellular Thermal Insulation in Sheet and Tubular Form
C547-03	Specification for Mineral Fiber Pipe Insulation
C552-03	Specification for Cellular Glass Thermal Insulation
C553-02	Specification for Mineral Fiber Blanket Thermal Insulation for Commercial and Industrial Applications
C578-04A	Specification for Rigid, Cellular Polystyrene Thermal Insulation
C585-90(2004)	Practice for Inner and Outer Diameters of Rigid Thermal Insulation for Nominal Sizes of Pipe and Tubing (NPS System)
C591-01	Specification for Unfaced Preformed Rigid Cellular Polyisocyanurate Thermal Insulation
C612-04	Specification for Mineral Fiber Block and Board Thermal Insulation
C680-04e1	Practice for Estimate of the Heat Gain or Loss and the Surface Temperatures of Insulated Flat, Cylindrical, and Spherical Systems by Use of Computer Programs
795-03	Specification for Thermal Insulation for Use in Contact with Austentic Stainless Steel
C921-03a	Practice for Determining the Properties of Jacketing Materials for Thermal Insulation
C1055-99	Guide for Heated System Surface Conditions That Produce Contact Burn Injuries
C1071-00	Specification for Fibrous Glass Duct Lining Insulation (Thermal and Sound Absorbing Material)
C1126-04	Specification for Faced or Unfaced Rigid Cellular Phenolic Thermal Insulation
C1136-03	Specification for Flexible Low Permeance Vapor Retarders for Thermal Insulation
C1427-99a	Specification for Preformed Flexible Cellular Polyolefin Thermal Insulation in Sheet and Tubular Form
D1621-04a	Test Method for Compressive Properties of Rigid Cellular Plastics
E84-05	Test Method for Surface Burning Characteristics of Building Materials
E96-00	Test Methods for Water Vapor Transmission of Materials
E119-00a	Test Methods for Fire Tests of Building Construction and Materials
E136-04	Test Method for Behavior of Materials in a Vertical Tube Furnace at 750°C
E795-00	Practice for Mounting Test Specimens during Sound Absorption Tests
E1222-90(2002)	Test Method for Laboratory Measurement of the Insertion Loss of Pipe Lagging Systems
E1529-00	Test Methods for Determining Effects of Large Hydrocarbon Pool Fires on Structural Members and Assemblies
E2231-02	Practice for Specimen Preparation and Mounting of Pipe and Duct Insulation Materials to Assess Surface Burning Characteristics

MICA

1999	*National Commercial and Industrial Insulation Standards*, 5th ed.

NACE

RP0198-2004	The Control of Corrosion under Thermal Insulation and Fireproofing Materials—A Systems Approach

NFPA

Standard 90A	Installation of Air-Conditioning and Ventilating Systems
90B	Installation of Warm Air Heating and Air-Conditioning Systems
255	Method of Test of Surface Burning Characteristics of Building Materials
259	Test Method for Potential Heat of Building Materials

UL/UL Canada

Standard 181	Factory-Made Air Ducts and Air Connectors
CAN/ULC-S101	Methods of Fire Endurance Tests of Building Construction and Materials
CAN/ULC-S102	Method of Test for Surface Burning Characteristics of Building Materials and Assemblies

CAN4-S114-1980 Method of Test for Determination of Non-Combustibility in Building Materials (Rev 1997)

U.S. Navy

Standard MIL-1-2781 Insulation, Pipe, Thermal

REFERENCES

Brower, G. 2000. A new solution for controlling water vapor problems in low temperature insulation systems. *Insulation Outlook* (September).

Crall, G.C.P. 2002., The use of wicking technology to manage moisture in below ambient insulation systems. *Insulation Materials, Testing and Applications*, vol. 4, pp. 326-334, A.O. Desjarlais and R.R. Zarr, eds. ASTM STP 1426. American Society for Testing and Materials, West Conshohocken, PA.

Gordon, J. 1996. An investigation into freezing and bursting water pipes in residential construction. *Research Report* 90-1. University of Illinois Building Research Council.

Hart, G. 2006. Thermal insulation coatings (TICs): How effective are they as insulation? *Insulation Outlook* (July).

Korsgaard, V. 1993. Innovative concept to prevent moisture formation and icing of cold pipe insulation. *ASHRAE Transactions* 99(1):270-273.

Kuntz, H.L. and R.M. Hoover. 1987. The interrelationship between the physical properties of fibrous duct lining materials and lined duct sound attenuation (RP-478). *ASHRAE Transactions* 93(2).

Marion, W. and K. Urban. 1995. *User's manual for TMY2's typical meteorological years*. National Renewable Energy Laboratory, Golden, CO.

Miller, W.S. 2001. Acoustical lagging systems. *Insulation Outlook* (April): 41-46.

Mumaw, J.R. 2001. Below ambient piping insulation systems. *Insulation Outlook* (September).

Mumaw, J.R., 2002. A test protocol for comparison of the moisture absorption behavior of below-ambient piping insulation systems operating in hot-humid environments. *Insulation Materials: Testing and Applications*, vol. 4, pp. 176-186, A.O. Desjarlais and R.R. Zarr, eds. ASTM STP 1426. American Society for Testing and Materials, West Conshohocken, PA.

Turner, W.C. and J.F. Malloy. 1981. *Thermal insulation handbook*. Robert E. Kreiger Publishing, McGraw Hill Book Company, New York.

CHAPTER 24

AIRFLOW AROUND BUILDINGS

AIRFLOW around buildings affects worker safety, process and building equipment operation, weather and pollution protection at inlets, and the ability to control indoor temperature, humidity, air motion, and contaminants. Wind causes variable surface pressures on buildings that change intake and exhaust system flow rates, natural ventilation, infiltration and exfiltration, and interior pressures. The mean flow patterns and turbulence of wind passing over a building can recirculate exhaust gases to air intakes. This chapter provides basic information for evaluating windflow patterns, estimating wind pressures, and identifying problems caused by the effects of wind on intakes, exhausts, and equipment. In most cases, detailed solutions are addressed in other chapters. Related information can be found in Chapters 11, 14, 16, and 36 of this volume; in Chapters 29, 30, 44, 46, and 52 of the 2007 *ASHRAE Handbook—HVAC Applications*; and in Chapters 29, 34, and 39 of the 2008 *ASHRAE Handbook—HVAC Systems and Equipment.*

FLOW PATTERNS

Buildings having even moderately complex shapes, such as L- or U-shaped structures, can generate flow patterns too complex to generalize for design. To determine flow conditions influenced by surrounding buildings or topography, wind tunnel or water channel tests of physical scale models, tests of existing buildings, or careful computational modeling efforts are required (see the section on Physical and Computational Modeling). Only isolated, rectangular block buildings are discussed here. English and Fricke (1997), Hosker (1984, 1985), Khanduri et al. (1998), Saunders and Melbourne (1979), and Walker et al. (1996) review the effects of nearby buildings.

As wind impinges on a building, airflow separates at the building edges, generating recirculation zones over downwind surfaces (roof, side and downwind walls) and extending into the downwind wake (Figure 1). On the upwind wall, surface flow patterns are largely influenced by approach wind characteristics. Figure 1 shows that the mean speed of wind U_H approaching a building increases with height H above the ground. Higher wind speed at roof level causes a larger pressure on the upper part of the wall than near the ground, which leads to **downwash** on the lower one-half to two-thirds of the building. On the upper one-quarter to one-third of the building, windflow is directed upward over the roof (**upwash**). For a building with height H three or more times width W of the upwind face, an intermediate stagnation zone can exist between the upwash and downwash regions, where surface streamlines pass horizontally around the building, as shown in Figures 1 (inset) and 2. (In Figure 2, the upwind building surface is "folded out" to illustrate upwash, downwash, and stagnation zones.) Downwash on the lower surface of the upwind face separates from the building before it reaches ground level and moves upwind to form a vortex that can generate high velocities close to the ground ("area of strong surface wind" in

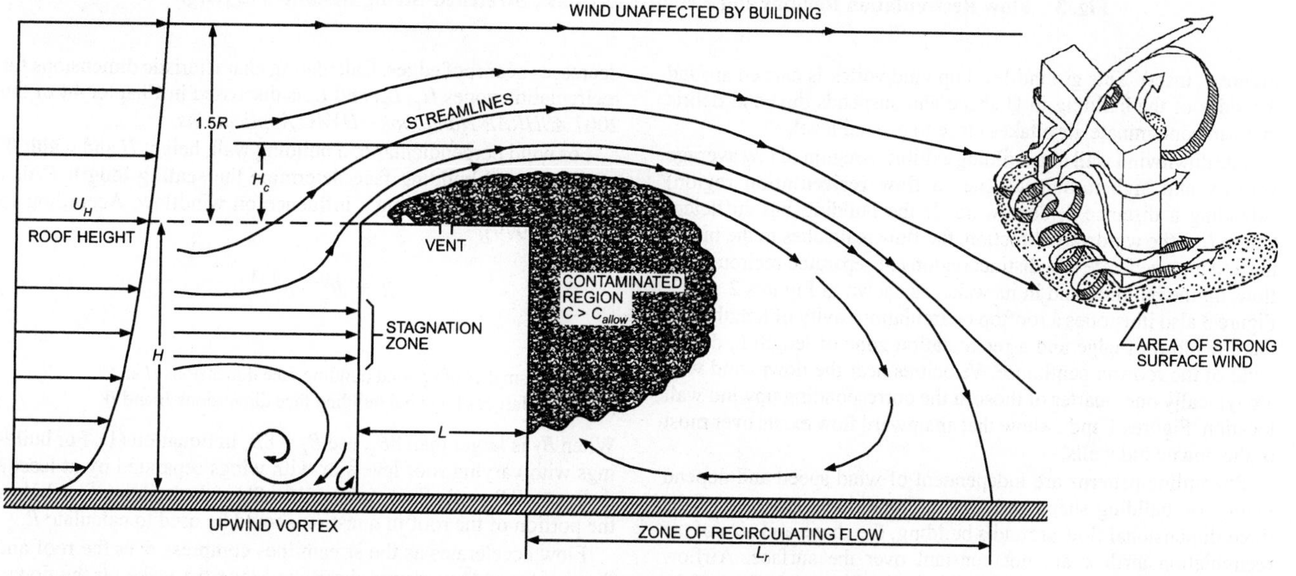

Fig. 1 Flow Patterns Around Rectangular Building

The preparation of this chapter is assigned to TC 4.3, Ventilation Requirements and Infiltration.

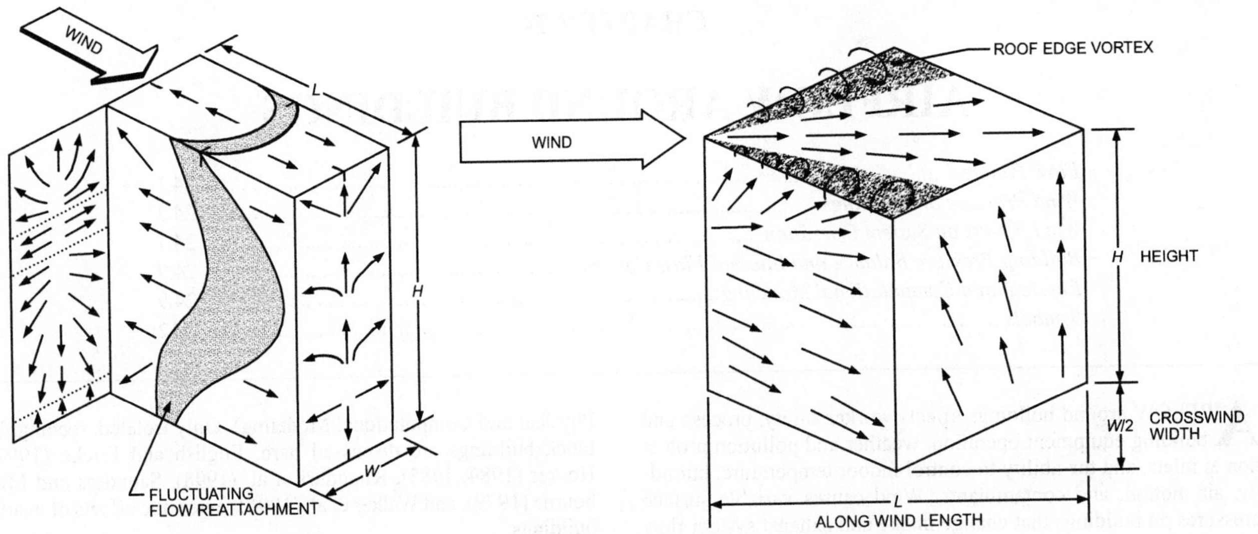

Fig. 2 Surface Flow Patterns for Normal and Oblique Winds
(Wilson 1979)

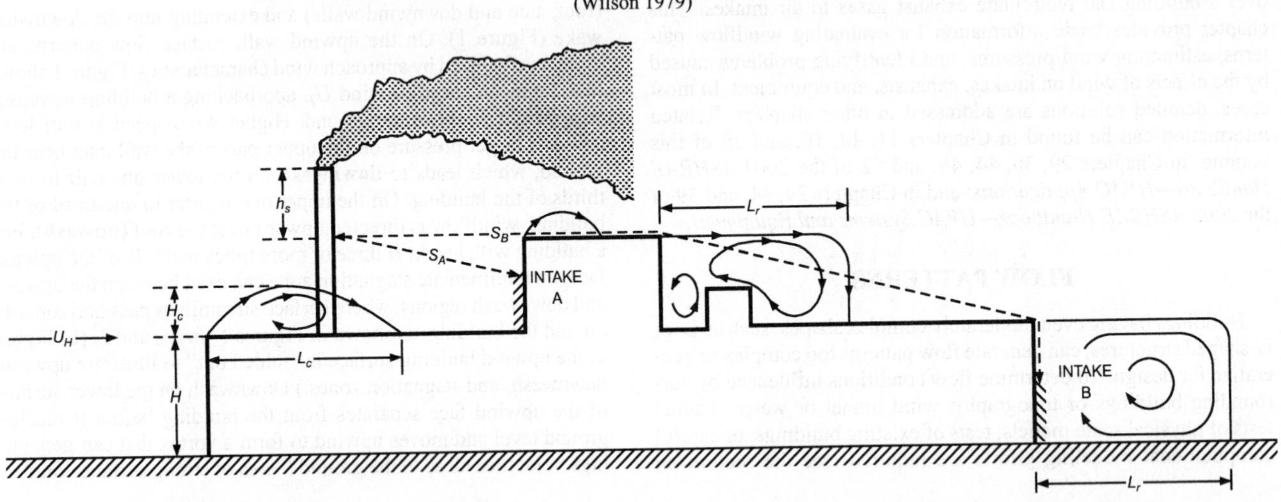

Fig. 3 Flow Recirculation Regions and Exhaust-to-Intake Stretched-String Distances (S_A, S_B)

Figure 1, inset). This ground-level upwind vortex is carried around the sides of the building in U shape and suspends dust and debris that can contaminate air intakes close to ground level.

The downwind wall of a building exhibits a region of low average velocity and high turbulence (i.e., a **flow recirculation** region) extending a distance L_r downwind. If the building has sufficient length L in the windward direction, the flow reattaches to the building and may generate two distinct regions of separated recirculation flow, on the building and in its wake, as shown in Figures 2 and 3. Figure 3 also illustrates a rooftop recirculation cavity of length L_c at the upwind roof edge and a recirculation zone of length L_r downwind of the rooftop penthouse. Velocities near the downwind wall are typically one-quarter of those at the corresponding upwind wall location. Figures 1 and 2 show that an upward flow exists over most of the downwind walls.

Streamline patterns are independent of wind speed and depend mainly on building shape and upwind conditions. Because of the three-dimensional flow around a building, the shape and size of the recirculation airflow are not constant over the surface. Airflow reattaches closer to the upwind building face along the edges of the building than it does near the middle of the roof and sidewalls (Figure 2). Recirculation cavity height H_c (Figures 1 and 3) also decreases near roof edges. Calculating characteristic dimensions for recirculation zones H_c, L_c, and L_r is discussed in Chapter 44 of the 2007 *ASHRAE Handbook—HVAC Applications*.

For wind perpendicular to a building wall, height H and width W of the upwind building face determine the **scaling length *R*** that characterizes the building's influence on windflow. According to Wilson (1979),

$$R = B_s^{0.67} B_L^{0.33} \quad (1)$$

where

B_s = smaller of upwind building face dimensions H and W
B_L = larger of upwind building face dimensions H and W

When B_L is larger than $8B_s$, use $B_L = 8B_s$ in Equation (1). For buildings with varying roof levels or with wings separated by at least a distance of B_s, only the height and width of the building face below the portion of the roof in question should be used to calculate R.

Flow accelerates as the streamlines compress over the roof and decelerates as they spread downward over the wake on the downwind side of the building. The distance above roof level where a building influences the flow is approximately $1.5R$, as shown in

Figure 1. In addition, roof pitch also begins to affect flow when it exceeds about 15° (1:4). When roof pitch reaches 20° (1:3), flow remains attached to the upwind pitched roof and produces a recirculation region downwind of the roof ridge that is larger than that for a flat roof.

If the angle of the approach wind is not perpendicular to the upwind face, complex flow patterns result. Strong vortices develop from the upwind edges of a roof, causing strong downwash onto the roof (Figure 2). High speeds in these vortices (vorticity) cause large negative pressures near roof corners that can be a hazard to roof-mounted equipment during high winds. When the angle between the wind direction and the upwind face of the building is less than about 70°, the upwash/downwash patterns on the upwind face of the building are less pronounced, as is the ground-level vortex shown in Figure 1. Figure 2 shows that, for an approach flow angle of 45°, streamlines remain close to the horizontal in their passage around the sides of the building, except near roof level, where the flow is sucked upward into the roof edge vortices (Cochran 1992).

Both the upwind velocity profile shape and its turbulence intensity strongly influence flow patterns and surface pressures (Melbourne 1979).

WIND PRESSURE ON BUILDINGS

In addition to flow patterns described previously, the turbulence or gustiness of approaching wind and the unsteady character of separated flows cause surface pressures to fluctuate. Pressures discussed here are time-averaged values, with an averaging period of about 600 s. This is approximately the shortest time period considered to be a "steady-state" condition when considering atmospheric winds; the longest is typically 3600 s. Instantaneous pressures may vary significantly above and below these averages, and peak pressures two or three times the mean values are possible. Although peak pressures are important with regard to structural loads, mean values are more appropriate for computing infiltration and ventilation rates. Time-averaged surface pressures are proportional to wind velocity pressure p_v given by Bernoulli's equation:

$$p_v = \frac{\rho_a U_H^2}{2} \tag{2}$$

where

U_H = approach wind speed at upwind wall height H, m/s [see Equation (4)]

ρ_a = ambient (outdoor) air density, kg/m^3

The proportional relationship is shown in the following equation, in which the difference p_s between the pressure on the building surface and the local outdoor atmospheric pressure at the same level in an undisturbed wind approaching the building is

$$p_s = C_p p_v \tag{3}$$

where C_p is the local wind pressure coefficient at a point on the building surface.

The local wind speed U_H at the top of the wall that is required for Equation (2) is estimated by applying terrain and height corrections to the hourly wind speed U_{met} from a nearby meteorological station. U_{met} is generally measured in flat, open terrain (i.e., category 3 in Table 1). The anemometer that records U_{met} is located at height H_{met}, usually 10 m above ground level. The hourly average wind speed U_H (Figures 1 and 3) in the undisturbed wind approaching a building in its local terrain can be calculated from U_{met} as follows:

$$U_H = U_{met}\left(\frac{\delta_{met}}{H_{met}}\right)^{a_{met}}\left(\frac{H}{\delta}\right)^a \tag{4}$$

Table 1 Atmospheric Boundary Layer Parameters

Terrain Category	Description	Exponent *a*	Layer Thickness δ, m
1	Large city centers, in which at least 50% of buildings are higher than 25 m, over a distance of at least 0.8 km or 10 times the height of the structure upwind, whichever is greater	0.33	460
2	Urban and suburban areas, wooded areas, or other terrain with numerous closely spaced obstructions having the size of single-family dwellings or larger, over a distance of at least 460 m or 10 times the height of the structure upwind, whichever is greater	0.22	370
3	Open terrain with scattered obstructions having heights generally less than 9 m, including flat open country typical of meteorological station surroundings	0.14	270
4	Flat, unobstructed areas exposed to wind flowing over water for at least 1.6 km, over a distance of 460 m or 10 times the height of the structure inland, whichever is greater	0.10	210

The atmospheric boundary layer thickness δ and exponent a for the local building terrain and a_{met} and δ_{met} for the meteorological station are determined from Table 1. Typical values for meteorological stations (category 3 in Table 1) are $a_{met} = 0.14$ and $\delta_{met} = 270$ m. The values and terrain categories in Table 1 are consistent with those adopted in other engineering applications (e.g., ASCE *Standard* 7). Equation (4) gives the wind speed at height H above the average height of local obstacles, such as buildings and vegetation, weighted by the plan-area. At heights at or below this average obstacle height (e.g., at roof height in densely built-up suburbs), speed depends on the geometrical arrangement of the buildings, and Equation (4) is less reliable.

An alternative mathematical description of the atmospheric boundary layer, which uses a logarithmic function, is given by Deaves and Harris (1978). Although their model is more complicated than the power law used in Equation (4), it more closely models the real physics of the atmosphere and has been adopted by several foreign codes (e.g., SA/SNZ *Standard* AS/NZS 1170.2 from Australia).

Example 1. Assuming a 10 m/s anemometer wind speed for a height H_{met} of 10 m at a nearby airport, determine the wind speed U_H at roof level $H = 15$ m for a building located in a city suburb.

Solution: From Table 1, the atmospheric boundary layer properties for the anemometer are a_{met} = 0.14 and δ_{met} = 270 m. The atmospheric boundary layer properties at the building site are $a = 0.22$ and δ = 370 m. Using Equation (4), wind speed U_H at 15 m is

$$U_H = 10\left(\frac{270}{10}\right)^{0.14}\left(\frac{15}{370}\right)^{0.22} = 7.8 \text{ m/s}$$

Local Wind Pressure Coefficients

Values of the mean local wind pressure coefficient C_p used in Equation (3) depend on building shape, wind direction, and influence of nearby buildings, vegetation, and terrain features. Accurate determination of C_p can be obtained only from wind tunnel model tests of the specific site and building or full-scale tests. Ventilation rate calculations for single, unshielded rectangular buildings can be reasonably estimated using existing wind tunnel data. Many wind load codes (e.g., ASCE *Standard* ASCE/SEI 7-05, SA/SNZ *Standard* AS/NZS 1170.2) give mean pressure coefficients for common building shapes.

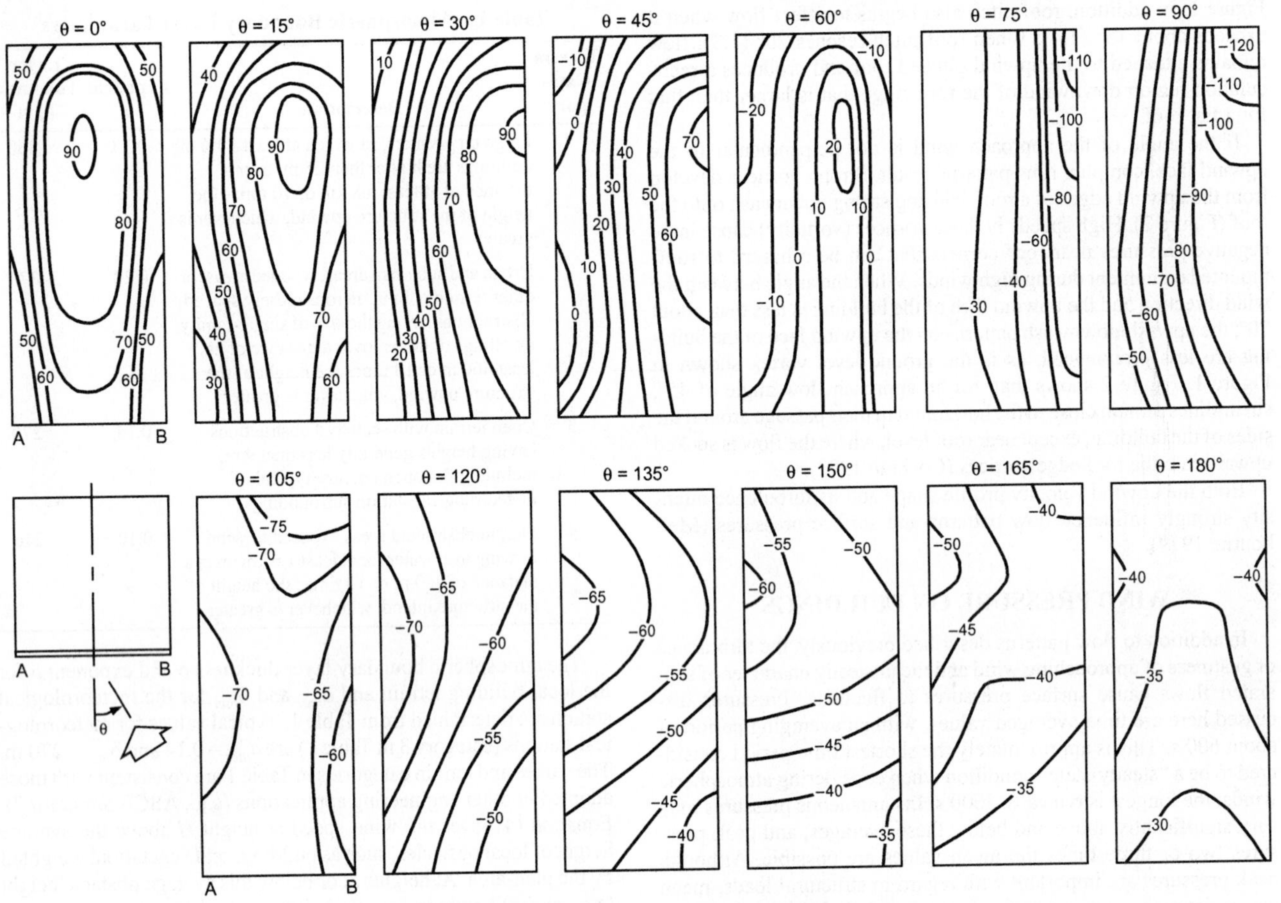

Fig. 4 Local Pressure Coefficients ($C_p \times 100$) for Tall Building with Varying Wind Direction
(Davenport and Hui 1982)

Figure 4 shows pressure coefficients for walls of a tall rectangular cross section building (high-rise) sited in urban terrain (Davenport and Hui 1982). Figure 5 shows pressure coefficients for walls of a low-rise building (Holmes 1986). Generally, for high-rise buildings, height H is more than three times the crosswind width W. For $H > 3W$, use Figure 4; for $H < 3W$, use Figure 5. At a wind angle $\theta = 0°$ (e.g., wind perpendicular to the face in question), pressure coefficients are positive, and their magnitudes decrease near the sides and the top as flow velocities increase.

As seen in Figure 4, C_p generally increases with height, which reflects increasing velocity pressure in the approach flow as wind speed increases with height. As wind direction moves off normal ($\theta = 0°$), the region of maximum pressure occurs closer to the upwind edge (B in Figure 4) of the building. At a wind angle of $\theta = 45°$, pressures become negative at the downwind edge (A in Figure 4) of the front face. At some angle θ between 60° and 75°, pressures become negative over the whole front face. For $\theta = 90°$, maximum suction (negative) pressure occurs near the upwind edge (B in Figure 4) of the building side and then recovers towards a lower-magnitude negative coefficient as the downwind edge (A in Figure 4) is approached. The degree of this recovery depends on the length of the side in relation to the width W of the structure. For wind angles larger than $\theta = 100°$, the side is completely within the separated flow of the wake and spatial variations in pressure over the face are not as great. The average pressure on a face is positive for wind angles from $\theta = 0°$ to almost 60° and negative (suction) for $\theta = 60°$ to 180°.

A similar pattern of behavior in wall pressure coefficients for a low-rise building is shown in Figure 5. Here, recovery from strong suction with distance from the upwind edge is more rapid.

Surface-Averaged Wall Pressures

Surface-averaged pressure coefficients may be used to determine ventilation and/or infiltration rates, as discussed in Chapter 16. Figure 6 shows the surface pressure coefficient C_s averaged over a complete wall of a low-rise building (Swami and Chandra 1987). The figure also includes values calculated from pressure distributions in Figure 5. Similar results for a tall building are shown in Figure 7 (Akins et al. 1979).

The wind-induced indoor/outdoor pressure difference is found using the coefficient $C_{p\,(in\text{-}out)}$, which is defined as

$$C_{p\,(in\text{-}out)} = C_p - C_{in} \qquad (5)$$

where C_{in} is the internal wind-induced pressure coefficient. For uniformly distributed air leakage sites in all the walls, C_{in} is about –0.2, as can be found easily by integration.

Roof Pressures

Surface pressures on the roof of a low-rise building depend strongly on roof slope. Figure 8 shows typical distributions for a wind direction normal to a side of the building. Note that the direction and magnitude of pressure coefficients are indicated by the direction and length of the arrows. For very low slopes (less than about 10°), pressures are negative over the whole roof surface. The magnitude is greatest within the separated flow zone near the leading edge and recovers toward the free stream pressure downwind of the edge. For intermediate slopes (about 10 to 20°), two large-magnitude low-pressure regions are formed, one at the leading roof edge and one at the roof peak. For steeper slopes (greater than about 20°), pressures are weakly positive on the upwind slope and

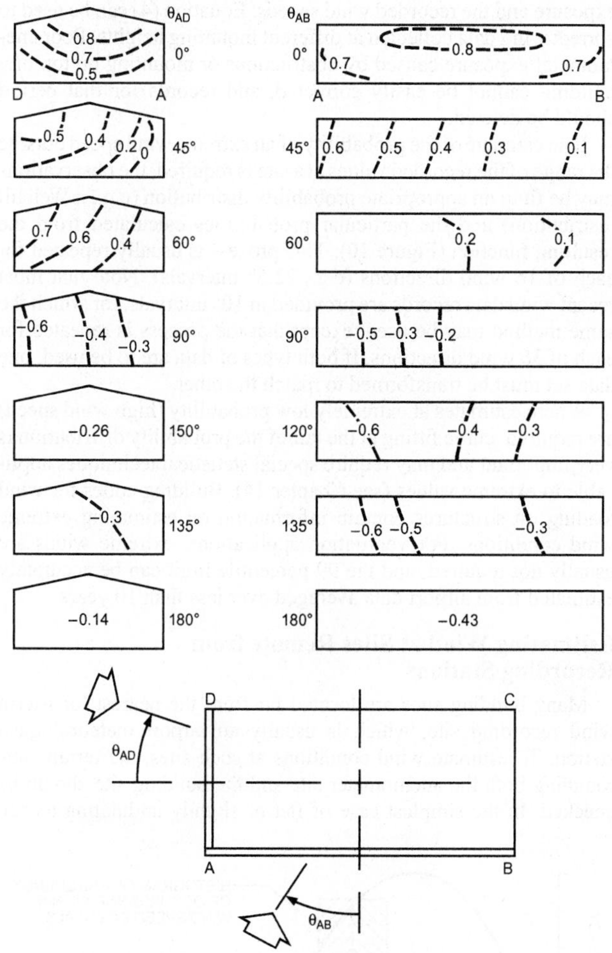

Fig. 5 Local Pressure Coefficients for Walls of Low-Rise Building with Varying Wind Direction

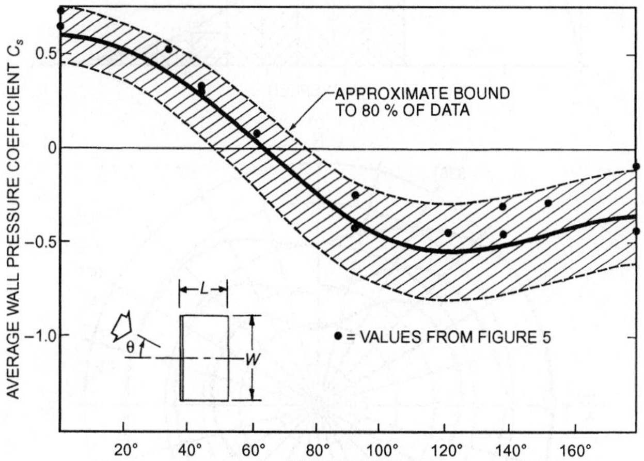

Fig. 6 Variation of Surface-Averaged Wall Pressure Coefficients for Low-Rise Buildings
Courtesy of Florida Solar Energy Center
(Swami and Chandra 1987)

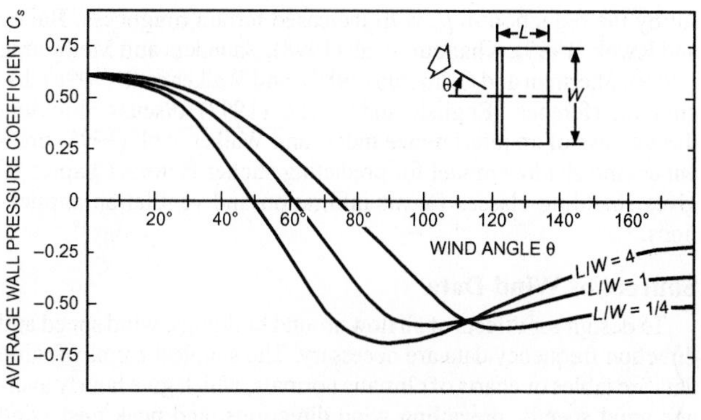

Fig. 7 Surface-Averaged Wall Pressure Coefficients for Tall Buildings
(Akins et al. 1979)

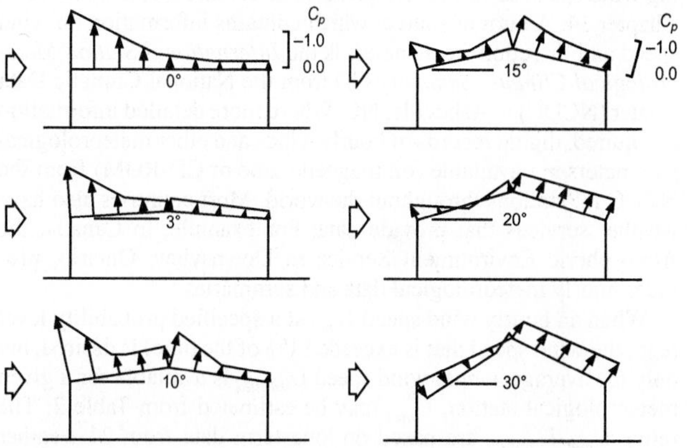

Fig. 8 Local Roof Pressure Coefficients for Roof of Low-Rise Buildings
(Holmes 1986)

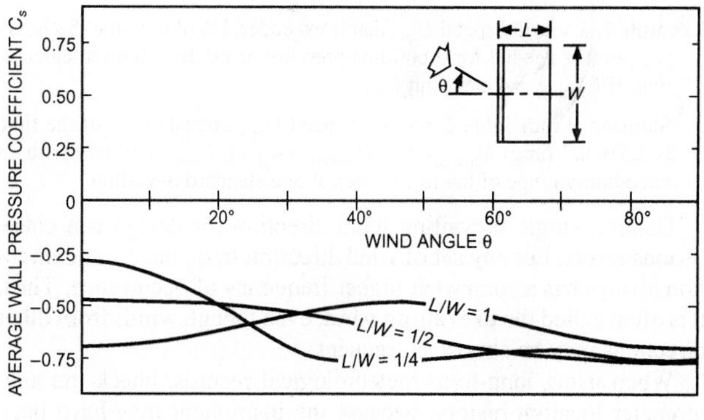

Fig. 9 Surface-Averaged Roof Pressure Coefficients for Tall Buildings
(Akins et al. 1979)

negative within the separated flow over the downwind slope. With a wind angle of about 45°, the vortices originating at the leading corner of a roof with a low slope can induce very large, localized negative pressures (see Figure 2). A similar vortex forms on the downwind side of a leading ridge end on a steep roof, as discussed in Cochran et al. (1999). Roof corner vortices and how to disrupt their influence are discussed in Cochran and Cermak (1992) and Cochran and English (1997). Figure 9 shows the average pressure coefficient over the roof of a tall building (Akins et al. 1979).

Interference and Shielding Effects on Pressures

Nearby structures strongly influence surface pressures on both high- and low-rise buildings, particularly for spacing-to-height ratios less than five, where distributions of pressure shown in Figures 4 to 9 do not apply. Although the effect of shielding for low-rise buildings is still significant at larger spacing, it is largely accounted for by the reduction in p_v with increased terrain roughness. Bailey and Kwok (1985), Khanduri et al. (1998), Saunders and Melbourne (1979), Sherman and Grimsrud (1980), and Walker et al. (1996) discuss interference. English and Fricke (1997) discuss shielding through use of an interference index, and Walker et al. (1996) present a wind shadow model for predicting shelter factors. Chapter 16 gives shielding classes for air infiltration and ventilation applications.

Sources of Wind Data

To design for effects of airflow around buildings, wind speed and direction frequency data are necessary. The simplest forms of wind data are tables or charts of climatic normals, which give hourly average wind speeds, prevailing wind directions, and peak gust wind speeds for each month. This information can be found in sources such as *The Weather Almanac* (Bair 1992) and the *Climatic Atlas of the United States* (DOC 1968). Climatic design information, including wind speed at various frequencies of occurrence, is included in Chapter 14. A current source, which contains information on wind speed and direction frequencies, is the *International Station Meteorological Climatic Summary* CD from the National Climatic Data Center (NCDC) in Asheville, NC. Where more detailed information is required, digital records of hourly winds and other meteorological parameters are available (on magnetic tape or CD-ROM) from the NCDC for stations throughout the world. Most countries also have weather services that provide data. For example, in Canada, the Atmospheric Environment Service in Downsview, Ontario, provides hourly meteorological data and summaries.

When an hourly wind speed U_{met} at a specified probability level (e.g., the wind speed that is exceeded 1% of the time) is desired, but only the average annual wind speed U_{annual} is available for a given meteorological station, U_{met} may be estimated from Table 2. The ratios U_{met}/U_{annual} are based on long-term data from 24 weather stations widely distributed over North America. At these stations, U_{annual} ranges from 3.1 to 6.3 m/s The uncertainty ranges listed in Table 2 are one standard deviation of the wind speed ratios. The following example demonstrates the use of Table 2.

Example 2. The wind speed U_{met} that is exceeded 1% of the time (88 hours per year) is needed for a building pressure or exhaust dilution calculation. If U_{annual} = 4 m/s, find U_{met}.

Solution: From Table 2, the wind speed U_{met} exceeded 1% of the time is 2.5 ± 0.4 times U_{annual}. For U_{annual} = 4 m/s, U_{met} is 10 m/s with an uncertainty range of 8.4 to 11.6 m/s at one standard deviation.

Using a single prevailing wind direction for design can cause serious errors. For any set of wind direction frequencies, one direction always has a somewhat higher frequency of occurrence. Thus, it is often called the **prevailing wind**, even though winds from other directions may be almost as frequent.

When using long-term meteorological records, check the anemometer location history, because the instrument may have been relocated and its height varied. This can affect its directional exposure and the recorded wind speeds. Equation (4) can be used to correct wind data collected at different mounting heights. Poor anemometer exposure caused by obstructions or mounting on top of a building cannot be easily corrected, and records for that period should be deleted.

If an estimate of the probability of an extreme wind speed outside the range of the recorded values at a site is required, the observations may be fit to an appropriate probability distribution (e.g., a Weibull distribution) and the particular probabilities calculated from the resulting function (Figure 10). This process is usually repeated for each of 16 wind directions (e.g., 22.5° intervals). Note that most recent wind data records are provided in 10° intervals, for which the same method may be used, except that the process is repeated for each of 36 wind directions. If both types of data are to be used, one data set must be transformed to match the other.

Where estimates at extremely low probability (high wind speed) are required, curve fitting at the tail of the probability distribution is very important and may require special statistical techniques applicable to extreme values (see Chapter 14). Building codes for wind loading on structures contain information on estimating extreme wind conditions. For ventilation applications, extreme winds are usually not required, and the 99 percentile limit can be accurately estimated from airport data averaged over less than 10 years.

Estimating Wind at Sites Remote from Recording Stations

Many building sites are located far from the nearest long-term wind recording site, which is usually an airport meteorological station. To estimate wind conditions at such sites, the terrain surrounding both the anemometer site and the building site should be checked. In the simplest case of flat or slightly undulating terrain

Table 2 Typical Relationship of Hourly Wind Speed U_{met} to Annual Average Wind Speed U_{annual}

Percentage of Hourly Values That Exceed U_{met}	Wind Speed Ratio U_{met}/U_{annual}
90%	0.2 ± 0.1
75%	0.5 ± 0.1
50%	0.8 ± 0.1
25%	1.2 ± 0.15
10%	1.6 ± 0.2
5%	1.9 ± 0.3
1%	2.5 ± 0.4

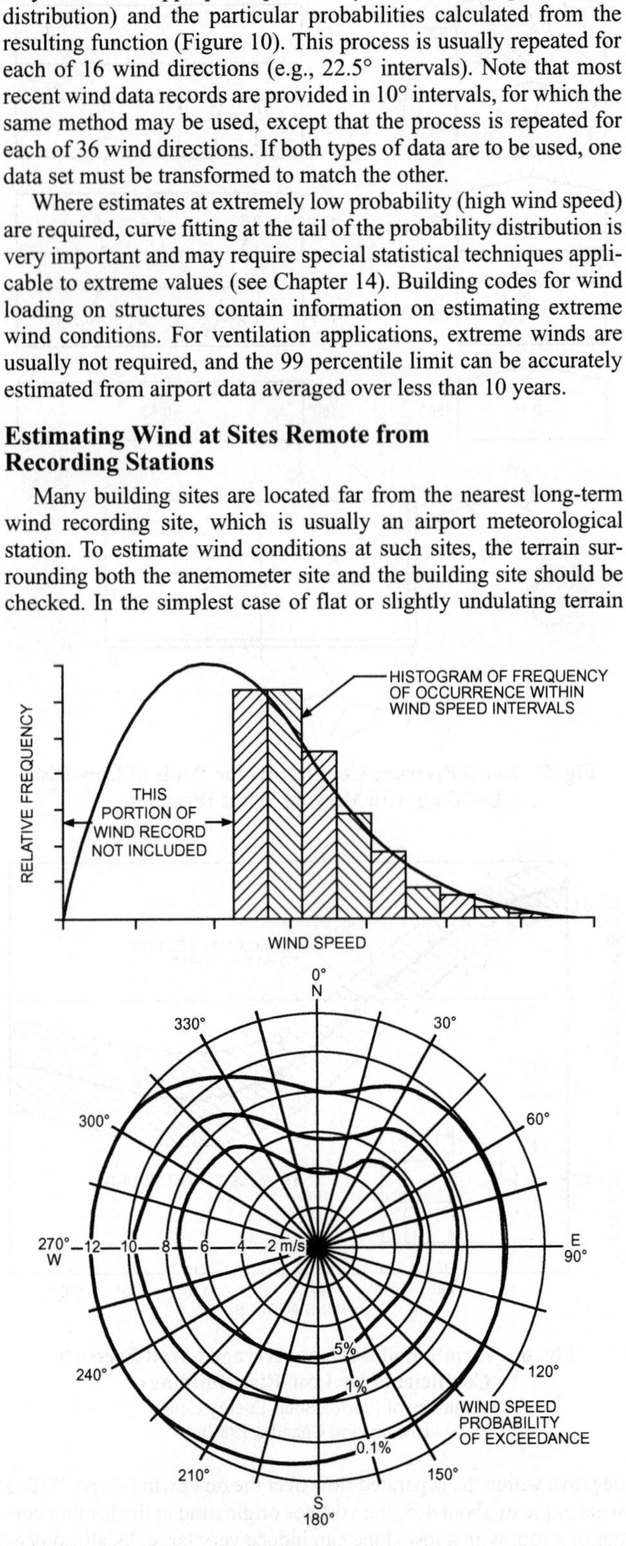

Fig. 10 Frequency Distribution of Wind Speed and Direction

with few obstructions extending for large distances around and between the anemometer site and building site, recorded wind data can be assumed to be representative of that at the building site. Wind direction occurrence frequency at a building site should be inferred from airport data only if the two locations are on the same terrain, with no terrain features that could alter wind direction between them.

In cases where the only significant difference between the anemometer site terrain and the building site terrain is surface roughness, the mean wind speed can be adjusted using Equation (4) and Table 1, to yield approximate wind velocities at the building site. Wind direction frequencies at the site are assumed to be the same as at the recording station.

In using Equation (4), cases may be encountered where, for a given wind direction, the terrain upwind of either the building or recording site does not fall into just one of the categories in Table 1. The terrain immediately upwind of the site may fall into one category, while that somewhat further upwind falls into a different category. For example, at a downtown airport the terrain may be flat and open (category 3) immediately around the recording instrument, but urban or suburban (category 2) a relatively short distance away. This difference in terrains also occurs when a building or recording site is in an urban area near open water or at the edge of town. In these cases, the suggested approach is to use the terrain category most representative of the average condition within approximately 1.6 km upwind of the site (Deaves 1981). If the average condition is somewhere between two categories described in Table 1, the values of a and δ can be interpolated from those given in the table.

Several other factors are important in causing wind speed and direction at a building site to differ from values recorded at a nearby meteorological station. Wind speeds for buildings on hillcrests or in valleys where the wind is accelerated or channeled can be 1.5 times higher than meteorological station data. Wind speeds for buildings sheltered in the lee of hills and escarpments can be reduced to 0.5 times the values at nearby flat meteorological station terrain.

Solar heating of valley slopes can cause light winds of 1 to 4 m/s to occur as warm air flows upslope. At night, radiant cooling of the ground can produce similar speeds as cold air drains downslope. In general, rolling terrain experiences a smaller fraction of low speeds than nearly flat terrain.

When wind is calm or light in the rural area surrounding a city, urban air tends to rise in a buoyant plume over the city center. This rising air, heated by anthropogenic sources and higher solar absorption in the city, is replaced by air pushed toward the city center from the edges. In this way, the urban heat island can produce light wind speeds and direction frequencies significantly different than those at a rural meteorological station.

In more complex terrain, both wind speed and direction may be significantly different from those at the distant recording site. In these cases, building site wind conditions should not be estimated from airport data. Options are either to establish an on-site wind recording station or to commission a detailed wind tunnel correlation study between the building site and long-term meteorological station wind observations.

WIND EFFECTS ON SYSTEM OPERATION

A building with only upwind openings is under a positive pressure (Figure 11A). Building pressures are negative when there are only downwind openings (Figure 11B). A building with internal partitions and openings (Figure 11C) is under various pressures, depending on the relative sizes of openings and wind direction. With larger openings on the upwind face, the building interior tends toward positive pressure; the reverse is also true (see Figures 4 to 9, and Chapter 16).

With few exceptions, building intakes and exhausts cannot be located or oriented such that a prevailing wind ensures ventilation and air-conditioning system operation. Wind can assist or hinder inlet and exhaust fans, depending on their positions on the building, but even in locations with a predominant wind direction, the ventilating system must perform adequately for all other directions. To avoid variable system flow rates, use Figures 4, 5, and 8 as a guide to placing inlets and exhausts in locations where surface pressure coefficients do not vary greatly with wind direction.

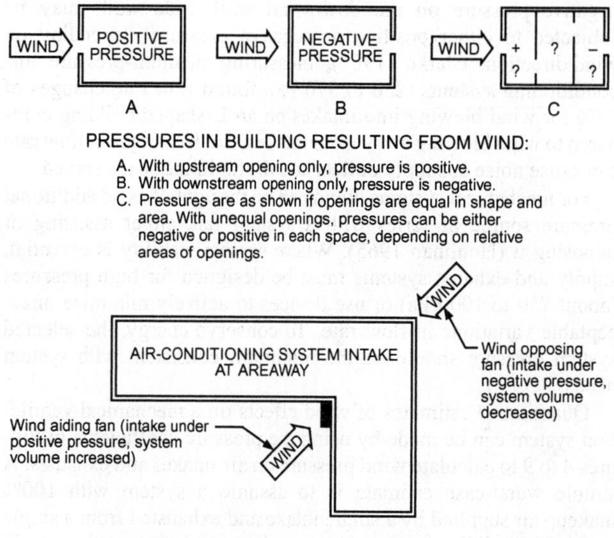

WIND
POSITIVE PRESSURE
WIND
NEGATIVE PRESSURE
WIND
+
?
–
?
?
A
B
C
PRESSURES IN BUILDING RESULTING FROM WIND:
A. With upstream opening only, pressure is positive.
B. With downstream opening only, pressure is negative.
C. Pressures are as shown if openings are equal in shape and area. With unequal openings, pressures can be either negative or positive in each space, depending on relative areas of openings.
WIND
AIR-CONDITIONING SYSTEM INTAKE AT AREAWAY
Wind opposing fan (intake under negative pressure, system volume decreased)
Wind aiding fan (intake under positive pressure, system volume increased)
WIND

Fig. 11 Sensitivity of System Volume to Locations of Building Openings, Intakes, and Exhausts

Airflow through a wall opening results from differential pressures, which may exceed 125 Pa during high winds. Supply and exhaust systems, openings, dampers, louvers, doors, and windows make building flow conditions too complex for direct calculation. Iterative calculations are required because of the nonlinear dependence of volume flow rate on the differential pressure across an opening. Several multizone airflow models are available for these iterative calculations (Feustel and Dieris 1992; Walton and Dols 2005). Opening and closing of doors and windows by building occupants add further complications. In determining $C_{p(in\text{-}out)}$ from Equation (5), wind direction is more important than the position of an opening on a wall, as shown in Figures 4 and 5. Refer to Chapter 16 for details on wind effects on building ventilation, including natural and mechanical systems.

Cooling towers and similar equipment should be oriented to take advantage of prevailing wind directions, if possible, based on careful study of meteorological data and flow patterns on the building for the area and time of year.

Natural and Mechanical Ventilation

With natural ventilation, wind may augment, impede, or sometimes reverse the airflow through a building. For flat roof areas with large along-wind sides, wind can reattach to the roof downwind of the leading edge (see Figure 2). For peaked roofs, the upwind slope may be positively pressurized while the downwind slope may be negatively pressurized, as shown in Figure 8. Thus, any natural ventilation openings could see either a positive or negative pressure, dependent on wind speed and direction. Positive pressure existing where negative pressures were expected could reverse expected natural ventilation. These reversals can be avoided by using stacks, continuous roof ventilators, or other exhaust devices in which flow is augmented by wind.

Mechanical ventilation is also affected by wind conditions. A low-pressure wall exhaust fan (12 to 25 Pa) can suffer drastic reduction in capacity. Flow can be reduced or reversed by wind pressure on upwind walls, or increased substantially when subjected to negative pressure on the downwind wall. Side walls may be subjected to either positive or negative pressure, depending on wind direction. Clarke (1967), measuring medium-pressure air-conditioning systems (250 to 370 Pa), found flow rate changes of 25% for wind blowing into intakes on an L-shaped building compared to wind blowing away from intakes. Such changes in flow rate can cause noise at supply outlets and drafts in the space served.

For mechanical systems, wind can be thought of as an additional pressure source in series with a system fan, either assisting or opposing it (Houlihan 1965). Where system stability is essential, supply and exhaust systems must be designed for high pressures (about 750 to 1000 Pa) or use devices to actively minimize unacceptable variations in flow rate. To conserve energy, the selected system pressure should be the minimum consistent with system needs.

Quantitative estimates of wind effects on a mechanical ventilation system can be made by using the pressure coefficients in Figures 4 to 9 to calculate wind pressure on air intakes and exhausts. A simple worst-case estimate is to assume a system with 100% makeup air supplied by a single intake and exhausted from a single outlet. The building is treated as a single zone, with an exhaust-only fan as shown in Figure 12. This overestimates the effect of wind on system volume flow.

Combining Equations (2) and (3), surface wind pressures at air intake and exhaust locations are

$$p_{s\ intake} = C_{p\ intake}\frac{\rho_a U_h^2}{2} \tag{6}$$

$$p_{s\ exhaust} = C_{p\ exhaust}\frac{\rho_a U_h^2}{2} \tag{7}$$

For the single-zone building shown in Figure 12, a worst-case estimate of wind effect neglects any flow resistance in the intake grill and duct, making interior building pressure $p_{interior}$ equal to outdoor wind pressure on the intake ($p_{interior} = p_{s\ intake}$). Then, with all system flow resistance assigned to the exhaust duct in Figure 12, and a pressure rise Δp_{fan} across the fan, pressure drop from outdoor intake to outdoor exhaust yields

$$(p_{s\ intake} - p_{s\ exhaust}) + \Delta p_{fan} = F_{sys}\frac{\rho Q^2}{A_L^2} \tag{8}$$

where F_{sys} is system flow resistance, A_L is flow leakage area, and Q is system volume flow rate. This result shows that, for the worst-case estimate, the wind-induced pressure difference simply adds to or subtracts from the fan pressure rise. With inlet and exhaust pressures from Equations (6) and (7), the effective fan pressure rise $\Delta p_{fan\ eff}$ is

$$\Delta p_{fan\ eff} = \Delta p_{fan} + \Delta p_{wind} \tag{9}$$

where

$$\Delta p_{wind} = (C_{p\ intake} - C_{p\ exhaust})\frac{\rho_a U_h^2}{2} \tag{10}$$

The fan is wind-assisted when $C_{p\ intake} > C_{p\ exhaust}$ and wind-opposed when the wind direction changes, causing $C_{p\ intake} < C_{p\ exhaust}$. The effect of wind-assisted and wind-opposed pressure differences is illustrated in Figure 13.

Example 3. Make a worst-case estimate for the effect of wind on the supply fan for a low-rise building with height H = 15 m, located in a city suburb. Use the hourly average wind speed that will be exceeded only 1% of the time and assume an annual hourly average speed of U_{annual} = 4 m/s measured on a meteorological tower at height H_{met} = 10 m at a nearby airport. Outdoor air density is ρ_a = 1.2 kg/m³.

Solution: From Table 2, the wind speed exceeded only 1% of the hours each year is a factor of 2.5 ± 0.4 higher than the annual average of 4 m/s, so the 1% maximum speed at the airport meteorological station is

$$U_{met} = 2.5 \times 4 = 10 \text{ m/s}$$

From Example 1, building wind speed U_H is 7.8 m/s.

A worst-case estimate of wind effect must assume intake and exhaust locations on the building that produce the largest difference ($C_{p\ intake} - C_{p\ exhaust}$) in Equations (9) and (10). From Figure 5, the largest difference occurs for the intake on the upwind wall AB and the exhaust on the downwind wall CD, with a wind angle θ_{AB} = 0°. For this worst case, $C_{p\ intake}$ = +0.8 on the upwind wall and $C_{p\ exhaust}$ = –0.43 on the downwind wall. Using these coefficients in Equations (9) and (10) to evaluate effective fan pressure $\Delta p_{fan\ eff}$,

$$\Delta p_{fan\ eff} = \Delta p_{fan} + [0.8 - (-0.43)]\frac{1.2(7.8)^2}{2}$$

$$= \Delta p_{fan} + 44.9 \text{ Pa}$$

This wind-assisted hourly averaged pressure is exceeded only 1% of the time (88 hours per year). When wind direction reverses, the outlet will be on the upwind wall and the inlet on the downwind wall, producing wind-opposed flow, changing the sign from +44.9

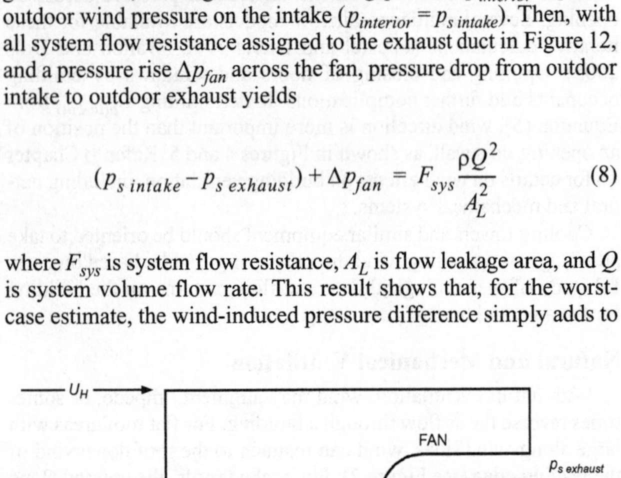

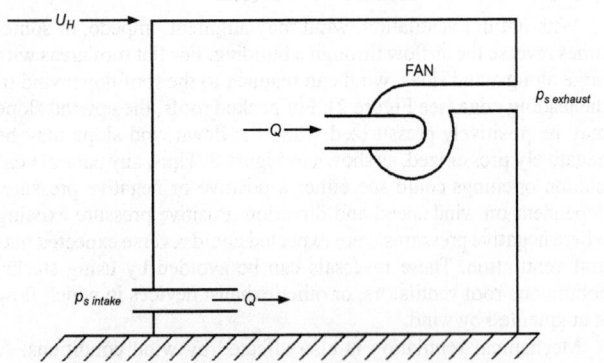

Fig. 12 Intake and Exhaust Pressures on Exhaust Fan in Single-Zone Building

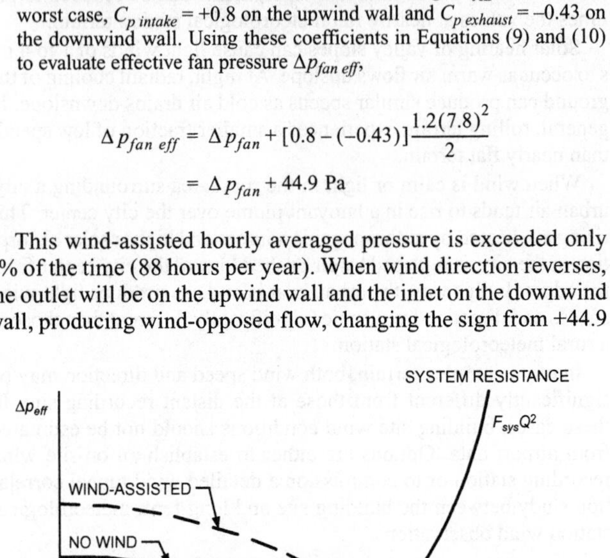

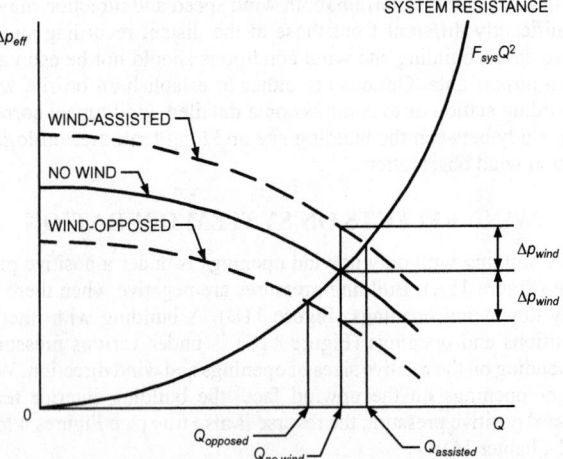

Fig. 13 Effect of Wind-Assisted and Wind-Opposed Flow

to −44.9 Pa. The importance of these pressures depends on their size relative to the fan pressure rise Δp_{fan}, as shown in Figure 13.

Minimizing Wind Effect on System Volume

Wind effect can be reduced by careful selection of inlet and exhaust locations. Because wall surfaces are subject to a wide variety of positive and negative pressures, wall openings should be avoided when possible. When they are required, wall openings should be away from corners formed by building wings (see Figure 11). Mechanical ventilation systems should operate at a pressure high enough to minimize wind effect. Low-pressure systems and propeller exhaust fans should not be used with wall openings unless their ventilation rates are small or they are used in noncritical services (e.g., storage areas).

Although roof air intakes in flow recirculation zones best minimize wind effect on system flow rates, current and future air quality in these zones must be considered. These locations should be avoided if a contamination source exists or may be added in the future. The best area is near the middle of the roof, because the negative pressure there is small and least affected by changes in wind direction (see Figure 8). Avoid edges of the roof and walls, where large pressure fluctuations occur. Either vertical or horizontal (mushroom) openings can be used. On roofs with large areas, where intake may be outside the roof recirculation zone, mushroom or 180° gooseneck designs minimize impact pressure from wind flow. Vertical louvered openings or 135° goosenecks are undesirable for this purpose or for rain protection.

Heated air or contaminants should be exhausted vertically through stacks, above the roof recirculation zone. Horizontal, louvered (45° down), and 135° gooseneck discharges are undesirable, even for heat removal systems, because of their sensitivity to wind effects. A 180° gooseneck for hot-air systems may be undesirable because of air impingement on tar and felt roofs. Vertically discharging stacks in a recirculation region (except near a wall) have the advantage of being subjected only to negative pressure created by wind flow over the tip of the stack. See Chapter 44 of the 2007 *ASHRAE Handbook—HVAC Applications* for information on stack design.

Chemical Hood Operation

Wind effects can interfere with safe chemical hood operation. Supply volume variations can cause both disturbances at hood faces and a lack of adequate hood makeup air. Volume surges, caused by fluctuating wind pressures acting on the exhaust system, can cause momentary inadequate hood exhaust. If highly toxic contaminants are involved, surging is unacceptable. The system should be designed to eliminate this condition. On low-pressure exhaust systems, it is impossible to test the hoods under wind-induced, surging conditions. These systems should be tested during calm conditions for safe flow into the hood faces, and rechecked by smoke tests during high wind conditions. For more information on chemical hoods, see Chapter 14 of the 2007 *ASHRAE Handbook—HVAC Applications*. For more information on stack and intake design, see Chapter 44 of that volume.

BUILDING PRESSURE BALANCE AND INTERNAL FLOW CONTROL

Proper building pressure balance avoids flow conditions that make doors hard to open and cause drafts. In some cases (e.g., office buildings), pressure balance may be used to prevent confinement of contaminants to specific areas. In other cases (e.g., laboratories), the correct internal airflow is towards the contaminated area.

Pressure Balance

Although supply and exhaust systems in an internal area may be in nominal balance, wind can upset this balance, not only because of its effects on fan capacity but also by superimposing infiltrated or exfiltrated air (or both) on the area. These effects can make it impossible to control environmental conditions. Where building balance and minimum infiltration are important, consider the following:

- Design HVAC system with pressure adequate to minimize wind effects
- Include controls to regulate flow rate, pressure, or both
- Separate supply and exhaust systems to serve each building area requiring control or balance
- Use revolving or other self-closing doors or double-door air locks to noncontrolled adjacent areas, particularly outside doors
- Seal windows and other leakage sources
- Close natural ventilation openings

Internal Flow Control

Airflow direction is maintained by controlling pressure differentials between spaces. In a laboratory building, for example, peripheral rooms such as offices and conference rooms are kept at positive pressure, and laboratories at negative pressure, both with reference to corridor pressure. Pressure differentials between spaces are normally obtained by balancing supply system airflows in the spaces in conjunction with exhaust systems in the laboratories. Differential pressure instrumentation is normally used to control the airflow.

The pressure differential for a room adjacent to a corridor can be controlled using the corridor pressure as the reference. Outdoor pressure cannot usually control pressure differentials within internal spaces, even during periods of relatively constant wind velocity (wind-induced pressure). A single pressure sensor can measure the outside pressure at one point only and may not be representative of pressures elsewhere.

Airflow (or pressure) in corridors is sometimes controlled by an outdoor reference probe that senses static pressure at doorways and air intakes. The differential pressure measured between the corridor and the outside may then signal a controller to increase or decrease airflow to (or pressure in) the corridor. Unfortunately, it is difficult to locate an external probe where it will sense the proper external static pressure. High wind velocity and resulting pressure changes around entrances can cause great variations in pressure.

To measure ambient static pressure, the probe should be located where airflow streamlines are not affected by the building or nearby buildings. One possibility is at a height of $1.5R$, as shown in Figure 1. However, this is usually not feasible. If an internal space is to be pressurized relative to ambient conditions, the pressure must be known on each exterior surface in contact with the space. For example, a room at the northeast corner of the building should be pressurized with respect to pressure on both the north and east building faces, and possibly the roof. In some cases, multiple probes on a single building face may be required. Figures 4 to 8 may be used as guides in locating external pressure probes. System volume and pressure control is described in Chapter 46 of the 2007 *ASHRAE Handbook—HVAC Applications*.

PHYSICAL AND COMPUTATIONAL MODELING

For many routine design applications, flow patterns and wind pressures can be estimated using the data and equations presented in the previous sections. Exhaust dilution for simple building geometries in homogeneous terrain environments (e.g., no larger buildings or terrain features nearby) can be estimated using the data and equations presented in the previous sections and in Chapter 44 of the 2007 *ASHRAE Handbook—HVAC Applications*. However, in critical applications, such as where health and safety are of concern, more accurate estimates may be required.

Computational Modeling

Computational fluid dynamics (CFD) models attempt to resolve airflow around buildings by solving the Navier-Stokes equations at finite grid locations. CFD models are currently used to model internal flows (see Chapter 13), but are insufficient to accurately model atmospheric turbulence. According to Stathopoulos (2000, 2002), there is great potential for computational wind engineering (CWE), but the numerical wind tunnel "is still virtual rather than real." According to Murakami (2000), CWE has become a more popular tool, but results usually include numerical errors and prediction inaccuracies. Murakami also notes that, although issues remaining for improving CWE are not many, they are very difficult.

Different methods for predicting turbulent flow around buildings are described and compared in the following paragraphs.

Direct numerical simulation (DNS) directly resolves all the spatial and temporal scales in the flow based on the exact Navier-Stokes equations. This requires very extensive computational resources (runs lasting from several hours to days, depending on computer characteristics, power, and capacity) and can at present only be applied for flow in simple geometries and at low Reynolds numbers. For the complex, high-Re-number flows in wind engineering, application of DNS will not be possible in the foreseeable future.

Large eddy simulation (LES) is a simplified method in which the spatially filtered Navier-Stokes equations are solved. Turbulent structures larger than the filter (sometimes taken equal to the grid size) are explicitly solved, while those smaller than the filter are modeled (i.e., approximated) by a subfilter model. Information on filtering and subfilter models can be found in Ferzinger and Peric (2002), Geurts (2003), and Meyers et al. (2008).

In **Reynolds-averaged Navier-Stokes (RANS) simulation,** equations are obtained by averaging the Navier-Stokes equations (time-averaging if the flow is statistically steady or ensemble-averaging for time-dependent flows). With RANS, only the mean flow is solved, whereas all scales of turbulence must be modeled. Averaging generates additional unknowns for which turbulence models are required. Many turbulence models are available, but no single turbulence model is universally accepted as being the best for all types of applications.

In addition, hybrid RANS/LES approaches are available, in which **unsteady RANS (URANS)** is used near the wall, and LES in the rest of the flow field. This avoids the excessively high near-wall grid resolution required for application of LES near walls in high-Reynolds-number flow problems. An example of a hybrid RANS/LES approach is **detached eddy simulation (DES)**, as proposed by Spalart et al. (1997).

The statistically steady RANS method is the most widely applied and validated in CWE. It has been used for a wide range of building applications, including estimating pressure coefficients (Meroney et al. 2002; Murakami et al. 1992; Oliveira and Younis 2000; Richards and Hoxey 1992; Stathopoulos 1997; Stathopoulos and Zhou 1993); wind-driven rain (Blocken and Carmeliet 2002, 2004; Choi 1993, 1994; Tang and Davidson 2004); pollutant dispersion (Cowan et al. 1997; Dawson et al. 1991; Leitl et al. 1997; Li and Stathopoulos 1997; Meroney 2004; Meroney et al. 1999); pedestrian wind conditions (Blocken et al. 2008; Richards et al. 2002; Stathopoulos and Baskaran 1996; Yoshie et al. 2007); snow drift (Sundsbo 1998; Thiis 2000); and cooling tower drift (Meroney 2006, 2008). Although many past applications of RANS have been limited to isolated buildings or relatively simple building arrangements, large and sometimes very large discrepancies have been found in comparisons with wind tunnel and full-scale measurements. These are at least partly attributed to turbulence model limitations and to the statistically steady solution of flows that exhibit pronounced transient features, such as intermittent separation, recirculation zones, and vortex shedding. In addition, a wide range of other computational aspects can contribute to uncertainties and errors, divided by COST (2007) into two broad categories: physical and numerical. Physical modeling errors and uncertainties result from assumptions and approximations made in the mathematical description of the physical process. Examples are simplifications of the actual physical complexity (e.g., using RANS instead of DNS) and uncertainties and/or simplifications of the geometric and physical boundary conditions. Numerical errors and uncertainties are the result of the numerical solution of the mathematical model. Examples are computer programming errors, computer round-off errors, spatial and temporal discretization errors, and iterative convergence errors.

LES is a time-dependent approach in which more of the turbulence is resolved. It therefore has a larger potential to provide accurate results than statistically steady RANS simulations (Murakami et al. 1992; Tominaga et al. 1997). LES also provides more information about the flow, such as instantaneous and peak wind speeds, pressures, and pollutant concentrations. However, it requires considerably higher CPU times and memory than RANS. It also requires time- and space-resolved data as boundary conditions to properly simulate the inflow. Such experimental data are rarely available in practice (COST 2007). LES is also considered to require more experience for users to apply effectively than does RANS. These drawbacks imply that the practical application of CWE will continue to be based on statistically steady RANS for a considerable while.

Guidelines for using CFD have been developed and assembled to help users avoid, reduce, and estimate errors and uncertainties in applying CFD. ERCOFTAC (2000) provides extensive guidelines for industrial CFD applications, many of which are also applicable to CWE. COST (2007) assembled a comprehensive best-practice guideline document for CFD simulation of flows in the urban environment. Guidelines for application of CFD to pedestrian wind conditions around buildings and for predicting wind loads on buildings have been developed by the Architectural Institute of Japan and reported by Mochida et al. (2002), Tamura et al. (2008), Tominaga et al. (2008), and Yoshie et al. (2007). Other efforts have focused on specific problems, such as those encountered in simulating equilibrium atmospheric boundary layers in computational domains [e.g., Blocken et al. (2007a, 2007b); Hargreaves and Wright (2007); Richards and Hoxey (1993); Yang et al. (2008)]. Most of these guidelines apply to statistically steady RANS simulations.

Independent of whether RANS or LES is employed, evaluating the accuracy of CFD results by comparing them with wind tunnel or field experiments is very important because turbulence models are based on assumptions; no turbulence model is universally valid for all applications. Physical modeling therefore remains an indispensable tool in wind engineering.

Physical Modeling

Measurements on small-scale models in wind tunnels or water channels can provide information for design before construction. These measurements can also be used as an economical method of performance evaluation for existing facilities. Full-scale testing is not generally useful in the initial design phase because of the time and expense required to obtain meaningful information, but it is useful for verifying data derived from physical modeling and for planning remedial changes to improve existing facilities (Cochran 2006).

Detailed accounts of physical modeling, field measurements and applications, and engineering problems resulting from atmospheric flow around buildings are available in international journals, proceedings of conferences, and research reports on wind engineering (see the Bibliography).

The wind tunnel is the main tool used to assess and understand airflow around buildings. Water channels or tanks can also be used, but are more difficult to implement and give only qualitative results for some cases. Models of buildings, complexes, and the local surrounding topography are constructed and tested in a simulated turbulent atmospheric boundary layer. Airflow, wind pressures, snow loads, structural response, or pollutant concentrations can then be measured directly by properly scaling wind, building geometry, and exhaust flow characteristics. Dagliesh (1975) and Petersen (1987a) found generally good agreement between the results of wind tunnel simulations and corresponding full-scale data. Cochran (1992) and Cochran and Cermak (1992) found good agreement between model- and full-scale measurements of low-rise architectural aerodynamics and cladding pressures, respectively. Stathopoulos et al. (1999, 2002, 2004) obtained good agreement between model- and full-scale measurements of the dispersion of gaseous pollutants from rooftop stacks on two different buildings in an urban environment.

Similarity Requirements

Physical modeling is most appropriate for applications involving small-scale atmospheric motions, such as recirculation of exhaust downwind of a laboratory, wind loads on structures, wind speeds around building clusters, snow loads on roofs, and airflow over hills or other terrain features. Winds associated with tornadoes, thunderstorms, and large-scale atmospheric motion cannot currently be physically modeled accurately.

Snyder (1981) gives guidelines for fluid modeling of atmospheric diffusion. This report contains explicit directions and should be used whenever designing wind tunnel studies to assess concentration levels of air pollutants. ASCE *Standard* 7, ASCE *Manual of Practice* 67 (ASCE 1999), and AWES *Quality Assurance Manual* (AWES 2001) also provide guidance when wind tunnels are used for evaluating wind effects on structures.

A complete and exact simulation of airflow over buildings and the resulting concentration or pressure distributions cannot be achieved in a physical model. However, this is not a serious limitation. Cermak (1971, 1975, 1976a, 1976b), Petersen (1987a, 1987b), and Snyder (1981) found that transport and dispersion of laboratory exhaust can be modeled accurately if the following criteria are met in the model and full scale:

1. Match exhaust velocity to wind speed ratios, V_e/U_H.
2. Match exhaust to ambient air density ratios, ρ_e/ρ_a.
3. Match exhaust Froude numbers. $Fr^2 = \rho_a V_e^2/[(\rho_e - \rho_a)gd]$, where d is effective exhaust stack diameter.
4. Ensure fully turbulent stack gas flow by ensuring stack flow Reynolds number ($Re_s = V_e d/\nu$) is greater than 2000 [where ν is the kinematic viscosity of ambient (outdoor) air], or by placing an obstruction inside the stack to enhance turbulence.
5. Ensure fully turbulent wind flow.
6. Scale all dimensions and roughness by a common factor.
7. Match atmospheric stability by the bulk Richardson number (Cermak 1975). For most applications related to airflow around buildings, neutral stratification is assumed, and no Richardson number matching is required.
8. Match mean velocity and turbulence distributions in the wind.
9. Ensure building wind Reynolds number ($Re_b = U_H R/\nu$) is greater than 11 000 for sharp-edged structures, or greater than 90 000 for round-edged structures.
10. Ensure less than 5% blockage of wind tunnel cross section.

For wind speeds, flow patterns, or pressure distributions around buildings, only conditions 5 to 10 are necessary. Usually, each wind tunnel study requires a detailed assessment to determine the appropriate parameters to match in the model and full scale.

In wind tunnel simulations of exhaust gas recirculation, buoyancy of the exhaust gas (condition 3) is often not modeled. This allows using a high wind tunnel speed or a smaller model to achieve high enough Reynolds numbers (conditions 4, 5, and 9). Neglecting buoyancy is justified if the density of building exhaust air is within 10% of the ambient (outdoor) air. Also, critical minimum dilution D_{crit} occurs generally at wind speeds high enough to produce a well-mixed, neutrally stable atmosphere, allowing stability matching (condition 7) to be neglected (see Chapter 44 of the 2007 *ASHRAE Handbook—HVAC Applications* for discussion of D_{crit}). However, in some cases and depending on emission sources, calm conditions may produce critical dilution. Nevertheless, omission of conditions 3 and 7 simplifies the test procedure considerably, reducing both testing time and cost.

Buoyancy should be properly simulated for high-temperature exhausts such as boilers and diesel generators. Equality of model and prototype Froude numbers (condition 3) requires tunnel speeds of less than 0.5 m/s for testing. However, greater tunnel speeds may be needed to meet the minimum building Reynolds number requirement (condition 4).

Wind Simulation Facilities

Boundary layer wind tunnels are required for conducting most wind studies. The wind tunnel test section should be long enough to establish, upwind of the model building, a deep boundary layer that slowly changes with downwind distance.

Other important wind tunnel characteristics include width and height of the test section, range of wind speeds, roof adjustability, and temperature control. Larger models can be used in tunnels that are wider and taller, which, in turn, give better measurement resolution. Model blockage effects can be minimized by an adjustable roof height. Temperature control of the tunnel surface and airflow is required when atmospheric conditions other than neutral stability are to be simulated. Boundary layer characteristics appropriate for the site are established by using roughness elements on the tunnel floor that produce mean velocity, turbulence intensity profiles, and spectra characteristic of full scale.

Water can also be used for the modeling fluid if an appropriate flow facility is available. Flow facilities may be in the form of a tunnel, tank, or open channel. Water tanks with a free surface ranging in size up to that of a wind tunnel test section have been used by towing a model (upside down) through the nonflowing fluid. Stable stratification can be obtained by adding a salt solution. This technique does not allow development of a boundary layer and therefore yields only approximate, qualitative information on flow around buildings. Water channels can be designed to develop thick turbulent boundary layers similar to those developed in the wind tunnel. One advantage of such a flow system is ease of flow visualization, but this is offset by a greater difficulty in developing the correct turbulence structure and the measurement of flow variables and concentrations.

Designing Model Test Programs

The first step in planning a test program is selecting the model length scale. This choice depends on cross-sectional dimensions of the test section, dimensions of the buildings to be modeled, and/or topographic features and thickness of the simulated atmospheric boundary layer. Typical geometric scales range from about 120:1 to 1000:1.

Because a large model is desirable to meet minimum Reynolds and Froude number requirements, a wide test section is advantageous. In general, the model at any section should be small compared to the test section area so that blockage is less than 5% (Melbourne 1982).

The test program must include specifications of the meteorological variables to be considered (e.g., wind direction, wind speed, thermal stability). Data taken at the nearest meteorological station should be reviewed to obtain a realistic assessment of wind climate for a particular site. Ordinarily, local winds around a building, pressures, and/or concentrations are measured for 16 wind directions (e.g., 22.5° intervals). This is easily accomplished by mounting the building model and its nearby surroundings on a turntable. More than 16 wind directions are required for highly toxic exhausts or for finding peak fluctuating pressures on a building. If only local wind information and pressures are of interest, testing at one wind speed with neutral stability is sufficient.

SYMBOLS

a = exponent in power law wind speed profile for local building terrain, Equation (4) and Table 1, dimensionless
A_L = flow leakage area, Equation (8), m^2
a_{met} = exponent a for the meteorological station, Equation (4) and Table 1, dimensionless
B_L = larger of two upwind building face dimensions H and W, Equation (1), m
B_s = smaller of two upwind building face dimensions H and W, Equation (1), m
C_p = local wind pressure coefficient for building surface, Equation (3), dimensionless
$C_{p\,in}$ = internal wind-induced pressure coefficient, Equation (5), dimensionless
$C_{p(in\text{-}out)}$ = difference between outdoor and indoor pressure coefficients, Equation (5), dimensionless
C_s = surface-averaged pressure coefficient, Figure 6, dimensionless
d = effective stack diameter, m
D_{crit} = critical dilution factor at roof level for uncapped vertical exhaust at critical wind speed (see Chapter 44 of the 2007 *ASHRAE Handbook—HVAC Applications*), dimensionless
Fr = Froude number, dimensionless
F_{sys} = system flow resistance, Equation (8), dimensionless
g = acceleration of gravity, 9.8 m/s^2
H = wall height above ground on upwind building face, Equation (4) and Figure 1, m
H_c = maximum height above roof level of upwind roof edge flow recirculation zone, Figures 1 and 3, m
H_{met} = height of anemometer at meteorological station, Equation (4), m
h_s = exhaust stack height (typically above roof unless otherwise specified, m (see Figure 3, and Chapter 44 in the 2007 *ASHRAE Handbook—HVAC Applications*)
L = length of building in wind direction, Figures 1 and 2, m
L_c = length of upwind roof edge recirculation zone, Figure 3, m
L_r = length of flow recirculation zone behind rooftop obstacle or building, Figures 1 and 3, m
p_s = wind pressure difference between exterior building surface and local ambient (outdoor) atmospheric pressure at same elevation in undisturbed approach wind, Equation (3), Pa
p_v = wind velocity pressure at roof level, Equation (2), Pa
Q = volumetric flow rate, Equation (8), m^3/s
R = scaling length for roof flow patterns, Equation (1), m
Re_b = building Reynolds number, dimensionless
Re_s = stack flow Reynolds number, dimensionless
S = stretched-string distance; shortest distance from exhaust to intake over obstacles and along building surface, m (see Figure 3, and Chapter 44 in the 2007 *ASHRAE Handbook—HVAC Applications*)
U_{annual} = annual average of hourly wind speeds U_{met}, Table 2, m/s
U_H = mean wind speed at height H of upwind wall in undisturbed flow approaching building, Equation (2) and Figures 1, 2, and 3, m/s
U_{met} = meteorological station hourly wind speed, measured at height H_{met} above ground in smooth terrain, Equation (4) and Table 2, m/s
V_e = exhaust face velocity, m/s
W = width of upwind building face, Figure 2, m

Greek

δ = fully developed atmospheric boundary layer thickness, Equation (4) and Table 1, m
δ_{met} = atmospheric boundary layer thickness at meteorological station, Equation (4) and Table 1, m
Δp_{fan} = pressure rise across fan, Equation (8), Pa
$\Delta p_{fan\,eff}$ = effective pressure rise across fan, Equation (9), Pa
Δp_{wind} = wind-induced pressure, Equations (9) and (10), Pa
θ = angle between perpendicular line from upwind building face and wind direction, Figures 4 to 7, degrees
ν = kinematic viscosity of ambient (outdoor) air, m^2/s
ρ_a = ambient (outdoor) air density, Equation (2), kg/m^3
ρ_e = density of exhaust gas mixture, kg/m^3

REFERENCES

Akins, R.E., J.A. Peterka, and J.E. Cermak. 1979. Averaged pressure coefficients for rectangular buildings. *Wind Engineering: Proceedings of the Fifth International Conference*, vol. 7, pp. 369-380.

ASCE. 2006. Minimum design loads for buildings and other structures. *Standard* ASCE/SEI 7-05. American Society of Civil Engineers, New York.

ASCE. 1999. Wind tunnel studies of buildings and structures. *ASCE Manuals and Reports on Engineering Practice* 67. American Society of Civil Engineers, New York.

AWES. 2001. *Quality assurance manual—Wind engineering studies of buildings*. AWES-QAM-1-2001. The Australasian Wind Engineering Society, Melbourne.

Bailey, P.A. and K.C.S. Kwok. 1985. Interference excitation of twin fall buildings. *Wind Engineering and Industrial Aerodynamics* 21:323-338.

Bair, F.E. 1992. *The weather almanac*, 6th ed. Gale Research, Inc., Detroit.

Blocken, B. and J. Carmeliet. 2002. Spatial and temporal distribution of driving rain on a low-rise building. *Wind and Structures* 5(5):441-462.

Blocken, B. and J. Carmeliet. 2004. A review of wind-driven rain research in building science. *Journal of Wind Engineering and Industrial Aerodynamics* 92(13):1079-1130.

Blocken, B., J. Carmeliet, and T. Stathopoulos. 2007a. CFD evaluation of the wind speed conditions in passages between buildings—Effect of wall-function roughness modifications on the atmospheric boundary layer flow. *Journal of Wind Engineering and Industrial Aerodynamics* 95(9-11):941-962.

Blocken, B., T. Stathopoulos, and J. Carmeliet. 2007b. CFD simulation of the atmospheric boundary layer: Wall function problems. *Atmospheric Environment* 41(2):238-252.

Blocken, B., P. Moonen, T. Stathopoulos, and J. Carmeliet. 2008. A numerical study on the existence of the Venturi-effect in passages between perpendicular buildings. *Journal of Engineering Mechanics—ASCE* 134(12).

Cermak, J.E. 1971. Laboratory simulation of the atmospheric boundary layer. *AIAA Journal* 9(9):1746.

Cermak, J.E. 1975. Applications of fluid mechanics to wind engineering. *Journal of Fluid Engineering, Transactions of ASME* 97:9.

Cermak, J.E. 1976a. Nature of airflow around buildings. *ASHRAE Transactions* 82(1):1044-1060.

Cermak, J.E. 1976b. Aerodynamics of buildings. *Annual Review of Fluid Mechanics* 8:75.

Choi, E.C.C. 1993. Simulation of wind-driven rain around a building. *Journal of Wind Engineering and Industrial Aerodynamics* 46/47:721-729.

Choi, E.C.C. 1994. Determination of wind-driven rain intensity on building faces. *Journal of Wind Engineering and Industrial Aerodynamics* 51:55-69.

Clarke, J.H. 1967. Airflow around buildings. *Heating, Piping and Air Conditioning* 39(5):145.

Cochran, L.S. 1992. Low-rise architectural aerodynamics: The Texas Tech University experimental building. *Architectural Science Review* 35(4): 131-136.

Cochran, L.S. 2006. State of the art review of wind tunnels and physical modeling to obtain structural loads and cladding pressures. *Architectural Science Review* 50(1):7-16.

Cochran, L.S. and J.E. Cermak. 1992. Full and model scale cladding pressures on the Texas Tech University experimental building. *Journal of Wind Engineering and Industrial Aerodynamics* 41-44:1589-1600.

Cochran, L.S. and E.C. English. 1997. Reduction of wind loads by architectural features. *Architectural Science Review* 40(3):79-87.

Cochran, L.S., J.A. Peterka, and R.J. Derickson. 1999. Roof surface wind speed distributions on low-rise buildings. *Architectural Science Review* 42(3):151-160.

COST. 2007. *Best practice guideline for the CFD simulation of flows in the urban environment. COST action 732: Quality assurance and improvement of microscale meteorological models.* J. Franke, A. Hellsten, H. Schlünzen, and B. Carissimo, eds. European Cooperation in the field of Scientific and Technical Research, Brussels.

Cowan, I.R., I.P. Castro, and A.G. Robins. 1997. Numerical considerations for simulations of flow and dispersion around buildings. *Journal of Wind Engineering and Industrial Aerodynamics* 67/68:535-545.

Dagliesh, W.A. 1975. Comparison of model/full-scale wind pressures on a high-rise building. *Journal of Industrial Aerodynamics* 1:55-66.

Davenport, A.G. and H.Y.L. Hui. 1982. *External and internal wind pressures on cladding of buildings.* Boundary Layer Wind Tunnel Laboratory, University of Western Ontario, London, Canada. BLWT-820133.

Dawson, P., D.E. Stock, and B. Lamb. 1991. The numerical simulation of airflow and dispersion in three-dimensional atmospheric recirculation zones. *Journal of Applied Meteorology* 30:1005-1024.

Deaves, D.M. 1981. Computations of wind flow over changes in surface roughness. *Journal of Wind Engineering and Industrial Aerodynamics* 7:65-94.

Deaves, D.M. and R.I. Harris. 1978. A mathematical model of the structure of strong winds. *Report* 76. Construction Industry Research and Information Association (U.K.).

DOC. 1968. *Climatic atlas of the United States*. U.S. Department of Commerce, Washington, D.C.

English, E.C. and F.R. Fricke. 1997. The interference index and its prediction using a neural network analysis of wind tunnel data. *Fourth Asia-Pacific Symposium on Wind Engineering*, APSOWE IV University of Queensland, pp. 363-366.

ERCOFTAC. 2000. *Special interest group on quality and trust in industrial CFD: Best practice guidelines*. M. Casey, and T. Wintergerste, eds. European Research Community on Flow, Turbulence and Combustion, Brussels.

Ferziger, J.H. and M. Peric. 2002. *Computational methods for fluid mechanics*. Springer.

Feustel, H.E. and J. Dieris. 1992. A survey of airflow models for multizone buildings. *Energy and Buildings* 18:79-100.

Geurts, B.J. 2003. *Elements of direct and large-eddy simulation*. Edwards Publishing, Las Vegas.

Hargreaves, D.M. and N.G. Wright. 2007. On the use of the k-ε model in commercial CFD software to model the neutral atmospheric boundary layer. *Journal of Wind Engineering and Industrial Aerodynamics* 95(5):355-369.

Holmes, J.D. 1983. *Wind loads on low rise buildings—A review*. Commonwealth Scientific and Industrial Research Organisation (CSIRO), Division of Building Research, Australia.

Holmes, J.D. 1986. *Wind loads on low-rise buildings: The structural and environmental effects of wind on buildings and structures*, Chapter 12. Faculty of Engineering, Monash University, Melbourne, Australia.

Hosker, R.P. 1984. Flow and diffusion near obstacles. In *Atmospheric science and power production*. U.S. Department of Energy DOE/TIC-27601 (DE 84005177).

Hosker, R.P. 1985. Flow around isolated structures and building clusters: A review. *ASHRAE Transactions* 91(2b):1671-1692.

Houlihan, T.F. 1965. Effects of relative wind on supply air systems. *ASHRAE Journal* 7(7):28.

Khanduri, A.C., T. Stathopoulos, and C. Bédard. 1998. Wind-induced interference effects on buildings—A review of the state-of-the-art. *Engineering Structures* 20(7):617-630.

Leitl, B.M., P. Kastner-Klein, M. Rau, and R.N. Meroney. 1997. Concentration and flow distributions in the vicinity of U-shaped buildings: Wind-tunnel and computational data. *Journal of Wind Engineering and Industrial Aerodynamics* 67/68:745-755.

Li, Y. and T. Stathopoulos. 1997. Numerical evaluation of wind-induced dispersion of pollutants around a building. *Journal of Wind Engineering and Industrial Aerodynamics* 67/68:757-766.

Melbourne, W.H. 1979. Turbulence effects on maximum surface pressures; A mechanism and possibility of reduction. *Proceedings of the Fifth International Conference on Wind Engineering*, J.E. Cermak, ed., pp. 541-551.

Melbourne, W.H. 1982. Wind tunnel blockage effects and corrections. *Proceedings of the International Workshop on Wind Tunnel Modeling Criteria and Techniques in Civil Engineering Applications*, T.A. Reinhold, ed., pp. 197-216.

Meroney, R.N. 2004. *Wind tunnel and numerical simulation of pollution dispersion: A hybrid approach*. Invited lecture at Croucher Advanced Study Institute on Wind Tunnel Modeling, Hong Kong University of Science and Technology, 6-10 December, 2004. Available at www.engr.colostate.edu/~meroney/projects/ASI Crocher Paper Final.pdf.

Meroney, R.N. 2006. CFD prediction of cooling tower drift. *Journal of Wind Engineering and Industrial Aerodynamics* 94(6):463-490.

Meroney, R.N. 2008. Protocol for CFD prediction of cooling-tower drift in an urban environment. *Journal of Wind Engineering and Industrial Aerodynamics* 96(10-11):1789-1804.

Meroney, R.N., B.M. Leitl, S. Rafailidis, and M. Schatzmann. 1999. Wind-tunnel and numerical modeling of flow and dispersion about several building shapes. *Journal of Wind Engineering and Industrial Aerodynamics* 81(1-3):333-345.

Meroney, R.N., C.W. Letchford, and P.P. Sarkar. 2002. Comparison of numerical and wind tunnel simulation of wind loads on smooth, rough and dual domes immersed in a boundary layer. *Wind and Structures* 5(2-4):347-358.

Meyers, J., B.J. Geurts, and P. Sagaut, eds. 2008. Quality and reliability of large-eddy simulations. *ERCOFTAC Series*, vol. 12. European Research Community on Flow, Turbulence, and Combustion, Lausanne, Switzerland, and Springer, Netherlands.

Mochida, A., Y. Tominaga, S. Murakami, R. Yoshie, T. Ishihara, and R. Ooka. 2002. Comparison of various k-ε models and DSM to flow around a high rise building—Report of AIJ cooperative project for CFD prediction of wind environment. *Wind and Structures* 5(2-4):227-244.

Murakami, S. 2000. Overview of CWE 2000. International Symposium on Computational Wind Engineering. PF Consultants.

Murakami, S., A. Mochida, Y. Hayashi, and S. Sakamoto. 1992. Numerical study on velocity-pressure field and wind forces for bluff bodies by k-ε, ASM and LES. *Journal of Wind Engineering and Industrial Aerodynamics* 41-44:2841-2852.

NCDC. Updated periodically. *International station meteorological climatic summary* (CD-ROM). National Climatic Data Center, Asheville, NC. Published jointly with U.S. Air Force and U.S. Navy.

Oliveira, P.J. and B.A. Younis. 2000. On the prediction of turbulent flows around full-scale buildings. *Journal of Wind Engineering and Industrial Aerodynamics* 86(2-3):203-220.

Petersen, R.L. 1987a. Wind tunnel investigation of the effect of platform-type structures on dispersion of effluents from short stacks. *Journal of Air Pollution Control Association* 36:1347-1352.

Petersen, R.L. 1987b. Designing building exhausts to achieve acceptable concentrations of toxic effluent. *ASHRAE Transactions* 93(2):2165-2185.

Richards, P.J. and R.P. Hoxey. 1992. Computational and wind tunnel modelling of mean wind loads on the Silsoe structures building. *Journal of Wind Engineering and Industrial Aerodynamics* 43(1-3):1641-1652.

Richards, P.J. and R.P. Hoxey. 1993. Appropriate boundary conditions for computational wind engineering models using the k-ε turbulence model. *Journal of Wind Engineering and Industrial Aerodynamics* 46/47:145-153.

Richards, P.J., G.D. Mallison, D. McMillan, and Y.F. Li. 2002. Pedestrian level wind speeds in downtown Auckland. *Wind and Structures* 5(2-4): 151-164.

SA/SNZ. 2002. Structural design actions—Part 2: Wind actions. *Standard* AS/NZS 1170.2:2002. Standards Australia International Ltd., Sydney.

Saunders, J.W. and W.H. Melbourne. 1979. Buffeting effect of upwind buildings. *Fifth International Conference on Wind Engineering*. Pergamon Press, pp. 593-606.

Sherman, M.H. and D.T. Grimsrud. 1980. The measurement of infiltration using fan pressurization and weather data. *Report* LBL-10852. Lawrence Berkeley Laboratory, University of California.

Snyder, W.H. 1981. Guideline for fluid modeling of atmospheric diffusion. Environmental Protection Agency *Report* EPA-600/881-009.

Spalart, P., W.-H. Jou, M. Strelets, and S. Allmaras. 1997. Comments on the feasibility of LES for wings and on the hybrid RANS/LES approach. *Advances in DNS/LES, 1st AFOSR International Conference on DNS/LES*, Greden Press.

Stathopoulos, T. 1997. Computational wind engineering: Past achievements and future challenges. *Journal of Wind Engineering and Industrial Aerodynamics* 67/68:509-532.

Stathopoulos, T. 2000. The numerical wind tunnel for industrial aerodynamics: Real or virtual in the new millennium? Third International Symposium on Computational Wind Engineering. PF Consultants.

Stathopoulos, T. 2002. The numerical wind tunnel for industrial aerodynamics: Real or virtual in the new millennium? *Wind and Structures* 5(2-4):193-208.

Stathopoulos, T. and B.A. Baskaran. 1996. Computer simulation of wind environmental conditions around buildings. *Engineering Structures* 18 (11):876-885.

Stathopoulos, T. and Y.S. Zhou. 1993. Numerical simulation of wind-induced pressures on buildings of various geometries. *Journal of Wind Engineering and Industrial Aerodynamics* 46/47:419-430.

Stathopoulos, T., L. Lazure, and P. Saathoff. 1999. Tracer gas investigation of reingestion of building exhaust in an urban environment. IRSST *Report* R-213, Robert-Sauvé Institute of Occupational Health and Safety Research (IRSST), Montreal, Canada.

Stathopoulos, T., L. Lazure, P. Saathoff, and X. Wei. 2002. Dilution of exhaust from a rooftop stack on a cubical building in an urban environment. *Atmospheric Environment* 36:4577-4591.

Stathopoulos, T., L. Lazure, P. Saathoff, and A. Gupta. 2004. The effect of stack height, stack location and rooftop structures on air intake contamination. A laboratory and full-scale study. IRSST *Report* R-392. Robert-Sauvé Institute of Occupational Health and Safety Research (IRSST), Montreal, Canada.

Sundsbo, P.A. 1998. Numerical simulations of wind deflection fins to control snow accumulation in building steps. *Journal of Wind Engineering and Industrial Aerodynamics* 74-76:543-552.

Swami, M.V. and S. Chandra. 1987. Procedures for calculating natural ventilation airflow rates in buildings. *Final Report* FSEC-CR-163-86. Florida Solar Energy Center, Cape Canaveral.

Tamura, T., K. Nozawa, and K. Kondo. 2008 AIJ guide for numerical prediction of wind loads on buildings. *Journal of Wind Engineering and Industrial Aerodynamics* 96(10-11):1974-1984.

Tang, W. and C.I. Davidson. 2004. Erosion of limestone building surfaces caused by wind-driven rain: 2. Numerical modeling. *Atmospheric Environment* 38(33):5601-5609.

Thiis, T.K. 2000. A comparison of numerical simulations and full-scale measurements of snowdrifts around buildings. *Wind and Structures* 3(2): 73-81.

Tominaga, Y., S. Murakami, and A. Mochida. 1997. CFD prediction of gaseous diffusion around a cubic model using a dynamic mixed SGS model based on composite grid technique. *Journal of Wind Engineering and Industrial Aerodynamics* 67/68: 827-841.

Tominaga, Y., A. Mochida, R. Yoshie, H. Kataoka, T. Nozu, M. Yoshikawa, and T. Shirasawa. 2008. AIJ guidelines for practical applications of CFD to pedestrian wind environment around buildings. *Journal of Wind Engineering and Industrial Aerodynamics* 96(10-11):1749-1761.

Walker, I.S., D.J. Wilson, and T.W. Forest. 1996. Wind shadow model for air infiltration sheltering by upwind obstacles. *International Journal of HVAC&R Research* (now *HVAC&R Research*) 2(4):265-283.

Walton, G.N. and W.S. Dols. 2005. *CONTAM 2.4 user guide and program documentation*. NISTIR 7251. National Institute of Standards and Technology, Gaithersburg, Maryland.

Wilson, D.J. 1979. Flow patterns over flat roofed buildings and application to exhaust stack design. *ASHRAE Transactions* 85(2):284-295.

Yang, W., Y. Quan, X. Jin, Y. Tamura, and M. Gu. 2008. Influences of equilibrium atmosphere boundary layer and turbulence parameters on wind load distributions of low-rise buildings. *Journal of Wind Engineering and Industrial Aerodynamics* 96(10-11):2080-2092.

Yoshie, R., A. Mochida, Y. Tominaga, H. Kataoka, K. Harimoto, T. Nozu, and T. Shirasawa. 2007. Cooperative project for CFD prediction of pedestrian wind environment in the architectural institute of Japan. *Journal of Wind Engineering and Industrial Aerodynamics* 95(9-11):1551-1578.

BIBLIOGRAPHY

AIHA. 2003. Laboratory ventilation. ANSI/AIHA *Standard* Z9.5-2003. American Industrial Hygiene Association, Fairfax, VA.

ASCE. 1987. Wind tunnel model studies of building and structures. *ASCE Manuals and Reports on Engineering Practice* 67. American Society of Civil Engineers, New York.

Cermak, J.E. 1977. Wind-tunnel testing of structures. *Journal of the Engineering Mechanics Division*, ASCE 103, EM6:1125.

Cermak, J.E., ed. 1979. Wind engineering. *Wind Engineering: Proceedings of the Fifth International Conference*, Colorado State University, Fort Collins, CO. Pergamon Press, New York.

Clarke, J.H. 1965. The design and location of building inlets and outlets to minimize wind effect and building reentry of exhaust fumes. *Journal of American Industrial Hygiene Association* 26:242.

CWE. 1993. *Proceedings of the 1st International Symposium on Computational Wind Engineering*, Tokyo, Japan. Elsevier.

CWE. 1997. *Proceedings of the 2nd International Symposium on Computational Wind Engineering*, Colorado State University, Fort Collins. Elsevier.

CWE. 2000. *Proceedings of the 3rd International Symposium on Computational Wind Engineering*. PF Consultants.

CWE. 2006. *Proceedings of the 4th International Symposium on Computational Wind Engineering,* Yokohama, Japan. Elsevier.

Defant, F. 1951. Local winds. In *Compendium of meteorology*, pp. 655-672. American Meteorology Society, Boston.

Elliot, W.P. 1958. The growth of the atmospheric internal boundary layer. *Transactions of the American Geophysical Union* 39:1048-1054.

ESDU. 1990. Strong winds in the atmospheric boundary layer. Part 1: Mean hourly wind speeds, pp. 15-17. *Engineering Science Data Unit*, Item 82-26, London.

Geiger, R. 1966. *The climate near the ground*. Harvard University, Cambridge.

Houghton, E.L. and N.B. Carruthers. 1976. *Wind forces on buildings and structures: An introduction*. Edward Arnold, London.

Landsberg, H. 1981. *The urban climate*. Academic Press, New York.

Meroney, R.N. and B. Bienkiewicz, eds. 1997. *Computational wind engineering 2*. Elsevier, Amsterdam.

Panofsky, H.A. and J.A. Dutton. 1984. *Atmospheric turbulence: Models and methods for engineering applications*. John Wiley & Sons, New York.

Simiu, V. and R. Scanlan. 1986. *Wind effects on structures: An introduction to wind engineering*, 2nd ed. Wiley Interscience, New York.

WERC. 1985. *Proceedings of the 5th U.S. National Conference on Wind Engineering*, 6-8 November, Texas Tech University, Lubbock. Mehta, K.C. and R.A. Dillingham, eds. Wind Engineering Research Center, Lubbock.

CHAPTER 25

HEAT, AIR, AND MOISTURE CONTROL IN BUILDING ASSEMBLIES—FUNDAMENTALS

PROPER design of space heating, cooling, and air conditioning requires detailed knowledge of the building envelope's overall heat, air, and moisture control performance. This chapter provides guidance in the analysis and design of building envelope assemblies for good heat, air, and moisture control performance. Guidance for designing mechanical systems is found in other chapters of the ASHRAE Handbook series. This chapter discusses the fundamentals of combined heat, air, and moisture movement as it relates to envelope assemblies.

Because heat, air, and moisture transfer are coupled and closely interact with each other, they should not be treated separately. In fact, improving a building envelope's energy performance may cause moisture-related problems. Evaporation of water or removal of moisture by any other means are processes that may require considerable energy that is not always available. Only a sophisticated moisture control strategy can ensure hygienic conditions and adequate durability for modern, energy-efficient building assemblies. Effective moisture control design must deal with all hygrothermal loads (heat and humidity) acting on the building envelope.

TERMINOLOGY AND SYMBOLS

The following heat, air, and moisture definitions and symbols are commonly used.

A **building envelope** or **building enclosure** provides physical separation between the indoor and outdoor environments. A **building assembly** is any part of the building enclosure, such as wall assembly, window assembly, or roof assembly, that has boundary conditions at the interior and the exterior of the building. A **building component** is any element or material within a building assembly.

Heat

Specific heat capacity c is the change in heat (energy) of unit mass of material for unit change of temperature in J/(kg·K).

Volumetric heat capacity ρc is the change in heat stored in unit volume of material for unit change of temperature, in J/(m^3·K).

The vector **heat flux** q is the time rate of heat transfer through a unit area, in W/m^2.

Thermal conductivity k [also often the Greek letter λ (lambda)] is the steady-state heat flux through a unit thickness of a homogeneous material in a direction perpendicular to the isothermal planes, induced by a unit temperature difference. (ASTM *Standard* C168 (defines homogeneity.) Units are W/(m·K). Thermal conductivity must be evaluated for a specific mean temperature, thickness, age, and moisture content. For porous materials, heat flows by a combination of conduction, convection, radiation, and latent heat exchange and may depend on orientation, direction, or both. The measured property of such materials is called **apparent thermal conductivity**. The specific test conditions (i.e., sample thickness, orientation, environment, environmental pressure, surface temperature, mean temperature, temperature difference, and moisture distribution) should be reported with the values. The symbol k_{app} is used to denote the lack of pure conduction or to indicate that all values reported are apparent. Materials with a low apparent thermal conductivity are called *insulation* materials (see Chapter 26 for more detail).

Thermal resistivity R_u is the reciprocal of thermal conductivity. Units are (m·K)/W.

Thermal conductance C is the heat flux through a flat body induced by a unit temperature difference between the surfaces of that body. Units are W/(m^2·K). When the two defined surfaces have unequal areas, as with heat flux through materials of nonuniform thickness, an appropriate mean area and mean thickness must be given. Thermal conductance formulas involving materials that are not uniform slabs must contain shape factors to account for the area variation involved. When heat flux occurs by conduction alone, the thermal conductance of a layer may be obtained by dividing the material's thermal conductivity by its thickness. When several modes of heat transfer are involved, the **apparent thermal conductance** may be obtained by dividing the material's apparent thermal conductivity by its thickness. When air circulates within or passes through insulation, as may happen in low-density fibrous materials, the apparent thermal conductance is affected. Thermal conductances and resistances of common building and insulation materials are listed in Chapter 26.

Thermal resistance R is the mean temperature difference between two defined surfaces of material or construction under steady-state conditions that induces a unit heat flux, in (m^2·K)/W.

Heat transfer film coefficient h_i or h_o is heat transferred by convection and radiation between an inside or outside surface and the surrounding environment per unit time and unit area, induced by a unit temperature difference between the surface and reference temperature in the surrounding environment. Units are W/(m^2·K).

Surface film resistance R_i or R_o is the reciprocal of the inside or outside surface heat transfer film coefficient, in (m^2·K)/W. For convection to occur, the surrounding space must be filled with air or another fluid. If the space is evacuated, heat flow occurs by radiation only.

Thermal transmittance U is the heat flux under steady-state conditions from the environment on the one side of a body to the environment on the other side, per unit temperature difference between the two environments, in W/(m^2·K). Thermal transmittance is sometimes called the **overall coefficient of heat transfer** or

The preparation of this chapter is assigned to TC 4.4, Building Materials and Building Envelope Performance.

U-factor. Thermal transmittance includes surface film conductance.

Thermal emittance ε is the ratio of radiant flux emitted by a surface to that emitted by a black surface at the same temperature.

Effective emittance of an air space E is the combined effect of emittances from the boundary surfaces of an air space, where the boundaries are parallel and of a dimension much larger than the distance between them. Chapter 26 lists values of E for various air spaces.

Air

Air transfer M_a is airflow induced by an air pressure difference, caused by wind, stack effect, or mechanical systems, in kg/s.

Air flux m_a, a vector, is the time rate of air transfer through a unit area, in kg/(s·m²).

Air permeability k_a is the air flux through a unit thickness of homogeneous material in a direction perpendicular to the isobaric planes, induced by a unit air pressure difference. Units are in kg/(Pa·s·m) or s.

Air permeance K_a is the time rate of air transfer through a unit surface of a porous membrane or layer induced by a unit air pressure difference over that layer. Units are kg/(Pa·s·m²), kg/(Pa·s·m), or kg/(Pa·s).

Moisture

Moisture content w is the amount of moisture per unit volume of porous material, in kg/m³.

Moisture ratio X (in mass) or Ψ (in volume) is the amount of moisture per unit weight of dry porous material or the volume of moisture per unit volume of dry material, in percent.

Specific moisture content is the ratio between a change in moisture content and the corresponding change in driving potential.

Specific moisture ratio is the ratio between a change in moisture ratio and the corresponding change in driving potential.

Water vapor flux m_v is the time rate of water vapor transfer through a unit area, in kg/(s·m²).

Water vapor permeance M is the water vapor flux by diffusion through a unit area of a flat layer, induced by a unit partial water vapor pressure difference across that layer, in kg/(Pa·s·m²).

Water vapor permeability μ_p is the water vapor flux through a unit thickness of homogeneous material in a direction perpendicular to the isobaric planes, induced by a unit partial water vapor pressure difference, under specified temperature and humidity. Units are kg/(Pa·s·m). When permeability varies with psychrometric conditions, the specific permeability defines the property at a specific condition.

Water vapor resistance Z is the reciprocal of water vapor permeance, in (m²·s·Pa)/kg.

Moisture transfer M_m is the moisture flow induced by a difference in suction or in relative humidity, in kg/s.

Moisture flux m_m, a vector, is the time rate of moisture transfer through a unit area, in kg/(s·m²).

Moisture permeability k_m is the moisture flux through a unit thickness of a homogeneous material in a direction perpendicular to the isosuction planes, induced by a unit difference in suction. Units are kg/(Pa·s·m) (suction).

Moisture diffusivity D_m is the ratio between the moisture permeability and the volumetric moisture capacity, in m²/s.

ENVIRONMENTAL HYGROTHERMAL LOADS

The main function of the building enclosure is separation of indoor spaces from the outdoor climate. This section describes the hygrothermal loads acting on the building envelope. The purpose of these load descriptions is to predict their influence on the hygrothermal behavior of building assemblies, as a basis for design recommendations and moisture control measures (Künzel and Karagiozis 2004). Load estimations for sizing mechanical systems can be found in Chapters 17 and 18.

In Figure 1, the hygrothermal loads relevant for building envelope design are represented schematically for an external wall. Generally, they show diurnal and seasonal variations at the exterior surface and mainly seasonal variations at the interior surface. During daytime, the exterior wall surface heats by solar radiation, leading to evaporation of moisture from the surface layer. Around sunset, when solar radiation decreases, long-wave (infrared) emission may lead to overcooling (cooling below ambient air temperature) of the façade, and exterior surface condensation may occur. The exterior surface is also exposed to moisture from wind-driven precipitation.

Usually, several load cycles overlap (e.g., summer/winter, day/night, rain/sun). Therefore, a precise analysis of the expected hygrothermal loads should be done before starting to design any building envelope component. However, the magnitude of the loads is not always independent of building geometry and the component's properties. Analysis of the transient hygrothermal loads is generally based on hourly meteorological data. However, the determination of local conditions at the envelope's surface is rather complicated and requires specific experience. In some cases, computer simulations are necessary to assess the microclimate acting on differently oriented or inclined building assemblies.

Ambient Temperature and Humidity

Ambient temperature and humidity with respect to (res.) partial vapor pressure are the boundary conditions always affecting both sides of the building envelope. The climate-dependent exterior conditions may show large diurnal and seasonal variations. Therefore, hourly data are required for most building simulations. ASHRAE provides such meteorological data sets, including temperature and relative humidity, for many locations worldwide (see Chapter 14). These data sets usually represent average meteorological years based on long-term observations at specific locations. However, data of more extreme climate conditions may be important to assess the risks of moisture damage. Therefore, Sanders (1996) proposed using data of the coldest or warmest year in 10 years for hygrothermal analysis instead of data from an average year. However, the temperature at the building site may differ from the meteorological reference data when the site's altitude differs from that of the station recording the data. On average, there is a temperature shift of ∓1 K for every ±200 m. The microclimate around the building may result

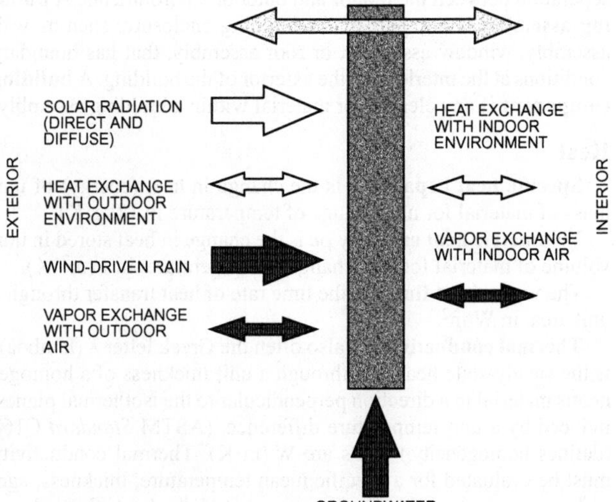

Fig. 1 Hygrothermal Loads and Alternating Diurnal or Seasonal Directions Acting on Building Envelope

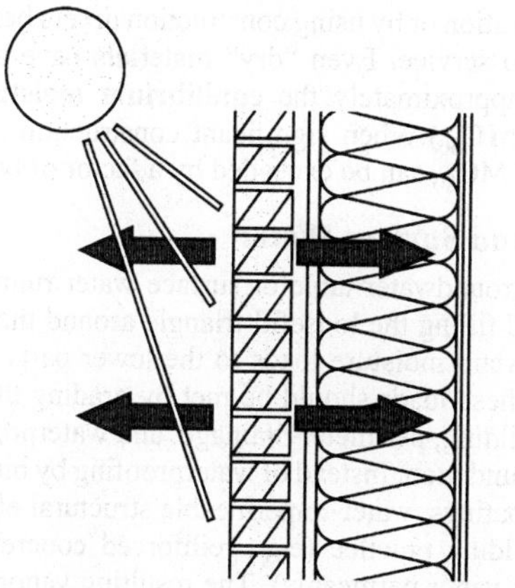

Fig. 2 Solar Vapor Drive and Interstitial Condensation

in an additional temperature shift that depends on the season. For example, the proximity of a lake can moderate seasonal temperature variations, with higher temperatures in winter and lower temperatures in summer compared to sites without water nearby. A low-lying site experiences lower temperatures in winter, whereas city temperatures are higher year round (METEOTEST 2007).

Indoor climate conditions depend on the purpose and occupation of the building. For most commercial constructions, temperature and humidity are controlled by HVAC systems with usually well-defined set points. Indoor conditions in residential buildings are influenced by the outdoor climate and by occupant behavior. The moisture release in an average household is highly variable. According to Sanders (1996), it may range from 3 to 20 kg/day, with an average of approximately 8 kg/day. This moisture must be removed by ventilation or air conditioning. The resulting relative humidity may be determined by hygrothermal whole-building simulation or by simple estimation methods using information on moisture production, air change rates, and climate-dependent HVAC operation (TenWolde and Walker 2001). The presence of spa or swimming pools may increase the load substantially. Information on typical indoor climate conditions of special-purpose constructions like spas, ice rinks, or agricultural buildings and production plants may be found in the 2007 *ASHRAE Handbook—HVAC Applications*.

Solar Radiation

Incident solar radiation is the major thermal load at the building envelope's exterior. For mainly direct solar radiation, the resultant heat source depends on the angle between the sun and the normal of the exposed surface and on its color (short-wave absorptivity). For calculation of incident solar heat flux and spectra, see Chapter 15.

Regarding moisture control, solar radiation is usually considered beneficial unless an envelope component is completely shaded. However, in some cases solar radiation combined with water from precipitation or other sources (e.g., construction moisture) can lead to severe moisture problems. For example, as shown in Figure 2, if the water-absorbing exterior layer of an assembly (e.g., brick veneer, a typical example of "reservoir" cladding) has been wetted by wind-driven rain, heat from solar radiation may drive some of the evaporating water inwards. The resulting high vapor pressure in the cladding causes vapor diffusion toward the ambient air as well as toward the interior of the building assembly, leading to condensation on material layers within the assemblies such as sheathing boards or vapor retarders. Adapting the permeance of vapor retarders and weather-resistive barriers (WRB) to the potential loads may improve the situation. ASHRAE Research Project RP-1091 (Burnett et al. 2004) showed that cladding ventilation is also an effective remedy within specified exterior air humidity limits.

Exterior Condensation

Long-Wave Radiant Effects. Long-wave radiation exchange of the envelope surface with the cold layers of the lower atmosphere is a major heat transfer process. At night or with the sun at a low angle, it results in a net heat flux to the sky (i.e., heat energy sink) (see Chapter 15). Depending on the building assembly's thermal properties, this may lead to a drop in the envelope's surface temperature below the ambient air temperature (overcooling). If the surface temperature reaches the air's dew point, condensation will occur on the exterior surface of the building assembly. Massive structures with a high thermal inertia do not usually lose enough heat to the nighttime radiation sink to bring the surface temperature below the dew point for a significant period of time. However, many modern building assemblies, such as lightweight roofs or exterior insulation finish systems (EIFS), have little thermal inertia in their exterior surface layers and are therefore subject to considerable amounts of exterior condensation (Künzel 2007).

Interior Temperature Differential. Exterior condensation can also occur on poorly insulated assemblies in cooling climates because of the operation of air-conditioning systems. Repeated exterior condensation or long-lasting, high relative humidity often provides the basis for soiling or microbial growth (fungi or algae), which may not be acceptable even though the durability of the assembly is unlikely to be affected.

Effect on Other Layers. Under exterior condensation conditions, ventilated assemblies may also experience condensation within the ventilated air layer. This phenomenon has been discovered by investigating pitched roofs with cathedral ceiling insulation (Hens 1992; Janssens 1998; Künzel and Grosskinski 1989). However, damage cases because of condensation in the ventilation plane are rare, except in metal roofs (Zheng et al. 2004). Occasionally, soiling because of condensate runoff has been reported.

Wind-Driven Rain

The load from rain, especially wind-driven rain, is the main reason for moisture-related building failure. Because the requirements of sometimes costly rain-protection measures depend on the local climate, some countries have introduced regional driving-rain classifications. Generally, coastal regions and those on the windward side of mountains receive the highest precipitation load. Areas of low rainfall do not have the potential for severe wind-driven rain.

Regional precipitation and wind loads are significant factors in determining local wind-driven rain load, but local exposure conditions are of equal importance. A building in the open field receives a higher load than one sheltered by a forest or other buildings. A quantification of exposure conditions for walls depending on landscape, neighborhood, and building size and geometry can be found in the British *Standard* BS 8104 and in the European ISO/DIN *Standard* 15927-3:2006. The average wind-driven rain load R_D in the open ground was investigated by Lacy (1965). It may be estimated from normal rain R_N and the wind velocity component v parallel to the considered orientation, as shown in the following equation:

$$R_D = f v R_N \quad (1)$$

where

R_D = wind-driven rain intensity, kg/(s·m²)
f = empirical factor = approximately 0.2 s/m
v = mean wind velocity, m/s
R_N = rain intensity on a horizontal surface in the open field, kg/(s·m²)

Figure 3 shows a typical plot (a "rain rose") of results from Equation (1) plotted in polar coordinates indicating the amount of wind-driven rain in mass per unit area hitting an unobstructed and isolated vertical surface in the open ground.

The driving rain load close to a façade is considerably less than in the open ground (as shown in Figure 4), and it becomes irregular. Tops and edges of walls generally receive the highest amount of driving rain deposition. This is caused by the airflow pattern around a building (see Chapter 24 for more information). At the windward side, high pressure gradients coincide with large changes in air velocity. The building acts as an obstacle for the wind, slowing down the airflow and subsequently reducing the wind-driven rain load near the façade. Gravity and the momentum of the rain droplets prevent them from following the airflow around the building, causing them to strike the façade mainly at the edges of the flow obstacle (Straube and Burnett 2000).

However, the irregular driving rain deposition is often evened out by water running off the hard-hit areas, especially when the façade surface has low water absorptivity or the wind-driven rain load is high enough to saturate the most exposed surface layers.

Roof overhangs can reduce the driving rain load on low-rise buildings. Slightly inclined wall sections or protruding façade elements may receive a considerable amount of splash water from façade areas above them, in addition to the direct driving rain deposition. This is often a problem for buildings with walls slightly out of vertical (Hens 2008).

Construction Moisture

Building damage as a result of migrating construction moisture has become more frequent because tight construction schedules leave little time for building materials to dry. Although often disregarded, construction moisture is either delivered with the building products or absorbed by the materials during storage or construction. Cast-in-place concrete, autoclaved aerated concrete (AAC), calcium silicate brick (CSB) and "green" wood are examples of materials that contain significant moisture when delivered. Stucco, mortar, clay brick, and concrete blocks are examples of materials that are either mixed or brought into contact with water at the construction site. All other porous building materials may take up considerable amounts of precipitation or groundwater when left unprotected during storage or construction before the enclosure of the building.

A single-family house made of AAC may initially contain more than 13 Mg of water in its walls. Care must be taken to safely remove that water, either by additional ventilation during the first years of operation or by using construction dryers before putting the building into service. Even "dry" materials have an initial water content of approximately the **equilibrium moisture content at 80% rh (EMC_{80})**.When significant construction moisture is encountered, EMC_{80} can be exceeded by a factor of two or more.

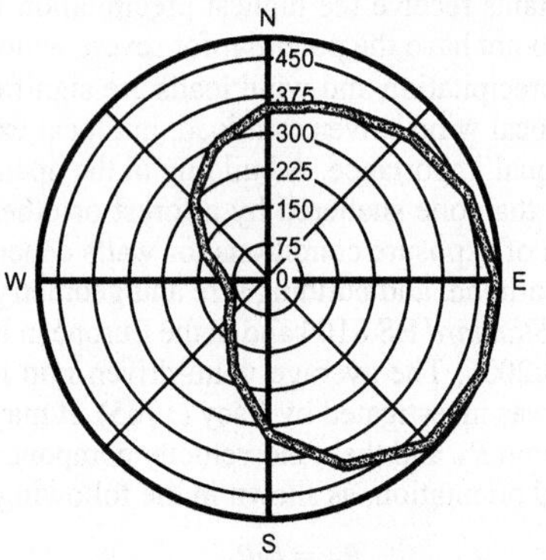

Fig. 3 Typical Wind-Driven Rain Rose for Open Ground

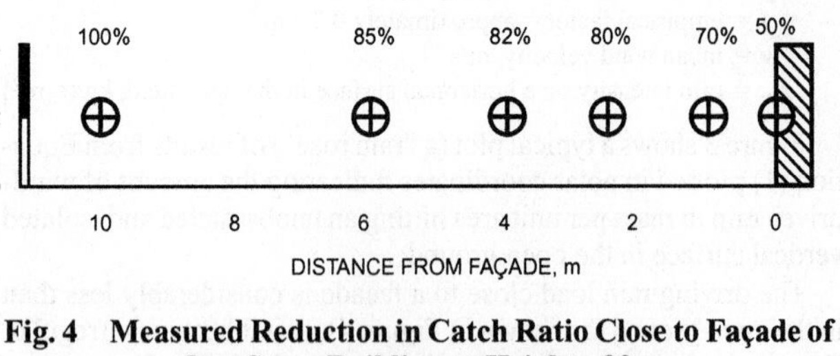

Fig. 4 Measured Reduction in Catch Ratio Close to Façade of One-Story Building at Height of 2 m

Ground- and Surface Water

A high groundwater table or surface water running toward the building and filling the loosefill triangle around the basement represent important moisture loads to the lower parts of the building envelope. These loads should be met by grading the ground away from the building, perimeter drainage, and waterproofing the basement and foundation. Instead of waterproofing by bituminous membranes or coatings, water-impermeable structural elements may be used in building practice (e.g., reinforced concrete, which may, however, be vapor permeable). The resulting vapor flux also presents a load that must be accounted for (e.g., by basement ventilation). Moisture loads in the ground may impair the performance of exterior basement insulation applied on the outside of the waterproofing layer. Therefore, special care must be taken to protect insulation from moisture accumulation unless the insulation material is itself impermeable to water and vapor (e.g., foam glass).

Wicking of ground- or surface water into porous walls by capillary action is called **rising damp**. This phenomenon may be a sign of poor drainage or waterproofing of the building's basement or foundation. However, other phenomena show moisture patterns similar to rising damp. If the wall is contaminated with salts, which may be the case in historic buildings, there might also be an elevated moisture content in the wall caused by a hygroscopicity increase resulting from water uptake by the salt crystals. Another reason for the appearance of rising damp may actually be surface condensation in unheated buildings during summer.

Air Pressure Differentials

Wind and stack effects caused by differences between indoor and outdoor temperature result in air pressure differentials over the building envelope. In contrast to wind, stack effect is a permanent load that may not be neglected. Worse, stack pressure may act in the same direction as vapor pressure: from inside to outside during the heating season, and in the opposite direction during the cooling season. Therefore, airflow through cracks, imperfect joints, or air-permeable assembly layers may cause interstitial condensation in a manner similar to vapor diffusion. However, condensation caused by stack-induced airflow is likely to be more intense and concentrated around leaks in the building envelope. This can become a problem at the top of a building, which may be especially vulnerable because of leaks at the parapets. To avoid moisture damage, airflow through and within the building envelope should be prevented by a continuous air barrier. Because it is difficult to guarantee total airtightness of the building envelope, the hygrothermal effect of airflow can be quite important, especially when high pressure differentials are expected (e.g., in multistory or mechanically pressurized buildings). For the practical determination of pressure differentials and airflow, see Chapter 16. Air pressures across the envelope may also drive liquid water inward or outward.

HEAT TRANSFER

Heat flow through the building envelope is mainly associated with the energy performance of buildings. However, other aspects of heat transfer are equally important. Interior surface temperature serves not only as an indicator for hygienic conditions in the building (e.g., conditions preventing surface condensation or mold growth), it can also be a major factor for thermal comfort. Temperature peaks and fluctuations within the building envelope or on its surfaces may also affect the envelope's durability. At low temperature, building materials tend to become less elastic and sometimes brittle, making them vulnerable to strain or mechanical impact. At high temperature, some materials degrade because of chemical reactions or irreversible deformation. Deformation and local mechanical failure can also occur under the influence of steep temperature gradients or transients. Whereas some of these aspects can be assessed by steady state calculations (e.g., heating energy losses), others require transient simulations for accurate evaluation.

As explained in Chapter 4, heat transfer by apparent conduction in a solid is governed by Fourier's law:

$$q = -k\,\mathrm{grad}(t)$$

$$q = -\left(k_x\frac{dt}{dx} + k_y\frac{dt}{dy} + k_z\frac{dt}{dz}\right) \quad (2)$$

where

q = heat flux, W/m^2
t = temperature, °C
k_x, k_y, k_z = apparent thermal conductivity in direction of x, y, and z axes, W/(m·K)
grad(t) = gradient of temperature (change in temperature per unit length, perpendicular to isothermal surfaces in solid), K/m
dt/dx = gradient of temperature along x axis, K/m
dt/dy = gradient of temperature along y axis, K/m
dt/dz = gradient of temperature along z axis, K/m

The thermal conductivity k of the material may be directionally dependent. In fact, many building materials show considerable anisotropy. Examples are wood and wood-based materials, mineral fiber insulation, and perforated bricks. Therefore, k_x, k_y, and k_z are generally not equal.

Substituting Equation (2) into the relationship for conservation of energy yields

$$\frac{\partial h}{\partial t} \times \frac{\partial t}{\partial \tau} = \mathrm{div}[k\,\mathrm{grad}(t)] + S$$
$$= \frac{\partial}{\partial x}\left(k_x\frac{\partial t}{\partial x}\right) + \frac{\partial}{\partial y}\left(k_y\frac{\partial t}{\partial y}\right) + \frac{\partial}{\partial z}\left(k_z\frac{\partial t}{\partial z}\right) + S \quad (3)$$

where

h = enthalpy per unit volume, J/m^3
S = heat sources and sinks (e.g., caused by latent heat of evaporation/condensation in presence of moisture or chemical reactions such as in concrete hydration), W/m^3

with

$$\frac{\partial h}{\partial \tau} = \rho_s c_s + w c_w \quad (4)$$

where

ρ_s = density of solid (dry material), kg/m^3
c_s = specific heat capacity of dry solid, J/(kg·K)
c_w = specific heat capacity of liquid water, J/(kg·K)
w = moisture content, kg/m^3

STEADY-STATE THERMAL RESPONSE

In steady state without sources or sinks, Equation (3) reduces to

$$\frac{\partial}{\partial x}\left(k_x\frac{\partial t}{\partial x}\right) + \frac{\partial}{\partial y}\left(k_y\frac{\partial t}{\partial y}\right) + \frac{\partial}{\partial z}\left(k_z\frac{\partial t}{\partial z}\right) = 0 \quad (5)$$

If the steady-state heat flux is only in one direction (e.g., perpendicular to the building envelope), Equation (2) can be rewritten for each material layer within the building envelope as

$$q = -k_m\frac{\Delta t}{\Delta x} = -C\,\Delta t = -\frac{1}{R}\Delta t \quad (6)$$

where

Δt = temperature difference between two interfaces of one material layer, K
Δx = layer thickness, m
k_m = mean thermal conductivity of material layer with thickness Δx, W/(m·K)
C = thermal conductance of layer with thickness Δx, W/(m^2·K)
R = thermal resistance of layer with thickness Δx, (m^2·K)/W

Under steady-state conditions, the one-dimensional heat flux is the same through all material layers, but their individual thermal conductance or resistance is usually different.

Thermal Resistance of a Flat Assembly

A single layer's thermal resistance to heat flow is given by the ratio of its thickness to its apparent thermal conductivity. Accordingly, the surface-to-surface thermal resistance of a flat building assembly composed of parallel layers (e.g., a ceiling, floor, or wall), or a curved component if the curvature is small, consists of the sum of the resistances (R-values) of all layers in series:

$$R_s = R_1 + R_2 + R_3 + R_4 + \cdots + R_n \quad (7)$$

where

$R_1, R_2, \ldots, R_n$ = resistances of individual layers, (m^2·K)/W
R_s = resistance of building assembly surface to surface (system resistance), (m^2·K)/W

For building components with nonuniform or irregular sections, such as hollow clay and concrete blocks, use the R-value of the unit as manufactured. To obtain the overall resistance (air to air), the surface film resistances R_i and R_o must be added to R.

The surface film resistance and its reciprocal, the heat transfer film coefficient, specify the heat transfer to or from a surface by the combined effect of convection and conduction. Although these contributions are affected by surface roughness and temperature difference between the air and surface, the largest influence is that of air movement, turbulence, and velocity close to the surface. Because air movement at the envelope surface depends on wind speed and direction, as well as flow patterns around the building, which are usually unknown, average film coefficients for interior and exterior heat transfer are normally used. Correlations such as that of Schwarz (1971) link the convective film coefficient to wind speed recorded at a height of 10 m and to orientation of the surface (windward or leeward side). However, because the surface-to-surface thermal resistance of a wall is usually high compared with the surface film resistances, an exact value is of minor importance for most applications.

Heat is also transported between the envelope's surface and the environment by thermal radiation. Because air is rather permeable to long-wave radiation, the radiative heat exchange takes place between the surface and objects in the environment, not the surrounding air. Heat transfer by radiation between two surfaces is controlled by the character of the surfaces (emittance and reflectance), the temperature difference between them, and the angle factor through which they see each other. Indoors, the external wall surface exchanges radiation with partition walls, floor, and ceiling, furniture, and other external walls. In winter, most of the other surfaces have a higher temperature than the external wall surface; therefore, there is a net heat flux to the external wall by radiative exchange. Outdoors, the external wall surface sees the ground, neighboring buildings, and the sky. Without the sun, thermal radiation from the sky is normally low compared to the radiation from the wall. This means the wall is losing energy to the sky. Especially during clear nights, the temperature of the exterior surface of the external wall may drop below the ambient air temperature. In this case, convective and radiative heat transfer at the surface are opposed to each other.

Combined Convective and Radiative Surface Transfer

For simplicity, convective and radiative surface transfer coefficients are often combined, leading to the **apparent transfer coefficient** h:

$$q = h(t_{en} - t_s) \tag{8}$$

with

$$h = h_c + h_r \tag{9}$$

where

q = total surface heat transfer, W/m²
h = apparent surface transfer coefficient, W/(m²·K)
h_r = surface transfer coefficient to account for long-wave radiation exchange, W/(m²·K)
h_c = convective surface transfer coefficient (also called surface film coefficient), W/(m²·K)
t_{en} = environmental temperature, °C
t_s = surface temperature, °C

For indoor surface heat transfer, this approach is acceptable when only the heat transport through the building envelope is considered. Environmental temperature t_{en} includes the temperature of surfaces within the field of view of the considered envelope assembly. When all these surfaces are of partition walls and floors that have the same temperature as the indoor air, t_{en} may be replaced by the indoor air temperature.

This approach becomes questionable when heat transfer at the outdoor surface is concerned. Because radiation to the sky can lead to surface temperatures below ambient air temperature, Equation (8) underestimates the real heat flux when environmental temperature is replaced by outdoor air temperature. Therefore, t_{en} must include all short- and long-wave radiation contributions perpendicular to the assembly's exterior surface. However, t_{en} cannot be used for moisture transfer calculations. Therefore, a more convenient way may be to treat the heat transfer by convection and the radiation exchange separately. In this case, h_r in Equation (9) becomes zero and t_{en} is equal to the outdoor air temperature. The heat exchange by radiation is then calculated by balancing the solar and environmental radiation onto the assembly's exterior surface with the long-wave emission from it.

Steady-state calculation of thermal transport through the building envelope is generally done using surface resistances based on combined surface transfer coefficients, with R being the inverse of h. Because of greater air movement outdoors, the mean thermal resistance at the exterior surface is lower than at the interior surface. Typical ranges for the apparent exterior and interior surface transfer coefficient with surface infrared reflectance ≤0.1 (nonmetallic) are

$$R_o = 0.03 \text{ to } 0.06 \text{ (m}^2\text{·K)/W}$$

$$R_i = 0.12 \text{ to } 0.20 \text{ (m}^2\text{·K)/W}$$

To calculate thermal transmittance U, the lower values of R should be used. To calculate interior surface film temperature for risk assessment of surface condensation or mold growth, the higher interior and lower exterior R values should be used.

Heat Flow Across an Air Space

Heat flow across an air space is affected by the nature of the boundary surfaces, orientation of the air space, distance between boundary surfaces, and direction of heat flow. Air space thermal conductance, the reciprocal of the air space thermal resistance, is the sum of a radiation component, a conduction component, and a convection component. For computational purposes, spaces are considered airtight, with neither air leakage nor air washing along the boundary surfaces.

The radiation portion is affected by the temperature of the two boundary surfaces and by their respective surface properties. For surfaces that can be considered ideal gray, the surface properties are emittance, absorptance, and reflectance. Chapter 4 explains all three in depth. For an opaque surface, reflectance is equal to one minus the emittance, which varies with surface type and condition and radiation wavelength. The combined effect of the emittances of the two boundary surfaces is expressed by the effective emittance E of the air space. Table 2 in Chapter 26 lists typical emittance values for reflective surfaces and building materials, and the corresponding effective emittance for air spaces. More exact surface emittance values should be obtained by tests. The radiation component is not affected by the thickness of the air space, its orientation, direction of heat flow, or order of emittance (i.e., which surface is hot or cold).

In contrast, heat transfer by convection is affected markedly by the orientation of the air space, direction of heat flow, temperature difference across the space, and, in some cases, thickness of the space. It is also slightly affected by the mean temperatures of both surfaces. For air spaces in building components, radiation and convection components both contribute to the total heat flow. An example of the magnitudes of heat flow by radiation and convection/ conduction across a vertical or horizontal airspace (up and down) is given in Figure 5.

Table 3 in Chapter 26 lists typical thermal resistance values of sealed air spaces of uniform thickness with moderately smooth, plane, parallel surfaces. These data are based on experimental measurements (Robinson et al. 1954). Resistance values for systems with air spaces can be estimated from these results if emittance values are corrected for field conditions. However, for some common composite building insulation systems involving mass-type insulation with a reflective surface in conjunction with an air space, the resistance value may be appreciably lower than the estimated value, particularly if the air space is not sealed or of uniform thickness (Palfey 1980). For critical applications, a particular design's effectiveness should be confirmed by actual test data undertaken by using the ASTM hot-box method (ASTM *Standard* C1363). This test is especially necessary for constructions combining reflective and nonreflective thermal insulation.

Total Thermal Resistance of a Flat Building Assembly

Total thermal resistance to heat flow through a flat building component composed of parallel layers between the environments at both sides is given by

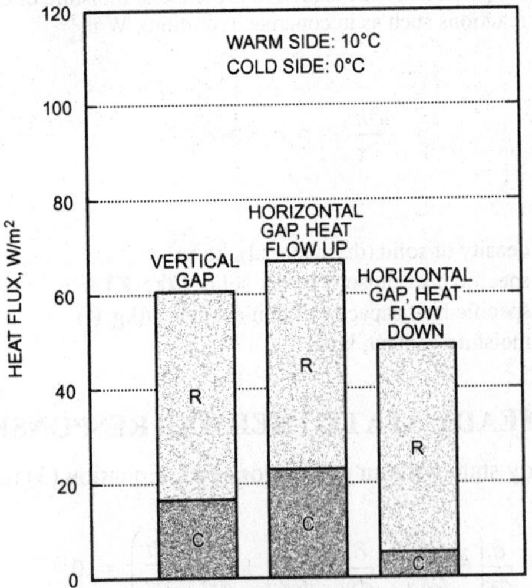

Fig. 5 Heat Flux by Thermal Radiation and Combined Convection and Conduction Across Vertical or Horizontal Air Layer

$$R_T = R_i + R_s + R_o \quad (10)$$

where

R_i = apparent thermal resistance of interior surface film, (m²·K)/W
R_o = apparent thermal resistance of exterior surface film, (m²·K)/W
R_s = resistance of building assembly surface to surface (system resistance), (m²·K)/W

Thermal Transmittance of a Flat Building Assembly

The thermal transmittance or U-factor of a flat building assembly is the reciprocal of R_T:

$$U = 1/R_T \quad (11)$$

Calculating thermal transmittance requires knowing the (1) apparent thermal resistance of all homogeneous layers, (2) thermal resistance of the nonhomogeneous layers, (3) surface film resistances at both sides of the construction, and (4) thermal resistances of air spaces in the construction. The steady-state heat flux Q_n across the building envelope assembly is then defined by

$$Q_n = A_n U_n (t_i - t_o) \quad (12)$$

where

t_i, t_o = indoor and outdoor reference temperatures, °C
A_n = component area, m²
U_n = U-factor of component, W/(m²·K)

Interface Temperatures in a Flat Building Component

The temperature drop through any layer of an assembly is proportional to its resistance. Thus, the temperature drop Δt_j through R_j is

$$\Delta t_j = \frac{R_j(t_i - t_o)}{R_T} \quad (13)$$

The temperature in an interface j then becomes ($t_o < t_i$)

$$t_j = t_o + \frac{R_o^j}{R_T}(t_i - t_o) \quad (14)$$

where R_o^j is the sum of thermal resistances between inside and interface j in flat assembly, in (m²·K)/W.

If the apparent thermal conductivity of materials in a building component is highly temperature-dependent, the mean temperature must be known before assigning an appropriate thermal resistance. In such a case, use trial and error: first, select the R-values for the particular layers. Then calculate total resistance R_T with Equation (10) and the temperature at each interface using Equation (14). The mean temperature in each layer (arithmetic mean of its surface temperatures) can then be used to obtain second-generation R-values. The procedure is repeated until the R-values are correctly selected for the resulting mean temperatures. Generally, this is done in two or three trial calculations.

Series and Parallel Heat Flow Paths

In many building assemblies (e.g., wood-frame construction), components are arranged so that heat flows in parallel paths of different conductances. If no heat flows through lateral paths, the thermal transmittance through each path may be calculated. The average transmittance of the enclosure is then

$$U_{av} = aU_a + bU_b + \cdots + nU_n \quad (15)$$

where $a, b, \ldots, n$ are the surface-weighted path fractions for a typical basic area composed of several different paths with transmittances $U_a, U_b, \ldots, U_n$.

If heat can flow laterally with little resistance in any continuous layer, so that transverse isothermal planes result, the flat construction performs as a series combination of layers, of which one or more provide parallel paths. Total average resistance $R_{T(av)}$ in that case is the sum of the resistance of the layers between the isothermal planes, each layer being calculated and the results weighted by contributing surface area. For further information, see Chapter 27.

The U-factor, assuming parallel heat flow only, is usually lower than that assuming combined series-parallel heat flow. The actual U-factor lies between the two. Without test results, a best choice must be selected. Generally, if the construction contains a layer in which lateral conduction is somewhat high compared to heat flux through the wall, a value closer to the series-parallel calculation should be used. If, however, there is no layer of high lateral conductance, use a value closer to the parallel calculation. For assemblies with large differences in material conductivities (e.g., assemblies using metal structural elements), the zone method is recommended (see Chapter 27). An alternative is using linear and punctual thermal transmittances. These characterize the excess heat transfer per degree temperature difference caused by a linear or local thermal bridge.

Thermal Bridges and Whole-Assembly Thermal Transmittance

In many envelope constructions, heat flow develops two- or three-dimensionally (**thermal bridging**). Heat loss and gain through thermal bridges are higher than their share in total surface may suggest. In heating climates, the inside surface may also be colder than the surrounding surfaces. This makes thermal bridges likely places for dirt deposit and mold growth because of elevated moisture content of surfaces in equilibrium with higher relative humidity.

The hot-box method (ASTM *Standard* C1363) or a multidimensional computer model should be used to determine the overall thermal transmittance of a wall with thermal bridges. Computer models also give the temperatures and heat fluxes.

For flat-wall thermal bridging calculations, refer to the zone and modified zone methods described in Chapter 27. Two- and three-dimensional thermal bridging estimates require the use of appropriate computer modeling tools.

TRANSIENT THERMAL RESPONSE

Steady-state calculations are used to define the average heating energy demand in cold climates. However, in climates where daily temperature swings oscillate around a comfortable mean temperature, transient analysis is more appropriate. The thermal response of a building to daily swings in temperature and solar radiation depends on the properties of its opaque and transparent (fenestration) envelope components and on its operation. The effects on the mutual dependences of the different factors are rather complex and there is no simplified approach that can account for these interactions. Therefore, whole-building simulations complying with ANSI/ASHRAE *Standard* 140 are recommended.

AIRFLOW

Air transfer in and through building components develops when the air permeance of the component differs from zero. Driving forces are stack pressure, wind pressure, and pressure differences induced by the mechanical system; see Chapters 16 and 24 for more details. When performing air flux calculations through a building component, distinguish between open porous materials and the openings that occur with layers, cavities, cracks, leaks, and intentionally installed vents. Air flux through an open porous material is given by

$$m_a = -k_a \, \text{grad}(P_a) \tag{16}$$

where

m_a = air flux, kg/(s·m²)
k_a = air permeability of open porous material, kg/(Pa·s·m)
grad(P_a) = gradient in total air pressure (stack, wind, and mechanical systems), Pa/m

For openings in layers, cavities, cracks, leaks, and intentionally installed vents, the air flux (fractionated layers) or air transfer equation (all other) is

$$m_a \text{ or } M_a = C(\Delta P_a)^n \tag{17}$$

where the flow coefficient C and flow exponent n are determined experimentally.

A single layer with low air permeability (an **airflow retarder**) minimizes air flux through an assembly. The main function of an airflow retarder is to minimize airflow through an assembly, so the retarder must be continuous and leak-free. It must also be strong enough to withstand the air pressure difference.

When a building component contains coupled discrete layers, cavities, cracks, leaks, and intentionally installed vents, airflow becomes three-dimensional. For such cases, Kronvall (1982) developed an equivalent hydraulic network methodology, which was adapted by Janssens (1998) to calculate airflow in lightweight sloped roofs.

Water Vapor Flow by Air Movement

Air not only transports heat but also the water vapor the air contains. The water vapor flux is represented by

$$m_v = Wm_a \approx \frac{0.62}{P_a} m_a p \tag{18}$$

where

W = humidity ratio of moving air
m_a = air flux, kg/(s·m²)
p = partial water vapor pressure in air, Pa
P_a = atmospheric air pressure, Pa

Even small air fluxes can carry large amounts of water vapor when compared to vapor diffusion. However, potentially damaging airflow always takes place through cracks and leaky joints rather than through the entire area of a building component.

Heat Flux with Airflow

Air leakage through building components may increase ventilation in a building beyond that needed for comfort and indoor air quality (see Chapter 16). Air also carries heat that may degrade a building's thermal performance. Airflow changes the assumption at the basis of Equation (2) that no mass flow develops in the solid. The sensible heat flux q that moves together with the air is

$$q = c_a m_a t \tag{19}$$

where q is in W/m² and c_a is the specific heat capacity of air, J/(kg·K).

MOISTURE TRANSFER

Moisture may enter a building envelope by various paths, including built-in moisture, water leaks, wind-driven rain, and foundation leaks. Water vapor activates sorption in the envelope materials, and water vapor flow in and through the envelope may cause condensation on both nonporous and wet, porous surfaces.

Visible and invisible degradation caused by moisture is an important factor limiting the useful life of a building. Invisible degradation includes the decrease of thermal resistance of building and insulating materials and the decrease in strength and stiffness of load-bearing materials. Visible degradation includes (1) mold on surfaces, (2) decay of wood-based materials, (3) spalling of masonry and concrete caused by freeze/thaw cycles, (4) hydration of plastic materials, (5) corrosion of metals, (6) damage from expansion of materials (e.g., buckling of wood floors), and (7) decline in appearance. In addition, high moisture levels can lead to odors and mold spores in indoor air.

MOISTURE STORAGE IN BUILDING MATERIALS

Many building materials are porous. The pores provide a large internal surface, which generally has an affinity for water molecules. In some materials, such as wood, moisture may also be adsorbed in the cell wall itself. The amount of water in these **hygroscopic** (water-attracting) materials is related to the relative humidity of surrounding air. When relative humidity rises, hygroscopic materials gain moisture (**adsorption**), and when relative humidity drops, they lose moisture (**desorption**). The relationship between relative humidity and moisture content at a particular temperature is represented in a graph called the **sorption isotherm** (Figure 6). Isotherms obtained by adsorption are not identical to isotherms obtained by desorption; this difference is called **hysteresis**. At high relative humidity, small pores become entirely filled with water by capillary condensation. The maximum moisture content should be reached at 100% rh, when all pores are water-filled, but experimentally this can only be achieved in a vacuum, by boiling the material or by keeping it in contact with water for an extremely long time. In practice, the maximum moisture content of a porous material is lower. That value is referred to as **free water saturation** w_f or sometimes **capillary moisture content**. Figure 6 shows a typical sorption curve, giving the equilibrium moisture content as a function of relative humidity. The equilibrium moisture content increases with relative humidity, especially above 80% rh. It decreases slightly with increasing temperature. Moisture contents above w_{95} (the equilibrium water content at 95% rh) cannot be achieved solely by vapor adsorption, because this region is characterized by capillary (unbound) water.

Chapter 32 describes hygroscopic substances and their use as dehumidifying agents. Chapter 26 has data on the moisture content of various materials in equilibrium with the atmosphere at various relative humidity steps. Wood and many other hygroscopic materials change dimensions with variations in moisture content.

Porous materials also absorb liquid water when in contact with it. Liquid water may be present because of leaks, rain penetration, flooding, or surface condensation. Wetting may be so complete that the material reaches free water saturation when the largest pores are filled with water. Up to this point there is still a distinct equilibrium between the moisture content of the material and its environment. This becomes evident when different porous materials are brought in direct (capillary) contact with each other. In that case, there is capillary flow from one material to the other until all pores at a certain size are filled with water in both materials; all pores with sizes above this limit remain empty because smaller capillaries have a higher suction force than larger ones. This phenomenon is used to determine the moisture storage function above 95% rh, which represents the limit of vapor sorption tests in climatic chambers. Dalehaug et al. (2005), Krus (1996), and Roels et al. (2003) described using a pressure plate apparatus, in which water-saturated material samples are placed on a porous membrane permeable to water but impermeable to air. Then pressure is applied in different steps each time until capillary equilibrium is achieved. The equilibrium moisture content at each pressure step is determined by weighing the samples. The moisture storage function from zero pressure (free

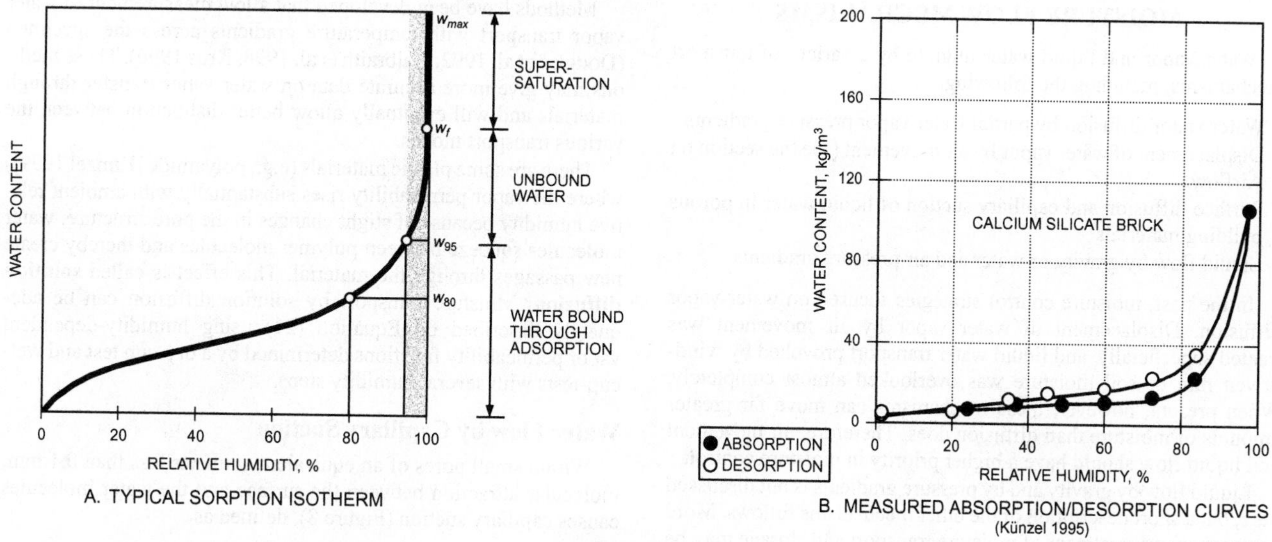

Fig. 6 Sorption Isotherms for Porous Building Materials

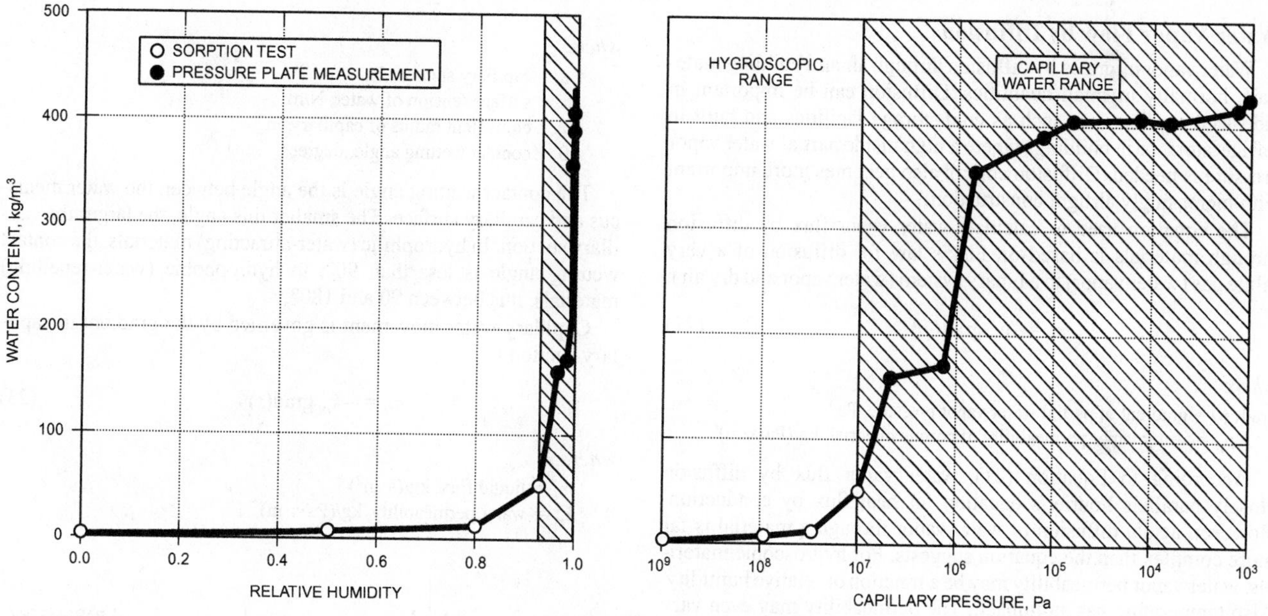

Fig. 7 Sorption Isotherm and Suction Curve for Autoclaved Aerated Concrete (AAC)
(Künzel and Holm 2001)

water saturation at 100% rh) up to 10 MPa, which corresponds to approximately 93% rh, is defined by plotting the equilibrium water content over the applied pressure (Figure 7), which is assumed to be equal to the suction pressure of the largest still-water-filled capillaries.

For a continuous moisture storage function from the dry state to 100% rh, the sorption isotherm and the resultant curve from the pressure plate test are combined, either by converting the suction pressure into relative humidity or vice versa, using Kelvin's equation:

$$\phi = \exp\left(-\frac{s}{\rho_W R_D T}\right) \tag{20}$$

where

ϕ = relative humidity of air in pores
s = suction pressure, Pa
ρ_w = density of water, kg/m³
R_D = gas constant for water vapor, J/(kg·K)
T = absolute temperature, K

The hatched zones in Figure 7 represent the overhygroscopic range where the converted results from the pressure plate tests are plotted to complete the sorption isotherm. This narrow range is less important if vapor diffusion is the dominant moisture transport mechanism, for which an approximative interpolation of the moisture storage function between the end of the sorption isotherm and the free water saturation suffices. However, if capillary water flow from one material to the other becomes dominant (e.g., water absorption by bricks from mortar or stucco), the influence of the pressure plate results on the outcome of the calculation may not be negligible (Krus 1996). In that case, the detailed suction curve (Figure 7, right) should be used for simulations.

MOISTURE FLOW MECHANISMS

Water vapor and liquid water migrate by a variety of transport mechanisms, including the following:

- Water vapor diffusion by partial water vapor pressure gradients
- Displacement of water vapor by air movement (see the section on Airflow)
- Surface diffusion and capillary suction of liquid water in porous building materials
- Liquid flow by gravity or water and air pressure gradients

In the past, moisture control strategies focused on water vapor diffusion. Displacement of water vapor by air movement was treated superficially, and liquid water transport provoked by wind-driven rain or soil moisture was overlooked almost completely. When present, however, these mechanisms can move far greater amounts of moisture than diffusion does. Therefore, air movement and liquid flow should have a higher priority in moisture control.

Liquid flow by gravity and by pressure gradients is not discussed here, but a short description of the other mechanisms follows. More comprehensive treatment of moisture transport and storage may be found in Hens (1996), Künzel (1995), and Pedersen (1990). For a discussion of water vapor in air, see Chapter 1.

Water Vapor Flow by Diffusion

Water vapor migrates by diffusion through air and building materials, normally in small quantities. Diffusion can be important in industrial applications, such as cold-storage facilities and built-in refrigerators, or in buildings where a high inside partial water vapor pressure is needed. Diffusion control also becomes more important with increasingly airtight construction.

The equation used to calculate water vapor flux by diffusion through materials is based on Fick's law for diffusion of a very dilute gas (water vapor) in a binary system (water vapor and dry air):

$$m_v = -\mu_p \,\text{grad}(p) \tag{21}$$

where

grad(p) = gradient of partial water vapor pressure, Pa
μ_p = water vapor permeability of porous material, kg/(Pa·s·m)

According to Equation (21), water vapor flux by diffusion closely parallels Fourier's equation for heat flux by conduction. However, actual diffusion of water vapor through a material is far more complex than the equation suggests. For hygroscopic materials, water vapor permeability may be a function of relative humidity. Also temperature has an impact., The permeability may even vary spatially or by orientation because of variations or anisotropy in the material's porous system.

Test methods for measuring water vapor permeability are described in ASTM *Standard* E96. Water vapor flux through a material is determined gravimetrically while maintaining constant temperature and partial water vapor pressure differential across the specimen. Tests are usually done in a climatic chamber at controlled temperature (20 or 23°C) and 50% rh. The material samples are sealed to the top of a cup that contains either a desiccant (dry-cup) or water res. salt solution (wet-cup).

Permeability is usually expressed in kg/(Pa·s·m) and permeance in kg/(Pa·s·m^2). Whereas *permeability* refers to the water vapor flux per unit thickness, *permeance* is used in reference to a material of a specific thickness. For example, a material that is 50 mm thick generally is assumed to have half the permeance of a 25 mm thick material, even though permeances of many materials often are not strictly proportional to thickness. In many cases, the property ignores the effect of cracks or holes in the surface. It is inappropriate to refer to permeability with regard to inhomogeneous or composite materials, such as structural insulated panels (SIPs) or film-faced insulation batts.

Methods have been developed that allow measurement of water vapor transport with temperature gradients across the specimen (Douglas et al. 1992; Galbraith et al. 1998; Krus 1996). These methods may give more accurate data on water vapor transfer through materials and will eventually allow better distinction between the various transport modes.

There are some plastic materials (e.g., polyamide [Künzel 1999]) where the vapor permeability rises substantially with ambient relative humidity because of slight changes in the pore structure: water molecules squeeze between polymer molecules and thereby create new passages through the material. This effect is called **solution diffusion**. Moisture transport by solution diffusion can be adequately described by Equation (21) using humidity-dependent vapor permeability functions determined by a dry-cup test and wet-cup-tests with several humidity steps.

Water Flow by Capillary Suction

Within small pores of an equivalent diameter less than 0.1 mm, molecular attraction between the surface and the water molecules causes capillary suction (Figure 8), defined as

$$s = \frac{2\sigma\cos\theta}{r} \tag{22}$$

where

s = capillary suction, Pa
σ = surface tension of water, N/m
r = equivalent radius of capillary, m
θ = contact wetting angle, degrees

The contact wetting angle is the angle between the water meniscus and capillary surface. The smaller this angle, the larger the capillary suction. In hydrophilic (water-attracting) materials, the contact wetting angle is less than 90°; in hydrophobic (water-repelling) materials, it is between 90 and 180°.

Capillary water movement is governed by the gradient in capillary suction s:

$$m_l = -k_m \,\text{grad}(s) \tag{23}$$

where

m_l = liquid flux, kg/(s·m^2)
k_m = water permeability, kg/(Pa·s·m)

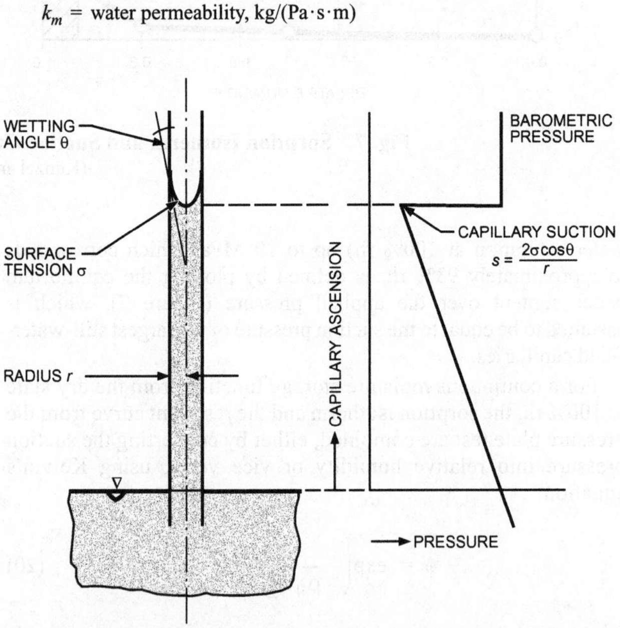

Fig. 8 Capillary Rise in Hydrophilic Materials

Alternatively, replace s with relative humidity [for conversion, see Equation (20)]:

$$m_l = -\delta_\phi \,\text{grad}(\phi) \tag{24}$$

where δ_ϕ is the liquid transport coefficient related to the relative humidity as driving potential, in kg/(m·s).

Capillary suction is greater in smaller capillaries, so water moves from larger to smaller capillaries. In pores with constant equivalent radius, water moves toward zones with smaller contact wetting angles. Although surface tension is a decreasing function of temperature (the higher the temperature, the lower the surface tension) and water moves toward zones with lower temperature, that effect is small compared to the effect of equivalent pore diameter and contact angle.

Capillary suction increases linearly with the inverse of the radius [see Equation (22)], but the flow resistance increases proportionally to the fourth power of the inverse radius. Therefore, larger pores have a much greater liquid transport capacity than smaller pores. Because larger pores can only be filled with water when the smaller pores are already saturated, the liquid transport capacity is a function of moisture content. Thus, water permeability k_m and liquid transport coefficient δ_ϕ are also functions of water content. Determination of these functions is, however, quite difficult because it requires the measurement of suction res. relative humidity distributions during transient water absorption and drying tests (Plagge et al. 2007).

Whereas measuring suction requires experience and special preparation of material samples, determining one-dimensional moisture content distributions in porous building materials can be done accurately with state-of-the-art scanning technologies using nuclear magnetic resonance (NMR), or gamma ray or x-ray attenuation (Krus 1996; Kumaran 1991; van Besien et al. 2002). Transient water content profiles recorded during such scanning tests serve to determine the liquid diffusivity D_w of the examined material, which is defined by

$$m_l = -D_w \,\text{grad}(w) \tag{25}$$

where

w = moisture content, kg/m³
D_w = liquid diffusivity, m²/s

For most hygroscopic building materials, D_w is a function of moisture content. The diffusivity of calcium silicate brick, a masonry block with hygrothermal behavior that has been investigated extensively, shows an almost exponential increase with water content. As shown in Figure 9, the straight line indicates an exponential increase because the ordinate has a logarithmic scale. This exponential dependence of D_w has been found for many porous materials. Therefore, an exponential approximation is often used when D_w is determined from simple water absorption tests (Kumaran 1999; Künzel 1995).

Although Equation (25), which resembles Fick's law for diffusion, would seem a natural choice for calculating liquid flow, its use is not recommended because water content is not a continuous potential in building envelopes consisting of different materials. Using Equation (23) or (24) is recommended because relative humidity ϕ and capillary suction s are considered to be continuous potentials (no jumps at material interfaces). Where diffusivity functions are available, the liquid transport coefficient δ_ϕ in Equation (24) can be determined by

$$\delta_\phi = D_w \, dw/d\phi \tag{26}$$

where $dw/d\phi$ is the slope of sorption isotherm res. moisture retention curve, in kg/m³.

Liquid Flow at Low Moisture Content

The explanation of liquid flow at low moisture content is still a matter of controversy. Some researchers assume it is surface diffusion (e.g., Krus 1996), whereas others believe liquid flow only fully starts beyond critical moisture content (Carmeliet et al. 1999; Kumaran et al. 2003; Vos and Coelman 1967). Liquid flow begins within the hygroscopic range, and is often mistaken for a part of vapor diffusion. In porous materials with a fixed pore structure, the apparent increase in vapor permeability during a wet-cup test may be partly due to liquid transport phenomena, and partly to shorter diffusion paths among water islands in the porous system formed by capillary condensation. Surface diffusion is defined as molecular movement of water adsorbed at the pore walls of the material. The driving potential is the mobility of the molecules, which depends on relative humidity in the pores (i.e., the adsorbed water migrates from zones of high to low relative humidity). Liquid flow, if present at low moisture content, can be described by Equations (23) or (24), as for capillary flow.

Under isothermal conditions, it is impossible to differentiate between vapor and liquid flow at low moisture content. However, in the presence of a temperature gradient, both transport processes may oppose each other in a pore; the fluxes may go in opposite directions (Künzel 1995). This can be explained by looking at the physical processes in a single capillary going through a wall, as shown in Figure 10. In winter, the indoor vapor pressure is usually higher than outdoors while the indoor humidity is lower than outdoor relative humidity. Therefore, the partial vapor pressure gradient is opposed to the relative humidity gradient over the cross section of a exterior wall. Looking at one capillary in that wall under very dry conditions (Figure 10), the only moisture transport mechanism is vapor diffusion and the total flux is directed towards the exterior. If the average humidity in the wall rises to 50 to 80% rh, liquid water begins to move in the opposite direction either by surface diffusion or by capillary suction in the nanopores. Under these conditions, the total moisture flux may go to zero if both fluxes are of the same magnitude (Krus 1996). When conditions are very wet (e.g., from wind-driven rain), most of the capillary pores are filled with water, and the dominant transport mechanism is flow by capillary suction.

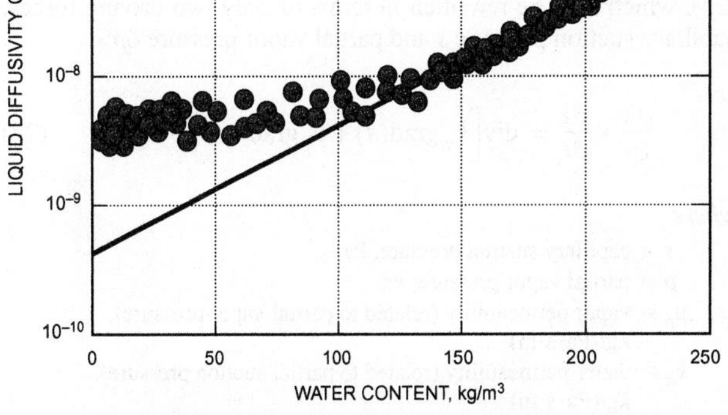

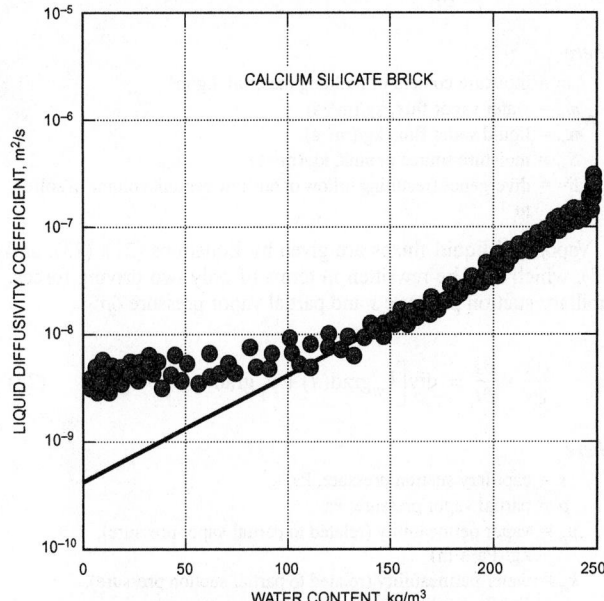

Fig. 9 Moisture Dependent Diffusivity of Calcium Silicate Brick (CSB) Determined from NMR Scans During Water Absorption Tests
(Krus 1996)

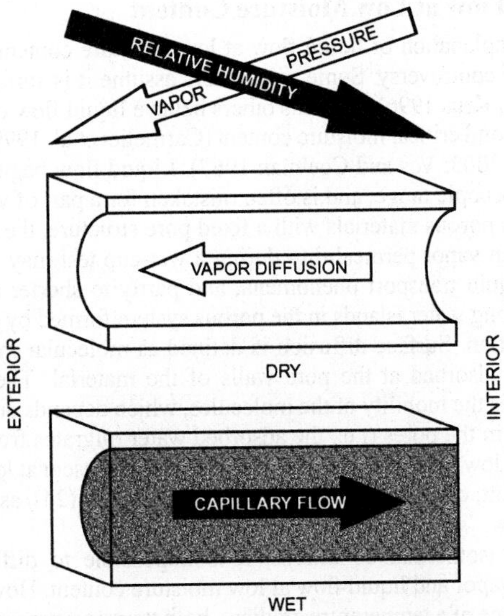

Fig. 10 Moisture Fluxes by Vapor Diffusion and Liquid Flow in Single Capillary of Exterior Wall under Winter Conditions

Transient Moisture Flow

It is difficult to experimentally distinguish between liquid flow by suction and water vapor flow by diffusion in porous, hygroscopic materials. Because these materials have a very complex porous system and each surface is transversed by liquid-filled pore fractions and vapor-filled pore fractions, vapor and liquid flow are often treated as parallel processes. This allows expression of moisture flow as the summation of the two transport equations, one using water vapor pressure to drive water vapor flow by diffusion, and the other using either capillary suction or relative humidity ϕ to drive liquid moisture flow. The conservation equation in that case can be written as

$$\frac{\partial w}{\partial t} = -\text{div}(m_w + m_v) + S_w \qquad (27)$$

where

w = moisture content of building material, kg/m³
m_v = water vapor flux, kg/(m²·s)
m_w = liquid water flux, kg/(m²·s)
S_w = moisture source or sink, kg/(m³·s)
div = divergence (resulting inflow or outflow per unit volume of solid), m⁻¹

Vapor and liquid fluxes are given by Equations (21), (23), and (24), which may be rewritten in terms of only two driving forces, capillary suction pressure s and partial vapor pressure δp:

$$\frac{\partial w}{\partial s} \times \frac{\partial s}{\partial t} = \text{div}\left[k_m \text{grad}(s) + \mu_p \text{grad}(p)\right] + S_w \qquad (28)$$

where

s = capillary suction pressure, Pa
p = partial vapor pressure, Pa
μ_p = vapor permeability (related to partial vapor pressure), kg/(Pa·s·m)
k_m = water permeability (related to partial suction pressure), kg/(Pa·s·m)
S_w = moisture source or sink, kg/(m³·s)

Alternatively, suction pressure s in Equation (28) can be replaced by relative humidity as the sole variable, with the saturation pressure p_{sat} only a function of temperature:

$$\frac{\partial w}{\partial \phi} \times \frac{\partial \phi}{\partial \tau} = \text{div}\left[\delta_\phi \text{grad}(\phi) + \mu_p \text{grad}(\phi p_{sat})\right] + S_w \qquad (29)$$

where

ϕ = relative humidity, %
p_{sat} = saturation vapor pressure, Pa
μ_p = vapor permeability (related to partial vapor pressure), kg/(Pa·s·m)
δ_ϕ = liquid transport coefficient (related to relative humidity), kg/(s·m)

Because of the strong temperature dependence of vapor pressure res. saturation vapor pressure, Equation (28) res. (29) must be coupled with Equation (3) to describe nonisothermal moisture flow. Under isothermal conditions, Equation (28) res. (29) could be solved independently. However, pure isothermal conditions hardly ever exist in reality because as soon as water evaporates or condenses, the latent heat effect leads to temperature differences. Other potentials may be used if material properties appropriate to those potentials are available.

COMBINED HEAT, AIR, AND MOISTURE TRANSFER

The consequences of combined heat, air, and moisture transfer can be detrimental to a building's thermal performance, occupant comfort, and indoor air quality. Air in- and exfiltration short-circuit the U-factor as a designed wall performance. Wind washing, inside air washing, and stack-induced air movement may increment the U-factor by a factor of 2.5 or more. High moisture levels in building materials may also have a negative effect on the thermal performance of the building envelope. Therefore, it is advisable to analyze the combined heat, air, and moisture transfer through building assemblies. However, some of these transport phenomena, especially those involving airflow, are three-dimensional in nature and difficult to predict because they only occur through accidental gaps, cracks, or imperfect joints. Research that attempts to describe these effects is ongoing, but at present, practitioners can only use simplified tools or hygrothermal models that do not yet cover all airflow aspects.

SIMPLIFIED HYGROTHERMAL DESIGN CALCULATIONS AND ANALYSES

SURFACE HUMIDITY AND CONDENSATION

Surface condensation occurs when water vapor contacts a nonporous surface that has a temperature lower than the dew point of the surrounding air. Insulation should therefore be thick enough to ensure that the surface temperature on the warm side of an insulated assembly always exceeds the dew-point temperature there. However, even without reaching the dew point, relative humidity at the surface may become so high that, given enough time, mold growth occurs. According to Hens (1990), a design rule is that surface relative humidity should not exceed 80% on a monthly mean basis.

The temperature ratio f_{h_i} is useful for calculating the surface temperature:

$$f_{h_i} = \frac{t_s - t_o}{t_i - t_o} \qquad (30)$$

where

t_s = surface temperature on warm side, °C
t_o = ambient temperature on cold side, °C
t_i = ambient temperature on warm side, °C

The minimum temperature ratio to avoid surface condensation is

$$f_{h_i,min} = \frac{t_{d,i} - t_o}{t_i - t_o} \quad (31)$$

where $t_{d,i}$ is the dew point of ambient air on the warm side, °C.

The minimum insulation thickness to avoid surface condensation on a flat element can be calculated from

$$L_{min} = k\left[\frac{f_{h_i,min}}{h_i(1 - f_{h_i,min})} - R_{add}\right] \quad (32)$$

where R_{add} is the thermal resistance between the surface on the warm side and the cold ambient for the wall without thermal insulation, $(m^2 \cdot K)/W$.

The condensation resistance of glazing is often estimated from outdoor and indoor design temperature, U-factor of the window assembly, and air film resistance. A window assembly may have different U-factors at the glass, frame, and the edge where the glass meets the frame; condensation resistance must be calculated at each of these locations. A procedure for these calculations can be found in NFRC (2004). The likelihood of window condensation depends strongly on the indoor air film resistance. This resistance may be reduced by washing the window with supply air. It may be increased with the use of window treatments such as blinds or curtains. Condensation on glazing is not inherently damaging, unless water is allowed to run onto painted or other surfaces that can be damaged by water.

INTERSTITIAL CONDENSATION AND DRYING

Dew-Point Methods

The best-known simple steady-state design tools for evaluating interstitial condensation and drying within exterior envelopes (walls, roofs, and ceilings) are the dew-point method and the Glaser method (which uses the same underlying principles as the dew-point method, but uses graphic rather than computational methods). These methods assume that steady-state conduction governs heat flow and steady-state diffusion governs water vapor flow. Both analyses compare partial water vapor pressures within the envelope, as calculated by steady-state water vapor diffusion, with saturation water vapor pressures, which are based on calculated steady-state temperatures within the envelope.

The condition where the calculated partial water vapor pressure is greater than saturation has been called **condensation**. Strictly speaking, condensation is the change in phase from vapor to liquid, as occurs on glass, metal, etc. For porous and hygroscopic building materials (e.g., wood, gypsum, masonry materials), vapor may be adsorbed or absorbed and never form the droplets usually associated with true condensation. Nevertheless, the term *condensation* is used for this method to indicate vapor pressure in excess of saturation vapor pressure, although this could be misleading about actual water conditions on porous and hygroscopic surfaces. This is one of the unfortunate simplifications inherent in a steady-state analytic tool.

Steady-state heat conduction and vapor diffusion impose severe limitations on applicability and interpretation. The greatest one is that the main focus is on preventing sustained interstitial condensation, as indicated by vapor pressures beyond saturation vapor pressures. Many building failures (e.g., mold, buckling of siding, paint failure) are not necessarily related to interstitial condensation; conversely, limited interstitial condensation can often be tolerated, depending on the materials involved, temperature conditions, and speed at which the material dries out. (Drying can only be approximated because both the dew-point and Glaser methods neglect moisture storage and capillary flow.) Because all moisture transfer mechanisms except water vapor diffusion are excluded, results should be considered as approximations and should be used with extreme care. Their validity and usefulness depend on judicious selection of boundary conditions, initial conditions, and material properties. Specifically, the methods should be used to estimate monthly or seasonal mean conditions only, rather than daily or weekly means. Furthermore, water vapor permeances may vary with relative humidity, and rain, flashing imperfections, leaky or poorly formed joints, rain exposure, airflow, and sunshine can have overriding effects. The dew-point and Glaser methods, however, are still used by design professionals and actually form the basis for most codes dealing with moisture control and vapor retarders.

For those who want to use this simple tool despite its shortcomings, a description of the dew-point method is presented in this chapter, with two application examples in Chapter 27. A comprehensive description of the dew-point and Glaser methods can be found in TenWolde (1994).

The dew-point method uses the equations for steady-state heat conduction and diffusion in a flat component, with the vapor flux in a layer written as

$$-m_v = \mu_p \frac{\Delta p}{d} = \frac{\Delta p}{Z} \quad (33)$$

where

m_v = water vapor flux through layer of material, ng/(s·m²)
Δp = partial water vapor pressure difference across layer, Pa
μ_p = water vapor permeability of material, ng/(Pa·s·m)
d = thickness of layer, m
Z = water vapor resistance, (Pa·s·m²)/ng

Over time, upgrades have been added to the dew-point method: (1) the concept of critical moisture content allows accounting for moisture build-up and upgraded calculation of drying, and (2) carried vapor flow has been included, underlining the importance of airtightness to avoid moisture deposition by condensation in building assemblies (Hens 2007; Vos and Coleman 1967).

TRANSIENT COMPUTATIONAL ANALYSIS

Computer models can analyze and predict the heat, air, and moisture response of building components. These transient models can predict the varying hygrothermal situations in building components for different design configurations under various conditions and climates, and their capabilities are continually improved. Hens (1996) reviewed the state of the art of heat, air, and moisture transport modeling for buildings and identified 37 different models, most of which were research tools that are not readily available and may have been too complex for use by practitioners. Some, however, were available either commercially, free of charge, or through a consultant. Also, Trechsel (2001) provides an update on existing tools and approaches.

For many applications and for design guide development, the actual behavior of an assembly under transient climatic conditions must be simulated, to account for short-term processes such as driving rain absorption, summer condensation, and phase changes. Understanding the application limits of a model is an important part of that process.

The features of a complete moisture analysis model include transient heat, air, and moisture transport formulation, incorporating the physics of contact conditions between layers and materials. Interfaces may be bridgeable for vapor diffusion, airflow, and gravity or pressure liquid flow only. They may be ideally capillary (no flow resistance from one layer to the next) or behave as a real contact (have an additional capillary resistance at the interface).

Not all these features are required for every analysis, though additional features may be needed in some applications (e.g., moisture flow through unintentional cracks and intentional openings, rain penetration through veneer walls and exterior cladding). To model these phenomena accurately, experiments may be needed to define subsystem performance under various loads (Straube and

Burnett 1997). It is usually preferable to take performance measurements of system and subsystems in field situations, because only then are all exterior loads and influences captured.

Validation, verification, and benchmarking of combined heat, air, and moisture models is a formidable task. Currently, only limited internationally accepted experimental data exist. The main difficulty lies in the fact that it is difficult to measure air and moisture fluxes and moisture transport potentials, even under laboratory conditions. In addition, even an already validated model should be verified for each new application.

In most full hygrothermal models, common outputs are air pressure; temperature; moisture content; relative humidity; and air, heat, and moisture fluxes. Results must be checked for consistency, accuracy, grid independence, and sensitivity to parameter changes. The results may be used to evaluate the moisture tolerance of an envelope system subjected to various interior and exterior loads. Heat fluxes may be used to determine thermal performance under the influence of moisture and airflow. Furthermore, the transient output data may be used for durability and indoor air quality assessment. Postprocessing tools concerning durability (e.g., corrosion, mold growth, freeze and thaw, hygrothermal stress and strain, indoor air humidity) have been developed or are under development. For instance, Carmeliet (1992) linked full hygrothermal modeling to probability-based fracture mechanics to predict the risk of crack development and growth in an exterior insulation finish system (EIFS) by weathering. A transient model to estimate the rate of mold growth was developed by Sedlbauer (2001).

Transient models have enabled timestep-by-timestep analysis of heat, air, and moisture conditions in building components, and give much more realistic results than steady-state conduction/diffusion and conduction/diffusion/airflow models. However, they are complex and usually not transparent, and require judgment and expertise on the part of the user. Existing models are one- or two-dimensional, requiring the user to devise a realistic representation of a three-dimensional building component. Users should be aware which transport phenomena and types of boundary conditions are included and which are not. For instance, some models are not able to handle air transport or rain wetting of the exterior. The results also tend to be very sensitive to the choice of indoor and outdoor conditions. Usually, exact conditions are not known. Indoor and outdoor conditions to be used have been established by proposed ASHRAE *Standard* 160P. More extensive data on material properties have become available (e.g., Kumaran 2006), but it can be problematic finding accurate data for all the materials in a component. Finally, interpretation of results is not easy: accurate data on the moisture and temperature conditions that materials can tolerate are often not available.

Combined heat, air, and moisture models also have limitations. Rain absorption, for example, can be modeled, but rainwater runoff and its consequences at joints, sills, and parapets cannot, although runoff followed by gravity-induced local penetration is one of the main causes of severe moisture problems. Even an apparently simple problem, such as predicting rain leakage through a brick veneer, is beyond many tools' capabilities. In such cases, simple qualitative schemes and field tests still are the way to proceed.

CRITERIA TO EVALUATE HYGROTHERMAL SIMULATION RESULTS

At the building assembly and whole building level, combined heat, air, and moisture transfer has consequences for thermal comfort, perceived indoor air quality, health, durability, and energy efficiency. The hygrothermal conditions in a building or within a building envelope assembly can be crucial for the overall performance of the construction and its mechanical systems. Therefore, simulation results should be compared to limit conditions and widely accepted performance criteria determined for the following performance issues.

Thermal Comfort

Thermal comfort, defined as a condition of mind that expresses satisfaction with the thermal environment (ASHRAE *Standard* 55), depends on two human parameters (clothing and metabolism) and a set of environmental variables, among them relative humidity. At effective temperatures below 25°C, relative humidity's effect on thermal comfort is minimal, but above 25°C, its importance increases as latent heat loss becomes a main mechanism in getting rid of metabolic heat. If, at those temperatures, the air feels too moist, the thermal environment is perceived as uncomfortable. At low relative humidity, polluted air can irritate the mucosa, and electric discharges when touching insulators (e.g., plastic chairs) are felt. However, in most residential buildings and in many offices, temperature is controlled but not relative humidity, except in hot and humid climates. Its instantaneous value depends on the equilibrium between vapor release indoors, ventilation, airflow among rooms, and temporary vapor storage by finishes and furnishings (often called moisture buffering). The average value over longer periods depends on ventilation and vapor release only, whereas buffering reduces temporary extremes only.

Perceived Air Quality

Air quality may be defined exactly by measuring the pollutants present. However, occupants typically perceive dryer, cooler air as smelling "fresher" than humid, warmer air. Thus, temperature and relative humidity affect perception of air freshness. Together, they define the air's enthalpy. Testing has shown that higher enthalpy lowers the perception of freshness (Fang et al. 1998). Despite this fact, in most buildings, relative humidity is an uncontrolled parameter.

Human Health

Mold in buildings is offensive to occupants. Mold will grow on most surfaces if the relative humidity at the surface is above a critical value, the surface temperature is conducive to growth, and the substrate provides nutritional value to the organism. The growth rate depends on the magnitude and duration of surface relative humidity. Surface relative humidity is a complex function of material moisture content, local surface temperature, and humidity conditions in the space. In recognition of the issue's complexity, the International Energy Agency established a surface relative humidity criterion for design purposes: monthly average values should remain below 80% (Hens 1990). Other proposals include the Canada Mortgage and Housing Corporation's stringent requirement of always keeping surface relative humidity below 65% (CMHC 1999). Although there still is no agreement on which criterion is most appropriate, mold growth can usually be avoided by allowing surface relative humidity over 80% only for short time periods. The relative humidity criterion may be relaxed for nonporous surfaces that are regularly cleaned. Most molds only grow at temperatures above 5°C. Moisture accumulation below 5°C may not cause mold growth if the material is allowed to dry out below the hygroscopic moisture content for a relative humidity of 80% before the temperature rises above 5°C. Mathematical models for predicting a mold growth index were developed by Hukka and Viitanen (1999) and Sedlbauer (2001); these can be linked to results from hygrothermal analysis.

Dust mites trigger allergies and asthma. Dust mites thrive at high relative humidities (over 70%) at room temperature, but will not survive sustained relative humidities below 50% (Burge et al. 1994). Note that these values relate to local conditions in the places that mites tend to inhabit (e.g., mattresses, carpets, soft furniture).

Durability of Finishes and Structure

Moisture behind paint films may cause paint failure, and water or condensation may also cause streaking or staining. Excessive changes in moisture content of wood-based panels or boards may cause buckling or warp. Excessive moisture in masonry and concrete may cause salt efflorescence, or, when combined with low temperatures, freeze/thaw damage and spalling (chipping).

Structural failures caused by wood decay are rare but have occurred (Merrill and TenWolde 1989). Decay generally requires wood moisture content at fiber saturation (usually about 30%) or higher and temperatures between 10 and 40°C. Such high wood moisture contents are possible in green lumber or by absorption of liquid water from condensation, leaks, groundwater, or saturated materials in contact with the wood. To maintain a safety margin, 20% moisture content is sometimes used as the maximum allowable moisture level. Because wood moisture content can vary widely with sample location, a local moisture content of 20% or higher may indicate fiber saturation elsewhere. Once established, decay fungi produce water that enables them to maintain moisture conditions conducive to their growth.

Rusting of nails, nail plates, or other metal building components is also a potential cause of structural failure. Corrosion may occur at relative humidities near the metal surface above 60% or as a result of liquid water from elsewhere. Wood moisture content over 20% encourages corrosion of steel fasteners in the wood, especially if the wood is treated with preservatives. In buildings, metal fasteners are often the coldest surfaces, encouraging condensation and corrosion.

Energy Efficiency

Moisture can significantly degrade the thermal performance of most insulation materials. Moisture contributes to heat transfer in both sensible and latent forms, as well as through mass transfer. The effect depends on the type of insulation material, moisture content, temperature of the insulation material and its thermal history, the location of moisture in the insulation material, and the building envelope's interior and exterior environments. Reported relationships between thermal performance of the insulation material and moisture content vary significantly. Kyle and Desjarlais (1994) estimated that water distribution accounts for a difference of up to 25% in heat flux in some cases. Evaporation on the warm side and condensation or adsorption on the cold side add important latent heat components to the heat flux (Kumaran 1987).

Hedlin (1988) and Shuman (1980) experimentally showed that, for building envelopes containing permeable fibrous insulations that were undergoing temperature reversals, the heat flux transferred by that moisture drive increased sharply as the moisture content increased to approximately 1% by volume. The rate of heat transfer increase diminished rapidly with further increases in moisture content. Heat transfer for permeable insulation with 1% moisture content by volume was roughly double that of dry insulation. Pedersen-Rode et al. (1991) analytically reproduced Hedlin's results. They demonstrated the high mobility of moisture in a permeable insulation and showed that latent effects are appreciable for a wide variety of North American climates. Latent effects typically add to the building's energy load and can increase peak energy demand. The extra load is added in the warm afternoon, and nearly the same amount of heat is removed in the cool evening.

Under conditions where water vapor pressure gradients change slowly or where the insulation layer has an extremely low water vapor permeance, little water vapor is transported, but moisture still affects sensible heat transfer in the building envelope component. Epstein and Putnam (1977) and Larsson et al. (1977) showed a nearly linear increase in sensible heat transfer of approximately 3 to 5% for each volume percent increase in moisture content in cellular plastic insulations. For example, an insulation material with a 5% moisture content by volume has 15 to 25% greater heat transfer than when dry. Other field studies by Dechow and Epstein (1978) and Ovstaas et al. (1983) showed similar results for insulations installed in below-grade applications such as foundation walls.

REFERENCES

ASHRAE. 2004. Thermal environmental conditions for human occupancy. ANSI/ASHRAE *Standard* 55-2004.

ASHRAE. 2007. Method of test for the evaluation of building energy analysis computer programs. ANSI/ASHRAE *Standard* 140-2004.

ASTM. 2008. Terminology relating to thermal insulating materials. *Standard* C168-05a. American Society for Testing and Materials, West Conshohocken, PA.

ASTM. 2005. Test method for thermal performance of building materials and envelope assemblies by means of a hot box apparatus. *Standard* C1363-05. American Society for Testing and Materials, West Conshohocken, PA.

ASTM. 2005. Test methods for water vapor transmission of materials. *Standard* E96/E96M-05. American Society for Testing and Materials, West Conshohocken, PA.

BSI. 1992. Code of practice for assessing exposure of walls to wind-driven rain. *Standard* BS 8104:1992. British Standards Institution, London.

Burge, H.A., H.J. Su, and J.D. Spengler. 1994. Moisture, organisms, and health effects. Chapter 6 in *Moisture control in buildings*, ASTM *Manual* MNL 18. American Society for Testing and Materials, West Conshohocken, PA.

Burnett, E., J. Straube, and A. Karagiozis. 2004. Development of design strategies for rainscreen and sheathing membrane performance in wood frame walls. ASHRAE Research Project RP-1091, *Final Report*.

Carmeliet, J. 1992. *Durability of fiber-reinforced rendering for exterior insulation systems*. Ph.D. dissertation, Catholic University–Leuven, Belgium.

Carmeliet, J., G. Houvenaghel, and F. Descamps. 1999. Multiscale network for simulating liquid water and water vapour transfer properties of porous materials. *Transport in Porous Materials* 35:67-88.

CMHC. 1999. *Best practice guide, wood frame envelopes*. Canada Mortgage and Housing Corporation and Canada Wood Council, Ottawa.

Dalehaug, A., O. Aunronning, and B. Time. 2005. Measurement of water retention properties of plaster: A parameter study of the influence on moisture balance of an external wall construction from variations of this parameter. *Proceedings of the 7th Symposium on Building Physics in the Nordic Countries*, Reykjavik, pp. 94-101.

Dechow, F.J. and K.A. Epstein. 1978. Laboratory and field investigations of moisture absorption and its effect on thermal performance of various insulations. ASTM *Special Technical Publication* STP 660:234-260.

Douglas, J.S., T.H. Kuehn, and J.W. Ramsey. 1992. A new moisture permeability measurement method and representative test data. *ASHRAE Transactions* 98(2):513-519.

Epstein, K.A. and L.E. Putnam. 1977. Performance criteria for the protected membrane roof system. *Proceedings of the Symposium on Roofing Technology*. National Institute of Standards and Technology, Gaithersburg, MD, and National Roofing Contractors Association, Rosemont, IL.

Fang, L., G. Clausen, and P.O. Fanger. 1998. Impact of temperature and humidity on the perception of indoor air quality. *Indoor Air* 8:80-90.

Galbraith, G.H., R.C. McLean, and J.S. Guo. 1998. Moisture permeability data presented as a mathematical relationship. *Building Research & Information* 20(6):364-372.

Hedlin, C.P. 1988. Heat flow through a roof insulation having moisture contents between 0 and 1% by volume, in summer. *ASHRAE Transactions* 94(2):1579-1594.

Hens, H. 1990. *Guidelines & practice*. International Energy Agency Annex XIV, Leuven, Belgium.

Hens, H. 1992. Air/windtightness of pitched roofs—How they really behave (in German). *Bauphysik* 14(6):161-174.

Hens, H. 1996. Heat, air and moisture transfer in highly insulated envelope parts, task 1: Modelling. *Final Report*, vol. 1, International Energy Agency, Annex 24. Catholic University–Leuven, Laboratorium for Building Physics, Belgium.

Hens, H. 2007. Does heat, air moisture modeling really help in solving hygrothermal problems? *Proceedings Rakennusfysiikka*, Technical University of Tampere, Finland.

Hens, H. 2008. *Building physics: Heat, air and moisture—Fundamentals and engineering methods with examples and exercises*. Ernst & Sohn, Berlin.

Hukka, A. and H. Viitanen. 1999. A mathematical model of mold growth on wooden material. *Wood Science and Technology* 33(6):475-485.

ISO/DIN. 2006. Hygrothermal performance of buildings—Part 3: Calculation of a driving rain index for vertical surfaces from hourly wind and rain data. *Standard* 15927-3:2006. International Organization for Standardization, Geneva, and Deutsches Institut für Normung, Berlin.

Janssens, A. 1998. *Reliable control of interstitial condensation in lightweight roof systems.* Ph.D. dissertation, Catholic University–Leuven, Belgium.

Kronvall, J. 1982. Air flows in building components. *Report* TVBH-1002. Division of Building Technology, Lund University of Technology, Sweden.

Krus, M. 1996. *Moisture transport and storage coefficients of porous mineral building materials: Theoretical principles and new test methods.* Fraunhofer IRB Verlag, Stuttgart.

Kumaran, M.K. 1987. Vapor transport characteristics of mineral fiber insulation from heat flow measurements. In *Water vapor transmission through building materials and systems: Mechanisms and measurements.* ASTM *Special Technical Publication* STP 1039:19-27.

Kumaran, M.K. 1991. Application of gamma-ray spectroscopy for determination of moisture distribution in insulating materials. *Proceedings of the International Centre for Heat and Mass Transfer*, pp. 95-103.

Kumaran, M.K. 1999. Moisture diffusivity of building materials from water absorption measurements. *Journal of Thermal Envelope and Building Science* 22:349-355.

Kumaran, M.K. 2006. A thermal and moisture transport database for common building and insulating materials (RP-1018). *ASHRAE Transactions* 112(2):485-497.

Kumaran, M., J. Lackey, N. Normandin, F. Tariku, and D. Van Reenen. 2003. Variations in the hygrothermal properties of several wood-based building products. In *Research in Building Physics: Proceedings of the Second International Conference on Building Physics*, Leuven, Belgium, pp. 35-42. J. Carmeliet, H. Hens, and G. Vermeir, eds. Taylor and Francis, London.

Künzel, H.M. 1995. *Simultaneous heat and moisture transport in building components: One- and two-dimensional calculation using simple parameters*. Fraunhofer IRB Verlag, Stuttgart.

Künzel, H.M. 1999. More moisture load tolerance of construction assemblies through the application of a smart vapor retarder. In *Thermal Performance of Exterior Envelopes of Buildings VII*, pp. 129-132, Conference Proceedings. ASHRAE.

Künzel, H.M. 2007. Factors determining surface moisture on external walls. In *Thermal Performance of Exterior Envelopes of Buildings X*, Conference Proceedings. ASHRAE.

Künzel, H.M. and T. Grosskinski. 1989. Non-ventilated and fully insulated—The best solution for the pitched roof (in German). *Warme- und Kalteschutz im Bau* 27.

Künzel, H.M. and A. Holm. 2001. *Simulation of heat and moisture transfer in construction assemblies*. Fraunhofer IBP, Holzkirchen. http://publica.fraunhofer.de/eprints/urn:nbn:de:0011-n-268883.pdf

Künzel, H.M. and A. Karagiozis. 2004. Vapor control in cold and coastal climate zones. *Proceedings of the Canadian Conference on Building Energy Simulation, eSim 2004*, pp. 55-60.

Kyle, D.M. and A.O. Desjarlais. 1994. Assessment of technologies for constructing self-drying low-slope roofs. Oak Ridge National Laboratory *Report* ORNL/CON-380. Oak Ridge, TN.

Lacy, R.E. 1965. Driving-rain maps and the onslaught of rain on buildings. *Proceedings of the RILEM/CIB Symposium on Moisture Problems in Buildings*, Helsinki, Finland.

Larsson, L.E., J. Ondrus, and B.A. Petersson. 1977. The protected membrane roof (PMR)—A study combining field and laboratory tests. *Proceedings of the Symposium on Roofing Technology.* National Institute of Standards and Technology, Gaithersburg, MD, and National Roofing Contractors Association, Rosemont, IL.

Merrill, J.L. and A. TenWolde. 1989. Overview of moisture-related damage in one group of Wisconsin manufactured homes. *ASHRAE Transactions* 95(1):405-414.

METEOTEST. 2007. *Handbook of METEONORM—Global meteorological database for engineers, planners and education.* METEOTEST, Bern, Switzerland.

NFRC. 2004. Procedure for determining fenestration product condensation resistance values. *Technical Document* 500. National Fenestration Rating Council, Silver Spring, MD.

Ovstaas, G., S. Smith, W. Strzepek, and G. Titley. 1983. Thermal performance of various insulations in below-earth-grade perimeter application. ASTM *Special Technical Publication* STP 789:435-454.

Palfey, A.J. 1980. Thermal performance of low emittance building sheathing. *Journal of Thermal Insulation* (now *Journal of Building Physics*) 3:129-141.

Pedersen, C.R. 1990. Combined heat and moisture transfer in building constructions. *Report* 214. Technical University of Denmark.

Pedersen-Rode, C., T.W. Petrie, G.E. Courville, P.W. Childs, and K.E. Wilkes. 1991. Moisture migration and drying rates for low slope roofs—Preliminary results. *Proceedings of the 3rd International Symposium on Roofing Technology.* National Roofing Contractors Association, Rosemont, IL.

Plagge, R., G. Scheffler, and A. Nicolai. 2007. Experimental methods to derive hygrothermal material functions for numerical simulation tools. In *Thermal Performance of Exterior Envelopes of Buildings X*, Conference Proceedings. ASHRAE.

Robinson, H.E., F.J. Powlitch, and R.S. Dill. 1954. The thermal insulating value of airspaces. Housing and Home Finance Agency, *Housing Research Paper* 32, U.S. Government Printing Office, Washington, D.C.

Roels, S., J. Carmeliet, and H. Hens. 2003. Hamstad, WP 1: Moisture transfer properties and material characterisation. *Final Report* (GRD1-1999-2007), KUL2003-18, Catholic University–Leuven, Belgium.

Sanders, C. 1996. Environmental conditions. IEA Annex 24 *Report*, vol. 2, Catholic University–Leuven, Belgium.

Schwarz, B. 1971. *Die Wärme- und Stoffübertragung an Außenwandoberflächen.* (*Heat and mass transfer at exterior wall surfaces.*) Dissertation, University of Stuttgart.

Sedlbauer, K. 2001. *Prediction of mould fungus formation on the surface of and inside building components*. Ph.D. dissertation, University of Stuttgart.

Shuman, E.C. 1980. Field measurement of heat flux through a roof with saturated thermal insulation and covered with black and white granules. ASTM *Special Technical Publication* STP 718:519-539.

Straube, J. and E. Burnett. 1997. Rain control and screened wall systems. *7th Conference on Building Science and Technology, Durability of Buildings—Design, Maintenance, Codes and Practices*, pp. 17-37.

Straube J. and E. Burnett. 2000. Simplified prediction of driving rain on buildings. *Proceedings of the First International Building Physics Conference*, Technische Universiteit–Eindhoven, the Netherlands, pp. 375-382.

TenWolde, A. 1994. Design tools. Chapter 11 in *Moisture control in buildings*. ASTM *Manual* MNL 18. American Society for Testing and Materials, West Conshohocken, PA.

TenWolde, A. and I. Walker. 2001. Interior moisture design loads for residences. In *Thermal Performance of Exterior Envelopes of Buildings VIII*, Conference Proceedings. ASHRAE.

Trechsel, H. 2001. *Moisture analysis and condensation control in building envelopes*. ASTM *Manual* MNL 40. American Society for Testing and Materials, West Conshohocken, PA.

Van Besien, T., S. Roels, and J. Carmeliet. 2002. Experimental determination of moisture: Diffusivity of porous building materials using x-ray radiography. *Proceedings of the 6th Nordic Symposium on Building Physics*, Trondheim, Norway.

Vos, B.H. and E.J.W. Coelman. 1967. Condensation in structures. *Report* BI-67-33/23, TNO-IBBC, Rijswijk, the Netherlands.

Zheng, R., A. Janssens, J. Carmeliet, W. Bogaerts, and H. Hens. 2004. An evaluation of highly insulated cold zinc roofs in a moderate humid climate, Part 2—Corrosion behaviour of zinc sheeting. *Construction and Building Materials* 18(1):61-71.

CHAPTER 26

HEAT, AIR, AND MOISTURE CONTROL IN BUILDING ASSEMBLIES—MATERIAL PROPERTIES

THIS chapter presents thermal and water vapor transmission data based on steady-state or equilibrium conditions. This information can be used in the simplified calculation methods described in Chapter 27, or in software-based methods that develop step-wise steady-state conditions into a time-dependent solution. Chapter 4 covers heat transfer under transient or changing temperature conditions. Chapter 25 discusses combined heat-air-moisture transport. For information on insulation for mechanical systems, see Chapter 23.

Ideal conditions of components and installations are assumed in calculating overall R-values (i.e., insulating materials are of uniform nominal thickness and thermal resistance, air spaces are of uniform thickness and surface temperature, moisture effects are not involved, and installation details are in accordance with design). Robinson et al. (1957) showed that measured values differ from calculated values for certain insulated constructions. To account for this, some engineers moderately decrease calculated R-values.

The overall thermal resistance of an assembly comprises its surface-to-surface conductance and the resistances to heat transfer between assembly surfaces and interior and exterior spaces. This chapter includes standardized surface and air cavity resistances in typical building assemblies. Typical thermal properties (density, thermal conductivity, and specific heat) are provided for a wide range of building materials.

Material properties related to hygric performance (e.g., water vapor permeance, permeability, air permeance, sorption isotherms) are also given for several materials.

THERMAL PROPERTIES

AIR SPACES

Surface Resistances

As explained in Chapter 25, the overall R-value of an assembly comprises its surface-to-surface conductance C and the resistances to heat transfer between assembly surfaces and interior and exterior spaces (R_i and R_o, respectively). Table 1 presents standardized surface resistances R as well as conductances h_i and h_o, which are sometimes referenced in fenestration applications [see Chapter 15 and ASHRAE (1998)]. As shown, the resistance to heat transfer from a heated area to the surface (or from the surface to a cooler area) through natural convection (called "still air" in Table 1, although air does move through buoyancy) depends on the position of the surface, direction of heat transfer, temperature of the surface and the air, difference between the surface temperature and that of the surroundings, and the surface's long-wave emittance. Where air is moved by wind or fans, the resistance to heat transfer to or from the surface depends on air speed, surface temperature, difference between the surface temperature and that of the surroundings, and the surface's long-wave emittance. Values in Table 1 are for typical situations encountered in construction. For other temperatures and conditions, use ASHRAE (1998) to determine surface conductances or resistances.

Note that it is not appropriate to compute an overall R-value that assigns both a surface resistance and an air-space resistance to the same air space; that should be considered double-counting, and is not an accurate representation of the thermal resistance of the assembly (see Note 2 in Table 1).

Table 1 Surface Conductances and Resistances for Air

		Surface Emittance, ε					
		Nonreflective		Reflective			
	Direction of	ε = 0.90		ε = 0.20		ε = 0.05	
Position of Surface	Heat Flow	h_i	R	h_i	R	h_i	R
Still Air							
Horizontal	Upward	9.26	0.11	5.17	0.19	4.32	0.23
Sloping at 45°	Upward	9.09	0.11	5.00	0.20	4.15	0.24
Vertical	Horizontal	8.29	0.12	4.20	0.24	3.35	0.30
Sloping at 45°	Downward	7.50	0.13	3.41	0.29	2.56	0.39
Horizontal	Downward	6.13	0.16	2.10	0.48	1.25	0.80
Moving Air (any position)		h_o	R				
Wind (for winter) at 6.7 m/s	Any	34.0	0.030	—	—	—	—
Wind (for summer) at 3.4 m/s	Any	22.7	0.044	—	—	—	—

Notes:
1. Surface conductance h_i and h_o measured in W/(m²·K); resistance R in (m²·K)/W.
2. No surface has both an air space resistance value and a surface resistance value.
3. Conductances are for surfaces of the stated emittance facing virtual black-body surroundings at same temperature as ambient air. Values based on surface/air temperature difference of 5.5 K and surface temperatures of 21°C.
4. See Chapter 4 for more detailed information.
5. Condensate can have significant effect on surface emittance (see Table 2).

Air Cavities

When air is enclosed in the assembly, the enclosed cavity's thermal resistance can contribute to the resistance of the overall assembly. Even under steady-state conditions, convective air movement driven by buoyancy defines the thermal resistance of the cavity. Like the surface condition described above, the magnitude of this resistance depends on the slope of the cavity, direction of heat transfer, mean temperature in the cavity, and temperature and long-wave emittance of cavity surfaces. Table 3 provides thermal resistance values for enclosed cavities for various conditions, depending on the

The preparation of this chapter is assigned to TC 4.4, Building Materials and Building Envelope Performance.

Table 2 Emittance Values of Various Surfaces and Effective Emittances of Air Spaces[a]

Surface	Average Emittance ε	Effective Emittance ε_{eff} of Air Space: One Surface Emittance ε; Other, 0.9	Effective Emittance ε_{eff} of Air Space: Both Surfaces Emittance ε
Aluminum foil, bright	0.05	0.05	0.03
Aluminum foil, with condensate just visible (>0.5 g/m²)	0.30[b]	0.29	—
Aluminum foil, with condensate clearly visible (>2.0 g/m²)	0.70[b]	0.65	—
Aluminum sheet	0.12	0.12	0.06
Aluminum coated paper, polished	0.20	0.20	0.11
Steel, galvanized, bright	0.25	0.24	0.15
Aluminum paint	0.50	0.47	0.35
Building materials: wood, paper, masonry, nonmetallic paints	0.90	0.82	0.82
Regular glass	0.84	0.77	0.72

[a]Values apply in 4 to 40 μm range of electromagnetic spectrum.
[b]Values based on data in Bassett and Trethowen (1984).

combined or **effective emittance** of the cavity's hot and cold surfaces. The effective emittance is the combined value of the emittances of both surfaces according to $1/\varepsilon_{eff} = 1/\varepsilon_1 + 1/\varepsilon_2 - 1$. Some values for combined emittance are listed in Table 2, to be used to determine the resistance of cavities in Table 3.

Tables 2 and 3 give values for well-sealed cavities constructed with care. Field applications can differ substantially from laboratory test conditions. Air gaps into the cavity can seriously degrade thermal performance because of air movement through both natural and forced convection. Sabine et al. (1975) found that tabular values are not necessarily additive for multiple-layer, low-emittance air spaces, and tests on actual constructions should be conducted to accurately determine thermal resistance values.

Values for foil insulation products supplied by manufacturers must also be used with caution because they apply only to systems that are identical to the configuration in which the product was tested. In addition, surface oxidation, dust accumulation, condensation, and other factors that change the condition of the low-emittance surface can reduce the thermal effectiveness of these insulation systems (Hooper and Moroz 1952). Deterioration results from contact with several types of solutions, either acidic or basic (e.g., wet cement mortar, preservatives found in decay-resistant lumber). Polluted environments may cause rapid and severe material degradation. However, site inspections show a predominance of well-preserved installations, and only a small number of cases in which rapid and severe deterioration has occurred. An extensive review of the reflective building insulation system performance literature is provided by Goss and Miller (1989).

Note that reflective foils are only effective if the reflective surface faces an air space, because radiative heat transfer cannot be reduced where there is no air space to allow radiative heat transfer. Also, multiple layers of reflective foil are no more effective than a single layer, unless the reflective surfaces adjoin different air spaces in the assembly.

Figure 1 shows how surface conductance for surfaces with different roughness is affected by air movement. Other tests on smooth surfaces show that the average value of the convection part of surface conductance decreases as surface length increases.

The following conditions are assumed in calculating design R-values for construction assemblies:

- Equilibrium or steady-state heat transfer, disregarding effects of thermal storage

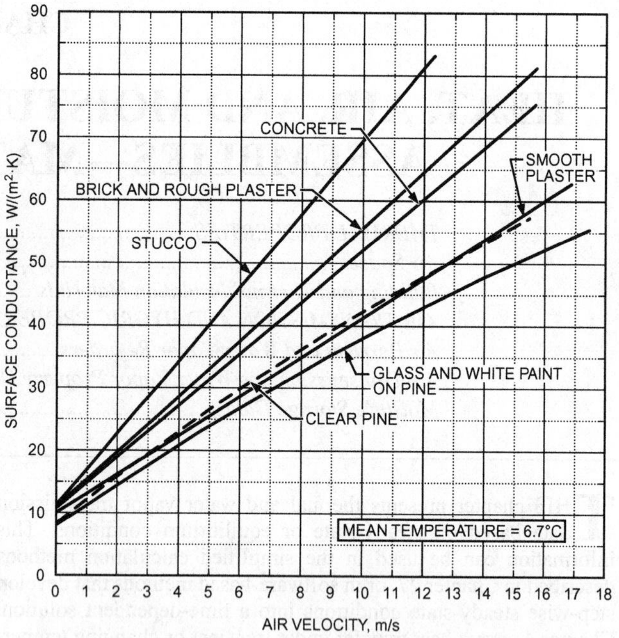

Fig. 1 Surface Conductance for Different Surfaces as Affected by Air Movement

- Surrounding surfaces at ambient air temperature
- Exterior wind velocity of 6.7 m/s for winter [surface with R = 0.03 (m²·K)/W] and 3.4 m/s for summer [surface with R = 0.044 (m²·K)/W]
- Surface emittance of ordinary building materials is 0.9

BUILDING AND THERMAL INSULATION MATERIALS

Thermal Insulation Materials

When properly applied, thermal insulation materials retard conductive, convective, and radiative heat flux. Thermal insulation in building envelopes does at least one of the following:

- Conserves energy by reducing the building's heat loss or gain
- Controls surface temperatures for comfort
- Helps control temperatures in a structure
- Reduces the tendency for water condensation on inside and outside surfaces
- Reduces temperature fluctuations in unconditioned or partly conditioned spaces

Thermal insulation materials may also serve additional functions, although these should be consistent with the capabilities of the materials and their primary purpose:

- Adding structural strength to a wall, ceiling, or floor section
- Providing support for a surface finish
- Impeding water vapor transmission and air infiltration
- Preventing or reducing damage to structures from exposure to fire and freezing conditions
- Reducing noise and vibration

Poorly designed or improperly installed thermal insulation may promote interstitial moisture condensation and subsequent damage within a building envelope. When thermal insulation is used to control heat flow at all temperatures, the limiting value is its survival temperature.

Table 3 Thermal Resistances of Plane Air Spaces,[a,b,c] $(m^2 \cdot K)/W$

Position of Air Space	Direction of Heat Flow	Mean Temp.,[d] °C	Temp. Diff.,[d] K	13 mm Air Space[c] ε_{eff} 0.03	0.05	0.2	0.5	0.82	20 mm Air Space[c] ε_{eff} 0.03	0.05	0.2	0.5	0.82
Horiz.	Up	32.2	5.6	0.37	0.36	0.27	0.17	0.13	0.41	0.39	0.28	0.18	0.13
		10.0	16.7	0.29	0.28	0.23	0.17	0.13	0.30	0.29	0.24	0.17	0.14
		10.0	5.6	0.37	0.36	0.28	0.20	0.15	0.40	0.39	0.30	0.20	0.15
		−17.8	11.1	0.30	0.30	0.26	0.20	0.16	0.32	0.32	0.27	0.20	0.16
		−17.8	5.6	0.37	0.36	0.30	0.22	0.18	0.39	0.38	0.31	0.23	0.18
		−45.6	11.1	0.30	0.29	0.26	0.22	0.18	0.31	0.31	0.27	0.22	0.19
		−45.6	5.6	0.36	0.35	0.31	0.25	0.20	0.38	0.37	0.32	0.26	0.21
45° Slope	Up	32.2	5.6	0.43	0.41	0.29	0.19	0.13	0.52	0.49	0.33	0.20	0.14
		10.0	16.7	0.36	0.35	0.27	0.19	0.15	0.35	0.34	0.27	0.19	0.14
		10.0	5.6	0.45	0.43	0.32	0.21	0.16	0.51	0.48	0.35	0.23	0.17
		−17.8	11.1	0.39	0.38	0.31	0.23	0.18	0.37	0.36	0.30	0.23	0.18
		−17.8	5.6	0.46	0.45	0.36	0.25	0.19	0.48	0.46	0.37	0.26	0.20
		−45.6	11.1	0.37	0.36	0.31	0.25	0.21	0.36	0.35	0.31	0.25	0.20
		−45.6	5.6	0.46	0.45	0.38	0.29	0.23	0.45	0.43	0.37	0.29	0.23
Vertical	Horiz.	32.2	5.6	0.43	0.41	0.29	0.19	0.14	0.62	0.57	0.37	0.21	0.15
		10.0	16.7	0.45	0.43	0.32	0.22	0.16	0.51	0.49	0.35	0.23	0.17
		10.0	5.6	0.47	0.45	0.33	0.22	0.16	0.65	0.61	0.41	0.25	0.18
		−17.8	11.1	0.50	0.48	0.38	0.26	0.20	0.55	0.53	0.41	0.28	0.21
		−17.8	5.6	0.52	0.50	0.39	0.27	0.20	0.66	0.63	0.46	0.30	0.22
		−45.6	11.1	0.51	0.50	0.41	0.31	0.24	0.51	0.50	0.42	0.31	0.24
		−45.6	5.6	0.56	0.55	0.45	0.33	0.26	0.65	0.63	0.51	0.36	0.27
45° Slope	Down	32.2	5.6	0.44	0.41	0.29	0.19	0.14	0.62	0.58	0.37	0.21	0.15
		10.0	16.7	0.46	0.44	0.33	0.22	0.16	0.60	0.57	0.39	0.24	0.17
		10.0	5.6	0.47	0.45	0.33	0.22	0.16	0.67	0.63	0.42	0.26	0.18
		−17.8	11.1	0.51	0.49	0.39	0.27	0.20	0.66	0.63	0.46	0.30	0.22
		−17.8	5.6	0.52	0.50	0.39	0.27	0.20	0.73	0.69	0.49	0.32	0.23
		−45.6	11.1	0.56	0.54	0.44	0.33	0.25	0.67	0.64	0.51	0.36	0.28
		−45.6	5.6	0.57	0.56	0.45	0.33	0.26	0.77	0.74	0.57	0.39	0.29
Horiz.	Down	32.2	5.6	0.44	0.41	0.29	0.19	0.14	0.62	0.58	0.37	0.21	0.15
		10.0	16.7	0.47	0.45	0.33	0.22	0.16	0.66	0.62	0.42	0.25	0.18
		10.0	5.6	0.47	0.45	0.33	0.22	0.16	0.68	0.63	0.42	0.26	0.18
		−17.8	11.1	0.52	0.50	0.39	0.27	0.20	0.74	0.70	0.50	0.32	0.23
		−17.8	5.6	0.52	0.50	0.39	0.27	0.20	0.75	0.71	0.51	0.32	0.23
		−45.6	11.1	0.57	0.55	0.45	0.33	0.26	0.81	0.78	0.59	0.40	0.30
		−45.6	5.6	0.58	0.56	0.46	0.33	0.26	0.83	0.79	0.60	0.40	0.30
Air Space				**40 mm Air Space[c]**					**90 mm Air Space[c]**				
Horiz.	Up	32.2	5.6	0.45	0.42	0.30	0.19	0.14	0.50	0.47	0.32	0.20	0.14
		10.0	16.7	0.33	0.32	0.26	0.18	0.14	0.27	0.35	0.28	0.19	0.15
		10.0	5.6	0.44	0.42	0.32	0.21	0.16	0.49	0.47	0.34	0.23	0.16
		−17.8	11.1	0.35	0.34	0.29	0.22	0.17	0.40	0.38	0.32	0.23	0.18
		−17.8	5.6	0.43	0.41	0.33	0.24	0.19	0.48	0.46	0.36	0.26	0.20
		−45.6	11.1	0.34	0.34	0.30	0.24	0.20	0.39	0.38	0.33	0.26	0.21
		−45.6	5.6	0.42	0.41	0.35	0.27	0.22	0.47	0.45	0.38	0.29	0.23
45° Slope	Up	32.2	5.6	0.51	0.48	0.33	0.20	0.14	0.56	0.52	0.35	0.21	0.14
		10.0	16.7	0.38	0.36	0.28	0.20	0.15	0.40	0.38	0.29	0.20	0.15
		10.0	5.6	0.51	0.48	0.35	0.23	0.17	0.55	0.52	0.37	0.24	0.17
		−17.8	11.1	0.40	0.39	0.32	0.24	0.18	0.43	0.41	0.33	0.24	0.19
		−17.8	5.6	0.49	0.47	0.37	0.26	0.20	0.52	0.51	0.39	0.27	0.20
		−45.6	11.1	0.39	0.38	0.33	0.26	0.21	0.41	0.40	0.35	0.27	0.22
		−45.6	5.6	0.48	0.46	0.39	0.30	0.24	0.51	0.49	0.41	0.31	0.24
Vertical	Horiz.	32.2	5.6	0.70	0.64	0.40	0.22	0.15	0.65	0.60	0.38	0.22	0.15
		10.0	16.7	0.45	0.43	0.32	0.22	0.16	0.47	0.45	0.33	0.22	0.16
		10.0	5.6	0.67	0.62	0.42	0.26	0.18	0.64	0.60	0.41	0.25	0.18
		−17.8	11.1	0.49	0.47	0.37	0.26	0.20	0.51	0.49	0.38	0.27	0.20
		−17.8	5.6	0.62	0.59	0.44	0.29	0.22	0.61	0.59	0.44	0.29	0.22
		−45.6	11.1	0.46	0.45	0.38	0.29	0.23	0.50	0.48	0.40	0.30	0.24
		−45.6	5.6	0.58	0.56	0.46	0.34	0.26	0.60	0.58	0.47	0.34	0.26
45° Slope	Down	32.2	5.6	0.89	0.80	0.45	0.24	0.16	0.85	0.76	0.44	0.24	0.16
		10.0	16.7	0.63	0.59	0.41	0.25	0.18	0.62	0.58	0.40	0.25	0.18
		10.0	5.6	0.90	0.82	0.50	0.28	0.19	0.83	0.77	0.48	0.28	0.19
		−17.8	11.1	0.68	0.64	0.47	0.31	0.22	0.67	0.64	0.47	0.31	0.22
		−17.8	5.6	0.87	0.81	0.56	0.34	0.24	0.81	0.76	0.53	0.33	0.24
		−45.6	11.1	0.64	0.62	0.49	0.35	0.27	0.66	0.64	0.51	0.36	0.28
		−45.6	5.6	0.82	0.79	0.60	0.40	0.30	0.79	0.76	0.58	0.40	0.30
Horiz.	Down	32.2	5.6	1.07	0.94	0.49	0.25	0.17	1.77	1.44	0.60	0.28	0.18
		10.0	16.7	1.10	0.99	0.56	0.30	0.20	1.69	1.44	0.68	0.33	0.21
		10.0	5.6	1.16	1.04	0.58	0.30	0.20	1.96	1.63	0.72	0.34	0.22
		−17.8	11.1	1.24	1.13	0.69	0.39	0.26	1.92	1.68	0.86	0.43	0.29
		−17.8	5.6	1.29	1.17	0.70	0.39	0.27	2.11	1.82	0.89	0.44	0.29
		−45.6	11.1	1.36	1.27	0.84	0.50	0.35	2.05	1.85	1.06	0.57	0.38
		−45.6	5.6	1.42	1.32	0.86	0.51	0.35	2.28	2.03	1.12	0.59	0.39

Column headings: Air Space; Effective Emittance ε_{eff}[d,e].

[a]See Chapter 25. Thermal resistance values were determined from $R = 1/C$, where $C = h_c + \varepsilon_{eff} h_r$, h_c is conduction/convection coefficient, $\varepsilon_{eff} h_r$ is radiation coefficient $\approx 0.227\varepsilon_{eff}[(t_m + 273)/100]^3$, and t_m is mean temperature of air space. Values for h_c were determined from data developed by Robinson et al. (1954). Equations (5) to (7) in Yarbrough (1983) show data in this table in analytic form. For extrapolation from this table to air spaces less than 12.5 mm (e.g., insulating window glass), assume $h_c = 21.8(1 + 0.00274t_m)/l$, where l is air space thickness in mm, and h_c is heat transfer in $W/(m^2 \cdot K)$ through the air space only.

[b]Values based on data presented by Robinson et al. (1954). (Also see Chapter 4, Tables 5 and 6, and Chapter 33). Values apply for ideal conditions (i.e., air spaces of uniform thickness bounded by plane, smooth, parallel surfaces with no air leakage to or from the space). For greater accuracy, use overall U-factors determined through calibrated hot box (ASTM *Standard* C976) or guarded hot box (ASTM *Standard* C236) testing. Thermal resistance values for multiple air spaces must be based on careful estimates of mean temperature differences for each air space.

[c]A single resistance value cannot account for multiple air spaces; each air space requires a separate resistance calculation that applies only for established boundary conditions. Resistances of horizontal spaces with heat flow downward are substantially independent of temperature difference.

[d]Interpolation is permissible for other values of mean temperature, temperature difference, and effective emittance ε_{eff}. Interpolation and moderate extrapolation for air spaces greater than 90 mm are also permissible.

[e]Effective emittance ε_{eff} of air space is given by $1/\varepsilon_{eff} = 1/\varepsilon_1 + 1/\varepsilon_2 - 1$, where ε_1 and ε_2 are emittances of surfaces of air space (see Table 2).

Basic Materials

Thermal insulation normally consists of the following basic materials and composites:

- Inorganic, fibrous, or cellular materials such as glass, rock, or slag wool
- Calcium silicate, bonded perlite, vermiculite, and ceramic products (asbestos was also used, but its use has been discouraged or banned for several years; use caution if it is encountered in existing buildings)
- Organic fibrous materials such as cellulose, cotton, wool, wood, pulp, cane, or synthetic fibers, and organic cellular materials such as cork, foamed rubber, polystyrene, polyurethane, and other polymers
- Metallic or metallized organic reflective membranes, which must face an air-filled, gas-filled, or evacuated space to be effective

Physical Structure and Form

Physical forms of building insulation include the following:

Loose-fill insulation consists of fibers, powders, granules, or nodules, usually poured or blown into walls or other spaces. **Insulating cement** is a loose material that is mixed with water or a suitable binder to obtain plasticity and adhesion. It is troweled or blown wet on a surface and dried in place. Both loose fill and insulating cement are suited for covering irregular spaces.

Flexible and **semirigid insulation** consists of organic and inorganic materials with and without binders and with varying degrees of compressibility and flexibility. This insulation is generally available as blanket, batt, or felt, and in either sheets or rolls. Coverings and facings may be fastened to one or both sides and serve as reinforcing, airflow or vapor retarders (or both), reflective surfaces, or surface finishes. These coverings include combinations of laminated foil, glass, cloth or plastics and paper, or wire mesh. Although standard sizes are generally used, thickness and shape of insulation can be any convenient dimension.

Rigid materials are available in rectangular blocks, boards, or sheets, which are preformed during manufacture to standard lengths, widths, and thickness.

Reflective materials are available in sheets and rolls of single-layer or multilayer construction and in preformed shapes with integral air spaces.

Formed-in-place insulations are available as liquid components or expandable pellets that can be poured, frothed, or sprayed in place to form rigid or semirigid foam insulation. Fibrous materials mixed with liquid binders can also be sprayed in place; in some products, the binder is also a foam.

Accessories for thermal insulation include mechanical and adhesive fasteners, exterior and interior finishes, vapor- and airflow-retarding coatings, sealants, lagging adhesives, membranes, and flashing compounds. ASTM *Standard* C168 defines terms related to thermal insulating materials.

Apparent Thermal Conductivity

A low apparent thermal conductivity is the primary property of a thermal insulation, but selecting a material may also involve secondary criteria (e.g., resiliency or rigidity, acoustical energy absorption, water vapor permeability, airflow resistance, fire hazard and fire resistance, ease of application, applied cost, health and safety aspects, or other parameters), which can affect the choice among materials that have almost equal thermal performance.

Thermal conductivity k is a property of a homogeneous, nonporous material. Most thermal insulation is porous and consists of combinations of solid matter with small voids, which comprise 90% or more of the volume. Heat transmission is therefore a combination of gas and solid conduction, radiation, and convection, and is affected by factors such as length of heat flow paths, temperature, temperature difference, and environmental conditions. In fact, a wide variety of physical, environmental, application, and, in some cases, aging factors affect the thermal performance of insulation. In some materials with low thermal conductivity (e.g., opacified silica aerogel, corkboard), heat transfer is almost purely conductive.

Although heat transmission characteristics are usually determined by measuring thermal conductivity, this property does not strictly apply to thermal insulation. A particular sample of a material has a unique value of thermal conductivity for a particular set of conditions. This value may not be representative of the material at other conditions and should be called **apparent thermal conductivity**. For details, refer to ASTM *Standards* C168, C177, C335, C518, C976, and C1045.

Reflective insulation reduces radiant heat transfer because the surfaces have high reflectance and low emittance values. Conventional calculation methods ascribe the radiative properties to the associated air cavity, rather than to the insulation layer, to avoid incorrectly ascribing the benefits of reflective insulation that does not face an air cavity. Tables 1 and 2 give typical design values for air cavities faced with reflective layers. Multiple layers of reflective materials and smooth and parallel sealed air spaces increase overall thermal resistance. Air exchange and movement must be inhibited, however, or the reduction in radiative heat transfer is overshadowed by increased convection.

Mass-type insulation can be combined with reflective surfaces and air spaces to increase thermal resistance. However, each design must be evaluated, because maximum thermal performance of these systems depends on factors such as condition of the insulation, shape and form of construction, means to avoid air leakage and movement, and condition and aging characteristics of installed reflective surfaces.

Design values of apparent thermal conductivity, thermal conductance, and thermal resistance for most common insulation materials are listed in Table 4. These values have been selected as typical and useful for engineering calculations. Test results of insulation under appropriate conditions give values for that particular case.

Insulation's form and physical structure, environment, and application conditions can affect its apparent thermal conductivity. Form and physical structure vary with the basic material and manufacturing process. Typical variations include density, cell size, diameter and arrangement of fibers or particles, degree and extent of bonding materials, transparency to thermal radiation, and type and pressure of gas within the insulation.

Figure 2 illustrates the variation with density of the apparent thermal conductivity at one mean temperature for a number of insulation materials used in building envelopes. For most mass-type insulation, there is a minimum that depends on the type and form of the material, temperature, and direction of heat flow. For fibrous materials, the values of density at which the minimum occurs increase as both the fiber diameter (or cell size) and the mean temperature increase. These effects are shown in Figures 3 (Lotz 1969) and 4.

Other structural factors that affect thermal performance include compaction and settling of insulation, air permeability, type and amount of binder used, additives that may influence the bond or contact between fibers or particles, and type and form of radiation transfer inhibitor, if used. In cellular materials, most factors that influence strength also control thermal conductivity: size, shape, and orientation of the cells, and thickness of the cell walls. However, gas contained in the cells and radiation characteristics of cell surfaces also influence the effective conductivity.

Density changes caused by compaction affect the apparent thermal conductivity of insulation powders. Insulating concretes made from lightweight aggregates can be produced in a wide range of densities, with corresponding thermal conductivity. Fibrous insulation reaches a minimum conductivity when fibers are uniformly spaced and perpendicular to the direction of heat flow. Generally, a

Table 4 Typical Thermal Properties of Common Building and Insulating Materials: Design Values[a]

Description	Density, kg/m³	Conductivity[b] k, W/(m·K)	Resistance R, (m²·K)/W	Specific Heat, kJ/(kg·K)	Reference[n]
Building Board and Siding					
Board					
Asbestos/cement board	1900	0.57	—	1.00	Nottage (1947)
Cement board	1150	0.25	—	0.84	Kumaran (2002)
Fiber/cement board	1400	0.25	—	0.84	Kumaran (2002)
	1000	0.19	—	0.84	Kumaran (1996)
	400	0.07	—	1.88	Kumaran (1996)
	300	0.06	—	1.88	Kumaran (1996)
Gypsum or plaster board	640	0.16	—	1.15	Kumaran (2002)
Oriented strand board (OSB) 9 to 11 mm	650	—	0.11	1.88	Kumaran (2002)
12.7 mm	650	—	0.12	1.88	Kumaran (2002)
Plywood (douglas fir) 12.7 mm	460	—	0.14	1.88	Kumaran (2002)
15.9 mm	540	—	0.15	1.88	Kumaran (2002)
Plywood/wood panels 19.0 mm	450	—	0.19	1.88	Kumaran (2002)
Vegetable fiber board				—	
Sheathing, regular density[e] 12.7 mm	290	—	0.23	1.30	Lewis (1967)
intermediate density[e] 12.7 mm	350	—	0.19	1.30	Lewis (1967)
Nail-base sheathing[e] 12.7 mm	400	—	0.19	1.30	
Shingle backer 9.5 mm	290	—	0.17	1.30	
Sound deadening board 12.7 mm	240	—	0.24	1.26	
Tile and lay-in panels, plain or acoustic	290	0.058	—	0.59	
Laminated paperboard	480	0.072	—	1.38	Lewis (1967)
Homogeneous board from repulped paper	480	0.072	—	1.17	
Hardboard[e]					
medium density	800	0.105	—	1.30	Lewis (1967)
high density, service-tempered grade and service grade	880	0.12	—	1.34	Lewis (1967)
high density, standard-tempered grade	1010	0.144	—	1.34	Lewis (1967)
Particleboard[e]					
low density	590	0.102	—	1.30	Lewis (1967)
medium density	800	0.135	—	1.30	Lewis (1967)
high density	1000	1.18	—	—	Lewis (1967)
underlayment 15.9 mm	640	—	1.22	1.21	Lewis (1967)
Waferboard	700	0.072	—	1.88	Kumaran (1996)
Shingles					
Asbestos/cement	1900	—	0.037	—	
Wood, 400 mm, 190 mm exposure	—	—	0.15	1.30	
Wood, double, 400 mm, 300 mm exposure	—	—	0.21	1.17	
Wood, plus ins. backer board 8 mm	—	—	0.25	1.30	
Siding				—	
Asbestos/cement, lapped 6.4 mm	—	—	0.037	1.01	
Asphalt roll siding	—	—	0.026	1.47	
Siding					
Asphalt insulating siding (12.7 mm bed)	—	—	0.26	1.47	
Hardboard siding 11 mm	—	—	0.12	1.17	
Wood, drop, 200 mm 25 mm	—	—	0.14	1.17	
Wood, bevel					
200 mm, lapped 13 mm	—	—	0.14	1.17	
250 mm, lapped 19 mm	—	—	0.18	1.17	
Wood, plywood, lapped 9.5 mm	—	—	0.10	1.22	
Aluminum, steel, or vinyl,[j, k] over sheathing				—	
hollow-backed	—	—	0.11	1.22[k]	
insulating-board-backed				—	
9.5 mm	—	—	0.32	1.34	
foil-backed 9.5 mm	—	—	0.52	—	
Architectural (soda-lime float) glass	2500	1.0	—	0.84	
Building Membrane					
Vapor-permeable felt	—	—	0.011	—	
Vapor: seal, 2 layers of mopped 0.73 kg/m² felt	—	—	0.21	—	
Vapor: seal, plastic film	—	—	Negligible	—	

Table 4 Typical Thermal Properties of Common Building and Insulating Materials: Design Values[a] (*Continued*)

Description	Density, kg/m³	Conductivity[b] k, W/(m·K)	Resistance R, (m²·K)/W	Specific Heat, kJ/(kg·K)	Reference[n]
Finish Flooring Materials					
Carpet and rebounded urethane pad .... 19 mm	110	—	0.42	—	NIST (2000)
Carpet and rubber pad (one-piece) .... 9.5 mm	320	—	0.12	—	NIST (2000)
Pile carpet with rubber pad .... 9.5 to 12.7 mm	290	—	0.28	—	NIST (2000)
Linoleum/cork tile .... 6.4 mm	465	—	0.09	—	NIST (2000)
PVC/Rubber floor covering	—	0.40	—	—	CIBSE (2006)
Rubber tile .... 25 mm	1900	—	0.06	—	NIST (2000)
Terrazzo .... 25 mm	—	—	0.014	0.80	
Insulating Materials					
Blanket and batt[c,d]					
Glass-fiber batts .... 85 to 90 mm	10 to 14	0.043	—	0.84	Kumaran (2002)
.... 50 mm	8 to 13	0.045 to 0.048	—	0.84	Kumaran (2002)
Mineral fiber .... 140 mm	30	0.036	—	0.84	Kumaran (1996)
Mineral wool, felted	16 to 48	0.040	—	—	CIBSE (2006), NIST (2000)
....	65 to 130	0.035	—	—	NIST (2000)
Slag wool	50 to 190	0.038	—	—	Raznjevic (1976)
....	255	0.040	—	—	Raznjevic (1976)
....	305	0.043	—	—	Raznjevic (1976)
....	350	0.048	—	—	Raznjevic (1976)
....	400	0.050	—	—	Raznjevic (1976)
Board and slabs					
Cellular glass	130	0.048	—	0.75	(Manufacturer)
Cement fiber slabs, shredded wood with Portland cement binder	400 to 430	0.072 to 0.076	—	—	
with magnesia oxysulfide binder	350	0.082	—	1.30	
Glass fiber board	160	0.032 to 0.040	—	0.84	Kumaran (1996)
Expanded rubber (rigid)	70	0.032	—	1.67	Nottage (1947)
Expanded polystyrene extruded (smooth skin)	25 to 40	0.022 to 0.030	—	1.47	Kumaran (1996)
Expanded polystyrene, molded beads	15 to 25	0.032 to 0.039	—	1.47	Kumaran (1996)
Mineral fiberboard, wet felted	160	0.038	—	0.84	Kumaran (1996)
core or roof insulation	255 to 270	0.049	—	—	
acoustical tile[g]	290	0.050	—	0.80	
....	335	0.053	—	—	
wet-molded, acoustical tile[g]	370	0.061	—	0.59	
Perlite board	160	0.052	—	—	Kumaran (1996)
Polyisocyanurate, aged					
unfaced	25 to 35	0.020 to 0.027	—	—	Kumaran (2002)
with facers	65	0.019	—	1.47	Kumaran (1996)
Phenolic foam board with facers, aged	65	0.019	—	—	Kumaran (1996)
Loose fill					
Cellulosic (milled paper or wood pulp)	35 to 50	0.039 to 0.045	—	1.38	NIST (2000), Kumaran (1996)
Perlite, expanded	30 to 65	0.039 to 0.045	—	1.09	(Manufacturer)
....	65 to 120	0.045 to 0.052	—	—	(Manufacturer)
....	120 to 180	0.052 to 0.061	—	—	(Manufacturer)
Mineral fiber (rock, slag, or glass)[d]					
.... approx. 95 to 130 mm	10 to 30	—	1.92	0.71	
.... approx. 170 to 220 mm	10 to 30	—	3.33	—	
.... approx. 190 to 250 mm	10 to 30	—	3.85	—	
.... approx. 260 to 350 mm	10 to 30	—	5.26	—	
.... 90 mm (closed sidewall application)	30 to 55	—	2.1 to 2.5	—	
Vermiculite, exfoliated	110 to 130	0.068	—	1.34	Sabine et al. (1975)
....	64 to 96	0.063	—	—	(Manufacturer)
Spray-applied					
Cellulosic fiber	55 to 95	0.042 to 0.049	—	—	Yarbrough et al. (1987)
Glass fiber	55 to 70	0.038 to 0.039	—	—	Yarbrough et al. (1987)
Polyurethane foam (low density)	6 to 8	0.042	—	1.47	Kumaran (2002)
	40	0.026	—	1.47	Kumaran (2002)
aged and dry .... 40 mm	30	—	1.6	1.47	Kumaran (1996)
.... 50 mm	55	—	1.92	1.47	Kumaran (1996)
.... 120 mm	30	—	3.69	—	Kumaran (1996)
Ureaformaldehyde foam, dry	8 to 20	0.030 to 0.032	—	—	CIBSE (2006)
Metals					
(See Chapter 33, Table 3)					

Table 4 Typical Thermal Properties of Common Building and Insulating Materials: Design Values[a] (*Continued*)

Description		Density, kg/m³	Conductivity[b] k, W/(m·K)	Resistance R, (m²·K)/W	Specific Heat, kJ/(kg·K)	Reference[n]
Roofing						
Asbestos/cement shingles		1120	—	0.037	1.00	
Asphalt (bitumen with inert fill)		1600	0.43	—		CIBSE (2006)
		1900	0.58	—		CIBSE (2006)
		2300	1.15	—	—	CIBSE (2006)
Asphalt roll roofing		920	—	0.027	1.51	
Asphalt shingles		920	—	0.078	1.26	
Built-up roofing	10 mm	920	—	0.059	1.47	
Mastic asphalt (heavy, 20% grit)		950	0.19	—	—	CIBSE (2006)
Reed thatch		270	0.09	—	—	CIBSE (2006)
Roofing felt		2250	1.20	—	—	CIBSE (2006)
Slate	13 mm	—	—	0.009	1.26	
Straw thatch		240	0.07	—	—	CIBSE (2006)
Wood shingles, plain and plastic-film-faced		—	—	0.166	1.30	
Plastering Materials						
Cement plaster, sand aggregate		1860	0.72	—	0.84	
Sand aggregate						
	10 mm	—	—	0.013	0.84	
	20 mm	—	—	0.026	0.84	
Gypsum plaster		1120	0.38	—	—	CIBSE (2006)
		1280	0.46	—	—	CIBSE (2006)
Lightweight aggregate						
	13 mm	720	—	0.056	—	
	16 mm	720	—	0.066	—	
on metal lath	19 mm	—	—	0.083	—	
Perlite aggregate		720	0.22	—	1.34	
Sand aggregate		1680	0.81	—	0.84	
on metal lath	19 mm	—	—	0.023	—	
Vermiculite aggregate		480	0.14	—	—	CIBSE (2006)
		600	0.20	—	—	CIBSE (2006)
		720	0.25	—	—	CIBSE (2006)
		840	0.26	—	—	CIBSE (2006)
		960	0.30	—	—	CIBSE (2006)
Perlite plaster		400	0.08	—	—	CIBSE (2006)
		600	0.19	—	—	CIBSE (2006)
Pulpboard or paper plaster		600	0.07	—	—	CIBSE (2006)
Sand/cement plaster, conditioned		1560	0.63	—	—	CIBSE (2006)
Sand/cement/lime plaster, conditioned		1440	0.48	—	—	CIBSE (2006)
Sand/gypsum (3:1) plaster, conditioned		1550	0.65	—	—	CIBSE (2006)
Masonry Materials						
Masonry units						
Brick, fired clay		2400	1.21 to 1.47	—	—	Valore (1988)
		2240	1.07 to 1.30	—	—	Valore (1988)
		2080	0.92 to 1.12	—	—	Valore (1988)
		1920	0.81 to 0.98	—	0.80	Valore (1988)
		1760	0.71 to 0.85	—	—	Valore (1988)
		1600	0.61 to 0.74	—	—	Valore (1988)
		1440	0.52 to 0.62	—	—	Valore (1988)
		1280	0.43 to 0.53	—	—	Valore (1988)
		1120	0.36 to 0.45	—	—	Valore (1988)
Clay tile, hollow						
1 cell deep	75 mm	—	—	0.14	0.88	Rowley (1937)
	100 mm	—	—	0.20	—	Rowley (1937)
2 cells deep	150 mm	—	—	0.27	—	Rowley (1937)
	200 mm	—	—	0.33	—	Rowley (1937)
	250 mm	—	—	0.39	—	Rowley (1937)
3 cells deep	300 mm	—	—	0.44	—	Rowley (1937)
Lightweight brick		800	0.20	—	—	Kumaran (1996)
		770	0.22	—	—	Kumaran (1996)
Concrete blocks[h, i]						
Limestone aggregate						
~200 mm, 16.3 kg, 2200 kg/m³ concrete, 2 cores		—	—	—	—	
with perlite-filled cores		—	—	0.37	—	Valore (1988)
~300 mm, 25 kg, 2200 kg/m³ concrete, 2 cores		—	—	—	—	
with perlite-filled cores		—	—	0.65	—	Valore (1988)
Normal-weight aggregate (sand and gravel)						
~200 mm, 16 kg, 2100 kg/m³ concrete, 2 or 3 cores		—	—	0.20 to 0.17	0.92	Van Geem (1985)

Table 4 Typical Thermal Properties of Common Building and Insulating Materials: Design Values[a] (*Continued*)

Description	Density, kg/m³	Conductivity[b] k, W/(m·K)	Resistance R, (m²·K)/W	Specific Heat, kJ/(kg·K)	Reference[n]
with perlite-filled cores	—	—	0.35	—	Van Geem (1985)
with vermiculite-filled cores	—	—	0.34 to 0.24	—	Valore (1988)
~300 mm, 22.7 kg, 2000 kg/m³ concrete, 2 cores	—	—	0.217	0.92	Valore (1988)
Medium-weight aggregate (combinations of normal and lightweight aggregate)					
~200 mm, 13 kg, 1550 to 1800 kg/m³					
concrete, 2 or 3 cores	—	—	0.30 to 0.22	—	Van Geem (1985)
with perlite-filled cores	—	—	0.65 to 0.41	—	Van Geem (1985)
with vermiculite-filled cores	—	—	0.58	—	Van Geem (1985)
with molded-EPS-filled (beads) cores	—	—	0.56	—	Van Geem (1985)
with molded EPS inserts in cores	—	—	0.47	—	Van Geem (1985)
Low-mass aggregate (expanded shale, clay, slate or slag, pumice)					
~150 mm, 7 1/2 kg, 1400 kg/m²					
concrete, 2 or 3 cores	—	—	0.34 to 0.29	—	Van Geem (1985)
with perlite-filled cores	—	—	0.74	—	Van Geem (1985)
with vermiculite-filled cores	—	—	0.53	—	Van Geem (1985)
200 mm, 8 to 10 kg, 1150 to 1380 kg/m² concrete	—	—	0.56 to 0.33	0.88	Van Geem (1985)
with perlite-filled cores	—	—	1.20 to 0.77	—	Van Geem (1985)
with vermiculite-filled cores	—	—	0.93 to 0.69	—	Shu et al. (1979)
with molded-EPS-filled (beads) cores	—	—	0.85	—	Shu et al. (1979)
with UF foam-filled cores	—	—	0.79	—	Shu et al. (1979)
with molded EPS inserts in cores	—	—	0.62	—	Shu et al. (1979)
300 mm, 16 kg, 1400 kg/m³,					
concrete, 2 or 3 cores	—	—	0.46 to 0.40	—	Van Geem (1985)
with perlite-filled cores	—	—	1.6 to 1.1	—	Van Geem (1985)
with vermiculite-filled cores	—	—	1.0	—	Valore (1988)
Stone, lime, or sand	2880	10.4	—	—	Valore (1988)
Quartzitic and sandstone	2560	6.2	—	—	Valore (1988)
	2240	3.46	—	—	Valore (1988)
	1920	1.88	—	0.88	Valore (1988)
Calcitic, dolomitic, limestone, marble, and granite	2880	4.33	—	—	Valore (1988)
	2560	3.17	—	—	Valore (1988)
	2240	2.31	—	—	Valore (1988)
	1920	1.59	—	0.88	Valore (1988)
	1600	1.15	—	—	Valore (1988)
Gypsum partition tile					
75 by 300 by 760 mm, solid	—	—	0.222	0.79	Rowley (1937)
4 cells	—	—	0.238	—	Rowley (1937)
100 by 300 by 760 mm, 3 cells	—	—	0.294	—	Rowley (1937)
Limestone	2400	0.57	—	0.84	Kumaran (2002)
	2600	0.93	—	0.84	Kumaran (2002)
Concretes[i]					
Sand and gravel or stone aggregate concretes (concretes with >50% quartz or quartzite sand have conductivities in higher end of range)	2400	1.4 to 2.9	—	—	Valore (1988)
	2240	1.3 to 2.6	—	0.80 to 1.00	Valore (1988)
	2080	1.0 to 1.9	—	—	Valore (1988)
Low-mass aggregate or limestone concretes	1920	0.9 to 1.3	—	—	Valore (1988)
Expanded shale, clay, or slate; expanded slags; cinders; pumice (with density up to 1600 kg/m³); scoria (sanded concretes have conductivities in higher end of range)	1600	0.68 to 0.89	—	0.84	Valore (1988)
	1280	0.48 to 0.59	—	0.84	Valore (1988)
	960	0.30 to 0.36	—	—	Valore (1988)
	640	0.18	—	—	Valore (1988)
Gypsum/fiber concrete (87.5% gypsum, 12.5% wood chips)	800	0.24	—	0.84	Rowley (1937)
Cement/lime, mortar, and stucco	1920	1.40	—	—	Valore (1988)
	1600	0.97	—	—	Valore (1988)
	1280	0.65	—	—	Valore (1988)
Perlite, vermiculite, and polystyrene beads	800	0.26 to 0.27	—	—	Valore (1988)
	640	0.20 to 0.22	—	0.63 to 0.96	Valore (1988)
	480	0.16	—	—	Valore (1988)
	320	0.12	—	—	Valore (1988)
Foam concretes	1920	0.75	—	—	Valore (1988)
	1600	0.60	—	—	Valore (1988)

Table 4 Typical Thermal Properties of Common Building and Insulating Materials: Design Values[a] (*Continued*)

Description	Density, kg/m³	Conductivity[b] *k*, W/(m·K)	Resistance *R*, (m²·K)/W	Specific Heat, kJ/(kg·K)	Reference[n]
....	1280	0.44	—	—	Valore (1988)
....	1120	0.36	—	—	Valore (1988)
Foam concretes and cellular concretes	960	0.30	—	—	Valore (1988)
....	640	0.20	—	—	Valore (1988)
....	320	0.12	—	—	Valore (1988)
Aerated concrete (oven-dried)	430 to 800	0.20	—	0.84	Kumaran (1996)
Polystyrene concrete (oven-dried)	255 to 800	0.37	—	0.84	Kumaran (1996)
Polymer concrete	1950	1.64	—	—	Kumaran (1996)
....	2200	1.03	—	—	Kumaran (1996)
Polymer cement	1870	0.78	—	—	Kumaran (1996)
Slag concrete	960	0.22	—	—	Touloukian et al (1970)
....	1280	0.32	—	—	Touloukian et al. (1970)
....	1600	0.43	—	—	Touloukian et al. (1970)
....	2000	1.23	—	—	Touloukian et al. (1970)
Woods (12% moisture content)[l]					
Hardwoods	—	—	—	1.63[m]	Wilkes (1979)
Oak	660 to 750	0.16 to 0.18	—	—	Cardenas and Bible (1987)
Birch	680 to 725	0.17 to 0.18	—	—	Cardenas and Bible (1987)
Maple	635 to 700	0.16 to 0.17	—	—	Cardenas and Bible (1987)
Ash	615 to 670	0.15 to 0.16	—	—	Cardenas and Bible (1987)
Softwoods	—	—	—	1.63[m]	Wilkes (1979)
Southern pine	570 to 660	0.14 to 0.16	—	—	Cardenas and Bible (1987)
Southern yellow pine	500	0.13	—	—	Kumaran (2002)
Eastern white pine	400	0.10	—	—	Kumaran (2002)
Douglas fir/larch	535 to 580	0.14 to 0.15	—	—	Cardenas and Bible (1987)
Southern cypress	500 to 515	0.13	—	—	Cardenas and Bible (1987)
Hem/fir, spruce/pine/fir	390 to 500	0.11 to 0.13	—	—	Cardenas and Bible (1987)
Spruce	400	0.09	—	—	Kumaran (2002)
Western red cedar	350	0.09	—	—	Kumaran (2002)
West coast woods, cedars	350 to 500	0.10 to 0.13	—	—	Cardenas and Bible (1987)
Eastern white cedar	360	0.10	—	—	Kumaran (2002)
California redwood	390 to 450	0.11 to 0.12	—	—	Cardenas and Bible (1987)
Pine (oven-dried)	370	0.092	—	1.88	Kumaran (1996)
Spruce (oven-dried)	395	0.10	—	1.88	Kumaran (1996)

Notes for Table 4

[a]Values are for mean temperature of 24°C. Representative values for dry materials are intended as design (not specification) values for materials in normal use. Thermal values of insulating materials may differ from design values depending on in-situ properties (e.g., density and moisture content, orientation, etc.) and manufacturing variability. For properties of specific product, use values supplied by manufacturer or unbiased tests.

[b]Symbol λ also used to represent thermal conductivity.

[c]Does not include paper backing and facing, if any. Where insulation forms boundary (reflective or otherwise) of airspace, see Tables 2 and 3 for insulating value of airspace with appropriate effective emittance and temperature conditions of space.

[d]Conductivity varies with fiber diameter (see Chapter 25). Batt, blanket, and loose-fill mineral fiber insulations are manufactured to achieve specified R-values, the most common of which are listed in the table. Because of differences in manufacturing processes and materials, the product thicknesses, densities, and thermal conductivities vary over considerable ranges for a specified R-value.

[e]Values are for aged products with gas-impermeable facers on the two major surfaces. An aluminum foil facer of 25 μm thickness or greater is generally considered impermeable to gases. For change in conductivity with age of expanded polyisocyanurate, see SPI Bulletin U108.

[f]Cellular phenolic insulation may no longer be manufactured. Thermal conductivity and resistance values do not represent aged insulation, which may have higher thermal conductivity and lower thermal resistance.

[g]Insulating values of acoustical tile vary, depending on density of board and on type, size, and depth of perforations.

[h]Values for fully grouted block may be approximated using values for concrete with similar unit density.

[i]Values for concrete block and concrete are at moisture contents representative of normal use.

[j]Values for metal or vinyl siding applied over flat surfaces vary widely, depending on ventilation of the airspace beneath the siding; whether airspace is reflective or nonreflective; and on thickness, type, and application of insulating backing-board used. Values are averages for use as design guides, and were obtained from several guarded hot box tests (ASTM *Standard* C236) or calibrated hot box (ASTM *Standard* C976) on hollow-backed types and types made using backing of wood fiber, foamed plastic, and glass fiber. Departures of ±50% or more from these values may occur.

[k]Vinyl specific heat = 1.0 kJ/(kg·K)

[l]See Adams (1971), MacLean (1941), and Wilkes (1979). Conductivity values listed are for heat transfer across the grain. Thermal conductivity of wood varies linearly with density, and density ranges listed are those normally found for wood species given. If density of wood species is not known, use mean conductivity value. For extrapolation to other moisture contents, the following empirical equation developed by Wilkes (1979) may be used:

$$k = 0.1791 + \frac{(1.874 \times 10^{-2} + 5.753 \times 10^{-4} M)\rho}{1 + 0.01M}$$

where ρ is density of moist wood in kg/m³, and M is moisture content in percent.

[m]From Wilkes (1979), an empirical equation for specific heat of moist wood at 24°C is as follows:

$$c_p = \frac{(0.299 + 0.01M)}{(1 + 0.01M)} + \Delta c_p$$

where Δc_p accounts for heat of sorption and is denoted by

$$\Delta c_p = M(1.921 \times 10^{-3} - 3.168 \times 10^{-5} M)$$

where M is moisture content in percent by mass.

[n]Blank space in reference column indicates historical values from previous volumes of *ASHRAE Handbook*. Source of information could not be determined.

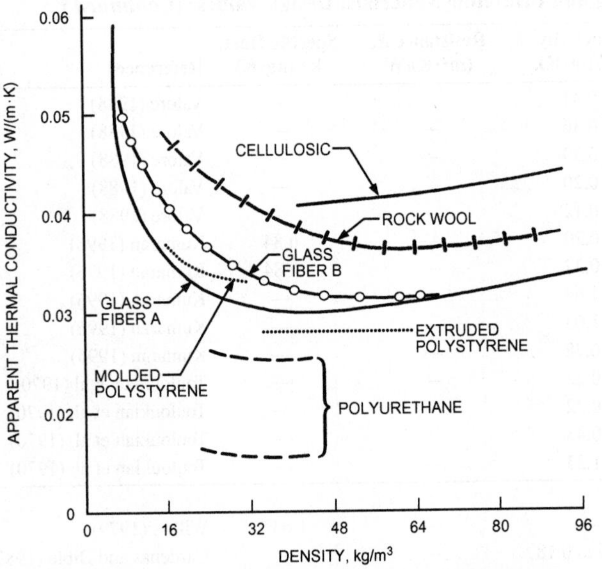

Fig. 2 Apparent Thermal Conductivity Versus Density of Several Thermal Insulations Used as Building Insulations

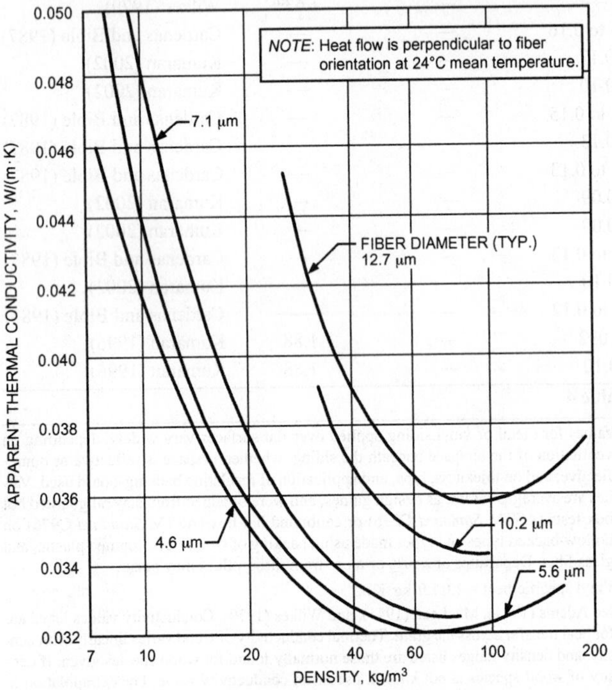

Fig. 3 Variation of Apparent Thermal Conductivity with Fiber Diameter and Density

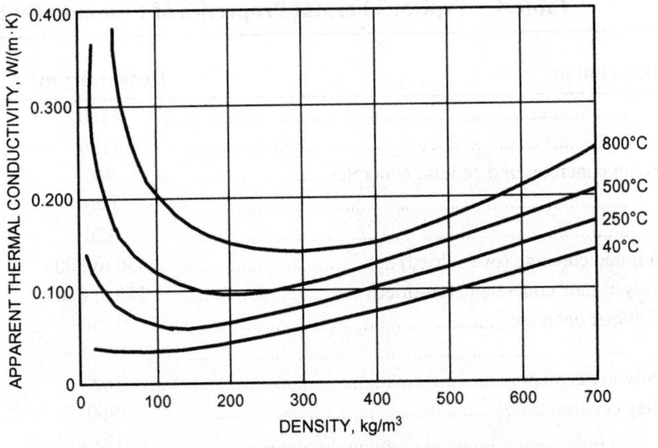

Fig. 4 Typical Variation of Apparent Thermal Conductivity with Mean Temperature and Density for Fibrous Insulations

decrease in fiber diameter lowers conductivity for the same density (Figure 4). For cellular insulation, a specific combination of cell size, density, and gas composition produces optimum thermal conductivity.

At temperatures below 200 to 300°C, a large portion of heat transfer occurs by conduction through air or another gas in the insulation (Lander 1955; Rowley et al. 1952; Simons 1955; Verschoor and Greebler 1952).The overall heat transfer can be closely approximated by supposition of gas conduction with all other mechanisms, each determined separately. If the gas in the insulation is replaced by another gas with a different thermal conductivity, the apparent thermal conductivity changes by an amount approximately equal to the difference in conductivity of the two gases. For example, replacing air with a fluorinated hydrocarbon (HFC) can lower the apparent thermal conductivity of insulation by as much as 50%.

Fluorocarbon-expanded cellular plastic foams with a high proportion (greater than 90%) of closed cells retain the fluorocarbon for extended periods of time. Newly produced, they have apparent thermal conductivities of approximately 0.016 W/(m·K) at 24°C, but this value increases with time as air diffuses into the cells and the fluorocarbon gas gradually dissolves in the polymer or diffuses out. Diffusion rates and increase in apparent thermal conductivity depend on several factors, including permeance of cell walls to the gases involved, foam age, temperature, geometry of the insulation (thickness), and integrity of the surface protection provided. Brandreth (1986) and Tye (1988) showed that aging of polyurethane and polyisocyanurate is reasonably well understood analytically and confirmed experimentally. The dominant parameters for minimum aging are as follows:

- Closed-cell content >90%, preferably >95%
- Small, uniform cell diameter <<1 mm, with larger proportion of polymer in windows between cells
- Small anisotropy in cell structure
- High density
- Increased thickness
- High initial pressure of fluorocarbon blowing agent in cell
- Polymer highly resistant to gas diffusion and solubility
- Polymer distributed evenly in struts and windows of cells
- Low aging temperature

Aging is further reduced, particularly for laminated and spray-applied products, with higher-density polymer skins, or by well-adhered facings and coverings with low gas and moisture permeance. An oxygen diffusion rate of less than 3.5 $mm^3/(m^2 \cdot day)$ for a 25 μm thick barrier is one criterion used by some industry organizations for manufacturers of laminated products. The adhesion of any facing must be continuous, and every effort must be made during manufacturing to eliminate or minimize the shear plane layer at the foam/substrate interface (Ostrogorsky and Glicksman 1986). Before 1987, chlorinated fluorocarbons were commonly used as cell gas. Because of their high ozone-depleting potential, chlorofluorocarbons (CFCs) were phased out during the 1990s in accordance with the Montreal Protocol of 1987. Alternatives used today are fluorocarbons, CO_2, N-pentane, and C-pentane.

Closed-cell phenolic-type materials and products, which are blown with similar gases, age differently and much more slowly.

For homogeneous, dense materials, the primary mode of heat transfer is conduction. However, as temperatures increase, heat transfer by radiation (and possibly convection) becomes a greater part of the total. The magnitude of radiation and convection depends on temperature difference, direction of heat flow, nature of the materials involved, and geometry. Because of radiative heat transfer in low-density insulation, measured apparent thermal conductivity depends on test thickness. That thickness effect increases the apparent thermal conductivity measured at installed thickness over that commonly determined at 25 mm (Pelanne 1979). From a thermal resistance standpoint, the effect is small, typically less than 10%, even for thin (e.g., 25 mm thick), low-density (e.g., 5.5 kg/m^3) insulation. The effect becomes negligible for typical building applications (e.g., 150 mm insulation with a density of 11 kg/m^3).

Environment and application conditions include mean temperature, temperature gradient, moisture content, air infiltration, orientation, and direction of heat flow. The magnitude of effect each has on apparent thermal conductivity varies according to insulation material and form.

The apparent thermal conductivity of insulating materials generally increases with temperature. The rate of change varies with material type and density. Figure 5 shows typical variations with mean temperature. However, some materials, such as fluorocarbon-expanded, closed-cell polyurethanes, have an inflection in the curve where the fluorocarbon changes phase from gas to liquid (see Table 7B in Chapter 25). The apparent thermal conductivity of a sample at one mean temperature (average of the two surface temperatures)

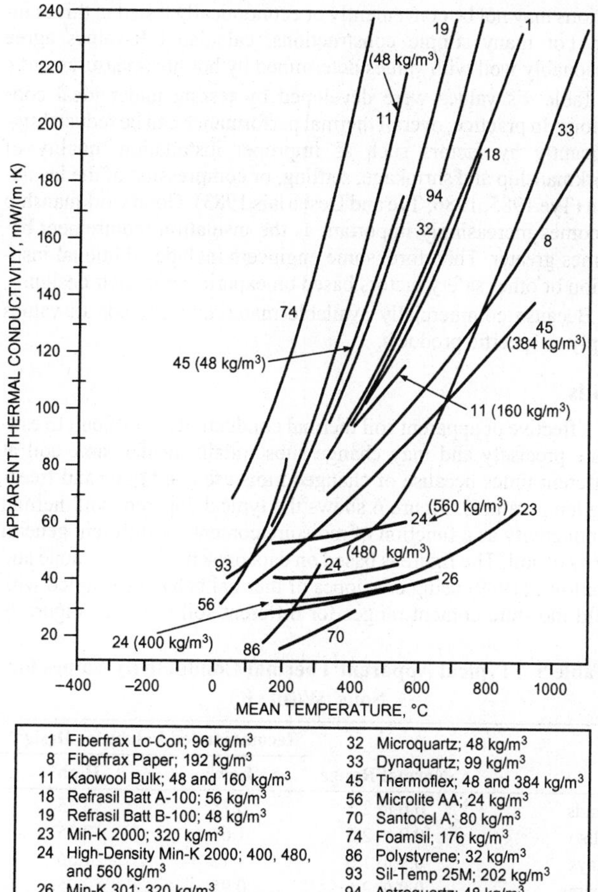

Fig. 5 Apparent Thermal Conductivity Versus Mean Temperature for Various Materials (in Air at Atmospheric Pressure)
(Glaser et al. 1967; Pelanne 1977)

only applies to the material at the particular thickness tested. Further testing is required to obtain values suitable for all thicknesses.

Insulating materials that allow a large percentage of heat transfer by radiation, such as low-density fibrous and cellular products, show the greatest change in apparent thermal conductivity with temperature and surrounding surface emittance.

The effect of temperature on structural integrity is ordinarily not important for most insulation materials in low-temperature applications. In any case, decomposition, excessive linear shrinkage, softening, or other effects limit the maximum temperature for which a material is suited. At extreme temperatures, both high and low, selecting suitable materials is more difficult and must be based on experience and performance data (see Tables 4 and 7B in Chapter 25).

Convection and air infiltration in or through some insulation systems may increase heat transfer across them. Low-density, loose-fill, large open-cell, and fibrous insulation, and poorly designed or installed reflective systems are the most susceptible. The temperature difference across the insulation and the height and width of the insulated space influence the amount of convection. In some cases, natural convection may be inherent to the system (Wilkes and Childs 1992; Wilkes and Rucker 1983), but in many cases it is a consequence of careless design and/or careless construction of the insulated structure (Donnelly et al. 1976). Gaps between board- and batt-type insulations lower their effectiveness. Board-type insulation may not be perfectly square, may be installed improperly, and may be applied to uneven surfaces. A 4% void area around batt insulation can produce a 50% loss in effective thermal resistance for ceiling application with R = 3.4 (m^2·K)/W (Verschoor 1977). Similar results have been obtained for wall configurations (Brown et al. 1993; Hedlin 1985; Lecompte 1989; Lewis 1979; Rasmussen et al. 1993; Tye and Desjarlais 1981). As a solution, preformed joints in board-type insulation allow boards to fit together without air gaps. Boards and batts can be installed in two layers, with joints between layers offset and staggered.

The apparent thermal conductivity of insulation materials increases with moisture content. If moisture condenses in the insulation, it not only reduces thermal resistance, but may also physically damage the system. Reduction in thermal resistance depends on material, moisture content, and moisture distribution. Section A3 of the *CIBSE Guide A* (CIBSE 2006) covers thermal properties of building structures affected by moisture.

Apparent thermal conductivity for insulation materials and systems is obtained by standard methods listed in ASTM (2008). The methods apply mainly to laboratory measurements on dried or conditioned samples at specific mean temperatures and temperature gradient conditions. Although fundamental heat transmission characteristics of a material or system can be determined accurately, actual performance in a structure may vary from laboratory results; only field measurements can clarify the differences. Field-test procedures continue to be developed. Envelope design, construction, and material may all affect the procedure to be followed, as detailed in ASTM (1985a, 1985b, 1988, 1990, 1991).

Mechanical Properties

Some insulation is used occasionally to support load-bearing roofs and floors, form self-supporting partitions, or stiffen structural panels. For such applications, the material's strength in compression, tension, shear, impact, flexure, and resistance to vibration may be important. These properties vary with basic composition of the insulation, density, cell size, fiber diameter and orientation, type and amount of binder (if any), and temperature and environmental conditioning.

Health and Safety

Many thermal insulation materials have good resistance to fire, vermin, rot, objectionable odors, and vapors. Some are a potential risk to health and safety, presenting either (1) risk related to storage, handling, and installation or (2) risk that occurs after installation (e.g., aging, fire, or physical disturbance). Potential hazards during manufacture are not considered here. Correct handling, installation, and precautionary measures may reduce or eliminate risks.

Combustion of insulation materials and accessories may release heat, hazardous gases, fibers, and particulates. Manufacturers' recommendations and applicable codes and standards (e.g., ASTM *Standard* C930) give more details.

Acoustics

Some thermal insulation with open, porous surfaces is used as sound absorption material, regardless of whether thermal performance is a design requirement. Thermal insulation with high density and resilient characteristics can act as vibration insulators, either alone or in combination with other materials. Some flexible and semirigid, formed-in-place fibrous materials and rigid fibrous insulation help reduce sound transmission when placed in a composite construction.

Sound-absorbing insulation is normally installed on interior surfaces or used as interior surfacing materials. Rigid sound-absorbing insulation is fabricated into tiles or blocks, edge-treated to facilitate mechanical or adhesive application, and prefinished during manufacture. Insulation units can have a natural porous surface or mechanical perforations to facilitate entry of sound waves; others use a diaphragm or decorative film surfacing attached only to the edges of the units, which allows sound waves to reach the fibrous backing by diaphragm action.

Flexible, semirigid, and formed-in-place fibrous materials used for sound absorption are available in a variety of thickness and densities that determine their sound absorption characteristics.

When density is increased by reducing material thickness, sound absorption is generally reduced; however, as thickness increases, the influence of density decreases.

A wall of staggered-stud construction, finished with airtight gypsum board, that uses resilient clips or channels on one side of the stud reduces sound transmission. Another option is resilient insulation boards of special manufacture to prevent acoustic coupling between surfaces. A sound absorption thermal insulation blanket in a wall cavity also reduces sound transmission, depending on the type of construction.

In floors, resilient channels or separate airtight finished floor and ceiling joists form a discontinuous construction. Sound-absorbing thermal insulation placed in this construction reduces sound transmission. Sound-deadening boards underlying finish flooring absorb impact sounds and reduce airborne and impact sound transmission.

Thermal insulation boards can be placed under mechanical equipment to isolate vibration. The imposed loading and natural resonant frequency of these materials are critical for proper design. Because material must deflect properly under load to provide isolation, the system should be neither over- nor underloaded.

For further information on sound and vibration control, refer to Chapter 47 of the 2007 *ASHRAE Handbook—HVAC Applications*.

Other Properties

Other properties of insulating materials that can be important, depending on application, include density, resilience, resistance to settling, air and vapor permeance, reuse or salvage value, ease of handling, dimensional uniformity and stability, resistance to chemical action and chemical change, resistance to moisture penetration, ease in fabrication, application of finishes, and sizes and thickness obtainable.

Building Materials

The values listed in Table 4 are typically for a mean temperature of 24°C. Thermal conductivity values may vary with temperature: polymers' conductivity generally decreases with temperature, until the glass-transition temperature is reached. This transition occurs at different temperatures for different materials, but is typically at –30 or –40°C; below this threshold, thermal conductivity increases quickly as the temperature decreases.

Table 4 also lists resistance values for materials of specific thickness. Where conductance is required for a material for which only the conductivity is listed, the conductance value can be determined by dividing the conductivity by the desired thickness x, or $C = k/x$. Thermal resistance is the reciprocal of conductance: $R = 1/C$. Resistivity (resistance per unit thickness) is the reciprocal of conductivity, or $1/k$.

Table 4 was revised as a result of ASHRAE research project RP-905 (McGowan 2007). Where possible, sources of data are shown in the Reference column; if no source is specified, the value for that material has been carried over from previous editions of this chapter.

Property Data

Building and Insulating Materials. Steady-state thermal resistances (R-values) of building assemblies (walls, floors, windows, roof systems, etc.) can be calculated from thermal properties of the materials in the component, provided by Table 4, or heat flow through the assembled component can be measured directly with laboratory equipment such as the guarded hot box (ASTM *Standard* C236) or the calibrated hot box (ASTM *Standard* C976). Direct measurement is the most accurate method of determining the overall thermal resistance for a combination of building materials assembled as a building envelope component. However, all combinations may not be conveniently or economically tested in this manner. For many simple constructions, calculated R-values agree reasonably well with values determined by hot box measurement.

Table 4's values were developed by testing under ideal conditions. In practice, overall thermal performance can be reduced significantly by factors such as improper installation, quality of workmanship and shrinkage, settling, or compression of the insulation (Tye 1985, 1986; Tye and Desjarlais 1983). Good workmanship becomes increasingly important as the insulation requirement becomes greater. Therefore, some engineers include additional insulation or other safety factors based on experience in their design.

Because commercially available materials vary, not all values apply to specific products.

Soils

Effective or apparent soil thermal conductivity is difficult to estimate precisely and may change substantially in the same soil at different times because of changed moisture conditions and freezing temperatures. Figure 6 shows the typical apparent soil thermal conductivity as a function of moisture content for different general types of soil. The figure is based on data presented in Salomone and Marlowe (1989) using envelopes of thermal behavior coupled with field moisture content ranges for different soil types. In Figure 6,

Table 5 Typical Apparent Thermal Conductivity Values for Soils, W/(m · K)

		Recommended Values for Design[a]	
	Normal Range	Low[b]	High[c]
Sands	0.6 to 2.5	0.78	2.25
Silts	0.9 to 2.5	1.64	2.25
Clays	0.9 to 1.6	1.12	1.56
Loams	0.9 to 2.5	0.95	2.25

[a]Reasonable values for use when no site- or soil-specific data are available.
[b]Moderately conservative values for minimum heat loss through soil (e.g., use in soil heat exchanger or earth-contact cooling calculations). Values are from Salomone and Marlowe (1989).
[c]Moderately conservative values for maximum heat loss through soil (e.g., use in peak winter heat loss calculations). Values are from Salomone and Marlowe (1989).

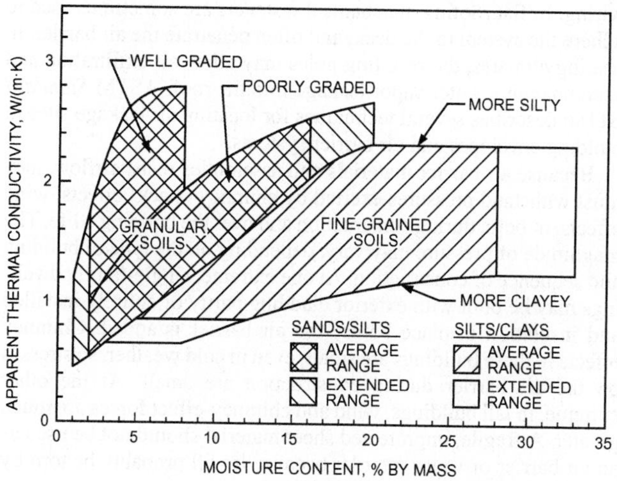

Fig. 6 Trends of Apparent Thermal Conductivity of Moist Soils

Table 6 Typical Apparent Thermal Conductivity Values for Rocks, W/(m · K)

	Normal Range
Pumice, tuff, obsidian	0.5 to 2.2
Basalt	0.5 to 2.6
Shale	0.9 to 4.0
Granite	1.7 to 4.3
Limestone, dolomite, marble	1.2 to 4.3
Quartzose sandstone	1.4 to 7.8

"well-graded" applies to granular soils with good representation of all particle sizes from largest to smallest. "Poorly graded" refers to granular soils with either uniform gradation, in which most particles are about the same size, or skip (or gap) gradation, in which particles of one or more intermediate sizes are not present.

Although thermal conductivity varies greatly over the complete range of possible moisture contents, this range can be narrowed if it is assumed that the moisture contents of most field soils lie between the "wilting point" of the soil (i.e., the moisture content of a soil below which a plant cannot alleviate its wilting symptoms) and the "field capacity" of the soil (i.e., the moisture content of a soil that has been thoroughly wetted and then drained until the drainage rate has become negligibly small). After a prolonged dry spell, moisture is near the wilting point, and after a rainy period, soil has moisture content near its field capacity. Moisture contents at these limits have been studied by many agricultural researchers, and data for different types of soil are given by Kersten (1949) and Salomone and Marlowe (1989). Shaded areas in Figure 6 approximate (1) the full range of moisture contents for different soil types and (2) a range between average values of each limit.

Table 5 summarizes design values for thermal conductivities of the basic soil classes. Table 6 gives ranges of thermal conductivity for some basic classes of rock. The value chosen depends on whether heat transfer is being calculated for minimum heat loss through the soil, as in a ground heat exchange system, or a maximum value, as in peak winter heat loss calculations for a basement. Hence, high and low values are given for each soil class.

As heat flows through soil, moisture tends to move away from the heat source. This moisture migration provides initial mass transport of heat, but it also dries the soil adjacent to the heat source, thus lowering the apparent thermal conductivity in that zone of soil.

Typically, when other factors are held constant,

- k increases with moisture content
- k increases with increasing dry density of a soil
- k decreases with increasing organic content of a soil
- k tends to decrease for soils with uniform gradations and rounded soil grains (because grain-to-grain contacts are reduced)
- k of a frozen soil may be higher or lower than that of the same unfrozen soil (because the conductivity of ice is higher than that of water but lower than that of typical soil grains). Differences in k below moisture contents of 7 to 8% are quite small. At approximately 15% moisture content, k may vary up to 30% from unfrozen values.

When calculating annual energy use, choose values that represent typical site conditions as they vary during the year. In climates where ground freezing is significant, accurate heat transfer simulations should include the effect of the latent heat of fusion of water. Energy released during this phase change significantly retards the progress of the frost front in moist soils.

For further information, see Chapter 17, which includes a method for estimating heat loss through foundations.

AIR TRANSMISSION AND HYGRIC PROPERTIES

AIR BARRIERS AND WATER VAPOR RETARDERS

Although the functions of water vapor and air barriers are different, a single component may serve both purposes. The designer should assess needs for vapor and air movement control in the building envelope and provide a system that guarantees the required vapor and air barrier properties.

Air Barriers

An effective air barrier must

- Meet material permeability requirements.
- Be continuous when installed (i.e., tight joints in the air barrier assembly, effective bonds in air barrier materials at intersections such as wall/roof and wall/foundation, tightly sealed penetrations).
- Accommodate dimensional changes caused by temperature or shrinkage without damage to joints or air barrier material.
- Be strong enough to support the stresses applied to the air barrier material or assembly. The air barrier must not be ruptured or excessively deformed by wind or stack effect. Where an adhesive is used to complete a joint, the assembly must be designed to withstand forces that might gradually peel the air barrier material away. Where the air barrier material is not strong enough to withstand anticipated wind and other loads, it must be supported on both sides to account for positive and negative wind gust pressures.

In addition, the following properties may be important, depending on the application:

- Elasticity
- Thermal stability
- Fire and flammability resistance
- Inertness to deteriorating elements
- Ease of fabrication, application, and joint sealing

Control of airflow requires an effective air barrier (also called an **airflow retarder** or **air infiltration barrier**) as well as a vapor retarder. Although flow of dry air may accelerate drying of a wet building component (Karagiozis and Salonvaara 1999a, 1999b), without effective control of airflow, vapor retarders are completely ineffective.

A retarder may control both vapor and airflow (i.e., act as an air/vapor retarder). Many designs are based on this idea, with measures taken to ensure that the vapor retarder is continuous to control airflow. Some designs treat airflow and vapor retarders as separate entities, but an airflow retarder should not be where it can cause moisture to condense if it also has vapor-retarding properties. For example, an air barrier placed on the cold side of a building envelope may cause condensation, particularly if the vapor retarder at the other side is ineffective. Instead, a carefully installed, sealed cold-side air/vapor retarder that has sufficient thermal resistance may lower the potential for condensation by raising the temperature at its indoor surface during the cold season (Ojanen et al. 1994).

Air leakage characteristics can be determined with the ASTM *Standard* E1186 test method for air barriers on the interior side of the building envelope, and described according to ASTM *Standard* E1677. Specific air leakage criteria for air barriers in cold heating climates can be found in Di Lenardo et al. (1995). These specifications call for maximum permissible air leakage rates between 0.05 and 0.2 L/s per square metre (as measured with an air pressure difference of 75 Pa), depending on the water vapor permeance of the outermost layer of the building envelope. The highest leakage rate applies if the permeance of the outermost layer is greater than 600 ng/(Pa·s·m^2); the lowest rate applies if the permeance is less than 60 ng/(Pa·s·m^2). Intermediate values are provided. The recommendations apply only to heating climates. (See the section on Air Transmission and Water Vapor Property Data for water vapor permeances of various building materials.)

The required air permeance of an air barrier material has been set by some building codes at 0.02 L/(s·m^2) at a pressure difference of 75 Pa. An addendum to ASHRAE *Standard* 90.1 in 2008 also referenced this value. ASTM *Standard* E1677 provides an alternative minimum air barrier testing and criteria specifically suitable for framed walls of low-rise buildings.

Air leakage characteristics of an air barrier assembly can be determined with the ASTM *Standard* E2357 test method, which determines the air leakage of three wall specimens: (1) with the air barrier material installed using air barrier accessories alone, (2) with the air barrier material installed and connected to air barrier components (window, doors, and other premanufactured elements) using air barrier accessories, and (3) with an air barrier wall assembly connected to a foundation assembly and roof assembly using air barrier accessories. The test method reports the air leakage rate at a reference pressure difference of 75 Pa.

Specific air leakage criteria for air barrier assemblies can be found in Di Lenardo et al (1995), as well as a 2008 addendum to ASHRAE *Standard* 90.1. These specifications provides classes for air leakage rates of 0.05, 0.10, 0.15, and 0.20 L/(s·m^2) when measured with an air pressure difference of 75 Pa, depending on the water vapor permeance of the outermost layer of the building envelope. The highest leakage rate applies if the permeance of the outermost layer is greater than 600 ng/ (Pa·s·m^2); the lowest rate applies if the permeance is less than 60 ng/(Pa·s·m^2). ASTM *Standard* E1677's alternative minimum air barrier testing and criteria are specifically suitable for framed walls of low-rise buildings.

All of the building assemblies are put together and the various air barrier assemblies are connected to form an air barrier system affecting the whole building. A building's air leakage characteristics can be determined with the ASTM *Standard* E779 test method. A 2008 addendum to ASHRAE *Standard* 90.1 referenced a requirement of 2.0 L/(s·m^2) at 75 Pa pressure difference.

The effectiveness of an air barrier can be greatly reduced if openings, even small ones, exist in it. These openings can be caused by poor design, poor workmanship during application, insufficient coating thickness, improper caulking and flashing, uncompensated thermal expansion, mechanical forces, aging, and other forms of degradation. Faults or leaks typically occur at electrical boxes, plumbing penetrations, telephone and television wiring, and other unsealed openings in the structure. A ceiling air barrier should be continuous at chases for plumbing, ducts, flues, and electrical wiring. In flat roofing, mechanical fasteners are sometimes used to adhere the system to the deck, and often penetrate the air barrier. In heating climates, the resulting holes may allow air exfiltration and accompanying water vapor leakage into the roof. ASTM *Standard* E1186 describes several techniques for locating air leakage sites in building envelopes and air barrier systems.

Because air barrier materials and assemblies resist airflow, they must withstand pressures exerted by chimney (stack) effects, wind effects, or both, during construction and over the building's life. The magnitude of pressure may vary, depending on the type of building and sequence of construction. At one extreme, single-family dwellings may be built with exterior cladding partly or entirely installed and insulation in place before the air barrier is added. Chimney effects in these buildings are small, even in cold weather, so stresses on the air barrier during construction are small. At the other extreme, in tall buildings, wind and chimney-effect forces are much greater. A fragile, unprotected sheet material should not be used as an air barrier or vapor retarder because it will probably be torn by wind before construction is completed.

Note that a small penetration across an air barrier assembly may seriously affect its performance by concentrating air/vapor flow in a small area, resulting in large deposits of water (in some cases turning into ice). As mentioned, calculations of water vapor flow, interstitial condensation, and related moisture accumulation using only water vapor resistances are useless when airflow is involved. More information on air leakage in buildings may be found in Chapter 16.

Vapor Retarders

Water vapor retarders need to be considered in every building design. The need for and type of water vapor retarder used depend on the climate zone, construction type, and building use. Water vapor retarders were designed to protect building elements from water vapor permeating through building materials and then condensing. It is now recognized that it is just as important to allow the building assembly to dry as it is to keep the building assembly from getting wet. In some cases, to allow the building assembly to dry, a water vapor retarder may not be needed or may need to be semipermeable. In other cases, the environmental conditions, building construction, and building use may dictate that a material with very low water vapor permeance should be installed to protect the building components.

The 2007 supplement to the International Codes now lists three water vapor retarder classes:

- **Class I:** 5.7 ng/(Pa·s·m^2) or less
- **Class II:** 5.7 ng/(Pa·s·m^2) but less than or equal to 57 ng/(Pa·s·m^2)
- **Class III:** more than 57 ng/(Pa·s·m^2) but less than or equal to 570 ng/(Pa·s·m^2)

The designer determines the appropriate type of water vapor retarder and its proper location in the building assembly based on climate conditions, other materials used in the building assembly, and the building's use (e.g., intended relative humidity).

Functions and Properties

A vapor retarder slows the rate of water vapor diffusion, but does not totally prevent it. Requirements for vapor retarders in building components are not extremely stringent, because conditions on the inside and outside of buildings vary continually, air movement and ventilation can provide wetting as well as drying at various times, and water vapor entering one side of a building component can be stored and released later.

If conditions are conducive to condensation, water vapor retarders help (1) keep insulation dry; (2) prevent structural damage by rot, corrosion, or expansion of freezing water; and (3) reduce paint problems on exterior wall construction (ASTM *Standard* C755). Vapor retarders control vapor diffusion, so that water vapor enters an assembly more slowly than it leaves. If this can be accomplished through judicious placement of a vapor retarder, the assembly tends to dry out. Another way to look at vapor retarders is that they are the most vapor-resistant layer in the assembly; a capable designer knows where this layer is and ensures that it does not promote condensation or prevent the assembly from drying.

In addition to vapor permeance, the following properties of vapor retarders are important, depending on the application:

- Mechanical strength in tension, shear, impact, and flexure
- Adhesion
- Elasticity
- Thermal stability
- Fire and flammability resistance
- Resistance to other deteriorating elements (e.g., chemicals, UV radiation)
- Ease of fabrication, application, and joint sealing

The vapor retarder's effectiveness depends on its vapor permeance, installation, and location in the insulated section. It is usually located at or near the surface exposed to higher water vapor pressure and higher temperature. For residences with heating systems, this is usually the winter-warm side.

Vapor retarder material is usually a thin sheet or coating. However, a construction of several materials, some perhaps of substantial thickness, can also constitute a vapor retarder system. In fact, designers have many options. For example, airflow and moisture movement might be controlled using an interior finish, such as drywall, to provide strength and stiffness, along with a low-permeability coating, such as vapor-retarding paint, to provide the required low permeance. Other designs may use more than one component. However, (1) any component that qualifies as a vapor retarder usually also impedes airflow, and is thus subject to pressure differences that it must resist; and (2) any component that impedes airflow may also retard vapor movement and promote condensation or frost formation.

Several studies found a significant increase in apparent permeance as a result of small holes in the vapor retarder. For example, Seiffert (1970) reported a 100-fold increase in the vapor permeance of aluminum foil when it is 0.014% perforated, and a 4000-fold increase when 0.22% of the surface is perforated. In general, penetrations particularly degrade a vapor retarder's effectiveness if it has very low permeance (e.g., polyethylene or aluminum foil). In addition, perforations may lead to air leakage, which further erodes effectiveness.

Smart vapor retarders allow substantial summer drying while functioning as effective vapor retarders during the cold season. One type of smart vapor retarder has low permeance to vapor, but is permeable to liquid water, allowing condensed moisture to dry. Korsgaard and Pedersen (1989, 1992) describe such a vapor retarder composed of synthetic fabric sandwiched between staggered strips of plastic film. The fabric wicks free water from the building envelope while the plastic film retards vapor flow into it.

Another type of smart vapor retarder provides low vapor permeance at low relative humidities, but much higher permeance at high relative humidity. During the heating season, indoor humidity usually is below 50% and the smart vapor retarder's permeance is low. In the summer, and on winter days with high solar-heat gains, when the temperature gradient is inward, moisture moving from the exterior of the wall or roof raises the relative humidity at the vapor retarder. This leads to higher vapor permeance and the potential for the wall or roof to dry out. One such vapor retarder is described by Kuenzel (1999). Below 50% rh, the film's permeance is less than 60 ng/($Pa \cdot s \cdot m^2$), but it increases above 60% rh, reaching 2070 ng/($Pa \cdot s \cdot m^2$) at 90% rh.

Water vapor permeances and permeabilities of some vapor retarders and other building materials are given in Tables 7 and 8. Additional information on control of moisture and airflow using vapor and air barriers may be found in Construction Specifications Canada (1990) and Kumaran (1989).

Classifications

Historically, a material or system with permeance of 60 ng/($Pa \cdot s \cdot m^2$) or less qualified as a vapor retarder. Refining this, the Canadian General Standards Board (CGSB) specifies type I vapor retarders as having a permeance of 15 ng/($Pa \cdot s \cdot m^2$), and type II as having a permeance of 45 ng/($Pa \cdot s \cdot m^2$) or less before aging and 60 ng/($Pa \cdot s \cdot m^2$) or less after aging.

Water vapor retarders are classified as rigid, flexible, or coating materials. **Rigid retarders** include reinforced plastics, aluminum, and stainless steel. These usually are mechanically fastened in place and are vapor-sealed at the joints. **Flexible retarders** include metal foils, laminated foil and treated papers, coated felts and papers, and plastic films or sheets. They are supplied in roll form or as an integral part of a building material (e.g., insulation). Accessory materials are required for sealing joints. **Coating retarders** may be semifluid or mastic; paint (arbitrarily called surface coatings); or hot melt, including thermofusible sheet materials. Their basic composition may be asphaltic, resinous, or polymeric, with or without pigments and solvents, as required to meet design conditions. They can be applied by spray, brush, trowel, roller, dip or mop, or in sheet form, depending on the type of coating and surface to which it is applied. Potentially, each of these materials is an air barrier; however, to meet air barrier specifications, it must satisfy requirements for strength, continuity, and air permeance.

AIR TRANSMISSION AND WATER VAPOR PROPERTY DATA

Table 7 gives typical water vapor permeance and permeability values for common building materials. These values can be used to calculate water vapor flow through building components and assemblies using equations in Chapter 25.

Water vapor permeability of most building materials is a function of their moisture content, which, in turn, is a function of ambient relative humidity. Permeability values at various relative humidities are presented in Table 8 for several building materials. The same data are presented in Figure 7 for oriented strand board (OSB) and plywood samples. Data in this table and chart are from Kumaran (2002).

Users of the dew-point method may use constant values found in Table 7. However, if condensation in the assembly is predicted, then a more appropriate value should be used. Transient hygrothermal modeling typically uses vapor permeability values that vary with relative humidity, such as those given in Table 8. Table 8 also gives mean air permeability data.

MOISTURE STORAGE DATA

Transient analysis of assemblies requires consideration of the materials' moisture storage capacity. Some materials (called hygroscopic) adsorb or reject moisture to achieve equilibrium with adjacent air. Storage capacity of these materials is typically illustrated by graphs of moisture content versus humidity. The curve showing uptake of moisture (the **sorption isotherm**) is usually above the curve showing drying (the **desorption isotherm**) because the material's uptake of moisture is inhibited by surface tension, as is its release of moisture. Table 9 provides data for these curves for several hygroscopic materials, and Kumaran (1996, 2002) and McGowan (2007) provide actual curves, additional data, and conditions under which they were determined.

Values in Table 9 express moisture content as percentage of dry weight, followed by a subscript value of the relative air humidity at which this moisture content occurs. Note that these values are based on measurement of materials that have reached equilibrium with their surroundings, which in some cases can take many weeks. Most

Table 7 Typical Water Vapor Permeance and Permeability for Common Building Materials[a]

Material	Mass, kg/m²	Thickness, mm	Permeance, ng/(Pa·s·m²) Dry-Cup	Wet-Cup	Other Method	Permeability, ng/(Pa·s·m)
Plastic and Metal Foils and Films[b]						
Aluminum foil		0.025	0.0			
		0.009	2.9			
Polyethylene		0.051	9.1			4.7×10^{-4}
		0.1	4.6			4.7×10^{-4}
		0.15	3.4[b]			4.7×10^{-4}
		0.2	2.3[b]			4.7×10^{-4}
		0.25			1.7	4.7×10^{-4}
Polyvinylchloride, unplasticized		0.051	39[b]			
Polyvinylchloride, plasticized		0.1	46 to 80			
Polyester		0.025	42			
		0.09	13			
		0.19	4.6			
Cellulose acetate		0.25	263			
		3.2	18			
Liquid-Applied Coating Materials						
Commercial latex paints (dry film thickness)						
Vapor retarder paint		0.07			26	
Primer-sealer		0.03			360	
Vinyl acetate/acrylic primer		0.05			424	
Vinyl/acrylic primer		0.04			491	
Semigloss vinyl/acrylic enamel		0.06			378	
Exterior acrylic house and trim		0.04			313	
Paint, 2 coats						
Asphalt paint on plywood					23	
Aluminum varnish on wood					17 to 29	
Enamels on smooth plaster					29 to 86	
Primers and sealers on interior insulation board					51 to 120	
Various primers plus 1 coat flat oil paint on plaster					91 to 172	
Flat paint on interior insulation board					229	
Water emulsion on interior insulation board					1716 to 4863	
Paint, 3 coats						
Exterior paint, white lead and oil on wood siding			17 to 57			
Exterior paint, white lead/zinc oxide and oil on wood			51			
Styrene/butadiene latex coating	0.6		629			
Polyvinyl acetate latex coating	1.2		315			
Chlorosulfonated polyethylene mastic	1.1		97			
	2.2		3.4			
Asphalt cutback mastic						
1.6 mm, dry			8.0			
4.8 mm, dry			0.0			
Hot-melt asphalt	0.6		29			
	1.1		5.7			
Building Paper, Felts, Roofing Papers[c]						
Duplex sheet, asphalt laminated, aluminum foil one side	0.42		0.1	10		
Saturated and coated roll roofing	3.18		2.9	14		
Kraft paper and asphalt laminated, reinforced	0.33		17	103		
Blanket thermal insulation back-up paper, asphalt coated	0.30		23	34 to 240		
Asphalt, saturated and coated vapor retarder paper	0.42		11 to 17	34		
Asphalt, saturated, but not coated, sheathing paper	0.21		190	1160		
asphalt felt, 0.73 kg/m²	0.68		57	320		
tar felt, 0.73 kg/m²	0.68		230	1040		
Single kraft, double	0.16		1170	2400		
Polyamide film, 2 mil			62.9	1174		

[a]This table allows comparisons of materials, but when selecting vapor retarder materials, exact values for permeance or permeability should be obtained from manufacturer or from laboratory tests. Values shown indicate variations among mean values for materials that are similar but of different density, orientation, lot, or source. Values should not be used as design or specification data. Values from dry- and wet-cup methods were usually obtained from investigations using ASTM *Standards* C355 and E96; other values were obtained by two-temperature, special cell, and air velocity methods.

[b]Usually installed as vapor retarders, although sometimes used as exterior finish and elsewhere near the cold side, where special considerations are then required for warm-side barrier effectiveness.

[c]Low-permeance sheets used as vapor retarders. High permeance used elsewhere in construction.

[d]*Source*: Lotz (1964).

Table 8 Water Vapor Permeability of Building Materials at Various Relative Humidities

Material	Permeability at Various Relative Humidities, ng/(Pa·s·m) 10%	30%	50%	70%	90%	Water Absorption Coefficient, (kg·s^½)/m²	Mean Air Permeability, kg/(Pa·s·m)	References/ Comments
Building Board and Siding								
Asbestos cement board, 3 mm thickness		← 0.66 to 1.37 →		← N/A →				Dry cup*
with oil-base finishes		← 0.05 to 0.09 →		← N/A →				
Cement board, 13 mm, 1130 kg/m³	7.4	7.4	9.3	12	16	0.013	3×10^{-8}	Kumaran (2002)
Fiber cement board, 8 mm, 1380 kg/m³	0.21	0.58	1.6	4.7	14.8	0.025	3×10^{-12}	Kumaran (2002)
Gypsum board		21		23	30			Kumaran (1996)/NRC
asphalt impregnated			← 0.038 →					
Gypsum wall board, 13 mm, 625 kg/m³	23.4	27.2	31.9	37.6	44.7	0.0019[c]	4.2×10^{-9}	Kumaran (2002)
with one coat primer	6.83	14.9	22.0	28.9	35.9	N/A	2.2×10^{-8}	Kumaran (2002)
with one coat primer/two coats latex paint	1.1	2.1	4.0	8.0	16.5	N/A	2.5×10^{-9}	Kumaran (2002)
Hardboard siding, 11 mm, 740 kg/m³	3.92	4.28	4.67	5.10	5.58	0.00072	4.5×10^{-9}	Kumaran (2002)
Oriented strand board (OSB), 9.5 mm, 660 kg/m³	0.0064	0.177	0.487	1.35	3.83	0.0016	1×10^{-9}	Kumaran (2002)
11.1 mm	0.026	0.60	1.23	2.30	4.08	0.0022	2×10^{-9}	Kumaran (2002)
12.7 mm	0.044	0.344	0.90	1.70	2.75	0.0016	1×10^{-9}	Kumaran (2002)
Particleboard		4.4	6.0	10.2	15.2			Kumaran (1996)
Douglas fir plywood, 12 mm, 470 kg/m³	0.19	0.59	1.46	3.19	6.50	0.0042[d]	4×10^{-11}	Kumaran (2002)
15 mm, 550 kg/m³	0.15	0.41	1.09	2.91	7.99	0.0031	1×10^{-9}	Kumaran (2002)
Canadian softwood plywood, 18 mm, 445 kg/m³	0.06	0.57	2.28	6.12	13.30	0.0037	2×10^{-11}	Kumaran (2002)
Plywood (exterior-grade), 12 mm, 580 kg/m³	0.21	0.36		0.80	8.62			Burch et al.
Wood fiber board, 11 mm, 320 kg/m³	12.4	13.6	15.0	16.4	18.1	0.00094	2.5×10^{-7}	Kumaran (2002)
25 mm, 300 kg/m³	71.5	58.4		86.7	77.2			Burch and Desjarlais (1995)
Masonry Materials								
Aerated concrete, 460 kg/m³	11.2	15.9	22.9	33.4	50	0.036	5×10^{-9}	Kumaran (2002)
600 kg/m³	18	21.6	22	42	63			Kumaran (1996)
Cement mortar, 1600 kg/m³	13.6	16.5	20.1	24.5	30.2	0.02	1.5×10^{-9}	Kumaran (2002)
Clay brick, 100 by 100 by 200 mm, 1980 kg/m³	4.14	4.44	4.77	5.12	5.50	0.17	2 to 5×10^{-10}	Kumaran (2002)
Concrete, 2200 kg/m³		1.26	1.4	2.5	6.5			Kumaran (1996)
Concrete block (cored, limestone aggregate), 200 mm			← 27.4 →					
Lightweight concrete, 1100 kg/m³		12.3		11.4	18.7			Kumaran (1996)
Limestone, 2500 kg/m³	0.26	0.26	0.26	0.26	0.26	0.00033	negligible	Kumaran (2002)
Perlite board		28		33	82			Kumaran (1996)
Plaster, on metal lath, 19 mm			← 16.3 →					
on wood lath			← 12.0 →					
on plain gypsum lath (with studs)			← 21.7 →					
Polystyrene concrete, 530 kg/m³		0.88		1.1	2.7			Kumaran (1996)
Portland stucco mix, 1985 kg/m³	0.81	1.15	1.63	2.31	3.26	0.012	1×10^{-11}	Kumaran (2002)
Tile masonry, glazed, 100 mm			← 0.69 →					
Woods								
Eastern white cedar, 20 mm, 360 kg/m³ (transverse)	0.013	0.078	0.48	3.05	20.9	0.0016	negligible	Kumaran (2002)
Eastern white pine, 19 mm, 460 kg/m³ (transverse)	0.47	0.17	0.67	2.58	10.2	0.0066	1×10^{-12}	Kumaran (2002)
Pine	0.35	0.51	1.1	3.1	6.3			Kumaran (1996)
Southern yellow pine, 20 mm, 350 kg/m³ (transverse)	0.12	0.404	1.37	4.7	16.9	0.0014	3×10^{-11}	Kumaran (2002)
Spruce (longitudinal)	53	74	84	86	87			Kumaran (1996)
20 mm, 400 kg/m³ (transverse)	0.37	1.08	3.13	9.27	29.5	0.002	5×10^{-11}	Kumaran (2002)
Western red cedar, 18 mm, 350 kg/m³ (transverse)	0.106	0.228	0.491	1.06	2.29	0.001	$<1 \times 10^{-12}$	Kumaran (2002)
Insulation								
Air (still)			← 174 →					
Cellular glass			← 0.0 →					
Cellulose insulation, dry blown, 30 kg/m³	112	140	156	168	178	0.1	2.9×10^{-4}	Kumaran (2002)
Corkboard		3.0 to 3.8		14				
Glass fiber batt, 11.5 kg/m³	172	172	172	172	172	N/A	2.5×10^{-4}	Kumaran (2002)
Glass-fiber insulation board, 24 mm, 120 kg/m³		238			152			Burch et al.
facer, 1.6 mm, 880 kg/m³	0.004	0.00251		0.0184	0.0389			Burch et al.
Mineral fiber insulation, 30 to 190 kg/m³		70		88	250			Kumaran (1996)
Mineral wool (unprotected)			← 245 →					

Table 8 Water Vapor Permeability of Building Materials at Various Relative Humidities (*Continued*)

Material	Permeability at Various Relative Humidities, ng/(Pa·s·m) 10%	30%	50%	70%	90%	Water Absorption Coefficient, (kg·s^½)/m²	Mean Air Permeability, kg/(Pa·s·m)	References/ Comments
Phenolic foam (covering removed)	←		38		→			
Polystyrene								
expanded, 14.8 kg/m³	2.85	3.36	3.96	4.66	5.50	N/A	1.1×10^{-8}	Kumaran (2002)
extruded, 28.6 kg/m³	1.22	1.22	1.22	1.22	1.22	N/A		Kumaran (2002)
Polyurethane								
expanded board stock [(R = 1.94 W/(m²·K)]		0.58 to 2.3						
sprayed foam, 39.0 kg/m³	2.34	2.54	2.75	2.97	3.22	N/A	1×10^{-11}	Kumaran (2002)
6.5 to 8.5 kg/m³	87.5	87.5	87.5	87.5	87.5	N/A	4.2×10^{-9}	Kumaran (2002)
Polyisocyanurate insulation, 26.5 kg/m³	4.04	4.56	5.14	5.80	6.55	N/A		Kumaran (2002)
Polyisocyanurate glass-mat facer, 0.8 mm, 430 kg/m³	0.49	0.90		1.30	2.29			Burch et al.
Structural insulating board, sheathing quality	←		29 to 73		→			
interior, uncoated, 13 mm	←		37.2 to 67		→			
Unicellular synthetic flexible rubber foam		0.029						
Foil, Felt, Paper								
Bituminous paper (#15 felt), 0.72 mm, 515 g/m² (transverse)	0.29	0.29	0.29	0.40	1.17	0.0005	2.5×10^{-6}	Kumaran (2002)
Asphalt-impregnated paper								
10 min rating, 0.2 mm, 170 g/m² (transverse)	0.24	0.43	0.78	1.48	3.06	0.001	1.1×10^{-6}	Kumaran (2002)
30 min rating, 0.22 mm, 200 g/m² (transverse)	0.44	0.74	1.28	2.31	4.67	0.093	6.6×10^{-6}	Kumaran (2002)
60 min rating, 0.34 mm, 280 g/m² (transverse)	1.51	1.91	2.44	3.18	4.24	0.0011	7.1×10^{-6}	Kumaran (2002)
Spun bonded polyolefin (SBPO)								
0.14 to 0.15 mm, 65 g/m² (transverse)	4.37	4.37	4.37	4.37	4.37	0.00031	4.6×10^{-7}	Kumaran (2002)
with crinkled surface, 0.1 to 0.11 mm, 67 g/m² (transverse)	3.17	3.17	3.17	3.17	3.17	0.00024	3×10^{-7}	Kumaran (2002)
Wallpaper								
paper		0.12		1.2 to 1.7				Kumaran (1996)
textile		0.05		0.74 to 2.34				Kumaran (1996)
vinyl, 0.205 mm, 170 g/m² (transverse)	0.08	0.14	0.21	0.32	0.46	0.00025	5×10^{-9}	Kumaran (2002)
Other Construction Materials								
Built-up roofing (hot-mopped)	←		0.0		→			
Exterior insulated finish system (EIFS), 4.4 mm acrylic, 1140 kg/m³	0.09	0.09	0.09	0.09	0.09	0.00053	0	Kumaran (2002)
Glass fiber reinforced sheet,								
acrylic, 1.4 mm	←		0.01		→			
polyester, 1.2 mm	←		0.035		→			

*Historical data, no reference available

N/A = Not applicable

hygrothermal simulation software programs that use these values assume that equilibrium is achieved instantaneously.

Maximum values in Table 9 are those that could be realistically measured in laboratory conditions, so not all materials have a listing for a maximum moisture content at 100% rh. For those that do, there are sometimes two listings: the moisture content measured when the material's capillary pores were saturated (shown as 100c) and the value at total saturation (shown as 100t). It is understood that the moisture content of any material would be 0.0 at a theoretical relative humidity of 0%, so this point is not shown in the table.

Figure 8 shows example of as a conventional sorption isotherm graph. Curves show sorption (wetting) and desorption (drying), for data in Table 9 and from Kumaran (2002). As Figure 8 illustrates, data in Table 9 were selected to provide an accurate representation of the sorption isotherm, although not all data from the original source are represented.

CODES AND STANDARDS

ASHRAE. 2007. Energy standard for buildings except low-rise residential buildings. ANSI/ASHRAE/IESNA *Standard* 90.1-2007.

ASTM. 2005. Standard terminology relating to thermal insulation. *Standard* C168-05a. American Society for Testing and Materials, West Conshohocken, PA.

ASTM. 2004. Standard test method for steady-state heat flux measurements and thermal transmission properties by means of the guarded-hot-plate apparatus. *Standard* C177-04. American Society for Testing and Materials, West Conshohocken, PA.

ASTM. 2005. Standard test method for steady-state heat transfer properties of horizontal pipe insulation. *Standard* C335-05ae1. American Society for Testing and Materials, West Conshohocken, PA.

ASTM. 2004. Standard test method for steady-state heat thermal transmission properties by means of the heat flow meter apparatus. *Standard* C518-04. American Society for Testing and Materials, West Conshohocken, PA.

ASTM. 2003. Standard practice for selection of vapor retarders for thermal insulation. *Standard* C755-03. American Society for Testing and Materials, West Conshohocken, PA.

ASTM. 2005. Standard classification of potential health and safety concerns associated with thermal insulation materials and accessories. *Standard* C930-05. American Society for Testing and Materials, West Conshohocken, PA.

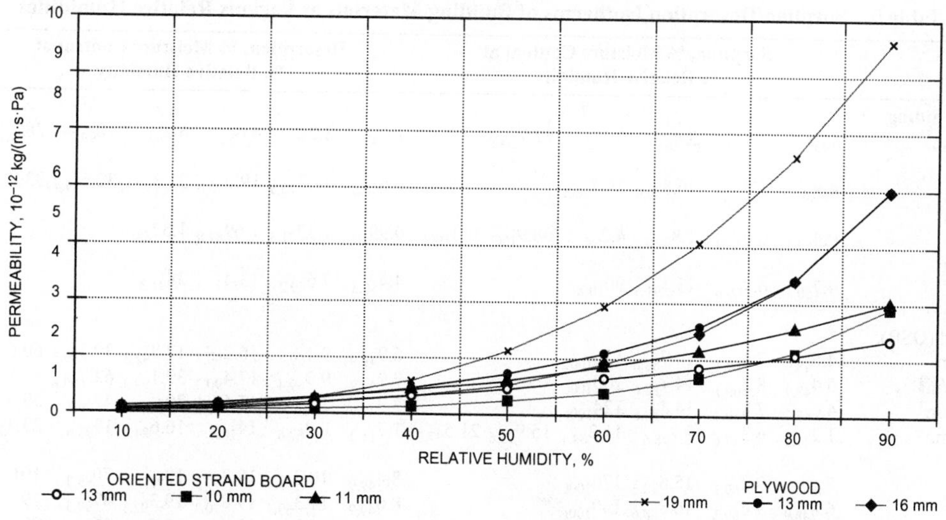

Fig. 7 Permeability of Wood-Based Sheathing Materials at Various Relative Humidities

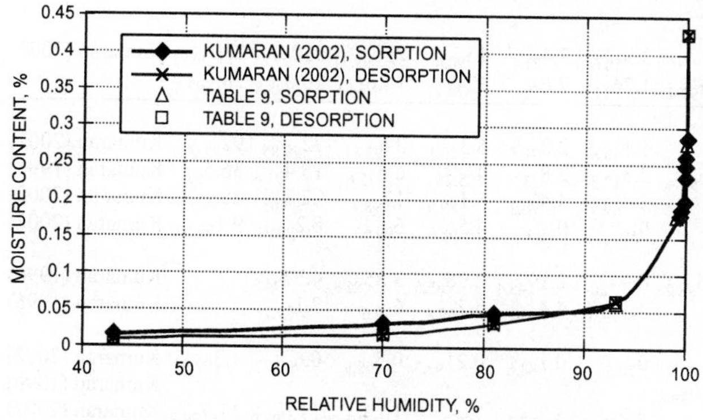

Fig. 8 Sorption/Desorption Isotherms, Cement Board

ASTM. 2007. Standard practice for calculating thermal transmission properties from steady-state measurements. *Standard* C1045-07. American Society for Testing and Materials, West Conshohocken, PA.

ASTM. 2005. Standard test method for thermal performance of building materials and envelope assemblies by means of a guarded hot box apparatus. *Standard* C1363-05. American Society for Testing and Materials, West Conshohocken, PA.

ASTM. 2005. Standard test methods for water vapor transmission of materials. *Standard* E96/E96M-05. American Society for Testing and Materials, West Conshohocken, PA.

ASTM. 2003. Standard practices for air leakage site detection in building envelopes and air barrier systems. *Standard* E1186-03. American Society for Testing and Materials, West Conshohocken, PA.

ASTM. 2005. Standard specification for an air retarder (AR) material or system for low-rise framed building walls. *Standard* E1677-05. American Society for Testing and Materials, West Conshohocken, PA.

ASTM. 2005. Standard test method for determining air leakage of air barrier assemblies. *Standard* E2357-05. American Society for Testing and Materials, West Conshohocken, PA.

REFERENCES

Adams, L. 1971. Supporting cryogenic equipment with wood. *Chemical Engineering* (May):156-158.

ASHRAE. 1998. Standard method for determining and expressing the heat transfer and total optical properties of fenestration products. SPC 142.

ASTM. 1974. Heat transmission measurements in thermal insulations. *Special Technical Publication* STP 544. American Society for Testing and Materials, West Conshohocken, PA.

ASTM. 1978. Thermal transmission measurements of insulation. *Special Technical Publication* STP 660. American Society for Testing and Materials, West Conshohocken, PA.

ASTM. 1980. Thermal insulation performance. *Special Technical Publication* STP 718. American Society for Testing and Materials, West Conshohocken, PA.

ASTM. 1983. Thermal insulations, materials, and systems for energy conservation in the '80s. *Special Technical Publication* STP 789. American Society for Testing and Materials, West Conshohocken, PA.

ASTM. 1985a. Guarded hot plate and heat flow meter methodology. *Special Technical Publication* STP 879. American Society for Testing and Materials, West Conshohocken, PA.

ASTM. 1985b. Building applications of heat flux transducers. *Special Technical Publication* STP 885. American Society for Testing and Materials, West Conshohocken, PA.

ASTM. 1988. Thermal insulation: Material and systems. *Special Technical Publication* STP 922. American Society for Testing and Materials, West Conshohocken, PA.

ASTM. 1990. Insulation materials: Testing and applications. *Special Technical Publication* STP 1030. American Society for Testing and Materials, West Conshohocken, PA.

ASTM. 1991. Insulation materials: Testing and applications, 2nd vol. *Special Technical Publication* STP 1116. American Society for Testing and Materials, West Conshohocken, PA.

Bassett, M.R. and H.A. Trethowen. 1984. Effect of condensation on emittance of reflective insulation. *Journal of Thermal Insulation* 8(October):127.

Brandreth, D.A., ed. 1986. *Advances in foam aging—A topic in energy conservation series*. Caissa Editions, Yorklyn, DE.

Brown, W.C., M.T. Bomberg, J. Rasmussen, and J. Ullett. 1993. Measured thermal resistance of frame walls with defects in the installation of mineral fibre insulation. *Journal of Thermal Insulation and Building Envelopes* 16(April):318-339.

CIBSE. 2006. Thermal properties of building structures. Chapter 3 in CIBSE *Guide A*: *Environmental Design*. The Chartered Institution of Building Services Engineers, London, U.K.

Construction Specifications Canada. 1990. *Tek-AID on air barrier systems*. Toronto.

Di Lenardo, B., W.C. Brown, W.A. Dalgleish, K. Kumaran, and G.F. Poirier. 1995. *Technical guide for air barrier systems for exterior walls of low-rise buildings*. Canadian Construction Materials Centre, National Research Council Canada, Ottawa, Ontario.

Donnelly, R.G., V.J. Tennery, D.L. McElroy, T.G. Godfrey, and J.O. Kolb. 1976. Industrial thermal insulation: An assessment. Oak Ridge National Laboratory *Reports* TM-5283, TM-5515, and TID-27120.

Glaser, P.E., I.A. Black, R.S. Lindstrom, F.E. Ruccia, and A.E. Wechsler. 1967. Thermal insulation systems—A survey. NASA *Report* SP5027.

Goss, W.P. and R.G. Miller. 1989. Literature review of measurement and prediction of reflective building insulation system performance: 1900-1989. *ASHRAE Transactions* 95(2).

Hedlin, C.P. 1985. Effect of insulation joints on heat loss through flat roofs. *ASHRAE Transactions* 91(2B):608-622.

Hooper, F.C. and W.J. Moroz. 1952. The impact of aging factors on the emissivity of reflective insulations. ASTM *Bulletin* (May):92-95.

Table 9 Sorption/Desorption Isotherms of Building Materials at Various Relative Humidities

Material	Sorption, % Moisture Content at % Relative Humidity						Desorption, % Moisture Content at % Relative Humidity						References
Building Board and Siding													
Cement board, 13 mm, 1130 kg/m³	1_{43}	1.9_{70}	3.4_{81}	6.1_{93}	42.7_{100t}		1.6_{43}	3.2_{70}	4.6_{81}	6.2_{93}	$18_{99.27}$	$28_{99.93}$	Kumaran (2002)
Fiber cement board, 8 mm, 1380 kg/m³	$4_{50.6}$	$5.8_{70.4}$	$16.8_{89.9}$	34.7_{100t}			$6.6_{50.5}$	$12.3_{70.5}$	$19.6_{90.6}$	$31.3_{95.32}$	$32.5_{99.49}$	$33.9_{99.93}$	Kumaran (2002)
Gypsum wall board, 13 mm, 625 kg/m³	$0.4_{50.5}$	$0.65_{70.5}$	$1.8_{90.8}$	4.2_{94}	68.9_{100c}	113_{100t}	$0.99_{50.4}$	$1.32_{71.5}$	$1.69_{84.8}$	$1.82_{88.3}$			Kumaran (2002)
Hardboard siding, 11 mm, 740 kg/m³	$4.7_{50.3}$	$6.9_{69.6}$	$13.1_{91.3}$	90_{100t}			$4.4_{50.3}$	$7.6_{69.2}$	$13.4_{91.3}$	$38_{91.3}$			Kumaran (2002)
Oriented strand board (OSB), 9.5 mm, 660 kg/m³	$4.6_{48.9}$	$7.6_{69.1}$	$14.7_{88.6}$	126_{100c}			$6.9_{49.9}$	$9.1_{69.4}$	$16.2_{90.3}$	$17.3_{92.3}$	$39.3_{99.3}$	$60.6_{99.8}$	Kumaran (2002)
11.1 mm, 650 kg/m³	$5.4_{48.9}$	$8.2_{69.1}$	$14.7_{88.6}$	160_{100t}			$7.9_{49.9}$	$9.9_{69.4}$	$17.4_{90.3}$	$39.1_{99.3}$	$62.7_{99.8}$		Kumaran (2002)
12.7 mm, 650 kg/m³	$4.6_{48.9}$	$7.8_{69.1}$	$14.8_{88.6}$	124_{100t}			$7.9_{49.9}$	$10_{69.4}$	$17.6_{90.3}$	$20_{92.3}$	$42_{99.3}$	59.5	Kumaran (2002)
Particle board, 19 mm, 760 kg/m³	$1.2_{11.3}$	$6.3_{57.6}$	$9.7_{78.6}$	$11.3_{84.1}$	$15.9_{93.6}$	$21.5_{97.3}$	$1.7_{11.3}$	$8.8_{57.6}$	$14_{78.6}$	$16.6_{84.1}$	$19_{93.6}$	$23.3_{97.6}$	Kumaran (1996)
Plywood, 13 mm	$7_{48.9}$	$9.2_{69.1}$	$15.8_{88.6}$	170_{100t}			$8.4_{49.9}$	$10.8_{69.4}$	$18.2_{90.3}$	$19_{92.3}$	$70_{99.3}$	101	Kumaran (2002)
16 mm	$6.8_{48.9}$	$9.6_{69.1}$	$16.8_{88.6}$	140_{100t}			$8.6_{49.9}$	$11.3_{69.4}$	$19.8_{90.3}$	$19.3_{92.3}$	$47_{99.3}$	79	Kumaran (2002)
19 mm	$6.7_{48.9}$	$10.1_{69.1}$	$17.6_{88.6}$	190_{100t}			$8.9_{49.9}$	$11.3_{69.4}$	$19.3_{90.3}$	$20.7_{92.3}$	$66_{99.3}$	$99_{99.8}$	Kumaran (2002)
Plywood (exterior-grade), 12 mm, 580 kg/m³	$1.83_{11.3}$	6.9_{58}	$9.5_{78.7}$	$12.1_{84.5}$	$17.9_{93.8}$	22.1	$2.09_{11.3}$	9.3_{58}	$13.7_{78.7}$	$15.2_{84.5}$	$19.8_{93.8}$	23.4	Burch et al.
Wood fiber board, 11 mm, 320 kg/m³	$4.6_{50.6}$	$7.4_{70.5}$	$15.8_{91.1}$	304			$3.9_{50.6}$	$7.4_{71.1}$	$15_{90.6}$	$230_{99.71}$	$230_{99.85}$	$230_{99.93}$	Kumaran (2002)
25 mm, 300 kg/m³	$0.63_{11.3}$	5.7_{58}	$9.2_{78.7}$	$11.3_{84.5}$	$16.4_{93.8}$	$24.6_{97.4}$	$1.26_{11.3}$	7.6_{58}	$12_{78.7}$	$14.6_{84.5}$	$20.6_{93.8}$	$28.1_{97.4}$	
Masonry Materials													
Aerated concrete, 460 kg/m³	$1.1_{50.6}$	$2.1_{71.5}$	$5_{88.1}$	83_{100c}	172		$1.1_{50.6}$	$2.2_{71.5}$	$6.3_{88.1}$	$34_{97.81}$	$72_{99.85}$	$92_{99.99}$	Kumaran (2002)
600 kg/m³	$1.8_{17.8}$	$3.2_{75.8}$	$4.6_{90.3}$	$6.4_{92.4}$	$9.6_{95.9}$	$17.5_{98.4}$	$2.3_{17.8}$	2.8_{33}	$4_{55.2}$	$6.6_{75.6}$	$15.4_{91.6}$	36.5_{98}	Kumaran (1996)
Cement mortar, 1600 kg/m³	$0.42_{49.9}$	$2.3_{70.1}$	$5.3_{89.9}$	26_{100t}			$3.4_{49.9}$	$4.4_{70.2}$	$6.1_{89.9}$	$17_{98.9}$	$22_{99.63}$	$25_{99.93}$	Kumaran (2002)
Clay brick, 100 × 100 × 200 mm, 1980 kg/m³	0.08_{50}	$0.12_{69.1}$	$0.1_{91.2}$	9.9_{100t}			0_{50}	$0_{91.2}$	$4.5_{98.9}$	$6_{99.63}$	$8.2_{99.71}$	$9.1_{99.93}$	Kumaran (2002)
Concrete, 2200 kg/m³	$0.88_{25.2}$	$1.15_{44.9}$	1.74_{65}	2.62_{80}	$3.35_{89.8}$	$4.45_{98.2}$	0.94_{20}	$2.19_{45.4}$	$2.98_{65.6}$	$3.85_{84.8}$	$4.57_{94.8}$		Kumaran (1996)
Lightweight concrete, 1100 kg/m³	$2.9_{24.4}$	$3.4_{45.2}$	$4_{65.2}$	4.6_{85}	6.6_{98}		$3.1_{19.6}$	4.4_{40}	$5.2_{59.8}$	$6_{79.6}$	$7.1_{94.7}$		Kumaran (1996)
Limestone, 2500 kg/m³	0_{50}	0_{70}	$0.1_{88.5}$	1.8_{100t}			$0_{70.5}$	$0.1_{88.6}$	$0.21_{95.3}$	$0.5_{98.9}$	$0.6_{99.27}$	$1.3_{99.93}$	Kumaran (2002)
Perlite board	130_{33}	160_{52}	260_{75}	380_{86}	800_{97}	$1170_{99.8}$							Kumaran (1996)
Portland stucco mix, 1985 kg/m³	3_{50}	$3.7_{70.3}$	$5.8_{89.9}$	12_{100t}			4.2_{50}	$5.2_{70.3}$	$7_{90.3}$	$10.3_{95.29}$	$11.6_{98.9}$	$11.7_{99.93}$	Kumaran (2002)
Woods													
Eastern white cedar, 25 mm, 360 kg/m³	$3.4_{49.8}$	7.6_{70}	$12.8_{88.5}$	228_{100t}			1.7_{50}	$7.4_{70.5}$	$11.9_{88.7}$	$85_{98.9}$	$118_{99.63}$	$176_{99.92}$	
Eastern white pine, 25 mm, 460 kg/m³	$3.2_{49.8}$	7.6_{70}	$12_{88.5}$	192_{100t}			3.2_{50}	$9_{70.5}$	$12.4_{88.7}$	$84_{99.78}$			
Southern yellow pine, 25 mm, 500 kg/m³	$3.6_{49.8}$	8.1_{70}	$15.2_{88.5}$	158_{100t}			4.3_{50}	$10_{70.5}$	$15.6_{88.7}$	$57_{99.78}$			
Spruce (transverse)	$4.1_{49.8}$	9.2_{70}	$16.7_{88.5}$	228_{100t}			4.9_{50}	$11.3_{70.5}$	$17.7_{88.7}$	$148_{95.96}$	$187_{99.78}$		
Western red cedar, 25 mm, 350 kg/m³	$3.4_{49.8}$	6_{70}	$9.6_{88.5}$	228_{100t}			1_{50}	$9_{70.5}$	$13.3_{88.7}$	$113_{99.78}$			
Insulation													
Cellulose, dry-blown, 30 kg/m³	$6.1_{50.5}$	$9.6_{71.5}$	$24_{88.1}$				$5_{50.2}$	$12_{72.8}$	26_{88}				Kumaran (2002)
Glass fiber batt, 11.5 kg/m³	$0.21_{50.6}$	$0.34_{71.5}$	$0.75_{88.1}$				$0.24_{50.4}$	$0.35_{71.4}$	$0.67_{88.2}$				Kumaran (2002)
Glass-fiber board, 24 mm, 120 kg/m³	$0.16_{11.3}$	0.75	$0.82_{78.7}$	$0.96_{84.5}$	$1.3_{93.8}$	$2.03_{97.4}$	$0.43_{11.3}$	$0.86_{32.8}$	1.11_{58}	$1.26_{84.5}$	$1.74_{93.8}$	$2.16_{97.4}$	Burch et al.
Glass-fiber board facer, 1.6 mm, 880 kg/m³	$0.09_{11.3}$	0.53_{58}	$0.76_{78.7}$	$0.84_{84.5}$	$1.14_{93.8}$	$1.54_{97.4}$	$0.18_{11.3}$	0.56_{58}	$0.87_{78.7}$	$1.09_{84.5}$	$1.45_{93.8}$	$1.81_{97.4}$	Burch et al.
Mineral fiber, 40 kg/m³	$0.5_{20.1}$	$0.55_{45.4}$	0.59_{65}	$0.7_{85.2}$	$0.76_{94.5}$	$0.8_{97.5}$	$0.5_{20.1}$	$0.58_{44.9}$	$0.63_{64.9}$	$0.81_{84.5}$	$1.1_{94.7}$	$1.6_{97.8}$	Kumaran (1996)
Polystyrene, expanded, 14.8 kg/m³	$0.4_{50.4}$	$0.3_{68.3}$	$0.2_{88.3}$				$0.4_{50.1}$	$0.5_{67.9}$	$0.5_{87.9}$				Kumaran (2002)
extruded, 28.6 kg/m³	$0.6_{50.4}$	$0.5_{68.3}$	$0.4_{88.3}$				$0.5_{50.1}$	$0.5_{67.9}$	$0.4_{87.9}$				Kumaran (2002)
Polyurethane, sprayed foam, 39 kg/m³	$1.3_{50.4}$	$1.7_{68.3}$	$2_{88.4}$				$1.1_{50.1}$	$1.5_{67.9}$	$1.8_{87.9}$				Kumaran (2002)
6.5 to 8.5 kg/m³	$0.5_{50.4}$	$1_{70.2}$	$1.6_{90.3}$				$1_{50.5}$	$2.1_{70.9}$	$7_{91.3}$				Kumaran (2002)
Polyisocyanurate, 26.5 kg/m³	$1.3_{50.4}$	$1.7_{68.3}$	$2.1_{88.3}$				$1.1_{50.1}$	$1.5_{67.9}$	$1.9_{87.9}$				Kumaran (2002)
Polyisocyanurate glass facer, 1 mm, 430 kg/m³	$1.36_{11.3}$	4.5_{58}	$6.8_{78.7}$	$9_{84.5}$	$12.5_{93.8}$	$17.9_{97.4}$	$0.89_{11.3}$	5.8_{58}	$8.3_{78.7}$	10.9	$14.4_{93.8}$	$18.4_{97.4}$	Burch et al.

ICC. 2007. *2007 code development*. International Code Council, Washington, D.C. (Available at http://www.iccsafe.org/cs/codes/2007-08cycle/2007Supplement/index.html)

ISO. 2003. Thermal performance of windows, doors, and shading devices—Detailed calculations. *Standard* 15099. International Organization for Standardization, Geneva.

Karagiozis, A.N. and H.M. Salonvaara. 1999a. Hygrothermal performance of EIFS-clad walls: Effect of vapor diffusion and air leakage on the drying of construction moisture. *Special Technical Publication* STP 1352, pp. 32-51. American Society for Testing and Materials, West Conshohocken, PA.

Karagiozis, A.N. and H.M. Salonvaara. 1999b. *Whole building hygrothermal performance: Proceedings of the 5th Symposium on Building Physics in the Nordic Countries*, Goteborg, vol. 2, pp. 745-753. C.E. Hagentoft and P.I. Sandberg, eds.

Kersten, M.S. 1949. Thermal properties of soils. University of Minnesota, Engineering Experiment Station *Bulletin* 28 (June).

Korsgaard, V. and C.R. Pedersen. 1989. Transient moisture distribution in flat roofs with hygro diode vapor retarder. *Proceedings of ASHRAE/DOE/BTECC/CIBSE Conference on Thermal Performance of Exterior Envelopes of Buildings IV.*

Korsgaard, V. and C.R. Pedersen. 1992. Laboratory and practical experience with a novel water-permeable vapor retarder. *Proceedings of ASHRAE/DOE/BTECC/CIBSE Conference on Thermal Performance of Exterior Envelopes of Buildings V*, pp. 480-490.

Kuenzel, H.M. 1999. More moisture load tolerance of construction assemblies through the application of a smart vapor retarder. *Proceedings of Thermal Performance of the Exterior Envelopes of Buildings VII*, pp. 129-132. ASHRAE.

Kumaran, M.K. 1989. Experimental investigation on simultaneous heat and moisture transport through thermal insulation. *Proceedings of the Conseil International du Batiment/International Building Council (CIB) 11th International Conference* 2:275-284.

Kumaran, M.K. 2002. A thermal and moisture transport database for common building and insulating materials. ASHRAE Research Project RP-1018, *Final Report*. National Research Council, Canada.

Lander, R.M. 1955. Gas is an important factor in the thermal conductivity of most insulating materials. *ASHRAE Transactions* 61:151.

Lecompte, J. 1989. The influence of natural convection in an insulated cavity on the thermal performance of the wall. *Special Technical Publication* STP 1000:397-420. American Society for Testing and Materials, West Conshohocken, PA.

Lewis, W.C. 1967. Thermal conductivity of wood-base fiber and particle panel materials. Forest Products Laboratory, *Research Paper* FPL 77, June.

Lewis, J.E. 1979. Thermal evaluation of the effects of gaps between adjacent roof insulation panels. *Journal of Thermal Insulation* (October):80-103.

Lotz, W.A. 1964. Vapor barrier design, neglected key to freezer insulation effectiveness. *Quick Frozen Foods* (November):122.

Lotz, W.A. 1969. Facts about thermal insulation. *ASHRAE Journal* (June): 83-84.

MacLean, J.D. 1941. Thermal conductivity of wood. *ASHVE Transactions* 47:323.

McGowan, A.G. 2007. Catalog of material thermal property data (RP-905). ASHRAE Research Project, *Final Report.*

NIST. 2000. *NIST standard reference database 81: NIST heat transmission properties of insulating and building materials*. Available at http://srdata.nist.gov/insulation/. U.S. Department of Commerce, National Institute of Standards and Materials, Gaithersburg, MD.

Nottage, H.B. 1947. Thermal properties of building materials used in heat flow calculations. *ASHVE Transactions* 53:215-243.

Ojanen, T., R. Kohonen, and M.K Kumaran. 1994. Modeling heat, air, and moisture transport through building materials and components. Chapter 2 in *Manual* MNL 18, *Moisture control in buildings*. American Society for Testing and Materials, West Conshohocken, PA.

Ostrogorsky, A.G. and L.R. Glicksman. 1986. Laboratory tests of effectiveness of diffusion barriers. *Journal of Cellular Plastics* 22:303.

Pelanne, C.M. 1977. Heat flow principles in thermal insulation. *Journal of Thermal Insulation* 1:48.

Pelanne, C.M. 1979. Thermal insulation heat flow measurements: Requirements for implementation. *ASHRAE Journal* 21(3):51.

Rasmussen J., W.C. Brown, M. Bomberg, and J.M. Ullett. 1993. Measured thermal performance of frame walls with defects in the installation of mineral fibre insulation. *Proceedings of the 3rd Symposium on Building Physics in the Nordic Countries*, pp. 209-217.

Raznjevic, K. 1976. Thermal conductivity tables. In *Handbook of thermodynamic tables and charts*. McGraw-Hill, New York.

Robinson, H.E., F.J. Powlitch, and R.S. Dill. 1954. The thermal insulation value of airspaces. *Housing Research Paper* 32, Housing and Home Finance Agency.

Robinson, H.E., F.J. Powell, and L.A. Cosgrove. 1957. Thermal resistance of airspaces and fibrous insulations bounded by reflective surfaces. National Bureau of Standards, *Building Materials and Structures Report* BMS 151.

Rowley, F.B. and A.B. Algren. 1932. Heat transmission through building materials. University of Minnesota *Bulletin* #8, Minneapolis.

Rowley, F.B. and A.B. Algren. 1937. Thermal conductivity of building materials. University of Minnesota *Bulletin* #12, Minneapolis.

Rowley, F.B., R.C. Jordan, C.E. Lund, and R.M. Lander. 1952. Gas is an important factor in the thermal conductivity of most insulating materials. *ASHVE Transactions* 58:155.

Sabine, H.J., M.B. Lacher, D.R. Flynn, and T.L. Quindry. 1975. Acoustical and thermal performance of exterior residential walls, doors and windows. NBS *Building Science Series* 77. National Institute of Standards and Technology, Gaithersburg, MD.

Salomone, L.A. and J.I. Marlowe. 1989. *Soil and rock classification according to thermal conductivity: Design of ground-coupled heat pump systems*. EPRI CU-6482. Electric Power Research Institute, Palo Alto, CA.

Seiffert, K. 1970. *Damp diffusion and buildings*. Elsevier, Amsterdam, the Netherlands.

Shu, L.S., A.E. Fiorato, and J.W. Howanski. 1979. Heat transmission coefficients of concrete block walls with core insulation. *Proceedings of the ASHRAE/DOE-ORNL Conference on Thermal Performance of the Exterior Envelopes of Buildings*, ASHRAE SP 28, pp. 421-435.

Simons, E. 1955. In-place studies of insulated structures. *Refrigerating Engineering* 63:40, 128.

Touloukian, Y.S., R.W. Powell, C.Y. Ho, and I.G. Clemens. 1970. Thermophysical properties of matter. *Thermal conductivity data tables of nonmetallic solids*. IFI/Plenum, New York.

Tye, R.P. 1985. Upgrading thermal insulation performance of industrial processes. *Chemical Engineering Progress* (February):30-34.

Tye, R.P. 1986. Effects of product variability on thermal performance of thermal insulation. *Proceedings of the First Asian Thermal Properties Conference*, Beijing, People's Republic of China.

Tye, R.P. 1988. Aging of cellular plastics: A comprehensive bibliography. *Journal of Thermal Insulation* 11:196-222.

Tye, R.P. and A.O. Desjarlais. 1981. *Performance characteristics of foam-in-place urea formaldehyde insulation*. ORNL/Sub-78/86993/1. Oak Ridge National Laboratory, Oak Ridge, TN.

Tye, R.P. and A.O. Desjarlais. 1983. Factors influencing the thermal performance of thermal insulations for industrial applications. In *Thermal insulation, materials, and systems for energy conservation in the '80s*, F.A. Govan, D.M. Greason, and J.D. McAllister, eds. ASTM STP 789: 733-748.

Valore, R.C. 1988. *Thermophysical properties of masonry and its constituents, parts I and II*. International Masonry Institute, Washington, D.C.

Van Geem, M.G. 1985. Thermal transmittance of concrete block walls with core insulation. *ASHRAE Transactions* 91(2).

Verschoor, J.D. 1977. Effectiveness of building insulation applications. USN/CEL *Report* CR78.006—NTIS AD-AO53 452/9ST.

Verschoor, J.D. and P. Greebler. 1952. Heat transfer by gas conductivity and radiation in fibrous insulations. *ASME Transactions* 74(6):961-68.

Wilkes, K.E. 1979. Thermophysical properties data base activities at Owens-Corning Fiberglas. *Proceedings of the ASHRAE/DOE-ORNL Conference on Thermal Performance of the Exterior Envelopes of Buildings*, ASHRAE SP 28, pp. 662-677.

Wilkes, K.E. and P.W. Childs. 1992. Thermal performance of fiberglass and cellulose attic insulations. *Proceedings of the ASHRAE/DOE/BTECC/CIBSE Conference on Thermal Performance of the Exterior Envelopes of Buildings V*, pp. 357-367.

Wilkes, K.E. and J.L. Rucker. 1983. Thermal performance of residential attic insulation. *Energy and Buildings* 5:263-277.

Yarbrough, E.W. 1983. *Assessment of reflective insulations for residential and commercial applications*. ORNL/TM-8891. Oak Ridge National Laboratory, Oak Ridge, TN.

Yarbrough, D.W., R.S. Graves, D.L. McElroy, A.O. Desjarlais, and R.P. Tye. 1987. The thermal resistance of spray-applied fiber insulations. *Journal of Thermal Insulation* 11(2):81-95.

BIBLIOGRAPHY

ASHRAE 1996. Building insulation system thermal anomalies. ASHRAE *Research Report* RP-758. Enermodal Engineering, Ltd.

ASTM. 2008. *Annual book of ASTM standards*, vol. 04.06, *Thermal insulation; building and environmental acoustics*. American Society for Testing and Materials, West Conshohocken, PA.

Hedlin, C.P. 1988. Heat flow through a roof insulation having moisture contents between 0 and 1% by volume, in summer. *ASHRAE Transactions* 94(2):1579-1594.

CHAPTER 27

HEAT, AIR, AND MOISTURE CONTROL IN BUILDING ASSEMBLIES—EXAMPLES

THERMAL and moisture design as well as long-term performance must be considered during the planning phase of buildings. Installing appropriate insulation layers and taking appropriate air and moisture control measures can be much more economical during construction than later. Design and material selection should be based on

- Building use
- Interior and exterior climate
- Space availability
- Thermal and moisture properties of materials
- Other properties required by location of materials
- Durability of materials
- Compatibility with adjacent materials
- Performance expectations of the assembly

Designers and builders often rely on generic guidelines and past building practice as the basis for system and material selection. In many cases, this may still be a valuable approach, but for more difficult cases, selections and performance expectations should be set through engineering analysis. Recent developments have increased the capabilities of available tools and methods of thermal and moisture analysis.

This chapter draws on Chapter 25's fundamental information on heat, air and moisture transport in building assemblies, as well as Chapter 26's material property data. Examples here demonstrate calculation of heat, moisture, and air transport in typical assemblies. For design guidance for common building envelope assemblies and conditions, see Chapter 43 of the 2007 *ASHRAE Handbook—HVAC Applications*.

Insulation specifically for mechanical systems is discussed in Chapter 23. For specific industrial applications of insulated assemblies, see the appropriate chapter in other ASHRAE Handbook volumes. In the 2006 *ASHRAE Handbook—Refrigeration*, for refrigerators and freezers, see Chapters 46, 47, and 48; for insulation systems for refrigerant piping, see Chapter 33; for refrigerated facility design, see Chapters 14 and 39; for trucks, trailers, rail cars, and containers, see Chapter 30; for marine refrigeration, see Chapter 31. For environmental test facilities, see Chapter 37 in the 2002 *ASHRAE Handbook—Refrigeration*.

Engineering practice is predicated on the assumption that performance effects can be viewed in functional format, where discrete input values lead to discrete output values that may be assessed for acceptability. Heat transfer in solids lends itself to engineering analysis because material properties are relatively constant and easy to characterize, the transport equations are well established, analysis results tend toward linearity, and, for well-defined input values, output values are well defined. Airflow and moisture transport analysis, in contrast, is difficult: material properties are difficult to characterize, transport equations are not well-defined, analysis results tend toward nonlinearity, and both input and output values include great uncertainty. Air movement is even more difficult to characterize than moisture transport.

Engineering makes use of the continuum in understanding from physical principles, to simple applications, to complex applications, to design guidance. Complex design applications can be handled by computers; however, this chapter presents simpler examples as a learning tool. Because complex applications are built up from simpler ones, understanding the simpler applications ensures that a critical engineering oversight of complex (computer) applications is retained. Computers have facilitated the widespread use of two- and three-dimensional analysis as well as transient (time-dependent) calculations. As a consequence, steady-state calculations are less widely used. Design guidance, notably guidance regarding use of air and vapor barriers, faces changes in light of sophisticated transient calculations. ASHRAE *Standard* 160P creates a framework for using transient hygrothermal calculations in building envelope design.

The preparation of this chapter is assigned to TC 4.4, Building Materials and Building Envelope Performance.

HEAT TRANSFER

ONE-DIMENSIONAL U-FACTOR CALCULATION

Wall U-Factor

The U-factor for a building envelope assembly determines the rate of steady-state heat conduction through the assembly. One-dimensional heat flow through building envelope assemblies is the starting point for determining whole-building heat transmittance.

Example 1. Calculate the system R-value R_{system}, average total resistance [$R_{T(av)}$], and U-factor of the structural insulated panel assembly shown in Figure 1, assuming winter conditions.

Solution: Determine indoor and outdoor air film resistances from Table 1 in Chapter 26, and thermal resistance of all components from Table 4 in that chapter. If any elements are described by conductivity

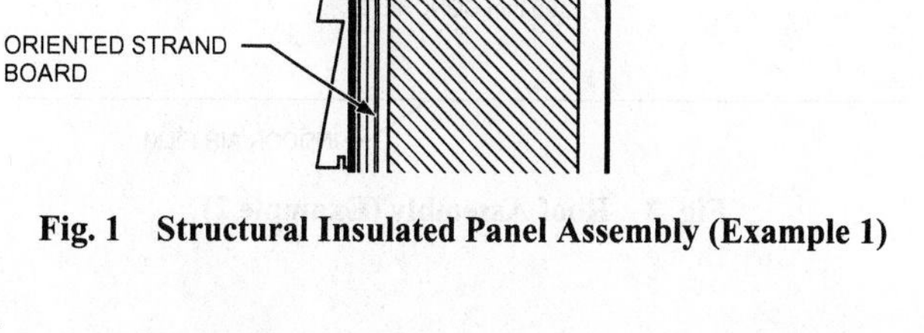

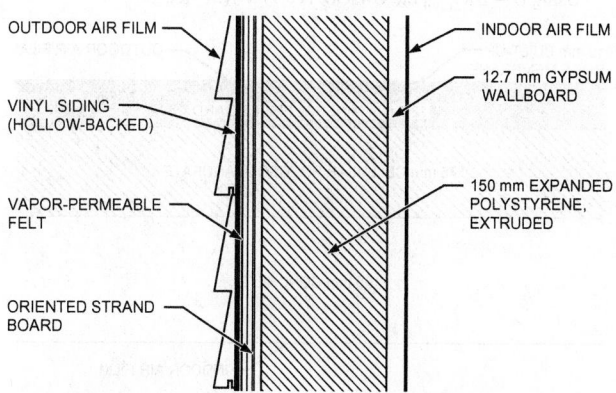

Fig. 1 Structural Insulated Panel Assembly (Example 1)

(independent of thickness) rather than thermal resistance (thickness-dependent), then calculate the resistance.

Element	R, (m²·K)/W
1. Outdoor air film	0.030
2. Vinyl siding (hollow backed)	0.107
3. Vapor-permeable felt	0.011
4. Oriented strand board (OSB), 11 mm	0.11
5. 150 mm expanded polystyrene, extruded (smooth skin)	5.28
6. 13 mm gypsum wallboard	0.079
7. Indoor air film	0.120
Total	5.70

The conductivity k of expanded polystyrene is 0.029 W/(m·K). For 150 mm thickness,

$$R_{foam} = x/k = 0.153/0.029 = 5.28 \text{ (m}^2\text{·K)/W}$$

To calculate the system's R-value in the example, sum the R-values of the system components only, disregarding indoor and outdoor air films.

$$R_{system} = 0.107 + 0.011 + 0.07 + 5.28 + 0.079 = 5.55 \text{ (m}^2\text{·K)/W}$$

The average total R-value ($R_{T(av)}$) consists of the system's R-value plus the thermal resistance of the interior and exterior air films.

$$R_{T(av)} = R_o + R_{system} + R_i = 5.70 \text{ (m}^2\text{·K)/W}$$

The U-factor for the wall is $1/R_{T(av)}$, or 0.175 W/(m²·K).

Roof U-Factor

Example 2. Find the U-factor of the roof assembly shown in Figure 2, assuming summer conditions.

Solution: The calculation procedure is similar to that shown in Example 1. Note the U-factor of nonvertical assemblies depends on the direction of heat flow [i.e., whether the calculation is for winter (heat flow up) or summer (heat flow down)], because the resistances of indoor air films and plane air spaces in ceilings differ, based on the heat flow direction (see Table 3 in Chapter 26). The effects of mechanical fasteners are not addressed in this example.

Element	R, (m²·K)/W
1. Indoor air film	0.16
2. 100 mm concrete, k = 0.7	0.07
3. 75 mm cellular polyisocyanurate (CFC-11 exp.) (gas-impermeable facers)	4.97
4. 25 mm mineral fiberboard	0.52
5. 9 mm built-up roof membrane	0.06
6. Outdoor air film	0.04
Total	5.81

Using $U = 1/R_{T(av)}$, the U-factor is 0.17 W/(m²·K).

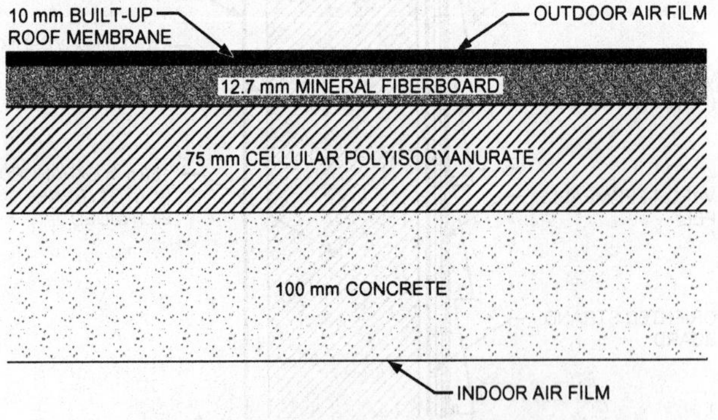

Fig. 2 Roof Assembly (Example 2)

Attics

During sunny periods, unconditioned attics may be hotter than outdoor air. Peak attic temperatures on a hot, sunny day may be 10 to 45 K above outdoor air temperature, depending on factors such as shingle color, roof framing type, air exchange rate through vents, and use of radiant barriers. Energy efficiency estimates can be obtained using models such as Wilkes (1991).

Basement Walls and Floors

Heat transfer through basement walls and floors to the ground depends on the following factors: (1) the difference between the air temperature in the room and that of the ground and outside air, (2) the material of the walls or floor, and (3) the thermal conductivity of surrounding earth. The latter varies with local conditions and is usually unknown. Because of the great thermal inertia of surrounding soil, ground temperature varies with depth, and there is a substantial time lag between changes in outdoor air temperatures and corresponding changes in ground temperatures. As a result, ground-coupled heat transfer is less amenable to steady-state representation than above-grade building elements. However, there are several simplified procedures for estimating ground-coupled heat transfer. These fall into two main categories: (1) those that reduce the ground heat transfer problem to a closed-form solution, and (2) those that use simple regression equations developed from statistically reduced multidimensional transient analyses.

Closed-form solutions, including Latta and Boileau's (1969) procedure discussed in Chapter 17, generally reduce the problem to one-dimensional, steady-state heat transfer. These procedures use simple, "effective" U-factors or ground temperatures or both. Methods differ in the various parameters averaged or manipulated to obtain these effective values. Closed-form solutions provide acceptable results in climates that have a single dominant season, because the dominant season persists long enough to allow a reasonable approximation of steady-state conditions at shallow depths. The large errors (percentage) that are likely during transition seasons should not seriously affect building design decisions, because these heat flows are relatively insignificant compared to those of the principal season.

The ASHRAE arc-length procedure (Latta and Boileau 1969) is a reliable method for wall heat losses in cold winter climates. Chapter 17 discusses a slab-on-grade floor model developed by one study. Although both procedures give results comparable to transient computer solutions for cold climates, their results for warmer U.S. climates differ substantially.

Research conducted by Dill et al. (1945) and Hougten et al. (1942) indicates a heat flow of approximately 6.3 W/m² through an uninsulated concrete basement floor with a temperature difference of 11 K between the basement floor and the air 150 mm above it. A U-factor of 5.7 W/(m²·K) is sometimes used for concrete basement floors on the ground. For basement walls below grade, the temperature difference for winter design conditions is greater than for the floor. Test results indicate that, at the mid-height of the below-grade portion of the basement wall, the unit area heat loss is approximately twice that of the floor.

For small concrete slab floors (equal in area to a 7.5 by 7.5 m house) in contact with the ground at grade level, tests indicate that heat loss can be calculated as proportional to the length of exposed edge rather than total area. This amounts to 1.4 W per linear metre of exposed edge per degree temperature difference between indoor air and the average outdoor air temperature. This value can be reduced appreciably by installing insulation under the ground slab and along the edge between the floor and abutting walls. In most calculations, if the perimeter loss is calculated accurately, no other floor losses need to be considered. Chapter 17 contains data for load calculations and heat loss values for below-grade walls and floors at different depths.

The second category of simplified procedures uses transient two-dimensional computer models to generate ground heat transfer data, which are then reduced to compact form by regression analysis (Mitalas 1982, 1983; Shipp 1983). These are the most accurate procedures available, but the database is very expensive to generate. In addition, these methods are limited to the range of climates and constructions specifically examined. Extrapolating beyond the outer bounds of the regression surfaces can produce significant errors.

Guide details and recommendations related to application of concepts for basements are provided in Chapter 43 of the 2007 *ASHRAE Handbook—HVAC Applications*. Detailed analysis of heat transfer through foundation insulation may also be found in the *Building Foundation Design Handbook* (Labs et al. 1988).

TWO-DIMENSIONAL U-FACTOR CALCULATION

The following examples show three methods of two-dimensional, steady-state conductive heat transfer analysis through wall assemblies. They offer approximations to overall rates of heat transfer (U-factor) when assemblies contain a layer composed of dissimilar materials. The methods are described in Chapter 25. The **parallel-path method** is used when the thermal conductivity of the dissimilar materials in the layer are rather close in value (within the same order of magnitude), as with wood-frame walls. The **isothermal-planes method** is appropriate for materials with conductivities moderately different from those of adjacent materials (e.g., masonry). The **zone method** and the **modified zone method** are appropriate for materials with a very high difference in conductivity (two orders of magnitude or more), such as with assemblies containing metal.

Two-dimensional, steady-state heat transfer analysis is often conducted using computer-based finite difference methods. If the resolution of the analysis is sufficiently fine, computer methods provide better simulations than any of the methods described here, and the results typically show better agreement with measured values.

The methods described here do not take into account heat storage in the materials, nor do they account for varying material properties (e.g., when thermal conductivity is affected by moisture content or temperature). Transient analysis is often used in such cases.

Wood-Frame Walls

The average overall R-values and U-factors of wood-frame walls can be calculated by assuming either parallel heat flow paths through areas with different thermal resistances or by assuming isothermal planes. Equation (15) in Chapter 25 provides the basis for the two methods.

The **framing factor** expresses the fraction of the total building component (wall or roof) area that is framing. The value depends on the specific type of construction, and may vary based on local construction practices, even for the same type of construction. For stud walls 400 mm on center (OC), the fraction of insulated cavity may be as low as 0.75, where the fraction of studs, plates, and sills is 0.21 and the fraction of headers is 0.04. For studs 600 mm OC, the respective values are 0.78, 0.18, and 0.04. These fractions contain an allowance for multiple studs, plates, sills, extra framing around windows, headers, and band joists. These assumed framing fractions are used in Example 3, to illustrate the importance of including the effect of framing in determining a building's overall thermal conductance. The actual framing fraction should be calculated for each specific construction.

Example 3. Calculate the U-factor of the 38 by 90 mm stud wall shown in Figure 3. The studs are at 400 mm OC. There is 90 mm mineral fiber batt insulation (R-13) in the stud space. The inside finish is 13 mm gypsum wallboard, and the outside is finished with rigid foam insulating sheathing (R-4) and vinyl siding. The insulated cavity occupies approximately 75% of the transmission area; the studs, plates, and sills occupy 21%; and the headers occupy 4%.

Solution: Obtain the R-values of the various building elements from Tables 1 and 4 of Chapter 26. Assume $R = 7.0$ (m^2·K)/W for the wood framing. Also, assume the headers are solid wood, and group them with the studs, plates, and sills.

Two simple methods may be used to determine the U-factor of wood frame walls: parallel path and isothermal planes. For highly conductive framing members such as metal studs, the modified zone method must be used.

Parallel-Path Method:

Element	*R* (Insulated Cavity), (m^2·K)/W	*R* (Studs, Plates, and Headers), (m^2·K)/W
1. Outside air film, 24 km/h wind	0.03	0.03
2. Vinyl siding (hollow-backed)	0.14	0.14
3. Rigid foam insulating sheathing	0.70	0.70
4. Mineral fiber batt insulation, 90 mm	2.30	—
5. Wood stud, nominal 38 by 90 mm	—	0.77
6. Gypsum wallboard, 13 mm	0.08	0.08
7. Inside air film, still air	0.12	0.12
	$R_1 = 3.37$	$R_2 = 1.85$

Individual U-factors are reciprocals of the R-value, so $U_1 = 0.297$ and $U_2 = 0.588$ W/(m^2·K). If the wood framing is accounted for using the parallel-path flow method, the wall's U-factor is determined using Equation (15) from Chapter 25. The fractional area of insulated cavity is 0.75 and the fractional area of framing members is 0.25.

$$U_{av} = (0.75 \times 0.297) + (0.25 \times 0.588) = 0.37 \text{ W/(m}^2\cdot\text{K)}$$

$$R_{T(av)} = 1/U_{av} = 2.70 \text{ (m}^2\cdot\text{K)/W}$$

With the isothermal-planes method, the fractional areas are applied only to the building layer that contains the studs and cavity-fill insulation. The average R-value for this layer (R_{avs}) is added to the R-values of the other components for a total *R* for the assembly.

Isothermal-Planes Method:

Element	*R* (Stud Cavity Elements), (m^2·K)/W	*R* (Studs, Plates, and Headers), (m^2·K)/W
1. Outside air film, 24 km/h wind		0.03
2. Vinyl siding (hollow-backed)		0.14
3. Rigid foam insulating sheathing		0.70
4. Mineral fiber batt insulation, 90 mm	2.30	1.53 (R_{avs})
5. Wood stud, nominal 38 by 90 mm	0.77	
6. Gypsum wallboard, 13 mm		0.08
7. Inside air film, still air		0.12
		$R_T = 2.61$

The average R-value R_{avs} of the stud cavity is calculated using the fractional area of stud and insulation using Equation (15) from Chapter 25.

$$U_{avs} = 0.75(1/2.3) + 0.25(1/0.77) = 0.652$$

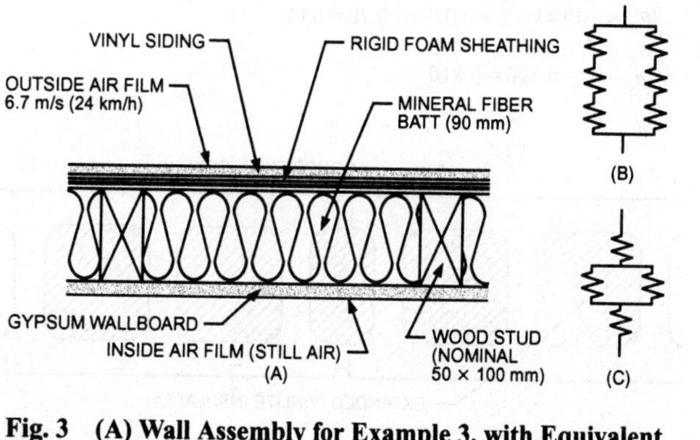

Fig. 3 (A) Wall Assembly for Example 3, with Equivalent Electrical Circuits: (B) Parallel Path and (C) Isothermal Planes

$$R_{avs} = 1/U_{avs} = 1.53\ (\text{m}^2\cdot\text{K})/\text{W}$$

If the wood framing is included using the isothermal-planes method, the U-factor of the wall is determined using Equations (10) and (11) from Chapter 25 as follows:

$$R_T = 2.61\ (\text{m}^2\cdot\text{K})/\text{W}$$

$$U_{av} = 1/R_T = 0.383\ \text{W}/(\text{m}^2\cdot\text{K})$$

For a frame wall with a 300 mm OC stud space, the average overall R-value is 2.67 (m²·K)/W. Similar calculation procedures may be used to evaluate other wall designs, except those with thermal bridges.

Masonry Walls

The average overall R-values of masonry walls can be estimated by assuming a combination of layers in series, one or more of which provides parallel paths. This method is used because heat flows laterally through block face shells so that transverse isothermal planes result. Average total resistance $R_{T(av)}$ is the sum of the resistances of the layers between such planes, each layer calculated as shown in Example 4.

Example 4. Calculate the overall thermal resistance and average U-factor of the 194 mm thick insulated concrete block wall shown in Figure 4. The two-core block has an average web thickness of 25 mm and a face shell thickness of 30 mm. Overall block dimensions are 194 by 194 by 395 mm. Measured thermal resistances of 1700 kg/m³ concrete and 110 kg/m³ expanded perlite insulation are 0.70 and 20 (m²·K)/W, respectively.

Solution: The equation used to determine the overall thermal resistance of the insulated concrete block wall is derived from Equations (7) and (15) from Chapter 25 and is given below:

$$R_{T(av)} = R_i + R_f + \left(\frac{a_w}{R_w} + \frac{a_c}{R_c}\right)^{-1} + R_o$$

where

$R_{T(av)}$ = overall thermal resistance based on assumption of isothermal planes
R_i = thermal resistance of inside air surface film (still air)
R_o = thermal resistance of outside air surface film (24 km/h wind)
R_f = total thermal resistance of face shells
R_c = thermal resistance of cores between face shells
R_w = thermal resistance of webs between face shells
a_w = fraction of total area transverse to heat flow represented by webs of blocks
a_c = fraction of total area transverse to heat flow represented by cores of blocks

From the information given and the data in Tables 3 and 4, Chapter 26, determine the values needed to compute the overall thermal resistance.

$R_i = 0.12$
$R_o = 0.03$
$R_f = 2 \times 0.032 \times 0.70 = 0.045$
$R_c = (0.194 - 2 \times 0.032) \times 20 = 2.60$
$R_w = (0.194 - 2 \times 0.032) \times 0.70 = 0.091$
$a_w = 3 \times 25/395 = 0.190$
$a_c = 1 - 0.190 = 0.810$

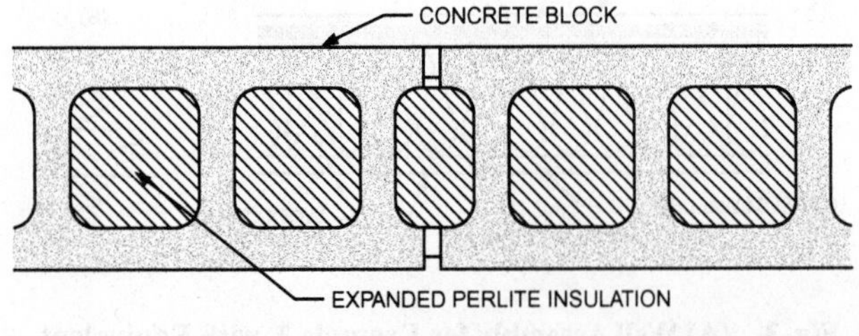

Fig. 4 Insulated Concrete Block Wall (Example 4)

Using the equation given, the overall thermal resistance and average U-factor are calculated as follows:

$$R_{T(av)} = 0.12 + 0.045 + \frac{(0.091 \times 2.60)}{(0.81 \times 0.091) + (0.19 \times 2.60)} + 0.03$$

$$= 0.612\ (\text{m}^2\cdot\text{K})/\text{W}$$

$$U_{av} = 1/0.612 = 1.63\ \text{W}/(\text{m}^2\cdot\text{K})$$

Based on guarded hot-box tests of this wall without mortar joints, Tye and Spinney (1980) measured the average R-value for this insulated concrete block wall as 0.551 (m²·K)/W.

Assuming parallel heat flow only, the calculated resistance is higher than that calculated on the assumption of isothermal planes. The actual resistance generally is some value between the two calculated values. In the absence of test values, examination of the construction usually reveals whether a value closer to the higher or lower calculated R-value should be used. Generally, if the construction contains a layer in which lateral conduction is high compared with transmittance through the construction, the calculation with isothermal planes should be used. If the construction has no layer of high lateral conductance, the parallel heat flow calculation should be used.

Hot-box tests of insulated and uninsulated masonry walls constructed with block of conventional configuration show that thermal resistances calculated using the isothermal planes heat flow method agree well with measured values (Shu et al. 1979; Valore 1980; Van Geem 1985). Neglecting horizontal mortar joints in conventional block can result in thermal transmittance values up to 16% lower than actual, depending on the masonry's density and thermal properties, and 1 to 6% lower, depending on the core insulation material (McIntyre 1984; Van Geem 1985). For aerated concrete block walls, other solid masonry, and multicore block walls with full mortar joints, neglecting mortar joints can cause errors in R-values up to 40% (Valore 1988). Horizontal mortar joints, usually found in concrete block wall construction, are neglected in Example 4.

Constructions Containing Metal

Curtain and metal stud-wall constructions often include metallic and other thermal bridges, which can significantly reduce the thermal resistance. However, the capacity of the adjacent facing materials to transmit heat transversely to the metal is limited, and some contact resistance between all materials in contact limits the reduction. Contact resistances in building structures are only 0.01 to 0.1 (m²·K)/W, too small to be of concern in many cases. However, the contact resistances of steel framing members may be important. Also, in many cases (as illustrated in Example 5), the area of metal in contact with the facing greatly exceeds the thickness of metal, which mitigates contact resistance effects.

Thermal characteristics for panels of sandwich construction can be computed by combining the thermal resistances of the layers. R-values for assembled sections should be determined on a representative sample by using a hot-box method. If the sample is a wall section with air cavities on both sides of fibrous insulation, the sample must be of representative height because convective airflow can contribute significantly to heat flow through the test section. Computer modeling can also be useful, but all heat transfer mechanisms must be considered.

The metal studs in Examples 5 and 7 are 90 mm deep and placed at 400 mm on center. In Example 5, the metal member is only 0.5 mm thick, but it is in contact with adjacent facings over a 32 mm wide area. The steel member is 32 mm deep, has a thermal resistance of approximately 0.0019 (m²·K)/W, and is virtually isothermal. The calculation involves careful selection of the thickness for the steel member. If the member is assumed to be 0.5 mm thick, the fact that the flange transmits heat to the adjacent facing is ignored, and heat flow through the steel is underestimated. If the member is assumed to be 32 mm thick, heat flow through the steel is overestimated. In Example 5, the steel member behaves in much the same way as a rectangular member 90 mm thick and 32 mm deep with a thermal resistance of $0.0019(32/0.5) = 0.12$ (m²·K)/W.

Example 5. Calculate the system R (i.e., the R-value of the assembly less the resistances of indoor and outdoor air films) of the insulated steel frame wall shown in Figure 5. The C-factor is the reciprocal of the system R. Assume that the steel member has an R-value of 0.12 (m²·K)/W and that the framing behaves as though it occupies approximately 8% of the transmission area.

Solution: Obtain the R-values of the various building elements from Table 4 in Chapter 26.

Element	*R* (Insul.)	*R* (Framing)
1. 12.7 mm gypsum wallboard	0.08	0.08
2. 90 mm mineral fiber batt insulation	1.94	—
3. Steel framing member	—	0.12
4. 12.7 mm gypsum wallboard	0.08	0.08
	$R_1 = 2.10$	$R_2 = 0.28$

Because $C = 1/R$, $C_1 = 0.476$ and $C_2 = 3.57$ W/(m²·K).

If the steel framing (thermal bridging) is not considered, the C-factor of the wall is calculated using Equation (11) from Chapter 25 as follows:

$$C_{av} = C_1 = 1/R_1 = 0.476 \text{ W/(m}^2\text{·K)}$$

If the steel framing is accounted for using the parallel-flow method, the wall's C-factor is determined using Equation (15) from Chapter 25 as follows:

$$C_{av} = (0.92 \times 0.476) + (0.08 \times 3.57)$$
$$= 0.724 \text{ W/(m}^2\text{·K)}$$
$$R_{T(av)} = 1.38 \text{ (m}^2\text{·K)/W}$$

If the steel framing is included using the isothermal planes method, the C-factor of the wall is determined using Equations (10) and (11) from Chapter 25 as follows:

$$R_{T(av)} = 0.08 + 1/[(0.92/1.94) + (0.08/0.12)] + 0.08$$
$$= 1.037 \text{ (m}^2\text{·K)/W}$$
$$C_{av} = 0.96 \text{ W/(m}^2\text{·K)}$$

For this insulated steel frame wall, Farouk and Larson (1983) measured an average R-value of 1.16 (m²·K)/W. For the same assembly, the recommended modified zone method (see Example 7) gives an average R-value of 1.18 (m²·K)/W. Two-dimensional analysis (THERM) yields $U_{av} = 1.0$ or $R = 1.00$ (m²·K)/W. ASHRAE/IESNA *Standard* 90.1 describes how to determine the thermal resistance of wall assemblies containing metal framing by using insulation/framing adjustment factors in Table A9.2B of the standard. For 38 by 90 mm steel framing, 400 mm OC, $F_c = 0.50$. Using the correction factor method, an R-value of 1.13 (m²·K)/W [0.08 + 1.94(0.50) + 0.08] is obtained for the wall described here.

Zone Method of Calculation

For structures with widely spaced metal members of substantial cross-sectional area, the isothermal planes method can give thermal resistance values that are too low. For these constructions, the **zone method** can be used. This method involves two separate computations: one for a chosen limited portion, zone A, containing the highly conductive element; the other for the remaining portion of simpler construction, zone B. The two computations are then combined using the parallel-flow method, and the average transmittance per unit overall area is calculated. The basic laws of heat transfer are applied by adding the area conductances CA of elements in parallel, and adding area resistances R/A of elements in series.

The surface shape of zone A is determined by the metal element. For a metal beam (see Figure 6), the zone A surface is a strip of width W that is centered on the beam. For a rod perpendicular to panel surfaces, it is a circle of diameter W. The value of W is calculated from Equation (1), which is empirical. The value of d should not be less than 13 mm for still air.

$$W = m + 2d \tag{1}$$

where

m = width or diameter of metal heat path terminal, mm
d = depth from panel surface to metal, mm

Generally, W should be calculated using Equation (1) for each end of the metal heat path; the larger value, within the limits of the basic area, should be used as illustrated in Example 6.

Example 6. Calculate transmittance of the roof deck shown in Figure 6. Tee-bars at 600 mm OC support glass fiber form boards, gypsum concrete, and built-up roofing. Conductivities of components are: steel, 45 W/(m·K); gypsum concrete, 0.24 W/(m·K); and glass fiber form board, 0.036 W/(m·K). Conductance of built-up roofing is 17 W/(m·K).

Solution: The basic area is 0.6 m² with a tee-bar (1 m long) across the middle. This area is divided into zones A and B. Zone A is determined from Equation (1) as follows:

Top side $W = m + 2d = 15 + (2 \times 40) = 95$ mm

Bottom side $W = m + 2d = 50 + (2 \times 13) = 76$ mm

Using the larger value of W, the area of zone A is $(1.0 \times 95/1000) = 0.095$ m². The area of zone B is $0.600 - 0.095 = 0.505$ m².

To determine area transmittance for zone A, divide the structure within the zone into five sections parallel to the top and bottom surfaces (Figure 6). The area conductance CA of each section is calculated by adding the area conductances of its metal and nonmetal paths. Area

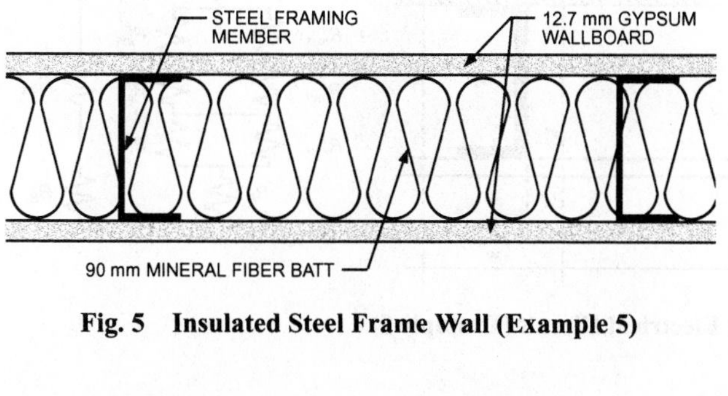

Fig. 5 Insulated Steel Frame Wall (Example 5)

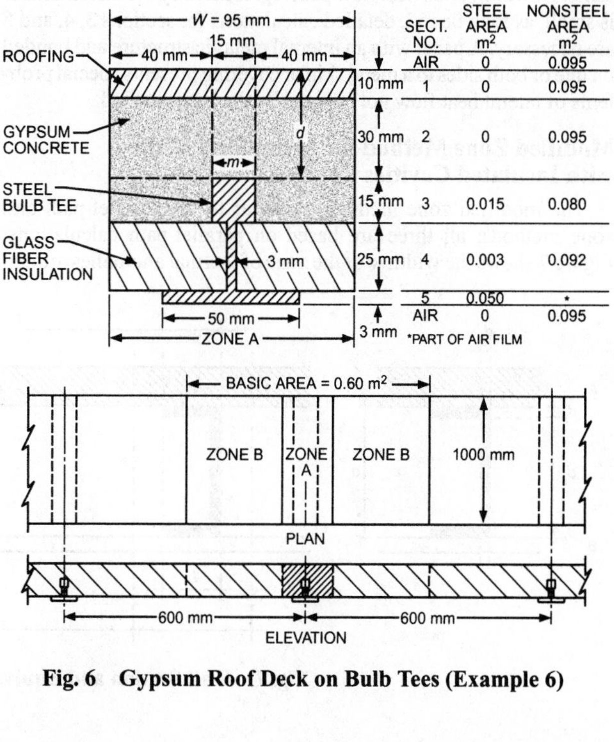

Fig. 6 Gypsum Roof Deck on Bulb Tees (Example 6)

conductances of the sections are converted to area resistances R/A and added to obtain the total resistance of zone A.

Section	Area × Conductance	= CA	$\frac{1}{CA} = \frac{R}{A}$
Air (outside, 24 km/h)	0.095 × 34	= 3.23	0.31
1. Roofing	0.095 × 17	= 1.62	0.62
2. Gypsum concrete	0.095 × 0.24/0.030	= 0.76	1.32
3. Steel	0.015 × 45/0.015	= 45	0.022
Gypsum concrete	0.080 × 0.24/0.015	= 1.28	
4. Steel	0.003 × 45/0.025	= 5.4	0.181
Glass fiberboard	0.092 × 0.036/0.025	= 0.13	
5. Steel	0.050 × 45/0.005	= 450	0.002
Air (inside)	0.095 × 9.26	= 0.88	1.14
		Total R/A =	3.59

Area transmittance of zone A = $1/(R/A)$ = 1/3.59 = 0.279.

For zone B, the unit resistances are added and then converted to area transmittance.

Section	Resistance R
Air (outside, 24 km/h)	1/34 = 0.029
Roofing	1/17 = 0.059
Gypsum concrete	0.045/0.24 = 0.188
Glass fiberboard	0.025/0.036 = 0.694
Air (inside)	1/9.26 = 0.108
Total resistance	= 1.078

Because unit transmittance = $1/R$ = 0.927, the total area transmittance UA is calculated as follows:

Zone B = 0.505 × 0.927	= 0.468
Zone A	= 0.279
Total area transmittance of basic area	= 0.747
Transmittance	= 0.747 W/(m²·K)
Resistance	= 0.80 (m²·K)/W

Overall R-values of 0.805 and 0.854 (m²·K)/W were measured in two guarded hot-box tests of a similar construction.

When the steel member represents a relatively large proportion of the total heat flow path, as in Example 6, detailed calculations of resistance in sections 3, 4, and 5 of zone A are unnecessary; if only the steel member is considered, the final result of Example 6 is the same. However, if the heat flow path represented by the steel member is small, as for a tie rod, detailed calculations for sections 3, 4, and 5 are necessary. A panel with an internal metallic structure and bonded on one or both sides to a metal skin or covering presents special problems of lateral heat flow not covered by the zone method.

Modified Zone Method for Metal Stud Walls with Insulated Cavities

The modified zone method is similar to the parallel-path and zone methods; all three are based on parallel-path calculations. Figure 7 shows the width w of the zone of thermal anomalies around a metal stud. This zone can be assumed to equal the length of the stud flange L (parallel-path method), or can be calculated as a sum of the length of stud flange and a distance double that from wall surface to metal Σd_i (zone method). In the modified zone method, the width of the zone depends on three parameters:

- Ratio between thermal resistivity of sheathing material and cavity insulation
- Size (depth) of stud
- Thickness of sheathing material

Example 7. Calculate the U-factor of the wall section shown in Figure 7 using the modified zone method.

Solution: The wall cross section is divided into two zones: the zone of thermal anomalies around the metal stud (zone W), and the cavity zone (zone *cav*). Wall material layers are grouped into exterior and interior surface sections A (sheathing, siding) and B (wallboard), and interstitial sections I and II (cavity insulation, metal stud flange).

Assuming that the wall materials in section A are thicker than those in section B, as shown, they can be described as follows:

$$\sum_{i=1}^{n} d_i \geq \sum_{j=1}^{m} d_j$$

where

n = number of material layer (of thickness d_i) between metal stud flange and wall surface for section A

m = number of material layer (of thickness d_j) for section B

Then, the width W of zone W can be estimated by

$$W = L + z_f \sum_{i=1}^{n} d_i$$

where

L = stud flange size

d_i = thickness of material layer in section A

z_f = zone factor, shown in Figure 8 (z_f = 2 for zone method)

Kosny and Christian (1995) verified the accuracy of the modified zone method for over 200 simulated cases of metal frame walls with insulated cavities. For all configurations considered, the discrepancy between results were within ±2%. Hot-box-measured R-values for 15 metal stud walls tested by Barbour et al. (1994) were compared with results obtained by Kosny and Christian (1995) and McGowan and Desjarlais (1997). The modified zone method was found to be the most accurate simple method for estimating the clear-wall R-value of light-gage steel stud walls with insulated cavities. However, this analysis does not apply to construction with metal sheathing. Also, ASHRAE *Standard* 90.1 may require a different method of analysis.

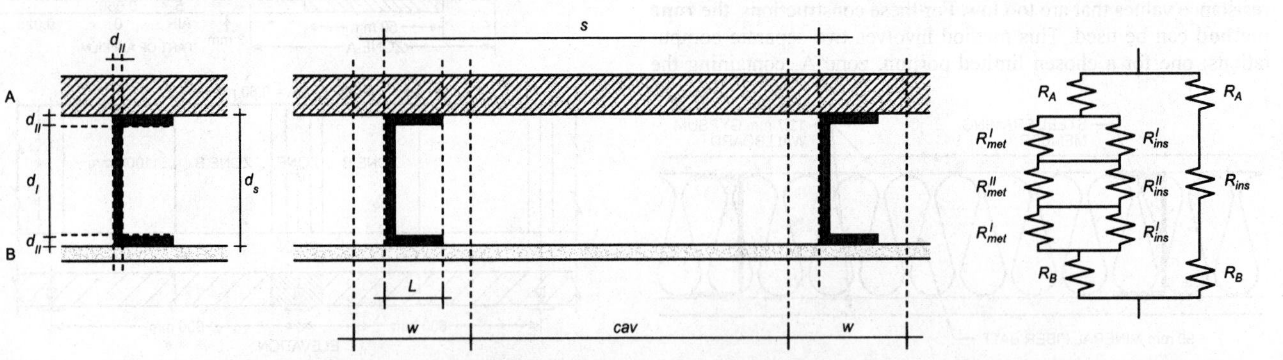

Fig. 7 Wall Section and Equivalent Electrical Circuit (Example 7)

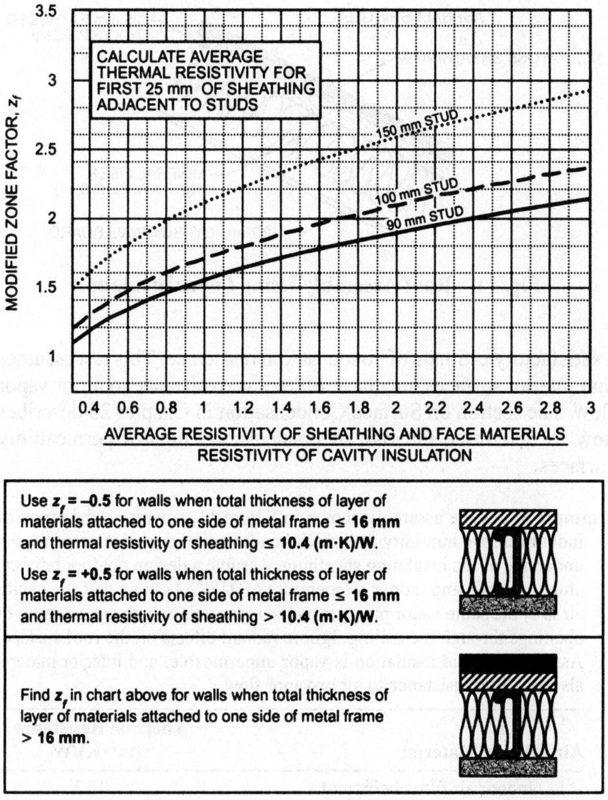
CALCULATE AVERAGE THERMAL RESISTIVITY FOR FIRST 25 mm OF SHEATHING ADJACENT TO STUDS
150 mm STUD
100 mm STUD
90 mm STUD
MODIFIED ZONE FACTOR, z_f
1
1.5
2
2.5
3
3.5
0.4 0.6 0.8 1 1.2 1.4 1.6 1.8 2 2.2 2.4 2.6 2.8 3
AVERAGE RESISTIVITY OF SHEATHING AND FACE MATERIALS
RESISTIVITY OF CAVITY INSULATION
Use z_f = –0.5 for walls when total thickness of layer of materials attached to one side of metal frame ≤ 16 mm and thermal resistivity of sheathing ≤ 10.4 (m·K)/W.
Use z_f = +0.5 for walls when total thickness of layer of materials attached to one side of metal frame ≤ 16 mm and thermal resistivity of sheathing > 10.4 (m·K)/W.
Find z_f in chart above for walls when total thickness of layer of materials attached to one side of metal frame > 16 mm.

Fig. 8 Modified Zone Factor for Calculating R-Value of Metal Stud Walls with Cavity Insulation

Step 1. Determine zone factor z_f, and the ratio of the exterior sheathing material's resistivity to the cavity material's resistivity. Resistivity r is the reciprocal of conductivity; Table 4 in Chapter 26, lists conductivities of various materials.

Element	Symbol	Value	Units
Stud spacing	s	0.406	m
Resistivity of sheathing material	r_i	34.67	(m·K)/W
Resistivity of cavity insulation	r_{ins}	23.92	(m·K)/W
Ratio r_i/r_{ins}		1.449	(no units)
Zone factor from chart	z_f	1.71	(no units)

Step 2. Calculate width W of affected zone W:

$$W = L + z_f \sum d_i$$

Element	Symbol	Value	Units
Cavity thickness	d_s	0.089	m
Thickness of metal	d_{II}	0.0010	m
Interior dimension between flanges	d_I	0.088	m
Thickness of exterior insulating materials		0.051	m
Flange length	L	0.038	m
Affected zone thickness	W	0.125	m

Step 3. Calculate the exterior and interior thermal resistances, using conductivity or thermal resistance values from step 1.

Element	Symbol	Value	Units
Exterior materials			
Thickness of first exterior material	d_e	0.0381	m
Resistivity of first exterior material	r_e	34.7	(m·K)/W
Resistance of first material		1.32	(m²·K)/W
Resistances of other materials		0.145	
Sum of resistances of exterior materials	R_A	1.47	(m²·K)/W

Element	Symbol	Value	Units
Interior materials			
Thickness of interior material	d_j	0.00127	m
Resistivity of interior material	r_j	6.24	(m·K)/W
Resistance of interior material	R_B	0.043	(m²·K)/W

Step 4. Calculate the thermal resistance of the sections in zone around the metal element. The building elements in series from outside to inside are shown in Figure 7.

Element	Symbol	Value	Units
Resistivity of steel	r_{met}	0.0208	(m·K)/W
R^I_{ins}	d^I_{xri}	2.10	(m²·K)/W
R^{II}_{ins}	d^{II}_{xri}	0.024	(m²·K)/W
R^I_{met}	d^I_{xrmet}	0.00183	(m²·K)/W
R^{II}_{met}	d^{II}_{xrmet}	0.00002	(m²·K)/W

The particular thermal resistances of the zone elements are then calculated.

Zone W is the zone at the web of the metal member. For width W, the thermal conductance C is calculated as the sum of the contributory areas. Because the thickness of the web of the metal member is d_I and the length along the flange section is L,

$$C_I = \frac{W - d_I}{W}C_{ins} + \frac{d_I}{W}C_{met} \quad \text{and} \quad C_{II} = \frac{W - L}{W}C_{ins} + \frac{L}{W}C_{met}$$

Using resistance rather than conductance, the contributing R-values are calculated as

$$R_I = \frac{R^I_{met}R^I_{ins}W}{d_I(R^I_{ins} - R^I_{met}) + WR^I_{met}} \quad \text{and} \quad R_{II} = \frac{R^{II}_{met}R^{II}_{ins}W}{L(R^{II}_{ins} - R^{II}_{met}) + WR^{II}_{met}}$$

At the cavity, the sum of the series R-values is

$$\sum R_{cav} = R_A + R_B + R^I_{ins} + 2R^{II}_{ins}$$

In zone W, the sum of the R-values is

$$\sum R_W = R_A + R_B + R_I + 2R_{II}$$

The total conductivity across the length s is proportional to the contributing lengths of zone W and the cavity:

$$C_{tot} = \frac{W}{s}C_W + \frac{cav}{s}C_{cav}$$

or

$$R_{tot} = \frac{\sum R_W \sum R_{cav} s}{W\left(\sum R_{cav} - \sum R_W\right) + s\sum R_W}$$

Element	Symbol	Value	Units
Resistance at web	R_I	0.203	(m²·K)/W
Resistance at flange	R_{II}	0.00007	(m²·K)/W
Sum of resistances at cavity	ΣR_{cav}	3.66	(m²·K)/W
Sum of resistances at zone W	ΣR_W	1.713	(m²·K)/W
Total R	R_{tot}	2.71	(m²·K)/W
Total U	U_{tot}	0.369	W/(m²·K)

In this example, the calculated total R-value for the wall is 2.71 (m²·K)/W, and the wall's U-factor is 0.369 W/(m²·K).

Complex Assemblies

Building enclosure geometry of two- and three-dimensional assemblies may be complex, including corners, terminations of materials, and junctures of different materials. Such assemblies cannot be analyzed effectively with explicit calculations; rather, they require iterative calculations using computers.

Figure 9 shows a corner composed of homogeneous material. Surface temperatures can be estimated from the intersections of isotherms and the surface. If, in this figure, the interior were warm with respect to outside, then the line at the corner would be colder than the

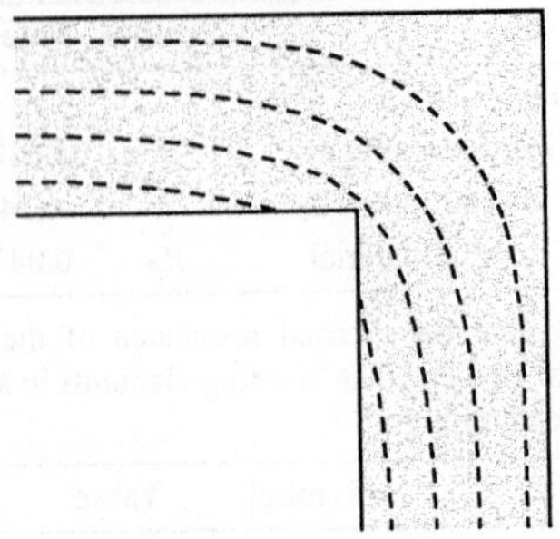

Fig. 9 Corner Composed of Homogeneous Material Showing Locations of Isotherms

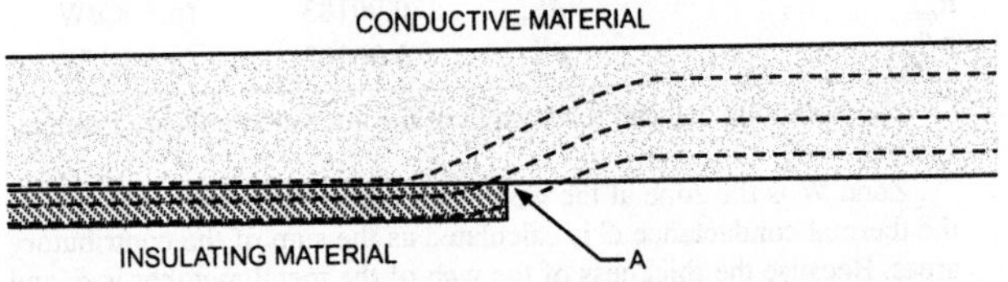

Fig. 10 Insulating Material Installed on Conductive Material, Showing Temperature Anomaly (Point A) at Insulation Edge

remainder of the interior surface. This effect may be exacerbated by the air film at the corner, which would have a greater effective thickness than on the plane of the wall, and would therefore offer greater thermal resistance, further lowering the corner temperature.

Figure 10 shows an insulating material applied to a conductive material. Insulation is placed at the inside, during a period of cold outdoor temperatures. A computer program may be used to trace the isotherms. The interior isotherm is cut where the insulating material is interrupted, indicating lowered temperature at that location (point A). In fact, the temperature at the edge of the interrupted insulation is even lower than the temperature at the surface of the uninsulated wall. Interruptions in insulation can lead to thermal bridges. For this reason, insulation of conductive assemblies such as masonry or concrete is often more successful when applied to the outside rather than to the inside of the building.

Windows and Doors

Table 4 of Chapter 15 lists U-factors for various fenestration products. For heat transmission coefficients for wood and steel doors, see Table 6 in Chapter 15. All U-factors are approximate, because a significant portion of the resistance of a window or door is contained in the air film resistances, and some parameters that may have important effects are not considered. For example, the listed U-factors assume the surface temperatures of surrounding bodies are equal to the ambient air temperature. However, the indoor surface of a window or door in an actual installation may be exposed to nearby radiating surfaces, such as radiant heating panels, or opposite walls with much higher or lower temperatures than the indoor air. Air movement across the surface of a window or door, such as that caused by nearby heating and cooling outlet grilles or by wind outdoors, increases the U-factor.

MOISTURE TRANSPORT

The following examples build on the previous sections by discussing methods that combine heat and moisture transport analysis. The methods include fundamental calculations that can be performed by hand as well as more advanced transient calculations that require computer modeling.

WALL OR ROOF WITH INSULATED SHEATHING

When insulating materials with low water vapor permeability are included in a building assembly, a simple moisture test can provide a satisfactory estimate of condensation resistance. This test assumes that interior surfaces may have little or no resistance to air or vapor flow. The section on Surface Condensation in Chapter 25 describes how to determine the risk of condensation on low-permeability surfaces.

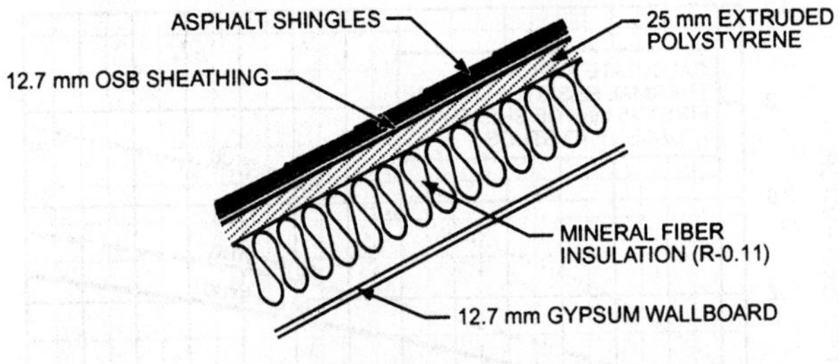

Fig. 11 Roof Assembly Using Foam Insulation

Example 8. For the assembly shown in Figure 11, determine the range of indoor relative humidity for which condensation does not occur on the underside of the insulating sheathing. Assume a design outdoor temperature of −1°C, and indoor temperature of 21°C. Assume that the cavity air is at the same vapor pressure as the indoor air, which can occur with openings through the ceiling. Ignore radiant effects on the roof surface. Assume the rigid insulation is vapor impermeable, and interior materials have little resistance to air or vapor flow.

Air Film or Material	Thermal Resistance, $(m^2 \cdot K)/W$
1. Indoor air film coefficient	0.12
2. Gypsum wallboard	0.08
3. Mineral fiber insulation	3.34
4. 25 mm extruded polystyrene	1.23
5. OSB sheathing, 13 mm	0.12
6. Asphalt shingles	0.06
7. Exterior air film coefficient	0.03
Total R-value	4.98

Solution: The temperature difference is 22 K. The sum of the R-values from the foam/mineral fiber interface inward is 3.54 $(m^2 \cdot K)/W$. The sum of the R-values from that interface outward is 1.44 $(m^2 \cdot K)/W$. The temperature difference ratio [Equation (14), Chapter 25] is 1.44/4.98, or 0.29. The interface temperature is 5.4°C. The saturation vapor pressure of indoor air is 2476 Pa, and the saturation vapor pressure at the interface is 894 Pa (see Chapter 1). The upper bound for indoor relative humidity is therefore 894/2476, or 36% rh.

Many factors influence the likelihood (or not) of damage in an assembly such as this with exterior rigid insulation. Solar effects generally ensure a period of high temperatures that allows drying. On the other hand, cold sky temperatures may increase heat loss from the assembly, which lowers the surface temperature below ambient. Even when indoor humidity is high enough that condensation at the interface is indicated, the rate of water formation may be slowed by airtightness at the ceiling and by vapor diffusion protection.

VAPOR PRESSURE PROFILE (GLASER OR DEW-POINT) ANALYSIS

The common steady-state one-dimension tool for evaluating moisture accumulation and drying within exterior envelopes (walls, roofs, and ceilings) is the dew-point or Glaser method. Users should recognize its limitations, which include the following:

- Strictly speaking, condensation is a phase change from vapor to liquid. Water that is attached to the surfaces of building materials is adsorbed or absorbed water, not liquid water. Increase in the moisture content of porous and hygroscopic building materials is properly called sorption, not condensation. Dew-point method results have often been interpreted to indicate condensation, when, in fact, increases in moisture content were through sorption, not condensation.

- Heat and moisture storage effects are not included in dew-point analysis. Experience shows storage effects to play a significant role in heat and moisture performance of assemblies.
- Diffusion is the only moisture transport mechanism considered. Airflow, capillary transport, rain wetting, initial conditions, latent effects, solar effects, and ventilation cannot be included in the method, and they may have a dominant effect on building assembly performance.
- The dew-point method allows calculation of a rate of moisture accumulation or rate of drying from a critical location within the assembly. However, the method has not shown how to estimate damage associated with any rate of accumulation or drying.

Chapter 25 discusses the Glaser method and its limitations in more detail.

ASHRAE does not recommend the dew-point method as the sole basis for hygrothermal design of building envelope assemblies. ASHRAE *Standard* 160P is being developed to assist in hygrothermal analysis for design purposes. The dew-point method is presented here for reasons of historical continuity, and because it serves as an illustration of the fundamental principles of conduction in heat transport and diffusion in moisture transport.

Winter Wall Wetting Examples

Example 9. For a wood-framed wall, assume monthly mean conditions of 21°C, 40% rh indoors and –6.6°C, 50% rh outdoors. Indoor and outdoor vapor pressures are 995 and 175 Pa, respectively.

Solution:

Step 1. List the components in the building assembly, with their R-values and permeances.

Air Film or Material	Thermal Resistance, (m²·K)/W	Proportional Temperature Drop	Vapor Permeance, ng/(Pa·s·m²)	Vapor Diffusion Resistance, (Pa·s·m²)/ng	Proportional Vapor Pressure Drop
1. Surface film coefficient	0.12	0.050	9200	0.00011	0.003
2. Gypsum board, painted, cracked joints	0.08	0.033	290	0.00345	0.088
3. Insulation, mineral fiber	1.90	0.785	1700	0.00059	0.015
4. OSB sheathing	0.1	0.045	29	0.00050	0.881
5. Wood siding	0.18	0.074	2010	0.00002	0.013
6. Surface film coefficient	0.03	0.012	57 000	0.04	0.000
Totals	2.21	1.000		0.0447	1.000

Step 2. List the indoor and outdoor temperature and relative humidity. Vapor pressure at indoor and outdoor locations is determined by multiplying the saturation vapor pressure at that temperature by the relative humidity.

Boundary or Interface Between Materials	Temperature, °C	Saturation Vapor Pressure, Pa	Relative Humidity, %	Initial Vapor Pressure, Pa	Corrected Vapor Pressure, Pa
Indoor air	21	2488	40	995	995
1-2 interface	19.6	2286		995	760
2-3 interface	18.7	2161		921	756
3-4 interface	–2.9	478		908	478
4-5 interface	–4.2	430		186	477
5-6 interface	–6.3	361		175	184
Outdoor air	–6.6	350	50	175	175
Difference	27.6		Difference	820	

Step 3. Calculate the proportional temperature drop across each layer. The temperature drop is proportional to the R-value:

$$\frac{\Delta t_{layer}}{t_i - t_o} = \frac{R_{layer}}{R_T}$$

The table in step 1 lists the resulting proportional temperature drops. Calculate the proportional water vapor pressure drops across each layer. These are calculated the same way as the proportional temperature drops in step 1:

$$\frac{\Delta p_{layer}}{p_i - p_o} = \frac{Z_{layer}}{Z_T}$$

where

Z_T = total water vapor diffusion resistance of wall (sum of diffusion resistances of all layers), (Pa·s·m²)/ng

p = partial water vapor pressure, Pa

Step 4. Determine the temperature at each interface, using the temperature difference from indoors to outdoors, and the proportional temperature drop. Find the saturation water vapor pressure corresponding to the interface temperatures from step 1. These values can be found in Table 2 in Chapter 1.

Step 5. From step 1, the total water vapor diffusion resistance of the wall without the vapor retarder is

$$Z_{wall} = 1/9200 + 1/290 + 1/1700 + 1/29 + 1/2010 + 1/57\,000$$
$$= 0.04 \text{ (Pa·s·m}^2\text{)/ng}$$

The partial water vapor pressure drop across the whole wall is calculated from the indoor and outdoor saturation water vapor pressures and relative humidities (see the table in step 2).

$$p_{wall} = p_i - p_o = (40/100)2488 - (50/100)350 = 820 \text{ Pa}$$

Step 6. Figure 12 shows the calculated saturation and partial water vapor pressures. Comparison reveals that the calculated partial water vapor pressure on the interior surface of the sheathing is well above saturation. This indicates incipient accumulation of water (condensation or sorption), probably on the surface of the sheathing, not within the insulation. If the accumulation rate is of interest, two additional steps are necessary.

Step 7. The calculated water vapor pressure exceeds the saturation water vapor pressure by the greatest amount at the back side of the sheathing (Figure 12). Therefore, this is the most likely location for accumulation. Under conditions of phase change (condensation or sorption), the water vapor pressure should equal the saturation water vapor pressure at that interface (see the corrected vapor pressure column in step 2 of Example 9).

Step 8. The change of water vapor pressure on the OSB sheathing alters all other partial water vapor pressures as well as water vapor flux through the wall. Calculating partial water vapor pressures is similar to

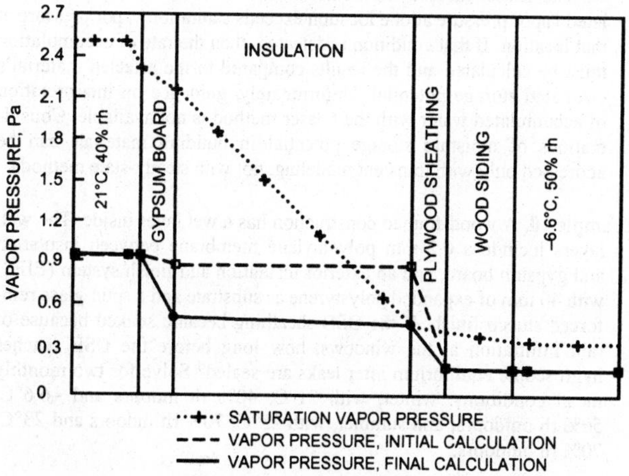

Fig. 12 Dew-Point Calculation in Wood-Framed Wall (Example 9)

the calculation in step 3, but the wall is now divided in two parts: one on the interior of the condensation interface (i.e., gypsum board and insulation) and the other on the exterior (OSB sheathing and wood siding). Water vapor pressure drop over the first (interior) part of the wall is

$$\Delta p_1 = 995 - 478 = 517 \text{ Pa}$$

and over the second (exterior) part is

$$\Delta p_2 = 478 - 175 = 303 \text{ Pa}$$

The diffusion resistances of both parts of the wall are

$$Z_1 = 1/9200 + 1/290 + 1/1700 = 0.004 \text{ (Pa·s·m}^2\text{)/ng}$$

$$Z_2 = 1/29 + 1/2010 + 1/57\,000 = 0.035 \text{ (Pa·s·m}^2\text{)/ng}$$

The water vapor pressure drops across each material can be calculated from the part between the inside and sheathing

$$\frac{\Delta p_{layer}}{p_i - p'_{sheathing}} = \frac{Z_{layer}}{Z_i^{sheathing}}$$

and the part between the sheathing and outside

$$\frac{\Delta p_{layer}}{p'_{sheathing} - p_o} = \frac{Z_{layer}}{Z^o_{sheathing}}$$

	Z_{tot}, (Pa·s·m²)/ng	Vapor Pressure Difference, Pa	Vapor Flow, ng/(s·m²)
Indoor air to critical interface	0.004	517	124 746
Critical interface to outdoor air	0.035	303	8 661
Net accumulation, ng/(s·m²)			116 085

As shown in Figure 12, final calculations of water vapor pressure no longer exceed saturation, which means that the condensation plane was chosen correctly. However, vapor flux is no longer the same throughout the wall. The flux from inside increases; to the outside it decreases. The difference between both is the rate of moisture accumulation by interstitial condensation at the back side of the sheathing:

$$m_c = \frac{p_i - p'_{sheathing}}{Z_i^{sheathing}} - \frac{p'_{sheathing} - p_o}{Z^o_{sheathing}}$$

In this case m_c = 116 000 ng/(s·m²). Assume the 12 mm OSB sheathing (density of 500 kg/m³) begins with moisture content of 10%. The weight of dry OSB at that thickness is 6.5 kg/m², so the mass of water is 0.65 kg. If these conditions persist for 30 days (720 h), then the amount of accumulated water is 0.30 kg. This raises the moisture content of the wood to 12.5%. It is evident that wetting by diffusion is very slow.

The Glaser method should not be used to show simply that calculated vapor pressure at one location exceeds saturation vapor pressure at that location. If that condition is detected, then the rate of accumulation must be calculated and the results compared to the affected material's estimated storage potential. Unfortunately, guidance on interpretation of accumulated water with the Glaser method is not available. Considerations of moisture storage potential in building materials can be addressed only with transient modeling, not with steady-state methods.

Example 10. A wood-framed construction has a wet layer inside. The wall layers include a 0.2 mm polyethylene membrane between insulation and gypsum board, and an exterior insulation and finish system (EIFS) with 40 mm of expanded polystyrene as substrate and a spun-glass reinforced stucco finish. If the OSB sheathing became soaked because of rain infiltration at the windows, how long before the OSB reaches hygroscopic equilibrium after leaks are sealed? Solve for two monthly mean conditions: winter, with 21°C, 40% rh indoors and −6.6°C, 50% rh outdoors; and summer, with 25°C, 70% rh indoors and 23°C, 70% rh outdoors.

Solution:

Step 1. List the components in the building assembly, with their R-values and permeances.

Air Film or Material	Thermal Resistance R, (m²·K)/W	Proportional Temperature Drop	Vapor Permeance, ng/(Pa·s·m²)	Vapor Diffusion Resistance, (Pa·s·m²)/ng	Proportional Vapor Pressure Drop
1. Air film coefficient	0.12	0.038	9200	0.0001	0.000
2. Gypsum board, painted	0.079	0.025	290	0.003	0.001
3. Polyethylene foil	0.0	0.000	0.435	2.299	0.975
4. Insulation, mineral fiber	1.9	0.595	1700	0.001	0.000
5. OSB sheathing	0.055	0.017	29	0.034	0.015
6. EPS	1	0.313	72.5	0.014	0.006
7. EIFS stucco lamina and finish	0.01	0.003	185	0.005	0.002
8. Air film coefficient	0.03	0.009	57 000	0.00002	0.000
Total	3.19	1.000		2.36	1.000

Step 2. List the indoor and outdoor temperature and relative humidity. As in Example 9, indoor and outdoor vapor pressure is determined by multiplying the saturation vapor pressure at that temperature by the relative humidity.

Winter conditions:

	Temperature, °C	Saturated Vapor Pressure, Pa	Relative Humidity, %	Vapor Pressure, Pa
Indoors	21	2488	40	995
1 and 2	20.0	2334		995
2 and 3	19.3	2237		995
3 and 4	19.3	2237		751
4 and 5	2.9	751		**751**
5 and 6	2.4	726		**726**
6 and 7	−6.3	361		330
7 and 8	−6.3	358		176
Outdoors	−6.6	350	50	175
Difference	27.6			

Summer conditions:

	Temperature, °C	Saturated Vapor Pressure, Pa	Relative Humidity, %	Vapor Pressure, Pa
Indoors	25	3169	70	2219
1 and 2	24.9	3155		2219
2 and 3	24.9	3146		2220
3 and 4	24.9	3146		2929
4 and 5	23.7	2929		**2929**
5 and 6	23.7	2923		**2923**
6 and 7	23.0	2815		2237
7 and 8	23.0	2814		1968
Outdoors	23	2811	70	1967
Difference	2.0			

Step 3. Indoor and outdoor vapor pressures are calculated from the given conditions of temperature and relative humidity. The vapor pressure at each side of the OSB sheathing is assigned the value of the saturation vapor pressure at that temperature (see bold values in the summer and winter condition tables).

Step 4. Calculate the total vapor resistance on either side of the critical OSB layer. Between inside and sheathing,

$$\frac{\Delta p_{layer}}{p_i - p'_{sheathing}} = \frac{Z_{layer}}{Z_i^{sheathing}}$$

Between sheathing and outside,

$$\frac{\Delta p_{layer}}{p'_{sheathing} - p_o} = \frac{Z_{layer}}{Z^o_{sheathing}}$$

From the summer and winter condition tables, the diffusion resistances of both parts of the wall are

$$Z_1 = 0.0001 + 0.003 + 2.299 + 0.001 = 2.303\ (\text{Pa}\cdot\text{s}\cdot\text{m}^2)/\text{ng}$$

$$Z_2 = 0.014 + 0.005 + 0.00002 = 0.019\ (\text{Pa}\cdot\text{s}\cdot\text{m}^2)/\text{ng}$$

Step 5. Calculate the vapor pressure difference on either side of the critical OSB layer (the last column in the summer and winter condition tables). From the vapor resistance on each side and the vapor pressure difference on each side, vapor flow in each direction can be calculated.

Winter

$$m_{sheathing,i} = \frac{p_i - p'_{sheathing}}{Z^i_{sheathing}} = 106\ \text{ng/(s}\cdot\text{m}^2)$$

$$m_{sheathing,o} = \frac{p'_{sheathing} - p_o}{Z^{sheathing}_o} = 28\ 659\ \text{ng/(s}\cdot\text{m}^2)$$

	Z_{tot}, (Pa·s·m²)/ng	Vapor Pressure Difference, Pa	Vapor Flow, ng/(s·m²)
Indoor air to critical interface	2.303	244.4	106
Critical interface to outdoor air	0.019	550.7	28 659
		Net drying, ng/s	28 553
		Net drying, g/m² per month	74

Summer

$$m_{sheathing,i} = \frac{p_i - p'_{sheathing}}{Z^i_{sheathing}} = -309\ \text{ng/(s}\cdot\text{m}^2)$$

$$m_{sheathing,o} = \frac{p'_{sheathing} - p_o}{Z^{sheathing}_o} = 49\ 744\ \text{ng/(s}\cdot\text{m}^2)$$

	Z_{tot}, (Pa·s·m²)/ng	Vapor Pressure Difference, Pa	Vapor Flow, ng/(s·m²)
Indoor air to critical interface	2.303	−710.8	−309
Critical interface to outdoor air	0.019	955.9	49 744
		Net drying, ng/s	50 052
		Net drying, g/m² per month	129.7

Drying consequently amounts to 74 g/m² per month in winter and 130 g/m² per month in summer. OSB soaked with water can have excess moisture content of up to 4.8 kg/m². Drying only by one-dimensional diffusion would appear to take several years at this rate. Radiation, air movement, and two- and three-dimensional effects can change the rate of drying.

Figures 13 and 14 show the calculated water vapor pressure in winter and summer. The OSB is at water vapor saturation pressure; saturation is not reached at any other interface.

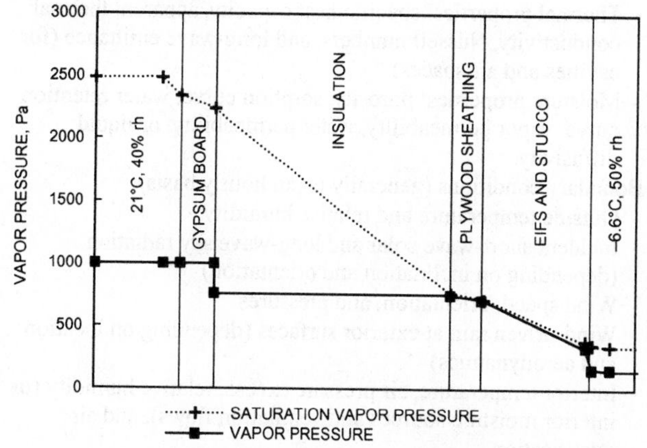

Fig. 13 Drying Wet Sheathing, Winter (Example 10)

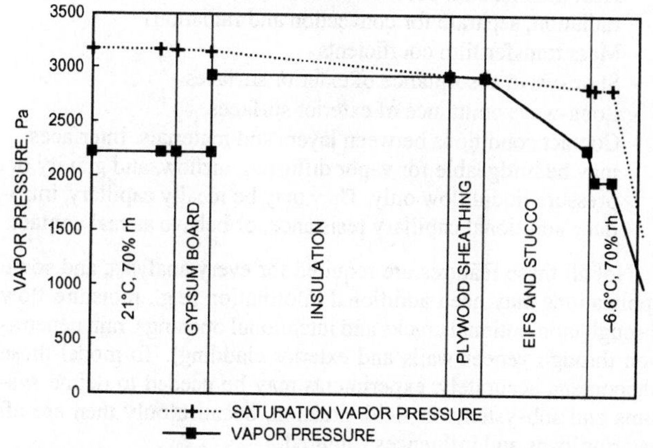

Fig. 14 Drying Wet Sheathing, Summer (Example 10)

TRANSIENT HYGROTHERMAL MODELING

Fundamentals of hygrothermal modeling tools, including modeling criteria and method of reporting, are discussed in Chapter 25. Although this chapter does not provide a complete example, it introduces input data commonly required by these programs and discusses considerations for analyzing output when using these tools.

For many applications and for design guide development, actual behavior of an assembly under transient climatic conditions may be simulated to account for short-term processes such as driving rain absorption, summer condensation, and phase changes. Computer simulations allow designers to model these conditions over time. It is important, however, to understand the model's application limits.

Applying one of these models requires at least the following information: exterior climate conditions, indoor temperature and humidity, and building assembly materials and sizes. Many programs include a material property database and exterior climate and indoor condition data, allowing simple modeling to be performed without customization. However, using generic material property and weather data may not accurately recreate actual target conditions.

Features of a complete moisture analysis model include

- Transient heat, air, and moisture transport formulation, incorporating the physics of
  - Airflow
  - Water vapor transport by advection (combination of water vapor diffusion and air-driven vapor flow)
  - Liquid transport by capillary action, gravity, and pressure differences
  - Heat flow by apparent conduction, convection, and radiation
  - Heat and moisture storage/capacity of materials
  - Condensation and evaporation processes with linked latent-to-sensible heat transformation
  - Freezing and thawing processes with linked latent-to-sensible heat transformation and based on laws of conservation of heat, mass, and momentum
- Material properties as functions of moisture content, relative humidity, and temperature, such as
  - Density
  - Air properties: permeability and permeance

  - Thermal properties: specific heat capacity, apparent thermal conductivity, Nusselt numbers, and long-wave emittance (for cavities and air spaces)
  - Moisture properties: porosity, sorption curve, water retention curve, vapor permeability, water permeability, or liquid diffusivity
- Boundary conditions (generally on an hourly basis)
  - Outside temperature and relative humidity
  - Incident short-wave solar and long-wave sky radiation (depending on inclination and orientation)
  - Wind speed, orientation, and pressures
  - Wind-driven rain at exterior surfaces (depending on location and aerodynamics)
  - Interior temperature, air pressure excess, relative humidity (or interior moisture sources and ventilation flows), and air stratification
  - Surface conditions
  - Heat transfer film coefficients (combined convection and radiation, separate for convection and radiation)
  - Mass transfer film coefficients
  - Short-wave absorptance of exterior surfaces
  - Long-wave emittance of exterior surfaces
  - Contact conditions between layers and materials. Interfaces may be bridgeable for vapor diffusion, airflow, and gravity or pressure liquid flow only. They may be ideally capillary, introduce additional capillary resistance, or behave as real contact.

Not all these features are required for every analysis, and some applications may need additional information (e.g., moisture flow through unintentional cracks and intentional openings, rain penetration through veneer walls and exterior cladding). To model these phenomena accurately, experiments may be needed to define systems and subsystems in field situation, because only then are all exterior loads and influences captured.

It is important to recognize that simulation results are based on input data. Therefore, the more accurate the input data used, the closer the results will match real-world conditions. Exterior weather conditions, material properties, and interior operating conditions all vary widely, so it is important to get the best data available on materials being modeled. For most users, this is a difficult task. Many product manufacturers do not provide the material property data needed for the simulations. Developing weather data for a particular site is also beyond the expertise of many.

Combined hear, air, and moisture models also have limitations. Users should be aware which transport phenomena and types of boundary conditions are included and which are not. For instance, some models cannot handle air transport or rain wetting of the exterior. Even an apparently simple problem, such as predicting rain leakage through a brick veneer, is beyond existing tools' capabilities. In such cases, simple qualitative schemes and field tests still are the way to proceed. In addition, results also tend to be very sensitive to the choice of indoor and outdoor conditions. Usually, exact conditions are not known.

Outputs from these programs typically include the moisture content of materials as well as relative humidity within the assembly. Interpretation of results is not easy: accurate data on moisture and temperature conditions that materials can tolerate are often not available. Although moisture accumulation may result in indoor air quality issues or material degradation, the effect of moisture accumulation in building assemblies depends on many factors, including choice of construction materials, and varies by building, making interpretation of results even more difficult.

AIR MOVEMENT

Research has demonstrated that air movement is more effective than water vapor diffusion for transporting water vapor within building envelopes. To minimize moisture penetration by air leakages, the building envelope should be as airtight as possible. The airflow retarder must also be sufficiently strong and well supported to resist wind loads.

In older residential buildings, air leakage provided sufficient ventilation and rarely led to interstitial condensation. However, in airtight buildings, mechanical ventilation is needed to ensure acceptable air quality and prevent moisture and health problems caused by excessive indoor humidity. Ventilation or drainage must go to the outside of the airtight layer of construction, or it will increase building air leakage. To avoid condensation on the airtight layer, either the layer temperature must be kept above the dew point by locating it on the warm side of the insulation, or the layer permeance must allow vapor transmission.

As described in detail in the section on Leakage Distribution in Chapter 16, air leakage through building envelopes is not confined to doors and windows. Although 6 to 22% of air leakage occurs there, 18 to 50% typically takes place through walls, and 3 to 30% through the ceiling. Leakage often occurs between sill plate and foundation, through interior walls, electrical outlets, plumbing penetrations, and cracks at top and bottom of exterior walls.

Not all cracks and openings can be sealed in existing buildings, nor can absolutely tight construction be achieved in new buildings. Provide as tight an enclosure as possible to reduce leakage, minimize potential condensation within the envelope, and reduce energy loss.

Moisture accumulation in building envelopes can also be minimized by controlling the dominant direction of airflow by operating the building at a small negative or positive air pressure, depending on climate. In cooling climates, pressure should be positive to keep out humid outside air. In heating climates, pressure should be neither strongly negative, which could risk drawing soil gas or combustion products indoors, nor strongly positive, which could risk driving moisture into building envelope cavities.

Equivalent Permeance

Dew-point analysis allows simple estimation of the effect of wall and roof cavity ventilation on heat and vapor transport by using parallel thermal and vapor diffusion resistances (TenWolde and Carll 1992; Trethowen 1979). These parallel resistances account for heat and vapor that bypass exterior material layers with ventilation air from outside. Equivalent thermal and water vapor diffusion resistances are approximated from the following equations:

$$R_{par} = \frac{1}{m_a c}$$

$$Z_{par} = \frac{1}{m_a \xi}$$

where

R_{par} = parallel equivalent thermal resistance, $(m^2 \cdot K)/W$
Z_{par} = parallel equivalent water vapor diffusion vapor flow resistance, $(Pa \cdot s \cdot m^2)/kg$
m_a = ventilation flux, $kg/(m^2 \cdot s)$
ξ = $0.62/P_a$, where P_a is atmospheric pressure, Pa
c = 6.13 J/(kg·K)

REFERENCES

ASHRAE. 2006. Design criteria for moisture control in buildings. *Draft Standard* 160P.

ASHRAE. 2007. Energy standard for buildings except low-rise residential buildings. ANSI/ASHRAE/IESNA *Standard* 90.1-2007.

Barbour, E., J. Goodrow, J. Kosny, and J.E. Christian. 1994. *Thermal performance of steel-framed walls.* Prepared for American Iron and Steel Institute by NAHB Research Center.

Dill, R.S., W.C. Robinson, and H.E. Robinson. 1945. Measurements of heat losses from slab floors. National Bureau of Standards. *Building Materials and Structures Report* BMS 103.

Farouk, B. and D.C. Larson. 1983. Thermal performance of insulated wall systems with metal studs. *Proceedings of the 18th Intersociety Energy Conversion Engineering Conference*, Orlando, FL.

Hougten, F.C., S.I. Taimuty, C. Gutberlet, and C.J. Brown. 1942. Heat loss through basement walls and floors. *ASHVE Transactions* 48:369.

Kosny, J. and J.E. Christian. 1995. Reducing the uncertainties associated with using the ASHRAE zone method for R-value calculations of metal frame walls. *ASHRAE Transactions* 101(2):779-788.

Labs, K., J. Carmody, R. Sterling, L. Shen, Y.J. Huang, and D. Parker. 1988. Building foundation design handbook. *Report* ORNL/SUB/86-72143/1. Oak Ridge National Laboratory, Oak Ridge, TN.

Latta, J.K. and G.G. Boileau. 1969. Heat losses from house basements. *Canadian Building* 19(10).

McGowan, A. and A.O. Desjarlais. 1997. An investigation of common thermal bridges in walls. *ASHRAE Transactions* 103(1):509-517.

McIntyre, D.A. 1984. *The increase in U-value of a wall caused by mortar joints*. ECRC/M1843. The Electricity Council Research Centre, Copenhurst, U.K.

Mitalas, G.P. 1982. *Basement heat loss studies at DBR/NRC*. NRCC 20416. Division of Building Research, National Research Council of Canada, September.

Mitalas, G.P. 1983. Calculation of basement heat loss. *ASHRAE Transactions* 89(1B):420.

Shipp, P.H. 1983. Basement, crawlspace and slab-on-grade thermal performance. *Proceedings of the ASHRAE/DOE Conference, Thermal Performance of the Exterior Envelopes of Buildings II*, ASHRAE SP 38:160-179.

Shu, L.S., A.E. Fiorato, and J.W. Howanski. 1979. Heat transmission coefficients of concrete block walls with core insulation. *Proceedings of the ASHRAE/DOE-ORNL Conference, Thermal Performance of the Exterior Envelopes of Buildings*, ASHRAE SP 28:421-435.

TenWolde A. and C. Carll. 1992. Effect of cavity ventilation on moisture in walls and roofs. *Proceedings of ASHRAE Conference, Thermal Performance of the Exterior Envelopes of Buildings V*, pp. 555-562.

Trethowen, H.A. 1979. The Kieper method for building moisture design. BRANZ *Reprint* 12, Building Research Association of New Zealand.

Tye, R.P. and S.C. Spinney. 1980. A study of various factors affecting the thermal performance of perlite insulated masonry construction. Dynatech *Report* PII-2. Holometrix, Inc. (formerly Dynatech R/D Company), Cambridge, MA.

Valore, R.C. 1980. Calculation of U-values of hollow concrete masonry. American Concrete Institute, *Concrete International* 2(2):40-62.

Valore, R.C. 1988. *Thermophysical properties of masonry and its constituents*, parts I and II. International Masonry Institute, Washington, D.C.

Van Geem, M.G. 1985. Thermal transmittance of concrete block walls with core insulation. *ASHRAE Transactions* 91(2).

Wilkes, K.E. 1991. Thermal model of attic systems with radiant barriers. *Report* ORNL/CON-262. Oak Ridge National Laboratory, TN.

BIBLIOGRAPHY

Hens, H. 1978. Condensation in concrete flat roofs. *Building Research and Practice* Sept./Oct.:292-309.

TenWolde, A. 1994. Design tools. Chapter 11 in *Moisture control in buildings*. ASTM *Manual* MNL 18. American Society for Testing and Materials, West Conshohocken, PA.

Vos, B.H. and E.J.W. Coelman. 1967. Condensation in structures. *Report* B-67-33/23, TNO-IBBC, Rijswijk, the Netherlands.

CHAPTER 28

COMBUSTION AND FUELS

PRINCIPLES OF COMBUSTION

COMBUSTION is a chemical reaction in which an oxidant reacts rapidly with a fuel to liberate stored energy as thermal energy, generally in the form of high-temperature gases. Small amounts of electromagnetic energy (light), electric energy (free ions and electrons), and mechanical energy (noise) are also produced during combustion. Except in special applications, the oxidant for combustion is oxygen in the air. The oxidation normally occurs with the fuel in vapor form. One notable exception is oxidation of solid carbon, which occurs directly with the solid phase.

Conventional fuels contain primarily hydrogen and carbon, in elemental form or in various compounds (hydrocarbons). Their complete combustion produces mainly carbon dioxide (CO_2) and water (H_2O); however, small quantities of carbon monoxide (CO) and partially reacted flue gas constituents (gases and liquid or solid aerosols) may form. Most conventional fuels also contain small amounts of sulfur, which is oxidized to sulfur dioxide (SO_2) or sulfur trioxide (SO_3) during combustion, and noncombustible substances such as mineral matter (ash), water, and inert gases. Flue gas is the product of complete or incomplete combustion and includes excess air (if present), but not dilution air (air added to flue gas downstream of the combustion process, such as through the relief opening of a draft hood).

Fuel combustion rate depends on the (1) rate of chemical reaction of combustible fuel constituents with oxygen, (2) rate at which oxygen is supplied to the fuel (mixing of air and fuel), and (3) temperature in the combustion region. The reaction rate is fixed by fuel selection. Increasing the mixing rate or temperature increases the combustion rate.

With **complete combustion** of hydrocarbon fuels, all hydrogen and carbon in the fuel are oxidized to H_2O and CO_2. Generally, complete combustion requires excess oxygen or excess air beyond the amount theoretically required to oxidize the fuel. Excess air is usually expressed as a percentage of the air required to completely oxidize the fuel.

In **stoichiometric combustion** of a hydrocarbon fuel, fuel is reacted with the exact amount of oxygen required to oxidize all carbon, hydrogen, and sulfur in the fuel to CO_2, H_2O, and SO_2. Therefore, exhaust gas from stoichiometric combustion theoretically contains no incompletely oxidized fuel constituents and no unreacted oxygen (i.e., no carbon monoxide and no excess air or oxygen). The percentage of CO_2 contained in products of stoichiometric combustion is the maximum attainable and is referred to as the **stoichiometric** CO_2, **ultimate** CO_2, or **maximum theoretical percentage of** CO_2.

Stoichiometric combustion is seldom realized in practice because of imperfect mixing and finite reaction rates. For economy and safety, most combustion equipment should operate with some excess air. This ensures that fuel is not wasted and that combustion is complete despite variations in fuel properties and supply rates of fuel and air. The amount of excess air to be supplied to any combustion equipment depends on (1) expected variations in fuel properties and in fuel and air supply rates, (2) equipment application, (3) degree of operator supervision required or available, and (4) control requirements. For maximum efficiency, combustion at low excess air is desirable.

Incomplete combustion occurs when a fuel element is not completely oxidized during combustion. For example, a hydrocarbon may not completely oxidize to carbon dioxide and water, but may form partially oxidized compounds, such as carbon monoxide, aldehydes, and ketones. Conditions that promote incomplete combustion include (1) insufficient air and fuel mixing (causing local fuel-rich and fuel-lean zones), (2) insufficient air supply to the flame (providing less than the required amount of oxygen), (3) insufficient reactant residence time in the flame (preventing completion of combustion reactions), (4) flame impingement on a cold surface (quenching combustion reactions), or (5) flame temperature that is too low (slowing combustion reactions).

Incomplete combustion uses fuel inefficiently, can be hazardous because of carbon monoxide production, and contributes to air pollution.

Combustion Reactions

The reaction of oxygen with combustible elements and compounds in fuels occurs according to fixed chemical principles, including

- Chemical reaction equations
- Law of matter conservation: the mass of each element in the reaction products must equal the mass of that element in the reactants
- Law of combining masses: chemical compounds are formed by elements combining in fixed mass relationships
- Chemical reaction rates

Oxygen for combustion is normally obtained from air, which is a mixture of nitrogen, oxygen, small amounts of water vapor, carbon dioxide, and inert gases. For practical combustion calculations, dry air consists of 20.95% oxygen and 79.05% inert gases (nitrogen, argon, etc.) by volume, or 23.15% oxygen and 76.85% inert gases by mass. For calculation purposes, nitrogen is assumed to pass through the combustion process unchanged (although small quantities of nitrogen oxides form). Table 1 lists oxygen and air requirements for stoichiometric combustion and the products of stoichiometric combustion of some pure combustible materials (or constituents) found in common fuels.

Flammability Limits

Fuel burns in a self-sustained reaction only when the volume percentages of fuel and air in a mixture at standard temperature and pressure are within the upper and lower flammability limits (UFL and LFL), also called explosive limits (UEL and LEL; see Table 2). Both temperature and pressure affect these limits. As mixture temperature increases, the upper limit increases and the lower limit decreases. As the pressure of the mixture decreases below atmospheric

The preparation of this chapter is assigned to TC 6.10, Fuels and Combustion.

Table 1 Combustion Reactions of Common Fuel Constituents

Constituent	Molecular Formula	Combustion Reactions	Stoichiometric Oxygen and Air Requirements, kg/kg Fuel[a] O_2	kg/kg Fuel[a] Air	m³/m³ Fuel O_2	m³/m³ Fuel Air	Flue Gas from Stoichiometric Combustion with Air: Ultimate CO_2, %	Dew Point,[c] °C	m³/m³ Fuel CO_2	m³/m³ Fuel H_2O	kg/kg Fuel CO_2	kg/kg Fuel H_2O
Carbon (to CO)	C	$C + 0.5O_2 \rightarrow CO$	1.33	5.75	b	b	—	—	—	—	—	—
Carbon (to CO_2)	C	$C + O_2 \rightarrow CO_2$	2.66	11.51	b	b	29.30	—	—	—	3.664	—
Carbon monoxide	CO	$CO + 0.5O_2 \rightarrow CO_2$	0.57	2.47	0.50	2.39	34.70	—	1.0	—	1.571	—
Hydrogen	H_2	$H_2 + 0.5O_2 \rightarrow H_2O$	7.94	34.28	0.50	2.39	—	72	—	1.0	—	8.937
Methane	CH_4	$CH_4 + 2O_2 \rightarrow CO_2 + 2H_2O$	3.99	17.24	2.00	9.57	11.73	59	1.0	2.0	2.744	2.246
Ethane	C_2H_6	$C_2H_6 + 3.5O_2 \rightarrow 2CO_2 + 3H_2O$	3.72	16.09	3.50	16.75	13.18	57	2.0	3.0	2.927	1.798
Propane	C_3H_8	$C_3H_8 + 5O_2 \rightarrow 3CO_2 + 4H_2O$	3.63	15.68	5.00	23.95	13.75	55	3.0	4.0	2.994	1.634
Butane	C_4H_{10}	$C_4H_{10} + 6.5O_2 \rightarrow 4CO_2 + 5H_2O$	3.58	15.47	6.50	31.14	14.05	54	4.0	5.0	3.029	1.550
Alkanes	C_nH_{2n+2}	$C_nH_{2n+2} + (1.5n + 0.5)O_2 \rightarrow nCO_2 + (n + 1)H_2O$	—	—	$1.5n + 0.5$	$7.18n + 2.39$	—	53	n	$n + 1$	$\frac{44.01n}{14.026n + 2.016}$	$\frac{18.01(n + 1)}{14.026n + 2.016}$
Ethylene	C_2H_4	$C_2H_4 + 3O_2 \rightarrow 2CO_2 + 2H_2O$	3.42	14.78	3.00	14.38	15.05	52	2.0	2.0	3.138	1.285
Propylene	C_3H_6	$C_3H_6 + 4.5O_2 \rightarrow 3CO_2 + 3H_2O$	3.42	14.78	4.50	21.53	15.05	52	3.0	3.0	3.138	1.285
Alkenes	C_nH_{2n}	$C_nH_{2n} + 1.5nO_2 \rightarrow nCO_2 + nH_2O$	3.42	14.78	$1.50n$	$7.18n$	15.05	52	n	n	3.138	1.285
Acetylene	C_2H_2	$C_2H_2 + 2.5O_2 \rightarrow 2CO_2 + H_2O$	3.07	13.27	2.50	11.96	17.53	39	2.0	1.0	3.834	0.692
Alkynes	C_nH_{2m}	$C_nH_{2m} + (n + 0.5m)O_2 \rightarrow nCO_2 + mH_2O$	—	—	$n + 0.5m$	$4.78n + 2.39m$	—	—	n	m	$\frac{22.005n}{6.005n + 1.008m}$	$\frac{9.008m}{6.005n + 1.008m}$
									SO_x	H_2O	SO_x	H_2O
Sulfur (to SO_2)	S	$S + O_2 \rightarrow SO_2$	1.00	4.31	b	b	—	—	$1.0SO_2$	—	1.998 (SO_2)	—
Sulfur (to SO_3)	S	$S + 1.5O_2 \rightarrow SO_3$	1.50	6.47	b	b	—	—	$1.0SO_3$	—	2.497 (SO_3)	—
Hydrogen sulfide	H_2S	$H_2S + 1.5O_2 \rightarrow SO_2 + H_2O$	1.41	6.08	1.50	7.18	—	52	$1.0SO_2$	1.0	1.880 (SO_2)	0.528

Adapted, in part, from *Gas Engineers Handbook* (1965).
[a]Atomic masses: H = 1.008, C = 12.01, O = 16.00, S = 32.06.
[b]Volume ratios are not given for fuels that do not exist in vapor form at reasonable temperatures or pressure.
[c]Dew point is determined from Figure 2.

Table 2 Flammability Limits and Ignition Temperatures of Common Fuels in Fuel/Air Mixtures

Substance	Molecular Formula	Lower Flammability Limit, %	Upper Flammability Limit, %	Ignition Temperature, °C	References
Carbon	C	—		660	Hartman (1958)
Carbon monoxide	CO	12.5	74	609	Scott et al. (1948)
Hydrogen	H_2	4.0	75.0	520	Zabetakis (1956)
Methane	CH_4	5.0	15.0	705	*Gas Engineers Handbook* (1965)
Ethane	C_2H_6	3.0	12.5	520 to 630	Trinks (1947)
Propane	C_3H_8	2.1	10.1	466	NFPA (1962)
n-Butane	C_4H_{10}	1.86	8.41	405	NFPA (1962)
Ethylene	C_2H_4	2.75	28.6	490	Scott et al. (1948)
Propylene	C_3H_6	2.00	11.1	450	Scott et al. (1948)
Acetylene	C_2H_2	2.50	81	406 to 440	Trinks (1947)
Sulfur	S	—		190	Hartman (1958)
Hydrogen sulfide	H_2S	4.3	45.50	292	Scott et al. (1948)

Flammability limits adapted from Coward and Jones (1952). All values corrected to 16°C, 104 kPa, dry.

pressure, the upper limit decreases and the lower limit increases. However, as pressure increases above atmospheric, the upper limit increases and the lower limit is relatively constant.

Ignition Temperature

Ignition temperature is the lowest temperature at which heat is generated by combustion faster than it is lost to the surroundings and combustion becomes self-propagating. (See Table 2). The fuel/air mixture will not burn freely and continuously below the ignition temperature unless heat is supplied, but chemical reaction between the fuel and air may occur. Ignition temperature is affected by a large number of factors.

The ignition temperature and flammability limits of a fuel/air mixture, together, are a measure of the potential for ignition (*Gas Engineers Handbook* 1965).

Combustion Modes

Combustion reactions occur in either continuous or pulse flame modes. **Continuous combustion** burns fuel in a sustained manner as long as fuel and air are continuously fed to the combustion zone and the fuel/air mixture is within the flammability limits. Continuous combustion is more common than pulse combustion and is used in most fuel-burning equipment.

Pulse combustion is an acoustically resonant process that burns various fuels in small, discrete fuel/air mixture volumes in a very rapid series of combustions.

The introduction of fuel and air into the pulse combustor is controlled by mechanical or aerodynamic valves. Typical combustors consist of one or more valves, a combustion chamber, an exit pipe, and a control system (ignition means, fuel-metering devices, etc.). Typically, combustors for warm-air furnaces, hot-water boilers, and commercial cooking equipment use mechanical valves. Aerodynamic valves are usually used in higher-pressure applications, such as thrust engines. Separate valves for air and fuel, a single valve for premixed air and fuel, or multiple valves of either type can be used. Premix valve systems may require a flame trap at the combustion chamber entrance to prevent flashback.

In a mechanically valved pulse combustor, air and fuel are forced into the combustion chamber through the valves under pressures less than 3.5 kPa. An ignition source, such as a spark, ignites the fuel/ air mixture, causing a positive pressure build-up in the combustion chamber. The positive pressure causes the valves to close, leaving only the exit pipe of the combustion chamber as a pressure relief opening. Combustion chamber and exit pipe geometry determine the resonant frequency of the combustor.

The pressure wave from initial combustion travels down the exit pipe at sonic velocity. As this wave exits the combustion chamber, most of the flue gases present in the chamber are carried with it into the exit pipe. Flue gases remaining in the combustion chamber begin to cool immediately. Contraction of cooling gases and momentum of gases in the exit pipe create a vacuum inside the chamber that opens the valves and allows more fuel and air into the chamber. While the fresh charge of fuel/air enters the chamber, the pressure wave reaches the end of the exit pipe and is partially reflected from the open end of the pipe. The fresh fuel/air charge is ignited by residual combustion and/or heat. The resulting combustion starts another cycle.

Typical pulse combustors operate at 30 to 100 cycles per second and emit resonant sound, which must be considered in their application. The pulses produce high convective heat transfer rates.

Heating Value

Combustion produces thermal energy (heat). The quantity of heat generated by complete combustion of a unit of specific fuel is constant and is called the **heating value**, **heat of combustion**, or **caloric value** of that fuel. A fuel's heating value can be determined by measuring the heat evolved during combustion of a known quantity of the fuel in a calorimeter, or it can be estimated from quantitative chemical analysis of the fuel and the heating values of the various chemical elements in the fuel. For information on calculating heating values, see the sections on Characteristics of Fuel Oils and Characteristics of Coal.

Higher heating value (HHV), **gross heating value**, or **total heating value** includes the latent heat of vaporization and is determined when water vapor in the fuel combustion products is cooled and condensed at standard temperature and pressure. Conversely, **lower heating value (LHV)** or **net heating value** does *not* include latent heat of vaporization. In the United States, when the heating value of a fuel is specified without designating higher or lower, it generally means the higher heating value. (LHV is mainly used for internal combustion engine fuels.)

Heating values are usually expressed in kJ/L or MJ/m^3 for gaseous fuels, MJ/L for liquid fuels, and MJ/kg for solid fuels. Heating values are always given in relation to standard temperature and pressure, usually 16, 20, or 25°C and 101.325 kPa, depending on the particular industry practice. Heating values in the United States and Canada are based on standard conditions of 15°C and 101.4 kPa (760 mm Hg), dry. Heating values of several substances in common fuels are listed in Table 3.

With incomplete combustion, not all fuel is completely oxidized, and the heat produced is less than the heating value of the fuel. Therefore, the quantity of heat produced per unit of fuel consumed decreases (lower combustion efficiency).

Not all heat produced during combustion can be used effectively. The greatest heat loss is the thermal energy of the increased temperature of hot exhaust gases above the temperature of incoming air and fuel. Other heat losses include radiation and convection heat transfer from the outer walls of combustion equipment to the environment.

Altitude Compensation

Air at altitudes above sea level is less dense and has less mass of oxygen per unit volume. The volume concentration of oxygen, however, remains the same as sea level. Therefore, combustion at altitudes above sea level has less available oxygen to burn with the fuel unless compensation is made for the altitude. Combustion occurs, but the amount of excess air is reduced. If excess air is reduced enough by an increase in altitude, combustion is incomplete or ceases.

Table 3 Heating Values of Substances Occurring in Common Fuels

Substance	Molecular Formula	Higher Heating Values,[a] MJ/m^3	Higher Heating Values,[a] MJ/kg	Lower Heating Values,[a] MJ/kg	Specific Density,[b] kg/m^3
Carbon (to CO)	C	—	9.188	9.188	—
Carbon (to CO_2)	C	—	32.780	32.780	—
Carbon monoxide	CO	12.0	10.111	10.111	1.187
Hydrogen	H_2	12.1	142.107	120.075	0.085
Methane	CH_4	37.7	55.533	49.997	0.679
Ethane	C_2H_6	66.1	51.923	47.492	1.28
Propane	C_3H_8	94.0	50.402	46.373	1.92
Butane	C_4H_{10}	128.9	49.593	45.771	2.53
Ethylene	C_2H_4	59.8[c]	50.325	47.160	—
Propylene	C_3H_6	87.2[c]	48.958	45.792	1.78
Acetylene	C_2H_2	55.0	50.014	48.309	1.120
Sulfur (to SO_2)	S	—	9.257	9.257	—
Sulfur (to SO_3)	S	—	13.816	13.816	—
Hydrogen sulfide	H_2S	24.1	16.508	15.205	1.456

Adapted from *Gas Engineers Handbook* (1965).
[a]All values corrected to 16°C, 101.4 kPa, dry. For gases saturated with water vapor at 16°C, deduct 1.74% of value to adjust for gas volume displaced by water vapor.
[b]At 0°C and 101.3 kPa.
[c]*North American Combustion Handbook* (1986).

When gas-fired appliances operate at altitudes substantially above sea level, three notable effects occur (see Chapter 30 of the 2008 *ASHRAE Handbook—HVAC Systems and Equipment*):

- Oxygen available for combustion is reduced in proportion to the atmospheric pressure reduction.
- With gaseous fuels, the heat of combustion per unit volume of fuel gas (gas heat content) is reduced because of reduced fuel gas density in proportion to the atmospheric pressure reduction.
- Reduced air density affects the performance and operating temperature of heat exchangers and appliance cooling mechanisms.

Altitude compensation matches fuel and air supply rates to attain complete combustion without too much excess air or too much fuel. This can be done at increased altitude by increasing the air supply rate to the combustion zone with a combustion air blower, or by decreasing the fuel supply rate to the combustion zone by decreasing the fuel input (derating).

Power burners use combustion air blowers and can increase the air supply rate to compensate for altitude. The combustion zone can be pressurized to attain the same air density in the combustion chamber as that at sea level.

Derating can be used as an alternative to power combustion. U.S. fuel gas codes generally do not require derating of nonpower burners at altitudes up to 600 m. At altitudes above 600 m, many fuel gas codes require that burners be derated 4% for each 300 m above sea level (NFPA/AGA *National Fuel Gas Code*). Chimney or vent operation also must be considered at high altitudes (see Chapter 34 of the 2008 *ASHRAE Handbook—HVAC Systems and Equipment*).

ASHRAE research project RP-1182 (Fleck et al. 2007) concluded that the tested fan-assisted furnaces experienced a natural derate of 1.8% in gas input rate per 305 m increase in altitude above sea level. Such a gas input derate for altitude may provide safe combustion operation (less than 400 parts per million of carbon monoxide concentration in air-free flue gas) for fan-assisted residential gas furnaces up to 2040 m altitude. These tests suggest that

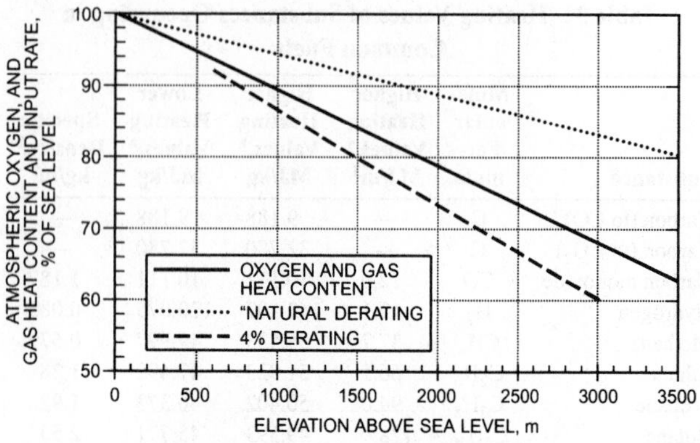

Note: Natural derating applies for fixed injector (orifice) size and pressure.

Fig. 1 Altitude Effects on Gas Combustion Appliances

some furnaces as currently designed and constructed can be installed and operated safely and acceptably at some high altitudes with no modifications to the sea-level gas orifices, gas manifold pressure, etc., as are currently needed for the 4% per 300 m altitude derating requirements. However, the research project did not sufficiently evaluate furnace operation for high-altitude effects on heat exchanger and other component temperatures, endurance, and performance, which should be considered by manufacturers and standards developers. New research is under way to evaluate the effects of high-altitude on gas-fired water heaters and boilers.

In addition to reducing the gas heat content of fuel gas, reduced fuel gas density also causes increased gas velocity through flow metering orifices. The net effect is for gas input rate to decrease naturally with increases in altitude, but at less than the rate at which atmospheric oxygen decreases. This effect is one reason that derating is required when appliances are operated at altitudes significantly above sea level. Early research with draft hood-equipped appliances established that appliance input rates should be reduced at the rate of 4% per 300 m above sea level, for altitudes higher than 600 m above sea level (Figure 1).

Experience with recently developed appliances having fan-assisted combustion systems demonstrated that the 4% rule may not apply in all cases. It is therefore important to consult the manufacturer's listed appliance installation instructions, which are based on how the combustion system operates, and on other factors, such as impaired heat transfer. Note also that manufacturers of appliances having tracking-type burner systems may not require derating at altitudes above 600 m. In those systems, fuel gas and combustion airflow are affected in the same proportion by density reduction.

It is important for appliance specifiers to be aware that the heating capacity of appliances is substantially reduced at altitudes significantly above sea level. To ensure adequate delivery of heat, derating of heating capacity must also be considered and quantified.

By definition, fuel gas HHV value remains constant for all altitudes because (in North America) it is based on standard conditions of 760 mm Hg, dry, and 15°C. Some fuel gas suppliers at high altitudes (e.g., at Denver, Colorado, at 1524 m) may report fuel gas heat content at local barometric pressure instead of standard pressure. This can be calculated using the following equation:

$$HC = HHV \times \frac{B}{P_s} \tag{1}$$

where

HC = local gas heat content at local barometric pressure and standard temperature conditions, MJ/m³

HHV = gas higher heating value at standard temperature and pressure of 15°C and 760 mm Hg, respectively, MJ/m³

B = local barometric pressure, mm Hg (not corrected to sea level: do not use barometric pressure as reported by weather forecasters, because it is corrected to sea level)

P_s = standard pressure = 760 mm Hg

For example, at 1524 m, the barometric pressure is 84.316 kPa. If the HHV of a fuel gas sample is 37.5 MJ/m^3 (at standard temperature and pressure), local gas heat content is 31.21 MJ/m^3 at 84.316 kPa barometric pressure 1524 m above sea level.

$$HC = 37.5 \text{ MJ/m}^3 \times 84.316 \text{ kPa}/101.325 \text{ kPa} = 31.21 \text{ MJ/m}^3$$

Therefore, local gas heat content of a sample of fuel gas can be expressed as 31.21 MJ/m^3 at local barometric pressure of 84.316 kPa and standard temperature, or as 37.5 MJ/m^3 (HHV). Both gas heat contents are correct, but the application engineer must understand the difference to use each one correctly. As described earlier, local heat content HC can be used to determine appliance input rate.

When gas heat value (either HHV or HC) is used to determine gas input rate, the gas pressure and temperature in the meter must also be considered. Add the gage pressure of gas in the meter to the local barometric pressure to calculate the heat content of the gas at the pressure in the meter. Gas temperature in the meter also affects the heat content of the gas in the meter. Gas heat value is directly proportional to gas pressure and inversely proportional to its absolute temperature in accordance with the perfect gas laws, as illustrated in the following example calculations for gas input rate with either the HHV or local heat content method.

Example 1. Calculate the gas input rate for 37.5 MJ/m^3 HHV fuel gas, 2.800 m^3/h volumetric flow rate of 24°C fuel gas at 84.316 kPa barometer pressure (1525 m altitude) with 1.700 kPa fuel gas pressure in the gas meter.

HHV Method:

$$Q = 0.2778 HHV \times VFR_s$$

where

Q = fuel gas input rate, kW

0.2778 = conversion factor, MJ/h to kW

HHV = fuel gas higher heating value at standard temperature and pressure, MJ/m³

VFR_s = fuel gas volumetric flow rate adjusted to standard temperature and pressure, m³/h = $VFR(T_s \times P)/(T \times P_s)$

VFR = fuel gas volumetric flow rate at local temperature and pressure conditions, m³/h

T_s = standard temperature, 288.15 K (15.0°C + 273.15 K)

P = gas meter absolute pressure, kPa (local barometer pressure + gas pressure in meter relative to barometric pressure) = 84.316 kPa + 1.700 kPa = 86.016 kPa gas meter absolute pressure

T = absolute temperature of fuel gas, K (fuel gas temperature in °C + 273.15 K)

P_s = standard pressure, 101.325 kPa

Substituting given values into the equation for VFR_s gives

$$VFR_s = \frac{2.800 \text{ m}^3/\text{h} \times 288.15 \text{ K} \times 86.016 \text{ kPa}}{(24.00°\text{C} + 273.15 \text{ K})101.325 \text{ kPa}} = 2.305 \text{ m}^3/\text{h}$$

Then,

$$Q = 0.2778 \times 37.5 \text{ MJ/m}^3 \times 2.305 \text{ m}^3/\text{h} = 24.012 \text{ kW}$$

Local Gas Heat Content Method: The local gas heat content is simply the HHV adjusted to local gas meter pressure and temperature conditions. The gas input rate is simply the observed volumetric gas flow rate times the local gas heat content.

$$Q = 0.2778 HC \times VFR$$

where

Q = fuel gas input rate, kW

0.2778 = conversion factor, MJ/h to kW

HC = fuel gas heat content at local gas meter pressure and temperature conditions, MJ/m^3
VFR = fuel gas volumetric flow rate, referenced to local gas meter pressure and temperature conditions, m^3/h

$$HC = HHV(T_s \times P)/(T \times P_s)$$

T_s = standard temperature, 288.15 K (15.00°C + 273.15 K)
P = gas meter absolute pressure, kPa (local barometer pressure + gas pressure in gas meter relative to barometric pressure)
P_s = standard pressure = 101.325 kPa
P_l = local barometric pressure = 84.316 kPa
T = absolute temperature of fuel gas, 297.15 K (24.00°C fuel gas temperature + 273.15 K)

Substituting given values into the equation for HC gives

$$HC = \frac{37.5 \times 288.15(84.316 + 1.700)}{297.15 \times 101.325} = 30.87 \text{ MJ/m}^3$$

Then,

$$Q = 0.2778 \times 30.87 \text{ MJ/m}^3 \times 2.800 \text{ m}^3\text{/h} = 24.012 \text{ kW}$$

The gas input rate is exactly the same for both calculation methods.

FUEL CLASSIFICATION

Generally, hydrocarbon fuels are classified according to physical state (gas, liquid, or solid). Different types of combustion equipment are usually needed to burn fuels in the different physical states. Gaseous fuels can be burned in premix or diffusion burners. Liquid fuel burners must include a means for atomizing or vaporizing fuel and must provide adequate mixing of fuel and air. Solid fuel combustion equipment must (1) heat fuel to vaporize sufficient volatiles to initiate and sustain combustion, (2) provide residence time to complete combustion, and (3) provide space for ash containment.

Principal fuel applications include space heating and cooling of residential, commercial, industrial, and institutional buildings; service water heating; steam generation; and refrigeration. Major fuels for these applications are natural and liquefied petroleum gases (LPG), fuel oils, diesel and gas turbine fuels (for on-site energy applications), and coal. Fuels of limited use, such as manufactured gases, kerosene, liquid fuels derived from biological materials (wood, vegetable oils, and animal fat products), briquettes, wood, and coke, are not discussed here.

Fuel choice is based on one or more of the following:

Fuel factors

- Availability, including dependability of supply
- Convenience of use and storage
- Economy
- Cleanliness, including amount of contamination in unburned fuel [affecting (1) usability in fuel-burning equipment and (2) environmental impact]

Combustion equipment factors

- Operating requirements
- Cost
- Service requirements
- Ease of control

GASEOUS FUELS

Although various gaseous fuels have been used as energy sources in the past, heating and cooling applications are presently limited to natural gas and liquefied petroleum gases.

Types and Properties

Natural gas is a nearly odorless, colorless gas that accumulates in the upper parts of oil and gas reservoirs. Raw natural gas is a mixture of methane (55 to 98%), higher hydrocarbons (primarily ethane), and noncombustible gases. Some constituents, principally water vapor, hydrogen sulfide, helium, liquefied petroleum gases, and gasoline, are removed before distribution.

Natural gas used as fuel typically contains methane, CH_4 (70 to 96%); ethane, C_2H_6 (1 to 14%); propane, C_3H_8 (0 to 4%); butane, C_4H_{10} (0 to 2%); pentane, C_5H_{12} (0 to 0.5%); hexane, C_6H_{14} (0 to 2%); carbon dioxide, CO_2 (0 to 2%); oxygen, O_2 (0 to 1.2%); and nitrogen, N_2 (0.4 to 17%).

The composition of natural gas depends on its geographical source. Because the gas is drawn from various sources, the composition of gas distributed in a given location can vary slightly, but a fairly constant heating value is usually maintained for control and safety. Local gas utilities are the best sources of current gas composition data for a particular area.

Heating values of natural gases vary from 34 to 45 MJ/m^3; the usual range is 37.3 to 39.1 MJ/m^3 at sea level. The heating value for a particular gas can be calculated from the composition data and values in Table 3.

For safety purposes, odorants (e.g., mercaptans) are added to natural gas and LPG to give them noticeable odors.

Liquefied petroleum gases (LPG) consist primarily of propane and butane, and are usually obtained as a byproduct of oil refinery operations or by stripping liquefied petroleum gases from the natural gas stream. Propane and butane are gaseous under usual atmospheric conditions, but can be liquefied under moderate pressures at normal temperatures.

Commercial propane consists primarily of propane but generally contains about 5 to 10% propylene. Its heating value is about 50.15 MJ/kg, about 93 MJ/m^3 of gas, or about 25.4 GJ/m^3 of liquid propane. At atmospheric pressure, commercial propane has a boiling point of about –42°C. The low boiling point of propane allows it to be used during winter in the northern United States and southern Canada. Tank heaters and vaporizers allow its use also in colder climates and where high fuel flow rates are required. The American Society for Testing and Materials (ASTM) *Standard* D1835 and Gas Processors Association (GPA) *Standard* 2140, which are similar, provide formulating specifications for required properties of liquefied petroleum gases at the time of delivery. Propane is shipped in cargo tank vehicles, rail cars, and barges. It is stored at consumer sites in tanks that comply with requirements of the ASME *Boiler and Pressure Vessel Code* or transportable cylinders that comply with requirements of the U.S. Department of Transportation.

HD-5 propane is a special LPG product for use in internal combustion engines under moderate to high severity. Its specifications are included in ASTM *Standard* D1835 and GPA *Standard* 2140.

Propane/air mixtures are used in place of natural gas in small communities and by natural gas companies to supplement normal supplies at peak loads. Table 4 lists heating values and densities for various fuel/air ratios.

Commercial butane consists primarily of butane but may contain up to 5% butylene. It has a heating value of about 49.3 MJ/kg, about 120 MJ/m^3 of gas, or about 28.4 GJ/m^3 of liquid butane. At atmospheric pressure, commercial butane has a relatively high boiling point of about 0°C. Therefore, butane cannot be used in cold weather unless the gas temperature is maintained above 0°C or the partial pressure is decreased by dilution with a gas having a lower boiling point. Butane is usually available in bottles, tank trucks, or tank cars, but not in cylinders.

Butane/air mixtures are used in place of natural gas in small communities and by natural gas companies to supplement normal supplies at peak loads. Table 4 lists heating values and specific gravities for various fuel/air ratios.

Commercial propane/butane mixtures with various ratios of propane and butane are available. Their properties generally fall between those of the unmixed fuels.

Manufactured gases are combustible gases produced from coal, coke, oil, liquefied petroleum gases, or natural gas. For more detailed information, see the *Gas Engineers Handbook* (1965).

Table 4 Propane/Air and Butane/Air Gas Mixtures

Heating Value, MJ/m³	Propane/Air[a]			Butane/Air[b]		
	% Gas	% Air	Density, kg/m³	% Gas	% Air	Density, kg/m³
18	19.16	80.84	1.41	14.81	85.19	1.48
22	23.41	76.59	1.44	18.11	81.89	1.52
26	27.67	72.33	1.46	21.40	78.60	1.56
30	31.93	68.07	1.49	24.69	75.31	1.60
34	36.18	63.82	1.52	27.98	72.02	1.64
38	40.44	59.56	1.54	31.27	68.73	1.68
42	44.70	55.30	1.57	34.57	65.43	1.72
46	48.95	51.05	1.60	37.86	62.14	1.76
50	53.21	46.79	1.63	41.15	58.85	1.80
54	57.47	42.53	1.65	44.44	55.56	1.84
58	61.72	38.28	1.68	47.74	52.26	1.88
62	65.98	34.02	1.71	51.03	48.97	1.92
66	70.24	29.76	1.73	54.32	45.68	1.96

Adapted from *Gas Engineers Handbook* (1965).
Air density at 0°C and 101.325 kPa is 1.292 kg/m³.
[a]Values used for calculation: 93.97 MJ/m³; propane = 1.92 kg/m³.
[b]Values used for calculation: 121.5 MJ/m³; butane = 2.53 kg/m³.

These fuels are used primarily for industrial in-plant operations or as specialty fuels (e.g., acetylene for welding).

LIQUID FUELS

Significant liquid fuels include various fuel oils for firing combustion equipment and engine fuels for on-site energy systems. Liquid fuels, with few exceptions, are mixtures of hydrocarbons derived by refining crude petroleum. In addition to hydrocarbons, crude petroleum usually contains small quantities of sulfur, oxygen, nitrogen, vanadium, other trace metals, and impurities such as water and sediment. Refining produces a variety of fuels and other products. Nearly all lighter hydrocarbons are refined into fuels (e.g., liquefied petroleum gases, gasoline, kerosene, jet fuels, diesel fuels, and light heating oils). Heavy hydrocarbons are refined into residual fuel oils and other products (e.g., lubricating oils, waxes, petroleum coke, and asphalt).

Crude petroleums from different oil fields vary in hydrocarbon molecular structure. Crude is paraffin-base (principally chain-structured paraffin hydrocarbons), naphthene- or asphaltic-base (containing relatively large quantities of saturated ring-structural naphthenes), aromatic-base (containing relatively large quantities of unsaturated, ring-structural aromatics, including multi-ring compounds such as asphaltenes), or mixed- or intermediate-base (between paraffin- and naphthene-base crudes). Except for heavy fuel oils, the crude type has little significant effect on resultant distillate products and combustion applications.

Types of Fuel Oils

Fuel oils for heating are broadly classified as **distillate fuel oils** (lighter oils) or **residual fuel oils** (heavier oils). ASTM *Standard* D396 has specifications for fuel oil properties that subdivide the oils into various grades. Grades No. 1 and 2 are distillates; grades 4, 5 (Light), 5 (Heavy), and 6 are residual. Specifications for the grades are based on required characteristics of fuel oils for use in different types of burners.

Grade No. 1 is a light distillate intended for vaporizing-type burners. High volatility is essential to continued evaporation with minimum residue. This fuel is also used in extremely cold climates for residential heating using pressure-atomizing burners.

Grade No. 2 is heavier than No. 1 and is used primarily with pressure-atomizing (gun) burners that spray oil into a combustion chamber. Vapor from the atomized oil mixes with air and burns. This grade is used in most domestic burners and many medium-capacity commercial/industrial burners. A dewaxed No. 2 oil with a pour point of –50°C is supplied only to areas where regular No. 2 oil would jell. Grade No. 2—low sulfur is a relatively new category that has a sulfur content of 0.05%. Lower fuel sulfur content reduces fouling rates of boiler heat exchangers (Butcher et al. 1997).

Grade No. 4 is an intermediate fuel that is considered either a heavy distillate or a light residual. Intended for burners that atomize oils of higher viscosity than domestic burners can handle, its permissible viscosity range allows it to be pumped and atomized at relatively low storage temperatures.

Grade No. 5 (Light) is a residual fuel of intermediate viscosity for burners that handle fuel more viscous than No. 4 without preheating. Preheating may be necessary in some equipment for burning and, in colder climates, for handling.

Grade No. 5 (Heavy) is a residual fuel more viscous than No. 5 (Light), but intended for similar purposes. Preheating is usually necessary for burning and, in colder climates, for handling.

Grade No. 6, sometimes referred to as Bunker C, is a high-viscosity oil used mostly in commercial and industrial heating. It requires preheating in the storage tank to allow pumping, and additional preheating at the burner to allow atomizing.

Low-sulfur residual oils are marketed in many areas to allow users to meet sulfur dioxide emission regulations. These fuel oils are produced (1) by refinery processes that remove sulfur from the oil (hydrodesulfurization), (2) by blending high-sulfur residual oils with low-sulfur distillate oils, or (3) by a combination of these methods. These oils have significantly different characteristics from regular residual oils. For example, the viscosity/temperature relationship can be such that low-sulfur fuel oils have viscosities of No. 6 fuel oils when cold, and of No. 4 when heated. Therefore, normal guidelines for fuel handling and burning can be altered when using these fuels.

Another liquid fuel of increasing interest is biodiesel. It is made from biological sources (e.g., vegetable oils, used cooking oils, tallow). ASTM's recent *Standard* D6751 addresses biodiesel; requirements are largely similar to those for petroleum diesel (cetane number, flash point, etc.; see the section on Types and Properties of Liquid Fuels for Engines). In practice, biodiesel is almost always blended, most often with ASTM heating oils when used for stationary heating applications, because of cost and cold-flow properties of 100% biodiesel. However, the benefits of a renewable fuel that has very low net carbon dioxide emission in its life cycle, reduced particulate and sulfur emissions, and lower NO_x emissions in many heating applications balance the need for mixing.

Fuel oil grade selection for a particular application is usually based on availability and economic factors, including fuel cost, clean air requirements, preheating and handling costs, and equipment cost. Installations with low firing rates and low annual fuel consumption cannot justify the cost of preheating and other methods that use residual fuel oils. Large installations with high annual fuel consumption cannot justify the premium cost of distillate fuel oils.

Characteristics of Fuel Oils

Characteristics that determine grade classification and suitability for given applications are (1) viscosity, (2) flash point, (3) pour point, (4) water and sediment content, (5) carbon residue, (6) ash, (7) distillation qualities or distillation temperature ranges, (8) density, (9) sulfur content, (10) heating value, (11) carbon/ hydrogen content, (12) aromatic content, and (13) asphaltene content. Not all of these are included in ASTM *Standard* D396.

Viscosity is an oil's resistance to flow. It is significant because it indicates the ease with which oil flows or can be pumped and the ease of atomization. Differences in fuel oil viscosities are caused by variations in the concentrations of fuel oil constituents and different refining methods. Approximate viscosities of fuel oils are shown in Figure 2.

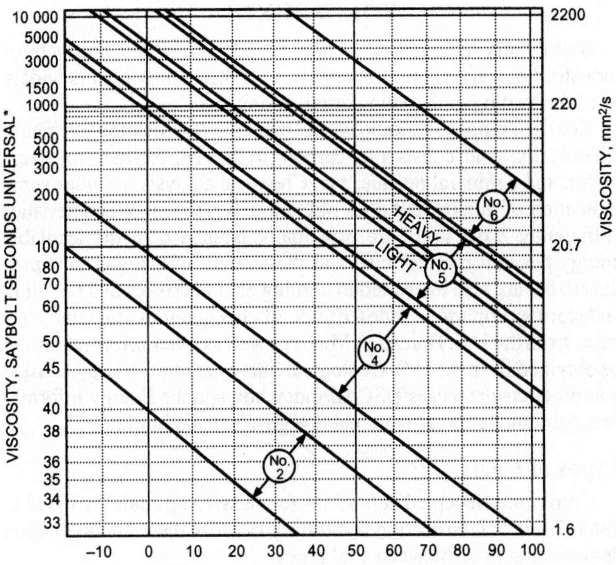

* 1 Saybolt Second (SSU, or SUS) = time required for 60 mL to gravity-flow through Saybolt universal viscometer.

Fig. 2 Approximate Viscosity of Fuel Oils

Flash point is the lowest temperature to which an oil must be heated for its vapors to ignite in a flame. Minimum permissible flash point is usually prescribed by state and municipal laws.

Pour point is the lowest temperature at which a fuel can be stored and handled. Fuels with higher pour points can be used when heated storage and piping facilities are provided.

Water and **sediment content** should be low to prevent fouling the facilities. Sediment accumulates on filter screens and burner parts. Water in distillate fuels can cause tanks to corrode and emulsions to form in residual oil.

Carbon residue is obtained by a test in which the oil sample is destructively distilled in the absence of air. When commercial fuels are used in proper burners, this residue has almost no relationship to soot deposits, except indirectly when deposits are formed by vaporizing burners.

Ash is the noncombustible material in an oil. An excessive amount indicates the presence of materials that cause high wear on burner pumps.

The **distillation** test shows the volatility and ease of vaporization of a fuel.

Relative density is the ratio of the density of a fuel oil to the density of water at a specific temperature. Relative densities cover a range in each grade, with some overlap between distillate and residual grades.

Air pollution considerations are important in determining the allowable **sulfur content** of fuel oils. Sulfur content is frequently limited by legislation aimed at reducing sulfur oxide emissions from combustion equipment; usual maximum allowable sulfur content levels are 1.0, 0.5, or 0.3%. Table 5 lists sulfur levels of some marketed fuel oils. New research (Lee et al. 2002a, 2002b) suggests that fuel sulfur content affects the sulfate content of particulate emissions, which are reported to be associated with adverse health effects.

Sulfur in fuel oils is also undesirable because sulfur compounds in flue gas are corrosive. Although low-temperature corrosion can be minimized by maintaining the stack at temperatures above the dew point of the flue gas, this limits the overall thermal efficiency of combustion equipment. The presence of sulfur oxides in the flue gas raises the dew point temperature (see the section on Combustion Calculations).

Table 5 Sulfur Content of Marketed Fuel Oils

Grade of Oil	No. 1	No. 2	No. 4	No. 5 (Light)	No. 5 (Heavy)	No. 6
Total fuel samples	31	61	13	15	16	96
Sulfur content, % mass						
minimum	0.001	0.03	0.46	0.90	0.57	0.32
maximum	0.120	0.50	1.44	3.50	2.92	4.00
average	0.023	0.20	0.83	1.46	1.46	1.41
No. samples with S						
over 0.3%	0	17	13	15	16	96
over 0.5%	0	2	11	15	16	93
over 1.0%	0	0	3	9	11	60
over 3.0%	0	0	0	2	0	8

Data for No. 1 and No. 2 oil derived from Dickson and Sturm (1994).
Data for No. 4, 5, and 6 oil derived from Shelton (1974).

Table 6 Typical Density and Higher Heating Value of Standard Grades of Fuel Oil

Grade No.	Density, kg/m³	Higher Heating Value, GJ/m³
1	833 to 800	38.2 to 37.0
2	874 to 834	39.5 to 38.2
4	933 to 886	41.3 to 39.9
5L	951 to 921	41.8 to 40.9
5H	968 to 945	42.4 to 41.6
6	1012 to 965	43.5 to 42.2

For certain industrial applications (e.g., direct-fired metallurgy, where work is performed in the combustion zone), fuel sulfur content must be limited because of adverse effects on product quality. Sulfur contents of typical fuel oils are listed in Table 5.

Heating value is an important property, although ASTM *Standard* D396 does not list it as one of the criteria for fuel oil classification. Table 6 shows the relationship between heating value and density for several oil grades. In the absence of more specific data, heating values can be calculated as derived from the *North American Combustion Handbook* (1978):

$$\text{Higher heating value, MJ/kg} = 51.92 - 8.79 \times 10^{-6}\rho^2 \quad (2)$$

Distillate fuel oils (grades 1 and 2) have a **carbon/hydrogen content** of 84 to 86% carbon, with the remainder predominantly hydrogen. Heavier residual fuel oils (grades 4, 5, and 6) may contain up to 88% carbon and as little as 11% hydrogen. An approximate relationship for determining the hydrogen content of fuel oils is

$$\text{Hydrogen, \%} = 26 - (15 \times \text{Relative density}) \quad (3)$$

ASTM *Standard* D396 is more a classification than a specification, distinguishing between six generally nonoverlapping grades, one of which characterizes any commercial fuel oil. Quality is not defined, as a refiner might control it; for example, the standard lists the distillation temperature 90% point for grade No. 2 as having a maximum of 338°C, whereas commercial practice rarely exceeds 315°C.

Types and Properties of Liquid Fuels for Engines

The primary stationary engine fuels are diesel and gas turbine oils, natural gases, and LPGs. Other fuels include sewage gas, manufactured gas, and other commercial gas mixtures. Gasoline and the JP series of gas turbine fuels are rarely used for stationary engines.

Only properties of diesel and gas turbine fuel oils are covered here; properties of natural and liquefied petroleum gases are found in the section on Gaseous Fuels. For properties of gasolines and JP turbine fuel, consult texts on internal combustion engines and gas turbines. Properties of currently marketed gasolines can be found in ASTM *Standard* D4814.

Properties of the three **grades of diesel fuel oils** (1-D, 2-D, and 4D) are listed in ASTM *Standard* D975.

Grade No. 1-D includes the class of volatile fuel oils from kerosene to intermediate distillates. They are used in high-speed engines with frequent and relatively wide variations in loads and speeds and where abnormally low fuel temperatures are encountered.

Grade No. 2-D includes the class of lower-volatility distillate gas oils. They are used in high-speed engines with relatively high loads and uniform speeds, or in engines not requiring fuels with the higher volatility or other properties specified for grade No. 1-D.

Grade No. 4-D covers the more viscous distillates and blends of these distillates with residual fuel oils. They are used in low- and medium-speed engines involving sustained loads at essentially constant speed.

Property specifications and test methods for grade No. 1-D, 2-D, and 4-D diesel fuel oils are essentially identical to specifications of grade No. 1, 2, and 4 fuel oils, respectively. However, diesel fuel oils have an additional specification for **cetane number**, which measures ignition quality and influences combustion roughness. Cetane number requirements depend on engine design, size, speed and load variations, and starting and atmospheric conditions. An increase in cetane number over values actually required does not improve engine performance. Thus, the cetane number should be as low as possible to ensure maximum fuel availability. ASTM *Standard* D975 provides several methods for estimating cetane number from other fuel oil properties.

ASTM *Standard* D2880 for gas turbine fuel oils relates gas turbine fuel oil grades to fuel and diesel fuel oil grades. Test methods for determining properties of gas turbine fuel oils are essentially identical to those for fuel oils. However, gas turbine specifications limit quantities of some trace elements that may be present, to prevent excessive corrosion in gas turbine engines. For a detailed discussion of fuels for gas turbines and combustion in gas turbines, see Chapters 5 and 9, respectively, in Hazard (1971).

SOLID FUELS

Solid fuels include coal, coke, wood, and waste products of industrial and agricultural operations. Of these, only coal is widely used for heating and cooling applications.

Coal's complex composition makes classification difficult. Chemically, coal consists of carbon, hydrogen, oxygen, nitrogen, sulfur, and a mineral residue, ash. Chemical analysis provides some indication of quality, but does not define its burning characteristics sufficiently. Coal users are principally interested in the available energy per unit mass of coal and the amount of ash and dust produced, but are also interested in burning characteristics and handling and storing properties. A description of coal qualities and characteristics from the U.S. Bureau of Mines as well as other information can be obtained from the U.S. Geological Survey at http://energy.er.usgs.gov/products/databases/USCoal/index.htm and the Energy Information Administration at www.eia.doe.gov/fuelcoal.html.

Types of Coals

Commonly accepted definitions for classifying coals are listed in Table 7. This classification is arbitrary because there are no distinct demarcation lines between coal types.

Anthracite is a clean, dense, hard coal that creates little dust in handling. It is comparatively hard to ignite, but burns freely once started. It is noncaking and burns uniformly and smokelessly with a short flame.

Semianthracite has a higher volatile content than anthracite. It is not as hard and ignites more easily. Otherwise, its properties are similar to those of anthracite.

Bituminous coal includes many types of coal with distinctly different compositions, properties, and burning characteristics. Coals range from high-grade bituminous, such as those found in the eastern United States, to low-rank coals, such as those found in the western United States. Caking properties range from coals that melt or become fully plastic, to those from which volatiles and tars are distilled without changing form (classed as noncaking or free-burning). Most bituminous coals are strong and nonfriable enough to allow screened sizes to be delivered free of fines. Generally, they

Table 7 Classification of Coals by Rank[a]

Class	Group	Limits of Fixed Carbon or Energy Content, Mineral-Matter-Free Basis	Requisite Physical Properties
I Anthracite	1. Metaanthracite	Dry FC, 98% or more (Dry VM, 2% or less)	Nonagglomerating
	2. Anthracite	Dry FC, 92% or more, and less than 98% (Dry VM, 8% or less, and more than 2%)	
	3. Semianthracite	Dry FC, 86% or more, and less than 92% (Dry VM, 14% or less, and more than 8%)	
II Bituminous[d]	1. Low-volatile bituminous coal	Dry FC, 78% or more, and less than 86% (Dry VM, 22% or less, and more than 14%)	Either agglomerating[b] or nonweathering[f]
	2. Medium-volatile bituminous coal	Dry FC, 69% or more, and less than 78% (Dry VM, 31% or less, and more than 22%)	
	3. High-volatile Type A bituminous coal	Dry FC, less than 69% (Dry VM, more than 31%), and moist,[c] about 32.6 MJ/kg[e] or more	
	4. High-volatile Type B bituminous coal	Moist,[c] about 30.2 MJ/kg or more, and less than 32.6 MJ/kg[e]	
	5. High-volatile Type C bituminous coal	Moist,[c] about 25.6 MJ/kg or more, and less than 30.2 MJ/kg[e]	
III Subbituminous	1. Subbituminous Type A coal	Moist,[c] about 25.6 MJ/kg or more, and less than 30.2 MJ/kg[e]	Both weathering and nonagglomerating[b]
	2. Subbituminous Type B coal	Moist,[c] about 22.1 MJ/kg or more, and less than 25.6 MJ/kg[e]	
	3. Subbituminous Type C coal	Moist,[c] about 19.3 MJ/kg or more, and less than 22.1 MJ/kg[e]	
IV Lignitic	1. Lignite	Moist,[c] less than 19.3 MJ/kg	Consolidated
	2. Brown coal	Moist,[c] less than 19.3 MJ/kg	Unconsolidated

Source: Adapted from ASTM *Standard* D388.
FC = fixed carbon; VM = volatile matter; MMF = mineral-matter-free
[a]Classification does not include a few coals of unusual physical and chemical properties that come within limits of fixed carbon or energy content of high-volatile bituminous and subbituminous ranks. All these coals either contain less than 48% dry, MMF FC, or have more than about 36.1 MJ/kg, which is moist, MMF.
[b]If agglomerating, classify in group 1 of class II.
[c]*Moist* refers to coal containing natural bed moisture but without visible water on coal surface.
[d]There may be noncaking varieties in each group of class II.
[e]Coals with 69% or more fixed carbon on dry, MMF basis are classified according to FC, regardless of energy content.
[f]There are three varieties of coal in group 5: variety 1, agglomerating and nonweathering; variety 2, agglomerating and weathering; and variety 3, nonagglomerating and nonweathering.

ignite easily and burn freely. Flame length is long and varies with different coals. If improperly fired, much smoke and soot are possible, especially at low burning rates.

Semibituminous coal is soft and friable, and handling creates fines and dust. It ignites slowly and burns with a medium-length flame. Its caking properties increase as volatile matter increases, but the coke formed is weak. With only half the volatile matter content of bituminous coals, burning produces less smoke; hence, it is sometimes called smokeless coal.

Subbituminous coal, such as that found in the western United States, is high in moisture when mined and tends to break up as it dries or is exposed to the weather; it is likely to ignite spontaneously when piled or stored. It ignites easily and quickly, has a medium-length flame, and is noncaking and free-burning. The lumps tend to break into small pieces if poked. Very little smoke and soot are formed.

Lignite is woody in structure, very high in moisture when mined, of low heating value, and clean to handle. It has a greater tendency than subbituminous coals to disintegrate as it dries and is also more likely to ignite spontaneously. Because of its high moisture, freshly mined lignite ignites slowly and is noncaking. The char left after moisture and volatile matter are driven off burns very easily, like charcoal. The lumps tend to break up in the fuel bed and pieces of char that fall into the ash pit continue to burn. Very little smoke or soot forms.

Characteristics of Coal

The characteristics of coals that determine classification and suitability for given applications are the proportions of (1) volatile matter, (2) fixed carbon, (3) moisture, (4) sulfur, and (5) ash. Each of these is reported in the proximate analysis. Coal analyses can be reported on several bases: as-received, moisture-free (or dry), and mineral-matter-free (or ash-free). As-received is applicable for combustion calculations; moisture-free and mineral-matter-free, for classification purposes.

Volatile matter is driven off as gas or vapor when the coal is heated according to a standard temperature test. It consists of a variety of organic gases, generally resulting from distillation and decomposition. Volatile products given off by heated coals differ materially in the ratios (by mass) of the gases to oils and tars. No heavy oils or tars are given off by anthracite, and very small quantities are given off by semianthracite. As volatile matter increases to as much as 40% of the coal (dry and ash-free basis), increasing amounts of oils and tars are released. However, for coals of higher volatile content, the quantity of oils and tars decreases and is relatively low in the subbituminous coals and in lignite.

Fixed carbon is the combustible residue left after the volatile matter is driven off. It is not all carbon. Its form and hardness are an indication of fuel coking properties and, therefore, guide the choice of combustion equipment. Generally, fixed carbon represents that portion of fuel that must be burned in the solid state.

Moisture is difficult to determine accurately because a sample can lose moisture on exposure to the atmosphere, particularly when reducing the sample size for analysis. To correct for this loss, total moisture content of a sample is customarily determined by adding the moisture loss obtained when air-drying the sample to the measured moisture content of the dried sample. Moisture does not represent all of the water present in coal; water of decomposition (combined water) and of hydration are not given off under standardized test conditions.

Ash is the noncombustible residue remaining after complete coal combustion. Generally, the mass of ash is slightly less than that of mineral matter before burning.

Sulfur is an undesirable constituent in coal, because sulfur oxides formed when it burns contribute to air pollution and cause combustion system corrosion. Table 8 lists the sulfur content of typical coals. Legislation has limited the sulfur content of coals burned in certain locations.

Table 8 Typical Ultimate Analyses for Coals

Rank	As Received, MJ/kg	Constituents, Percent by Mass O	H	C	N	S	Ash
Anthracite	29.5	5.0	2.9	80.0	0.9	0.7	10.5
Semianthracite	31.6	5.0	3.9	80.4	1.1	1.1	8.5
Low-volatile bituminous	33.4	5.0	4.7	81.7	1.4	1.2	6.0
Medium-volatile bituminous	32.6	5.0	5.0	81.4	1.4	1.5	6.0
High-volatile bituminous							
Type A	32.1	9.3	5.3	75.9	1.5	1.5	6.5
B	29.1	13.8	5.5	67.8	1.4	3.0	8.5
C	25.6	20.6	5.8	59.6	1.1	3.5	9.4
Subbituminous							
Type B	20.9	29.5	6.2	52.5	1.0	1.0	9.8
C	19.8	35.7	6.5	46.4	0.8	1.0	9.6
Lignite	16.0	44.0	6.9	40.1	0.7	1.0	7.3

Heating value may be reported on an as-received, dry, dry and mineral-matter-free, or moist and mineral-matter-free basis. Higher heating values of coals are frequently reported with their proximate analysis. When more specific data are lacking, the higher heating value of higher-quality coals can be calculated by the Dulong formula:

$$\text{Higher heating value, MJ/kg} = 33.829C + 144.28[H - (O/8)] + 9.42S \quad (4)$$

where C, H, O, and S are the mass fractions of carbon, hydrogen, oxygen, and sulfur in the coal obtained from the ultimate analysis.

Other important parameters in judging coal suitability include

- **Ultimate analysis**, which is another method of reporting coal composition. Percentages of C, H, O, N, S, and ash in the coal sample are reported. Ultimate analysis is used for detailed fuel studies and for computing a heat balance when required in heating device testing. Typical ultimate analyses of various coals are shown in Table 8.
- **Ash-fusion temperature**, which indicates the fluidity of the ash at elevated temperatures. It is helpful in selecting coal to be burned in a particular furnace and in estimating the possibility of ash handling and slagging problems.
- The **grindability index**, which indicates the ease with which a coal can be pulverized and is helpful in estimating ball mill capacity with various coals. There are two common methods for determining the index: Hardgrove (see Hardgrove Grindability Index at www.energy.psu.edu/HGI) and ball mill.
- The **free-swelling index**, which denotes the extent of coal swelling on combustion on a fuel bed and indicates the coking characteristics of coal.

COMBUSTION CALCULATIONS

Calculations of the quantities of (1) air required for combustion and (2) flue gas products generated during combustion are frequently needed for sizing system components and as input to efficiency calculations. Other calculations, such as values for excess air and theoretical CO_2, are useful in estimating combustion system performance.

Frequently, combustion calculations can be simplified by using relative molecular mass. The relative molecular mass of a compound equals the sum of the atomic masses of the elements in the compound. Molecular mass can be expressed in any mass units. The gram molecular mass or gram mole is the molecular mass of the compound expressed in grams. The molecular mass of any substance contains the same number of molecules as the molecular mass of any other substance.

Corresponding to measurement standards common to the industries, calculations involving gaseous fuels are generally based on volume, and those involving liquid and solid fuels generally use mass.

Some calculations described here require data on concentrations of carbon dioxide, carbon monoxide, and oxygen in the flue gas. Gas analyses for CO_2, CO, and O_2 can be obtained by volumetric chemical analysis and other analytical techniques, including electromechanical cells used in portable electronic flue gas analyzers.

Air Required for Combustion

Stoichiometric (or theoretical) air is the exact quantity of air required to provide oxygen for complete combustion.

The three most prevalent components in hydrocarbon fuels (C, H_2, and S) are completely burned as in the following fundamental reactions:

$$C + O_2 \rightarrow CO_2$$

$$H_2 + 0.5O_2 \rightarrow H_2O$$

$$S + O_2 \rightarrow SO_2$$

In the reactions, C, H_2, and S can be taken to represent 1 kg mole of carbon, hydrogen, and sulfur, respectively. Using approximate atomic masses (C = 12, H = 1, S = 32, and O = 16), 12 kg of C are oxidized by 32 kg of O_2 to form 44 kg of CO_2, 2 kg of H_2 are oxidized by 16 kg of O_2 to form 18 kg of H_2O, and 32 kg of S are oxidized by 32 kg of O_2 to form 64 kg of SO_2. These relationships can be extended to include hydrocarbons.

The mass of dry air required to supply a given quantity of oxygen is 4.32 times the mass of the oxygen. The mass of air required to oxidize the fuel constituents listed in Table 1 was calculated on this basis. Deduct oxygen contained in the fuel, except the amount in ash, from the amount of oxygen required, because this oxygen is already combined with fuel components. In addition, when calculating the mass of supply air for combustion, allow for water vapor, which is always present in atmospheric air.

Combustion calculations for gaseous fuels are based on volume. **Avogadro's law** states that, for any gas, one mole occupies the same volume at a given temperature and pressure. Therefore, in reactions involving gaseous compounds, the gases react in volume ratios identical to the gram mole ratios. That is, to oxidize hydrogen in the preceding reaction, one volume (or one kg mole) of hydrogen reacts with one-half volume (or one-half kg mole) of oxygen to form one volume (or one kg mole) of water vapor.

The volume of air required to supply a given volume of oxygen is 4.78 times the volume of oxygen. The volumes of dry air required to oxidize the fuel constituents listed in Table 1 were calculated on this basis. Volume ratios are not given for fuels that do not exist in vapor form at reasonable temperatures or pressures. Again, oxygen contained in the fuel should be deducted from the quantity of oxygen required, because this oxygen is already combined with fuel components. Allow for water vapor, which increases the volume of dry air by 1 to 3%.

From the relationships just described, the theoretical mass m_a of dry air required for stoichiometric combustion of a unit mass of any hydrocarbon fuel is

$$m_a = 0.0144(8C + 24H + 3S - 3O) \tag{5}$$

where C, H, S, and O are the mass percentages of carbon, hydrogen, sulfur, and oxygen in the fuel.

Analyses of gaseous fuels are generally based on hydrocarbon components rather than elemental content.

If fuel analysis is based on mass, the theoretical mass m_a of dry air required for stoichiometric combustion of a unit mass of gaseous fuel is

$$\begin{aligned} m_a = {} & 2.47CO + 34.28H_2 + 17.24CH_4 + 16.09C_2H_6 \\ & + 15.68C_3H_8 + 15.47C_4H_{10} + 13.27C_2H_2 \\ & + 14.78C_2H_4 + 6.08H_2S - 4.32O_2 \end{aligned} \tag{6}$$

If fuel analysis is reported on a volumetric or molecular basis, it is simplest to calculate air requirements based on volume and, if necessary, convert to mass. The theoretical volume V_a of air required for stoichiometric combustion of a unit volume of gaseous fuels is

$$\begin{aligned} V_a = {} & 2.39CO + 2.39H_2 + 9.57CH_4 + 16.75C_2H_6 \\ & + 23.95C_3H_8 + 31.14C_4H_{10} + 11.96C_2H_2 \\ & + 14.38C_2H_4 + 7.18H_2S - 4.78O_2 \\ & + 30.47 \text{ illuminants} \end{aligned} \tag{7}$$

where CO, H_2, and so forth are the volumetric fractions of each constituent in the fuel gas.

Illuminants include a variety of compounds not separated by usual gas analysis. In addition to ethylene (C_2H_4) and acetylene (C_2H_2), the principal illuminants included in Equation (7), and the dry air required for combustion, per unit volume of each gas, are as follows: propylene (C_3H_6), 21.44; butylene (C_4H_8), 28.58; pentene (C_5H_{10}), 35.73; benzene (C_6H_6); 35.73, toluene (C_7H_8), 42.88; and xylene (C_8H_{10}), 50.02. Because toluene and xylene are normally scrubbed from the gas before distribution, they can be disregarded in computing air required for combustion of gaseous fuels. The percentage of illuminants present in gaseous fuels is small, so the values can be lumped together, and an approximate value of 30 unit volumes of dry air per unit volume of gas can be used. If ethylene and acetylene are included as illuminants, a value of 20 unit volumes of dry air per unit volume of gaseous illuminants can be used.

For many combustion calculations, only approximate values of air requirements are necessary. If approximate values for theoretical air are sufficient, or if complete information on the fuel is not available, the values in Tables 9 and 10 can be used. Another value used for estimating air requirements is 0.24 m^3 of air for 1 MJ of fuel.

In addition to the amount theoretically required for combustion, **excess air** must be supplied to most practical combustion systems to ensure complete combustion:

$$\text{Excess air, \%} = \frac{\text{Air supplied} - \text{Theoretical air}}{\text{Theoretical air}} \tag{8}$$

The excess air level at which a combustion process operates significantly affects its overall efficiency. Too much excess air dilutes flue gas excessively, lowering its heat transfer temperature and increasing sensible flue gas loss. Conversely, too little excess air can lead to incomplete combustion and loss of unburned combustible gases. Combustion efficiency is usually maximized when just enough excess air is supplied and properly mixed with combustible gases to ensure complete combustion. The general practice is to supply 5 to 50% excess air, depending on the type of fuel burned, combustion equipment, and other factors.

Table 9 Approximate Air Requirements for Stoichiometric Combustion of Fuels

Type of Fuel	Air Required, kg/kg Fuel	Air Required, m³/Unit Fuel*	Approx. Precision, %	Exceptions
Solid	MJ/kg × 0.314	MJ/kg × 0.26	3	Fuels containing more than 30% water
Liquid	MJ/kg × 0.305	MJ/kg × 0.35	3	Results low for gasoline and kerosene
Gas	MJ/kg × 0.288	MJ/m³ × 0.24	5	11.2 MJ/m³ or less

Source: Data based on Shnidman (1954).
*Unit fuel for solid and liquid fuels in kg, for gas in L.

Table 10 Approximate Air Requirements for Stoichiometric Combustion of Various Fuels

Type of Fuel	Theoretical Air Required for Combustion
Solid fuels	kg/kg fuel
Anthracite	9.6
Semibituminous	11.2
Bituminous	10.3
Lignite	6.2
Coke	11.2
Liquid fuels	Mg/m^3 fuel
No. 1 fuel oil	12.34
No. 2 fuel oil	12.70
No. 5 fuel oil	13.42
No. 6 fuel oil	13.66
Gaseous fuels	m^3/m^3 fuel
Natural gas	9.6
Butane	31.1
Propane	24.0

The amount of dry air supplied per unit mass of fuel burned can be obtained from the following equation, which is reasonably precise for most solid and liquid fuels:

$$\text{Dry air supplied} = \frac{C(3.04N_2)}{CO_2 + CO} \tag{9}$$

where

Dry air supplied = unit mass per unit mass of fuel
C = unit mass of carbon burned per unit mass of fuel, corrected for carbon in ash
CO_2, CO, N_2 = percentages by volume from flue gas analysis

These values of dry air supplied and theoretical air can be used in Equation (8) to determine excess air.

Excess air can also be calculated from unit volumes of stoichiometric combustion products and air, and from volumetric analysis of the flue gas:

$$\text{Excess air, \%} = 100\left(\frac{P}{A}\right)\left(\frac{U - CO_2}{CO_2}\right) \tag{10}$$

where

U = ultimate carbon dioxide of flue gases resulting from stoichiometric combustion, %
CO_2 = carbon dioxide content of flue gases, %
P = dry products from stoichiometric combustion, unit volume per unit volume of gas burned
A = air required for stoichiometric combustion, unit volume per unit volume of gas burned

Because the ratio P/A is approximately 0.9 for most natural gases, a value of 90 can be substituted for $100(P/A)$ in Equation (10) for rough calculation.

Because excess air calculations are almost invariably made from flue gas analysis results and theoretical air requirements are not always known, another convenient method of expressing Equation (8) is

$$\text{Excess air, \%} = \frac{100[O_2 - (CO/2)]}{0.264N_2 - [O_2 - (CO/2)]} \tag{11}$$

where O_2, CO, and N_2 are percentages by volume from the flue gas analysis, dry basis.

Theoretical CO_2

The theoretical (or ultimate, stoichiometric, or maximum) CO_2 concentration attainable in the products from the combustion of a hydrocarbon fuel with air is obtained when the fuel is completely

Table 11 Approximate Maximum Theoretical (Stoichiometric) CO_2 Values, and CO_2 Values of Various Fuels with Different Percentages of Excess Air

Type of Fuel	Theoretical or Maximum CO_2, %	Percent CO_2 at Given Excess Air Values		
		20%	40%	60%
Gaseous fuels				
Natural gas	12.1	9.9	8.4	7.3
Propane gas (commercial)	13.9	11.4	9.6	8.4
Butane gas (commercial)	14.1	11.6	9.8	8.5
Mixed gas (natural and carbureted water gas)	11.2	12.5	10.5	9.1
Carbureted water gas	17.2	14.2	12.1	10.6
Coke oven gas	11.2	9.2	7.8	6.8
Liquid fuels				
No. 1 and 2 fuel oil	15.0	12.3	10.5	9.1
No. 6 fuel oil	16.5	13.6	11.6	10.1
Solid fuels				
Bituminous coal	18.2	15.1	12.9	11.3
Anthracite	20.2	16.8	14.4	12.6
Coke	21.0	17.5	15.0	13.0

burned with the theoretical quantity of air and zero excess air. Theoretical CO_2 varies with the carbon/hydrogen ratio of the fuel. For combustion with excess air present, theoretical CO_2 values can be calculated from the flue gas analysis:

$$\text{Theoretical } CO_2\text{, \%} = U = \frac{CO_2}{1 - (O_2/20.95)} \tag{12}$$

where CO_2 and O_2 are percentages by volume from the flue gas analysis, dry basis.

Table 11 gives approximate theoretical CO_2 values for stoichiometric combustion of several common types of fuel, as well as CO_2 values attained with different amounts of excess air. In practice, desirable CO_2 values depend on the excess air, fuel, firing method, and other considerations.

Quantity of Flue Gas Produced

The mass of dry flue gas produced per mass of fuel burned is required in heat loss and efficiency calculations. This mass is equal to the sum of the mass of (1) fuel (minus ash retained in the furnace), (2) air theoretically required for combustion, and (3) excess air. For solid fuels, this mass, determined from the flue gas analysis, is

$$\text{Dry flue gas} = \frac{11CO_2 + 8O_2 + 7(CO + N_2)}{3(CO_2 + CO)} \tag{13}$$

where

Dry flue gas = kg/kg of fuel
C = kg of carbon burned per kg of fuel, corrected for carbon in ash
CO_2, O_2, CO, N_2 = percentages by volume from flue gas analysis

The total dry gas volume of flue gases from combustion of one unit volume of gaseous fuels for various percentages of CO_2 is

$$\text{Dry flue gas} = \left(\frac{\text{Volume of } CO_2 \text{ produced}}{\text{Unit vol. of gas burned}}\right)\left(\frac{100}{CO_2}\right) \tag{14}$$

where

Dry flue gas = unit volume per unit volume of gaseous fuel
CO_2 = percentage by volume from the flue gas analysis

Excess air quantity can be estimated by subtracting the quantity of dry flue gases resulting from stoichiometric combustion from the total volume of flue gas.

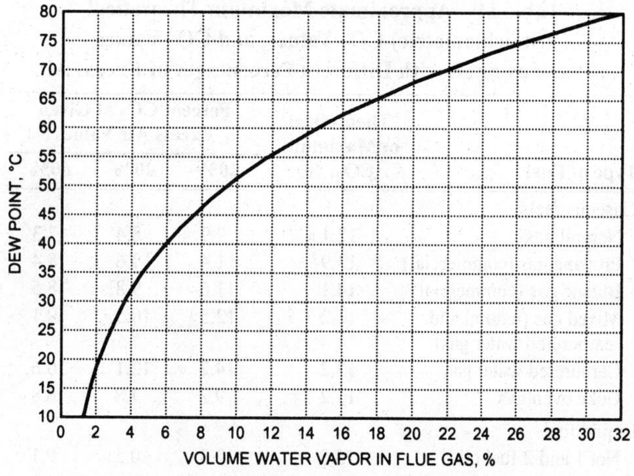

Fig. 3 Water Vapor and Dew Point of Flue Gas
Adapted from *Gas Engineers Handbook* (1965). Printed with permission of Industrial Press and American Gas Association.

Water Vapor and Dew Point of Flue Gas

Water vapor in flue gas is the total of the water (1) contained in the fuel, (2) contained in the stoichiometric and excess air, and (3) produced from combustion of hydrogen or hydrocarbons in the fuel. The amount of water vapor in stoichiometric combustion products may be calculated from the fuel burned by using the water data in Table 1.

The dew point is the temperature at which condensation begins and can be determined using Figure 3. The volume fraction of water vapor P_{wv} in the flue gas can be determined as follows:

$$P_{wv} = \frac{V_w}{(100V_c/P_c) + V_w} \qquad (15)$$

where

V_w = total water vapor volume (from fuel; stoichiometric, excess, and dilution air; and combustion)
V_c = unit volume of CO_2 produced per unit volume of gaseous fuel
P_c = percent CO_2 in flue gas

Using Figure 4, the dew points of solid, liquid, or gaseous fuels may be estimated. For example, to find the dew point of flue gas resulting from the combustion of a solid fuel with a mass ratio (hydrogen to carbon-plus-sulfur) of 0.088 and sufficient excess air to produce 11.4% oxygen in the flue gas, start with the mass ratio of 0.088. Proceed vertically to the intersection of the solid fuels curve and then to the theoretical dew point of 46°C on the dew-point scale (see dashed lines in Figure 4). Follow the curve fixed by this point (down and to the right) to 11.4% oxygen in the flue gas (on the abscissa). The actual dew point is 34°C and is found on the dew-point scale.

The dew point can be estimated for flue gas from natural gas having a higher heating value (HHV) of 38 MH/m³ with 6.3% oxygen or 31.5% air. Start with 38 MJ/m³ and proceed vertically to the intersection of the gaseous fuels curve and then to the theoretical dew point of 59°C on the dew-point scale. Follow the curve fixed by this point to 6.3% oxygen or 31.5% air in the flue gas. The actual dew point is 53°C.

The presence of sulfur dioxide, and particularly sulfur trioxide, influences the vapor pressure of condensate in flue gas, and the dew point can be raised by as much as 14 to 42°C, as shown in Figure 5. To illustrate the use of Figure 5, for a manufactured gas with an HHV of 20.5 MJ/m³ containing 340 mg of sulfur per cubic metre being burned with 40% excess air, the proper curve in Figure 5 is determined as follows:

$$\frac{\text{Mass sulfur in fuel, mg/m}^3}{\text{Fuel heating value, MJ/m}^3} = \frac{340}{20.5} = 16.6 \qquad (16)$$

This curve lies between the 0 and 20 curves and is close to the 20 curve. The dew point for any percentage of excess air from zero to 100% can be determined on this curve. For this flue gas with 40% excess air, the dew point is about 80°C, instead of 65°C for zero sulfur at 40% excess air.

Sample Combustion Calculations

Example 2. Analysis of flue gases from burning a natural gas shows 10.0% CO_2, 3.1% O_2, and 86.9% N_2 by volume. Analysis of the fuel is 90% CH_4, 5% N_2, and 5% C_2H_6 by volume. Find U (maximum theoretical percent CO_2), and percentage of excess air.

Solution: From Equation (12),

$$U = \frac{10.0}{1-(3.1/20.95)} = 11.74\%\ CO_2$$

From Equation (10), using $100(P/A) = 90$,

$$\text{Excess air} = \frac{(11.74-10.0)90}{10} = 15.7\%$$

Example 3. For the same analysis as in Example 2, find, per cubic metre of fuel gas, the volume of dry air required for combustion, the volume of each constituent in the flue gases, and the total volume of dry and wet flue gases.

Solution: From Equation (7), the volume of dry air required for combustion is

$$9.57CH_4 + 16.75C_2H_6 = (9.57 \times 0.90) + (16.75 \times 0.05)$$
$$= 9.45\ \text{m}^3 \text{ per m}^3 \text{ of fuel gas}$$

(The volume of dry air may also be calculated using Table 10.)

From Table 1, the cubic metres of flue gas constituents per cubic metre of fuel gas are as follows:

Nitrogen, N_2	
From methane	$(0.9CH_4)(9.57 - 2.0) = 6.81$
From ethane	$(0.05C_2H_6)(16.75 - 3.5) = 0.66$
Nitrogen in fuel	$= 0.05$
Nitrogen in excess air	$0.791 \times 0.157 \times 9.45 = 1.17$
	Total nitrogen = 8.69 m³
Oxygen, O_2	
In excess air	$0.209 \times 0.157 \times 9.45 = 0.31$ m³
Carbon dioxide, CO_2	
From methane	$(0.9CH_4)(1.0) = 0.90$
From ethane	$(0.05C_2H_6)(2.0) = 0.10$
	Total carbon dioxide = 1.00 m³
Water vapor, H_2O (does not appear in some flue gas analyses)	
From methane	$(0.9CH_4)(2.0) = 1.8$
From ethane	$(0.05C_2H_6)(3.0) = 0.15$
	Total water vapor = 1.95 m³

Total volume of dry gas per cubic metre of fuel gas

$$8.69 + 0.31 + 1.00 = 10.0\ \text{m}^3$$

Total volume of wet gases per cubic metre of fuel gas (neglecting water vapor in combustion air)

$$10.0 + 1.95 = 11.95\ \text{m}^3$$

The cubic metres of dry flue gas per cubic metre of fuel gas can also be computed from Equation (14):

$$(1.00)(100)/10.0 = 10.0\ \text{m}^3$$

EFFICIENCY CALCULATIONS

In analyzing heating appliance efficiency, an energy balance is made that accounts (as much as possible) for disposition of all thermal energy released by combustion of the fuel quantity consumed.

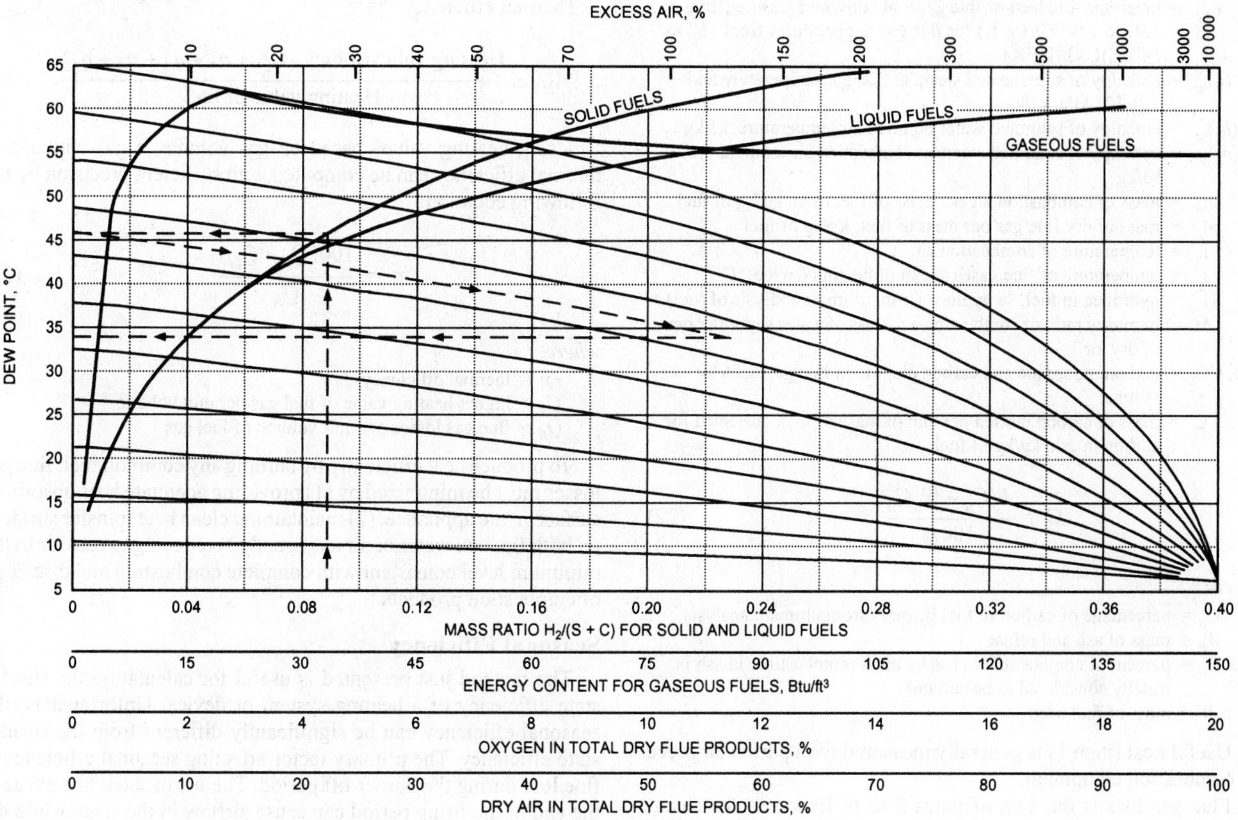

Fig. 4 Theoretical Dew Points of Combustion Products of Industrial Fuels

Adapted from *Gas Engineers Handbook* (1965). Printed with permission of Industrial Press and American Gas Association.

The various components of this balance are generally expressed in terms of megajoules per kilogram of fuel burned or as a percentage of its higher heating value. The following are major components of an energy balance and their calculation methods:

1. Useful heat q_1, or heat transferred to the heated medium; for convection heating equipment, this value is computed as the product of the mass rate of flow and enthalpy change.
2. Heat loss as sensible heat in the dry flue gases

$$q_2 = m_g c_{pg}(t_g - t_a) \tag{17}$$

where m_g (mass of dry flue gas per mass of fuel, kg/kg) is calculated as in Equation (13).

3. Heat loss in water vapor in products formed by combustion of hydrogen

$$q_3 = (9H_2/100)[(h)_{tg} - (h_f)_{ta}] \tag{18}$$

4. Heat loss in water vapor in the combustion air

$$q_4 = Mm_a[(h)_{tg} - (h_g)_{ta}] \tag{19}$$

where m_a is calculated as in Equations (5) and (6).

5. Heat loss from incomplete combustion of carbon

$$q_5 = 23\,591C\left(\frac{CO}{CO_2 + CO}\right) \tag{20}$$

6. Heat loss from unburned carbon in the ash or refuse

$$q_6 = 33\,957[(C_u/100) - C] \tag{21}$$

7. Unaccounted-for heat losses, q_7

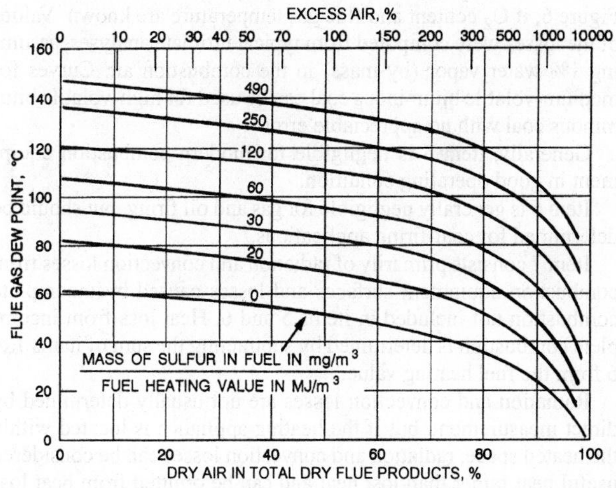

Fig. 5 Influence of Sulfur Oxides on Flue Gas Dew Point

The following symbols are used in Equations (17) to (21):

q_1 = useful heat, kJ/kg of fuel
q_2 = heat loss in dry flue gases, kJ/kg of fuel
q_3 = heat loss in water vapor from combustion of hydrogen, kJ/kg of fuel
q_4 = heat loss in water vapor in combustion air, kJ/kg of fuel
q_5 = heat loss from incomplete combustion of carbon, kJ/kg of fuel
q_6 = heat loss from unburned carbon in ash, kJ/kg of fuel
q_7 = unaccounted-for heat losses, kJ/kg of fuel

c_{pg} = mean specific heat of flue gases at constant pressure [from 1.01 to 1.06 kJ/(kg·K) for flue gas temperatures from 150 to 540°C)], kJ/(kg·K)
$(h)_{tg}$ = enthalpy of superheated steam at flue gas temperature and 101.325 kPa, kJ/kg
$(h_f)_{ta}$ = enthalpy of saturated water liquid at air temperature, kJ/kg
$(h_g)_{ta}$ = enthalpy of saturated steam at combustion air temperature, kJ/kg
m_a = mass of combustion air per mass of fuel used, kg/kg of fuel
m_g = mass of dry flue gas per mass of fuel, kg/kg of fuel
t_a = temperature of combustion air, °C
t_g = temperature of flue gases at exit of heating device, °C
H_2 = hydrogen in fuel, % by mass (from ultimate analysis of fuel)
M = humidity ratio of combustion air, mass of water vapor per mass of dry air
CO, CO_2 = carbon monoxide and carbon dioxide in flue gases, % by volume
C = mass of carbon burned per unit of mass of fuel, corrected for carbon in ash, kg/kg of fuel

$$C = \frac{WC_u - W_aC_a}{100W} \tag{22}$$

where

C_u = percentage of carbon in fuel by mass from ultimate analysis
W_a = mass of ash and refuse
C_a = percent of combustible in ash by mass (combustible in ash is usually considered to be carbon)
W = mass of fuel used

Useful heat (item 1) is generally measured for a particular piece of combustion equipment.

Flue gas loss is the sum of items 2 to 6. However, for clean-burning gas- and oil-fired equipment, items 5 and 6 are usually negligible and flue gas loss is the sum of items 2, 3, and 4.

Flue gas losses (the sum of items 2, 3, and 4) can be determined with sufficient precision for most purposes from the curves in Figure 6, if O_2 content and flue gas temperature are known. Values of the losses were computed from typical ultimate analyses, assuming 1% water vapor (by mass) in the combustion air. Curves for medium-volatile bituminous coal can be used for high-volatile bituminous coal with no appreciable error.

Generally, item 5 is negligible for modern combustion equipment in good operating condition.

Item 6 is generally negligible for gas and oil firing, but should be determined for coal-firing applications.

Item 7 consists primarily of radiation and convection losses from combustion equipment surfaces and losses caused by incomplete combustion not included in items 5 and 6. Heat loss from incomplete combustion is determined by subtracting the sum of items 1 to 6 from the fuel heating value.

Radiation and convection losses are not usually determined by direct measurement, but if the heating appliance is located within the heated space, radiation and convection losses can be considered useful heat rather than lost heat and can be omitted from heat loss calculations or added to item 1.

If CO is present in flue gases, small amounts of unburned hydrogen and hydrocarbons may also be present. The small losses caused by incomplete combustion of these gases would be included in item 7, if item 7 was determined by subtracting items 1 to 6 from the fuel heating value.

The overall thermal efficiency of combustion equipment is defined as

$$\text{Thermal efficiency, \%} = 100 \times \frac{\text{Useful heat}}{\text{Heating value of fuel}} \tag{23}$$

Equation (24) can be used to estimate efficiency for equipment where item 7 is small or radiation and convection are useful heat:

Thermal efficiency, % =

$$100 \times \frac{\text{Heating value of fuel} - (q_2 + q_3 + q_4 + q_5 + q_6)}{\text{Heating value of fuel}} \tag{24}$$

Using heating values based on gas volume, a gas appliance's thermal efficiency can be computed with sufficient precision by the following equation:

$$\eta = \frac{100(Q_h - Q_{fl})}{Q_h} \tag{25}$$

where

η = thermal efficiency, %
Q_h = higher heating value of fuel gas per unit volume
Q_{fl} = flue gas losses per unit volume of fuel gas

To produce heat efficiently by burning any common fuel, flue gas losses must be minimized by (1) providing adequate heat-absorbing surface in the appliance, (2) maintaining clean heat transfer surfaces on both fire and water or air sides, and (3) reducing excess air to the minimum level consistent with complete combustion and discharge of combustion products.

Seasonal Efficiency

The method just presented is useful for calculating the steady-state efficiency of a heating system or device. Unfortunately, the seasonal efficiency can be significantly different from the steady-state efficiency. The primary factor affecting seasonal efficiency is flue loss during the burner-off period. The warm stack that exists at the end of the firing period can cause airflow in the stack while the burner is off, which can remove heat from furnace and heat exchanger components, the structure itself, and pilot flames. Also, if combustion air is drawn from the heated space within the structure, the heated air lost must be at least partly replaced with cold infiltrated air. For further discussion of seasonal efficiency, see Chapters 9 and 32 of the 2008 *ASHRAE Handbook—HVAC Systems and Equipment* and Chapter 19 of this volume.

COMBUSTION CONSIDERATIONS

Air Pollution

Combustion processes constitute the largest single source of anthropogenic (human-caused) air pollution. Pollutants can be grouped into five categories:

- Products of incomplete fuel combustion
  - Combustible aerosols (solid and liquid), including smoke, soot, and organics, but excluding ash
  - Carbon monoxide CO
  - Gaseous hydrocarbons
- Carbon dioxide CO_2
- Oxides of nitrogen (collectively referred to as NO_x)
  - Nitric oxide NO
  - Nitrogen dioxide NO_2
- Emissions resulting from fuel contaminants
  - Sulfur oxides, primarily sulfur dioxide SO_2 and small quantities of sulfur trioxide SO_3
  - Ash
  - Trace metals
- Emissions resulting from additives
  - Combustion-controlling additives
  - Mercaptans
  - Other additives

Emission levels of nitrogen oxides and products of incomplete combustion are directly related to the combustion process and can be controlled, to some extent, by process modification. Emissions from

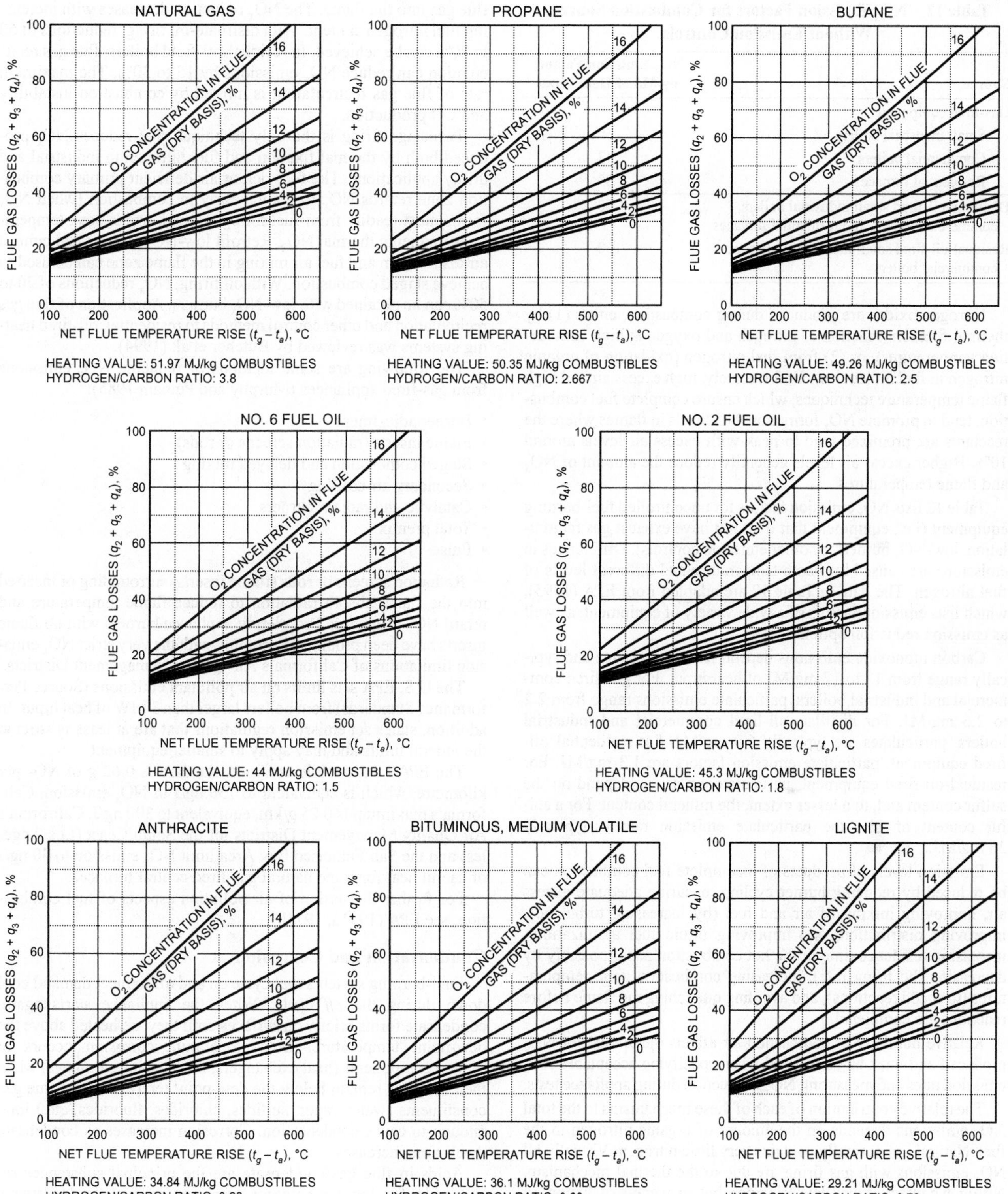

Fig. 6 Flue Gas Losses with Various Fuels
(Flue gas temperature rise shown. Loss based on 18°C room temperature.)

fuel contaminants are related to fuel selection and are slightly affected by the combustion process. Emissions from additives must be considered in the overall evaluation of the merits of using additives.

Carbon dioxide as a pollutant has gained attention because of its suspected effect on global warming. Carbon dioxide is produced by HVAC&R equipment (either directly or as a result of generating the electric power to operate the HVAC&R equipment), transportation, industry, and other sources. Carbon dioxide emissions can be minimized by increasing appliance operating efficiencies and using fuels with higher hydrogen content.

Table 12 NO_x Emission Factors for Combustion Sources Without Emission Controls

Source	NO_x Emission Factor, mg/MJ of Heat Input
Gas-fired equipment	
Small industrial boilers	60
Commercial boilers	43
Residential furnaces	39
Distillate-oil-fired small industrial boilers, commercial boilers, and residential furnaces	60
Residual-oil-fired small industrial boilers and commercial boilers	160

Nitrogen oxides are produced during combustion, either (1) by thermal fixation (reaction of nitrogen and oxygen at high combustion temperatures), or (2) from fuel nitrogen (oxidation of organic nitrogen in fuel molecules). Unfortunately, high excess air and high flame temperature techniques, which ensure complete fuel combustion, tend to promote NO_x formation. NO levels in flames where the reactants are premixed tend to peak with excess air levels around 10%. Higher excess air levels generally reduce the amount of NO_x and flame temperatures.

Table 12 lists NO_x emission factors for uncontrolled fuel-burning equipment (i.e., equipment that does not have exhaust gas recirculation, low-NO_x burners, or other emission controls). Differences in emissions are caused by flame temperature and different levels of fuel nitrogen. The data in Table 12 are adapted from EPA (1995), which lists emission factors of a wide variety of equipment, as well as emission reduction options.

Carbon monoxide emissions depend less on fuel type and typically range from 13 to 17 mg/MJ of heat input. For gas-fired commercial and industrial boilers, particulate emissions range from 2.2 to 2.6 mg/MJ. For distillate-oil-fired commercial and industrial boilers, particulates are typically 6.0 mg/MJ. For residential oil-fired equipment, particulate emission factors are 1.3 mg/MJ. For residual-oil-fired equipment, particulate emissions depend on the sulfur content and, to a lesser extent, the mineral content. For a sulfur content of 1%, the particulate emission rate is typically 36 mg/MJ.

Emission levels of products of incomplete fuel combustion can be reduced by reducing burner cycling, ensuring adequate excess air, improving mixing of air and fuel (by increasing turbulence, improving distribution, and improving liquid fuel atomization), increasing residence time in the hot combustion zone (possibly by decreasing the firing rate), increasing combustion zone temperatures (to speed reactions), and avoiding quenching the flame before reactions are completed.

Relative humidity of combustion air affects the amount of NO_x produced and must be considered when specifying acceptable NO_x emission rates and measuring NO_x production during appliance tests.

The relative contribution of each of these mechanisms to the total NO_x emissions depends on the amount of organic nitrogen in the fuel. Natural gas normally contains very little nitrogen. Virtually all NO_x emissions with gas firing are due to the thermal mechanism. Nitrogen content of distillate oil varies, but an average of 20 ppm of fuel NO_x is produced (about 20 to 30% of the total NO_x). Levels in residual oil can be significantly higher, with fuel NO_x contributing heavily to the total emissions.

Thermal fixation depends strongly on flame maximum temperature. For example, increasing the flame temperature from 1400 to 1500°C increases thermal NO_x tenfold. Therefore, methods to control thermal NO_x are based on methods to reduce the maximum flame temperature. Flue gas recirculation is perhaps the most effective method for commercial and industrial boilers. In gas-fired boilers, NO_x can be reduced 70% with 15 to 20% recirculation of flue gas into the flame. The NO_x reduction decreases with increasing fuel nitrogen content. With distillate-oil firing, reductions of 60 to 70% can be achieved. In residual-oil-fired boilers, flue gas recirculation can reduce NO_x emissions by 15 to 30%. The maximum rate of flue gas recirculation is limited by combustion instability and CO production.

Two-stage firing is the only technique that reduces NO_x produced both by thermal fixation and fuel nitrogen in industrial and utility applications. The fuel-rich or air-deficient primary combustion zone retards NO_x formation early in combustion (when NO_x forms most readily from fuel nitrogen), and avoids peak temperatures, reducing thermal NO_x. Retrofit low-NO_x burners that control air distribution and fuel air mixing in the flame zone can be used to achieve staged combustion. With oil firing, NO_x reductions of 20 to 50% can be obtained with low-NO_x burners. Application of flue gas recirculation and other control methods to residential, oil-fired heating systems was reviewed by Butcher et al. (1994).

The following are some methods of reducing NO_x emissions from gas-fired appliances (Murphy and Putnam 1985):

- Burner adjustment
- Flame inserts (radiation screens or rods)
- Staged combustion and delayed mixing
- Secondary air baffling
- Catalytic and radiant burners
- Total premix
- Pulse

Radiation screens or rods (flame inserts) surrounding or inserted into the flame absorb radiation to reduce flame temperature and retard NO_x formation. Proprietary appliance burners with no flame inserts have been produced to comply with the very strict NO_x emission limitations of California's Air Quality Management Districts.

The U.S. EPA sets limits on air pollutant emissions (Source Performance Standards) from boilers larger than 3 MW of heat input. In addition, states set emission regulations that are at least as strict at the federal limits and may apply to smaller equipment.

The EPA's automobile emission standard is 0.62 g of NO_2 per kilometre, which is equivalent to 750 ng/J of NO_x emission. California's maximum is 0.25 g/km, equivalent to 300 ng/J. California's Air Quality Management Districts for the South Coast (Los Angeles) and the San Francisco Bay Area limit NO_x emission to 40 ng/J of useful heat for some natural gas-fired central furnaces.

For further discussion of air pollution aspects of fuel combustion, see EPA (1971a, 1971b).

Condensation and Corrosion

Fuel-burning systems that cycle on and off to meet demand cool down during the *off* cycle. When the appliance starts again, condensate forms briefly on surfaces until they are heated above the dew-point temperature. Low-temperature corrosion occurs in system components (heat exchangers, flues, vents, chimneys) when their surfaces remain below the dew-point temperature of flue gas constituents (water vapor, sulfides, chlorides, fluorides, etc.) long enough to cause condensation. Corrosion increases as condensate dwell time increases.

Acids in flue gas condensate are the principal substances responsible for low-temperature corrosion in fuel-fired systems. Sulfuric, hydrochloric, and other acids are formed when acidic compounds in fuel and air combustion products combine with condensed moisture in appliance heat exchangers, flues, or vents. Corrosion can be avoided by maintaining these surfaces above the flue gas dew point.

In high-efficiency, condensing-type appliances and economizers, flue gas temperatures are intentionally reduced below the flue gas dew-point temperatures to achieve efficiencies approaching 100%. In these systems, surfaces subjected to condensate must be made of corrosion-resistant materials. The most corrosive conditions exist at the leading edge of the condensing region, especially areas that experience evaporation during each cycle (Stickford et al. 1988). Draining condensate retards the concentration of acids on system surfaces; regions from which condensate partially or completely drains away before evaporation are less severely attacked than regions from which condensate does not drain before evaporation.

The metals most resistant to condensate corrosion are stainless-steel alloys with high chromium and molybdenum content, and nickel-chromium alloys with high molybdenum content (Stickford et al. 1988). Aluminum experiences general corrosion rather than pitting when exposed to flue gas condensate. If applied in sufficiently thick cross section to allow for metal loss, aluminum can be used in condensing regions. Most ceramic and high-temperature polymer materials resist the corrosive effects of flue gas condensate. These materials may have application in the condensing regions, if they can meet the structural and temperature requirements of a particular application.

In coal-fired power plants, the rate of corrosion for carbon steel condensing surfaces by mixed acids (primarily sulfuric and hydrochloric) is reported to be maximum at about 50°C ± 10 K (Davis 1987). Mitigation techniques include (1) acid neutralization with a base such as NH_3 or $Ca(OH)_2$; (2) use of protective linings of glass-filled polyester or coal-tar epoxy; and (3) replacement of steel with molybdenum-bearing stainless steels, nickel alloys, polymers, or other corrosion-resistant materials. Other elements in residual fuel oils and coals that contribute to high-temperature corrosion include sodium, potassium, and vanadium. Each fuel-burning system component should be evaluated during installation, or when modified, to determine the potential for corrosion and the means to retard corrosion (Paul et al. 1988).

If fuel-burning appliances accumulate condensate that does not evaporate, the condensate must be routed into a trapped drainage system. Because the condensate may be acidic, the drainage system must be suitable and environmentally acceptable. Condensate freezing must be considered in cold climates.

Abnormal Combustion Noise in Gas Appliances

During development of a new boiler, furnace, or other gas-fired appliance, tonal noise can be an unacceptable problem. Because the frequency of the tone is equal to a resonance frequency of the system, this problem is often called a *combustion resonance*, but this term is misleading: changing the appliance's resonance frequency merely changes the frequency of the tone without much effect on the amplitude.

The proper term is **combustion-driven oscillation**, which is caused by feedback instability. Pressure oscillations in the combustion chamber (which manifest themselves as objectionable noise) also interact with the flame, modulating the instantaneous rate of combustion, which, in turn, causes more pressure oscillations (Putnam 1971). This feedback involves the acoustic response of the combustion chamber and of the fuel-air supply system, as well as that of the flame. For some combinations of response properties, the feedback loop is unstable.

Predicting instability in a design is generally not practical for domestic or small commercial appliances because there is not enough information to predict the acoustic response of some of the components, particularly the flame.

A model of the feedback loop (Baade 1978) is very useful, however, for solving existing oscillation problems, where the only concern is the particular frequency at which the oscillation occurs. Reducing the response of the flame, fuel/air mixture supply, or combustion chamber at that frequency should be the focus. This concept can be easily demonstrated with a small brazing torch in a tube of variable length (Baade 1987, 2004).

In some systems, the flame can be modified to reduce its response at the oscillation frequency. Often, this involves simply changing the fuel/air ratio further away from the stochiometric ratio (Elsari and Cummings 2003; Goldschmidt et al. 1978), thus lengthening the flame, which can also be done by increasing the size of burner ports (Matsui 1981; Schimmer 1979). Other possibilities for reducing flame response are using a suitable mix of differently sized burner ports (Kagiya 2000) and modifying the heat transfer characteristics of the burner matrix (Schreel et al. 2002).

The fuel supply system response can be reduced by avoiding resonance at or near the frequency of oscillation (Kilham et al. 1964) or by tuning the supply system to an antiresonance at that frequency (Neumann 1974). Designs for this can be evaluated by modeling the mixture supply system using transmission matrices (Munjal 1987) and computer programs for matrix multiplication, which are widely available (Baade and Tomarchio 2008).

For the combustion chamber, changing the resonance frequency is generally futile, but increasing the damping always works, provided that the system can increase damping sufficiently. Any damping less than the critical amount will have very little effect.

In some systems, the oscillation frequency may be a function of the flue pipe length. In such cases, investigate changing the length as well as adding damping.

For large systems, combustion oscillations may possibly be eliminated by using active feedback (Sattinger et al. 2000). Active feedback is not likely to be cost-effective for residential and small commercial systems.

Soot

Soot deposits on flue surfaces of a boiler or heater act as an insulating layer over the surface, reducing heat transfer to the water or air. Soot can also clog flues, reduce draft and available air, and prevent proper combustion. Proper burner adjustment can minimize soot accumulation. Using off-specification fuel can contribute to soot generation.

REFERENCES

ASME. 2007. *Boiler and pressure vessel code*. American Society of Mechanical Engineers, New York.

ASTM. 1999. Standard classification of coals by rank. *Standard* D388-99. American Society for Testing and Materials, West Conshohocken, PA.

ASTM. 2002. Standard specification for fuel oils. ANSI/ASTM *Standard* D396-02A. American Society for Testing and Materials, West Conshohocken, PA.

ASTM. 2004. Standard specification for diesel fuel oils. ANSI/ASTM *Standard* D975-04. American Society for Testing and Materials, West Conshohocken, PA.

ASTM. 2003. Standard specification for liquefied petroleum (LP) gases. ANSI/ASTM *Standard* D1835-03a. American Society for Testing and Materials, West Conshohocken, PA.

ASTM. 2003. Standard specification for gas turbine fuel oils. ANSI/ASTM *Standard* D2880-03. American Society for Testing and Materials, West Conshohocken, PA.

ASTM. 2008. Specification for automotive spark-ignition engine fuel. *Standard* D4814-08. American Society for Testing and Materials, West Conshohocken, PA.

ASTM. 2007. Specification for biodiesel fuel blend stock (B100) for middle distillate fuels. *Standard* D6751-07be1. American Society for Testing and Materials, West Conshohocken, PA.

Baade, P.K. 1978. Design criteria and models for preventing combustion oscillations. *ASHRAE Transactions* 84(1):449.

Baade, P.K. 1987. Demonstration of methods for solving combustion "resonance" noise problems. *NOISE-CON'87 Proceedings*, pp. 195-200.

Baade, P.K. 2004. How to solve abnormal combustion noise problems. *Sound and Vibration* 4(7):22-27.

Baade, P.K. and M.J. Tomarchio. 2008. Tricks and tools for solving abnormal combustion noise problems. *Sound and Vibration* (July):12-17.

Butcher, T.A., L. Fisher, B. Kamath, T. Kirchstetter, and J. Batey. 1994. Nitrogen oxides (NO_x) and oil burners. *Proceedings of the 1994 Oil Heat Technology Conference and Workshops*. BNL *Report* 52430. Brookhaven National Laboratory, Upton, NY.

Butcher, T.A., S.W. Lee, Y. Celebi, and W. Litzke. 1997. Fouling of heat-transfer surfaces in oil-fired boilers for domestic heating. *Journal of the Institute of Energy* 70:151-159.

Coward, H.F. and G.W. Jones. 1952. Limits of flammability of gases and vapors. *Bulletin* 503. U.S. Bureau of Mines, Washington, D.C.

Davis, J.R., ed. 1987. *Metals handbook*, 9th ed., vol. 13, *Corrosion*. ASM International, Metals Park, OH.

Dickson, C.L. and G.P. Sturm, Jr. 1994. *Heating oils*. National Institute for Petroleum and Energy Research, Bartlesville, OK.

Elsari, M. and A. Cummings. 2003. Combustion oscillations in gas fired appliances: Eigen-frequencies and stability regimes. *Applied Acoustics* 64(6):565-580.

EPA. 1971a. Standards of performance for new stationary sources, Group I. *Federal Register* 36, August 17. U.S. Environmental Protection Agency, Washington, D.C.

EPA. 1971b. Standards of performance for new stationary sources, Group I, Part II. *Federal Register* 36, December 23. U.S. Environmental Protection Agency, Washington, D.C.

EPA. 1995. Compilation of air pollutant emission factors. *Report* AP-42. U.S. Environmental Protection Agency, Washington, D.C. http://www.epa.gov/ttn/chief/ap42/.

Fleck, B.A., S.C. Arnold, M.Y. Ackerman, J.D. Dale, W.E. Klaczek, and D.J. Wilson. 2007. Field testing and residential fan-assisted gas-fired furnaces: Effects of altitude and assessment of current derating standards (RP-1182). ASHRAE Research Project, *Final Report*.

Fricker, N. and C.A. Roberts, 1979. An experimental and theoretical approach to combustion driven oscillations. *Gas Waerme International* 28(13).

Gas engineers handbook. 1965. Industrial Press, New York.

Goldschmidt, V., R.G. Leonard, J.F. Riley, G. Wolfbrandt, and P.K. Baade. 1978. Transfer functions of gas flames: Methods of measurement and representative data. *ASHRAE Transactions* 84(1):466-476.

GPA. 1997. Liquefied petroleum gas specifications and test methods. *Standard* 2140-97. Gas Processors Association, Tulsa, OK.

Hartman, I. 1958. Dust explosions. In *Mechanical engineers' handbook*, 6th ed., Section 7, pp. 41-48. McGraw-Hill, New York.

Hazard, H.R. 1971. Gas turbine fuels. In *Gas turbine handbook*. Gas Turbine Publications, Stamford, CT.

Kagiya, S. 2000. Practical burner design for the suppression of combustion oscillations. *Annual Technical Report Digest*, vol. 10. Tokyo Gas Co.

Kilham, J.K., E.G. Jackson, and T.J.B. Smith. 1964. Oscillatory combustion in tunnel burners. *10th Symposium (International) on Combustion*, England, pp. 1231-1240. The Combustion Institute, Pittsburgh, PA.

Lee, S.W., I. He, T. Herage, V. Razbin, E. Kelly, and B. Young. 2002a. *Influence of fuel sulphur in particulate emissions from pilot-scale research furnaces*. Natural Resources Canada. CETC 02-08 (CF).

Lee, S.W., I. He, T. Herage, B. Young, and E. Kelly. 2002b. *Fuel sulphur effects on particulate emissions from oil combustion systems under accelerated laboratory conditions*. Natural Resources Canada. CETC 02-09 (CF).

Matsui, Y. 1981. An experimental study on pyro-acoustic amplification of premixed laminar flames. *Combustion and Flame* 43:199-209.

Munjal, M.L. 1987. *Acoustics of ducts and mufflers*. Wiley Interscience, Hoboken, NJ.

Murphy, M.J. and A.A. Putnam. 1985. Burner technology bulletin: Control of NO_x emissions from residential gas appliances. *Report* GRI-85/0132. Battelle Columbus Division for Gas Research Institute.

Neumann, E.G. 1974. An impedance condition for avoiding acoustic oscillations generated by gas flames. *Acustica* 30:229-235.

NFPA. 1962. Fire-hazard properties of flammable liquids, gases and volatile solids. In *Fire protection handbook*, 12th ed., Tables 6-126, pp. 6-131 ff. National Fire Protection Association, Quincy, MA.

NFPA/AGA. 2006. National fuel gas code, Section 11.1.2. ANSI/NFPA *Standard* 54-2006. National Fire Protection Association, Quincy, MA. ANSI/AGA *Standard* Z223.1-1999. American Gas Association, Washington, D.C.

North American combustion handbook, 3rd ed. 1986. North American Manufacturing Co., Cleveland, OH.

Paul, D.D., A.L. Rutz, S.G. Talbert, J.J. Crisafolli, G.R. Whitacre, and R.D. Fischer. 1988. User's manual for Vent-II Ver. 3.0—A dynamic microcomputer program for analyzing gas venting systems. *Report* GRI-88/0304. Battelle Columbus Division for Gas Research Institute.

Putnam, A. 1971. *Combustion-driven oscillations in industry*. Elsevier, New York.

Sattinger, S.S., Y. Neumeier, A. Nabi, B.T. Zinn, D.J. Amos, and D.D. Darling. 2000. Sub-scale demonstration of the active feedback control of gas-turbine combustion instabilities. *ASME Transactions, Journal of Engineering for Gas Turbines and Power* 122(2):262-268.

Schimmer, H. 1979. Selbsterregte Schwingungen in Brennkammern—Ihre Entstehung und Massnahmen zu ihrer Vermeidung. *Gas Waerme International* 26:17-23.

Schreel, K.R.A.M., R. Rook, and L.P.H. de Goey. 2002. The acoustic response of burner stabilized flat flames. *Proceedings of the Combustion Institute*, Sapporo, Japan, vol. 29, pp. 115-121.

Scott, G.S., G.W. Jones, and F.E. Scott. 1948. Determination of ignition temperatures of combustible liquids and gases. *Analytical Chemistry* 20: 238-241.

Shelton, E.M. 1974. Burner oil fuels. *Petroleum Products Survey* 86. U.S. Bureau of Mines, Washington, D.C.

Shnidman, L. 1954. *Gaseous fuels*. American Gas Association, Arlington, VA.

Stickford, G.H., S.G. Talbert, B. Hindin, and D.W. Locklin. 1988. Research on corrosion-resistant materials for condensing heat exchangers. *Proceedings of the 39th Annual International Appliance Technical Conference*.

Trinks, W. 1947. Simplified calculation of radiation from non-luminous furnace gases. *Industrial Heating* 14:40-46.

U.S. Bureau of Mines. Semiannually. *Mineral industry surveys, motor gasolines*. Washington, D.C.

Zabetakis, M.G. 1956. Research on the combustion and explosion hazards of hydrogen-water vapor-air mixtures. Division of Explosives Technology, *Progress Report* 1. U.S. Bureau of Mines, Washington, D.C.

BIBLIOGRAPHY

ANSI. 2004. American National Standard acoustical terminology. *Standard* S1.1-1994 (R2004). American National Standards Institute, New York.

Bonne, U. and A. Patani. 1982. Combustion system performance analysis and simulation study. *Report* GRI-81/0093 (PB 83-161 406). Honeywell SSPL, Bloomington, MN.

Gas Appliance Technology Center, Gas Research Institute. *Manufacturer update on status of GATC research on heat-exchanger corrosion, May 1984*. Battelle Columbus Laboratories and American Gas Association Laboratories.

Lewis, B. and G. von Elbe. 1987. *Combustion, flames, and explosion of gases*, 3rd ed. Academic Press, New York.

Stickford, G.H., S.G. Talbert, and D.W. Locklin. 1987. Condensate corrosivity in residential condensing appliances. *Proceedings of the International Symposium on Condensing Heat Exchangers*, Paper 3, BNL *Report* 52068, 1 and 2. Brookhaven National Laboratory, Upton, NY.

CHAPTER 29

REFRIGERANTS

REFRIGERANTS are the working fluids in refrigeration, air-conditioning, and heat-pumping systems. They absorb heat from one area, such as an air-conditioned space, and reject it into another, such as outdoors, usually through evaporation and condensation, respectively. These phase changes occur both in absorption and mechanical vapor compression systems, but not in systems operating on a gas cycle using a fluid such as air. (See Chapter 2 for more information on refrigeration cycles.) The design of the refrigeration equipment depends strongly on the selected refrigerant's properties. Tables 1 and 2 list standard refrigerant designations, some properties, and safety classifications from ASHRAE *Standard* 34.

Refrigerant selection involves compromises between conflicting desirable thermophysical properties. A refrigerant must satisfy many requirements, some of which do not directly relate to its ability to transfer heat. Chemical stability under conditions of use is an essential characteristic. Safety codes may require a nonflammable refrigerant of low toxicity for some applications. Environmental consequences of refrigerant leaks must also be considered. Cost, availability, efficiency, and compatibility with compressor lubricants and equipment materials are other concerns.

Latent heat of vaporization is another important property. On a molar basis, fluids with similar boiling points have almost the same latent heat. Because compressor displacement is defined on a volumetric basis, refrigerants with similar boiling points produce similar refrigeration effect with a given compressor. On a mass basis, latent heat varies widely among fluids. Efficiency of a theoretical vapor compression cycle is maximized by fluids with low vapor heat capacity. This property is associated with fluids having a simple molecular structure and low molecular mass.

Transport properties (e.g., thermal conductivity and viscosity) affect performance of heat exchangers and piping. High thermal conductivity and low viscosity are desirable.

No single fluid satisfies all the attributes desired of a refrigerant; consequently, various refrigerants are used. This chapter describes the basic characteristics of various refrigerants, and Chapter 30 lists thermophysical properties.

REFRIGERANT PROPERTIES

Global Environmental Properties

Chlorofluorocarbons (CFCs) and hydrochlorofluorocarbons (HCFCs) can affect both stratospheric ozone and climate change, whereas hydrofluorocarbons (HFCs) can affect climate change. Minimizing all refrigerant releases from systems is important not only because of environmental impacts, but also because charge losses lead to insufficient system charge levels, which in turn results in suboptimal operation and lowered efficiency.

Stratospheric Ozone Depletion. The stratospheric ozone layer filters out the UV-B portion of the sun's ultraviolet (UV) radiation. Overexposure to this radiation increases the risk of skin cancer, cataracts, and impaired immune systems. It also can damage sensitive crops, reduce crop yields, and stress marine phytoplankton (and thus human food supplies from the oceans). In addition, exposure to UV radiation degrades plastics and wood.

Stratospheric ozone depletion has been linked to the presence of chlorine and bromine in the stratosphere. Chemicals with long atmospheric lifetimes can migrate to the stratosphere, where the molecules break down from interaction with ultraviolet light or through chemical reaction. Chemicals such as CFCs and HCFCs release chlorine, which reacts with stratospheric ozone.

Ozone-depleting substances, including CFCs and HCFCs, are to be phased out of production under the Montreal Protocol (UNEP 2003, 2006). U.S. regulations for CFC and HCFC refrigerants, including phaseout schedules, may be found at http://www.epa.gov/ozone/strathome.html. The Alliance for Responsible Atmospheric Policy (http://www.arap.org/regs/) also briefly summarizes regulations for several countries. Reclaimed CFC and HCFC refrigerants that meet the requirements of ARI *Standard* 700 can continue to be used for servicing existing systems.

Global Climate Change. The average global temperature is determined by the balance of energy from the sun heating the earth and its atmosphere and of energy radiated from the earth and the atmosphere to space. **Greenhouse gases (GHGs)**, such as carbon dioxide (CO_2) and water vapor, as well as small particles trap heat at and near the surface, maintaining the average temperature of the Earth's surface about 34 K warmer than would be the case if these gases and particles were not present (the **greenhouse effect**).

Global warming (also called **global climate change**) is a concern because of an increase in the greenhouse effect from increasing concentrations of GHGs attributed to human activities. The major GHG of concern is CO_2 released to the atmosphere when fossil fuels (coal, oil, and natural gas) are burned for energy. Methane (CH_4), nitrous oxide (N_2O), CFCs, HCFCs, HFCs, perfluorocarbons (PFCs), and sulfur hexafluoride (SF_6) are also GHGs.

In 1988, the United Nations Environment Programme (UNEP) and the World Meteorological Organization (WMO) established the Intergovernmental Panel on Climate Change (IPCC) to provide an objective source of information about the causes of climate change, its potential environmental and socioeconomic consequences, and the adaptation and mitigation options to respond to it. According to IPCC (2007a), atmospheric concentration of carbon dioxide has increased by more than 35% over the past 250 years, primarily from burning fossil fuels, with some contribution from deforestation. Concentration of methane has increased by over 145%, and nitrous oxide by about 18%. IPCC (2007a) deems atmospheric concentrations of fluorochemicals, including fluorocarbon gases (CFCs, HCFCs, and HFCs) and sulfur hexafluoride, to be a smaller contributor to global climate change. On whether observed warming is attributable to human influence, IPCC (2007b) concludes that "Most of the observed increase in global averaged temperatures since the mid-twentieth century [about 0.65 K] is very likely [90% confident] due to the observed increase in anthropogenic greenhouse gas concentrations."

The preparation of this chapter is assigned to TC 3.1, Refrigerants and Secondary Coolants.

Table 1 Refrigerant Data and Safety Classifications

Refrigerant Number	Chemical Name[a,b]	Chemical Formula[a]	Molecular Mass[a]	Normal Boiling Point,[a] °C	Safety Group
Methane Series					
11	Trichlorofluoromethane	CCl_3F	137.4	24	A1
12	Dichlorodifluoromethane	CCl_2F_2	120.9	–30	A1
12B1	Bromochlorodifluoromethane	$CBrClF_2$	165.4	–4	
13	Chlorotrifluoromethane	$CClF_3$	104.5	–81	A1
14	Tetrafluoromethane (carbon tetrafluoride)	CF_4	88.0	–128	A1
21	Dichlorofluoromethane	$CHCl_2F$	102.9	9	B1
22	Chlorodifluoromethane	$CHClF_2$	86.5	–41	A1
23	Trifluoromethane	CHF_3	70.0	–82	A1
30	Dichloromethane (methylene chloride)	CH_2Cl_2	84.9	40	B2
31	Chlorofluoromethane	CH_2ClF	68.5	–9	
32	Difluoromethane (methylene fluoride)	CH_2F_2	52.0	–52	A2
40	Chloromethane (methyl chloride)	CH_3Cl	50.4	–24	B2
41	Fluoromethane (methyl fluoride)	CH_3F	34.0	–78	
50	Methane	CH_4	16.0	–161	A3
Ethane Series					
113	1,1,2-trichloro-1,2,2-trifluoroethane	CCl_2FCClF_2	187.4	48	A1
114	1,2-dichloro-1,1,2,2-tetrafluoroethane	$CClF_2CClF_2$	170.9	4	A1
115	Chloropentafluoroethane	$CClF_2CF_3$	154.5	–39	A1
116	Hexafluoroethane	CF_3CF_3	138.0	–78	A1
123	2,2-dichloro-1,1,1-trifluoroethane	$CHCl_2CF_3$	153.0	27	B1
124	2-chloro-1,1,1,2-tetrafluoroethane	$CHClFCF_3$	136.5	–12	A1
125	Pentafluoroethane	CHF_2CF_3	120.0	–79	A1
134a	1,1,1,2-tetrafluoroethane	CH_2FCF_3	102.0	–26	A1
141b	1,1-dichloro-1-fluoroethane	CH_3CCl_2F	117.0	32	
142b	1-chloro-1,1-difluoroethane	CH_3CClF_2	100.5	–10	A2
143a	1,1,1-trifluoroethane	CH_3CF_3	84.0	–47	A2
152a	1,1-difluoroethane	CH_3CHF_2	66.0	–25	A2
170	Ethane	CH_3CH_3	30.0	–89	A3
Ethers					
E170	Dimethyl ether	CH_3OCH_3	46.0	–25	A3
Propane Series					
218	Octafluoropropane	$CF_3CF_2CF_3$	188.0	–37	A1
236fa	1,1,1,3,3,3-hexafluoropropane	$CF_3CH_2CF_3$	152.0	–1	A1
245fa	1,1,1,3,3-pentafluoropropane	$CF_3CH_2CHF_2$	134.0	15	B1
290	Propane	$CH_3CH_2CH_3$	44.0	–42	A3
Cyclic Organic Compounds (see Table 2 for blends)					
C318	Octafluorocyclobutane	$-(CF_2)_4-$	200.0	–6	A1
Miscellaneous Organic Compounds					
Hydrocarbons					
600	Butane	$CH_3CH_2CH_2CH_3$	58.1	0	A3
600a	Isobutane	$CH(CH_3)_2CH_3$	58.1	–12	A3
601	Pentane	$CH_3(CH_2)_3CH_3$	72.15	36.1	A3
601a	Isopentane	$(CH_3)_2CHCH_2CH_3$	72.15	27.8	A3
Oxygen Compounds					
610	Ethyl ether	$CH_3CH_2OCH_2CH_3$	74.1	35	
611	Methyl formate	$HCOOCH_3$	60.0	32	B2
Sulfur Compounds					
620	(Reserved for future assignment)				
Nitrogen Compounds					
630	Methyl amine	CH_3NH_2	31.1	–7	
631	Ethyl amine	$CH_3CH_2(NH_2)$	45.1	17	
Inorganic Compounds					
702	Hydrogen	H_2	2.0	–253	A3
704	Helium	He	4.0	–269	A1
717	Ammonia	NH_3	17.0	–33	B2
718	Water	H_2O	18.0	100	A1
720	Neon	Ne	20.2	–246	A1
728	Nitrogen	N_2	28.1	–196	A1
732	Oxygen	O_2	32.0	–183	
740	Argon	Ar	39.9	–186	A1
744	Carbon dioxide	CO_2	44.0	–78[c]	A1
744A	Nitrous oxide	N_2O	44.0	–90	
764	Sulfur dioxide	SO_2	64.1	–10	B1
Unsaturated Organic Compounds					
1150	Ethene (ethylene)	$CH_2{=}CH_2$	28.1	–104	A3
1270	Propene (propylene)	$CH_3CH{=}CH_2$	42.1	–48	A3

Source: ANSI/ASHRAE *Standard* 34-2007.

[a]Chemical name, chemical formula, molecular mass, and normal boiling point are not part of this standard.

[b]Preferred chemical name is followed by the popular name in parentheses.

[c]Sublimes.

Table 2 Data and Safety Classifications for Refrigerant Blends

Refrigerant Number	Composition (Mass %)	Composition Tolerances	Azeotropic Temperature, °C	Molecular Mass[a]	Normal Boiling Point, °C	Safety Group
Zeotropes						
400	R-12/114 (must be specified)		none			A1
401A	R-22/152a/124 (53.0/13.0/34.0)	(±2/+0.5,–1.5/±1)				A1
401B	R-22/152a/124 (61.0/11.0/28.0)	(±2/+0.5,–1.5/±1)				A1
401C	R-22/152a/124 (33.0/15.0/52.0)	(±2/+0.5,–1.5/±1)				A1
402A	R-125/290/22 (60.0/2.0/38.0)	(±2/±0.1,–1/±2)				A1
402B	R-125/290/22 (38.0/2.0/60.0)	(±2/±0.1,–1/±2)				A1
403A	R-290/22/218 (5.0/75.0/20.0)	(+0.2,–2/±2/±2)				A1
403B	R-290/22/218 (5.0/56.0/39.0)	(+0.2,–2/±2/±2)				A1
404A	R-125/143a/134a (44.0/52.0/4.0)	(±2/±1/±2)				A1
405A	R-22/152a/142b/C318 (45.0/7.0/5.5/42.5)	(±2/±1/±1/±2)				
406A	R-22/600a/142b (55.0/4.0/41.0)	(±2/±1/±1)				A2
407A	R-32/125/134a (20.0/40.0/40.0)	(±2/±2/±2)				A1
407B	R-32/125/134a (10.0/70.0/20.0)	(±2/±2/±2)				A1
407C	R-32/125/134a (23.0/25.0/52.0)	(±2/±2/±2)				A1
407D	R-32/125/134a (15.0/15.0/70.0)	(±2/±2/±2)				A1
407E	R-32/125/134a (25.0/15.0/60.0)	(±2,±2,±2)				A1
408A	R-125-143a-22 (7.0/46.0/47.0)	(±2/±1/±2)				A1
409A	R-22/124/142b (60.0/25.0/15.0)	(±2/±2/±1)				A1
409B	R-22/124/142b (65.0/25.0/10.0)	(±2/±2/±1)				A1
410A	R-32/125 (50.0/50.0)	(+0.5,–1.5/+1.5,–0.5)				A1
410B	R-32/125 (45.0/55.0)	(±1/±1)				A1
411A	R-1270/22/152a (1.5/87.5/11.0)	(+0,–1/+2,–0/+0,–1)				A2
411B	R-1270/22/152a (3.0/94.0/3.0)	(+0,–1/+2,–0/+0,–1)				A2
412A	R-22/218/142b (70.0/5.0/25.0)	(±2/±1/±1)				A2
413A	R-218/134a/600a (9.0/88.0/3.0)	(±1/±2/±0,–1)				A2
414A	R-22/124/600a/142b (51.0/28.5/4.0/16.5)	(±2/±2/±0.5/±0.5,–1)				A1
414B	R-22/124/600a/142b (50.0/39.0/1.5/9.5)	(±2/±2/±0.5/±0.5,–1)				A1
415A	R-22/152a (82.0/18.0)	(±1/±1)				A2
415B	R-22/152a (25.0/75.0)	(±1/±1)				A2
416A	R-134a/124/600 (59.0/39.5/1.5)	(+0.5,–1/+1,–0.5/+1,–0.2)				A1
417A	R-125/134a/600 (46.6/50.0/3.4)	(±1/±1/±0.1,–0.4)				A1
418A	R-290/22/152a (1.5/96.0/2.5)	(±0.5/±1/±0.5				A2
419A	R-125/134a/E170 (77.0/19.0/4.0)	(±1/±1/±1)				A2
420A	R-134a/142b (88.0/12.0)	(±1,–0,+0,–1)				A1
421A	R-125/134a (58.0/42.0)	(±1/ ±1)				A1
421B	R125/134a (85.0/15.0)	(±1/±1)				A1
422A	R-125/134a/600a (85.1/11.5/3.4)	(±1/ ±1/+0.1,–0.4)				A1
422B	R-125/134a/600a (55.0/42.0/3.0)	(±1/ ±1/+0.1,–0.5)				A1
422C	R-125/134a/600a (82.0/15.0/3.0)	(±1/ ±1/+0.1,–0.5)				A1
423A	R-134a/227ea (52.5/47.5)	(±1/±1)				A1
424A	R-125/134a/600a/600/601a (50.5/47.0/0.9/1.0/0.6)	(±1/ ±1/+0.1,–0.2/+0.1, –0.2/+0.1,–0.2)				A1
425A	R-32/134a/227ea (18.5/69.5/12.0)	(±0.5/±0.5/±0.5)				A1
426A	R-125/134a/600a/601a (5.1/93.0/1.3/0.6)	(±1/ ±1/+0.1,–0.2/+0.1,–0.2)				A1
427A	R-32/125/143a/134a (15.0/25.0/10.0/50.0)	(±2/ ±2/±2/ ±2)				A1
428A	R-125/143a/290/600a (77.5/20.0/0.6/1.9)	(±1/ ±1/+0.1, –0.2/+0.1,–0.2)				A1
Azeotropes[b]						
500	R-12/152a (73.8/26.2)		0	99.3	–33	A1
501	R-22/12 (75.0/25.0)[c]		–41	93.1	–41	A1
502	R-22/115 (48.8/51.2)		19	112.0	–45	A1
503	R-23/13 (40.1/59.9)		88	87.5	–88	
504	R-32/115 (48.2/51.8)		17	79.2	–57	
505	R-12/31 (78.0/22.0)[c]		115	103.5	–30	
506	R-31/114 (55.1/44.9)		18	93.7	–12	
507A[d]	R-125/143a (50.0/50.0)		–40	98.9	–46.7	A1
508A[d]	R-23/116 (39.0/61.0)		–86	100.1	–86	A1
508B	R-23/116 (46.0/54.0)		–45.6	95.4	–88.3	A1
509A[d]	R-22/218 (44.0/56.0)		0	124.0	–47	A1

Source: ANSI/ASHRAE *Standard* 34-2007.

[a]Molecular mass and normal boiling point are not part of this standard.

[b]Azeotropic refrigerants exhibit some segregation of components at conditions of temperature and pressure other than those at which they were formulated. Extent of segregation depends on the particular azeotrope and hardware system configuration.

[c]Exact composition of this azeotrope is in question, and additional experimental studies are needed.

[d]R-507, R-508, and R-509 are allowed designations for R-507A, R-508A, and R-509A because of a change in designations after assignment of R-500 through R-509. Corresponding changes were not made for R-500 through R-506.

Global Environmental Characteristics of Refrigerants. Atmospheric release of CFC and HCFC refrigerants such as R-11, R-12, R-22, and R-502 contributes to depletion of the ozone layer. The measure of a material's ability to deplete stratospheric ozone is its **ozone depletion potential (ODP)**, a value relative to that of R-11 which is 1.0.

Halocarbons (CFCs, HCFCs, and HFCs) and many nonhalocarbons (e.g., hydrocarbons, carbon dioxide) are also greenhouse gases. The **global warming potential (GWP)** of a GHG is an index describing its relative ability to trap radiant energy compared to CO_2 (R-744), which has a very long atmospheric lifetime. GWP may be calculated for any particular **integration time horizon (ITH)**. Typically, a 100 year ITH is used for regulatory purposes, and may be designated as GWP_{100}.

The energy refrigeration appliances consume is often produced from fossil fuels, which results in emission of CO_2, a contributor to global warming. This indirect effect associated with energy consumption is frequently much larger than the direct effect of refrigerant emissions. The **total equivalent warming impact (TEWI)** of an HVAC&R system is the sum of direct refrigerant emissions expressed in terms of CO_2 equivalents, and indirect emissions of CO_2 from the system's energy use over its service life. Another measure is **life-cycle climate performance (LCCP)**, which includes TEWI and adds direct and indirect emissions effects associated with manufacturing the refrigerant.

Ammonia (R-717), hydrocarbons, HCFCs, and most HFCs have shorter atmospheric lifetimes than CFCs because they are largely destroyed in the lower atmosphere by reactions with OH radicals. A shorter atmospheric lifetime generally results in lower ODP and GWP_{100} values. Environmentally preferred refrigerants (1) have low or zero ODP, (2) have relatively short atmospheric lifetimes, (3) have low GWP_{100}, (4) provide good system efficiency, (5) have appropriate safety properties, and (6) yield a low TEWI or LCCP in system applications (i.e., leaks are minimized or prevented, and performance is optimized).

Table 3 shows atmospheric lifetime, ODP, and GWP_{100} of refrigerants being phased out under the Montreal Protocol and of refrigerants being used to replace them, alone or as components of blends. Because HFCs do not contain chlorine or bromine, their ODP values are negligible (Ravishankara et al. 1994) and thus are shown as 0 in Table 3. Nonhalocarbon refrigerants listed have zero ODP and very low GWP_{100}.

There are some differences between the values stipulated for reporting under the Montreal and Kyoto protocols and the latest scientific values. These are not of sufficient magnitude to significantly alter design decisions based on the numbers in the table. All these values have rather wide error bands and may change with each assessment of the science. Changes in GWP assessments are largely dominated by changes in understanding of CO_2, which is the reference chemical.

Table 4 shows the calculated ODPs and GWP_{100}s for refrigerant blends, using the latest scientific assessment values as reported in Calm and Hourahan (2007).

Table 3 Refrigerant Environmental Properties

Refrigerant	Atmospheric Lifetime, years[a]	ODP[b]	GWP_{100}[c]
R-11	45	1	4750
R-12	100	1	10 900
R-13	640	1	14 400
R-22	12	0.055	1810
R-23	270	0	14 800
R-32	4.9	0	675
R-113	85	0.8	6130
R-114	300	1	10 000
R-115	1700	0.6	7370
R-116	10 000	0	12 200
R-123	1.3	0.02	77
R-124	5.8	0.022	609
R-125	29	0	3500
R-134a	14	0	1430
R-141b	9.3	0.11	725
R-142b	17.9	0.065	2310
R-143a	52	0	4470
R-152a	1.4	0	124
R-218	2600	0	8830
R-227ea	34.2	0	3220
R-236fa	240	0	9810
R-245ca	6.2[d]	0	693[d]
R-245fa	7.6	0	1030
R-C318	3200	0	10 300
R-744	Variable	0	1
R-290	0.41[d]	0	~20[d]
R-600	0.018[d]	0	~20[d]
R-600a	0.019[d]	0	~20[d]
R-601a	0.01[d]	0	~20[d]
R-717	0.01[d]	0	<1[d]
R-1270	0.001[d]	0	~20[d]

[a]Atmospheric lifetimes from Table 2.14 of IPCC (2007b) except where indicated.
[b]ODP from UNEP (2006), Section 1.1, Annexes A, B, and C, pp. 23-25.
[c]GWP_{100} from Table 2.14 of IPCC (2007b) except where indicated.
[d]Calm and Hourahan (2007).

Physical Properties

Table 5 lists some physical properties of commonly used refrigerants, a few very-low-boiling-point cryogenic fluids, some newer refrigerants, and some older refrigerants of historical interest. These refrigerants are arranged in increasing order of atmospheric boiling point.

Table 5 also includes the freezing point, critical properties, and refractive index. Of these properties, normal boiling point is most important because it is a direct indicator of the temperature at which a refrigerant can be used. The freezing point must be lower than any contemplated usage. The critical properties describe a material at the

Table 4 Environmental Properties of Refrigerant Blends

Refrigerant Number	ODP*	GWP_{100}*	Refrigerant Number	ODP*	GWP_{100}*
401A	0.033	1200	415B	0.013	550
401B	0.036	1300	416A	0.008	1100
401C	0.027	930	417A	0.000	2300
402A	0.019	2800	418A	0.048	1700
402B	0.030	2400	419A	0	3000
403A	0.038	3100	420A	0.008	1500
403B	0.028	4500	421A	0	2600
404A	0	3900	421B	0	3200
405A	0.026	5300	422A	0	3100
406A	0.056	1900	422B	0	2500
407A	0	2100	422C	0	3100
407B	0	2800	422D	0	2700
407C	0	1800	423A	0	2300
407D	0	1600	424A	0	2400
407E	0	1600	425A	0	1500
408A	0.024	3200	426A	0	1500
409A	0.046	1600	427A	0	2100
409B	0.045	1600	428A	0	3600
410A	0	2100	500	0.738	8100
411A	0.044	1600	502	0.250	4700
411B	0.047	1700	503	0.599	15 000
412A	0.053	2300	507A	0	4000
413A	0	2100	508A	0	13 000
414A	0.043	1500	508B	0	13 000
414B	0.039	1400	509A	0.022	5700
415A	0.028	1500			

*ODPs and GWP_{100}s from Calm and Hourahan (2007), computed based on mass-weighted averages of values for individual components.

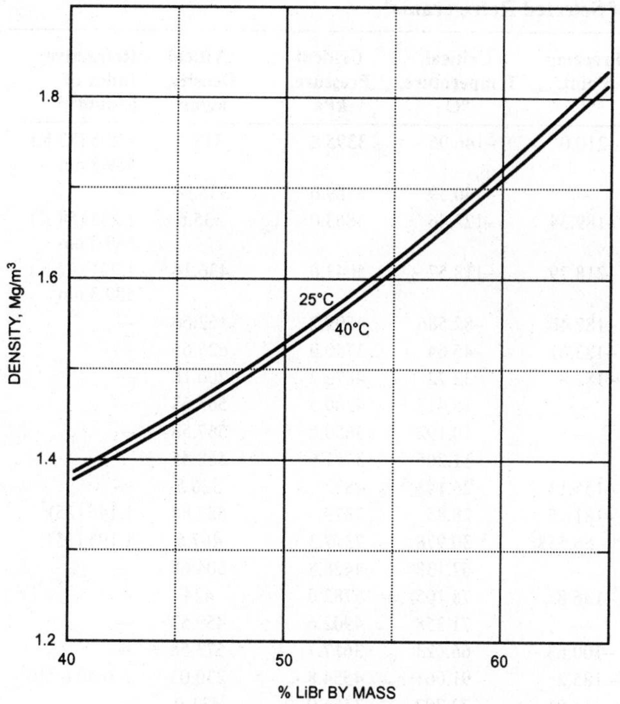

Fig. 1 Specific Density of Aqueous Solutions of Lithium Bromide

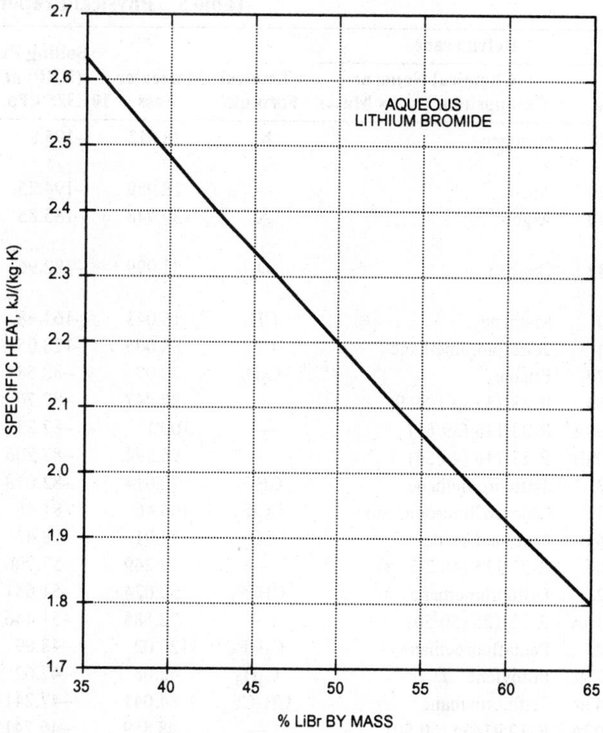

Fig. 2 Specific Heat of Aqueous Lithium Bromide Solutions

point where the distinction between liquid and gas is lost. At higher temperatures, no separate liquid phase is possible for pure fluids. In refrigeration cycles involving condensation, a refrigerant must be chosen that allows this change of state to occur at a temperature somewhat below the critical. Cycles that reject heat at supercritical temperatures (such as cycles using carbon dioxide) are also possible.

Lithium Bromide/Water and Ammonia/Water Solutions. These are the most commonly used working fluids in absorption refrigeration systems. Figure 1 shows density, Figure 2 shows specific heat, and Figure 3 shows viscosity of lithium bromide/water solutions. Chapter 30 has an enthalpy-concentration diagram and a vapor pressure diagram for lithium bromide/water solutions. Chapter 30 also has equilibrium properties of water/ammonia solutions.

Electrical Properties

Tables 6 and 7 list the electrical characteristics of refrigerants that are especially important in hermetic systems.

Sound Velocity

The practical velocity of a gas in piping or through openings is limited by the velocity of sound in the gas.

Table 8 gives examples of the velocity of sound in the vapor phase of various refrigerants. Chapter 30 has sound velocity data for many refrigerants. The velocity increases when temperature is increased and decreases when pressure is increased. The velocity of sound can be calculated from the equation

$$V_a = \sqrt{(dp/d\rho)_S} = \sqrt{\gamma(dp/d\rho)_T} \tag{1}$$

where

V_a = sound velocity, m/s
p = pressure, Pa
ρ = density, kg/m³
$\gamma = c_p/c_v$ = ratio of specific heats
S = entropy, kJ/(kg·K)
T = temperature, K

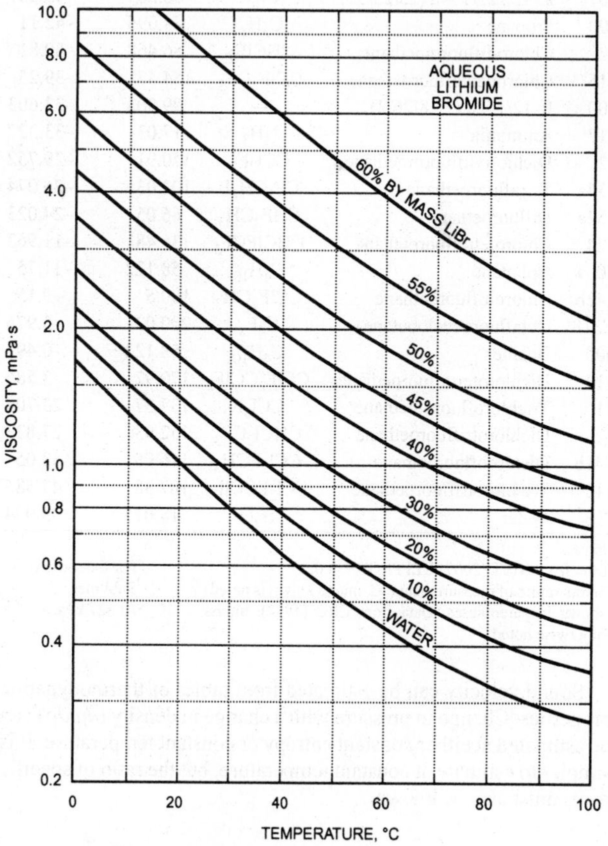

Fig. 3 Viscosity of Aqueous Solutions of Lithium Bromide

Table 5 Physical Properties of Selected Refrigerants[a]

Refrigerant No.	Chemical Name or Composition (% by Mass)	Chemical Formula	Molecular Mass	Boiling Pt. (NBP) at 101.325 kPa, °C	Freezing Point, °C	Critical Temperature, °C	Critical Pressure, kPa	Critical Density, kg/m^3	Refractive Index of Liquid[b,c]
728	Nitrogen	N_2	28.013	–195.8	–210.0	–146.96	3395.8	313.3	1.205 (83 K) 589.3 nm
729	Air	—	28.959	–194.25	—	–140.59	3789.6	335.94	—
740	Argon	Ar	39.948	–185.85	–189.34	–122.46	4863.0	535.6	1.233 (84 K) 589.3 nm
732	Oxygen	O_2	31.999	–182.96	–218.79	–118.57	5043.0	436.14	1.221 (92 K) 589.3 nm
50	Methane	CH_4	16.043	–161.48	–182.46	–82.586	4599.2	162.66	—
14	Tetrafluoromethane	CF_4	88.005	–128.05	–183.61	–45.64	3750.0	625.66	—
170	Ethane	C_2H_6	30.07	–88.581	–182.8	32.72	4872.2	206.18	—
503	R-23/13 (40.1/59.9)	—	87.247	–87.76	—	18.417	4280.5	565.68	—
508A[4]	R-23/116 (39/61)	—	100.1	–87.233	—	10.192	3650.8	567.58	—
508B[4]	R-23/116 (46/54)	—	95.394	–87.206	—	11.205	3771.6	568.45	—
23	Trifluoromethane	CHF_3	70.014	–82.018	–155.13	26.143	4832	526.5	—
13	Chlorotrifluoromethane	$CClF_3$	104.46	–81.48	–181.15	28.85	3879	582.88	1.146 (25)[2]
744	Carbon dioxide	CO_2	44.01	–78.4[d]	–56.558[e]	30.978	7377.3	467.6	1.195 (15)
504	R-32/115 (48.2/51.8)	—	79.249	–57.906	—	62.138	4428.8	504.68	—
32	Difluoromethane	CH_2F_2	52.024	–51.651	–136.81	78.105	5782.0	424	—
410A	R-32/125 (50/50)	—	72.585	–51.446	—	71.358	4902.6	459.53	—
125	Pentafluoroethane	C_2HF_5	120.02	–48.09	–100.63	66.023	3617.7	573.58	—
1270	Propylene	C_3H_6	42.08	–47.62	–185.2	91.061	4554.8	230.03	1.3640 (–50)[1]
143a	Trifluoroethane	CH_3CF_3	84.041	–47.241	–111.81	72.707	3761.0	431.0	—
507A	R-125/143a (50/50)	—	98.859	–46.741	—	70.617	3705	490.77	—
404A	R-125/143a/134a (44/52/4)	—	97.604	–46.222	—	72.046	3728.9	486.53	—
502	R-22/115 (48.8/51.2)	—	111.63	–45.174	—	80.507	4016.8	568.70	—
407C	R-32/125/134a (23/25/52)	—	86.204	–43.627	—	86.034	4629.8	484.23	—
290	Propane	C_3H_8	44.096	–42.11	–187.62	96.74	4251.2	220.4	1.3397 (–42)
22	Chlorodifluoromethane	$CHClF_2$	86.468	–40.81	–157.42	96.145	4990.0	523.84	1.234 (25)[2]
115	Chloropentafluoroethane	$CClF_2CF_3$	154.47	–39.25	–99.39	79.95	3129.0	614.8	1.221 (25)[2]
500	R-12/152a (73.8/26.2)	—	99.303	–33.603	—	102.09	4168.6	495.1	—
717	Ammonia	NH_3	17.03	–33.327	–77.655	132.25	11 333.0	225.0[d]	1.325 (16.5)
12	Dichlorodifluoromethane	CCl_2F_2	120.91	–29.752	–157.05	111.97	4136.1	565.0	1.288 (25)[2]
134a	Tetrafluoroethane	CF_3CH_2F	102.03	–26.074	–103.3	101.06	4059.3	511.9	—
152a	Difluoroethane	CHF_2CH_3	66.051	–24.023	–118.59	113.26	4516.8	368	—
124	Chlorotetrafluoroethane	$CHClFCF_3$	136.48	–11.963	–199.15	122.28	3624.3	560.0	—
600a	Isobutane	C_4H_{10}	58.122	–11.75	–159.42	134.66	3629.0	225.5	1.3514 (–25)[1]
142b	Chlorodifluoroethane	$CClF_2CH_3$	100.5	–9.15	–130.43	137.11	4055.0	466.0	—
C318	Octafluorocyclobutane	C_4F_8	200.03	–5.975	–39.8	115.23	2777.5	619.97	
600	Butane	C_4H_{10}	58.122	–0.49	–102.7	151.98	3796.0	227.94	1.3562 (–15)[1]
114	Dichlorotetrafluoroethane	$CClF_2CClF_2$	170.92	3.586	–94.15	145.68	3257.0	579.97	1.294 (25)
11	Trichlorofluoromethane	CCl_3F	137.37	23.708	–110.47	197.96	4407.6	554.0	1.362 (25)[2]
123	Dichlorotrifluoroethane	$CHCl_2CF_3$	152.93	27.823	–107.15	183.68	3661.8	550.0	—
141b	Dichlorofluoroethane	CCl_2FCH_3	116.95	32.05	–103.5	204.4	4212.0	458.6	—
113	Trichlorotrifluoroethane	CCl_2FCClF_2	187.38	47.585	–36.22	214.06	3392.2	560.0	1.357 (25)[2]
718[3]	Water	H_2O	18.015	99.974	0.01	373.95	22 064.0	322.0	—

Notes:
[a]Data from NIST (2007) REFPROP v. 8.0.
[b]Temperature of measurement (°C, unless kelvin is noted) shown in parentheses. Data from CRC (1987), unless otherwise noted.
[c]For the sodium D line.
[d]Sublimes.
[e]At 527 kPa.

References:
[1]Kirk and Othmer (1956).
[2]*Bulletin* B-32A (DuPont).
[3]*Handbook of Chemistry* (1967).
[4]*NIST Standard Reference Database 23*, v. 7 (Lemmon et al. 2002).

Sound velocity can be estimated from tables of thermodynamic properties. Change in pressure with a change in density ($dp/d\rho$) can be estimated at either constant entropy or constant temperature. It is simpler to estimate at constant temperature, but the ratio of specific heats must also be known.

REFRIGERANT PERFORMANCE

Chapter 2 describes several methods of calculating refrigerant performance, and Chapter 30 includes tables of thermodynamic properties of refrigerants.

Table 9 shows the theoretical calculated performance of a number of refrigerants for a standard cycle of 258 K evaporation and 303 K condensation. In most cases, suction vapor is assumed to be saturated, and compression is assumed adiabatic or at constant entropy. For R-113 and R-114, for example, these assumptions cause some liquid in the discharge vapor. In these cases, it is assumed that discharge vapor is saturated and that suction vapor is slightly superheated. Note that actual operating conditions and performance differ somewhat from numbers in the table because of additional factors such as compressor efficiency and transport properties.

Table 6 Electrical Properties of Liquid Refrigerants

Refrigerant No.	Chemical Name or Composition (% By Mass)	Temp., °C	Dielectric Constant	Volume Resistivity, MΩ·m	Ref.
11	Trichlorofluoromethane	28.9	2.28		1
		a	1.92	63 680	2
		25	2.5	90	3
		25	2.32		10
12	Dichlorodifluoromethane	28.9	2.13		1
		a	1.74	53 900	2
		25	2.1	>120	3
		25	2.100		4
		25	2.14		10
13	Chlorotrifluoromethane	−30	2.3	120	4
		20	1.64		
22	Chlorodifluoromethane	23.9	6.11		1
		a	6.12	0.83	2
		25	6.6	75	3
		25	6.42		10
23	Trifluoromethane	−30	6.3		3
		20	5.51		4
32	Difluoromethane	a	14.27		6
		25	14.67		10
113	Trichlorotrifluoroethane	30	2.44		1
		a	1.68	45 490	2
		25	2.6	>120	3
114	Dichlorotetrafluoroethane	31.1	2.17		1
		a	1.83	66 470	2
		25	2.2	>70	3
123	2,2-dichloro-1,1,1-trifluoroethane	a	4.50	14 700	7
124	2-chloro-1,1,1,2-tetrafluoroethane	25	4.89		10
124a	Chlorotetrafluoroethane	25	4.0	50	3
125	Pentafluoroethane	20	4.94		8
		25	5.10		10
134a	1,1,1,2-tetrafluoroethane	a	9.51	17 700	7
		25	9.87		10
143a	1,1,1-trifluoroethane	25	9.78		10
236fa	1,1,1,3,3,3-hexafluoropropane	25	7.89		10
245fa	1,1,1,3,3-pentafluoropropane	25	6.82		10
290	Propane	a	1.27	73 840	2
404A	R-125/143a/134a (44/52/4)	a	7.58	8450	9
		25	8.06		10
407C	R-32/125/134a (23/25/52)	a	8.74	7420	9
		25	10.21		10
410A	R-32/125 (50/50)	a	7.78	3920	9
		25	5.37		10
500	R-12/152a (73.8/26.2)	a	1.80	55 750	2
507A	R-125/143a (50/50)	a	6.97	5570	9
		25	7.94		10
508A	R-23/116 (39/61)	−30	6.60		1
		0	5.02		1
508B	R-23/116 (46/54)	−30	7.24		1
		0	5.48		1
717	Ammonia	20.6	15.5		5
744	Carbon dioxide	0	1.59		5

a = ambient temperature

References:

1 Data from E.I. DuPont de Nemours & Co., Inc.
2 Beacham and Divers (1955)
3 Eiseman (1955)
4 Fellows et al. (1991)
5 CRC (1987)
6 Bararo et al. (1997)
7 Fellows et al. (1991)
8 Pereira et al. (1999)
9 Meurer et al. (2001)
10 Gbur (2005)

Table 7 Electrical Properties of Refrigerant Vapors

Refrigerant No.	Chemical Name or Composition (% by mass)	Pressure, kPa	Temp., °C	Dielectric Constant	Relative Dielectric Strength, Nitrogen = 1	Volume Resistivity, GΩ·m	Ref.
11	Trichlorofluoromethane	50.7	26.1	1.0019			3
		a	b	1.009		74.35	2
		101.3	22.8		3.1		4
12	Dichlorodifluoromethane	50.7	28.9	1.0016			3
		a	b	1.012	452^c	72.77	2
		101.3	22.8		2.4		4
		101.3	25	1.0064			6
13	Chlorotrifluoromethane	50.7	28.9	1.0013			3
		101.3	22.8		1.4		4
14	Tetrafluoromethane	50.7	24.4	1.0006			3
		101.3	22.8		1.0		4
22	Chlorodifluoromethane	50.7		1.0035			3
		a	b	1.004	460^c	2113	2
		101.3	22.8		1.3		4
		101.3	25	1.0068			6
32	Difluoromethane	101.3	25	1.0102			6
113	Trichlorotrifluoroethane	a	b	1.010	440^c	94.18	2
		40.5	22.8		2.6		4
114	Dichlorotetrafluoroethane	50.7	26.7	1.0021			3
		a	b	1.002	295^c	148.3	2
		101.3	22.8		2.8		4
116	Hexafluoroethane	95.2	22.8	1.002			3
124	2-chloro-1,1,1,2-tetrafluoroethane	101.3	25	1.0060			6
125	Pentafluoroethane	101.3	25	1.0072			6
134a	1,1,1,2-tetrafluoroethane	101.3	25	1.0125			6
142b	Chlorodifluoroethane	94.2	27.2	1.013			3
143a	Trifluoroethane	86.1	25	1.013			3
		101.3	25	1.0170			6
170	Ethane	101.3	0	1.0015			1
236fa	1,1,1,3,3,3-hexafluoropropane	101.3	25	1.0121			6
245fa	1,1,1,3,3-pentafluoropropane	101.3	25	1.0066			6
290	Propane	a	b	1.009	440^c	105.3	2
404A	R-125/143a/134a (44/52/4)	101.3	25	1.0121			6
407C	R-32/125/134a (23/25/52)	101.3	25	1.0113			6
410A	R-32/125 (50/50)	101.3	25	1.0078			6
500	R-12/152a (73.8/26.2)	a	b	1.024	470^c	76.45	2
507A	R-125/143a (50/50)	101.3	25	1.0119			6
508A	R-23/116 (39/61)	a	−30	1.12			5
		a	0	1.31			5
		101.3	25	1.0042			6
508B	R-23/116 (46/54)	a	−30	1.13			5
		a	0	1.34			5
		101.3	25	1.0042			6
717	Ammonia	101.3	0	1.0072			1
		a	0		0.82		4
729	Air	101.3	0	1.00059			1
744	Carbon dioxide	101.3	0	1.00099			1
		101.3	b		0.88		4
1150	Ethylene	101.3	0	1.00144			1
		101.3	22.8		1.21		4

Notes:
a = saturation vapor pressure
b = ambient temperature
c = measured breakdown voltage, volts/mil

References:

1 CRC (1987)
2 Beacham and Divers (1955)
3 Fuoss (1938)
4 Charlton and Cooper (1937)
5 Data from E.I. DuPont de Nemours & Co., Inc.
6 Gbur (2005)

Table 8 Velocity of Sound in Refrigerant Vapors

Refrigerant	Pressure, kPa	Temperature, °C 10	50	100
		Velocity of Sound, m/s		
11	100	b	144.52	156.06
12	100	145.94	156.20	167.93
	1000	b	136.60	156.04
	1500	b	b	148.45
22	100	177.08	188.81	202.24
	1000	b	173.97	193.09
	1500	b	163.78	187.56
23	100	199.83	212.33	226.78
	1000	188.21	204.92	222.29
	1500	180.89	200.66	219.83
32	100	235.50	250.33	267.05
	1000	212.11	236.68	258.78
	1500	b	228.18	254.02
113	100	b	119.64	130.01
114	100	118.04	127.18	137.39
123	100	b	134.30	145.46
	1000	b	b	b
	1500	b	b	b
124	100	133.96	143.96	155.12
	1000	b	b	139.55
	1500	b	b	128.84
134a	100	157.21	168.39	180.99
	1000	b	146.88	168.59
	1500	b	b	160.87
143a	100	174.73	186.74	200.45
	1000	b	168.36	189.26
	1500	b	156.00	182.68
404A	100	161.39	172.60	185.37
	1000	b	155.51	178.05
	1500	b	143.93	168.98
407C	100	173.85	185.72	199.20
	1000	b	169.30	189.38
	1500	b	158.12	183.56
410A	100	192.84	205.56	220.06
	1000	170.15	192.17	211.92
	1500	b	183.78	207.24
502	100	152.01	162.45	174.43
	1000	b	147.40	165.17
	1500	b	136.70	159.59
507A	100	160.32	174.45	184.14
	1000	b	154.67	174.00
	1500	b	143.34	168.04
508A	100	161.68	172.35	184.74
	1000	149.98	164.89	180.22
	1500	142.71	160.67	177.84
508B	100	166.23	177.14	189.76
	1000	154.64	169.74	185.31
	1500	147.46	165.55	182.94
600	100	204.59	219.88	236.83
	1000	b	b	206.17
	1500	b	b	181.53
600a	100	205.58	220.45	237.15
	1000	b	b	210.17
	1500	b	b	190.26
717	100	422.02	450.44	482.17
	1000	b	430.71	470.71
	1500	b	417.84	463.93
744	100	262.37	278.69	297.64
	1000	253.98	273.23	294.31
	1500	248.95	270.12	292.48

Source: NIST Standard Reference Database 23, v.7.0 (Lemmon et al. 2002)
b = Below saturation temperature.

SAFETY

Tables 1 and 2 summarize toxicity and flammability characteristics of many refrigerants. In ASHRAE *Standard* 34, refrigerants are classified according to the hazard involved in their use. The toxicity and flammability classifications yield six safety groups (A1, A2, A3, B1, B2, and B3) for refrigerants. Group A1 refrigerants are the least hazardous, Group B3 the most hazardous.

The safety classification in ASHRAE *Standard* 34 consists of a capital letter and a numeral. The capital letter designates a toxicity class based on allowable exposure:

- Class A: Toxicity has not been identified at concentrations less than or equal to 400 ppm by volume, based on data used to determine threshold limit value/time-weighted average (TLV/TWA) or consistent indices.
- Class B: There is evidence of toxicity at concentrations below 400 ppm by volume, based on data used to determine TLV/TWA or consistent indices.

The numeral denotes flammability:

- Class 1: No flame propagation in air at 21°C and 101 kPa
- Class 2: Lower flammability limit (LFL) greater than 0.10 kg/m^3 at 21°C and 101 kPa and heat of combustion less than 19 000 kJ/kg
- Class 3: Highly flammable as defined by LFL less than or equal to 0.10 kg/m^3 at 21°C and 101 kPa or heat of combustion greater than or equal to 19 000 kJ/kg

LEAK DETECTION

Leak detection in refrigeration equipment is of major importance for manufacturers and service engineers.

Electronic Detection

Electronic detectors are widely used in manufacture and assembly of refrigeration equipment. Instrument operation depends on the variation in current flow caused by ionization of decomposed refrigerant between two oppositely charged platinum electrodes. This instrument can detect any of the halogenated refrigerants except R-14; however, it is not recommended for use in atmospheres that contain explosive or flammable vapors. Other vapors, such as alcohol and carbon monoxide, may interfere with the test.

The electronic detector is the most sensitive of the various leak detection methods, reportedly capable of sensing a leak of 0.3 g of R-12 per year. A portable model is available for field testing. Other models are available with automatic balancing systems that correct for refrigerant vapors that might be present in the atmosphere around the test area.

Bubble Method

The object to be tested is pressurized with air or nitrogen. A pressure corresponding to operating conditions is generally used. If possible, the object is immersed in water, and any leaks are detected by observing bubbles in the liquid. Adding a detergent to the water decreases surface tension, prevents escaping gas from clinging to the side of the object, and promotes formation of a regular stream of small bubbles. Kerosene or other organic liquids are sometimes used for the same reason. A solution of soap or detergent can be brushed or poured onto joints or other spots where leakage is suspected. Leaking gas forms soap bubbles that can be readily detected.

Leaks can also be determined by pressurizing or evacuating and observing the change in pressure or vacuum over a period of time. This is effective in checking system tightness but does not locate the point of leakage.

UV Dye Method

A stable UV-fluorescent dye is introduced into the system to be tested. Operating the system mixes the UV dye uniformly in the

Table 9 Comparative Refrigerant Performance per Ton of Refrigeration

Refrigerant No.	Refrigerant Chemical Name or Composition (% by mass)	Evaporator Pressure, MPa	Condenser Pressure, MPa	Compression Ratio	Net Refrigerating Effect, kJ/kg	Refrigerant Circulated, g/s	Liquid Circulated, L/s	Specific Volume of Suction Gas, m³/kg	Compressor Displacement, L/s	Power Consumption, kW	Coefficient of Performance	Compressor Discharge Temp., °C
170	Ethane	1.608	4.639	2.88	161.71	6.10	0.0219	0.0338	0.206	0.365	2.7	323
744	Carbon dioxide	2.254	7.18	3.19	133.23	3.88	0.0064	0.0168	0.065	0.192	2.69	343
1270	Propylene	0.358	1.304	3.64	286.17	3.46	0.0070	0.1299	0.449	0.220	4.5	315
290	Propane	0.286	1.075	3.76	277.90	3.53	0.0073	0.1562	0.551	0.218	4.5	309
502	R-22/115 (48.8/51.2)	0.343	1.312	3.83	105.95	9.43	0.0079	0.0508	0.479	0.228	4.38	311
507A	R-125/143a (50/50)	0.379	1.459	3.85	110.14	9.07	0.0089	0.0508	0.461	0.239	4.18	308
404A	R-125/143a/134a (44/52/4)	0.365	1.42	3.89	114.15	8.75	0.0086	0.0537	0.470	0.237	4.21	309
410A	R-32/125 (50/50)	0.478	1.872	3.92	167.89	5.84	0.0056	0.0545	0.318	0.222	4.41	324
125	Pentafluoroethane	0.403	1.561	3.87	85.30	11.41	0.0098	0.0394	0.449	0.244	3.99	304
22	Chlorodifluoromethane	0.295	1.187	4.02	162.67	6.13	0.0052	0.0779	0.478	0.214	4.66	326
12	Dichlorodifluoromethane	0.181	0.741	4.09	117.02	8.49	0.0066	0.0923	0.784	0.212	4.7	311
500	R-12/152a (73.8/26.2)	0.214	0.876	4.09	139.68	7.08	0.0063	0.0939	0.665	0.212	4.66	314
407C	R-32/125/134a (23/25/52)	0.288	1.26	4.38	163.27	6.11	0.0054	0.0805	0.492	0.222	4.5	321
600a	Isobutane*	0.088	0.403	4.58	263.91	3.76	0.0069	0.4073	1.533	0.215	4.62	303
134a	Tetrafluoroethane	0.163	0.767	4.71	148.03	6.71	0.0056	50.1214	0.814	0.216	4.6	310
124	Chlorotetrafluoroethane*	0.0088	0.443	5.03	117.83	8.41	0.0063	0.1711	11.439	0.214	4.62	303
717	Ammonia	0.235	1.162	4.94	1103.1	0.90	0.0015	0.5117	0.463	0.210	4.76	372
600	Butane*	0.056	0.283	5.05	292.24	3.53	0.0062	0.6446	2.274	0.218	4.74	303
11	Trichlorofluoromethane	0.02	0.125	6.25	155.95	6.36	0.0043	0.7689	4.891	0.197	5.02	316
123	Dichlorotrifluoroethane	0.016	0.109	6.81	142.28	7.02	0.0048	0.8914	6.259	0.204	4.9	306
113	Trichlorotrifluoroethane*	0.007	0.054	7.71	122.58	7.84	0.0051	1.6818	13.187	0.200	4.81	303

*Superheat required.

oil/refrigerant system. The dye, which usually prefers oil, shows up at the leak's location, and can be detected using an appropriate UV lamp. Ensure that the dye is compatible with system components and that no one is exposed to UV radiation from the lamp. This method is often more effective for liquid leaks than for vapor.

Another, more expensive method is to use dispersive and nondispersive infrared analyzers. Although these analyzers are expensive, they can not only find the refrigerant leak but also identify the refrigerant.

Ammonia Leaks

Ammonia can be detected by any of the previously described methods, or by bringing a solution of hydrochloric acid near the object. If ammonia vapor is present, a white cloud or smoke of ammonium chloride forms. Ammonia can also be detected with indicator paper that changes color in the presence of a base.

EFFECT ON CONSTRUCTION MATERIALS

Metals

Halogenated refrigerants can be used satisfactorily under normal conditions with most common metals, such as steel, cast iron, brass, copper, tin, lead, and aluminum. Under more severe conditions, various metals affect properties such as hydrolysis and thermal decomposition in varying degrees. The tendency of metals to promote thermal decomposition of halogenated compounds is in the following order:

(least decomposition) Inconel < 18-8 stainless steel < nickel < copper < 1040 steel < aluminum < bronze < brass < zinc < silver (most decomposition)

This order is only approximate, and there may be exceptions for individual compounds or for special use conditions. The effect of metals on hydrolysis is probably similar.

Table 10 Swelling of Elastomers in Liquid Refrigerants at Room Temperature, % Linear Swell

Refrigerant Number	Polyisoprene (Sulfur Cure)	Polychloroprene	Butyl Rubber	Styrene Butadiene Rubber	Nitrile Rubber	Fluoroelastomer
22	10.2	6.1	3.9	9.8	51.4	33.2
123	48.0	15.3	16.3	40.8	83.7	31.6
124	5.8	2.8	3.2	4.1	45.9	29.0
142b	10.2	6.5	6.2	7.3	8.7	31.8
32	2.7	1.0	1.0	2.0	8.3	23.2
125	4.2	2.7	2.6	3.6	3.9	11.7
134a	1.2	1.2	0.6	1.0	5.1	25.6
143a	1.9	1.2	1.3	1.5	2.0	13.6
152a	4.2	3.0	1.7	2.8	8.8	3.91

Magnesium alloys and aluminum containing more than 2% magnesium are not recommended for use with halogenated compounds where even trace amounts of water may be present. Zinc is not recommended for use with CFC-113. Experience with zinc and other fluorinated compounds has been limited, but no unusual reactivity has been observed under normal conditions of use in dry systems.

Ammonia should never be used with copper, brass, or other alloys containing copper. Further discussion of the compatibility of refrigerants and lubricants with construction materials may be found in Chapter 5 of the 2006 *ASHRAE Handbook—Refrigeration*.

Elastomers

Linear swelling of some elastomers in the liquid phase of HCFC and HFC refrigerants is shown in Table 10. Swelling data can be used to a limited extent in comparing the effect of refrigerants on elastomers. However, other factors, such as the amount of extraction, tensile strength, and degree of hardness of the exposed elastomer, must be considered. When other fluids (e.g., lubricants) are present in addition to the refrigerant, the combined effect on elastomers should be determined. Extensive test data for compatibility of elastomers and gasketing materials with refrigerants and lubricants

Table 11 Diffusion of Water and R-22 Through Elastomers

Elastomer	Diffusion Rate Water[a]	R-22[b]
Polychloroprene	970	4.63
Nitrile rubber	150	69.4
Chlorosulfonated polyethylene	620	1.85
Butyl rubber	58	1.04
Fluoroelastomer	—	12.7
Polyethylene	167	—
Natural	1940	—

Adapted from Eiseman (1955).
[a]75 μm film, 100% rh at 38°C. Water diffusion rate is in micrograms per second per square metre of elastomer.
[b]Film thickness = 25 μm; temperature = 25°C. Gas at 101.3 kPa and 0°C. Diffusion rate in cubic centimetres of gas per second per square metre of elastomer.

are reported by Hammed et al. (1994). Diffusion of fluids through elastomers is another consideration; Table 11 shows the diffusion rate of water and R-22 through elastomers.

Plastics

The effect of a refrigerant on a plastic material should be thoroughly examined under conditions of intended use, including the presence of lubricants. Plastics are often mixtures of two or more basic types, and it is difficult to predict the refrigerant's effect. Swelling data can be used as a general guide of effect, but, as with elastomers, the effect on properties of the plastic should also be examined. Extensive test data for compatibility of plastics with refrigerants and lubricants are reported by Cavestri (1993), including 23 plastics, 10 refrigerants, 7 lubricants, and 17 refrigerant/lubricant combinations. Refrigerants and lubricants had little effect on most of the plastics. Three plastics (acrylonitrile-butadiene-styrene, polyphenylene oxide, and polycarbonate) were affected enough to be considered incompatible. In a separate study by DuPont Fluoroproducts, two additional plastics (acrylic and polystyrene plastics) were determined to have questionable compatibility with HCFC and HFC refrigerants.

REFERENCES

ASHRAE. 2007. Designation and safety classification of refrigerants. ANSI/ASHRAE *Standard* 34-2004.

Bararo, M.T., U.V. Mardolcar, and C.A. Nieto de Castro. 1997. Molecular properties of alternative refrigerants derived from dielectric-constant measurements. *Journal of Thermophysics* 18(2):419-438.

Beacham, E.A. and R.T. Divers. 1955. Some aspects of the dielectric properties of refrigerants. *Refrigerating Engineering* 7:33.

Calm, J.M. and G.C. Hourahan. 2007. Refrigerant data update. *Heating/Piping/Air Conditioning Engineering* 79(1):50-64.

Cavestri, R.C. 1993. Compatibility of refrigerants and lubricants with engineering plastics. *Report* DOE/CE/23810-15. Air Conditioning and Refrigeration Technology Institute (ARTI), Arlington, VA.

Charlton, E.E. and F.S. Cooper. 1937. Dielectric strengths of insulating fluids. *General Electric Review* 865(9):438.

Chemical engineer's handbook, 5th ed. 1973. McGraw-Hill, New York.

CRC handbook of chemistry and physics, 68th ed. 1987. CRC Press, Boca Raton, FL.

DuPont. *Bulletin* B-32A. Freon Products Division. E.I. DuPont de Nemours & Co., Wilmington, DE.

DuPont Fluoroproducts. *Technical Information Bulletins for HFC-134a, R-407C and R-410A*. E.I. DuPont de Nemours & Co., Wilmington, DE.

Eiseman, B.J., Jr. 1955. How electrical properties of Freon compounds affect hermetic system's insulation. *Refrigerating Engineering* 4:61.

Fellows, B.R., R.G. Richard, and I.R. Shankland. 1991. Electrical characterization of alternate refrigerants. *Actes Congrès International du Froid* 18(2). International Institute of Refrigeration, Paris.

Fuoss, R.M. 1938. Dielectric constants of some fluorine compounds. *Journal of the American Chemical Society* 64:1633.

Hammed, G.R., R.H. Seiple, and O. Taikum. 1994. Compatibility of refrigerants and lubricants with elastomers. *Report* DOE/CE/23810-14. Air Conditioning and Refrigeration Technology Institute, Arlington, VA.

Handbook of chemistry, 10th ed. 1967. McGraw-Hill, New York.

Handbook of chemistry and physics, 41st ed. 1959-1960. Chemical Rubber Publishing, Cleveland, OH.

IPCC. 2007a. *Climate change 2007: Synthesis report. Contribution of working groups I, II, and III to the fourth assessment report of the Intergovernmental Panel on Climate Change*. B.P. Jallow, L. Kajfez-Bogataj, R. Bojaru, D. Hawkins, S. Diaz, H. Lee, A. Allali, I. Elgizouli, D. Wratt, O. Hohmeyer, D. Griggs, and N. Leary, eds. http:// www.ipcc.ch/ipccreports/ar4-syr.htm.

IPCC. 2007b. *Climate change 2007: The physical science basis*. S. Solomon, D. Qin, M. Manning, Z. Chen, M. Marquis, K.B. Averyt, M. Tignor, and H.L. Miller, eds. Cambridge University Press, Cambridge, U.K. http://www.ipcc.ch/ipccreports/ar4-wg1.htm.

Kirk and Othmer. 1956. *The encyclopedia of chemical technology*. Interscience Encyclopedia, New York.

Lemmon, E.W., M.O. McLinden, and M.L. Huber. 2002. *NIST standard reference database 23*, v. 7.0. National Institute of Standards and Technology, Gaithersburg, MD.

Matheson gas data book. 1966. Matheson Company, East Rutherford, NJ.

Meurer C., G. Pietsch, and M. Haacke M. 2001. Electrical properties of CFC- and HCFC-substitutes. *International Journal of Refrigeration* 24(2):171-175.

Pereira L.F., F.E. Brito, A.N. Gurova, U.V. Mardolcar, and C.A. Nieta de Castro. 1999. Dipole moment, expansivity and compressibility coefficients of HFC 125 derived from dielectric constant measurements. 1st International Workshop on Thermochemical, Thermodynamic and Transport Properties of Halogenated Hydrocarbons and Mixtures, Pisa, Italy.

Ravishankara, A.R., A.A. Turnipseed, N.R. Jensen, and R.F. Warren. 1994. Do hydrofluorocarbons destroy stratospheric ozone? *Science* 248:1217-1219.

Stewart, R.B., R.T. Jacobsen, and S.G. Penoncello. 1986. *ASHRAE thermodynamic properties of refrigerants*.

U.N. 1994. *1994 report of the refrigeration, air conditioning, and heat pumps technical options committee*. United Nations Environment Programme, Nairobi, Kenya.

UNEP. 2003. *Handbook for the international treaties for the protection of the ozone layer*. United Nations Environment Programme, Nairobi, Kenya.

UNEP. 2006. *Handbook for the international treaties for the protection of the ozone layer*, 7th ed. UNEP Ozone Secretariat, Nairobi, Kenya. http:// ozone.unep.org/Publications/MP_Handbook/.

BIBLIOGRAPHY

Brown, J.A. 1960. Effect of propellants on plastic valve components. *Soap and Chemical Specialties* 3:87.

Eiseman, B.J., Jr. 1949. Effect on elastomers of Freon compounds and other halohydrocarbons. *Refrigerating Engineering* 12:1171.

U.N. 1996. World policy roundup. *OzonAction: The Newsletter of the United Nations Environment Programme Industry and Environment OzonAction Programme* 20(October):10.

CHAPTER 30

THERMOPHYSICAL PROPERTIES OF REFRIGERANTS

THIS chapter presents data for thermodynamic and transport properties of refrigerants, arranged for the occasional user. The refrigerants have a thermodynamic property chart on pressure-enthalpy coordinates with an abbreviated set of tabular data for saturated liquid and vapor on the facing page. In addition, tabular data in the superheated vapor region are given for R-134a to assist students working on compression cycle examples.

For each cryogenic fluid, a second table of properties is provided for vapor at a pressure of one standard atmosphere; these data are needed when such gases are used in heat transfer or purge gas applications. For zeotropic blends, including R-729 (air), tables are incremented in pressure, with properties given for liquid on the bubble line and vapor on the dew line. This arrangement is used because pressure is more commonly measured in the field while servicing equipment; it also highlights the difference between bubble and dew-point temperatures (the "temperature glide" experienced with blends).

Most CFC refrigerants have been deleted. Tables for R-11, R-13, R-113, R-114, R-141b, R-142b, R-500, R-502, R-503, and R-720 (neon) may be found in the 1997 *ASHRAE Handbook—Fundamentals*. R-12 has been retained to assist in making comparisons. Revised formulations have been used for many refrigerants; these conform to international standards, where applicable. Thermodynamic properties of R-12, R-22, R-32, R-123, R-125, R-134a, R-143a, R-152a, R-717 (ammonia), and R-744 (carbon dioxide) and refrigerant blends R-404A, R-407C, R-410A, and R-507 conform to ISO/DIS *Draft Standard* 17584, Refrigerant Properties.

Reference states used for most refrigerants correspond to the international convention of 200 kJ/kg for enthalpy and 1 kJ/(kg·K) for entropy, both for saturated liquid at 0°C. Exceptions are water and fluids with very low critical temperatures (e.g., ethylene, cryogens).

These data are intended to help engineers make preliminary comparisons among unfamiliar fluids. For greater detail and a wider range of data, see the sources in the References.

The preparation of this chapter is assigned to TC 3.1, Refrigerants and Secondary Coolants.

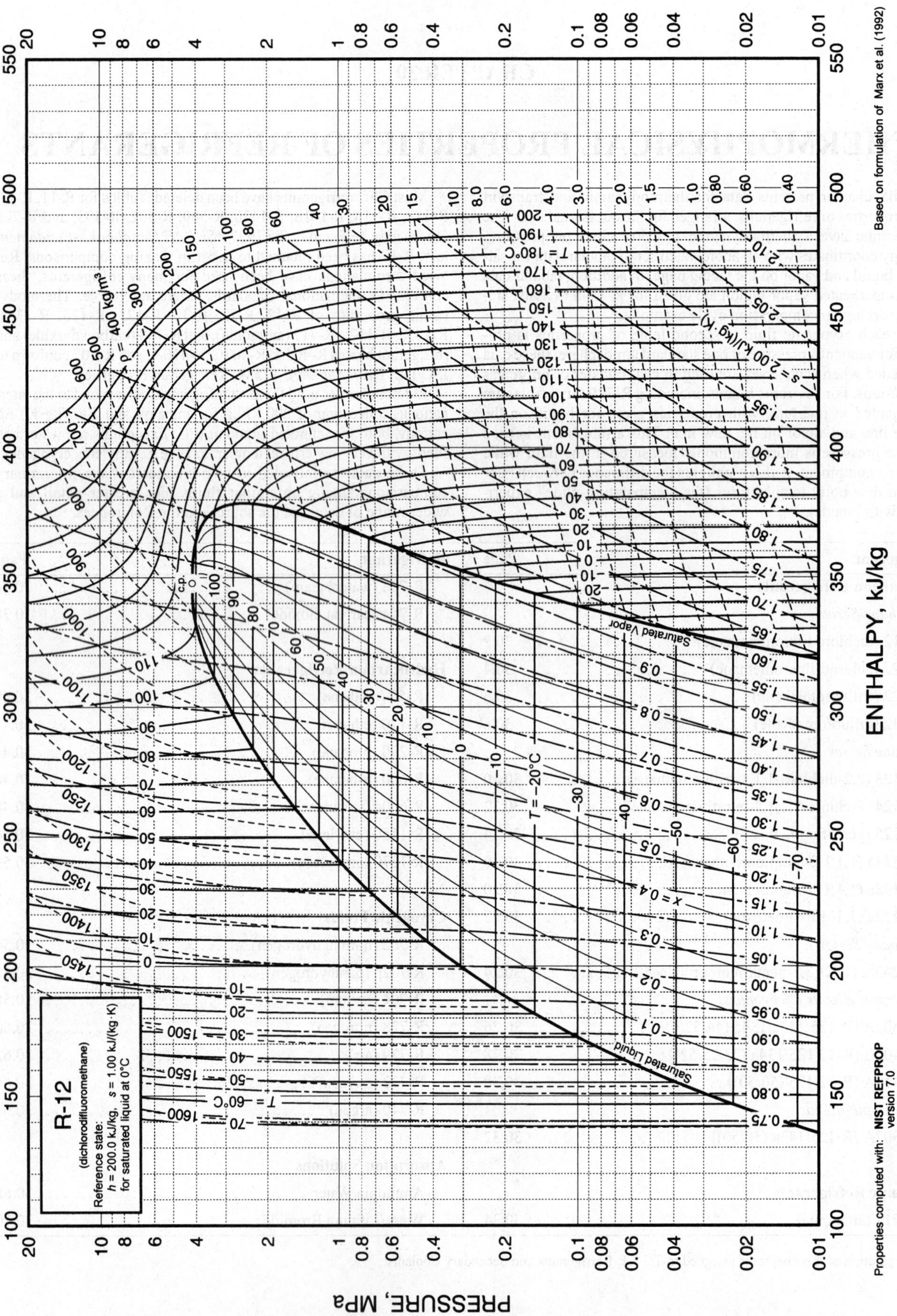

Fig. 1 Pressure-Enthalpy Diagram for Refrigerant 12

Refrigerant 12 (Dichlorodifluoromethane) Properties of Saturated Liquid and Saturated Vapor

Temp.,* °C	Pressure, MPa	Density, kg/m³ Liquid	Volume, m³/kg Vapor	Enthalpy, kJ/kg Liquid	Enthalpy, kJ/kg Vapor	Entropy, kJ/(kg·K) Liquid	Entropy, kJ/(kg·K) Vapor	Specific Heat c_p, kJ/(kg·K) Liquid	Specific Heat c_p, kJ/(kg·K) Vapor	c_p/c_v Vapor	Velocity of Sound, m/s Liquid	Velocity of Sound, m/s Vapor	Viscosity, µPa·s Liquid	Viscosity, µPa·s Vapor	Thermal Cond., mW/(m·K) Liquid	Thermal Cond., mW/(m·K) Vapor	Surface Tension, mN/m	Temp.,* °C
–100	0.00119	1679.1	10.0040	113.32	306.09	0.6077	1.7210	0.819	0.449	1.182	1035	118.5	1005.0	6.78	116.7	4.27	26.48	–100
–90	0.00286	1652.8	4.3948	121.53	310.59	0.6538	1.6861	0.824	0.465	1.176	990	121.4	819.0	7.18	112.0	4.67	24.90	–90
–80	0.00619	1626.3	2.1355	129.81	315.19	0.6978	1.6576	0.831	0.481	1.172	945	124.1	684.9	7.58	107.4	5.08	23.35	–80
–70	0.01228	1599.5	1.1286	138.17	319.87	0.7400	1.6344	0.840	0.497	1.168	902	126.7	584.0	7.97	103.0	5.50	21.81	–70
–60	0.02261	1572.3	0.63992	146.62	324.61	0.7806	1.6156	0.850	0.513	1.166	859	129.1	505.1	8.37	98.8	5.93	20.30	–60
–50	0.03911	1544.7	0.38494	155.18	329.39	0.8197	1.6004	0.861	0.530	1.165	816	131.2	441.8	8.76	94.7	6.38	18.81	–50
–40	0.06409	1516.5	0.24342	163.86	334.18	0.8577	1.5882	0.873	0.548	1.166	775	133.0	389.8	9.16	90.7	6.84	17.35	–40
–30	0.10026	1487.7	0.16057	172.67	338.94	0.8946	1.5784	0.886	0.566	1.169	733	134.5	346.2	9.55	86.9	7.32	15.91	–30
–29.75[b]	0.10133	1487.0	0.15900	172.89	339.06	0.8955	1.5782	0.887	0.567	1.169	732	134.5	345.2	9.56	86.8	7.33	15.88	–29.75
–28	0.10910	1481.9	0.14841	174.44	339.89	0.9019	1.5767	0.889	0.570	1.170	725	134.7	338.3	9.63	86.1	7.41	15.63	–28
–26	0.11854	1476.0	0.13736	176.23	340.83	0.9091	1.5751	0.892	0.574	1.171	717	135.0	330.6	9.71	85.3	7.51	15.35	–26
–24	0.12860	1470.1	0.12731	178.02	341.78	0.9163	1.5735	0.895	0.578	1.171	709	135.2	323.2	9.79	84.6	7.61	15.06	–24
–22	0.13931	1464.1	0.11815	179.81	342.72	0.9234	1.5720	0.898	0.582	1.172	701	135.4	316.0	9.87	83.8	7.71	14.78	–22
–20	0.15070	1458.1	0.10978	181.62	343.65	0.9305	1.5706	0.901	0.586	1.174	693	135.6	309.0	9.95	83.1	7.80	14.50	–20
–18	0.16279	1452.1	0.10213	183.42	344.59	0.9376	1.5693	0.904	0.590	1.175	684	135.8	302.2	10.03	82.4	7.90	14.23	–18
–16	0.17562	1446.1	0.09512	185.24	345.52	0.9447	1.5680	0.907	0.594	1.176	676	136.0	295.6	10.10	81.6	8.01	13.95	–16
–14	0.18920	1440.0	0.08870	187.06	346.44	0.9517	1.5667	0.910	0.598	1.178	668	136.1	289.2	10.18	80.9	8.11	13.67	–14
–12	0.20358	1433.8	0.08280	188.89	347.37	0.9587	1.5655	0.913	0.602	1.179	660	136.3	283.0	10.26	80.2	8.21	13.40	–12
–10	0.21878	1427.6	0.07737	190.72	348.29	0.9656	1.5644	0.917	0.607	1.181	652	136.4	276.9	10.34	79.4	8.31	13.12	–10
–8	0.23483	1421.4	0.07237	192.56	349.20	0.9726	1.5633	0.920	0.611	1.183	644	136.5	271.0	10.42	78.7	8.41	12.85	–8
–6	0.25176	1415.1	0.06777	194.41	350.11	0.9795	1.5623	0.923	0.616	1.184	636	136.6	265.2	10.50	78.0	8.52	12.58	–6
–4	0.26960	1408.8	0.06352	196.27	351.01	0.9863	1.5613	0.927	0.620	1.186	628	136.6	259.6	10.58	77.3	8.62	12.31	–4
–2	0.28839	1402.5	0.05959	198.13	351.91	0.9932	1.5603	0.930	0.625	1.189	620	136.7	254.1	10.66	76.6	8.73	12.04	–2
0	0.30815	1396.1	0.05595	200.00	352.81	1.0000	1.5594	0.934	0.630	1.191	612	136.7	248.7	10.74	75.9	8.84	11.77	0
2	0.32891	1389.6	0.05258	201.88	353.69	1.0068	1.5586	0.938	0.635	1.193	604	136.7	243.5	10.82	75.1	8.95	11.51	2
4	0.35071	1383.1	0.04946	203.76	354.57	1.0136	1.5577	0.942	0.640	1.196	596	136.7	238.4	10.90	74.4	9.06	11.24	4
6	0.37358	1376.5	0.04656	205.65	355.45	1.0203	1.5569	0.946	0.645	1.199	588	136.7	233.4	10.98	73.7	9.17	10.98	6
8	0.39756	1369.9	0.04386	207.56	356.32	1.0270	1.5561	0.950	0.650	1.202	580	136.6	228.6	11.07	73.0	9.28	10.71	8
10	0.42267	1363.2	0.04135	209.46	357.18	1.0337	1.5554	0.954	0.656	1.205	572	136.5	223.8	11.15	72.3	9.39	10.45	10
12	0.44895	1356.5	0.03901	211.38	358.03	1.0404	1.5547	0.958	0.661	1.208	564	136.5	219.1	11.23	71.6	9.51	10.19	12
14	0.47643	1349.7	0.03683	213.31	358.88	1.0471	1.5540	0.962	0.667	1.211	556	136.3	214.6	11.31	70.9	9.62	9.94	14
16	0.50514	1342.8	0.03480	215.24	359.71	1.0537	1.5533	0.967	0.672	1.215	548	136.2	210.1	11.40	70.2	9.74	9.68	16
18	0.53513	1335.9	0.03290	217.18	360.54	1.0603	1.5527	0.971	0.678	1.219	540	136.1	205.7	11.48	69.6	9.86	9.42	18
20	0.56642	1328.9	0.03112	219.14	361.36	1.0669	1.5521	0.976	0.685	1.223	532	135.9	201.4	11.57	68.9	9.98	9.17	20
22	0.59905	1321.8	0.02946	221.10	362.17	1.0735	1.5515	0.981	0.691	1.228	524	135.7	197.2	11.65	68.2	10.10	8.92	22
24	0.63305	1314.6	0.02790	223.07	362.97	1.0801	1.5509	0.986	0.697	1.232	516	135.5	193.1	11.74	67.5	10.23	8.67	24
26	0.66846	1307.4	0.02643	225.05	363.76	1.0866	1.5503	0.991	0.704	1.237	508	135.2	189.0	11.83	66.8	10.36	8.42	26
28	0.70531	1300.1	0.02506	227.04	364.54	1.0932	1.5498	0.997	0.711	1.242	499	134.9	185.0	11.92	66.1	10.49	8.17	28
30	0.74365	1292.7	0.02377	229.04	365.31	1.0997	1.5492	1.002	0.718	1.248	491	134.7	181.1	12.01	65.4	10.62	7.92	30
32	0.78350	1285.2	0.02256	231.06	366.07	1.1062	1.5487	1.008	0.726	1.254	483	134.3	177.3	12.10	64.8	10.75	7.68	32
34	0.82491	1277.6	0.02142	233.08	366.81	1.1127	1.5481	1.014	0.734	1.260	475	134.0	173.5	12.19	64.1	10.89	7.43	34
36	0.86791	1269.9	0.02034	235.12	367.54	1.1192	1.5476	1.020	0.742	1.267	467	133.6	169.8	12.28	63.4	11.03	7.19	36
38	0.91253	1262.2	0.01933	237.16	368.26	1.1257	1.5470	1.026	0.750	1.274	459	133.2	166.1	12.38	62.7	11.18	6.95	38
40	0.95882	1254.3	0.01838	239.22	368.96	1.1322	1.5465	1.033	0.759	1.282	450	132.8	162.5	12.48	62.1	11.33	6.72	40
42	1.00680	1246.3	0.01748	241.29	369.65	1.1387	1.5459	1.040	0.768	1.290	442	132.4	159.0	12.57	61.4	11.48	6.48	42
44	1.05660	1238.1	0.01662	243.38	370.33	1.1451	1.5454	1.048	0.778	1.299	434	131.9	155.5	12.67	60.7	11.63	6.25	44
46	1.10810	1229.9	0.01582	245.47	370.98	1.1516	1.5448	1.055	0.788	1.308	426	131.4	152.0	12.78	60.0	11.79	6.01	46
48	1.16140	1221.5	0.01505	247.59	371.62	1.1580	1.5443	1.063	0.798	1.318	417	130.9	148.6	12.88	59.4	11.96	5.78	48
50	1.21660	1213.0	0.01433	249.71	372.24	1.1645	1.5437	1.072	0.810	1.329	409	130.3	145.3	12.99	58.7	12.13	5.55	50
52	1.27370	1204.4	0.01365	251.85	372.85	1.1710	1.5431	1.081	0.821	1.340	400	129.7	141.9	13.10	58.0	12.31	5.33	52
54	1.33270	1195.6	0.01300	254.01	373.43	1.1774	1.5425	1.090	0.834	1.353	392	129.1	138.7	13.21	57.3	12.49	5.10	54
56	1.39380	1186.6	0.01238	256.18	373.99	1.1839	1.5418	1.100	0.847	1.366	383	128.4	135.4	13.33	56.7	12.68	4.88	56
58	1.45680	1177.5	0.01180	258.38	374.53	1.1904	1.5411	1.111	0.861	1.381	375	127.7	132.2	13.45	56.0	12.87	4.66	58
60	1.52190	1168.1	0.01124	260.58	375.05	1.1969	1.5404	1.122	0.876	1.397	366	127.0	129.1	13.57	55.3	13.08	4.44	60
62	1.58920	1158.6	0.01071	262.81	375.54	1.2033	1.5397	1.135	0.892	1.414	357	126.3	125.9	13.70	54.7	13.29	4.23	62
64	1.65860	1148.9	0.01021	265.06	376.00	1.2099	1.5389	1.148	0.910	1.433	348	125.5	122.8	13.83	54.0	13.51	4.01	64
66	1.73020	1139.0	0.00973	267.33	376.44	1.2164	1.5381	1.162	0.929	1.453	339	124.6	119.7	13.96	53.3	13.75	3.80	66
68	1.80410	1128.8	0.00927	269.62	376.84	1.2229	1.5372	1.177	0.949	1.476	330	123.8	116.7	14.11	52.6	13.99	3.59	68
70	1.88020	1118.3	0.00883	271.94	377.22	1.2295	1.5363	1.193	0.971	1.501	321	122.9	113.6	14.26	52.0	14.25	3.39	70
75	2.08110	1090.9	0.00782	277.84	377.99	1.2461	1.5337	1.241	1.037	1.576	298	120.4	106.1	14.66	50.3	14.96	2.88	75
80	2.29750	1061.4	0.00691	283.94	378.48	1.2629	1.5306	1.302	1.122	1.677	274	117.7	98.6	15.11	48.7	15.80	2.40	80
85	2.53040	1029.1	0.00608	290.27	378.64	1.2801	1.5268	1.384	1.239	1.817	249	114.7	91.1	15.65	47.2	16.82	1.93	85
90	2.78080	993.2	0.00533	296.91	378.35	1.2978	1.5220	1.501	1.410	2.026	224	111.4	83.4	16.29	45.9	18.11	1.49	90
95	3.05010	952.2	0.00463	303.95	377.45	1.3163	1.5159	1.679	1.683	2.362	197	107.8	75.6	17.11	45.1	19.81	1.07	95
100	3.33990	903.8	0.00396	311.58	375.60	1.3360	1.5076	1.996	2.192	2.990	169	103.7	67.3	18.20	45.7	22.27	0.69	100
105	3.65250	842.2	0.00330	320.24	372.08	1.3581	1.4952	2.754	3.458	4.544	139	99.3	58.1	19.87	51.7	26.34	0.35	105
110	3.99240	742.7	0.00252	331.82	363.95	1.3874	1.4712	7.81	11.440	14.140	105	94.0	46.3	23.46	113.7	39.46	0.07	110
111.97[c]	4.13610	565.0	0.00177	347.76	347.76	1.4283	1.4283	∞	∞	∞	0	0.0	—	—	∞	∞	0.00	111.97

*Temperatures on ITS-90 scale

[b]Normal boiling point

[c]Critical point

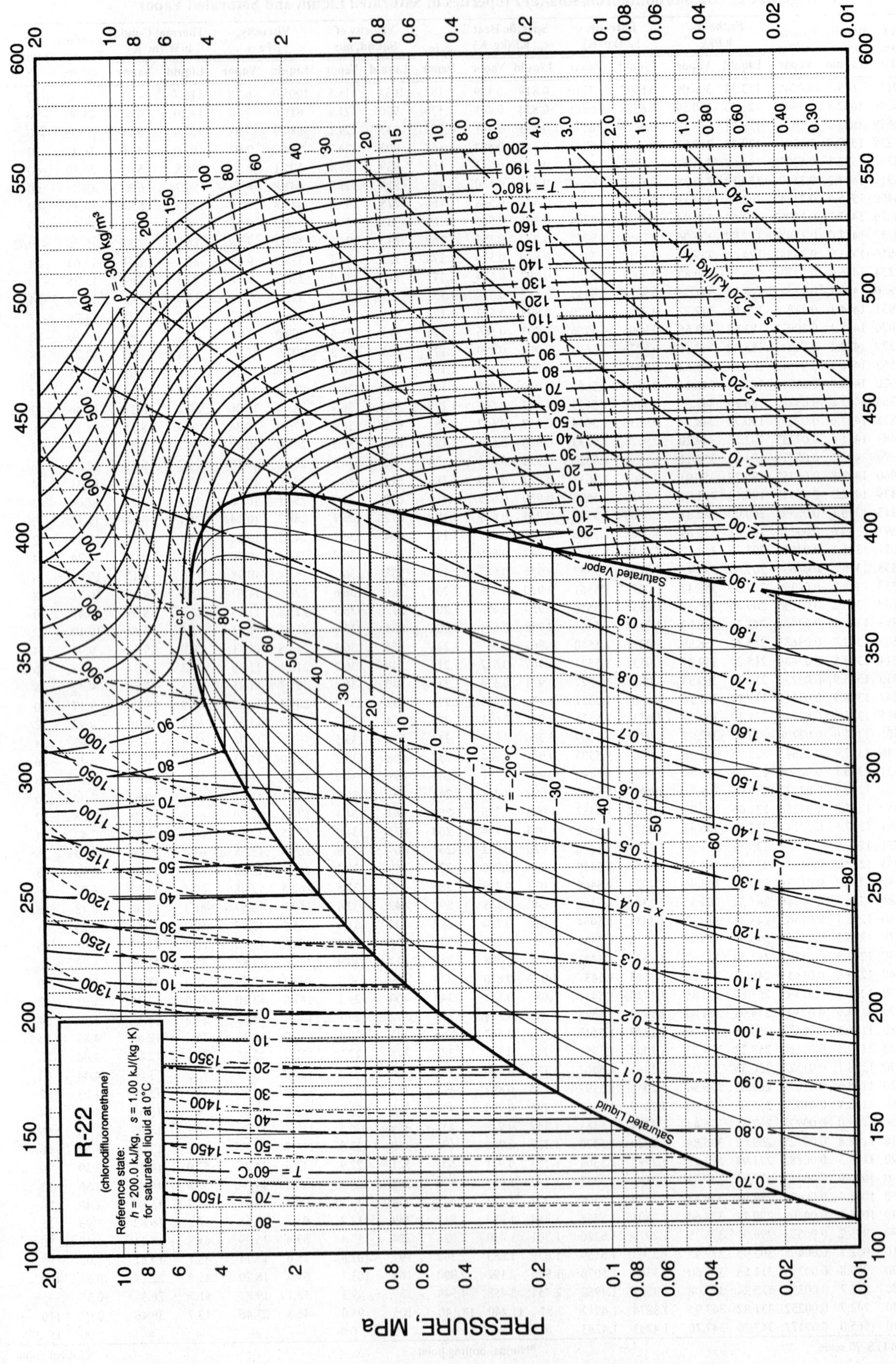

Based on formulation of Kamei et al. (1995)

Properties computed with: **NIST REFPROP** version 7.0

Fig. 2 Pressure-Enthalpy Diagram for Refrigerant 22

Refrigerant 22 (Chlorodifluoromethane) Properties of Saturated Liquid and Saturated Vapor

Temp.,* °C	Pressure, MPa	Density, kg/m³ Liquid	Volume, m³/kg Vapor	Enthalpy, kJ/kg Liquid	Enthalpy, kJ/kg Vapor	Entropy, kJ/(kg·K) Liquid	Entropy, kJ/(kg·K) Vapor	Specific Heat c_p, kJ/(kg·K) Liquid	Specific Heat c_p, kJ/(kg·K) Vapor	c_p/c_v Vapor	Velocity of Sound, m/s Liquid	Velocity of Sound, m/s Vapor	Viscosity, μPa·s Liquid	Viscosity, μPa·s Vapor	Thermal Cond., mW/(m·K) Liquid	Thermal Cond., mW/(m·K) Vapor	Surface Tension, mN/m	Temp.,* °C
–100	0.00201	1571.3	8.26600	90.71	358.97	0.5050	2.0543	1.061	0.497	1.243	1127	143.6	845.8	7.25	143.1	4.46	28.12	–100
–90	0.00481	1544.9	3.64480	101.32	363.85	0.5646	1.9980	1.061	0.512	1.237	1080	147.0	699.4	7.67	137.8	4.84	26.36	–90
–80	0.01037	1518.2	1.77820	111.94	368.77	0.6210	1.9508	1.062	0.528	1.233	1033	150.3	591.0	8.09	132.6	5.25	24.63	–80
–70	0.02047	1491.2	0.94342	122.58	373.70	0.6747	1.9108	1.065	0.545	1.231	986	153.3	507.6	8.52	127.6	5.68	22.92	–70
–60	0.03750	1463.7	0.53680	133.27	378.59	0.7260	1.8770	1.071	0.564	1.230	940	156.0	441.4	8.94	122.6	6.12	21.24	–60
–50	0.06453	1435.6	0.32385	144.03	383.42	0.7752	1.8480	1.079	0.585	1.232	893	158.3	387.5	9.36	117.8	6.59	19.58	–50
–48	0.07145	1429.9	0.29453	146.19	384.37	0.7849	1.8428	1.081	0.589	1.233	884	158.7	377.8	9.45	116.9	6.69	19.25	–48
–46	0.07894	1424.2	0.26837	148.36	385.32	0.7944	1.8376	1.083	0.594	1.234	875	159.1	368.6	9.53	115.9	6.79	18.92	–46
–44	0.08705	1418.4	0.24498	150.53	386.26	0.8039	1.8327	1.086	0.599	1.235	865	159.5	359.6	9.62	115.0	6.89	18.59	–44
–42	0.09580	1412.6	0.22402	152.70	387.20	0.8134	1.8278	1.088	0.603	1.236	856	159.9	351.0	9.70	114.0	6.99	18.27	–42
–40.81[b]	0.10132	1409.2	0.21260	154.00	387.75	0.8189	1.8250	1.090	0.606	1.236	851	160.1	346.0	9.75	113.5	7.05	18.08	–40.81
–40	0.10523	1406.8	0.20521	154.89	388.13	0.8227	1.8231	1.091	0.608	1.237	847	160.3	342.6	9.79	113.1	7.09	17.94	–40
–38	0.11538	1401.0	0.18829	157.07	389.06	0.8320	1.8186	1.093	0.613	1.238	838	160.6	334.5	9.87	112.2	7.19	17.62	–38
–36	0.12628	1395.1	0.17304	159.27	389.97	0.8413	1.8141	1.096	0.619	1.239	828	160.9	326.7	9.96	111.2	7.29	17.30	–36
–34	0.13797	1389.1	0.15927	161.47	390.89	0.8505	1.8098	1.099	0.624	1.241	819	161.2	319.1	10.04	110.3	7.40	16.98	–34
–32	0.15050	1383.2	0.14682	163.67	391.79	0.8596	1.8056	1.102	0.629	1.242	810	161.5	311.7	10.12	109.4	7.51	16.66	–32
–30	0.16389	1377.2	0.13553	165.88	392.69	0.8687	1.8015	1.105	0.635	1.244	800	161.8	304.6	10.21	108.5	7.61	16.34	–30
–28	0.17819	1371.1	0.12528	168.10	393.58	0.8778	1.7975	1.108	0.641	1.246	791	162.0	297.7	10.29	107.5	7.72	16.02	–28
–26	0.19344	1365.0	0.11597	170.33	394.47	0.8868	1.7937	1.112	0.646	1.248	782	162.3	291.0	10.38	106.6	7.83	15.70	–26
–24	0.20968	1358.9	0.10749	172.56	395.34	0.8957	1.7899	1.115	0.653	1.250	772	162.5	284.4	10.46	105.7	7.94	15.39	–24
–22	0.22696	1352.7	0.09975	174.80	396.21	0.9046	1.7862	1.119	0.659	1.253	763	162.7	278.1	10.55	104.8	8.06	15.07	–22
–20	0.24531	1346.5	0.09268	177.04	397.06	0.9135	1.7826	1.123	0.665	1.255	754	162.8	271.9	10.63	103.9	8.17	14.76	–20
–18	0.26479	1340.3	0.08621	179.30	397.91	0.9223	1.7791	1.127	0.672	1.258	744	163.0	265.9	10.72	103.0	8.29	14.45	–18
–16	0.28543	1334.0	0.08029	181.56	398.75	0.9311	1.7757	1.131	0.678	1.261	735	163.1	260.1	10.80	102.1	8.40	14.14	–16
–14	0.30728	1327.6	0.07485	183.83	399.57	0.9398	1.7723	1.135	0.685	1.264	726	163.2	254.4	10.89	101.1	8.52	13.83	–14
–12	0.33038	1321.2	0.06986	186.11	400.39	0.9485	1.7690	1.139	0.692	1.267	716	163.3	248.8	10.98	100.2	8.65	13.52	–12
–10	0.35479	1314.7	0.06527	188.40	401.20	0.9572	1.7658	1.144	0.699	1.270	707	163.3	243.4	11.06	99.3	8.77	13.21	–10
–8	0.38054	1308.2	0.06103	190.70	401.99	0.9658	1.7627	1.149	0.707	1.274	697	163.4	238.1	11.15	98.4	8.89	12.91	–8
–6	0.40769	1301.6	0.05713	193.01	402.77	0.9744	1.7596	1.154	0.715	1.278	688	163.4	233.0	11.24	97.5	9.02	12.60	–6
–4	0.43628	1295.0	0.05352	195.33	403.55	0.9830	1.7566	1.159	0.722	1.282	679	163.4	227.9	11.32	96.6	9.15	12.30	–4
–2	0.46636	1288.3	0.05019	197.66	404.30	0.9915	1.7536	1.164	0.731	1.287	669	163.4	223.0	11.41	95.7	9.28	12.00	–2
0	0.49799	1281.5	0.04710	200.00	405.05	1.0000	1.7507	1.169	0.739	1.291	660	163.3	218.2	11.50	94.8	9.42	11.70	0
2	0.53120	1274.7	0.04424	202.35	405.78	1.0085	1.7478	1.175	0.748	1.296	650	163.2	213.5	11.59	93.9	9.56	11.40	2
4	0.56605	1267.8	0.04159	204.71	406.50	1.0169	1.7450	1.181	0.757	1.301	641	163.1	208.9	11.68	93.1	9.70	11.10	4
6	0.60259	1260.8	0.03913	207.09	407.20	1.0254	1.7422	1.187	0.766	1.307	632	163.0	204.4	11.77	92.2	9.84	10.81	6
8	0.64088	1253.8	0.03683	209.47	407.89	1.0338	1.7395	1.193	0.775	1.313	622	162.8	200.0	11.86	91.3	9.99	10.51	8
10	0.68095	1246.7	0.03470	211.87	408.56	1.0422	1.7368	1.199	0.785	1.319	613	162.6	195.7	11.96	90.4	10.14	10.22	10
12	0.72286	1239.5	0.03271	214.28	409.21	1.0505	1.7341	1.206	0.795	1.326	603	162.4	191.5	12.05	89.5	10.29	9.93	12
14	0.76668	1232.2	0.03086	216.70	409.85	1.0589	1.7315	1.213	0.806	1.333	594	162.2	187.3	12.14	88.6	10.45	9.64	14
16	0.81244	1224.9	0.02912	219.14	410.47	1.0672	1.7289	1.220	0.817	1.340	584	161.9	183.2	12.24	87.7	10.61	9.35	16
18	0.86020	1217.4	0.02750	221.59	411.07	1.0755	1.7263	1.228	0.828	1.348	575	161.6	179.2	12.33	86.8	10.77	9.06	18
20	0.91002	1209.9	0.02599	224.06	411.66	1.0838	1.7238	1.236	0.840	1.357	565	161.3	175.3	12.43	85.9	10.95	8.78	20
22	0.96195	1202.3	0.02457	226.54	412.22	1.0921	1.7212	1.244	0.853	1.366	555	161.0	171.5	12.53	85.0	11.12	8.50	22
24	1.01600	1194.6	0.02324	229.04	412.77	1.1004	1.7187	1.252	0.866	1.375	546	160.6	167.7	12.63	84.1	11.30	8.22	24
26	1.07240	1186.7	0.02199	231.55	413.29	1.1086	1.7162	1.261	0.879	1.385	536	160.2	163.9	12.74	83.2	11.49	7.94	26
28	1.13090	1178.8	0.02082	234.08	413.79	1.1169	1.7136	1.271	0.893	1.396	527	159.7	160.3	12.84	82.3	11.69	7.66	28
30	1.19190	1170.7	0.01972	236.62	414.26	1.1252	1.7111	1.281	0.908	1.408	517	159.2	156.7	12.95	81.4	11.89	7.38	30
32	1.25520	1162.6	0.01869	239.19	414.71	1.1334	1.7086	1.291	0.924	1.420	507	158.7	153.1	13.06	80.5	12.10	7.11	32
34	1.32100	1154.3	0.01771	241.77	415.14	1.1417	1.7061	1.302	0.940	1.434	497	158.2	149.6	13.17	79.6	12.31	6.84	34
36	1.38920	1145.8	0.01679	244.38	415.54	1.1499	1.7036	1.314	0.957	1.448	487	157.6	146.1	13.28	78.7	12.54	6.57	36
38	1.46010	1137.3	0.01593	247.00	415.91	1.1582	1.7010	1.326	0.976	1.463	478	157.0	142.7	13.40	77.8	12.77	6.30	38
40	1.53360	1128.5	0.01511	249.65	416.25	1.1665	1.6985	1.339	0.995	1.480	468	156.4	139.4	13.52	76.9	13.02	6.04	40
42	1.60980	1119.6	0.01433	252.32	416.55	1.1747	1.6959	1.353	1.015	1.498	458	155.7	136.1	13.64	76.0	13.28	5.77	42
44	1.68870	1110.6	0.01360	255.01	416.83	1.1830	1.6933	1.368	1.037	1.517	448	155.0	132.8	13.77	75.1	13.55	5.51	44
46	1.77040	1101.4	0.01291	257.73	417.07	1.1913	1.6906	1.384	1.061	1.538	437	154.2	129.5	13.90	74.1	13.83	5.25	46
48	1.85510	1091.9	0.01226	260.47	417.27	1.1997	1.6879	1.401	1.086	1.561	427	153.4	126.3	14.04	73.2	14.13	5.00	48
50	1.94270	1082.3	0.01163	263.25	417.44	1.2080	1.6852	1.419	1.113	1.586	417	152.6	123.1	14.18	72.3	14.45	4.74	50
52	2.03330	1072.4	0.01104	266.05	417.56	1.2164	1.6824	1.439	1.142	1.614	407	151.7	120.0	14.32	71.4	14.78	4.49	52
54	2.12700	1062.3	0.01048	268.89	417.63	1.2248	1.6795	1.461	1.173	1.644	396	150.8	116.9	14.47	70.4	15.14	4.24	54
56	2.22390	1052.0	0.00995	271.76	417.66	1.2333	1.6766	1.485	1.208	1.677	386	149.8	113.8	14.63	69.5	15.52	4.00	56
58	2.32400	1041.3	0.00944	274.66	417.63	1.2418	1.6736	1.511	1.246	1.714	375	148.8	110.7	14.80	68.6	15.92	3.75	58
60	2.42750	1030.4	0.00896	277.61	417.55	1.2504	1.6705	1.539	1.287	1.755	364	147.7	107.6	14.98	67.6	16.36	3.51	60
65	2.70120	1001.4	0.00785	285.18	417.06	1.2722	1.6622	1.626	1.413	1.881	337	144.9	100.0	15.46	65.3	17.61	2.92	65
70	2.99740	969.7	0.00685	293.10	416.09	1.2945	1.6529	1.743	1.584	2.056	309	141.7	92.4	16.02	62.9	19.16	2.36	70
75	3.31770	934.4	0.00595	301.46	414.49	1.3177	1.6424	1.913	1.832	2.315	280	138.1	84.6	16.70	60.6	21.16	1.82	75
80	3.66380	893.7	0.00512	310.44	412.01	1.3423	1.6299	2.181	2.231	2.735	249	134.2	76.6	17.55	58.6	23.87	1.30	80
85	4.03780	844.8	0.00434	320.38	408.19	1.3690	1.6142	2.682	2.984	3.532	215	129.7	68.1	18.71	57.4	27.82	0.83	85
90	4.44230	780.1	0.00356	332.09	401.87	1.4001	1.5922	3.981	4.975	5.626	177	124.6	58.3	20.48	59.3	34.55	0.40	90
95	4.88240	662.9	0.00262	349.56	387.28	1.4462	1.5486	17.31	25.29	26.43	128	118.0	44.4	24.76	83.5	59.15	0.05	95
96.15[c]	4.99000	523.8	0.00191	366.90	366.90	1.4927	1.4927	∞	∞	∞	0	0.0	—	—	∞	∞	0.00	96.15

*Temperatures on ITS-90 scale

[b]Normal boiling point

[c]Critical point

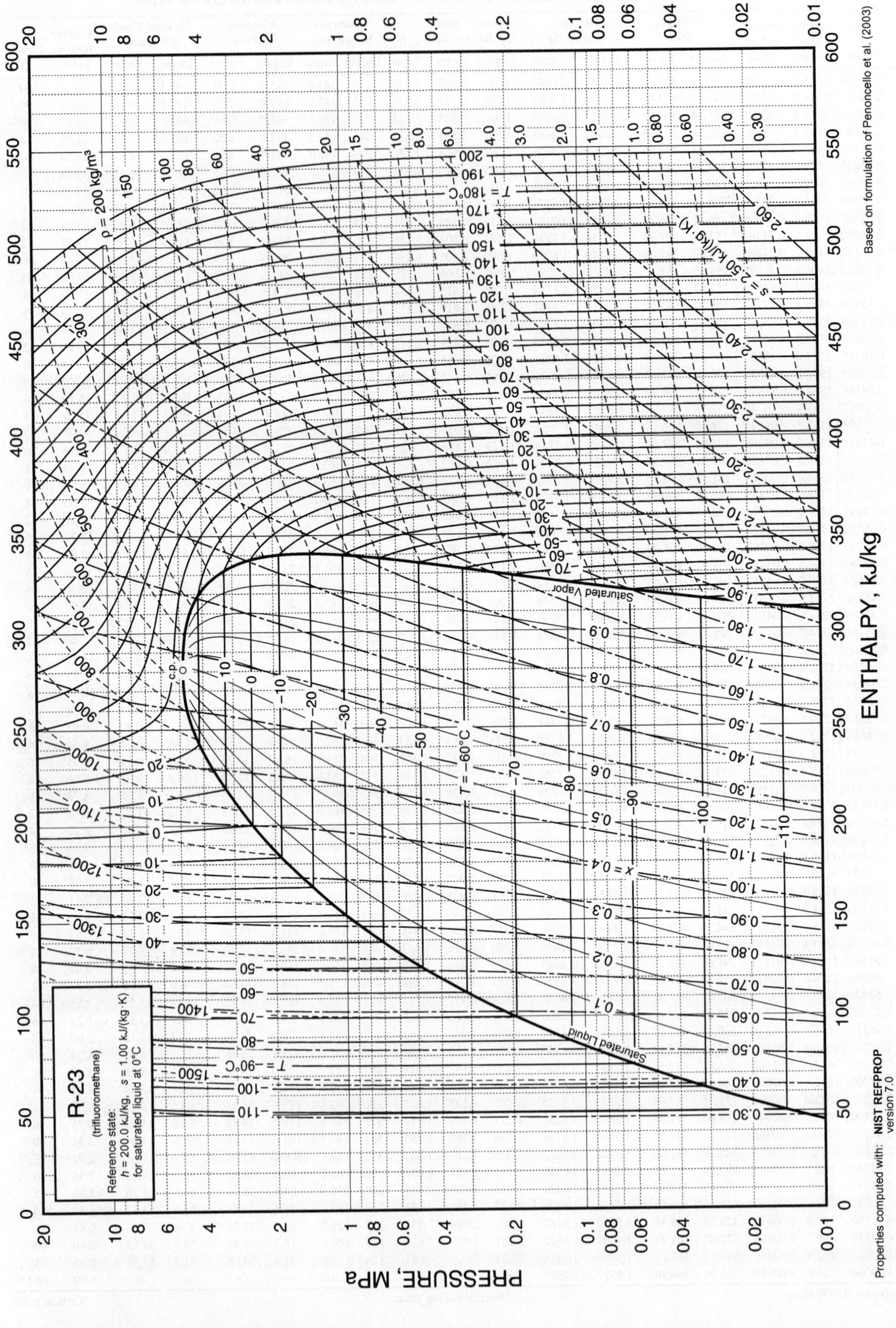

Fig. 3 Pressure-Enthalpy Diagram for Refrigerant 23

Refrigerant 23 (Trifluoromethane) Properties of Saturated Liquid and Saturated Vapor

Temp.,* °C	Pres- sure, MPa	Density, kg/m³ Liquid	Volume, m³/kg Vapor	Enthalpy, kJ/kg Liquid	Enthalpy, kJ/kg Vapor	Entropy, kJ/(kg·K) Liquid	Entropy, kJ/(kg·K) Vapor	Specific Heat c_p, kJ/(kg·K) Liquid	Specific Heat c_p, kJ/(kg·K) Vapor	c_p/c_v Vapor	Velocity of Sound, m/s Liquid	Velocity of Sound, m/s Vapor	Viscosity, μPa·s Liquid	Viscosity, μPa·s Vapor	Thermal Cond., mW/(m·K) Liquid	Thermal Cond., mW/(m·K) Vapor	Surface Tension, mN/m	Temp.,* °C
–155.13[a]	0.00006	1701.9	241.360	–3.67	289.21	–0.0705	2.4111	1.221	0.500	1.315	1211	135.7	2055.0	5.35	268.6	3.80	34.37	–155.13
–150	0.00014	1685.3	105.950	2.54	291.73	–0.0190	2.3293	1.205	0.506	1.311	1200	138.4	1662.0	5.64	250.2	4.07	33.12	–150
–140	0.00060	1652.0	26.330	14.53	296.65	0.0746	2.1934	1.195	0.522	1.304	1151	143.3	1153.0	6.22	220.9	4.61	30.71	–140
–130	0.00206	1617.9	8.21940	26.48	301.56	0.1612	2.0828	1.195	0.541	1.297	1092	147.9	845.9	6.80	198.2	5.15	28.35	–130
–120	0.00588	1583.3	3.06950	38.45	306.45	0.2420	1.9919	1.199	0.565	1.292	1033	152.2	648.3	7.37	180.1	5.70	26.03	–120
–110	0.01447	1548.2	1.32190	50.47	311.27	0.3179	1.9165	1.205	0.593	1.289	976	156.0	514.4	7.93	165.3	6.25	23.75	–110
–100	0.03157	1512.3	0.63807	62.56	315.98	0.3898	1.8534	1.213	0.625	1.290	921	159.5	419.2	8.48	152.9	6.82	21.53	–100
–90	0.06239	1475.7	0.33766	74.76	320.51	0.4582	1.8000	1.225	0.661	1.294	866	162.4	349.0	9.03	142.4	7.42	19.35	–90
–82.02[b]	0.10132	1445.6	0.21446	84.60	323.96	0.5106	1.7630	1.237	0.694	1.301	823	164.3	305.1	9.47	135.0	7.92	17.65	–82.02
–80	0.11370	1437.9	0.19248	87.10	324.81	0.5236	1.7543	1.241	0.702	1.304	812	164.7	295.3	9.58	133.2	8.05	17.23	–80
–78	0.12712	1430.2	0.17333	89.59	325.63	0.5364	1.7459	1.245	0.711	1.306	801	165.1	286.1	9.69	131.5	8.18	16.81	–78
–76	0.14175	1422.5	0.15644	92.09	326.44	0.5491	1.7378	1.249	0.721	1.309	790	165.4	277.2	9.80	129.8	8.31	16.40	–76
–74	0.15768	1414.7	0.14151	94.60	327.24	0.5617	1.7299	1.253	0.730	1.312	779	165.8	268.8	9.91	128.2	8.45	15.98	–74
–72	0.17496	1406.8	0.12828	97.12	328.03	0.5742	1.7221	1.258	0.740	1.315	769	166.1	260.7	10.01	126.6	8.59	15.57	–72
–70	0.19370	1398.9	0.11652	99.64	328.79	0.5866	1.7146	1.262	0.750	1.319	758	166.3	253.0	10.12	125.1	8.73	15.16	–70
–68	0.21395	1390.9	0.10605	102.18	329.55	0.5990	1.7073	1.267	0.760	1.323	747	166.6	245.6	10.23	123.5	8.87	14.76	–68
–66	0.23582	1382.8	0.09669	104.72	330.29	0.6112	1.7001	1.272	0.771	1.327	736	166.8	238.5	10.34	122.0	9.02	14.36	–66
–64	0.25937	1374.7	0.08832	107.28	331.01	0.6234	1.6931	1.278	0.782	1.332	725	167.0	231.6	10.45	120.5	9.16	13.96	–64
–62	0.28469	1366.4	0.08081	109.85	331.71	0.6356	1.6863	1.283	0.793	1.337	714	167.1	225.1	10.56	119.1	9.32	13.56	–62
–60	0.31188	1358.1	0.07406	112.43	332.40	0.6476	1.6796	1.290	0.805	1.342	703	167.2	218.7	10.67	117.7	9.47	13.16	–60
–58	0.34102	1349.7	0.06798	115.02	333.06	0.6596	1.6731	1.296	0.817	1.347	692	167.3	212.6	10.78	116.2	9.63	12.77	–58
–56	0.37220	1341.3	0.06249	117.62	333.71	0.6716	1.6667	1.303	0.830	1.354	681	167.3	206.7	10.89	114.9	9.79	12.38	–56
–54	0.40552	1332.7	0.05753	120.24	334.33	0.6835	1.6604	1.310	0.843	1.360	670	167.4	201.1	11.00	113.5	9.96	11.99	–54
–52	0.44106	1324.0	0.05303	122.88	334.94	0.6953	1.6542	1.317	0.856	1.367	659	167.3	195.6	11.11	112.1	10.13	11.61	–52
–50	0.47893	1315.3	0.04895	125.53	335.52	0.7071	1.6482	1.325	0.870	1.375	648	167.3	190.3	11.22	110.8	10.30	11.22	–50
–48	0.51921	1306.4	0.04523	128.19	336.07	0.7189	1.6422	1.333	0.885	1.383	637	167.2	185.1	11.34	109.5	10.48	10.85	–48
–46	0.56201	1297.4	0.04185	130.87	336.61	0.7306	1.6363	1.342	0.900	1.392	625	167.0	180.1	11.45	108.2	10.66	10.47	–46
–44	0.60743	1288.3	0.03877	133.57	337.11	0.7423	1.6305	1.351	0.915	1.401	614	166.8	175.3	11.57	106.9	10.85	10.10	–44
–42	0.65557	1279.0	0.03595	136.29	337.59	0.7539	1.6248	1.361	0.932	1.411	603	166.6	170.6	11.68	105.6	11.04	9.73	–42
–40	0.70653	1269.7	0.03336	139.02	338.04	0.7655	1.6191	1.371	0.949	1.422	591	166.4	166.0	11.80	104.3	11.24	9.36	–40
–38	0.76042	1260.2	0.03100	141.78	338.46	0.7771	1.6135	1.382	0.967	1.433	580	166.1	161.6	11.92	103.1	11.45	9.00	–38
–36	0.81734	1250.5	0.02882	144.56	338.85	0.7887	1.6080	1.393	0.985	1.446	569	165.7	157.3	12.04	101.8	11.66	8.64	–36
–34	0.87740	1240.7	0.02682	147.36	339.21	0.8002	1.6025	1.405	1.005	1.459	557	165.3	153.1	12.16	100.5	11.88	8.28	–34
–32	0.94071	1230.7	0.02498	150.18	339.53	0.8118	1.5970	1.418	1.026	1.474	545	164.9	149.0	12.29	99.3	12.10	7.93	–32
–30	1.00740	1220.5	0.02328	153.03	339.82	0.8233	1.5915	1.432	1.048	1.490	534	164.4	144.9	12.42	98.0	12.33	7.58	–30
–28	1.07750	1210.1	0.02171	155.90	340.06	0.8348	1.5861	1.447	1.072	1.507	522	163.9	141.0	12.55	96.8	12.57	7.23	–28
–26	1.15130	1199.6	0.02026	158.80	340.27	0.8464	1.5806	1.462	1.097	1.526	510	163.3	137.2	12.68	95.5	12.82	6.89	–26
–24	1.22880	1188.8	0.01892	161.73	340.43	0.8579	1.5752	1.479	1.123	1.546	498	162.7	133.4	12.81	94.3	13.08	6.55	–24
–22	1.31000	1177.8	0.01767	164.69	340.55	0.8695	1.5697	1.497	1.152	1.569	486	162	129.7	12.95	93.1	13.35	6.21	–22
–20	1.39530	1166.6	0.01651	167.68	340.62	0.8810	1.5642	1.517	1.182	1.593	474	161.3	126.1	13.10	91.8	13.63	5.88	–20
–18	1.48460	1155.0	0.01544	170.71	340.63	0.8927	1.5586	1.538	1.215	1.620	462	160.5	122.6	13.25	90.5	13.92	5.56	–18
–16	1.57810	1143.2	0.01443	173.77	340.59	0.9043	1.5530	1.561	1.251	1.650	449	159.7	119.1	13.40	89.3	14.23	5.23	–16
–14	1.67600	1131.1	0.01350	176.88	340.49	0.9160	1.5473	1.586	1.290	1.682	437	158.8	115.6	13.56	88.0	14.55	4.92	–14
–12	1.77840	1118.7	0.01263	180.02	340.33	0.9277	1.5416	1.613	1.333	1.719	424	157.9	112.2	13.73	86.7	14.88	4.60	–12
–10	1.88530	1105.9	0.01181	183.21	340.09	0.9395	1.5357	1.643	1.38	1.759	411	156.9	108.9	13.90	85.4	15.23	4.29	–10
–8	1.99710	1092.7	0.01105	186.45	339.78	0.9514	1.5297	1.676	1.432	1.805	399	155.8	105.6	14.09	84.1	15.60	3.99	–8
–6	2.11370	1079.1	0.01033	189.75	339.39	0.9634	1.5235	1.712	1.491	1.857	386	154.7	102.3	14.28	82.7	15.99	3.69	–6
–4	2.23540	1064.9	0.00966	193.10	338.91	0.9755	1.5172	1.754	1.556	1.916	372	153.5	99.0	14.49	81.4	16.40	3.40	–4
–2	2.36240	1050.3	0.00902	196.51	338.33	0.9877	1.5107	1.800	1.630	1.983	359	152.3	95.8	14.71	80.0	16.83	3.11	–2
0	2.49470	1035.1	0.00843	200.00	337.64	1.0000	1.5039	1.853	1.715	2.061	345	151.0	92.5	14.94	78.5	17.29	2.83	0
2	2.63260	1019.2	0.00786	203.56	336.83	1.0125	1.4969	1.915	1.814	2.152	332	149.6	89.3	15.19	77.1	17.79	2.55	2
4	2.77620	1002.5	0.00733	207.22	335.89	1.0252	1.4895	1.986	1.929	2.259	318	148.1	86.1	15.47	75.6	18.32	2.28	4
6	2.92590	985.0	0.00683	210.97	334.78	1.0382	1.4817	2.071	2.067	2.388	303	146.5	82.8	15.77	74.0	18.89	2.02	6
8	3.08170	966.5	0.00635	214.84	333.50	1.0514	1.4735	2.173	2.234	2.545	289	144.9	79.6	16.10	72.4	19.51	1.76	8
10	3.24380	946.7	0.00589	218.84	332.01	1.0650	1.4647	2.300	2.441	2.742	274	143.2	76.2	16.47	70.7	20.20	1.52	10
12	3.41270	925.6	0.00545	223.00	330.27	1.0790	1.4552	2.461	2.704	2.993	259	141.3	72.9	16.89	68.9	20.95	1.28	12
14	3.58850	902.6	0.00502	227.37	328.22	1.0936	1.4448	2.673	3.053	3.325	243	139.4	69.4	17.38	67.0	21.80	1.05	14
16	3.77150	877.4	0.00461	231.98	325.79	1.1089	1.4333	2.966	3.536	3.787	227	137.3	65.8	17.95	65.0	22.76	0.83	16
18	3.96220	849.1	0.00421	236.93	322.84	1.1252	1.4203	3.404	4.252	4.474	210	135.0	62.0	18.64	62.7	23.88	0.63	18
20	4.16100	816.4	0.00381	242.36	319.17	1.1430	1.4050	4.130	5.429	5.602	193	132.5	57.9	19.51	60.2	25.25	0.44	20
25	4.69860	680.1	0.00263	261.94	301.55	1.2067	1.3396	18.870	26.84	26.080	141	124.3	44.3	24.79	53.4	35.21	0.05	25
26.14[c]	4.83200	526.5	0.00190	280.97	280.97	1.2697	1.2697	∞	∞	∞	0	0.0	—	—	∞	∞	0.00	26.14

*Temperatures on ITS-90 scale [a]Triple point [b]Normal boiling point [c]Critical point

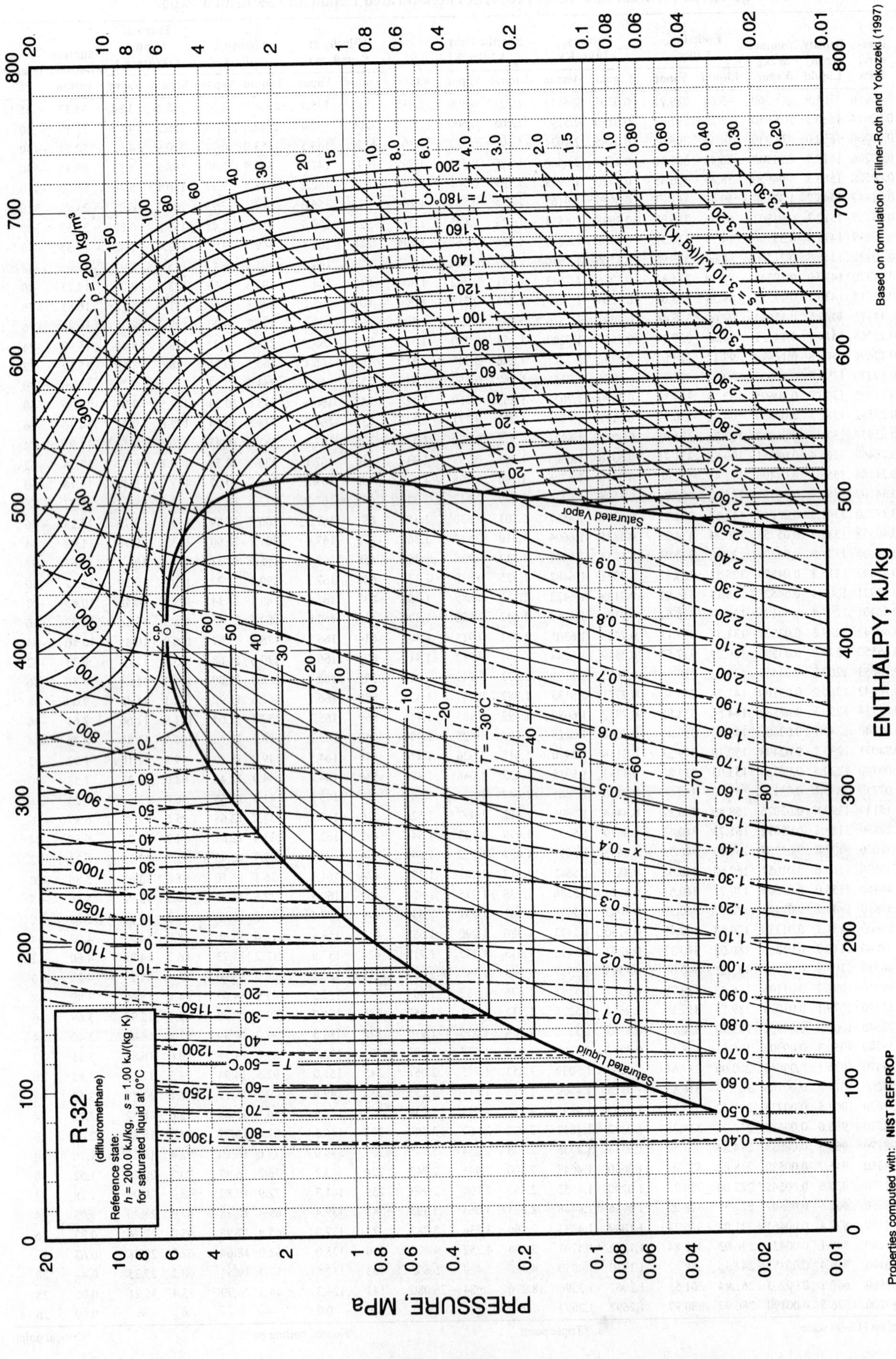

Fig. 4 Pressure-Enthalpy Diagram for Refrigerant 32

Refrigerant 32 (Difluoromethane) Properties of Saturated Liquid and Saturated Vapor

Temp.,* °C	Pressure, MPa	Density, kg/m³	Volume, m³/kg	Enthalpy, kJ/kg		Entropy, kJ/(kg·K)		Specific Heat c_p, kJ/(kg·K)		c_p/c_v	Velocity of Sound, m/s		Viscosity, μPa·s		Thermal Cond., mW/(m·K)		Surface Tension, mN/m	Temp.,* °C
		Liquid	Vapor	Liquid	Vapor	Liquid	Vapor	Liquid	Vapor	Vapor	Liquid	Vapor	Liquid	Vapor	Liquid	Vapor		
−136.81[a]	0.00005	1429.3	453.850	−19.07	444.31	−0.1050	3.2937	1.592	0.660	1.321	1414	169.6	1226.0	5.70	242.9	6.95	39.01	−136.81
−130	0.00013	1412.7	174.360	−8.26	448.77	−0.0276	3.1651	1.583	0.665	1.318	1378	173.6	1023.0	5.97	240.6	6.97	37.47	−130
−120	0.00048	1388.4	51.1840	7.52	455.33	0.0790	3.0030	1.573	0.674	1.315	1326	179.2	811.8	6.39	236.1	7.02	35.23	−120
−110	0.00145	1363.8	17.9070	23.20	461.86	0.1782	2.8668	1.565	0.686	1.312	1273	184.5	664.6	6.80	230.6	7.12	33.02	−110
−100	0.00381	1339.0	7.22200	38.83	468.31	0.2711	2.7515	1.560	0.703	1.310	1221	189.5	556.1	7.22	224.3	7.27	30.83	−100
−90	0.00887	1313.9	3.27210	54.42	474.61	0.3586	2.6529	1.559	0.725	1.310	1169	194.1	472.6	7.64	217.4	7.45	28.68	−90
−80	0.01865	1288.4	1.63160	70.02	480.72	0.4415	2.5679	1.561	0.754	1.311	1118	198.3	406.4	8.06	210.0	7.68	26.56	−80
−70	0.03607	1262.4	0.88072	85.66	486.57	0.5204	2.4939	1.566	0.790	1.314	1066	202.0	352.7	8.48	202.2	7.96	24.48	−70
−60	0.06496	1235.7	0.50786	101.38	492.11	0.5958	2.4289	1.576	0.833	1.320	1014	205.1	308.2	8.91	194.2	8.28	22.42	−60
−51.65[b]	0.10133	1212.9	0.33468	114.59	496.45	0.6565	2.3805	1.587	0.875	1.328	971	207.4	276.7	9.26	187.4	8.60	20.74	−51.65
−50	0.11014	1208.4	0.30944	117.22	497.27	0.6683	2.3714	1.589	0.883	1.329	962	207.7	271.0	9.33	186.0	8.66	20.41	−50
−40	0.17741	1180.2	0.19743	133.23	502.02	0.7382	2.3200	1.608	0.940	1.343	910	209.7	239.4	9.75	177.8	9.10	18.44	−40
−38	0.19409	1174.4	0.18134	136.45	502.91	0.7519	2.3103	1.612	0.952	1.347	900	210.1	233.6	9.84	176.1	9.19	18.05	−38
−36	0.21197	1168.6	0.16680	139.69	503.78	0.7655	2.3008	1.616	0.965	1.350	889	210.4	228.1	9.92	174.5	9.29	17.66	−36
−34	0.23111	1162.8	0.15365	142.93	504.63	0.7791	2.2916	1.621	0.977	1.354	879	210.6	222.6	10.01	172.8	9.39	17.27	−34
−32	0.25159	1156.9	0.14173	146.18	505.47	0.7926	2.2824	1.626	0.990	1.358	868	210.9	217.4	10.09	171.2	9.50	16.89	−32
−30	0.27344	1151.0	0.13091	149.45	506.27	0.8060	2.2735	1.631	1.004	1.363	858	211.1	212.3	10.18	169.5	9.60	16.50	−30
−28	0.29675	1145.0	0.12107	152.72	507.06	0.8193	2.2647	1.637	1.017	1.367	847	211.3	207.4	10.26	167.9	9.71	16.12	−28
−26	0.32157	1138.9	0.11211	156.01	507.83	0.8326	2.2561	1.642	1.031	1.372	837	211.4	202.6	10.35	166.3	9.83	15.74	−26
−24	0.34796	1132.9	0.10393	159.31	508.57	0.8458	2.2476	1.648	1.045	1.377	826	211.5	197.9	10.43	164.6	9.95	15.36	−24
−22	0.37600	1126.7	0.09646	162.62	509.28	0.8589	2.2392	1.654	1.060	1.383	816	211.6	193.3	10.52	163.0	10.07	14.99	−22
−20	0.40575	1120.6	0.08963	165.94	509.97	0.8720	2.2310	1.661	1.075	1.389	805	211.7	188.9	10.61	161.3	10.19	14.61	−20
−18	0.43728	1114.3	0.08337	169.28	510.64	0.8850	2.2229	1.668	1.090	1.395	794	211.7	184.6	10.70	159.7	10.32	14.24	−18
−16	0.47067	1108.0	0.07762	172.63	511.28	0.8979	2.2149	1.675	1.106	1.401	784	211.7	180.5	10.78	158.1	10.46	13.87	−16
−14	0.50597	1101.7	0.07234	175.99	511.89	0.9109	2.2070	1.682	1.122	1.408	773	211.7	176.4	10.87	156.5	10.60	13.50	−14
−12	0.54327	1095.2	0.06749	179.37	512.47	0.9237	2.1992	1.690	1.139	1.416	762	211.6	172.4	10.96	154.9	10.74	13.14	−12
−10	0.58263	1088.8	0.06301	182.76	513.02	0.9365	2.1915	1.698	1.156	1.423	751	211.5	168.5	11.05	153.2	10.89	12.77	−10
−8	0.62414	1082.2	0.05889	186.18	513.54	0.9493	2.1839	1.706	1.174	1.432	741	211.4	164.8	11.14	151.6	11.04	12.41	−8
−6	0.66786	1075.6	0.05508	189.60	514.03	0.9620	2.1764	1.715	1.192	1.440	730	211.2	161.1	11.23	150.0	11.21	12.05	−6
−4	0.71388	1068.9	0.05155	193.05	514.49	0.9747	2.1690	1.725	1.211	1.450	719	211.0	157.5	11.32	148.4	11.38	11.69	−4
−2	0.76226	1062.1	0.04829	196.52	514.91	0.9874	2.1616	1.735	1.231	1.460	708	210.8	154.0	11.42	146.8	11.55	11.34	−2
0	0.81310	1055.3	0.04527	200.00	515.30	1.0000	2.1543	1.745	1.251	1.470	697	210.5	150.6	11.51	145.3	11.73	10.99	0
2	0.86647	1048.3	0.04246	203.50	515.65	1.0126	2.1471	1.756	1.272	1.481	686	210.2	147.3	11.61	143.7	11.93	10.63	2
4	0.92245	1041.3	0.03986	207.03	515.96	1.0252	2.1399	1.767	1.294	1.493	675	209.8	144.0	11.70	142.1	12.13	10.29	4
6	0.98113	1034.2	0.03743	210.58	516.24	1.0377	2.1327	1.779	1.317	1.506	664	209.4	140.8	11.80	140.5	12.34	9.94	6
8	1.04260	1027.0	0.03518	214.15	516.47	1.0503	2.1256	1.792	1.341	1.519	652	209.0	137.7	11.90	139.0	12.56	9.60	8
10	1.10690	1019.7	0.03308	217.74	516.66	1.0628	2.1185	1.806	1.367	1.534	641	208.5	134.6	12.00	137.4	12.79	9.25	10
12	1.17420	1012.2	0.03112	221.36	516.80	1.0753	2.1114	1.820	1.393	1.549	630	208.0	131.6	12.10	135.9	13.04	8.91	12
14	1.24450	1004.7	0.02929	225.01	516.90	1.0878	2.1043	1.835	1.421	1.565	618	207.5	128.7	12.48	134.3	13.29	8.58	14
16	1.31790	997.1	0.02758	228.68	516.95	1.1003	2.0972	1.851	1.450	1.583	607	206.9	125.8	12.60	132.8	13.56	8.24	16
18	1.39460	989.3	0.02598	232.39	516.95	1.1128	2.0902	1.868	1.481	1.602	595	206.3	123.0	12.73	131.2	13.85	7.91	18
20	1.47460	981.4	0.02448	236.12	516.90	1.1253	2.0831	1.886	1.514	1.622	584	205.6	120.3	12.86	129.7	14.16	7.59	20
22	1.55790	973.3	0.02307	239.89	516.79	1.1378	2.0760	1.905	1.548	1.644	572	204.9	117.5	13.00	128.2	14.48	7.26	22
24	1.64480	965.2	0.02175	243.69	516.62	1.1503	2.0688	1.926	1.585	1.668	560	204.1	114.9	13.14	126.6	14.83	6.94	24
26	1.73530	956.8	0.02051	247.53	516.39	1.1629	2.0616	1.948	1.624	1.693	548	203.3	112.2	13.28	125.1	15.19	6.62	26
28	1.82950	948.3	0.01935	251.40	516.09	1.1755	2.0544	1.972	1.667	1.721	536	202.4	109.7	13.43	123.6	15.59	6.30	28
30	1.92750	939.6	0.01826	255.32	515.72	1.1881	2.0471	1.997	1.712	1.750	524	201.5	107.1	13.58	122.1	16.01	5.99	30
32	2.02940	930.7	0.01722	259.28	515.29	1.2007	2.0397	2.025	1.760	1.783	512	200.6	104.6	13.74	120.6	16.46	5.68	32
34	2.13530	921.7	0.01625	263.28	514.77	1.2134	2.0322	2.055	1.813	1.819	499	199.6	102.1	13.90	119.1	16.95	5.37	34
36	2.24540	912.4	0.01533	267.34	514.17	1.2262	2.0246	2.088	1.870	1.858	487	198.5	99.7	14.07	117.6	17.47	5.07	36
38	2.35970	902.8	0.01447	271.45	513.49	1.2391	2.0169	2.124	1.933	1.901	474	197.4	97.3	14.25	116.1	18.04	4.77	38
40	2.47830	893.0	0.01365	275.61	512.71	1.2520	2.0091	2.163	2.001	1.948	461	196.2	94.9	14.44	114.6	18.65	4.47	40
42	2.60140	883.0	0.01287	279.84	511.82	1.2650	2.0011	2.206	2.077	2.001	448	194.9	92.5	14.64	113.1	19.32	4.18	42
44	2.72920	872.6	0.01214	284.13	510.83	1.2781	1.9929	2.255	2.160	2.060	435	193.6	90.2	14.84	111.6	20.05	3.89	44
46	2.86160	861.9	0.01144	288.50	509.72	1.2914	1.9845	2.309	2.254	2.126	421	192.3	87.8	15.06	110.1	20.85	3.61	46
48	2.99890	850.8	0.01078	292.95	508.48	1.3048	1.9759	2.369	2.358	2.201	408	190.8	85.5	15.29	108.6	21.73	3.33	48
50	3.14120	839.3	0.01015	297.49	507.10	1.3183	1.9670	2.439	2.477	2.287	394	189.3	83.2	15.54	107.0	22.69	3.06	50
52	3.28870	827.3	0.00955	302.12	505.57	1.3321	1.9578	2.518	2.613	2.385	379	187.7	80.8	15.80	105.5	23.77	2.79	52
54	3.44150	814.8	0.00897	306.87	503.86	1.3461	1.9482	2.609	2.771	2.499	365	186.0	78.5	16.09	104.0	24.97	2.52	54
56	3.59970	801.7	0.00843	311.74	501.95	1.3603	1.9382	2.717	2.956	2.633	350	184.3	76.1	16.39	102.5	26.31	2.26	56
58	3.76350	787.9	0.00790	316.75	499.82	1.3749	1.9277	2.845	3.175	2.793	335	182.4	73.8	16.73	100.9	27.83	2.01	58
60	3.93320	773.3	0.00740	321.93	497.44	1.3898	1.9166	3.001	3.441	2.987	320	180.4	71.4	17.09	99.4	29.55	1.76	60
62	4.10890	757.8	0.00691	327.30	494.76	1.4052	1.9048	3.193	3.771	3.228	304	178.3	68.9	17.49	97.8	31.54	1.52	62
64	4.29090	741.1	0.00644	332.90	491.73	1.4211	1.8922	3.438	4.190	3.535	288	176.1	66.4	17.95	96.3	33.85	1.29	64
66	4.47930	723.0	0.00598	338.78	488.26	1.4377	1.8785	3.761	4.743	3.938	271	173.7	63.8	18.46	94.8	36.59	1.06	66
68	4.67450	703.2	0.00553	345.02	484.25	1.4553	1.8634	4.207	5.508	4.495	254	171.2	61.1	19.06	93.3	39.90	0.85	68
70	4.87680	680.9	0.00508	351.73	479.52	1.4740	1.8464	4.865	6.639	5.316	236	168.4	58.2	19.76	92.0	44.04	0.64	70
75	5.41680	605.9	0.00391	372.39	461.72	1.5314	1.7880	10.130	15.600	11.720	186	159.6	49.5	22.56	91.5	62.91	0.19	75
78.11[c]	5.78200	424.0	0.00236	414.15	414.15	1.6486	1.6486	∞	∞	∞	0	0.0	—	—	∞	∞	0.00	78.11

*Temperatures on ITS-90 scale   [a]Triple point   [b]Normal boiling point   [c]Critical point

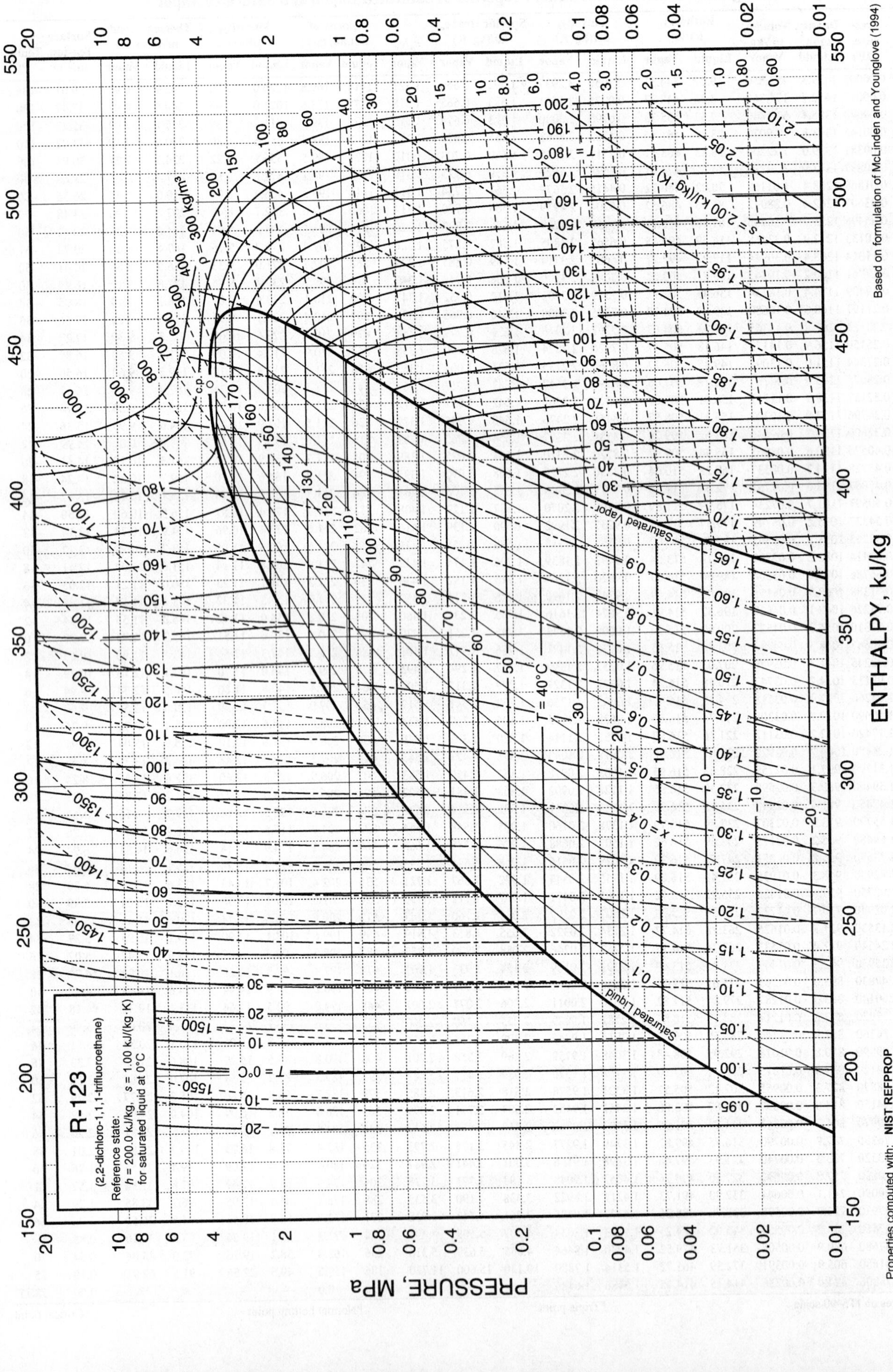

Fig. 5 Pressure-Enthalpy Diagram for Refrigerant 123

Refrigerant 123 (2,2-Dichloro-1,1,1-Trifluoroethane) Properties of Saturated Liquid and Saturated Vapor

Temp.,* °C	Pressure, MPa	Density, kg/m³ Liquid	Volume, m³/kg Vapor	Enthalpy, kJ/kg Liquid	Enthalpy, kJ/kg Vapor	Entropy, kJ/(kg·K) Liquid	Entropy, kJ/(kg·K) Vapor	Specific Heat c_p, kJ/(kg·K) Liquid	Specific Heat c_p, kJ/(kg·K) Vapor	c_p/c_v Vapor	Velocity of Sound, m/s Liquid	Velocity of Sound, m/s Vapor	Viscosity, μPa·s Liquid	Viscosity, μPa·s Vapor	Thermal Cond., mW/(m·K) Liquid	Thermal Cond., mW/(m·K) Vapor	Surface Tension, mN/m	Temp.,* °C
–80	0.00013	1709.6	83.6670	123.92	335.98	0.6712	1.7691	0.924	0.520	1.117	1133	108.3	2093.0	6.68	107.4	3.22	28.42	–80
–70	0.00034	1687.4	32.8420	133.17	341.25	0.7179	1.7422	0.927	0.537	1.113	1091	110.8	1680.0	7.09	104.8	3.79	27.09	–70
–60	0.00081	1665.1	14.3330	142.46	346.66	0.7625	1.7206	0.932	0.553	1.110	1049	113.3	1383.0	7.50	102.0	4.35	25.78	–60
–50	0.00177	1642.6	6.84600	151.81	352.21	0.8054	1.7034	0.939	0.569	1.107	1006	115.6	1160.0	7.91	99.1	4.92	24.48	–50
–40	0.00358	1620.0	3.53190	161.25	357.88	0.8468	1.6901	0.948	0.585	1.105	964	117.9	986.4	8.31	96.1	5.49	23.19	–40
–30	0.00675	1597.0	1.94700	170.78	363.65	0.8868	1.6800	0.958	0.601	1.103	923	120.0	848.0	8.70	93.0	6.05	21.92	–30
–20	0.01200	1573.8	1.13640	180.41	369.52	0.9256	1.6726	0.968	0.617	1.102	881	122.0	735.4	9.09	89.8	6.61	20.66	–20
–10	0.02025	1550.1	0.69690	190.15	375.45	0.9633	1.6675	0.979	0.634	1.102	841	123.8	642.4	9.47	86.7	7.18	19.41	–10
0	0.03265	1526.1	0.44609	200.00	381.44	1.0000	1.6642	0.990	0.651	1.102	801	125.4	564.6	9.84	83.7	7.74	18.18	0
2	0.03574	1521.3	0.40991	201.98	382.64	1.0072	1.6638	0.993	0.654	1.103	793	125.7	550.6	9.91	83.1	7.86	17.94	2
4	0.03907	1516.4	0.37720	203.97	383.84	1.0144	1.6634	0.995	0.658	1.103	785	126.0	537.0	9.99	82.5	7.97	17.70	4
6	0.04264	1511.5	0.34759	205.97	385.05	1.0216	1.6631	0.997	0.661	1.103	777	126.3	523.8	10.06	81.9	8.08	17.45	6
8	0.04647	1506.6	0.32075	207.96	386.25	1.0287	1.6628	0.999	0.665	1.103	769	126.6	511.1	10.13	81.3	8.20	17.21	8
10	0.05057	1501.6	0.29637	209.97	387.46	1.0358	1.6626	1.002	0.668	1.104	761	126.8	498.8	10.20	80.7	8.31	16.97	10
12	0.05495	1496.7	0.27420	211.97	388.66	1.0428	1.6625	1.004	0.672	1.104	754	127.1	486.8	10.28	80.1	8.43	16.73	12
14	0.05963	1491.7	0.25401	213.99	389.87	1.0499	1.6624	1.006	0.675	1.104	746	127.3	475.3	10.35	79.5	8.54	16.49	14
16	0.06463	1486.7	0.23559	216.00	391.08	1.0569	1.6623	1.009	0.679	1.105	738	127.6	464.0	10.42	79.0	8.66	16.25	16
18	0.06995	1481.7	0.21877	218.02	392.29	1.0638	1.6623	1.011	0.682	1.105	730	127.8	453.2	10.49	78.4	8.77	16.01	18
20	0.07561	1476.6	0.20338	220.05	393.49	1.0707	1.6624	1.014	0.686	1.106	723	128.0	442.6	10.56	77.8	8.89	15.77	20
22	0.08163	1471.5	0.18929	222.08	394.70	1.0776	1.6625	1.016	0.690	1.106	715	128.2	432.4	10.63	77.3	9.01	15.53	22
24	0.08802	1466.4	0.17637	224.12	395.91	1.0845	1.6626	1.018	0.693	1.107	707	128.4	422.4	10.70	76.7	9.12	15.30	24
26	0.09480	1461.3	0.16451	226.16	397.12	1.0913	1.6628	1.021	0.697	1.107	700	128.6	412.8	10.77	76.1	9.24	15.06	26
27.82[b]	0.10133	1456.6	0.15453	228.03	398.22	1.0975	1.6630	1.023	0.701	1.108	693	128.7	404.2	10.84	75.6	9.35	14.84	27.82
28	0.10198	1456.2	0.15360	228.21	398.32	1.0981	1.6630	1.023	0.701	1.108	692	128.7	403.4	10.84	75.6	9.36	14.82	28
30	0.10958	1451.0	0.14356	230.26	399.53	1.1049	1.6633	1.026	0.705	1.109	684	128.9	394.3	10.91	75.0	9.48	14.59	30
32	0.11762	1445.8	0.13431	232.31	400.73	1.1116	1.6635	1.028	0.709	1.109	677	129.0	385.4	10.98	74.5	9.60	14.35	32
34	0.12611	1440.6	0.12577	234.38	401.93	1.1183	1.6639	1.031	0.712	1.110	669	129.1	376.8	11.05	74.0	9.72	14.12	34
36	0.13507	1435.4	0.11789	236.44	403.14	1.1250	1.6642	1.033	0.716	1.111	662	129.3	368.4	11.12	73.4	9.84	13.89	36
38	0.14452	1430.1	0.11060	238.51	404.34	1.1317	1.6646	1.036	0.720	1.112	654	129.4	360.3	11.19	72.9	9.96	13.66	38
40	0.15447	1424.8	0.10385	240.59	405.54	1.1383	1.6651	1.038	0.724	1.113	647	129.5	352.4	11.26	72.4	10.08	13.43	40
42	0.16495	1419.4	0.09759	242.67	406.73	1.1449	1.6655	1.041	0.728	1.114	639	129.5	344.7	11.33	71.8	10.20	13.20	42
44	0.17597	1414.1	0.09179	244.76	407.93	1.1515	1.6660	1.044	0.732	1.115	632	129.6	337.2	11.40	71.3	10.32	12.97	44
46	0.18755	1408.7	0.08641	246.86	409.12	1.1581	1.6665	1.046	0.736	1.116	624	129.7	329.9	11.46	70.8	10.45	12.74	46
48	0.19971	1403.3	0.08140	248.95	410.31	1.1646	1.6670	1.049	0.741	1.117	617	129.7	322.8	11.53	70.3	10.57	12.51	48
50	0.21246	1397.8	0.07674	251.06	411.50	1.1711	1.6676	1.052	0.745	1.119	610	129.7	315.9	11.60	69.8	10.70	12.28	50
52	0.22584	1392.3	0.07240	253.17	412.69	1.1776	1.6682	1.055	0.749	1.120	602	129.7	309.1	11.67	69.3	10.82	12.05	52
54	0.23985	1386.8	0.06836	255.28	413.87	1.1840	1.6688	1.058	0.753	1.121	595	129.7	302.6	11.74	68.8	10.95	11.83	54
56	0.25451	1381.2	0.06458	257.41	415.05	1.1905	1.6694	1.060	0.758	1.123	588	129.7	296.2	11.80	68.3	11.08	11.60	56
58	0.26985	1375.6	0.06106	259.53	416.23	1.1969	1.6701	1.063	0.762	1.124	580	129.7	289.9	11.87	67.8	11.21	11.38	58
60	0.28589	1370.0	0.05777	261.67	417.40	1.2033	1.6707	1.066	0.767	1.126	573	129.6	283.9	11.94	67.3	11.34	11.16	60
62	0.30264	1364.3	0.05469	263.81	418.57	1.2096	1.6714	1.069	0.771	1.127	566	129.6	277.9	12.01	66.8	11.47	10.93	62
64	0.32013	1358.6	0.05180	265.95	419.73	1.2160	1.6721	1.072	0.776	1.129	558	129.5	272.1	12.07	66.3	11.61	10.71	64
66	0.33838	1352.8	0.04910	268.10	420.89	1.2223	1.6728	1.076	0.781	1.131	551	129.4	266.5	12.14	65.9	11.74	10.49	66
68	0.35740	1347.0	0.04656	270.26	422.05	1.2286	1.6735	1.079	0.785	1.133	544	129.3	261.0	12.21	65.4	11.88	10.27	68
70	0.37722	1341.2	0.04418	272.42	423.20	1.2349	1.6743	1.082	0.790	1.135	536	129.2	255.6	12.28	64.9	12.01	10.05	70
72	0.39787	1335.3	0.04195	274.60	424.35	1.2411	1.6750	1.085	0.795	1.137	529	129.0	250.4	12.35	64.5	12.15	9.84	72
74	0.41936	1329.3	0.03985	276.77	425.50	1.2474	1.6758	1.089	0.800	1.139	522	128.9	245.2	12.42	64.0	12.29	9.62	74
76	0.44171	1323.4	0.03787	278.96	426.63	1.2536	1.6766	1.092	0.806	1.142	515	128.7	240.2	12.49	63.5	12.44	9.40	76
78	0.46494	1317.3	0.03601	281.15	427.77	1.2598	1.6774	1.096	0.811	1.144	507	128.5	235.3	12.55	63.1	12.58	9.19	78
80	0.48909	1311.2	0.03426	283.35	428.89	1.2660	1.6781	1.100	0.816	1.147	500	128.3	230.5	12.63	62.6	12.73	8.97	80
82	0.51416	1305.1	0.03261	285.55	430.01	1.2722	1.6789	1.103	0.822	1.150	493	128.1	225.9	12.70	62.2	12.87	8.76	82
84	0.54019	1298.9	0.03105	287.77	431.13	1.2783	1.6797	1.107	0.827	1.152	486	127.8	221.3	12.77	61.7	13.02	8.55	84
86	0.56720	1292.6	0.02958	289.99	432.23	1.2845	1.6806	1.111	0.833	1.156	478	127.6	216.8	12.84	61.3	13.17	8.34	86
88	0.59520	1286.3	0.02819	292.22	433.33	1.2906	1.6814	1.115	0.839	1.159	471	127.3	212.5	12.91	60.8	13.33	8.13	88
90	0.62423	1279.9	0.02687	294.45	434.43	1.2967	1.6822	1.120	0.845	1.162	464	127.0	208.2	12.98	60.4	13.48	7.92	90
92	0.65430	1273.5	0.02563	296.70	435.51	1.3028	1.6830	1.124	0.851	1.166	457	126.6	204.0	13.06	59.9	13.64	7.71	92
94	0.68544	1266.9	0.02445	298.95	436.59	1.3089	1.6838	1.129	0.858	1.169	449	126.3	199.9	13.14	59.5	13.80	7.50	94
96	0.71768	1260.3	0.02334	301.21	437.66	1.3150	1.6846	1.133	0.864	1.173	442	125.9	195.9	13.21	59.1	13.96	7.30	96
98	0.75103	1253.7	0.02228	303.49	438.72	1.3211	1.6854	1.138	0.871	1.177	435	125.5	191.9	13.29	58.6	14.13	7.09	98
100	0.78553	1246.9	0.02128	305.77	439.77	1.3271	1.6862	1.143	0.878	1.182	427	125.1	188.1	13.37	58.2	14.29	6.89	100
110	0.97603	1211.9	0.01697	317.32	444.88	1.3572	1.6902	1.172	0.917	1.208	391	122.8	169.9	13.80	56.0	15.17	5.88	110
120	1.19900	1174.4	0.01361	329.15	449.67	1.3872	1.6938	1.207	0.964	1.243	354	119.8	153.4	14.29	53.9	16.14	4.91	120
130	1.45780	1133.6	0.01094	341.32	454.07	1.4173	1.6969	1.254	1.026	1.294	317	116.0	138.1	14.89	51.7	17.22	3.98	130
140	1.75630	1088.3	0.00879	353.92	457.94	1.4475	1.6992	1.318	1.111	1.369	279	111.5	123.8	15.65	49.5	18.44	3.09	140
150	2.09870	1036.8	0.00703	367.10	461.05	1.4782	1.7003	1.415	1.240	1.493	239	106.0	110.2	16.68	47.2	19.87	2.24	150
160	2.49010	975.7	0.00555	381.13	463.01	1.5101	1.6991	1.584	1.473	1.726	198	99.3	96.8	18.19	44.8	21.63	1.45	160
170	2.93720	896.9	0.00425	396.61	462.89	1.5443	1.6939	1.979	2.033	2.309	154	91.1	82.7	20.71	42.3	24.05	0.74	170
180	3.45060	765.9	0.00292	416.22	456.82	1.5867	1.6763	4.549	5.661	6.158	102	80.6	64.3	26.59	39.7	28.82	0.15	180
183.68[c]	3.66180	550.0	0.00182	437.39	437.39	1.6325	1.6325	∞	∞	∞	0	0.0	—	—	∞	∞	0.00	183.68

*Temperatures on ITS-90 scale

[b]Normal boiling point

[c]Critical point

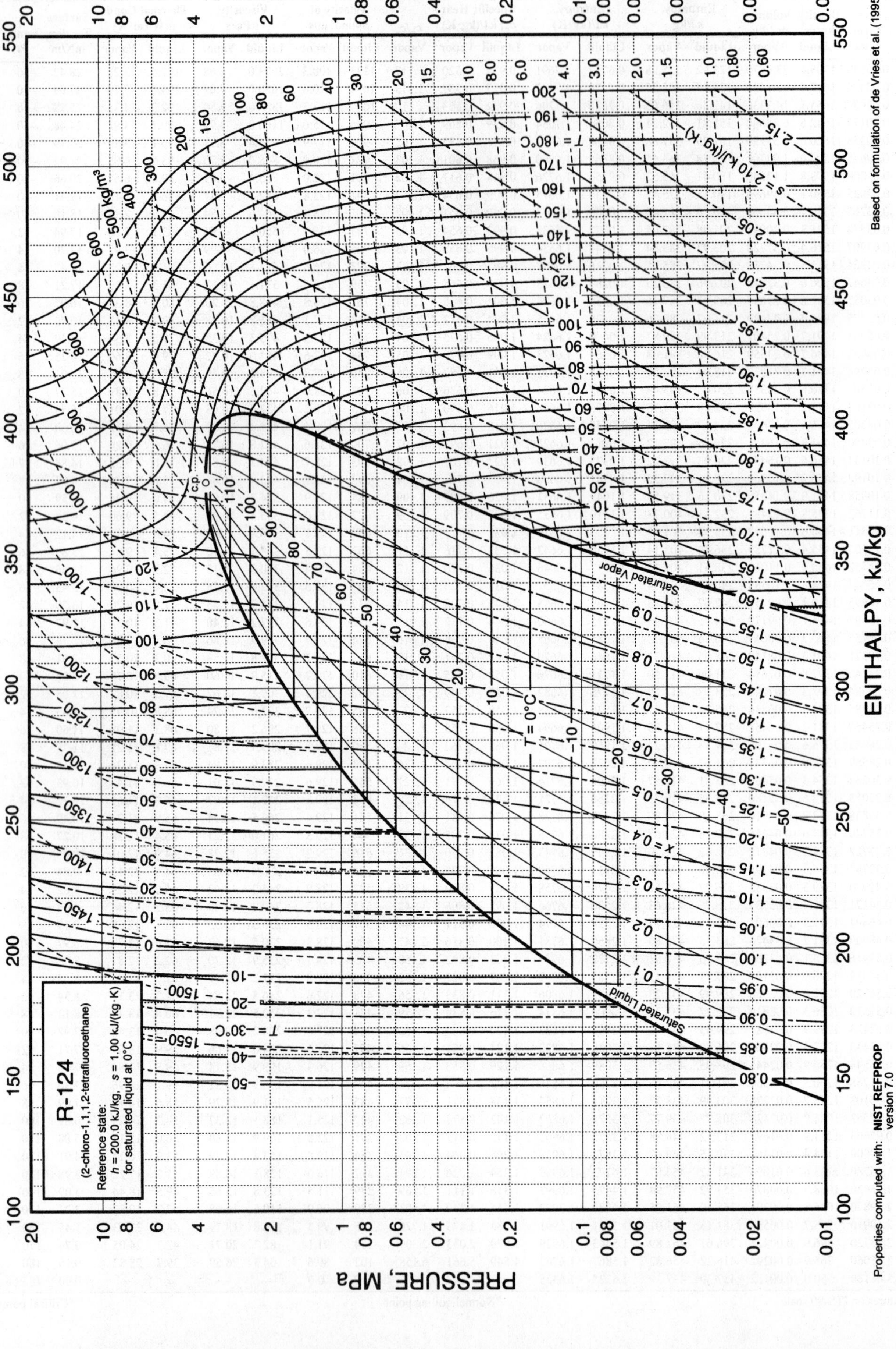

Fig. 6 Pressure-Enthalpy Diagram for Refrigerant 124

Refrigerant 124 (2-Chloro-1,1,1,2-Tetrafluoroethane) Properties of Saturated Liquid and Saturated Vapor

Temp.,*	Pres- sure,	Density, kg/m³	Volume, m³/kg	Enthalpy, kJ/kg		Entropy, kJ/(kg·K)		Specific Heat c_p, kJ/(kg·K)		c_p/c_v	Velocity of Sound, m/s		Viscosity, μPa·s		Thermal Cond., mW/(m·K)		Surface Tension,	Temp.,*
°C	MPa	Liquid	Vapor	Liquid	Vapor	Liquid	Vapor	Liquid	Vapor	Vapor	Liquid	Vapor	Liquid	Vapor	Liquid	Vapor	mN/m	°C
−100	0.00024	1714.6	44.37500	98.87	302.29	0.5417	1.7165	0.953	0.534	1.129	1052	109.1	1964.0	6.66	111.8	4.81	26.10	−100
−90	0.00067	1688.6	16.53100	108.45	307.68	0.5954	1.6832	0.962	0.551	1.125	1007	111.9	1521.0	7.05	108.7	5.26	24.69	−90
−80	0.00169	1662.3	6.96450	118.13	313.21	0.6469	1.6569	0.972	0.569	1.122	963	114.6	1215.0	7.45	105.4	5.74	23.30	−80
−70	0.00379	1635.9	3.25230	127.91	318.86	0.6962	1.6362	0.983	0.586	1.119	919	117.2	994.1	7.84	101.9	6.23	21.92	−70
−60	0.00779	1609.1	1.65600	137.80	324.62	0.7437	1.6202	0.995	0.605	1.117	875	119.6	829.0	8.23	98.5	6.74	20.56	−60
−50	0.01482	1582.0	0.90713	147.81	330.46	0.7896	1.6081	1.007	0.624	1.116	832	121.8	701.6	8.62	94.9	7.27	19.21	−50
−40	0.02642	1554.3	0.52863	157.95	336.36	0.8340	1.5993	1.020	0.644	1.116	790	123.8	600.9	9.01	91.3	7.82	17.88	−40
−30	0.04452	1526.1	0.32470	168.23	342.29	0.8772	1.5930	1.034	0.665	1.118	748	125.5	519.4	9.39	87.7	8.39	16.56	−30
−20	0.07145	1497.3	0.20856	178.66	348.23	0.9191	1.5890	1.049	0.688	1.120	706	126.9	452.4	9.78	84.1	8.98	15.26	−20
−18	0.07813	1491.4	0.19180	180.76	349.42	0.9274	1.5884	1.052	0.693	1.121	698	127.1	440.4	9.86	83.4	9.10	15.00	−18
−16	0.08529	1485.5	0.17665	182.87	350.61	0.9356	1.5879	1.056	0.698	1.122	690	127.3	428.8	9.93	82.7	9.22	14.74	−16
−14	0.09296	1479.6	0.16293	184.99	351.79	0.9438	1.5874	1.059	0.703	1.123	682	127.5	417.6	10.01	82.0	9.34	14.49	−14
−12	0.10117	1473.6	0.15048	187.11	352.97	0.9519	1.5870	1.062	0.708	1.124	673	127.7	406.8	10.09	81.2	9.46	14.23	−12
−11.96[b]	0.10133	1473.5	0.15026	187.15	352.99	0.9521	1.5870	1.062	0.708	1.124	673	127.7	406.6	10.09	81.2	9.46	14.23	−11.96
−10	0.10993	1467.6	0.13917	189.24	354.15	0.9600	1.5867	1.065	0.713	1.125	665	127.9	396.3	10.16	80.5	9.59	13.98	−10
−8	0.11928	1461.6	0.12888	191.38	355.33	0.9681	1.5864	1.069	0.718	1.126	657	128.1	386.2	10.24	79.8	9.71	13.72	−8
−6	0.12923	1455.5	0.11950	193.52	356.51	0.9761	1.5862	1.072	0.723	1.127	649	128.2	376.4	10.32	79.1	9.84	13.47	−6
−4	0.13983	1449.4	0.11093	195.68	357.68	0.9841	1.5860	1.076	0.729	1.128	641	128.3	366.9	10.40	78.4	9.96	13.22	−4
−2	0.15108	1443.2	0.10310	197.83	358.86	0.9921	1.5859	1.079	0.734	1.129	633	128.5	357.7	10.47	77.7	10.09	12.97	−2
0	0.16303	1437.0	0.09593	200.00	360.02	1.0000	1.5858	1.083	0.740	1.131	625	128.6	348.8	10.55	77.0	10.22	12.72	0
2	0.17570	1430.8	0.08936	202.17	361.19	1.0079	1.5858	1.087	0.746	1.132	617	128.6	340.2	10.63	76.3	10.35	12.47	2
4	0.18911	1424.5	0.08333	204.35	362.35	1.0158	1.5858	1.090	0.751	1.134	609	128.7	331.8	10.71	75.6	10.49	12.22	4
6	0.20331	1418.1	0.07779	206.54	363.51	1.0236	1.5859	1.094	0.757	1.135	601	128.7	323.7	10.79	74.9	10.62	11.97	6
8	0.21830	1411.8	0.07268	208.74	364.67	1.0314	1.5860	1.098	0.763	1.137	593	128.8	315.8	10.87	74.2	10.75	11.72	8
10	0.23414	1405.3	0.06798	210.94	365.82	1.0392	1.5861	1.102	0.769	1.139	585	128.8	308.2	10.95	73.5	10.89	11.48	10
12	0.25084	1398.9	0.06364	213.15	366.97	1.0469	1.5863	1.106	0.776	1.141	577	128.7	300.8	11.03	72.8	11.03	11.23	12
14	0.26844	1392.3	0.05964	215.37	368.11	1.0546	1.5865	1.110	0.782	1.143	569	128.7	293.5	11.11	72.1	11.17	10.99	14
16	0.28696	1385.7	0.05593	217.60	369.25	1.0623	1.5868	1.114	0.788	1.145	561	128.7	286.5	11.19	71.4	11.31	10.74	16
18	0.30644	1379.1	0.05250	219.84	370.38	1.0700	1.5870	1.119	0.795	1.148	553	128.6	279.7	11.28	70.8	11.46	10.50	18
20	0.32692	1372.4	0.04932	222.09	371.51	1.0776	1.5873	1.123	0.802	1.150	545	128.5	273.1	11.36	70.1	11.61	10.26	20
22	0.34842	1365.6	0.04636	224.34	372.63	1.0852	1.5876	1.128	0.809	1.153	537	128.4	266.6	11.44	69.4	11.75	10.02	22
24	0.37097	1358.8	0.04362	226.60	373.75	1.0928	1.5880	1.132	0.816	1.156	529	128.2	260.3	11.53	68.7	11.91	9.78	24
26	0.39462	1351.9	0.04107	228.88	374.85	1.1004	1.5883	1.137	0.823	1.159	521	128.1	254.2	11.61	68.1	12.06	9.54	26
28	0.41938	1345.0	0.03870	231.16	375.96	1.1079	1.5887	1.142	0.830	1.162	513	127.9	248.2	11.70	67.4	12.22	9.30	28
30	0.44530	1337.9	0.03648	233.45	377.05	1.1154	1.5891	1.147	0.838	1.165	505	127.7	242.4	11.79	66.8	12.38	9.06	30
32	0.47241	1330.8	0.03442	235.75	378.14	1.1229	1.5895	1.152	0.845	1.169	497	127.5	236.7	11.88	66.1	12.54	8.83	32
34	0.50075	1323.7	0.03249	238.07	379.22	1.1304	1.5900	1.157	0.853	1.172	489	127.2	231.2	11.97	65.5	12.71	8.59	34
36	0.53034	1316.4	0.03069	240.39	380.29	1.1379	1.5904	1.163	0.861	1.176	481	126.9	225.8	12.06	64.8	12.88	8.36	36
38	0.56123	1309.1	0.02901	242.72	381.36	1.1453	1.5909	1.168	0.870	1.180	473	126.6	220.5	12.16	64.2	13.05	8.13	38
40	0.59345	1301.6	0.02743	245.07	382.41	1.1528	1.5913	1.174	0.878	1.185	465	126.3	215.4	12.25	63.5	13.23	7.90	40
42	0.62704	1294.1	0.02596	247.43	383.45	1.1602	1.5918	1.180	0.887	1.189	457	125.9	210.4	12.35	62.9	13.41	7.67	42
44	0.66202	1286.5	0.02457	249.79	384.49	1.1676	1.5923	1.187	0.897	1.194	449	125.6	205.5	12.45	62.3	13.59	7.44	44
46	0.69845	1278.8	0.02327	252.17	385.51	1.1750	1.5928	1.193	0.906	1.199	441	125.2	200.7	12.55	61.7	13.79	7.21	46
48	0.73635	1271.0	0.02205	254.56	386.52	1.1824	1.5933	1.200	0.916	1.205	433	124.7	196.0	12.66	61.0	13.98	6.98	48
50	0.77577	1263.1	0.02090	256.97	387.53	1.1897	1.5937	1.207	0.926	1.211	425	124.3	191.4	12.77	60.4	14.18	6.76	50
52	0.81675	1255.1	0.01982	259.39	388.51	1.1971	1.5942	1.214	0.937	1.217	417	123.8	187.0	12.88	59.8	14.39	6.53	52
54	0.85931	1247.0	0.01880	261.82	389.49	1.2044	1.5947	1.221	0.948	1.224	409	123.3	182.6	12.99	59.2	14.61	6.31	54
56	0.90350	1238.7	0.01784	264.26	390.45	1.2118	1.5951	1.229	0.959	1.231	401	122.7	178.3	13.11	58.6	14.83	6.09	56
58	0.94937	1230.3	0.01693	266.73	391.39	1.2191	1.5956	1.238	0.971	1.239	393	122.1	174.1	13.27	58.0	15.08	5.87	58
60	0.99695	1221.8	0.01607	269.20	392.33	1.2265	1.5960	1.246	0.984	1.247	385	121.5	169.9	13.40	57.5	15.32	5.65	60
62	1.04630	1213.2	0.01527	271.69	393.24	1.2338	1.5965	1.255	0.997	1.256	376	120.9	165.9	13.53	56.9	15.57	5.43	62
64	1.09740	1204.3	0.01450	274.20	394.14	1.2411	1.5969	1.265	1.011	1.266	368	120.2	161.9	13.67	56.3	15.83	5.21	64
66	1.15040	1195.4	0.01378	276.72	395.01	1.2485	1.5972	1.275	1.026	1.276	360	119.5	158.0	13.82	55.7	16.10	5.00	66
68	1.20520	1186.2	0.01309	279.27	395.87	1.2558	1.5976	1.286	1.042	1.287	351	118.7	154.2	13.97	55.2	16.38	4.79	68
70	1.26200	1176.9	0.01244	281.83	396.71	1.2631	1.5979	1.297	1.058	1.299	343	117.9	150.4	14.12	54.6	16.68	4.58	70
72	1.32070	1167.4	0.01183	284.41	397.52	1.2705	1.5982	1.310	1.076	1.313	334	117.1	146.7	14.28	54.1	16.98	4.37	72
74	1.38150	1157.6	0.01124	287.01	398.31	1.2779	1.5985	1.323	1.095	1.327	326	116.2	143.0	14.45	53.5	17.30	4.16	74
76	1.44430	1147.7	0.01069	289.63	399.08	1.2852	1.5987	1.337	1.115	1.343	317	115.3	139.4	14.63	53.0	17.64	3.95	76
78	1.50930	1137.5	0.01016	292.28	399.81	1.2926	1.5989	1.352	1.137	1.360	309	114.4	135.8	14.82	52.5	17.99	3.75	78
80	1.57640	1127.0	0.00965	294.95	400.52	1.3001	1.5990	1.368	1.160	1.379	300	113.4	132.3	15.01	51.9	18.36	3.54	80
85	1.75400	1099.6	0.00849	301.75	402.14	1.3187	1.5990	1.415	1.229	1.436	278	110.7	123.7	15.54	50.6	19.39	3.05	85
90	1.94620	1070.1	0.00746	308.74	403.51	1.3376	1.5986	1.475	1.318	1.513	255	107.8	115.2	16.16	49.4	20.58	2.56	90
95	2.15420	1037.8	0.00653	315.97	404.56	1.3568	1.5975	1.554	1.437	1.618	231	104.4	106.9	16.88	48.2	22.00	2.09	95
100	2.37870	1001.8	0.00569	323.50	405.20	1.3766	1.5955	1.665	1.607	1.773	207	100.7	98.4	17.75	47.0	23.73	1.64	100
105	2.62120	960.8	0.00492	331.44	405.26	1.3971	1.5923	1.835	1.873	2.022	182	96.6	89.8	18.85	46.0	25.94	1.21	105
110	2.88310	912.1	0.00419	339.99	404.46	1.4188	1.5870	2.135	2.357	2.478	156	91.9	80.8	20.30	45.1	28.94	0.80	110
115	3.16620	849.5	0.00347	349.58	402.13	1.4428	1.5782	2.837	3.513	3.576	127	86.6	70.7	22.45	45.0	33.62	0.43	115
120	3.47390	749.1	0.00267	361.94	395.71	1.4734	1.5593	6.828	9.976	9.676	93	80.2	57.3	26.73	48.2	44.96	0.11	120
122.28[c]	3.62430	560.0	0.00179	378.79	378.79	1.5156	1.5156	∞	∞	∞	0	0.0	—	—	∞	∞	0.00	122.28

*Temperatures on ITS-90 scale

[b]Normal boiling point

[c]Critical point

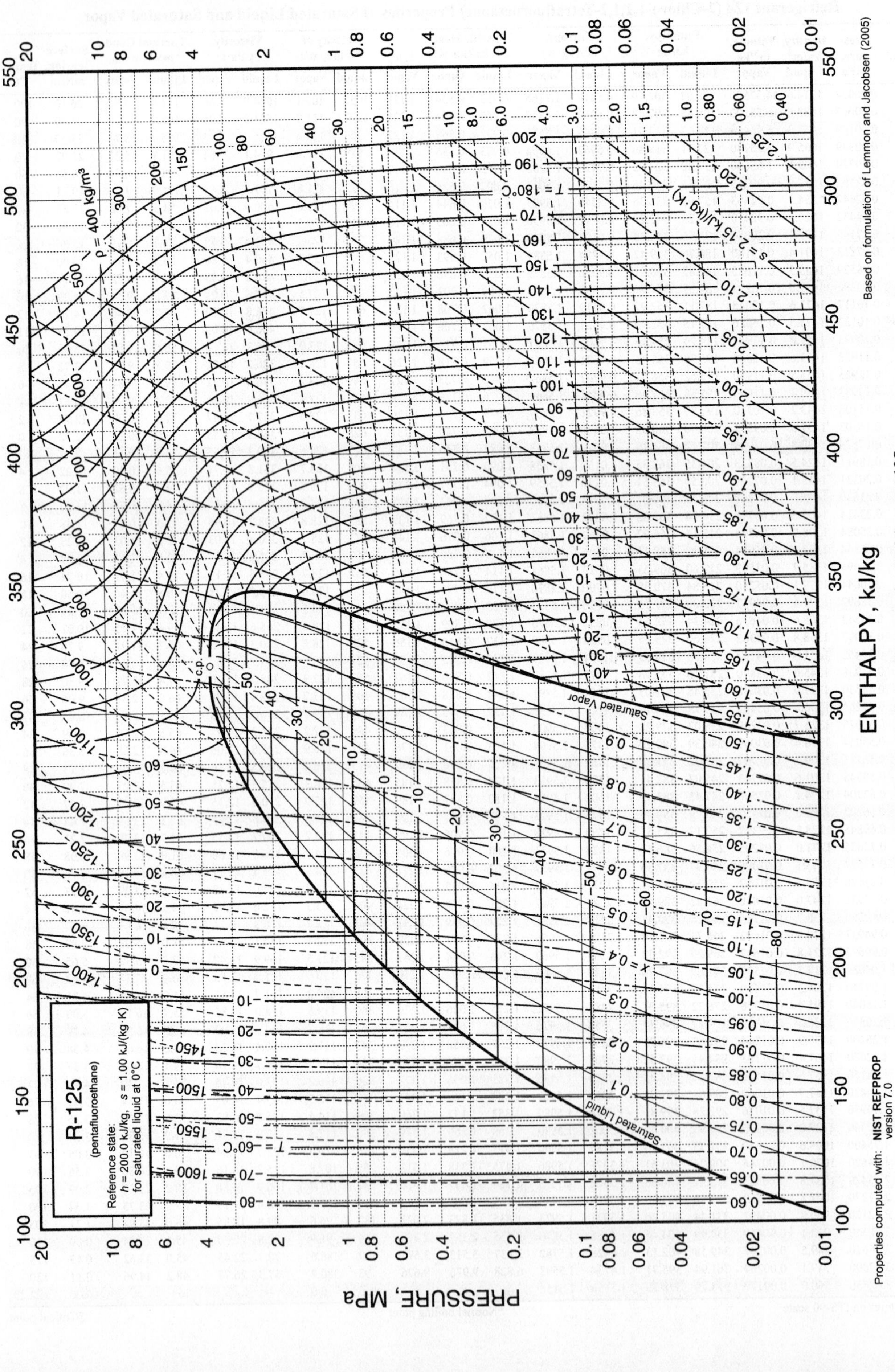

Fig. 7 Pressure-Enthalpy Diagram for Refrigerant 125

Refrigerant 125 (Pentafluoroethane) Properties of Saturated Liquid and Saturated Vapor

Temp.,[a] °C	Pressure, MPa	Density, kg/m³	Volume, m³/kg	Enthalpy, kJ/kg		Entropy, kJ/(kg·K)		Specific Heat c_p, kJ/(kg·K)		c_p/c_v	Velocity of Sound, m/s		Viscosity, µPa·s		Thermal Cond., mW/(m·K)		Surface Tension, mN/m	Temp., °C
		Liquid	Vapor	Liquid	Vapor	Liquid	Vapor	Liquid	Vapor	Vapor	Liquid	Vapor	Liquid	Vapor	Liquid	Vapor		
–100.63[b]	0.00291	1690.7	4.0880	87.13	277.39	0.4902	1.5931	1.035	0.569	1.142	933	116.4	1152	7.43	116.0	5.23	21.79	–100.63
–100	0.00309	1688.7	3.8709	87.78	277.74	0.4940	1.5911	1.035	0.570	1.141	929	116.6	1134	7.46	115.7	5.28	21.69	–100
–90	0.00729	1656.2	1.7303	98.18	283.36	0.5524	1.5634	1.045	0.592	1.138	878	119.4	890.8	7.90	111.0	5.92	20.08	–90
–80	0.01547	1623.4	0.85534	108.70	289.06	0.6082	1.5421	1.058	0.615	1.136	827	121.9	720.6	8.34	106.3	6.58	18.50	–80
–70	0.03008	1589.9	0.45942	119.36	294.83	0.6620	1.5257	1.074	0.639	1.136	779	124.1	595.2	8.77	101.6	7.25	16.94	–70
–60	0.05432	1555.7	0.26432	130.19	300.60	0.7140	1.5135	1.091	0.664	1.138	731	126.0	499.3	9.20	96.8	7.92	15.41	–60
–58	0.06066	1548.7	0.23836	132.38	301.75	0.7242	1.5114	1.095	0.669	1.138	721	126.3	482.8	9.29	95.9	8.06	15.11	–58
–56	0.06758	1541.7	0.21542	134.57	302.91	0.7343	1.5095	1.099	0.675	1.139	712	126.6	467.0	9.37	95.0	8.20	14.81	–56
–54	0.07511	1534.7	0.19510	136.78	304.06	0.7444	1.5077	1.103	0.680	1.140	702	126.9	452.0	9.46	94.0	8.33	14.51	–54
–52	0.08329	1527.6	0.17706	138.99	305.20	0.7544	1.5060	1.107	0.686	1.141	693	127.2	437.6	9.54	93.1	8.47	14.21	–52
–50	0.09216	1520.5	0.16100	141.21	306.35	0.7644	1.5044	1.111	0.692	1.142	683	127.4	423.8	9.63	92.2	8.61	13.91	–50
–48.09[c]	0.10132	1513.6	0.14728	143.34	307.44	0.7739	1.5030	1.115	0.697	1.143	674	127.6	411.1	9.71	91.3	8.75	13.63	–48.09
–48	0.10177	1513.3	0.14668	143.44	307.49	0.7743	1.5029	1.115	0.697	1.143	674	127.6	410.5	9.71	91.3	8.75	13.61	–48
–46	0.11214	1506.0	0.13387	145.68	308.63	0.7842	1.5016	1.119	0.703	1.144	664	127.8	397.9	9.80	90.3	8.89	13.32	–46
–44	0.12332	1498.8	0.12240	147.92	309.77	0.7940	1.5003	1.123	0.709	1.145	655	128.0	385.7	9.89	89.4	9.03	13.02	–44
–42	0.13536	1491.4	0.11209	150.18	310.90	0.8037	1.4991	1.128	0.715	1.146	645	128.2	374.0	9.97	88.5	9.17	12.73	–42
–40	0.14830	1484.0	0.10283	152.44	312.03	0.8134	1.4980	1.132	0.722	1.148	636	128.3	362.8	10.06	87.6	9.32	12.44	–40
–38	0.16218	1476.6	0.09448	154.71	313.16	0.8231	1.4969	1.137	0.728	1.150	627	128.5	352.0	10.14	86.7	9.46	12.15	–38
–36	0.17705	1469.1	0.08693	157.00	314.28	0.8327	1.4960	1.142	0.734	1.151	617	128.6	341.6	10.23	85.7	9.61	11.86	–36
–34	0.19295	1461.5	0.08011	159.29	315.40	0.8423	1.4951	1.146	0.741	1.153	608	128.7	331.6	10.32	84.8	9.75	11.57	–34
–32	0.20994	1453.8	0.07393	161.59	316.51	0.8519	1.4943	1.151	0.748	1.155	599	128.7	321.9	10.40	83.9	9.90	11.29	–32
–30	0.22806	1446.1	0.06831	163.90	317.61	0.8614	1.4935	1.157	0.755	1.157	589	128.7	312.6	10.49	83.0	10.05	11.00	–30
–28	0.24735	1438.4	0.06321	166.22	318.71	0.8708	1.4928	1.162	0.762	1.160	580	128.7	303.6	10.58	82.1	10.20	10.72	–28
–26	0.26787	1430.5	0.05855	168.56	319.80	0.8802	1.4922	1.167	0.769	1.162	570	128.7	294.9	10.66	81.2	10.35	10.44	–26
–24	0.28968	1422.6	0.05431	170.90	320.88	0.8896	1.4916	1.173	0.776	1.165	561	128.7	286.5	10.75	80.3	10.50	10.15	–24
–22	0.31281	1414.5	0.05043	173.26	321.96	0.8990	1.4911	1.178	0.784	1.167	552	128.6	278.4	10.84	79.4	10.65	9.88	–22
–20	0.33733	1406.4	0.04688	175.62	323.03	0.9083	1.4906	1.184	0.791	1.170	542	128.5	270.5	10.93	78.5	10.81	9.60	–20
–18	0.36328	1398.3	0.04363	178.00	324.09	0.9176	1.4901	1.190	0.799	1.173	533	128.4	262.9	11.02	77.7	10.97	9.32	–18
–16	0.39072	1390.0	0.04064	180.39	325.14	0.9268	1.4897	1.196	0.807	1.177	523	128.2	255.5	11.11	76.8	11.12	9.05	–16
–14	0.41970	1381.6	0.03789	182.80	326.19	0.9361	1.4894	1.203	0.815	1.181	514	128.0	248.4	11.21	75.9	11.29	8.78	–14
–12	0.45028	1373.1	0.03536	185.21	327.22	0.9453	1.4890	1.209	0.824	1.184	505	127.8	241.4	11.30	75.0	11.45	8.50	–12
–10	0.48252	1364.5	0.03303	187.64	328.24	0.9544	1.4887	1.216	0.832	1.189	495	127.5	234.7	11.40	74.1	11.62	8.23	–10
–8	0.51646	1355.8	0.03088	190.08	329.25	0.9636	1.4884	1.223	0.841	1.193	486	127.3	228.1	11.49	73.3	11.79	7.97	–8
–6	0.55218	1347.0	0.02890	192.54	330.25	0.9727	1.4882	1.231	0.850	1.198	476	126.9	221.8	11.59	72.4	11.96	7.70	–6
–4	0.58972	1338.1	0.02706	195.01	331.23	0.9818	1.4879	1.238	0.860	1.203	467	126.6	215.6	11.69	71.6	12.14	7.44	–4
–2	0.62915	1329.0	0.02535	197.50	332.20	0.9909	1.4877	1.246	0.870	1.209	457	126.2	209.6	11.79	70.7	12.32	7.17	–2
0	0.67052	1319.8	0.02377	200.00	333.16	1.0000	1.4875	1.255	0.880	1.215	448	125.8	203.7	11.89	69.8	12.50	6.91	0
2	0.71390	1310.5	0.02230	202.52	334.10	1.0091	1.4873	1.263	0.890	1.222	439	125.3	198.0	12.00	69.0	12.69	6.65	2
4	0.75935	1301.0	0.02093	205.05	335.02	1.0181	1.4870	1.273	0.902	1.229	429	124.9	192.4	12.11	68.1	12.88	6.40	4
6	0.80694	1291.3	0.01966	207.60	335.92	1.0272	1.4868	1.282	0.913	1.237	420	124.3	187.0	12.22	67.3	13.08	6.14	6
8	0.85672	1281.5	0.01848	210.17	336.80	1.0362	1.4866	1.292	0.926	1.246	410	123.8	181.7	12.33	66.5	13.29	5.89	8
10	0.90875	1271.5	0.01737	212.76	337.66	1.0452	1.4863	1.303	0.939	1.255	400	123.2	176.5	12.45	65.6	13.50	5.64	10
12	0.96312	1261.3	0.01634	215.37	338.50	1.0542	1.4860	1.314	0.954	1.265	391	122.5	171.4	12.57	64.8	13.72	5.39	12
14	1.0199	1250.9	0.01537	218.00	339.31	1.0633	1.4857	1.326	0.969	1.277	381	121.9	166.5	12.70	64.0	13.95	5.14	14
16	1.0791	1240.3	0.01447	220.65	340.10	1.0723	1.4854	1.339	0.986	1.289	371	121.1	161.6	12.83	63.1	14.18	4.90	16
18	1.1408	1229.4	0.01362	223.32	340.85	1.0813	1.4850	1.352	1.003	1.303	362	120.4	156.9	12.96	62.3	14.43	4.66	18
20	1.2052	1218.3	0.01283	226.02	341.58	1.0904	1.4846	1.367	1.023	1.318	352	119.6	152.2	13.10	61.5	14.69	4.42	20
22	1.2722	1206.9	0.01208	228.74	342.28	1.0995	1.4842	1.382	1.044	1.334	342	118.7	147.6	13.25	60.7	14.96	4.18	22
24	1.3420	1195.3	0.01138	231.49	342.95	1.1085	1.4836	1.399	1.067	1.352	332	117.8	143.1	13.40	59.8	15.24	3.95	24
26	1.4146	1183.3	0.01072	234.26	343.57	1.1176	1.4831	1.417	1.093	1.372	322	116.8	138.7	13.57	59.0	15.55	3.72	26
28	1.4901	1171.0	0.01010	237.07	344.16	1.1268	1.4824	1.436	1.121	1.395	312	115.8	134.4	13.74	58.2	15.87	3.49	28
30	1.5685	1158.4	0.00951	239.91	344.71	1.1359	1.4817	1.457	1.152	1.420	302	114.8	130.1	13.92	57.4	16.21	3.26	30
32	1.6501	1145.4	0.00895	242.78	345.22	1.1452	1.4809	1.481	1.186	1.448	292	113.7	125.9	14.11	56.6	16.57	3.04	32
34	1.7347	1131.9	0.00843	245.69	345.67	1.1544	1.4799	1.507	1.224	1.480	282	112.5	121.7	14.32	55.8	16.97	2.82	34
36	1.8226	1117.9	0.00793	248.64	346.07	1.1637	1.4789	1.536	1.267	1.516	272	111.3	117.6	14.54	54.9	17.39	2.60	36
38	1.9138	1103.5	0.00746	251.63	346.42	1.1731	1.4778	1.568	1.316	1.558	261	109.9	113.5	14.77	54.1	17.86	2.39	38
40	2.0085	1088.4	0.00702	254.67	346.69	1.1826	1.4764	1.605	1.372	1.606	251	108.6	109.4	15.03	53.3	18.37	2.18	40
42	2.1067	1072.7	0.00659	257.76	346.90	1.1921	1.4750	1.647	1.436	1.662	240	107.1	105.4	15.31	52.5	18.93	1.97	42
44	2.2084	1056.2	0.00619	260.92	347.02	1.2018	1.4733	1.697	1.511	1.728	229	105.6	101.3	15.61	51.7	19.55	1.77	44
46	2.3140	1038.9	0.00580	264.14	347.05	1.2116	1.4714	1.755	1.600	1.808	218	104.0	97.3	15.95	50.9	20.25	1.57	46
48	2.4234	1020.6	0.00543	267.44	346.96	1.2216	1.4692	1.824	1.708	1.906	207	102.3	93.3	16.32	50.1	21.04	1.38	48
50	2.5368	1001.1	0.00507	270.83	346.75	1.2318	1.4667	1.910	1.842	2.029	196	100.5	89.2	16.75	49.3	21.95	1.19	50
52	2.6544	980.2	0.00472	274.33	346.38	1.2422	1.4638	2.019	2.014	2.187	184	98.6	85.1	17.23	48.5	23.02	1.01	52
54	2.7763	957.5	0.00439	277.95	345.82	1.2529	1.4604	2.162	2.241	2.398	172	96.6	80.9	17.79	47.7	24.29	0.84	54
56	2.9027	932.6	0.00406	281.75	345.00	1.2641	1.4563	2.359	2.559	2.695	159	94.5	76.5	18.45	47.0	25.83	0.67	56
58	3.0339	904.5	0.00373	285.77	343.85	1.2758	1.4512	2.652	3.036	3.142	146	92.2	71.9	19.25	46.3	27.80	0.51	58
60	3.1703	872.1	0.00340	290.10	342.21	1.2884	1.4448	3.139	3.833	3.889	132	89.8	67.1	20.27	45.9	30.44	0.36	60
62	3.3121	832.4	0.00305	294.95	339.79	1.3024	1.4362	4.120	5.435	5.389	116	87.3	61.6	21.67	46.0	34.37	0.22	62
64	3.4602	777.5	0.00265	300.86	335.77	1.3195	1.4230	7.17	10.29	9.90	100	84.4	54.8	23.90	47.8	41.79	0.09	64
66.02[d]	3.6177	573.6	0.00174	318.06	318.06	1.3696	1.3696	∞	∞	∞	0	0.0	—	—	∞	∞	0.00	66.02

[a]Temperatures on ITS-90 scale [b]Triple point [c]Normal boiling point [d]Critical point

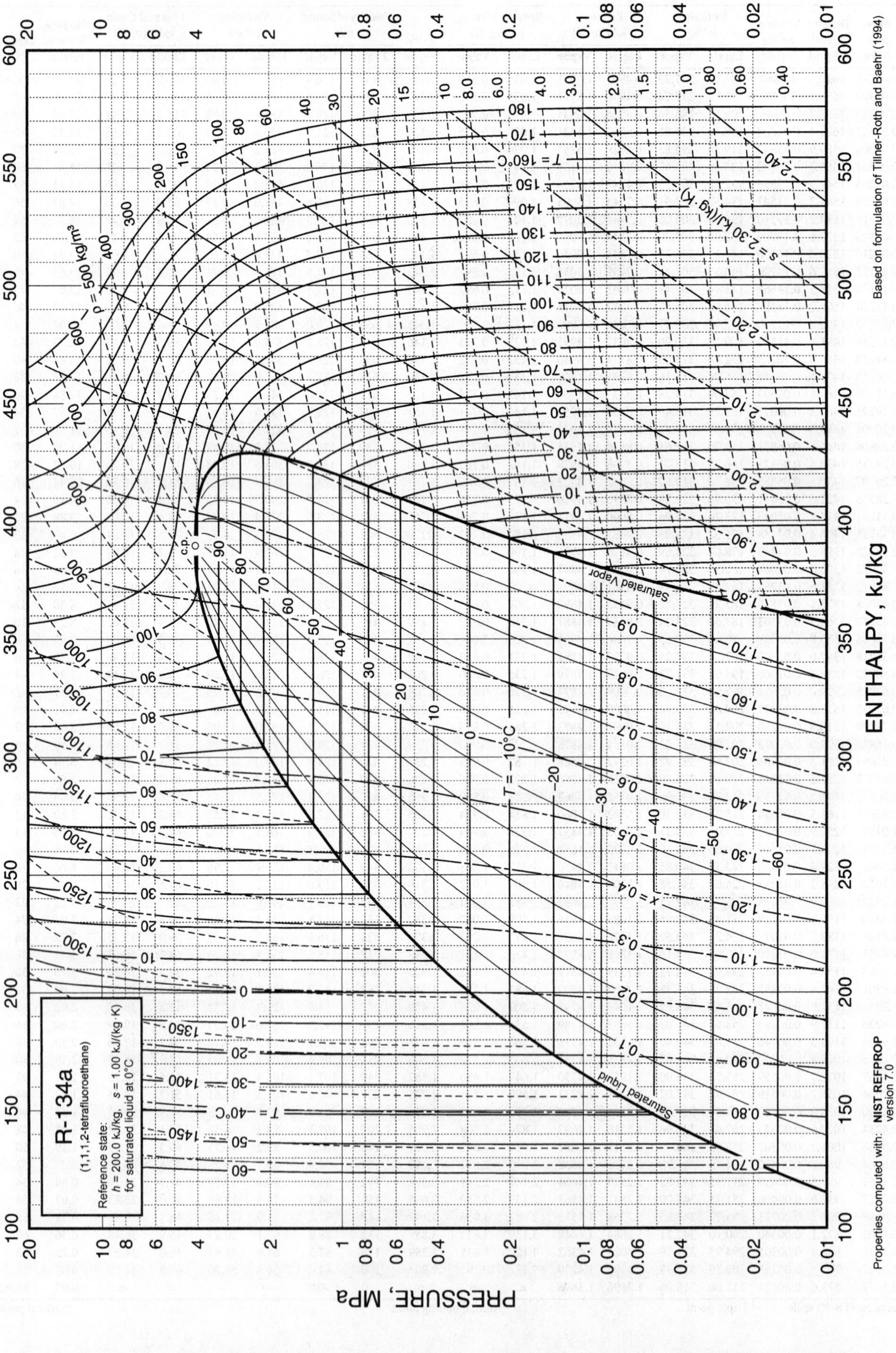

Fig. 8 Pressure-Enthalpy Diagram for Refrigerant 134a

Refrigerant 134a (1,1,1,2-Tetrafluoroethane) Properties of Saturated Liquid and Saturated Vapor

Temp.,* °C	Pressure, MPa	Density, kg/m³	Volume, m³/kg	Enthalpy, kJ/kg		Entropy, kJ/(kg·K)		Specific Heat c_p, kJ/(kg·K)		c_p/c_v	Velocity of Sound, m/s		Viscosity, µPa·s		Thermal Cond., mW/(m·K)		Surface Tension, mN/m	Temp.,* °C
		Liquid	Vapor	Liquid	Vapor	Liquid	Vapor	Liquid	Vapor	Vapor	Liquid	Vapor	Liquid	Vapor	Liquid	Vapor		
–103.30[a]	0.00039	1591.1	35.4960	71.46	334.94	0.4126	1.9639	1.184	0.585	1.164	1120	126.8	2175.0	6.46	145.2	3.08	28.07	–103.30
–100	0.00056	1582.4	25.1930	75.36	336.85	0.4354	1.9456	1.184	0.593	1.162	1103	127.9	1893.0	6.60	143.2	3.34	27.50	–100
–90	0.00152	1555.8	9.7698	87.23	342.76	0.5020	1.8972	1.189	0.617	1.156	1052	131.0	1339.0	7.03	137.3	4.15	25.79	–90
–80	0.00367	1529.0	4.2682	99.16	348.83	0.5654	1.8580	1.198	0.642	1.151	1002	134.0	1018.0	7.46	131.5	4.95	24.10	–80
–70	0.00798	1501.9	2.0590	111.20	355.02	0.6262	1.8264	1.210	0.667	1.148	952	136.8	809.2	7.89	126.0	5.75	22.44	–70
–60	0.01591	1474.3	1.0790	123.36	361.31	0.6846	1.8010	1.223	0.692	1.146	903	139.4	663.1	8.30	120.7	6.56	20.80	–60
–50	0.02945	1446.3	0.60620	135.67	367.65	0.7410	1.7806	1.238	0.720	1.146	855	141.7	555.1	8.72	115.6	7.36	19.18	–50
–40	0.05121	1417.7	0.36108	148.14	374.00	0.7956	1.7643	1.255	0.749	1.148	807	143.6	472.2	9.12	110.6	8.17	17.60	–40
–30	0.08438	1388.4	0.22594	160.79	380.32	0.8486	1.7515	1.273	0.781	1.152	760	145.2	406.4	9.52	105.8	8.99	16.04	–30
–28	0.09270	1382.4	0.20680	163.34	381.57	0.8591	1.7492	1.277	0.788	1.153	751	145.4	394.9	9.60	104.8	9.15	15.73	–28
–26.07[b]	0.10133	1376.7	0.19018	165.81	382.78	0.8690	1.7472	1.281	0.794	1.154	742	145.7	384.2	9.68	103.9	9.31	15.44	–26.07
–26	0.10167	1376.5	0.18958	165.90	382.82	0.8694	1.7471	1.281	0.794	1.154	742	145.7	383.8	9.68	103.9	9.32	15.43	–26
–24	0.11130	1370.4	0.17407	168.47	384.07	0.8798	1.7451	1.285	0.801	1.155	732	145.9	373.1	9.77	102.9	9.48	15.12	–24
–22	0.12165	1364.4	0.16006	171.05	385.32	0.8900	1.7432	1.289	0.809	1.156	723	146.1	362.9	9.85	102.0	9.65	14.82	–22
–20	0.13273	1358.3	0.14739	173.64	386.55	0.9002	1.7413	1.293	0.816	1.158	714	146.3	353.0	9.92	101.1	9.82	14.51	–20
–18	0.14460	1352.1	0.13592	176.23	387.79	0.9104	1.7396	1.297	0.823	1.159	705	146.4	343.5	10.01	100.1	9.98	14.21	–18
–16	0.15728	1345.9	0.12551	178.83	389.02	0.9205	1.7379	1.302	0.831	1.161	695	146.6	334.3	10.09	99.2	10.15	13.91	–16
–14	0.17082	1339.7	0.11605	181.44	390.24	0.9306	1.7363	1.306	0.838	1.163	686	146.7	325.4	10.17	98.3	10.32	13.61	–14
–12	0.18524	1333.4	0.10744	184.07	391.46	0.9407	1.7348	1.311	0.846	1.165	677	146.8	316.9	10.25	97.4	10.49	13.32	–12
–10	0.20060	1327.1	0.09959	186.70	392.66	0.9506	1.7334	1.316	0.854	1.167	668	146.9	308.6	10.33	96.5	10.66	13.02	–10
–8	0.21693	1320.8	0.09242	189.34	393.87	0.9606	1.7320	1.320	0.863	1.169	658	146.9	300.6	10.41	95.6	10.83	12.72	–8
–6	0.23428	1314.3	0.08587	191.99	395.06	0.9705	1.7307	1.325	0.871	1.171	649	147.0	292.9	10.49	94.7	11.00	12.43	–6
–4	0.25268	1307.9	0.07987	194.65	396.25	0.9804	1.7294	1.330	0.880	1.174	640	147.0	285.4	10.57	93.8	11.17	12.14	–4
–2	0.27217	1301.4	0.07436	197.32	397.43	0.9902	1.7282	1.336	0.888	1.176	631	147.0	278.1	10.65	92.9	11.34	11.85	–2
0	0.29280	1294.8	0.06931	200.00	398.60	1.0000	1.7271	1.341	0.897	1.179	622	146.9	271.1	10.73	92.0	11.51	11.56	0
2	0.31462	1288.1	0.06466	202.69	399.77	1.0098	1.7260	1.347	0.906	1.182	612	146.9	264.3	10.81	91.1	11.69	11.27	2
4	0.33766	1281.4	0.06039	205.40	400.92	1.0195	1.7250	1.352	0.916	1.185	603	146.8	257.6	10.90	90.2	11.86	10.99	4
6	0.36198	1274.7	0.05644	208.11	402.06	1.0292	1.7240	1.358	0.925	1.189	594	146.7	251.2	10.98	89.4	12.04	10.70	6
8	0.38761	1267.9	0.05280	210.84	403.20	1.0388	1.7230	1.364	0.935	1.192	585	146.5	244.9	11.06	88.5	12.22	10.42	8
10	0.41461	1261.0	0.04944	213.58	404.32	1.0485	1.7221	1.370	0.945	1.196	576	146.4	238.8	11.15	87.6	12.40	10.14	10
12	0.44301	1254.0	0.04633	216.33	405.43	1.0581	1.7212	1.377	0.956	1.200	566	146.2	232.9	11.23	86.7	12.58	9.86	12
14	0.47288	1246.9	0.04345	219.09	406.53	1.0677	1.7204	1.383	0.967	1.204	557	146.0	227.1	11.32	85.9	12.77	9.58	14
16	0.50425	1239.8	0.04078	221.87	407.61	1.0772	1.7196	1.390	0.978	1.209	548	145.7	221.5	11.40	85.0	12.95	9.30	16
18	0.53718	1232.6	0.03830	224.66	408.69	1.0867	1.7188	1.397	0.989	1.214	539	145.5	216.0	11.49	84.1	13.14	9.03	18
20	0.57171	1225.3	0.03600	227.47	409.75	1.0962	1.7180	1.405	1.001	1.219	530	145.1	210.7	11.58	83.3	13.33	8.76	20
22	0.60789	1218.0	0.03385	230.29	410.79	1.1057	1.7173	1.413	1.013	1.224	520	144.8	205.5	11.67	82.4	13.53	8.48	22
24	0.64578	1210.5	0.03186	233.12	411.82	1.1152	1.7166	1.421	1.025	1.230	511	144.5	200.4	11.76	81.6	13.72	8.21	24
26	0.68543	1202.9	0.03000	235.97	412.84	1.1246	1.7159	1.429	1.038	1.236	502	144.1	195.4	11.85	80.7	13.92	7.95	26
28	0.72688	1195.2	0.02826	238.84	413.84	1.1341	1.7152	1.437	1.052	1.243	493	143.6	190.5	11.95	79.8	14.13	7.68	28
30	0.77020	1187.5	0.02664	241.72	414.82	1.1435	1.7145	1.446	1.065	1.249	483	143.2	185.8	12.04	79.0	14.33	7.42	30
32	0.81543	1179.6	0.02513	244.62	415.78	1.1529	1.7138	1.456	1.080	1.257	474	142.7	181.1	12.14	78.1	14.54	7.15	32
34	0.86263	1171.6	0.02371	247.54	416.72	1.1623	1.7131	1.466	1.095	1.265	465	142.1	176.6	12.24	77.3	14.76	6.89	34
36	0.91185	1163.4	0.02238	250.48	417.65	1.1717	1.7124	1.476	1.111	1.273	455	141.6	172.1	12.34	76.4	14.98	6.64	36
38	0.96315	1155.1	0.02113	253.43	418.55	1.1811	1.7118	1.487	1.127	1.282	446	141.0	167.7	12.44	75.6	15.21	6.38	38
40	1.0166	1146.7	0.01997	256.41	419.43	1.1905	1.7111	1.498	1.145	1.292	436	140.3	163.4	12.55	74.7	15.44	6.13	40
42	1.0722	1138.2	0.01887	259.41	420.28	1.1999	1.7103	1.510	1.163	1.303	427	139.7	159.2	12.65	73.9	15.68	5.88	42
44	1.1301	1129.5	0.01784	262.43	421.11	1.2092	1.7096	1.523	1.182	1.314	418	138.9	155.1	12.76	73.0	15.93	5.63	44
46	1.1903	1120.6	0.01687	265.47	421.92	1.2186	1.7089	1.537	1.202	1.326	408	138.2	151.0	12.88	72.1	16.18	5.38	46
48	1.2529	1111.5	0.01595	268.53	422.69	1.2280	1.7081	1.551	1.223	1.339	399	137.4	147.0	13.00	71.3	16.45	5.13	48
50	1.3179	1102.3	0.01509	271.62	423.44	1.2375	1.7072	1.566	1.246	1.354	389	136.6	143.1	13.12	70.4	16.72	4.89	50
52	1.3854	1092.9	0.01428	274.74	424.15	1.2469	1.7064	1.582	1.270	1.369	379	135.7	139.2	13.24	69.6	17.01	4.65	52
54	1.4555	1083.2	0.01351	277.89	424.83	1.2563	1.7055	1.600	1.296	1.386	370	134.7	135.4	13.37	68.7	17.31	4.41	54
56	1.5282	1073.4	0.01278	281.06	425.47	1.2658	1.7045	1.618	1.324	1.405	360	133.8	131.6	13.51	67.8	17.63	4.18	56
58	1.6036	1063.2	0.01209	284.27	426.07	1.2753	1.7035	1.638	1.354	1.425	350	132.7	127.9	13.65	67.0	17.96	3.95	58
60	1.6818	1052.9	0.01144	287.50	426.63	1.2848	1.7024	1.660	1.387	1.448	340	131.7	124.2	13.79	66.1	18.31	3.72	60
62	1.7628	1042.2	0.01083	290.78	427.14	1.2944	1.7013	1.684	1.422	1.473	331	130.5	120.6	13.95	65.2	18.68	3.49	62
64	1.8467	1031.2	0.01024	294.09	427.61	1.3040	1.7000	1.710	1.461	1.501	321	129.4	117.0	14.11	64.3	19.07	3.27	64
66	1.9337	1020.0	0.00969	297.44	428.02	1.3137	1.6987	1.738	1.504	1.532	311	128.1	113.5	14.28	63.4	19.50	3.05	66
68	2.0237	1008.3	0.00916	300.84	428.36	1.3234	1.6972	1.769	1.552	1.567	301	126.8	109.9	14.46	62.6	19.95	2.83	68
70	2.1168	996.2	0.00865	304.28	428.65	1.3332	1.6956	1.804	1.605	1.607	290	125.5	106.4	14.65	61.7	20.45	2.61	70
72	2.2132	983.8	0.00817	307.78	428.86	1.3430	1.6939	1.843	1.665	1.653	280	124.0	102.9	14.85	60.8	20.98	2.40	72
74	2.3130	970.8	0.00771	311.33	429.00	1.3530	1.6920	1.887	1.734	1.705	269	122.6	99.5	15.07	59.9	21.56	2.20	74
76	2.4161	957.3	0.00727	314.94	429.04	1.3631	1.6899	1.938	1.812	1.766	259	121.0	96.0	15.30	59.0	22.21	1.99	76
78	2.5228	943.1	0.00685	318.63	428.98	1.3733	1.6876	1.996	1.904	1.838	248	119.4	92.5	15.56	58.1	22.92	1.80	78
80	2.6332	928.2	0.00645	322.39	428.81	1.3836	1.6850	2.065	2.012	1.924	237	117.7	89.0	15.84	57.2	23.72	1.60	80
85	2.9258	887.2	0.00550	332.22	427.76	1.4104	1.6771	2.306	2.397	2.232	207	113.1	80.2	16.67	54.9	26.22	1.14	85
90	3.2442	837.8	0.00461	342.93	425.42	1.4390	1.6662	2.756	3.121	2.820	176	107.9	70.9	17.81	52.8	29.91	0.71	90
95	3.5912	772.7	0.00374	355.25	420.67	1.4715	1.6492	3.938	5.020	4.369	141	101.9	60.4	19.61	51.7	36.40	0.33	95
100	3.9724	651.2	0.00268	373.30	407.68	1.5188	1.6109	17.59	25.35	20.81	101	94.0	45.1	24.21	59.9	60.58	0.04	100
101.06[c]	4.0593	511.9	0.00195	389.64	389.64	1.5621	1.5621	∞	∞	∞	0	0.0	—	—	∞	∞	0.00	101.06

*Temperatures on ITS-90 scale [a]Triple point [b]Normal boiling point [c]Critical point

Refrigerant 134a Properties of Superheated Vapor

Pressure = 0.101325 MPa
Saturation temperature = −26.07°C

Temp.,* °C	Density, kg/m³	Enthalpy, kJ/kg	Entropy, kJ/(kg·K)	Vel. of Sound, m/s
Saturated				
Liquid	1374.34	166.07	0.8701	747.1
Vapor	5.26	382.90	1.7476	145.7
−20	5.11	387.68	1.7667	147.8
−10	4.89	395.65	1.7976	151.0
0	4.69	403.74	1.8278	154.2
10	4.50	411.97	1.8574	157.2
20	4.34	420.34	1.8864	160.1
30	4.18	428.85	1.9150	162.9
40	4.04	437.52	1.9431	165.7
50	3.91	446.33	1.9708	168.4
60	3.78	455.30	1.9981	171.0
70	3.67	464.43	2.0251	173.6
80	3.56	473.70	2.0518	176.1
90	3.46	483.13	2.0781	178.6
100	3.36	492.71	2.1041	181.0
110	3.27	502.44	2.1298	183.4
120	3.19	512.32	2.1553	185.7
130	3.11	522.35	2.1805	188.1
140	3.03	532.52	2.2054	190.3
150	2.96	542.83	2.2301	192.6

Pressure = 0.200 MPa
Saturation temperature = −10.07°C

Temp.,* °C	Density, kg/m³	Enthalpy, kJ/kg	Entropy, kJ/(kg·K)	Vel. of Sound, m/s
Saturated				
Liquid	1325.78	186.69	0.9506	672.8
Vapor	10.01	392.71	1.7337	146.9
−10	10.01	392.77	1.7339	147.0
0	9.54	401.21	1.7654	150.6
10	9.13	409.73	1.7961	154.0
20	8.76	418.35	1.8260	157.3
30	8.42	427.07	1.8552	160.4
40	8.12	435.90	1.8839	163.4
50	7.83	444.87	1.9121	166.3
60	7.57	453.97	1.9398	169.2
70	7.33	463.20	1.9671	171.9
80	7.11	472.57	1.9940	174.6
90	6.89	482.08	2.0206	177.2
100	6.70	491.74	2.0468	179.7
110	6.51	501.53	2.0727	182.2
120	6.34	511.47	2.0983	184.7
130	6.17	521.55	2.1236	187.1
140	6.01	531.76	2.1486	189.4
150	5.87	542.12	2.1734	191.7

Pressure = 0.400 MPa
Saturation temperature = 8.94°C

Temp.,* °C	Density, kg/m³	Enthalpy, kJ/kg	Entropy, kJ/(kg·K)	Vel. of Sound, m/s
Saturated				
Liquid	1263.84	212.08	1.0432	583.8
Vapor	19.52	403.80	1.7229	146.6
10	19.41	404.78	1.7263	147.0
20	18.45	414.00	1.7583	151.2
30	17.61	423.21	1.7892	155.0
40	16.87	432.46	1.8192	158.6
50	16.20	441.76	1.8485	162.0
60	15.60	451.15	1.8771	165.3
70	15.05	460.63	1.9051	168.4
80	14.54	470.21	1.9326	171.4
90	14.08	479.91	1.9597	174.3
100	13.65	489.72	1.9864	177.1
110	13.24	499.65	2.0126	179.8
120	12.87	509.71	2.0386	182.4
130	12.51	519.90	2.0641	185.0
140	12.18	530.21	2.0894	187.5
150	11.87	540.66	2.1144	190.0

Pressure = 0.600 MPa
Saturation temperature = 21.58°C

Temp.,* °C	Density, kg/m³	Enthalpy, kJ/kg	Entropy, kJ/(kg·K)	Vel. of Sound, m/s
Saturated				
Liquid	1219.08	229.62	1.1035	524.0
Vapor	29.13	410.67	1.7178	145.0
30	27.79	418.97	1.7455	149.0
40	26.41	428.72	1.7772	153.4
50	25.21	438.44	1.8077	157.4
60	24.16	448.16	1.8374	161.2
70	23.22	457.93	1.8662	164.7
80	22.37	467.75	1.8944	168.0
90	21.59	477.65	1.9221	171.2
100	20.88	487.64	1.9492	174.3
110	20.22	497.72	1.9759	177.3
120	19.61	507.92	2.0022	180.1
130	19.04	518.22	2.0280	182.9
140	18.51	528.63	2.0536	185.6
150	18.01	539.17	2.0787	188.2
160	17.54	549.82	2.1036	190.8
170	17.10	560.59	2.1282	193.3
180	16.68	571.48	2.1525	195.8
190	16.29	582.50	2.1766	198.2
200	15.91	593.63	2.2003	200.6

Pressure = 0.800 MPa
Saturation temperature = 31.33°C

Temp.,* °C	Density, kg/m³	Enthalpy, kJ/kg	Entropy, kJ/(kg·K)	Vel. of Sound, m/s
Saturated				
Liquid	1181.92	243.58	1.1495	477.4
Vapor	38.99	415.58	1.7144	142.9
40	36.98	424.61	1.7437	147.6
50	35.03	434.85	1.7758	152.4
60	33.36	444.98	1.8067	156.8
70	31.90	455.08	1.8366	160.8
80	30.62	465.17	1.8656	164.6
90	29.46	475.30	1.8939	168.1
100	28.41	485.49	1.9215	171.5
110	27.46	495.74	1.9486	174.7
120	26.58	506.07	1.9753	177.8
130	25.77	516.50	215	180.8
140	25.01	527.03	2.0272	183.7
150	24.31	537.66	2.0527	186.4
160	23.65	548.40	2.0777	189.2
170	23.03	559.24	2.1025	191.8
180	22.45	570.20	2.1270	194.4
190	21.89	581.28	2.1511	196.9
200	21.37	592.46	2.1750	199.4

Pressure = 1.000 MPa
Saturation temperature = 39.39°C

Temp.,* °C	Density, kg/m³	Enthalpy, kJ/kg	Entropy, kJ/(kg·K)	Vel. of Sound, m/s
Saturated				
Liquid	1149.06	255.44	1.1874	438.6
Vapor	49.16	419.31	1.7117	140.6
40	48.95	419.99	1.7139	141.0
50	45.86	430.91	1.7482	146.9
60	43.34	441.56	1.7807	152.0
70	41.21	452.05	1.8117	156.7
80	39.36	462.47	1.8416	160.9
90	37.74	472.86	1.8706	164.9
100	36.29	483.26	1.8989	168.6
110	34.99	493.69	1.9265	172.1
120	33.80	504.19	1.9535	175.4
130	32.71	514.75	1.9800	178.6
140	31.70	525.39	2.0061	181.7
150	30.76	536.12	2.0318	184.6
160	29.90	546.95	2.0571	187.5
170	29.08	557.88	2.0820	190.3
180	28.32	568.91	2.1066	193.0
190	27.60	580.05	2.1309	195.6
200	26.92	591.29	2.1550	198.2

Pressure = 1.200 MPa
Saturation temperature = 46.32°C

Temp.,* °C	Density, kg/m³	Enthalpy, kJ/kg	Entropy, kJ/(kg·K)	Vel. of Sound, m/s
Saturated				
Liquid	1118.89	265.91	1.2200	405.0
Vapor	59.73	422.22	1.7092	138.2
50	58.09	426.51	1.7226	140.7
60	54.32	437.83	1.7571	146.9
70	51.26	448.81	1.7896	152.3
80	48.69	459.61	1.8206	157.1
90	46.49	470.30	1.8504	161.5
100	44.55	480.94	1.8794	165.6
110	42.83	491.58	1.9075	169.4
120	41.28	502.25	1.9350	173.0
130	39.87	512.95	1.9619	176.4
140	38.58	523.72	1.9882	179.7
150	37.39	534.56	2.0142	182.8
160	36.29	545.48	2.0397	185.8
170	35.26	556.50	2.0648	188.8
180	34.31	567.60	2.0896	191.6
190	33.40	578.80	2.1141	194.4
200	32.56	590.11	2.1382	197.1
210	31.76	601.51	2.1621	199.7
220	31.01	613.02	2.1856	202.3
230	30.29	624.64	2.2090	204.8
240	29.61	636.36	2.2320	207.2
250	28.96	648.18	2.2548	209.7

Pressure = 1.400 MPa
Saturation temperature = 52.43°C

Temp.,* °C	Density, kg/m³	Enthalpy, kJ/kg	Entropy, kJ/(kg·K)	Vel. of Sound, m/s
Saturated				
Liquid	1090.50	275.38	1.2488	375.1
Vapor	70.76	424.50	1.7068	135.6
60	66.61	433.69	1.7347	141.2
70	62.25	445.31	1.7691	147.5
80	58.74	456.56	1.8014	153.0
90	55.79	467.60	1.8322	158.0
100	53.24	478.53	1.8619	162.5
110	51.03	489.39	1.8906	166.6
120	49.05	500.25	1.9186	170.5
130	47.28	511.11	1.9459	174.2
140	45.67	522.02	1.9726	177.7
150	44.19	532.97	1.9988	181.0
160	42.83	544	2.0246	184.2
170	41.57	555.10	2.0499	187.2
180	40.41	566.28	2.0748	190.2
190	39.31	577.55	2.0994	193.1
200	38.28	588.92	2.1237	195.9
210	37.32	600.38	2.1477	198.6
220	36.41	611.94	2.1714	201.3
230	35.55	623.60	2.1948	203.9
240	34.73	635.35	2.2179	206.4
250	33.96	647.22	2.2408	208.9

Pressure = 1.600 MPa
Saturation temperature = 57.91°C

Temp.,* °C	Density, kg/m³	Enthalpy, kJ/kg	Entropy, kJ/(kg·K)	Vel. of Sound, m/s
Saturated				
Liquid	1063.28	284.11	1.2748	348.1
Vapor	82.34	426.27	1.7042	132.9
60	80.74	428.99	1.7124	134.7
70	74.43	441.47	1.7493	142.3
80	69.61	453.30	1.7833	148.7
90	65.71	464.76	1.8153	154.2
100	62.43	476.01	1.8458	159.2
110	59.62	487.13	1.8753	163.8
120	57.14	498.19	1.9038	168.0
130	54.95	509.23	1.9315	171.9
140	52.98	520.28	1.9586	175.6
150	51.18	531.36	1.9851	179.1
160	49.54	542.49	2.0111	182.5
170	48.03	553.68	2.0366	185.7
180	46.63	564.94	2.0617	188.8
190	45.32	576.29	2.0865	191.8
200	44.10	587.71	2.1109	194.7
210	42.96	599.23	2.1350	197.6
220	41.88	610.84	2.1588	200.3
230	40.87	622.55	2.1823	203.0
240	39.91	634.35	2.2055	205.6
250	39.00	646.25	2.2285	208.2

*Temperatures on ITS-90 scale

Refrigerant 134a Properties of Superheated Vapor (*Concluded*)

Pressure = 1.800 MPa, Saturation temperature = 62.90°C

Temp.,* °C	Density, kg/m^3	Enthalpy, kJ/kg	Entropy, kJ/(kg·K)	Vel. of Sound, m/s
Saturated Liquid	1036.81	292.26	1.2987	323.2
Vapor	94.53	427.59	1.7014	130.1
70	88.23	437.17	1.7296	136.5
80	81.54	449.76	1.7657	144.0
90	76.38	461.74	1.7992	150.3
100	72.17	473.36	1.8308	155.9
110	68.64	484.78	1.8610	160.8
120	65.60	496.06	1.8900	165.4
130	62.91	507.29	1.9183	169.6
140	60.53	518.50	1.9457	173.5
150	58.37	529.71	1.9725	177.3
160	56.42	540.95	1.9988	180.8
170	54.62	552.24	2.0246	184.2
180	52.97	563.59	2.0499	187.4
190	51.44	575.01	2.0748	190.6
200	50.01	586.50	2.0993	193.6
210	48.68	598.08	2.1236	196.5
220	47.43	609.74	2.1475	199.4
230	46.25	621.50	2.1710	202.1
240	45.14	633.34	2.1944	204.9
250	44.09	645.28	2.2174	207.5

Pressure = 2.000 MPa, Saturation temperature = 67.49°C

Temp.,* °C	Density, kg/m^3	Enthalpy, kJ/kg	Entropy, kJ/(kg·K)	Vel. of Sound, m/s
Saturated Liquid	1010.74	299.96	1.3209	300.1
Vapor	107.46	428.52	1.6983	127.2
70	104.37	432.22	1.7091	129.9
80	94.85	445.86	1.7483	138.9
90	87.97	458.49	1.7835	146.2
100	82.58	470.57	1.8164	152.4
110	78.17	482.32	1.8474	157.8
120	74.44	493.86	1.8772	162.7
130	71.18	505.30	1.9059	167.2
140	68.33	516.68	1.9338	171.4
150	65.78	528.03	1.9609	175.4
160	63.47	539.39	1.9875	179.1
170	61.37	550.79	2.0135	182.6
180	59.45	562.23	2.0390	186.0
190	57.67	573.72	2.0641	189.3
200	56.02	585.28	2.0888	192.4
210	54.49	596.92	2.1131	195.5
220	53.05	608.64	2.1371	198.4
230	51.70	620.44	2.1608	201.3
240	50.43	632.33	2.1842	204.1
250	49.23	644.30	2.2073	206.8

Pressure = 2.200 MPa, Saturation temperature = 71.74°C

Temp.,* °C	Density, kg/m^3	Enthalpy, kJ/kg	Entropy, kJ/(kg·K)	Vel. of Sound, m/s
Saturated Liquid	984.76	307.32	1.3417	278.4
Vapor	121.25	429.08	1.6948	124.3
80	110.03	441.49	1.7303	133.3
90	100.70	454.98	1.7680	141.8
100	93.78	467.61	1.8023	148.7
110	88.25	479.75	1.8344	154.7
120	83.70	491.59	1.8649	160.0
130	79.79	503.25	1.8942	164.9
140	76.41	514.81	1.9226	169.3
150	73.40	526.32	1.9501	173.5
160	70.71	537.81	1.9769	177.4
170	68.28	549.31	2.0032	181.1
180	66.06	560.84	2.0289	184.6
190	64.02	572.42	2.0542	188.0
200	62.13	584.06	2.0790	191.3
210	60.38	595.76	2.1035	194.4
220	58.74	607.53	2.1276	197.5
230	57.21	619.38	2.1514	200.4
240	55.77	631.31	2.1749	203.3
250	54.42	643.33	2.1981	206.1

Pressure =2.400 MPa, Saturation temperature = 75.70°C

Temp.,* °C	Density, kg/m^3	Enthalpy, kJ/kg	Entropy, kJ/(kg·K)	Vel. of Sound, m/s
Saturated Liquid	958.58	314.40	1.3616	257.9
Vapor	136.07	429.27	1.6908	121.4
80	127.96	436.42	1.7112	126.9
90	114.90	451.12	1.7523	137.0
100	105.89	464.44	1.7885	144.8
110	99.00	477.04	1.8218	151.5
120	93.44	489.22	1.8532	157.2
130	88.79	501.14	1.8831	162.4
140	84.77	512.90	1.9119	167.2
150	81.27	524.57	1.9398	171.6
160	78.15	536.20	1.9670	175.7
170	75.35	547.82	1.9935	179.6
180	72.81	559.45	2.0195	183.3
190	70.48	571.11	2.0449	186.8
200	68.34	582.82	2.0699	190.2
210	66.36	594.58	2.0945	193.4
220	64.51	606.41	2.1188	196.6
230	62.79	618.31	2.1427	199.6
240	61.18	630.29	2.1662	202.5
250	59.66	642.35	2.1895	205.4

Pressure = 2.600 MPa, Saturation temperature = 79.41°C

Temp.,* °C	Density, kg/m^3	Enthalpy, kJ/kg	Entropy, kJ/(kg·K)	Vel. of Sound, m/s
Saturated Liquid	931.88	321.29	1.3806	238.2
Vapor	152.12	429.08	1.6863	118.3
80	150.48	430.22	1.6895	119.3
90	131.08	446.81	1.7359	131.7
100	119.15	461.03	1.7745	140.8
110	110.50	474.19	1.8093	148.1
120	103.72	486.75	1.8417	154.4
130	98.17	498.96	1.8724	160.0
140	93.46	510.94	1.9017	165.0
150	89.39	522.79	1.9301	169.7
160	85.80	534.57	1.9576	174.0
170	82.59	546.30	1.9844	178.1
180	79.70	558.04	2.0106	181.9
190	77.07	569.79	2.0362	185.5
200	74.65	581.57	2.0614	189.0
210	72.43	593.40	2.0861	192.4
220	70.36	605.29	2.1105	195.6
230	68.44	617.24	2.1345	198.8
240	66.64	629.27	2.1581	201.8
250	64.95	641.37	2.1815	204.8

Pressure = 2.800 MPa, Saturation temperature = 82.90°C

Temp.,* °C	Density, kg/m^3	Enthalpy, kJ/kg	Entropy, kJ/(kg·K)	Vel. of Sound, m/s
Saturated Liquid	904.29	328.05	1.3990	219.1
Vapor	169.71	428.50	1.6812	115.3
90	150.13	441.84	1.7183	125.9
100	133.85	457.32	1.7603	136.4
110	122.89	471.16	1.7970	144.6
120	114.63	484.17	1.8305	151.5
130	108.00	496.70	1.8620	157.5
140	102.49	508.93	1.8919	162.9
150	97.78	520.97	1.9207	167.8
160	93.66	532.90	1.9486	172.3
170	90.01	544.77	1.9757	176.5
180	86.74	556.61	2.0021	180.5
190	83.78	568.45	2.0279	184.3
200	81.08	580.31	2.0533	187.9
210	78.59	592.21	2.0782	191.4
220	76.29	604.16	2.1027	194.7
230	74.15	616.17	2.1268	198.0
240	72.16	628.25	2.1505	201.1
250	70.30	640.39	2.1740	204.1

Pressure = 3.000 MPa, Saturation temperature = 86.20°C

Temp.,* °C	Density, kg/m^3	Enthalpy, kJ/kg	Entropy, kJ/(kg·K)	Vel. of Sound, m/s
Saturated Liquid	875.30	334.75	1.4171	200.4
Vapor	189.25	427.47	1.6752	112.2
90	173.82	435.84	1.6983	119.1
100	150.47	453.20	1.7455	131.8
110	136.36	467.93	1.7845	141.0
120	126.23	481.47	1.8194	148.5
130	118.34	494.36	1.8518	155.0
140	111.89	506.86	1.8824	160.7
150	106.45	519.11	1.9117	165.9
160	101.75	531.21	1.9399	170.6
170	97.62	543.21	1.9673	175.0
180	93.94	555.16	1.9940	179.2
190	90.62	567.10	2.0201	183.1
200	87.61	579.05	2.0456	186.8
210	84.84	591.02	2.0706	190.4
220	82.30	603.03	2.0952	193.8
230	79.94	615.10	2.1195	197.2
240	77.74	627.22	2.1433	200.4
250	75.69	639.41	2.1668	203.4
260	73.77	651.66	2.1900	206.5
270	71.96	664	2.2130	209.4
280	70.25	676.41	2.2356	212.2
290	68.63	688.89	2.2580	215.0
300	67.10	701.46	2.2801	217.8

Pressure = 4.000 MPa, Saturation temperature = 100.35°C

Temp.,* °C	Density, kg/m^3	Enthalpy, kJ/kg	Entropy, kJ/(kg·K)	Vel. of Sound, m/s
Saturated Liquid	626.95	376.48	1.5272	101.3
Vapor	396.29	404.57	1.6024	93.4
110	233.68	446.28	1.7131	119.8
120	199.79	465.29	1.7621	132.5
130	179.83	481.11	1.8018	142.0
140	165.73	495.51	1.8371	149.7
150	154.89	509.13	1.8697	156.4
160	146.10	522.25	1.9004	162.4
170	138.74	535.07	1.9296	167.8
180	132.41	547.69	1.9578	172.7
190	126.88	560.17	1.9850	177.4
200	121.97	572.58	2.0115	181.7
210	117.55	584.95	2.0374	185.8
220	113.56	597.30	2.0627	189.7
230	109.90	609.66	2.0875	193.4
240	106.55	622.05	2.1119	197.0
250	103.44	634.47	2.1359	200.5
260	100.56	646.93	2.1595	203.8
270	97.87	659.45	2.1827	207.1
280	95.35	672.03	2.2057	210.2
290	92.98	684.67	2.2283	213.3
300	90.75	697.38	2.2507	216.2

Pressure = 6.00 MPa, Saturation temperature = n/a (supercritical)

Temp.,* °C	Density, kg/m^3	Enthalpy, kJ/kg	Entropy, kJ/(kg·K)	Vel. of Sound, m/s
Saturated Liquid				
Vapor				
110	762.66	375.61	1.5174	173.6
120	591.77	405.75	1.5950	127.4
130	418.90	439.87	1.6807	120.4
140	333.91	465.19	1.7428	130.1
150	289.37	484.69	1.7894	139.9
160	260.70	501.52	1.8288	148.3
170	239.96	516.92	1.8639	155.7
180	223.87	531.45	1.8963	162.2
190	210.82	545.43	1.9269	168.1
200	199.88	559.04	1.9559	173.6
210	190.50	572.39	1.9839	178.6
220	182.31	585.57	2.0109	183.4
230	175.06	598.64	2.0371	187.8
240	168.56	611.63	2.0626	192.1
250	162.68	624.57	2.0876	196.2
260	157.33	637.50	2.1121	200.0
270	152.41	650.43	2.1361	203.8
280	147.88	663.38	2.1598	207.4
290	143.67	676.35	2.1830	210.9
300	139.75	689.36	2.2059	214.3

*Temperatures on ITS-90 scale

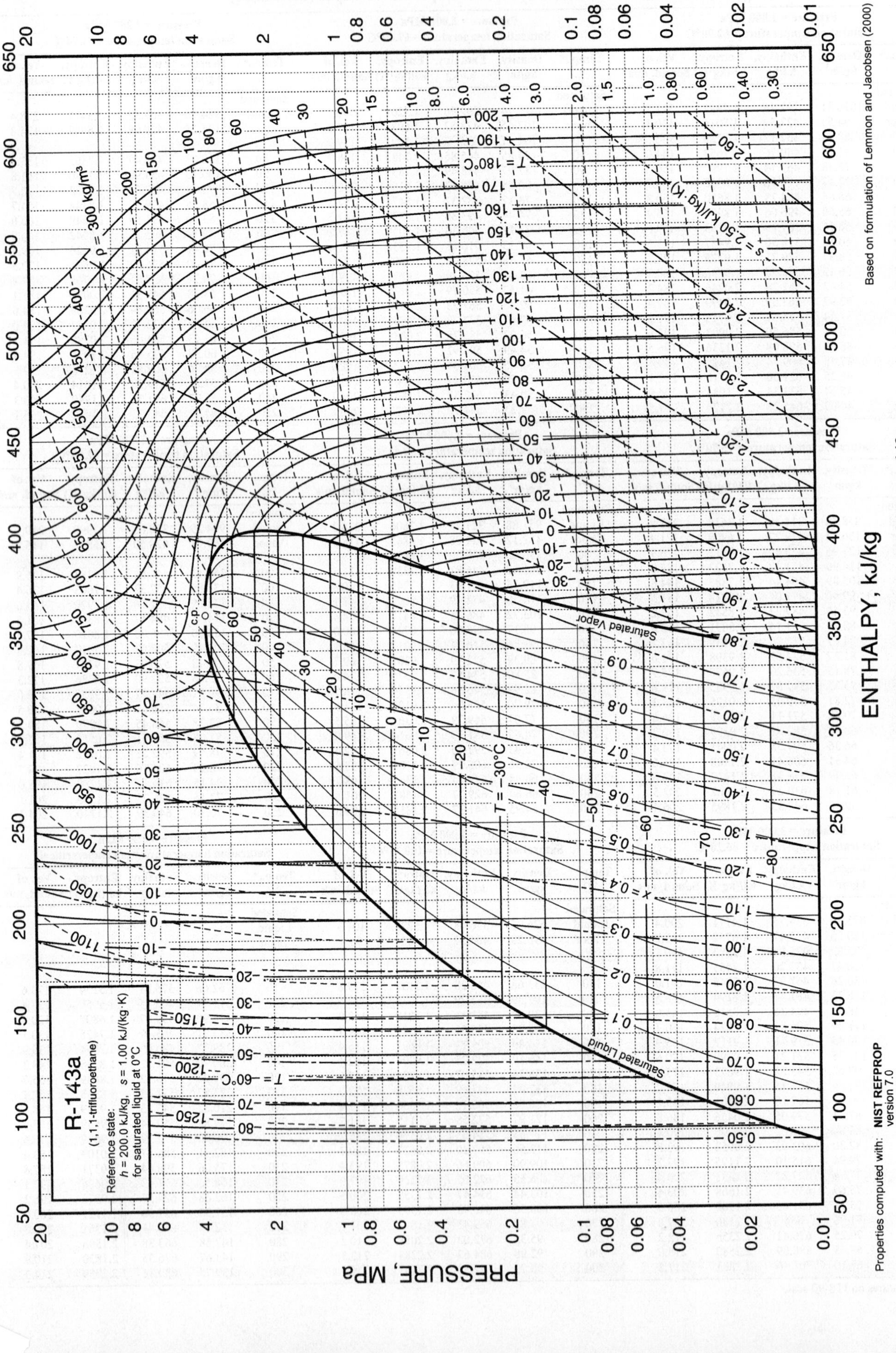

Fig. 9 Pressure-Enthalpy Diagram for Refrigerant 143a

Refrigerant 143a (1,1,1-Trifluoroethane) Properties of Saturated Liquid and Saturated Vapor

Temp.,* °C	Pressure, MPa	Density, kg/m³ Liquid	Volume, m³/kg Vapor	Enthalpy, kJ/kg Liquid	Enthalpy, kJ/kg Vapor	Entropy, kJ/(kg·K) Liquid	Entropy, kJ/(kg·K) Vapor	Specific Heat c_p, kJ/(kg·K) Liquid	Specific Heat c_p, kJ/(kg·K) Vapor	c_p/c_v Vapor	Velocity of Sound, m/s Liquid	Velocity of Sound, m/s Vapor	Viscosity, μPa·s Liquid	Viscosity, μPa·s Vapor	Thermal Cond., mW/(m·K) Liquid	Thermal Cond., mW/(m·K) Vapor	Surface Tension, mN/m	Temp.,* °C
–111.81[a]	0.00107	1330.5	14.807	52.52	319.59	0.3142	1.9695	1.211	0.630	1.192	1058	137.6	912.1	5.91	137.0	4.90	13.72	–111.81
–110	0.00129	1326.2	12.430	54.71	320.68	0.3277	1.9579	1.212	0.635	1.191	1049	138.2	867.9	5.97	135.8	5.00	13.75	–110
–100	0.00333	1301.9	5.1127	66.87	326.81	0.4000	1.9012	1.220	0.664	1.185	1002	141.7	680.1	6.34	129.5	5.53	13.80	–100
–90	0.00761	1277.2	2.3596	79.13	333.06	0.4688	1.8553	1.233	0.694	1.181	954	144.9	553.4	6.72	123.5	6.10	13.71	–90
–80	0.01572	1252.2	1.1971	91.55	339.40	0.5348	1.8180	1.250	0.726	1.178	907	147.8	462.1	7.08	117.8	6.70	13.48	–80
–70	0.02991	1226.7	0.65675	104.16	345.80	0.5984	1.7879	1.270	0.759	1.177	859	150.4	393.0	7.45	112.5	7.34	13.11	–70
–60	0.05307	1200.6	0.38446	116.99	352.21	0.6599	1.7635	1.293	0.794	1.178	811	152.5	338.8	7.82	107.4	8.02	12.61	–60
–50	0.08874	1173.9	0.23754	130.05	358.58	0.7197	1.7438	1.318	0.833	1.182	764	154.2	294.9	8.19	102.5	8.73	12.00	–50
–48	0.09773	1168.5	0.21695	132.69	359.85	0.7314	1.7403	1.323	0.841	1.184	754	154.5	287.1	8.26	101.6	8.88	11.86	–48
–47.24[b]	0.10133	1166.4	0.20971	133.70	360.33	0.7359	1.7391	1.325	0.844	1.184	751	154.6	284.2	8.29	101.2	8.94	11.81	–47.24
–46	0.10742	1163.0	0.19849	135.35	361.11	0.7431	1.7370	1.328	0.850	1.185	745	154.7	279.6	8.33	100.6	9.03	11.72	–46
–44	0.11786	1157.5	0.18191	138.01	362.37	0.7548	1.7339	1.334	0.858	1.186	735	154.9	272.3	8.41	99.7	9.18	11.57	–44
–42	0.12907	1152.0	0.16697	140.69	363.62	0.7664	1.7308	1.339	0.867	1.188	726	155.1	265.3	8.48	98.8	9.33	11.42	–42
–40	0.14109	1146.4	0.15350	143.38	364.86	0.7779	1.7279	1.345	0.876	1.189	716	155.3	258.6	8.56	97.8	9.49	11.27	–40
–38	0.15398	1140.8	0.14133	146.08	366.10	0.7894	1.7251	1.351	0.885	1.191	707	155.5	252.0	8.63	96.9	9.65	11.11	–38
–36	0.16775	1135.1	0.13031	148.79	367.34	0.8008	1.7224	1.357	0.894	1.193	697	155.6	245.7	8.70	96.0	9.81	10.95	–36
–34	0.18247	1129.4	0.12032	151.52	368.56	0.8122	1.7198	1.363	0.904	1.195	688	155.7	239.6	8.78	95.1	9.97	10.79	–34
–32	0.19816	1123.7	0.11124	154.25	369.78	0.8236	1.7173	1.369	0.913	1.198	678	155.8	233.6	8.85	94.2	10.13	10.62	–32
–30	0.21488	1117.9	0.10297	157.00	370.99	0.8348	1.7149	1.375	0.923	1.200	669	155.8	227.8	8.93	93.3	10.30	10.44	–30
–28	0.23267	1112.1	0.09544	159.77	372.19	0.8461	1.7126	1.382	0.933	1.203	659	155.9	222.3	9.18	92.4	10.49	10.27	–28
–26	0.25156	1106.2	0.08857	162.54	373.39	0.8573	1.7104	1.388	0.944	1.206	650	155.9	216.8	9.26	91.6	10.66	10.09	–26
–24	0.27161	1100.3	0.08228	165.33	374.57	0.8685	1.7083	1.395	0.955	1.209	640	155.8	211.6	9.33	90.7	10.83	9.90	–24
–22	0.29286	1094.3	0.07652	168.13	375.74	0.8796	1.7062	1.402	0.966	1.212	630	155.8	206.4	9.41	89.8	11.01	9.72	–22
–20	0.31535	1088.3	0.07125	170.95	376.91	0.8907	1.7043	1.409	0.977	1.216	621	155.7	201.4	9.48	89.0	11.19	9.53	–20
–18	0.33915	1082.2	0.06640	173.78	378.06	0.9018	1.7024	1.417	0.988	1.219	611	155.6	196.6	9.56	88.1	11.37	9.33	–18
–16	0.36428	1076.0	0.06194	176.63	379.20	0.9128	1.7005	1.424	1.000	1.223	602	155.4	191.8	9.64	87.2	11.55	9.14	–16
–14	0.39081	1069.8	0.05784	179.49	380.33	0.9238	1.6987	1.432	1.012	1.227	592	155.2	187.2	9.71	86.4	11.74	8.94	–14
–12	0.41877	1063.6	0.05405	182.37	381.44	0.9347	1.6970	1.440	1.025	1.232	582	155.0	182.7	9.79	85.5	11.94	8.74	–12
–10	0.44823	1057.2	0.05056	185.27	382.54	0.9457	1.6953	1.449	1.038	1.237	573	154.8	178.4	9.87	84.7	12.13	8.53	–10
–8	0.47923	1050.8	0.04733	188.18	383.63	0.9566	1.6937	1.457	1.051	1.242	563	154.5	174.1	9.95	83.9	12.33	8.32	–8
–6	0.51182	1044.3	0.04434	191.11	384.70	0.9675	1.6921	1.466	1.065	1.247	553	154.2	169.9	10.04	83.0	12.53	8.12	–6
–4	0.54606	1037.7	0.04158	194.05	385.75	0.9783	1.6906	1.476	1.079	1.253	544	153.9	165.8	10.12	82.2	12.74	7.90	–4
–2	0.58199	1031.0	0.03901	197.02	386.79	0.9892	1.6890	1.485	1.093	1.260	534	153.5	161.8	10.21	81.4	12.96	7.69	–2
0	0.61967	1024.3	0.03662	200.00	387.81	1.0000	1.6876	1.495	1.109	1.266	524	153.1	157.9	10.29	80.5	13.17	7.47	0
2	0.65916	1017.4	0.03440	203.00	388.81	1.0108	1.6861	1.505	1.124	1.273	515	152.6	154.1	10.38	79.7	13.40	7.25	2
4	0.70051	1010.5	0.03234	206.03	389.79	1.0216	1.6846	1.516	1.141	1.281	505	152.1	150.3	10.47	78.9	13.63	7.03	4
6	0.74378	1003.5	0.03042	209.07	390.75	1.0324	1.6832	1.528	1.158	1.289	495	151.6	146.6	10.57	78.1	13.87	6.81	6
8	0.78901	996.3	0.02862	212.13	391.68	1.0432	1.6818	1.539	1.176	1.298	485	151.0	143.0	10.66	77.2	14.12	6.59	8
10	0.83628	989.1	0.02695	215.22	392.60	1.0539	1.6804	1.552	1.194	1.307	475	150.4	139.5	10.76	76.4	14.38	6.36	10
12	0.88564	981.7	0.02538	218.33	393.48	1.0647	1.6790	1.565	1.214	1.317	465	149.8	136.0	10.86	75.6	14.64	6.14	12
14	0.93714	974.2	0.02392	221.47	394.35	1.0755	1.6775	1.578	1.234	1.328	455	149.1	132.6	10.96	74.8	14.92	5.91	14
16	0.99085	966.5	0.02255	224.63	395.18	1.0863	1.6761	1.593	1.256	1.340	445	148.4	129.3	11.07	74.0	15.21	5.68	16
18	1.0468	958.7	0.02126	227.81	395.98	1.0970	1.6747	1.608	1.278	1.353	435	147.6	126.0	11.18	73.2	15.51	5.45	18
20	1.1052	950.8	0.02005	231.02	396.76	1.1078	1.6732	1.624	1.302	1.366	425	146.8	122.7	11.29	72.4	15.82	5.22	20
22	1.1659	942.7	0.01892	234.27	397.50	1.1186	1.6717	1.641	1.328	1.381	415	145.9	119.5	11.40	71.5	16.15	4.99	22
24	1.2290	934.4	0.01785	237.54	398.20	1.1295	1.6701	1.659	1.355	1.398	405	145.0	116.4	11.52	70.7	16.50	4.76	24
26	1.2947	926.0	0.01685	240.84	398.87	1.1403	1.6685	1.679	1.384	1.416	394	144.0	113.3	11.64	69.9	16.87	4.53	26
28	1.3630	917.3	0.01591	244.18	399.49	1.1512	1.6669	1.699	1.416	1.435	384	143.0	110.2	11.77	69.1	17.26	4.30	28
30	1.4340	908.4	0.01501	247.56	400.07	1.1621	1.6652	1.722	1.449	1.457	374	141.9	107.2	11.91	68.3	17.67	4.07	30
32	1.5077	899.3	0.01417	250.97	400.61	1.1730	1.6634	1.746	1.486	1.480	363	140.8	104.2	12.04	67.5	18.11	3.84	32
34	1.5842	890.0	0.01338	254.42	401.09	1.1840	1.6616	1.772	1.526	1.507	352	139.6	101.2	12.19	66.6	18.58	3.61	34
36	1.6636	880.4	0.01262	257.91	401.52	1.1951	1.6596	1.801	1.570	1.536	342	138.4	98.3	12.34	65.8	19.09	3.38	36
38	1.7460	870.5	0.01191	261.45	401.89	1.2062	1.6575	1.832	1.618	1.569	331	137.1	95.4	12.50	65.0	19.63	3.16	38
40	1.8314	860.3	0.01123	265.04	402.19	1.2174	1.6553	1.867	1.671	1.606	320	135.7	92.5	12.67	64.2	20.22	2.93	40
42	1.9200	849.7	0.01059	268.68	402.42	1.2286	1.6530	1.906	1.732	1.648	309	134.3	89.7	12.85	63.3	20.87	2.71	42
44	2.0117	838.7	0.00998	272.39	402.56	1.2400	1.6505	1.949	1.799	1.696	298	132.8	86.8	13.03	62.5	21.57	2.49	44
46	2.1068	827.3	0.00940	276.15	402.62	1.2515	1.6478	1.998	1.877	1.752	286	131.2	84.0	13.24	61.7	22.35	2.27	46
48	2.2053	815.4	0.00884	279.98	402.58	1.2631	1.6448	2.054	1.966	1.817	275	129.6	81.1	13.45	60.8	23.20	2.06	48
50	2.3073	803.0	0.00831	283.90	402.43	1.2748	1.6416	2.118	2.070	1.894	263	127.9	78.3	13.69	60.0	24.16	1.85	50
52	2.4130	789.9	0.00780	287.90	402.15	1.2868	1.6381	2.194	2.194	1.985	251	126.1	75.4	13.94	59.1	25.23	1.64	52
54	2.5224	776.1	0.00731	292.00	401.72	1.2989	1.6343	2.285	2.343	2.097	238	124.2	72.5	14.23	58.2	26.45	1.44	54
56	2.6357	761.5	0.00684	296.22	401.12	1.3113	1.6300	2.395	2.528	2.236	226	122.2	69.6	14.54	57.4	27.84	1.24	56
58	2.7530	745.8	0.00639	300.57	400.31	1.3240	1.6252	2.534	2.762	2.413	213	120.1	66.6	14.89	56.5	29.45	1.05	58
60	2.8744	728.9	0.00594	305.09	399.24	1.3371	1.6197	2.714	3.069	2.647	200	117.9	63.6	15.29	55.6	31.37	0.87	60
65	3.1977	678.3	0.00486	317.45	394.94	1.3726	1.6018	3.564	4.532	3.763	164	111.8	55.4	16.64	53.6	38.41	0.45	65
70	3.5527	600.8	0.00370	333.19	385.42	1.4172	1.5694	7.720	11.500	9.040	122	104.2	45.1	19.30	53.2	55.97	0.11	70
72.71[c]	3.7610	431.0	0.00232	358.91	358.91	1.4906	1.4906	∞	∞	∞	0	0.0	—	—	∞	∞	0.00	72.71

*Temperatures on ITS-90 scale [a]Triple point [b]Normal boiling point [c]Critical point

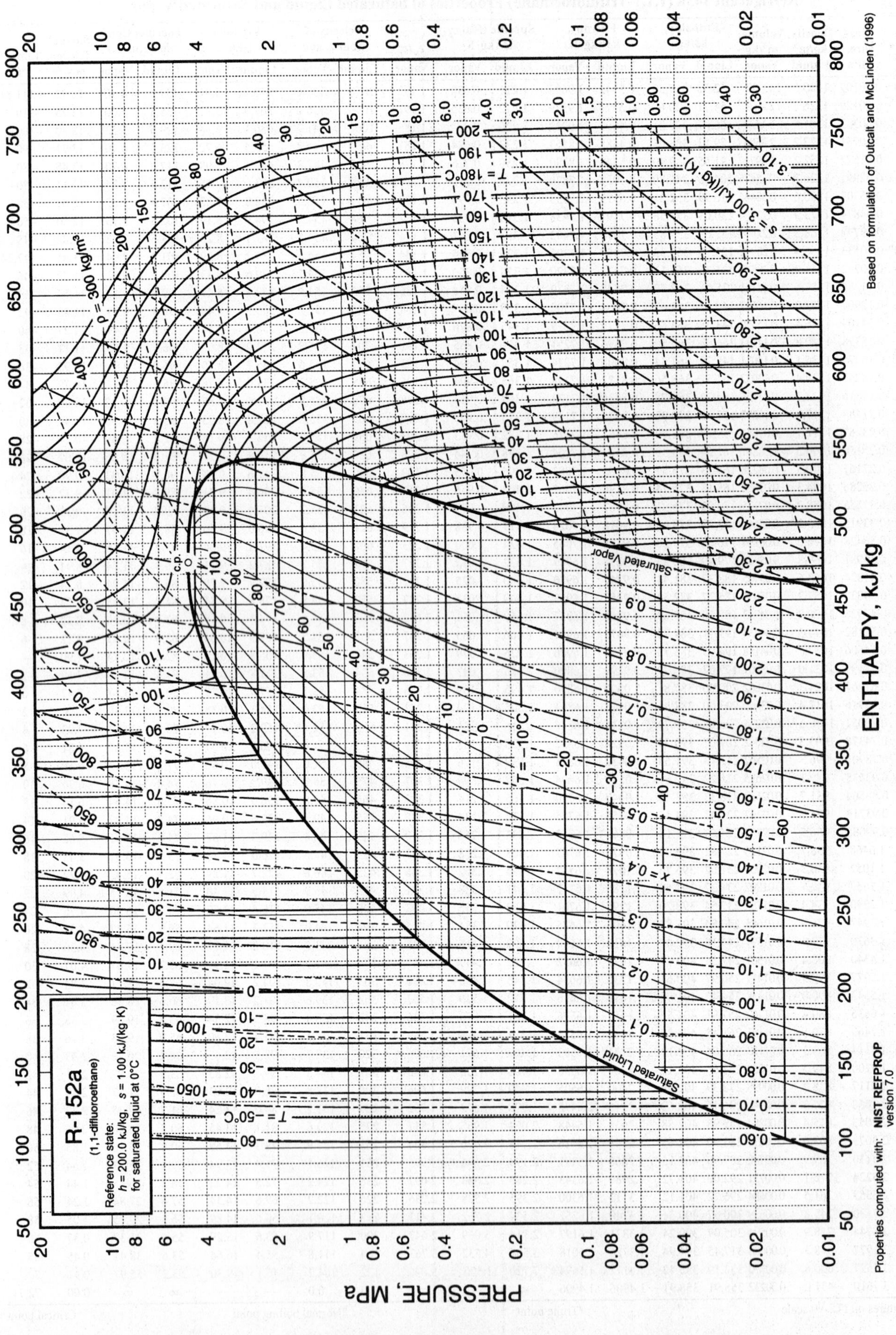

Fig. 10 Pressure-Enthalpy Diagram for Refrigerant 152a

Refrigerant 152a (1,1-Difluoroethane) Properties of Saturated Liquid and Saturated Vapor

Temp.,* °C	Pressure, MPa	Density, kg/m³	Volume, m³/kg	Enthalpy, kJ/kg		Entropy, kJ/(kg·K)		Specific Heat c_p, kJ/(kg·K)		c_p/c_v	Velocity of Sound, m/s		Viscosity, μPa·s		Thermal Cond., mW/(m·K)		Surface Tension, mN/m	Temp.,* °C
		Liquid	Vapor	Liquid	Vapor	Liquid	Vapor	Liquid	Vapor	Vapor	Liquid	Vapor	Liquid	Vapor	Liquid	Vapor		
–118.59[a]	0.00006	1192.9	303.290	13.79	419.32	0.1119	2.7357	1.477	0.699	1.220	1401	154.0	2025.0	5.20	176.3	0.10	31.65	–118.59
–110	0.00019	1177.1	107.740	26.62	425.38	0.1927	2.6368	1.505	0.717	1.214	1337	157.8	1528.0	5.48	170.2	0.94	30.23	–110
–100	0.00058	1158.7	37.6170	41.75	432.59	0.2827	2.5399	1.518	0.740	1.207	1275	162.0	1153.0	5.81	163.4	1.91	28.58	–100
–90	0.00153	1140.1	15.0520	56.96	439.97	0.3681	2.4593	1.524	0.763	1.201	1219	166.0	904.0	6.14	156.9	2.89	26.96	–90
–80	0.00359	1121.3	6.74380	72.23	447.48	0.4492	2.3920	1.530	0.789	1.196	1166	169.8	730.2	6.47	150.7	3.86	25.34	–80
–70	0.00765	1102.4	3.31970	87.57	455.08	0.5266	2.3357	1.539	0.816	1.192	1115	173.4	603.5	6.80	144.7	4.84	23.75	–70
–60	0.01500	1083.2	1.76820	103.02	462.74	0.6009	2.2885	1.551	0.845	1.190	1066	176.6	507.4	7.14	139.0	5.82	22.18	–60
–50	0.02742	1063.7	1.00640	118.62	470.40	0.6723	2.2487	1.567	0.877	1.189	1016	179.5	432.5	7.47	133.5	6.81	20.63	–50
–40	0.04721	1043.8	0.60583	134.40	478.02	0.7414	2.2152	1.587	0.913	1.190	967	182.1	372.5	7.80	128.2	7.80	19.09	–40
–30	0.07718	1023.5	0.38242	150.39	485.55	0.8085	2.1868	1.610	0.952	1.193	919	184.2	323.6	8.14	123.1	8.80	17.58	–30
–28	0.08469	1019.4	0.35056	153.62	487.04	0.8216	2.1817	1.615	0.960	1.194	909	184.5	314.8	8.21	122.1	9.01	17.29	–28
–26	0.09276	1015.3	0.32186	156.86	488.52	0.8348	2.1767	1.620	0.968	1.195	899	184.9	306.4	8.27	121.2	9.21	16.99	–26
–24.02[b]	0.10133	1011.2	0.29622	160.07	489.98	0.8477	2.1719	1.625	0.977	1.196	889	185.2	298.4	8.34	120.2	9.41	16.69	–24.02
–24	0.10142	1011.1	0.29595	160.11	490.00	0.8478	2.1719	1.625	0.977	1.196	889	185.2	298.3	8.34	120.2	9.41	16.69	–24
–22	0.11072	1006.9	0.27253	163.37	491.47	0.8608	2.1672	1.630	0.985	1.197	880	185.5	290.5	8.41	119.2	9.62	16.39	–22
–20	0.12068	1002.7	0.25131	166.64	492.94	0.8737	2.1627	1.635	0.994	1.199	870	185.8	282.9	8.48	118.2	9.82	16.10	–20
–18	0.13133	998.5	0.23206	169.92	494.40	0.8866	2.1583	1.641	1.003	1.200	860	186.1	275.6	8.54	117.3	10.03	15.80	–18
–16	0.14271	994.2	0.21457	173.21	495.85	0.8994	2.1541	1.647	1.013	1.202	850	186.3	268.6	8.61	116.3	10.23	15.51	–16
–14	0.15484	989.9	0.19865	176.52	497.29	0.9122	2.1500	1.653	1.022	1.203	841	186.5	261.7	8.68	115.4	10.44	15.22	–14
–12	0.16777	985.6	0.18414	179.83	498.72	0.9249	2.1460	1.658	1.032	1.205	831	186.7	255.1	8.75	114.5	10.65	14.93	–12
–10	0.18152	981.3	0.17090	183.16	500.15	0.9375	2.1421	1.665	1.041	1.207	821	186.9	248.7	8.82	113.5	10.86	14.64	–10
–8	0.19614	976.9	0.15879	186.50	501.56	0.9501	2.1383	1.671	1.051	1.209	811	187.0	242.6	8.88	112.6	11.07	14.35	–8
–6	0.21166	972.5	0.14770	189.86	502.96	0.9627	2.1347	1.677	1.062	1.211	801	187.1	236.6	8.95	111.7	11.28	14.06	–6
–4	0.22812	968.1	0.13754	193.22	504.36	0.9752	2.1311	1.684	1.072	1.213	792	187.2	230.8	9.02	110.8	11.50	13.77	–4
–2	0.24555	963.6	0.12821	196.61	505.74	0.9876	2.1277	1.690	1.083	1.215	782	187.3	225.1	9.09	109.8	11.71	13.48	–2
0	0.26399	959.1	0.11963	200.00	507.11	1.0000	2.1243	1.697	1.094	1.218	772	187.4	219.7	9.16	108.9	11.93	13.20	0
2	0.28349	954.6	0.11174	203.41	508.47	1.0124	2.1211	1.704	1.105	1.221	762	187.4	214.4	9.23	108.0	12.14	12.91	2
4	0.30407	950.0	0.10447	206.83	509.82	1.0247	2.1179	1.711	1.116	1.224	752	187.4	209.2	9.30	107.1	12.36	12.63	4
6	0.32578	945.4	0.09776	210.27	511.16	1.0370	2.1148	1.719	1.128	1.227	742	187.4	204.2	9.37	106.2	12.58	12.35	6
8	0.34867	940.8	0.09156	213.72	512.48	1.0492	2.1118	1.726	1.139	1.230	733	187.3	199.4	9.44	105.4	12.80	12.07	8
10	0.37277	936.1	0.08583	217.19	513.78	1.0614	2.1089	1.734	1.152	1.233	723	187.2	194.7	9.51	104.5	13.03	11.79	10
12	0.39812	931.3	0.08052	220.67	515.08	1.0736	2.1060	1.742	1.164	1.237	713	187.1	190.1	9.58	103.6	13.25	11.51	12
14	0.42476	926.6	0.07560	224.17	516.36	1.0857	2.1032	1.750	1.177	1.240	703	187.0	185.6	9.65	102.7	13.48	11.23	14
16	0.45275	921.8	0.07104	227.69	517.62	1.0978	2.1005	1.759	1.190	1.244	693	186.8	181.3	9.73	101.8	13.71	10.96	16
18	0.48211	916.9	0.06680	231.22	518.86	1.1098	2.0978	1.768	1.203	1.249	683	186.6	177.1	9.80	101.0	13.95	10.68	18
20	0.51291	912.0	0.06286	234.77	520.09	1.1219	2.0952	1.776	1.217	1.253	673	186.4	173.0	9.87	100.1	14.18	10.41	20
22	0.54517	907.0	0.05919	238.34	521.30	1.1339	2.0926	1.786	1.231	1.258	663	186.1	169.0	9.95	99.3	14.42	10.14	22
24	0.57894	902.0	0.05577	241.93	522.50	1.1459	2.0901	1.795	1.246	1.263	653	185.8	165.1	10.02	98.4	14.66	9.87	24
26	0.61428	896.9	0.05258	245.53	523.67	1.1578	2.0876	1.805	1.261	1.268	643	185.5	161.3	10.10	97.5	14.91	9.60	26
28	0.65122	891.8	0.04960	249.16	524.83	1.1698	2.0852	1.815	1.277	1.274	633	185.1	157.6	10.18	96.7	15.16	9.33	28
30	0.68982	886.6	0.04682	252.80	525.96	1.1817	2.0828	1.826	1.293	1.280	623	184.7	154.0	10.26	95.9	15.41	9.06	30
32	0.73012	881.4	0.04422	256.47	527.07	1.1936	2.0804	1.837	1.309	1.286	613	184.3	150.4	10.34	95.0	15.67	8.80	32
34	0.77216	876.0	0.04179	260.16	528.16	1.2055	2.0780	1.848	1.326	1.293	602	183.9	147.0	10.42	94.2	15.93	8.54	34
36	0.81600	870.7	0.03951	263.86	529.23	1.2174	2.0757	1.860	1.344	1.300	592	183.4	143.6	10.50	93.3	16.20	8.27	36
38	0.86169	865.2	0.03737	267.60	530.27	1.2292	2.0734	1.872	1.362	1.307	582	182.9	140.3	10.58	92.5	16.47	8.01	38
40	0.90927	859.7	0.03536	271.35	531.28	1.2411	2.0711	1.885	1.381	1.315	572	182.3	137.1	10.66	91.7	16.74	7.75	40
42	0.95879	854.1	0.03348	275.13	532.27	1.2529	2.0689	1.898	1.401	1.324	561	181.7	134.0	10.75	90.8	17.03	7.50	42
44	1.01030	848.4	0.03170	278.93	533.23	1.2648	2.0666	1.912	1.421	1.333	551	181.1	130.9	10.84	90.0	17.32	7.24	44
46	1.06390	842.6	0.03004	282.76	534.16	1.2766	2.0643	1.926	1.443	1.342	541	180.4	127.9	11.21	89.2	17.60	6.99	46
48	1.11960	836.7	0.02846	286.62	535.06	1.2884	2.0620	1.941	1.465	1.353	530	179.7	125.0	11.32	88.4	17.90	6.73	48
50	1.17740	830.8	0.02699	290.50	535.93	1.3003	2.0598	1.957	1.489	1.364	520	178.9	122.1	11.42	87.5	18.22	6.48	50
52	1.23740	824.7	0.02559	294.41	536.77	1.3121	2.0575	1.974	1.513	1.375	509	178.2	119.2	11.53	86.7	18.54	6.23	52
54	1.29970	818.6	0.02427	298.35	537.56	1.3240	2.0552	1.992	1.539	1.388	499	177.3	116.5	11.64	85.9	18.87	5.98	54
56	1.36430	812.3	0.02303	302.33	538.32	1.3358	2.0528	2.010	1.566	1.402	488	176.4	113.7	11.76	85.1	19.21	5.74	56
58	1.43130	805.9	0.02185	306.34	539.04	1.3477	2.0504	2.030	1.595	1.416	478	175.5	111.1	11.88	84.2	19.56	5.50	58
60	1.50070	799.4	0.02074	310.38	539.72	1.3596	2.0480	2.051	1.626	1.432	467	174.6	108.4	12.00	83.4	19.92	5.25	60
62	1.57260	792.7	0.01968	314.45	540.35	1.3716	2.0456	2.073	1.658	1.450	456	173.6	105.8	12.12	82.6	20.30	5.01	62
64	1.64710	785.9	0.01868	318.57	540.94	1.3835	2.0431	2.097	1.693	1.468	445	172.5	103.3	12.26	81.8	20.70	4.78	64
66	1.72420	779.0	0.01774	322.72	541.47	1.3955	2.0405	2.122	1.730	1.488	435	171.4	100.8	12.39	80.9	21.11	4.54	66
68	1.80390	771.9	0.01684	326.92	541.95	1.4076	2.0379	2.150	1.769	1.511	424	170.2	98.3	12.53	80.1	21.54	4.31	68
70	1.88640	764.6	0.01598	331.16	542.37	1.4196	2.0351	2.179	1.812	1.535	413	169.0	95.9	12.68	79.3	22.00	4.08	70
72	1.97170	757.2	0.01517	335.45	542.73	1.4318	2.0323	2.211	1.859	1.562	402	167.8	93.5	12.83	78.5	22.48	3.85	72
74	2.05990	749.5	0.01440	339.79	543.02	1.4440	2.0294	2.245	1.909	1.591	390	166.5	91.1	12.99	77.6	22.98	3.62	74
76	2.15100	741.6	0.01366	344.18	543.24	1.4562	2.0264	2.283	1.964	1.624	379	165.1	88.7	13.16	76.8	23.51	3.40	76
78	2.24520	733.5	0.01296	348.63	543.38	1.4686	2.0232	2.324	2.025	1.661	368	163.7	86.4	13.34	76.0	24.08	3.18	78
80	2.34240	725.2	0.01228	353.15	543.43	1.4810	2.0198	2.370	2.092	1.702	356	162.2	84.1	13.52	75.2	24.69	2.96	80
90	2.87800	678.5	0.00933	376.87	542.06	1.5451	2.0000	2.703	2.586	2.016	297	153.7	72.6	14.64	71.0	28.54	1.91	90
100	3.50500	618.5	0.00686	403.59	536.28	1.6151	1.9707	3.495	3.776	2.805	233	143.1	60.7	16.35	67.0	35.03	0.96	100
110	4.24320	517.4	0.00446	439.22	517.31	1.7058	1.9096	9.260	12.220	8.530	158	129.1	45.6	20.19	67.5	53.48	0.17	110
113.26[c]	4.51680	368.0	0.00272	477.55	477.55	1.8037	1.8037	∞	∞	∞	0	0.0	—	—	∞	∞	0.00	113.26

*Temperatures on ITS-90 scale   [a]Triple point   [b]Normal boiling point   [c]Critical point

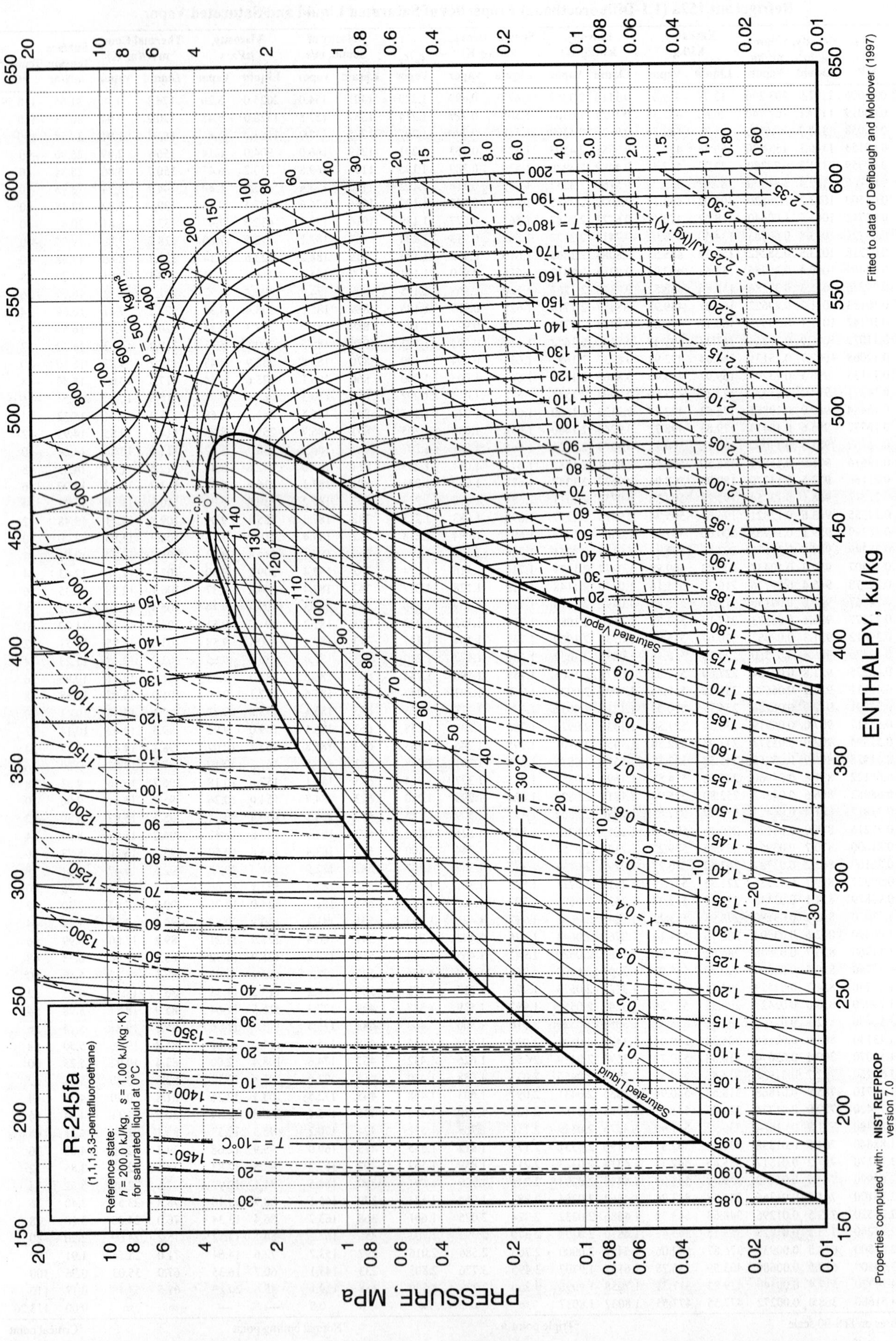

Fig. 11 Pressure-Enthalpy Diagram for Refrigerant 245fa

Refrigerant 245fa (1,1,1,3,3-Pentafluoropropane) Properties of Saturated Liquid and Saturated Vapor

Temp.,[a] °C	Pressure, MPa	Density, kg/m³ Liquid	Volume, m³/kg Vapor	Enthalpy, kJ/kg Liquid	Enthalpy, kJ/kg Vapor	Entropy, kJ/(kg·K) Liquid	Entropy, kJ/(kg·K) Vapor	Specific Heat c_p, kJ/(kg·K) Liquid	Specific Heat c_p, kJ/(kg·K) Vapor	c_p/c_v Vapor	Velocity of Sound, m/s Liquid	Velocity of Sound, m/s Vapor	Viscosity, µPa·s Liquid	Viscosity, µPa·s Vapor	Thermal Cond., mW/(m·K) Liquid	Thermal Cond., mW/(m·K) Vapor	Surface Tension, mN/m	Temp., °C
−60	0.00127	1548.7	10.380	126.08	361.82	0.6949	1.8009	1.200	0.701	1.101	1041	120.3	2026.	7.36	115.5	9.08	24.67	−60
−50	0.00281	1525.2	4.9038	138.12	368.68	0.7501	1.7834	1.208	0.725	1.099	994	122.7	1501.	7.71	111.9	9.27	23.47	−50
−40	0.00572	1501.6	2.5079	150.24	375.67	0.8033	1.7702	1.218	0.751	1.098	948	125.0	1174.	8.06	108.5	9.54	22.26	−40
−30	0.01085	1477.7	1.3726	162.48	382.76	0.8547	1.7606	1.229	0.778	1.098	902	127.1	951.2	8.40	105.2	9.89	21.03	−30
−20	0.01937	1453.6	0.79638	174.84	389.94	0.9044	1.7541	1.242	0.806	1.099	859	129.0	790.1	8.75	102.1	10.30	19.78	−20
−10	0.03277	1429.0	0.48586	187.34	397.18	0.9528	1.7502	1.257	0.837	1.100	815	130.7	668.3	9.09	99.0	10.77	18.52	−10
0	0.05292	1404.0	0.30955	200.00	404.47	1.0000	1.7486	1.274	0.868	1.103	773	132.1	573.2	9.42	95.9	11.31	17.25	0
2	0.05795	1398.9	0.28419	202.55	405.93	1.0093	1.7484	1.277	0.875	1.104	765	132.3	556.7	9.49	95.3	11.43	16.99	2
4	0.06336	1393.8	0.26129	205.11	407.39	1.0186	1.7484	1.281	0.881	1.104	756	132.5	540.8	9.56	94.7	11.55	16.74	4
6	0.06916	1388.7	0.24057	207.68	408.86	1.0278	1.7484	1.284	0.888	1.105	748	132.8	525.6	9.62	94.0	11.67	16.48	6
8	0.07538	1383.5	0.22180	210.25	410.32	1.0369	1.7485	1.288	0.895	1.106	740	133.0	511.0	9.69	93.4	11.79	16.22	8
10	0.08204	1378.3	0.20477	212.84	411.79	1.0461	1.7487	1.292	0.901	1.107	731	133.2	497.0	9.76	92.8	11.91	15.97	10
12	0.08917	1373.1	0.18929	215.43	413.25	1.0552	1.7489	1.296	0.908	1.108	723	133.4	483.5	9.82	92.2	12.04	15.71	12
14	0.09677	1367.9	0.17520	218.02	414.72	1.0642	1.7492	1.299	0.915	1.109	715	133.5	470.6	9.89	91.5	12.17	15.46	14
15.14[b]	0.10133	1364.9	0.16774	219.51	415.55	1.0694	1.7494	1.302	0.919	1.109	710	133.6	463.4	9.93	91.2	12.24	15.31	15.14
16	0.10488	1362.6	0.16236	220.63	416.18	1.0733	1.7496	1.303	0.922	1.110	707	133.7	458.1	9.96	90.9	12.30	15.20	16
18	0.11352	1357.3	0.15063	223.24	417.65	1.0822	1.7500	1.307	0.929	1.111	698	133.8	446.1	10.02	90.3	12.43	14.94	18
20	0.12270	1352.0	0.13992	225.86	419.12	1.0912	1.7504	1.312	0.936	1.112	690	133.9	434.5	10.09	89.7	12.56	14.69	20
22	0.13247	1346.6	0.13012	228.49	420.58	1.1001	1.7509	1.316	0.943	1.113	682	134.1	423.3	10.16	89.0	12.70	14.43	22
24	0.14283	1341.3	0.12113	231.13	422.04	1.1090	1.7515	1.320	0.950	1.114	674	134.1	412.5	10.22	88.4	12.84	14.17	24
26	0.15383	1335.8	0.11288	233.78	423.51	1.1178	1.7521	1.324	0.958	1.115	666	134.2	402.1	10.29	87.8	12.98	13.92	26
28	0.16547	1330.4	0.10530	236.44	424.97	1.1267	1.7527	1.329	0.965	1.117	657	134.3	392.0	10.36	87.2	13.12	13.66	28
30	0.17779	1324.9	0.09833	239.10	426.43	1.1355	1.7534	1.333	0.973	1.118	649	134.3	382.3	10.42	86.5	13.27	13.40	30
32	0.19081	1319.3	0.09191	241.78	427.89	1.1442	1.7541	1.338	0.980	1.120	641	134.4	372.8	10.49	85.9	13.42	13.15	32
34	0.20456	1313.7	0.08599	244.46	429.35	1.1529	1.7549	1.342	0.988	1.121	633	134.4	363.7	10.56	85.3	13.57	12.89	34
36	0.21907	1308.1	0.08053	247.15	430.81	1.1617	1.7557	1.347	0.996	1.123	625	134.4	354.8	10.62	84.6	13.72	12.63	36
38	0.23436	1302.4	0.07548	249.86	432.26	1.1703	1.7566	1.352	1.003	1.125	617	134.4	346.2	10.69	84.0	13.87	12.38	38
40	0.25046	1296.7	0.07080	252.57	433.71	1.1790	1.7574	1.357	1.011	1.126	609	134.3	337.9	10.76	83.4	14.02	12.12	40
42	0.26741	1291.0	0.06647	255.29	435.16	1.1876	1.7583	1.362	1.019	1.128	600	134.3	329.8	10.83	82.7	14.18	11.87	42
44	0.28522	1285.2	0.06246	258.03	436.61	1.1962	1.7593	1.367	1.028	1.130	592	134.2	321.9	10.89	82.1	14.34	11.61	44
46	0.30394	1279.3	0.05873	260.77	438.05	1.2048	1.7603	1.373	1.036	1.132	584	134.1	314.3	10.96	81.4	14.50	11.36	46
48	0.32358	1273.4	0.05527	263.52	439.49	1.2133	1.7613	1.378	1.044	1.135	576	134.0	306.9	11.03	80.8	14.66	11.10	48
50	0.34417	1267.4	0.05205	266.29	440.93	1.2219	1.7623	1.383	1.053	1.137	568	133.8	299.7	11.10	80.2	14.83	10.85	50
52	0.36576	1261.4	0.04905	269.07	442.36	1.2304	1.7633	1.389	1.061	1.139	560	133.7	292.6	11.17	79.5	15.00	10.60	52
54	0.38836	1255.3	0.04625	271.85	443.78	1.2389	1.7644	1.395	1.070	1.142	552	133.5	285.8	11.24	78.9	15.17	10.34	54
56	0.41201	1249.2	0.04365	274.65	445.21	1.2474	1.7655	1.401	1.079	1.145	544	133.3	279.1	11.32	78.2	15.34	10.09	56
58	0.43674	1243.0	0.04122	277.46	446.62	1.2558	1.7666	1.407	1.088	1.147	536	133.1	272.6	11.39	77.6	15.51	9.84	58
60	0.46259	1236.8	0.03894	280.29	448.04	1.2642	1.7678	1.413	1.098	1.150	527	132.8	266.2	11.46	76.9	15.69	9.59	60
62	0.48957	1230.4	0.03682	283.12	449.44	1.2727	1.7689	1.419	1.107	1.153	519	132.6	260.1	11.54	76.3	15.86	9.34	62
64	0.51773	1224.1	0.03482	285.97	450.84	1.2811	1.7701	1.426	1.117	1.157	511	132.3	254.0	11.61	75.6	16.04	9.09	64
66	0.54710	1217.6	0.03296	288.83	452.23	1.2894	1.7713	1.433	1.127	1.160	503	132.0	248.1	11.69	75.0	16.23	8.84	66
68	0.57771	1211.1	0.03121	291.70	453.62	1.2978	1.7724	1.439	1.137	1.164	495	131.6	242.3	11.77	74.4	16.41	8.59	68
70	0.60960	1204.4	0.02957	294.59	455.00	1.3062	1.7736	1.447	1.147	1.168	487	131.3	236.7	11.85	73.7	16.60	8.35	70
72	0.64279	1197.8	0.02803	297.49	456.36	1.3145	1.7748	1.454	1.158	1.172	479	130.9	231.2	11.93	73.1	16.79	8.10	72
74	0.67732	1191.0	0.02658	300.40	457.72	1.3229	1.7760	1.461	1.169	1.176	470	130.5	225.8	12.01	72.4	16.98	7.85	74
76	0.71323	1184.1	0.02521	303.33	459.08	1.3312	1.7773	1.469	1.180	1.181	462	130.0	220.5	12.10	71.8	17.18	7.61	76
78	0.75055	1177.2	0.02393	306.28	460.42	1.3395	1.7785	1.477	1.192	1.186	454	129.5	215.3	12.18	71.2	17.38	7.37	78
80	0.78931	1170.1	0.02272	309.24	461.75	1.3478	1.7797	1.486	1.204	1.191	446	129.0	210.2	12.27	70.5	17.58	7.13	80
82	0.82956	1163.0	0.02158	312.21	463.06	1.3561	1.7809	1.494	1.217	1.196	437	128.5	205.3	12.37	69.9	17.79	6.88	82
84	0.87132	1155.7	0.02050	315.20	464.37	1.3644	1.7821	1.503	1.230	1.202	429	127.9	200.4	12.46	69.3	18.00	6.65	84
86	0.91464	1148.4	0.01949	318.21	465.66	1.3727	1.7833	1.512	1.243	1.209	421	127.4	195.6	12.56	68.6	18.22	6.41	86
88	0.95955	1140.9	0.01853	321.24	466.94	1.3810	1.7845	1.522	1.257	1.215	412	126.7	190.9	12.66	68.0	18.44	6.17	88
90	1.0061	1133.3	0.01762	324.28	468.20	1.3893	1.7856	1.532	1.272	1.223	404	126.1	186.3	12.76	67.4	18.66	5.93	90
92	1.0543	1125.6	0.01676	327.34	469.45	1.3976	1.7868	1.543	1.287	1.230	396	125.4	181.8	12.87	66.7	18.89	5.70	92
94	1.1042	1117.7	0.01594	330.42	470.68	1.4059	1.7879	1.554	1.303	1.239	387	124.7	177.3	12.98	66.1	19.13	5.47	94
96	1.1559	1109.7	0.01517	333.52	471.89	1.4142	1.7890	1.565	1.320	1.247	379	123.9	172.9	13.10	65.5	19.38	5.24	96
98	1.2093	1101.6	0.01444	336.64	473.09	1.4225	1.7901	1.577	1.337	1.257	370	123.1	168.6	13.22	64.9	19.63	5.01	98
100	1.2646	1093.3	0.01374	339.78	474.26	1.4308	1.7912	1.590	1.356	1.267	362	122.3	164.3	13.35	64.3	19.89	4.78	100
105	1.4110	1071.8	0.01215	347.74	477.09	1.4516	1.7936	1.625	1.408	1.297	340	120.0	154.0	13.70	62.8	20.59	4.22	105
110	1.5698	1049.1	0.01074	355.85	479.74	1.4725	1.7959	1.667	1.469	1.335	319	117.4	143.9	14.09	61.3	21.36	3.68	110
115	1.7417	1025.0	0.00949	364.13	482.19	1.4936	1.7977	1.716	1.544	1.383	296	114.6	134.2	14.54	59.9	22.24	3.15	115
120	1.9275	999.2	0.00837	372.62	484.39	1.5148	1.7991	1.777	1.638	1.445	274	111.4	124.7	15.07	58.5	23.27	2.64	120
125	2.1280	971.2	0.00736	381.35	486.25	1.5364	1.7998	1.854	1.762	1.530	250	107.9	115.3	15.71	57.1	24.49	2.15	125
130	2.3442	940.4	0.00644	390.39	487.70	1.5584	1.7997	1.959	1.932	1.652	226	103.9	106.0	16.49	55.9	25.99	1.68	130
135	2.5773	905.8	0.00560	399.81	488.57	1.5810	1.7984	2.113	2.188	1.840	201	99.5	96.6	17.48	54.7	27.93	1.24	135
140	2.8287	865.6	0.00481	409.80	488.59	1.6046	1.7953	2.367	2.617	2.161	174	94.5	87.0	18.82	53.6	30.55	0.83	140
145	3.1003	815.9	0.00404	420.68	487.22	1.6300	1.7891	2.888	3.504	2.835	144	88.8	76.6	20.77	53.0	34.48	0.47	145
150	3.3946	744.6	0.00324	433.55	482.85	1.6597	1.7762	4.720	6.517	5.146	111	82.2	64.1	24.20	54.2	42.04	0.16	150
154.01[c]	3.6510	516.1	0.00194	460.34	460.34	1.7217	1.7217	∞	∞	∞	0	0.0	—	—	∞	∞	0.00	154.01

[a]Temperatures on ITS-90 scale [b]Normal boiling point [c]Critical point

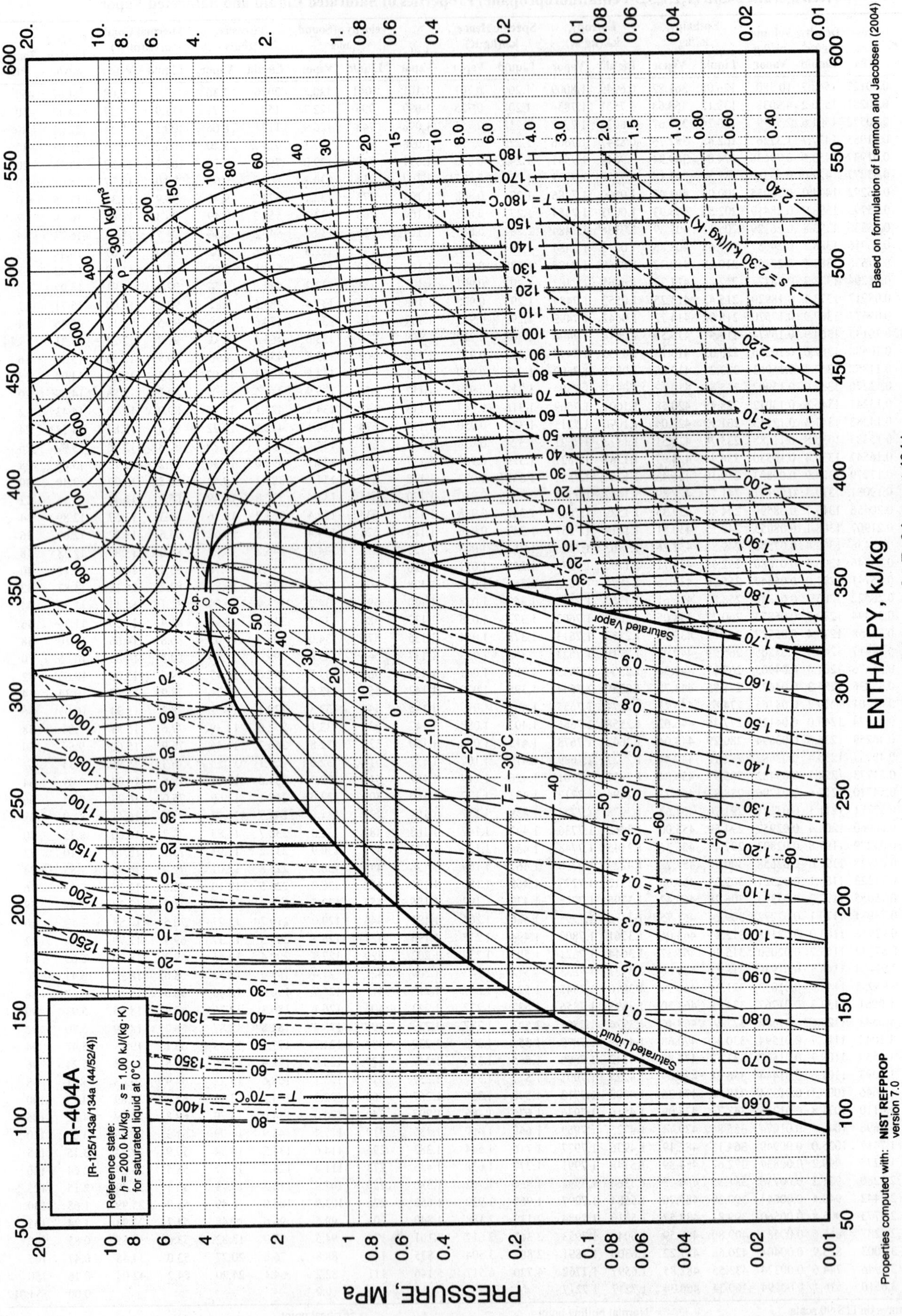

Fig. 12 Pressure-Enthalpy Diagram for Refrigerant 404A

Refrigerant 404A [R-125/143a/134a (44/52/4)] Properties of Liquid on Bubble Line and Vapor on Dew Line

Pres-sure, MPa	Temperature,* °C		Density, kg/m³	Volume, m³/kg	Enthalpy, kJ/kg		Entropy, kJ/(kg·K)		Specific Heat c_p, kJ/(kg·K)		c_p/c_v	Velocity of Sound, m/s		Viscosity, μPa·s		Thermal Cond., mW/(m·K)		Surface Tension, mN/m	Pres-sure, MPa
	Bubble	Dew	Liquid	Vapor	Liquid	Vapor	Liquid	Vapor	Liquid	Vapor	Vapor	Liquid	Vapor	Liquid	Vapor	Liquid	Vapor		
0.005	−93.70	−92.50	1447.1	3.05794	81.16	311.61	0.4716	1.7532	1.220	0.640	1.163	998	132.9	764.9	7.32	122.5	6.15	17.78	0.005
0.006	−91.48	−90.32	1440.6	2.57690	83.85	312.92	0.4865	1.7450	1.218	0.646	1.162	980	133.6	727.8	7.41	121.2	6.28	17.58	0.006
0.007	−89.56	−88.42	1434.9	2.22992	86.19	314.06	0.4993	1.7382	1.216	0.651	1.161	966	134.1	697.9	7.48	120.1	6.40	17.40	0.007
0.008	−87.86	−86.74	1429.9	1.96748	88.26	315.07	0.5106	1.7324	1.215	0.655	1.161	953	134.6	673.0	7.55	119.2	6.50	17.24	0.008
0.009	−86.32	−85.22	1425.4	1.76182	90.13	315.99	0.5206	1.7273	1.214	0.660	1.160	942	135.0	651.7	7.61	118.3	6.60	17.09	0.009
0.01	−84.93	−83.84	1421.3	1.59620	91.83	316.83	0.5296	1.7229	1.214	0.663	1.160	933	135.4	633.3	7.66	117.5	6.68	16.96	0.01
0.02	−75.05	−74.08	1392.4	0.83425	103.81	322.78	0.5917	1.6953	1.215	0.691	1.159	870	137.9	523.7	8.04	112.2	7.31	16.00	0.02
0.04	−63.85	−62.97	1359.4	0.43619	117.48	329.58	0.6587	1.6707	1.225	0.725	1.159	807	140.4	431.3	8.47	106.4	8.05	14.85	0.04
0.06	−56.57	−55.75	1337.7	0.29837	126.44	334.00	0.7007	1.6578	1.234	0.749	1.161	770	141.7	383.8	8.74	102.8	8.55	14.08	0.06
0.08	−51.03	−50.25	1321.0	0.22779	133.31	337.36	0.7320	1.6494	1.243	0.767	1.163	742	142.6	352.7	8.95	100.1	8.93	13.48	0.08
0.1	−46.50	−45.74	1307.1	0.18467	138.97	340.08	0.7571	1.6434	1.251	0.784	1.166	719	143.2	329.8	9.12	98.0	9.25	12.98	0.1
0.10132[b]	−46.22	−45.47	1306.3	0.18240	139.31	340.25	0.7586	1.6430	1.252	0.785	1.166	718	143.2	328.5	9.13	97.8	9.27	12.95	0.10132
0.12	−42.63	−41.90	1295.1	0.15551	143.83	342.40	0.7783	1.6387	1.259	0.798	1.169	700	143.6	311.9	9.26	96.2	9.53	12.55	0.12
0.14	−39.24	−38.53	1284.5	0.13443	148.12	344.41	0.7967	1.6349	1.266	0.811	1.171	684	143.9	297.3	9.39	94.6	9.78	12.17	0.14
0.16	−36.20	−35.51	1275.0	0.11846	151.97	346.20	0.8130	1.6318	1.273	0.823	1.174	669	144.1	285.0	9.50	93.2	10.01	11.82	0.16
0.18	−33.45	−32.78	1266.2	0.10592	155.49	347.81	0.8277	1.6292	1.279	0.834	1.177	656	144.2	274.4	9.60	91.9	10.21	11.51	0.18
0.2	−30.93	−30.27	1258.0	0.09581	158.73	349.28	0.8411	1.6270	1.285	0.844	1.179	644	144.3	265.1	9.69	90.8	10.40	11.21	0.2
0.22	−28.59	−27.94	1250.4	0.08748	161.75	350.63	0.8534	1.6250	1.291	0.855	1.182	633	144.3	256.9	9.78	89.7	10.58	10.94	0.22
0.24	−26.42	−25.78	1243.3	0.08049	164.57	351.88	0.8649	1.6233	1.297	0.864	1.185	623	144.4	249.5	9.86	88.7	10.75	10.69	0.24
0.26	−24.37	−23.75	1236.5	0.07454	167.23	353.04	0.8755	1.6217	1.303	0.873	1.188	613	144.3	242.8	9.94	87.8	10.91	10.45	0.26
0.28	−22.45	−21.83	1230.1	0.06941	169.75	354.13	0.8855	1.6203	1.308	0.882	1.190	604	144.3	236.7	10.01	87.0	11.06	10.22	0.28
0.3	−20.62	−20.02	1223.9	0.06494	172.14	355.15	0.8950	1.6190	1.313	0.891	1.193	595	144.2	231.1	10.08	86.2	11.21	10.01	0.3
0.32	−18.89	−18.29	1218.0	0.06101	174.43	356.12	0.9039	1.6179	1.319	0.899	1.196	587	144.1	225.9	10.15	85.4	11.34	9.81	0.32
0.34	−17.24	−16.65	1212.4	0.05752	176.61	357.03	0.9125	1.6168	1.324	0.907	1.199	579	144.0	221.1	10.21	84.7	11.48	9.61	0.34
0.36	−15.66	−15.08	1206.9	0.05441	178.71	357.90	0.9206	1.6158	1.329	0.915	1.202	572	143.9	216.6	10.27	84.0	11.61	9.42	0.36
0.38	−14.15	−13.57	1201.6	0.05162	180.73	358.72	0.9283	1.6149	1.334	0.923	1.205	565	143.8	212.4	10.33	83.3	11.73	9.24	0.38
0.4	−12.69	−12.12	1196.5	0.04909	182.68	359.51	0.9358	1.6141	1.339	0.931	1.208	558	143.7	208.4	10.39	82.7	11.85	9.07	0.4
0.42	−11.29	−10.73	1191.6	0.04680	184.56	360.26	0.9429	1.6133	1.344	0.938	1.211	551	143.5	204.7	10.44	82.1	11.97	8.90	0.42
0.44	−9.94	−9.39	1186.7	0.04471	186.38	360.98	0.9498	1.6125	1.349	0.946	1.214	545	143.4	201.2	10.49	81.5	12.08	8.74	0.44
0.46	−8.64	−8.09	1182.0	0.04279	188.15	361.67	0.9564	1.6118	1.353	0.953	1.217	538	143.2	197.8	10.55	81.0	12.19	8.58	0.46
0.48	−7.37	−6.83	1177.5	0.04103	189.86	362.33	0.9628	1.6112	1.358	0.960	1.220	532	143.0	194.6	10.60	80.4	12.30	8.43	0.48
0.5	−6.15	−5.61	1173.0	0.03940	191.53	362.96	0.9690	1.6105	1.363	0.967	1.223	527	142.8	191.6	10.65	79.9	12.41	8.28	0.5
0.55	−3.24	−2.72	1162.3	0.03584	195.51	364.45	0.9837	1.6091	1.374	0.984	1.231	513	142.4	184.6	10.77	78.7	12.66	7.93	0.55
0.6	−0.53	−0.02	1152.0	0.03284	199.26	365.81	0.9973	1.6078	1.386	1.001	1.239	500	141.9	178.2	10.88	77.5	12.91	7.61	0.6
0.65	2.02	2.52	1142.3	0.03029	202.81	367.06	1.0101	1.6066	1.397	1.018	1.247	488	141.3	172.5	10.99	76.5	13.16	7.30	0.65
0.7	4.42	4.91	1132.9	0.02809	206.18	368.21	1.0222	1.6055	1.409	1.034	1.256	476	140.8	167.2	11.10	75.5	13.41	7.01	0.7
0.75	6.70	7.18	1123.8	0.02618	209.41	369.28	1.0336	1.6044	1.420	1.051	1.264	465	140.2	162.4	11.20	74.5	13.65	6.74	0.75
0.8	8.87	9.34	1115.1	0.02449	212.49	370.27	1.0444	1.6035	1.432	1.067	1.274	455	139.6	157.9	11.30	73.6	13.89	6.48	0.8
0.85	10.94	11.40	1106.5	0.02300	215.46	371.19	1.0547	1.6025	1.443	1.084	1.283	445	139.0	153.6	11.40	72.8	14.12	6.23	0.85
0.9	12.92	13.37	1098.2	0.02166	218.32	372.05	1.0646	1.6016	1.455	1.100	1.293	435	138.3	149.7	11.50	72.0	14.35	5.99	0.9
0.95	14.81	15.26	1090.2	0.02046	221.09	372.85	1.0741	1.6007	1.466	1.117	1.303	426	137.7	146.0	11.59	71.2	14.59	5.76	0.95
1.0	16.64	17.08	1082.2	0.01937	223.77	373.59	1.0832	1.5999	1.478	1.134	1.313	417	137.1	142.5	11.69	70.4	14.82	5.54	1.0
1.1	20.09	20.52	1066.9	0.01749	228.89	374.94	1.1005	1.5982	1.503	1.169	1.336	400	135.7	136.1	11.88	69.0	15.29	5.13	1.1
1.2	23.32	23.73	1052.0	0.01590	233.75	376.12	1.1166	1.5965	1.528	1.206	1.360	384	134.4	130.2	12.07	67.7	15.76	4.75	1.2
1.3	26.35	26.75	1037.5	0.01455	238.37	377.14	1.1318	1.5949	1.554	1.244	1.386	368	133.0	124.9	12.26	66.5	16.23	4.39	1.3
1.4	29.22	29.60	1023.4	0.01338	242.81	378.02	1.1462	1.5932	1.582	1.285	1.414	354	131.6	119.9	12.45	65.3	16.71	4.06	1.4
1.5	31.93	32.30	1009.5	0.01236	247.07	378.78	1.1599	1.5914	1.611	1.329	1.445	340	130.1	115.3	12.65	64.2	17.21	3.75	1.5
1.6	34.51	34.87	995.7	0.01146	251.19	379.42	1.1730	1.5896	1.643	1.376	1.478	327	128.7	111.0	12.84	63.1	17.72	3.45	1.6
1.7	36.97	37.32	982.1	0.01066	255.17	379.95	1.1856	1.5878	1.676	1.426	1.515	314	127.2	107.0	13.05	62.1	18.24	3.17	1.7
1.8	39.33	39.67	968.6	0.00994	259.05	380.38	1.1977	1.5858	1.712	1.481	1.556	301	125.7	103.2	13.25	61.2	18.80	2.91	1.8
1.9	41.58	41.91	955.1	0.00930	262.83	380.70	1.2095	1.5838	1.751	1.541	1.601	289	124.1	99.5	13.47	60.2	19.37	2.66	1.9
2.0	43.75	44.07	941.6	0.00871	266.52	380.92	1.2208	1.5817	1.794	1.607	1.652	277	122.6	96.1	13.70	59.3	19.98	2.43	2.0
2.1	45.84	46.15	928.1	0.00817	270.14	381.05	1.2319	1.5794	1.841	1.681	1.709	266	121.0	92.7	13.93	58.5	20.62	2.21	2.1
2.2	47.85	48.15	914.4	0.00768	273.70	381.08	1.2427	1.5770	1.893	1.763	1.774	254	119.4	89.5	14.18	57.6	21.31	2.00	2.2
2.3	49.80	50.08	900.6	0.00723	277.20	381.01	1.2532	1.5745	1.952	1.856	1.847	243	117.8	86.5	14.44	56.8	22.04	1.80	2.3
2.4	51.68	51.95	886.5	0.00680	280.66	380.83	1.2635	1.5718	2.019	1.962	1.932	232	116.2	83.5	14.72	56.0	22.83	1.61	2.4
2.5	53.50	53.76	872.2	0.00641	284.09	380.55	1.2737	1.5689	2.095	2.085	2.032	222	114.5	80.5	15.02	55.3	23.69	1.43	2.5
2.6	55.26	55.51	857.5	0.00604	287.50	380.15	1.2837	1.5658	2.183	2.229	2.149	211	112.9	77.7	15.34	54.5	24.62	1.26	2.6
2.7	56.97	57.21	842.4	0.00569	290.89	379.62	1.2937	1.5624	2.288	2.401	2.289	200	111.2	74.9	15.69	53.8	25.65	1.10	2.7
2.8	58.63	58.86	826.8	0.00536	294.29	378.96	1.3036	1.5587	2.414	2.609	2.459	190	109.5	72.1	16.07	53.2	26.79	0.94	2.8
2.9	60.24	60.46	810.5	0.00505	297.70	378.14	1.3135	1.5547	2.569	2.868	2.672	179	107.7	69.3	16.49	52.6	28.06	0.80	2.9
3.0	61.81	62.01	793.4	0.00475	301.15	377.15	1.3234	1.5503	2.765	3.197	2.944	169	106.0	66.5	16.95	52.0	29.51	0.67	3.0
3.2	64.82	64.99	755.6	0.00417	308.25	374.49	1.3438	1.5397	3.381	4.233	3.797	148	102.3	60.9	18.09	51.2	33.17	0.43	3.2
3.4	67.67	67.81	709.8	0.00361	315.97	370.45	1.3657	1.5255	4.771	6.536	5.689	126	98.5	54.7	19.68	51.3	38.73	0.23	3.4
3.729[c]	72.05	72.05	486.5	0.00206	343.92	343.92	1.4455	1.4455	—	—	—	—	—	—	—	—	—	0.00	3.729

*Temperatures on ITS-90 scale

[b]Bubble and dew points at one standard atmosphere

[c]Critical point

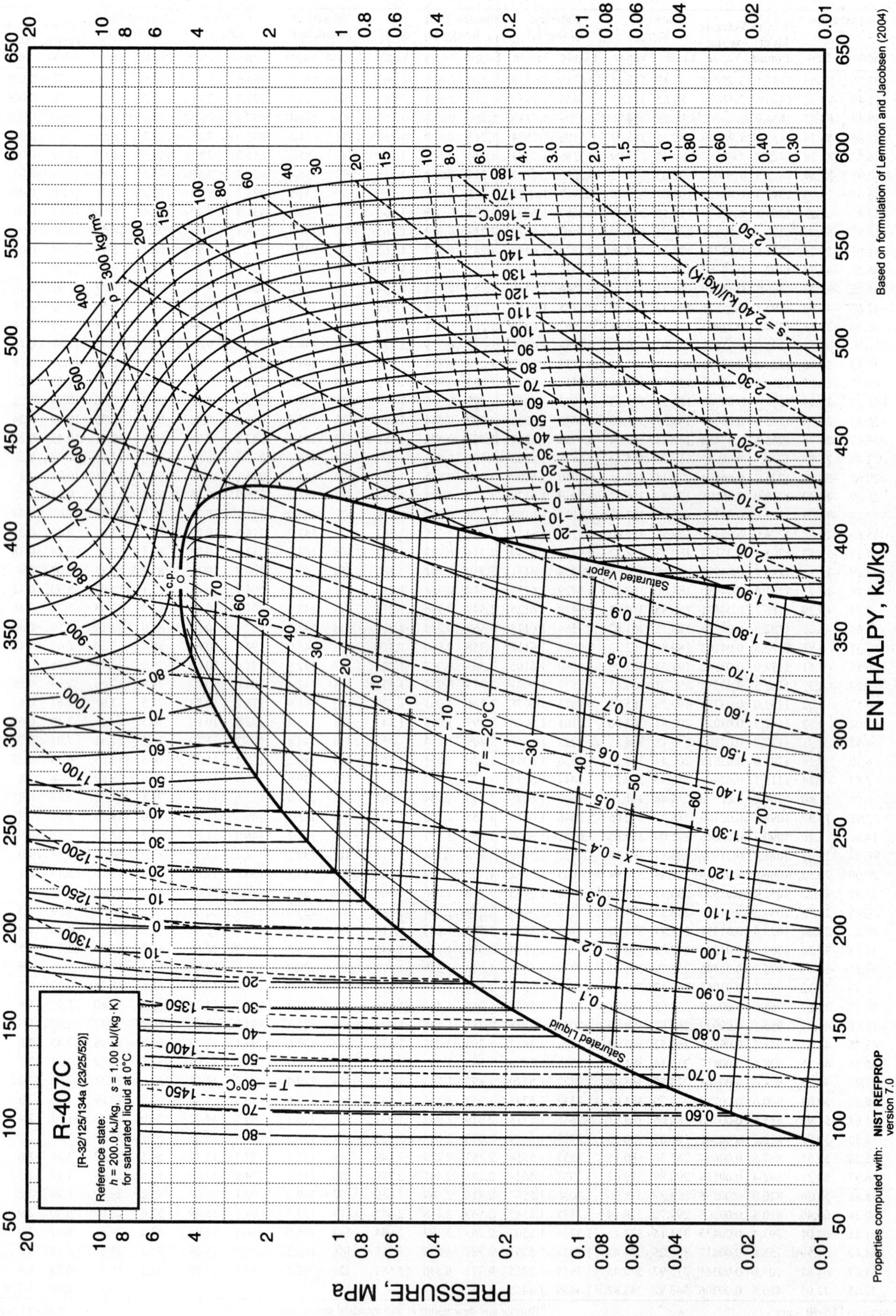

Fig. 13 Pressure-Enthalpy Diagram for Refrigerant 407C

Refrigerant 407C [R-32/125/134a (23/25/52)] Properties of Liquid on Bubble Line and Vapor on Dew Line

Pressure, MPa	Temperature,* °C Bubble	Temperature,* °C Dew	Density, kg/m³ Liquid	Volume, m³/kg Vapor	Enthalpy, kJ/kg Liquid	Enthalpy, kJ/kg Vapor	Entropy, kJ/(kg·K) Liquid	Entropy, kJ/(kg·K) Vapor	Specific Heat c_p, kJ/(kg·K) Liquid	Specific Heat c_p, kJ/(kg·K) Vapor	c_p/c_v Vapor	Velocity of Sound, m/s Liquid	Velocity of Sound, m/s Vapor	Viscosity, μPa·s Liquid	Viscosity, μPa·s Vapor	Thermal Cond., mW/(m·K) Liquid	Thermal Cond., mW/(m·K) Vapor	Surface Tension, mN/m	Pressure, MPa
0.01	–82.45	–74.81	1495.5	1.89703	90.48	366.78	0.5259	1.9471	1.281	0.668	1.182	1008	149.1	779.8	8.43	151.5	6.94	24.75	0.01
0.02	–72.50	–65.02	1466.7	0.99017	103.24	372.75	0.5910	1.9104	1.283	0.694	1.181	953	151.8	632.8	8.83	145.4	7.52	22.93	0.02
0.04	–61.25	–53.95	1433.7	0.51705	117.72	379.47	0.6612	1.8761	1.291	0.727	1.182	893	154.6	513.1	9.28	138.5	8.19	20.91	0.04
0.06	–53.96	–46.79	1412.0	0.35346	127.17	383.77	0.7050	1.8573	1.299	0.750	1.184	856	156.1	453.1	9.57	134.1	8.64	19.62	0.06
0.08	–48.42	–41.34	1395.3	0.26975	134.39	386.99	0.7374	1.8445	1.306	0.769	1.187	828	157.1	414.4	9.79	130.7	8.99	18.65	0.08
0.1	–43.90	–36.90	1381.5	0.21865	140.31	389.59	0.7635	1.8349	1.312	0.786	1.190	806	157.8	386.2	9.97	128.1	9.28	17.87	0.1
0.10132[b]	–43.63	–36.63	1380.7	0.21595	140.67	389.75	0.7650	1.8343	1.312	0.787	1.190	804	157.8	384.6	9.98	127.9	9.29	17.82	0.10132
0.12	–40.05	–33.11	1369.7	0.18411	145.39	391.78	0.7854	1.8273	1.318	0.800	1.193	787	158.3	364.3	10.12	125.8	9.52	17.21	0.12
0.14	–36.67	–29.79	1359.1	0.15916	149.86	393.68	0.8043	1.8210	1.324	0.813	1.196	770	158.7	346.6	10.25	123.8	9.75	16.63	0.14
0.16	–33.65	–26.83	1349.7	0.14025	153.86	395.36	0.8211	1.8156	1.329	0.825	1.199	755	159.0	331.8	10.37	122.0	9.94	16.12	0.16
0.18	–30.92	–24.15	1341.0	0.12542	157.51	396.86	0.8362	1.8110	1.334	0.837	1.201	742	159.3	319.1	10.48	120.4	10.13	15.66	0.18
0.2	–28.41	–21.69	1333.0	0.11347	160.87	398.22	0.8499	1.8069	1.339	0.848	1.204	730	159.5	308.0	10.57	119.0	10.29	15.24	0.2
0.22	–26.09	–19.41	1325.5	0.10362	163.99	399.47	0.8625	1.8033	1.344	0.858	1.207	719	159.6	298.2	10.66	117.6	10.45	14.86	0.22
0.24	–23.93	–17.29	1318.4	0.09536	166.91	400.62	0.8742	1.8000	1.349	0.868	1.210	708	159.7	289.5	10.75	116.4	10.60	14.50	0.24
0.26	–21.90	–15.31	1311.8	0.08833	169.65	401.69	0.8851	1.7970	1.354	0.877	1.213	698	159.8	281.6	10.83	115.2	10.74	14.16	0.26
0.28	–19.99	–13.43	1305.5	0.08227	172.24	402.69	0.8954	1.7942	1.358	0.886	1.216	689	159.8	274.4	10.90	114.2	10.87	13.85	0.28
0.3	–18.19	–11.66	1299.5	0.07699	174.71	403.62	0.9050	1.7917	1.362	0.895	1.219	680	159.8	267.8	10.97	113.1	10.99	13.56	0.3
0.32	–16.47	–9.98	1293.7	0.07235	177.06	404.49	0.9141	1.7894	1.367	0.903	1.222	672	159.8	261.8	11.04	112.2	11.11	13.28	0.32
0.34	–14.83	–8.38	1288.2	0.06824	179.30	405.32	0.9228	1.7872	1.371	0.911	1.224	664	159.8	256.1	11.11	111.2	11.23	13.01	0.34
0.36	–13.27	–6.85	1282.9	0.06457	181.45	406.10	0.9310	1.7851	1.375	0.919	1.227	656	159.8	250.9	11.17	110.4	11.35	12.76	0.36
0.38	–11.77	–5.38	1277.8	0.06127	183.52	406.85	0.9389	1.7832	1.379	0.927	1.230	649	159.7	246.0	11.23	109.5	11.46	12.52	0.38
0.4	–10.33	–3.97	1272.8	0.05830	185.52	407.55	0.9465	1.7814	1.383	0.934	1.233	642	159.7	241.4	11.28	108.7	11.57	12.29	0.4
0.42	–8.94	–2.61	1268.0	0.05559	187.44	408.23	0.9537	1.7796	1.387	0.942	1.236	635	159.6	237.1	11.34	107.9	11.68	12.07	0.42
0.44	–7.61	–1.31	1263.4	0.05313	189.30	408.87	0.9607	1.7780	1.391	0.949	1.239	629	159.5	233.0	11.39	107.2	11.78	11.85	0.44
0.46	–6.31	–0.04	1258.8	0.05087	191.11	409.48	0.9674	1.7764	1.395	0.956	1.242	622	159.4	229.1	11.45	106.5	11.88	11.65	0.46
0.48	–5.06	1.18	1254.4	0.04879	192.86	410.07	0.9739	1.7750	1.399	0.963	1.245	616	159.3	225.4	11.50	105.8	11.98	11.45	0.48
0.5	–3.85	2.36	1250.1	0.04687	194.56	410.64	0.9801	1.7735	1.403	0.970	1.248	610	159.2	221.9	11.54	105.1	12.08	11.26	0.5
0.55	–0.98	5.17	1239.8	0.04267	198.61	411.95	0.9950	1.7702	1.413	0.987	1.255	596	158.9	213.9	11.66	103.5	12.31	10.81	0.55
0.6	1.70	7.79	1230.0	0.03915	202.42	413.15	1.0087	1.7672	1.422	1.004	1.262	583	158.6	206.7	11.77	102.1	12.54	10.40	0.6
0.65	4.22	10.24	1220.7	0.03615	206.02	414.25	1.0216	1.7644	1.432	1.020	1.270	571	158.2	200.1	11.88	100.7	12.75	10.01	0.65
0.7	6.60	12.56	1211.7	0.03356	209.44	415.25	1.0338	1.7618	1.441	1.036	1.278	559	157.8	194.1	11.98	99.4	12.96	9.64	0.7
0.75	8.85	14.76	1203.1	0.03131	212.71	416.18	1.0452	1.7594	1.451	1.052	1.286	548	157.4	188.6	12.08	98.2	13.17	9.30	0.75
0.8	11.00	16.85	1194.9	0.02933	215.83	417.03	1.0561	1.7571	1.460	1.067	1.294	537	157.0	183.6	12.17	97.1	13.37	8.98	0.8
0.85	13.04	18.84	1186.8	0.02757	218.83	417.83	1.0665	1.7550	1.469	1.082	1.302	527	156.6	178.8	12.26	96.0	13.58	8.67	0.85
0.9	15.00	20.74	1179.1	0.02600	221.71	418.57	1.0764	1.7529	1.479	1.098	1.310	518	156.1	174.4	12.35	94.9	13.78	8.38	0.9
0.95	16.88	22.56	1171.5	0.02460	224.50	419.25	1.0859	1.7509	1.488	1.113	1.319	508	155.6	170.3	12.44	93.9	13.98	8.11	0.95
1.0	18.69	24.32	1164.1	0.02332	227.19	419.89	1.0950	1.7491	1.498	1.128	1.327	499	155.2	166.4	12.52	93.0	14.18	7.84	1.0
1.1	22.11	27.63	1149.9	0.02111	232.34	421.03	1.1122	1.7455	1.517	1.159	1.346	482	154.2	159.2	12.68	91.1	14.59	7.35	1.1
1.2	25.30	30.73	1136.2	0.01926	237.20	422.03	1.1283	1.7421	1.537	1.190	1.365	466	153.2	152.8	12.84	89.5	14.99	6.89	1.2
1.3	28.30	33.63	1123.0	0.01768	241.82	422.89	1.1434	1.7389	1.557	1.222	1.385	451	152.1	146.9	13.01	87.9	15.39	6.47	1.3
1.4	31.14	36.37	1110.2	0.01631	246.24	423.63	1.1577	1.7358	1.578	1.255	1.406	436	151.0	141.5	13.15	86.4	15.80	6.07	1.4
1.5	33.83	38.97	1097.7	0.01512	250.48	424.27	1.1713	1.7328	1.600	1.289	1.428	423	150.0	136.5	13.31	85.0	16.22	5.70	1.5
1.6	36.39	41.43	1085.5	0.01408	254.57	424.80	1.1843	1.7298	1.622	1.324	1.452	409	148.8	131.8	13.47	83.7	16.64	5.35	1.6
1.7	38.84	43.78	1073.5	0.01315	258.51	425.25	1.1967	1.7269	1.645	1.361	1.477	397	147.7	127.5	13.62	82.4	17.07	5.02	1.7
1.8	41.18	46.03	1061.7	0.01231	262.33	425.61	1.2086	1.7241	1.669	1.400	1.504	385	146.6	123.4	13.78	81.2	17.52	4.71	1.8
1.9	43.43	48.18	1050.0	0.01157	266.05	425.89	1.2200	1.7212	1.695	1.440	1.533	373	145.4	119.6	13.94	80.1	17.98	4.42	1.9
2.0	45.59	50.25	1038.5	0.01089	269.66	426.10	1.2311	1.7184	1.722	1.483	1.564	361	144.2	115.9	14.10	78.9	18.45	4.14	2.0
2.1	47.67	52.24	1027.1	0.01027	273.19	426.23	1.2418	1.7155	1.750	1.529	1.597	350	143.0	112.5	14.27	77.9	18.94	3.87	2.1
2.2	49.68	54.15	1015.7	0.00971	276.64	426.29	1.2522	1.7126	1.780	1.577	1.633	339	141.8	109.2	14.44	76.8	19.45	3.62	2.2
2.3	51.63	56.00	1004.4	0.00919	280.02	426.28	1.2624	1.7097	1.813	1.629	1.671	329	140.6	106.0	14.62	75.8	19.98	3.38	2.3
2.4	53.51	57.79	993.1	0.00871	283.34	426.20	1.2723	1.7068	1.847	1.684	1.713	318	139.4	103.0	14.79	74.9	20.54	3.15	2.4
2.5	55.34	59.51	981.8	0.00827	286.60	426.06	1.2819	1.7038	1.884	1.744	1.758	308	138.2	100.0	14.98	73.9	21.12	2.93	2.5
2.6	57.11	61.19	970.5	0.00786	289.82	425.85	1.2914	1.7007	1.924	1.810	1.808	298	136.9	97.2	15.17	73.0	21.73	2.72	2.6
2.7	58.83	62.81	959.0	0.00747	292.99	425.57	1.3006	1.6976	1.968	1.881	1.863	288	135.6	94.5	15.37	72.1	22.38	2.52	2.7
2.8	60.51	64.38	947.5	0.00711	296.12	425.21	1.3097	1.6944	2.016	1.958	1.923	279	134.4	91.9	15.58	71.3	23.06	2.33	2.8
2.9	62.14	65.91	935.9	0.00677	299.23	424.79	1.3187	1.6911	2.069	2.044	1.990	269	133.1	89.3	15.80	70.4	23.79	2.14	2.9
3.0	63.73	67.40	924.1	0.00645	302.31	424.29	1.3276	1.6877	2.128	2.139	2.065	259	131.7	86.8	16.03	69.6	24.56	1.96	3.0
3.2	66.80	70.25	899.9	0.00587	308.43	423.06	1.3450	1.6805	2.268	2.365	2.243	240	129.1	81.9	16.53	68.1	26.26	1.63	3.2
3.4	69.73	72.94	874.6	0.00533	314.54	421.46	1.3622	1.6726	2.451	2.657	2.475	222	126.4	77.1	17.09	66.6	28.22	1.33	3.4
3.6	72.53	75.50	847.6	0.00484	320.71	419.45	1.3795	1.6639	2.701	3.050	2.789	203	123.6	72.5	17.75	65.2	30.54	1.05	3.6
3.8	75.22	77.92	818.1	0.00439	327.02	416.91	1.3970	1.6540	3.065	3.613	3.239	184	120.7	67.7	18.52	64.0	33.33	0.79	3.8
4.0	77.82	80.21	785.1	0.00395	333.64	413.66	1.4152	1.6424	3.647	4.486	3.935	165	117.7	62.9	19.48	63.1	36.86	0.56	4.0
4.2	80.32	82.37	746.0	0.00352	340.83	409.34	1.4348	1.6281	4.726	6.029	5.159	146	114.6	57.6	20.75	62.7	41.59	0.36	4.2
4.63[c]	86.03	86.03	484.2	0.00207	378.48	378.48	1.5384	1.5384	—	—	—	—	—	—	—	—	—	0.00	4.63

*Temperatures on ITS-90 scale

[b]Bubble and dew points at one standard atmosphere

[c]Critical point

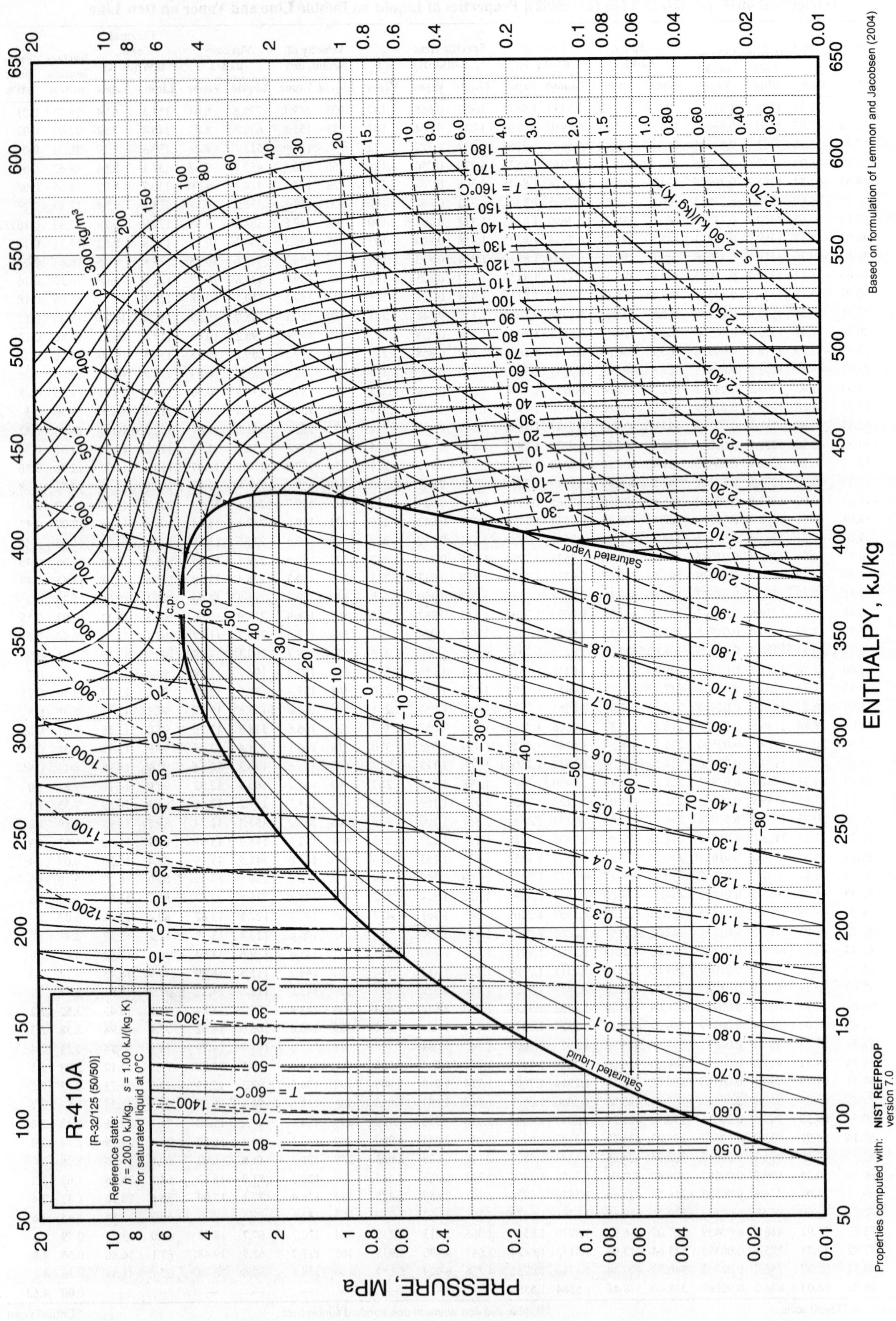

Fig. 14 Pressure-Enthalpy Diagram for Refrigerant 410A

Refrigerant 410A [R-32/125 (50/50)] Properties of Liquid on Bubble Line and Vapor on Dew Line

Pressure, MPa	Temperature,* °C		Density, kg/m³	Volume, m³/kg	Enthalpy, kJ/kg		Entropy, kJ/(kg·K)		Specific Heat c_p, kJ/(kg·K)		c_p/c_v	Velocity of Sound, m/s		Viscosity, μPa·s		Thermal Cond., mW/(m·K)		Surface Tension, mN/m	Pressure, MPa
	Bubble	Dew	Liquid	Vapor	Liquid	Vapor	Liquid	Vapor	Liquid	Vapor	Vapor	Liquid	Vapor	Liquid	Vapor	Liquid	Vapor		
0.01	−88.23	−88.14	1460.6	2.09888	76.56	378.76	0.4588	2.0927	1.344	0.668	1.227	1004	159.7	669.9	8.29	177.3	7.44	24.72	0.01
0.02	−78.79	−78.70	1432.9	1.09659	89.26	384.25	0.5258	2.0432	1.345	0.696	1.228	958	162.8	552.9	8.71	170.8	7.79	22.91	0.02
0.04	−68.12	−68.04	1401.1	0.57309	103.64	390.29	0.5978	1.9956	1.351	0.734	1.231	906	165.8	454.8	9.17	163.3	8.21	20.90	0.04
0.06	−61.22	−61.14	1380.0	0.39193	113.00	394.10	0.6426	1.9687	1.358	0.762	1.235	872	167.5	404.6	9.47	158.3	8.50	19.62	0.06
0.08	−55.98	−55.90	1363.9	0.29918	120.14	396.92	0.6758	1.9500	1.364	0.785	1.239	847	168.7	371.8	9.70	154.6	8.73	18.66	0.08
0.1	−51.70	−51.62	1350.5	0.24256	125.99	399.17	0.7024	1.9358	1.369	0.805	1.243	826	169.5	347.8	9.88	151.5	8.93	17.88	0.1
0.10132[b]	−51.44	−51.36	1349.7	0.23957	126.34	399.31	0.7040	1.9350	1.370	0.807	1.244	824	169.5	346.4	9.90	151.3	8.94	17.84	0.10132
0.12	−48.06	−47.98	1339.0	0.20427	130.99	401.05	0.7247	1.9243	1.375	0.823	1.247	808	170.1	329.0	10.04	148.9	9.11	17.23	0.12
0.14	−44.87	−44.79	1328.8	0.17661	135.39	402.67	0.7441	1.9147	1.380	0.839	1.251	792	170.6	313.8	10.18	146.6	9.26	16.65	0.14
0.16	−42.02	−41.94	1319.6	0.15565	139.34	404.09	0.7612	1.9065	1.385	0.854	1.255	778	170.9	300.9	10.30	144.6	9.40	16.15	0.16
0.18	−39.44	−39.36	1311.2	0.13921	142.93	405.36	0.7766	1.8993	1.390	0.868	1.259	765	171.2	289.9	10.41	142.8	9.53	15.69	0.18
0.2	−37.07	−36.99	1303.4	0.12595	146.23	406.50	0.7905	1.8928	1.395	0.881	1.263	753	171.5	280.3	10.51	141.1	9.66	15.27	0.2
0.22	−34.89	−34.80	1296.2	0.11503	149.29	407.53	0.8034	1.8871	1.399	0.893	1.266	743	171.6	271.8	10.61	139.5	9.77	14.89	0.22
0.24	−32.85	−32.76	1289.4	0.10587	152.15	408.49	0.8153	1.8818	1.404	0.904	1.270	732	171.8	264.2	10.70	138.1	9.88	14.54	0.24
0.26	−30.94	−30.85	1283.0	0.09807	154.84	409.36	0.8264	1.8770	1.408	0.916	1.274	723	171.9	257.2	10.78	136.7	9.98	14.21	0.26
0.28	−29.14	−29.05	1276.9	0.09135	157.38	410.18	0.8368	1.8726	1.413	0.926	1.277	714	172.0	251.0	10.86	135.5	10.08	13.90	0.28
0.3	−27.44	−27.35	1271.1	0.08550	159.80	410.94	0.8466	1.8685	1.417	0.936	1.281	705	172.0	245.2	10.93	134.3	10.18	13.60	0.30
0.32	−25.82	−25.73	1265.5	0.08035	162.10	411.65	0.8558	1.8647	1.421	0.946	1.285	697	172.0	239.8	11.00	133.10	10.27	13.33	0.32
0.34	−24.28	−24.19	1260.2	0.07579	164.29	412.32	0.8646	1.8611	1.426	0.956	1.288	689	172.1	234.9	11.07	132.10	10.36	13.06	0.34
0.36	−22.81	−22.72	1255.0	0.07172	166.40	412.95	0.8703	1.8577	1.430	0.965	1.292	682	172.1	230.3	11.13	131.00	10.46	12.81	0.36
0.38	−21.40	−21.31	1250.1	0.06806	168.43	413.54	0.8810	1.8545	1.434	0.975	1.295	675	172.0	226.0	11.19	130.10	10.55	12.57	0.38
0.4	−20.04	−19.95	1245.3	0.06476	170.38	414.10	0.8887	1.8514	1.438	0.983	1.299	668	172.0	221.9	11.25	129.10	10.64	12.35	0.40
0.42	−18.74	−18.65	1240.6	0.06176	172.26	414.64	0.8960	1.8486	1.443	0.992	1.303	661	172.0	218.1	11.31	128.20	10.73	12.13	0.42
0.44	−17.48	−17.39	1236.1	0.05902	174.08	415.14	0.9031	1.8458	1.447	1.001	1.306	655	171.9	214.5	11.36	127.30	10.82	11.92	0.44
0.46	−16.27	−16.18	1231.8	0.05652	175.84	415.63	0.9099	1.8432	1.451	1.009	1.310	649	171.8	211.1	11.42	126.50	10.91	11.71	0.46
0.48	−15.10	−15.00	1227.5	0.05421	177.55	416.09	0.9165	1.8407	1.455	1.017	1.313	643	171.8	207.8	11.47	125.70	10.99	11.52	0.48
0.5	−13.96	−13.86	1223.3	0.05209	179.21	416.53	0.9228	1.8383	1.459	1.025	1.317	637	171.7	204.7	11.52	124.90	11.08	11.33	0.50
0.55	−11.26	−11.16	1213.4	0.04743	183.17	417.54	0.9379	1.8326	1.469	1.045	1.326	623	171.4	197.6	11.64	123.10	11.28	10.89	0.55
0.6	−8.74	−8.64	1203.9	0.04352	186.89	418.46	0.9518	1.8275	1.479	1.064	1.335	610	171.2	191.2	11.75	121.40	11.48	10.47	0.60
0.65	−6.38	−6.28	1194.9	0.04019	190.40	419.28	0.9649	1.8227	1.489	1.083	1.344	597	170.9	185.3	11.86	119.70	11.68	10.09	0.65
0.7	−4.15	−4.05	1186.3	0.03732	193.74	420.03	0.9772	1.8183	1.499	1.101	1.354	586	170.5	180.0	11.96	118.20	11.88	9.73	0.70
0.75	−2.04	−1.93	1178.1	0.03482	196.92	420.71	0.9888	1.8141	1.509	1.119	1.363	574	170.2	175.1	12.06	116.80	12.07	9.39	0.75
0.8	−0.03	0.08	1170.1	0.03262	199.96	421.33	0.9998	1.8102	1.519	1.136	1.373	564	169.8	170.6	12.15	115.50	12.26	9.07	0.80
0.85	1.89	1.99	1162.4	0.03068	202.88	421.89	1.0103	1.8065	1.529	1.154	1.382	554	169.4	166.4	12.24	114.20	12.45	8.77	0.85
0.9	3.72	3.83	1154.9	0.02894	205.69	422.41	1.0204	1.8030	1.540	1.171	1.392	544	169.0	162.4	12.33	113.00	12.64	8.48	0.90
0.95	5.48	5.58	1147.6	0.02738	208.40	422.88	1.0300	1.7996	1.550	1.188	1.402	535	168.6	158.7	12.41	111.80	12.82	8.21	0.95
1.0	7.17	7.27	1140.5	0.02596	211.02	423.31	1.0392	1.7964	1.560	1.205	1.413	525	168.1	155.3	12.49	110.70	13.01	7.95	1.00
1.1	10.36	10.47	1126.8	0.02351	216.03	424.07	1.0567	1.7903	1.581	1.239	1.434	508	167.2	148.8	12.65	108.60	13.39	7.46	1.10
1.2	13.34	13.46	1113.7	0.02145	220.76	424.68	1.0730	1.7846	1.603	1.274	1.457	492	166.3	143.1	12.81	106.70	13.79	7.01	1.20
1.3	16.15	16.26	1101.0	0.01970	225.26	425.19	1.0883	1.7792	1.624	1.31	1.481	477	165.4	137.8	12.95	104.80	14.19	6.59	1.30
1.4	18.79	18.91	1088.8	0.01819	229.56	425.59	1.1027	1.7741	1.647	1.347	1.506	462	164.4	133.0	13.12	103.10	14.60	6.20	1.40
1.5	21.30	21.41	1076.9	0.01687	233.68	425.89	1.1165	1.7691	1.670	1.385	1.532	448	163.4	128.5	13.23	101.50	15.03	5.83	1.50
1.6	23.68	23.80	1065.2	0.01571	237.65	426.11	1.1296	1.7644	1.694	1.424	1.560	435	162.4	124.3	13.38	99.98	15.46	5.49	1.60
1.7	25.96	26.07	1053.8	0.01468	241.48	426.25	1.1421	1.7597	1.719	1.465	1.590	422	161.4	120.4	13.52	98.53	15.91	5.16	1.70
1.8	28.13	28.25	1042.6	0.01376	245.19	426.31	1.1542	1.7552	1.745	1.509	1.621	410	160.3	116.8	13.66	97.15	16.38	4.86	1.80
1.9	30.22	30.34	1031.6	0.01293	248.79	426.31	1.1657	1.7508	1.772	1.555	1.655	398	159.3	113.3	13.81	95.82	16.86	4.57	1.90
2.0	32.22	32.34	1020.7	0.01218	252.29	426.24	1.1769	1.7464	1.800	1.603	1.690	386	158.2	110.1	13.95	94.56	17.36	4.29	2.00
2.1	34.16	34.28	1009.9	0.0115	255.71	426.10	1.1878	1.7421	1.830	1.655	1.728	375	157.1	107.0	14.10	93.34	17.88	4.03	2.10
2.2	36.02	36.14	999.2	0.01088	259.05	425.90	1.1983	1.7379	1.861	1.709	1.769	364	156.0	104.0	14.25	92.17	18.42	3.78	2.20
2.3	37.82	37.94	988.6	0.01031	262.32	425.64	1.2085	1.7336	1.894	1.768	1.813	353	154.9	101.2	14.40	91.05	18.99	3.54	2.30
2.4	39.56	39.68	978.0	0.00978	265.52	425.33	1.2185	1.7294	1.929	1.831	1.860	343	153.8	98.5	14.55	89.96	19.58	3.31	2.40
2.5	41.25	41.37	967.5	0.00929	268.67	424.95	1.2282	1.7251	1.967	1.898	1.911	332	152.6	95.9	14.71	88.91	20.21	3.10	2.50
2.6	42.89	43.00	957.0	0.00883	271.77	424.51	1.2377	1.7209	2.008	1.971	1.966	322	151.5	93.4	14.87	87.89	20.87	2.89	2.60
2.7	44.48	44.59	946.4	0.00841	274.82	424.02	1.2470	1.7166	2.052	2.050	2.026	313	150.3	91.0	15.03	86.91	21.56	2.69	2.70
2.8	46.02	46.14	935.8	0.00802	277.84	423.47	1.2561	1.7123	2.100	2.136	2.091	303	149.1	88.6	15.21	85.96	22.29	2.50	2.80
2.9	47.53	47.64	925.2	0.00764	280.82	422.85	1.2651	1.7079	2.153	2.230	2.163	293	147.9	86.3	15.38	85.04	23.07	2.31	2.90
3.0	48.99	49.10	914.5	0.00729	283.78	422.18	1.2740	1.7035	2.211	2.333	2.243	284	146.7	84.1	15.57	84.14	23.89	2.14	3.00
3.2	51.81	51.91	892.6	0.00665	289.62	420.62	1.2913	1.6944	2.348	2.575	2.429	265	144.2	79.9	15.96	82.42	25.70	1.81	3.20
3.4	54.49	54.59	870.0	0.00607	295.43	418.78	1.3085	1.6849	2.522	2.879	2.663	247	141.7	75.7	16.39	80.81	27.77	1.50	3.40
3.6	57.05	57.15	846.3	0.00555	301.26	416.60	1.3254	1.6747	2.752	3.276	2.970	229	139.0	71.7	16.87	79.29	30.17	1.22	3.60
3.8	59.50	59.59	821.0	0.00506	307.16	414.03	1.3425	1.6638	3.070	3.815	3.386	210	136.3	67.7	17.43	77.90	33.02	0.97	3.80
4.0	61.85	61.93	793.5	0.00460	313.24	410.97	1.3600	1.6517	3.541	4.596	3.987	192	133.4	63.7	18.08	76.68	36.48	0.74	4.00
4.2	64.10	64.17	762.6	0.00417	319.65	407.24	1.3783	1.6380	4.306	5.826	4.929	173	130.4	59.4	18.87	75.77	40.86	0.53	4.20
4.903[c]	71.36	71.36	459.5	0.00218	368.55	368.55	1.5181	1.5181	—	—	—	—	—	—	—	—	—	0.00	4.903

*Temperatures on ITS-90 scale

[b]Bubble and dew points at one standard atmosphere

[c]Critical point

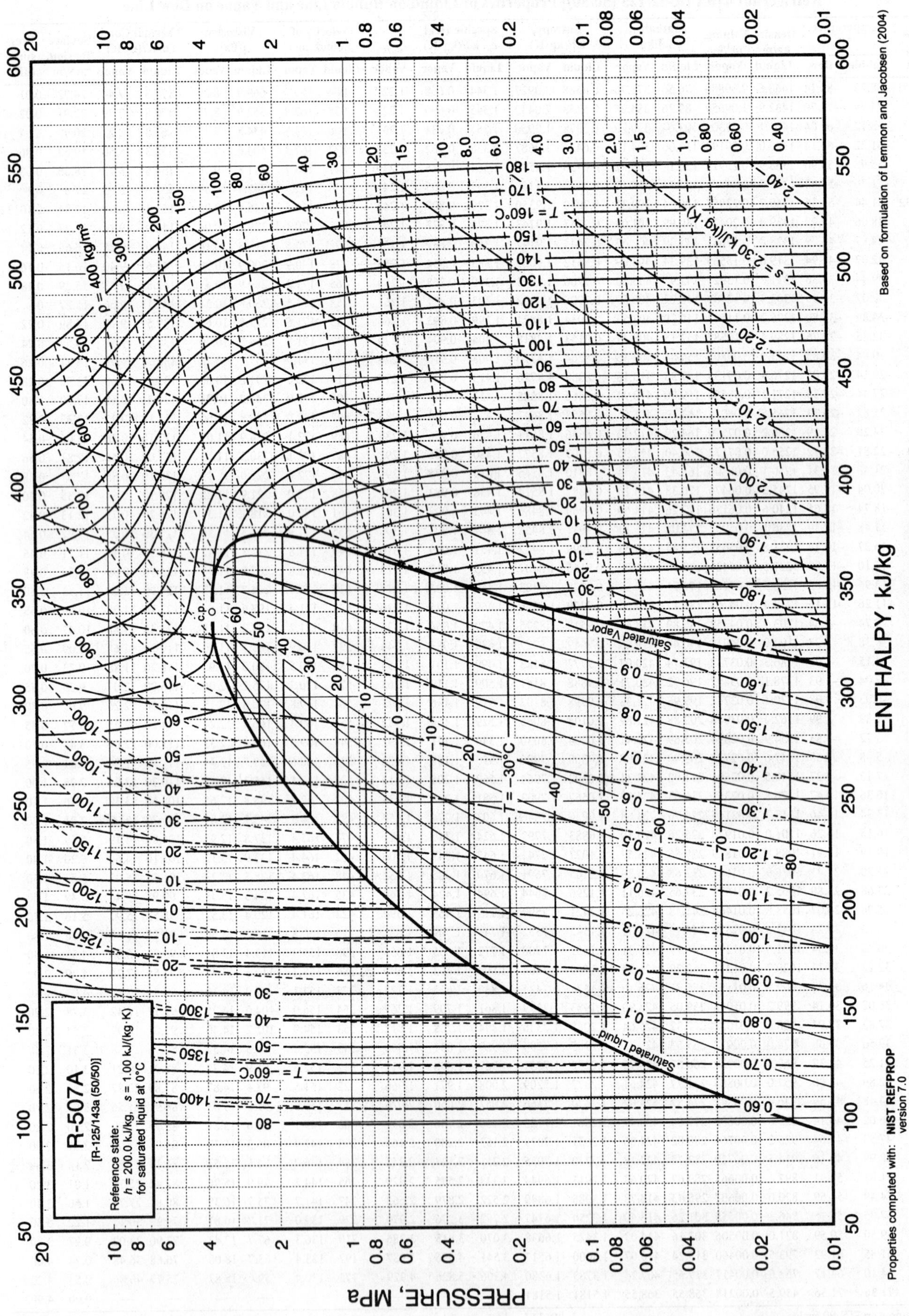

Fig. 15 Pressure-Enthalpy Diagram for Refrigerant 507A

Refrigerant 507A [R-125/143[a] (50/50)] Properties of Saturated Liquid and Saturated Vapor

Temp.,* °C	Pressure,** MPa	Density, kg/m³ Liquid	Volume, m³/kg Vapor	Enthalpy, kJ/kg Liquid	Enthalpy, kJ/kg Vapor	Entropy, kJ/(kg·K) Liquid	Entropy, kJ/(kg·K) Vapor	Specific Heat c_p, kJ/(kg·K) Liquid	Specific Heat c_p, kJ/(kg·K) Vapor	c_p/c_v Vapor	Velocity of Sound, m/s Liquid	Velocity of Sound, m/s Vapor	Viscosity, μPa·s Liquid	Viscosity, μPa·s Vapor	Thermal Cond., mW/(m·K) Liquid	Thermal Cond., mW/(m·K) Vapor	Surface Tension, mN/m	Temp.,* °C
–100	0.00295	1476.9	4.92920	74.41	303.90	0.4323	1.7579	1.219	0.618	1.164	1046	129.6	—	—	124.6	5.77	18.35	–100
–95	0.00458	1461.7	3.25360	80.48	306.85	0.4669	1.7377	1.210	0.631	1.162	1000	131.2	784.2	7.29	121.7	6.06	17.88	–95
–90	0.00693	1446.8	2.20850	86.51	309.83	0.5003	1.7197	1.205	0.644	1.161	960	132.6	701.5	7.49	118.8	6.36	17.41	–90
–85	0.01019	1431.9	1.53750	92.53	312.83	0.5327	1.7036	1.203	0.658	1.159	925	134.0	631.9	7.68	116.1	6.67	16.92	–85
–80	0.01464	1417.1	1.09510	98.54	315.85	0.5642	1.6893	1.203	0.672	1.159	892	135.4	572.7	7.88	113.4	6.99	16.43	–80
–75	0.02058	1402.3	0.79638	104.57	318.88	0.5950	1.6766	1.205	0.686	1.158	862	136.6	521.7	8.07	110.8	7.31	15.92	–75
–70	0.02836	1387.4	0.59012	110.60	321.92	0.6250	1.6652	1.208	0.701	1.158	833	137.8	477.4	8.27	108.2	7.63	15.40	–70
–65	0.03837	1372.5	0.44482	116.66	324.96	0.6545	1.6552	1.213	0.716	1.159	806	138.9	438.5	8.46	105.7	7.96	14.88	–65
–60	0.05105	1357.4	0.34056	122.74	328.00	0.6833	1.6463	1.220	0.732	1.160	779	139.8	404.3	8.65	103.2	8.30	14.34	–60
–55	0.06688	1342.3	0.26444	128.87	331.03	0.7116	1.6384	1.227	0.749	1.161	754	140.7	373.8	8.84	100.8	8.65	13.80	–55
–50	0.08638	1326.9	0.20801	135.03	334.05	0.7395	1.6314	1.235	0.766	1.164	729	141.4	346.5	9.02	98.4	9.00	13.24	–50
–48	0.09533	1320.7	0.18960	137.51	335.25	0.7505	1.6288	1.239	0.773	1.165	719	141.6	336.4	9.10	97.4	9.14	13.02	–48
–46.74[b]	0.10132	1316.8	0.17902	139.07	336.01	0.7574	1.6273	1.241	0.777	1.166	713	141.8	330.2	9.15	96.8	9.23	12.88	–46.74
–46	0.10499	1314.5	0.17313	139.99	336.45	0.7615	1.6264	1.243	0.780	1.166	709	141.9	326.7	9.17	96.5	9.28	12.80	–46
–44	0.11541	1308.2	0.15836	142.48	337.65	0.7724	1.6241	1.247	0.787	1.167	699	142.1	317.4	9.25	95.5	9.42	12.57	–44
–42	0.12662	1301.9	0.14510	144.99	338.84	0.7832	1.6219	1.251	0.795	1.169	690	142.3	308.4	9.32	94.6	9.57	12.34	–42
–40	0.13867	1295.6	0.13317	147.49	340.03	0.7940	1.6198	1.255	0.803	1.170	680	142.5	299.8	9.40	93.7	9.71	12.12	–40
–38	0.15159	1289.2	0.12240	150.01	341.21	0.8047	1.6178	1.259	0.810	1.172	670	142.6	291.4	9.47	92.7	9.86	11.89	–38
–36	0.16542	1282.8	0.11268	152.54	342.38	0.8153	1.6159	1.264	0.818	1.174	661	142.7	283.4	9.55	91.8	10.01	11.66	–36
–34	0.18022	1276.3	0.10388	155.08	343.55	0.8260	1.6141	1.269	0.826	1.176	651	142.8	275.7	9.62	90.9	10.16	11.42	–34
–32	0.19602	1269.7	0.09590	157.63	344.72	0.8365	1.6123	1.274	0.835	1.178	642	142.9	268.3	9.70	90.0	10.31	11.19	–32
–30	0.21287	1263.2	0.08865	160.18	345.88	0.8470	1.6107	1.279	0.843	1.180	632	142.9	261.1	9.77	89.1	10.46	10.96	–30
–28	0.23081	1256.5	0.08205	162.75	347.03	0.8575	1.6092	1.284	0.852	1.183	622	143.0	254.1	9.85	88.2	10.61	10.72	–28
–26	0.24989	1249.8	0.07604	165.33	348.17	0.8679	1.6077	1.289	0.861	1.186	613	143.0	247.4	9.93	87.3	10.77	10.49	–26
–24	0.27016	1243.1	0.07055	167.92	349.30	0.8783	1.6063	1.295	0.870	1.188	603	142.9	240.9	10.00	86.5	10.93	10.25	–24
–22	0.29167	1236.3	0.06553	170.52	350.43	0.8886	1.6049	1.301	0.879	1.191	594	142.9	234.5	10.08	85.6	11.08	10.02	–22
–20	0.31446	1229.4	0.06094	173.13	351.54	0.8989	1.6037	1.307	0.888	1.195	584	142.8	228.4	10.15	84.7	11.24	9.78	–20
–18	0.33858	1222.5	0.05673	175.76	352.65	0.9091	1.6024	1.313	0.898	1.198	575	142.7	222.5	10.23	83.8	11.40	9.54	–18
–16	0.36408	1215.4	0.05286	178.39	353.75	0.9193	1.6013	1.319	0.908	1.202	566	142.5	216.8	10.31	83.0	11.56	9.30	–16
–14	0.39102	1208.4	0.04931	181.04	354.83	0.9295	1.6001	1.326	0.918	1.206	556	142.3	211.2	10.39	82.1	11.73	9.06	–14
–12	0.41945	1201.2	0.04603	183.71	355.91	0.9397	1.5991	1.333	0.929	1.210	547	142.1	205.7	10.47	81.2	11.89	8.82	–12
–10	0.44941	1193.9	0.04301	186.39	356.97	0.9498	1.5980	1.340	0.940	1.214	537	141.9	200.5	10.55	80.4	12.06	8.58	–10
–8	0.48096	1186.6	0.04023	189.08	358.02	0.9599	1.5971	1.348	0.951	1.219	528	141.6	195.3	10.63	79.5	12.23	8.34	–8
–6	0.51416	1179.2	0.03765	191.78	359.06	0.9699	1.5961	1.355	0.962	1.224	518	141.3	190.3	10.71	78.7	12.41	8.10	–6
–4	0.54906	1171.7	0.03527	194.51	360.08	0.9800	1.5952	1.363	0.974	1.230	508	141.0	185.5	10.79	77.8	12.58	7.86	–4
–2	0.58571	1164.0	0.03306	197.25	361.08	0.9900	1.5943	1.372	0.987	1.236	499	140.6	180.7	10.88	77.0	12.76	7.62	–2
0	0.62417	1156.3	0.03101	200.00	362.07	1.0000	1.5934	1.381	0.999	1.242	489	140.2	176.1	10.97	76.2	12.96	7.37	0
2	0.66450	1148.5	0.02910	202.77	363.05	1.0100	1.5925	1.390	1.012	1.249	480	139.8	171.6	11.05	75.3	13.16	7.13	2
4	0.70676	1140.5	0.02733	205.56	364.00	1.0199	1.5917	1.399	1.026	1.256	470	139.3	167.2	11.14	74.5	13.36	6.89	4
6	0.75099	1132.4	0.02568	208.37	364.94	1.0299	1.5908	1.410	1.040	1.264	460	138.8	162.9	11.23	73.7	13.57	6.65	6
8	0.79728	1124.2	0.02415	211.20	365.85	1.0398	1.5900	1.420	1.055	1.272	451	138.2	158.7	11.33	72.8	13.79	6.41	8
10	0.84566	1115.9	0.02271	214.04	366.75	1.0498	1.5891	1.431	1.071	1.282	441	137.6	154.5	11.43	72.0	14.01	6.17	10
12	0.89622	1107.4	0.02138	216.91	367.61	1.0597	1.5883	1.443	1.088	1.291	431	137.0	150.5	11.52	71.2	14.24	5.93	12
14	0.94900	1098.7	0.02012	219.80	368.46	1.0696	1.5874	1.455	1.105	1.302	422	136.3	146.6	11.63	70.4	14.49	5.69	14
16	1.00410	1089.9	0.01895	222.71	369.28	1.0796	1.5865	1.468	1.124	1.314	412	135.6	142.7	11.73	69.6	14.75	5.45	16
18	1.06150	1080.9	0.01785	225.65	370.07	1.0895	1.5856	1.482	1.144	1.327	402	134.9	138.9	11.86	68.8	15.01	5.21	18
20	1.12140	1071.7	0.01683	228.61	370.83	1.0995	1.5846	1.497	1.165	1.341	392	134.1	135.1	11.97	67.9	15.29	4.97	20
22	1.18370	1062.4	0.01586	231.60	371.55	1.1094	1.5836	1.513	1.188	1.356	382	133.2	131.5	12.09	67.1	15.58	4.74	22
24	1.24860	1052.8	0.01495	234.61	372.25	1.1194	1.5826	1.530	1.212	1.372	372	132.3	127.9	12.22	66.3	15.89	4.50	24
26	1.31610	1043.0	0.01410	237.66	372.91	1.1294	1.5815	1.548	1.239	1.391	362	131.4	124.3	12.35	65.5	16.21	4.27	26
28	1.38640	1032.9	0.01329	240.73	373.52	1.1394	1.5804	1.568	1.268	1.411	352	130.4	120.8	12.48	64.7	16.54	4.04	28
30	1.45940	1022.6	0.01253	243.84	374.10	1.1495	1.5792	1.589	1.299	1.433	341	129.3	117.4	12.62	63.9	16.90	3.81	30
32	1.53520	1011.9	0.01182	246.98	374.63	1.1595	1.5779	1.612	1.333	1.458	331	128.2	114.0	12.77	63.1	17.28	3.58	32
34	1.61400	1001.0	0.01114	250.16	375.11	1.1697	1.5765	1.637	1.371	1.485	321	127.1	110.6	12.93	62.2	17.68	3.35	34
36	1.69580	989.7	0.01050	253.39	375.54	1.1799	1.5750	1.664	1.413	1.516	310	125.9	107.3	13.10	61.4	18.12	3.12	36
38	1.78070	978.1	0.00989	256.65	375.91	1.1901	1.5734	1.695	1.459	1.551	300	124.6	104.0	13.28	60.6	18.58	2.90	38
40	1.86880	966.0	0.00932	259.96	376.22	1.2004	1.5717	1.729	1.511	1.591	289	123.2	100.7	13.47	59.8	19.09	2.68	40
42	1.96020	953.5	0.00877	263.33	376.46	1.2108	1.5698	1.767	1.570	1.636	278	121.8	97.5	13.68	59.0	19.63	2.47	42
44	2.05490	940.5	0.00825	266.74	376.61	1.2213	1.5678	1.811	1.638	1.689	267	120.4	94.3	13.90	58.1	20.23	2.25	44
46	2.15310	926.9	0.00776	270.23	376.68	1.2320	1.5655	1.860	1.716	1.750	256	118.8	91.0	14.14	57.3	20.89	2.04	46
48	2.25480	912.7	0.00728	273.78	376.66	1.2427	1.5631	1.918	1.807	1.823	245	117.2	87.8	14.41	56.5	21.62	1.83	48
50	2.36030	897.7	0.00683	277.41	376.52	1.2536	1.5603	1.985	1.915	1.910	233	115.5	84.6	14.70	55.7	22.43	1.63	50
55	2.64090	856.2	0.00578	286.91	375.54	1.2818	1.5519	2.225	2.304	2.228	203	110.8	76.4	15.59	53.6	24.98	1.15	55
60	2.94760	806.1	0.00480	297.28	373.26	1.3120	1.5401	2.677	3.060	2.855	171	105.5	67.7	16.86	51.7	28.77	0.70	60
65	3.28380	739.1	0.00384	309.30	368.44	1.3465	1.5215	3.940	5.190	4.625	135	99.3	57.9	18.93	50.7	35.54	0.31	65
70	3.65570	599.6	0.00260	328.32	353.47	1.4007	1.4740	31.960	44.630	36.780	92	90.7	42.0	25.07	63.2	67.27	0.02	70
70.62[c]	3.70500	490.8	0.00204	340.45	340.45	1.4358	1.4358	∞	∞	∞	0	0.0	—	—	—	—	0.00	70.62

*Temperatures on ITS-90 scale

**Small deviations from azeotropic behavior occur at some conditions; tabulated pressures are average of bubble and dew-point pressures

[b]Normal boiling point

[c]Critical point

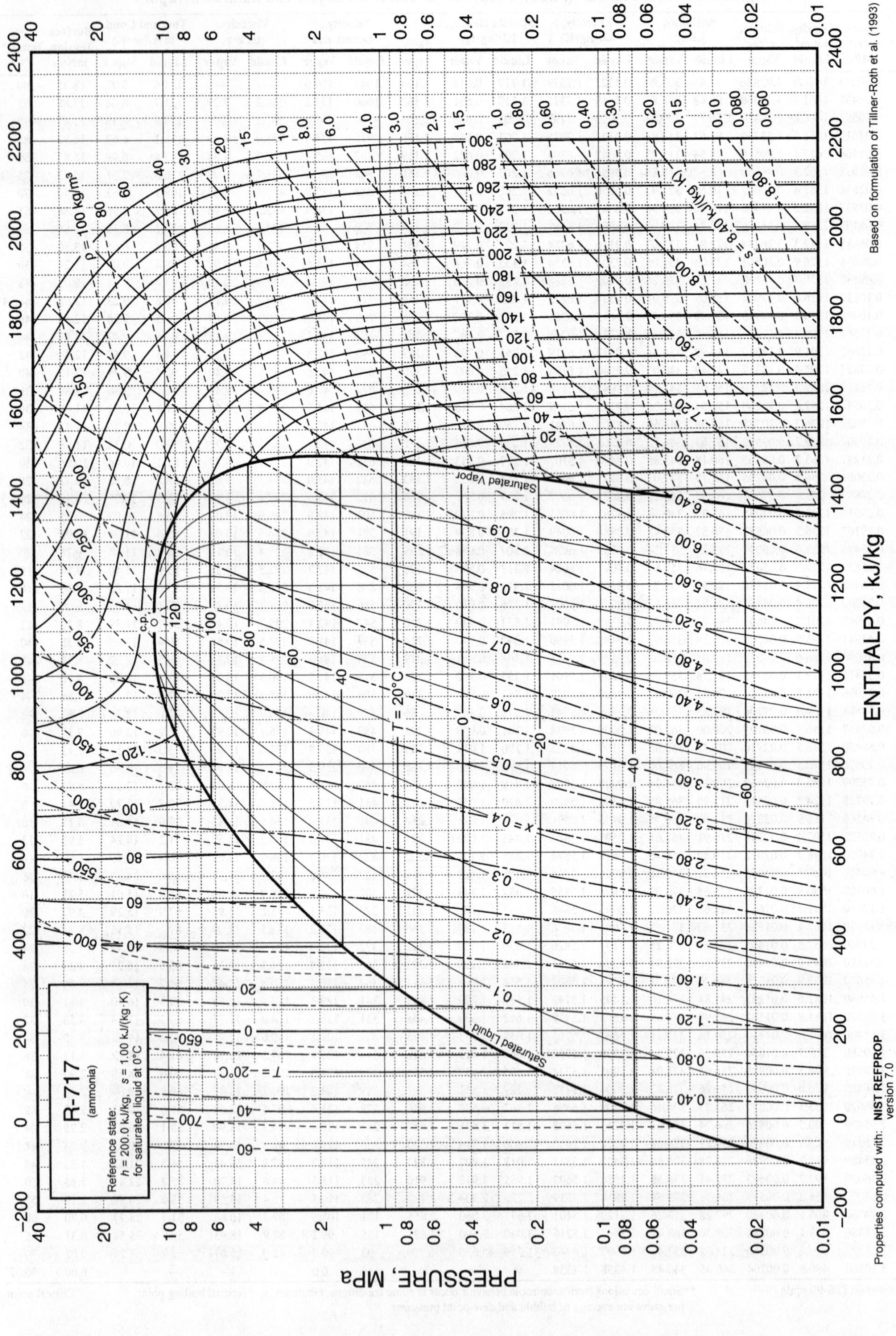

Fig. 16 Pressure-Enthalpy Diagram for Refrigerant 717 (Ammonia)

Refrigerant 717 (Ammonia) Properties of Saturated Liquid and Saturated Vapor

Temp.,* °C	Pressure, MPa	Density, kg/m³ Liquid	Volume, m³/kg Vapor	Enthalpy, kJ/kg Liquid	Enthalpy, kJ/kg Vapor	Entropy, kJ/(kg·K) Liquid	Entropy, kJ/(kg·K) Vapor	Specific Heat c_p, kJ/(kg·K) Liquid	Specific Heat c_p, kJ/(kg·K) Vapor	c_p/c_v Vapor	Velocity of Sound, m/s Liquid	Velocity of Sound, m/s Vapor	Viscosity, µPa·s Liquid	Viscosity, µPa·s Vapor	Thermal Cond., mW/(m·K) Liquid	Thermal Cond., mW/(m·K) Vapor	Surface Tension, mN/m	Temp.,* °C
–77.65[a]	0.00609	732.9	15.602	–143.15	1341.23	–0.4716	7.1213	4.202	2.063	1.325	2124	354.1	559.6	6.84	819.0	19.64	62.26	–77.65
–70	0.01094	724.7	9.0079	–110.81	1355.55	–0.3094	6.9088	4.245	2.086	1.327	2051	360.5	475.0	7.03	792.1	19.73	59.10	–70
–60	0.02189	713.6	4.7057	–68.06	1373.73	–0.1040	6.6602	4.303	2.125	1.330	1967	368.4	391.3	7.30	757.0	19.93	55.05	–60
–50	0.04084	702.1	2.6277	–24.73	1391.19	0.0945	6.4396	4.360	2.178	1.335	1890	375.6	328.9	7.57	722.3	20.24	51.11	–50
–40	0.07169	690.2	1.5533	19.17	1407.76	0.2867	6.2425	4.414	2.244	1.342	1816	382.2	281.2	7.86	688.1	20.64	47.26	–40
–38	0.07971	687.7	1.4068	28.01	1410.96	0.3245	6.2056	4.424	2.259	1.343	1802	383.4	273.1	7.92	681.4	20.73	46.51	–38
–36	0.08845	685.3	1.2765	36.88	1414.11	0.3619	6.1694	4.434	2.275	1.345	1787	384.6	265.3	7.98	674.6	20.83	45.75	–36
–34	0.09795	682.8	1.1604	45.77	1417.23	0.3992	6.1339	4.444	2.291	1.347	1773	385.8	257.9	8.03	667.9	20.93	45.00	–34
–33.33[b]	0.10133	682.0	1.1242	48.76	1418.26	0.4117	6.1221	4.448	2.297	1.348	1768	386.2	255.5	8.05	665.7	20.97	44.75	–33.33
–32	0.10826	680.3	1.0567	54.67	1420.29	0.4362	6.0992	4.455	2.308	1.349	1759	387.0	250.8	8.09	661.3	21.04	44.26	–32
–30	0.11943	677.8	0.96396	63.60	1423.31	0.4730	6.0651	4.465	2.326	1.351	1744	388.1	244.1	8.15	654.6	21.15	43.52	–30
–28	0.13151	675.3	0.88082	72.55	1426.28	0.5096	6.0317	4.474	2.344	1.353	1730	389.2	237.6	8.21	648.0	21.26	42.78	–28
–26	0.14457	672.8	0.80614	81.52	1429.21	0.5460	5.9989	4.484	2.363	1.355	1716	390.2	231.4	8.27	641.5	21.38	42.05	–26
–24	0.15864	670.3	0.73896	90.51	1432.08	0.5821	5.9667	4.494	2.383	1.358	1702	391.2	225.5	8.33	634.9	21.51	41.32	–24
–22	0.17379	667.7	0.67840	99.52	1434.91	0.6180	5.9351	4.504	2.403	1.360	1687	392.2	219.8	8.39	628.4	21.63	40.60	–22
–20	0.19008	665.1	0.62373	108.55	1437.68	0.6538	5.9041	4.514	2.425	1.363	1673	393.2	214.4	8.45	622.0	21.77	39.88	–20
–18	0.20756	662.6	0.57428	117.60	1440.39	0.6893	5.8736	4.524	2.446	1.365	1659	394.1	209.2	8.51	615.5	21.90	39.16	–18
–16	0.22630	660.0	0.52949	126.67	1443.06	0.7246	5.8437	4.534	2.469	1.368	1645	395.0	204.2	8.57	609.1	22.05	38.45	–16
–14	0.24637	657.3	0.48885	135.76	1445.66	0.7597	5.8143	4.543	2.493	1.371	1631	395.8	199.3	8.63	602.8	22.19	37.74	–14
–12	0.26782	654.7	0.45192	144.88	1448.21	0.7946	5.7853	4.553	2.517	1.375	1616	396.7	194.7	8.69	596.4	22.35	37.04	–12
–10	0.29071	652.1	0.41830	154.01	1450.70	0.8293	5.7569	4.564	2.542	1.378	1602	397.5	190.2	8.75	590.1	22.50	36.34	–10
–8	0.31513	649.4	0.38767	163.16	1453.14	0.8638	5.7289	4.574	2.568	1.382	1588	398.2	185.9	8.81	583.9	22.67	35.65	–8
–6	0.34114	646.7	0.35970	172.34	1455.51	0.8981	5.7013	4.584	2.594	1.385	1574	398.9	181.7	8.87	577.7	22.83	34.96	–6
–4	0.36880	644.0	0.33414	181.54	1457.81	0.9323	5.6741	4.595	2.622	1.389	1559	399.6	177.7	8.93	571.5	23.00	34.27	–4
–2	0.39819	641.3	0.31074	190.76	1460.06	0.9662	5.6474	4.606	2.651	1.393	1545	400.2	173.8	8.99	565.3	23.18	33.59	–2
0	0.42938	638.6	0.28930	200.00	1462.24	1.0000	5.6210	4.617	2.680	1.398	1531	400.8	170.1	9.06	559.2	23.37	32.91	0
2	0.46246	635.8	0.26962	209.27	1464.35	1.0336	5.5951	4.628	2.710	1.402	1516	401.4	166.5	9.12	553.1	23.55	32.24	2
4	0.49748	633.1	0.25153	218.55	1466.40	1.0670	5.5695	4.639	2.742	1.407	1502	401.9	162.9	9.18	547.1	23.75	31.57	4
6	0.53453	630.3	0.23489	227.87	1468.37	1.1003	5.5442	4.651	2.774	1.412	1487	402.4	159.5	9.24	541.1	23.95	30.91	6
8	0.57370	627.5	0.21956	237.20	1470.28	1.1334	5.5192	4.663	2.807	1.417	1473	402.8	156.2	9.30	535.1	24.15	30.24	8
10	0.61505	624.6	0.20543	246.57	1472.11	1.1664	5.4946	4.676	2.841	1.422	1458	403.2	153.0	9.36	529.1	24.37	29.59	10
12	0.65866	621.8	0.19237	255.95	1473.88	1.1992	5.4703	4.689	2.877	1.428	1443	403.6	149.9	9.43	523.2	24.58	28.94	12
14	0.70463	618.9	0.18031	265.37	1475.56	1.2318	5.4463	4.702	2.913	1.434	1429	403.9	146.9	9.49	517.3	24.81	28.29	14
16	0.75303	616.0	0.16914	274.81	1477.17	1.2643	5.4226	4.716	2.951	1.440	1414	404.2	144.0	9.55	511.5	25.04	27.65	16
18	0.80395	613.1	0.15879	284.28	1478.70	1.2967	5.3991	4.730	2.990	1.446	1399	404.4	141.1	9.61	505.6	25.27	27.01	18
20	0.85748	610.2	0.14920	293.78	1480.16	1.3289	5.3759	4.745	3.030	1.453	1384	404.6	138.3	9.68	499.9	25.52	26.38	20
22	0.91369	607.2	0.14029	303.31	1481.53	1.3610	5.3529	4.760	3.071	1.460	1370	404.8	135.6	9.74	494.1	25.77	25.75	22
24	0.97268	604.3	0.13201	312.87	1482.82	1.3929	5.3301	4.776	3.113	1.468	1355	404.9	133.0	9.80	488.4	26.03	25.12	24
26	1.03450	601.3	0.12431	322.47	1484.02	1.4248	5.3076	4.793	3.158	1.475	1340	404.9	130.4	9.87	482.7	26.29	24.50	26
28	1.09930	598.2	0.11714	332.09	1485.14	1.4565	5.2853	4.810	3.203	1.484	1324	405.0	127.9	9.93	477.0	26.57	23.89	28
30	1.16720	595.2	0.11046	341.76	1486.17	1.4881	5.2631	4.828	3.250	1.492	1309	404.9	125.5	10.00	471.4	26.85	23.28	30
32	1.23820	592.1	0.10422	351.45	1487.11	1.5196	5.2412	4.847	3.299	1.501	1294	404.8	123.1	10.06	465.7	27.14	22.67	32
34	1.31240	589.0	0.09840	361.19	1487.95	1.5509	5.2194	4.867	3.349	1.510	1279	404.7	120.7	10.13	460.1	27.43	22.07	34
36	1.39000	585.8	0.09296	370.96	1488.70	1.5822	5.1978	4.888	3.401	1.520	1263	404.5	118.4	10.19	454.6	27.74	21.47	36
38	1.47090	582.6	0.08787	380.78	1489.36	1.6134	5.1763	4.909	3.455	1.530	1248	404.3	116.2	10.26	449.1	28.05	20.88	38
40	1.55540	579.4	0.08310	390.64	1489.91	1.6446	5.1549	4.932	3.510	1.541	1232	404.0	114.0	10.33	443.5	28.38	20.29	40
42	1.64350	576.2	0.07863	400.54	1490.36	1.6756	5.1337	4.956	3.568	1.553	1216	403.7	111.9	10.39	438.0	28.71	19.71	42
44	1.73530	572.9	0.07445	410.48	1490.70	1.7065	5.1126	4.981	3.628	1.565	1201	403.3	109.8	10.46	432.6	29.06	19.13	44
46	1.83100	569.6	0.07052	420.48	1490.94	1.7374	5.0915	5.007	3.691	1.577	1185	402.9	107.8	10.53	427.1	29.41	18.56	46
48	1.93050	566.3	0.06682	430.52	1491.06	1.7683	5.0706	5.034	3.756	1.591	1169	402.4	105.8	10.60	421.7	29.78	17.99	48
50	2.03400	562.9	0.06335	440.62	1491.07	1.7990	5.0497	5.064	3.823	1.605	1153	401.9	103.8	10.67	416.3	30.16	17.43	50
55	2.31110	554.2	0.05554	466.10	1490.57	1.8758	4.9977	5.143	4.005	1.643	1112	400.3	99.0	10.86	402.9	31.16	16.04	55
60	2.61560	545.2	0.04880	491.97	1489.27	1.9523	4.9458	5.235	4.208	1.687	1070	398.3	94.5	11.05	389.6	32.26	14.69	60
65	2.94910	536.0	0.04296	518.26	1487.09	2.0288	4.8939	5.341	4.438	1.739	1028	396.0	90.1	11.25	376.4	33.47	13.37	65
70	3.31350	526.3	0.03787	545.04	1483.94	2.1054	4.8415	5.465	4.699	1.799	984	393.3	85.9	11.47	363.2	34.80	12.08	70
75	3.71050	516.2	0.03342	572.37	1479.72	2.1823	4.7885	5.610	5.001	1.870	940	390.1	81.9	11.70	350.2	36.30	10.83	75
80	4.14200	505.7	0.02951	600.34	1474.31	2.2596	4.7344	5.784	5.355	1.955	895	386.5	78.0	11.95	337.1	38.00	9.61	80
85	4.61000	494.5	0.02606	629.04	1467.53	2.3377	4.6789	5.993	5.777	2.058	848	382.5	74.2	12.23	324.1	39.95	8.44	85
90	5.11670	482.8	0.02300	658.61	1459.19	2.4168	4.6213	6.250	6.291	2.187	800	377.9	70.5	12.55	311.0	42.24	7.30	90
95	5.66430	470.2	0.02027	689.19	1449.01	2.4973	4.5612	6.573	6.933	2.349	751	372.7	66.8	12.91	297.9	44.99	6.20	95
100	6.25530	456.6	0.01782	721.00	1436.63	2.5797	4.4975	6.991	7.762	2.562	701	367.0	63.2	13.32	284.8	48.36	5.15	100
105	6.89230	441.9	0.01561	754.35	1421.57	2.6647	4.4291	7.555	8.877	2.851	649	360.5	59.6	13.82	271.5	52.65	4.15	105
110	7.57830	425.6	0.01360	789.68	1403.08	2.7533	4.3542	8.360	10.46	3.26	594	353.3	56.0	14.42	258.1	58.33	3.20	110
115	8.31700	407.2	0.01174	827.74	1379.99	2.8474	4.2702	9.630	12.91	3.91	538	345.0	52.3	15.19	244.6	66.28	2.31	115
120	9.11250	385.5	0.00999	869.92	1350.23	2.9502	4.1719	11.940	17.21	5.04	477	335.4	48.3	16.21	231.2	78.40	1.50	120
125	9.97002	357.8	0.00828	919.68	1309.12	3.0702	4.0483	17.660	27.00	7.62	411	323.6	43.8	17.73	219.1	100.01	0.77	125
130	10.89770	312.3	0.00638	992.02	1239.32	3.2437	3.8571	54.210	76.49	20.66	334	306.6	37.3	20.63	221.9	160.39	0.18	130
132.25[c]	11.33300	225.0	0.00444	1119.22	1119.22	3.5542	3.5542	∞	∞	∞	0	0.0	—	—	∞	∞	0.00	132.25

*Temperatures on ITS-90 scale [a]Triple point [b]Normal boiling point [c]Critical point

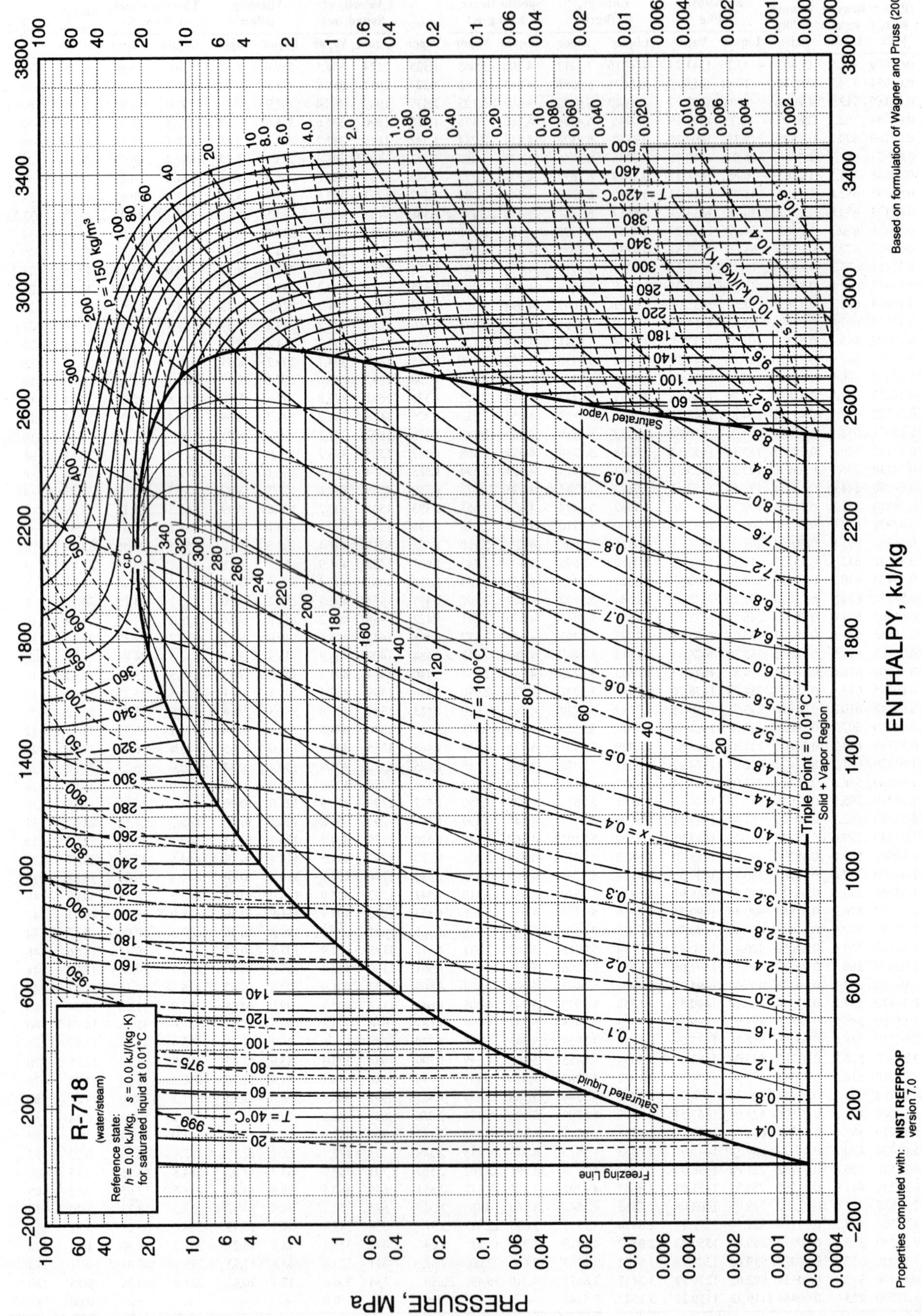

Fig. 17 Pressure-Enthalpy Diagram for Refrigerant 718 (Water/Steam)

Refrigerant 718 (Water/Steam) Properties of Saturated Liquid and Saturated Vapor

Temp.,* °C	Pressure, MPa	Density, kg/m³ Liquid	Volume, m³/kg Vapor	Enthalpy, kJ/kg Liquid	Enthalpy, kJ/kg Vapor	Entropy, kJ/(kg·K) Liquid	Entropy, kJ/(kg·K) Vapor	Specific Heat c_p, kJ/(kg·K) Liquid	Specific Heat c_p, kJ/(kg·K) Vapor	c_p/c_v Vapor	Velocity of Sound, m/s Liquid	Velocity of Sound, m/s Vapor	Viscosity, μPa·s Liquid	Viscosity, μPa·s Vapor	Thermal Cond., mW/(m·K) Liquid	Thermal Cond., mW/(m·K) Vapor	Surface Tension, mN/m	Temp.,* °C
0.01[a]	0.00061	999.8	205.990	0.00	2500.92	0.0000	9.1555	4.220	1.884	1.329	1402	409.0	1791.2	9.22	561.0	17.07	75.65	0.01
5	0.00087	999.9	147.010	21.02	2510.06	0.0763	9.0248	4.205	1.889	1.328	1426	412.6	1518.3	9.34	570.5	17.34	74.94	5
10	0.00123	999.7	106.300	42.02	2519.21	0.1511	8.8998	4.196	1.895	1.328	1447	416.2	1306.0	9.46	580.0	17.62	74.22	10
15	0.00171	999.1	77.8750	62.98	2528.33	0.2245	8.7803	4.189	1.900	1.328	1466	419.7	1137.6	9.59	589.3	17.92	73.49	15
20	0.00234	998.2	57.7570	83.91	2537.43	0.2965	8.6660	4.184	1.906	1.327	1482	423.2	1001.6	9.73	598.4	18.23	72.74	20
25	0.00317	997.0	43.3370	104.83	2546.51	0.3672	8.5566	4.182	1.912	1.327	1497	426.6	890.1	9.87	607.2	18.55	71.97	25
30	0.00425	995.6	32.8780	125.73	2555.55	0.4368	8.4520	4.180	1.918	1.327	1509	430.0	797.4	10.01	615.5	18.89	71.19	30
35	0.00563	994.0	25.2050	146.63	2564.55	0.5051	8.3517	4.180	1.925	1.327	1520	433.4	719.3	10.16	623.3	19.24	70.40	35
40	0.00738	992.2	19.5150	167.53	2573.51	0.5724	8.2555	4.180	1.931	1.327	1529	436.7	653.0	10.31	630.6	19.60	69.60	40
45	0.00959	990.2	15.2520	188.43	2582.43	0.6386	8.1633	4.180	1.939	1.327	1536	440.0	596.1	10.46	637.3	19.97	68.78	45
50	0.01235	988.0	12.0270	209.34	2591.29	0.7038	8.0748	4.182	1.947	1.328	1542	443.2	546.8	10.62	643.6	20.36	67.94	50
55	0.01576	985.7	9.5643	230.26	2600.09	0.7680	7.9898	4.183	1.955	1.328	1547	446.4	504.0	10.77	649.2	20.77	67.10	55
60	0.01995	983.2	7.6672	251.18	2608.83	0.8313	7.9081	4.185	1.965	1.328	1551	449.5	466.4	10.93	654.3	21.19	66.24	60
65	0.02504	980.5	6.1935	272.12	2617.50	0.8937	7.8296	4.187	1.975	1.329	1553	452.6	433.2	11.10	659.0	21.62	65.37	65
70	0.03120	977.7	5.0395	293.07	2626.10	0.9551	7.7540	4.190	1.986	1.330	1555	455.6	403.9	11.26	663.1	22.07	64.48	70
75	0.03860	974.8	4.1289	314.03	2634.60	1.0158	7.6812	4.193	1.999	1.331	1555	458.5	377.7	11.43	666.8	22.53	63.58	75
80	0.04741	971.8	3.4052	335.01	2643.02	1.0756	7.6111	4.197	2.012	1.332	1554	461.4	354.3	11.59	670.0	23.01	62.67	80
85	0.05787	968.6	2.8258	356.01	2651.33	1.1346	7.5434	4.201	2.027	1.333	1553	464.2	333.3	11.76	672.8	23.51	61.75	85
90	0.07018	965.3	2.3591	377.04	2659.53	1.1929	7.4781	4.205	2.043	1.334	1550	466.9	314.4	11.93	675.3	24.02	60.82	90
95	0.08461	961.9	1.9806	398.09	2667.61	1.2504	7.4151	4.210	2.061	1.335	1547	469.6	297.3	12.10	677.3	24.55	59.87	95
99.97[b]	0.10133	958.4	1.6732	419.06	2675.53	1.3069	7.3544	4.216	2.080	1.337	1543	472.2	281.8	12.27	679.1	25.09	58.92	99.97
100	0.10142	958.3	1.6718	419.17	2675.57	1.3072	7.3541	4.216	2.080	1.337	1543	472.2	281.7	12.27	679.1	25.10	58.91	100
105	0.12090	954.7	1.4184	440.27	2683.39	1.3633	7.2952	4.222	2.101	1.339	1538	474.7	267.6	12.44	680.5	25.66	57.94	105
110	0.14338	950.9	1.2093	461.42	2691.06	1.4188	7.2381	4.228	2.124	1.341	1533	477.1	254.7	12.61	681.7	26.24	56.96	110
115	0.16918	947.1	1.0358	482.59	2698.58	1.4737	7.1828	4.236	2.150	1.343	1527	479.5	242.9	12.78	682.6	26.85	55.97	115
120	0.19867	943.1	0.89121	503.81	2705.93	1.5279	7.1291	4.244	2.177	1.346	1520	481.7	232.1	12.96	683.2	27.47	54.97	120
125	0.23224	939.0	0.77003	525.07	2713.10	1.5816	7.0770	4.252	2.207	1.349	1512	483.9	222.1	13.13	683.6	28.11	53.96	125
130	0.27028	934.8	0.66800	546.38	2720.08	1.6346	7.0264	4.261	2.239	1.352	1504	486.0	212.9	13.30	683.7	28.76	52.93	130
135	0.31323	930.5	0.58173	567.74	2726.87	1.6872	6.9772	4.272	2.274	1.355	1496	487.9	204.4	13.47	683.6	29.44	51.90	135
140	0.36154	926.1	0.50845	589.16	2733.44	1.7392	6.9293	4.283	2.311	1.359	1486	489.8	196.5	13.65	683.3	30.14	50.86	140
145	0.41568	921.6	0.44596	610.64	2739.80	1.7907	6.8826	4.294	2.351	1.363	1476	491.6	189.2	13.82	682.8	30.86	49.80	145
150	0.47616	917.0	0.39245	632.18	2745.93	1.8418	6.8371	4.307	2.394	1.368	1466	493.3	182.5	13.99	682.0	31.60	48.74	150
155	0.54350	912.3	0.34646	653.79	2751.81	1.8924	6.7926	4.321	2.440	1.373	1455	494.8	176.1	14.16	681.1	32.35	47.67	155
160	0.61823	907.4	0.30678	675.47	2757.44	1.9426	6.7491	4.335	2.488	1.379	1443	496.3	170.2	14.34	680.0	33.13	46.59	160
165	0.70093	902.5	0.27243	697.24	2762.81	1.9923	6.7066	4.351	2.540	1.385	1431	497.6	164.7	14.51	678.6	33.93	45.50	165
170	0.79219	897.5	0.24259	719.08	2767.90	2.0417	6.6650	4.368	2.594	1.392	1419	498.9	159.6	14.68	677.0	34.75	44.41	170
175	0.89260	892.3	0.21658	741.02	2772.71	2.0906	6.6241	4.386	2.652	1.399	1405	500.0	154.7	14.85	675.3	35.59	43.30	175
180	1.00280	887.0	0.19384	763.05	2777.21	2.1392	6.5840	4.405	2.713	1.407	1392	501.0	150.1	15.03	673.3	36.45	42.19	180
185	1.12350	881.6	0.17390	785.19	2781.41	2.1875	6.5447	4.425	2.777	1.416	1378	501.9	145.8	15.20	671.1	37.33	41.07	185
190	1.25520	876.1	0.15636	807.43	2785.28	2.2355	6.5059	4.447	2.844	1.425	1363	502.7	141.8	15.37	668.8	38.24	39.95	190
195	1.39880	870.4	0.14089	829.79	2788.82	2.2832	6.4678	4.471	2.915	1.436	1348	503.4	137.9	15.54	666.1	39.16	38.81	195
200	1.55490	864.7	0.12721	852.27	2792.01	2.3305	6.4302	4.496	2.990	1.447	1332	503.9	134.3	15.71	663.3	40.11	37.67	200
205	1.72430	858.8	0.11508	874.88	2794.83	2.3777	6.3930	4.523	3.068	1.459	1316	504.3	130.9	15.89	660.3	41.09	36.53	205
210	1.90770	852.7	0.10429	897.63	2797.27	2.4245	6.3563	4.551	3.150	1.472	1299	504.6	127.6	16.06	657.0	42.09	35.38	210
215	2.10580	846.5	0.09468	920.53	2799.32	2.4712	6.3200	4.582	3.237	1.486	1282	504.8	124.5	16.24	653.4	43.11	34.23	215
220	2.31960	840.2	0.08609	943.58	2800.95	2.5177	6.2840	4.615	3.329	1.501	1264	504.8	121.5	16.41	649.7	44.17	33.07	220
225	2.54970	833.7	0.07840	966.80	2802.15	2.5640	6.2483	4.650	3.426	1.518	1246	504.6	118.7	16.59	645.6	45.26	31.90	225
230	2.79710	827.1	0.07150	990.19	2802.90	2.6101	6.2128	4.688	3.528	1.536	1228	504.4	116.0	16.76	641.3	46.38	30.74	230
235	3.06250	820.3	0.06530	1013.77	2803.17	2.6561	6.1775	4.728	3.638	1.556	1209	503.9	113.4	16.94	636.7	47.53	29.57	235
240	3.34690	813.4	0.05970	1037.55	2802.96	2.7020	6.1423	4.772	3.754	1.578	1189	503.3	110.9	17.12	631.8	48.73	28.39	240
245	3.65120	806.2	0.05465	1061.55	2802.22	2.7478	6.1072	4.819	3.878	1.601	1169	502.6	108.4	17.31	626.7	49.97	27.22	245
250	3.97620	798.9	0.05008	1085.77	2800.93	2.7935	6.0721	4.870	4.011	1.627	1148	501.6	106.1	17.49	621.2	51.26	26.04	250
255	4.32290	791.4	0.04594	1110.23	2799.07	2.8392	6.0369	4.925	4.153	1.655	1127	500.5	103.9	17.68	615.4	52.61	24.87	255
260	4.69230	783.6	0.04217	1134.96	2796.60	2.8849	6.0016	4.986	4.308	1.686	1105	499.2	101.7	17.88	609.2	54.03	23.69	260
265	5.08530	775.7	0.03875	1159.96	2793.49	2.9307	5.9661	5.051	4.475	1.720	1083	497.7	99.6	18.07	602.8	55.53	22.51	265
270	5.50300	767.5	0.03562	1185.27	2789.69	2.9765	5.9304	5.123	4.656	1.757	1060	496.0	97.5	18.28	595.9	57.11	21.34	270
275	5.94640	759.0	0.03277	1210.90	2785.17	3.0224	5.8944	5.202	4.855	1.798	1037	494.1	95.5	18.48	588.7	58.80	20.16	275
280	6.41660	750.3	0.03015	1236.88	2779.87	3.0685	5.8579	5.289	5.073	1.845	1013	491.9	93.5	18.70	581.1	60.61	18.99	280
285	6.91470	741.3	0.02776	1263.25	2773.73	3.1147	5.8209	5.385	5.314	1.896	988	489.5	91.6	18.92	573.2	62.57	17.83	285
290	7.44180	731.9	0.02555	1290.03	2766.70	3.1612	5.7834	5.493	5.582	1.954	962	486.9	89.7	19.15	565.0	64.71	16.66	290
295	7.99910	722.2	0.02353	1317.27	2758.70	3.2080	5.7451	5.614	5.882	2.019	936	483.9	87.8	19.40	556.3	67.05	15.51	295
300	8.58790	712.1	0.02166	1345.01	2749.64	3.2552	5.7059	5.750	6.220	2.094	909	480.7	85.9	19.65	547.4	69.65	14.36	300
310	9.86510	690.7	0.01833	1402.22	2727.95	3.3510	5.6244	6.085	7.045	2.277	853	473.3	82.2	20.21	528.7	75.84	12.09	310
320	11.28430	667.1	0.01547	1462.22	2700.59	3.4494	5.5372	6.537	8.159	2.528	793	464.4	78.4	20.85	509.2	83.91	9.86	320
330	12.85810	640.8	0.01298	1525.87	2666.03	3.5518	5.4422	7.186	9.753	2.889	729	453.7	74.5	21.61	489.1	94.94	7.70	330
340	14.60070	610.7	0.01078	1594.53	2621.85	3.6601	5.3356	8.210	12.24	3.45	658	440.7	70.4	22.55	468.5	110.91	5.63	340
350	16.52940	574.7	0.00880	1670.89	2563.64	3.7784	5.2110	10.120	16.69	4.46	578	424.4	65.9	23.82	447.4	135.95	3.67	350
360	18.66600	527.6	0.00695	1761.66	2481.49	3.9167	5.0536	15.000	27.36	6.83	480	402.4	60.3	25.72	425.7	181.51	1.88	360
370	21.04360	451.4	0.00495	1890.69	2334.52	4.1112	4.8012	45.160	96.60	21.15	360	362.8	52.1	29.68	425.0	323.84	0.39	370
373.95[c]	22.06400	322.0	0.00311	2084.26	2084.26	4.4070	4.4070	∞	∞	∞	0	0.0	—	—	∞	∞	0.00	373.95

*Temperatures on ITS-90 scale [a]Triple point [b]Normal boiling point [c]Critical point

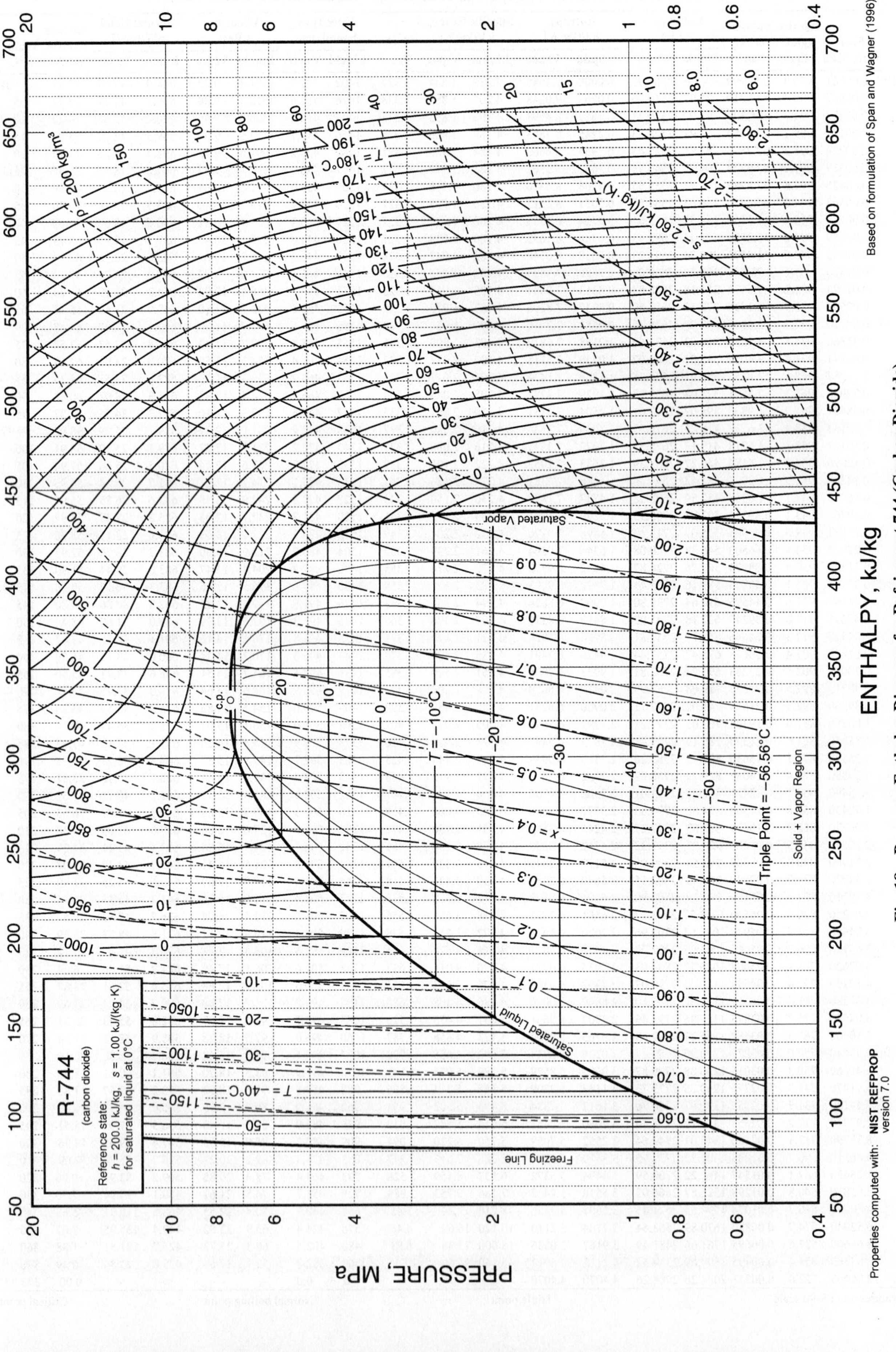

Fig. 18 Pressure-Enthalpy Diagram for Refrigerant 744 (Carbon Dioxide)

Refrigerant 744 (Carbon Dioxide) Properties of Saturated Liquid and Saturated Vapor

Temp.,* °C	Pressure, MPa	Density, kg/m³	Volume, m³/kg	Enthalpy, kJ/kg		Entropy, kJ/(kg·K)		Specific Heat c_p, kJ/(kg·K)		c_p/c_v	Velocity of Sound, m/s		Viscosity, μPa·s		Thermal Cond., mW/(m·K)		Surface Tension, mN/m	Temp.,* °C
		Liquid	Vapor	Liquid	Vapor	Liquid	Vapor	Liquid	Vapor	Vapor	Liquid	Vapor	Liquid	Vapor	Liquid	Vapor		
–56.56[a]	0.51796	1178.5	0.07267	80.04	430.42	0.5213	2.1390	1.953	0.909	1.444	976	222.8	256.7	10.95	180.6	11.01	17.16	–56.56
–50	0.68234	1154.6	0.05579	92.94	432.68	0.5794	2.1018	1.971	0.952	1.468	928	223.4	229.3	11.31	172.1	11.58	15.53	–50
–48	0.73949	1147.1	0.05162	96.90	433.29	0.5968	2.0909	1.978	0.967	1.477	914	223.5	221.6	11.42	169.5	11.76	15.04	–48
–46	0.80015	1139.6	0.04782	100.88	433.86	0.6142	2.0801	1.985	0.982	1.486	900	223.6	214.3	11.53	166.9	11.95	14.56	–46
–44	0.86445	1132.0	0.04435	104.87	434.39	0.6314	2.0694	1.993	0.998	1.496	885	223.6	207.2	11.64	164.4	12.14	14.07	–44
–42	0.93252	1124.2	0.04118	108.88	434.88	0.6486	2.0589	2.002	1.015	1.507	871	223.6	200.3	11.75	161.8	12.34	13.60	–42
–40	1.00450	1116.4	0.03828	112.90	435.32	0.6656	2.0485	2.012	1.033	1.518	856	223.5	193.8	11.87	159.3	12.54	13.12	–40
–38	1.08050	1108.5	0.03562	116.95	435.72	0.6826	2.0382	2.022	1.052	1.530	842	223.4	187.4	11.98	156.8	12.75	12.65	–38
–36	1.16070	1100.5	0.03318	121.01	436.07	0.6995	2.0281	2.033	1.072	1.544	827	223.2	181.3	12.10	154.3	12.97	12.18	–36
–34	1.24520	1092.4	0.03093	125.10	436.37	0.7163	2.0180	2.045	1.094	1.558	813	223.1	175.4	12.22	151.8	13.20	11.72	–34
–32	1.33420	1084.1	0.02886	129.20	436.62	0.7331	2.0079	2.059	1.116	1.573	798	222.8	169.7	12.34	149.3	13.43	11.26	–32
–30	1.42780	1075.7	0.02696	133.34	436.82	0.7498	1.9980	2.073	1.141	1.590	783	222.5	164.2	12.46	146.9	13.68	10.80	–30
–28	1.52610	1067.2	0.02519	137.50	436.96	0.7665	1.9880	2.089	1.166	1.608	768	222.2	158.9	12.59	144.4	13.94	10.35	–28
–26	1.62930	1058.6	0.02356	141.69	437.04	0.7831	1.9781	2.105	1.194	1.627	753	221.8	153.8	12.72	141.9	14.20	9.90	–26
–24	1.73750	1049.8	0.02205	145.91	437.06	0.7997	1.9683	2.124	1.223	1.648	738	221.4	148.8	12.85	139.5	14.49	9.46	–24
–22	1.85090	1040.8	0.02065	150.16	437.01	0.8163	1.9584	2.144	1.255	1.671	723	220.9	144.0	12.98	137.1	14.78	9.02	–22
–20	1.96960	1031.7	0.01934	154.45	436.89	0.8328	1.9485	2.165	1.289	1.696	708	220.4	139.3	13.12	134.6	15.09	8.59	–20
–19	2.03100	1027.0	0.01873	156.61	436.81	0.8411	1.9436	2.177	1.307	1.709	700	220.1	137.1	13.18	133.4	15.25	8.37	–19
–18	2.09380	1022.3	0.01813	158.77	436.70	0.8494	1.9386	2.189	1.326	1.723	692	219.8	134.8	13.26	132.2	15.42	8.16	–18
–17	2.15810	1017.6	0.01756	160.95	436.58	0.8576	1.9337	2.201	1.346	1.738	684	219.5	132.6	13.33	131.0	15.59	7.95	–17
–16	2.22370	1012.8	0.01700	163.14	436.44	0.8659	1.9287	2.215	1.366	1.753	676	219.2	130.4	13.40	129.8	15.77	7.74	–16
–15	2.29080	1008.0	0.01647	165.34	436.27	0.8742	1.9237	2.228	1.388	1.768	668	218.8	128.3	13.47	128.6	15.95	7.53	–15
–14	2.35930	1003.1	0.01595	167.55	436.09	0.8825	1.9187	2.243	1.410	1.785	660	218.5	126.2	13.55	127.4	16.14	7.32	–14
–13	2.42940	998.1	0.01545	169.78	435.89	0.8908	1.9137	2.258	1.433	1.802	651	218.1	124.1	13.63	126.2	16.34	7.11	–13
–12	2.50100	993.1	0.01497	172.01	435.66	0.8991	1.9086	2.273	1.457	1.821	643	217.7	122.0	13.70	125.0	16.54	6.90	–12
–11	2.57400	988.1	0.01450	174.26	435.41	0.9074	1.9036	2.290	1.483	1.840	635	217.4	120.0	13.78	123.8	16.74	6.70	–11
–10	2.64870	982.9	0.01405	176.52	435.14	0.9157	1.8985	2.307	1.509	1.860	626	216.9	118.0	13.86	122.5	16.96	6.50	–10
–9	2.72490	977.7	0.01361	178.80	434.84	0.9240	1.8934	2.325	1.537	1.881	617	216.5	116.1	13.95	121.3	17.18	6.29	–9
–8	2.80270	972.5	0.01319	181.09	434.51	0.9324	1.8882	2.345	1.566	1.904	609	216.1	114.1	14.03	120.1	17.42	6.09	–8
–7	2.88210	967.1	0.01278	183.39	434.17	0.9408	1.8830	2.365	1.597	1.927	600	215.6	112.2	14.12	118.9	17.66	5.89	–7
–6	2.96320	961.7	0.01238	185.71	433.79	0.9491	1.8778	2.386	1.629	1.952	591	215.2	110.3	14.20	117.7	17.91	5.70	–6
–5	3.04590	956.2	0.01200	188.05	433.38	0.9576	1.8725	2.408	1.663	1.979	582	214.7	108.4	14.30	116.5	18.17	5.50	–5
–4	3.13030	950.6	0.01162	190.40	432.95	0.9660	1.8672	2.432	1.699	2.007	573	214.2	106.6	14.39	115.3	18.44	5.30	–4
–3	3.21640	945.0	0.01126	192.77	432.48	0.9744	1.8618	2.457	1.737	2.037	564	213.7	104.8	14.48	114.1	18.73	5.11	–3
–2	3.30420	939.2	0.01091	195.16	431.99	0.9829	1.8563	2.484	1.777	2.068	555	213.1	102.9	14.58	112.9	19.03	4.92	–2
–1	3.39380	933.4	0.01057	197.57	431.46	0.9914	1.8509	2.512	1.819	2.102	546	212.6	101.2	14.68	111.6	19.34	4.73	–1
0	3.48510	927.4	0.01024	200.00	430.89	1.0000	1.8453	2.542	1.865	2.138	536	212.0	99.4	14.79	110.4	19.67	4.54	0
1	3.57830	921.4	0.00992	202.45	430.29	1.0086	1.8397	2.574	1.913	2.176	527	211.5	97.6	14.89	109.2	20.02	4.35	1
2	3.67330	915.2	0.00961	204.93	429.65	1.0172	1.8340	2.609	1.965	2.218	518	210.9	95.9	15.00	108.0	20.38	4.17	2
3	3.77010	909.0	0.00931	207.43	428.97	1.0259	1.8282	2.645	2.020	2.262	508	210.3	94.2	15.12	106.8	20.76	3.99	3
4	3.86880	902.6	0.00901	209.95	428.25	1.0346	1.8223	2.685	2.080	2.309	499	209.6	92.5	15.24	105.5	21.17	3.80	4
5	3.96950	896.0	0.00872	212.50	427.48	1.0434	1.8163	2.727	2.144	2.360	489	209.0	90.8	15.36	104.3	21.60	3.62	5
6	4.07200	889.4	0.00845	215.08	426.67	1.0523	1.8102	2.772	2.213	2.416	480	208.3	89.1	15.49	103.1	22.06	3.45	6
7	4.17650	882.6	0.00817	217.69	425.81	1.0612	1.8041	2.822	2.289	2.476	470	207.6	87.5	15.62	101.8	22.54	3.27	7
8	4.28310	875.6	0.00791	220.34	424.89	1.0702	1.7977	2.875	2.370	2.541	460	206.9	85.8	15.76	100.6	23.06	3.10	8
9	4.39160	868.4	0.00765	223.01	423.92	1.0792	1.7913	2.934	2.460	2.612	451	206.2	84.2	15.91	99.4	23.61	2.93	9
10	4.50220	861.1	0.00740	225.73	422.88	1.0884	1.7847	2.998	2.558	2.690	441	205.4	82.6	16.06	98.1	24.21	2.76	10
11	4.61490	853.6	0.00715	228.49	421.79	1.0976	1.7779	3.068	2.666	2.776	431	204.6	80.9	16.22	96.9	24.84	2.59	11
12	4.72970	845.9	0.00691	231.29	420.62	1.1070	1.7710	3.145	2.786	2.871	421	203.8	79.3	16.39	95.6	25.53	2.42	12
13	4.84660	837.9	0.00668	234.13	419.37	1.1165	1.7638	3.232	2.919	2.977	411	203.0	77.7	16.56	94.4	26.27	2.26	13
14	4.96580	829.7	0.00645	237.03	418.05	1.1261	1.7565	3.328	3.068	3.095	401	202.1	76.1	16.75	93.1	27.08	2.10	14
15	5.08701	821.2	0.00622	239.99	416.64	1.1359	1.7489	3.436	3.237	3.228	391	201.2	74.4	16.95	91.9	27.96	1.95	15
16	5.21080	812.4	0.00600	243.01	415.12	1.1458	1.7411	3.558	3.429	3.378	381	200.3	72.8	17.16	90.6	28.93	1.79	16
17	5.33680	803.3	0.00578	246.10	413.50	1.1559	1.7329	3.698	3.649	3.550	370	199.3	71.2	17.39	89.4	29.99	1.64	17
18	5.46510	793.8	0.00557	249.26	411.76	1.1663	1.7244	3.858	3.905	3.748	360	198.3	69.5	17.64	88.1	31.16	1.49	18
19	5.59580	783.8	0.00536	252.52	409.89	1.1769	1.7155	4.044	4.204	3.979	349	197.2	67.8	17.90	86.9	32.47	1.35	19
20	5.72910	773.4	0.00515	255.87	407.87	1.1877	1.7062	4.264	4.560	4.252	338	196.1	66.1	18.19	85.7	33.94	1.20	20
21	5.86480	762.4	0.00494	259.33	405.67	1.1989	1.6964	4.526	4.990	4.578	326	194.9	64.4	18.50	84.5	35.61	1.06	21
22	6.00310	750.8	0.00474	262.93	403.26	1.2105	1.6860	4.846	5.519	4.976	314	193.6	62.7	18.85	83.4	37.52	0.93	22
23	6.14400	738.4	0.00453	266.68	400.63	1.2225	1.6749	5.248	6.185	5.472	302	192.3	60.9	19.23	82.4	39.74	0.80	23
24	6.28770	725.0	0.00433	270.61	397.70	1.2352	1.6629	5.767	7.049	6.107	288	190.8	59.0	19.66	81.5	42.35	0.67	24
25	6.43420	710.5	0.00412	274.78	394.43	1.2485	1.6498	6.467	8.212	6.949	274	189.1	57.0	20.16	80.8	45.51	0.55	25
26	6.58370	694.5	0.00391	279.26	390.71	1.2627	1.6353	7.460	9.862	8.121	259	187.2	55.0	20.73	80.5	49.44	0.44	26
27	6.73610	676.4	0.00369	284.14	386.39	1.2783	1.6189	8.970	12.38	9.870	243	185.0	52.8	21.42	80.7	54.56	0.33	27
28	6.89180	655.3	0.00346	289.62	381.20	1.2958	1.5999	11.550	16.69	12.780	225	182.1	50.3	22.27	81.9	61.73	0.23	28
29	7.05090	629.4	0.00320	296.07	374.61	1.3163	1.5763	16.950	25.74	18.630	205	178.2	47.5	23.41	85.2	73.19	0.13	29
30	7.21370	593.3	0.00290	304.55	365.13	1.3435	1.5433	35.340	55.82	36.660	177	171.3	43.8	25.17	95.4	98.02	0.05	30
30.98[c]	7.37730	467.6	0.00214	332.25	332.25	1.4336	1.4336	∞	∞	∞	0	0.0	—	—	∞	∞	0.00	30.98

*Temperatures on ITS-90 scale

[a]Triple point

[c]Critical point

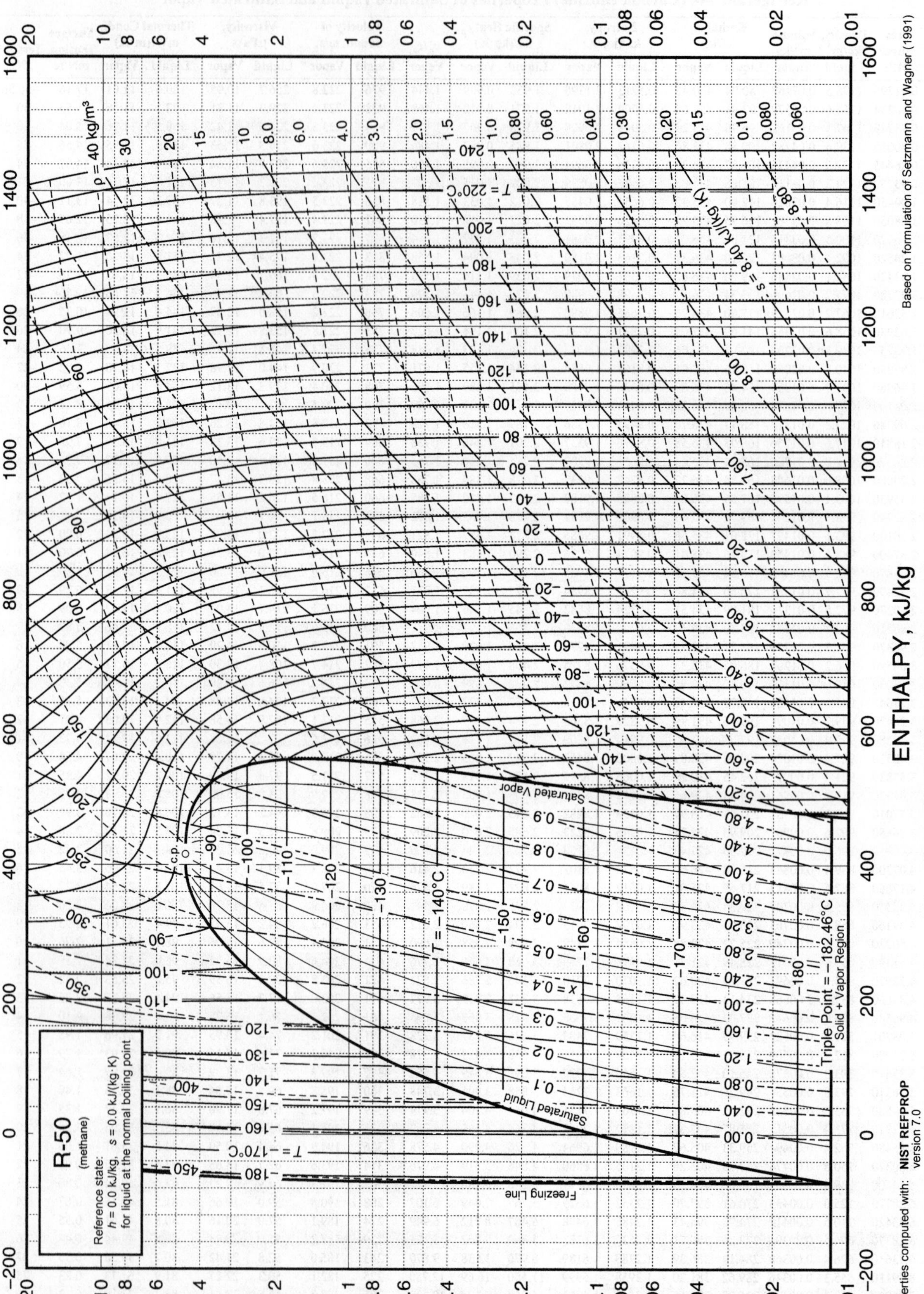

Fig. 19 Pressure-Enthalpy Diagram for Refrigerant 50 (Methane)

Refrigerant 50 (Methane) Properties of Saturated Liquid and Saturated Vapor

Temp.,* °C	Pressure, MPa	Density, kg/m³ Liquid	Volume, m³/kg Vapor	Enthalpy, kJ/kg Liquid	Enthalpy, kJ/kg Vapor	Entropy, kJ/(kg·K) Liquid	Entropy, kJ/(kg·K) Vapor	Specific Heat c_p, kJ/(kg·K) Liquid	Specific Heat c_p, kJ/(kg·K) Vapor	c_p/c_v Vapor	Velocity of Sound, m/s Liquid	Velocity of Sound, m/s Vapor	Viscosity, μPa·s Liquid	Viscosity, μPa·s Vapor	Thermal Cond., mW/(m·K) Liquid	Thermal Cond., mW/(m·K) Vapor	Surface Tension, mN/m	Temp.,* °C
–182.46[a]	0.01170	451.5	3.9881	–71.82	472.44	–0.7099	5.2911	3.368	2.110	1.341	1539	249.1	204.5	3.64	211.2	8.85	18.76	–182.46
–180	0.01590	448.2	3.0071	–63.53	477.22	–0.6199	5.1853	3.377	2.118	1.343	1516	252.2	189.5	3.73	208.3	9.15	18.09	–180
–175	0.02823	441.4	1.7755	–46.58	486.76	–0.4429	4.9910	3.399	2.137	1.348	1470	258.0	163.9	3.93	202.1	9.78	16.74	–175
–170	0.04723	434.5	1.1081	–29.49	495.99	–0.2735	4.8208	3.426	2.162	1.355	1422	263.4	143.4	4.12	195.5	10.42	15.43	–170
–165	0.07509	427.4	0.72466	–12.24	504.85	–0.1108	4.6704	3.457	2.192	1.365	1373	268.3	126.8	4.32	188.7	11.09	14.17	–165
–161.48[b]	0.10133	422.4	0.55054	0.00	510.83	0.0000	4.5746	3.481	2.218	1.373	1338	271.5	116.8	4.46	183.9	11.58	13.30	–161.48
–160	0.11429	420.2	0.49291	5.19	513.28	0.0459	4.5363	3.492	2.229	1.377	1323	272.7	112.9	4.52	181.8	11.79	12.94	–160
–155	0.16757	412.7	0.34665	22.82	521.22	0.1973	4.4156	3.533	2.274	1.392	1273	276.5	101.3	4.73	174.8	12.53	11.75	–155
–150	0.23784	405.0	0.25077	40.69	528.60	0.3440	4.3058	3.580	2.328	1.412	1221	279.7	91.4	4.95	167.7	13.30	10.60	–150
–145	0.32817	397.1	0.18583	58.84	535.34	0.4866	4.2049	3.635	2.393	1.436	1168	282.3	82.8	5.17	160.5	14.13	9.49	–145
–140	0.44177	388.8	0.14054	77.30	541.38	0.6257	4.1111	3.701	2.472	1.466	1114	284.3	75.2	5.40	153.4	15.01	8.43	–140
–135	0.58192	380.2	0.10813	96.13	546.63	0.7618	4.0228	3.780	2.569	1.504	1059	285.6	68.6	5.63	146.3	15.96	7.42	–135
–130	0.75201	371.1	0.08440	115.39	550.97	0.8956	3.9384	3.876	2.690	1.552	1002	286.2	62.7	5.88	139.2	16.99	6.44	–130
–125	0.95550	361.6	0.06666	135.17	554.29	1.0276	3.8566	3.996	2.842	1.613	943	286.2	57.3	6.15	132.1	18.13	5.52	–125
–120	1.1959	351.4	0.05315	155.58	556.43	1.1585	3.7759	4.148	3.038	1.694	882	285.4	52.4	6.43	125.0	19.39	4.64	–120
–118	1.3033	347.2	0.04865	163.94	556.91	1.2108	3.7437	4.220	3.133	1.733	858	284.8	50.5	6.55	122.1	19.95	4.31	–118
–116	1.4174	342.8	0.04457	172.44	557.16	1.2631	3.7112	4.302	3.240	1.777	832	284.2	48.7	6.68	119.3	20.53	3.98	–116
–114	1.5384	338.3	0.04087	181.08	557.15	1.3155	3.6785	4.393	3.362	1.827	807	283.4	47.0	6.81	116.4	21.15	3.66	–114
–112	1.6668	333.6	0.03750	189.88	556.87	1.3681	3.6454	4.497	3.501	1.885	780	282.5	45.3	6.95	113.5	21.81	3.35	–112
–110	1.8026	328.8	0.03442	198.85	556.28	1.4209	3.6117	4.615	3.662	1.951	754	281.4	43.6	7.09	110.7	22.52	3.04	–110
–108	1.9462	323.7	0.03160	208.03	555.37	1.4741	3.5773	4.751	3.848	2.028	726	280.2	42.0	7.24	107.8	23.28	2.75	–108
–106	2.0978	318.4	0.02900	217.42	554.09	1.5278	3.5419	4.910	4.068	2.119	698	278.9	40.4	7.40	104.9	24.12	2.46	–106
–104	2.2578	312.9	0.02662	227.06	552.39	1.5821	3.5054	5.097	4.331	2.227	670	277.4	38.8	7.57	102.0	25.05	2.19	–104
–102	2.4264	307.1	0.02441	236.99	550.24	1.6372	3.4675	5.322	4.650	2.358	641	275.7	37.2	7.76	99.0	26.09	1.92	–102
–100	2.6040	301.0	0.02236	247.25	547.56	1.6934	3.4278	5.596	5.044	2.520	610	273.9	35.6	7.96	96.1	27.28	1.66	–100
–95	3.0895	283.6	0.01781	274.80	537.86	1.8408	3.3174	6.654	6.608	3.153	529	268.4	31.7	8.55	88.6	31.27	1.07	–95
–90	3.6399	261.7	0.01384	306.71	521.52	2.0062	3.1791	9.10	10.37	4.64	437	261.3	27.5	9.39	81.2	38.68	0.55	–90
–85	4.2648	227.5	0.00993	349.75	488.81	2.2241	2.9632	21.88	30.57	12.16	320	250.2	22.3	10.95	77.5	62.99	0.13	–85
–82.59[c]	4.5992	162.7	0.00615	415.59	415.59	2.5624	2.5624	∞	∞	∞	0	0.0	—	—	∞	∞	0.00	–82.59

*Temperatures on ITS-90 scale [a]Triple point [b]Normal boiling point [c]Critical point

Refrigerant 50 (Methane) Properties of Gas at 0.101 325 MPa (one standard atmosphere)

Temp., °C	Density, kg/m³	Enthalpy, kJ/kg	Entropy, kJ/(kg·K)	c_p, kJ/(kg·K)	c_p/c_v	Vel. of Sound, m/s	Visc., μPa·s	Thermal Cond., mW/(m·K)
–161.5[a]	1.8164	510.83	4.5746	2.218	1.373	271.5	4.46	11.58
–160	1.7899	514.11	4.6037	2.208	1.371	273.5	4.52	11.74
–155	1.7064	525.08	4.6986	2.183	1.366	280.3	4.71	12.30
–150	1.6310	535.95	4.7887	2.165	1.362	286.9	4.90	12.87
–145	1.5626	546.74	4.8746	2.151	1.359	293.2	5.10	13.45
–140	1.5000	557.47	4.9567	2.141	1.356	299.4	5.29	14.03
–135	1.4425	568.15	5.0355	2.132	1.354	305.4	5.48	14.62
–130	1.3894	578.79	5.1112	2.125	1.351	311.2	5.67	15.21
–120	1.2947	599.99	5.2543	2.116	1.348	322.5	6.06	16.40
–110	1.2124	621.11	5.3879	2.109	1.345	333.3	6.44	17.58
–100	1.1403	642.18	5.5133	2.106	1.343	343.8	6.81	18.77
–90	1.0764	663.23	5.6315	2.104	1.341	353.8	7.19	19.96
–80	1.0194	684.27	5.7433	2.105	1.339	363.5	7.56	21.15
–70	0.9683	705.33	5.8496	2.107	1.337	372.9	7.92	22.31
–60	0.9221	726.42	5.9509	2.111	1.335	382.0	8.29	23.49
–50	0.8802	747.57	6.0479	2.118	1.332	390.7	8.64	24.68
–40	0.8419	768.78	6.1409	2.126	1.330	399.2	9.00	25.89
–30	0.8069	790.10	6.2304	2.137	1.327	407.5	9.35	27.12
–20	0.7747	811.53	6.3168	2.149	1.324	415.4	9.69	28.36
–10	0.7450	833.09	6.4003	2.164	1.320	423.2	10.03	29.63
0	0.7175	854.82	6.4814	2.181	1.316	430.7	10.37	30.93
10	0.6919	876.72	6.5601	2.200	1.312	437.9	10.70	32.25
20	0.6682	898.82	6.6368	2.221	1.308	445.0	11.02	33.61
30	0.6460	921.14	6.7117	2.243	1.304	451.9	11.35	34.99
40	0.6252	943.69	6.7849	2.268	1.299	458.6	11.66	36.41

Temp., °C	Density, kg/m³	Enthalpy, kJ/kg	Entropy, kJ/(kg·K)	c_p, kJ/(kg·K)	c_p/c_v	Vel. of Sound, m/s	Visc., μPa·s	Thermal Cond., mW/(m·K)
50	0.6058	966.50	6.8565	2.293	1.295	465.1	11.98	37.86
60	0.5875	989.57	6.9269	2.321	1.290	471.4	12.29	39.35
70	0.5703	1012.92	6.9959	2.350	1.285	477.6	12.60	40.87
80	0.5541	1036.57	7.0638	2.380	1.281	483.7	12.90	42.42
90	0.5388	1060.52	7.1307	2.411	1.276	489.6	13.20	44.01
100	0.5243	1084.79	7.1967	2.443	1.271	495.5	13.49	45.63
110	0.5106	1109.39	7.2617	2.476	1.266	501.2	13.79	47.28
120	0.4975	1134.32	7.3259	2.510	1.262	506.8	14.08	48.96
130	0.4852	1159.60	7.3894	2.545	1.257	512.3	14.36	50.67
140	0.4734	1185.22	7.4522	2.580	1.253	517.7	14.64	52.41
150	0.4622	1211.21	7.5143	2.616	1.248	523.1	14.92	54.18
160	0.4515	1237.55	7.5759	2.652	1.244	528.3	15.20	55.97
170	0.4413	1264.25	7.6368	2.689	1.240	533.5	15.47	57.79
180	0.4315	1291.32	7.6972	2.726	1.236	538.6	15.74	59.63
190	0.4222	1318.76	7.7571	2.763	1.232	543.7	16.01	61.50
200	0.4132	1346.57	7.8165	2.800	1.228	548.7	16.28	63.39
210	0.4047	1374.76	7.8755	2.837	1.224	553.6	16.54	65.30
220	0.3965	1403.32	7.9340	2.875	1.221	558.5	16.80	67.23
230	0.3886	1432.26	7.9921	2.912	1.217	563.4	17.06	69.18
240	0.3810	1461.57	8.0498	2.950	1.214	568.2	17.31	71.15
250	0.3737	1491.26	8.1071	2.988	1.211	572.9	17.56	73.14
260	0.3667	1521.32	8.1640	3.025	1.207	577.6	17.81	75.14
270	0.3599	1551.76	8.2205	3.062	1.204	582.3	18.06	77.16
280	0.3534	1582.57	8.2768	3.100	1.201	586.9	18.31	79.20
290	0.3471	1613.75	8.3326	3.137	1.198	591.5	18.55	81.25
300	0.3411	1645.31	8.3882	3.174	1.196	596.0	18.79	83.31

[a]Saturated vapor at normal boiling point

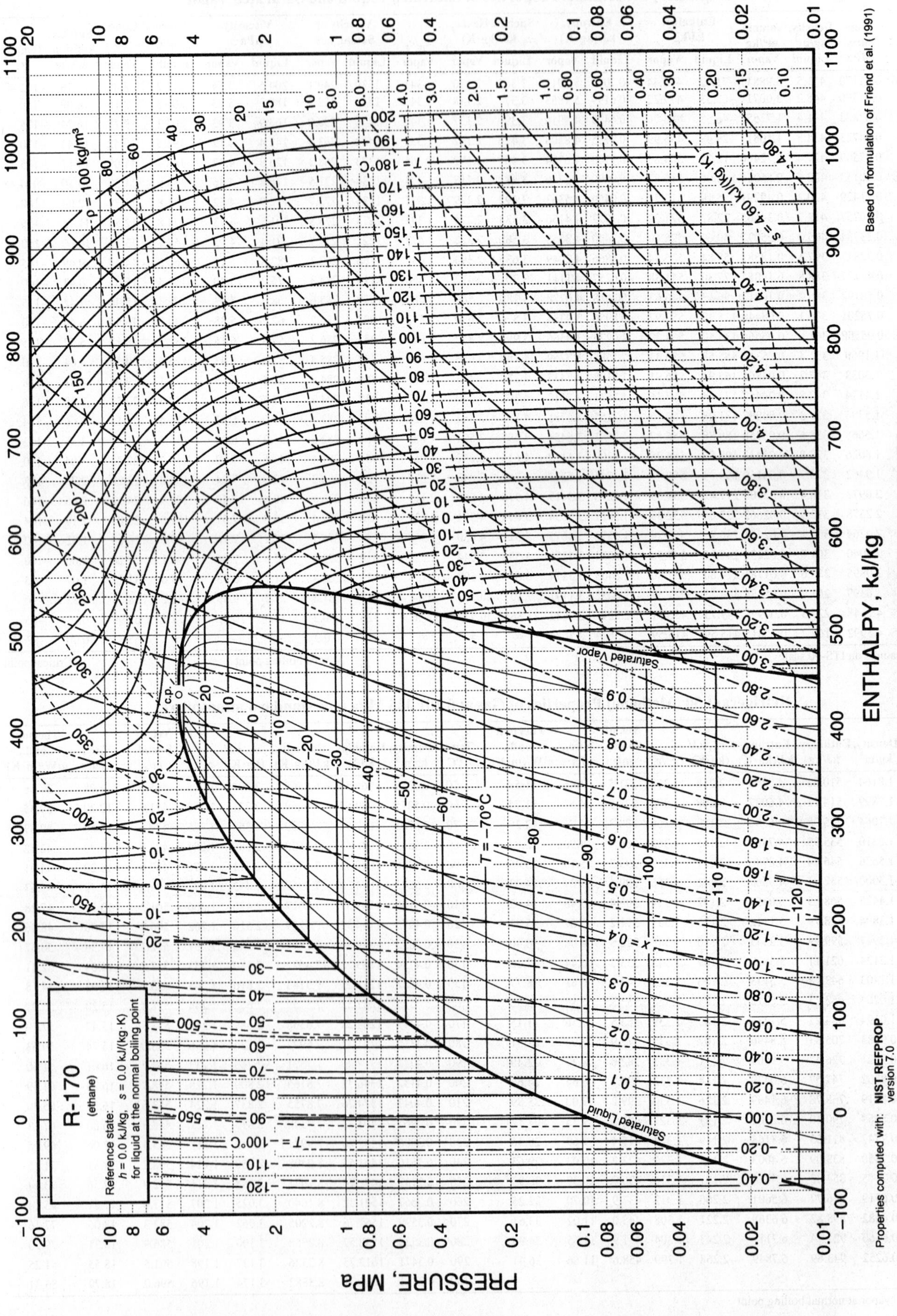

Fig. 20 Pressure-Enthalpy Diagram for Refrigerant 170 (Ethane)

Refrigerant 170 (Ethane) Properties of Saturated Liquid and Saturated Vapor

Temp.,[a] °C	Pressure, MPa	Density, kg/m³ Liquid	Volume, m³/kg Vapor	Enthalpy, kJ/kg Liquid	Enthalpy, kJ/kg Vapor	Entropy, kJ/(kg·K) Liquid	Entropy, kJ/(kg·K) Vapor	Specific Heat c_p, kJ/(kg·K) Liquid	Specific Heat c_p, kJ/(kg·K) Vapor	c_p/c_v Vapor	Velocity of Sound, m/s Liquid	Velocity of Sound, m/s Vapor	Viscosity, µPa·s Liquid	Viscosity, µPa·s Vapor	Thermal Cond., mW/(m·K) Liquid	Thermal Cond., mW/(m·K) Vapor	Surface Tension, mN/m	Temp., °C
–175	0.00001	643.0	3649.3	–201.26	384.73	–1.4643	4.5060	2.288	1.184	1.305	1952	188.2	933.9	3.26	249.4	3.35	30.35	–175
–170	0.00002	637.5	1353.1	–189.85	390.67	–1.3510	4.2770	2.277	1.194	1.302	1916	192.7	783.6	3.41	245.2	3.64	29.51	–170
–165	0.00005	632.0	555.95	–178.48	396.66	–1.2433	4.0747	2.273	1.204	1.298	1880	197.0	669.0	3.55	240.8	3.93	28.67	–165
–160	0.00013	626.5	249.56	–167.11	402.69	–1.1405	3.8953	2.274	1.215	1.295	1844	201.3	579.6	3.70	236.3	4.23	27.83	–160
–155	0.00027	621.0	120.95	–155.73	408.76	–1.0421	3.7356	2.278	1.226	1.292	1808	205.4	508.5	3.84	231.6	4.54	26.99	–155
–150	0.00054	615.5	62.674	–144.33	414.87	–0.9476	3.5932	2.283	1.238	1.289	1772	209.4	450.9	3.99	226.9	4.86	26.15	–150
–145	0.00103	609.9	34.435	–132.89	421.00	–0.8566	3.4657	2.290	1.251	1.287	1735	213.3	403.6	4.14	222.1	5.18	25.31	–145
–140	0.00185	604.3	19.920	–121.42	427.16	–0.7688	3.3513	2.299	1.265	1.284	1699	217.0	364.1	4.29	217.3	5.50	24.48	–140
–135	0.00316	598.7	12.060	–109.90	433.34	–0.6839	3.2484	2.308	1.279	1.282	1663	220.7	330.8	4.44	212.4	5.84	23.64	–135
–130	0.00519	593.0	7.6020	–98.34	439.53	–0.6017	3.1557	2.318	1.293	1.280	1626	224.2	302.4	4.59	207.5	6.18	22.81	–130
–125	0.00821	587.3	4.9668	–86.72	445.71	–0.5219	3.0719	2.328	1.307	1.278	1589	227.6	277.8	4.74	202.5	6.54	21.98	–125
–120	0.01255	581.5	3.3504	–75.04	451.89	–0.4445	2.9962	2.340	1.320	1.277	1552	230.9	256.4	4.90	197.6	6.90	21.15	–120
–115	0.01863	575.7	2.3254	–63.31	458.04	–0.3691	2.9274	2.353	1.333	1.277	1515	234.0	237.6	5.05	192.7	7.28	20.33	–115
–110	0.02691	569.8	1.6556	–51.50	464.15	–0.2957	2.8649	2.366	1.347	1.277	1478	237.0	220.9	5.21	187.7	7.67	19.51	–110
–105	0.03793	563.9	1.2060	–39.62	470.20	–0.2241	2.8078	2.381	1.362	1.278	1440	239.7	206.0	5.36	182.8	8.07	18.69	–105
–100	0.05230	557.9	0.89662	–27.66	476.16	–0.1542	2.7556	2.397	1.380	1.280	1403	242.3	192.5	5.52	178.0	8.48	17.88	–100
–95	0.07068	551.8	0.67900	–15.61	482.04	–0.0858	2.7076	2.415	1.401	1.282	1365	244.7	180.4	5.68	173.1	8.92	17.07	–95
–90	0.09380	545.6	0.52278	–3.46	487.79	–0.0188	2.6635	2.434	1.425	1.286	1326	246.9	169.3	5.84	168.3	9.36	16.26	–90
–88.58[b]	0.10132	543.8	0.48676	0.00	489.40	0.0000	2.6516	2.439	1.433	1.287	1316	247.4	166.4	5.89	167.0	9.49	16.03	–88.58
–85	0.12243	539.3	0.40856	8.79	493.42	0.0469	2.6227	2.455	1.454	1.290	1288	248.8	159.2	6.00	163.6	9.83	15.46	–85
–80	0.15741	532.9	0.32361	21.15	498.91	0.1115	2.5850	2.478	1.487	1.295	1249	250.4	149.9	6.16	158.9	10.31	14.67	–80
–78	0.17338	530.3	0.29583	26.13	501.07	0.1370	2.5707	2.487	1.501	1.297	1234	251.0	146.4	6.23	157.0	10.51	14.35	–78
–76	0.19055	527.7	0.27094	31.13	503.20	0.1623	2.5567	2.497	1.515	1.300	1218	251.6	143.0	6.30	155.2	10.72	14.04	–76
–74	0.20899	525.1	0.24859	36.16	505.30	0.1875	2.5432	2.508	1.531	1.302	1203	252.1	139.6	6.36	153.3	10.92	13.72	–74
–72	0.22877	522.5	0.22847	41.20	507.38	0.2125	2.5300	2.519	1.546	1.305	1187	252.5	136.4	6.43	151.5	11.13	13.41	–72
–70	0.24993	519.8	0.21033	46.27	509.43	0.2373	2.5172	2.530	1.562	1.308	1171	252.9	133.3	6.50	149.7	11.35	13.09	–70
–68	0.27255	517.1	0.19394	51.36	511.45	0.2621	2.5048	2.542	1.579	1.312	1156	253.3	130.3	6.56	147.9	11.56	12.78	–68
–66	0.29668	514.4	0.17909	56.48	513.44	0.2867	2.4926	2.554	1.596	1.315	1140	253.6	127.3	6.63	146.0	11.79	12.47	–66
–64	0.32238	511.6	0.16563	61.62	515.40	0.3111	2.4808	2.567	1.614	1.319	1124	253.9	124.4	6.70	144.2	12.01	12.16	–64
–62	0.34972	508.9	0.15339	66.79	517.34	0.3355	2.4692	2.580	1.633	1.323	1108	254.2	121.6	6.77	142.4	12.24	11.86	–62
–60	0.37877	506.1	0.14224	71.99	519.23	0.3597	2.4580	2.594	1.651	1.327	1092	254.3	118.9	6.84	140.6	12.48	11.55	–60
–58	0.40958	503.2	0.13208	77.21	521.10	0.3838	2.4470	2.608	1.671	1.331	1076	254.5	116.2	6.91	138.9	12.72	11.24	–58
–56	0.44223	500.4	0.12279	82.47	522.93	0.4078	2.4362	2.623	1.691	1.336	1060	254.6	113.6	6.99	137.1	12.96	10.94	–56
–54	0.47677	497.5	0.11429	87.75	524.73	0.4317	2.4257	2.638	1.711	1.342	1044	254.6	111.1	7.06	135.3	13.21	10.63	–54
–52	0.51328	494.6	0.10650	93.07	526.48	0.4556	2.4154	2.654	1.732	1.347	1028	254.6	108.6	7.13	133.6	13.46	10.33	–52
–50	0.55183	491.6	0.09935	98.42	528.20	0.4793	2.4053	2.671	1.754	1.353	1012	254.6	106.2	7.21	131.8	13.73	10.03	–50
–48	0.59247	488.7	0.09277	103.80	529.88	0.5029	2.3954	2.689	1.777	1.359	996	254.5	103.9	7.28	130.1	13.99	9.73	–48
–46	0.63529	485.7	0.08671	109.22	531.52	0.5265	2.3856	2.707	1.800	1.366	979	254.4	101.5	7.36	128.4	14.26	9.44	–46
–44	0.68034	482.6	0.08113	114.68	533.11	0.5500	2.3760	2.726	1.824	1.373	963	254.2	99.3	7.44	126.7	14.54	9.14	–44
–42	0.72770	479.5	0.07597	120.18	534.66	0.5735	2.3666	2.746	1.850	1.381	947	253.9	97.1	7.51	125.0	14.83	8.85	–42
–40	0.77744	476.4	0.07120	125.71	536.16	0.5969	2.3573	2.767	1.876	1.390	930	253.6	94.9	7.59	123.3	15.12	8.55	–40
–38	0.82963	473.2	0.06679	131.29	537.60	0.6202	2.3481	2.789	1.904	1.399	914	253.2	92.8	7.68	121.6	15.42	8.26	–38
–36	0.88433	470.0	0.06269	136.91	539.00	0.6435	2.3390	2.812	1.932	1.408	897	252.8	90.7	7.76	119.9	15.73	7.97	–36
–34	0.94163	466.7	0.05889	142.57	540.34	0.6668	2.3301	2.836	1.963	1.419	880	252.4	88.7	7.84	118.2	16.04	7.68	–34
–32	1.0016	463.4	0.05536	148.28	541.62	0.6900	2.3211	2.862	1.995	1.430	864	251.8	86.7	7.93	116.6	16.37	7.40	–32
–30	1.0643	460.0	0.05207	154.04	542.85	0.7133	2.3123	2.889	2.028	1.442	847	251.2	84.7	8.02	114.9	16.70	7.11	–30
–28	1.1298	456.6	0.04900	159.86	544.00	0.7365	2.3035	2.918	2.064	1.455	830	250.6	82.7	8.11	113.3	17.05	6.83	–28
–26	1.1982	453.1	0.04614	165.72	545.10	0.7597	2.2947	2.948	2.102	1.469	813	249.9	80.8	8.20	111.6	17.40	6.55	–26
–24	1.2696	449.6	0.04347	171.64	546.12	0.7829	2.2859	2.980	2.142	1.485	796	249.1	79.0	8.30	110.0	17.77	6.27	–24
–22	1.3440	446.0	0.04097	177.62	547.06	0.8062	2.2772	3.014	2.185	1.501	778	248.3	77.1	8.40	108.4	18.15	6.00	–22
–20	1.4215	442.3	0.03863	183.67	547.93	0.8295	2.2684	3.050	2.231	1.519	761	247.4	75.3	8.50	106.7	18.55	5.72	–20
–18	1.5023	438.5	0.03644	189.78	548.72	0.8528	2.2596	3.089	2.281	1.539	744	246.4	73.5	8.61	105.1	18.96	5.45	–18
–16	1.5863	434.7	0.03439	195.95	549.41	0.8761	2.2507	3.130	2.334	1.561	726	245.4	71.8	8.71	103.5	19.38	5.18	–16
–14	1.6737	430.8	0.03245	202.20	550.02	0.8996	2.2417	3.175	2.392	1.584	708	244.3	70.0	8.83	101.9	19.83	4.92	–14
–12	1.7645	426.8	0.03064	208.53	550.52	0.9231	2.2326	3.223	2.455	1.610	690	243.1	68.3	8.94	100.3	20.29	4.65	–12
–10	1.8588	422.6	0.02892	214.94	550.91	0.9467	2.2234	3.275	2.523	1.639	672	241.9	66.6	9.07	98.7	20.78	4.39	–10
–8	1.9568	418.4	0.02731	221.43	551.19	0.9704	2.2140	3.331	2.598	1.671	654	240.6	64.9	9.19	97.1	21.30	4.13	–8
–6	2.0585	414.1	0.02579	228.02	551.35	0.9942	2.2045	3.393	2.681	1.706	635	239.2	63.3	9.33	95.6	21.84	3.88	–6
–4	2.1640	409.7	0.02435	234.71	551.37	1.0182	2.1947	3.460	2.773	1.746	617	237.7	61.6	9.46	94.0	22.41	3.63	–4
–2	2.2734	405.1	0.02298	241.50	551.24	1.0423	2.1847	3.534	2.875	1.791	598	236.1	60.0	9.61	92.4	23.02	3.38	–2
0	2.3867	400.3	0.02169	248.41	550.96	1.0667	2.1743	3.617	2.990	1.841	579	234.5	58.4	9.77	90.8	23.68	3.13	0
5	2.6883	387.7	0.01874	266.27	549.46	1.1287	2.1468	3.871	3.352	2.001	531	229.9	54.3	10.20	86.9	25.53	2.54	5
10	3.0172	373.7	0.01612	285.14	546.55	1.1928	2.1161	4.227	3.878	2.236	480	224.8	50.3	10.71	83.0	27.85	1.97	10
15	3.3755	357.9	0.01377	305.36	541.71	1.2602	2.0804	4.773	4.713	2.611	427	218.9	46.2	11.34	79.0	30.90	1.43	15
20	3.7655	339.0	0.01160	327.57	533.99	1.3328	2.0369	5.746	6.249	3.299	368	212.1	41.8	12.17	75.2	35.30	0.93	20
25	4.1903	315.0	0.00952	353.26	521.20	1.4152	1.9785	8.05	10.02	4.96	302	204.1	37.0	13.38	72.0	42.79	0.48	25
30	4.6551	276.3	0.00723	388.24	494.95	1.5263	1.8783	21.69	32.79	14.35	220	192.0	30.6	15.75	74.9	64.07	0.11	30
32.17[c]	4.8722	206.2	0.00485	438.99	438.99	1.6901	1.6901	∞	∞	∞	0	0.0	—	—	∞	∞	0.00	32.17

[a]Temperatures on ITS-90 scale [b]Normal boiling point [c]Critical point

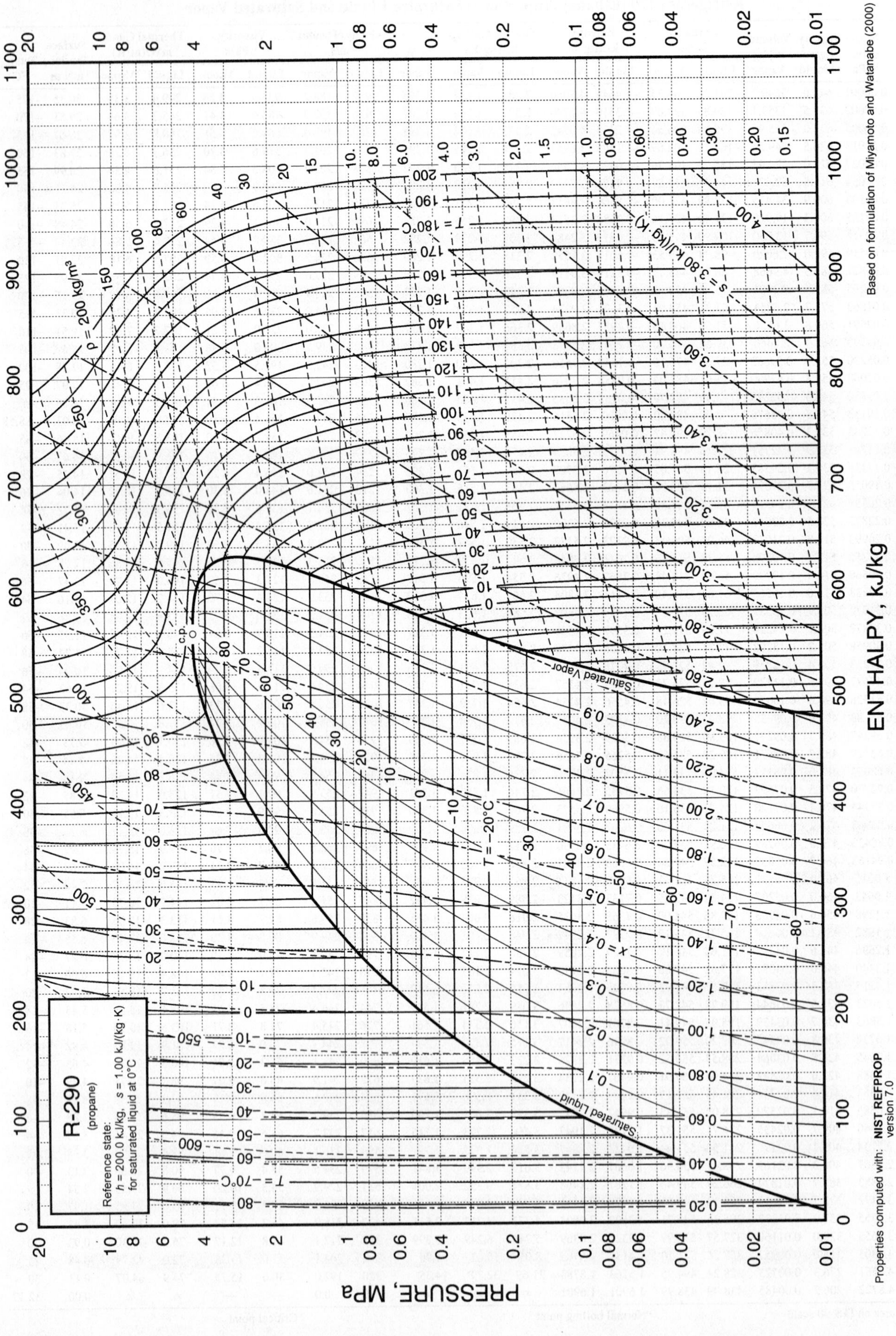

Fig. 21 Pressure-Enthalpy Diagram for Refrigerant 290 (Propane)

Refrigerant 290 (Propane) Properties of Saturated Liquid and Saturated Vapor

Temp., °C	Pressure, MPa	Density, kg/m³ Liquid	Volume, m³/kg Vapor	Enthalpy, kJ/kg Liquid	Enthalpy, kJ/kg Vapor	Entropy, kJ/(kg·K) Liquid	Entropy, kJ/(kg·K) Vapor	Specific Heat c_p, kJ/(kg·K) Liquid	Specific Heat c_p, kJ/(kg·K) Vapor	c_p/c_v Vapor	Velocity of Sound, m/s Liquid	Velocity of Sound, m/s Vapor	Viscosity, μPa·s Liquid	Viscosity, μPa·s Vapor	Thermal Cond., mW/(m·K) Liquid	Thermal Cond., mW/(m·K) Vapor	Surface Tension, mN/m	Temp., °C
–150	0.00001	694.6	4316.4	–123.78	402.06	–0.6903	3.5796	1.962	1.020	1.227	1880	168.8	1343.0	3.55	192.9	3.68	31.84	–150
–140	0.00003	684.5	864.49	–104.09	412.43	–0.5366	3.3426	1.977	1.054	1.218	1813	174.9	985.4	3.80	187.7	4.28	30.29	–140
–130	0.00012	674.4	223.53	–84.23	423.12	–0.3929	3.1514	1.994	1.087	1.210	1745	180.7	761.7	4.05	182.2	4.90	28.76	–130
–120	0.00041	664.3	70.785	–64.21	434.11	–0.2576	2.9962	2.012	1.119	1.203	1679	186.3	611.6	4.31	176.4	5.55	27.24	–120
–110	0.00116	654.0	26.386	–43.99	445.38	–0.1298	2.8697	2.032	1.151	1.197	1612	191.7	505.0	4.56	170.4	6.23	25.73	–110
–100	0.00290	643.7	11.231	–23.56	456.88	–0.0083	2.7664	2.054	1.184	1.192	1545	196.8	425.7	4.82	164.4	6.94	24.23	–100
–90	0.00645	633.3	5.3300	–2.90	468.58	0.1077	2.6820	2.078	1.220	1.188	1478	201.5	364.5	5.08	158.2	7.67	22.74	–90
–80	0.01305	622.8	2.7676	18.03	480.44	0.2189	2.6130	2.106	1.258	1.184	1411	205.9	315.9	5.34	152.1	8.43	21.27	–80
–70	0.02440	612.0	1.5487	39.25	492.41	0.3259	2.5566	2.137	1.300	1.182	1345	209.9	276.4	5.60	145.9	9.22	19.81	–70
–60	0.04269	601.1	0.92250	60.81	504.44	0.4294	2.5107	2.172	1.346	1.181	1278	213.5	243.6	5.85	139.8	10.04	18.37	–60
–50	0.07057	589.9	0.57905	82.75	516.48	0.5298	2.4734	2.212	1.397	1.182	1213	216.5	216.0	6.11	133.8	10.88	16.94	–50
–42.11[b]	0.10133	580.9	0.41388	100.36	525.95	0.6070	2.4491	2.246	1.440	1.183	1161	218.4	197.2	6.31	129.2	11.57	15.83	–42.11
–40	0.11112	578.4	0.37985	105.12	528.48	0.6275	2.4433	2.256	1.453	1.184	1147	218.9	192.6	6.36	128.0	11.76	15.54	–40
–38	0.12105	576.1	0.35076	109.65	530.87	0.6468	2.4380	2.265	1.464	1.185	1134	219.3	188.3	6.41	126.8	11.94	15.26	–38
–36	0.13166	573.8	0.32437	114.20	533.26	0.6660	2.4330	2.275	1.476	1.185	1121	219.6	184.1	6.47	125.6	12.12	14.98	–36
–34	0.14297	571.4	0.30037	118.77	535.64	0.6851	2.4282	2.285	1.488	1.186	1108	220.0	180.1	6.52	124.5	12.30	14.70	–34
–32	0.15502	569.0	0.27853	123.36	538.01	0.7041	2.4236	2.295	1.501	1.187	1095	220.3	176.1	6.57	123.3	12.48	14.42	–32
–30	0.16783	566.6	0.25861	127.97	540.38	0.7231	2.4192	2.305	1.513	1.188	1082	220.6	172.3	6.62	122.2	12.67	14.15	–30
–28	0.18144	564.2	0.24041	132.61	542.75	0.7419	2.4150	2.316	1.526	1.189	1069	220.9	168.6	6.67	121.1	12.86	13.87	–28
–26	0.19589	561.8	0.22376	137.26	545.11	0.7607	2.4109	2.327	1.539	1.191	1056	221.1	165.0	6.73	120.0	13.05	13.60	–26
–24	0.21119	559.4	0.20851	141.94	547.46	0.7795	2.4071	2.338	1.553	1.192	1043	221.3	161.5	6.78	118.8	13.24	13.33	–24
–22	0.22739	556.9	0.19452	146.64	549.80	0.7982	2.4034	2.349	1.566	1.193	1030	221.5	158.1	6.83	117.7	13.43	13.06	–22
–20	0.24452	554.5	0.18167	151.36	552.13	0.8168	2.3999	2.361	1.580	1.195	1016	221.6	154.7	6.89	116.6	13.63	12.79	–20
–18	0.26261	552.0	0.16984	156.11	554.46	0.8353	2.3965	2.373	1.595	1.197	1003	221.8	151.5	6.94	115.5	13.83	12.52	–18
–16	0.28170	549.5	0.15894	160.88	556.77	0.8538	2.3933	2.385	1.609	1.198	990	221.8	148.3	6.99	114.4	14.03	12.25	–16
–14	0.30181	546.9	0.14889	165.68	559.08	0.8722	2.3903	2.397	1.624	1.200	977	221.9	145.2	7.05	113.4	14.23	11.98	–14
–12	0.32300	544.4	0.13961	170.50	561.37	0.8906	2.3874	2.410	1.639	1.202	964	221.9	142.2	7.10	112.3	14.44	11.71	–12
–10	0.34528	541.8	0.13103	175.35	563.65	0.9090	2.3846	2.423	1.655	1.205	951	221.9	139.3	7.16	111.2	14.65	11.45	–10
–8	0.36870	539.2	0.12308	180.22	565.92	0.9273	2.3819	2.436	1.671	1.207	938	221.8	136.4	7.22	110.1	14.86	11.18	–8
–6	0.39329	536.6	0.11571	185.12	568.18	0.9455	2.3794	2.450	1.687	1.209	925	221.8	133.6	7.27	109.1	15.08	10.92	–6
–4	0.41909	533.9	0.10887	190.05	570.42	0.9637	2.3769	2.464	1.704	1.212	912	221.6	130.9	7.33	108.0	15.29	10.65	–4
–2	0.44613	531.3	0.10252	195.01	572.65	0.9819	2.3746	2.478	1.721	1.215	899	221.5	128.2	7.39	107.0	15.52	10.39	–2
0	0.47446	528.6	0.09661	200.00	574.87	1.0000	2.3724	2.493	1.739	1.218	885	221.3	125.6	7.45	106.0	15.74	10.13	0
2	0.50410	525.9	0.09111	205.02	577.06	1.0181	2.3703	2.508	1.757	1.221	872	221.1	123.0	7.51	104.9	15.97	9.87	2
4	0.53510	523.1	0.08598	210.06	579.24	1.0362	2.3682	2.524	1.776	1.225	859	220.8	120.5	7.57	103.9	16.20	9.62	4
6	0.56749	520.4	0.08120	215.14	581.41	1.0542	2.3663	2.540	1.795	1.229	846	220.5	118.1	7.63	102.9	16.44	9.36	6
8	0.60131	517.6	0.07673	220.25	583.55	1.0722	2.3644	2.556	1.815	1.232	833	220.2	115.7	7.69	101.9	16.68	9.10	8
10	0.63660	514.7	0.07255	225.40	585.67	1.0902	2.3626	2.573	1.835	1.237	819	219.8	113.3	7.75	100.9	16.93	8.85	10
12	0.67340	511.9	0.06865	230.57	587.77	1.1082	2.3608	2.591	1.856	1.241	806	219.3	111.0	7.82	99.9	17.18	8.60	12
14	0.71175	509.0	0.06498	235.79	589.85	1.1261	2.3592	2.609	1.878	1.246	793	218.9	108.8	7.88	99.0	17.44	8.34	14
16	0.75168	506.0	0.06155	241.03	591.91	1.1440	2.3575	2.627	1.901	1.251	780	218.4	106.6	7.95	98.0	17.70	8.09	16
18	0.79324	503.1	0.05833	246.32	593.94	1.1620	2.3560	2.646	1.925	1.256	766	217.8	104.4	8.02	97.0	17.97	7.85	18
20	0.83646	500.1	0.05530	251.64	595.95	1.1799	2.3544	2.666	1.949	1.262	753	217.2	102.3	8.09	96.1	18.24	7.60	20
22	0.88139	497.0	0.05246	256.99	597.93	1.1978	2.3529	2.687	1.975	1.268	739	216.6	100.2	8.16	95.1	18.53	7.35	22
24	0.92807	493.9	0.04978	262.39	599.88	1.2157	2.3514	2.708	2.001	1.275	726	215.9	98.1	8.23	94.2	18.81	7.11	24
26	0.97653	490.8	0.04726	267.83	601.80	1.2336	2.3500	2.730	2.029	1.282	713	215.2	96.1	8.31	93.3	19.11	6.87	26
28	1.0268	487.6	0.04488	273.31	603.68	1.2515	2.3486	2.753	2.058	1.290	699	214.4	94.1	8.38	92.3	19.41	6.62	28
30	1.0790	484.4	0.04264	278.83	605.54	1.2695	2.3471	2.777	2.088	1.298	685	213.5	92.2	8.46	91.4	19.72	6.38	30
32	1.1331	481.1	0.04053	284.40	607.35	1.2874	2.3457	2.802	2.119	1.307	672	212.6	90.3	8.54	90.5	20.05	6.15	32
34	1.1891	477.8	0.03853	290.01	609.13	1.3053	2.3443	2.827	2.152	1.316	658	211.7	88.4	8.63	89.6	20.38	5.91	34
36	1.2472	474.4	0.03664	295.68	610.87	1.3233	2.3429	2.855	2.187	1.326	645	210.7	86.5	8.71	88.7	20.72	5.68	36
38	1.3072	471.0	0.03485	301.39	612.57	1.3413	2.3414	2.883	2.224	1.337	631	209.7	84.7	8.80	87.8	21.07	5.44	38
40	1.3694	467.5	0.03315	307.15	614.21	1.3594	2.3399	2.913	2.263	1.349	617	208.6	82.8	8.89	86.9	21.43	5.21	40
42	1.4337	463.9	0.03154	312.96	615.81	1.3774	2.3384	2.944	2.304	1.362	603	207.4	81.0	8.99	86.0	21.81	4.98	42
44	1.5002	460.3	0.03002	318.83	617.36	1.3955	2.3368	2.977	2.348	1.375	589	206.2	79.3	9.08	85.2	22.20	4.76	44
46	1.5690	456.5	0.02857	324.76	618.86	1.4137	2.3352	3.012	2.395	1.391	575	204.9	77.5	9.19	84.3	22.60	4.53	46
48	1.6400	452.7	0.02720	330.75	620.29	1.4319	2.3335	3.050	2.445	1.407	561	203.6	75.8	9.29	83.5	23.03	4.31	48
50	1.7133	448.9	0.02589	336.80	621.66	1.4502	2.3317	3.089	2.499	1.425	547	202.2	74.1	9.40	82.6	23.47	4.09	50
55	1.9072	438.8	0.02288	352.23	624.77	1.4962	2.3268	3.201	2.652	1.478	511	198.3	69.8	9.70	80.5	24.65	3.55	55
60	2.1168	428.0	0.02020	368.14	627.36	1.5429	2.3210	3.337	2.841	1.548	474	194.1	65.7	10.03	78.4	26.00	3.02	60
65	2.3430	416.3	0.01781	384.60	629.29	1.5903	2.3139	3.509	3.086	1.641	437	189.3	61.5	10.42	76.3	27.56	2.52	65
70	2.5868	403.6	0.01565	401.75	630.37	1.6389	2.3052	3.735	3.421	1.773	398	184.0	57.4	10.86	74.3	29.41	2.03	70
75	2.8493	389.5	0.01367	419.76	630.33	1.6891	2.2939	4.053	3.914	1.970	358	178.2	53.2	11.40	72.2	31.71	1.56	75
80	3.1319	373.3	0.01185	438.93	628.73	1.7417	2.2791	4.545	4.707	2.288	315	171.6	48.8	12.07	70.2	34.75	1.12	80
85	3.4361	354.0	0.01012	459.81	624.75	1.7980	2.2586	5.433	6.182	2.883	269	164.1	44.1	12.96	68.3	39.13	0.72	85
90	3.7641	328.8	0.00840	483.71	616.47	1.8616	2.2272	7.623	9.888	4.374	218	155.5	38.8	14.28	67.1	46.66	0.36	90
95	4.1195	286.5	0.00640	516.33	595.81	1.9476	2.1635	23.59	36.07	14.62	158	144.1	31.4	17.00	73.6	69.48	0.06	95
96.74[c]	4.2512	220.5	0.00454	555.24	555.24	2.0516	2.0516	∞	∞	∞	0	0.0	—	—	∞	∞	0.00	96.74

[b]Normal boiling point

[c]Critical point

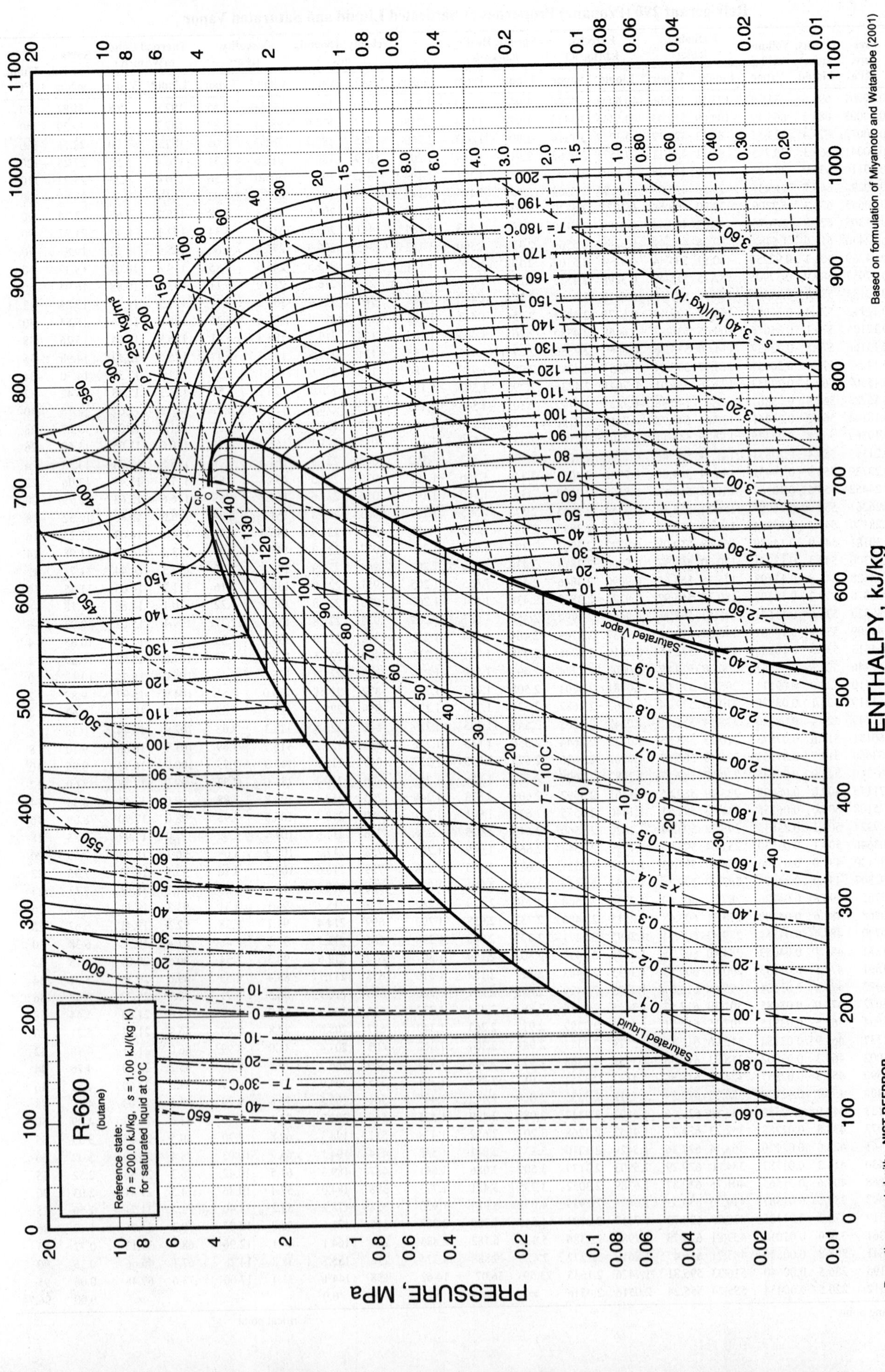

Fig. 22 Pressure-Enthalpy Diagram for Refrigerant 600 (*n*-Butane)

Refrigerant 600 (*n*-Butane) Properties of Saturated Liquid and Saturated Vapor

Temp.,[a] °C	Pressure, MPa	Density, kg/m³ Liquid	Volume, m³/kg Vapor	Enthalpy, kJ/kg Liquid	Enthalpy, kJ/kg Vapor	Entropy, kJ/(kg·K) Liquid	Entropy, kJ/(kg·K) Vapor	Specific Heat c_p, kJ/(kg·K) Liquid	Specific Heat c_p, kJ/(kg·K) Vapor	c_p/c_v Vapor	Velocity of Sound, m/s Liquid	Velocity of Sound, m/s Vapor	Viscosity, µPa·s Liquid	Viscosity, µPa·s Vapor	Thermal Cond., mW/(m·K) Liquid	Thermal Cond., mW/(m·K) Vapor	Surface Tension, mN/m	Temp., °C
–100	0.00016	699.3	150.44	–13.65	450.85	0.0318	2.7144	2.013	1.231	1.132	1592	167.4	792.2	4.30	161.6	6.83	28.03	–100
–95	0.00028	694.6	91.606	–3.57	457.02	0.0892	2.6746	2.021	1.247	1.130	1563	169.6	719.0	4.43	159.4	7.12	27.33	–95
–90	0.00045	689.9	57.588	6.56	463.27	0.1453	2.6389	2.029	1.263	1.128	1534	171.8	655.9	4.55	157.2	7.43	26.64	–90
–85	0.00072	685.2	37.271	16.73	469.58	0.2000	2.6069	2.038	1.279	1.127	1505	174.0	601.2	4.68	154.9	7.73	25.94	–85
–80	0.00111	680.5	24.773	26.94	475.97	0.2536	2.5784	2.048	1.295	1.125	1477	176.1	553.2	4.81	152.6	8.05	25.26	–80
–75	0.00168	675.8	16.873	37.21	482.41	0.3061	2.5529	2.058	1.312	1.124	1449	178.1	510.9	4.93	150.2	8.38	24.57	–75
–70	0.00247	671.0	11.752	47.53	488.92	0.3575	2.5303	2.069	1.330	1.122	1420	180.1	473.4	5.06	147.9	8.71	23.89	–70
–65	0.00355	666.2	8.3565	57.90	495.50	0.4080	2.5103	2.081	1.347	1.121	1392	182.1	439.9	5.18	145.5	9.05	23.22	–65
–60	0.00501	661.4	6.0558	68.34	502.13	0.4575	2.4926	2.094	1.366	1.120	1364	184.0	409.8	5.31	143.1	9.40	22.54	–60
–55	0.00695	656.6	4.4659	78.85	508.82	0.5062	2.4772	2.108	1.385	1.119	1336	185.8	382.8	5.43	140.8	9.75	21.88	–55
–50	0.00947	651.7	3.3470	89.42	515.56	0.5541	2.4638	2.122	1.404	1.118	1309	187.5	358.3	5.55	138.4	10.11	21.21	–50
–45	0.01270	646.8	2.5462	100.07	522.35	0.6013	2.4522	2.137	1.425	1.118	1281	189.2	336.1	5.68	136.0	10.48	20.55	–45
–40	0.01679	641.9	1.9638	110.80	529.19	0.6478	2.4423	2.153	1.446	1.117	1253	190.8	315.8	5.80	133.6	10.86	19.90	–40
–35	0.02190	636.9	1.5341	121.62	536.08	0.6937	2.4340	2.170	1.468	1.117	1226	192.3	297.3	5.92	131.3	11.25	19.25	–35
–30	0.02821	631.9	1.2127	132.52	543.01	0.7389	2.4271	2.188	1.490	1.116	1198	193.8	280.3	6.04	128.9	11.64	18.60	–30
–25	0.03591	626.8	0.96911	143.51	549.98	0.7836	2.4216	2.206	1.514	1.116	1171	195.1	264.7	6.16	126.6	12.05	17.96	–25
–20	0.04521	621.7	0.78237	154.60	556.98	0.8278	2.4173	2.226	1.538	1.116	1144	196.3	250.3	6.28	124.3	12.46	17.32	–20
–15	0.05635	616.6	0.63759	165.79	564.02	0.8715	2.4141	2.246	1.563	1.117	1116	197.5	237.0	6.41	122.0	12.88	16.69	–15
–10	0.06955	611.4	0.52415	177.08	571.08	0.9147	2.4120	2.267	1.589	1.117	1089	198.5	224.7	6.53	119.8	13.30	16.06	–10
–5	0.08509	606.1	0.43441	188.48	578.17	0.9576	2.4108	2.289	1.616	1.118	1062	199.4	213.2	6.65	117.5	13.74	15.44	–5
–0.49[b]	0.10132	601.3	0.36910	198.87	584.58	0.9959	2.4105	2.310	1.641	1.119	1038	200.1	203.5	6.76	115.5	14.14	14.88	–0.49
0	0.10323	600.7	0.36275	200.00	585.27	1.0000	2.4105	2.312	1.644	1.119	1035	200.2	202.5	6.77	115.3	14.19	14.82	0
2	0.11127	598.6	0.33818	204.64	588.12	1.0169	2.4106	2.321	1.655	1.120	1024	200.5	198.4	6.82	114.4	14.37	14.58	2
4	0.11980	596.4	0.31562	209.30	590.97	1.0337	2.4108	2.331	1.667	1.120	1014	200.7	194.4	6.87	113.6	14.55	14.33	4
6	0.12882	594.2	0.29488	213.98	593.82	1.0505	2.4112	2.341	1.678	1.121	1003	201.0	190.6	6.91	112.7	14.74	14.09	6
8	0.13837	592.0	0.27578	218.68	596.67	1.0672	2.4116	2.350	1.690	1.122	992	201.2	186.8	6.96	111.8	14.93	13.85	8
10	0.14845	589.8	0.25817	223.40	599.53	1.0838	2.4122	2.360	1.702	1.122	981	201.4	183.2	7.01	111.0	15.11	13.60	10
12	0.15909	587.6	0.24192	228.13	602.38	1.1005	2.4129	2.371	1.715	1.123	971	201.6	179.6	7.06	110.1	15.31	13.36	12
14	0.17031	585.4	0.22691	232.89	605.24	1.1170	2.4137	2.381	1.727	1.124	960	201.7	176.1	7.11	109.3	15.50	13.12	14
16	0.18213	583.1	0.21302	237.68	608.09	1.1335	2.4146	2.391	1.740	1.125	949	201.9	172.7	7.16	108.4	15.69	12.88	16
18	0.19457	580.9	0.20016	242.48	610.95	1.1500	2.4156	2.402	1.752	1.126	938	202.0	169.4	7.21	107.6	15.89	12.65	18
20	0.20765	578.6	0.18823	247.30	613.80	1.1665	2.4167	2.413	1.765	1.127	928	202.0	166.2	7.26	106.7	16.09	12.41	20
22	0.22139	576.3	0.17717	252.15	616.66	1.1829	2.4179	2.424	1.778	1.128	917	202.1	163.0	7.31	105.9	16.29	12.17	22
24	0.23582	574.0	0.16688	257.02	619.51	1.1992	2.4191	2.435	1.792	1.129	906	202.1	159.9	7.36	105.1	16.49	11.94	24
26	0.25095	571.7	0.15732	261.91	622.36	1.2155	2.4205	2.446	1.805	1.130	895	202.2	156.9	7.41	104.3	16.70	11.70	26
28	0.26680	569.3	0.14842	266.82	625.21	1.2318	2.4219	2.458	1.819	1.131	885	202.1	153.9	7.47	103.5	16.90	11.47	28
30	0.28341	567.0	0.14012	271.76	628.06	1.2481	2.4234	2.470	1.833	1.133	874	202.1	151.1	7.52	102.7	17.11	11.24	30
32	0.30079	564.6	0.13238	276.72	630.91	1.2643	2.4250	2.481	1.847	1.134	863	202.0	148.2	7.57	101.9	17.33	11.00	32
34	0.31897	562.2	0.12516	281.71	633.75	1.2805	2.4266	2.494	1.862	1.136	853	201.9	145.5	7.62	101.1	17.54	10.77	34
36	0.33796	559.8	0.11841	286.72	636.59	1.2966	2.4283	2.506	1.876	1.137	842	201.8	142.8	7.68	100.3	17.76	10.54	36
38	0.35779	557.4	0.11209	291.76	639.42	1.3127	2.4301	2.518	1.891	1.139	831	201.7	140.2	7.73	99.5	17.98	10.32	38
40	0.37849	554.9	0.10618	296.82	642.25	1.3288	2.4319	2.531	1.906	1.141	820	201.5	137.6	7.79	98.7	18.21	10.09	40
42	0.40007	552.4	0.10065	301.90	645.08	1.3449	2.4338	2.544	1.922	1.143	810	201.3	135.0	7.84	97.9	18.43	9.86	42
44	0.42256	550.0	0.09545	307.02	647.90	1.3609	2.4358	2.557	1.937	1.145	799	201.1	132.5	7.90	97.2	18.66	9.64	44
46	0.44599	547.4	0.09058	312.15	650.71	1.3769	2.4378	2.571	1.953	1.147	788	200.8	130.1	7.95	96.4	18.90	9.41	46
48	0.47038	544.9	0.08600	317.32	653.52	1.3929	2.4398	2.585	1.970	1.149	777	200.5	127.7	8.01	95.7	19.14	9.19	48
50	0.49575	542.3	0.08170	322.51	656.32	1.4089	2.4419	2.598	1.986	1.151	767	200.2	125.4	8.07	94.9	19.38	8.97	50
55	0.56365	535.8	0.07201	335.62	663.28	1.4488	2.4473	2.635	2.029	1.158	740	199.2	119.7	8.22	93.1	20.00	8.42	55
60	0.63824	529.1	0.06366	348.91	670.19	1.4885	2.4529	2.673	2.075	1.165	713	198.1	114.3	8.38	91.3	20.64	7.87	60
65	0.71991	522.3	0.05642	362.39	677.02	1.5282	2.4587	2.713	2.123	1.173	685	196.7	109.1	8.54	89.5	21.32	7.34	65
70	0.80908	515.2	0.05012	376.06	683.77	1.5679	2.4646	2.756	2.174	1.183	658	195.1	104.1	8.71	87.8	22.03	6.81	70
75	0.90616	507.9	0.04462	389.95	690.41	1.6075	2.4705	2.802	2.229	1.194	631	193.3	99.3	8.89	86.1	22.77	6.29	75
80	1.0116	500.4	0.03978	404.06	696.94	1.6471	2.4765	2.851	2.288	1.207	603	191.2	94.7	9.08	84.5	23.56	5.78	80
85	1.1258	492.6	0.03552	418.40	703.32	1.6868	2.4824	2.905	2.353	1.223	575	188.8	90.2	9.29	82.9	24.39	5.28	85
90	1.2493	484.5	0.03175	433.00	709.53	1.7266	2.4881	2.964	2.425	1.241	546	186.1	85.8	9.51	81.3	25.28	4.79	90
95	1.3825	476.0	0.02840	447.87	715.53	1.7665	2.4936	3.029	2.506	1.263	518	183.1	81.6	9.75	79.7	26.23	4.31	95
100	1.5259	467.1	0.02541	463.03	721.29	1.8066	2.4987	3.102	2.599	1.290	488	179.8	77.4	10.01	78.2	27.26	3.84	100
105	1.6801	457.8	0.02273	478.51	726.75	1.8469	2.5034	3.186	2.708	1.324	458	176.1	73.3	10.29	76.8	28.37	3.38	105
110	1.8456	447.9	0.02032	494.36	731.87	1.8876	2.5075	3.285	2.841	1.366	428	172.0	69.3	10.61	75.3	29.60	2.93	110
115	2.0230	437.3	0.01813	510.61	736.55	1.9287	2.5108	3.403	3.004	1.420	396	167.5	65.4	10.96	73.9	30.96	2.50	115
120	2.2131	425.9	0.01615	527.34	740.69	1.9704	2.5131	3.552	3.213	1.492	364	162.5	61.4	11.37	72.5	32.50	2.08	120
125	2.4166	413.4	0.01432	544.65	744.15	2.0129	2.5140	3.748	3.493	1.592	331	157.0	57.4	11.83	71.1	34.29	1.68	125
130	2.6344	399.6	0.01264	562.68	746.70	2.0566	2.5130	4.023	3.891	1.739	296	150.8	53.4	12.39	69.8	36.44	1.30	130
135	2.8675	383.7	0.01105	581.69	747.97	2.1020	2.5094	4.450	4.511	1.973	260	144.1	49.2	13.07	68.4	39.16	0.94	135
140	3.1172	364.7	0.00953	602.17	747.29	2.1502	2.5015	5.227	5.631	2.405	222	136.5	44.7	13.97	67.3	42.94	0.60	140
145	3.3853	339.9	0.00801	625.32	743.11	2.2041	2.4858	7.147	8.349	3.462	182	128.0	39.6	15.27	66.7	49.21	0.31	145
150	3.6746	297.7	0.00621	656.27	729.01	2.2755	2.4474	19.80	25.55	10.14	136	117.8	32.5	17.87	73.0	67.32	0.06	150
151.98[c]	3.7960	228.0	0.00439	693.91	693.91	2.3631	2.3631	∞	∞	∞	0	0.0	—	—	∞	∞	0.00	151.98

[a]Temperatures on ITS-90 scale [b]Normal boiling point [c]Critical point

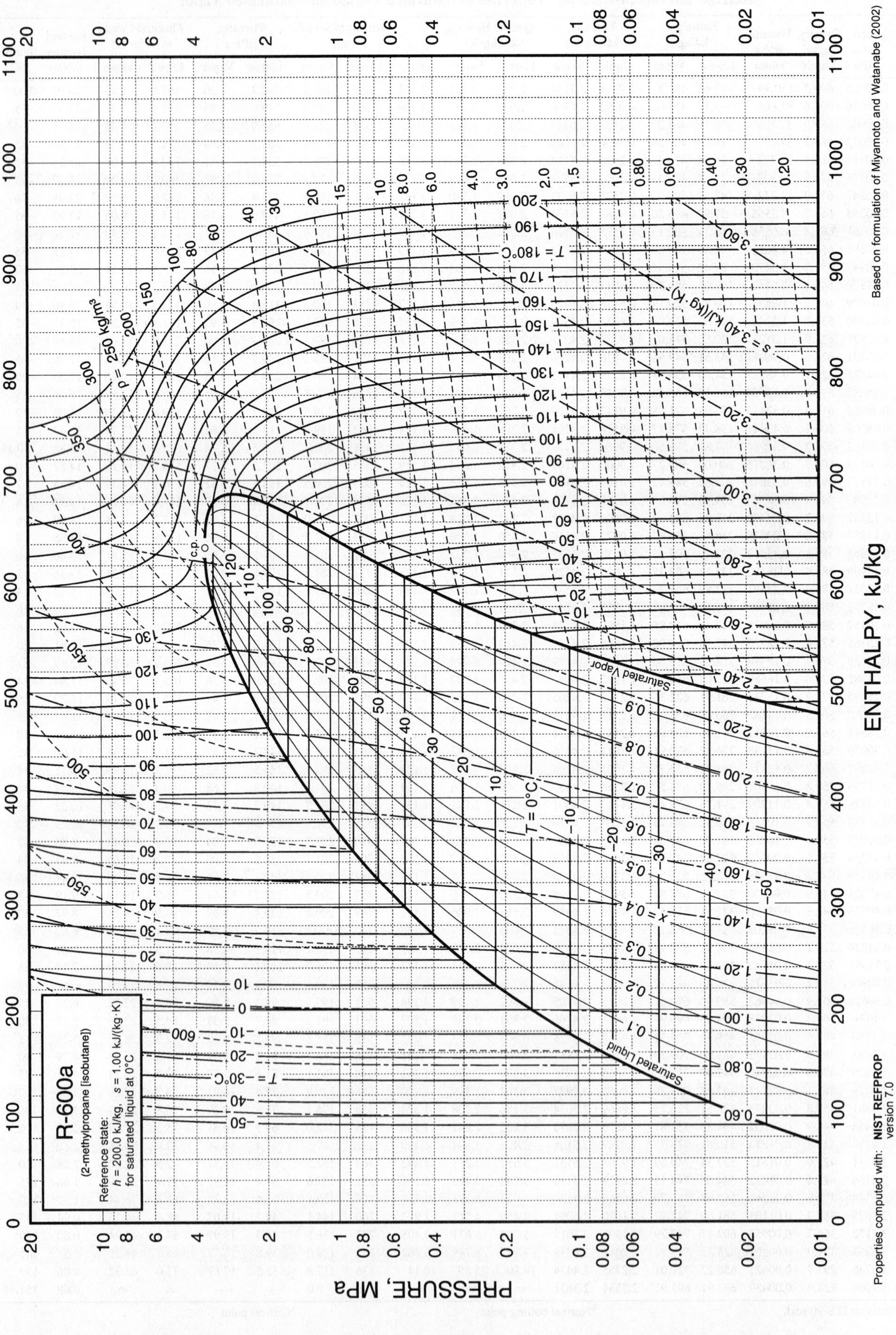

Fig. 23 Pressure-Enthalpy Diagram for Refrigerant 600a (Isobutane)

Refrigerant 600a (Isobutane) Properties of Saturated Liquid and Saturated Vapor

Temp.,[a] °C	Pressure, MPa	Density, kg/m³ Liquid	Volume, m³/kg Vapor	Enthalpy, kJ/kg Liquid	Enthalpy, kJ/kg Vapor	Entropy, kJ/(kg·K) Liquid	Entropy, kJ/(kg·K) Vapor	Specific Heat c_p, kJ/(kg·K) Liquid	Specific Heat c_p, kJ/(kg·K) Vapor	c_p/c_v Vapor	Velocity of Sound, m/s Liquid	Velocity of Sound, m/s Vapor	Viscosity, µPa·s Liquid	Viscosity, µPa·s Vapor	Thermal Cond., mW/(m·K) Liquid	Thermal Cond., mW/(m·K) Vapor	Surface Tension, mN/m	Temp., °C
–100	0.00038	683.9	65.234	–6.40	428.19	0.0671	2.5770	1.878	1.131	1.145	1558	168.3	936.5	4.40	140.0	6.03	25.52	–100
–95	0.00062	679.1	41.078	3.04	433.86	0.1208	2.5391	1.894	1.151	1.143	1526	170.5	837.2	4.53	138.0	6.39	24.88	–95
–90	0.00098	674.2	26.648	12.55	439.62	0.1734	2.5052	1.911	1.171	1.140	1494	172.6	753.2	4.65	136.0	6.76	24.24	–90
–85	0.00151	669.4	17.764	22.14	445.46	0.2251	2.4750	1.927	1.191	1.138	1462	174.7	681.3	4.78	134.0	7.13	23.59	–85
–80	0.00227	664.5	12.140	31.82	451.39	0.2759	2.4481	1.944	1.212	1.136	1431	176.7	619.2	4.91	131.9	7.50	22.96	–80
–75	0.00333	659.5	8.4874	41.59	457.40	0.3258	2.4242	1.961	1.233	1.134	1400	178.7	565.3	5.03	129.8	7.88	22.32	–75
–70	0.00478	654.6	6.0592	51.44	463.48	0.3749	2.4031	1.979	1.254	1.132	1370	180.6	518.1	5.16	127.7	8.27	21.68	–70
–65	0.00671	649.6	4.4096	61.38	469.63	0.4232	2.3845	1.997	1.276	1.130	1340	182.4	476.6	5.28	125.6	8.67	21.05	–65
–60	0.00927	644.6	3.2662	71.41	475.86	0.4708	2.3683	2.015	1.298	1.129	1309	184.2	439.8	5.41	123.5	9.06	20.41	–60
–55	0.01258	639.5	2.4590	81.54	482.14	0.5177	2.3541	2.034	1.321	1.128	1280	185.9	407.0	5.53	121.3	9.47	19.78	–55
–50	0.01680	634.4	1.8792	91.76	488.49	0.5640	2.3419	2.054	1.344	1.126	1250	187.5	377.6	5.65	119.2	9.88	19.16	–50
–45	0.02211	629.3	1.4561	102.09	494.89	0.6098	2.3315	2.074	1.368	1.126	1220	189.0	351.2	5.78	117.1	10.29	18.53	–45
–40	0.02870	624.1	1.1427	112.51	501.35	0.6549	2.3227	2.094	1.393	1.125	1191	190.4	327.4	5.90	115.0	10.71	17.91	–40
–35	0.03680	618.9	0.90737	123.04	507.85	0.6995	2.3154	2.115	1.418	1.125	1162	191.8	305.8	6.02	112.9	11.14	17.29	–35
–30	0.04662	613.6	0.72839	133.68	514.40	0.7437	2.3095	2.137	1.444	1.125	1133	193.0	286.2	6.14	110.8	11.57	16.67	–30
–25	0.05843	608.3	0.59062	144.43	520.99	0.7874	2.3048	2.159	1.471	1.125	1104	194.1	268.3	6.26	108.7	12.01	16.05	–25
–20	0.07248	602.9	0.48339	155.30	527.61	0.8306	2.3013	2.182	1.499	1.125	1075	195.1	251.9	6.38	106.6	12.45	15.44	–20
–15	0.08905	597.4	0.39904	166.29	534.26	0.8735	2.2989	2.206	1.527	1.126	1047	196.0	236.9	6.50	104.6	12.90	14.83	–15
–11.75[b]	0.10133	593.8	0.35378	173.49	538.60	0.9012	2.2979	2.222	1.547	1.126	1028	196.5	227.8	6.58	103.3	13.20	14.44	–11.75
–10	0.10845	591.9	0.33204	177.40	540.93	0.9160	2.2975	2.231	1.557	1.127	1018	196.8	223.1	6.62	102.6	13.36	14.23	–10
–5	0.13098	586.3	0.27833	188.63	547.63	0.9582	2.2969	2.256	1.587	1.128	990	197.4	210.3	6.74	100.6	13.83	13.63	–5
0	0.15696	580.6	0.23491	200.00	554.34	1.0000	2.2972	2.283	1.619	1.130	961	197.9	198.6	6.86	98.6	14.30	13.03	0
2	0.16839	578.3	0.21989	204.59	557.02	1.0167	2.2975	2.293	1.632	1.131	950	198.0	194.1	6.91	97.9	14.49	12.79	2
4	0.18045	576.0	0.20604	209.19	559.71	1.0333	2.2980	2.304	1.645	1.132	939	198.2	189.8	6.96	97.1	14.68	12.55	4
6	0.19316	573.6	0.19324	213.82	562.40	1.0498	2.2985	2.316	1.658	1.132	928	198.3	185.6	7.01	96.3	14.88	12.32	6
8	0.20654	571.3	0.18140	218.47	565.09	1.0663	2.2992	2.327	1.672	1.133	916	198.3	181.5	7.06	95.5	15.07	12.08	8
10	0.22061	568.9	0.17044	223.15	567.78	1.0828	2.3000	2.338	1.686	1.135	905	198.4	177.5	7.11	94.8	15.27	11.84	10
12	0.23541	566.5	0.16028	227.85	570.47	1.0993	2.3008	2.350	1.699	1.136	894	198.4	173.7	7.16	94.0	15.47	11.61	12
14	0.25094	564.2	0.15086	232.57	573.15	1.1157	2.3018	2.362	1.714	1.137	883	198.4	170.0	7.21	93.3	15.67	11.38	14
16	0.26724	561.7	0.14210	237.32	575.84	1.1320	2.3028	2.374	1.728	1.138	871	198.4	166.3	7.26	92.5	15.88	11.14	16
18	0.28432	559.3	0.13395	242.09	578.52	1.1484	2.3039	2.386	1.743	1.140	860	198.3	162.8	7.31	91.8	16.08	10.91	18
20	0.30222	556.9	0.12637	246.88	581.21	1.1647	2.3051	2.398	1.757	1.141	849	198.2	159.3	7.37	91.1	16.29	10.68	20
22	0.32095	554.4	0.11930	251.70	583.89	1.1810	2.3064	2.411	1.772	1.143	838	198.1	156.0	7.42	90.3	16.50	10.45	22
24	0.34054	551.9	0.11271	256.55	586.56	1.1972	2.3078	2.424	1.788	1.144	826	198.0	152.7	7.47	89.6	16.72	10.22	24
26	0.36102	549.4	0.10655	261.42	589.24	1.2134	2.3093	2.437	1.803	1.146	815	197.8	149.5	7.52	88.9	16.93	9.99	26
28	0.38240	546.9	0.10080	266.32	591.91	1.2296	2.3108	2.450	1.819	1.148	804	197.6	146.5	7.58	88.2	17.15	9.76	28
30	0.40472	544.3	0.09542	271.24	594.57	1.2458	2.3123	2.463	1.835	1.150	793	197.4	143.4	7.63	87.5	17.37	9.53	30
32	0.42800	541.7	0.09038	276.19	597.23	1.2619	2.3140	2.477	1.852	1.152	781	197.1	140.5	7.69	86.8	17.59	9.31	32
34	0.45226	539.1	0.08566	281.17	599.88	1.2780	2.3157	2.491	1.869	1.154	770	196.8	137.6	7.74	86.1	17.82	9.08	34
36	0.47753	536.5	0.08124	286.18	602.53	1.2941	2.3174	2.505	1.886	1.157	759	196.5	134.8	7.80	85.4	18.05	8.86	36
38	0.50384	533.9	0.07708	291.22	605.17	1.3102	2.3192	2.520	1.903	1.159	747	196.2	132.1	7.85	84.7	18.29	8.63	38
40	0.53121	531.2	0.07317	296.28	607.80	1.3263	2.3211	2.535	1.921	1.162	736	195.8	129.4	7.91	84.1	18.52	8.41	40
42	0.55966	528.5	0.06950	301.37	610.43	1.3423	2.3230	2.550	1.939	1.165	725	195.3	126.8	7.97	83.4	18.77	8.19	42
44	0.58923	525.8	0.06605	306.50	613.04	1.3583	2.3249	2.566	1.958	1.168	714	194.9	124.2	8.03	82.7	19.01	7.97	44
46	0.61995	523.0	0.06279	311.65	615.65	1.3744	2.3269	2.582	1.977	1.171	702	194.4	121.7	8.09	82.1	19.26	7.75	46
48	0.65182	520.2	0.05973	316.84	618.24	1.3904	2.3289	2.598	1.997	1.174	691	193.9	119.3	8.15	81.4	19.52	7.53	48
50	0.68490	517.4	0.05683	322.06	620.82	1.4064	2.3309	2.615	2.017	1.178	680	193.3	116.9	8.22	80.8	19.78	7.31	50
55	0.77299	510.2	0.05029	335.25	627.22	1.4464	2.3361	2.659	2.069	1.188	651	191.7	111.1	8.38	79.2	20.45	6.78	55
60	0.86916	502.7	0.04459	348.66	633.53	1.4863	2.3414	2.706	2.125	1.199	622	189.9	105.6	8.56	77.6	21.16	6.24	60
65	0.97386	495.0	0.03962	362.29	639.72	1.5263	2.3467	2.757	2.186	1.213	593	187.8	100.3	8.74	76.1	21.92	5.72	65
70	1.0875	487.0	0.03525	376.17	645.77	1.5664	2.3520	2.812	2.252	1.229	564	185.4	95.2	8.94	74.6	22.72	5.21	70
75	1.2107	478.6	0.03140	390.31	651.64	1.6065	2.3572	2.874	2.326	1.248	535	182.7	90.4	9.16	73.2	23.59	4.71	75
80	1.3438	469.9	0.02799	404.73	657.31	1.6469	2.3621	2.942	2.409	1.272	505	179.7	85.6	9.39	71.8	24.53	4.21	80
85	1.4874	460.7	0.02496	419.46	662.73	1.6874	2.3667	3.020	2.507	1.301	475	176.3	81.0	9.65	70.4	25.56	3.73	85
90	1.6420	451.1	0.02226	434.54	667.86	1.7283	2.3708	3.110	2.625	1.338	444	172.6	76.6	9.95	69.1	26.70	3.26	90
95	1.8081	440.7	0.01983	450.00	672.62	1.7696	2.3743	3.217	2.769	1.385	413	168.4	72.1	10.27	67.8	27.98	2.80	95
100	1.9865	429.6	0.01764	465.90	676.94	1.8114	2.3769	3.347	2.951	1.447	381	163.8	67.8	10.65	66.6	29.44	2.36	100
105	2.1778	417.6	0.01565	482.33	680.70	1.8539	2.3785	3.513	3.189	1.531	348	158.7	63.4	11.09	65.4	31.14	1.93	105
110	2.3826	404.3	0.01383	499.39	683.74	1.8974	2.3785	3.736	3.517	1.650	313	153.1	59.0	11.62	64.2	33.18	1.53	110
115	2.6019	389.4	0.01214	517.26	685.81	1.9423	2.3765	4.059	4.002	1.831	278	146.9	54.5	12.27	63.1	35.72	1.14	115
120	2.8366	372.0	0.01056	536.26	686.46	1.9893	2.3714	4.585	4.806	2.139	240	139.9	49.8	13.09	62.2	39.05	0.78	120
125	3.0880	350.6	0.00902	557.01	684.81	2.0400	2.3610	5.629	6.428	2.770	200	132.1	44.6	14.22	61.8	43.91	0.46	125
130	3.3578	321.0	0.00742	581.26	678.44	2.0985	2.3396	8.91	11.56	4.77	156	123.0	38.5	15.99	63.3	52.88	0.18	130
134.66[c]	3.6290	225.5	0.00443	633.94	633.94	2.2259	2.2259	∞	∞	∞	0	0.0	—	—	∞	∞	0.00	134.66

[a]Temperatures on ITS-90 scale [b]Normal boiling point [c]Critical point

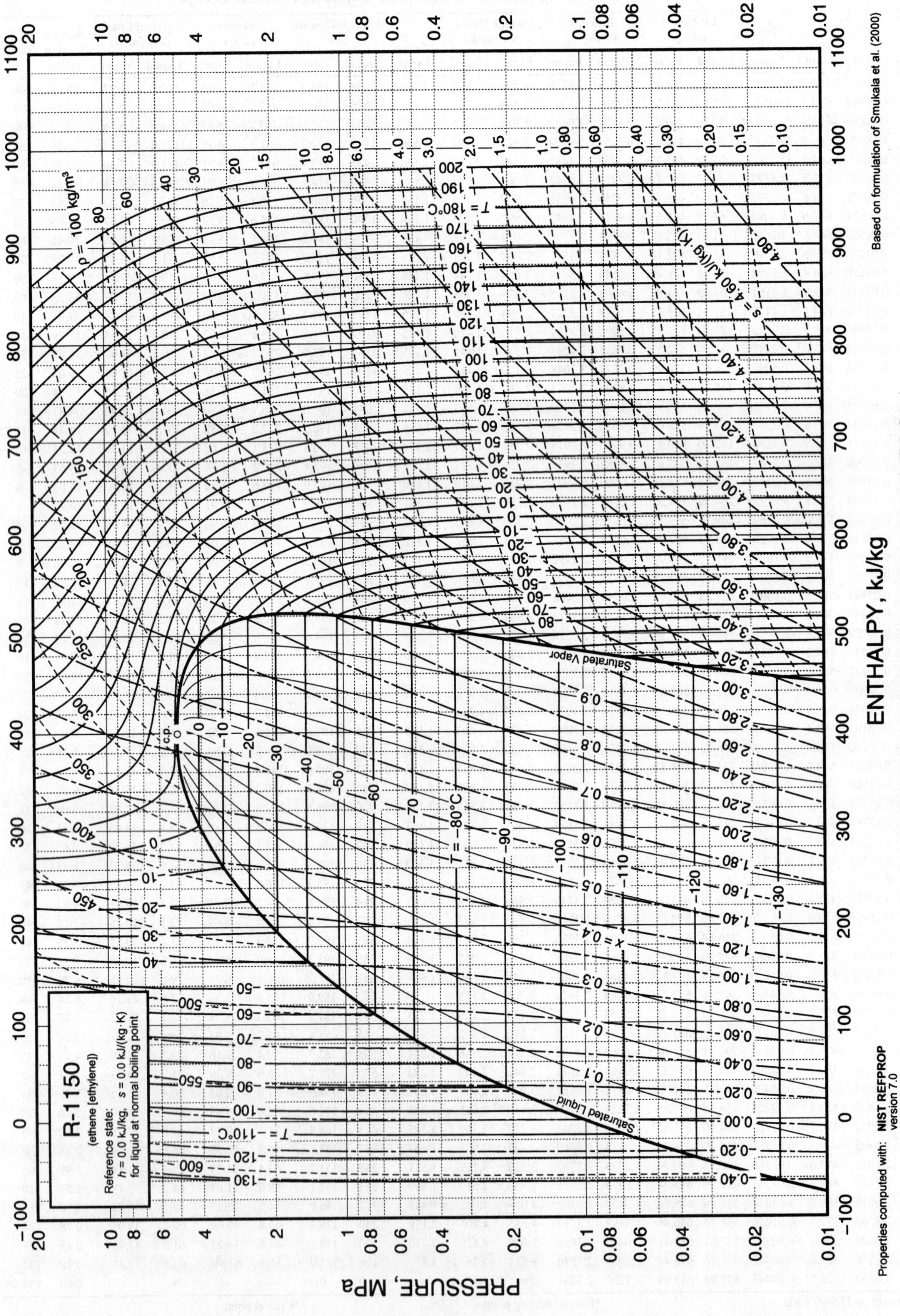

Fig. 24 Pressure-Enthalpy Diagram for Refrigerant 1150 (Ethylene)

Refrigerant 1150 (Ethylene) Properties of Saturated Liquid and Saturated Vapor

Temp.,*	Pres- sure,	Density, kg/m³	Volume, m³/kg	Enthalpy, kJ/kg		Entropy, kJ/(kg·K)		Specific Heat c_p, kJ/(kg·K)		c_p/c_v	Velocity of Sound, m/s		Viscosity, μPa·s		Thermal Cond., mW/(m·K)		Surface Tension,	Temp.,*
°C	MPa	Liquid	Vapor	Liquid	Vapor	Liquid	Vapor	Liquid	Vapor	Vapor	Liquid	Vapor	Liquid	Vapor	Liquid	Vapor	mN/m	°C
–169.16[a]	0.00012	654.6	252.640	–158.09	409.42	–1.1789	4.2787	2.429	1.187	1.333	1767	202.7	685.7	0.77	270.6	6.80	28.14	–169.16
–165	0.00025	649.3	129.690	–147.97	414.35	–1.0835	4.1160	2.432	1.188	1.333	1740	206.7	598.1	1.64	264.9	6.62	27.31	–165
–160	0.00053	643.0	62.7190	–135.81	420.24	–0.9736	3.9408	2.432	1.189	1.333	1707	211.3	514.5	2.47	258.1	6.59	26.33	–160
–155	0.00107	636.6	32.5570	–123.66	426.12	–0.8685	3.7848	2.429	1.191	1.334	1673	215.9	448.6	3.13	251.3	6.71	25.35	–155
–150	0.00203	630.1	17.9740	–111.52	431.97	–0.7679	3.6454	2.424	1.194	1.334	1639	220.3	395.8	3.66	244.5	6.92	24.38	–150
–145	0.00362	623.6	10.4720	–99.41	437.78	–0.6715	3.5204	2.419	1.198	1.335	1604	224.5	352.7	4.09	237.9	7.18	23.42	–145
–140	0.00614	617.1	6.39510	–87.33	443.54	–0.5790	3.4080	2.414	1.203	1.336	1569	228.6	317.2	4.44	231.2	7.47	22.47	–140
–135	0.01000	610.5	4.07100	–75.27	449.24	–0.4902	3.3065	2.409	1.210	1.337	1534	232.5	287.5	4.74	224.7	7.78	21.53	–135
–130	0.01565	603.8	2.68800	–63.22	454.85	–0.4046	3.2145	2.406	1.218	1.339	1498	236.3	262.3	5.00	218.3	8.09	20.59	–130
–125	0.02368	597.1	1.83310	–51.19	460.37	–0.3220	3.1310	2.404	1.228	1.341	1463	239.8	240.7	5.23	212.0	8.39	19.66	–125
–120	0.03474	590.3	1.28650	–39.16	465.79	–0.2423	3.0548	2.404	1.240	1.344	1427	243.2	222.0	5.44	205.8	8.70	18.74	–120
–115	0.04961	583.4	0.92612	–27.12	471.08	–0.1651	2.9850	2.406	1.254	1.348	1390	246.3	205.7	5.63	199.7	9.00	17.83	–115
–110	0.06911	576.5	0.68196	–15.06	476.22	–0.0903	2.9210	2.409	1.271	1.353	1354	249.2	191.3	5.81	193.7	9.30	16.93	–110
–105	0.09420	569.4	0.51239	–2.97	481.21	–0.0176	2.8619	2.416	1.290	1.358	1316	251.8	178.5	5.99	187.9	9.61	16.04	–105
–103.77[b]	0.10133	567.7	0.47899	0.00	482.41	0.0000	2.8481	2.418	1.295	1.360	1307	252.4	175.6	6.03	186.5	9.68	15.83	–103.77
–100	0.12585	562.2	0.39198	9.16	486.03	0.0532	2.8073	2.424	1.312	1.365	1279	254.2	167.0	6.16	182.2	9.92	15.16	–100
–98	0.14059	559.3	0.35377	14.02	487.90	0.0810	2.7866	2.429	1.321	1.368	1264	255.1	162.7	6.23	179.9	10.04	14.82	–98
–96	0.15662	556.4	0.32007	18.90	489.74	0.1085	2.7664	2.434	1.331	1.371	1249	255.9	158.6	6.30	177.7	10.17	14.47	–96
–94	0.17402	553.5	0.29026	23.79	491.55	0.1358	2.7468	2.439	1.342	1.375	1233	256.7	154.7	6.37	175.5	10.30	14.12	–94
–92	0.19285	550.5	0.26382	28.69	493.32	0.1628	2.7277	2.445	1.353	1.379	1218	257.4	150.9	6.44	173.3	10.44	13.78	–92
–90	0.21320	547.5	0.24030	33.60	495.06	0.1896	2.7092	2.451	1.365	1.383	1203	258.1	147.2	6.51	171.2	10.57	13.44	–90
–88	0.23514	544.5	0.21933	38.53	496.76	0.2161	2.6911	2.458	1.377	1.387	1187	258.7	143.6	6.58	169.0	10.71	13.10	–88
–86	0.25874	541.4	0.20058	43.48	498.43	0.2425	2.6734	2.465	1.391	1.392	1172	259.3	140.2	6.65	166.9	10.85	12.76	–86
–84	0.28409	538.4	0.18378	48.44	500.05	0.2686	2.6562	2.473	1.404	1.397	1156	259.9	136.9	6.72	164.8	11.00	12.42	–84
–82	0.31127	535.3	0.16869	53.41	501.64	0.2945	2.6394	2.482	1.419	1.402	1140	260.4	133.7	6.80	162.7	11.15	12.09	–82
–80	0.34034	532.2	0.15510	58.41	503.18	0.3202	2.6229	2.491	1.434	1.408	1125	260.8	130.6	6.87	160.7	11.30	11.75	–80
–78	0.37141	529.0	0.14284	63.43	504.68	0.3457	2.6069	2.501	1.450	1.414	1109	261.2	127.5	6.95	158.6	11.46	11.42	–78
–76	0.40454	525.8	0.13176	68.47	506.14	0.3711	2.5911	2.512	1.467	1.420	1093	261.5	124.6	7.02	156.6	11.62	11.09	–76
–74	0.43982	522.6	0.12172	73.53	507.55	0.3963	2.5757	2.524	1.484	1.427	1077	261.8	121.7	7.10	154.6	11.79	10.77	–74
–72	0.47733	519.3	0.11260	78.61	508.91	0.4214	2.5606	2.536	1.503	1.435	1061	262.1	118.9	7.18	152.6	11.96	10.44	–72
–70	0.51716	516.1	0.10431	83.72	510.23	0.4463	2.5457	2.549	1.522	1.443	1044	262.3	116.2	7.26	150.6	12.14	10.12	–70
–68	0.55939	512.7	0.09675	88.86	511.49	0.4710	2.5311	2.563	1.543	1.451	1028	262.4	113.6	7.34	148.6	12.33	9.80	–68
–66	0.60411	509.4	0.08985	94.03	512.70	0.4957	2.5168	2.578	1.565	1.460	1012	262.5	111.0	7.42	146.7	12.52	9.48	–66
–64	0.65141	506.0	0.08354	99.23	513.85	0.5202	2.5026	2.594	1.588	1.470	995	262.5	108.5	7.51	144.7	12.72	9.16	–64
–62	0.70136	502.5	0.07776	104.46	514.95	0.5446	2.4887	2.611	1.612	1.480	978	262.4	106.0	7.60	142.8	12.92	8.85	–62
–60	0.75406	499.0	0.07246	109.72	515.99	0.5689	2.4749	2.629	1.638	1.491	962	262.3	103.6	7.68	140.9	13.14	8.53	–60
–58	0.80960	495.5	0.06758	115.02	516.97	0.5932	2.4614	2.648	1.665	1.503	945	262.2	101.2	7.78	139.0	13.36	8.23	–58
–56	0.86807	491.9	0.06310	120.36	517.88	0.6173	2.4479	2.668	1.694	1.516	928	262.0	98.9	7.87	137.1	13.59	7.92	–56
–54	0.92955	488.2	0.05896	125.74	518.73	0.6414	2.4346	2.690	1.725	1.529	911	261.7	96.6	7.96	135.2	13.84	7.61	–54
–52	0.99414	484.5	0.05514	131.16	519.51	0.6654	2.4214	2.714	1.757	1.544	894	261.3	94.4	8.06	133.4	14.09	7.31	–52
–50	1.0619	480.8	0.05161	136.62	520.21	0.6894	2.4083	2.739	1.792	1.560	876	260.9	92.2	8.16	131.5	14.35	7.01	–50
–48	1.1330	476.9	0.04834	142.14	520.84	0.7133	2.3953	2.766	1.829	1.577	859	260.5	90.1	8.27	129.7	14.63	6.71	–48
–46	1.2075	473.0	0.04530	147.70	521.39	0.7372	2.3824	2.795	1.869	1.596	841	259.9	87.9	8.38	127.8	14.91	6.42	–46
–44	1.2854	469.1	0.04249	153.32	521.86	0.7611	2.3694	2.826	1.912	1.616	823	259.3	85.8	8.49	126.0	15.22	6.13	–44
–42	1.3669	465.0	0.03987	158.99	522.24	0.7850	2.3565	2.859	1.958	1.638	806	258.7	83.8	8.60	124.2	15.53	5.84	–42
–40	1.4521	460.9	0.03743	164.73	522.53	0.8089	2.3436	2.895	2.007	1.662	787	257.9	81.8	8.72	122.3	15.86	5.55	–40
–38	1.5410	456.7	0.03515	170.52	522.72	0.8328	2.3306	2.934	2.061	1.688	769	257.1	79.7	8.84	120.5	16.21	5.27	–38
–36	1.6339	452.4	0.03303	176.39	522.81	0.8568	2.3176	2.976	2.119	1.717	751	256.3	77.8	8.97	118.7	16.58	4.99	–36
–34	1.7307	448.0	0.03105	182.33	522.79	0.8809	2.3045	3.022	2.182	1.749	732	255.3	75.8	9.10	116.8	16.97	4.71	–34
–32	1.8315	443.5	0.02919	188.35	522.65	0.9050	2.2913	3.072	2.252	1.784	714	254.3	73.8	9.24	115.0	17.38	4.44	–32
–30	1.9366	438.9	0.02745	194.45	522.38	0.9292	2.2779	3.127	2.328	1.823	695	253.2	71.9	9.39	113.2	17.82	4.17	–30
–28	2.0459	434.1	0.02581	200.65	521.98	0.9535	2.2643	3.188	2.413	1.866	676	252.0	70.0	9.54	111.3	18.29	3.90	–28
–26	2.1596	429.2	0.02427	206.94	521.44	0.9780	2.2505	3.254	2.507	1.914	656	250.7	68.1	9.69	109.5	18.78	3.64	–26
–24	2.2779	424.2	0.02283	213.34	520.74	1.0027	2.2365	3.329	2.612	1.969	637	249.4	66.2	9.86	107.6	19.32	3.38	–24
–22	2.4008	419.0	0.02146	219.85	519.86	1.0276	2.2221	3.412	2.731	2.031	617	248.0	64.3	10.04	105.8	19.90	3.13	–22
–20	2.5284	413.6	0.02017	226.49	518.80	1.0527	2.2074	3.506	2.866	2.101	596	246.4	62.4	10.22	103.9	20.53	2.88	–20
–18	2.6610	408.0	0.01895	233.27	517.53	1.0781	2.1922	3.612	3.021	2.182	576	244.8	60.5	10.42	102.0	21.22	2.63	–18
–16	2.7985	402.2	0.01780	240.21	516.04	1.1039	2.1765	3.735	3.200	2.277	555	243.1	58.7	10.63	100.0	21.98	2.39	–16
–14	2.9412	396.1	0.01670	247.32	514.28	1.1300	2.1602	3.878	3.411	2.387	533	241.3	56.8	10.86	98.1	22.83	2.15	–14
–12	3.0893	389.8	0.01565	254.63	512.24	1.1567	2.1431	4.046	3.661	2.520	511	239.3	54.9	11.10	96.1	23.78	1.92	–12
–10	3.2428	383.0	0.01466	262.17	509.87	1.1839	2.1252	4.247	3.965	2.680	489	237.3	52.9	11.36	94.1	24.88	1.70	–10
–8	3.4019	375.9	0.01370	269.96	507.10	1.2118	2.1062	4.493	4.339	2.877	465	235.1	51.0	11.65	92.0	26.15	1.48	–8
–6	3.5669	368.3	0.01278	278.07	503.89	1.2406	2.0859	4.802	4.815	3.127	441	232.8	49.0	11.98	89.9	27.66	1.26	–6
–4	3.7379	360.1	0.01189	286.56	500.12	1.2705	2.0640	5.201	5.438	3.452	416	230.3	46.9	12.34	87.8	29.52	1.06	–4
–2	3.9152	351.1	0.01103	295.51	495.66	1.3018	2.0400	5.739	6.291	3.894	390	227.6	44.8	12.75	85.6	31.88	0.86	–2
0	4.0990	341.2	0.01018	305.06	490.32	1.3350	2.0132	6.507	7.526	4.526	362	224.6	42.6	13.23	83.5	35.04	0.67	0
5	4.5896	308.8	0.00802	333.52	470.25	1.4327	1.9243	11.680	16.100	8.720	283	214.9	36.2	15.01	79.8	52.44	0.25	5
9.20[c]	5.0418	214.2	0.00467	399.43	399.43	1.6614	1.6614	∞	∞	∞	0	0.0	—	—	∞	∞	0.00	9.20

*Temperatures on ITS-90 scale [a]Triple point [b]Normal boiling point [c]Critical point

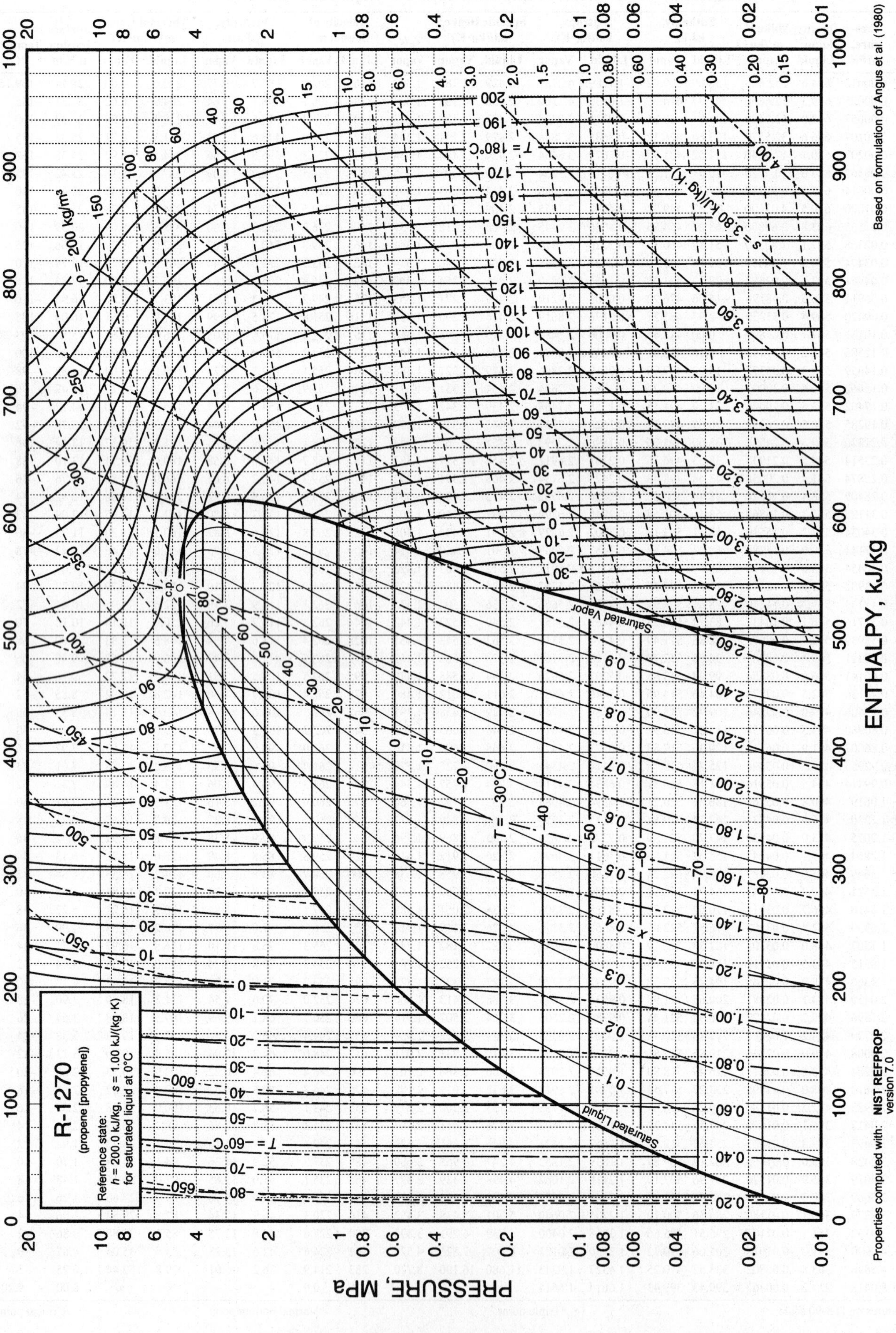

Fig. 25 Pressure-Enthalpy Diagram for Refrigerant 1270 (Propylene)

Refrigerant 1270 (Propylene) Properties of Saturated Liquid and Saturated Vapor

Temp.,* °C	Pressure, MPa	Density, kg/m³ Liquid	Volume, m³/kg Vapor	Enthalpy, kJ/kg Liquid	Enthalpy, kJ/kg Vapor	Entropy, kJ/(kg·K) Liquid	Entropy, kJ/(kg·K) Vapor	Specific Heat c_p, kJ/(kg·K) Liquid	Specific Heat c_p, kJ/(kg·K) Vapor	c_p/c_v Vapor	Velocity of Sound, m/s Liquid	Velocity of Sound, m/s Vapor	Viscosity, μPa·s Liquid	Viscosity, μPa·s Vapor	Thermal Cond., mW/(m·K) Liquid	Thermal Cond., mW/(m·K) Vapor	Surface Tension, mN/m	Temp.,* °C
–150	0.00001	727.9	2789.30000	–117.02	419.51	–0.6521	3.7046	1.834	0.991	1.249	1834	174.3	1324.0	3.51	179.9	4.60	33.49	–150
–140	0.00005	716.3	583.08000	–98.37	429.53	–0.5066	3.4582	1.893	1.015	1.242	1754	180.7	945.7	3.79	177.6	5.07	31.76	–140
–130	0.00018	704.9	156.04000	–79.20	439.78	–0.3677	3.2577	1.939	1.039	1.235	1683	186.9	718.7	4.06	175.0	5.55	30.05	–130
–120	0.00059	693.6	50.84700	–59.62	450.25	–0.2356	3.0936	1.974	1.064	1.229	1617	192.7	571.2	4.34	172.2	6.06	28.36	–120
–110	0.00166	682.2	19.42300	–39.73	460.91	–0.1098	2.9588	2.002	1.090	1.223	1554	198.3	468.9	4.62	169.1	6.60	26.69	–110
–100	0.00404	670.8	8.44420	–19.59	471.73	0.0100	2.8475	2.026	1.118	1.218	1493	203.5	394.1	4.90	165.8	7.16	25.04	–100
–90	0.00881	659.4	4.08250	0.80	482.68	0.1244	2.7555	2.050	1.149	1.214	1432	208.4	337.1	5.18	162.3	7.75	23.41	–90
–80	0.01754	647.8	2.15470	21.43	493.72	0.2341	2.6793	2.075	1.183	1.211	1370	212.9	292.2	5.46	158.6	8.36	21.80	–80
–70	0.03232	636.1	1.22310	42.34	504.79	0.3395	2.6159	2.103	1.220	1.209	1309	216.9	255.9	5.73	154.7	9.01	20.22	–70
–60	0.05578	624.1	0.73772	63.55	515.84	0.4412	2.5631	2.135	1.263	1.209	1247	220.4	226.1	6.01	150.6	9.69	18.66	–60
–50	0.09111	611.9	0.46816	85.11	526.79	0.5398	2.5191	2.171	1.309	1.211	1184	223.4	201.1	6.29	146.4	10.40	17.14	–50
–48	0.09991	609.4	0.42975	89.47	528.96	0.5592	2.5112	2.179	1.319	1.211	1171	223.9	196.6	6.35	145.6	10.55	16.83	–48
–47.69[b]	0.10133	609.1	0.42416	90.14	529.30	0.5621	2.5100	2.180	1.321	1.211	1169	224.0	195.9	6.36	145.4	10.58	16.79	–47.69
–46	0.10935	606.9	0.39515	93.84	531.13	0.5784	2.5035	2.187	1.330	1.212	1158	224.4	192.2	6.40	144.7	10.70	16.53	–46
–44	0.11949	604.4	0.36390	98.23	533.29	0.5976	2.4962	2.195	1.340	1.213	1145	224.8	188.0	6.46	143.8	10.86	16.23	–44
–42	0.13033	601.9	0.33564	102.64	535.45	0.6167	2.4891	2.203	1.351	1.214	1133	225.3	183.9	6.52	143.0	11.01	15.93	–42
–40	0.14192	599.4	0.31004	107.06	537.59	0.6356	2.4822	2.212	1.362	1.215	1120	225.7	179.9	6.57	142.1	11.17	15.63	–40
–38	0.15429	596.8	0.28680	111.51	539.73	0.6545	2.4756	2.221	1.373	1.216	1107	226.1	176.0	6.63	141.2	11.33	15.34	–38
–36	0.16748	594.3	0.26566	115.97	541.85	0.6733	2.4692	2.230	1.385	1.217	1094	226.4	172.3	6.69	140.3	11.49	15.04	–36
–34	0.18152	591.7	0.24642	120.45	543.97	0.6921	2.4630	2.239	1.396	1.218	1081	226.7	168.7	6.75	139.4	11.65	14.75	–34
–32	0.19644	589.1	0.22886	124.95	546.08	0.7107	2.4570	2.249	1.408	1.220	1068	227.0	165.1	6.80	138.5	11.82	14.45	–32
–30	0.21228	586.5	0.21282	129.47	548.17	0.7292	2.4512	2.259	1.421	1.221	1056	227.3	161.7	6.86	137.6	11.99	14.16	–30
–28	0.22908	583.8	0.19814	134.01	550.26	0.7477	2.4456	2.269	1.433	1.223	1043	227.5	158.4	6.92	136.7	12.16	13.87	–28
–26	0.24687	581.2	0.18469	138.57	552.33	0.7661	2.4402	2.279	1.446	1.225	1030	227.7	155.1	6.98	135.7	12.34	13.58	–26
–24	0.26569	578.5	0.17234	143.15	554.38	0.7845	2.4350	2.290	1.459	1.227	1017	227.9	152.0	7.04	134.8	12.52	13.29	–24
–22	0.28558	575.8	0.16100	147.76	556.43	0.8027	2.4299	2.300	1.473	1.229	1004	228.1	148.9	7.10	133.9	12.70	13.00	–22
–20	0.30657	573.1	0.15056	152.38	558.46	0.8209	2.4250	2.311	1.487	1.231	991	228.2	145.9	7.17	132.9	12.89	12.72	–20
–18	0.32871	570.4	0.14093	157.03	560.48	0.8391	2.4203	2.323	1.501	1.234	978	228.3	143.0	7.23	132.0	13.08	12.43	–18
–16	0.35203	567.6	0.13206	161.71	562.48	0.8571	2.4157	2.335	1.515	1.236	965	228.3	140.2	7.29	131.0	13.28	12.15	–16
–14	0.37657	564.8	0.12385	166.40	564.46	0.8752	2.4112	2.347	1.530	1.239	952	228.3	137.4	7.36	130.1	13.48	11.87	–14
–12	0.40237	562.0	0.11626	171.12	566.43	0.8931	2.4068	2.359	1.546	1.242	939	228.3	134.8	7.42	129.1	13.68	11.59	–12
–10	0.42947	559.2	0.10924	175.87	568.37	0.9111	2.4026	2.372	1.562	1.245	925	228.2	132.1	7.49	128.2	13.89	11.31	–10
–8	0.45791	556.3	0.10272	180.64	570.30	0.9289	2.3985	2.385	1.578	1.248	912	228.1	129.6	7.56	127.2	14.11	11.03	–8
–6	0.48773	553.5	0.09667	185.44	572.22	0.9468	2.3945	2.398	1.594	1.252	899	228.0	127.1	7.63	126.2	14.33	10.76	–6
–4	0.51897	550.6	0.09105	190.27	574.11	0.9645	2.3907	2.412	1.612	1.256	886	227.8	124.6	7.69	125.3	14.55	10.48	–4
–2	0.55167	547.6	0.08582	195.12	575.98	0.9823	2.3869	2.426	1.629	1.260	873	227.6	122.2	7.77	124.3	14.78	10.21	–2
0	0.58588	544.6	0.08094	200.00	577.82	1.0000	2.3832	2.441	1.648	1.264	860	227.4	119.9	7.84	123.3	15.02	9.94	0
2	0.62163	541.6	0.07640	204.91	579.65	1.0177	2.3796	2.456	1.666	1.268	847	227.1	117.6	7.91	122.3	15.27	9.67	2
4	0.65896	538.6	0.07216	209.85	581.45	1.0353	2.3761	2.471	1.686	1.273	834	226.7	115.4	7.99	121.3	15.52	9.40	4
6	0.69793	535.5	0.06820	214.82	583.22	1.0529	2.3726	2.487	1.706	1.278	820	226.4	113.2	8.07	120.3	15.79	9.13	6
8	0.73856	532.4	0.06449	219.83	584.97	1.0705	2.3693	2.504	1.726	1.284	807	226.0	111.1	8.15	119.3	16.06	8.87	8
10	0.78091	529.3	0.06102	224.86	586.69	1.0881	2.3660	2.521	1.748	1.289	794	225.5	109.0	8.23	118.3	16.33	8.60	10
12	0.82502	526.1	0.05777	229.93	588.39	1.1056	2.3627	2.538	1.770	1.296	781	225.0	106.9	8.31	117.3	16.62	8.34	12
14	0.87093	522.9	0.05472	235.03	590.05	1.1231	2.3595	2.557	1.793	1.302	767	224.5	104.9	8.4	116.3	16.92	8.08	14
16	0.91868	519.7	0.05186	240.17	591.68	1.1407	2.3563	2.575	1.817	1.309	754	223.9	102.9	8.48	115.3	17.23	7.82	16
18	0.96832	516.4	0.04917	245.34	593.28	1.1582	2.3532	2.595	1.842	1.316	741	223.3	101.0	8.57	114.3	17.55	7.56	18
20	1.01990	513.0	0.04664	250.55	594.84	1.1756	2.3501	2.615	1.867	1.324	727	222.6	99.1	8.67	113.3	17.88	7.31	20
22	1.07350	509.6	0.04426	255.8	596.37	1.1931	2.3470	2.637	1.894	1.333	714	221.9	97.2	8.76	112.2	18.22	7.05	22
24	1.12900	506.2	0.04202	261.09	597.86	1.2106	2.3440	2.659	1.923	1.342	701	221.1	95.4	8.86	111.2	18.58	6.80	24
26	1.18670	502.7	0.03990	266.42	599.31	1.2281	2.3409	2.682	1.952	1.351	687	220.3	93.6	8.97	110.2	18.95	6.55	26
28	1.24650	499.2	0.03791	271.79	600.72	1.2456	2.3378	2.706	1.983	1.362	674	219.4	91.8	9.06	109.2	19.34	6.31	28
30	1.30840	495.6	0.03602	277.21	602.08	1.2631	2.3348	2.731	2.015	1.373	661	218.5	90.0	9.17	108.1	19.74	6.06	30
32	1.37250	491.9	0.03424	282.67	603.40	1.2807	2.3317	2.757	2.049	1.385	647	217.5	88.3	9.28	107.1	20.15	5.82	32
34	1.43900	488.2	0.03255	288.18	604.67	1.2982	2.3286	2.785	2.085	1.398	634	216.5	86.6	9.40	106.0	20.58	5.58	34
36	1.50770	484.4	0.03095	293.74	605.88	1.3158	2.3255	2.814	2.123	1.412	620	215.4	84.9	9.52	105.0	21.03	5.34	36
38	1.57880	480.6	0.02944	299.35	607.05	1.3334	2.3223	2.845	2.163	1.427	606	214.3	83.3	9.64	104.0	21.50	5.10	38
40	1.65230	476.7	0.02801	305.01	608.15	1.3510	2.3191	2.878	2.206	1.443	593	213.1	81.6	9.77	102.9	22.00	4.86	40
42	1.72820	472.7	0.02664	310.72	609.19	1.3687	2.3158	2.913	2.251	1.460	579	211.8	80.0	9.91	101.9	22.52	4.63	42
44	1.80670	468.6	0.02535	316.50	610.17	1.3865	2.3124	2.950	2.300	1.480	565	210.5	78.4	10.05	100.8	23.06	4.40	44
46	1.88780	464.4	0.02412	322.34	611.07	1.4043	2.3090	2.990	2.352	1.501	552	209.1	76.8	10.20	99.7	23.63	4.17	46
48	1.97150	460.2	0.02295	328.24	611.90	1.4221	2.3054	3.032	2.408	1.523	538	207.7	75.2	10.36	98.7	24.24	3.95	48
50	2.05790	455.8	0.02183	334.21	612.65	1.4401	2.3017	3.078	2.469	1.549	524	206.2	73.6	10.52	97.6	24.88	3.73	50
55	2.28610	444.4	0.01926	349.47	614.13	1.4854	2.2919	3.211	2.644	1.624	488	202.2	69.7	10.97	94.9	26.63	3.18	55
60	2.53250	432.1	0.01696	365.26	614.95	1.5315	2.2809	3.380	2.868	1.723	452	197.7	65.8	11.49	92.2	28.67	2.65	60
65	2.79810	418.8	0.01490	381.71	614.94	1.5786	2.2683	3.604	3.163	1.859	415	192.8	61.9	12.10	89.4	31.07	2.15	65
70	3.08420	404.1	0.01302	399.01	613.87	1.6273	2.2535	3.921	3.578	2.055	377	187.4	57.9	12.83	86.6	33.94	1.67	70
75	3.39220	387.4	0.01130	417.46	611.33	1.6785	2.2353	4.416	4.213	2.363	337	181.3	53.7	13.73	83.8	37.50	1.21	75
80	3.72380	367.5	0.00967	437.66	606.61	1.7335	2.2120	5.315	5.332	2.918	294	174.7	49.1	14.90	81.1	42.14	0.79	80
85	4.08100	341.7	0.00808	461.03	598.06	1.7964	2.1790	7.507	7.921	4.221	248	167.2	43.8	16.55	79.2	48.98	0.41	85
90	4.46680	298.9	0.00630	493.45	579.55	1.8829	2.1200	20.390	21.470	11.110	195	159.2	36.3	19.59	81.9	64.05	0.10	90
92.42[c]	4.66460	223.4	0.00448	540.41	540.41	2.0097	2.0097	∞	∞	∞	0	0.0	—	—	∞	∞	0.00	92.42

*Temperatures on IPTS-68 scale

[b]Normal boiling point

[c]Critical point

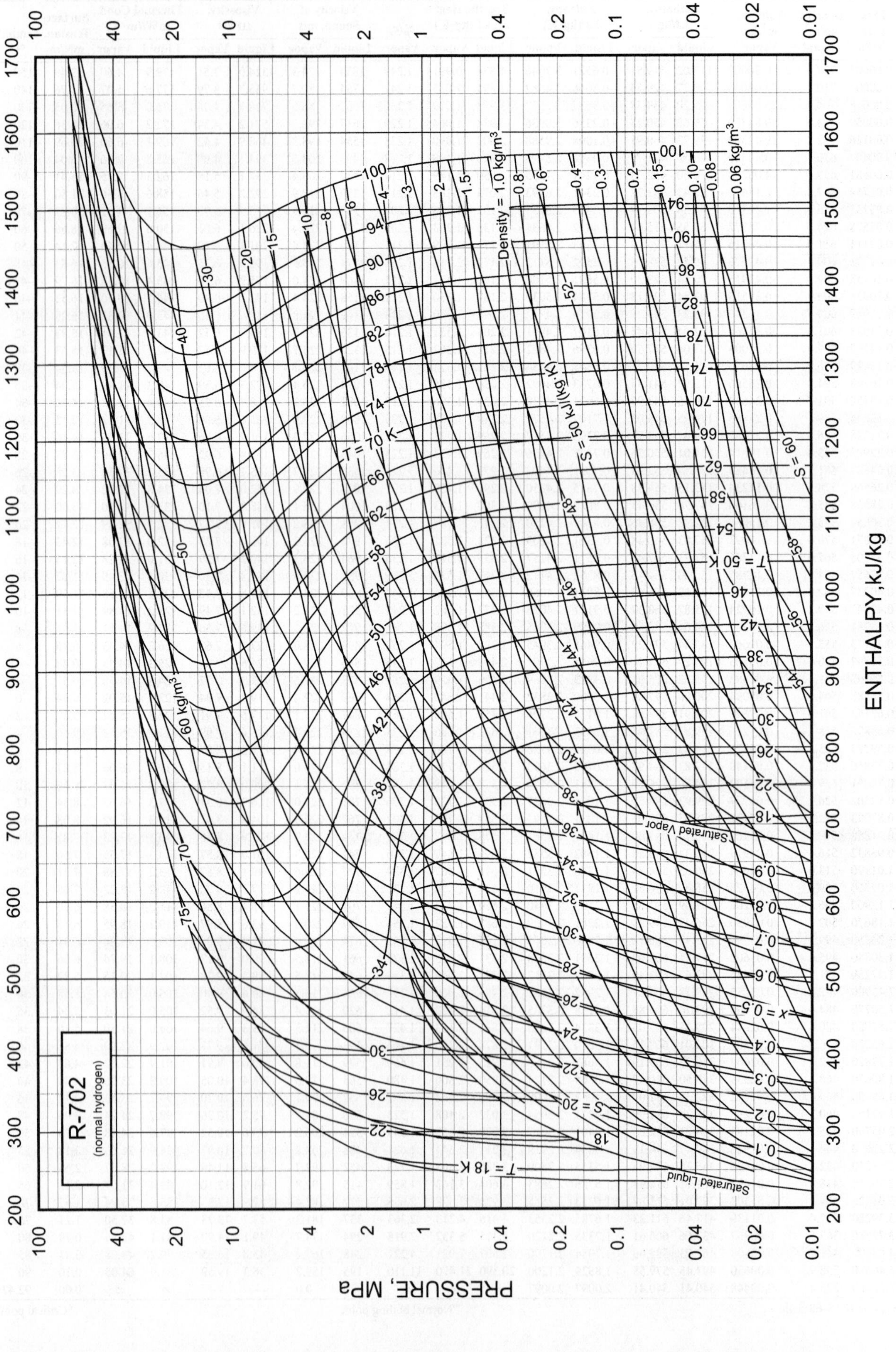

Fig. 26 Pressure-Enthalpy Diagram for Refrigerant 702 (Normal Hydrogen)

Refrigerant 702 (Normal Hydrogen) Properties of Saturated Liquid and Saturated Vapor

Temp.,* K	Absolute Pressure, MPa	Density, kg/m³ Liquid	Volume, m³/kg Vapor	Enthalpy, kJ/kg Liquid	Enthalpy, kJ/kg Vapor	Entropy, kJ/(kg·K) Liquid	Entropy, kJ/(kg·K) Vapor	Specific Heat c_p, kJ/(kg·K) Liquid	Specific Heat c_p, kJ/(kg·K) Vapor	c_p/c_v Vapor	Velocity of Sound, m/s Liquid	Velocity of Sound, m/s Vapor	Viscosity, μPa·s Liquid	Viscosity, μPa·s Vapor	Thermal Cond., mW/(m·K) Liquid	Thermal Cond., mW/(m·K) Vapor	Surface Tension, mN/m	Temp.,* K
13.95[a]	0.00776	76.90	7.2871	218.1	667.4	14.082	46.224	7.78	10.90	1.669	1362	304.5	25.5	0.66	76.2	10.37	3.181	13.95
14	0.00797	76.86	7.1136	218.6	667.8	14.108	46.147	7.71	10.89	1.672	1360	305.1	25.3	0.67	76.7	10.43	3.171	14
15	0.01334	76.02	4.5226	226.3	676.9	14.610	44.697	7.15	10.86	1.701	1318	316.2	22.2	0.74	84.1	11.62	2.970	15
16	0.02113	75.12	3.0172	233.4	685.6	15.075	43.411	7.30	11.00	1.719	1272	325.2	19.8	0.81	90.1	12.68	2.771	16
17	0.03200	74.18	2.0940	240.9	693.7	15.530	42.260	7.72	11.19	1.739	1226	333.2	17.8	0.87	94.8	13.68	2.575	17
18	0.04663	73.20	1.5017	249.0	701.3	15.984	41.220	8.26	11.43	1.764	1185	340.6	16.2	0.94	98.4	14.67	2.381	18
19	0.06577	72.18	1.1068	257.8	708.3	16.441	40.270	8.85	11.71	1.795	1147	347.3	14.8	1.00	101.1	15.68	2.191	19
20	0.09020	71.11	0.83478	267.3	714.6	16.904	39.393	9.49	12.04	1.833	1111	353.3	13.6	1.06	103.0	16.72	2.003	20
20.39[b]	0.10132	70.67	0.75195	271.2	716.8	17.086	39.068	9.74	12.20	1.851	1097	355.4	13.2	1.08	103.6	17.13	1.931	20.39
21	0.12072	69.96	0.64193	277.4	720.1	17.374	38.576	10.15	12.46	1.881	1075	358.6	12.6	1.12	104.2	17.81	1.819	21
22	0.15816	68.73	0.50178	288.3	724.8	17.852	37.806	10.88	12.96	1.940	1039	363.2	11.6	1.18	104.9	18.96	1.638	22
23	0.20336	67.41	0.39766	299.9	728.4	18.340	37.074	11.68	13.58	2.013	1001	367.2	10.8	1.25	105.0	20.18	1.460	23
24	0.25717	65.98	0.31878	312.3	731.0	18.840	36.369	12.58	14.35	2.106	960	370.6	10.1	1.32	104.6	21.50	1.287	24
25	0.32045	64.43	0.25795	325.8	732.3	19.351	35.683	13.65	15.34	2.224	918	373.3	9.4	1.39	103.8	22.92	1.117	25
26	0.39404	62.75	0.21028	340.3	732.2	19.877	35.007	14.94	16.63	2.378	872	375.4	8.7	1.46	102.5	24.48	0.953	26
27	0.47879	60.91	0.17233	356.1	730.4	20.421	34.331	16.56	18.36	2.586	824	376.9	8.1	1.54	100.8	26.23	0.793	27
28	0.57555	58.87	0.14165	373.5	726.5	20.989	33.642	18.72	20.79	2.877	772	377.8	7.5	1.63	98.7	28.22	0.639	28
29	0.68516	56.55	0.11647	392.7	720.2	21.596	32.925	21.85	24.41	3.310	715	378.2	6.9	1.74	96.0	30.56	0.492	29
30	0.80844	53.76	0.09540	414.7	710.5	22.267	32.157	27.13	30.32	4.013	650	378.1	6.4	1.86	92.6	33.46	0.352	30
31	0.94620	50.17	0.07735	441.4	696.2	23.059	31.298	38.73	41.37	5.321	573	377.7	5.8	2.04	88.3	37.32	0.222	31
32	1.0993	44.89	0.06132	477.9	674.4	24.112	30.271	84.77	67.41	8.383	482	377.6	5.1	2.35	82.3	43.40	0.105	32
33	1.2684	34.38	0.04665	547.5	640.5	26.097	28.951	—	—	—	—	—	—	—	—	—	0.011	33
33.19[c]	1.3152	30.11	0.03321	577.2	577.2	26.962	26.962	∞	∞	∞	0	0.0	—	—	∞	∞	0.000	33.19

*Temperatures on IPTS-68 scale [a]Triple point [b]Normal boiling point [c]Critical point

Refrigerant 702 (Normal Hydrogen) Properties of Gas at 0.101 325 MPa (one standard atmosphere)

Temp., °C	Density, kg/m³	Enthalpy, kJ/kg	Entropy, kJ/(kg·K)	c_p, kJ/(kg·K)	c_p/c_v	Vel. of Sound, m/s	Visc., μPa·s	Thermal Cond., mW/(m·K)
−252.8[b]	1.3299	716.8	39.068	12.20	1.851	355.4	1.08	17.10
−250	1.1366	749.3	40.564	11.45	1.793	385.4	1.22	19.29
−245	0.9089	805.0	42.744	10.91	1.744	431.8	1.47	23.26
−240	0.7609	859.0	44.508	10.69	1.720	472.2	1.72	27.06
−235	0.6557	912.1	46.001	10.58	1.706	508.7	1.95	30.62
−230	0.5767	964.8	47.300	10.52	1.696	542.3	2.18	34.00
−225	0.5150	1017.4	48.452	10.49	1.688	573.6	2.40	37.23
−220	0.4655	1069.7	49.487	10.47	1.682	603.0	2.60	40.37
−215	0.4247	1122.1	50.429	10.48	1.676	630.6	2.80	43.47
−210	0.3906	1174.6	51.294	10.51	1.668	656.6	2.98	46.55
−200	0.3366	1280.1	52.845	10.62	1.650	704.1	3.34	52.56
−190	0.2958	1387.2	54.217	10.81	1.629	746.5	3.67	58.30
−180	0.2639	1496.4	55.457	11.05	1.604	784.7	3.98	64.12
−170	0.2382	1608.2	56.597	11.32	1.580	819.7	4.28	70.43
−160	0.2171	1722.8	57.657	11.61	1.556	852.3	4.57	77.02
−150	0.1994	1840.3	58.652	11.89	1.534	883.2	4.85	83.56
−140	0.1844	1960.7	59.592	12.17	1.515	912.7	5.12	90.15
−130	0.1715	2083.7	60.483	12.44	1.499	941.2	5.38	96.62
−120	0.1603	2209.3	61.331	12.68	1.484	968.8	5.64	103.03
−110	0.1505	2337.3	62.140	12.90	1.471	995.7	5.89	109.55
−100	0.1418	2467.3	62.913	13.10	1.461	1022.1	6.14	115.95
−90	0.1340	2599.2	63.654	13.28	1.452	1047.9	6.38	122.20
−80	0.1271	2732.8	64.364	13.44	1.444	1073.2	6.62	128.33
−70	0.1208	2867.9	65.046	13.58	1.437	1098.0	6.85	134.30
−60	0.1152	3004.4	65.702	13.71	1.431	1122.5	7.08	140.15
−50	0.1100	3142.0	66.333	13.82	1.426	1146.5	7.31	145.84
−40	0.1053	3280.7	66.941	13.91	1.422	1170.1	7.53	151.44
−30	0.1010	3420.2	67.527	14.00	1.418	1193.4	7.75	156.92
−20	0.0970	3560.6	68.093	14.07	1.415	1216.3	7.97	162.24
−10	0.0933	3701.7	68.639	14.14	1.412	1238.8	8.19	167.47

Temp., °C	Density, kg/m³	Enthalpy, kJ/kg	Entropy, kJ/(kg·K)	c_p, kJ/(kg·K)	c_p/c_v	Vel. of Sound, m/s	Visc., μPa·s	Thermal Cond., mW/(m·K)
0	0.0899	3843.3	69.168	14.20	1.410	1261.1	8.40	172.58
5	0.0883	3914.4	69.425	14.22	1.409	1272.1	8.50	175.07
10	0.0867	3985.5	69.679	14.24	1.408	1283.0	8.61	177.56
15	0.0852	4056.8	69.928	14.27	1.407	1293.9	8.71	180.05
20	0.0838	4128.2	70.174	14.29	1.406	1304.7	8.81	182.48
25	0.0824	4199.7	70.416	14.31	1.405	1315.4	8.92	184.88
30	0.0810	4271.3	70.654	14.32	1.405	1326.0	9.02	187.28
35	0.0797	4342.9	70.888	14.34	1.404	1336.6	9.12	189.67
40	0.0784	4414.7	71.119	14.36	1.403	1347.1	9.22	192.01
45	0.0772	4486.5	71.347	14.37	1.403	1357.5	9.32	194.32
50	0.0760	4558.3	71.571	14.38	1.402	1367.9	9.42	196.78
55	0.0748	4630.3	71.792	14.39	1.402	1378.2	9.52	199.33
60	0.0737	4702.3	72.010	14.40	1.401	1388.4	9.62	201.86
65	0.0726	4774.3	72.224	14.41	1.401	1398.6	9.72	204.37
70	0.0716	4846.4	72.436	14.42	1.401	1408.7	9.81	206.88
75	0.0705	4918.5	72.644	14.43	1.400	1418.8	9.91	209.39
80	0.0695	4990.7	72.850	14.44	1.400	1428.8	10.01	211.88
85	0.0686	5062.9	73.053	14.44	1.400	1438.7	10.10	214.34
90	0.0676	5135.1	73.254	14.45	1.400	1448.6	10.20	216.72
95	0.0667	5207.4	73.451	14.45	1.399	1458.4	10.29	219.04
100	0.0658	5279.7	73.646	14.46	1.399	1468.2	10.39	221.42
110	0.0641	5424.3	74.029	14.47	1.399	1487.5	10.58	226.21
120	0.0625	5569.0	74.401	14.47	1.399	1506.7	10.77	230.86
130	0.0609	5713.8	74.765	14.48	1.398	1525.6	—	—
140	0.0594	5858.6	75.120	14.48	1.398	1544.3	—	—
150	0.0580	6003.4	75.466	14.49	1.398	1562.8	—	—
160	0.0567	6148.3	75.805	14.49	1.398	1581.0	—	—
170	0.0554	6293.2	76.135	14.49	1.398	1599.1	—	—
180	0.0542	6438.1	76.459	14.50	1.398	1616.9	—	—
190	0.0530	6583.1	76.775	14.50	1.398	1634.6	—	—
200	0.0519	6728.1	77.085	14.50	1.397	1652.0	—	—

[b]Saturated vapor at normal boiling point

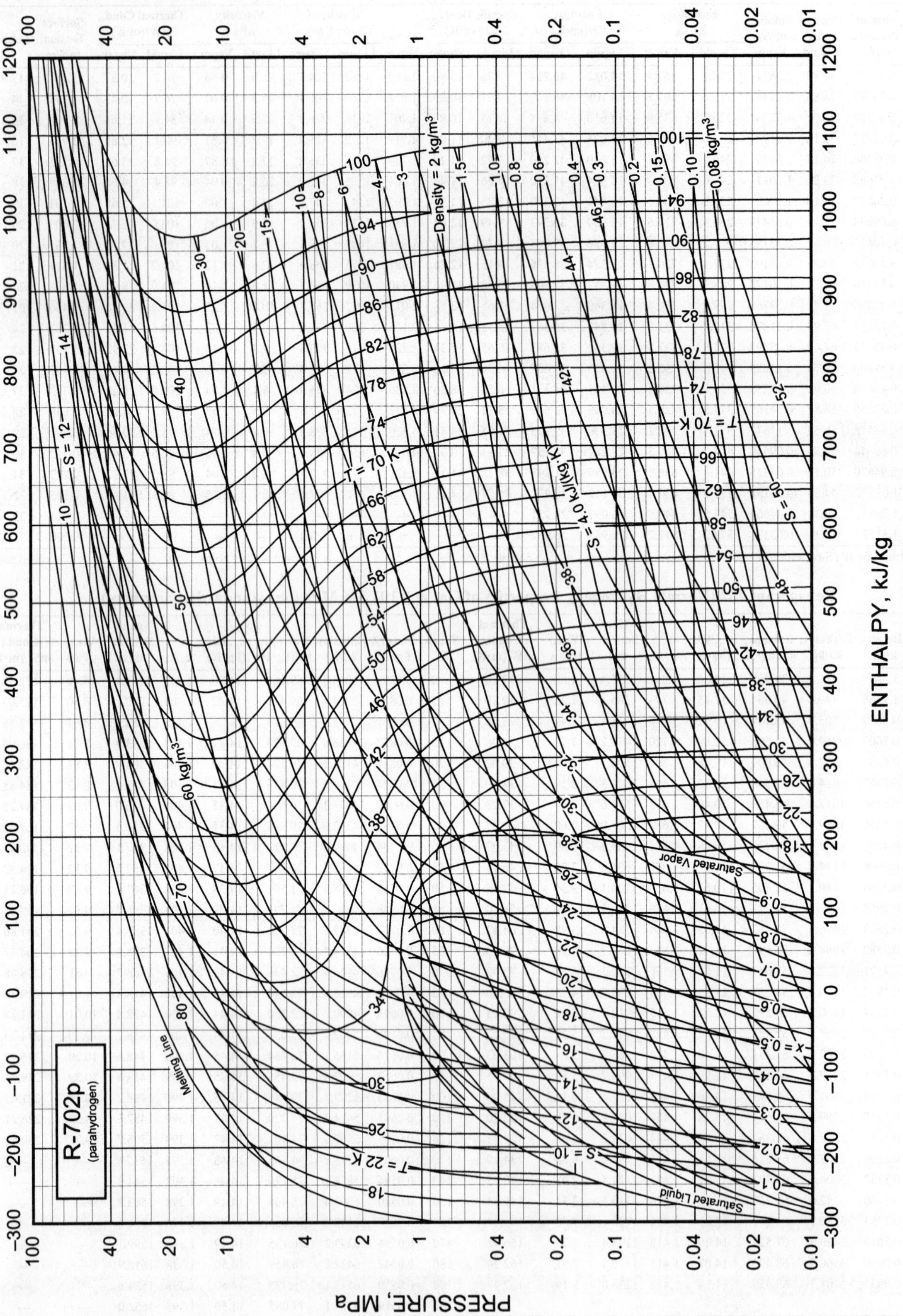

Fig. 27 Pressure-Enthalpy Diagram for Refrigerant 702p (Parahydrogen)

Refrigerant 702p (Parahydrogen) Properties of Saturated Liquid and Saturated Vapor

Temp.,* K	Absolute Pressure, MPa	Density, kg/m³ Liquid	Volume, m³/kg Vapor	Enthalpy, kJ/kg Liquid	Enthalpy, kJ/kg Vapor	Entropy, kJ/(kg·K) Liquid	Entropy, kJ/(kg·K) Vapor	Specific Heat c_p, kJ/(kg·K) Liquid	Specific Heat c_p, kJ/(kg·K) Vapor	c_p/c_v Vapor	Velocity of Sound, m/s Liquid	Velocity of Sound, m/s Vapor	Viscosity, μPa·s Liquid	Viscosity, μPa·s Vapor	Thermal Cond., mW/(m·K) Liquid	Thermal Cond., mW/(m·K) Vapor	Surface Tension, mN/m	Temp.,* K
13.80[a]	0.00705	77.04	7.8437	–307.2	140.1	4.980	37.428	7.72	10.68	1.690	1373	305.0	26.0	0.65	75.3	10.46	3.124	13.80
14	0.00790	76.87	7.1198	–305.7	141.9	5.088	37.115	7.53	10.70	1.692	1364	307.0	25.3	0.67	76.9	10.65	3.086	14
15	0.01343	76.01	4.4920	–298.3	150.9	5.588	35.628	7.13	10.84	1.704	1316	316.4	22.2	0.74	84.1	11.62	2.894	15
16	0.02152	75.12	2.9640	–291.1	159.5	6.051	34.295	7.30	11.01	1.720	1269	325.1	19.8	0.81	90.0	12.60	2.705	16
17	0.03284	74.19	2.0392	–283.5	167.5	6.504	33.107	7.72	11.22	1.741	1224	333.0	17.8	0.87	94.7	13.59	2.516	17
18	0.04807	73.22	1.4541	–275.4	175.0	6.958	32.042	8.26	11.46	1.767	1183	340.3	16.2	0.94	98.3	14.60	2.330	18
19	0.06796	72.19	1.0683	–266.6	181.8	7.416	31.077	8.85	11.76	1.800	1145	346.8	14.8	1.00	101.1	15.64	2.146	19
20	0.09326	71.11	0.80448	–257.2	188.0	7.880	30.193	9.48	12.12	1.840	1109	352.6	13.6	1.06	103.0	16.71	1.963	20
20.28[b]	0.10132	70.80	0.74656	–254.4	189.5	8.009	29.960	9.66	12.23	1.853	1099	354.1	13.3	1.07	103.4	17.01	1.913	20.28
20.50	0.10818	70.54	0.70371	–252.2	190.8	8.114	29.776	9.81	12.33	1.864	1091	355.3	13.1	1.09	103.7	17.25	1.873	20.50
21	0.12474	69.96	0.61847	–247.1	193.3	8.350	29.373	10.15	12.56	1.890	1073	357.8	12.6	1.12	104.2	17.82	1.783	21
21.50	0.14305	69.35	0.54589	–241.7	195.7	8.589	28.983	10.51	12.81	1.920	1055	360.2	12.1	1.15	104.7	18.39	1.693	21.50
22	0.16320	68.73	0.48372	–236.2	197.8	8.829	28.604	10.87	13.09	1.952	1036	362.3	11.6	1.18	104.9	18.98	1.605	22
22.50	0.18529	68.08	0.43016	–230.5	199.7	9.071	28.235	11.26	13.39	1.989	1018	364.3	11.2	1.21	105.0	19.59	1.517	22.50
23	0.20942	67.42	0.38378	–224.6	201.3	9.315	27.875	11.67	13.74	2.030	999	366.2	10.8	1.25	105.0	20.21	1.429	23
23.50	0.23570	66.72	0.34340	–218.5	202.6	9.562	27.521	12.10	14.12	2.075	979	367.9	10.4	1.28	104.9	20.86	1.342	23.50
24	0.26423	66.00	0.30808	–212.1	203.6	9.811	27.174	12.56	14.56	2.127	959	369.4	10.1	1.32	104.7	21.53	1.256	24
24.50	0.29511	65.25	0.27705	–205.5	204.4	10.064	26.832	13.06	15.04	2.185	939	370.8	9.7	1.35	104.3	22.23	1.171	24.50
25	0.32845	64.47	0.24966	–198.7	204.7	10.320	26.492	13.61	15.60	2.251	918	372.1	9.4	1.39	103.8	22.95	1.086	25
26	0.40291	62.80	0.20378	–184.2	204.4	10.843	25.820	14.87	16.96	2.414	873	374.1	8.7	1.46	102.6	24.51	0.920	26
27	0.48849	60.97	0.16716	–168.4	202.3	11.385	25.145	16.47	18.81	2.635	825	375.5	8.1	1.54	100.9	26.25	0.757	27
28	0.58610	58.93	0.13744	–151.2	198.1	11.954	24.454	18.61	21.44	2.948	773	376.3	7.5	1.63	98.7	28.23	0.599	28
29	0.69673	56.60	0.11286	–132.0	191.3	12.560	23.727	21.70	25.45	3.426	716	376.4	6.9	1.74	96.0	30.57	0.445	29
30	0.82143	53.86	0.09208	–110.2	180.6	13.223	22.933	26.73	32.31	4.238	653	375.9	6.4	1.86	92.6	33.45	0.299	30
31	0.96149	50.48	0.07387	–84.4	164.1	13.981	22.011	36.68	46.58	5.916	582	374.8	5.8	2.04	88.3	37.31	0.161	31
32	1.1185	45.81	0.05667	–51.0	135.8	14.938	20.788	66.67	93.30	11.357	501	373.2	5.1	2.35	82.3	43.38	0.038	32
32.94[c]	1.2838	31.36	0.03189	40.3	40.3	17.615	17.615	∞	∞	∞	0	0.0	—	—	∞	∞	0.000	32.94

*Temperatures on IPTS-68 scale [a]Triple point [b]Normal boiling point [c]Critical point

Refrigerant 702p (Parahydrogen) Properties of Gas at 0.101 325 MPa (one standard atmosphere)

Temp., °C	Density, kg/m³	Enthalpy, kJ/kg	Entropy, kJ/(kg·K)	c_p, kJ/(kg·K)	c_p/c_v	Vel. of Sound, m/s	Visc., μPa·s	Thermal Cond., mW/(m·K)
–252.9[b]	1.3395	189.5	29.960	12.23	1.853	354.1	1.07	17.01
–250	1.1364	223.4	31.524	11.45	1.793	385.5	1.22	19.33
–245	0.9088	279.1	33.703	10.91	1.744	431.8	1.47	23.27
–240	0.7608	333.0	35.467	10.69	1.720	472.2	1.72	27.03
–235	0.6557	386.2	36.960	10.58	1.706	508.7	1.95	30.58
–230	0.5767	438.9	38.260	10.54	1.694	542.0	2.18	33.99
–225	0.5150	491.6	39.415	10.53	1.683	572.8	2.40	37.34
–220	0.4655	544.3	40.456	10.57	1.672	601.2	2.60	40.72
–215	0.4247	597.3	41.410	10.66	1.656	627.0	2.80	44.21
–210	0.3906	651.0	42.295	10.81	1.637	650.4	2.98	47.87
–200	0.3366	761.4	43.918	11.31	1.587	690.5	3.34	55.69
–190	0.2958	877.9	45.409	12.01	1.532	723.9	3.67	64.19
–180	0.2639	1002.1	46.819	12.84	1.479	753.5	3.98	73.55
–170	0.2382	1134.8	48.171	13.69	1.435	781.3	4.28	83.79
–160	0.2171	1275.8	49.475	14.50	1.401	808.7	4.57	94.32
–150	0.1994	1424.3	50.732	15.17	1.376	836.2	4.85	104.41
–140	0.1844	1578.7	51.938	15.69	1.358	864.2	5.12	113.74
–130	0.1715	1737.6	53.088	16.05	1.347	892.4	5.38	122.26
–120	0.1603	1899.3	54.180	16.27	1.341	920.9	5.64	129.99
–110	0.1505	2062.6	55.213	16.37	1.338	949.5	5.89	136.76
–100	0.1418	2226.3	56.187	16.36	1.338	978.1	6.14	142.70
–90	0.1340	2389.6	57.104	16.29	1.340	1006.7	6.38	147.96
–80	0.1271	2551.9	57.967	16.17	1.343	1035.1	6.62	152.62
–70	0.1208	2712.9	58.779	16.03	1.347	1063.2	6.85	156.90
–60	0.1152	2872.4	59.546	15.87	1.352	1090.8	7.08	160.82
–50	0.1100	3030.3	60.270	15.71	1.356	1118.1	7.31	164.51
–40	0.1053	3186.7	60.955	15.56	1.361	1144.9	7.53	168.14
–30	0.1010	3341.5	61.605	15.41	1.366	1171.1	7.75	171.75
–20	0.0970	3495.0	62.224	15.28	1.370	1196.8	7.97	175.31
–10	0.0933	3647.2	62.814	15.16	1.374	1221.9	8.19	178.87
0	0.0899	3798.3	63.377	15.06	1.377	1246.5	8.40	182.44
5	0.0883	3873.5	63.650	15.01	1.379	1258.6	8.50	184.23
10	0.0867	3948.5	63.917	14.97	1.381	1270.5	8.61	186.05
15	0.0852	4023.2	64.179	14.93	1.382	1282.3	8.71	187.89
20	0.0838	4097.8	64.436	14.89	1.383	1294.0	8.81	189.73
25	0.0824	4172.1	64.687	14.86	1.384	1305.6	8.92	191.58
30	0.0810	4246.4	64.934	14.83	1.386	1317.0	9.02	193.46
35	0.0797	4320.4	65.176	14.80	1.387	1328.3	9.12	195.36
40	0.0784	4394.3	65.414	14.77	1.388	1339.5	9.22	197.29
45	0.0772	4468.1	65.648	14.75	1.388	1350.5	9.32	199.25
50	0.0760	4541.8	65.878	14.72	1.389	1361.5	9.42	201.20
55	0.0748	4615.4	66.104	14.70	1.390	1372.3	9.52	203.16
60	0.0737	4688.9	66.326	14.69	1.391	1383.1	9.62	205.18
65	0.0726	4762.2	66.545	14.67	1.391	1393.7	9.72	207.24
70	0.0716	4835.6	66.760	14.65	1.392	1404.3	9.81	209.33
75	0.0705	4908.8	66.972	14.64	1.392	1414.7	9.91	211.44
80	0.0695	4981.9	67.180	14.63	1.393	1425.1	10.01	213.53
85	0.0686	5055.1	67.386	14.62	1.393	1435.3	10.10	215.59
90	0.0676	5128.1	67.588	14.60	1.394	1445.5	10.20	217.63
95	0.0667	5201.1	67.788	14.60	1.394	1455.6	10.29	219.65
100	0.0658	5274.1	67.985	14.59	1.394	1465.6	10.39	221.73

[b]Saturated vapor at normal boiling point

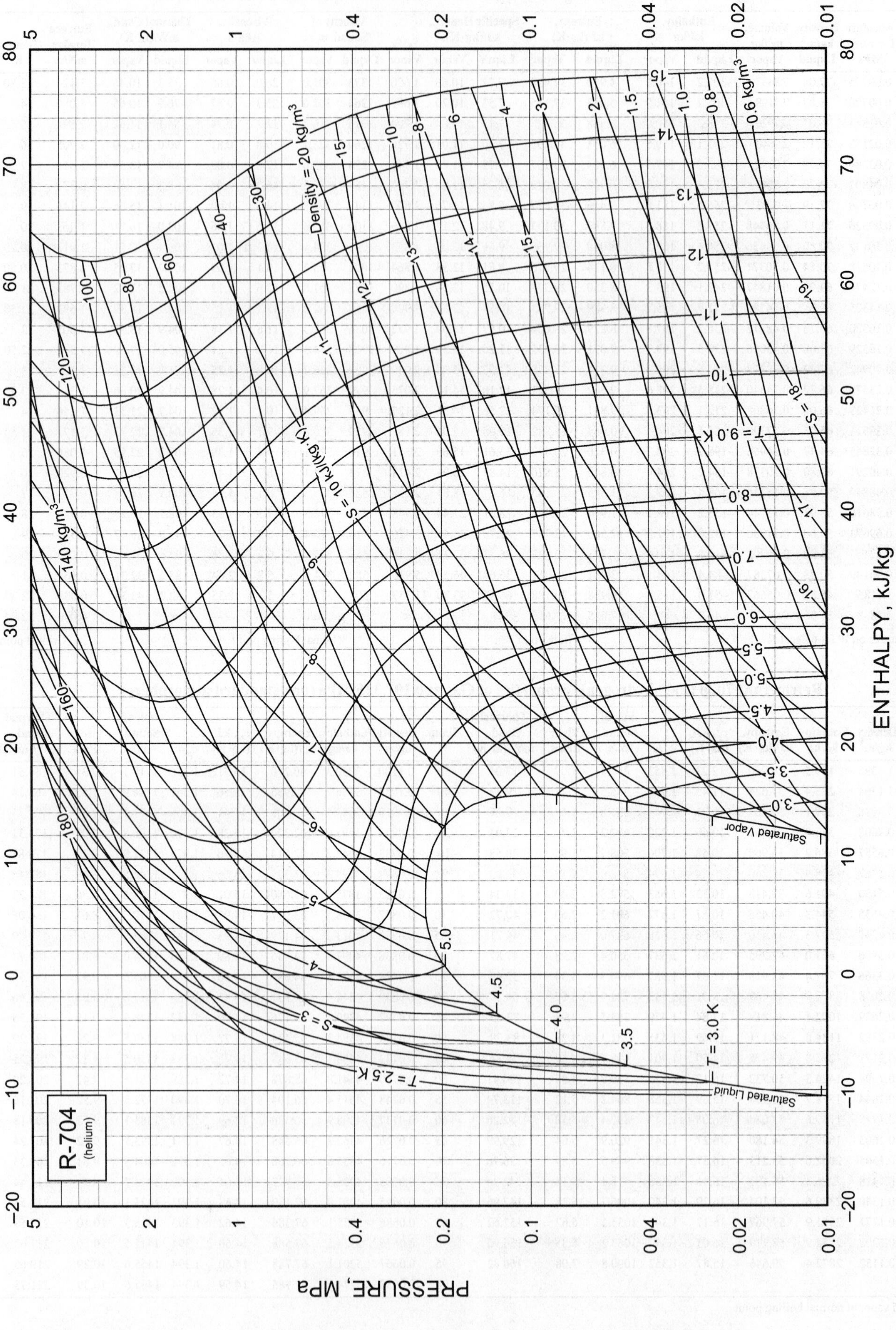

Fig. 28 Pressure-Enthalpy Diagram for Refrigerant 704 (Helium)

Note: The reference states for enthalpy and entropy differ from those in the table.

Refrigerant 704 (Helium) Properties of Saturated Liquid and Saturated Vapor

Temp.,* K	Absolute Pressure, MPa	Density, kg/m³ Liquid	Volume, m³/kg Vapor	Enthalpy, kJ/kg Liquid	Enthalpy, kJ/kg Vapor	Entropy, kJ/(kg·K) Liquid	Entropy, kJ/(kg·K) Vapor	Specific Heat c_p, kJ/(kg·K) Liquid	Specific Heat c_p, kJ/(kg·K) Vapor	c_p/c_v Vapor	Velocity of Sound, m/s Liquid	Velocity of Sound, m/s Vapor	Viscosity, μPa·s Liquid	Viscosity, μPa·s Vapor	Thermal Cond., mW/(m·K) Liquid	Thermal Cond., mW/(m·K) Vapor	Surface Tension, mN/m	Temp.,* K
2.18[a]	0.00486	146.24	0.87297	2.34	25.56	1.4040	12.0746	6.318	6.061	1.747	217	83.2	—	—	—	—	0.388	2.18
2.20	0.00515	146.19	0.83068	2.48	25.66	1.4682	12.0035	5.800	6.076	1.750	217	83.6	—	—	—	—	0.385	2.20
2.30	0.00653	145.87	0.67831	2.98	26.05	1.6865	11.7174	4.164	6.139	1.763	216	85.0	—	—	—	—	0.371	2.30
2.40	0.00814	145.46	0.56257	3.35	26.44	1.8414	11.4586	3.217	6.199	1.778	216	86.3	—	—	—	—	0.356	2.40
2.50	0.01000	144.96	0.47252	3.66	26.81	1.9607	11.2211	2.700	6.258	1.795	216	87.6	—	—	—	—	0.342	2.50
2.60	0.01213	144.38	0.40113	3.93	27.17	2.0604	11.0011	2.453	6.318	1.813	217	88.8	—	—	—	—	0.328	2.60
2.70	0.01454	143.72	0.34364	4.18	27.52	2.1502	10.7956	2.372	6.380	1.834	217	90.0	—	—	—	—	0.314	2.70
2.80	0.01727	143.00	0.29674	4.44	27.86	2.2356	10.6024	2.394	6.446	1.857	217	91.1	—	—	—	—	0.300	2.80
2.90	0.02032	142.21	0.25805	4.70	28.19	2.3196	10.4198	2.477	6.516	1.882	216	92.1	—	—	—	—	0.286	2.90
3.00	0.02373	141.34	0.22582	4.97	28.50	2.4039	10.2464	2.598	6.592	1.910	214	93.0	—	—	—	—	0.272	3.00
3.10	0.02750	140.42	0.19871	5.26	28.79	2.4894	10.0808	2.740	6.676	1.941	213	93.9	—	—	—	—	0.258	3.10
3.20	0.03166	139.43	0.17574	5.56	29.07	2.5765	9.9222	2.897	6.768	1.976	210	94.8	—	—	—	—	0.244	3.20
3.30	0.03622	138.38	0.15612	5.88	29.33	2.6653	9.7694	3.062	6.872	2.015	208	95.5	—	—	—	—	0.231	3.30
3.40	0.04121	137.25	0.13925	6.22	29.57	2.7559	9.6216	3.234	6.989	2.059	205	96.3	—	—	—	—	0.217	3.40
3.50	0.04664	136.06	0.12466	6.58	29.79	2.8482	9.4781	3.414	7.122	2.108	202	96.9	—	—	—	—	0.203	3.50
3.60	0.05252	134.80	0.11195	6.96	29.98	2.9422	9.3381	3.603	7.274	2.165	199	97.5	3.5	1.00	17.9	7.31	0.190	3.60
3.70	0.05888	133.45	0.10081	7.35	30.16	3.0380	9.2007	3.803	7.449	2.229	196	98.1	3.4	1.04	18.1	7.56	0.177	3.70
3.80	0.06573	132.03	0.09101	7.77	30.31	3.1355	9.0653	4.020	7.654	2.303	193	98.6	3.4	1.07	18.2	7.82	0.164	3.80
3.90	0.07310	130.51	0.08232	8.21	30.43	3.2351	8.9312	4.257	7.894	2.389	189	99.1	3.3	1.11	18.4	8.09	0.150	3.90
4.00	0.08100	128.90	0.07459	8.67	30.52	3.3367	8.7975	4.523	8.179	2.491	186	99.5	3.3	1.15	18.5	8.36	0.138	4.00
4.10	0.08945	127.17	0.06767	9.16	30.57	3.4407	8.6633	4.826	8.521	2.611	182	99.8	3.2	1.19	18.6	8.66	0.125	4.10
4.20	0.09847	125.32	0.06144	9.68	30.59	3.5475	8.5277	5.179	8.938	2.756	178	100.1	3.2	1.24	18.6	8.97	0.112	4.20
4.23[b]	0.10132	124.73	0.05967	9.84	30.59	3.5806	8.4861	5.299	9.083	2.806	176	100.2	3.2	1.25	18.7	9.06	0.108	4.23
4.30	0.10809	123.33	0.05581	10.22	30.57	3.6577	8.3896	5.600	9.455	2.934	173	100.4	3.1	1.28	18.7	9.30	0.099	4.30
4.40	0.11832	121.17	0.05067	10.80	30.50	3.7719	8.2476	6.118	10.110	3.158	169	100.6	3.1	1.33	18.8	9.66	0.087	4.40
4.50	0.12920	118.81	0.04596	11.42	30.36	3.8912	8.0999	6.776	10.964	3.448	164	100.8	3.0	1.38	18.8	10.07	0.075	4.50
4.60	0.14075	116.20	0.04161	12.09	30.16	4.0171	7.9440	7.646	12.117	3.838	159	100.9	3.0	1.43	18.8	10.54	0.063	4.60
4.70	0.15301	113.27	0.03753	12.83	29.87	4.1517	7.7767	8.863	13.754	4.388	153	101.0	2.9	1.48	18.9	11.08	0.051	4.70
4.80	0.16602	109.90	0.03367	13.64	29.45	4.2986	7.5924	10.700	16.244	5.224	147	101.1	2.8	1.55	19.0	11.76	0.040	4.80
4.90	0.17983	105.89	0.02993	14.57	28.87	4.4641	7.3821	13.813	20.464	6.637	140	101.3	2.7	1.62	19.1	12.63	0.029	4.90
5.00	0.19453	100.83	0.02617	15.69	28.02	4.6615	7.1273	20.240	29.094	9.531	133	101.6	2.6	1.70	19.3	13.86	0.018	5.00
5.10	0.21023	93.53	0.02206	17.20	26.63	4.9283	6.7774	40.770	55.866	18.545	124	102.5	2.5	1.80	19.9	15.77	0.008	5.10
5.20[c]	0.22746	69.64	0.01436	21.71	21.71	5.7639	5.7639	∞	∞	∞	0	0.0	—	—	∞	∞	0.000	5.20

*Temperatures on EPT-76 scale [a]Lower lambda point [b]Normal boiling point [c]Critical point

Refrigerant 704 (Helium) Properties of Gas at 0.101 325 MPa (one standard atmosphere)

Temp., °C	Density, kg/m³	Enthalpy, kJ/kg	Entropy, kJ/(kg·K)	c_p, kJ/(kg·K)	c_p/c_v	Vel. of Sound, m/s	Visc., μPa·s	Thermal Cond., mW/(m·K)
−268.9[b]	16.758	30.59	8.4861	9.083	2.806	100.2	1.25	9.05
−260	3.7508	82.19	15.2748	5.327	1.708	213.6	2.72	20.17
−250	2.1049	134.88	18.2572	5.236	1.678	284.4	3.93	28.69
−240	1.4677	187.10	20.1325	5.213	1.671	340.1	4.93	35.90
−220	0.9155	291.20	22.5899	5.200	1.668	430.1	6.60	48.56
−200	0.6655	395.16	24.2500	5.196	1.667	504.3	8.04	59.86
−180	0.5228	499.06	25.5057	5.195	1.667	568.8	9.35	70.30
−160	0.4305	602.95	26.5160	5.194	1.667	626.7	10.39	80.09
−140	0.3659	706.82	27.3614	5.194	1.667	679.7	11.56	89.41
−120	0.3182	810.69	28.0882	5.193	1.666	728.8	12.68	98.32
−100	0.2815	914.56	28.7256	5.193	1.666	774.9	13.75	106.90
−80	0.2524	1018.42	29.2932	5.193	1.667	818.3	14.79	115.20
−60	0.2287	1122.28	29.8049	5.193	1.667	859.6	15.80	123.25
−40	0.2091	1226.14	30.2707	5.193	1.667	898.9	16.79	131.09
−20	0.1926	1330.00	30.6980	5.193	1.667	936.7	17.75	138.73
0	0.1785	1433.87	31.0929	5.193	1.667	972.9	18.70	146.20
20	0.1663	1537.73	31.4599	5.193	1.667	1007.9	19.62	153.50
40	0.1557	1641.58	31.8026	5.193	1.667	1041.6	20.52	160.67
60	0.1464	1745.44	32.1241	5.193	1.667	1074.4	21.41	167.70
80	0.1381	1849.30	32.4269	5.193	1.667	1106.1	22.29	174.61
100	0.1307	1953.16	32.7129	5.193	1.667	1137.0	23.15	181.41
120	0.1240	2057.02	32.9840	5.193	1.667	1167.0	24.00	188.10
140	0.1180	2160.88	33.2417	5.193	1.667	1196.3	24.84	194.69
160	0.1126	2264.74	33.4872	5.193	1.667	1224.9	25.67	201.19
180	0.1076	2368.60	33.7216	5.193	1.667	1252.9	26.49	207.60
200	0.1031	2472.46	33.9459	5.193	1.667	1280.2	27.29	213.93
220	0.0989	2576.32	34.1609	5.193	1.667	1307.0	28.09	220.18
240	0.0950	2680.18	34.3673	5.193	1.667	1333.2	28.88	226.35
260	0.0915	2784.04	34.5659	5.193	1.667	1358.9	29.66	232.46
280	0.0882	2887.90	34.7571	5.193	1.667	1384.1	30.43	238.50
300	0.0851	2991.76	34.9416	5.193	1.667	1408.9	31.20	244.47
320	0.0822	3095.62	35.1197	5.193	1.667	1433.3	31.96	250.39
340	0.0795	3199.48	35.2919	5.193	1.667	1457.2	32.71	256.24
360	0.0770	3303.34	35.4586	5.193	1.667	1480.8	33.45	262.04
380	0.0747	3407.20	35.6201	5.193	1.667	1504.0	34.19	267.79
400	0.0725	3511.06	35.7767	5.193	1.667	1526.8	34.92	273.48
420	0.0704	3614.92	35.9288	5.193	1.667	1549.3	35.65	279.13
440	0.0684	3718.78	36.0765	5.193	1.667	1571.5	36.37	284.73
460	0.0665	3822.64	36.2201	5.193	1.667	1593.4	37.08	290.28
480	0.0648	3926.50	36.3599	5.193	1.667	1615.0	37.79	295.78
500	0.0631	4030.36	36.4960	5.193	1.667	1636.3	38.49	301.25

[b]Saturated vapor at normal boiling point

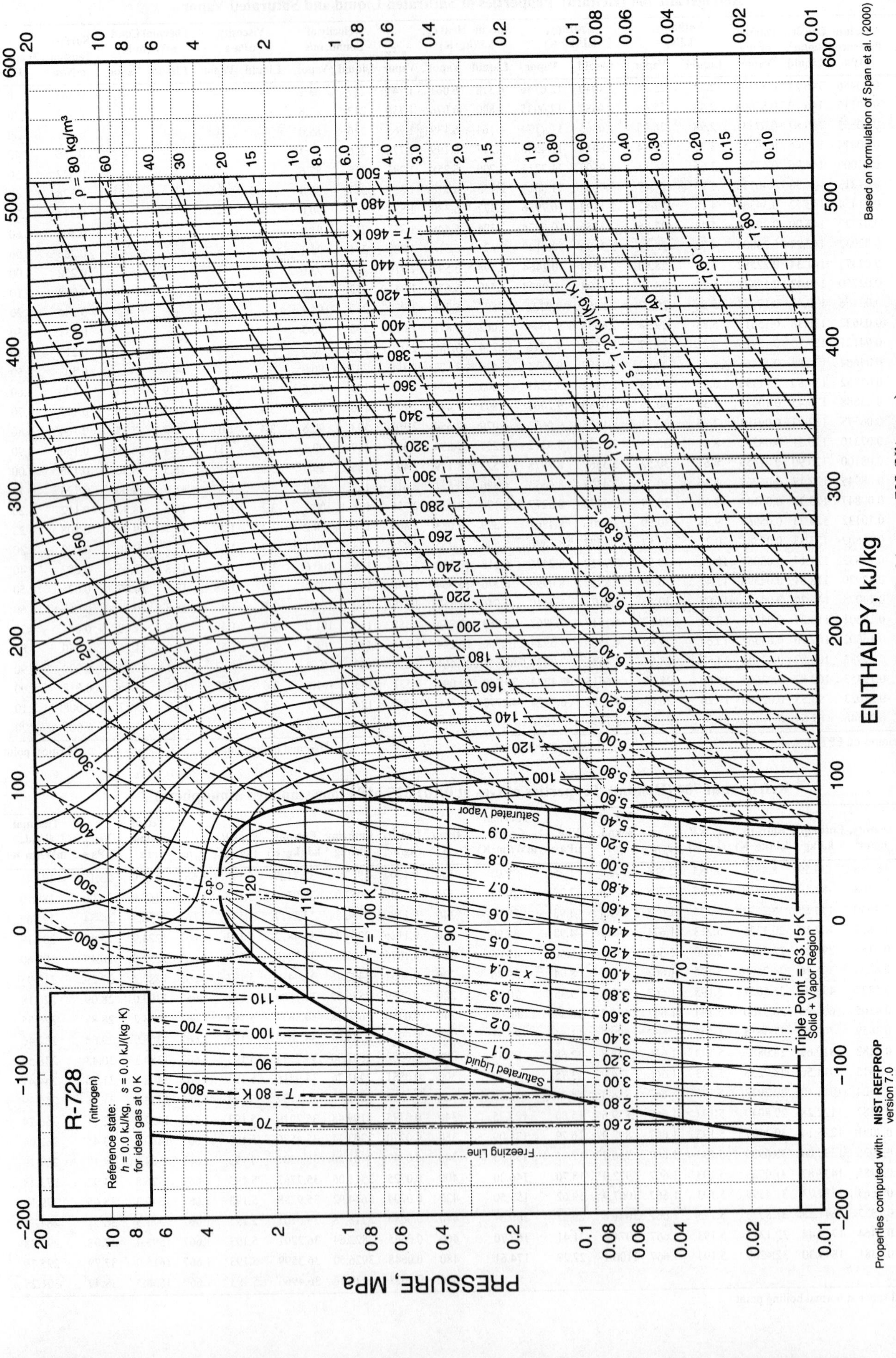

Fig. 29 Pressure-Enthalpy Diagram for Refrigerant 728 (Nitrogen)

Refrigerant 728 (Nitrogen) Properties of Saturated Liquid and Saturated Vapor

Temp.,* K	Absolute Pressure, MPa	Density, kg/m³ Liquid	Volume, m³/kg Vapor	Enthalpy, kJ/kg Liquid	Enthalpy, kJ/kg Vapor	Entropy, kJ/(kg·K) Liquid	Entropy, kJ/(kg·K) Vapor	Specific Heat c_p, kJ/(kg·K) Liquid	Specific Heat c_p, kJ/(kg·K) Vapor	c_p/c_v Vapor	Velocity of Sound, m/s Liquid	Velocity of Sound, m/s Vapor	Viscosity, µPa·s Liquid	Viscosity, µPa·s Vapor	Thermal Cond., mW/(m·K) Liquid	Thermal Cond., mW/(m·K) Vapor	Surface Tension, mN/m	Temp.,* K
63.15[a]	0.01252	867.2	1.48310	−150.73	64.78	2.4257	5.8383	2.000	1.058	1.411	995	161.1	311.6	4.38	173.2	5.62	12.24	63.15
64	0.01460	863.7	1.28720	−149.03	65.59	2.4524	5.8059	2.002	1.061	1.413	987	162.1	297.5	4.44	171.5	5.71	12.03	64
66	0.02062	855.4	0.93698	−145.02	67.47	2.5140	5.7336	2.005	1.066	1.417	966	164.3	267.8	4.59	167.5	5.92	11.55	66
68	0.02848	847.0	0.69642	−141.00	69.31	2.5739	5.6667	2.010	1.073	1.421	946	166.4	242.3	4.73	163.5	6.14	11.07	68
70	0.03854	838.5	0.52743	−136.97	71.10	2.6321	5.6045	2.014	1.082	1.427	926	168.4	220.2	4.88	159.5	6.35	10.59	70
72	0.05121	829.9	0.40625	−132.93	72.83	2.6889	5.5466	2.020	1.091	1.433	906	170.3	201.1	5.03	155.5	6.58	10.12	72
74	0.06691	821.1	0.31772	−128.87	74.50	2.7442	5.4925	2.027	1.102	1.441	885	172.1	184.3	5.19	151.5	6.80	9.65	74
76	0.08610	812.2	0.25192	−124.79	76.11	2.7983	5.4417	2.035	1.114	1.450	865	173.8	169.6	5.34	147.5	7.03	9.19	76
77.35[b]	0.10132	806.1	0.21682	−122.02	77.16	2.8342	5.4090	2.041	1.124	1.457	851	174.8	160.7	5.44	144.8	7.19	8.87	77.35
78	0.10926	803.1	0.20226	−120.70	77.64	2.8511	5.3939	2.045	1.129	1.461	845	175.3	156.6	5.49	143.5	7.26	8.73	78
80	0.13687	793.9	0.16422	−116.58	79.10	2.9028	5.3487	2.056	1.145	1.473	824	176.7	145.1	5.65	139.5	7.51	8.27	80
82	0.16947	784.6	0.13470	−112.43	80.47	2.9534	5.3059	2.068	1.163	1.487	804	178.0	134.8	5.81	135.6	7.76	7.83	82
84	0.20757	775.0	0.11152	−108.26	81.75	3.0031	5.2651	2.083	1.184	1.503	783	179.2	125.6	5.97	131.6	8.01	7.38	84
86	0.25174	765.2	0.09310	−104.05	82.93	3.0520	5.2262	2.099	1.208	1.521	762	180.2	117.2	6.14	127.7	8.29	6.94	86
88	0.30251	755.2	0.07831	−99.81	84.01	3.1000	5.1888	2.119	1.235	1.542	741	181.0	109.7	6.31	123.7	8.57	6.51	88
90	0.36046	745.0	0.06632	−95.52	84.97	3.1473	5.1527	2.141	1.266	1.567	719	181.8	102.8	6.48	119.8	8.87	6.09	90
92	0.42616	734.5	0.05651	−91.18	85.81	3.1940	5.1178	2.166	1.300	1.594	697	182.4	96.5	6.66	115.9	9.19	5.67	92
94	0.50020	723.8	0.04842	−86.79	86.52	3.2401	5.0839	2.196	1.341	1.626	675	182.8	90.7	6.84	111.9	9.53	5.25	94
96	0.58316	712.7	0.04169	−82.34	87.10	3.2858	5.0507	2.231	1.387	1.664	652	183.1	85.4	7.03	108.0	9.89	4.84	96
98	0.67565	701.2	0.03605	−77.81	87.51	3.3311	5.0181	2.271	1.440	1.707	629	183.3	80.4	7.23	104.0	10.29	4.44	98
100	0.77827	689.4	0.03129	−73.21	87.77	3.3761	4.9858	2.318	1.503	1.758	605	183.3	75.8	7.43	100.1	10.73	4.05	100
105	1.08330	657.5	0.02224	−61.27	87.56	3.4882	4.9055	2.479	1.714	1.931	543	182.5	65.3	7.98	90.3	12.04	3.10	105
110	1.46580	621.5	0.01598	−48.49	85.84	3.6015	4.8226	2.743	2.062	2.221	476	180.8	56.0	8.63	80.4	13.83	2.21	110
115	1.93700	578.7	0.01146	−34.39	81.91	3.7198	4.7311	3.240	2.749	2.778	403	177.7	47.3	9.44	70.6	16.58	1.39	115
120	2.51060	523.4	0.00799	−17.87	74.17	3.8514	4.6185	4.508	4.631	4.216	317	172.6	38.4	10.62	61.0	21.72	0.66	120
125	3.20690	426.1	0.00487	6.40	55.03	4.0373	4.4263	16.720	23.740	16.930	195	160.3	26.9	13.33	56.4	41.54	0.08	125
126.19[c]	3.39580	313.3	0.00319	29.23	29.23	4.2149	4.2149	∞	∞	∞	0	0.0	—	—	∞	∞	0.00	126.19

*Temperatures on ITS-90 scale [a]Triple point [b]Normal boiling point [c]Critical point

Refrigerant 728 (Nitrogen) Properties of Gas at 0.101 325 MPa (one standard atmosphere)

Temp., °C	Density, kg/m³	Enthalpy, kJ/kg	Entropy, kJ/(kg·K)	c_p, kJ/(kg·K)	c_p/c_v	Vel. of Sound, m/s	Visc., µPa·s	Thermal Cond., mW/(m·K)
−195.8[b]	4.6121	77.16	5.4090	1.124	1.457	174.8	5.44	7.19
−180	3.7571	94.51	5.6133	1.081	1.432	194.0	6.51	8.72
−160	3.0593	115.90	5.8213	1.061	1.419	215.2	7.81	10.63
−140	2.5858	137.02	5.9932	1.052	1.412	234.2	9.06	12.49
−120	2.2414	158.02	6.1402	1.048	1.409	251.6	10.27	14.28
−100	1.9789	178.95	6.2687	1.045	1.406	267.9	11.42	16.03
−90	1.8696	189.40	6.3273	1.045	1.405	275.6	11.99	16.88
−80	1.7719	199.85	6.3829	1.044	1.405	283.1	12.54	17.71
−70	1.6839	210.28	6.4355	1.043	1.404	290.4	13.08	18.54
−60	1.6043	220.71	6.4857	1.043	1.404	297.5	13.61	19.35
−50	1.5320	231.14	6.5335	1.042	1.403	304.4	14.14	20.15
−40	1.4659	241.56	6.5791	1.042	1.403	311.2	14.65	20.94
−30	1.4053	251.98	6.6229	1.042	1.403	317.9	15.16	21.72
−20	1.3496	262.40	6.6649	1.042	1.402	324.4	15.66	22.49
−10	1.2981	272.82	6.7053	1.042	1.402	330.7	16.15	23.25
0	1.2504	283.23	6.7441	1.041	1.402	337.0	16.63	24.00
10	1.2061	293.65	6.7815	1.041	1.402	343.1	17.10	24.74
20	1.1648	304.06	6.8177	1.041	1.401	349.1	17.57	25.47
30	1.1263	314.47	6.8526	1.041	1.401	355.0	18.03	26.20
40	1.0903	324.89	6.8864	1.041	1.401	360.8	18.49	26.91
50	1.0565	335.30	6.9191	1.042	1.401	366.5	18.94	27.62
60	1.0247	345.72	6.9509	1.042	1.400	372.1	19.38	28.32
70	0.9948	356.14	6.9817	1.042	1.400	377.7	19.82	29.01
80	0.9666	366.56	7.0117	1.042	1.400	383.1	20.25	29.69
90	0.9399	376.99	7.0408	1.043	1.400	388.5	20.68	30.37
100	0.9147	387.42	7.0691	1.043	1.399	393.7	21.10	31.04
110	0.8908	397.85	7.0967	1.044	1.399	398.9	21.52	31.70
120	0.8681	408.30	7.1236	1.044	1.398	404.0	21.93	32.36
130	0.8466	418.74	7.1498	1.045	1.398	409.1	22.34	33.01
140	0.8261	429.20	7.1755	1.046	1.397	414.1	22.74	33.66
150	0.8065	439.66	7.2005	1.047	1.397	419.0	23.14	34.30
160	0.7879	450.14	7.2249	1.048	1.396	423.8	23.53	34.93
170	0.7701	460.62	7.2489	1.049	1.396	428.6	23.92	35.56
180	0.7531	471.12	7.2723	1.050	1.395	433.3	24.31	36.18
190	0.7368	481.62	7.2952	1.051	1.394	438.0	24.69	36.80
200	0.7212	492.14	7.3177	1.053	1.394	442.6	25.07	37.42
210	0.7063	502.67	7.3397	1.054	1.393	447.1	25.44	38.03
220	0.6920	513.22	7.3613	1.055	1.392	451.6	25.81	38.63
230	0.6782	523.78	7.3825	1.057	1.391	456.0	26.18	39.23
240	0.6650	534.36	7.4033	1.059	1.390	460.4	26.54	39.83
250	0.6523	544.95	7.4238	1.060	1.389	464.7	26.90	40.42
260	0.6401	555.56	7.4439	1.062	1.389	468.9	27.26	41.01
270	0.6283	566.19	7.4636	1.064	1.388	473.2	27.62	41.59
280	0.6169	576.84	7.4831	1.066	1.387	477.3	27.97	42.17
290	0.6060	587.50	7.5022	1.068	1.386	481.5	28.32	42.75
300	0.5954	598.19	7.5210	1.070	1.385	485.5	28.66	43.32
310	0.5852	608.90	7.5395	1.072	1.384	489.6	29.00	43.89
320	0.5753	619.62	7.5577	1.074	1.383	493.6	29.35	44.46
330	0.5658	630.37	7.5757	1.076	1.381	497.5	29.68	45.02
340	0.5565	641.14	7.5934	1.078	1.380	501.4	30.02	45.58
350	0.5476	651.93	7.6109	1.080	1.379	505.3	30.35	46.13
360	0.5390	662.74	7.6281	1.082	1.378	509.1	30.68	46.69
370	0.5306	673.58	7.6451	1.085	1.377	512.9	31.01	47.23
380	0.5225	684.44	7.6618	1.087	1.376	516.7	31.34	47.78
390	0.5146	695.32	7.6783	1.089	1.375	520.4	31.66	48.33
400	0.5069	706.22	7.6947	1.092	1.374	524.1	31.98	48.87
420	0.4923	728.10	7.7267	1.096	1.371	531.4	32.62	49.94
440	0.4785	750.08	7.7580	1.101	1.369	538.6	33.24	51.00
460	0.4655	772.15	7.7885	1.106	1.367	545.6	33.87	52.06
480	0.4531	794.32	7.8183	1.111	1.365	552.6	34.48	53.10
500	0.4414	816.59	7.8475	1.116	1.363	559.4	35.08	54.14

[b]Saturated vapor at normal boiling point

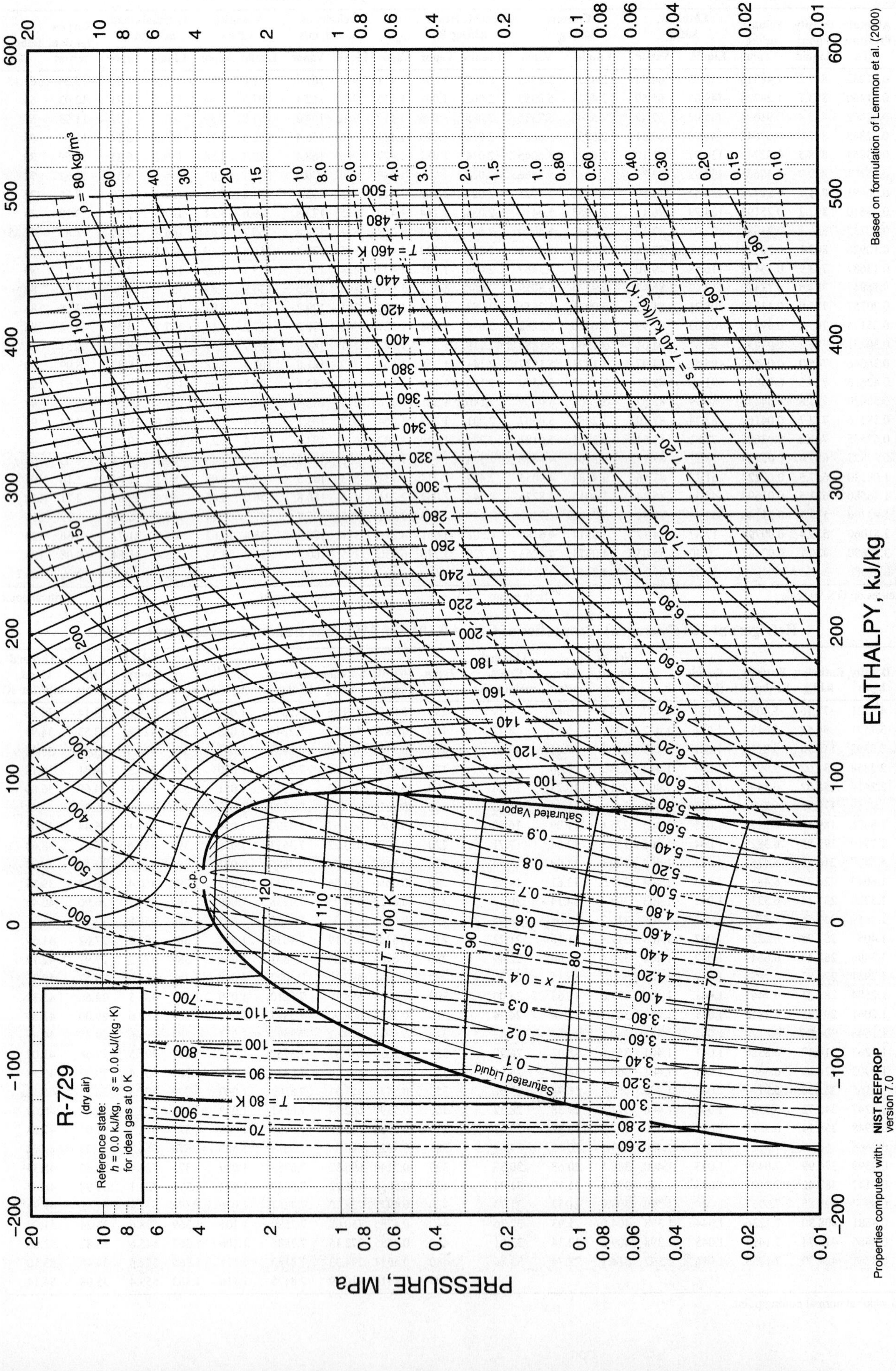

Fig. 30 Pressure-Enthalpy Diagram for Refrigerant 729 (Air)

Refrigerant 729 (Air) Properties of Liquid on the Bubble Line and Vapor on the Dew Line

Absolute Pressure, MPa	Temperature,* K		Density, kg/m³	Volume, m³/kg	Enthalpy, kJ/kg		Entropy, kJ/(kg·K)		Specific Heat c_p, kJ/(kg·K)		c_p/c_v	Velocity of Sound, m/s		Viscosity, μPa·s		Thermal Cond., mW/(m·K)		Surface Tension, mN/m
	Bubble	Dew	Liquid	Vapor	Liquid	Vapor	Liquid	Vapor	Liquid	Vapor	Vapor	Liquid	Vapor	Liquid	Vapor	Liquid	Vapor	
0.00526	59.75	63.09	957.8	3.42745	−162.40	62.73	2.4517	6.1507	1.895	1.014	1.405	1056	158.9	424.8	4.47	185.2	5.83	14.95
0.008	61.83	65.12	949.2	2.32401	−158.45	64.67	2.5165	6.0614	1.897	1.017	1.407	1035	161.3	377.9	4.62	181.2	6.04	14.41
0.01	63.00	66.27	944.4	1.88990	−156.22	65.75	2.5522	6.0142	1.899	1.019	1.408	1023	162.6	354.6	4.70	179.0	6.16	14.11
0.015	65.27	68.47	934.9	1.29870	−151.92	67.82	2.6193	5.9293	1.902	1.023	1.411	1001	165.0	315.3	4.87	174.7	6.38	13.54
0.02	66.99	70.15	927.6	0.99558	−148.64	69.35	2.6687	5.8697	1.904	1.026	1.414	984	166.8	289.6	4.99	171.4	6.55	13.11
0.03	69.58	72.68	916.5	0.68481	−143.68	71.62	2.7412	5.7866	1.909	1.033	1.420	959	169.4	256.4	5.18	166.5	6.80	12.46
0.04	71.57	74.61	907.9	0.52523	−139.88	73.30	2.7948	5.7282	1.913	1.039	1.425	940	171.3	234.8	5.33	162.7	7.00	11.97
0.05	73.19	76.19	900.8	0.42756	−136.77	74.63	2.8378	5.6832	1.917	1.044	1.430	925	172.8	219.0	5.45	159.7	7.16	11.57
0.06	74.58	77.53	894.7	0.36139	−134.10	75.75	2.8738	5.6467	1.921	1.050	1.434	911	174.0	206.8	5.55	157.0	7.29	11.24
0.08	76.89	79.78	884.3	0.27713	−129.64	77.55	2.9323	5.5893	1.928	1.060	1.443	889	175.9	188.7	5.72	152.7	7.52	10.68
0.1	78.79	81.62	875.7	0.22550	−125.95	78.96	2.9794	5.5450	1.936	1.070	1.452	871	177.3	175.6	5.86	149.1	7.71	10.22
0.10132[b]	78.90	81.73	875.1	0.22277	−125.73	79.05	2.9822	5.5424	1.936	1.071	1.452	869	177.4	174.8	5.87	148.9	7.72	10.20
0.15	82.51	85.23	858.4	0.15488	−118.68	81.55	3.0688	5.4648	1.953	1.094	1.471	834	179.9	153.5	6.15	142.1	8.07	9.35
0.2	85.39	88.02	844.6	0.11849	−113.01	83.38	3.1357	5.4079	1.969	1.117	1.409	806	181.6	139.3	6.37	136.8	8.37	8.68
0.3	89.82	92.32	822.7	0.08100	−104.17	85.84	3.2353	5.3272	2.002	1.162	1.527	762	183.7	120.9	6.72	128.5	8.88	7.67
0.4	93.26	95.65	805.0	0.06165	−97.17	87.42	3.3104	5.2691	2.034	1.207	1.564	727	184.9	108.9	7.00	122.1	9.37	6.90
0.5	96.12	98.42	789.7	0.04977	−91.26	88.49	3.3715	5.2231	2.068	1.253	1.601	697	185.6	100.1	7.25	116.8	9.82	6.28
0.6	98.59	100.80	776.0	0.04169	−86.07	89.22	3.4235	5.1848	2.102	1.299	1.639	670	186.0	93.3	7.47	112.2	10.24	5.75
0.8	102.76	104.83	751.9	0.03136	−77.12	89.99	3.5098	5.1221	2.176	1.398	1.721	625	186.3	83.0	7.86	104.4	11.03	4.88
1	106.23	108.18	730.4	0.02500	−69.40	90.12	3.5811	5.0708	2.258	1.506	1.813	585	186.0	75.3	8.21	98.0	11.81	4.18
1.5	113.15	114.83	682.6	0.01623	−53.12	88.65	3.7230	4.9678	2.515	1.844	2.101	500	184.2	61.9	9.00	85.2	13.87	2.85
2	118.58	120.02	638.2	0.01162	−39.06	85.27	3.8379	4.8805	2.899	2.359	2.538	427	181.4	52.5	9.79	75.2	16.31	1.89
2.5	123.11	124.32	592.9	0.00869	−25.82	80.04	3.9407	4.7966	3.558	3.27	3.286	359	177.8	44.8	10.68	66.9	19.55	1.16
3	127.03	127.99	541.8	0.00658	−12.26	72.34	4.0419	4.7056	5.008	5.303	4.895	290	173.4	37.7	11.82	60.0	24.56	0.59
3.78781[c]	132.53	132.53	342.6	0.00292	29.38	29.38	4.3479	4.3479	—	—	—	—	—	—	—	—	—	0.00

*Temperatures on ITS-90 scale

[b]Bubble and dew points at one standard atmosphere

[c]Critical point

Refrigerant 729 (Air) Properties of Gas at 0.101 325 MPa (one standard atmosphere)

Temp., °C	Density, kg/m³	Enthalpy, kJ/kg	Entropy, kJ/(kg·K)	c_p, kJ/(kg·K)	c_p/c_v	Vel. of Sound, m/s	Visc., μPa·s	Thermal Cond., mW/(m·K)
−191.4[d]	4.4889	79.05	5.5424	1.071	1.452	177.4	5.87	7.72
−180	3.8887	91.09	5.6804	1.044	1.435	190.8	6.68	8.84
−160	3.1648	111.75	5.8814	1.025	1.421	211.7	8.04	10.76
−140	2.6744	132.15	6.0474	1.016	1.414	230.4	9.35	12.63
−120	2.3178	152.43	6.1893	1.012	1.410	247.6	10.61	14.45
−100	2.0462	172.63	6.3133	1.009	1.408	263.5	11.82	16.20
−90	1.9332	182.71	6.3699	1.008	1.407	271.1	12.41	17.06
−80	1.8321	192.79	6.4235	1.007	1.406	278.5	12.99	17.91
−70	1.7411	202.86	6.4743	1.007	1.406	285.7	13.55	18.74
−60	1.6588	212.93	6.5227	1.007	1.405	292.7	14.11	19.56
−50	1.5840	222.99	6.5688	1.006	1.405	299.5	14.66	20.37
−40	1.5156	233.06	6.6130	1.006	1.404	306.2	15.20	21.17
−30	1.4530	243.11	6.6552	1.006	1.404	312.7	15.73	21.96
−20	1.3953	253.17	6.6957	1.006	1.404	319.1	16.25	22.74
−10	1.3421	263.23	6.7347	1.006	1.403	325.4	16.76	23.51
0	1.2927	273.29	6.7722	1.006	1.403	331.5	17.27	24.27
10	1.2469	283.35	6.8084	1.006	1.402	337.5	17.77	25.02
20	1.2043	293.41	6.8433	1.006	1.402	343.4	18.26	25.77
30	1.1644	303.48	6.8771	1.007	1.402	349.2	18.75	26.50
40	1.1272	313.55	6.9098	1.007	1.401	354.9	19.22	27.22
50	1.0922	323.62	6.9414	1.008	1.401	360.5	19.70	27.94
60	1.0594	333.70	6.9721	1.008	1.400	366.0	20.16	28.65
70	1.0284	343.79	7.0020	1.009	1.400	371.4	20.62	29.36
80	0.9993	353.88	7.0310	1.010	1.399	376.7	21.08	30.05
90	0.9717	363.98	7.0592	1.011	1.399	381.9	21.52	30.74
100	0.9456	374.09	7.0866	1.011	1.398	387.1	21.97	31.42
110	0.9209	384.21	7.1134	1.012	1.397	392.1	22.41	32.10
120	0.8975	394.34	7.1395	1.014	1.397	397.1	22.84	32.77
130	0.8752	404.49	7.1650	1.015	1.396	402.1	23.27	33.43
140	0.8540	414.64	7.1899	1.016	1.395	406.9	23.69	34.09

Temp., °C	Density, kg/m³	Enthalpy, kJ/kg	Entropy, kJ/(kg·K)	c_p, kJ/(kg·K)	c_p/c_v	Vel. of Sound, m/s	Visc., μPa·s	Thermal Cond., mW/(m·K)
150	0.8338	424.81	7.2142	1.017	1.394	411.7	24.11	34.75
160	0.8145	434.99	7.2379	1.019	1.394	416.4	24.52	35.39
170	0.7961	445.18	7.2612	1.020	1.393	421.1	24.93	36.04
180	0.7785	455.39	7.2840	1.022	1.392	425.7	25.34	36.67
190	0.7617	465.62	7.3063	1.023	1.391	430.2	25.74	37.31
200	0.7456	475.86	7.3282	1.025	1.390	434.7	26.13	37.93
210	0.7302	486.12	7.3497	1.027	1.389	439.1	26.53	38.56
220	0.7154	496.40	7.3707	1.029	1.388	443.5	26.92	39.17
230	0.7011	506.70	7.3914	1.031	1.387	447.8	27.30	39.79
240	0.6875	517.02	7.4117	1.033	1.386	452.0	27.69	40.40
250	0.6743	527.35	7.4317	1.035	1.385	456.2	28.06	41.00
260	0.6617	537.71	7.4513	1.037	1.384	460.4	28.44	41.60
270	0.6495	548.09	7.4705	1.039	1.383	464.5	28.81	42.20
280	0.6378	558.49	7.4895	1.041	1.381	468.6	29.18	42.80
290	0.6264	568.91	7.5082	1.043	1.380	472.6	29.55	43.39
300	0.6155	579.35	7.5266	1.045	1.379	476.6	29.91	43.97
310	0.6049	589.82	7.5447	1.048	1.378	480.5	30.27	44.56
320	0.5947	600.30	7.5625	1.050	1.377	484.4	30.63	45.14
330	0.5849	610.81	7.5801	1.052	1.376	488.3	30.98	45.71
340	0.5753	621.35	7.5974	1.055	1.375	492.1	31.34	46.29
350	0.5661	631.90	7.6145	1.057	1.373	495.9	31.69	46.86
360	0.5572	642.48	7.6313	1.059	1.372	499.7	32.03	47.42
370	0.5485	653.09	7.6479	1.062	1.371	503.4	32.38	47.99
380	0.5401	663.71	7.6643	1.064	1.370	507.1	32.72	48.55
390	0.5320	674.37	7.6805	1.066	1.369	510.7	33.06	49.11
400	0.5241	685.04	7.6965	1.069	1.368	514.3	33.40	49.66
420	0.5089	706.47	7.7279	1.074	1.365	521.5	34.06	50.76
440	0.4947	727.98	7.7585	1.078	1.363	528.5	34.72	51.86
460	0.4812	749.60	7.7884	1.083	1.361	535.4	35.37	52.94
480	0.4684	771.31	7.8176	1.088	1.359	542.3	36.02	54.01
500	0.4563	793.12	7.8461	1.093	1.357	549.0	36.65	55.08

[d]Saturated vapor at dew-point temperature

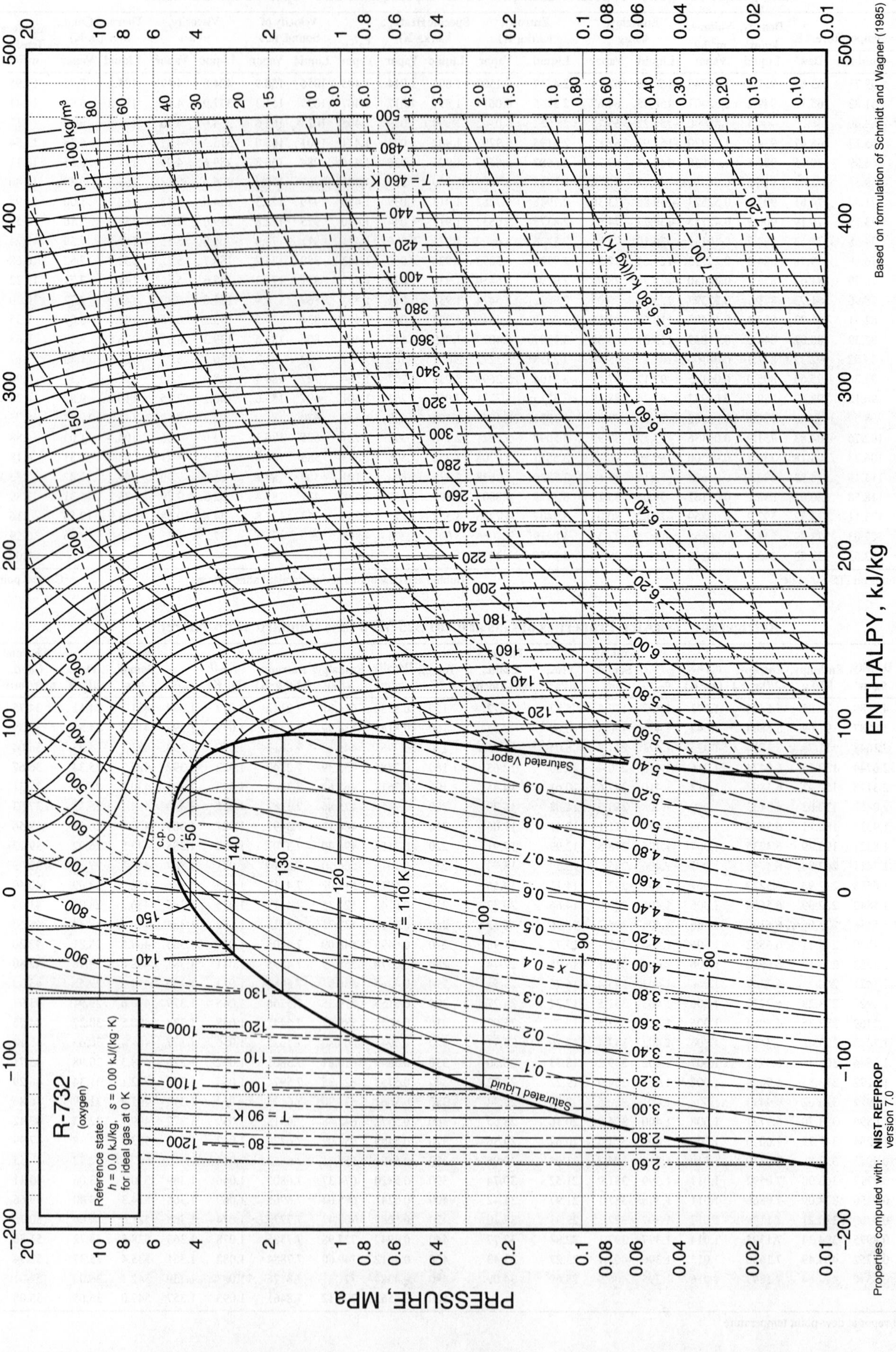

Fig. 31 Pressure-Enthalpy Diagram for Refrigerant 732 (Oxygen)

Refrigerant 732 (Oxygen) Properties of Saturated Liquid and Saturated Vapor

Temp.,* K	Absolute Pressure, MPa	Density, kg/m³ Liquid	Volume, m³/kg Vapor	Enthalpy, kJ/kg Liquid	Enthalpy, kJ/kg Vapor	Entropy, kJ/(kg·K) Liquid	Entropy, kJ/(kg·K) Vapor	Specific Heat c_p, kJ/(kg·K) Liquid	Specific Heat c_p, kJ/(kg·K) Vapor	c_p/c_v Vapor	Velocity of Sound, m/s Liquid	Velocity of Sound, m/s Vapor	Viscosity, μPa·s Liquid	Viscosity, μPa·s Vapor	Thermal Cond., mW/(m·K) Liquid	Thermal Cond., mW/(m·K) Vapor	Surface Tension, mN/m	Temp.,* K
54.36[a]	0.00015	1306.1	96.54300	–193.61	49.11	2.0921	6.5571	1.673	0.926	1.395	1123	140.3	773.6	4.10	201.9	4.42	22.68	54.36
55	0.00018	1303.5	80.00900	–192.55	49.68	2.1117	6.5159	1.672	0.928	1.394	1127	141.1	747.5	4.15	201.0	4.48	22.50	55
60	0.00073	1282.0	21.46200	–184.19	54.19	2.2571	6.2301	1.673	0.948	1.390	1127	147.0	578.1	4.55	193.9	4.98	21.12	60
65	0.00233	1259.7	7.21880	–175.81	58.66	2.3912	5.9985	1.677	0.967	1.387	1102	152.6	457.9	4.96	186.8	5.49	19.76	65
70	0.00626	1237.0	2.89250	–167.42	63.09	2.5156	5.8086	1.678	0.978	1.387	1066	158.1	371.8	5.36	179.7	5.99	18.41	70
75	0.01455	1213.9	1.32930	–159.02	67.45	2.6313	5.6510	1.679	0.979	1.392	1027	163.3	308.7	5.75	172.6	6.51	17.09	75
80	0.03012	1190.5	0.68099	–150.61	71.69	2.7397	5.5185	1.682	0.974	1.402	987	168.4	261.2	6.15	165.4	7.03	15.78	80
85	0.05683	1166.6	0.38047	–142.18	75.75	2.8417	5.4055	1.688	0.969	1.417	947	173.1	224.6	6.54	158.3	7.57	14.49	85
90	0.09935	1142.1	0.22794	–133.69	79.55	2.9383	5.3076	1.699	0.970	1.436	906	177.3	195.6	6.94	151.0	8.12	13.22	90
90.19[b]	0.10133	1141.2	0.22386	–133.37	79.69	2.9419	5.3042	1.699	0.971	1.437	904	177.5	194.7	6.95	150.8	8.15	13.17	90.19
95	0.16308	1116.9	0.14450	–125.12	83.04	3.0303	5.2215	1.715	0.982	1.460	864	181.0	172.1	7.33	143.8	8.71	11.98	95
100	0.25400	1090.9	0.09592	–116.45	86.16	3.1185	5.1445	1.738	1.006	1.491	822	184.1	152.6	7.73	136.6	9.34	10.75	100
105	0.37853	1063.8	0.06612	–107.64	88.85	3.2033	5.0746	1.767	1.046	1.528	779	186.4	135.9	8.13	129.2	10.01	9.56	105
110	0.54340	1035.5	0.04699	–98.64	91.05	3.2855	5.0100	1.807	1.101	1.576	735	188.1	121.5	8.55	121.9	10.75	8.39	110
115	0.75559	1005.6	0.03424	–89.42	92.72	3.3657	4.9495	1.858	1.177	1.638	689	189.1	108.8	8.98	114.6	11.57	7.25	115
120	1.02230	973.9	0.02544	–79.90	93.75	3.4444	4.8915	1.927	1.276	1.721	642	189.4	97.4	9.43	107.2	12.51	6.14	120
125	1.35090	939.7	0.01919	–70.02	94.06	3.5222	4.8349	2.021	1.411	1.835	592	189.0	87.1	9.91	99.9	13.61	5.07	125
130	1.74910	902.5	0.01463	–59.66	93.47	3.6001	4.7780	2.153	1.600	2.000	540	187.8	77.6	10.45	92.6	14.94	4.04	130
135	2.22500	861.0	0.01120	–48.65	91.74	3.6791	4.7191	2.354	1.886	2.252	484	185.7	68.7	11.06	85.4	16.64	3.05	135
140	2.78780	813.2	0.00856	–36.70	88.47	3.7612	4.6552	2.691	2.370	2.682	423	182.8	60.2	11.82	78.2	18.98	2.13	140
145	3.44770	755.1	0.00646	–23.22	82.83	3.8498	4.5812	3.368	3.369	3.561	355	178.8	51.9	12.88	71.1	22.58	1.27	145
150	4.21860	675.5	0.00465	–6.67	72.56	3.9546	4.4828	5.464	6.625	6.315	274	172.8	42.9	14.72	64.2	29.67	0.51	150
154.58[c]	5.04300	436.1	0.00229	32.42	32.42	4.2008	4.2008	∞	∞	∞	0	0.0	—	—	∞	∞	0.00	154.58

*Temperatures on ITS-90 scale [a]Triple point [b]Normal boiling point [c]Critical point

Refrigerant 732 (Oxygen) Properties of Gas at 0.101 325 MPa (one standard atmosphere)

Temp.,* °C	Density, kg/m³	Enthalpy, kJ/kg	Entropy, kJ/(kg·K)	c_p, kJ/(kg·K)	c_p/c_v	Vel. of Sound, m/s	Visc., μPa·s	Thermal Cond., mW/(m·K)
–183.0[b]	4.4671	79.69	5.3042	0.971	1.437	177.5	6.95	8.15
–180	4.3120	82.52	5.3352	0.948	1.439	181.1	7.18	8.43
–160	3.5050	101.23	5.5171	0.931	1.422	201.0	8.71	10.34
–140	2.9596	119.78	5.6681	0.924	1.414	218.8	10.18	12.22
–120	2.564	138.20	5.7970	0.919	1.409	235.2	11.59	14.07
–100	2.2629	156.56	5.9096	0.916	1.407	250.4	12.96	15.88
–90	2.1378	165.72	5.9611	0.916	1.406	257.6	13.62	16.76
–80	2.0258	174.87	6.0097	0.915	1.405	264.6	14.28	17.64
–70	1.9251	184.02	6.0559	0.915	1.404	271.5	14.92	18.51
–60	1.8340	193.16	6.0998	0.914	1.404	278.1	15.55	19.37
–50	1.7512	202.30	6.1418	0.914	1.403	284.6	16.17	20.22
–40	1.6756	211.45	6.1818	0.914	1.402	290.9	16.78	21.06
–30	1.6063	220.59	6.2202	0.915	1.401	297.1	17.39	21.90
–20	1.5425	229.74	6.2571	0.915	1.401	303.1	17.98	22.72
–10	1.4836	238.90	6.2926	0.916	1.400	309.0	18.57	23.54
0	1.4290	248.06	6.3268	0.917	1.399	314.8	19.14	24.35
10	1.3784	257.23	6.3597	0.918	1.398	320.5	19.71	25.15
20	1.3312	266.41	6.3916	0.919	1.397	326.0	20.27	25.95
30	1.2871	275.61	6.4225	0.920	1.396	331.4	20.83	26.73
40	1.2459	284.82	6.4524	0.922	1.395	336.7	21.37	27.51
50	1.2073	294.05	6.4814	0.924	1.394	342.0	21.91	28.29
60	1.1709	303.29	6.5095	0.926	1.392	347.1	22.44	29.05
70	1.1367	312.56	6.5369	0.928	1.391	352.1	22.97	29.82
80	1.1045	321.85	6.5636	0.930	1.390	357.0	23.49	30.57
90	1.0740	331.16	6.5896	0.932	1.388	361.9	24.00	31.32
100	1.0452	340.49	6.6150	0.935	1.387	366.6	24.51	32.06
110	1.0179	349.85	6.6397	0.937	1.385	371.3	25.01	32.80
120	0.9919	359.23	6.6639	0.940	1.384	375.9	25.50	33.53
130	0.9673	368.64	6.6875	0.943	1.382	380.5	25.99	34.26
140	0.9439	378.08	6.7107	0.945	1.38	384.9	26.48	34.98
150	0.9215	387.55	6.7333	0.948	1.379	389.3	26.96	35.69
160	0.9002	397.05	6.7555	0.951	1.377	393.7	27.43	36.41
170	0.8799	406.58	6.7772	0.954	1.375	398.0	27.90	37.11
180	0.8605	416.14	6.7986	0.957	1.373	402.2	28.37	37.81
190	0.8419	425.72	6.8195	0.961	1.372	406.4	28.83	38.51
200	0.8241	435.35	6.8400	0.964	1.370	410.5	29.28	39.21
210	0.8070	445.00	6.8602	0.967	1.368	414.5	29.73	39.89
220	0.7906	454.68	6.8801	0.970	1.367	418.5	30.18	40.58
230	0.7749	464.40	6.8996	0.973	1.365	422.5	30.63	41.26
240	0.7598	474.14	6.9188	0.976	1.363	426.4	31.06	41.94
250	0.6743	527.35	7.4345	1.035	1.385	456.2	27.56	40.55
260	0.7313	493.73	6.9562	0.983	1.360	434.2	31.93	43.28
270	0.7178	503.58	6.9745	0.986	1.359	438.0	32.36	43.94
280	0.7048	513.45	6.9925	0.989	1.357	441.7	32.78	44.61
290	0.6923	523.36	7.0103	0.992	1.355	445.4	33.20	45.27
300	0.6802	533.29	7.0278	0.995	1.354	449.1	33.62	45.92
310	0.6686	543.26	7.0450	0.998	1.352	452.8	34.04	46.57
320	0.6573	553.26	7.0620	1.001	1.351	456.4	34.45	47.22
330	0.6464	563.28	7.0788	1.004	1.350	460.0	34.85	47.87
340	0.6358	573.34	7.0953	1.007	1.348	463.6	35.26	48.51
350	0.6256	583.43	7.1116	1.010	1.347	467.1	35.66	49.15
360	0.6157	593.54	7.1277	1.013	1.345	470.6	36.06	49.78
370	0.6062	603.68	7.1436	1.016	1.344	474.1	36.46	50.42
380	0.5969	613.86	7.1593	1.019	1.343	477.5	36.85	51.05
390	0.5879	624.05	7.1748	1.021	1.342	480.9	37.24	51.68
400	0.5792	634.28	7.1901	1.024	1.340	484.3	37.63	52.30
420	0.5624	654.81	7.2202	1.029	1.338	491.0	38.39	53.54
440	0.5467	675.45	7.2495	1.034	1.336	497.6	39.15	54.78
460	0.5318	696.19	7.2782	1.039	1.334	504.2	39.90	56.00
480	0.5176	717.02	7.3062	1.044	1.332	510.6	40.64	57.21
500	0.5042	737.95	7.3336	1.049	1.330	517.0	41.36	58.42

*Temperatures on IPTS-68 scale

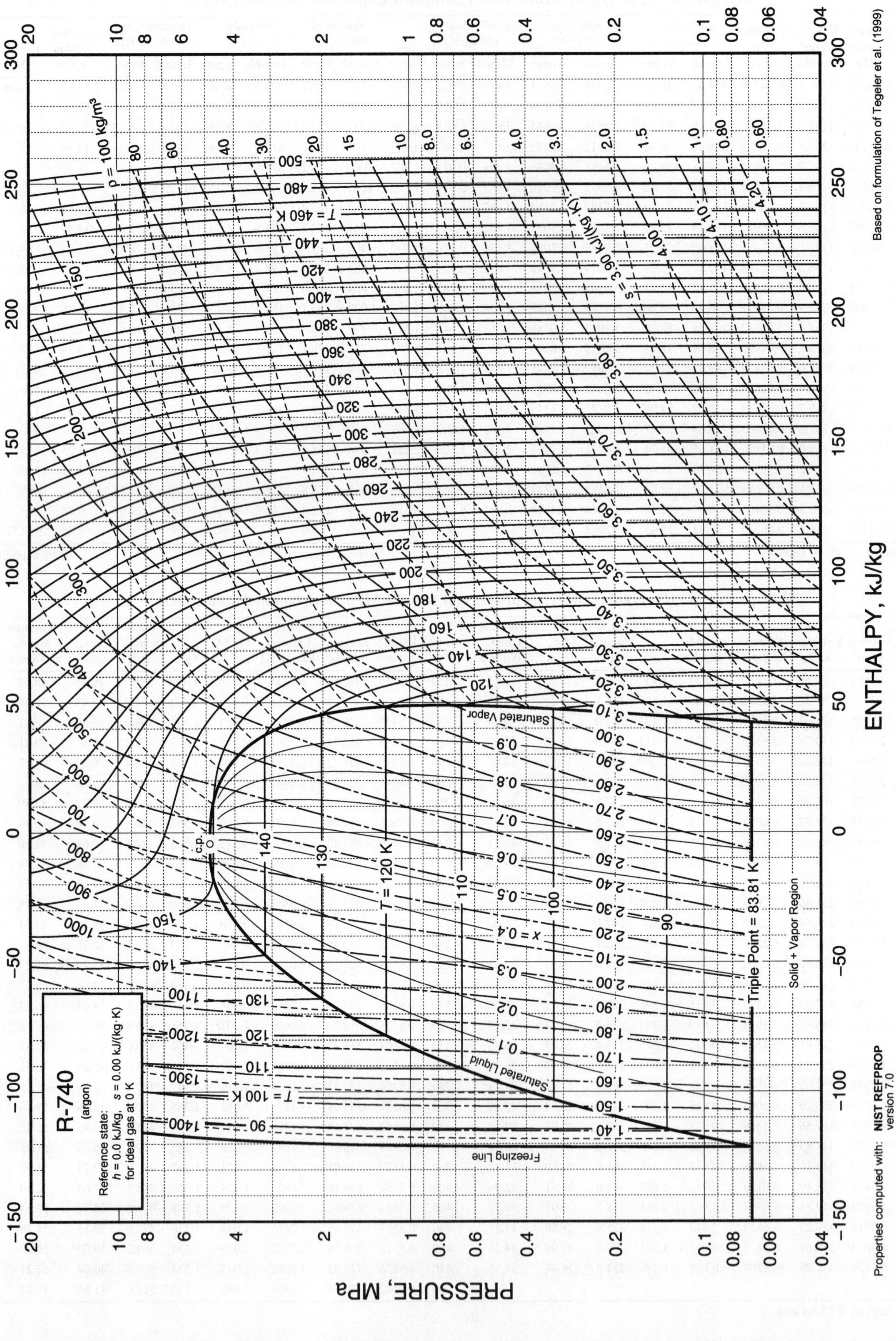

Fig. 32 Pressure-Enthalpy Diagram for Refrigerant 740 (Argon)

Refrigerant 740 (Argon) Properties of Saturated Liquid and Saturated Vapor

Temp.,* K	Absolute Pressure, MPa	Density, kg/m³ Liquid	Volume, m³/kg Vapor	Enthalpy, kJ/kg Liquid	Enthalpy, kJ/kg Vapor	Entropy, kJ/(kg·K) Liquid	Entropy, kJ/(kg·K) Vapor	Specific Heat c_p, kJ/(kg·K) Liquid	Specific Heat c_p, kJ/(kg·K) Vapor	c_p/c_v Vapor	Velocity of Sound, m/s Liquid	Velocity of Sound, m/s Vapor	Viscosity, μPa·s Liquid	Viscosity, μPa·s Vapor	Thermal Cond., mW/(m·K) Liquid	Thermal Cond., mW/(m·K) Vapor	Surface Tension, mN/m	Temp.,* K
83.81[a]	0.06889	1416.8	0.24663	−121.44	42.28	1.3295	3.2830	1.116	0.555	1.709	862	168.1	290.2	6.86	133.6	5.36	13.42	83.81
84	0.07045	1415.6	0.24164	−121.22	42.36	1.3321	3.2794	1.116	0.556	1.710	861	168.3	288.4	6.87	133.3	5.37	13.37	84
86	0.08811	1403.4	0.19687	−118.98	43.13	1.3583	3.2433	1.116	0.562	1.719	847	169.9	270.9	7.05	130.4	5.52	12.86	86
87.30[b]	0.10132	1395.4	0.17320	−117.52	43.62	1.3750	3.2208	1.117	0.566	1.725	838	170.9	260.3	7.17	128.5	5.62	12.53	87.3
88	0.10901	1391.1	0.16198	−116.74	43.87	1.3839	3.2090	1.118	0.568	1.728	833	171.4	254.8	7.23	127.4	5.68	12.35	88
90	0.13351	1378.6	0.13448	−114.49	44.57	1.4090	3.1763	1.121	0.576	1.740	819	172.8	240.0	7.41	124.5	5.83	11.85	90
92	0.16199	1366.0	0.11258	−112.23	45.23	1.4335	3.1451	1.125	0.584	1.752	805	174.2	226.4	7.60	121.6	6.00	11.36	92
94	0.19485	1353.2	0.09496	−109.96	45.85	1.4577	3.1152	1.131	0.593	1.766	791	175.5	213.8	7.78	118.7	6.16	10.86	94
96	0.23249	1340.3	0.08067	−107.68	46.41	1.4814	3.0865	1.137	0.603	1.782	776	176.7	202.2	7.97	115.8	6.33	10.38	96
98	0.27532	1327.1	0.06897	−105.38	46.93	1.5048	3.0590	1.145	0.614	1.800	762	177.8	191.3	8.16	113.0	6.51	9.89	98
100	0.32377	1313.7	0.05932	−103.06	47.40	1.5278	3.0324	1.154	0.627	1.820	747	178.9	181.3	8.35	110.2	6.69	9.42	100
102	0.37825	1300.1	0.05129	−100.72	47.81	1.5505	3.0068	1.164	0.641	1.842	732	179.9	172.0	8.54	107.4	6.88	8.94	102
104	0.43920	1286.2	0.04458	−98.37	48.17	1.5730	2.9819	1.175	0.656	1.867	717	180.8	163.3	8.74	104.6	7.08	8.48	104
106	0.50706	1272.0	0.03892	−95.98	48.46	1.5952	2.9578	1.188	0.673	1.894	701	181.6	155.2	8.95	101.9	7.28	8.02	106
108	0.58226	1257.6	0.03413	−93.57	48.68	1.6172	2.9343	1.202	0.691	1.926	685	182.4	147.6	9.15	99.1	7.50	7.56	108
110	0.66526	1242.8	0.03004	−91.13	48.84	1.6390	2.9114	1.218	0.712	1.960	669	183.0	140.4	9.37	96.4	7.73	7.11	110
112	0.75650	1227.6	0.02654	−88.65	48.92	1.6606	2.8890	1.235	0.736	2.000	653	183.6	133.7	9.59	93.7	7.98	6.67	112
114	0.85644	1212.1	0.02351	−86.14	48.93	1.6821	2.8669	1.255	0.762	2.044	636	184.1	127.4	9.81	91.0	8.24	6.23	114
116	0.96553	1196.2	0.02090	−83.59	48.85	1.7035	2.8452	1.278	0.791	2.094	619	184.5	121.4	10.04	88.4	8.52	5.80	116
118	1.08420	1179.7	0.01862	−81.00	48.68	1.7248	2.8238	1.303	0.825	2.151	602	184.8	115.7	10.29	85.7	8.82	5.38	118
120	1.21300	1162.8	0.01663	−78.35	48.41	1.7461	2.8025	1.332	0.863	2.216	584	185.1	110.2	10.54	83.1	9.15	4.96	120
125	1.58230	1117.9	0.01263	−71.49	47.27	1.7995	2.7495	1.425	0.986	2.426	538	185.3	97.6	11.23	76.7	10.14	3.95	125
130	2.02550	1068.1	0.00966	−64.16	45.30	1.8538	2.6957	1.564	1.172	2.741	488	184.8	85.9	12.03	70.4	11.45	3.00	130
135	2.55090	1011.5	0.00739	−56.18	42.21	1.9102	2.6390	1.790	1.482	3.262	433	183.7	74.7	13.02	64.2	13.34	2.10	135
140	3.16820	943.7	0.00559	−47.16	37.47	1.9712	2.5757	2.225	2.104	4.258	372	181.5	63.6	14.32	58.1	16.39	1.29	140
145	3.88960	854.3	0.00409	−36.19	29.76	2.0425	2.4973	3.399	3.896	6.880	297	176.6	52.1	16.27	52.0	22.53	0.58	145
150	4.73460	680.4	0.00253	−17.88	11.52	2.1589	2.3550	23.580	35.470	43.160	175	157.0	36.8	21.18	57.6	55.88	0.04	150
150.69[c]	4.86300	535.6	0.00187	−4.33	−4.33	2.2476	2.2476	∞	∞	∞	0	0.0	—	—	∞	∞	0.00	150.69

*Temperatures on ITS-90 scale [a]Triple point [b]Normal boiling point [c]Critical point

Refrigerant 740 (Argon) Properties of Gas at 0.101 325 MPa (one standard atmosphere)

Temp., °C	Density, kg/m³	Enthalpy, kJ/kg	Entropy, kJ/(kg·K)	c_p, kJ/(kg·K)	c_p/c_v	Vel. of Sound, m/s	Visc., μPa·s	Thermal Cond., mW/(m·K)
−185.8[b]	5.7736	43.62	3.2208	0.566	1.725	170.9	7.17	5.62
−180	5.3774	46.90	3.2571	0.556	1.715	177.2	7.66	6.01
−160	4.3721	57.80	3.3632	0.538	1.696	196.6	9.32	7.30
−140	3.6930	68.48	3.4501	0.531	1.686	214.0	10.93	8.56
−120	3.2000	79.06	3.5242	0.527	1.681	229.9	12.50	9.79
−100	2.8246	89.58	3.5887	0.525	1.677	244.7	14.02	10.99
−90	2.6684	94.83	3.6182	0.525	1.676	251.8	14.77	11.57
−80	2.5287	100.08	3.6461	0.524	1.675	258.6	15.50	12.15
−70	2.4031	105.31	3.6725	0.524	1.674	265.3	16.22	12.72
−60	2.2894	110.55	3.6977	0.523	1.673	271.8	16.94	13.28
−50	2.1861	115.78	3.7217	0.523	1.672	278.1	17.64	13.83
−40	2.0917	121.00	3.7446	0.523	1.672	284.3	18.33	14.38
−30	2.0052	126.23	3.7665	0.522	1.671	290.4	19.02	14.91
−20	1.9256	131.45	3.7876	0.522	1.671	296.3	19.69	15.44
−10	1.8520	136.67	3.8078	0.522	1.671	302.2	20.36	15.97
0	1.7840	141.89	3.8273	0.522	1.670	307.9	21.02	16.48
10	1.7207	147.11	3.8460	0.522	1.670	313.5	21.67	16.99
20	1.6618	152.33	3.8641	0.522	1.670	319.0	22.31	17.50
30	1.6068	157.54	3.8816	0.522	1.669	324.4	22.94	17.99
40	1.5554	162.76	3.8985	0.521	1.669	329.7	23.56	18.48
50	1.5071	167.97	3.9149	0.521	1.669	334.9	24.18	18.97
60	1.4618	173.18	3.9308	0.521	1.669	340.1	24.79	19.45
70	1.4191	178.39	3.9462	0.521	1.669	345.1	25.40	19.92
80	1.3788	183.61	3.9612	0.521	1.669	350.1	25.99	20.39
90	1.3408	188.82	3.9758	0.521	1.669	355.1	26.58	20.85
100	1.3048	194.03	3.9899	0.521	1.668	359.9	27.17	21.31
110	1.2707	199.24	4.0037	0.521	1.668	364.7	27.74	21.76
120	1.2383	204.45	4.0171	0.521	1.668	369.4	28.32	22.21
130	1.2076	209.66	4.0302	0.521	1.668	374.1	28.88	22.66
140	1.1783	214.87	4.0430	0.521	1.668	378.7	29.44	23.09
150	1.1504	220.08	4.0554	0.521	1.668	383.3	29.99	23.53
160	1.1239	225.28	4.0676	0.521	1.668	387.8	30.54	23.96
170	1.0985	230.49	4.0795	0.521	1.668	392.2	31.09	24.38
180	1.0742	235.70	4.0911	0.521	1.668	396.6	31.62	24.80
190	1.0510	240.91	4.1025	0.521	1.668	401.0	32.16	25.22
200	1.0288	246.12	4.1136	0.521	1.668	405.3	32.68	25.64
210	1.0075	251.32	4.1245	0.521	1.668	409.6	33.21	26.04
220	0.9870	256.53	4.1351	0.521	1.668	413.8	33.73	26.45
230	0.9674	261.74	4.1456	0.521	1.668	418.0	34.24	26.85
240	0.9485	266.94	4.1558	0.521	1.667	422.1	34.75	27.25
250	0.9304	272.15	4.1659	0.521	1.667	426.2	35.25	27.65
260	0.9129	277.36	4.1758	0.521	1.667	430.2	35.75	28.04
270	0.8961	282.56	4.1854	0.521	1.667	434.2	36.25	28.43
280	0.8799	287.77	4.1949	0.521	1.667	438.2	36.74	28.81
290	0.8643	292.98	4.2043	0.521	1.667	442.2	37.23	29.19
300	0.8492	298.18	4.2134	0.521	1.667	446.1	37.71	29.57
310	0.8346	303.39	4.2224	0.521	1.667	450.0	38.20	29.95
320	0.8206	308.59	4.2313	0.521	1.667	453.8	38.67	30.32
330	0.8069	313.80	4.2400	0.521	1.667	457.6	39.15	30.69
340	0.7938	319.01	4.2485	0.521	1.667	461.4	39.61	31.06
350	0.7810	324.21	4.2570	0.521	1.667	465.1	40.08	31.42
360	0.7687	329.42	4.2652	0.521	1.667	468.8	40.54	31.78
370	0.7567	334.62	4.2734	0.521	1.667	472.5	41.00	32.14
380	0.7452	339.83	4.2814	0.521	1.667	476.2	41.46	32.50
390	0.7339	345.03	4.2893	0.521	1.667	479.8	41.91	32.85
400	0.7230	350.24	4.2971	0.521	1.667	483.4	42.36	33.20
420	0.7022	360.65	4.3124	0.521	1.667	490.5	43.25	33.90
440	0.6825	371.06	4.3272	0.520	1.667	497.6	44.13	34.58
460	0.6638	381.47	4.3416	0.520	1.667	504.5	45.00	35.26
480	0.6462	391.88	4.3556	0.520	1.667	511.3	45.86	35.93
500	0.6295	402.29	4.3692	0.520	1.667	518.1	46.70	36.59

[b]Saturated vapor at normal boiling point

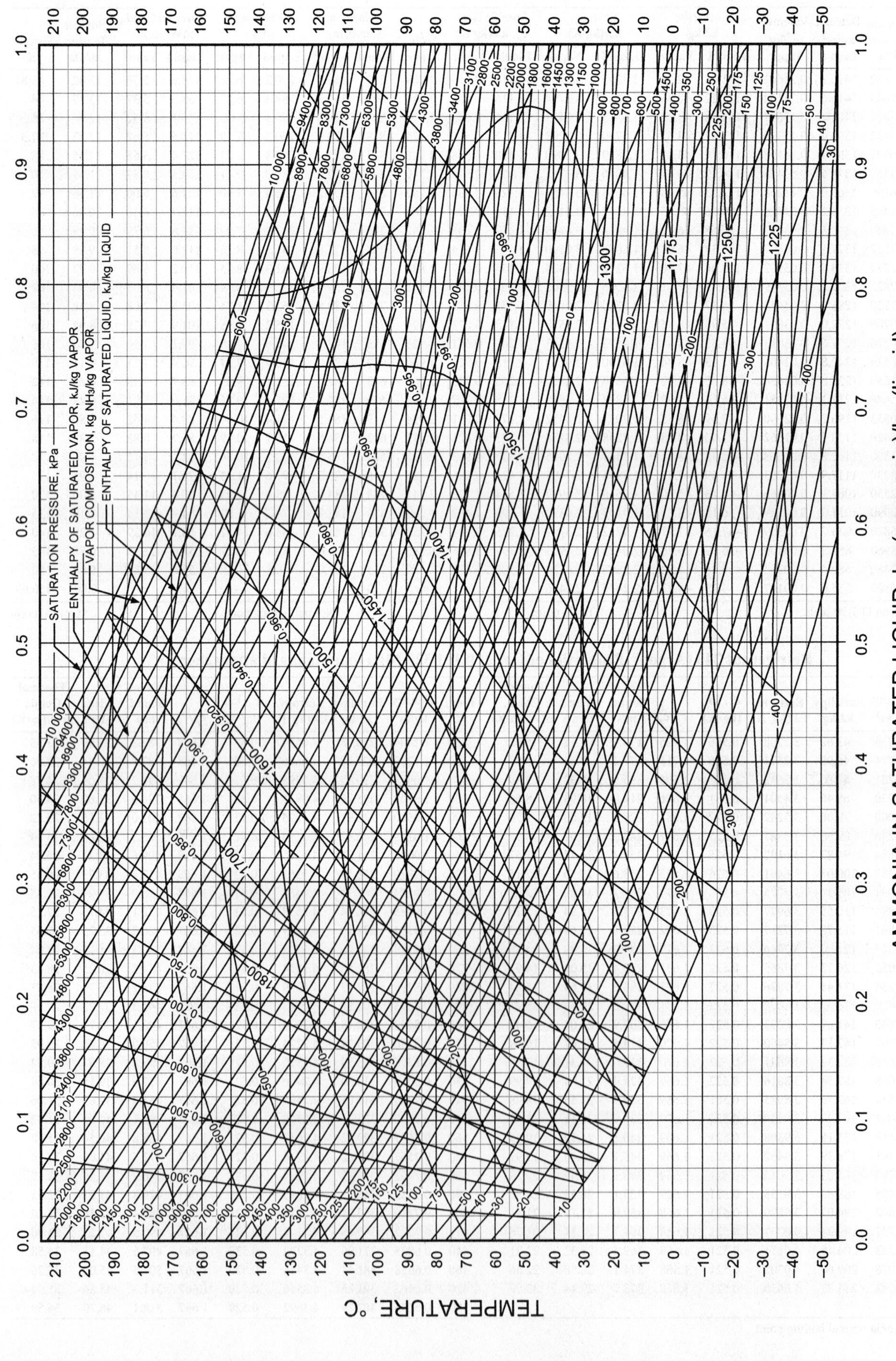

Fig. 33 Enthalpy-Concentration Diagram for Ammonia/Water Solutions

Prepared by Kwang Kim and Keith Herold, Center for Environmental Energy Engineering, University of Maryland at College Park

Specific Volume of Saturated Ammonia Solutions, m³/kg

Temp., °C	Concentration, Ammonia (Mass basis) 0	10	20	30	40	50	60	70	80	90	100	Temp., °C
−10	0.00100	0.00103	0.00106	0.00109	0.00114	0.00118	0.00122	0.00128	0.00135	0.00142	0.00151	−10
0	0.00100	0.00103	0.00107	0.00110	0.00114	0.00119	0.00124	0.00130	0.00137	0.00146	0.00156	0
10	0.00100	0.00104	0.00107	0.00111	0.00115	0.00120	0.00125	0.00132	0.00139	0.00149	0.00160	10
20	0.00100	0.00104	0.00108	0.00112	0.00116	0.00121	0.00127	0.00133	0.00142	0.00152	0.00164	20
30	0.00100	0.00105	0.00108	0.00113	0.00117	0.00123	0.00128	0.00135	0.00145	0.00156	0.00168	30
40	0.00101	0.00105	0.00109	0.00114	0.00119	0.00124	0.00130	0.00138	0.00148	0.00159	0.00173	40
50	0.00101	0.00106	0.00110	0.00115	0.00120	0.00125	0.00132	0.00140	0.00151	0.00163	0.00177	50
60	0.00102	0.00106	0.00111	0.00116	0.00121	0.00127	0.00134	0.00143	0.00154	0.00167	0.00183	60
70	0.00102	0.00107	0.00112	0.00117	0.00122	0.00129	0.00136	0.00146	0.00158	0.00172	0.00190	70
80	0.00103	0.00108	0.00113	0.00118	0.00124	0.00130	0.00139	0.00149	0.00162	0.00178	0.00198	80
90	0.00104	0.00109	0.00114	0.00119	0.00125	0.00132	0.00141	0.00153	0.00167	0.00184	0.00208	90
100	0.00104	0.00110	0.00115	0.00121	0.00127	0.00135	0.00145	0.00157	0.00172	0.00191	0.00219	100

Prepared under ASHRAE research project RP-271, sponsored by TC 8.3.
Data reference: B.H. Jennings, Ammonia water properties (paper presented at ASHRAE meeting, January 1965).

Refrigerant Temperature (t′ = °C) and Enthalpy (h = kJ/kg) of Lithium Bromide Solutions

Temp., (t = °C)		Percent LiBr 0	10	20	30	40	45	50	55	60	65	70
20	t′	20.0	19.1	17.7	15.0	9.8	5.8	−0.4	−7.7	−15.8	−23.4#	−29.3#
	h	84.0	67.4	52.6	40.4	33.5	33.5	38.9	53.2	78.0	111.0#	145.0#
30	t′	30.0	29.0	27.5	24.6	19.2	15.0	8.6	1.0	−7.3	−15.2#	−21.6#
	h	125.8	103.3	84.0	68.6	58.3	56.8	60.5	73.5	96.8	128.4#	161.7#
40	t′	40.0	38.9	37.3	34.3	28.5	24.1	17.5	9.8	1.3	−7.0#	−14.0#
	h	167.6	139.5	115.8	96.0	82.5	79.7	82.2	93.5	115.4	146.0#	178.3#
50	t′	50.0	48.8	47.2	44.0	37.9	33.3	26.5	18.5	9.9	1.3	−6.3#
	h	209.3	175.2	147.0	123.4	106.7	102.6	103.8	114.0	134.5	163.5	195.0#
60	t′	60.0	58.8	57.0	53.6	47.3	42.5	35.5	27.3	18.4	9.5	1.4#
	h	251.1	211.7	179.1	151.4	131.7	125.8	125.8	134.7	153.7	181.4	211.9#
70	t′	70.0	68.7	66.8	63.3	56.6	51.6	44.4	36.1	27.0	17.7	9.0#
	h	293.0	247.7	210.5	178.8	155.7	148.9	148.0	155.6	173.2	199.4	228.8#
80	t′	80.0	78.6	76.7	73.0	66.0	60.8	53.4	44.8	35.6	26.0	16.7#
	h	334.9	287.8	243.6	207.3	181.0	172.8	170.0	176.2	192.6	217.2	245.7#
90	t′	90.0	88.6	86.5	82.6	75.4	70.0	62.3	53.6	44.1	34.2	24.3#
	h	376.9	321.1	275.6	235.4	206.1	195.8	192.3	197.1	212.2	235.6	262.9#
100	t′	100.0	98.5	96.3	92.3	84.7	79.1	71.3	62.4	52.7	42.4	32.0
	h	419.0	357.6	307.9	263.8	231.0	219.9	214.6	218.2	231.5	253.5	279.7
110	t′	110.0	108.4	106.2	101.9	94.1	88.3	80.2	71.1	61.3	50.6	39.7
	h	461.3	394.3	340.1	292.4	255.9	243.3	236.8	239.1	251.0	271.4	296.3
120	t′	120.0*	118.3*	116.0*	111.6	103.4	97.5	89.2	79.9	69.8	58.9	47.3
	h	503.7*	431.0*	372.5*	320.9	281.0	267.0	259.0	260.0	270.2	289.5	313.4
130	t′	130.0*	128.3*	125.8*	121.3*	112.8	106.7	92.8	88.7	78.4	67.1	55.0
	h	546.5*	468.4*	404.5*	349.6*	306.2	290.7	281.0	280.4	289.1	306.9	330.2
140	t′	140.0*	138.2*	135.7*	130.9*	122.2*	115.8	107.1	97.4	87.0	75.3	62.7
	h	589.1*	505.6*	437.8*	377.9*	331.3*	314.2	303.2	301.1	308.1	324.7	346.9
150	t′	150.0*	148.1*	145.5*	140.6*	131.5*	125.0*	116.1*	106.2	95.5	83.5	70.3
	h	632.2*	542.7*	470.5*	406.8*	356.6*	337.8*	325.5*	321.6	327.3	342.7	363.6
160	t′	160.0*	158.1*	155.3*	150.3*	140.9*	134.2*	125.0*	115.0	104.1	91.8	78.9
	h	675.6*	580.8*	503.1*	435.4*	381.9*	361.2*	347.7*	342.2	346.1	360.3	380.1
170	t′	170.0*	168.0*	165.2*	159.9*	150.3*	143.3*	134.0*	123.7	112.7	100.0	85.7
	h	719.2*	618.9*	536.1*	464.3*	406.8*	384.9*	369.9*	362.9	365.4	378.3	396.0
180	t′	180.0*	177.9*	175.0*	169.6*	159.6*	152.5*	142.9*	132.5*	121.2*	108.2	93.3
	h	763.2*	657.1*	569.4*	493.4*	432.1*	408.8*	392.1*	383.4*	384.3*	395.8	411.3

*Extensions of data above 115°C are well above the original data and should be used with care.
#Supersaturated solution.

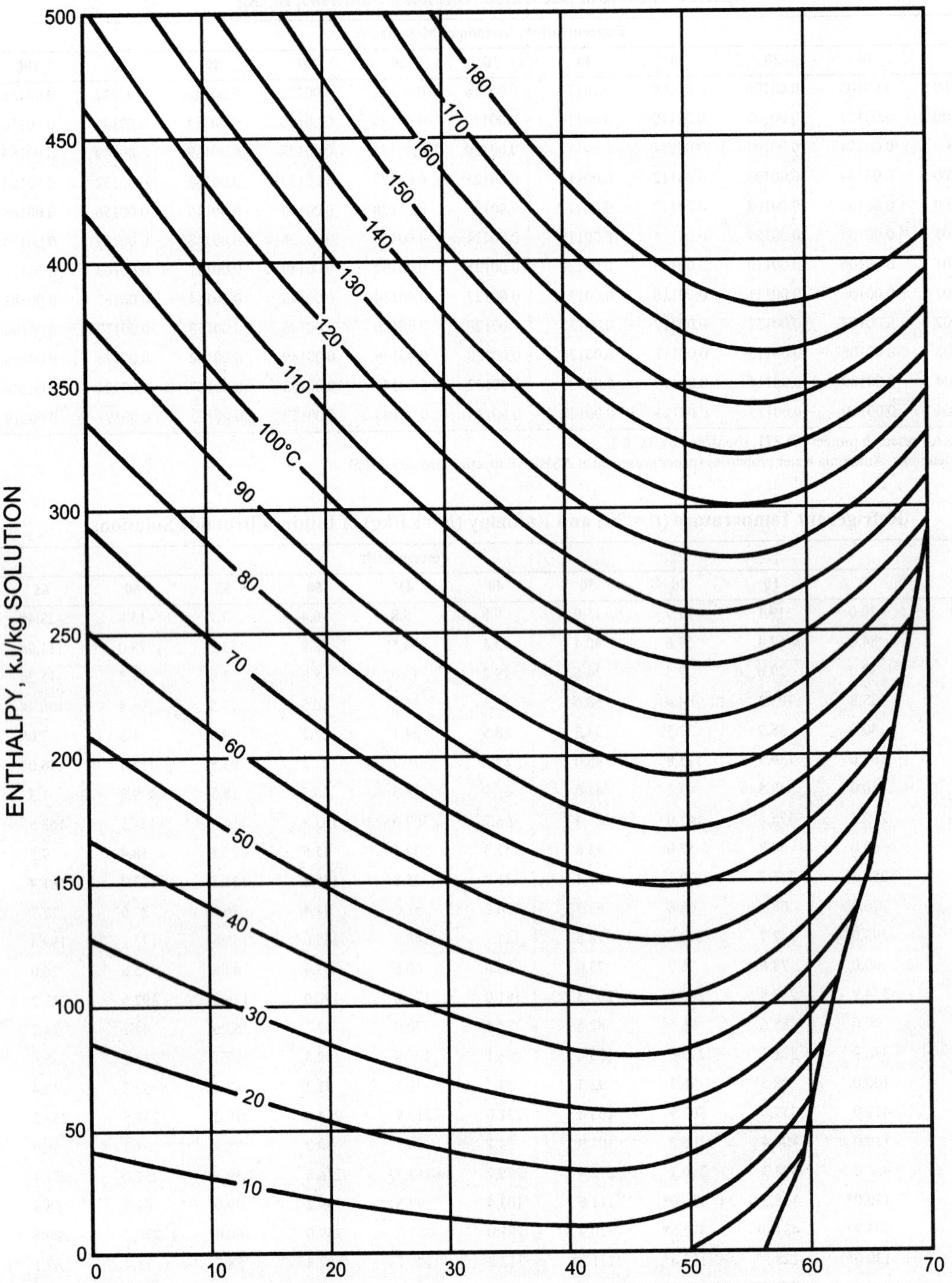

EQUATIONS **CONCENTRATION RANGE 40 < X < 70% LiBr** **TEMPERATURE RANGE 15 < t < 165°C**

$h = \Sigma_0^4 A_n X^n + t\Sigma_0^4 B_n X^n + t^2\Sigma_0^4 C_n X^n$ in kJ/kg, where t = °C and X = %LiBr

A_0 = −2024.33	B_0 = 18.2829	C_0 = −3.7008214 E-2
A_1 = 163.309	B_1 = −1.1691757	C_1 = 2.8877666 E-3
A_2 = −4.88161	B_2 = 3.248041 E-2	C_2 = −8.1313015 E-5
A_3 = 6.302948 E-2	B_3 = −4.034184 E-4	C_3 = 9.9116628 E-7
A_4 = −2.913705 E-4	B_4 = 1.8520569 E-6	C_4 = −4.4441207 E-9

Fig. 34 Enthalpy-Concentration Diagram for Water/Lithium Bromide Solutions

EQUATIONS

1. $t = \Sigma_0^3 B_n X^n + t' \Sigma_0^3 A_n X^n$ Solution Temperature, °C
2. $t' = (t - \Sigma_0^3 B_n X^n) / \Sigma_0^3 A_n X^n$ Refrigerant Temperature, °C
3. $\log P = C + D/T' + E/T'^2$ P = kPa; T' = K
4. $T' = \dfrac{-2E}{D + [D^2 - 4E(C - \log P)]^{0.5}}$

$A_0 = -2.007\ 55$	$B_0 = 124.937$	$C = 7.05$
$A_1 = 0.169\ 76$	$B_1 = -7.716\ 49$	$D = -1596.49$
$A_2 = -3.133\ 362$ E-03	$B_2 = 0.152\ 286$	$E = -104\ 095.5$
$A_3 = 1.976\ 68$ E-05	$B_3 = -7.950\ 90$ E-04	

RANGE: $-15 < t' < 110$°C
$5 < t < 175$°C
$45 < X < 70$% LiBr

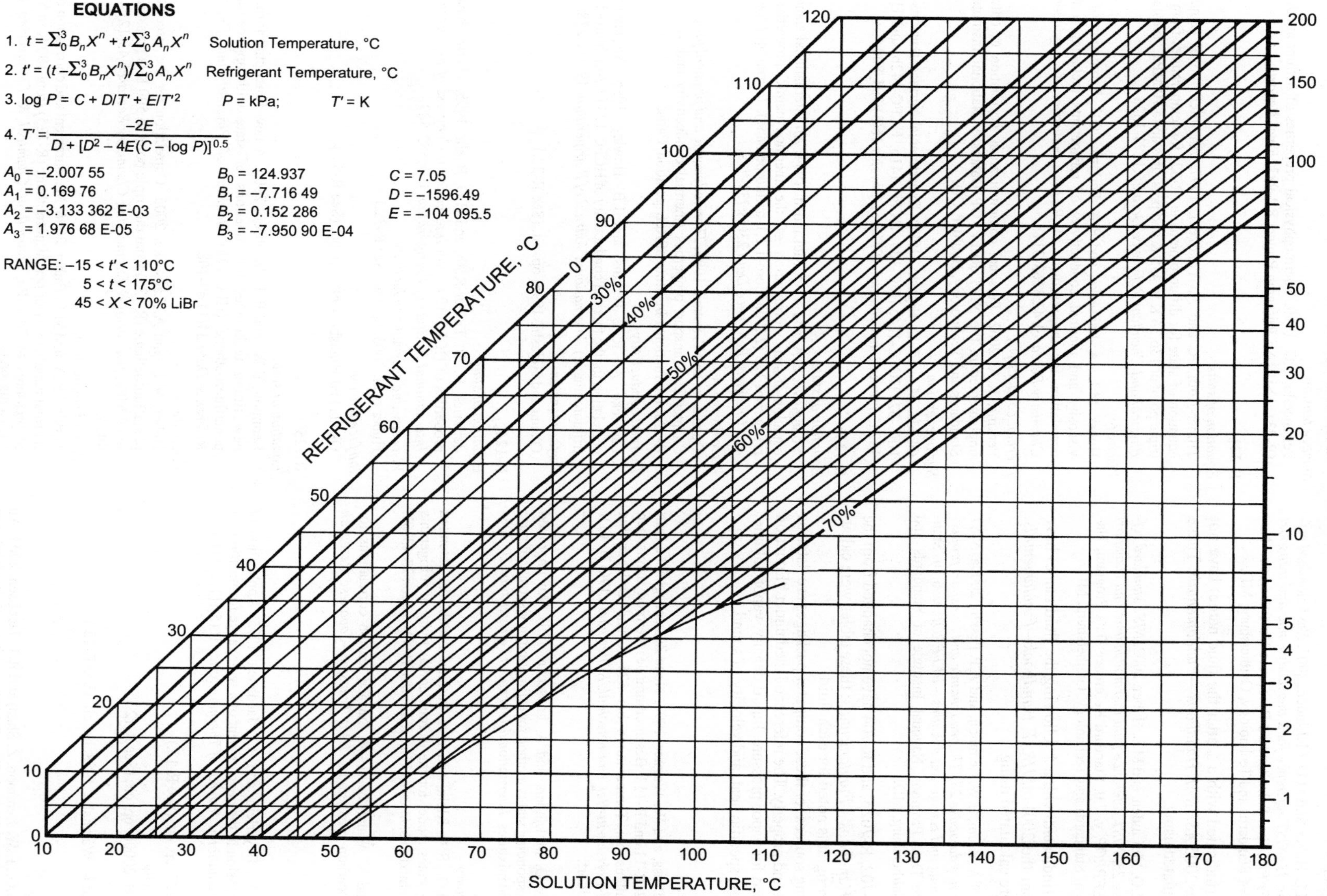

Fig. 35 Equilibrium Chart for Aqueous Lithium Bromide Solutions
Reprinted by permission of Carrier Corp.

REFERENCES

Tables revised for this edition (R-125, R-170, R-245fa, R-290, R-600, and R-600a) have been calculated using

Lemmon, E.W., M.L. Huber, and M.O. McLinden. 2007. *NIST standard reference database 23, NIST reference fluid thermodynamic and transport properties—REFPROP,* v. 8.0. Standard Reference Data Program, National Institute of Standards and Technology, Gaithersburg, MD.

Many tables (indicated with a ‡ after the fluid name) have not changed from the 2005 *ASHRAE Handbook—Fundamentals*. These tables were calculated using

Lemmon, E.W., M.O. McLinden, and M.L. Huber. 2002. *NIST standard reference database 23, NIST reference fluid thermodynamic and transport properties—REFPROP,* v. 7.0. Standard Reference Data Program, National Institute of Standards and Technology, Gaithersburg, MD.

Some tables (indicated with a † following the fluid name) have not changed from the 2001 *ASHRAE Handbook—Fundamentals*. These tables were calculated using

McLinden, M.O., S.A. Klein, E.W. Lemmon, and A.P. Peskin. 2000a. *NIST standard reference database 23: Thermodynamic and transport properties of refrigerants and refrigerant mixtures—REFPROP,* v. 6.10. Standard Reference Data Program, National Institute of Standards and Technology, Gaithersburg, MD.

Tables for R-702, R-702p, and R-704 have not changed from the 1997 *ASHRAE Handbook—Fundamentals*; these tables were calculated using the programs noted for each fluid.

The underlying sources for these computer packages are listed as follows by fluid and property. The reference listed under "Equation of state" was used for vapor pressure, liquid density, vapor volume, enthalpy, entropy, specific heat, and velocity of sound.

R-12†

Equation of state

Marx, V., A. Pruss, and W. Wagner. 1992. Neue Zustandsgleichungen für R-12, R-22, R-11 und R-113. Beschreibung des thermodynamischen Zustandsverhaltens bei Temperaturen bis 525 K und Drücken bis 200 MPa. *VDI-Fortschritt-Ber Wärmetechnik/Kältetechnik* 19(57). VDI Verlag, Düsseldorf.

Viscosity

Klein, S.A., M.O. McLinden, and A. Laesecke. 1997. An improved extended corresponding states method for estimation of viscosity of pure refrigerants and mixtures. *International Journal of Refrigeration* 20:208-217.

Thermal conductivity

McLinden, M.O., S.A. Klein, and R.A. Perkins. 2000b. An extended corresponding states model for the thermal conductivity of refrigerants and refrigerant mixtures. *International Journal of Refrigeration* 23:43-63.

Surface tension

Okada, M. and K. Watanabe. 1988. Surface tension correlations for several fluorocarbon refrigerants. *Heat Transfer—Japanese Research* 17:35-52.

R-22†

Equation of state

Kamei, A., S.W. Beyerlein, and R.T. Jacobsen. 1995. Application of nonlinear regression in the development of a wide range formulation for HCFC-22. *International Journal of Thermophysics* 16(5):1155-1164.

Viscosity

Klein et al. 1997. op. cit. (See R-12.)

Thermal conductivity

McLinden et al. 2000b. op. cit. (See R-12.)

Surface tension

Okada, M. and K. Watanabe. 1988. op. cit. (See R-12.)

R-23‡

Equation of state

Penoncello, S.G., E.W. Lemmon, Z. Shan, and R.T. Jacobsen. 2003. An equation of state for the calculation of the thermodynamic properties of trifluoromethane (R-23). *Journal of Physical and Chemical Reference Data* 32:1473.

Viscosity and thermal conductivity

Shan, Z., S.G. Penoncello, and R.T. Jacobsen. 2000. A generalized model for viscosity and thermal conductivity of trifluoromethane (R-23). *ASHRAE Transactions* 106(1):757-767.

Surface tension

Penoncello, S.G. 1999. Thermophysical properties of trifluoromethane (R-23). ASHRAE Research Project RP-997, *Final Report*.

R-32‡

Equation of state

Tillner-Roth, R. and A. Yokozeki. 1997. An international standard equation of state for difluoromethane (R-32) for temperatures from the triple point at 136.34 K to 435 K and pressures up to 70 MPa. *Journal of Physical and Chemical Reference Data* 26:1273-1328.

Viscosity

Huber, M.L., A. Laesecke, and R.A. Perkins. 2003. Estimation of the viscosity and thermal conductivity of refrigerants including a new correlation for the viscosity of R134a. *Industrial & Engineering Chemistry Research* 42:3163-3178.

Thermal conductivity

Perkins, R.A. 2002. Personal communication, correlation to data as implemented in the NIST REFPROP Database. National Institute of Standards and Technology, Boulder, CO.

Surface tension

Okada, M. and Y. Higashi. 1995. Experimental surface tensions for HFC-32, HCFC-124, HFC-125, HCFC-141b, HCFC-142b, and HFC-152a. *International Journal of Thermophysics* 16(3):791-800.

R-123†

Equation of state

Younglove, B.A. and M.O. McLinden. 1994. An international standard equation-of-state formulation of the thermodynamic properties of refrigerant 123 (2,2-dichloro-1,1,1-trifluoroethane). *Journal of Physical and Chemical Reference Data* 23(5):731-779.

Viscosity

Tanaka, Y. and T. Sotani. 1995. *Thermodynamic and physical properties*, Chapter 2: Transport properties (thermal conductivity and viscosity), R-123. International Institute of Refrigeration, Paris.

Thermal conductivity

Laesecke, A., R.A. Perkins, and J.B. Howley. 1996. An improved correlation for the thermal conductivity of HCFC-123 (2,2-dichloro-1,1,1-trifluoroethane). *International Journal of Refrigeration* 19:231-238.

Surface tension

Okada and Higashi. 1995. op. cit. (See R-32.)

R-124‡

Equation of state

de Vries, B., R. Tillner-Roth, and H.D. Baehr. 1995. Thermodynamic properties of HCFC-124. *19th International Congress of Refrigeration, International Institute of Refrigeration* IVa:582-589.

Viscosity and thermal conductivity

Huber et al. 2003. op. cit. (See R-32.)

Surface tension

Okada and Higashi. 1995. op. cit. (See R-32.)

R-125

Equation of state

Lemmon, E.W. and R.T. Jacobsen. 2005. A new functional form and new fitting techniques for equations of state with application to pentafluoroethane (HFC-125). *Journal of Physical and Chemical Reference Data* 34(1):69-108.

Viscosity

Huber, M.L. and A. Laesecke. 2006. Correlation for the viscosity of pentafluoroethane (R-125) from the triple point to 500 K at pressures up to 60 MPa. *Industrial & Engineering Chemistry Research* 45(12):4447-4453.

Thermal conductivity

Perkins, R.A. and M.L. Huber. 2006. Measurement and correlation of the thermal conductivity of pentafluoroethane (R-125) from 190 K to 512 K at pressures to 70 MPa. *Journal of Chemical & Engineering Data* 51(3):898-904.

Surface tension

Okada and Higashi. 1995. op. cit. (See R-32.)

R-134a†

Equation of state

Tillner-Roth, R. and H.D. Baehr. 1994. An international standard formulation of the thermodynamic properties of 1,1,1,2-tetrafluoroethane (HFC-134a) covering temperatures from 170 K to 455 K at pressures up to 70 MPa. *Journal of Physical and Chemical Reference Data* 23:657-729.

Viscosity

Huber et al. 2003. op. cit. (See R-32.)

Thermal conductivity

Perkins, R.A., A. Laesecke, J. Howley, M.L.V. Ramires, A.N. Gurova, and L. Cusco. 2000. Experimental thermal conductivity values for the IUPAC round-robin sample of 1,1,1,2-tetrafluoroethane (R134a). NISTIR 6605.

Surface tension

Okada, M. and Y. Higashi. 1994. Surface tension correlation of HFC-134a and HCFC-123. *CFCs, the Day After: Proceedings of Joint Meeting of IIR Commissions B1, B2, E1, and E2*, 541-548.

R-143a†

Equation of state

Lemmon, E.W. and R.T. Jacobsen. 2001. An international standard formulation for the thermodynamic properties of 1,1,1-trifluoroethane (HFC- 143a) for temperatures from 161 to 500 K and pressures to 60 MPa. *Journal of Physical and Chemical Reference Data* 29(4):521-552.

Viscosity

Klein et al. 1997. op. cit. (See R-12.)

Thermal conductivity

McLinden et al. 2000b. op. cit. (See R-12.)

Surface tension

Schmidt, J.W., E. Carrillo-Nava, and M.R. Moldover. 1996. Partially halogenated hydrocarbons $CHFCl\text{-}CF_3$, $CF_3\text{-}CH_3$, $CF_3\text{-}CHF\text{-}CHF_2$, $CF_3\text{-}CH_2\text{-}CF_3$, $CHF_2\text{-}CF_2\text{-}CH_2F$, $CF_3\text{-}CH_2\text{-}CHF_2$, $CF_3\text{-}O\text{-}CHF_2$: Critical temperature, refractive indices, surface tension and estimates of liquid, vapor and critical densities. *Fluid Phase Equilibria* 122:187-206.

R-152a‡

Equation of state

Outcalt, S.L. and M.O. McLinden. 1996. A modified Benedict-Webb-Rubin equation of state for the thermodynamic properties of R-152a (1,1-difluoroethane). *Journal of Physical and Chemical Reference Data* 25(2):605-636.

Viscosity

Klein et al. 1997. op. cit. (see R-12), ECS model of McLinden et al. (2000b) correlated to data as implemented in NIST REFPROP.

Thermal conductivity

Krauss, R., V.C. Weiss, T.A. Edison, J.V. Sengers, and K. Stephan. 1996. Transport properties of 1,1-difluoroethane (R-152a). *International Journal of Thermophysics* 17:731-757.

Surface tension

Okada and Higashi. 1995. op. cit. (See R-32.)

R-245fa

Equation of state

Extended corresponding states model of

Lemmon, E.W. and R. Span. 2006. Short fundamental equations of state for 20 industrial fluids. *Journal of Chemical & Engineering Data* 51(3):785-850.

Viscosity and thermal conductivity

Huber, M.L., A. Laesecke, and R.A. Perkins. 2003. Model for the viscosity and thermal conductivity of refrigerants, including a new correlation for the viscosity of R-134a. *Industrial & Engineering Chemistry Research* 42(13):3163-3178.

Surface tension

Schmidt et al. 1996. op. cit. (See R-143a.)

Pressure-enthalpy diagram based on data of

Defibaugh, D.R. and M.R. Moldover. 1997. Compressed and saturated liquid densities for 18 halogenated organic compounds. *Journal of Chemical and Engineering Data* 42:160-168.

R-404A‡

Equation of state

Lemmon, E.W. and R.T. Jacobsen. 2004a. Equations of state for mixtures of R-32, R-125, R-134a, R-143a, and R-152a. *Journal of Physical and Chemical Reference Data* 33(2):593-620.

Viscosity

Klein et al. 1997. op. cit. (See R-12.)

Thermal conductivity

McLinden et al. 2000b. op. cit. (See R-12.)

Surface tension

Moldover, M.R. and J.C. Rainwater. 1988. Interfacial tension and vapor-liquid equilibria in the critical region of mixtures. *Journal of Chemical Physics* 88:7772-7780.

R-407C‡

Equation of state

Lemmon and Jacobsen. 2004a. op. cit. (See R-404A.)

Viscosity

Klein et al. 1997. op. cit. (See R-12.)

Thermal conductivity

McLinden et al. 2000b. op. cit. (See R-12.)

Surface tension

Moldover and Rainwater. 1988. op. cit. (See R-404A.)

R-410A‡

Equation of state

Lemmon and Jacobsen. 2004a. op. cit. (See R-404A.)

Viscosity

Klein et al. 1997. op. cit. (See R-12.)

Thermal conductivity

McLinden et al. 2000b. op. cit. (See R-12.)

Surface tension

Moldover and Rainwater. 1988. op. cit. (See R-404A.)

R-507A‡

Equation of state

Lemmon and Jacobsen. 2004a. op. cit. (See R-404A.)

Viscosity

Klein et al. 1997. op. cit. (See R-12.)

Thermal conductivity

McLinden et al. 2000b. op. cit. (See R-12.)

Surface tension

Moldover and Rainwater. 1988. op. cit. (See R-404A.)

R-717 (Ammonia)†

Equation of state

Tillner-Roth, R., F. Harms-Watzenberg, and H.D. Baehr. 1993. Eine neue Fundamentalgleichung für Ammoniak. *DKV-Tagungsbericht* 20(II): 167181.

Viscosity

Fenghour, A., W.A. Wakeham, V. Vesovic, J.T.R. Watson, J. Millat, and E. Vogel. 1995a. The viscosity of ammonia. *Journal of Physical and Chemical Reference Data* 24:1649-1667.

Thermal conductivity

Tufeu, R., D.Y. Ivanov, Y. Garrabos, and B. Le Neindre. 1984. Thermal conductivity of ammonia in a large temperature and pressure range including the critical region. *Berichte der Bunsen-Gesellschaft—Physical Chemistry* 88:422-427.

Surface tension

Stairs, R.A. and M.J. Sienko. 1956. Surface tension of ammonia and of solutions of alkalai halides in ammonia. *Journal of American Chemical Society* 78:920-923.

R-718 (Water/Steam)†

Data computed using

Harvey, A.H., S.A. Klein, and A.P. Peskin. 1999. *NIST Standard Reference Database* 10. NIST/ASME steam properties database, v. 2.2. Standard Reference Data Program.

Equation of state

Wagner, W. and A. Pruss. 2002. The IAPWS formulation 1995 for the thermodynamic properties of ordinary water substance for general and scientific use. *Journal of Physical and Chemical Reference Data* 31:387-535.

Viscosity and thermal conductivity

Kestin, J., J.V. Sengers, B. Kamgar-Parsi, and J.M.H. Levelt Sengers. 1984. Thermophysical properties of fluid H_2O. *Journal of Physical and Chemical Reference Data* 13:175.

Surface tension

IAPWS. 1995. Physical chemistry of aqueous systems: Meeting the needs of industry. *Proceedings of the 12th International Conference on the Properties of Water and Steam*, Orlando. Begell House, Inc., A139-A142. International Association for the Properties of Steam.

R-744 (Carbon Dioxide)†

Equation of state

Span, R. and W. Wagner. 1996. A new equation of state for carbon dioxide covering the fluid region from the triple-point temperature to 1100 K at pressures up to 800 MPa. *Journal of Physical and Chemical Reference Data* 26:1509-1596.

Viscosity

Fenghour, A., W.A. Wakeham, and V. Vesovic. 1995b. The viscosity of carbon dioxide. *Journal of Physical and Chemical Reference Data* 27: 31-44.

Thermal conductivity

Vesovic, V., W.A. Wakeham, G.A. Olchowy, J.V. Sengers, J.T.R. Watson, and J. Millat. 1990. The transport properties of carbon dioxide. *Journal of Physical and Chemical Reference Data* 19:763-808.

Surface tension

Rathjen, W. and J. Straub. 1977. *Heat transfer in boiling*, Chapter 18, Temperature dependence of surface tension, coexistence curve, and vapor pressure of CO_2, $CClF_3$, $CBrF_3$, and SF_6. Academic Press, New York.

R-50 (Methane)†

Equation of state

Setzmann, U. and W. Wagner. 1991. A new equation of state and tables of thermodynamic properties for methane covering the range from the melting line to 625 K at pressures to 1000 MPa. *Journal of Physical and Chemical Reference Data* 20:1061-1151.

Viscosity

Younglove, B.A. and J.F. Ely. 1987. Thermophysical properties of fluids. II. Methane, ethane, propane, isobutane and normal butane. *Journal of Physical and Chemical Reference Data* 16:577-798.

Thermal conductivity

Friend, D.G., J.F. Ely, and H. Ingham. 1989. Thermophysical properties of methane. *Journal of Physical and Chemical Reference Data* 18(2): 583-638.

Surface tension

Somayajulu, G.R. 1988. A generalized equation for surface tension from the triple point to the critical point. *International Journal of Thermophysics* 9:559-566.

R-170 (Ethane)

Equation of state,

Bücker, D. and W. Wagner. 2006. A reference equation of state for the thermodynamic properties of ethane for temperatures from the melting line to 675 K and pressures up to 900 MPa. *Journal of Physical and Chemical Reference Data* 35:205.

Viscosity, and thermal conductivity

Friend, D.G., H. Ingham, and J.F. Ely. 1991. Thermophysical properties of ethane. *Journal of Physical and Chemical Reference Data* 20(2): 275-347.

Surface tension

Soares, V.A.M., B.d.J.V.S. Almeida, I.A. McLure, and R.A. Higgins. 1986. Surface tension of pure and mixed simple substances at low temperature. *Fluid Phase Equilibria* 32:9-16.

Pressure-enthalpy diagram based on data of

Friend, D.G., H. Ingham, and J.F. Ely. 1991. Thermophysical properties of ethane. *Journal of Physical and Chemical Reference Data* 20(2): 275-347.

R-290 (Propane)

Equation of state

Lemmon, E.W., W. Wagner, and M.O. McLinden. 2009. Thermodynamic properties of propane, IV: Equation of state. *Journal of Chemical & Engineering Data* (submitted for publication).

Viscosity

Vogel, E., C. Küchenmeister, E. Bich, and A. Laesecke. 1998. Reference correlation of the viscosity of propane. *Journal of Physical and Chemical Reference Data* 27:947-970.

Thermal conductivity

Marsh, K., R. Perkins, and M.L.V. Ramires. 2002. Measurement and correlation of the thermal conductivity of propane from 86 to 600 K at pressures to 70 MPa. *Journal of Chemical & Engineering Data* 47:932-940.

Surface tension

Baidakov, V.G. and I.I. Sulla. 1985. Surface tension of propane and isobutane at near-critical temperatures. *Russian Journal of Physical Chemistry* 59:551-554.

Pressure-enthalpy diagram based on data of

Miyamoto, H. and K. Watanabe. 2000. A thermodynamic property model for fluid-phase propane. *International Journal of Thermophysics* 21:1045-1072.

R-600 (*n*-Butane)

Equation of state

Bücker, D. and W. Wagner. 2006. Reference equations of state for the thermodynamic properties of fluid phase *n*-butane and isobutane. *Journal of Physical and Chemical Reference Data* 35:929.

Viscosity

Vogel, E., C. Kuchenmeister, and E. Bich. 1999. Viscosity for *n*-butane in the fluid region. *High Temperatures—High Pressures* 31:173-186.

Thermal conductivity

Perkins, R.A., M.L.V. Ramires, C.A. Nieto de Castro, and L. Cusco. 2002. Measurement and correlation of the thermal conductivity of butane. *Journal of Chemical and Engineering Data* 47:1263-1271.

Surface tension

Calado, J.C.G., I.A. McLure, and V.A.M. Soares. 1978. Surface tension for octafluorocyclobutane, *n*-butane and their mixtures from 233 K to 254 K, and vapour pressure, excess Gibbs function and excess volume for the mixture at 233 K. *Fluid Phase Equilibria* 2:199-213.

Coffin, C.C. and O. Maass. 1928. The preparation and physical properties of α-, β- and γ-butylene and normal and isobutane. *Journal of the American Chemical Society* 50(5):1427-1437.

Pressure-enthalpy diagram based on data of

Miyamoto, H. and K. Watanabe. 2001. Thermodynamic property model for fluid-phase *n*-butane. *International Journal of Thermophysics* 22:459-475.

R-600a (Isobutane)

Equation of state

Bücker, D. and W. Wagner. 2006. op cit. (See R-600.)

Viscosity

Vogel, E., C. Küchenmeister, and E. Bich. 2000. Viscosity correlation for isobutane over wide ranges of the fluid region. *International Journal of Thermophysics* 21:343-356.

Thermal conductivity

Perkins, R.A. 2002. Measurement and correlation of the thermal conductivity of isobutane. *Journal of Chemical Engineering Data* 47: 1272-1279.

Surface tension

Baidakov and Sulla. 1985. op. cit. (See R-290.)

Pressure-enthalpy diagram based on data of

Miyamoto, H. and K. Watanabe. 2002. A thermodynamic property model for fluid-phase isobutane. *International Journal of Thermophysics* 23:477-499.

R-1150 (Ethylene)†

Equation of state

Smukala, J., R. Span, and W. Wagner. 2000. A new equation of state for ethylene covering the fluid region for temperatures from the melting line to 450 K and pressures up to 300 MPa. *Journal of Physical and Chemical Reference Data* 29:1053-1122.

Viscosity and thermal conductivity

Holland, P.M., B.E. Eaton, and H.J.M. Hanley. 1983. A correlation of the viscosity and thermal conductivity data of gaseous and liquid ethylene. *Journal of Physical and Chemical Reference Data* 12:917-932.

Surface tension

Soares et al. op. cit. (See R-170.)

R-1270 (Propylene)‡

Equation of state

Angus, S., B. Armstrong, and K.M. de Reuck. 1980. *International thermodynamic tables of the fluid state—7: Propylene*. Pergamon Press, Oxford, U.K.

Viscosity and thermal conductivity

Huber et al. 2003. op. cit. (See R-32.)

Surface tension

Maass, O. and C.H. Wright. 1921. Some physical properties of hydrocarbons containing two and three carbon atoms. *Journal of the American Chemical Society* 43:1098-1111.

R-702 (Hydrogen)

Thermodynamic data computed using the ALLPROPS database, v. 4.0:

Lemmon, E.W., R.T. Jacobsen, S.G. Penoncello, and S.W. Beyerlein. 1994. Computer programs for the calculation of thermodynamic properties of cryogens and other fluids. *Advances in Cryogenic Engineering* 39:1891-1897.

Transport data computed using the NIST 12 database, v. 3.0:

Friend, D.G., R.D. McCarty, and V. Arp. 1992. *NIST thermophysical properties of pure fluids database*, v. 3.0. Standard Reference Data Program.

Equation of state, viscosity, and thermal conductivity

McCarty, R.D. 1975. *Hydrogen: Technology survey—Thermophysical properties*. NASA SP-3089.

Surface tension

Liley, P.E. and P.D. Desai. 1993. *ASHRAE thermophysical properties of refrigerants*.

R-702p (Parahydrogen)

Thermodynamic data computed using the ALLPROPS database, v. 4.0:

Lemmon et al. 1994. op. cit. (See R-702.)

Transport data computed using the NIST12 database, v. 3.0:

Friend et al. 1992. op. cit. (See R-702.)

Equation of state, viscosity, and thermal conductivity

Younglove, B.A. 1982. Thermophysical properties of fluids. I. Argon, ethylene, parahydrogen, nitrogen, nitrogen trifluoride, and oxygen. *Journal of Physical and Chemical Reference Data* 11(Supplement No. 1).

Surface tension

Liley and Desai. 1993. op. cit. (See R-702.)

R-704 (Helium)

Thermodynamic data computed using the ALLPROPS database, v. 4.0:

Lemmon et al. 1994. op. cit. (See R-702.)

Transport data computed using the NIST12 database, v. 3.0:

Friend et al. 1992. op. cit. (See R-702.)

Equation of state

Arp, V.D., R.D. McCarty, and D.G. Friend. 1995. Thermophysical properties of helium-4 from 0.8 to 1500 K with pressures to 2000 MPa. NIST *Technical Note* 1334 (revised).

Surface tension

Liley and Desai. 1993. op. cit. (See R-702.)

R-728 (Nitrogen)‡

Equation of state, viscosity, and thermal conductivity

Span, R., E.W. Lemmon, R.T. Jacobsen, W. Wagner, and A. Yokozeki. 2000. A reference equation of state for the thermodynamic properties of nitrogen for temperatures from 63.151 to 1000 K and pressures to 2200 MPa. *Journal of Physical and Chemical Reference Data* 29:1361-1433.

Viscosity and thermal conductivity

Lemmon, E.W. and R.T. Jacobsen. 2004b. Viscosity and thermal conductivity equations for nitrogen, oxygen, argon, and air. *International Journal of Thermophysics* 25:21-69.

Surface tension

Lemmon, E.W. and S.G. Penoncello. 1994. The surface tension of air and air component mixtures. *Advances in Cryogenic Engineering* 39:1927-1934.

R-729 (Air)‡

Equation of state

Lemmon, E.W., R.T. Jacobsen, S.G. Penoncello, and D.G. Friend. 2000. Thermodynamic properties of air and mixtures of nitrogen, argon, and oxygen from 60 to 2000 K at pressures to 2000 MPa. *Journal of Physical and Chemical Reference Data* 29:331-385.

Viscosity and thermal conductivity

Lemmon and Jacobsen. 2004b. op. cit. (See R-728.)

Surface tension

Lemmon and Penoncello. 1994. op. cit. (See R-728.)

R-732 (Oxygen)‡

Equation of state

Schmidt, R. and W. Wagner. 1985. A new form of the equation of state for pure substances and its application to oxygen. *Fluid Phase Equilibria* 19:175-200.

Viscosity and thermal conductivity

Lemmon and Jacobsen. 2004b. op. cit. (See R-728)

Surface tension

Lemmon and Penoncello. 1994. op. cit. (See R-728.)

R-740 (Argon)‡

Equation of state

Tegeler, C., R. Span, and W. Wagner. 1999. A new equation of state for argon covering the fluid region for temperatures from the melting line to 700 K at pressures up to 1000 MPa. *Journal of Physical and Chemical Reference Data* 28:779-850.

Viscosity and thermal conductivity

Lemmon and Jacobsen. 2004b. op. cit. (See R-728.)

Surface tension

Lemmon and Penoncello. 1994. op. cit. (See R-728.)

CHAPTER 31

PHYSICAL PROPERTIES OF SECONDARY COOLANTS (BRINES)

IN many refrigeration applications, heat is transferred to a **secondary coolant**, which can be any liquid cooled by the refrigerant and used to transfer heat without changing state. These liquids are also known as **heat transfer fluids, brines**, or **secondary refrigerants.**

Other ASHRAE Handbook volumes describe various applications for secondary coolants. In the 2006 *ASHRAE Handbook—Refrigeration*, refrigeration systems are discussed in Chapter 4, their uses in food processing in Chapters 14 to 29, and ice rinks in Chapter 35. In the 2007 *ASHRAE Handbook—HVAC Applications*, solar energy use is discussed in Chapter 33, thermal storage in Chapter 34, and snow melting and freeze protection in Chapter 50.

This chapter describes physical properties of several secondary coolants and provides information on their use. Additional, less widely used secondary coolants such as ethyl alcohol or potassium formate are not included in this chapter, but their physical properties are summarized in Melinder (2007). The chapter also includes information on corrosion protection. Additional information on corrosion inhibition can be found in Chapter 48 of the 2007 *ASHRAE Handbook—HVAC Applications* and Chapter 4 of the 2006 *ASHRAE Handbook—Refrigeration*.

BRINES

Physical Properties

Water solutions of calcium chloride and sodium chloride are the most common refrigeration brines. Tables 1 and 2 list the properties of pure calcium chloride brine and sodium chloride brine. For commercial grades, use the formulas in the footnotes to these tables. For calcium chloride brines, Figure 1 shows specific heat, Figure 2 shows the ratio of mass of solution to that of water, Figure 3 shows viscosity, and Figure 4 shows thermal conductivity. Figures 5 to 8 show the same properties for sodium chloride brines.

Table 1 Properties of Pure Calcium Chloride* Brines

Pure $CaCl_2$, % by Mass	Specific Heat at 15°C, J/(kg·K)	Crystallization Starts, °C	Density at 16°C, kg/m³		Density at Various Temperatures, kg/m³			
			$CaCl_2$	Brine	−20°C	−10°C	0°C	10°C
0	4184	0.0	0.0	999				
5	3866	−2.4	52.2	1044			1042	1041
6	3824	−2.9	63.0	1049			1051	1050
7	3757	−3.4	74.2	1059			1060	1059
8	3699	−4.1	85.5	1068			1070	1068
9	3636	−4.7	96.9	1078			1079	1077
10	3577	−5.4	108.6	1087			1088	1086
11	3523	−6.2	120.5	1095			1097	1095
12	3464	−7.1	132.5	1104			1107	1104
13	3414	−8.0	144.8	1113			1116	1114
14	3364	−9.2	157.1	1123			1126	1123
15	3318	−10.3	169.8	1132		1140	1136	1133
16	3259	−11.6	182.6	1141		1150	1145	1142
17	3209	−13.0	195.7	1152		1160	1155	1152
18	3163	−14.5	209.0	1161		1170	1165	1162
19	3121	−16.2	222.7	1171		1179	1175	1172
20	3084	−18.0	236.0	1180		1189	1185	1182
21	3050	−19.9	249.6	1189				
22	2996	−22.1	264.3	1201	1214	1210	1206	1202
23	2958	−24.4	278.7	1211				
24	2916	−26.8	293.5	1223	1235	1231	1227	1223
25	2882	−29.4	308.2	1232				
26	2853	−32.1	323.1	1242				
27	2816	−35.1	338.5	1253				
28	2782	−38.8	354.0	1264				
29	2753	−45.2	369.9	1275				
29.87	2741	−55.0	378.8	1289				
30	2732	−46.0	358.4	1294				
32	2678	−28.6	418.1	1316				
34	2636	−15.4	452.0	1339				

Source: CCI (1953)
*Mass of Type 1 (77% min.) $CaCl_2$ = (mass of pure $CaCl_2$)/(0.77). Mass of Type 2 (94% min.) $CaCl_2$ = (mass of pure $CaCl_2$)/(0.94).

The preparation of this chapter is assigned to TC 3.1, Refrigerants and Secondary Coolants.

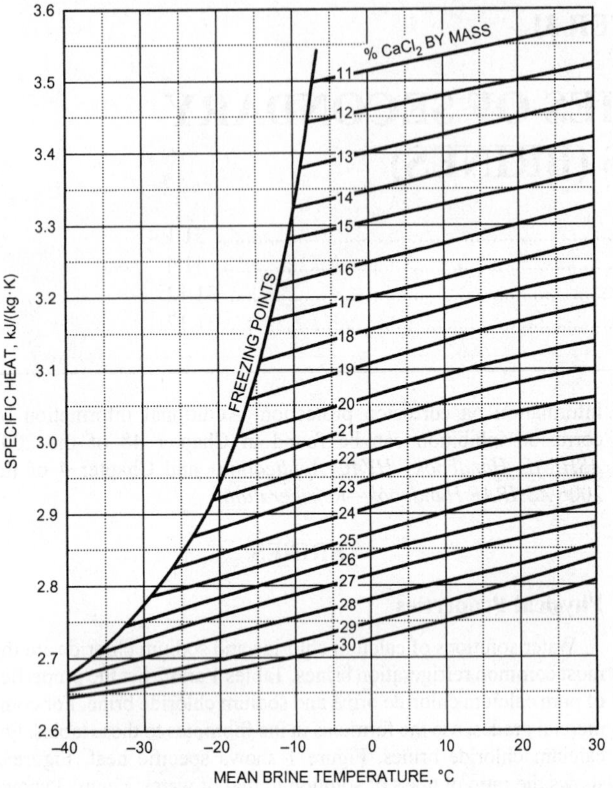

Fig. 1 Specific Heat of Calcium Chloride Brines
(CCI 1953)

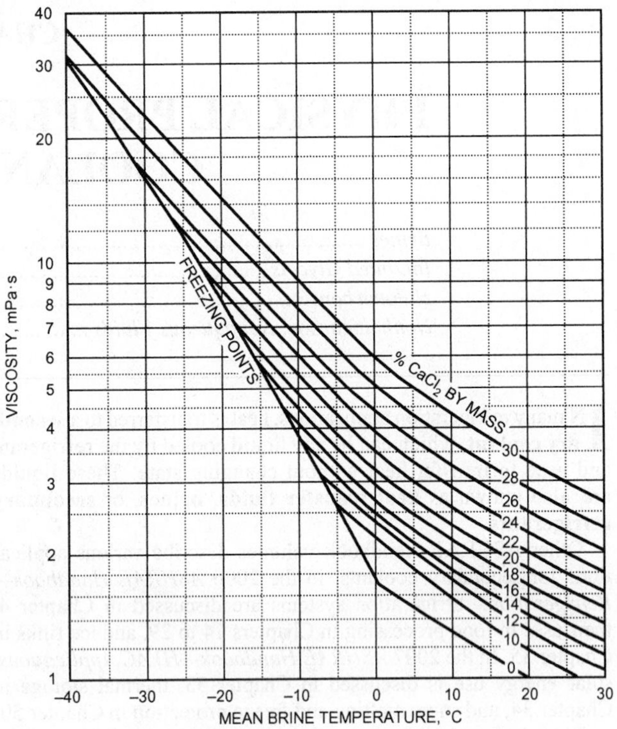

Fig. 3 Viscosity of Calcium Chloride Brines
(CCI 1953)

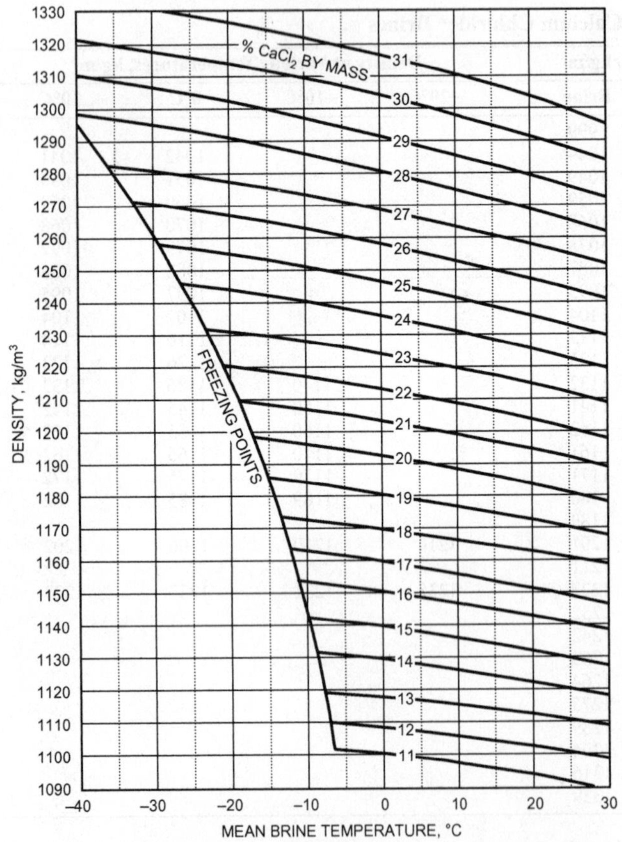

Fig. 2 Density of Calcium Chloride Brines
(CCI 1953)

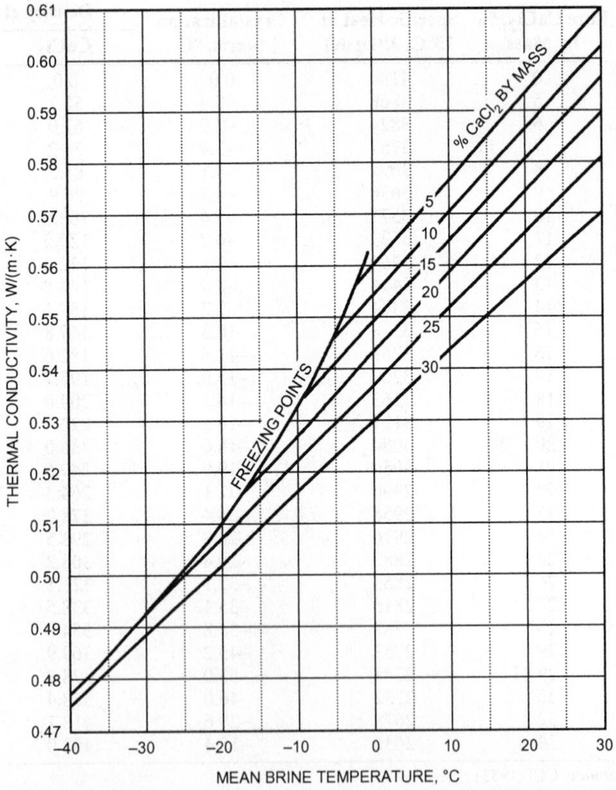

Fig. 4 Thermal Conductivity of Calcium Chloride Brines
(CCI 1953)

Table 2 Properties of Pure Sodium Chloride[a] Brines

Pure NaCl, % by Mass	Specific Heat at 15°C, J/(kg·K)	Crystallization Starts, °C	Density at 16°C, kg/m³ NaCl	Density at 16°C, kg/m³ Brine	Density at Various Temperatures, kg/m³ −10°C	−0°C	10°C	20°C
0	4184	0.0	0.0	1000				
5	3925	−2.9	51.7	1035		1038.1	1036.5	1034.0
6	3879	−3.6	62.5	1043		1045.8	1043.9	1041.2
7	3836	−4.3	73.4	1049		1053.7	1051.4	1048.5
8	3795	−5.0	84.6	1057		1061.2	1058.9	1055.8
9	3753	−5.8	95.9	1065		1069.0	1066.4	1063.2
10	3715	−6.6	107.2	1072		1076.8	1074.0	1070.6
11	3678	−7.3	118.8	1080		1084.8	1081.6	1078.1
12	3640	−8.2	130.3	1086		1092.4	1089.6	1085.6
13	3607	−9.1	142.2	1094		1100.3	1097.0	1093.2
14	3573	−10.1	154.3	1102		1108.2	1104.7	1100.8
15	3544	−10.9	166.5	1110	1119.4	1116.2	1112.5	1108.5
16	3515	−11.9	178.9	1118	1127.6	1124.2	1120.4	1116.2
17	3485	−13.0	191.4	1126	1135.8	1132.2	1128.3	1124.0
18	3456	−14.1	204.1	1134	1144.1	1140.3	1136.2	1131.8
19	3427	−15.3	217.0	1142	1153.4	1148.5	1144.3	1139.7
20	3402	−16.5	230.0	1150	1160.7	1156.7	1154.1	1147.7
21	3376	−17.8	243.2	1158	1169.1	1165.0	1160.5	1155.8
22	3356	−19.1	256.6	1166	1177.6	1173.3	1168.7	1163.9
23	3330	−20.6	270.0	1174	1186.1	1181.7	1177.0	1172.0
24	3310	−15.7	283.7	1182	1194.7	1190.1	1185.3	1180.3
25	3289	−8.8	297.5	1190				
25.2		0.0						

[a]Mass of commercial NaC1 required = (mass of pure NaCl required)/(% purity).

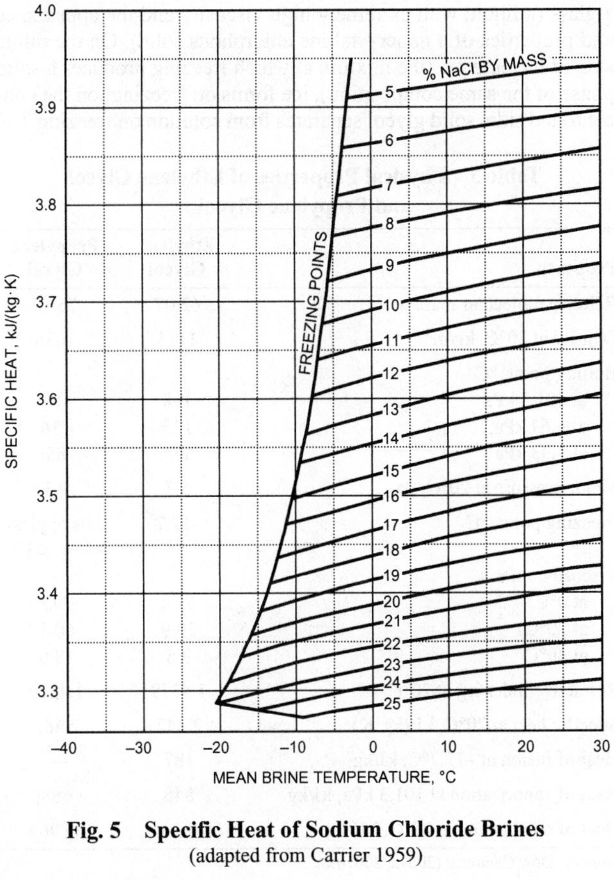

Fig. 5 Specific Heat of Sodium Chloride Brines
(adapted from Carrier 1959)

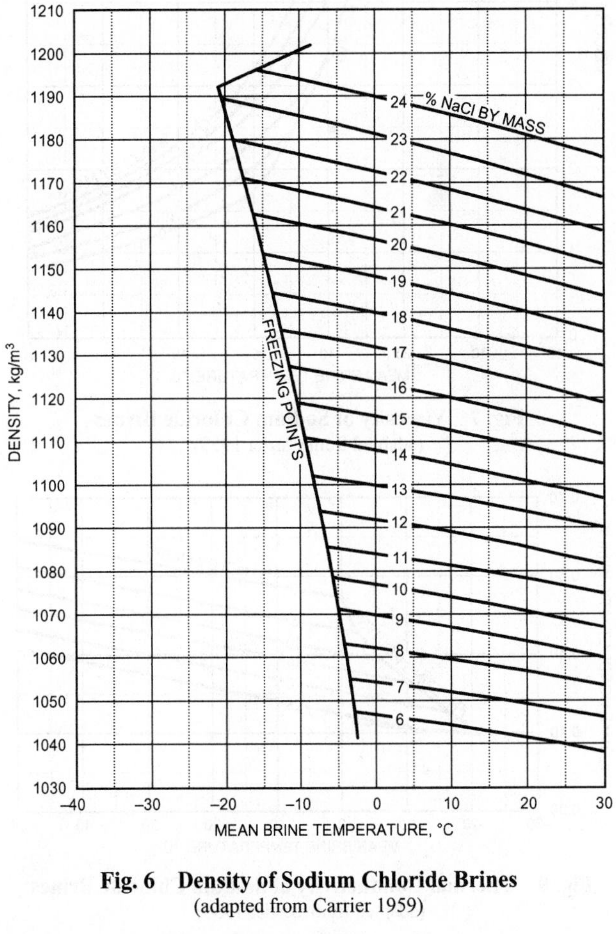

Fig. 6 Density of Sodium Chloride Brines
(adapted from Carrier 1959)

Brine applications in refrigeration are mainly in industrial machinery and in skating rinks. Corrosion is the principal problem for calcium chloride brines, especially in ice-making tanks where galvanized iron cans are immersed.

Ordinary salt (sodium chloride) is used where contact with calcium chloride is intolerable (e.g., the brine fog method of freezing fish and other foods). It is used as a spray to air-cool unit coolers to prevent frost formation on coils. In most refrigerating work, the lower freezing point of calcium chloride solution makes it more convenient to use.

Commercial calcium chloride, available as Type 1 (77% minimum) and Type 2 (94% minimum), is marketed in flake, solid, and solution forms; flake form is used most extensively. Commercial sodium chloride is available both in crude (rock salt) and refined grades. Because magnesium salts tend to form sludge, their presence in sodium or calcium chloride is undesirable.

Corrosion Inhibition

All brine systems must be treated to control corrosion and deposits. Historically, chloride-based brines were maintained at neutral pH and treated with sodium chromate. However, using chromate as a corrosion inhibitor is no longer deemed acceptable because of its environmental effect. Instead, most brines use a sodium-nitrite-based inhibitor ranging from approximately 3000 mg/kg in calcium brines to 4000 mg/kg in sodium brines. Other, proprietary organic inhibitors are also available to mitigate the inherent corrosiveness of brines.

Before using any inhibitor package, review federal, state, and local regulations concerning the use and disposal of the spent fluids. If the regulations prove too restrictive, an alternative inhibition system should be considered.

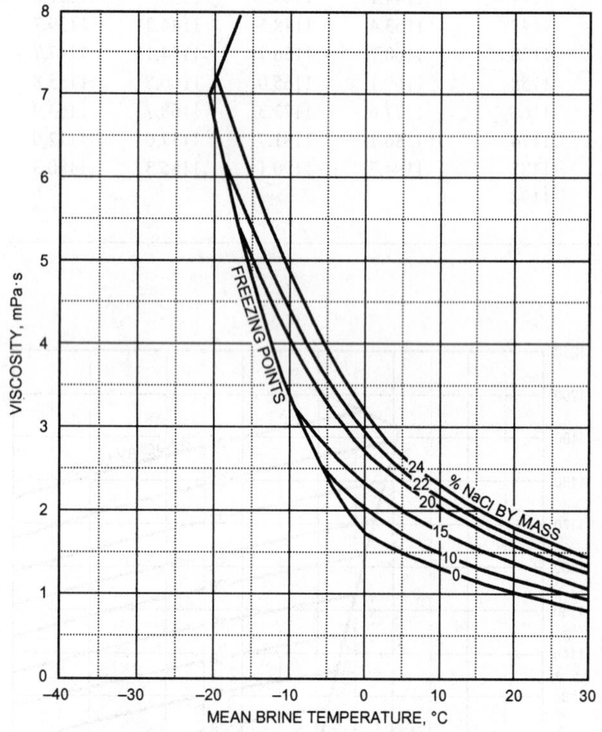

Fig. 7 Viscosity of Sodium Chloride Brines
(adapted from Carrier 1959)

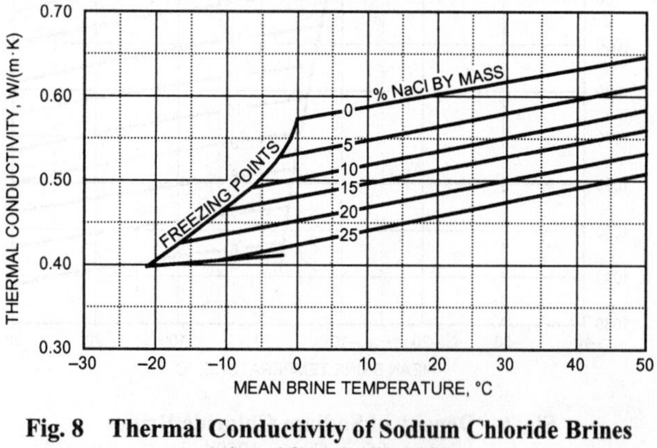

Fig. 8 Thermal Conductivity of Sodium Chloride Brines
(adapted from Carrier 1959)

INHIBITED GLYCOLS

Ethylene glycol and propylene glycol, when properly inhibited for corrosion control, are used as aqueous-freezing-point depressants (antifreeze) and heat transfer media. Their chief attributes are their ability to efficiently lower the freezing point of water, their low volatility, and their relatively low corrosivity when properly inhibited. Inhibited ethylene glycol solutions have better thermophysical properties than propylene glycol solutions, especially at lower temperatures. However, the less toxic propylene glycol is preferred for applications involving possible human contact or where mandated by regulations.

Physical Properties

Ethylene glycol and propylene glycol are colorless, practically odorless liquids that are miscible with water and many organic compounds. Table 3 shows properties of the pure materials.

The freezing and boiling points of aqueous solutions of ethylene glycol and propylene glycol are given in Tables 4 and 5. Note that increasing the concentration of ethylene glycol above 60% by mass causes the freezing point of the solution to increase. Propylene glycol solutions above 60% by mass do not have freezing points. Instead of freezing, propylene glycol solutions supercool and become a glass (a liquid with extremely high viscosity and the appearance and properties of a noncrystalline amorphous solid). On the dilute side of the eutectic (the mixture at which freezing produces a solid phase of the same composition), ice forms on freezing; on the concentrated side, solid glycol separates from solution on freezing. The

Table 3 Physical Properties of Ethylene Glycol and Propylene Glycol

Property	Ethylene Glycol	Propylene Glycol
Relative molecular mass	62.07	76.10
Density at 20°C, kg/m³	1113	1036
Boiling point, °C		
at 101.3 kPa	198	187
at 6.67 kPa	123	116
at 1.33 kPa	89	85
Vapor pressure at 20°C, Pa	6.7	9.3
Freezing point, °C	−12.7	Sets to glass below −51°C
Viscosity, mPa·s		
at 0°C	57.4	243
at 20°C	20.9	60.5
at 40°C	9.5	18.0
Refractive index n_D at 20°C	1.4319	1.4329
Specific heat at 20°C, kJ/(kg·K)	2.347	2.481
Heat of fusion at −12.7°C, kJ/kg	187	—
Heat of vaporization at 101.3 kPa, kJ/kg	846	688
Heat of combustion at 20°C, MJ/kg	19.246	23.969

Sources: Dow Chemical (2001a, 2001b)

Table 4 Freezing and Boiling Points of Aqueous Solutions of Ethylene Glycol

Percent Ethylene Glycol		Freezing Point, °C	Boiling Point, °C at 100.7 kPa
By Mass	By Volume		
0.0	0.0	0.0	100.0
5.0	4.4	–1.4	100.6
10.0	8.9	–3.2	101.1
15.0	13.6	–5.4	101.7
20.0	18.1	–7.8	102.2
21.0	19.2	–8.4	102.2
22.0	20.1	–8.9	102.2
23.0	21.0	–9.5	102.8
24.0	22.0	–10.2	102.8
25.0	22.9	–10.7	103.3
26.0	23.9	–11.4	103.3
27.0	24.8	–12.0	103.3
28.0	25.8	–12.7	103.9
29.0	26.7	–13.3	103.9
30.0	27.7	–14.1	104.4
31.0	28.7	–14.8	104.4
32.0	29.6	–15.4	104.4
33.0	30.6	–16.2	104.4
34.0	31.6	–17.0	104.4
35.0	32.6	–17.9	105.0
36.0	33.5	–18.6	105.0
37.0	34.5	–19.4	105.0
38.0	35.5	–20.3	105.0
39.0	36.5	–21.3	105.0
40.0	37.5	–22.3	105.6
41.0	38.5	–23.2	105.6
42.0	39.5	–24.3	105.6
43.0	40.5	–25.3	106.1
44.0	41.5	–26.4	106.1
45.0	42.5	–27.5	106.7
46.0	43.5	–28.8	106.7
47.0	44.5	–29.8	106.7
48.0	45.5	–31.1	106.7
49.0	46.6	–32.6	106.7
50.0	47.6	–33.8	107.2
51.0	48.6	–35.1	107.2
52.0	49.6	–36.4	107.2
53.0	50.6	–37.9	107.8
54.0	51.6	–39.3	107.8
55.0	52.7	–41.1	108.3
56.0	53.7	–42.6	108.3
57.0	54.7	–44.2	108.9
58.0	55.7	–45.6	108.9
59.0	56.8	–47.1	109.4
60.0	57.8	–48.3	110.0
65.0	62.8	*	112.8
70.0	68.3	*	116.7
75.0	73.6	*	120.0
80.0	78.9	–46.8	123.9
85.0	84.3	–36.9	133.9
90.0	89.7	–29.8	140.6
95.0	95.0	–19.4	158.3

Source: Dow Chemical (2001b)
*Freezing points are below –50°C.

Table 5 Freezing and Boiling Points of Aqueous Solutions of Propylene Glycol

Percent Propylene Glycol		Freezing Point, °C	Boiling Point, °C at 100.7 kPa
By Mass	By Volume		
0.0	0.0	0.0	100.0
5.0	4.8	–1.6	100.0
10.0	9.6	–3.3	100.0
15.0	14.5	–5.1	100.0
20.0	19.4	–7.1	100.6
21.0	20.4	–7.6	100.6
22.0	21.4	–8.0	100.6
23.0	22.4	–8.6	100.6
24.0	23.4	–9.1	100.6
25.0	24.4	–9.6	101.1
26.0	25.3	–10.2	101.1
27.0	26.4	–10.8	101.1
28.0	27.4	–11.4	101.7
29.0	28.4	–12.0	101.7
30.0	29.4	–12.7	102.2
31.0	30.4	–13.4	102.2
32.0	31.4	–14.1	102.2
33.0	32.4	–14.8	102.2
34.0	33.5	–15.6	102.2
35.0	34.4	–16.4	102.8
36.0	35.5	–17.3	102.8
37.0	36.5	–18.2	102.8
38.0	37.5	–19.1	103.3
39.0	38.5	–20.1	103.3
40.0	39.6	–21.1	103.9
41.0	40.6	–22.1	103.9
42.0	41.6	–23.2	103.9
43.0	42.6	–24.3	103.9
44.0	43.7	–25.5	103.9
45.0	44.7	–26.7	104.4
46.0	45.7	–27.9	104.4
47.0	46.8	–29.3	104.4
48.0	47.8	–30.6	105.0
49.0	48.9	–32.1	105.0
50.0	49.9	–33.5	105.6
51.0	50.9	–35.0	105.6
52.0	51.9	–36.6	105.6
53.0	53.0	–38.2	106.1
54.0	54.0	–39.8	106.1
55.0	55.0	–41.6	106.1
56.0	56.0	–43.3	106.1
57.0	57.0	–45.2	106.7
58.0	58.0	–47.1	106.7
59.0	59.0	–49.0	106.7
60.0	60.0	–51.1	107.2
65.0	65.0	*	108.3
70.0	70.0	*	110.0
75.0	75.0	*	113.9
80.0	80.0	*	118.3
85.0	85.0	*	125.0
90.0	90.0	*	132.2
95.0	95.0	*	154.4

Source: Dow Chemical (2001a)
*Above 60% by mass, solutions do not freeze but become a glass.

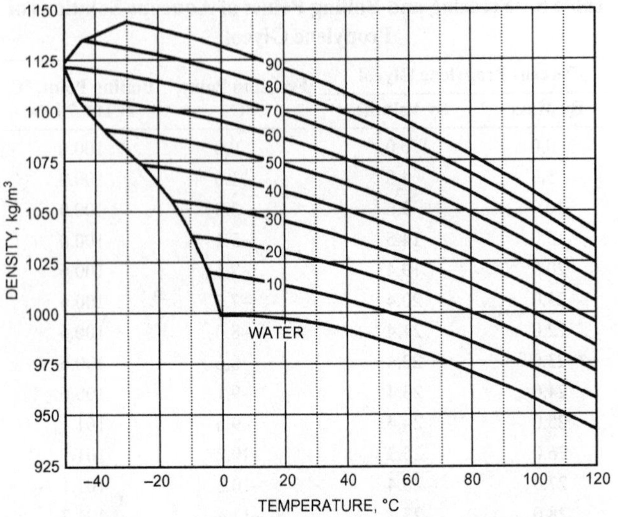

Fig. 9 Density of Aqueous Solutions of Industrially Inhibited Ethylene Glycol (vol. %)
(Dow Chemical 2001b)

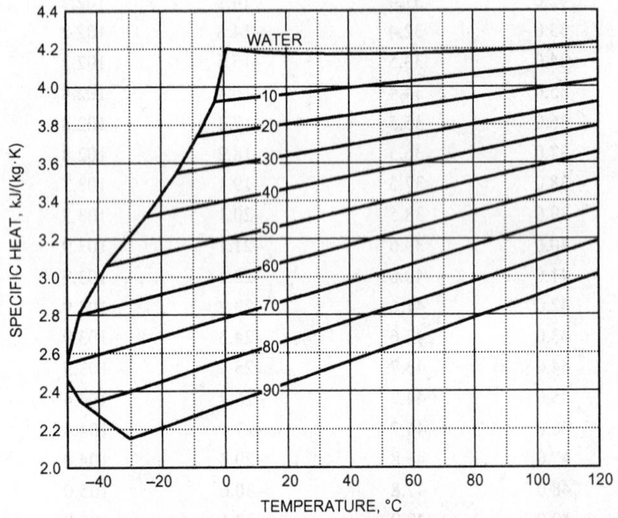

Fig. 10 Specific Heat of Aqueous Solutions of Industrially Inhibited Ethylene Glycol (vol. %)
(Dow Chemical 2001b)

freezing rate of such solutions is often quite slow, but, in time, they set to a hard, solid mass.

Physical properties (i.e., density, specific heat, thermal conductivity, and viscosity) for aqueous solutions of ethylene glycol can be found in Tables 6 to 9 and Figures 9 to 12; similar data for aqueous solutions of propylene glycol are in Tables 10 to 13 and Figures 13 to 16. Densities are for aqueous solutions of industrially inhibited glycols, and are somewhat higher than those for pure glycol and water alone. Typical corrosion inhibitor packages do not significantly affect other physical properties. Physical properties for the two fluids are similar, except for viscosity. At the same concentration, aqueous solutions of propylene glycol are more viscous than solutions of ethylene glycol. This higher viscosity accounts for the majority of the performance difference between the two fluids.

The choice of glycol concentration depends on the type of protection required by the application. If the fluid is being used to prevent equipment damage during idle periods in cold weather, such as winterizing coils in an HVAC system, 30% by volume ethylene glycol or 35% by volume propylene glycol is sufficient. These

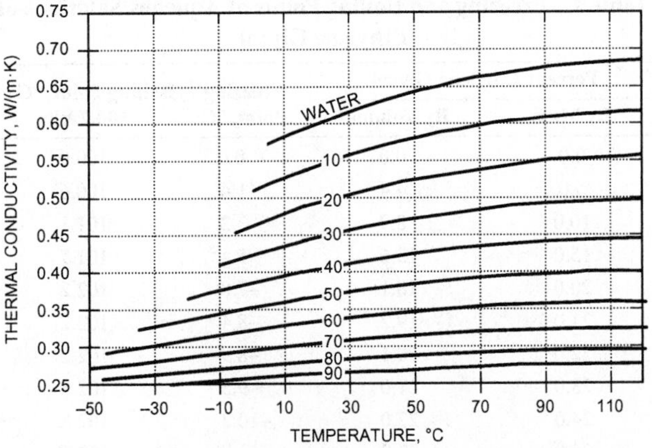

Fig. 11 Thermal Conductivity of Aqueous Solutions of Industrially Inhibited Ethylene Glycol (vol. %)
(Dow Chemical 2001b)

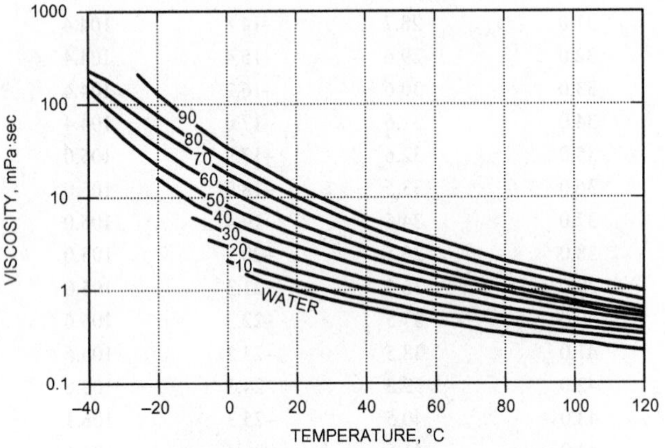

Fig. 12 Viscosity of Aqueous Solutions of Industrially Inhibited Ethylene Glycol (vol. %)
(Dow Chemical 2001b)

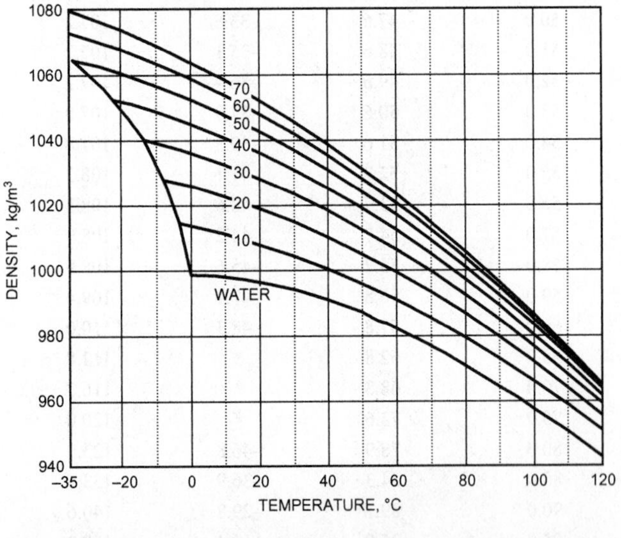

Fig. 13 Density of Aqueous Solutions of Industrially Inhibited Propylene Glycol (vol. %)
(Dow Chemical 2001b)

Table 6 Density of Aqueous Solutions of Ethylene Glycol

	Concentrations in Volume Percent Ethylene Glycol								
Temperature, °C	10%	20%	30%	40%	50%	60%	70%	80%	90%
−35					1089.94	1104.60	1118.61	1132.11	
−30					1089.04	1103.54	1117.38	1130.72	
−25					1088.01	1102.36	1116.04	1129.21	1141.87
−20				1071.98	1086.87	1101.06	1114.58	1127.57	1140.07
−15				1070.87	1085.61	1099.64	1112.99	1125.82	1138.14
−10			1054.31	1069.63	1084.22	1098.09	1111.28	1123.94	1136.09
−5		1036.85	1053.11	1068.28	1082.71	1096.43	1109.45	1121.94	1133.91
0	1018.73	1035.67	1051.78	1066.80	1081.08	1094.64	1107.50	1119.82	1131.62
5	1017.57	1034.36	1050.33	1065.21	1079.33	1092.73	1105.43	1117.58	1129.20
10	1016.28	1032.94	1048.76	1063.49	1077.46	1090.70	1103.23	1115.22	1126.67
15	1014.87	1031.39	1047.07	1061.65	1075.46	1088.54	1100.92	1112.73	1124.01
20	1013.34	1029.72	1045.25	1059.68	1073.35	1086.27	1098.48	1110.13	1121.23
25	1011.69	1027.93	1043.32	1057.60	1071.11	1083.87	1095.92	1107.40	1118.32
30	1009.92	1026.02	1041.26	1055.39	1068.75	1081.35	1093.24	1104.55	1115.30
35	1008.02	1023.99	1039.08	1053.07	1066.27	1078.71	1090.43	1101.58	1112.15
40	1006.01	1021.83	1036.78	1050.62	1063.66	1075.95	1087.51	1098.48	1108.89
45	1003.87	1019.55	1034.36	1048.05	1060.94	1073.07	1084.46	1095.27	1105.50
50	1001.61	1017.16	1031.81	1045.35	1058.09	1070.06	1081.30	1091.93	1101.99
55	999.23	1014.64	1029.15	1042.54	1055.13	1066.94	1078.01	1088.48	1098.36
60	996.72	1011.99	1026.36	1039.61	1052.04	1063.69	1074.60	1084.90	1094.60
65	994.10	1009.23	1023.45	1036.55	1048.83	1060.32	1071.06	1081.20	1090.73
70	991.35	1006.35	1020.42	1033.37	1045.49	1056.83	1067.41	1077.37	1086.73
75	988.49	1003.34	1017.27	1030.07	1042.04	1053.22	1063.64	1073.43	1082.61
80	985.50	1000.21	1014.00	1026.65	1038.46	1049.48	1059.74	1069.36	1078.37
85	982.39	996.96	1010.60	1023.10	1034.77	1045.63	1055.72	1065.18	1074.01
90	979.15	993.59	1007.09	1019.44	1030.95	1041.65	1051.58	1060.87	1069.53
95	975.80	990.10	1003.45	1015.65	1027.01	1037.55	1047.32	1056.44	1064.92
100	972.32	986.48	999.69	1011.74	1022.95	1033.33	1042.93	1051.88	1060.20
105	968.73	982.75	995.81	1007.71	1018.76	1028.99	1038.43	1047.21	1055.35
110	965.01	978.89	991.81	1003.56	1014.46	1024.52	1033.80	1042.41	1050.38
115	961.17	974.91	987.68	999.29	1010.03	1019.94	1029.05	1037.50	1045.29
120	957.21	970.81	983.43	994.90	1005.48	1015.23	1024.18	1032.46	1040.08
125	953.12	966.59	979.07	990.38	1000.81	1010.40	1019.19	1027.30	1034.74

Source: Dow Chemical (2001b)

Note: Density in kg/m³.

Table 7 Specific Heat of Aqueous Solutions of Ethylene Glycol

	Concentrations in Volume Percent Ethylene Glycol								
Temperature, °C	10%	20%	30%	40%	50%	60%	70%	80%	90%
−35					3.068	2.844	2.612	2.370	
−30					3.088	2.866	2.636	2.397	
−25					3.107	2.888	2.660	2.423	2.177
−20				3.334	3.126	2.909	2.685	2.450	2.206
−15				3.351	3.145	2.931	2.709	2.477	2.235
−10			3.560	3.367	3.165	2.953	2.733	2.503	2.264
−5		3.757	3.574	3.384	3.184	2.975	2.757	2.530	2.293
0	3.937	3.769	3.589	3.401	3.203	2.997	2.782	2.556	2.322
5	3.946	3.780	3.603	3.418	3.223	3.018	2.806	2.583	2.351
10	3.954	3.792	3.617	3.435	3.242	3.040	2.830	2.610	2.380
15	3.963	3.803	3.631	3.451	3.261	3.062	2.854	2.636	2.409
20	3.972	3.815	3.645	3.468	3.281	3.084	2.878	2.663	2.438
25	3.981	3.826	3.660	3.485	3.300	3.106	2.903	2.690	2.467
30	3.989	3.838	3.674	3.502	3.319	3.127	2.927	2.716	2.496
35	3.998	3.849	3.688	3.518	3.339	3.149	2.951	2.743	2.525
40	4.007	3.861	3.702	3.535	3.358	3.171	2.975	2.770	2.554
45	4.015	3.872	3.716	3.552	3.377	3.193	3.000	2.796	2.583
50	4.024	3.884	3.730	3.569	3.396	3.215	3.024	2.823	2.612
55	4.033	3.895	3.745	3.585	3.416	3.236	3.048	2.850	2.641
60	4.042	3.907	3.759	3.602	3.435	3.258	3.072	2.876	2.670
65	4.050	3.918	3.773	3.619	3.454	3.280	3.097	2.903	2.699
70	4.059	3.930	3.787	3.636	3.474	3.302	3.121	2.929	2.728
75	4.068	3.941	3.801	3.653	3.493	3.324	3.145	2.956	2.757
80	4.077	3.953	3.816	3.669	3.512	3.345	3.169	2.983	2.786
85	4.085	3.964	3.830	3.686	3.532	3.367	3.193	3.009	2.815
90	4.094	3.976	3.844	3.703	3.551	3.389	3.218	3.036	2.844
95	4.103	3.987	3.858	3.720	3.570	3.411	3.242	3.063	2.873
100	4.112	3.999	3.872	3.736	3.590	3.433	3.266	3.089	2.902
105	4.120	4.010	3.886	3.753	3.609	3.454	3.290	3.116	2.931
110	4.129	4.022	3.901	3.770	3.628	3.476	3.315	3.143	2.960
115	4.138	4.033	3.915	3.787	3.647	3.498	3.339	3.169	2.989
120	4.147	4.045	3.929	3.804	3.667	3.520	3.363	3.196	3.018
125	4.155	4.056	3.943	3.820	3.686	3.542	3.387	3.223	3.047

Source: Dow Chemical (2001b)

Note: Specific heat in kJ/(kg·K).

Table 8 Thermal Conductivity of Aqueous Solutions of Ethylene Glycol

	Concentrations in Volume Percent Ethylene Glycol								
Temperature, °C	10	20	30	40	50	60	70	80	90
−35						0.300	0.279	0.262	
−30					0.328	0.303	0.282	0.264	
−25					0.332	0.306	0.284	0.266	0.252
−20				0.366	0.336	0.310	0.287	0.268	0.253
−15				0.371	0.340	0.313	0.289	0.270	0.255
−10			0.411	0.376	0.344	0.316	0.292	0.271	0.256
−5		0.458	0.417	0.381	0.348	0.319	0.294	0.273	0.257
0	0.512	0.466	0.423	0.386	0.352	0.322	0.297	0.275	0.259
5	0.520	0.472	0.429	0.391	0.356	0.325	0.299	0.277	0.260
10	0.528	0.479	0.435	0.395	0.360	0.328	0.301	0.278	0.261
15	0.535	0.486	0.440	0.400	0.363	0.331	0.303	0.280	0.262
20	0.543	0.492	0.445	0.404	0.366	0.334	0.305	0.281	0.263
25	0.550	0.498	0.450	0.408	0.370	0.336	0.307	0.283	0.264
30	0.556	0.503	0.455	0.412	0.373	0.338	0.309	0.284	0.265
35	0.563	0.509	0.459	0.415	0.376	0.341	0.311	0.285	0.266
40	0.569	0.514	0.463	0.419	0.378	0.343	0.312	0.286	0.267
45	0.574	0.518	0.467	0.422	0.381	0.345	0.314	0.288	0.268
50	0.579	0.523	0.471	0.425	0.383	0.347	0.315	0.289	0.268
55	0.584	0.527	0.474	0.427	0.385	0.348	0.316	0.289	0.269
60	0.588	0.530	0.477	0.430	0.387	0.350	0.317	0.290	0.270
65	0.592	0.534	0.480	0.432	0.389	0.351	0.318	0.291	0.270
70	0.596	0.537	0.483	0.434	0.391	0.352	0.319	0.292	0.271
75	0.599	0.540	0.485	0.436	0.392	0.354	0.320	0.292	0.271
80	0.602	0.542	0.487	0.438	0.394	0.355	0.321	0.293	0.271
85	0.605	0.544	0.489	0.439	0.395	0.355	0.322	0.293	0.272
90	0.607	0.546	0.490	0.440	0.396	0.356	0.322	0.294	0.272
95	0.609	0.548	0.491	0.441	0.396	0.357	0.322	0.294	0.272
100	0.610	0.549	0.493	0.442	0.397	0.357	0.323	0.294	0.272
105	0.612	0.550	0.493	0.443	0.398	0.358	0.323	0.294	0.272
110	0.613	0.551	0.494	0.443	0.398	0.358	0.323	0.294	0.272
115	0.614	0.552	0.495	0.444	0.398	0.358	0.323	0.294	0.272
120	0.614	0.552	0.495	0.444	0.398	0.358	0.323	0.294	0.272
125	0.615	0.552	0.495	0.444	0.398	0.358	0.323	0.294	0.271

Source: Dow Chemical (2001b) *Note*: Thermal conductivity in W/(m·K).

Table 9 Viscosity of Aqueous Solutions of Ethylene Glycol

	Concentrations in Volume Percent Ethylene Glycol								
Temperature, °C	10	20	30	40	50	60	70	80	90
−35					66.93	93.44	133.53	191.09	
−30					43.98	65.25	96.57	141.02	
−25					30.50	46.75	70.38	102.21	196.87
−20				15.75	22.07	34.28	51.94	74.53	128.43
−15				11.74	16.53	25.69	38.88	55.09	87.52
−10			6.19	9.06	12.74	19.62	29.53	41.36	61.85
−5		3.65	5.03	7.18	10.05	15.25	22.76	31.56	45.08
0	2.08	3.02	4.15	5.83	8.09	12.05	17.79	24.44	33.74
5	1.79	2.54	3.48	4.82	6.63	9.66	14.09	19.20	25.84
10	1.56	2.18	2.95	4.04	5.50	7.85	11.31	15.29	20.18
15	1.37	1.89	2.53	3.44	4.63	6.46	9.18	12.33	16.04
20	1.21	1.65	2.20	2.96	3.94	5.38	7.53	10.05	12.95
25	1.08	1.46	1.92	2.57	3.39	4.52	6.24	8.29	10.59
30	0.97	1.30	1.69	2.26	2.94	3.84	5.23	6.90	8.77
35	0.88	1.17	1.50	1.99	2.56	3.29	4.42	5.79	7.34
40	0.80	1.06	1.34	1.77	2.26	2.84	3.76	4.91	6.21
45	0.73	0.96	1.21	1.59	2.00	2.47	3.23	4.19	5.30
50	0.67	0.88	1.09	1.43	1.78	2.16	2.80	3.61	4.56
55	0.62	0.81	0.99	1.29	1.59	1.91	2.43	3.12	3.95
60	0.57	0.74	0.90	1.17	1.43	1.69	2.13	2.72	3.45
65	0.53	0.69	0.83	1.06	1.29	1.51	1.88	2.39	3.03
70	0.50	0.64	0.76	0.97	1.17	1.35	1.67	2.11	2.67
75	0.47	0.59	0.70	0.89	1.07	1.22	1.49	1.87	2.37
80	0.44	0.55	0.65	0.82	0.98	1.10	1.33	1.66	2.12
85	0.41	0.52	0.60	0.76	0.89	1.00	1.20	1.49	1.90
90	0.39	0.49	0.56	0.70	0.82	0.92	1.09	1.34	1.71
95	0.37	0.46	0.52	0.65	0.76	0.84	0.99	1.21	1.54
100	0.35	0.43	0.49	0.60	0.70	0.77	0.90	1.10	1.40
105	0.33	0.40	0.46	0.56	0.65	0.71	0.82	1.00	1.27
110	0.32	0.38	0.43	0.53	0.60	0.66	0.76	0.91	1.16
115	0.30	0.36	0.41	0.49	0.56	0.61	0.70	0.83	1.07
120	0.29	0.34	0.38	0.46	0.53	0.57	0.64	0.77	0.98
125	0.28	0.33	0.36	0.43	0.49	0.53	0.60	0.71	0.90

Source: Dow Chemical (2001b) *Note*: Viscosity in mPa/s.

Table 10 Density of Aqueous Solutions of an Industrially Inhibited Propylene Glycol

	Concentrations in Volume Percent Propylene Glycol								
Temperature, °C	**10%**	**20%**	**30%**	**40%**	**50%**	**60%**	**70%**	**80%**	**90%**
−35						1072.92	1079.67	1094.50	1092.46
−30						1071.31	1077.82	1090.85	1088.82
−25					1062.11	1069.58	1075.84	1087.18	1085.15
−20					1060.49	1067.72	1073.74	1083.49	1081.46
−15				1050.43	1058.73	1065.73	1071.51	1079.77	1077.74
−10			1039.42	1048.79	1056.85	1063.61	1069.16	1076.04	1074.00
−5		1027.24	1037.89	1047.02	1054.84	1061.37	1066.69	1072.27	1070.24
0	1013.85	1025.84	1036.24	1045.12	1052.71	1059.00	1064.09	1068.49	1066.46
5	1012.61	1024.32	1034.46	1043.09	1050.44	1056.50	1061.36	1064.68	1062.65
10	1011.24	1022.68	1032.55	1040.94	1048.04	1053.88	1058.51	1060.85	1058.82
15	1009.75	1020.91	1030.51	1038.65	1045.52	1051.13	1055.54	1057.00	1054.96
20	1008.13	1019.01	1028.35	1036.24	1042.87	1048.25	1052.44	1053.12	1051.09
25	1006.40	1016.99	1026.06	1033.70	1040.09	1045.24	1049.22	1049.22	1047.19
30	1004.54	1014.84	1023.64	1031.03	1037.18	1042.11	1045.87	1045.30	1043.26
35	1002.56	1012.56	1021.09	1028.23	1034.15	1038.85	1042.40	1041.35	1039.32
40	1000.46	1010.16	1018.42	1025.30	1030.98	1035.47	1038.81	1037.38	1035.35
45	998.23	1007.64	1015.62	1022.24	1027.69	1031.95	1035.09	1033.39	1031.35
50	995.88	1004.99	1012.69	1019.06	1024.27	1028.32	1031.25	1029.37	1027.34
55	993.41	1002.21	1009.63	1015.75	1020.72	1024.55	1027.28	1025.33	1023.30
60	990.82	999.31	1006.44	1012.30	1017.04	1020.66	1023.19	1021.27	1019.24
65	988.11	996.28	1003.13	1008.73	1013.23	1016.63	1018.97	1017.19	1015.15
70	985.27	993.12	999.69	1005.03	1009.30	1012.49	1014.63	1013.08	1011.04
75	982.31	989.85	996.12	1001.21	1005.24	1008.21	1010.16	1008.95	1006.91
80	979.23	986.44	992.42	997.25	1001.05	1003.81	1005.57	1004.79	1002.76
85	976.03	982.91	988.60	993.17	996.73	999.28	1000.86	1000.62	998.58
90	972.70	979.25	984.65	988.95	992.28	994.63	996.02	996.41	994.38
95	969.25	975.47	980.57	984.61	987.70	989.85	991.06	992.19	990.16
100	965.68	971.56	976.36	980.14	983.00	984.94	985.97	987.94	985.91
105	961.99	967.53	972.03	975.54	978.16	979.90	980.76	983.68	981.64
110	958.17	963.37	967.56	970.81	973.20	974.74	975.42	979.38	977.35
115	954.24	959.09	962.97	965.95	968.11	969.45	969.96	975.07	973.03
120	950.18	954.67	958.26	960.97	962.89	964.03	964.38	970.73	968.69
125	945.99	950.14	953.41	955.86	957.55	958.49	958.67	966.37	964.33

Source: Dow Chemical (2001a) *Note*: Density in kg/m³.

Table 11 Specific Heat of Aqueous Solutions of Propylene Glycol

	Concentrations in Volume Percent Propylene Glycol								
Temperature, °C	**10%**	**20%**	**30%**	**40%**	**50%**	**60%**	**70%**	**80%**	**90%**
−35						3.096	2.843	2.572	2.264
−30						3.118	2.868	2.600	2.295
−25					3.358	3.140	2.893	2.627	2.326
−20					3.378	3.162	2.918	2.655	2.356
−15				3.586	3.397	3.184	2.943	2.683	2.387
−10			3.765	3.603	3.416	3.206	2.968	2.710	2.417
−5		3.918	3.779	3.619	3.435	3.228	2.993	2.738	2.448
0	4.042	3.929	3.793	3.636	3.455	3.250	3.018	2.766	2.478
5	4.050	3.940	3.807	3.652	3.474	3.272	3.042	2.793	2.509
10	4.058	3.951	3.820	3.669	3.493	3.295	3.067	2.821	2.539
15	4.067	3.962	3.834	3.685	3.513	3.317	3.092	2.849	2.570
20	4.075	3.973	3.848	3.702	3.532	3.339	3.117	2.876	2.600
25	4.083	3.983	3.862	3.718	3.551	3.361	3.142	2.904	2.631
30	4.091	3.994	3.875	3.735	3.570	3.383	3.167	2.931	2.661
35	4.099	4.005	3.889	3.751	3.590	3.405	3.192	2.959	2.692
40	4.107	4.016	3.903	3.768	3.609	3.427	3.217	2.987	2.723
45	4.115	4.027	3.917	3.784	3.628	3.449	3.242	3.014	2.753
50	4.123	4.038	3.930	3.801	3.648	3.471	3.266	3.042	2.784
55	4.131	4.049	3.944	3.817	3.667	3.493	3.291	3.070	2.814
60	4.139	4.060	3.958	3.834	3.686	3.515	3.316	3.097	2.845
65	4.147	4.071	3.972	3.850	3.706	3.537	3.341	3.125	2.875
70	4.155	4.082	3.985	3.867	3.725	3.559	3.366	3.153	2.906
75	4.163	4.093	3.999	3.883	3.744	3.581	3.391	3.180	2.936
80	4.171	4.104	4.013	3.900	3.763	3.603	3.416	3.208	2.967
85	4.179	4.115	4.027	3.916	3.783	3.625	3.441	3.236	2.997
90	4.187	4.126	4.040	3.933	3.802	3.647	3.465	3.263	3.028
95	4.195	4.136	4.054	3.949	3.821	3.670	3.490	3.291	3.058
100	4.203	4.147	4.068	3.966	3.841	3.692	3.515	3.319	3.089
105	4.211	4.158	4.082	3.982	3.860	3.714	3.540	3.346	3.119
110	4.219	4.169	4.095	3.999	3.879	3.736	3.565	3.374	3.150
115	4.227	4.180	4.109	4.015	3.898	3.758	3.590	3.402	3.181
120	4.235	4.191	4.123	4.032	3.918	3.780	3.615	3.429	3.211
125	4.243	4.202	4.137	4.049	3.937	3.802	3.640	3.457	3.242

Source: Dow Chemical (2001a) *Note*: Specific heat in kJ/(kg·K).

Table 12 Thermal Conductivity of Aqueous Solutions of Propylene Glycol

	Concentrations in Volume Percent Propylene Glycol								
Temperature, °C	10	20	30	40	50	60	70	80	90
−35						0.269	0.242	0.220	0.203
−30					0.302	0.272	0.245	0.222	0.204
−25					0.306	0.275	0.247	0.224	0.205
−20				0.346	0.311	0.278	0.250	0.226	0.206
−15				0.351	0.315	0.282	0.252	0.227	0.207
−10			0.397	0.356	0.319	0.285	0.254	0.229	0.208
−5		0.449	0.403	0.361	0.323	0.288	0.256	0.230	0.209
0	0.510	0.456	0.409	0.366	0.327	0.291	0.259	0.232	0.210
5	0.518	0.463	0.415	0.371	0.331	0.294	0.261	0.233	0.211
10	0.526	0.470	0.421	0.376	0.334	0.297	0.263	0.235	0.212
15	0.534	0.477	0.426	0.380	0.338	0.299	0.265	0.236	0.213
20	0.541	0.483	0.431	0.384	0.341	0.302	0.267	0.237	0.214
25	0.548	0.489	0.436	0.388	0.344	0.304	0.268	0.239	0.215
30	0.555	0.494	0.441	0.392	0.347	0.307	0.270	0.240	0.215
35	0.561	0.500	0.445	0.396	0.350	0.309	0.272	0.241	0.216
40	0.567	0.505	0.450	0.399	0.353	0.311	0.273	0.242	0.216
45	0.573	0.509	0.453	0.402	0.355	0.313	0.274	0.242	0.217
50	0.578	0.514	0.457	0.405	0.358	0.314	0.275	0.243	0.217
55	0.583	0.518	0.460	0.408	0.360	0.316	0.277	0.244	0.218
60	0.587	0.521	0.463	0.410	0.362	0.317	0.277	0.244	0.218
65	0.591	0.525	0.466	0.413	0.363	0.319	0.278	0.245	0.218
70	0.595	0.528	0.469	0.415	0.365	0.320	0.279	0.245	0.218
75	0.598	0.531	0.471	0.416	0.366	0.321	0.280	0.246	0.218
80	0.601	0.533	0.473	0.418	0.367	0.321	0.280	0.246	0.218
85	0.604	0.535	0.474	0.419	0.368	0.322	0.281	0.246	0.218
90	0.606	0.537	0.476	0.420	0.369	0.323	0.281	0.246	0.218
95	0.608	0.538	0.477	0.421	0.370	0.323	0.281	0.246	0.218
100	0.609	0.540	0.478	0.422	0.370	0.323	0.281	0.246	0.218
105	0.611	0.541	0.479	0.423	0.371	0.323	0.281	0.246	0.218
110	0.612	0.542	0.480	0.423	0.371	0.323	0.281	0.246	0.217
115	0.613	0.542	0.480	0.423	0.371	0.323	0.281	0.245	0.217
120	0.613	0.543	0.480	0.423	0.371	0.323	0.280	0.245	0.216

Source: Dow Chemical (2001a) *Note*: Thermal conductivity in W/(m·K).

Table 13 Viscosity of Aqueous Solutions of Propylene Glycol

	Concentrations in Volume Percent Propylene Glycol								
Temperature, °C	10	20	30	40	50	60	70	80	90
−35						524.01	916.18	1434.22	3813.29
−30					171.54	330.39	551.12	908.47	2071.34
−25					109.69	211.43	340.09	575.92	1176.09
−20				48.90	72.42	137.96	215.67	368.77	696.09
−15				33.07	49.29	92.00	140.62	239.86	428.19
−10			11.84	23.11	34.51	62.78	94.23	159.02	272.94
−5		4.98	9.07	16.63	24.81	43.84	64.83	107.64	179.78
0	2.68	4.05	7.07	12.30	18.28	31.32	45.74	74.45	122.03
5	2.23	3.34	5.61	9.32	13.77	22.87	33.04	52.63	85.15
10	1.89	2.79	4.52	7.21	10.59	17.05	24.41	37.99	60.93
15	1.63	2.36	3.69	5.70	8.30	12.96	18.41	28.00	44.62
20	1.42	2.02	3.06	4.59	6.62	10.04	14.15	21.04	33.38
25	1.25	1.74	2.57	3.75	5.36	7.91	11.08	16.10	25.45
30	1.11	1.52	2.19	3.12	4.41	6.34	8.81	12.55	19.76
35	0.99	1.34	1.88	2.62	3.68	5.15	7.12	9.94	15.60
40	0.89	1.18	1.63	2.24	3.10	4.25	5.84	7.99	12.49
45	0.81	1.06	1.43	1.93	2.65	3.55	4.85	6.52	10.15
50	0.73	0.95	1.26	1.68	2.28	3.00	4.08	5.39	8.35
55	0.67	0.86	1.13	1.48	1.99	2.57	3.46	4.51	6.95
60	0.62	0.78	1.01	1.31	1.75	2.22	2.98	3.82	5.85
65	0.57	0.71	0.92	1.18	1.55	1.93	2.58	3.28	4.97
70	0.53	0.66	0.83	1.06	1.38	1.70	2.26	2.83	4.26
75	0.49	0.60	0.76	0.96	1.24	1.51	1.99	2.47	3.69
80	0.46	0.56	0.70	0.88	1.12	1.35	1.77	2.18	3.22
85	0.43	0.52	0.65	0.81	1.02	1.22	1.59	1.94	2.83
90	0.40	0.49	0.60	0.75	0.93	1.10	1.43	1.73	2.50
95	0.38	0.45	0.56	0.69	0.86	1.01	1.30	1.56	2.23
100	0.35	0.43	0.53	0.65	0.79	0.92	1.18	1.42	2.00
105	0.33	0.40	0.50	0.60	0.74	0.85	1.08	1.29	1.80
110	0.32	0.38	0.47	0.57	0.69	0.79	1.00	1.19	1.63
115	0.30	0.36	0.45	0.54	0.64	0.74	0.93	1.09	1.48
120	0.28	0.34	0.42	0.51	0.60	0.69	0.86	1.02	1.35

Source: Dow Chemical (2001a) *Note*: Viscosity in mPa·s.

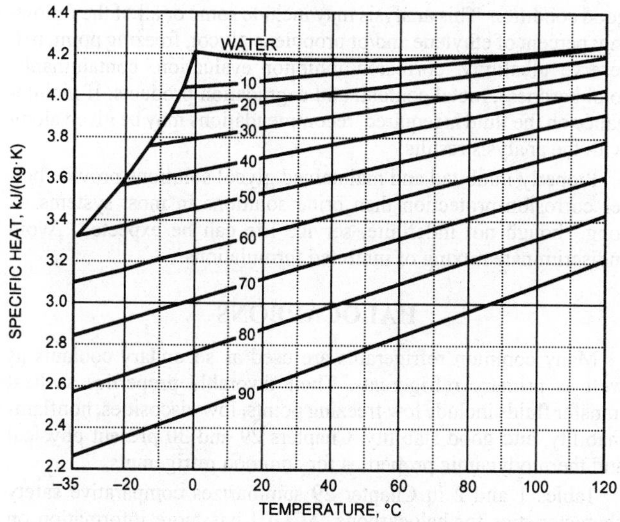

Fig. 14 Specific Heat of Aqueous Solutions of Industrially Inhibited Propylene Glycol (vol. %)
(Dow Chemical 2001b)

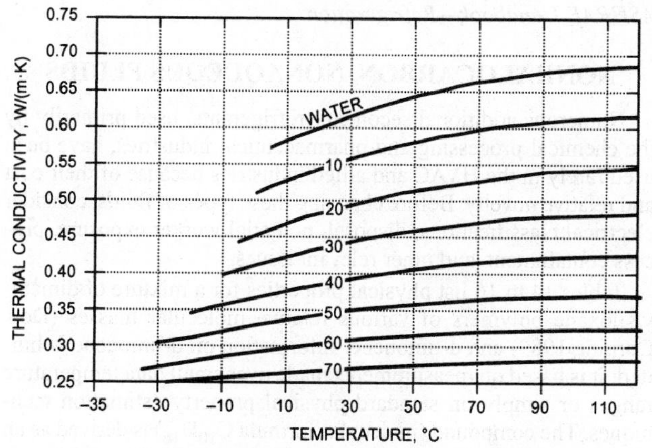

Fig. 15 Thermal Conductivity of Aqueous Solutions of Industrially Inhibited Propylene Glycol (vol. %)
(Dow Chemical 2001b)

concentrations allow the fluid to freeze. As the fluid freezes, it forms a slush that expands and flows into any available space. Therefore, expansion volume must be included with this type of protection. If the application requires that the fluid remain entirely liquid, use a concentration with a freezing point 3 K below the lowest expected temperature. Avoid excessive glycol concentration because it increases initial cost and adversely affects the fluid's physical properties.

Additional physical property data are available from suppliers of industrially inhibited ethylene and propylene glycol.

Corrosion Inhibition

Interestingly, ethylene glycol and propylene glycol, when not diluted with water, are actually less corrosive than water is with common construction metals. However, once diluted with water (as is typical), all aqueous glycol solutions are more corrosive than the water from which they are prepared. This is because uninhibited glycols oxidize with use to form acidic degradation products, and become increasingly more corrosive if not properly inhibited. The amount of oxidation is influenced by temperature, degree of aeration, and type of metal components to which the glycol solution is exposed. It is therefore necessary to use not only corrosion

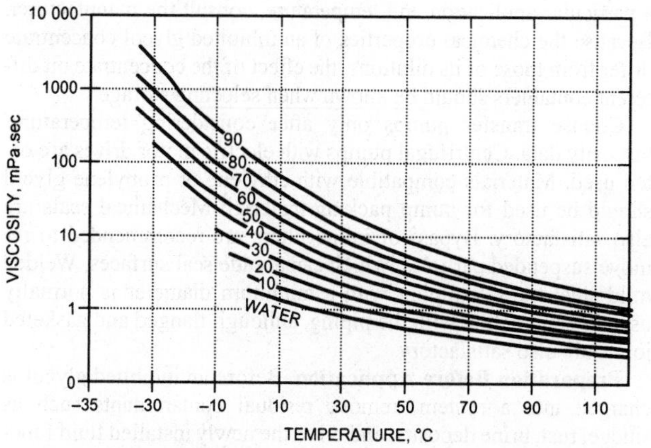

Fig. 16 Viscosity of Aqueous Solutions of Industrially Inhibited Propylene Glycol (vol. %)
(Dow Chemical 2001a)

inhibitors that are effective for water-based fluids, but also additional additives to buffer or neutralize the acidic glycol degradation products that form during use. Corrosion inhibitors form a surface barrier that protects metal from attack, but their effectiveness is highly dependent on solution pH. Failure to compensate for glycol degradation leads to a downward shift in solution pH, which negates the usefulness of the corrosion inhibitor at protecting iron-based alloys (particularly cast iron and carbon steels, but also solders). Properly inhibited glycol products are available from several suppliers.

Service Considerations

Design Considerations. Inhibited glycols can be used at temperatures as high as 175°C. However, maximum-use temperatures vary from fluid to fluid, so the manufacturer's suggested temperature-use ranges should be followed. In systems with a high degree of aeration, the bulk fluid temperature should not exceed 65°C; however, temperatures up to 175°C are permissible in a pressurized system if air intake is eliminated. Maximum film temperatures should not exceed 28 K above the bulk temperature. Nitrogen blanketing minimizes oxidation when the system operates at elevated temperatures for extended periods.

Minimum operating temperatures for a recirculating fluid are typically −29°C for ethylene glycol solutions and −18°C for propylene glycol solutions. Operation below these temperatures is generally impractical, because the fluids' viscosity builds dramatically, thus increasing pumping horsepower requirements and reducing heat transfer film coefficients.

Standard materials can be used with most inhibited glycol solutions, except galvanized metals, which form insoluble zinc salts with the corrosion inhibitors. This depletes corrosion inhibitors below effective limits, and can cause excessive insoluble salt (sludge) formation.

Because removal of sludge and other contaminants is critical, install suitable filters. If inhibitors are rapidly and completely adsorbed by such contamination, the fluid is ineffective for corrosion inhibition. Consider such adsorption when selecting filters.

Storage and Handling. Inhibited glycol concentrates are stable, relatively noncorrosive materials with high flash points. These fluids can be stored in mild steel, stainless steel, or aluminum vessels. However, aluminum should be used only when the fluid temperature is below 66°C. Corrosion in the vapor space of vessels may be a problem, because the fluid's inhibitor package cannot reach these surfaces to protect them. A protective coating may be necessary (e.g., novolac-based vinyl ester resins, high-bake phenolic resins, polypropylene, polyvinylidene fluoride). To ensure the coating is suitable for a particular application and temperature, consult the manufacturer. Because the chemical properties of an inhibited glycol concentrate differ from those of its dilutions, the effect of the concentrate on different containers should be known when selecting storage.

Choose transfer pumps only after considering temperature/viscosity data. Centrifugal pumps with electric motor drives are often used. Materials compatible with ethylene or propylene glycol should be used for pump packing material. Mechanical seals are also satisfactory. Bypass or inline filters are recommended to remove suspended particles, which can abrade seal surfaces. Welded mild steel transfer piping with a minimum diameter is normally used in conjunction with the piping, although flanged and gasketed joints are also satisfactory.

Preparation Before Application. Before an inhibited glycol is charged into a system, remove residual contaminants such as sludge, rust, brine deposits, and oil so the newly installed fluid functions properly. Avoid strong acid cleaners; if they are required, consider inhibited acids. Completely remove the cleaning agent before charging with inhibited glycol.

Dilution Water. Use distilled, deionized, or condensate water, because water from some sources contains elements that reduce the effectiveness of the inhibited formulation. If water of this quality is unavailable, water containing less than 25 mg/kg chloride, less than 25 mg/kg sulfate, and less than 100 mg/kg of total hardness may be used.

Fluid Maintenance. Glycol concentrations can be determined by refractive index, gas chromatography, or Karl Fischer analysis for water (assuming that the concentration of other fluid components, such as inhibitor, is known). Using density to determine glycol concentration is unsatisfactory because (1) density measurements are temperature-sensitive, (2) inhibitor concentrations can change density, (3) values for propylene glycol are close to those of water, and (4) propylene glycol values exhibit a maximum at 70 to 75% concentration.

An effective inhibitor monitoring and maintenance schedule is essential to keep a glycol solution relatively noncorrosive for a long period. Inspection immediately after installation, and annually thereafter, is normally an effective practice. Visual inspection of solution and filter residue can often detect potential system problems.

Many manufacturers of inhibited glycol-based heat transfer fluids provide analytical service to ensure that their product remains in good condition. This analysis may include some or all of the following: percent of ethylene and/or propylene glycol, freezing point, pH, reserve alkalinity, corrosion inhibitor evaluation, contaminants, total hardness, metal content, and degradation products. If maintenance on the fluid is required, recommendations may be given along with the analysis results.

Properly inhibited and maintained glycol solutions provide better corrosion protection than brine solutions in most systems. A long, though not indefinite, service life can be expected. Avoid indiscriminate mixing of inhibited formulations.

HALOCARBONS

Many common refrigerants are used as secondary coolants as well as primary refrigerants. Their favorable properties as heat transfer fluids include low freezing points, low viscosities, nonflammability, and good stability. Chapters 29 and 30 present physical and thermodynamic properties for common refrigerants.

Tables 1 and 2 in Chapter 29 summarizes comparative safety characteristics for halocarbons. ACGIH has more information on halocarbon toxicity threshold limit values and biological exposure indices (see the Bibliography).

Construction materials and stability factors in halocarbon use are discussed in Chapter 29 of this volume and Chapter 5 of the 2006 *ASHRAE Handbook—Refrigeration*.

NONHALOCARBON, NONAQUEOUS FLUIDS

Numerous additional secondary refrigerants, used primarily by the chemical processing and pharmaceutical industries, have been used rarely in the HVAC and allied industries because of their cost and relative novelty. Before choosing these types of fluids, consider electrical classifications, disposal, potential worker exposure, process containment, and other relevant issues.

Tables 14 to 16 list physical properties for a mixture of dimethylsiloxane polymers of various relative molecular masses (Dow Corning 1989) and d-limonene. Information on d-limonene is limited; it is based on measurements made over small data temperature ranges or simply on standard physical property estimation techniques. The compound (molecular formula $C_{10}H_{16}$) is derived as an extract from orange and lemon oils.

Table 14 Properties of a Polydimethylsiloxane Heat Transfer Fluid

Temperature, °C	Vapor Pressure, kPa	Viscosity, mPa·s	Density, kg/m³	Heat Capacity, kJ/(kg·K)	Thermal Conductivity, W/(m·K)
–73	0.00	12.4	924.6	1.410	0.1294
–70	0.00	11.2	922.1	1.418	0.1288
–60	0.00	8.26	913.5	1.443	0.1269
–50	0.00	6.24	905.0	1.469	0.1251
–40	0.00	4.83	896.4	1.495	0.1231
–30	0.00	3.81	887.9	1.520	0.1212
–20	0.00	3.07	879.3	1.546	0.1192
–10	0.01	2.51	870.7	1.572	0.1171
0	0.03	2.09	862.0	1.597	0.1150
10	0.08	1.76	853.3	1.623	0.1129
20	0.16	1.49	844.5	1.649	0.1108
30	0.32	1.29	835.5	1.674	0.1086
40	0.61	1.12	826.5	1.700	0.1064
50	1.09	0.98	817.3	1.726	0.1042
60	1.85	0.86	807.9	1.751	0.1019
70	3.02	0.77	798.4	1.777	0.0996
80	4.76	0.69	788.7	1.803	0.0973
90	7.25	0.62	778.8	1.828	0.0949
100	10.73	0.56	768.7	1.854	0.0925
110	15.45	0.51	758.3	1.880	0.0901
120	21.75	0.47	747.7	1.905	0.0877
130	29.95	0.43	736.8	1.931	0.0852
140	40.45	0.40	725.6	1.957	0.0827
150	53.67	0.37	714.1	1.982	0.0802
160	70.06	0.34	702.3	2.008	0.0777
170	90.10	0.32	690.2	2.033	0.0751
180	114.29	0.30	677.7	2.059	0.0725
190	143.17	0.28	664.8	2.085	0.0699
200	177.27	0.26	651.6	2.110	0.0673
210	217.14	0.25	638.0	2.136	0.0646
220	263.36	0.24	623.9	2.162	0.0620
230	316.47	0.22	609.5	2.187	0.0593
240	377.03	0.21	594.5	2.213	0.0566
250	445.61	0.20	579.1	2.239	0.0538
260	522.74	0.19	563.3	2.264	0.0511

Source: Dow Chemical (1998)

Table 15 Summary of Physical Properties of Polydimethylsiloxane Mixture and d-Limonene

	Polydimethylsiloxane Mixture	d-Limonene
Flash point, °C, closed cup	46.7	46.1
Boiling point, °C	175	154.4
Freezing point, °C	–111.1	–96.7
Operational temperature range, °C	–73.3 to 260	None published

Source: Dow Corning (1989).

Table 16 Physical Properties of d-Limonene

Temperature, °C	Specific Heat, kJ/(kg·K)	Viscosity, mPa·s	Density, kg/m³	Thermal Conductivity, W/(m·K)
–73	1.27	3.8	914.3	0.137
–50	1.39	3.0	897.1	0.133
–25	1.51	2.3	878.3	0.128
0	1.65	1.8	859.2	0.124
25	1.78	1.4	839.8	0.119
50	1.91	1.1	820.1	0.114
75	2.04	0.8	800.0	0.110
100	2.17	0.7	779.5	0.105
125	2.30	0.5	758.4	0.100
150	2.41	0.4	736.6	0.096

Source: Dow Corning (1989)
Note: Properties are estimated or based on incomplete data.

The mixture of dimethylsiloxane polymers can be used with most standard construction materials; d-limonene, however, can be quite corrosive, easily autooxidizing at ambient temperatures. This fact should be understood and considered before using d-limonene in a system.

REFERENCES

Carrier Air Conditioning Company. 1959. Basic data, Section 17M. Syracuse, NY.

CCI. 1953. Calcium chloride for refrigeration brine. *Manual* RM-1. Calcium Chloride Institute.

Dow Chemical. 1998. *Syltherm XLT heat transfer fluid*. Midland, MI.

Dow Chemical USA. 2001a. *Engineering and operating guideline for DOWFROST and DOWFROST HD inhibited propylene glycol heat transfer fluids*. Midland, MI.

Dow Chemical USA. 2001b. *Engineering manual for DOWTHERM SR-1 and DOWTHERM 4000 inhibited ethylene glycol heat transfer fluids*. Midland, MI.

Dow Corning USA. 1989. *Syltherm heat transfer liquids*. Midland, MI.

Melinder, Å. 2007. *Thermo-physical properties of aqueous solutions used as secondary working fluids*. Ph.D. dissertation, Department of Energy Technology, Kungliga Tekniska Högskolan, Stockholm. Available from http://urn.kb.se/resolve?urn=urn:nbn:se:kth:diva-4406.

BIBLIOGRAPHY

ACGIH. Annually. *TLVs® and BEIs®*. American Conference of Governmental Industrial Hygienists, Cincinnati.

ASM. 2000. *Corrosion: Understanding the basics*. J.R. Davis, ed. ASM International, Materials Park, OH.

Born, D.W. 1989. *Inhibited glycols for corrosion and freeze protection in water-based heating and cooling systems*. Midland, MI.

Fontana, M.G. 1986. *Corrosion engineering*. McGraw-Hill, New York.

NACE. 1973. *Corrosion inhibitors*. C.C. Nathan, ed. National Association of Corrosion Engineers, Houston.

NACE. 2002. *NACE corrosion engineer's reference book*, 3rd ed. R. Baboian, ed. National Association of Corrosion Engineers, Houston.

CHAPTER 32

SORBENTS AND DESICCANTS

SORPTION refers to the binding of one substance to another. **Sorbents** are materials that have an ability to attract and hold other gases or liquids. They can be used to attract gases or liquids other than water vapor, which makes them very useful in chemical separation processes. **Desiccants** are a subset of sorbents; they have a particular affinity for water.

Virtually all materials are desiccants; that is, they attract and hold water vapor. Wood, natural fibers, clays, and many synthetic materials attract and release moisture as commercial desiccants do, but they lack holding capacity. For example, woolen carpet fibers attract up to 23% of their dry mass in water vapor, and nylon can take up almost 6% of its mass in water. In contrast, a commercial desiccant takes up between 10 and 1100% of its dry mass in water vapor, depending on its type and on the moisture available in the environment. Furthermore, commercial desiccants continue to attract moisture even when the surrounding air is quite dry, a characteristic that other materials do not share.

All desiccants behave in a similar way: they attract moisture until they reach equilibrium with the surrounding air. Moisture is usually removed from the desiccant by heating it to temperatures between 50 and 260°C and exposing it to a scavenger airstream. After the desiccant dries, it must be cooled so that it can attract moisture once again. Sorption always generates sensible heat equal to the latent heat of the water vapor taken up by the desiccant plus an additional heat of sorption that varies between 5 and 25% of the latent heat of the water vapor. This heat is transferred to the desiccant and to the surrounding air.

The process of attracting and holding moisture is described as either adsorption or absorption, depending on whether the desiccant undergoes a chemical change as it takes on moisture. **Adsorption** does not change the desiccant, except by addition of the mass of water vapor; it is similar in some ways to a sponge soaking up water. **Absorption**, on the other hand, changes the desiccant. An example of an absorbent is table salt, which changes from a solid to a liquid as it absorbs moisture.

DESICCANT APPLICATIONS

Desiccants can dry either liquids or gases, including ambient air, and are used in many air-conditioning applications, particularly when the

- Latent load is large in comparison to the sensible load
- Energy cost to regenerate the desiccant is low compared to the cost of energy to dehumidify the air by chilling it below its dew point and reheating it
- Moisture control level for the space would require chilling the air to subfreezing dew points if compression refrigeration alone were used to dehumidify the air
- Temperature control level for the space or process requires continuous delivery of air at subfreezing temperatures

In any of these situations, the cost of running a vapor compression cooling system can be very high. A desiccant process may offer considerable advantages in energy, initial cost of equipment, and maintenance.

Because desiccants can attract and hold more than simply water vapor, they can remove contaminants from airstreams to improve indoor air quality. Desiccants have been used to remove organic vapors and, in special circumstances, to control microbiological contaminants (Battelle 1971; Buffalo Testing Laboratory 1974). Hines et al. (1991) also confirmed their usefulness in removing vapors that can degrade indoor air quality. Desiccant materials can adsorb hydrocarbon vapors while they are collecting moisture from air. These cosorption phenomena show promise of improving indoor air quality in typical building HVAC systems.

Desiccants are also used in drying compressed air to low dew points. In this application, moisture can be removed from the desiccant without heat. Desorption is accomplished using differences in vapor pressures compared to the total pressures of the compressed and ambient pressure airstreams.

Finally, desiccants are used to dry the refrigerant circulating in air-conditioning and refrigeration systems. This reduces corrosion in refrigerant piping and prevents valves and capillaries from becoming clogged with ice crystals. In this application, the desiccant is not regenerated; it is discarded when it has adsorbed its limit of water vapor.

This chapter discusses the water sorption characteristics of desiccant materials and explains some of the implications of those characteristics in ambient pressure air-conditioning applications. Information on other applications for desiccants can be found in Chapter 36 of this volume; Chapters 6, 26, 35, 41, and 45 of the 2006 *ASHRAE Handbook—Refrigeration*; Chapters 1, 2, 5, 9, 16, 18, 21, 28, and 45 of the 2007 *ASHRAE Handbook—HVAC Applications*; and Chapters 23 and 25 of the 2008 *ASHRAE Handbook—HVAC Systems and Equipment.*

DESICCANT CYCLE

Practically speaking, all desiccants function by the same way: by moisture transfer caused by a difference between water vapor pressures at their surface and of the surrounding air. When the vapor pressure at the desiccant surface is lower than that of the air, the desiccant attracts moisture. When the surface vapor pressure is higher than that of the surrounding air, the desiccant releases moisture.

Figure 1 shows the moisture content relationship between a desiccant and its surface vapor pressure. As the moisture content of the desiccant rises, so does the water vapor pressure at its surface. At some point, the vapor pressure at the desiccant surface is the same as that of the air: the two are in equilibrium. Then, moisture cannot move in either direction until some external force changes the vapor pressure at the desiccant or in the air.

The preparation of this chapter is assigned to TC 8.12, Desiccant Dehumidification Equipment and Components.

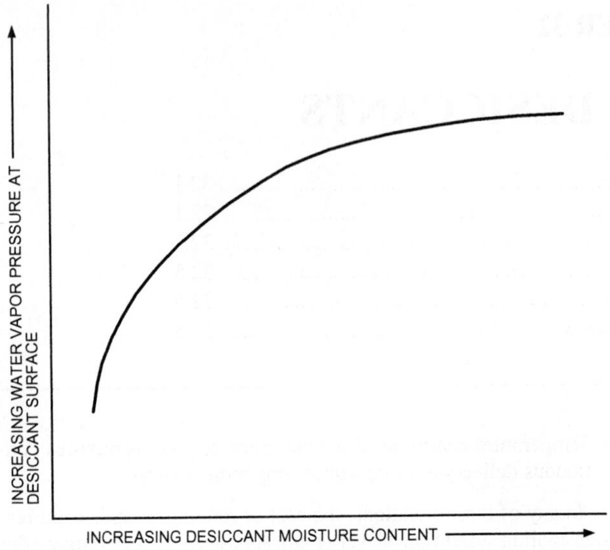

Fig. 1 Desiccant Water Vapor Pressure as Function of Moisture Content
(Harriman 2003)

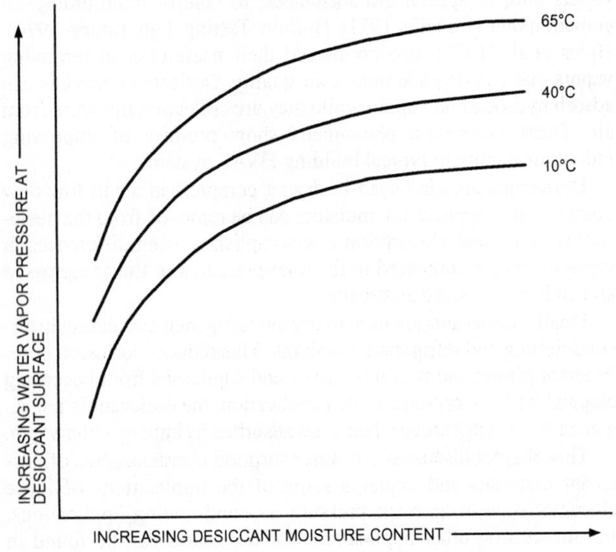

Fig. 2 Desiccant Water Vapor Pressure as Function of Desiccant Moisture Content and Temperature
(Harriman 2003)

Figure 2 shows the effect of temperature on vapor pressure at the desiccant surface. Both higher temperature and increased moisture content increase surface vapor pressure. When surface vapor pressure exceeds that of the surrounding air, moisture leaves the desiccant (**reactivation** or **regeneration**). After the desiccant is dried (reactivated) by the heat, its vapor pressure remains high, so it has very little ability to absorb moisture. **Cooling** the desiccant reduces its surface vapor pressure so that it can absorb moisture again. The complete cycle is illustrated in Figure 3.

The economics of desiccant operation depend on the energy cost of moving a given material through this cycle. Dehumidification of air (loading the desiccant with water vapor) generally proceeds without energy input other than fan and pump costs. The major portion of energy is invested in regenerating the desiccant (moving from point 2 to point 3) and cooling the desiccant (point 3 to point 1).

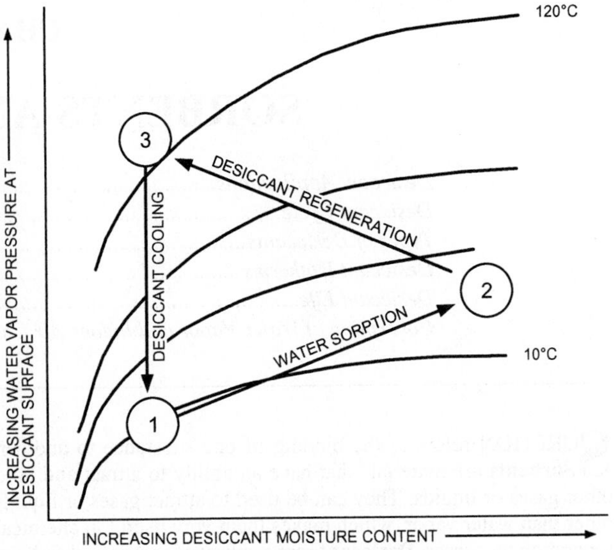

Fig. 3 Desiccant Cycle
(Harriman 2003)

Table 1 Vapor Pressures of Different Relative Humidities at 21°C

Relative Humidity at 21°C, %	Dew Point, °C	Vapor Pressure, kPa
10	−12.4	0.23
20	−3.6	0.47
30	1.9	0.70
40	6.0	0.94
50	9.3	1.17
60	12.0	1.40
70	14.4	1.64
80	16.5	1.87
90	18.3	2.11
100	20.0	2.34

Regeneration energy is equal to the sum of the heat

- Necessary to raise the desiccant to a temperature high enough to make its surface vapor pressure higher than that of the surrounding air
- Necessary to vaporize the moisture it contains (about 2465 kJ/kg)
- From desorption of water from the desiccant (a small amount)

The **cooling energy** is proportional to the (1) desiccant mass and (2) difference between its temperature after regeneration and the lower temperature that allows the desiccant to remove water from the airstream again.

The cycle is similar when desiccants are regenerated using pressure differences in a compressed air application. The desiccant is saturated in a high-pressure chamber (i.e., that of the compressed air). Then valves open, isolating the compressed air from the material, and the desiccant is exposed to air at ambient pressure. The saturated desiccant's vapor pressure is much higher than ambient air at normal pressures; thus, moisture leaves the desiccant for the surrounding air. An alternative desorption strategy returns a small portion of dried air to the moist desiccant bed to reabsorb moisture, then vents that moist air to the atmosphere.

Table 1 shows the range of vapor pressures over which the desiccant must operate in space-conditioning applications. It converts the relative humidity at 21°C to dew point and the corresponding vapor pressure. The greater the difference between the air and desiccant surface vapor pressures, the greater the ability of the material to absorb moisture from the air at that moisture content.

The ideal desiccant for a particular application depends on the range of water vapor pressures likely to occur in the air, temperature of the regeneration heat source, and moisture sorption and desorption characteristics of the desiccant within those constraints. In commercial practice, however, most desiccants can be made to perform well in a wide variety of operating situations through careful engineering of the mechanical aspects of the dehumidification system. Some of these hardware issues are discussed in Chapter 23 of the 2008 *ASHRAE Handbook—HVAC Systems and Equipment.*

TYPES OF DESICCANTS

Desiccants can be liquids or solids and can hold moisture through absorption or adsorption, as described earlier. Most absorbents are liquids, and most adsorbents are solids.

Liquid Absorbents

Liquid absorption dehumidification can best be illustrated by comparison to air washer operation. When air passes through an air washer, its dew point approaches the temperature of the water supplied to the machine. Air that is more humid is dehumidified, and air that is less humid is humidified. In a similar manner, a liquid absorption dehumidifier brings air into contact with a liquid desiccant solution. The liquid's vapor pressure is lower than water at the same temperature, and air passing over the solution approaches this reduced vapor pressure; it is dehumidified.

The vapor pressure of a liquid absorption solution is directly proportional to its temperature and inversely proportional to its concentration. Figure 4 illustrates the effect of increasing desiccant concentration on the water vapor pressure at its surface. The figure shows the vapor pressure of various solutions of water and triethylene glycol, a commercial liquid desiccant. As the mixture's glycol content increases, its vapor pressure decreases. This lower pressure allows the glycol solution to absorb moisture from the air whenever the air's vapor pressure is greater than that of the solution.

Viewed another way, the vapor pressure of a given concentration of absorbent solution approximates the vapor pressure values of a fixed relative humidity line on a psychrometric chart. Higher solution concentrations give lower equilibrium relative humidities, which allow the absorbent to dry air to lower levels.

Figure 5 illustrates the effect of temperature on the vapor pressure of various solutions of water and lithium chloride (LiCl), another common liquid desiccant. A solution that is 25% lithium chloride has a vapor pressure of 1.25 kPa at a temperature of 21°C. If the same 25% solution is heated to 37.8°C, its vapor pressure more than doubles to 3.3 kPa. Expressed another way, the 21°C, 25% solution is in equilibrium with air at a 10.5°C dew point. The same 25% solution at 37.8°C is at equilibrium with an airstream at a 26°C dew point. The warmer the desiccant, the less moisture it can attract from the air.

In standard practice, behavior of a liquid desiccant is controlled by adjusting its temperature, concentration, or both. Desiccant temperature is controlled by simple heaters and coolers. Concentration is controlled by heating the desiccant to drive moisture out into a waste airstream or directly to the ambient.

Commercially available liquid desiccants have an especially high water-holding capacity. Each molecule of LiCl, for example, can hold two water molecules, even in the dry state. Above two water molecules per molecule of LiCl, the desiccant becomes a liquid and continues to absorb water. If the solution is in equilibrium with air at 90% rh, approximately 26 water molecules are attached to each molecule of LiCl. This represents a water absorption of more than 1000% on a dry-mass basis.

As a practical matter, however, the absorption process is limited by the exposed surface area of desiccant and by the contact time allowed for reaction. More surface area and more contact time allow the desiccant to approach its theoretical capacity. Commercial desiccant systems stretch these limits by flowing liquid desiccant onto an extended surface, much like in a cooling tower.

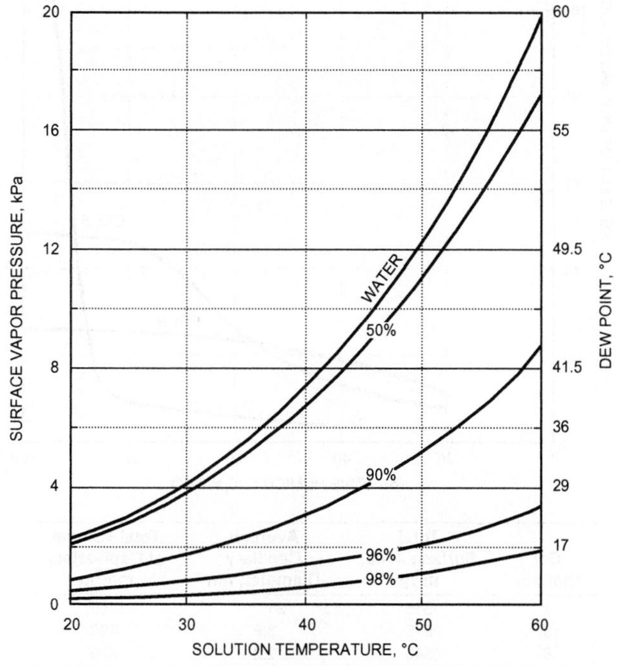

Fig. 4 Surface Vapor Pressure of Water/Triethylene Glycol Solutions
(from data of Dow 1981)

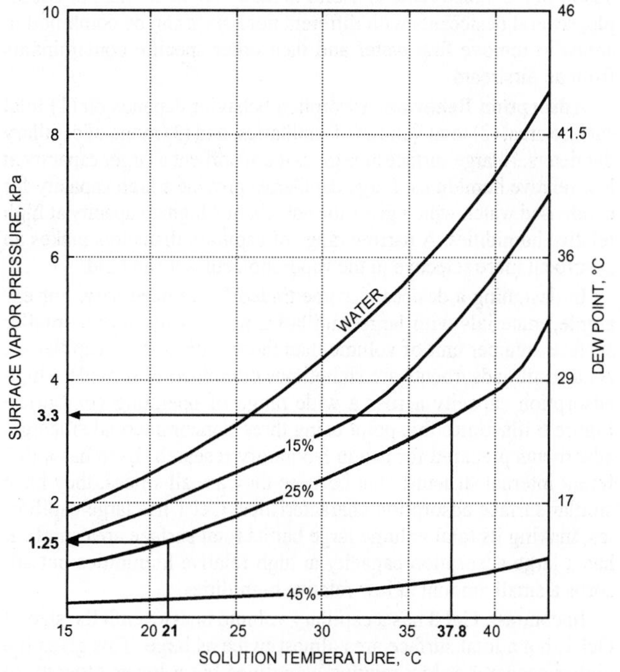

Fig. 5 Surface Vapor Pressure of Water/Lithium Chloride Solutions
(from data of Foote Mineral 1988)

Solid Adsorbents

Adsorbents are solid materials with a tremendous internal surface area per unit of mass; a single gram can have more than 4600 m^2 of surface area. Structurally, adsorbents resemble a rigid sponge, and the surface of the sponge in turn resembles the ocean coastline of a fjord. This analogy indicates the scale of the different surfaces in an adsorbent. The fjords can be compared to the **capillaries** in the adsorbent. The spaces between the grains of sand on the fjord beaches can be compared to the spaces between the individual molecules of adsorbent, all of which have the capacity to hold water molecules. The bulk of the adsorbed water is contained by condensation into the capillaries, and the majority of the surface area that attracts individual water molecules is in the crystalline structure of the material itself.

Adsorbents attract moisture because of the electrical field at the desiccant surface. The field is not uniform in either force or charge, so specific sites on the desiccant surface attract water molecules that have a net opposite charge. When the complete surface is covered, the adsorbent can hold still more moisture because vapor condenses into the first water layer and fills the capillaries throughout the material. As with liquid absorbents, the ability of an adsorbent to attract moisture depends on the difference in vapor pressure between its surface and the air.

The capacity of solid adsorbents is generally less than the capacity of liquid absorbents. For example, a typical molecular sieve adsorbent can hold 17% of its dry mass in water when the air is at 21 °C and 20% rh. In contrast, LiCl can hold 130% of its mass at the same temperature and relative humidity. But solid adsorbents have several other favorable characteristics.

For example, molecular sieves continue to adsorb moisture even when they are quite hot, allowing dehumidification of very warm airstreams. Also, several solid adsorbents can be manufactured to precise tolerances, with pore diameters that can be closely controlled. This means they can be tailored to adsorb molecules of a specific diameter. Water, for example, has an effective molecular diameter of 0.32 nm. A molecular sieve adsorbent with an average pore diameter of 0.40 nm adsorbs water but has almost no capacity for larger molecules, such as organic solvents. This selective adsorption characteristic is useful in many applications. For example, several desiccants with different pore sizes can be combined in series to remove first water and then other specific contaminants from an airstream.

Adsorption Behavior. Adsorption behavior depends on (1) total surface area, (2) total volume of capillaries, and (3) range of capillary diameters. A large surface area gives the adsorbent a larger capacity at low relative humidities. Large capillaries provide a high capacity for condensed water, which gives the adsorbent a higher capacity at high relative humidities. A narrow range of capillary diameters makes an adsorbent more selective in the vapor molecules it can hold.

In designing a desiccant, some tradeoffs are necessary. For example, materials with large capillaries necessarily have a smaller surface area per unit of volume than those with smaller capillaries. As a result, adsorbents are sometimes combined to provide a high adsorption capacity across a wide range of operating conditions. Figure 6 illustrates this point using three noncommercial silica gel adsorbents prepared for use in laboratory research. Each has a different internal structure, but because they are all silicas, they have similar surface adsorption characteristics. Gel 1 has large capillaries, making its total volume large but its total surface area small. It has a large adsorption capacity at high relative humidities but adsorbs a small amount at low relative humidities.

In contrast, Gel 8 has a capillary volume one-seventh the size of Gel 1, but a total surface area almost twice as large. This gives it a higher capacity at low relative humidities but a lower capacity to hold the moisture that condenses at high relative humidities.

Silica gels and most other adsorbents can be manufactured to provide optimum performance in a specific application, balancing capacity against strength, mass, and other favorable characteristics (Bry-Air 1986).

Types of Solid Adsorbents. General classes of solid adsorbents include

- Silica gels
- Zeolites
- Synthetic zeolites (molecular sieves)
- Activated aluminas
- Carbons
- Synthetic polymers

Silica gels are amorphous solid structures formed by condensing soluble silicates from solutions of water or other solvents. Advantages include relatively low cost and relative simplicity of structural customizing. They are available as large as spherical beads about 5 mm in diameter or as small as grains of a fine powder.

Zeolites are aluminosilicate minerals. They occur in nature and are mined rather than synthesized. Zeolites have a very open crystalline lattice that allows molecules like water vapor to be held inside the crystal itself like an object in a cage. Particular atoms of an aluminosilicate determine the size of the openings between the "bars" of the cage, which in turn governs the maximum size of the molecule that can be adsorbed into the structure.

Synthetic zeolites, also called **molecular sieves**, are crystalline aluminosilicates manufactured in a thermal process. Controlling the process temperature and the composition of the ingredient materials allows close control of the structure and surface characteristics of

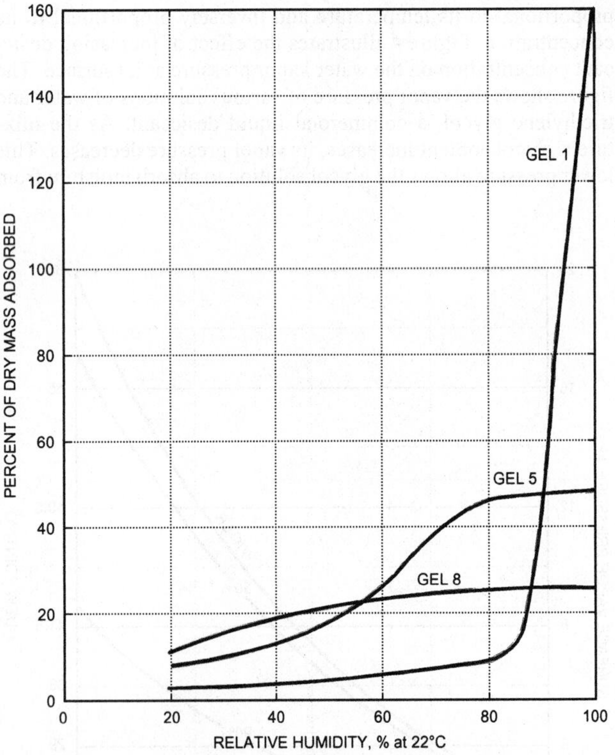

Gel Number	Total Surface Area, m^2/g	Average Capillary Diameter, nm	Total Volume of Capillaries, mm^3/g
1	315	21	1700
5	575	3.8	490
8	540	2.2	250

Fig. 6 Adsorption and Structural Characteristics of Some Experimental Silica Gels
(from data of Oscic and Cooper 1982)

the adsorbent. At a somewhat higher cost, this provides a much more uniform product than naturally occurring zeolites.

Activated aluminas are oxides and hydrides of aluminum that are manufactured in thermal processes. Their structural characteristics can be controlled by the gases used to produce them and by the temperature and duration of the thermal process.

Carbons are most frequently used for adsorption of gases other than water vapor because they have a greater affinity for the nonpolar molecules typical of organic solvents. Like other adsorbents, carbons have a large internal surface and especially large capillaries. This capillary volume gives them a high capacity to adsorb water vapor at relative humidities of 45 to 100%.

Synthetic polymers have potential for use as desiccants as well. Long molecules, like those found in polystyrenesulfonic acid sodium salt (PSSASS), are twisted together like strands of string. Each of the many sodium ions in the long PSSASS molecules has the potential to bind several water molecules, and the spaces between the packed strings can also contain condensed water, giving the polymer a capacity exceeding that of many other solid adsorbents.

DESICCANT ISOTHERMS

Figure 7 shows a rough comparison of the sorption characteristics of different desiccants. Large variations from these isotherms occur because manufacturers use different methods to optimize materials for different applications. The suitability of a given desiccant to a particular application is generally governed as much by the engineering of the mechanical system that presents the material to the airstreams as by the characteristics of the material itself.

Several sources give details of desiccant equipment design and information about desiccant isotherm characteristics. Brunauer (1945) considers five basic isotherm shape types. Each isotherm shape is determined by the dominant sorption mechanisms of the desiccant, which give rise to its specific capacity characteristics at different vapor pressures. Isotherm shape can be important in designing the optimum desiccant for applications where a narrow range of operating conditions can be expected. Collier (1986, 1988) illustrates how an optimum isotherm shape can be used to ensure a maximum coefficient of performance in one particular air-conditioning desiccant application.

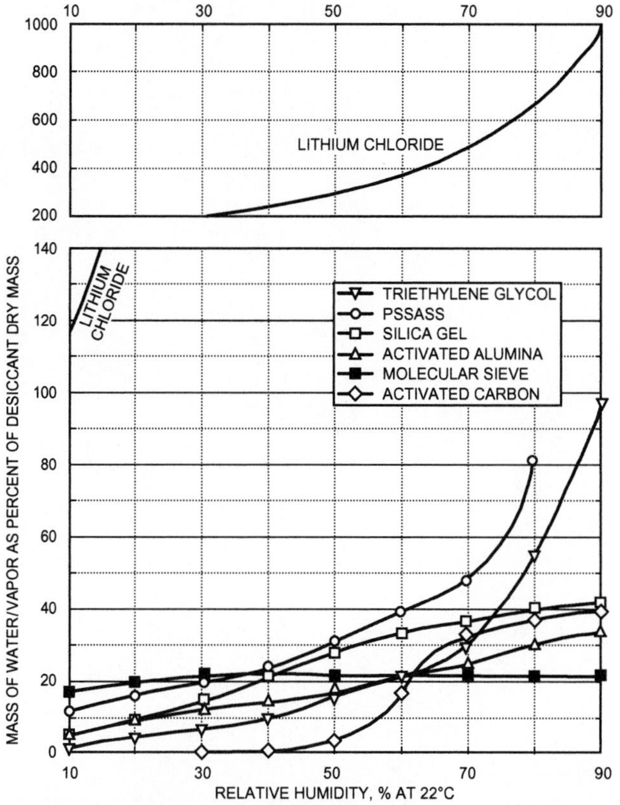

Sources for isotherms presented in the figure include
PSSASS: Czanderna (1988)
Lithium chloride: Munters Corporation: Cargocaire Division and Kathabar, Inc.
Triethylene glycol: Dow Chemical Corporation
Silica gel: Davison Chemical Division of W.R. Grace Co.
Activated carbon: Calgon Corporation
Activated alumina: LaRoche Industries Inc.
Molecular sieve: Davison Chemical Division of W.R. Grace Co.

Fig. 7 Sorption Isotherms of Various Desiccants

DESICCANT LIFE

The useful life of desiccant materials depends largely on the quantity and type of contamination in the airstreams they dry. In commercial equipment, desiccants last from 10 000 to 100 000 h or longer before they need replacement. Normally, two mechanisms cause the loss of desiccant capacity: (1) change in desiccant sorption characteristics through **chemical reactions** with contaminants and (2) loss of effective surface area through clogging or **hydrothermal degradation.**

Liquid absorbents are more susceptible to chemical reaction with airstream contaminants other than water vapor than are solid adsorbents. For example, certain sulfur compounds can react with LiCl to form lithium sulfate, which is not a desiccant. If the concentration of sulfur compounds in the airstream were below 10 mg/kg and the desiccant were in use 24 h a day, capacity reduction would be approximately 10 to 20% after three years of operation. If the concentration were 30 mg/kg, this reduction would occur after one year. In contaminated environments, equipment manufacturers often arrange filters to remove these products of reaction, and provide devices to replenish desiccant so that capacity stays constant.

Solid adsorbents tend to be less chemically reactive and more sensitive to clogging, a function of the type and quantity of particulate material in the airstream. Also, certain types of silica gel can be sensitive to saturated airstreams or to liquid moisture carried over from cooling coils into the desiccant bed. In more challenging applications, thermally stabilized desiccants are used in place of less durable materials.

In air-conditioning applications, desiccant equipment is designed to minimize the need for desiccant replacement in much the same way that vapor compression cooling systems are designed to avoid the need for compressor replacement. Unlike filters, desiccants are seldom intended to be frequently replaced during normal service in an air-drying application.

COSORPTION OF WATER VAPOR AND INDOOR AIR CONTAMINANTS

Hines et al. (1991) confirmed that many desiccant materials can collect common indoor pollutants while they collect water vapor from ambient air. This characteristic promises to become useful in future air-conditioning systems where indoor air quality is especially important.

The behavior of different desiccant and vapor mixtures is complex, but in general, pollutant sorption reactions can be classified into five categories:

- Humidity-neutral sorption
- Humidity-reduced sorption
- Humidity-enhanced sorption
- Humidity-pollutant displacement
- Desiccant-catalyzed pollutant conversion

Humidity-reduced sorption is illustrated by the behavior of water vapor and chloroform on activated carbon. Sorption is humidity-neutral until relative humidity exceeds 45%, when the uptake of chloroform is reduced. The adsorbed water blocks sites that would otherwise attract and hold chloroform. In contrast, water and carbonyl chloride mixtures on activated carbon demonstrate humidity-enhanced sorption (i.e., sorption of the pollutant increases at high relative humidities). Hines et al. (1991) attribute this phenomenon to the high water solubility of carbonyl chloride.

REFERENCES

Battelle. 1971. Project No. N-0914-5200-1971. Battelle Memorial Institute, Columbus, OH.

Brunauer, S. 1945. *The adsorption of gases and vapors*, vol. I. Princeton University Press, Princeton, NJ. Quoted and expanded in *The physical chemistry of surfaces*, by Arthur W. Adamson. John Wiley & Sons, New York, 1982.

Bry-Air. 1986. *MVB series engineering data*. Bry-Air Inc., Sunbury, OH.

Buffalo Testing Laboratory. 1974. *Report* No. 65711-1974.

Collier, R.K. 1986, 1988. Advanced desiccant materials assessment. *Research Report* 5084-243-1089. Phase I-1986, Phase II-1988. Gas Research Institute, Chicago.

Czanderna, A.W. 1988. Polymers as advanced materials for desiccant applications. *Research Report* NREL/PR-255-3308. National Renewable Energy Laboratory, Golden, CO.

Dow. 1981. *Guide to glycols*. Dow Chemical Corporation, Organic Chemicals Division, Midland, MI.

Foote Mineral. 1988. Lithium chloride technical data. *Bulletin* 151. Foote Mineral Corporation, Exton, PA.

Harriman, L.G., III. 2003. *The dehumidification handbook*, 2nd ed. Munters Corporation, Amesbury, MA.

Hines, A.J., T.K. Ghosh, S.K. Loyalka, and R.C. Warder, Jr. 1991. Investigation of co-sorption of gases and vapors as a means to enhance indoor air quality. ASHRAE *Research Project* 475-RP and Gas Research Institute *Project* GRI-90/0194. Gas Research Institute, Chicago.

Oscic, J. and I.L. Cooper. 1982. *Adsorption*. John Wiley & Sons, New York.

BIBLIOGRAPHY

Adamson, A.W. 1982. *The physical chemistry of surfaces*. John Wiley & Sons, New York.

Falcone, J.S., Jr., ed. 1982. Soluble silicates. *Symposium Series* 194. American Chemical Society, Washington, D.C.

Ruthven, D.M. 1984. *Principles of adsorption and adsorption processes*. John Wiley & Sons, New York.

SUNY Buffalo School of Medicine. Effects of glycol solution on microbiological growth. Niagrara Blower *Report* No. 03188.

Valenzuela, D. and A. Myers. 1989. *Adsorption equilibrium data handbook*. Simon & Schuster/Prentice-Hall, Englewood Cliffs, NJ.

CHAPTER 33

PHYSICAL PROPERTIES OF MATERIALS

VALUES in the following tables are in consistent units to assist the engineer looking for approximate values. For data on refrigerants, see Chapter 29; for secondary coolants, see Chapter 31. Chapter 26 gives more information on the values for materials used in building construction and insulation. Many properties vary with temperature, material density, and composition. The references document the source of the values and provide more detail or values for materials not listed here. The preparation of this chapter is assigned to TC 1.3, Heat Transfer and Fluid Flow.

Table 1 Properties of Vapor

Material	Relative Molecular Mass	Normal Boiling Point, °C	Critical Temperature, °C	Critical Pressure, kPa	Density, kg/m³	Specific Heat, J/(kg·K)	Thermal Conductivity, W/(m·K)	Viscosity, μPa·s
Alcohol, Ethyl	46.07[a]	78.6[a]	243.2[b]	6 394[b]		1520[j]	0.013[a]	14.2[j] (289)
Alcohol, Methyl	32.04[a]	65.0[a]	240.1[b]	7 977[b]		1350[j]	0.0301[r]	14.8[j] (272)
Ammonia	17.03[a]	–33.2[a]	132.6[b]	11 300[b]	7.72[b]	2200[aa]	0.0221[b]	9.30[aa]
Argon	39.948[a]	–185.9*	–122.5*	4 860[b]	1.785[b]	523[c]	0.016[a]	21.0[a]
Acetylene	26.04[a]	–83.7[a]	36.1[b]	6 280[b]	1.17[b]	1580[a]	0.0187[b]	9.34[a]
Benzene	78.11[a]	80.2[a]	289.6[d]	4 924[d]	2.68[e] (80)	1300[e] (80)	0.0071[e]	7.0[a]
Bromine	159.82[a]	58.8[a]	58.8[d]	10 340[d]	6.1[f] (59)	230[f] (100)	0.0061[a]	17[a]
Butane	58.12[a]	–0.5[a]	152.1[d]	3 797[d]	2.69[g]	1580[aa]	0.014[a]	7.0[a]
Carbon dioxide	44.01[a]	–78.5[a]	31.1[d]	7 384[d]	1.97[g]	840[g]	0.015[a]	14[h]
Carbon disulfide	76.13[h]	46.3[h]	278.9[h]	7 212[h]		599.0[p] (27)		
Carbon monoxide	28.01[a]	–191.5[a]	–140.3[d]	3 500[d]	1.25[d]	1100[f]	0.0230[a]	17[a]
Carbon tetrachloride	153.84[g]	76.6[h]	283.3[h]	4 560[h]		862[q] (27)		16.0[j]
Chlorine	70.91[a]	–34.7[a]	144.1[d]	7 710[d]	3.22[d]	490[a]	0.0080[a]	12[a]
Chloroform	119.39[h]	61.8[h]	263.4[h]	5 470[h]		528[j]	0.014[r]	16[j]
Ethyl chloride	64.52[h]	12.4[h]	187.3[h]	5 270[h]	2.872[b]	1780[r]	0.00872[j]	16.0[q]
Ethylene	28.03[h]	–103.7[h]	10.0[h]	5 120[h]	1.25[b]	1470[aa]	0.0176[aa]	9.60[aa]
Ethyl ether	74.12[h]	34.7[h]	192.7[h]	3 610[h]		2470[h] (35)		11.3[q]
Fluorine	38.00[h]	–187.0[h]	–129.2[h]	5 580[h]	1.637[b]	812[j]	0.0254[j]	37[j]
Helium	4.0026[a]	–269.0[i]	–267.9[h]	229[i]	0.178[i]	5192[aa]	0.142[aa]	19.0[aa]
Hydrogen	2.0159[a]	–253.1[i]	–240.0[i]	1 316[i]	0.0900[i]	14 200[j]	0.168[aa]	8.40[aa]
Hydrogen chloride	36.461[a]	–84.9[a]	51.4[d]	8 260[d]	1.640[b]	800[j]	0.0131[j]	13.3[j]
Hydrogen sulfide	34.080[a]	–60.8[a]	100.4[d]	9 012[d]	1.54[b]	996[j]	0.0130[j]	11.6[j]
Heptane (m)	100.21[a]	98.5[a]	266.8[b]	2 720[b]	3.4[k]	1990[j]	0.0185[j]	7.00[j]
Hexane (m)	86.18[a]	66.9[a]	234.8[d]	3 030[d]	3.4[k]	1880[j]	0.0168[j]	7.52[j]
Isobutane	58.12[f]	–11.6*	135.1[j]	3 648[j]	2.47[s] (21)	1570[aa]	0.014[aa]	6.94[aa]
Methane	16.04[a]	–164.0[a]	–81.8[j]	4 641[b]	0.718[b]	2180[aa]	0.0310[aa]	10.3[aa]
Methyl chloride	50.49[a]	–24.3[a]	143.2[j]	6 678[b]	2.307[b]	770[aa]	0.0093[aa]	10.1[aa]
Naphthalene	128.19[a]	218.0*	469.1[j]	3 972[j]		1310[q] (25)		
Neon	20.183[a]	–247.0[a]	–228.8[j]	2 698[j]		1030[aa]	0.0464[aa]	30.0[aa]
Nitric oxide	30.01[a]	–152.0[a]	–92.9[j]	6 546[j]		996[j]		29.4[j]
Nitrogen	28.01[a]	–195.8[a]	–146.9[j]	3 394[b]		1040[j]	0.0240[aa]	16.6[aa]
Nitrous oxide	44.01[a]	–88.5[a]	36.4[j]	7 235[j]		850[j]	0.01731[j] (26.8)	22.4[j]
Nitrogen tetroxide	92.02[a]		158.3[j]	10 133[j]		842[p] (27)	0.0401[r] (55)	
Oxygen	31.9977*	–183.0[a]	–118.6*	5 043*		913[j]	0.0244[aa]	19.1[aa]
n-Pentane	72.53[a]	36.1*	196.7[j]	3 375[j]		1680[a] (27)	0.0152[j] (26.8)	11.7[j]
Phenol	74.11[b]	181.4[b]	418.9[b]	6 130[b]	2.6[k]	1400[k]	0.017[k]	12[k]
Propane	44.09[g]	–42.1[g]	96.7*	4 248*	2.02[g]	1571[j] (4.5)	0.015[j]	7.40[j]
Propylene	42.08[b]	–47.7[l]	91.8[l]	4 622[l]	1.92[l]	1460[aa]	0.014[aa]	8.06[aa]
Sulfur dioxide	64.06[b]	–10.0[b]	156.9[b]	7 874[b]	2.93[b]	607[l]	0.0085[j]	11.6[j]
Water vapor	18.02[b]	100.0[m]	374.0*	22 064*	0.598[m]	2050[aa]	0.0247[m]	12.1[aa]

*Data source unknown.

Notes: 1. Properties at 101.325 kPa and 0°C, or the saturation temperature if higher than 0°C, unless otherwise noted in parentheses.

2. Superscript letters indicate data source from the References section.

Table 2 Properties of Liquids

Name or Description	Normal Boiling Point, °C at 101.325 kPa	Enthalpy of Vaporization, kJ/kg	Specific Heat, c_p J/(kg·K)	Specific Heat Temp., °C	Viscosity µPa·s	Viscosity Temp., °C	Enthalpy of Fusion, kJ/kg	Density kg/m³	Density Temp., °C	Thermal Conductivity W/(m·K)	Thermal Conductivity Temp., °C	Vapor Pressure kPa	Vapor Pressure Temp., °C	Freezing Point, °C
Acetic acid	118.6[a]	405.0[b]	2180[b]	26 to 95	1 222[f]	20	195[b]	1049[a]	20	0.17[b]	20	53.3[a]	99	16.7[a]
Acetone	56.3[a]	532.4[b]	2150[b]	3 to 23	331[f]	20	98.0[b]	791[a]	20	0.1761[b]	30	53.3[a]	40	-95.4[a]
Allyl alcohol	97.1[a]	684.1[b]	2740[b]	21 to 96	1 363[f]	20		853.9[a]	20	0.180[b]	25 to 30	53.3[a]	80	-129.0[a]
n–Amyl alcohol	138.2[i]	503.1[b]	2730[b]	25	4 004[f]	23	112[b]	817.9[f]	15	0.16[b]	30	13.3[a]	86	-79.0[a]
Ammonia	-33.2[a]	1357[b]	4601[b]	0	266[f]	-33	322.40[b]	696.8[b]	-45	0.50[b]	-15 to 30	53.3[a]	-45	-77.8[a]
Alcohol–ethyl	78.6[a]	854.8[b]	2840[b]	0 to 98	1 194[f]	20	108[b]	789.2[a]	20	0.182[b]	20	13.3[a]	35	117.3[a]
Alcohol–methyl	65.0[a]	1100[b]	2510[b]	15 to 20	592.8[f]	20	99.3[a]	791.3[a]	20	0.215[b]	20	13.3[a]	21	-97.8[a]
Aniline	184.4[a]	434.0[b]	2140[b]	8 to 82	4 467.0[f]	20	114[b]	1021[a]	20	0.173[b]	-2 to 20	1.3[a]	69	-6.2[a]
Benzene	80.2[a]	394.0[h]	1720[h]	20	653[a]	20	126[h]	879[d]	20	0.147[h]	20	10[d]	20	5.9[a]
Bromine	58.8[a]	185[d]	448[f]	20	988[a]	20	66.30[d]	3119[f]	20	0.122[a]	25	22.0[d]	20	-7.2[a]
n-Butyl alcohol	117.6[a]	591.5[h]	2350[f]	20	2950[f]	20	125[b]	811[a]	20	0.15[h]	20	0.7[d]	20	-90.2[a]
n-Butyric acid	163.6[a]	504.7[h]	2150[f]	20	1 540[a]	20	126[a]	964[a]	20	0.16[h]	12	0.09[d]	20	-6.2[a]
Calcium chloride brine (20% by mass)			3110[i]	20	2 000[i]	20		1180[i]	20	0.574[i]	20			-16.2[i]
Carbon disulfide	46.3[a]	346.1[h]	1000[i]	20	360[a]	20	57.70[d]	1260[d]	20	0.16[b]	30	39.3[d]	20	-111.2[a]
Carbon tetrachloride	76.7[a]	195[h]	842[f]	20	967[a]	20	29.80[d]	1590[d]	20	0.11[j]	20	12[d]	20	-22.8[a]
Chloroform	61.3[v]	247[v]	980[v]	20	562[v]	20		1489[v]	20	0.13[v]	20	21.3[v]	20	-63.3[v]
n-Decane	174.1[b]		2000[b]	20			202[b]	730[b]	20	0.15[b]	20	0.17[b]	20	-29.8[b]
Ethyl ether	34.5[v]	351[v]	2260[v]	20	230[v]	20	98.60[v]	714.6[v]	20	0.14[b]	20	58.7[v]	20	-116.3[v]
Ethyl acetate	77.2[v]	427.5[v]	1950[v]	20	451[v]	20	119[b]	838[v]	20	0.175[b]	20	9.6[b]	20	-82.4[v]
Ethyl chloride	12.4[j]	385.9[f] (20)	1540[f]	0			69.04[a]	897.8[a]	20	0.310[f]	1	53.3[y]	12	-136.4[a]
Ethyl iodide	72.3[a]	191[f] (71)	1540[f]	0	9.90[f]	20		1935.8[a]	20	0.370[f]	30	13.3[y]	18	-108.0*
Ethylene bromide	131.6[a]	231[f] (99)	729[f]	20	28.7[f]	20	57.73[a]	2179.3[a]	20			1.3[y]	19	9.6[a]
Ethylene chloride	83.6[a]	365.8[f] (153)	1260[f]	20	14.0[f]	20	88.43[a]	1235[a]	20			8.0[y]	18	-35.4[a]
Ethylene glycol	198.1[a]	800.1[f] (344)					181.10[a]	1109[a]	20	0.173[f]	20	0.1[y]	53	-10.8[a]
Formic acid	99.8[a]	502.0[f] (216)	2200[f]	20	29.7[f]	20	276.54[a]	1219[a]	20	0.180[a]	-2	5.3[y]	23	7.4[a]
Glycerin (glycerol)	179.9*				17 800[f]	20		1261[a]	20	0.195[a]	20	0.1[a]	51	18.9[a]
Heptane	97.5[a]	321[f]	2220[j]	20	409[a]	20	140[b]	684[a]	20	0.128[j]	20	4.73[y]	20	-92.2[a]
Hexane	65.9[a]	337[f]	2250[j]	20	320[d]	20	150[b]	658[a]	20	0.125[j]	20	16.00[y]	20	-96.2[a]
Hydrogen chloride	-85.9[a]	444[f]					54.9[f]	1190[d]	b.p.					-115.8[a]
Isobutyl alcohol	107.1[a]	579[f]	486[f]	20	3 910[f]	20		801[f]	20	0.14[f]	20	1.3[y]	20	-109.0[a]
Kerosene	204 to 293[b]		2000[n]	20	2 480[b]	20		820[a]	20	0.15[n]	20			
Linseed oil					42 900[b]	20		920[d]	20					-24.9[a]
Methyl acetate	56.1[a]	412[f]	1950[f]	20	389[f]	20		971[a]	20	0.16[f]	20	22.64[y]	20	-99.2†[a]
Methyl iodide	41.6[a]	192[f]			500[f]	20		2270[a]	20			42.7[y]	20	-67.5[a]
Naphthalene	209.8[a]	316[f]	1680[f]	m.p.	901[b]	m.p.	151[b]	976[y]	m.p.			0.291[b]	20	79.3[a]
Nitric acid	85.1[v]	628[v]	1700[v]	20	910[k]	20	166[v]	1512[v]	20	0.28[v]	20	0.236[v]	20	-42.7[v]
Nitrobenzene	209.9[b]	330[b]	1450[b]	20	2 150[b]	20	93.69[v]	1200[b]	20	1.7[b]	20	0.001[b]	20	4.8[b]
Octane	124.8[b]	306.3[b]	2100[b]	20	562[b]	20	180.70[b]	703[b]	20	0.15[b]	20	0.056[b]	20	-57.5[b]
Petroleum		230 to 384[w]	2000 to 3000[w]	20	7900 to 1.2¥10^{6}[w]	20		640 to 1000[w]	20					
n-Pentane	35.1[a]	357.3[h]	2330[h]	20	226[d]	20	117[h]	626[a]	20	0.11[h]	20	56.7[d]	20	-130.8[a]
Propionic acid	140.2[a]	413.6[f]	1980[h]	20	1 102[a]	20		992[a]	20	0.173*	12	0.4[d]	20	-21.8[a]
Sodium chloride brine														
20% by mass	103.9[a]		3110[x]	20	1 570[x]	20		1150[x]	20	0.583[x]	20	0.076[x]	20	-17.4[x]
10% by mass	100.9[a]		3620[x]	20	1 180[x]	20		1070[x]	20	0.593[x]	20	0.087[x]	20	-7.4[x]
Sodium hydroxide and water (15% by mass)	100.7[v]		3610[b]	20				1150[b]	20					-22.0[b]
Sulfuric acid and water														
100% by mass	286.8[v]		1400[b]	20	22 000[b]	20		1833[v]	20			0.001[b]	20	9.6[b]
95% by mass	300.9[v]		1460[v]	20	21 000[v]	20		1836[v]	20			0.001[v]	20	-29.2[v]
90% by mass	259.1[v]		1600[v]	20	25 000[v]	20		1816[v]	20	0.38[b]	20	0.001[v]	20	-10.5[v]
Toluene ($C_6H_5CH_3$)	108.9[b]	363[b]	1690[v]	20	587[v]	20	71.90[b]	867[b]	20	0.16[b]	20	0.12[b]	20	-96.0[b]
Turpentine	148.9[a]	286[v]	1700[b]	20	546[b]	20		863[b]	20	0.13[b]	20			
Water	100.0*	2257[m]	4180[m]	20	988[m]	20	333.8[b]	998.20[m]	20	0.602[m]	20	2.34*	20	-1.0[m]
Xylene [$C_6H_4(CH_3)_2$]														
Ortho	142.9[b]	347[b]	1720[b]	20	831[b]	20	128[b]	881[b]	20	1.6[b]	20	0.0260[b]	20	-26.2[b]
Meta	137.9[b]	342[b]	1670[b]	20	628[b]	20	109[b]	867[b]	0	1.6[b]	20	0.0290[b]	20	-48.2[b]
Para	136.9[b]	340[b]	1640[b]	20	670[b]	20	161[b]	862[b]	20			0.0300[b]	20	11.9[b]
Zinc sulfate and water														
10% by mass			3700[b]	20	1 570[a]	20		1110[r]	20	0.583[a]	20			-2.3[a]
1% by mass			3300[b]	20	1 100[a]	20		1010[r]	20	0.598[a]	20			-1.2[a]

*Data source unknown.
†Approximate solidification temperature.

Notes: Superscript letters indicate data source from the section on References.
m.p. = melting point b.p. = boiling point

Table 3 Properties of Solids

Material Description	Specific Heat, J/(kg·K)	Density, kg/m^3	Thermal Conductivity, W/(m·K)	Emissivity	
				Ratio	Surface Condition
Aluminum (alloy 1100)	896[b]	2 740[u]	221[u]	0.09[n]	Commercial sheet
				0.20[n]	Heavily oxidized
Aluminum bronze (76% Cu, 22% Zn, 2% Al)	400[n]	8 280[u]	100[u]		
Asbestos: Fiber	1050[b]	2 400[u]	0.170[u]		
Insulation	800[t]	580[b]	0.16[b]	0.93[b]	"Paper"
Ashes, wood	800[t]	640[b]	0.071[b] (50)		
Asphalt	920[b]	2 110[b]	0.74[b]		
Bakelite	1500[b]	1 300[u]	17[u]		
Bell metal	360[t] (50)				
Bismuth tin	170*		65.0*		
Brick, building	800[b]	1 970[u]	0.7[b]	0.93*	
Brass: Red (85% Cu, 15% Zn)	400[u]	8 780[u]	150[u]	0.030[b]	Highly polished
Yellow (65% Cu, 35% Zn)	400[u]	8 310[u]	120[u]	0.033[b]	Highly polished
Bronze	435[t]	8 490[t]	29[d] (0)		
Cadmium	230[a]	8 650[f]	92.9[b]	0.02[d]	
Carbon (gas retort)	710[a]		0.35[b] (−17)	0.81[a]	
Cardboard			0.07[b]		
Cellulose	1300[b]	54[t]	0.057[t]		
Cement (Portland clinker)	670[b]	1 920[i]	0.029[i]		
Chalk	900[t]	2 290[t]	0.83*	0.34*	About 120°C
Charcoal (wood)	840[t]	240[a]	0.05[a] (200)		
Chrome brick	710[b]	3 200[b]	1.2[b]		
Clay	920[b]	1 000[t]			
Coal	1000[b]	1 400[t]	0.17[f] (0)		
Coal tars	1500[b] (40)	1 200[b]	0.1[b]		
Coke (petroleum, powdered)	1500[b] (400)	990[b]	0.95[b] (400)		
Concrete (stone)	653[b] (200)	2 300[b]	0.93[b]		
Copper (electrolytic)	390[u]	8 910[u]	393[u]	0.072[n]	commercial, shiny
Cork (granulated)	2030[t]	86[t]	0.048[t] (−5)		
Cotton (fiber)	1340[u]	1 500[u]	0.042[u]		
Cryolite ($AlF_3 \cdot 3NaF$)	1060[b]	2 900[b]			
Diamond	616[b]	2 420[t]	47[t]		
Earth (dry and packed)		1 500[t]	0.064*	0.41*	
Felt		330[b]	0.05[b]		
Fireclay brick	829[b] (100)	1 790[t]	1[b] (200)	0.75[n]	At 1000°C
Fluorspar (CaF_2)	880[b]	3 190[v]	1.1[v]		
German silver (nickel silver)	400[u]	8 730[u]	33[u]	0.135[n]	Polished
Glass: Crown (soda-lime)	750[b]	2 470[u]	1.0[t] (93)	0.94[n]	Smooth
Flint (lead)	490[b]	4 280[u]	1.4[r]		
Heat-resistant	840[b]	2 230[t]	1.0[t] (93)		
"Wool"	657[b]	52.0[t]	0.038[t]		
Gold	131[u]	19 350[u]	297[t]	0.02[n]	Highly polished
Graphite: Powder	691*		0.183*		
Impervious	670[u]	1 870[u]	130[u]	0.75[n]	
Gypsum	1080[b]	1 200[b]	0.43[b]	0.903[b]	On a smooth plate
Hemp (fiber)	1352.3[u]	1 500[u]			
Ice: 0°C	2040[t]	921[b]	2.24[b]	0.95*	
−20°C	1950[t]		2.44*		
Iron: Cast	500[v] (100)	7 210[t]	47.7[b] (54)	0.435[b]	Freshly turned
Wrought		7 700[b]	60.4[b]	0.94[b]	Dull, oxidized
Lead	129[u]	11 300[u]	34.8[u]	0.28[n]	Gray, oxidized
Leather (sole)		1 000[b]	0.16[b]		
Limestone	909[b]	1 650[b]	0.93[b]	0.36* to 0.90	At 63 to 193°C
Linen			0.09[b]		
Litharge (lead monoxide)	230[b]	7 850[b]			
Magnesia: Powdered	980[b] (100)	796[b]	0.61[b] (47)		
Light carbonate		210[b]	0.059[b]		
Magnesite brick	930[b] (100)	2 530[b]	3.8[b] (204)		
Magnesium	1000[b]	1 730[u]	160[u]	0.55[n]	Oxidized
Marble	880[b]	2 600[b]	2.6[b]	0.931[b]	Light gray, polished
Nickel, polished	440[u]	8 890[u]	59.5[u]	0.045[n]	Electroplated
Paints: White lacquer				0.80[n]	
White enamel				0.91[n]	On rough plate
Black lacquer				0.80[n]	
Black shellac		1 000[u]	0.26[u]	0.91[n]	"Matte" finish
Flat black lacquer				0.96[n]	
Aluminum lacquer				0.39[n]	On rough plate

*Data source unknown.

Notes: 1. Values are for room temperature unless otherwise noted in parentheses. 2. Superscript letters indicate data source from the section on References.

Table 3 Properties of Solids (*Continued*)

Material Description	Specific Heat, J/(kg·K)	Density, kg/m³	Thermal Conductivity, W/(m·K)	Emissivity	
				Ratio	Surface Condition
Paper	1300*	930[b]	0.13[b]	0.92[b]	Pasted on tinned plate
Paraffin	1670[bb]	749[bb]	0.24[b] (0)		
Plaster		2 110[b]	0.74[b] (75)	0.91[b]	Rough
Platinum	130[u]	21 470[u]	69.0[u]	0.054[b]	Polished
Porcelain	750*	260[u]	2.2[u]	0.92[b]	Glazed
Pyrites (copper)	549[b]	4 200[b]			
Pyrites (iron)	569[b] (69)	4 970[v]			
Rock Salt	917[u]	2 180[u]			
Rubber, vulcanized: Soft	2000*	1 100[t]	0.1[t]	0.86[b]	Rough
Hard		1 190[t]	0.16[t]	0.95[b]	Glossy
Sand	800[b]	1 520[b]	0.33[b]		
Sawdust		190[b]	0.05[b]		
Silica	1320[b]	2 240[v]	1.4[t] (93)		
Silver	235[u]	10 500[u]	424[u]	0.02[n]	Polished and at 227°C
Snow: Freshly fallen		100[y]	0.598[t]		
At 0°C		500[t]	2.2[t]		
Steel (mild)	500[b]	7 830[b]	45.3[b]	0.12[n]	Cleaned
Stone (quarried)	800[b]	1 500[t]			
Tar: Pitch	2500[v]	1 100[u]	0.88[v]		
Bituminous		1 200[t]	0.71[u]		
Tin	233[u]	7 290[u]	64.9[u]	0.06[h]	Bright and at 50°C
Tungsten	130[u]	19 400[u]	201[u]	0.032[n]	Filament at 27°C
Wood: Hardwoods—	1900/2700[b]	370/1100[z]	0.11/0.255[z]		
Ash, white		690[z]	0.172[z]		
Elm, American		580[z]	0.153[z]		
Hickory		800[z]			
Mahogany		550[u]	0.13[u]		
Maple, sugar		720[z]	0.187[z]		
Oak, white	2390[b]	750[z]	0.176[z]	0.90[n]	Planed
Walnut, black		630[z]			
Softwoods—	See Table 4, Chapter 25	350/740[z]	0.11/0.16[z]		
Fir, white		430[z]	0.12[z]		
Pine, white		430[z]	0.11[z]		
Spruce		420[z]	0.11[z]		
Wool: Fiber	1360[u]	1 300[u]			
Fabric		110/330[u]	0.036/0.063[u]		
Zinc: Cast	390[u]	7 130[u]	110[u]	0.05[n]	Polished
Hot-rolled	390[b]	7 130[b]	110[b]		
Galvanizing				0.23[n]	Fairly bright

*Data source unknown.

Notes: 1. Values are for room temperature unless otherwise noted in parentheses.

2. Superscript letters indicate data source from the section on References.

REFERENCES

[a]*Handbook of chemistry and physics*, 63rd ed. 1982-83. Chemical Rubber Publishing Co., Cleveland, OH.

[b]Perry, R.H. *Chemical engineers' handbook*, 2nd ed., 1941, 5th ed., 1973. McGraw-Hill, New York.

[c]*Tables of thermodynamic and transport properties of air, argon, carbon dioxide, carbon monoxide, hydrogen, nitrogen, oxygen and steam.* 1960. Pergamon Press, Elmsford, NY.

[d]*American Institute of Physics handbook*, 3rd ed. 1972. McGraw-Hill, New York.

[e]Organick and Studhalter. 1948. *Thermodynamic properties of benzene. Chemical Engineering Progress* (November):847.

[f]Lange. 1972. *Handbook of chemistry*, rev. 12th ed. McGraw-Hill, New York.

[g]ASHRAE. 1969. *Thermodynamic properties of refrigerants.*

[h]Reid and Sherwood. 1969. *The properties of gases and liquids*, 2nd ed. McGraw-Hill, New York.

[i]Chapter 19, 1993 *ASHRAE Handbook—Fundamentals.*

[j]*T.P.R.C. data book*. 1966. Thermophysical Properties Research Center, W. Lafayette, IN.

[k]Estimated.

[l]Canjar, L.N., M. Goldman, and H. Marchman. 1951. Thermodynamic properties of propylene. *Industrial and Engineering Chemistry* (May):1183.

[m]*ASME steam tables*. 1967. American Society of Mechanical Engineers, New York.

[n]McAdams, W.H. 1954. *Heat transmission*, 3rd ed. McGraw-Hill, New York.

[o]Stull, D.R. 1947. Vapor pressure of pure substances (organic compounds). *Industrial and Engineering Chemistry* (April):517.

[p]*JANAF thermochemical tables*. 1965. PB 168 370. National Technical Information Service, Springfield, VA.

[q]*Physical properties of chemical compounds*. 1955-61. American Chemical Society, Washington, D.C.

[r]*International critical tables of numerical data*. 1928. National Research Council of USA, McGraw-Hill, New York.

[s]*Matheson gas data book*, 4th ed. 1966. Matheson Company, Inc., East Rutherford, NJ.

[t]Baumeister and Marks. 1967. *Standard handbook for mechanical engineers*. McGraw-Hill, New York.

[u]Miner and Seastone. *Handbook of engineering materials*. John Wiley and Sons, New York.

[v]Kirk and Othmer. 1966. *Encyclopedia of chemical technology.* Interscience Division, John Wiley and Sons, New York.

[w]Gouse and Stevens. 1960. *Chemical technology of petroleum*, 3rd ed. McGraw-Hill, New York.

[x]*Saline water conversion engineering data book*. 1955. M.W. Kellogg Co. for U.S. Department of Interior.

[y]Timmermans, J. *Physicochemical constants of pure organic compounds*, 2nd ed. American Elsevier, New York.

[z]*Wood handbook*. 1955. Handbook No. 72. Forest Products Laboratory, U.S. Department of Agriculture.

[aa]ASHRAE. 1976. *Thermophysical properties of refrigerants.*

[bb]Lane, G. ed. 1986. *Solar heat storage: Latent heat materials, Vol II—Technology.* CRC Press, Chicago.

CHAPTER 34

ENERGY RESOURCES

BECAUSE energy used in buildings and facilities composes a significant amount of the total energy used for all purposes, and thus affects energy resources, ASHRAE recognizes the "effect of its technology on the environment and natural resources to protect the welfare of posterity" (ASHRAE 2003).

Many governmental agencies regulate energy conservation, often through the procedures to obtain building permits. Required efficiency values for building energy use strongly influence selection of HVAC&R systems and equipment and how they are applied.

More information on sustainable design is available in the *ASHRAE GreenGuide* (2006) and in Chapter 35.

CHARACTERISTICS OF ENERGY AND ENERGY RESOURCE FORMS

The HVAC&R industry deals with energy forms as they occur on or arrive at a building site. Generally, these forms are fossil fuels (natural gas, oil, and coal) and electricity. Solar and wind energy are also available at most sites, as is low-level geothermal energy (an energy source for heat pumps). Direct-use (high-temperature) geothermal energy is available at some locations.

Forms of On-Site Energy

Fossil fuels and electricity are commodities that are usually metered or measured for payment at the facility's location. Solar or wind energy is freely available but does incur cost for the means to use it. High-temperature geothermal energy, which is not universally available, may or may not be a sold commodity, depending on the particular locale and local regulations. Chapter 32 of the 2007 *ASHRAE Handbook—HVAC Applications* has more information on geothermal energy.

Some on-site energy forms require further processing or conversion into more suitable forms for the particular systems and equipment in a building or facility. For instance, natural gas or oil is burned in a boiler to produce steam or hot water, which is then distributed to various use points (e.g., heating coils in air-handling systems, unit heaters, convectors, fin-tube elements, steam-powered cooling units, humidifiers, kitchen equipment) throughout the building. Although the methods and efficiencies of these processes fall within the scope of the HVAC&R designer, *how* an energy source arrives at a given facility site is not under direct control. On-site energy choices, if available, may be controlled by the designer based in part on the present and projected future availability of the resources.

The basic energy source for heating may be natural gas, oil, coal, or electricity. Cooling may be produced by electricity, thermal energy, or natural gas. If electricity is generated on site, the generator may be driven by an engine or fuel cell that consumes fossil fuels or hydrogen on site, or by a turbine using steam or gas directly.

The term **energy source** refers to on-site energy in the form in which it arrives at or occurs on a site (e.g., electricity, gas, oil, coal). **Energy resource** refers to the raw energy that (1) is extracted from the earth (wellhead or mine-mouth), (2) is used to generate the energy source delivered to a building site (e.g., coal used to generate electricity), or (3) occurs naturally and is available at a site (solar, wind, or geothermal energy).

Nonrenewable and Renewable Energy Resources

From the standpoint of energy conservation, energy resources can be classified as either (1) nonrenewable resources, which have definite, although sometimes unknown, limitations; or (2) renewable resources, which have the potential to regenerate in a reasonable period. Resources used most in industrialized countries are nonrenewable (ASHRAE 2003).

Note that *renewable* does not mean an infinite supply. For instance, hydropower is limited by rainfall and appropriate sites, usable geothermal energy is available only in limited areas, and crops are limited by the available farm area and competing nonenergy land uses. Other forms of renewable energy also have supply limitations.

Nonrenewable resources of energy include

- Coal
- Crude oil
- Natural gas
- Uranium or plutonium (nuclear energy)

Renewable resources of energy include

- Hydropower
- Solar
- Wind
- Earth heat (geothermal)
- Biomass (wood, wood wastes, and municipal solid waste, landfill methane, etc.)
- Tidal power
- Ocean thermal
- Atmosphere or large body of water (as used by the heat pump)
- Crops (for alcohol production or as boiler fuel)

Characteristics of Fossil Fuels and Electricity

Most on-site energy for buildings in developed countries involves electricity and fossil fuels as primary on-site energy sources. Both fossil fuels and electricity can be described by their energy content (joules). This implies that energy forms are comparable and that an equivalence can be established. In reality, however, they are only comparable in energy terms when they are used to generate heat. Fossil fuels, for example, cannot directly drive motors or energize light bulbs. Conversely, electricity gives off heat as a byproduct regardless of whether it is used for running a motor or lighting a light bulb, and regardless of whether that heat is needed. Thus,

The preparation of this chapter is assigned to TC 2.8, Building Environmental Impacts and Sustainability.

electricity and fossil fuels have different characteristics, uses, and capabilities aside from any differences in their derivation.

Other differences between energy forms include methods of extraction, transformation, transportation, and delivery, and characteristics of the resource itself. Natural gas arrives at the site in virtually the same form in which it was extracted from the earth. Oil is processed (distilled) before arriving at the site; having been extracted as crude oil, it arrives at a given site as, for example, No. 2 oil or diesel fuel. Electricity is created (converted) from a different energy form, often a fossil fuel, which itself may first be converted to a thermal form. The total electricity conversion, or generation, process includes energy losses governed largely by the laws of thermodynamics.

Fuel cells, which are used only on a small scale, convert a fossil fuel to electricity by chemical means.

Fossil fuels undergo a conversion process by combustion (oxidation) and heat transfer to thermal energy in the form of steam or hot water. The conversion equipment is a boiler or a furnace in lieu of a generator, and conversion usually occurs on a project site rather than off-site. (District heating or cooling is an exception.) Inefficiencies of the fossil fuel conversion occur on site, whereas inefficiencies of most electricity generation occur off site, before the electricity arrives at the building site. (Cogeneration is an exception.)

Sustainability is an important consideration for energy use. The United Nations' Brundtland Report (UN 1987) stated that the development of the built environment is sustainable if it "meets the needs of the present without compromising the ability of future generations to meet their own needs." More information may be found in Chapter 35.

ON-SITE ENERGY/ENERGY RESOURCE RELATIONSHIPS

An HVAC&R designer must select one or more forms of energy. Most often, these are fossil fuels and electricity, although installations are sometimes designed using a single energy source (e.g., only a fossil fuel or only electricity).

Solar energy normally impinges on the site (and on the facilities to be put there), so it affects the facility's energy consumption. The designer must account for this effect and may have to decide whether to make active use of solar energy. Other naturally occurring and distributed renewable forms such as wind power and earth heat (if available) might also be considered.

The designer should be aware of the relationship between on-site energy sources and raw energy resources, including how these resources are used and what they are used for. The relationship between energy sources and energy resources involves two parts: (1) quantifying the energy resource units expended and (2) considering the societal effect of depletion of one energy resource (caused by on-site energy use) with respect to others.

Quantifiable Relationships

As on-site energy sources are consumed, a corresponding amount of resources are consumed to produce that on-site energy. For instance, for every volume of No. 2 oil consumed by a boiler at a building site, some greater volume of crude oil is extracted from the earth. On leaving the well, the crude oil is transported and processed into its final form, perhaps stored, and then transported to the site where it will be used.

Even though natural gas often requires no significant processing, it is transported, often over long distances, to reach its final destination, which causes some energy loss. Electricity may have as its raw energy resource a fossil fuel, uranium, or an elevated body of water (hydroelectric generating plant).

Data are available to help determine the amount of resource use per delivered on-site energy source unit. In the United States, data are available from entities within the U.S. Department of Energy and from the agencies and associations listed at the end of this chapter.

A **resource utilization factor (RUF)** is the ratio of resources consumed to energy delivered (for each form of energy) to a building site. Specific RUFs may be determined for various energy sources normally consumed on site, including nonrenewable sources such as coal, gas, oil, and electricity, and renewable sources such as solar, geothermal, waste, and wood energy. With electricity, which may derive from several resources depending on the particular fuel mix of the generating stations in the region served, the overall RUF is the weighted combination of individual factors applicable to electricity and a particular energy resource. Grumman (1984) gives specific formulas for calculating RUFs.

There are great differences in the efficiency of equipment used in buildings. Although electricity incurs losses in its production, it is often much more efficient than direct fuel use at the building site, particularly for lighting or heat pump applications. Minimizing both energy cost and the amount of energy resources needed to accomplish a task effectively should be a major design goal, which requires consideration of both RUFs and end-use efficiency of building equipment.

Although a designer is usually not required to determine the amount of energy resources attributable to a given building or building site for its design or operation, this information may be helpful when assessing the long-range availability of energy for a building or the building's effect on energy resources. Fuel-quantity-to-energy resource ratios or factors are often used, which suggests that energy resources are of concern to the HVAC&R industry.

Intangible Relationships

Energy resources should not simply be converted into common energy units (e.g., gigajoule) because the commonality gives a misleading picture of the equivalence of these resources. Other differences and limitations of each of the resources defy easy quantification. For instance, electricity that arrives and is used on a site can be generated from coal, oil, natural gas, uranium, or hydropower. The end result is the same: electricity at *x* kV, *y* Hz. However, the societal impact of a megajoule of electricity generated by hydropower may not equal that of a megajoule generated by coal, uranium, domestic oil, or imported oil.

Intangible factors such as safety, environmental acceptability, availability, and national interest also are affected in different ways by the consumption of each resource. Heiman (1984) proposes a procedure for weighting the following intangible factors:

National/Global Considerations

- Balance of trade
- Environmental impacts
- International policy
- Employment
- Minority employment
- Availability
- Alternative uses
- National defense
- Domestic policy
- Effect on capital markets

Local Considerations

- Exterior environmental impact
  - Air
  - Solid waste
  - Water resources
- Local employment
- Local balance of trade
- Use of distribution infrastructure
- Local energy independence
- Land use
- Exterior safety

Site Considerations

- Reliability of supply
- Indoor air quality

- Aesthetics
- Interior safety
- Anticipated changes in energy resource prices

SUMMARY

In HVAC&R system design, the need to address immediate issues such as economics, performance, and space constraints often prevents designers from fully considering the energy resources affected. Today's energy resources are less certain because of issues such as availability, safety, national interest, environmental concerns, and the world political situation. As a result, the reliability, economics, and continuity of many common energy resources over the potential life of a building being designed are unclear. For this reason, the designer of building energy systems must consider the energy resources on which the long-term operation of the building will depend. If the continued viability of those resources is reason for concern, the design should provide for, account for, or address such an eventuality.

ENERGY RESOURCE PLANNING

The energy supplier (or suppliers) in a particular jurisdiction must plan for that jurisdiction's future energy needs. For competitive energy markets where these decisions do not have high societal costs, these plans are made by energy suppliers and are not revealed to governmental authorities or the public more than is absolutely necessary, because of the advantage competitors could gain by this knowledge. For electricity (and, to a lesser extent, natural gas), significant societal issues are involved in energy resource planning decisions that cannot be made by energy suppliers without approval by many different groups. Issues include

- **Reliability**, which is affected by the diversity of supply sources available. For gas, this includes the number of geographic supply sources and pipelines; for electricity, it includes the percentage of generation from various fuel sources. Consider the projected future supply and reliability of energy resources, including the possibility of supply disruption by natural or political events, and the likelihood of future supply shortages, which could reduce reliability.
- **Reserve margins**, or the ratio of total supply sources to expected peak supply source needs. Reserve levels that are too high result in waste of resources, higher environmental costs, and possibly poor financial health of the energy suppliers. Reserves that are too low result in volatile and very high peak energy prices and reduced reliability.
- **Land use.** Energy production and transmission often require governmental cooperation to condemn private property for energy production and transmission facilities. Construction and maintenance are also regulated to protect wetlands, prevent toxic waste releases, and other environmental issues.

Note that some energy deregulation plans provide no guidance at all on energy supplies, through integrated resource planning (IRP) or other methods. Energy suppliers choose whether to expand their capacity, and what types of fuel those facilities use, based on their own assessment of the future profitability of that investment. In these markets, decisions are made with little societal input other than permitting and pollution control regulations, just as a decision might be made by a manufacturer in an industry such as steel or paper.

INTEGRATED RESOURCE PLANNING (IRP)

In regulated utility markets, integrated resource planning is commonly used for planning significant new energy facilities, especially for electricity. Steps include (1) forecasting the amount of new resources needed and (2) determining the type and provider of this resource. Traditionally, the local utility provider forecasts future needs of a given energy resource, then either builds the necessary facility with the approval of regulators or uses a standard offer bid to determine what nonutility provider (or the utility itself) would provide the new energy resource.

Supplying new energy resources through either a standard bid process by a supplier or traditional utility regulation usually results in selection of the lowest-cost supply option, without regard for environmental costs or other societal needs. IRP allows a greater variety of resource options and allows environmental and other indirect societal costs to be given greater consideration.

IRP addresses a wider population of stakeholders than most other planning processes. Many regulatory agencies involve the public in the formulation and review of integrated resource plans. Customers, environmentalists, and other public interest groups are often prominent in these proceedings.

In deregulated energy markets, supplying markets with new energy resources is typically left up to competitive market forces. This has sometimes resulted in excessive reliance on one form of energy, such as natural gas generation. Another result has been highly volatile prices, when supply is not provided because of insufficient price signals, followed by much higher prices and energy shortages until new supply sources can be obtained (which may not be for several years because of the time required for construction and environmental approval processes). Energy efficiency and demand response programs are increasingly treated as an energy resource on a par with energy production options, with incentives and compensation provided for participants in these programs.

Demand-side management (DSM) is a common option for providing new energy resources, especially for electricity. These are actions taken to reduce the demand for energy, rather than increase the supply of energy. DSM is desirable because its environmental costs are almost always lower than those of building new energy facilities. However, the following factors have caused a decline in the number of DSM programs:

- Building and equipment codes and standards are a highly efficient form of DSM, reducing energy use with much lower administrative costs than programs that reward installation of more efficient equipment at a single site. However, they are more subtle than traditional DSM programs and may not always be recognized as a form of DSM.
- Opening markets to competing suppliers makes it more difficult to administer and implement DSM programs. However, they are still possible if regulators wish to continue them, and set appropriate rules and regulations for the market to allow implementation of DSM programs.

Many IRP participants may be interested in only one aspect of the process. For example, the energy industry's main interest may be cost minimization, whereas environmentalists may want to minimize pollutant emissions and prevent environmental damage from construction of energy facilities. Participation by all affected interest groups helps provide the best overall solution for society, including indirect costs and benefits from these energy resource decisions.

TRADABLE EMISSION CREDITS

Increasingly, quotas and limits apply to emissions of various pollutants. Often, a market-based system of tradable credits is used with these quotas. A company is given the right to produce a given level of emissions, and it earns a credit, which can be sold to others, if it produces fewer emissions than that level. If one company can reduce its emissions at a lower cost than another, it can do so and sell the emissions credit to the second company and earn a profit from its pollution control efforts. In the United States, emissions quota and trading programs currently include sulfur dioxide (SO_2) and nitrogen oxides (NO_x), with plans to implement carbon dioxide (CO_2) trading now under consideration, as well. In Europe, emissions trading for CO_2 began January 1, 2005. To date, this type of activity has largely involved large industrial plants, but it can also involve commercial

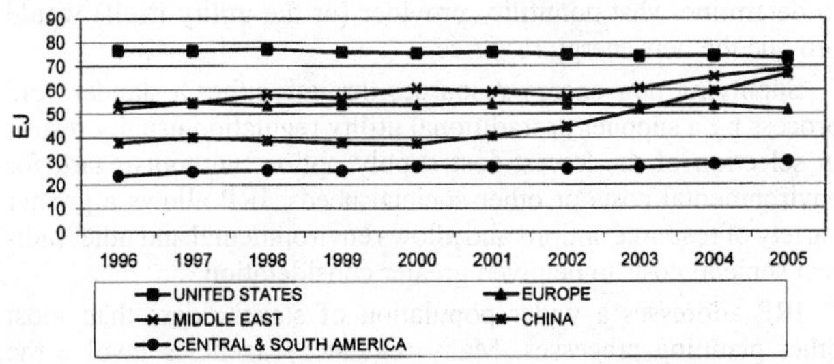

Fig. 1 Energy Production Trends: 1996-2005
(Basis: EIA 2007)

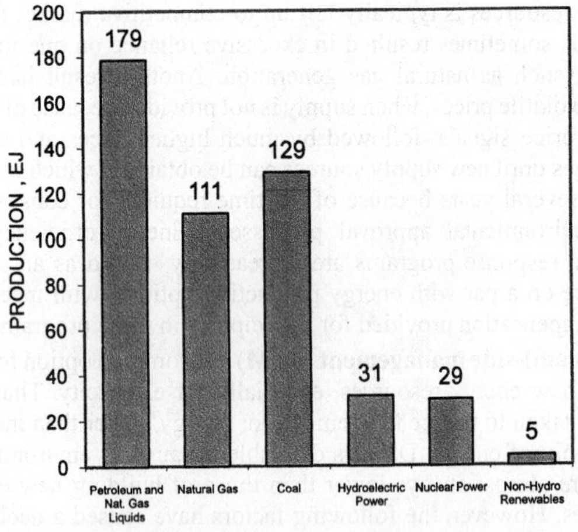

Fig. 2 World Primary Energy Production by Resource: 2005
(Basis: Table 2.9 in EIA 2007)

buildings with on-site emissions, such as generation equipment or gas engine-driven cooling.

Designers must be aware of any regulations concerning pollutant emissions; failure to comply with these regulations may result in civil or criminal penalties for designers or their clients. However, understand the options available under these regulations. The purchase or sale of emissions credits may allow reduced construction or building operations costs if the equipment can overcomply at a lower cost than the cost of another source of emissions to comply, or vice versa. In some cases, documentation of energy savings beyond what codes and regulations require can result in receiving emissions credits that may be sold later.

OVERVIEW OF GLOBAL ENERGY RESOURCES

WORLD ENERGY RESOURCES

Data in this section are from the U.S. Department of Energy's *International Energy Annual 2005* (EIA 2007).

Production

Energy production trends, by leading producers and world regions, from 1996 to 2005 are shown in Figure 1. World primary energy production, which essentially did not increase in the early 1990s, has risen about 2.4% per year from 1996 to 2005, as dramatic economic growth occurred in developing countries such as China. The largest total energy producers in 2005 were the United States (15%), China (14%), Russia (11%), and Saudi Arabia (6%). Together, they produce about 46% of the world's energy production. Total world energy production by resource type is shown in Figure 2.

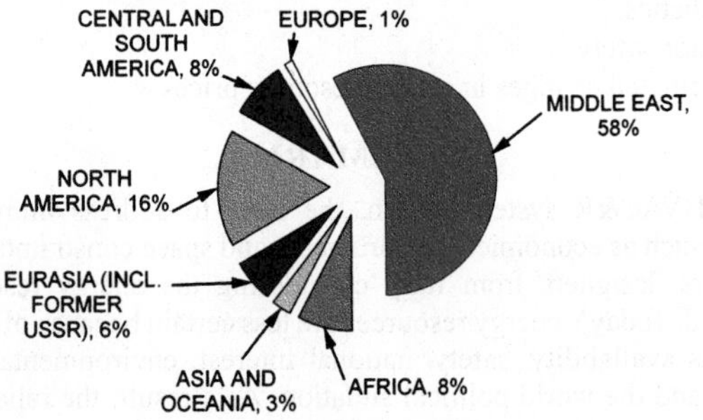

Fig. 3 World Crude Oil Reserves: 2006
(Basis: Table 8.1 in EIA 2007)

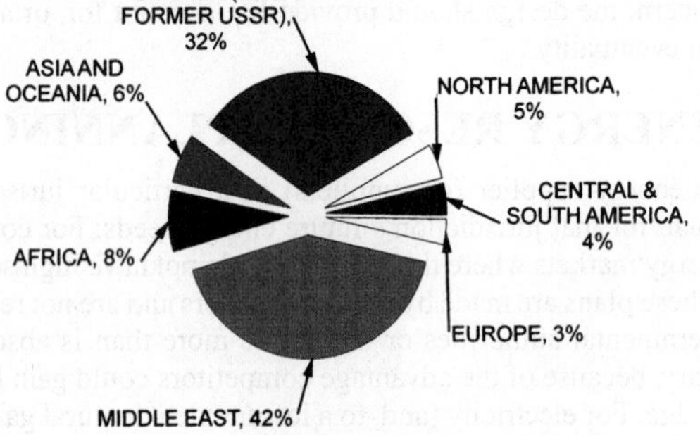

Fig. 4 World Natural Gas Reserves: 2006
(Basis: Table 8.1 in EIA 2007)

Crude Oil. World crude oil production was 8 801 000 m^3 per day in 2005. The biggest crude oil producers in 2005 were the Middle East (31%), Russia (12%), Central/South America (9%), the United States (7%), and Europe (7%). Since 1996, oil production declined by 25% in the United States, and increased 35% in Russia.

Natural Gas. World production reached 2.87×10^{12} m^3 in 2005, up 64% from the 1996 level. The biggest producers in 2005 were Russia (22%), the United States (18%), Canada (6%), and Iran (4%). Natural gas production in Iran has increased 150% since 1996.

Coal. At 5.89×10^9 Mg in 2005, coal production was up 26.5% since 1996. Leading producers of coal were China (37%), the United States (17%), India (7%), and Australia (6%). Since 1996, China, India, and Australia each increased coal production by more than 50%, and the United States increased production by 6%.

Reserves

On January 1, 2006, estimated world reserves of crude oil and gas were distributed by world region as shown in Figures 3 and 4. Countries with the largest reported crude oil reserves are Saudi Arabia (21%), Canada (14%), Iran (10%), and Iraq (9%). Most of Canada's crude oil reserves are in the form of tar sands, which have only recently been included as proven reserves. The largest gas reserves are in Russia (27%), Iran (16%), and Qatar (15%).

World coal reserves as of January 1, 2006, are shown by region in Figure 5. The most plentiful reserves, as a percent of total, were in the United States (27%), Russia (17%), China (13%), India (9%), and Australia (9%).

An important factor is the relative amount of these energy resources that has not yet been consumed. A standard measure is called **proved energy reserves**, which is the remaining known deposits that could be recovered economically given current economic and operating conditions. Dividing proved reserves by the

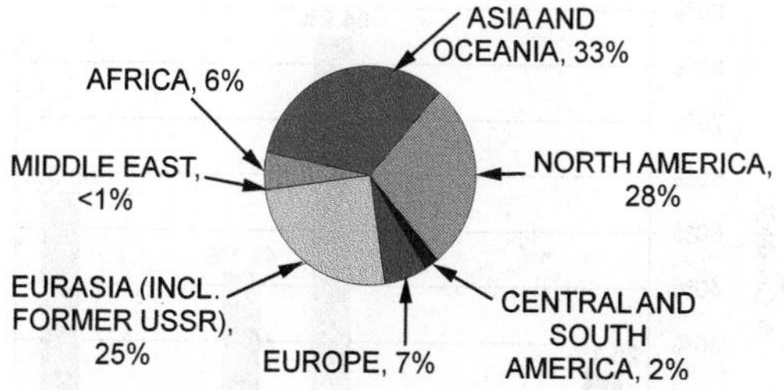

Fig. 5 World Recoverable Coal Reserves: 2006
(Basis: Table 8.2 in EIA 2007)

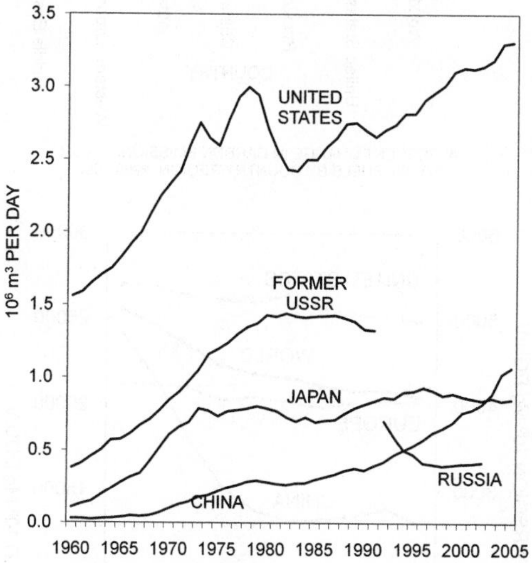

Fig. 6 World Petroleum Consumption: 2005
[Basis: Table 11.9 (EIA 2001) and Table 2.1 (EIA 2007)]

current production rate gives the number of years of the resource remaining. Using this measure, the reserve-to-production ratio at the end of 2005 for crude oil was 48.0 years; for natural gas, 60.3 years; and for coal, more than 153.7 years.

This does not mean that these resources will be depleted in that length of time: additional resources may be discovered in new areas, and improved technology may increase the amount of a resource that may be economically extracted. Also, the future rate of production and consumption may be higher or lower than current levels, which would decrease or increase the remaining years of a resource. However, reserve-to-production ratios provide insights into the limited nature of nonrenewable energy resources and the need to find alternatives, especially for resources with fewer years of remaining reserves.

Also note that, particularly for nations with nationalized energy production, there are limited opportunities to verify energy reserve data, and very large upward or downward revisions have occurred. This is independent of upward revisions that occur when new resources are discovered, or downward revisions as energy reserves are depleted. In recent years, some energy industry sources in particular have questioned the oil reserves of Saudi Arabia (Simmons 2006.)

Consumption

Data on world energy consumption are available only by type of resource rather than by total energy consumed.

Petroleum. Consumption trends of the leading consumers from 1960 to 2005 are depicted in Figure 6. In 2005, the United States consumed far more petroleum than any other country: 24.9% of the world total. Other major petroleum-consuming countries were China (8.0%), Japan (6.4%), Russia (3.3%), and Germany (3.1%).

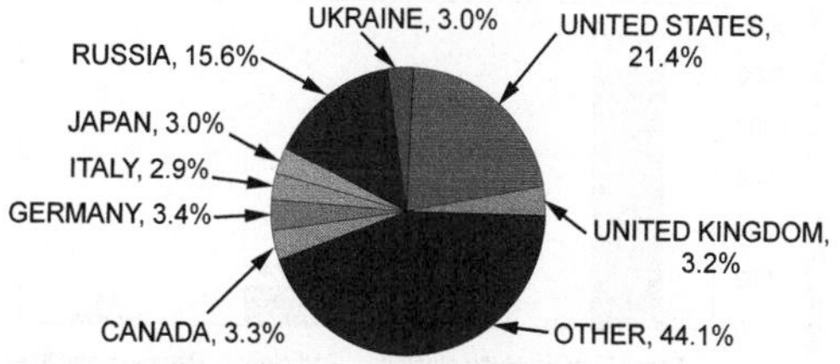

Fig. 7 World Natural Gas Consumption: 2005
(Basis: Table 1.3 in EIA 2007)

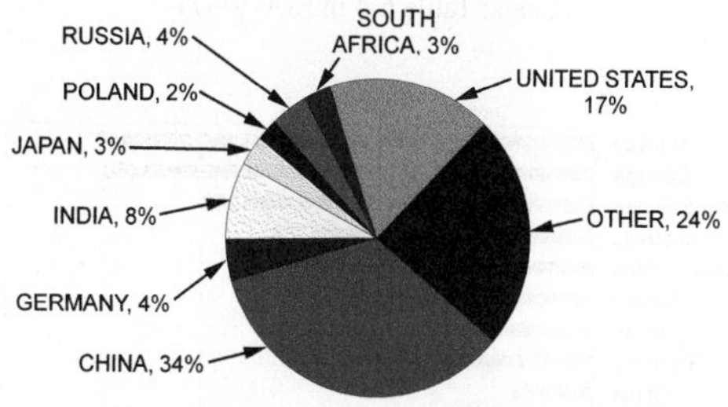

Fig. 8 World Coal Consumption: 2005
(Basis: Table 1.4 in EIA 2007)

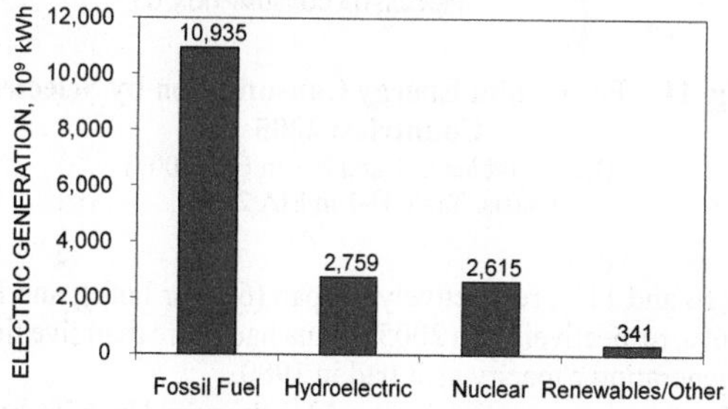

Fig. 9 World Electricity Generation by Resource: 2004
(Basis: Table 6.3 in EIA 2007)

Natural Gas. In 2005, the two biggest natural gas producers (the United States and Russia) were also the two biggest consumers. Figure 7 depicts natural gas consumption by the leading consumer countries as a percentage of world consumption. Of the major consumers, the United States consumed more than it produced (123%), and Russia consumed less (71%), as did Canada (52%). Germany produced very little, and consumption in the United Kingdom was slightly more than production (108%). World consumption of natural gas increased 26.1% between 1996 and 2005. After the United States and Russia, no single country consumed more than 5% of the world total.

Coal. Here, the two largest coal producers (China and the United States) were also the two largest consumers. China is by far the largest coal consumer, with consumption approximately double the United States' in 2005. Figure 8 depicts the percentage of world consumption by the leading consumers during 2005. Since 1980, world coal consumption has increased 57%, mostly in the last five years because of extremely rapid growth in China. Over the same period, consumption by China increased 229%, the United States 60%, and India 290%. Significant drops occurred in Germany, Poland, and Russia.

Electricity. Figure 9 shows the world's electricity generation by energy resource in 2004. Figure 10 shows installed capacity for the same resources at the beginning of 2005. Both net generation and installed capacity were dominated by the United States (23% and 25%, respectively). Comparable figures for the next largest are

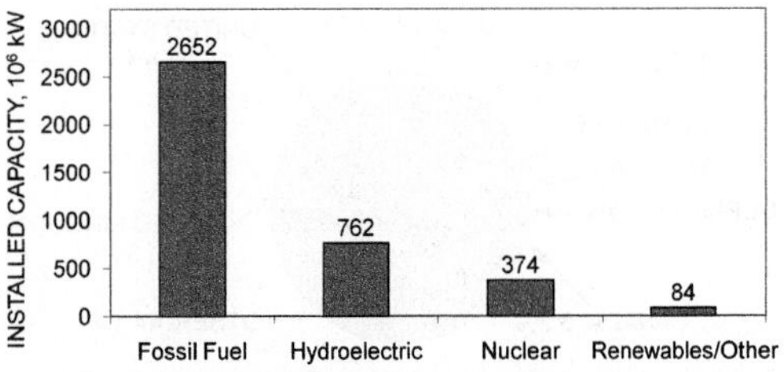

Fig. 10 World Installed Electricity Generation Capacity by Resource: 2005
(Basis: Table 6.4 in EIA 2007)

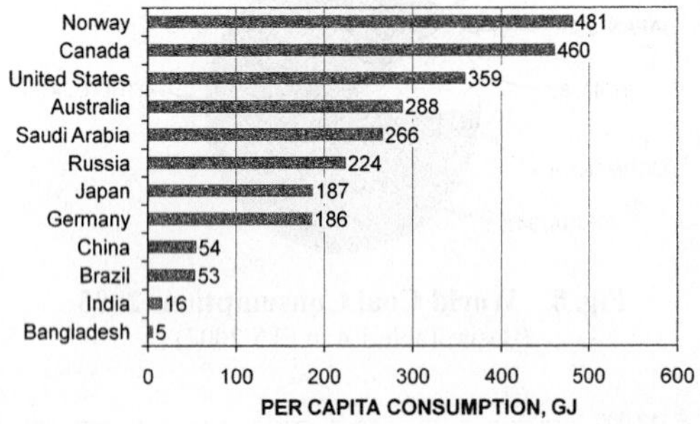

Fig. 11 Per Capita Energy Consumption by Selected Countries: 2005
(Basis: Tables B-1 and E-1 in EIA 2007)
(Basis: Table H-1 in EIA 2004)

China (14 and 11%, respectively), Japan (6% for both), and Russia (5 and 6%, respectively). In 2005, China had more than five times as much generating capacity as it had in 1980.

Hydroelectric generation increased in the world by 67% between 1980 and 2005, with the largest increases in Central and South America and China. The top countries for hydroelectric generation in 2005 were Canada, Brazil, the United States, and China, collectively accounting for 47% of the world total quantity of hydroelectric generation.

Total world electricity generation from nuclear resources increased 284% between 1980 and 2005, with higher-than-average increases occurring in Asia, Europe, and Africa. The top-generating countries in 2005 were the United States (30% of world total), France (16%), and Japan (11%).

Per Capita. Figure 11 compares the per capita energy consumption of selected countries for 2005. As is apparent, per capita energy consumption in cold-climate countries tends to be highest; also, the level in more developed countries is vastly different from that in less developed countries and differs considerably even among the more developed countries. Note that, although China's total energy use has grown very rapidly in recent years, on a per capita basis it is still far below the levels of more developed countries.

CARBON EMISSIONS

Worldwide carbon emissions from burning and flaring fossil fuels rose 25.1% from 1996 to 2005. Total carbon emissions were 28.193 billion metric tons of carbon dioxide in 2005, up from 22.531 billion metric tons in 1996. Figure 12 shows the changes in carbon emissions from burning fossil fuels from 1996 to 2005 for the total world and for selected countries. Russia, the United States, and Western Europe has small (under 10%) increases in carbon emissions. The developing countries and the Middle East show the largest increases, with extremely rapid carbon emissions growth in China in recent years. Note that although developing countries have the highest growth rates, their per capita carbon emissions are much less than in wealthier nations. A graph of per capita carbon emissions would look very similar to Figure 11, which shows per capita energy consumption of selected countries.

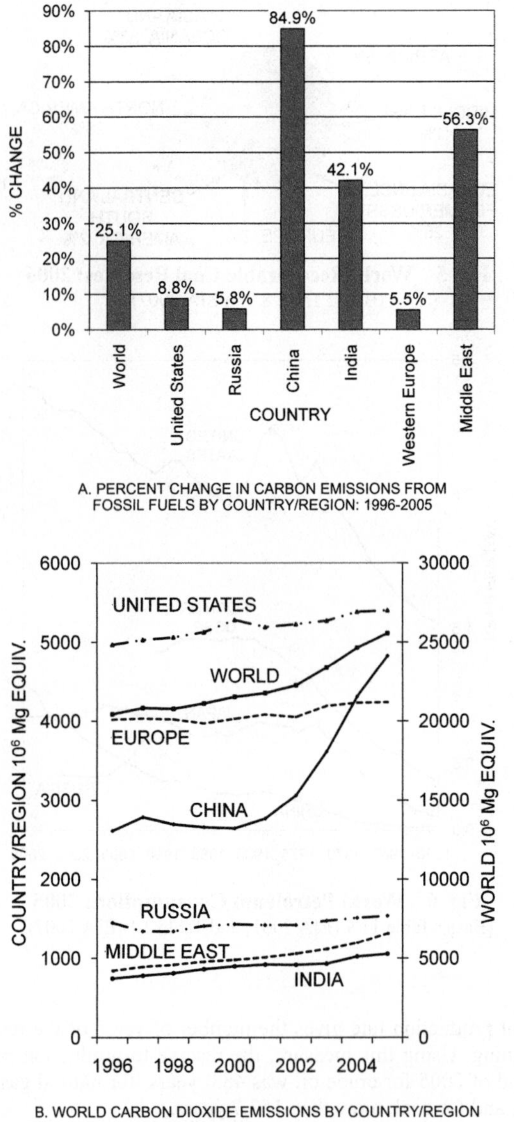

Fig. 12 World Carbon Emissions
(Basis: Table H-1 in EIA 2007)

U.S. ENERGY USE

Per Capita Energy Consumption

Figure 13, based on data from EIA (2006a), shows the growth in per capita energy use since 1950. The 1960s experienced a sharp increase in the per capita energy use growth rate, which leveled off during the 1970s because of higher energy prices and the emphasis on energy conservation. Since the early 1980s, however, per capita energy use growth has been relatively stable as energy efficiency increased. In recent years, per capita energy use has been slowly declining.

The *Annual Energy Outlook* is the basic source of data for projecting energy use in the United States (EIA 2006b). Figures 14 and 15 summarize data from this source.

EIA (2006b) forecasts energy trends based on macroeconomic growth scenarios, which include a variety of energy price and

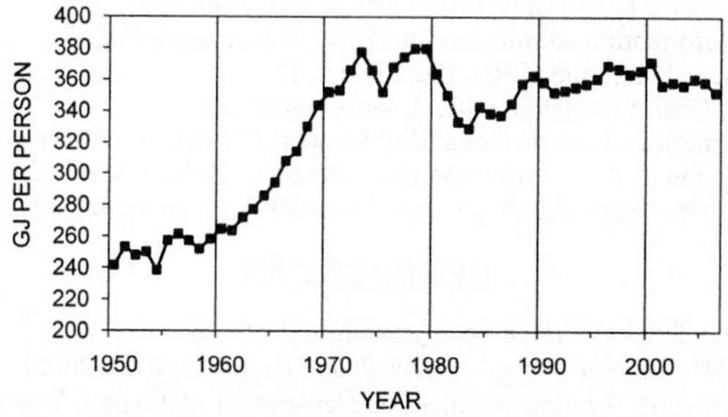

Fig. 13 Per Capita U.S. Energy Consumption
(Basis: Table 1.5 in EIA 2006a)

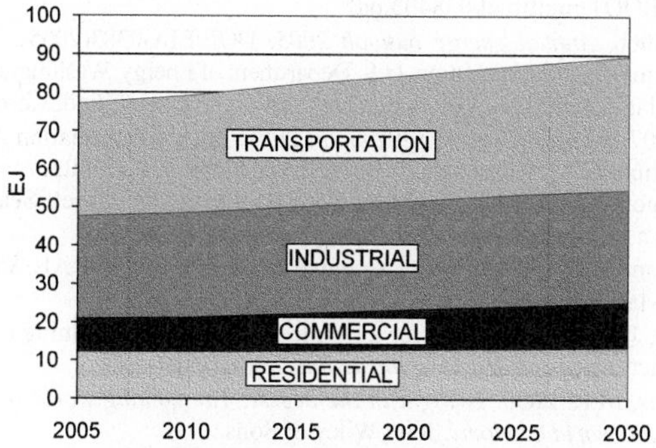

Fig. 14 Projected Total U.S. Energy Consumption by End-Use Sector
(Basis: Table A-2 in EIA 2007)

economic growth assumptions. Figures 14 and 15 (the baseline or reference case) assume average annual growth of the real gross domestic product (GDP) at 2.4%, of the labor force at 0.9%, and of productivity at 1.9%. The forecast, in order to be policy-neutral, also assumes that all federal, state, and local laws and regulations in effect December 31, 2007, remain unchanged through 2030. Note that this forecast includes the effects of the EISA 2007 energy bill, which included significant energy efficiency and conservation requirements, such as increased use of biofuels and higher fuel economy standards for automobiles and other personal transportation vehicles.

Projected Overall Energy Consumption

Figure 14 shows energy use by major end-use sector (i.e., residential, commercial, industrial, and transportation). HVAC&R engineers are primarily concerned with the first three sectors. Figure 15 shows energy consumption by type of resource. Figure 14 shows less total energy consumption than Figure 15, primarily because it excludes the thermodynamic losses of electricity generation and the processing and delivery burdens of various energy forms.

The following observations apply to the overall picture of projected energy use in the United States over the next two decades (Figures 14 and 15):

- Although a major issue in energy markets is carbon emissions, no specific programs such as cap-and-trade or carbon taxes are reflected in these forecasts, because no specific policies for carbon reductions had been enacted in 2007.
- Carbon emissions from energy use are projected to increase by an average of 0.6% per year through 2030 because of rising energy demand, increasing population, improvements in efficiency, and slow growth in the use of renewable sources. The 2030 level of carbon emissions is projected to be almost 16% higher than the 2006 levels.

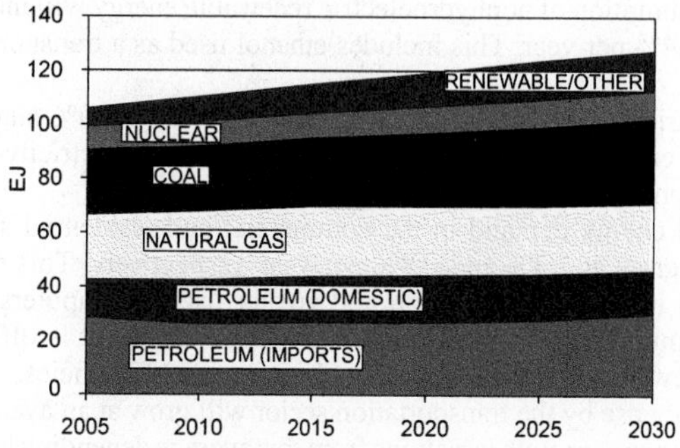

Fig. 15 Projected Total U.S. Energy Consumption by Resource
(Basis: Table A-1 in EIA 2007)

- Crude oil prices are expected to rise at an annual rate of 0.3% more than inflation. However, crude oil at any given time may fluctuate substantially because of short-term political or economic events affecting supplies.
- The wellhead price of natural gas was projected to rise at an annual rate of 0.3% more than inflation from 2006 through 2030. However, the U.S. Department of Energy (DOE) starts from a base price in 2006 that is well below actual market prices experienced in 2007 and 2008. This forecast assumes a long-term slow rise in price as lower-cost natural gas supply sources become less available. In recent years, U.S. natural gas markets have experienced extreme price volatility, making the outlook uncertain.
- The price of coal is expected to decline at an annual rate of 0.2% over the same period as a result of better productivity, more low-cost western coal production, and competitive labor pressures.
- Electricity prices are projected to show no change other than the effects of inflation from 2006 to 2030, because of improved technology and efficiency and the assumed very low increases in fuel costs.

  Nuclear power generation is expected to grow at an annual rate of 0.6% per year, because of construction of new nuclear power plants along with life extensions for existing plants. A total of 17 GW of new nuclear generation units are projected to be completed by 2030, which equates to 11 to 15 new units, depending on facility size and design.
- Electricity generation using renewable sources (which includes cogenerators) will increase by 2.1% per year, but is projected to become the third largest source of electricity after coal and nuclear power by 2025, surpassing natural gas generation between 2020 and 2025.
- Petroleum consumption will grow by 0.4% annually, led by the transportation sector, which is where most of it (74%) is used.
- The share of petroleum consumption met by net imports is projected to be about 64% in 2030, only a fraction of a percent higher than current levels. Over this period, U.S. crude oil production is projected to increase at an annual rate of 0.5%, reversing a multidecade slow decline since the 1970s. Reasons include higher prices encouraging more drilling, enhanced oil recovery projects at existing fields, and production of oil from shale. The forecast is for U.S. oil production to peak in approximately 2020, with declining production through 2030, but with production in 2030 still about 11% above current levels.
- Natural gas consumption will increase by 0.2% per year in all sectors. Natural gas use for electric generation is projected to decline after 2010, and direct use by residential and commercial consumers to increase.
- Coal consumption will increase at an average annual rate of 1.2%. Most of it (90%) will be used for electricity generation.

- Consumption of nonhydroelectric renewable energy will increase by 4.4% per year. This includes ethanol used as a transportation fuel.
- Electricity consumption is projected to grow by 0.9% annually, with efficiency gains offset by increased use of electricity-using equipment and an increasing population.
- Total energy demand in the commercial and residential sectors will grow at 1.4% and 0.8% per year, respectively. This results from increasing population and greater use of computers, telecommunications, and other office appliances, but it is offset by somewhat improved building and equipment efficiencies.
- Energy use by the transportation sector will grow at an average of 0.7% per year, with variations from this average depending heavily on prevailing fuel prices. The growth rate for transportation energy use is much lower than in recent forecasts, reflecting new mandatory fuel economy standards to be implemented during the forecast period.
- Per capita energy use is projected to decline by 0.1% annually, as increases in efficiency more than offset population growth and new energy-consuming products.
- Total energy use per dollar of gross domestic product (energy intensity), however, will continue to fall at an average rate of about 2.4% per year through 2030.

Outlook Summary

In general, the following key issues will dominate energy matters in the next two decades:

- Continued dependency of the United States on imported oil
- Potential increases in use of nuclear power for electric generation
- Role of technology developments, including energy conservation and energy efficiency as alternatives to energy production
- Substantial increases in use of renewable energy, rising from 9.4% of total U.S. production in 2006 to 13.6% in 2030
- Continued growth in total worldwide carbon emissions, and debate over actions to deal with the issue
- Relative merits of various energy alternatives, including nuclear power and different renewable energy options
- Population growth, coupled with the shift of large population segments into retirement

U.S. AGENCIES AND ASSOCIATIONS

American Gas Association (AGA), Washington, D.C.
American Petroleum Institute (API), Washington, D.C.
Bureau of Mines, Department of Interior, Washington, D.C.
Council on Environmental Quality (CEQ), Washington, D.C.
Edison Electric Institute (EEI), Washington, D.C.
Electric Power Research Institute (EPRI), Palo Alto, CA
Energy Information Administration (EIA), Washington, D.C.
Gas Research Institute (GRI), Des Plaines, IL
National Coal Association (NCA), Washington, D.C.
North American Electric Reliability Council (NAERC), Princeton, NJ
Organization of Petroleum Exporting Countries (OPEC), Vienna, Austria
United States Green Building Council (USGBC), Washington, D.C.

REFERENCES

ASHRAE. 2003. *ASHRAE energy position document.*

EIA. 2001. *Annual energy review 2000.* DOE/EIA-0384(2000). Energy Information Administration, U.S. Department of Energy, Washington, D.C. http:// www.eia.doe.gov.

EIA. 2006a. *Annual energy review 2005.* DOE/EIA-0384(2005). Energy Information Administration, U.S. Department of Energy, Washington, D.C. http:// www.eia.doe.gov. Available at http://tonto.eia.doe.gov/FTPROOT/multifuel/038405.pdf.

EIA. 2006b. *Annual energy outlook 2005.* DOE/EIA-0383(2005). Energy Information Administration, U.S. Department of Energy, Washington, D.C. Available at http://www.eia.doe.gov/oiaf/archive/aeo05/index.html.

EIA. 2007. *International energy annual 2005.* Energy Information Administration, U.S. Department of Energy, Washington, D.C. http://www.eia.doe.gov. Available at http://tonto.eia.doe.gov/bookshelf/SearchResults.asp?title=International+Energy+Annual.

Grumman, D.L. 1984. Energy resource accounting: ASHRAE *Standard* 90C-1977R. *ASHRAE Transactions* 90(1B):531-546.

Heiman, J.L. 1984. Proposal for a simple method for determining resource impact factors. *ASHRAE Transactions* 90(1B):564-570.

Simmons, M.R. 2006. *Twilight in the desert: The coming world oil shock and the world economy.* John Wiley & Sons.

UN. 1987. Our common future: Report of the World Commission on Environment and Development. Annex to General Assembly document A/42/427, *Development and International Co-operation: Environment.* United Nations. Available at http://www.un-documents.net/wced-ocf.htm.

BIBLIOGRAPHY

ASHRAE. 2003. *ASHRAE GreenGuide.* D. Grumman, ed.

DOE. 1979. *Impact assessment of a mandatory source-energy approach to energy conservation in new construction.* U.S. Department of Energy, Washington, D.C.

EISA. 2007. *Energy independence and security act of 2007.* HR-6. 110th Congress, 1st session. Available at http://frwebgate.access.gpo.gov/cgi-bin/getdoc.cgi?dbname=110_cong_bills&docid=f:h6enr.txt.pdf.

Pacific Northwest Laboratory. 1987. *Development of whole-building energy design targets for commercial buildings phase 1 planning.* PNL-5854, vol. 2. U.S. Department of Energy, Washington, D.C.

USGBC. 1999. *LEED™ reference guide.* U.S. Green Building Council, San Francisco.

CHAPTER 35

SUSTAINABILITY

THE Brundtland Commission of the United Nations (UN 1987) stated that development of the built environment is sustainable "...if it meets the needs of the present without compromising the ability of future generations to meet their own needs." Given the profound impact of buildings on the environment, the work of HVAC&R design engineers is inextricably linked to sustainability. The engineering sector has seminal influence on building performance, and HVAC&R designers' work is inherently related to overall sustainability in buildings.

HVAC&R engineering design on projects concerned with performance and sustainability requires understanding of and involvement with more than just HVAC, including projected energy and water demands, stormwater runoff generation, waste generation, and air quality impacts. This chapter is intended to provide key information and identify reference sources for further resources on

- Defining the energy, water, and other resource-consuming aspects of projects
- Quantifying the relative environmental impacts of competing design alternatives

These aspects of sustainability are addressed with respect to energy and water conservation, greenhouse gas and air quality impacts, and other impacts of buildings, such as stormwater runoff and potable water use.

The need to address sustainability in the built environment is being accelerated by external pressures such as environmental and resource concerns, rising energy prices, indoor environmental quality, global warming, and energy security. While economies transition from carbon-based to other forms of more sustainable energy, engineers will be challenged to meet an ever-increasing tide of regulation and demand.

DEFINITION

Sustainability has been defined in the *ASHRAE GreenGuide* (ASHRAE 2006a), in general terms, as "providing for the needs of the present without detracting from the ability to fulfill the needs of the future," a definition very similar to that developed in 1987 by the United Nations' Brundtland Commission (UN 1987). Others have defined sustainability as "the concept of maximizing the effectiveness of resource use while minimizing the impact of that use on the environment" (ASHRAE 2006b) and an environment in which "... an equilibrium ... exists between human society and stable ecosystems" (Townsend 2006).

Sustaining (i.e., keeping up or prolonging) those elements on which humankind's existence and that of the planet depend, such as energy, the environment, and health, are worthy goals.

The preparation of this chapter is assigned to TC 2.8, Building Environmental Impacts and Sustainability.

CHARACTERISTICS OF SUSTAINABILITY

Sustainability Addresses the Future

Sustainability is focused on the distant future (e.g., 30 to 50 years). Any actions taken under the name of sustainability must address the impact of present actions on conditions likely to prevail in that future time frame.

In designing the built environment, the emphasis has often been on the present or the near future, usually in the form of capital- or first-cost impact. As is apparent when life-cycle costing analysis is applied, capital cost assumes less importance the longer the future period under consideration.

This emphasis on the distant future can differentiate sustainable design from **green design**. Whereas green design addresses many of the same characteristics as sustainable design, it may also emphasize near-term impacts such as indoor environmental quality, operation and maintenance features, and meeting current client needs. Thus, green design may focus more on the immediate future (i.e., starting when the building is first constructed and then occupied). Sustainable design is of paramount importance to the global environment in the long-term while still incorporating features of green design that focus on the present and near future.

Sustainability Has Many Contributors

Sustainability is not just about energy, carbon emissions, pollution, waste disposal, or population growth. Although these are central ideas in thinking about sustainability, it is an oversimplification to think that addressing one factor, or even any one set of factors, can result in a sustainable future for the planet.

It is likewise a mistake to think that HVAC&R design practitioners, by themselves and just through activities within their purview, can create a sustainable result. To be sure, their activities can *contribute* to sustainability by creating a sustainable building, development, or other related project. But they cannot *by themselves* create global sustainability. Such an endeavor depends on many outside factors that cannot be controlled by HVAC&R engineers; however, they should make their fair-share contribution to sustainability in all their endeavors, and encourage other individuals and entities to do the same.

Sustainability Is Comprehensive

Sustainability has no borders or limits. A good faith effort to make a project sustainable does not mean that sustainability will be achieved globally. A superb design job on a building with sustainability as a goal will probably not contribute much to the global situation if a significant number of other buildings are not so designed, or if the transportation sector makes an inadequate contribution, or if only a few regions of the world do their fair share toward making the planet sustainable. A truly sustainable outcome thus depends on efforts in all sectors the world around.

Technology Plays Only a Partial Role

It may well be that in due time technology will have the theoretical *capability*, if diligently applied, to create a sustainable future for the planet and humankind. Having the capability to apply technology, however, does not guarantee that it will be applied; that must come from attitude or mindset. As with all things related to comprehensive change, there must be the *will.*

For example, automobile companies have the technical capability to make cars that are much more efficient, to the extent that some developed countries now dependent on imported oil could be self-sufficient. But that is not the case, perhaps because there is a lack of demand or because car companies are not required to build them. The technology is available, but the will is not there; motivation is absent.

Similarly, HVAC&R designers know how to design buildings that are much more energy efficient than they have been in the past, but such buildings are still relatively rare. ASHRAE's long-standing guidance in designing energy efficient—and now green and sustainable—buildings, along with the motivation provided by the U.S. Green Building Council's (USGBC) Leadership in Energy and Environmental Design (LEED®) Green Building Rating System™ and the American Institute of Architects' (AIA) commitment to stringent energy efficiency goals, have pointed the way technologically for the built environment and related industries to make their fair-share contribution to sustainability.

There is little ASHRAE, within its technological purview, can do directly about other, nontechnological barriers. It can, however, set a good example in its area of expertise and can also encourage and inspire other sectors to do their part to move towards sustainability.

FACTORS IMPACTING SUSTAINABILITY

The major factors impacting global sustainability are the following:

- Population growth
- Food supply
- Disease control and amelioration
- Energy resource availability
- Material resource availability and management
- Fresh water supply, both potable and nonpotable
- Effective and efficient usage practices for energy resources and water
- Air and water pollution
- Solid and liquid waste disposal
- Land use

The preceding are only broad categories, yet they encompass many subsidiary factors that have received public attention recently. For instance, climate change/global warming, carbon emissions, acid rain, deforestation, transportation, and watershed management are important factors as well. However, each of these can be viewed as a subset of one or more of the listed major areas.

PRIMARY HVAC&R CONSIDERATIONS IN SUSTAINABLE DESIGN

The main areas falling within an HVAC&R designer's (and ASHRAE's) purview on most projects are those dealing with energy and water use, material resources, air and water pollution, and solid waste disposal. Although HVAC&R professionals' expertise may impact issues such as land use and food supply on certain specialized projects, these more typically fall under the purview of other professionals and their organizations.

Energy Resource Availability

Although conventional energy resources and their availability largely fall beyond the scope of HVAC&R designers' work, an understanding of these topics is often required for participation in project discussions or utility programs relating to projects. Chapter 34 has more information on energy resources.

Some **renewable** energy resources, in contrast with traditional energy and fuels, are ubiquitous by nature and are thus available on many building sites. **Wind** and **solar** energy are widely distributed (if not always continuously available) on almost any site for use in active or passive ways. High-level (high-temperature) **geothermal** energy is only present at limited sites, and may thus be unavailable as a direct energy source on a multitude of relevant projects. Low-level geothermal, on the other hand, is dependent on the nearly constant temperature of the near-surface earth and thus can be used on almost any project if other factors align in its favor.

Designers should be familiar with the characteristics of common traditional (nonrenewable) energy resources (natural gas, heating oil, electricity) from the standpoint of their use in the relevant application. Designers are typically very familiar with the relative per-unit cost as it affects the operating cost of the building being designed. Other energy characteristics traditionally taken into account by the designer might also include ease of handling and use, cleanliness, emissions produced, and local availability, because these also have a direct effect on design and installation. Until recently, designers have not had reason to consider an energy resource's characteristics beyond the site line of the project at hand.

However, recent public focus on the impacts of building energy use on the environment has changed that approach. Designers now must consider a resource's broader characteristics that may affect the regional, national and global environment, such as its origin (domestic or foreign), future availability, emissions characteristics, broad economics, and social acceptability. Though responsible designers may not be able to do much about such factors, they should be aware of them; indeed, that awareness may affect decisions within the designer's control.

For instance, familiarity with an energy resource's emissions characteristics, whether at the well head, mine mouth, or generating station, may influence the designer to make the building more energy efficient, or provide the designer with arguments to convince the owner that energy-saving features in the building would be worth additional capital cost. Furthermore, as owners and developers of buildings become more aware of sustainability factors, designers must stay informed of the latest information and impacts.

One way to reduce a project's use of nonrenewable energy, beyond energy-efficient design itself, is to replace such energy use with renewable energy. Designers should develop familiarity with how projects might incorporate and benefit from renewable energy. Many kinds of passive design features can take advantage of naturally occurring energy.

Increasingly common examples of nonpassive approaches are solar systems, whether photovoltaic (electricity-generating) or solar thermal (hot-fluid generating). Low-level geothermal systems take advantage of naturally occurring and widely distributed earth-embedded energy. Wind systems are increasingly applied to supplement electric power grids, and are also sometimes incorporated on a smaller scale into on-site or distributed generation approaches.

Some large power users, such as municipalities or large industries, require that a minimum percentage of power they purchase be from renewable sources. Also, renewable portfolio standards are being imposed on electric utility companies by regulators.

Fresh Water Supply

HVAC&R systems can impact potable and nonpotable water supplies both directly and indirectly. First, some building systems use potable water, for example in evaporative cooling towers. Second, some building systems can discharge treated water or other waste streams with contaminants of concern that can impact local watersheds and water supplies. Indirect impacts include the use of water by utilities for electricity generation.

Effective and Efficient Use of Energy Resources and Water

This area is where HVAC&R engineers can have a profound impact on achieving sustainability goals. Impacts of building consumption can be at least partially mitigated through overall system performance improvement, as well as through increased use of on-site renewable energy and certain off-site energy resources. See the section on Designing for Effective Energy Resource Use for more information on addressing energy efficiency in the design process.

Building systems' water use can be reduced by reusing clean water from on-site, such as condensate drain water, or by using less potable water. For example, hybrid cooling towers can operate as water-to-air heat exchangers when run dry, and can operate their water sprays for additional evaporative capacity only when conditions require. In process control and refrigeration systems, similar opportunities exist. For more information on water use, the USGBC's LEED rating systems each include a section on water efficiency and provide guidance on controlling water use in buildings.

Discharge from building systems can be reduced through careful design, proper sequences and control, choice of lower impact chemical treatment regimes, or nonchemical water treatment. These techniques may not eliminate chemical treatment in all applications, but it can be substantially reduced.

Material Resource Availability and Management

Designers do not typically focus on embodied impacts of their systems design. For example, within the LEED framework, building systems under the purview of HVAC&R designers are currently excluded from credits for locally procured building materials and resources. However, the same concepts can be applied in selection and procurement of HVAC&R system components. For example, recycled steel content in system components could be required to be stated in HVAC&R product submittals. In some areas, locally assembled or manufactured components may be available that can reduce transportation impacts.

Air, Noise, and Water Pollution

HVAC&R systems and equipment can interact with both local and global environments. On a local scale, HVAC&R systems interact with the environment in ways such as acoustical noise generated by heat rejecting equipment (e.g., condensing units, cooling tower). Occasionally, this may require the addition of special barriers to prevent sound migration from the site, as shown in Figure 1.

Local impacts of combustion from on-site heat or electricity generation can be mitigated to an extent through careful consideration of the location of sources (emitters) with respect to nearby receptors, including outdoor air intakes and residences or other buildings with operable windows.

On a larger scale, air and water pollution occurs indirectly through the consumption of energy to operate building systems. This occurs in generating the electricity (whether from fossil fuel, nuclear, or hydroelectric resources), steam, or hot water for building heating or cooling. In this sense, improved efficiency is an approach to partial mitigation.

Solid and Liquid Waste Disposal

The solid waste disposal burden from installation and operations of building systems can be substantially reduced. Competing alternatives can be assessed through life cycle analysis. For example, an air-cooled unitary system with a shorter service life than a costlier water-cooled alternative could, over the course of the building's life, increase the solid waste burden when it is discarded.

An example of an HVAC&R design impacting liquid waste disposal is using glycol to protect coils from freezing, where the glycol must be eliminated in summer to provide required capacity. Because

Fig. 1 Cooling Tower Noise Barrier
(Courtesy Neil Moiseev)

reusing glycol is not a common practice, such a design would likely result in an annual glycol discharge.

In many locations, water quality regulations and agencies essentially limit or prohibit liquid waste disposal. Other approaches to pursue in reducing liquid waste disposal are discussed in the section on Effective and Efficient Use of Energy Resources and Water.

FACTORS DRIVING SUSTAINABILITY INTO DESIGN PRACTICE

HVAC&R designers face many challenges as they assimilate sustainability into their engineering practices. These challenges include climate change, a fast-changing regulatory and legal environment, and evolving standards of care. New tools, technologies, and approaches are required for well-prepared HVAC&R engineers. The challenges and the responses are creating new opportunities, just as changing project processes are allowing or requiring engineers to participate in projects in new ways.

Climate Change

In addition to their causal role (IPCC 2007), energy systems are exposed to significant vulnerabilities resulting from climate change. Increased volatility in weather profoundly affects HVAC&R practice. Historical weather data and extremes may inadequately describe conditions faced by a project built today, even over a modest lifespan for a building.

In 2001, the United Nations Environment Programme (UNEP) and the World Meteorological Organization (WMO) established the Intergovernmental Panel on Climate Change (IPCC) (www.ipcc.ch) to study and report on the scientific issues, potential impacts and mitigation methods associated with climate change. A series of publications were produced that discuss the possible outcomes and interventions required to mitigate the impacts of anthropogenic emissions.

Responsible designers are concerned with two dimensions of climate change: not only *what* they can do to reduce their designs' contribution, but also *whether* and *how* their designs should anticipate the future. It is the first that is the focus of this chapter and a majority of the available information on sustainable design. Warming trends currently occurring have been quantified with certainty. As a result, historical weather data may not be the best source for load calculations. Depending on the rate of change, anticipating future weather may become more significant in its impact on the climate control of building systems.

Regulatory Environment

The global community has responded to two major environmental issues during the past two decades. In the late 1980s, the Montreal Protocol (UNEP 2003) regulated the manufacture and trade of refrigerants which had been shown to damage the stratosphere and the troposphere by depleting atmospheric ozone. The effect on the HVAC&R industry was to require research and investment in alternative materials to those that had become the mainstays of the industry (Figure 2).

Next came the much more controversial issue of greenhouse gas emissions (and their potential for causing global warming) in the early 1990s. In response to these threats, many countries have signed and accepted the Kyoto Protocol (UNFCCC 1998), which places limits on these emissions.

Both the underlying science and the regulation of greenhouse gas emissions, primarily concerning (but not limited to) carbon dioxide (CO_2), have been embroiled in politics. A consensus has finally been expressed from within the scientific community, which has spurred political and regulatory action. The Fourth Assessment Report of the World Meteorological Organization's International Panel for Climate Change (IPCC 2007) cites widespread consensus from hundreds of scientists worldwide that rising CO_2 levels are primarily attributable to human factors as well as being responsible for warming of the lower atmosphere and associated major impact on the environment and societies.

An emissions trading program for CO_2 equivalents, already in place in the European Union, has started in the United States. Such a program will change the way of thinking for engineers and industry as new opportunities and challenges emerge. For example, a rigorous measurement and verification approach could quantify reduced building energy use and allow building owners to monetize the associated carbon reduction.

Evolving Standards of Care

Litigation relating to sustainability and global climate issues has increased. For example, a consortium of states successfully sued to force the U.S. Environmental Protection Agency (EPA) to consider CO_2 a pollutant that is harming the environment and thus take measures to regulate its emissions. This ruling is one of several developments in the continued and broadened response to CO_2 emissions by society at large. Building design and construction industries are already being impacted.

In the United States, some states have adopted carbon legislation, such as California's Global Warming Solutions Act of 2006. There and elsewhere, environmental impact reports are increasingly addressing not only local and immediate pollutant impacts, such as stormwater run-off, but greenhouse gas emissions as well.

Changing Design Process

Even in jurisdictions without regulatory change, change is happening in the HVAC&R industry. Today's engineer can contribute value to projects that include sustainability goals, using some of the many resources and approaches cited in this chapter.

ASHRAE, in partnership with the Illuminating Engineering Society of North America (IESNA) and the USGBC, has begun developing *Standard* 189 for high-performance green buildings, which intends to call for a determination of annual CO_2 equivalent emissions in addition to overall energy savings and other requirements. The component of such emissions from electricity use depends on the mix of fuels used to generate the electricity. In addition to regional variations, the overall fuel mix is projected to change, as shown in Figure 3.

Emissions considerations alone are not the only driver for design decision-making. Energy price pressures continue to mount. Examples of recent pressures include

- Antiquated electric transmission and distribution infrastructure
- Power plants being forced to become cleaner and more efficient, expediting closure of cheap, dirty generators
- Mandates imposed on utilities to provide more renewable energy to customers
- Influence of commodities trading markets on spot and future prices
- Constrained natural gas reserves and growth in demand continuing to increase volatility in the natural gas market
- Global warming, through environmental pressures to reduce carbon emissions in the face of increased demand for electricity, and infrastructure damage from more frequent storms

These and other pressures are changing project teams and their work, which are being asked to

- Incorporate sustainable design guidance and rating systems into their work
- Add a variety of new team members who bring additional expertise to address sustainability
- Gather quantitative data related to energy, water, greenhouse gas emissions, etc.
- Use new analysis tools to help maximize sustainability

Opportunities relating to sustainability for the well prepared engineer are growing. The increased focus on sustainability in the built

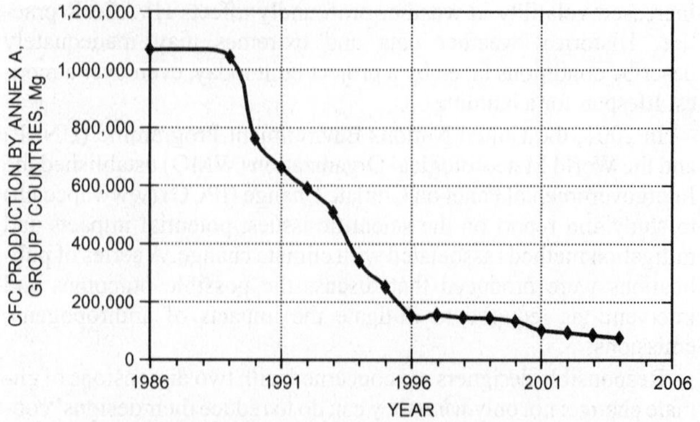

Fig. 2 Effect of Montreal Protocol on Global Chlorofluorocarbon (CFC) Production

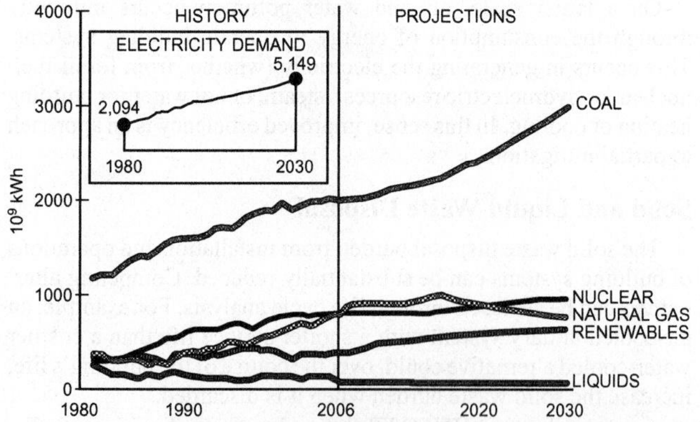

Fig. 3 Electricity Generation by Fuel, 1980–2030
(EIA 2008)

environment allows for more integrated, effective, and efficient ways to meet the nexus between environment, economy, and regulation. The challenge for the industry is how quickly it can adapt to these new opportunities and grow in an increasingly regulated environment. At the very least, the standard of care for engineers must be tracked and implemented to manage liability. Sustainability can provide an avenue for engineers and others to increase market share while exceeding current regulatory constraints and anticipating future regulations. More details on design considerations are provided in the section on Designing for Effective Energy Resource Use.

Integrating sustainability into HVAC&R system design can result in built environments that respect the greater environment and provide safe and comfortable indoor environments. The three occurrences of the letter *i* in *sustainability* can be thought of as representing key concepts in sustainable design: *interactive*, *iterative*, and *integrated*. Design processes that require greater interaction between team members and more iterative analysis to improve design solutions can be undertaken by teams through what has become known as integrated design.

Sustainability is inherently multidisciplinary. Recognizing this, teams often assemble a broad array of experts in a collaborative, interdisciplinary approach to achieve the highest levels of sustainability possible. This integrated design approach is addressed in Chapter 57 of the 2007 *ASHRAE Handbook—HVAC Applications*.

Other Opportunities

In addition to designing HVAC&R systems, engineers may increasingly be called upon to help address issues ranging from transportation to irrigation to on-site renewable energy. The approach to sustainable design alternatives opens the door for creativity and innovation in the design process. Rather than taking a "one-size-fits-all" approach to design, engineers can provide a range of available solutions and facilitate flexible implementation. Often, engineers will be asked to develop and evaluate measures based on economic and environmental performance. Success may require design iterations to achieve the desired performance.

DESIGNING FOR EFFECTIVE ENERGY RESOURCE USE

Most energy used in buildings is from nonrenewable resources, the cost of which historically has not considered replenishment or environmental impact. Thus, consideration of energy use in design has been based primarily on economic advantages, which are weighted to encourage more rather than less use.

As resources become less readily available and more exotic, and replenishable sources are investigated, the need to operate buildings effectively using less energy becomes paramount. Extensive study since the mid-1970s has shown that building energy use can be significantly reduced by applying the fundamental principles discussed in the following sections.

Energy Ethic: Resource Conservation Design Principles

The basic approach to energy-efficient design is reducing loads (power), improving transport systems, and providing efficient components and "intelligent" controls. Important design concepts include understanding the relationship between energy and power, maintaining simplicity, using self-imposed budgets, and applying energy-smart design practices.

Energy and Power

From an economic standpoint, more energy-efficient systems need not be more expensive than less efficient systems. Quite the opposite is true because of the simple relationship between energy and power, in which power is simply the time rate of energy use (or, conversely, energy is power times time). Power terms such as kilowatts are used in expressing the size of a motor, chiller, boiler, or transformer. Generally, the smaller the equipment, the less it costs. Other things being equal, as smaller equipment operates over time, it consumes less energy. Thus, in designing for energy efficiency, the first objective is always to reduce the power required to the bare minimum necessary to provide the desired performance, starting with the building's heating and cooling loads (a power term, in kilowatts and continuing with the various systems and subsystems.

Simplicity

Complex designs to save energy seldom function in the manner intended unless the systems are continually managed and operated by technically skilled individuals. Experience has shown that long-term, energy-efficient performance with a complex system is seldom achievable. Further, when complex systems are operated by minimally skilled individuals, both energy efficiency and performance suffer. Most techniques discussed in this chapter can be implemented with great simplicity.

Self-Imposed Budgets

Just as an engineer must work to a cost budget with most designs, self-imposed power budgets can be similarly helpful in achieving energy-efficient design. The series of Advanced Energy Design Guides from ASHRAE are a source for guidance on achievable design budgets. For example, the following are possible categories of power budgets for a mid-rise office building:

• Installed lighting (overall)	W/m^2
• Space sensible cooling	W/m^2
• Space heating load	W/m^2
• Electric power (overall)	W/m^2
• Thermal power (overall)	W/m^2
• Hydronic system head	kPa
• Water chiller (water-cooled)	kW/kW cooling
• Chilled-water system auxiliaries	kW/kW cooling
• Unitary air-conditioning systems	kW/kW cooling
• Annual electric energy	$MJ/(m^2 \cdot yr)$
• Annual thermal energy	$kJ/(m^2 \cdot yr \cdot K \cdot day)$

As the building and systems are designed, all decisions become interactive as each subsystem's power or energy performance is continually compared to the budget.

Design Process for Energy-Efficient Projects

Consider energy efficiency at the beginning of the building design process, because energy-efficient features are most easily and effectively incorporated at that time. Seek the active participation of all members of the design team, including the owner, architect, engineer, and often the contractor, early in the design process. Consider building attributes such as building function, form, orientation, window/wall ratio, and HVAC system types early in the process, because each has major energy implications. Identify meaningful energy performance benchmarks suited to the project, and set project-specific goals. Energy benchmarks for a sample project are shown in Table 1. Consider energy resources, on-site energy sources, and use of renewable energy, credits, or carbon offsets to mitigate environmental impacts of energy use.

Address a building's energy requirements in the following sequence:

1. **Minimize the impact of the building's functional requirements** by analyzing how the building relates to its external environment. Advocate changes in building form, aspect ratio, and other attributes that reduce, redistribute, or delay (shift) loads. The load calculation should be interactive so that the effect of those factors can be seen immediately.
2. **Minimize loads** by analyzing external and internal loads imposed on the building energy-using subsystems, both for peak- and part-load conditions. Design for efficient and effective

operation off-peak, where the majority of operating hours and energy use typically occurs.

3. **Maximize subsystem efficiency** by analyzing the diversified energy and power requirements of each energy-using subsystem serving the building's functional requirements. Consider static and dynamic efficiencies of energy conversion and energy transport subsystems, and consider opportunities to reclaim, redistribute, and store energy for later use.
4. **Study alternative ways to integrate subsystems** into the building by considering both power and time components of energy use. Identify, evaluate, and design each of these components to control overall design energy consumption. Consider the following when integrating major building subsystems:
   - Address more than one problem at a time when developing design solutions, and make maximum use of the building's advantageous features (e.g., windows, structural mass).
   - Examine design solutions that consider time (i.e., when energy use occurs), because sufficient energy may already be present from the environment (e.g., solar heat, night cooling) or from internal equipment (e.g., lights, computers) but available at times different from when needed. Active (e.g., heat pumps with water tanks) and passive (e.g., building mass) storage techniques may need to be considered.
   - Examine design solutions that consider the anticipated use of space. For example, in large but relatively unoccupied spaces, consider task or zone lighting. Consider transporting excess energy (light and heat) from locations of production and availability to locations of need instead of purchasing additional energy.
   - Never reject waste energy at temperatures usable for space conditioning or other practical purposes without calculating the economic benefit of energy recovery or treatment for reuse.
   - Consider or advocate design solutions that provide more comfortable surface temperatures or increase the availability of controlled daylight in buildings where human occupancy is a primary function.
   - Use easily understood design solutions, because they have a greater probability of use by building operators and occupants.
   - Where the functional requirements of a building are likely to change over time, design the installed environmental system to adapt to meet anticipated changes and to provide flexibility in meeting future changes in use, occupancy, or other functions.
   - Develop energy performance benchmarks, metrics, and targets that will allow building owners and operators to better realize the design intent. Differentiate between peak loads for system design and selection and lower operating loads that determine actual energy use.

Building Energy Use Elements

Envelope.

Control thermal conductivity by using insulation (including movable insulation), thermal mass, and/or phase-change thermal storage at levels that minimize net heating and cooling loads on a time-integrated (annual) basis.

- Minimize unintentional or uncontrolled thermal bridges, and include them in energy-related calculations because they can radically alter building envelope conductivity. Examples include wall studs, balconies, ledges, and extensions of building slabs.
- Minimize infiltration so that it approaches zero. (An exception is when infiltration provides the sole means of ventilation, such as in small residential units.) This minimizes fan energy consumption in pressurized buildings during occupied periods and minimizes heat loss (or unwanted heat gain, in warm climates) during unoccupied periods. In warm, humid climates, a tight envelope also improves indoor air quality. Reduce infiltration through design details that enhance the fit and integrity of building envelope joints in ways that may be readily achieved during construction (e.g., caulking, weatherstripping, vestibule doors, and/or revolving doors), with construction meeting accepted specifications.
- Consider operable windows to allow occupant-controlled ventilation. This requires careful design of the building's mechanical system to minimize unnecessary HVAC energy consumption, and building operators and occupants should be cautioned about improper use of operable windows. CIBSE (2005) provides comprehensive design considerations for natural ventilation.
- Strive to maintain occupant radiant comfort regardless of whether the building envelope is designed to be a static or dynamic membrane. Design opaque surfaces so that average inside surface temperatures remain within 3 K of room temperature in the coldest anticipated weather (i.e., winter design conditions) and so that the coldest inside surface remains within 14 K of room temperature (but always above the indoor dew point). In a building with time-varying internal heat generation, consider thermal mass for controlling radiant comfort. In the perimeter zone, thermal mass is more effective when it is positioned inside the envelope's insulation.

Table 1 Example Benchmark and Energy Targets for University Research Laboratory

	Gross	Lit/ Conditioned
Building area, m^2	15 793	10 266

Electric	**Electricity for Lighting**	**Electricity for Ventilation (Fans)**	**Electricity for In-Building Pumps**	**Electricity for Plug Loads**	**Electricity for Unidentified Loads**	**Total Electricity**	**Cogenerated Electricity**	**NGrid Electricity**
Design load, W/m^2	5.60	5.38	6.46	10.4	—	28.0	—	
Peak demand, W/m^2	4.52	5.38	4.52	7.86	0.0017	22.3	—	
Peak demand, kW (Projected submetered peak)	71	85	72	124	20	372	—	
Annual consumption, kWh/yr (Projected submetered reading)	218 154	346 598	191 245	891 503	175 200	1 823 000	966 000	857 000
Annual use index goal, kWh/yr	1.28	2.04	1.12	5.24	1.03	10.72		
Annual use index goal, site MJ/m^2 gross·yr	4378	6956	3838	17 893	3516	36 583		
Annual use index, kWh/m^2 gross·yr*	27.0 to 35.7	48.2 to 74.0	included elsewhere	47.3 to 61.0	NA	158.7 to 192.8		
Annual use index, site MJ/m^2 gross·yr*	97.3	173.6	—	170.1	—	571.1 to 694.0		

*From Labs21 program of U.S. Environmental Protection Agency (EPA) and U.S. Department of Energy (DOE). See http://www.epa.gov/lab21gov/index.htm.

- Effective control of solar radiation is critical to energy-efficient design because of the high level of internal heat production already present in most commercial buildings. In some climates, lighting energy consumption savings from daylighting techniques can be greater than the heating and cooling energy penalties that result from additional glazed surface area required, if the building envelope is properly designed for daylighting and lighting controls are installed and used. (In other climates, there may not be net savings.) Daylighting designs are most effective if direct solar beam radiation is not allowed to cause glare in building spaces.
- Design transparent parts of the building envelope to prevent solar radiant gain above that necessary for effective daylighting and solar heating. On south-facing facades (in the northern hemisphere), using low shading coefficients is generally not as effective as external physical shading devices in achieving this balance. Consider low-emissivity, high-visible-transmittance glazings for effective control of radiant heat gains and losses. For shading control, judicious use of vegetation may block excess gain year-round or seasonally, depending on the plant species chosen.

Lighting.

Lighting is both a major energy end use in commercial buildings (especially office buildings) and a major contributor to internal loads by increasing cooling loads and decreasing heating loads. Design should meet both the lighting functional criteria of the space and minimize energy use. IESNA (2000) recommends illuminance levels for visual tasks and surrounding lighted areas. Principles of energy-conserving design within that context include the following:

- Energy use is determined by the lighting load (demand power) and its duration of use (time). Minimize actual demand load rather than just apparent connected load. Control the load rather than just area switching, if switching may adversely affect the quality of the luminous environment.
- Consider daylighting with proper controls to reduce costs of electric lighting. Design should be sensitive to window glare, sudden changes in luminances, and general user acceptance of daylighting controls. Carefully select window treatment (blinds, drapes, and shades) and glazing to control direct solar penetration and luminance extremes while maintaining the view and daylight penetration.
- Design the lighting system so that illumination required for tasks is primarily limited to the location of the task and comes from a direction that minimizes direct glare and veiling reflections on the task. When the design is based on nonuniform illuminance, walls should be a light to medium color or illuminated to provide visual comfort. In densely occupied work spaces, uniform distribution of general lighting may be most appropriate. Where necessary, provide supplementary task illumination. General ambient illumination should not be lower than a third of the luminance required for the task, to help maintain visually comfortable luminance ratios.
- Use local task lighting to accommodate needs for higher lighting levels because of task visual difficulty, glare, intermittently changing requirements, or individual visual differences (poor or aging eyesight).
- Group similar activities so that high illuminance or special lighting for particular tasks can be localized in certain rooms or areas, and so that less-efficient fixtures required for critical glare control do not have to be installed uniformly when they are only required sparsely.
- Use lighting controls throughout so lighting is available when and where it is needed, but not wasted when tasks are less critical or spaces are not fully occupied. Also consider user acceptance of control strategies to maximize energy saving.
- Limit use of lower-efficiency lamps (e.g., incandescent) to applications where their color, lumens, or distribution characteristics cannot be duplicated by other sources. Limit use of extended-service incandescent lamps to applications where fixtures are difficult to reach and/or maintenance costs for replacing lamps would be excessive.
- Carry lighting design through the rest of the building's interior design. Reduced light absorption may be achieved by using lighter finishes, particularly on ceilings, walls, and partitions.

Other Loads.

- Minimize thermal impact of equipment and appliances on HVAC systems by using hoods, radiation shields, or other confining techniques, and by using controls to turn off equipment when not needed. Where practical, locate major heat-generating equipment where it can balance other heat losses. Computer centers or kitchen areas usually have separate, dedicated HVAC equipment. In addition, consider heat recovery for this equipment.
- Use storage techniques to level or distribute loads that vary on a time or spatial basis to allow operation of a device at maximum (often full-load) efficiency.

HVAC System Design.

- Consider separate HVAC systems to serve areas expected to operate on widely differing operating schedules or design conditions. For instance, systems serving office areas should generally be separate from those serving retail areas.
- Arrange systems so that spaces with relatively constant, weather-independent loads are served by systems separate from those serving perimeter spaces. Areas with special temperature or humidity requirements (e.g., computer rooms) should be served by systems separate from those serving areas that require comfort heating and cooling only. Alternatively, provide these areas with supplementary or auxiliary systems.
- Sequence the supply of zone cooling and heating to prevent simultaneous operation of heating and cooling systems for the same space, to the extent possible. Where this is not possible because of ventilation, humidity control, or air circulation requirements, reduce air quantities as much as possible before incorporating reheating, recooling, or mixing hot and cold airstreams. For example, if reheat is needed to dehumidify and prevent overcooling, *only* ventilation air needs to be treated, not the entire recirculated air quantity. Finally, reset supply air temperature up to the extent possible to reduce reheating, recooling, or mixing losses.
- Provide controls to allow operation in occupied and unoccupied modes. In the occupied mode, controls may provide for a gradually changing control point as system demands change from cooling to heating. In the unoccupied mode, ventilation and exhaust systems should be shut off if possible, and comfort heating and cooling systems should be shut off except to maintain space conditions ready for the next occupancy cycle.
- In geographical areas where diurnal temperature swings and humidity levels permit, consider judicious coupling of air distribution and building structural mass to allow nighttime cooling to reduce the requirement for daytime mechanical cooling.
- High ventilation rates, where required for special applications, can impose enormous heating and cooling loads on HVAC equipment. In these cases, consider recirculating filtered and cleaned air to the extent possible, rather than 100% outside air. Also, consider preheating outside air with reclaimed heat from other sources.

HVAC Equipment Selection.

- To allow HVAC equipment operation at the highest efficiencies, match conversion devices to load increments, and sequence the operation of modules. Oversized or large-scale systems should never serve small seasonal loads (e.g., a large heating boiler serving a summer-service water-heated load). Include specific low-load units and auxiliaries where prolonged use at minimal capacities is expected.

- Select the most efficient (or highest-COP) equipment practical at both design and reduced capacity (part-load) operating conditions.
- When selecting large-power devices such as chillers (including their auxiliary energy burdens), economic analysis of the complete life-cycle costs should be used. See Chapter 36 of the 2007 *ASHRAE Handbook—HVAC Applications* for more information on detailed economic analysis.
- Keep fluid temperatures for heating equipment devices as low as practical and for cooling equipment as high as practical, while still meeting loads and minimizing flow quantities.

Energy Transport Systems.

Energy should be transported as efficiently as possible. The following options are listed in order of efficiency, from the lowest energy transport burden (most efficient) to the highest (least efficient):

1. Electric wire or fuel pipe
2. Two-phase fluid pipe (steam or refrigerant)
3. Single-phase liquid/fluid pipe (water, glycol, etc.)
4. Air duct

Select a distribution system that complements other parameters such as control strategies, storage capabilities, conversion efficiency, and utilization efficiency.

The following specific design techniques may be applied to thermal energy transport systems:

Steam Systems.

- Include provisions for seasonal or non-use shutdown.
- Minimize venting of steam and ingestion of air, with design directed toward full-vapor performance.
- Avoid subcooling, if practical.
- Return condensate to boilers or source devices at the highest possible temperature.

Hydronic Systems.

- Minimize flow quantity by designing for the maximum practical temperature range.
- Vary flow quantity with load where possible.
- Design for the lowest practical pressure rise (or drop).
- Provide *operating* and *idle* control modes.
- When locating equipment, identify the critical pressure path and size runs for the minimum reasonable pressure drop.

Air Systems.

- Minimize airflow by careful load analysis and an effective distribution system. If the application allows, supply air quantity should vary with sensible load (i.e., VAV systems). Hold the fan pressure requirement to the lowest practical value and avoid using fan pressure as a source for control power.
- Provide *normal* and *idle* control modes for fan and psychrometric systems.
- Keep duct runs as short as possible, and keep runs on the critical pressure path sized for minimum practical pressure drop.

Power Distribution.

- Size transformers and generating units as closely as possible to the actual anticipated load (i.e., avoid oversizing to minimize fixed thermal losses).
- Consider distribution of electric power at the highest practical voltage and load selection at the maximum power factor consistent with safety.
- Consider tenant submetering in commercial and multifamily buildings as a cost-effective energy conservation measure. (A large portion of energy use in tenant facilities occurs simply because there is no economic incentive to conserve.)

Domestic Hot-Water Systems.

- Choose shower heads that provide and maintain user comfort and energy savings. They should not have removable flow-restricting inserts to meet flow limitation requirements.
- Consider point-of-use water heaters where their use will reduce energy consumption and annual energy cost.
- Consider using storage to facilitate heat recovery when the heat to be recovered is out of phase with the demand for hot water or when energy use for water heating can be shifted to take advantage of off-peak rates.

Controls.

Well-designed digital control provides information to managers and operators as well as to the data processor that serves as the intelligent controller. Include the energy-saving concepts discussed previously throughout the operating sequences and control logic. However, energy conservation should not be sought at the expense of inadequate performance; in a well-designed system, these two parameters are compatible. See Chapter 7 of this volume and Chapter 46 of the 2007 *ASHRAE Handbook—HVAC Applications* for more information on controls.

REFERENCES

ASHRAE. 2006a. *ASHRAE greenguide: The design, construction and operation of sustainable buildings*, 2nd ed. D. Grumman, ed.

ASHRAE. 2006b. *ASHRAE's sustainability roadmap—The approach to defining a leadership position in sustainability.* Presidential Ad Hoc Committee.

California. 2006. California global warming solutions act of 2006. State *Assembly Bill* 32. September 27.

CIBSE. 2005. *Natural ventilation in non-domestic buildings*. Applications Manual 10. Chartered Institution of Building Services Engineers, London.

EIA. 2008. *Annual energy outlook 2007.* DOE/EIA-0383(2007). Energy Information Administration, U.S. Department of Energy, Washington, D.C.

IPCC. 2007. *Fourth assessment report: Climate change 2007*. International Panel for Climate Change, World Meteorological Organization, Geneva.

Townsend, T.E. 2006. The ASHRAE promise: A sustainable future. Inaugural address, ASHRAE Annual Meeting, Quebec City.

UN. 1987. Our common future: Report of the world commission on environment and development. Annex to General Assembly document A/42/427, *Development and International Co-operation: Environment.* United Nations. http://www.un-documents.net/wced-ocf.htm. (14 Nov. 2007).

UNEP. 2003. *Montreal Protocol handbook for the international treaties for the protection of the ozone layer*, 6th ed., Annexes A, B, and C. Secretariat for the Vienna Convention for the Protection of the Ozone Layer and the Montreal Protocol on Substances that Deplete the Ozone Layer, United Nations Environment Programme, Nairobi.

UNFCCC. 1998. *Kyoto protocol to the united nations framework convention on climate change.* United Nations Framework Convention on Climate Change, New York. Available at http://unfccc.int/resource/docs/convkp/kpeng.pdf

BIBLIOGRAPHY

ASHRAE. 2004. *Advanced energy design guide for small office buildings.*

ASHRAE. 2006. *Advanced energy design guide for small retail buildings.*

ASHRAE. 2008. *Advanced energy design guide for K-12 school buildings.*

ASHRAE. 2008. *Advanced energy design guide for small warehouses and self-storage buildings.*

IESNA. 2000. *The IESNA lighting handbook.* Illuminating Engineering Society of North America, New York.

CHAPTER 36

MEASUREMENT AND INSTRUMENTS

HVAC engineers and technicians require instruments for both laboratory work and fieldwork. Precision is more essential in the laboratory, where research and development are undertaken, than in the field, where acceptance and adjustment tests are conducted. This chapter describes the characteristics and uses of some of these instruments.

TERMINOLOGY

The following definitions are generally accepted.

Accuracy. Capability of an instrument to indicate the true value of measured quantity. This is often confused with inaccuracy, which is the departure from the true value to which all causes of error (e.g., hysteresis, nonlinearity, drift, temperature effect, and other sources) contribute.

Amplitude. Magnitude of variation from its zero value in an alternating quantity.

Average. Sum of a number of values divided by the number of values.

Bandwidth. Range of frequencies over which a given device is designed to operate within specified limits.

Bias. Tendency of an estimate to deviate in one direction from a true value (a systematic error).

Calibration. (1) Process of comparing a set of discrete magnitudes or the characteristic curve of a continuously varying magnitude with another set or curve previously established as a standard. Deviation between indicated values and their corresponding standard values constitutes the correction (or calibration curve) for inferring true magnitude from indicated magnitude thereafter; (2) process of adjusting an instrument to fix, reduce, or eliminate the deviation defined in (1). Calibration reduces bias (systematic) errors.

Calibration curve. (1) Path or locus of a point that moves so that its graphed coordinates correspond to values of input signals and output deflections; (2) plot of error versus input (or output).

Confidence. Degree to which a statement (measurement) is believed to be true.

Deadband. Range of values of the measured variable to which an instrument will not effectively respond. The effect of deadband is similar to hysteresis, as shown in Figure 1.

Deviate. Any item of a statistical distribution that differs from the selected measure of control tendency (average, median, mode).

The preparation of this chapter is assigned to TC 1.2, Instruments and Measurements.

Deviation. Difference between a single measured value and the mean (average) value of a population or sample.

Deviation, standard. Square root of the average of the squares of the deviations from the mean (root mean square deviation). A measure of dispersion of a population.

Distortion. Unwanted change in wave form. Principal forms of distortion are inherent nonlinearity of the device, nonuniform response at different frequencies, and lack of constant proportionality between phase-shift and frequency. (A wanted or intentional change might be identical, but it is called **modulation**.)

Drift. Gradual, undesired change in output over a period of time that is unrelated to input, environment, or load. Drift is gradual; if variation is rapid and recurrent, with elements of both increasing and decreasing output, the fluctuation is referred to as **cycling**.

Dynamic error band. Spread or band of output-amplitude deviation incurred by a constant-amplitude sine wave as its frequency is varied over a specified portion of the frequency spectrum (see *Static error band*).

Emissivity. Ratio of the amount of radiation emitted by a real surface to that of an ideal (blackbody) emitter at the same temperature.

Error. Difference between the true or actual value to be measured (input signal) and the indicated value (output) from the measuring system. Errors can be systematic or random.

Error, accuracy. See *Error, systematic*.

Error, fixed. See *Error, systematic*.

Error, instrument. Error of an instrument's measured value that includes random or systematic errors.

Error, precision. See *Error, random*.

Error, probable. Error with a 50% or higher chance of occurrence. A statement of probable error is of little value.

Error, random. Statistical error caused by chance and not recurring. This term is a general category for errors that can take values on either side of an average value. To describe a random error, its distribution must be known.

Error, root mean square (RMS). Accuracy statement of a system comprising several items. For example, a laboratory potentiometer, volt box, null detector, and reference voltage source have individual accuracy statements assigned to them. These errors are generally independent of one another, so a system of these units displays an accuracy given by the square root of the sum of the squares of the individual limits of error. For example, four individual errors of 0.1% could yield a calibrated error of 0.4% but an RMS error of only 0.2%.

Error, systematic. Persistent error not due to chance; systematic errors are causal. It is likely to have the same magnitude and sign for every instrument constructed with the same components and

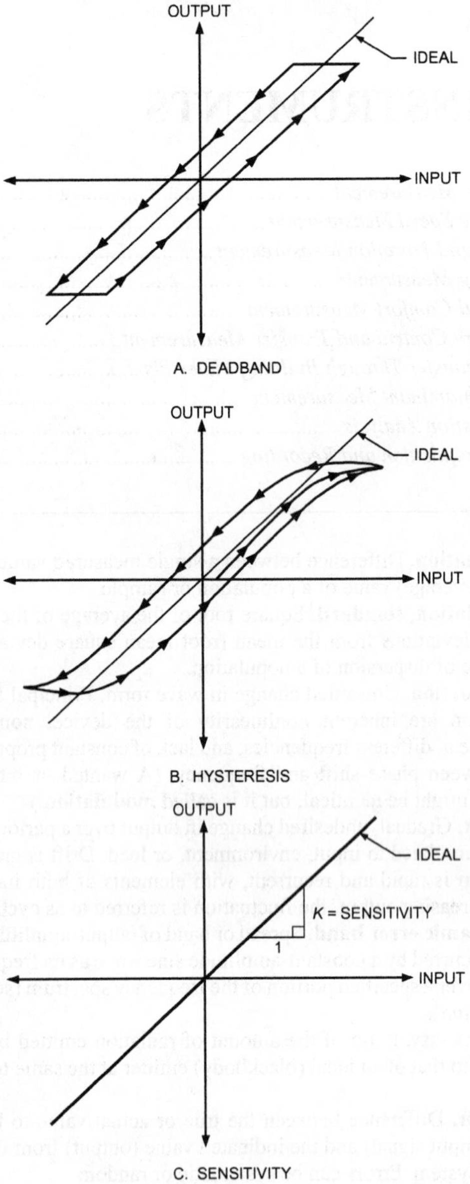

Fig. 1 Measurement and Instrument Terminology

procedures. Errors in calibrating equipment cause systematic errors because all instruments calibrated are biased in the direction of the calibrating equipment error. Voltage and resistance drifts over time are generally in one direction and are classed as systematic errors.

Frequency response (flat). Portion of the frequency spectrum over which the measuring system has a constant value of amplitude response and a constant value of time lag. Input signals that have frequency components within this range are indicated by the measuring system (without distortion).

Hydraulic diameter D_h. Defined as $4A_c/P_{wet}$, where A_c is flow cross-sectional area and P_{wet} is the wetted perimeter (perimeter in contact with the flowing fluid). For a rectangular duct with dimensions $W \times H$, the hydraulic diameter is $D_h = LW/(L+W)$. The related quantity *effective diameter* is defined as the diameter of a circular tube having the same cross-sectional area as the actual flow channel. For a rectangular flow channel, the effective diameter is $D_{eff} = \sqrt{4LW/\pi}$.

Hysteresis. Summation of all effects, under constant environmental conditions, that cause an instrument's output to assume different values at a given stimulus point when that point is approached with increasing or decreasing stimulus. Hysteresis includes backlash. It is usually measured as a percent of full scale when input varies over the full increasing and decreasing range. In instrumentation, hysteresis and deadband exhibit similar output error behavior in relation to input, as shown in Figure 1.

Linearity. The straight-lineness of the transfer curve between an input and an output (e.g., the ideal line in Figure 1); that condition prevailing when output is directly proportional to input (see *Nonlinearity*). Note that the generic term *linearity* does not consider any parallel offset of the straight-line calibration curve.

Loading error. Loss of output signal from a device caused by a current drawn from its output. It increases the voltage drop across the internal impedance, where no voltage drop is desired.

Mean. See *Average*.

Median. Middle value in a distribution, above and below which lie an equal number of values.

Mode. Value in a distribution that occurs most frequently.

Noise. Any unwanted disturbance or spurious signal that modifies the transmission, measurement, or recording of desired data.

Nonlinearity. Prevailing condition (and the extent of its measurement) under which the input/output relationship (known as the input/output curve, transfer characteristic, calibration curve, or response curve) fails to be a straight line. Nonlinearity is measured and reported in several ways, and the way, along with the magnitude, must be stated in any specification.

Minimum-deviation-based nonlinearity: maximum departure between the calibration curve and a straight line drawn to give the greatest accuracy; expressed as a percent of full-scale deflection.

Slope-based nonlinearity: ratio of maximum slope error anywhere on the calibration curve to the slope of the nominal sensitivity line; usually expressed as a percent of nominal slope.

Most other variations result from the many ways in which the straight line can be arbitrarily drawn. All are valid as long as construction of the straight line is explicit.

Population. Group of individual persons, objects, or items from which samples may be taken for statistical measurement.

Precision. Repeatability of measurements of the same quantity under the same conditions; not a measure of absolute accuracy. It describes the relative tightness of the distribution of measurements of a quantity about their mean value. Therefore, precision of a measurement is associated more with its repeatability than its accuracy. It combines uncertainty caused by random differences in a number of identical measurements and the smallest readable increment of the scale or chart. Precision is given in terms of deviation from a mean value.

Primary calibration. Calibration procedure in which the instrument output is observed and recorded while the input stimulus is applied under precise conditions, usually from a primary external standard traceable directly to the National Institute of Standards and Technology (NIST).

Range. Statement of upper and lower limits between which an instrument's input can be received and for which the instrument is calibrated.

Reliability. Probability that an instrument's precision and accuracy will continue to fall within specified limits.

Repeatability. See *Precision*.

Reproducibility. In instrumentation, the closeness of agreement among repeated measurements of the output for the same value of input made under the same operating conditions over a period of time, approaching from both directions; it is usually measured as a nonreproducibility and expressed as reproducibility in percent of span for a specified time period. Normally, this implies a long period of time, but under certain conditions, the period may be a short time so that drift is not included. Reproducibility includes hysteresis, dead band, drift, and repeatability. Between repeated measurements, the input may vary over the range, and operating conditions may vary within normal limits.

Resolution. Smallest change in input that produces a detectable change in instrument output. Resolution, unlike precision, is a psychophysical term referring to the smallest increment of humanly perceptible output (rated in terms of the corresponding increment of input). The precision, resolution, or both may be better than the accuracy. An ordinary six-digit instrument has a resolution of one part per million (ppm) of full scale; however, it is possible that the accuracy is no better than 25 ppm (0.0025%). Note that the practical resolution of an instrument cannot be any better than the resolution of the indicator or detector, whether internal or external.

Sensitivity. Slope of a calibration curve relating input signal to output, as shown in Figure 1. For linear instruments, sensitivity represents the change in output for a unit change in the input.

Sensitivity error. Maximum error in sensitivity displayed as a result of the changes in the calibration curve resulting from accumulated effects of systematic and random errors.

Stability. (1) Independence or freedom from changes in one quantity as the result of a change in another; (2) absence of drift.

Static error band. (1) Spread of error present if the indicator (pen, needle) stopped at some value (e.g., at one-half of full scale), normally reported as a percent of full scale; (2) specification or rating of maximum departure from the point where the indicator must be when an on-scale signal is stopped and held at a given signal level. This definition stipulates that the stopped position can be approached from either direction in following any random waveform. Therefore, it is a quantity that includes hysteresis and nonlinearity but excludes items such as chart paper accuracy or electrical drift (see *Dynamic error band*).

Step-function response. Characteristic curve or output plotted against time resulting from the input application of a step function (a function that is zero for all values of time before a certain instant, and a constant for all values of time thereafter).

Threshold. Smallest stimulus or signal that results in a detectable output.

Time constant. Time required for an exponential quantity to change by an amount equal to 0.632 times the total change required to reach steady state for first-order systems.

Transducer. Device for translating the changing magnitude of one kind of quantity into corresponding changes of another kind of quantity. The second quantity often has dimensions different from the first and serves as the source of a useful signal. The first quantity may be considered an input and the second an output. Significant energy may or may not transfer from the transducer's input to output.

Uncertainty. An estimated value for the bound on the error (i.e., what an error might be if it were measured by calibration). Although uncertainty may be the result of both systematic and precision errors, only precision error can be treated by statistical methods. Uncertainty may be either **absolute** (expressed in the units of the measured variable) or **relative** (absolute uncertainty divided by the measured value; commonly expressed in percent).

Zero shift. Drift in the zero indication of an instrument without any change in the measured variable.

UNCERTAINTY ANALYSIS

Uncertainty Sources

Measurement generally consists of a sequence of operations or steps. Virtually every step introduces a conceivable source of uncertainty, the effect of which must be assessed. The following list is representative of the most common, but not all, sources of uncertainty.

- Inaccuracy in the mathematical model that describes the physical quantity
- Inherent stochastic variability of the measurement process
- Uncertainties in measurement standards and calibrated instrumentation
- Time-dependent instabilities caused by gradual changes in standards and instrumentation
- Effects of environmental factors such as temperature, humidity, and pressure
- Values of constants and other parameters obtained from outside sources
- Uncertainties arising from interferences, impurities, inhomogeneity, inadequate resolution, and incomplete discrimination
- Computational uncertainties and data analysis
- Incorrect specifications and procedural errors
- Laboratory practice, including handling techniques, cleanliness, and operator techniques, etc.
- Uncertainty in corrections made for known effects, such as installation effect corrections

Uncertainty of a Measured Variable

For a measured variable *X*, the total error is caused by both **precision (random)** and **systematic (bias) errors**. This relationship is shown in Figure 2. The possible measurement values of the variable are scattered in a distribution around the parent population mean μ (Figure 2A). The curve (**normal** or **Gaussian distribution**) is the theoretical distribution function for the infinite population of measurements that generated *X*. The parent population mean differs from $(X)_{true}$ by an amount called the systematic (or bias) error β (Figure 2B). The quantity β is the total fixed error that remains after all calibration corrections have been made. In general, there are several sources of bias error, such as errors in calibration standard, data acquisition, data reduction, and test technique. There is usually no direct way to measure these errors. These errors are unknown and are assumed to be zero; otherwise, an additional correction would be applied to reduce them to as close to zero as possible. Figure 2B shows how the resulting deviation δ can be different for different random errors ε.

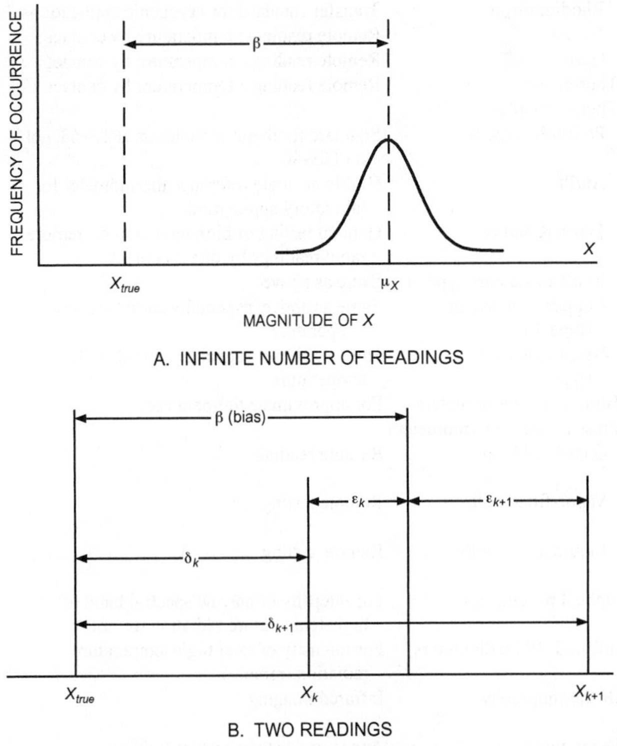

Fig. 2 Errors in Measurement of Variable *X*

The **precision uncertainty** for a variable, which is an estimate of the possible error associated with the repeatability of a particular measurement, is determined from the sample standard deviation, or the estimate of the error associated with the repeatability of a particular measurement. Unlike systematic error, precision error varies from reading to reading. As the number of readings of a particular variable tends to infinity, the distribution of these possible errors becomes Gaussian.

For each bias error source, the experimenter must estimate a **systematic uncertainty**. Systematic uncertainties are usually estimated from previous experience, calibration data, analytical models, and engineering judgment. The resultant uncertainty is the square root of the sum of the squares of the bias and precision uncertainties; see Coleman and Steele (1989).

For further information on measurement uncertainty, see ASME *Standards* MFC-2M and PTC 19.1, Abernethy et al. (1985), Brown et al. (1998), and Coleman and Steele (1995).

TEMPERATURE MEASUREMENT

Instruments for measuring temperature are listed in Table 1. Temperature sensor output must be related to an accepted temperature scale by manufacturing the instrument according to certain specifications or by calibrating it against a temperature standard. To help users conform to standard temperatures and temperature measurements, the International Committee of Weights and Measures (CIPM) adopted the International Temperature Scale of 1990 (ITS90).

The unit of temperature of the ITS-90 is the kelvin (K) and has a size equal to the fraction 1/273.16 of the thermodynamic temperature of the triple point of water.

In the United States, ITS-90 is maintained by the National Institute of Standards and Technology (NIST), which provides calibrations based on this scale for laboratories.

Benedict (1984), Considine (1985), DeWitt and Nutter (1988), Quinn (1990), and Schooley (1986, 1992) cover temperature measurement in more detail.

Sampling and Averaging

Although temperature is usually measured within, and is associated with, a relatively small volume (depending on the size of the thermometer), it can also be associated with an area (e.g., on a surface or in a flowing stream). To determine average stream temperature, the cross section must be divided into smaller areas and the temperature of each area measured. The temperatures measured are then combined into a weighted mass flow average by using either (1) equal areas and multiplying each temperature by the fraction of total mass flow in its area or (2) areas of size inversely proportional to mass flow and taking a simple arithmetic average of the temperatures in each. Mixing or selective sampling may be preferable to these cumbersome procedures. Although mixing can occur from turbulence alone, **transposition** is much more effective. In transposition, the stream is divided into parts determined by the type of stratification, and alternate parts pass through one another.

Table 1 Common Temperature Measurement Techniques

Measurement Means	Application	Approximate Range, °C	Uncertainty, K	Limitations
Liquid-in-glass thermometers				
Mercury-in-glass	Temperature of gases and liquids by contact	–38/550	0.03 to 2	In gases, accuracy affected by radiation
Organic fluid	Temperature of gases and liquids by contact	–200/200	0.03 to 2	In gases, accuracy affected by radiation
Resistance thermometers				
Platinum	Precision; remote readings; temperature of fluids or solids by contact	–259/1000	Less than 0.0001 to 0.1	High cost; accuracy affected by radiation in gases
Rhodium/iron	Transfer standard for cryogenic applications	–273/–243	0.0001 to 0.1	High cost
Nickel	Remote readings; temperature by contact	–250/200	0.01 to 1	Accuracy affected by radiation in gases
Germanium	Remote readings; temperature by contact	–273/–243	0.0001 to 0.1	
Thermistors	Remote readings; temperature by contact	Up to 200	0.0001 to 0.1	
Thermocouples				
Pt-Rh/Pt (type S)	Standard for thermocouples on IPTS-68, not on ITS-90	0/1450	0.1 to 3	High cost
Au/Pt	Highly accurate reference thermometer for laboratory applications	–50/1000	0.05 to 1	High cost
Types K and N	General testing of high temperature; remote rapid readings by direct contact	Up to 1250	0.1 to 10	Less accurate than Pt-Rh/Pt or Au/Pt thermocouples
Iron/Constantan (type J)	Same as above	Up to 750	0.1 to 6	Subject to oxidation
Copper/Constantan (type T)	Same as above; especially suited for low temperature	Up to 350	0.1 to 3	
Ni-Cr/Constantan (type E)	Same as above; especially suited for low temperature	Up to 900	0.1 to 7	
Bimetallic thermometers	For approximate temperature	–20/660	1, usually much more	Time lag; unsuitable for remote use
Pressure-bulb thermometers				
Gas-filled bulb	Remote reading	–75/660	2	Use caution to ensure installation is correct
Vapor-filled bulb	Remote testing	–5/250	2	Use caution to ensure installation is correct
Liquid-filled bulb	Remote testing	–50/1150	2	Use caution to ensure installation is correct
Optical pyrometers	For intensity of narrow spectral band of high-temperature radiation (remote)	800 and up	15	Generally requires knowledge of surface emissivity
Infrared (IR) radiometers	For intensity of total high-temperature radiation (remote)	Any range		
IR thermography	Infrared imaging	Any range		Generally requires knowledge of surface emissivity
Seger cones (fusion pyrometers)	Approximate temperature (within temperature source)	660/2000	50	

Static Temperature Versus Total Temperature

When a fluid stream impinges on a temperature-sensing element such as a thermometer or thermocouple, the element is at a temperature greater than the true stream temperature. The difference is a fraction of the temperature equivalent of the stream velocity t_e.

$$t_e = \frac{V^2}{2Jc_p} \tag{1}$$

where

t_e = temperature equivalent of stream velocity, °C
V = stream velocity, m/s
J = mechanical equivalent of heat = 1000 (N·m)/kJ
c_p = specific heat of stream at constant pressure, kJ/(kg·K)

This fraction of the temperature equivalent of the velocity is the **recovery factor**, which varies from 0.3 to 0.4 K for bare thermometers to 0.5 K for aerodynamically shielded thermocouples. For precise temperature measurement, each temperature sensor must be calibrated to determine its recovery factor. However, for most applications with air velocities below 10 m/s, the recovery factor can be omitted.

Various sensors are available for temperature measurement in fluid streams. The principal ones are the **static temperature thermometer**, which indicates true stream temperature but is cumbersome, and the **thermistor**, used for accurate temperature measurement within a limited range.

LIQUID-IN-GLASS THERMOMETERS

Any device that changes monotonically with temperature is a thermometer; however, the term usually signifies an ordinary liquid-in-glass temperature-indicating device. Mercury-filled thermometers have a useful range from –38.8°C, the freezing point of mercury, to about 550°C, near which the glass usually softens. Lower temperatures can be measured with organic-liquid-filled thermometers (e.g., alcohol-filled), with ranges of –200 to 200°C. During manufacture, thermometers are roughly calibrated for at least two temperatures, often the freezing and boiling points of water; space between the calibration points is divided into desired scale divisions. Thermometers that are intended for precise measurement applications have scales etched into the glass that forms their stems. The probable error for as-manufactured, etched-stem thermometers is ±1 scale division. The highest-quality mercury thermometers may have uncertainties of ±0.03 to 2 K if they have been calibrated by comparison against primary reference standards.

Liquid-in-glass thermometers are used for many HVAC applications, including local temperature indication of process fluids (e.g., cooling and heating fluids and air).

Mercury-in-glass thermometers are fairly common as temperature measurement standards because of their relatively high accuracy and low cost. If used as references, they must be calibrated on the ITS-90 by comparison in a uniform bath with a standard platinum resistance thermometer that has been calibrated either by the appropriate standards agency or by a laboratory that has direct traceability to the standards agency and the ITS-90. This calibration is necessary to determine the proper corrections to be applied to the scale readings. For application and calibration of liquid-in-glass thermometers, refer to NIST (1976, 1986).

Liquid-in-glass thermometers are calibrated by the manufacturer for total or partial stem immersion. If a thermometer calibrated for total immersion is used at partial immersion (i.e., with part of the liquid column at a temperature different from that of the bath), an emergent stem correction must be made, as follows:

$$\text{Stem correction} = Kn(t_b - t_s) \tag{2}$$

where

K = differential expansion coefficient of mercury or other liquid in glass. K is 0.00016 for Celsius mercury thermometers. For K values for other liquids and specific glasses, refer to Schooley (1992).
n = number of degrees that liquid column emerges from bath
t_b = temperature of bath, °C
t_s = average temperature of emergent liquid column of n degrees, °C

Because the true temperature of the bath is not known, this stem correction is only approximate.

Sources of Thermometer Errors

A thermometer measuring gas temperatures can be affected by radiation from surrounding surfaces. If the gas temperature is approximately the same as that of the surrounding surfaces, radiation effects can be ignored. If the temperature differs considerably from that of the surroundings, radiation effects should be minimized by shielding or aspiration (ASME *Standard* PTC 19.3). **Shielding** may be provided by highly reflective surfaces placed between the thermometer bulb and the surrounding surfaces such that air movement around the bulb is not appreciably restricted (Parmelee and Huebscher 1946). Improper shielding can increase errors. **Aspiration** involves passing a high-velocity stream of air or gas over the thermometer bulb.

When a **thermometer well** within a container or pipe under pressure is required, the thermometer should fit snugly and be surrounded with a high-thermal-conductivity material (oil, water, or mercury, if suitable). Liquid in a long, thin-walled well is advantageous for rapid response to temperature changes. The surface of the pipe or container around the well should be insulated to eliminate heat transfer to or from the well.

Industrial thermometers are available for permanent installation in pipes or ducts. These instruments are fitted with metal guards to prevent breakage. However, the considerable heat capacity and conductance of the guards or shields can cause errors.

Allowing ample time for the thermometer to attain temperature equilibrium with the surrounding fluid prevents excessive errors in temperature measurements. When reading a liquid-in-glass thermometer, keep the eye at the same level as the top of the liquid column to avoid parallax.

RESISTANCE THERMOMETERS

Resistance thermometers depend on a change of the electrical resistance of a sensing element (usually metal) with a change in temperature; resistance increases with increasing temperature. Use of resistance thermometers largely parallels that of thermocouples, although readings are usually unstable above about 550°C. Two-lead temperature elements are not recommended because they do not allow correction for lead resistance. Three leads to each resistor are necessary for consistent readings, and four leads are preferred. Wheatstone bridge circuits or 6-1/2-digit multimeters can be used for measurements.

A typical circuit used by several manufacturers is shown in Figure 3. This design uses a differential galvanometer in which coils L and H exert opposing forces on the indicating needle. Coil L is in series with the thermometer resistance AB, and coil H is in series with the constant resistance R. As the temperature falls, the resistance of AB decreases, allowing more current to flow through coil L than through coil H. This increases the force exerted by coil L, pulling the needle down to a lower reading. Likewise, as the temperature rises, the resistance of AB increases, causing less current to flow through coil L than through coil H and forcing the indicating needle to a higher reading. Rheostat S must be adjusted occasionally to maintain constant current.

The resistance thermometer is more costly to make and likely to have considerably longer response times than thermocouples. It gives best results when used to measure steady or slowly changing temperature.

Resistance Temperature Devices

Resistance temperature devices (RTDs) are typically constructed from platinum, rhodium/iron, nickel, nickel/iron, tungsten, or copper. These devices are further characterized by their simple circuit designs, high degree of linearity, good sensitivity, and excellent stability. The choice of materials for an RTD usually depends on the intended application; selection criteria include temperature range, corrosion protection, mechanical stability, and cost.

Presently, for HVAC applications, RTDs constructed of platinum are the most widely used. Platinum is extremely stable and resistant to corrosion. Platinum RTDs are highly malleable and can thus be drawn into fine wires; they can also be manufactured inexpensively as thin films. They have a high melting point and can be refined to high purity, thus attaining highly reproducible results. Because of these properties, platinum RTDs are used to define the ITS-90 for the range of 13.8033 K (triple point of equilibrium hydrogen) to 1234.93 K (freezing point of silver).

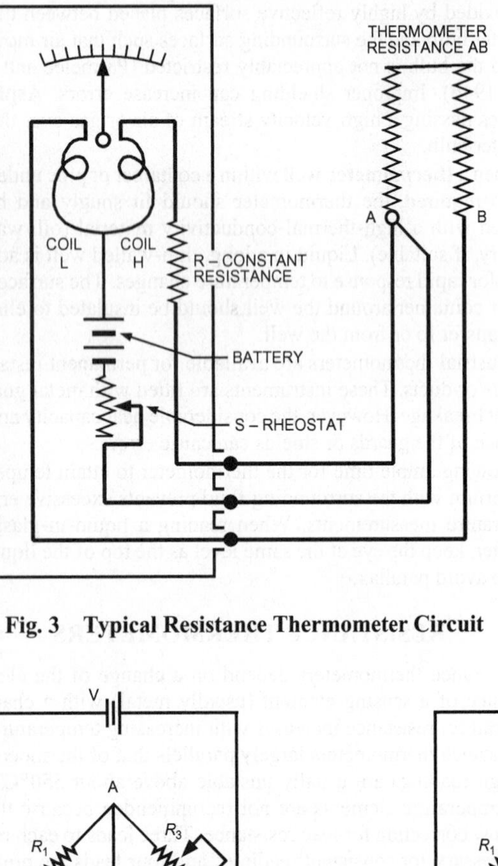

Fig. 3 Typical Resistance Thermometer Circuit

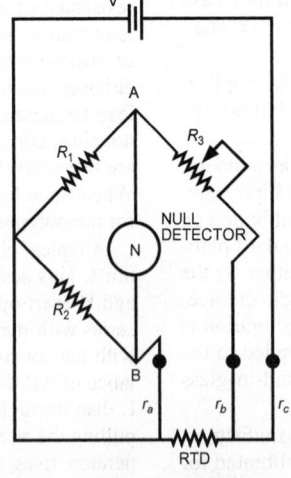

Platinum resistance temperature devices can measure the widest range of temperatures and are the most accurate and stable temperature sensors. Their resistance/temperature relationship is one of the most linear. The higher the purity of the platinum, the more stable and accurate the sensor. With high-purity platinum, primary-grade platinum RTDs can achieve reproducibility of ±0.00001 K, whereas the minimum uncertainty of a recently calibrated thermocouple is ±0.2 K.

The most widely used RTD is designed with a resistance of 100 Ω at 0°C (R_0 = 100 Ω). Other RTDs are available that use lower resistances at temperatures above 600°C. The lower the resistance value, the faster the response time for sensors of the same size.

Thin-Film RTDs. Thin-film 1000 Ω platinum RTDs are readily available. They have the excellent linear properties of lower-resistance platinum RTDs and are more cost-effective because they are mass produced and have lower platinum purity. However, many platinum RTDs with R_0 values of greater than 100 Ω are difficult to provide with transmitters or electronic interface boards from sources other than the RTD manufacturer. In addition to a nonstandard interface, higher-R_0-value platinum RTDs may have higher self-heating losses if the excitation current is not controlled properly.

Thin-film RTDs have the advantages of lower cost and smaller sensor size. They are specifically adapted to surface mounting. Thin-film sensors tend to have an accuracy limitation of ±0.1% or ±0.1 K. This may be adequate for most HVAC applications; only in tightly controlled facilities may users wish to install the standard wire-wound platinum RTDs with accuracies of 0.01% or ±0.01 K (available on special request for certain temperature ranges).

Assembly and Construction. Regardless of the R_0 value, RTD assembly and construction are relatively simple. Electrical connections come in three basic types, depending on the number of wires to be connected to the resistance measurement circuitry. Two, three, or four wires are used for electrical connection using a Wheatstone bridge or a variation (Figure 4).

In the basic two-wire configuration, the RTD's resistance is measured through the two connecting wires. Because the connecting wires extend from the site of the temperature measurement, any additional changes in resistivity caused by a change in temperature may affect the measured resistance. Three- and four-wire assemblies are built to compensate for the connecting lead resistance

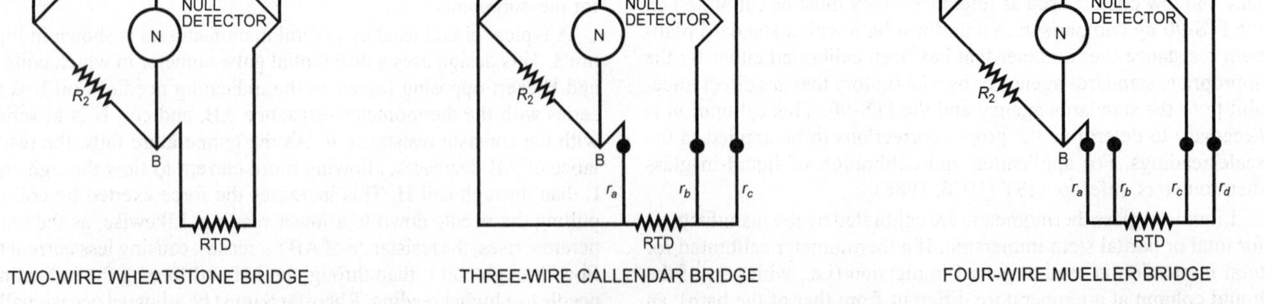

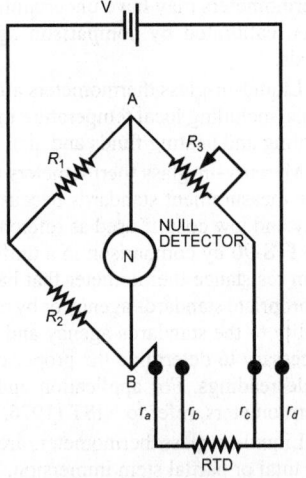

Fig. 4 Typical Resistance Temperature Device (RTD) Bridge Circuits

values. The original three-wire circuit improved resistance measurement by adding a compensating wire to the voltage side of the circuit. This helps reduce part of the connecting wire resistance. When more accurate measurements (better than ±0.1 K) are required, the four-wire bridge, which eliminates all connecting wire resistance errors, is recommended.

All bridges discussed here are direct current (dc) circuits and were used extensively until the advent of precision alternating current (ac) circuits using microprocessor-controlled ratio transformers, dedicated analog-to-digital converters, and other solid-state devices that measure resistance with uncertainties of less than 1 ppm. Resistance measurement technology now allows more portable thermometers, lower cost, ease of use, and high-precision temperature measurement in industrial uses.

Thermistors

Certain semiconductor compounds (usually sintered metallic oxides) exhibit large changes in resistance with temperature, usually decreasing as the temperature increases. For use, the thermistor element may be connected by lead wires into a galvanometer bridge circuit and calibrated. Alternatively, a 6-1/2-digit multimeter and a constant-current source with a means for reversing the current to eliminate thermal electromotive force (emf) effects may also be used. This method is easier and faster, and may be more precise and accurate. Thermistors are usually applied to electronic temperature compensation circuits, such as thermocouple reference junction compensation, or to other applications where high resolution and limited operating temperature ranges exist. Figure 5 illustrates a typical thermistor circuit.

Semiconductor Devices

In addition to positive-resistance-coefficient RTDs and negative-resistance-coefficient thermistors, there are two other types of devices that vary resistance or impedance with temperature. Although the principle of their operation has long been known, their reliability was questioned because of imprecise manufacturing techniques. Improved silicon microelectronics manufacturing techniques have brought semiconductors to the point where low-cost, precise temperature sensors are commercially available.

Elemental Semiconductors. Because of controlled doping of impurities into elemental germanium, a germanium semiconductor

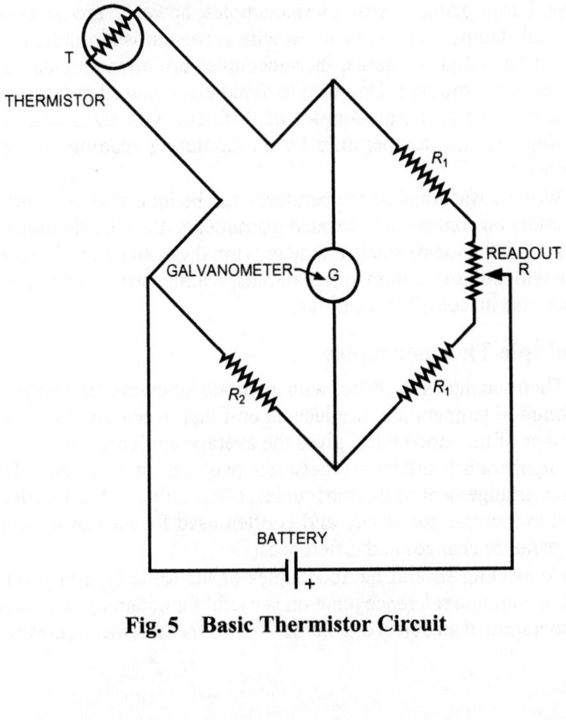

Fig. 5 Basic Thermistor Circuit

is a reliable temperature sensor for cryogenic temperature measurement in the range of 1 to 84 K.

Junction Semiconductors. The first simple junction semiconductor device consisted of a single diode or transistor, in which the forward-connected base emitter voltage was very sensitive to temperature. Today, the more common form is a pair of diode-connected transistors, which make the device suitable for ambient temperature measurement. Applications include thermocouple reference junction compensation.

The primary advantages of silicon transistor temperature sensors are their extreme linearity and exact R_0 value, as well as the incorporation of signal conditioning circuitry into the same device as the sensor element. As with thermocouples, these semiconductors require highly precise manufacturing techniques, extremely precise voltage measurements, multiple-point calibration, and temperature compensation to achieve an accuracy as high as ±0.01 K, but with a much higher cost. Lower-cost devices achieve accuracies of ±0.1 K using mass-manufacturing techniques and single-point calibration. A mass-produced silicon temperature sensor can be interchanged easily. If one device fails, only the sensor element need be changed. Electronic circuitry can be used to recalibrate the new device.

Winding Temperature. The winding temperature of electrical operating equipment is usually determined from the resistance change of these windings in operation. With copper windings, the relation between these parameters is

$$\frac{R_1}{R_2} = \frac{100 + t_1}{100 + t_2} \tag{3}$$

where

R_1 = winding resistance at temperature t_1, Ω
R_2 = winding resistance at temperature t_2, Ω
t_1, t_2 = winding temperatures, °C

The classical method of determining winding temperature is to measure the equipment when it is inoperative and temperature-stabilized at room temperature. After the equipment has operated sufficiently to stabilize temperature under load conditions, the winding resistance should be measured again by taking resistance measurements at known, short time intervals after shutdown. These values may be extrapolated to zero time to indicate the winding resistance at the time of shutdown. The obvious disadvantage of this method is that the device must be shut down to determine winding temperature. A circuit described by Seely (1955), however, makes it possible to measure resistances while the device is operating.

THERMOCOUPLES

When two wires of dissimilar metals are joined by soldering, welding, or twisting, they form a thermocouple junction or **thermojunction**. An emf that depends on the wire materials and the junction temperature exists between the wires. This is known as the **Seebeck voltage**.

Thermocouples for temperature measurement yield less precise results than platinum resistance thermometers, but, except for glass thermometers, thermocouples are the most common instruments of temperature measurement for the range of 0 to 1000°C. Because of their low cost, moderate reliability, and ease of use, thermocouples are widely accepted.

The most commonly used thermocouples in industrial applications are assigned letter designations. Tolerances of such commercially available thermocouples are given in Table 2.

Because the measured emf is a function of the difference in temperature and the type of dissimilar metals used, a known temperature at one junction is required; the remaining junction temperature may be calculated. It is common to call the one with known temperature the (cold) **reference** junction and the one with unknown temperature the (hot) **measured** junction. The reference junction is

Table 2 Thermocouple Tolerances on Initial Values of Electromotive Force Versus Temperature

Thermocouple Type	Material Identification	Temperature Range, °C	Reference Junction Tolerance at 0°C[a] Standard Tolerance (whichever is greater)	Special Tolerance (whichever is greater)
T	Copper versus Constantan	0 to 350	±1 K or ±0.75%	±0.5 K or ±0.4%
J	Iron versus Constantan	0 to 750	±2.2 K or ±0.75%	±1.1 K or ±0.4%
E	Nickel/10% Chromium versus Constantan	0 to 900	±1.7 K or ±0.5%	±1 K or ±0.4%
K	Nickel/10% Chromium versus 5% Aluminum, Silicon	0 to 1250	±2.2 K or ±0.75%	±1.1 K or ±0.4%
N	Nickel/14% Chromium, 1.5% Silicon versus Nickel/4.5% Silicon, 0.1% Magnesium	0 to 1250	±2.2 K or ±0.75%	±1.1 K or ±0.4%
R	Platinum/13% Rhodium versus Platinum	0 to 1450	±1.5 K or ±0.25%	±0.6 K or ±0.1%
S	Platinum/10% Rhodium versus Platinum	0 to 1450	±1.5 K or ±0.25%	±0.6 K or ±0.1%
B	Platinum/30% Rhodium versus Platinum/6% Rhodium	870 to 1700	±0.5%	±0.25%
T[b]	Copper versus Constantan	−200 to 0	±1 K or ±1.5%	c
E[b]	Nickel/10% Chromium versus Constantan	−200 to 0	±1.7 K or ±1%	c
K[b]	Nickel/10% Chromium versus 5% Aluminum, Silicon	−200 to 0	±2.2 K or ±2%	c

Source: ASTM *Standard* E230, Temperature-Electromotive Force (EMF) Tables for Standardized Thermocouples.

[a]Tolerances in this table apply to new thermocouple wire, normally in the size range of 0.25 to 3 mm diameter and used at temperatures not exceeding the recommended limits. Thermocouple wire is available in two grades: standard and special.

[b]Thermocouples and thermocouple materials are normally supplied to meet the tolerance specified in the table for temperatures above 0°C. The same materials, however, may not fall within the tolerances given in the second section of the table when operated below freezing (0°C). If materials are required to meet tolerances at subfreezing temperatures, the purchase order must state so.

[c]Little information is available to justify establishing special tolerances for below-freezing temperatures. Limited experience suggests the following special tolerances for types E and T thermocouples:

Type E −200 to 0°C; ±1 K or ±0.5% (whichever is greater)

Type T −200 to 0°C; ±0.5 K or ±0.8% (whichever is greater)

These tolerances are given only as a guide for discussion between purchaser and supplier.

typically kept at a reproducible temperature, such as the ice point of water.

Various systems are used to maintain the reference junction temperature (e.g., mixed ice and water in an insulated flask, or commercially available thermoelectric coolers to maintain the ice-point temperature automatically in a reference chamber). When these systems cannot be used in an application, measuring instruments with automatic reference junction temperature compensation may be used.

As previously described, the principle for measuring temperature with a thermocouple is based on accurate measurement of the Seebeck voltage. Acceptable dc voltage measurement methods are (1) millivoltmeter, (2) millivolt potentiometer, and (3) high-input impedance digital voltmeter. Many digital voltmeters include built-in software routines for direct calculation and display of temperature. Regardless of the method selected, there are many ways to simplify measurement.

Solid-state digital readout devices in combination with a milli- or microvoltmeter, as well as packaged thermocouple readouts with built-in cold junction and linearization circuits, are available. The latter requires a proper thermocouple to provide direct meter reading of temperature. Accuracy approaching or surpassing that of potentiometers can be attained, depending on the instrument quality. This method is popular because it eliminates the null balancing requirement and reads temperature directly in a digital readout.

Wire Diameter and Composition

Thermocouple wire is selected by considering the temperature to be measured, the corrosion protection afforded to the thermocouple, and the precision and service life required. Type T thermocouples are suitable for temperatures up to 350°C; type J, up to 750°C; and types K and N, up to 1250°C. Higher temperatures require noble metal thermocouples (type S, R, or B), which have a higher initial cost and do not develop as high an emf as the base metal thermocouples. Thermocouple wires of the same type have small compositional variation from lot to lot from the same manufacturer, and especially among different manufacturers. Consequently, calibrating samples from each wire spool is essential for precision. Calibration data on wire may be obtained from the manufacturer.

Computer-friendly reference functions are available for relating temperature and emf of letter-designated thermocouple types. The functions depend on thermocouple type and temperature range; they are used to generate reference tables of emf as a function of temperature, but are not well suited for calculating temperatures directly from values of emf. Approximate inverse functions are available, however, for calculating temperature and are of the form

$$t = \sum_{i=0}^{n} a_i E^i \tag{4}$$

where t = temperature, a_i = thermocouple constant coefficients, and E = voltage. Burns et al. (1992) give reference functions and approximate inverses for all letter-designated thermocouples.

The emf of a thermocouple, as measured with a high-input impedance device, is independent of the diameters of its constituent wires. Thermocouples with small-diameter wires respond faster to temperature changes and are less affected by radiation than larger ones. Large-diameter wire thermocouples, however, are necessary for high-temperature work when wire corrosion is a problem. For use in heated air or gases, thermocouples are often shielded and sometimes aspirated. One way to avoid error caused by radiation is using several thermocouples of different wire sizes and estimating the true temperature by extrapolating readings to zero diameter.

With thermocouples, temperatures can be indicated or recorded remotely on conveniently located instruments. Because thermocouples can be made of small-diameter wire, they can be used to measure temperatures within thin materials, within narrow spaces, or in otherwise inaccessible locations.

Multiple Thermocouples

Thermocouples in series, with alternate junctions maintained at a common temperature, produce an emf that, when divided by the number of thermocouples, gives the average emf corresponding to the temperature difference between two sets of junctions. This series arrangement of thermocouples, often called a **thermopile**, is used to increase sensitivity and is often used for measuring small temperature changes and differences.

Connecting several thermocouples of the same type in parallel with a common reference junction is useful for obtaining an average temperature of an object or volume. In such measurements, however, it is important that the electrical resistances of the individual thermocouples be the same. Use of thermocouples in series and parallel arrangements is discussed in ASTM *Manual* 12.

Surface Temperature Measurement

The thermocouple is useful in determining surface temperature. It can be attached to a metal surface in several ways. For permanent installations, soldering, brazing, or peening (i.e., driving the thermocouple measuring junction into a small drilled hole) is suggested. For temporary arrangements, thermocouples can be attached by tape, adhesive, or putty-like material. For boiler or furnace surfaces, use furnace cement. To minimize the possibility of error caused by heat conduction along wires, a surface thermocouple should be made of fine wires placed in close contact with the surface being measured for about 25 mm from the junction to ensure good thermal contact. Wires must be insulated electrically from each other and from the metal surface (except at the junction).

Thermocouple Construction

Thermocouple wires are typically insulated with fibrous glass, fluorocarbon resin, or ceramic insulators. In another form of thermocouple, the wires are insulated with compacted ceramic insulation inside a metal sheath, providing both mechanical protection and protection from stray electromagnetic fields. The measuring junction may be exposed or enclosed within the metal sheath. An enclosed junction may be either grounded or ungrounded to the metal sheath.

An exposed junction is in direct contact with the process stream; it is therefore subject to corrosion or contamination, but provides a fast temperature response. A grounded enclosed junction, in which the wires are welded to the metal sheath, provides electrical grounding, as well as mechanical and corrosion protection, but has a slower response time. Response time is even slower for ungrounded enclosed junctions, but the thermocouple wires are isolated electrically and are less susceptible to some forms of mechanical strain than those with grounded construction.

OPTICAL PYROMETRY

Optical pyrometry determines a surface's temperature from the color of the radiation it emits. As the temperature of a surface increases, it becomes deep red in color, then orange, and eventually white. This behavior follows from Wein's law, which indicates that the wavelength corresponding to the maximum intensity of emitted radiation is inversely proportional to the absolute temperature of the emitting surface. Thus, as temperature increases, the wavelength decreases.

To determine the unknown surface temperature, the color of the radiation from the surface is optically compared to the color of a heated filament. By adjusting the current in the filament, the color of the filament is made to match the color of radiation from the source surface. When in balance, the filament virtually disappears into the background image of the surface color. Filament calibration is required to relate the filament current to the unknown surface temperature. For further information, see Holman (2001).

INFRARED RADIATION THERMOMETERS

Infrared radiation (IR) thermometers, also known as *remote temperature sensors* (Hudson 1969) or *pyrometers*, allow noncontact measurement of surface temperature over a wide range. In these instruments, radiant flux from the observed object is focused by an optical system onto an infrared detector that generates an output signal proportional to the incident radiation that can be read from a meter or display unit. Both point and scanning radiometers are available; the latter can display the temperature variation in the field of view.

IR thermometers are usually classified according to the detector used: either thermal or photon. In **thermal detectors**, a change in electrical property is caused by the heating effect of the incident radiation. Examples of thermal detectors are the thermocouple, thermopile, and metallic and semiconductor bolometers. Typical response times are one-quarter to one-half second. In **photon detectors**, a change in electrical property is caused by the surface absorption of incident photons. Because these detectors do not require an increase in temperature for activation, their response time is much shorter than that of thermal detectors. Scanning radiometers usually use photon detectors.

An IR thermometer only measures the power level of radiation incident on the detector, a combination of thermal radiation emitted by the object and surrounding background radiation reflected from the object's surface. Very accurate measurement of temperature, therefore, requires knowledge of the long-wavelength emissivity of the object as well as the effective temperature of the thermal radiation field surrounding the object. Calibration against an internal or external source of known temperature and emissivity may be needed to obtain true surface temperature from the radiation measurements.

In other cases, using published emissivity factors for common materials may suffice. Many IR thermometers have an emissivity adjustment feature that automatically calculates the effect of emissivity on temperature once the emissivity factor is entered. Thermometers that do not have an emissivity adjustment are usually preset to calculate emissivity at 0.95, a good estimate of the emissivity of most organic substances, including paint. Moreover, IR thermometers are frequently used for relative, rather than absolute, measurement; in these cases, adjustment for emissivity may be unnecessary. The most significant practical problem is measuring shiny, polished objects. Placing electrical tape or painting the measurement area with flat black paint and allowing the temperature of the tape or paint to equilibrate can mitigate this problem.

A key factor in measurement quality can be the optical resolution or spot size of the IR thermometer, because this specification determines the instrument's measurement area from a particular distance and, thus, whether a user is actually measuring the desired area. Optical resolution is expressed as distance to spot size (*D*:*S*) at the focal. Part of the *D*:*S* specification is a description of the amount of target infrared energy encircled by the spot; typically it is 95%, but may be 90%.

Temperature resolution of an IR thermometer decreases as object temperature decreases. For example, a radiometer that can resolve a temperature difference of 0.3 K on an object near 20°C may only resolve a difference of 1 K on an object at 0°C.

INFRARED THERMOGRAPHY

Infrared thermography acquires and analyzes thermal information using images from an infrared imaging system. An infrared imaging system consists of (1) an infrared television camera and (2) a display unit. The infrared camera scans a surface and senses the self-emitted and reflected radiation viewed from the surface. The display unit contains either a cathode-ray tube (CRT) that displays a gray-tone or color-coded thermal image of the surface or a color liquid crystal display (LCD) screen. A photograph of the image on the CRT is called a *thermogram*. Introductions to infrared thermography are given by Madding (1989) and Paljak and Pettersson (1972).

Thermography has been used to detect missing insulation and air infiltration paths in building envelopes (Burch and Hunt 1978). Standard practices for conducting thermographic inspections of buildings are given in ASTM *Standard* C1060. A technique for quantitatively mapping heat loss in building envelopes is given by Mack (1986).

Aerial infrared thermography of buildings is effective in identifying regions of an individual built-up roof that have wet insulation (Tobiasson and Korhonen 1985), but it is ineffective in ranking a

Table 3 Humidity Sensor Properties

Type of Sensor	Sensor Category	Method of Operation	Approximate Range	Some Uses	Approximate Accuracy
Psychrometer	Evaporative cooling	Temperature measurement of wet bulb	0 to 80°C	Measurement, standard	±3 to 7% rh
Adiabatic saturation psychrometer	Evaporative cooling	Temperature measurement of thermodynamic wet bulb	5 to 30°C	Measurement, standard	±0.2 to 2% rh
Chilled mirror	Dew point	Optical determination of moisture formation	–75 to 95°C dp	Measurement, control, meteorology	±0.2 to 2 K
Heated saturated salt solution	Water vapor pressure	Vapor pressure depression in salt solution	–30 to 70°C dp	Measurement, control, meteorology	±1.5 K
Hair	Mechanical	Dimensional change	5 to 100% rh	Measurement, control	±5% rh
Nylon	Mechanical	Dimensional change	5 to 100% rh	Measurement, control	±5% rh
Dacron thread	Mechanical	Dimensional change	5 to 100% rh	Measurement	±7% rh
Goldbeater's skin	Mechanical	Dimensional change	5 to 100% rh	Measurement	±7% rh
Cellulosic materials	Mechanical	Dimensional change	5 to 100% rh	Measurement, control	±5% rh
Carbon	Mechanical	Dimensional change	5 to 100% rh	Measurement	±5% rh
Dunmore type	Electrical	Impedance	7 to 98% rh at 5 to 60°C	Measurement, control	±1.5% rh
Polymer film electronic hygrometer	Electrical	Impedance or capacitance	10 to 100% rh		±2 to 3% rh
Ion exchange resin	Electrical	Impedance or capacitance	10 to 100% rh at –40 to 90°C	Measurement, control	±5% rh
Porous ceramic	Electrical	Impedance or capacitance	Up to 200°C	Measurement, control	±1 to 1.5% rh
Aluminum oxide	Electrical	Capacitance	–80 to 60°C dp	Trace moisture measurement, control	±1 K dp
Electrolytic hygrometer	Electrolytic cell	Electrolyzes due to adsorbed moisture	1 to 1000 ppm	Measurement	
Infrared laser diode	Electrical	Optical diodes	0.1 to 100 ppm	Trace moisture measurement	±0.1 ppm
Surface acoustic wave	Electrical	SAW attenuation	85 to 98% rh	Measurement, control	±1% rh
Piezoelectric	Mass sensitive	Mass changes due to adsorbed moisture	–75 to –20°C	Trace moisture measurement, control	±1 to 5 K dp
Radiation absorption	Moisture absorption	Moisture absorption of UV or IR radiation	–20 to 80°C dp	Measurement, control, meteorology	±2 K dp, ±5% rh
Gravimetric	Direct measurement of mixing ratio	Comparison of sample gas with dry airstream	120 to 20 000 ppm mixing ratio	Primary standard, research and laboratory	±0.13% of reading
Color change	Physical	Color changes	10 to 80% rh	Warning device	±10% rh

Notes:
1. This table does not include all available technology for humidity measurement.
2. Approximate range for device types listed is based on surveys of device manufacturers.
3. Approximate accuracy is based on manufacturers' data.
4. Presently, NIST only certifies instruments with operating ranges within –75 to 100°C dp.

group of roofs according to their thermal resistance (Burch 1980; Goldstein 1978). In this latter application, the emittances of the separate roofs and outdoor climate (i.e., temperature and wind speed) throughout the microclimate often produce changes in the thermal image that may be incorrectly attributed to differences in thermal resistance.

Industrial applications include locating defective or missing pipe insulation in buried heat distribution systems, surveys of manufacturing plants to quantify energy loss from equipment, and locating defects in coatings (Bentz and Martin 1987). Madding (1989) discusses applications to electrical power systems and electronics.

HUMIDITY MEASUREMENT

Any instrument that can measure the humidity or psychrometric state of air is a hygrometer, and many are available. The indication sensors used on the instruments respond to different moisture property contents. These responses are related to factors such as wet-bulb temperature, relative humidity, humidity (mixing) ratio, dew point, and frost point.

Table 3 lists instruments for measuring humidity. Each is capable of accurate measurement under certain conditions and within specific limitations. The following sections describe the various instruments in more detail.

PSYCHROMETERS

A typical industrial psychrometer consists of a pair of matched electrical or mechanical temperature sensors, one of which is kept wet with a moistened wick. A blower aspirates the sensor, which lowers the temperature at the moistened temperature sensor. The lowest temperature depression occurs when the evaporation rate required to saturate the moist air adjacent to the wick is constant. This is a steady-state, open-loop, nonequilibrium process, which depends on the purity of the water, cleanliness of the wick, ventilation rate, radiation effects, size and accuracy of the temperature sensors, and transport properties of the gas.

ASHRAE *Standard* 41.6 recommends an airflow over both the wet and dry bulbs of 3 to 5 m/s for transverse ventilation and 1.5 to 2.5 m/s for axial ventilation.

The **sling psychrometer** consists of two thermometers mounted side by side in a frame fitted with a handle for whirling the device through the air. The thermometers are spun until their readings become steady. In the **ventilated** or **aspirated psychrometer**, the thermometers remain stationary, and a small fan, blower, or syringe moves air across the thermometer bulbs. Various designs are used in the laboratory, and commercial models are available.

Other temperature sensors, such as thermocouples and thermistors, are also used and can be adapted for recording temperatures or for use where a small instrument is required. Small-diameter wet-bulb sensors operate with low ventilation rates.

Charts and tables showing the relationship between the temperatures and humidity are available. Data are usually based on a barometric pressure equal to one standard atmosphere. To meet special needs, charts can be produced that apply to nonstandard pressure (e.g., the ASHRAE 2250 m psychrometric chart). Alternatively, mathematical calculations can be made (Kusuda 1965). Uncertainties of 3 to 7% rh are typical for psychrometer-based derivation. The degree of uncertainty is a function of the accuracy of temperature measurements (wet- and dry-bulb), knowledge of the barometric pressure, and conformance to accepted operational procedures such as those outlined in ASHRAE *Standard* 41.6.

In air temperatures below 0°C, water on the wick may either freeze or supercool. Because the wet-bulb temperature is different for ice and water, the state must be known and the proper chart or table used. Some operators remove the wick from the wet bulb for freezing conditions and dip the bulb in water a few times; this allows water to freeze on the bulb between dips, forming a film of ice. Because the wet-bulb depression is slight at low temperatures, precise temperature readings are essential. A psychrometer can be used at high temperatures, but if the wet-bulb depression is large, the wick must remain wet and water supplied to the wick must be cooled so as not to influence the wet-bulb temperature by carrying sensible heat to it (Richardson 1965; Worrall 1965).

Greenspan and Wexler (1968) and Wentzel (1961) developed devices to measure adiabatic saturation temperature.

DEW-POINT HYGROMETERS

Condensation Dew-Point Hygrometers

The condensation (chilled-mirror) dew-point hygrometer is an accurate and reliable instrument with a wide humidity range. However, these features are gained at increased complexity and cost compared to the psychrometer. In the condensation hygrometer, a surface is cooled (thermoelectrically, mechanically, or chemically) until dew or frost begins to condense out. The condensate surface is maintained electronically in vapor-pressure equilibrium with the surrounding gas, while surface condensation is detected by optical, electrical, or nuclear techniques. The measured surface temperature is then the dew-point temperature.

The largest source of error stems from the difficulty in measuring condensate surface temperature accurately. Typical industrial versions of the instrument are accurate to ±0.5 K over wide temperature spans. With proper attention to the condensate surface temperature measuring system, errors can be reduced to about ±0.2 K. Condensation hygrometers can be made surprisingly compact using solid-state optics and thermoelectric cooling.

Wide span and minimal errors are two of the main features of this instrument. A properly designed condensation hygrometer can measure dew points from 95°C down to frost points of –75°C. Typical condensation hygrometers can cool to 80 K below ambient temperature, establishing lower limits of the instrument to dew points corresponding to approximately 0.5% rh. Accuracies for measurements above –40°C can be ±1 K or better, deteriorating to ±2 K at lower temperatures.

The response time of a condensation dew-point hygrometer is usually specified in terms of its cooling/heating rate, typically 2 K/s for thermoelectric cooled mirrors. This makes it somewhat faster than a heated salt hygrometer. Perhaps the most significant feature of the condensation hygrometer is its fundamental measuring technique, which essentially renders the instrument self-calibrating. For calibration, it is necessary only to manually override the surface cooling control loop, causing the surface to heat, and confirm that the instrument recools to the same dew point when the loop is closed. Assuming that the surface temperature measuring system is correct, this is a reasonable check on the instrument's performance.

Although condensation hygrometers can become contaminated, they can easily be cleaned and returned to service with no impairment to performance.

Salt-Phase Heated Hygrometers

Another instrument in which the temperature varies with ambient dew-point temperature is variously designated as a self-heating salt-phase transition hygrometer or a heated electrical hygrometer. This device usually consists of a tubular substrate covered by glass fiber fabric, with a spiral bifilar winding for electrodes. The surface is covered with a salt solution, usually lithium chloride. The sensor is connected in series with a ballast and a 24 V (ac) supply. When the instrument is operating, electrical current flowing through the salt film heats the sensor. The salt's electrical resistance characteristics are such that a balance is reached with the salt at a critical moisture content corresponding to a saturated solution. The sensor temperature adjusts automatically so that the water vapor pressures of the salt film and ambient atmosphere are equal.

With lithium chloride, this sensor cannot be used to measure relative humidity below approximately 12% (the equilibrium relative humidity of this salt), and it has an upper dew-point limit of about 70°C. The regions of highest precision are between –23 and 34°C, and above 40°C dew point. Another problem is that the lithium chloride solution can be washed off when exposed to water. In addition, this type of sensor is subject to contamination problems, which limits its accuracy. Its response time is also very slow; it takes approximately 2 min for a 67% step change.

MECHANICAL HYGROMETERS

Many organic materials change in dimension with changes in humidity; this action is used in a number of simple and effective humidity indicators, recorders, and controllers (see Chapter 7). They are coupled to pneumatic leak ports, mechanical linkages, or electrical transduction elements to form hygrometers.

Commonly used organic materials are human hair, nylon, Dacron, animal membrane, animal horn, wood, and paper. Their inherent nonlinearity and hysteresis must be compensated for within the hygrometer. These devices are generally unreliable below 0°C. The response is generally inadequate for monitoring a changing process, and can be affected significantly by exposure to extremes of humidity. Mechanical hygrometers require initial calibration and frequent recalibration; however, they are useful because they can be arranged to read relative humidity directly, and they are simpler and less expensive than most other types.

ELECTRICAL IMPEDANCE AND CAPACITANCE HYGROMETERS

Many substances adsorb or lose moisture with changing relative humidity and exhibit corresponding changes in electrical impedance or capacitance.

Dunmore Hygrometers

This sensor consists of dual electrodes on a tubular or flat substrate; it is coated with a film containing salt, such as lithium chloride, in a binder to form an electrical connection between windings. The relation of sensor resistance to humidity is usually represented by graphs. Because the sensor is highly sensitive, the graphs are a series of curves, each for a given temperature, with intermediate values found by interpolation. Several resistance elements, called Dunmore elements, cover a standard range. Systematic calibration is essential because the resistance grid varies with time and contamination as well as with exposure to temperature and humidity extremes.

Polymer Film Electronic Hygrometers

These devices consist of a hygroscopic organic polymer deposited by means of thin or thick film processing technology on a water-permeable substrate. Both capacitance and impedance sensors are available. The impedance devices may be either ionic or electronic conduction types. These hygrometers typically have integrated circuits that provide temperature correction and signal conditioning. The primary advantages of this sensor technology are small size; low cost; fast response times (on the order of 1 to 120 s for 64% change in relative humidity); and good accuracy over the full range, including the low end, where most other devices are less accurate.

Ion Exchange Resin Electric Hygrometers

A conventional ion exchange resin consists of a polymer with a high relative molecular mass and polar groups of positive or negative charge in cross-link structure. Associated with these polar groups are ions of opposite charge that are held by electrostatic forces to the fixed polar groups. In the presence of water or water vapor, the electrostatically held ions become mobile; thus, when a voltage is impressed across the resin, the ions are capable of electrolytic conduction. The **Pope cell** is one example of an ion exchange element. It is a wide-range sensor, typically covering 15 to 95% rh; therefore, one sensor can be used where several Dunmore elements would be required. The Pope cell, however, has a nonlinear characteristic from approximately 1000 Ω at 100% rh to several megohms at 10% rh.

Impedance-Based Porous Ceramic Electronic Hygrometers

Using oxides' adsorption characteristics, humidity-sensitive ceramic oxide devices use either ionic or electronic measurement techniques to relate adsorbed water to relative humidity. Ionic conduction is produced by dissociation of water molecules, forming surface hydroxyls. The dissociation causes proton migration, so the device's impedance decreases with increasing water content. The ceramic oxide is sandwiched between porous metal electrodes that connect the device to an impedance-measuring circuit for linearizing and signal conditioning. These sensors have excellent sensitivity, are resistant to contamination and high temperature (up to 200°C), and may get fully wet without sensor degradation. These sensors are accurate to about ±1.5% rh (±1% rh when temperature-compensated) and have a moderate cost.

Aluminum Oxide Capacitive Sensor

This sensor consists of an aluminum strip that is anodized by a process that forms a porous oxide layer. A very thin coating of cracked chromium or gold is then evaporated over this structure. The aluminum base and cracked chromium or gold layer form the two electrodes of what is essentially an aluminum oxide capacitor.

Water vapor is rapidly transported through the cracked chromium or gold layer and equilibrates on the walls of the oxide pores in a manner functionally related to the vapor pressure of water in the atmosphere surrounding the sensor. The number of water molecules adsorbed on the oxide structure determines the capacitance between the two electrodes.

ELECTROLYTIC HYGROMETERS

In electrolytic hygrometers, air is passed through a tube, where moisture is adsorbed by a highly effective desiccant (usually phosphorous pentoxide) and electrolyzed. The airflow is regulated to 1.65 mL/s at a standard temperature and pressure. As the incoming water vapor is absorbed by the desiccant and electrolyzed into hydrogen and oxygen, the current of electrolysis determines the mass of water vapor entering the sensor. The flow rate of the entering gas is controlled precisely to maintain a standard sample mass flow rate into the sensor. The instrument is usually designed for use with moisture/air ratios in the range of less than 1 ppm to 1000 ppm, but can be used with higher humidities.

PIEZOELECTRIC SORPTION

This hygrometer compares the changes in frequency of two hygroscopically coated quartz crystal oscillators. As the crystal's mass changes because of absorption of water vapor, the frequency changes. The amount of water sorbed on the sensor is a function of relative humidity (i.e., partial pressure of water as well as ambient temperature).

A commercial version uses a hygroscopic polymer coating on the crystal. Humidity is measured by monitoring the change in the vibration frequency of the quartz crystal when the crystal is alternately exposed to wet and dry gas.

SPECTROSCOPIC (RADIATION ABSORPTION) HYGROMETERS

Radiation absorption devices operate on the principle that selective absorption of radiation is a function of frequency for different media. Water vapor absorbs **infrared** radiation at 2 to 3 μm wavelengths and **ultraviolet** radiation centered about the Lyman-alpha line at 0.122 μm. The amount of absorbed radiation is directly related to the absolute humidity or water vapor content in the gas mixture, according to Beer's law. The basic unit consists of an energy source and optical system for isolating wavelengths in the spectral region of interest, and a measurement system for determining the attenuation of radiant energy caused by water vapor in the optical path. Absorbed radiation is measured extremely quickly and independent of the degree of saturation of the gas mixture. Response times of 0.1 to 1 s for 90% change in moisture content are common. Spectroscopic hygrometers are primarily used where a noncontact application is required; this may include atmospheric studies, industrial drying ovens, and harsh environments. The primary disadvantages of this device are its high cost and relatively large size.

GRAVIMETRIC HYGROMETERS

Humidity levels can be measured by extracting and finding the mass of water vapor in a known quantity or atmosphere. For precise laboratory work, powerful desiccants, such as phosphorous pentoxide and magnesium perchlorate, are used for extraction; for other purposes, calcium chloride or silica gel is satisfactory.

When the highest level of accuracy is required, the gravimetric hygrometer, developed and maintained by NIST, is the ultimate in the measurement hierarchy. The gravimetric hygrometer gives the absolute water vapor content, where the mass of absorbed water and precise measurement of the gas volume associated with the water vapor determine the mixing ratio or absolute humidity of the sample. This system is the primary standard because the required measurements of mass, temperature, pressure, and volume can be made with extreme precision. However, its complexity and required attention to detail limit its usefulness.

CALIBRATION

For many hygrometers, the need for recalibration depends on the accuracy required, the sensor's stability, and the conditions to which the sensor is subjected. Many hygrometers should be calibrated regularly by exposure to an atmosphere maintained at a known humidity and temperature, or by comparison with a transfer standard hygrometer. Complete calibration usually requires observation of a series of temperatures and humidities. Methods for producing known humidities include saturated salt solutions (Greenspan 1977); sulfuric acid solutions; and mechanical systems, such as the divided flow, two-pressure (Amdur 1965); two-temperature (Till and Handegord 1960); and NIST two-pressure humidity generator (Hasegawa 1976). All these systems rely on precise methods of temperature and pressure control in a controlled environment to produce a known humidity, usually with accuracies of 0.5 to 1.0%. The operating range for the precision generator is typically 5 to 95% rh.

PRESSURE MEASUREMENT

Pressure is the force exerted per unit area by a medium, generally a liquid or gas. Pressure so defined is sometimes called **absolute pressure**. Thermodynamic and material properties are expressed in terms of absolute pressures; thus, the properties of a refrigerant are given in terms of absolute pressures. **Vacuum** refers to pressures below atmospheric.

Differential pressure is the difference between two absolute pressures, or the difference between two relative pressures measured with respect to the same reference pressure. Often, it can be very small compared to either of the absolute pressures (these are often referred to as low-range, high-line differential pressures). A common example of differential pressure is the pressure drop, or difference between inlet and outlet pressures, across a filter or flow element.

Gage pressure is a special case of differential pressure where the reference pressure is atmospheric pressure. Many pressure gages, including most refrigeration test sets, are designed to make gage pressure measurements, and there are probably more gage pressure measurements made than any other. Gage pressure measurements are often used as surrogates for absolute pressures. However, because of variations in atmospheric pressure caused by elevation (e.g., atmospheric pressure in Denver, Colorado, is about 81% of sea-level pressure) and weather changes, using gage pressures to determine absolute pressures can significantly restrict the accuracy of the measured pressure, unless corrections are made for the local atmospheric pressure at the time of measurement.

Pressures can be further classified as static or dynamic. **Static pressures** have a small or undetectable change with time; **dynamic pressures** include a significant pulsed, oscillatory, or other time-dependent component. Static pressure measurements are the most common, but equipment such as blowers and compressors can generate significant oscillatory pressures at discrete frequencies. Flow in pipes and ducts can generate resonant pressure changes, as well as turbulent "noise" that can span a wide range of frequencies.

Units

A plethora of pressure units, many of them poorly defined, are in common use. The international (SI) unit is the newton per square metre, called the pascal (Pa). Although the bar and standard atmosphere are used, they should not be introduced where they are not used at present.

INSTRUMENTS

Broadly speaking, pressure instruments can be divided into three different categories: standards, mechanical gages, and electromechanical transducers. Standards instruments are used for the most accurate calibrations. The liquid-column manometer, which is the most common and potentially the most accurate standard, is used for a variety of applications, including field applications. Mechanical pressure gages are generally the least expensive and the most common. However, electromechanical transducers have become much less expensive and are easier to use, so they are being used more often.

Pressure Standards

Liquid-column manometers measure pressure by determining the vertical displacement of a liquid of known density in a known gravitational field. Typically, they are constructed as a U-tube of transparent material (glass or plastic). The pressure to be measured is applied to one side of the U-tube. If the other (reference) side is evacuated (zero pressure), the manometer measures absolute pressure; if the reference side is open to the atmosphere, it measures gage pressure; if the reference side is connected to some other pressure, the manometer measures the differential between the two pressures. Manometers filled with water and different oils are often used to measure low-range differential pressures. In some low-range instruments, one tube of the manometer is inclined to enhance readability. Mercury-filled manometers are used for higher-range differential and absolute pressure measurements. In the latter case, the reference side is evacuated, generally with a mechanical vacuum pump. Typical full-scale ranges for manometers vary from 25 Pa to 300 kPa.

For pressures above the range of manometers, standards are generally of the piston-gage, pressure-balance, or deadweight-tester type. These instruments apply pressure to the bottom of a vertical piston, which is surrounded by a close-fitting cylinder (typical clearances are micrometres). The pressure generates a force approximately equal to the pressure times the area of the piston. This force is balanced by weights stacked on the top of the piston. If the mass of the weights, local acceleration of gravity, and area of the piston (or more properly, the "effective area" of the piston and cylinder assembly) are known, the applied pressure can be calculated. Piston gages usually generate gage pressures with respect to the atmospheric pressure above the piston. They can be used to measure absolute pressures either indirectly, by separately measuring the atmospheric pressure and adding it to the gage pressure determined by the piston gage, or directly, by surrounding the top of the piston and weights with an evacuated bell jar. Piston gage full-scale ranges vary from 35 kPa to 1.4 GPa.

At the other extreme, very low absolute pressures (below about 100 Pa), a number of different types of standards are used. These tend to be specialized and expensive instruments found only in major standards laboratories. However, one low-pressure standard, the **McLeod gage**, has been used for field applications. Unfortunately, although its theory is simple and straightforward, it is difficult to use accurately, and major errors can occur when it is used to measure gases that condense or are adsorbed (e.g., water). In general, other gages should be used for most low-pressure or vacuum applications.

Mechanical Pressure Gages

Mechanical pressure gages couple a pressure sensor to a mechanical readout, typically a pointer and dial. The most common type uses a **Bourdon tube** sensor, which is essentially a coiled metal tube of circular or elliptical cross section. Increasing pressure applied to the inside of the tube causes it to uncoil. A mechanical linkage translates the motion of the end of the tube to the rotation of a pointer. In most cases, the Bourdon tube is surrounded by atmospheric pressure, so that the gages measure gage pressure. A few instruments surround the Bourdon tube with a sealed enclosure that can be evacuated for absolute measurements or connected to another pressure for differential measurements. Available instruments vary widely in cost, size, pressure range, and accuracy. Full-scale ranges can vary from 35 kPa to 700 MPa. Accuracy of properly calibrated and used instruments can vary from 0.1 to 10% of full scale. Generally there is a strong correlation between size, accuracy, and price; larger instruments are more accurate and expensive.

For better sensitivity, some low-range mechanical gages (sometimes called **aneroid gages**) use corrugated diaphragms or capsules as sensors. The capsule is basically a short bellows sealed with end caps. These sensors are more compliant than a Bourdon tube, and a given applied pressure causes a larger deflection of the sensor. The inside of a capsule can be evacuated and sealed to measure absolute pressures or connected to an external fitting to allow differential pressures to be measured. Typically, these gages are used for low-range measurements of 100 kPa or less. In better-quality instruments, accuracies can be 0.1% of reading or better.

Electromechanical Transducers

Mechanical pressure gages are generally limited by inelastic behavior of the sensing element, friction in the readout mechanism, and limited resolution of the pointer and dial. These effects can be eliminated or reduced by using electronic techniques to sense the distortion or stress of a mechanical sensing element and electronically convert that stress or distortion to a pressure reading. A wide variety of sensors is used, including Bourdon tubes, capsules, diaphragms, and different resonant structures whose vibration frequency varies with the applied pressure. Capacitive, inductive, and optical lever sensors are used to measure the sensor element's displacement. In some cases, feedback techniques may be used to constrain the sensor in a null position, minimizing distortion and hysteresis of the sensing element. Temperature control or compensation is often included. Readout may be in the form of a digital display, analog voltage or current, or a digital code. Size varies, but for transducers using a diaphragm fabricated as part of a silicon chip, the sensor and signal-conditioning electronics can be contained in a small transistor package, and the largest part of the device is the pressure fitting. The best of these instruments achieve long-term instabilities of 0.01% or less of full scale, and corresponding accuracies when properly calibrated. Performance of less-expensive instruments can be more on the order of several percent.

Although the dynamic response of most mechanical gages is limited by the sensor and readout, the response of some electromechanical transducers can be much faster, allowing measurements of dynamic pressures at frequencies up to 1 kHz and beyond in the case of transducers specifically designed for dynamic measurements. Manufacturers' literature should be consulted as a guide to the dynamic response of specific instruments.

As the measured pressure drops below about 10 kPa, it becomes increasingly difficult to sense mechanically. A variety of gages have been developed that measure some other property of the gas that is related to the pressure. In particular, **thermal conductivity gages**, known as thermocouple, thermistor, Pirani, and convection gages, are used for pressures down to about 0.1 Pa. These gages have a sensor tube with a small heated element and a temperature sensor; the temperature of the heated element is determined by the thermal conductivity of the gas, and the output of the temperature sensor is displayed on an analog or digital electrical meter contained in an attached electronics unit. The accuracy of thermal conductivity gages is limited by their nonlinearity, dependence on gas species, and tendency to read high when contaminated. Oil contamination is a particular problem. However, these gages are small, reasonably rugged, and relatively inexpensive; in the hands of a typical user, they give far more reliable results than a McLeod gage. They can be used to check the base pressure in a system that is being evacuated before being filled with refrigerant. They should be checked periodically for contamination by comparing the reading with that from a new, clean sensor tube.

General Considerations

Accurate values of atmospheric or barometric pressure are required for weather prediction and aircraft altimetry. In the United States, a network of calibrated instruments, generally accurate to within 0.1% of reading and located at airports, is maintained by the National Weather Service, the Federal Aviation Administration, and local airport operating authorities. These agencies are generally cooperative in providing current values of atmospheric pressure that can be used to check the calibration of absolute pressure gages or to correct gage pressure readings to absolute pressures. However, pressure readings generally reported for weather and altimetry purposes are not the true atmospheric pressure, but rather a value adjusted to an equivalent sea level pressure. Therefore, unless the location is near sea level, it is important to ask for the station or true atmospheric pressure rather than using the adjusted values broadcast by radio stations. Further, atmospheric pressure decreases with increasing elevation at a rate (near sea level) of about 10 Pa/m, and corresponding corrections should be made to account for the difference in elevation between the instruments being compared.

Gage-pressure instruments are sometimes used to measure absolute pressures, but their accuracy can be compromised by uncertainties in atmospheric pressure. This error can be particularly serious when gage-pressure instruments are used to measure vacuum (negative gage pressures). For all but the most crude measurements, absolute-pressure gages should be used for vacuum measurements; for pressures below about 100 Pa, a thermal conductivity gage should be used.

All pressure gages are susceptible to temperature errors. Several techniques are used to minimize these errors: sensor materials are generally chosen to minimize temperature effects, mechanical readouts can include temperature compensation elements, electromechanical transducers may include a temperature sensor and compensation circuit, and some transducers are operated at a controlled temperature. Clearly, temperature effects are of greater concern for field applications, and it is prudent to check the manufacturers' literature for the temperature range over which the specified accuracy can be maintained. Abrupt temperature changes can also cause large transient errors that may take some time to decay.

Readings of some electromechanical transducers with a resonant or vibrating sensor can depend on the gas species. Although some of these units can achieve calibrated accuracies of the order of 0.01% of reading, they are typically calibrated with dry air or nitrogen, and readings for other gases can be in error by several percent, possibly much more for refrigerants and other high-density gases. High-accuracy readings can be maintained by calibrating these devices with the gas to be measured. Manufacturers' literature should be consulted.

Measuring dynamic pressures is limited not just by the frequency response of the pressure gage, but also by the hydraulic or pneumatic time constant of the connection between the gage and the system to be monitored. Generally, the longer the connecting lines and the smaller their diameter, the lower the system's frequency response. Further, even if only the static component of the pressure is of interest, and a gage with a low-frequency response is used, a significant pulsating or oscillating pressure component can cause significant errors in pressure gage readings and, in some cases, can damage the gage, particularly one with a mechanical readout mechanism. In these cases, a filter or snubber should be used to reduce the higher-frequency components.

AIR VELOCITY MEASUREMENT

HVAC engineers measure the flow of air more often than any other gas, and usually at or near atmospheric pressure. Under this condition, air can be treated as an incompressible (i.e., constant-density) fluid, and simple formulas give sufficient precision to solve many problems. Instruments that measure fluid velocity and their application range and precision are listed in Table 4.

AIRBORNE TRACER TECHNIQUES

Tracer techniques are suitable for measuring velocity in an open space. Typical tracers include smoke, feathers, pieces of lint, and radioactive or nonradioactive gases. Measurements are made by timing the rate of movement of solid tracers or by monitoring the change in concentration level of gas tracers.

Smoke is a useful qualitative tool in studying air movements. Smoke can be obtained from titanium tetrachloride (irritating to

Table 4 Air Velocity Measurement

Measurement Means	Application	Range, m/s	Precision	Limitations
Smoke puff or airborne solid tracer	Low air velocities in rooms; highly directional	0.025 to 0.25	10 to 20%	Awkward to use but valuable in tracing air movement.
Deflecting vane anemometer	Air velocities in rooms, at outlets, etc.; directional	0.15 to 120	5%	Requires periodic calibration check.
Revolving (rotating) vane anemometer	Moderate air velocities in ducts and rooms; somewhat directional	0.5 to 15	2 to 5%	Subject to significant errors when variations in velocities with space or time are present. Easily damaged. Affected by turbulence intensity. Requires periodic calibration.
Thermal (hot-wire or hot-film) anemometer	a. Low air velocities; directional and omnidirectional available b. Transient velocity and turbulence	0.25 to 50	2 to 10%	Requires accurate calibration at frequent intervals. Some are relatively costly. Affected by thermal plume because of self-heating.
Pitot-static tube	Standard (typically hand-held) instrument for measuring single-point duct velocities	0.9 to 50 with micromanometer; 3 to 50 with draft gages; 50 up with manometer	2 to 5%	Accuracy falls off at low end of range because of square-root relationship between velocity and dynamic pressure. Also affected by alignment with flow direction.
Impact tube and sidewall or other static tap	High velocities, small tubes, and where air direction may be variable	0.6 to 50 with micromanometer; 3 to 50 with draft gages; 50 up with manometer	2 to 5%	Accuracy depends on constancy of static pressure across stream section.
Cup anemometer	Meteorological	Up to 60	2 to 5%	Poor accuracy at low air velocity (<2.5 m/s).
Ultrasonic	Large instruments: meteorological Small instruments: in-duct and room air velocities	0.005 to 30	1 to 2%	High cost.
Laser Doppler velocimeter (LDV)	Calibration of air velocity instruments	0.005 to 30	1 to 3%	High cost and complexity limit LDVs to laboratory applications. Requires seeding of flow with particles, and transparent optical access (window).
Particle image velocimetry (PIV)	Full-field (2D, 3D) velocity measurements in rooms, outlets	0.005 to 30	10%	High cost and complexity limits measurements to laboratory applications. Requires seeding of flow with particles, and transparent optical access (window).
Pitot array, self-averaging differential pressure, typically using equalizing manifolds	In duct assemblies, ducted or fan inlet probes	3 to 50	±2 to >40% of reading	Performance depends heavily on quality and range of associated differential pressure transmitter. Very susceptible to measurement errors caused by duct placement and temperature changes. Nonlinear output (square-root function). Mathematical averaging errors likely because of sampling method. Must be kept clean to function properly. Must be set up and field-calibrated to hand-held reference, or calibrated against nozzle standard.
Piezometer and piezo-ring variations, self-averaging differential pressure using equalizing manifolds	Centrifugal fan inlet cone	3 to 50	±5 to >40% of reading	Performance depends heavily on quality and range of required differential pressure transmitter. Very susceptible to measurement errors caused by inlet cone placement, inlet obstructions, and temperature changes. Nonlinear output (square-root function). Must be kept clean. Must be field-calibrated to hand-held reference.
Vortex shedding	In-duct assemblies, ducted or fan inlet probes	2 to 30	±2.5 to 10% of reading	Highest cost per sensing point. Largest physical size. Low-temperature accuracy questionable. Must be set up and field-calibrated to hand-held reference.
Thermal (analog electronic) using thermistors	In-duct assemblies or ducted probes	0.25 to 25	±2 to 40% of reading	Mathematical averaging errors may be caused by analog electronic circuitry when averaging nonlinear signals. Sensing points may not be independent. May not be able to compensate for temperatures beyond a narrow range. Must be set up and field-calibrated to hand-held reference. Must be recalibrated regularly to counteract drift.
Thermal dispersion (microcontroller-based) using thermistors to independently determine temperatures and velocities	Ducted or fan inlet probes, bleed velocity sensors	0.1 to 50	±2 to 10% of reading	Cost increases with number of sensor assemblies in array. Not available with flanged frame. Honeycomb air straighteners not recommended by manufacturer. Accuracy verified only to −29°C. Not suitable for abrasive or high-temperature environments.
Thermal (analog electronic) using RTDs	In-duct assemblies or ducted probes; stainless steel and platinum RTDs have industrial environment capabilities	0.5 to 90	±1 to 20% of reading	Requires long duct/pipe runs. Sensitive to placement conditions. Mathematical averaging errors may be caused by analog electronic circuitry when averaging nonlinear signals. Must be recalibrated regularly to counteract drift. Fairly expensive.

nasal membranes) or by mixing potassium chlorate and powdered sugar (nonirritating) and firing the mixture with a match. The latter process produces considerable heat and should be confined to a pan away from flammable materials. Titanium tetrachloride smoke works well for spot tests, particularly for leakage through casings and ducts, because it can be handled easily in a small, pistol-like ejector. Another alternative is theatrical smoke, which is nontoxic, but requires proper illumination.

Fumes of ammonia water and sulfuric acid, if allowed to mix, form a white precipitate. Two bottles, one containing ammonia water and the other containing acid, are connected to a common nozzle by rubber tubing. A syringe forces air over the liquid surfaces in the bottles; the two streams mix at the nozzle and form a white cloud.

A satisfactory test smoke also can be made by bubbling an airstream through ammonium hydroxide and then hydrochloric acid (Nottage et al. 1952). Smoke tubes, smoke candles, and smoke bombs are available for studying airflow patterns.

ANEMOMETERS

Deflecting Vane Anemometers

The deflecting vane anemometer consists of a pivoted vane enclosed in a case. Air exerts pressure on the vane as it passes through the instrument from an upstream to a downstream opening. A hair spring and a damping magnet resist vane movement. The instrument gives instantaneous readings of directional velocities on an indicating scale. With fluctuating velocities, needle swings must be visually averaged. This instrument is useful for studying air motion in a room, locating objectionable drafts, measuring air velocities at supply and return diffusers and grilles, and measuring laboratory hood face velocities.

Propeller or Revolving (Rotating) Vane Anemometers

The propeller anemometer consists of a light, revolving, wind-driven wheel connected through a gear train to a set of recording dials that read linear metres of air passing in a measured length of time. It is made in various sizes, though 75, 100, and 150 mm are the most common. Each instrument requires individual calibration. At low velocities, the mechanism's friction drag is considerable, and is usually compensated for by a gear train that overspeeds. For this reason, the correction is often additive at the lower range and subtractive at the upper range, with the least correction in the middle range. The best instruments have starting speeds of 0.25 m/s or higher; therefore, they cannot be used below that air speed. Electronic revolving vane anemometers, with optical or magnetic pick-ups to sense the rotation of the vane, are available in vane sizes as small as 13 mm diameter.

Cup Anemometers

The cup anemometer is primarily used to measure outdoor, meteorological wind speeds. It consists of three or four hemispherical cups mounted radially from a vertical shaft. Wind from any direction with a vector component in the plane of cup rotation causes the cups and shaft to rotate. Because it is primarily used to measure meteorological wind speeds, the instrument is usually constructed so that wind speeds can be recorded or indicated electrically at a remote point.

Thermal Anemometers

The thermal (or hot-wire, or hot-film) anemometer consists of a heated RTD, thermocouple junction, or thermistor sensor constructed at the end of a probe; it is designed to provide a direct, simple method of determining air velocity at a point in the flow field. The probe is placed into an airstream, and air movement past the electrically heated velocity sensor tends to cool the sensor in proportion to the speed of the airflow. The electronics and sensor are commonly combined into a portable, hand-held device that interprets the sensor signal and provides a direct reading of air velocity in either analog or digital display format. Often, the sensor probe also incorporates an ambient temperature-sensing RTD or thermistor, in which case the indicated air velocity is "temperature compensated" to "standard" air density conditions (typically 1.20 kg/m^3).

Thermal anemometers have long been used in fluid flow research. Research anemometer sensors have been constructed using very fine wires in configurations that allow characterization of fluid flows in one, two, and three dimensions, with sensor/electronics response rates up to several hundred kilohertz. This technology has been incorporated into more ruggedized sensors suitable for measurements in the HVAC field, primarily for unidirectional airflow measurement. Omnidirectional sensing instruments suitable for thermal comfort studies are also available.

The principal advantages of thermal anemometers are their wide dynamic range and their ability to sense extremely low velocities. Commercially available portable instruments often have a typical accuracy (including repeatability) of 2 to 5% of reading over the entire velocity range. Accuracies of ±2% of reading or better are obtainable from microcontroller (microprocessor)-based thermistor and RTD sensor assemblies, some of which can be factory-calibrated to known reference standards (e.g., NIST air speed tunnels). An integrated microcontroller also allows an array of sensor assemblies to be combined in one duct or opening, providing independently derived velocity and temperature measurements at each point.

Limitations of thermistor-based velocity measuring devices depend on sensor configuration, specific thermistor type used, and the application. At low velocities, thermal anemometers can be significantly affected by their own thermal plumes (from self-heating). Products using this technology can be classified as hand-held instruments or permanently mounted probes and arrays, and as those with analog electronic transmitters and those that are microcontroller-based.

Limitations of hand-held and analog electronic thermal anemometers include the following: (1) the unidirectional sensor must be carefully aligned in the airstream (typically to within ±20° rotation) to achieve accurate results; (2) the velocity sensor must be kept clean because contaminant build-up can change the calibration (which may change accuracy performance); and (3) because of the inherent high speed of response of thermal anemometers, measurements in turbulent flows can yield fluctuating velocity measurements. Electronically controlled time-integrated functions are now available in many digital air velocity meters to help smooth these turbulent flow measurements.

Microcontroller-based thermal dispersion devices are typically configured as unidirectional instruments, but may have multiple velocity-sensing elements capable of detecting flow direction. These devices can be used to measure a "bleed" air velocity between two spaces or across a fixed orifice. With mathematical conversion, these measured velocities can closely approximate equivalents in differential pressure down to two decimal places (Pa). They can be used for space pressure control, to identify minute changes in flow direction, or for estimating volumetric flow rates across a fixed orifice by equating to velocity pressure.

In the HVAC field, thermal anemometers are suitable for a variety of applications. They are particularly well-suited to the low velocities associated with outside air intake measurement and control, return or relief fan tracking for pressurization in variable-air-volume (VAV) systems, VAV terminal box measurement, unit ventilator and packaged equipment intake measurement, space pressurization for medical isolation, and laboratory fume hood face velocity measurements (typically in the 0.25 to 1 m/s range). Thermal anemometers can also take multipoint traverse measurements in ventilation ductwork.

Laser Doppler Velocimeters (or Anemometers)

The laser Doppler velocimeter (LDV) or laser Doppler anemometer (LDA) is an extremely complex system that collects scattered light produced by particles (i.e., seed) passing through the intersection volume of two intersecting laser beams of the same light frequency, which produces a regularly spaced fringe pattern (Mease et al. 1992). The scattered light consists of bursts containing regularly spaced oscillations whose frequency is linearly proportional to the speed of the particle. Because of their cost and complexity, they are usually not suitable for in situ field measurements. Rather, the primary HVAC application of LDV systems is calibrating systems used to calibrate other air velocity instruments.

The greatest advantage of an LDV is its performance at low air speeds: as low as 0.075 m/s with uncertainty levels of 1% or less (Mease et al. 1992). In addition, it is nonintrusive in the flow; only optical access is required. It can be used to measure fluctuating components as well as mean speeds and is available in one-, two-, and even three-dimensional configurations. Its biggest disadvantages are its high cost and extreme technological complexity, which requires highly skilled operators. Modern fiber-optic systems require less-skilled operators but at a considerable increase in cost.

Particle Image Velocimetry (PIV)

Particle image velocimetry (PIV) is an optical method that measures fluid velocity by determining the displacement of approximately neutrally buoyant seed particles introduced in the flow. Particle displacements are determined from images of particle positions at two instants of time. Usually, statistical (correlation) methods are used to identify the displacement field.

The greatest advantage of PIV is its ability to examine two- and three-dimensional velocity fields over a region of flow. The method usually requires laser light (sheet) illumination, and is typically limited to a field area of less than 1 m^2. Accuracy is usually limited to about ±10% by the resolution of particle displacements, which must be small enough to remain in the field of view during the selected displacement time interval. For more comprehensive information on PIV, including estimates of uncertainty, see Raffel et al. (1998).

PITOT-STATIC TUBES

The pitot-static tube, in conjunction with a suitable manometer or differential pressure transducer, provides a simple method of determining air velocity at a point in a flow field. Figure 6 shows the construction of a standard pitot tube (ASHRAE *Standard* 51) and the method of connecting it with inclined manometers to display both static pressure and velocity pressure. The equation for determining air velocity from measured velocity pressure is

$$V = \sqrt{\frac{2p_w}{\rho}} \tag{5}$$

where

V = velocity, m/s
p_w = velocity pressure (pitot-tube manometer reading), Pa
ρ = density of air, kg/m^3

The type of manometer or differential pressure transducer used with a pitot-static tube depends on the magnitude of velocity pressure being measured and on the desired accuracy. Over 7.5 m/s, a draft gage of appropriate range is usually satisfactory. If the pitot-static tube is used to measure air velocities lower than 7.5 m/s, a precision manometer or comparable pressure differential transducer is essential.

Example Calculation

Step 1. Numerical evaluation. Let p_w = 93.16 ± 0.95 Pa and ρ = 1.185 ± 0.020 kg/m^3. Then,

$$V = \sqrt{\frac{2p_w}{\rho}} = \sqrt{\frac{2(93.16)}{(1.185)}} = 12.54 \text{ m/s}$$

Step 2. Uncertainty estimate. Let the typical bias (i.e., calibration) uncertainty of the pitot tube be $u_{V,bias}$ = ±1% of reading. The uncertainty in the velocity measurement is thus estimated to be

$$u_V = \sqrt{(u_{V,bias})^2 + (u_{V,prec})^2}$$

$$= \sqrt{(u_{V,bias})^2 + \left[\frac{1}{2}(u_{p_w})\right]^2 + \left[\frac{1}{2}(u_\rho)\right]^2}$$

$$= \sqrt{(0.01)^2 + \left[\frac{1}{2}\left(\frac{0.95}{93.16}\right)\right]^2 + \left[\frac{1}{2}\left(\frac{0.020}{1.185}\right)\right]^2}$$

$$= \pm 0.014 = \pm 1.4\%$$

Therefore,

$$U_V = \pm u_V V = \pm(0.014)(12.54 \text{ m/s}) = \pm 0.18 \text{ m/s}$$

In summary,

$$V = 12.54 \pm 0.18 \text{ m/s}$$

Other pitot-static tubes have been used and calibrated. To meet special conditions, various sizes of pitot-static tubes geometrically similar to the standard tube can be used. For relatively high velocities in ducts of small cross-sectional area, total pressure readings can be obtained with an impact (pitot) tube. Where static pressure across the stream is relatively constant, as in turbulent flow in a straight duct, a sidewall tap to obtain static pressure can be used with the impact tube to obtain the velocity pressure. One form of impact tube is a small streamlined tube with a fine hole in its upstream end and its axis parallel to the stream.

If the Mach number of the flow is greater than about 0.3, the effects of compressibility should be included in the computation of the air speed from pitot-static and impact (stagnation or pitot) tube measurements (Mease et al. 1992).

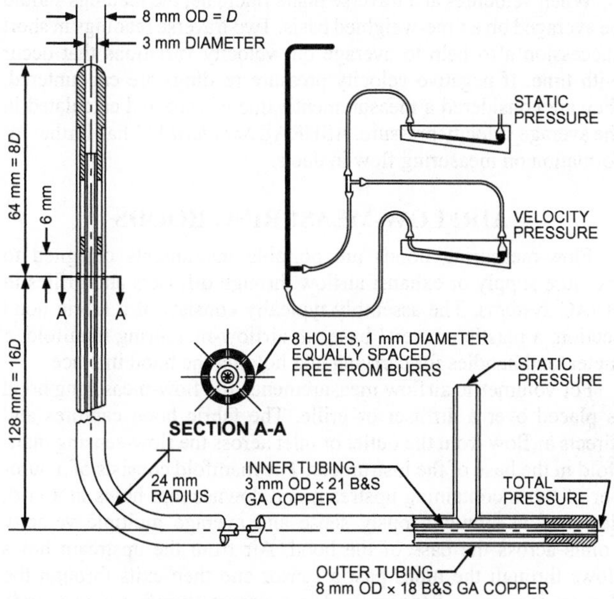

Fig. 6 Standard Pitot Tube

MEASURING FLOW IN DUCTS

Because velocity in a duct is seldom uniform across any section, and a pitot tube reading or thermal anemometer indicates velocity at only one location, a traverse is usually made to determine average velocity. Generally, velocity is lowest near the edges or corners and greatest at or near the center.

To determine velocity in a traverse plane, a straight average of individual point velocities gives satisfactory results when point

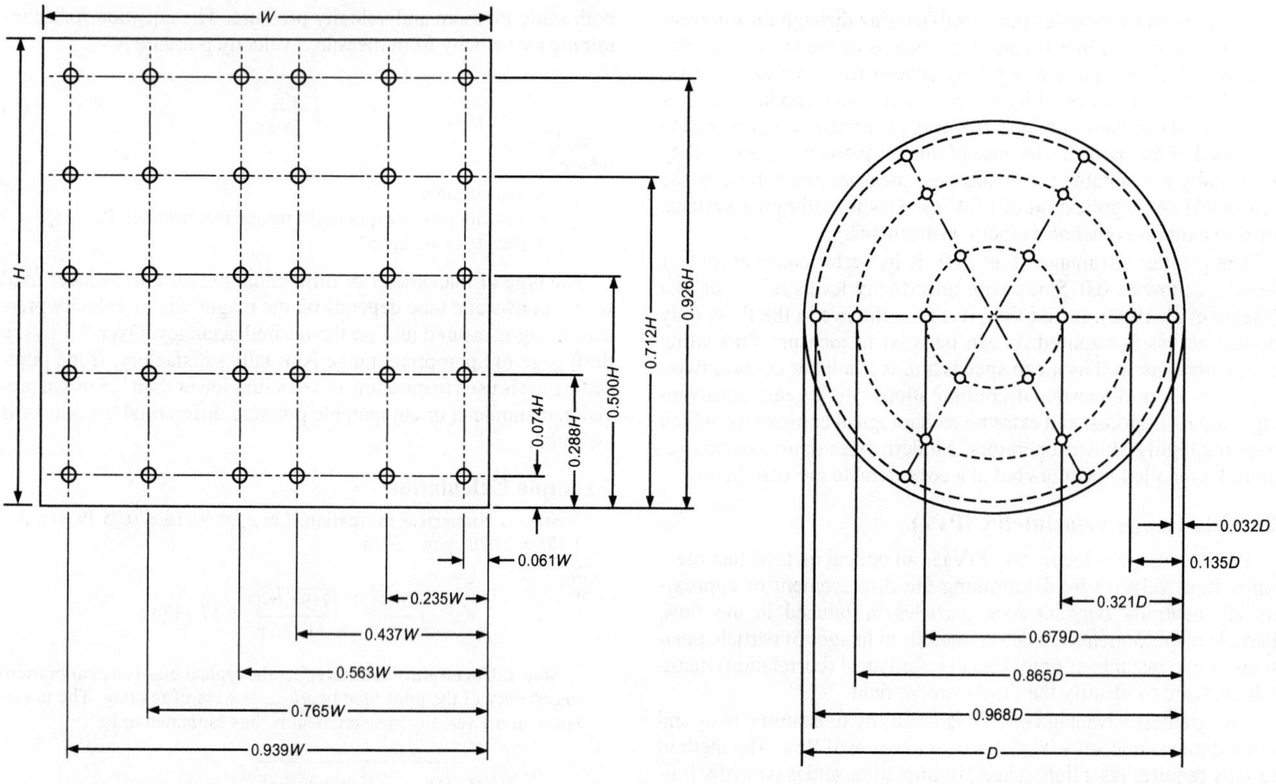

Duct Dimensions	No. of Points for Traverse Lines	Position Relative to Inner Wall
460 mm < *H*, *W* < 750 mm	5	0.074, 0.288, 0.500, 0.712, 0.926
750 mm ≤ *H*, *W* ≤ 900 mm	6	0.061, 0.235, 0.437, 0.563, 0.765, 0.939
H, *W* > 900 mm	7	0.053, 0.203, 0.366, 0.500, 0.634, 0.797, 0.947

Log-Tchebycheff Rule for Rectangular Ducts

No. of Measuring Points per Diameter	Position Relative to Inner Wall
6	0.032, 0.135, 0.321, 0.679, 0.865, 0.968
8	0.021, 0.117, 0.184, 0.345, 0.655, 0.816, 0.883, 0.979
10	0.019, 0.077, 0.153, 0.217, 0.361, 0.639, 0.783, 0.847, 0.923, 0.981

Log-Linear Rule for Circular Ducts

Note: Example duct has 5 × 6 (*H* × *W*) measurement pattern, as for rectangular duct of 600 × 750 mm.

Fig. 7 Measuring Points for Rectangular and Round Duct Traverse

velocities are determined by the **log-Tchebycheff (log-T) rule** or, if care is taken, by the **equal-area method**. Figure 7 shows suggested sensor locations for traversing round and rectangular ducts. The log-Tchebycheff rule provides the greatest accuracy because its location of traverse points accounts for the effect of wall friction and the fall-off of velocity near wall ducts. The log-T method is now recommended for rectangular ducts with *H* and *W* > 460 mm. For circular ducts, the log-T and log-linear methods are similar. Log-T minimizes the positive error (measured greater than actual) caused by the failure to account for losses at the duct wall. This error can occur when using the older method of equal subareas to traverse rectangular ducts.

When using the log-T method for a rectangular duct traverse, measure a minimum of 25 points. For a circular duct traverse, the log-linear rule and three symmetrically disposed diameters may be used (Figure 7). Points on two perpendicular diameters may be used where access is limited.

If possible, measuring points should be located at least 7.5 hydraulic diameters downstream and 3 hydraulic diameters upstream from a disturbance (e.g., caused by a turn). Compromised traverses as close as 2 hydraulic diameters downstream and 1 hydraulic diameter upstream can be performed with an increase in measurement error. Because field-measured airflows are rarely steady and uniform, particularly near disturbances, accuracy can be improved by increasing the number of measuring points. Straightening vanes (ASHRAE *Standard* 51) located 1.5 duct diameters ahead of the traverse plane improve measurement precision.

When velocities at a traverse plane fluctuate, the readings should be averaged on a time-weighted basis. Two traverse readings in short succession also help to average out velocity variations that occur with time. If negative velocity pressure readings are encountered, they are considered a measurement value of zero and calculated in the average velocity pressure. ASHRAE *Standard* 111 has further information on measuring flow in ducts.

AIRFLOW-MEASURING HOODS

Flow-measuring hoods are portable instruments designed to measure supply or exhaust airflow through diffusers and grilles in HVAC systems. The assembly typically consists of a fabric hood section, a plastic or metal base, an airflow-measuring manifold, a meter, and handles for carrying and holding the hood in place.

For volumetric airflow measurements, the flow-measuring hood is placed over a diffuser or grille. The fabric hood captures and directs airflow from the outlet or inlet across the flow-sensing manifold in the base of the instrument. The manifold consists of a number of tubes containing upstream and downstream holes in a grid, designed to simultaneously sense and average multiple velocity points across the base of the hood. Air from the upstream holes flows through the tubes past a sensor and then exits through the downstream holes. Sensors used by different manufacturers include swinging vane anemometers, electronic micromanometers, and thermal anemometers. In electronic micromanometers, air does not actually flow through the manifold, but the airtight sensor senses the pressure differential from the upstream to downstream series of holes. The meter on the base of the hood interprets the signal from the sensor and provides a direct reading of volumetric flow in either an analog or digital display format.

As a performance check in the field, the indicated flow of a measuring hood can be compared to a duct traverse flow measurement (using a pitot-tube or thermal anemometer). All flow-measuring hoods induce some back pressure on the air-handling system because the hood restricts flow out of the diffuser. This added resistance alters the true amount of air coming out of the diffuser. In most cases, this error is negligible and is less than the accuracy of the instrument. For proportional balancing, this error need not be taken into account because all similar diffusers have about the same amount of back pressure. To determine whether back pressure is significant, a velocity traverse can be made in the duct ahead of the diffuser with and without the hood in place. The difference in average velocity of the traverse indicates the degree of back-pressure compensation required on similar diffusers in the system. For example, if the average velocity is 4.0 m/s with the hood in place and 4.1 m/s without the hood, the indicated flow reading can be multiplied by 1.025 on similar diffusers in the system (4.1/4.0 = 1.025). As an alternative, the designer of the air-handling system can predict the head-induced airflow reduction by using a curve supplied by the hood manufacturer. This curve indicates the pressure drop through the hood for different flow rates.

FLOW RATE MEASUREMENT

Various means of measuring fluid flow rate are listed in Table 5. Values for volumetric or mass flow rate measurement (ASME *Standard* PTC 19.5; Benedict 1984) are often determined by measuring pressure difference across an orifice, nozzle, or venturi tube. The various meters have different advantages and disadvantages. For example, the orifice plate is more easily changed than the complete nozzle or venturi tube assembly. However, the nozzle is often preferred to the orifice because its discharge coefficient is more precise. The venturi tube is a nozzle followed by an expanding recovery section to reduce net pressure loss. Differential pressure flow measurement has benefited through workshops addressing fundamental issues, textbooks, research, and improved standards (ASME *Standards* B40.100, MFC-1M, MFC-9M, MFC-10M; DeCarlo 1984; Mattingly 1984; Miller 1983).

Fluid meters use a wide variety of physical techniques to measure flow (ASME *Standard* PTC 19.5; DeCarlo 1984; Miller 1983); more common ones are described in this section. To validate accuracy of flow rate measurement instruments, calibration procedures should include documentation of traceability to the calibration facility. The calibration facility should, in turn, provide documentation of traceability to national standards.

Flow Measurement Methods

Direct. Both gas and liquid flow can be measured accurately by timing a collected amount of fluid that is measured gravimetrically or volumetrically. This method is common for calibrating other metering devices, but it is particularly useful where flow rate is low or intermittent and where a high degree of accuracy is required. These systems are generally large and slow, but in their simplicity, they can be considered primary devices.

The **variable-area meter** or **rotameter** is a convenient direct-reading flowmeter for liquids and gases. This is a vertical, tapered tube in which the flow rate is indicated by the position of a float suspended in the upward flow. The float's position is determined by its buoyancy and the upward fluid drag.

Displacement meters measure total liquid or gas flow over time. The two major types of displacement meters used for gases are the conventional gas meter, which uses a set of bellows, and the wet test meter, which uses a water displacement principle.

Indirect. The **Thomas meter** is used in laboratories to measure high gas flow rates with low pressure losses. Gas is heated by electric heaters, and the temperature rise is measured by two resistance thermometer grids. When heat input and temperature rise are known, the mass flow of gas is calculated as the quantity of gas that removes the equivalent heat at the same temperature rise.

A velocity traverse (made using a pitot tube or other velocity-measuring instrument) measures airflow rates in the field or calibrates large nozzles. This method can be imprecise at low velocities and impracticable where many test runs are in progress.

Another field-estimating method measures pressure drop across elements with known pressure drop characteristics, such as heating and cooling coils or fans. If the pressure drop/flow rate relationship has been calibrated against a known reference (typically, at least four points in the operating range), the results can be precise. If the method depends on rating data, it should be used for check purposes only.

VENTURI, NOZZLE, AND ORIFICE FLOWMETERS

Flow in a pipeline can be measured by a venturi meter (Figure 8), flow nozzle (Figure 9), or orifice plate (Figure 10). American Society of Mechanical Engineers (ASME) *Standard* MFC-3M describes measurement of fluid flow in pipes using the orifice, nozzle, and venturi; ASME *Standard* PTC 19.5 specifies their construction.

Assuming an incompressible fluid (liquid or slow-moving gas), uniform velocity profile, frictionless flow, and no gravitational effects, the principle of conservation of mass and energy can be applied to the venturi and nozzle geometries to give

$$w = \rho V_1 A_1 = \rho V_2 A_2 = A_2 \sqrt{\frac{2\rho(p_1 - p_2)}{1 - \beta^4}} \qquad (6)$$

where

w = mass flow rate, kg/s
V = velocity of stream, m/s
A = flow area, m^2
ρ = density of fluid, kg/m^3
p = absolute pressure, Pa
β = ratio of diameters D_2/D_1 for venturi and sharp-edge orifice and d/D for flow nozzle, where D = pipe diameter and d = throat diameter

Note: Subscript 1 refers to entering conditions; subscript 2 refers to throat conditions.

Because flow through the meter is not frictionless, a correction factor C is defined to account for friction losses. If the fluid is at a high temperature, an additional correction factor F_a should be

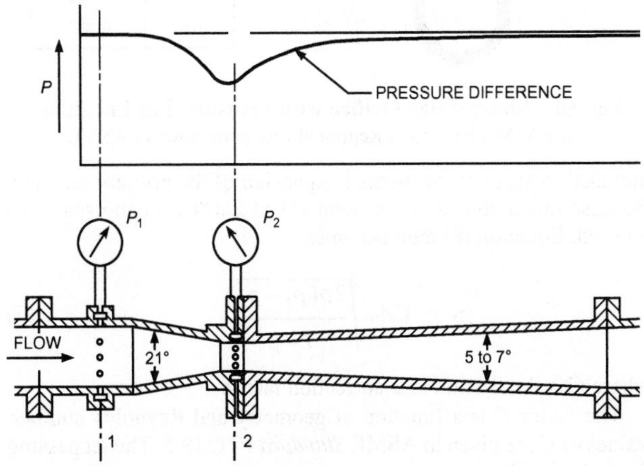

Fig. 8 Typical Herschel-Type Venturi Meter

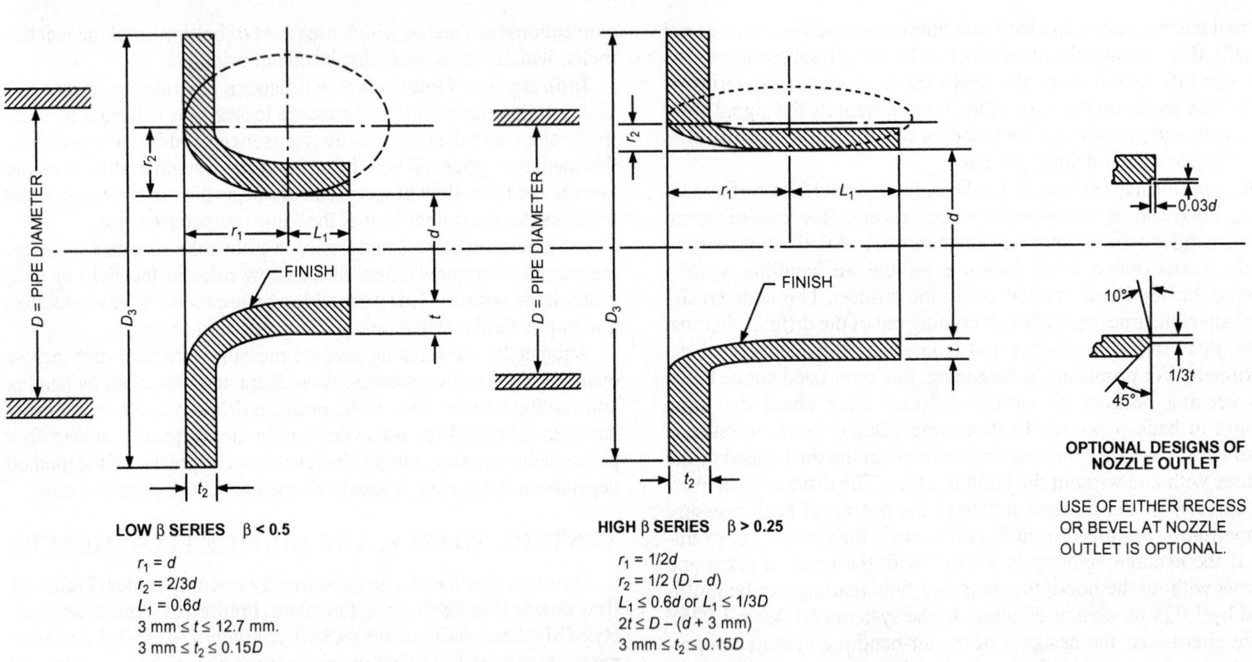

Fig. 9 Dimensions of ASME Long-Radius Flow Nozzles
From ASME PTC 19.5. Reprinted with permission of ASME.

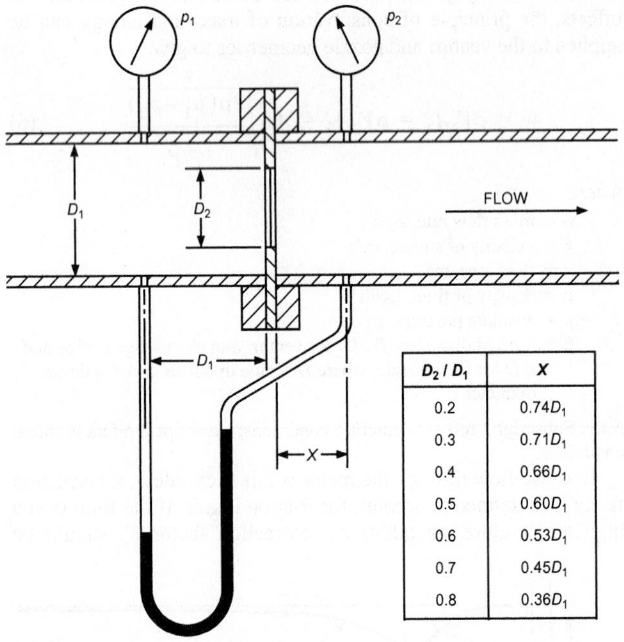

D_2 / D_1	X
0.2	$0.74D_1$
0.3	$0.71D_1$
0.4	$0.66D_1$
0.5	$0.60D_1$
0.6	$0.53D_1$
0.7	$0.45D_1$
0.8	$0.36D_1$

Fig. 10 Sharp-Edge Orifice with Pressure Tap Locations
From ASME PTC 19.5. Reprinted with permission of ASME.

included to account for thermal expansion of the primary element. Because this amounts to less than 1% at 260°C, it can usually be omitted. Equation (6) then becomes

$$w = CA_2\sqrt{\frac{2\rho(p_1 - p_2)}{1 - \beta^4}} \quad (7)$$

where *C* is the friction loss correction factor.

The factor *C* is a function of geometry and Reynolds number. Values of *C* are given in ASME *Standard* PTC 19.5. The jet passing through an orifice plate contracts to a minimum area at the vena contracta located a short distance downstream from the orifice plate. The contraction coefficient, friction loss coefficient *C*, and approach factor $1/(1 - \beta^4)^{0.5}$ can be combined into a single constant *K*, which is a function of geometry and Reynolds number. The orifice flow rate equations then become

$$Q = KA_2\sqrt{\frac{2(p_1 - p_2)}{\rho}} \quad (8)$$

where

Q = discharge flow rate, m³/s
A_2 = orifice area, m²
$p_1 - p_2$ = pressure drop as obtained by pressure taps, Pa

Values of *K* are shown in ASME *Standard* PTC 19.5.

Valves, bends, and fittings upstream from the flowmeter can cause errors. Long, straight pipes should be installed upstream and downstream from flow devices to ensure fully developed flow for proper measurement. ASHRAE *Standard* 41.8 specifies upstream and downstream pipe lengths for measuring flow of liquids with an orifice plate. ASME *Standard* PTC 19.5 gives piping requirements between various fittings and valves and the venturi, nozzle, and orifice. If these conditions cannot be met, flow conditioners or straightening vanes can be used (ASME *Standards* PTC 19.5, MFC-10M; Mattingly 1984; Miller 1983).

Compressibility effects must be considered for gas flow if pressure drop across the measuring device is more than a few percent of the initial pressure.

Nozzles are sometimes arranged in parallel pipes from a common manifold; thus, the capacity of the testing equipment can be changed by shutting off the flow through one or more nozzles. An apparatus designed for testing airflow and capacity of air-conditioning equipment is described by Wile (1947), who also presents pertinent information on nozzle discharge coefficients, Reynolds numbers, and resistance of perforated plates. Some laboratories refer to this apparatus as a code tester.

VARIABLE-AREA FLOWMETERS (ROTAMETERS)

In permanent installations where high precision, ruggedness, and operational ease are important, the variable-area flowmeter is

Table 5 Volumetric or Mass Flow Rate Measurement

Measurement Means	Application	Range	Precision	Limitations
Orifice and differential pressure measurement system	Flow through pipes, ducts, and plenums for all fluids	Above Reynolds number of 5000	1 to 5%	Discharge coefficient and accuracy influenced by installation conditions.
Nozzle and differential pressure measurement system	Flow through pipes, ducts, and plenums for all fluids	Above Reynolds number of 5000	0.5 to 2.0%	Discharge coefficient and accuracy influenced by installation conditions.
Venturi tube and differential pressure measurement system	Flow through pipes, ducts, and plenums for all fluids	Above Reynolds number of 5000	0.5 to 2.0%	Discharge coefficient and accuracy influenced by installation conditions.
Timing given mass or volumetric flow	Liquids or gases; used to calibrate other flowmeters	Any	0.1 to 0.5%	System is bulky and slow.
Rotameters	Liquids or gases	Any	0.5 to 5.0%	Should be calibrated for fluid being metered.
Displacement meter	Relatively small volumetric flow with high pressure loss	As high as 500 L/s, depending on type	0.1 to 2.0% depending on type	Most types require calibration with fluid being metered.
Gasometer or volume displacement	Short-duration tests; used to calibrate other flowmeters	Total flow limited by available volume of containers	0.5 to 1.0%	—
Thomas meter (temperature rise of stream caused by electrical heating)	Elaborate setup justified by need for good accuracy	Any	1%	Uniform velocity; usually used with gases.
Element of resistance to flow and differential pressure measurement system	Used for check where system has calibrated resistance element	Lower limit set by readable pressure drop	1 to 5%	Secondary reading depends on accuracy of calibration.
Turbine flowmeters	Liquids or gases	Any	0.25 to 2.0%	Uses electronic readout.
Single- or multipoint instrument for measuring velocity at specific point in flow	Primarily for installed air-handling systems with no special provision for flow measurement	Lower limit set by accuracy of velocity measurement instrumentation	2 to 10%	Accuracy depends on uniformity of flow and completeness of traverse. May be affected by disturbances near point of measurement.
Heat input and temperature changes with steam and water coil	Check value in heater or cooler tests	Any	1 to 3%	—
Laminar flow element and differential pressure measurement system	Measure liquid or gas volumetric flow rate; nearly linear relationship with pressure drop; simple and easy to use	50 mm³/s to 1 m³/s	1%	Fluid must be free of dirt, oil, and other impurities that could plug meter or affect its calibration.
Magnetohydrodynamic flowmeter (electromagnetic)	Measures electrically conductive fluids, slurries; meter does not obstruct flow; no moving parts	0.006 to 600 L/s	1%	At present state of the art, conductivity of fluid must be greater than 5 μmho/cm.
Swirl flowmeter and vortex shedding meter	Measure liquid or gas flow in pipe; no moving parts	Above Reynolds number of 10^4	1%	—

satisfactory. It is frequently used to measure liquids or gases in small-diameter pipes. For ducts or pipes over 150 mm in diameter, the expense of this meter may not be warranted. In larger systems, however, the meter can be placed in a bypass line and used with an orifice.

The variable-area meter (Figure 11) commonly consists of a float that is free to move vertically in a transparent tapered tube. The fluid to be metered enters at the narrow bottom end of the tube and moves upward, passing at some point through the annulus formed between the float and the inside wall of the tube. At any particular flow rate, the float assumes a definite position in the tube; a calibrated scale on the tube shows the float's location and the fluid flow rate.

The float's position is established by a balance between the fluid pressure forces across the annulus and gravity on the float. The buoyant force $V_f(\rho_f - \rho)g$ supporting the float is balanced by the pressure difference acting on the cross-sectional area of the float $A_f \Delta p$, where ρ_f, A_f, and V_f are, respectively, the float density, float cross-sectional area, and float volume. The pressure difference across the annulus is

$$\Delta p = \frac{V_f(\rho_f - \rho)g}{A_f} \quad (9)$$

The mass flow follows from Equation (8) as

$$w = KA_2 \sqrt{\frac{2V_f(\rho_f - \rho)g\rho}{A_f}} \quad (10)$$

Flow for any fluid is nearly proportional to the area, so that calibration of the tube is convenient. To use the meter for different fluids, the flow coefficient variation for any float must be known. Float design can reduce variation of the flow coefficient with Reynolds number; float materials can reduce the dependence of mass flow calibration on fluid density.

POSITIVE-DISPLACEMENT METERS

Many positive-displacement meters are available for measuring total liquid or gas volumetric flow rates. The measured fluid flows progressively into compartments of definite size. As the compartments fill, they rotate so that the fluid discharges from the meter.

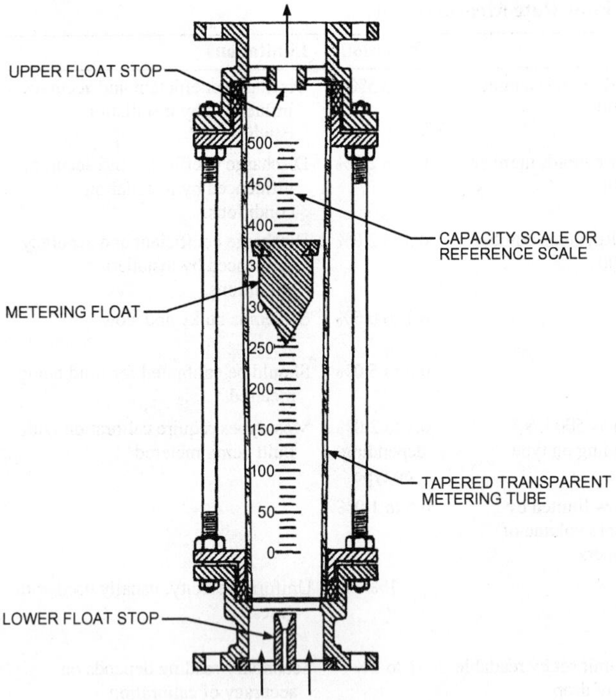

Fig. 11 Variable-Area Flowmeter

The flow rate through the meter equals the product of the compartment volume, number of compartments, and rotation rate of the rotor. Most of these meters have a mechanical register calibrated to show total flow.

TURBINE FLOWMETERS

Turbine flowmeters are volumetric flow-rate-sensing meters with a magnetic stainless steel turbine rotor suspended in the flow stream of a nonmagnetic meter body. The fluid stream exerts a force on the blades of the turbine rotor, setting it in motion and converting the fluid's linear velocity to an angular velocity. Design motivation for turbine meters is to have the rotational speed of the turbine proportional to the average fluid velocity and thus to the volume rate of fluid flow (DeCarlo 1984; Mattingly 1992; Miller 1983).

The rotor's rotational speed is monitored by an externally mounted pickoff assembly. The **magnetic pickoff** contains a permanent magnet and coil. As the turbine rotor blades pass through the field produced by the permanent magnet, a shunting action induces ac voltage in the winding of the coil wrapped around the magnet. A sine wave with a frequency proportional to the flow rate develops. With the **radio frequency pickoff**, an oscillator applies a high-frequency carrier signal to a coil in the pickoff assembly. The rotor blades pass through the field generated by the coil and modulate the carrier signal by shunting action on the field shape. The carrier signal is modulated at a rate corresponding to the rotor speed, which is proportional to the flow rate. With both pickoffs, pulse frequency is a measure of flow rate, and the total number of pulses measures total volume (Mattingly 1992; Shafer 1961; Woodring 1969).

Because output frequency of the turbine flowmeter is proportional to flow rate, every pulse from the turbine meter is equivalent to a known volume of fluid that has passed through the meter; the sum of these pulses yields total volumetric flow. Summation is done by electronic counters designed for use with turbine flowmeters; they combine a mechanical or electronic register with the basic electronic counter.

Turbine flowmeters should be installed with straight lengths of pipe upstream and downstream from the meter. The length of the inlet and outlet pipes should be according to manufacturers' recommendations or pertinent standards. Where recommendations of standards cannot be accommodated, the meter installation should be calibrated. Some turbine flowmeters can be used in bidirectional flow applications. A fluid strainer, used with liquids of poor or marginal lubricity, minimizes bearing wear.

The lubricity of the process fluid and the type and quality of rotor bearings determine whether the meter is satisfactory for the particular application. When choosing turbine flowmeters for use with fluorocarbon refrigerants, attention must be paid to the type of bearings used in the meter and to the oil content of the refrigerant. For these applications, sleeve-type rather than standard ball bearings are recommended. The amount of oil in the refrigerant can severely affect calibration and bearing life.

In metering liquid fluorocarbon refrigerants, the liquid must not flash to a vapor (cavitate), which tremendously increases flow volume. Flashing results in erroneous measurements and rotor speeds that can damage bearings or cause a failure. Flashing can be avoided by maintaining adequate back pressure on the downstream side of the meter (Liptak 1972).

AIR INFILTRATION, AIRTIGHTNESS, AND OUTDOOR AIR VENTILATION RATE MEASUREMENT

Air infiltration is the flow of outdoor air into a building through unintentional openings. **Airtightness** refers to the building envelope's ability to withstand flow when subjected to a pressure differential. The **outdoor air ventilation rate** is the rate of outdoor airflow intentionally introduced to the building for dilution of occupant- and building-generated contaminants. Measurement approaches to determine these factors are described briefly here, and in greater detail in Chapter 16.

Air infiltration depends on the building envelope's airtightness and the pressure differentials across the envelope. These differentials are induced by wind, stack effect, and operation of building mechanical equipment. For meaningful results, the air infiltration rate should be measured under typical conditions.

Airtightness of a residential building's envelope can be measured relatively quickly using building pressurization tests. In this technique, a large fan or blower mounted in a door or window induces a large and roughly uniform pressure difference across the building shell. The airflow required to maintain this pressure difference is then measured. The more leakage in the building, the more airflow is required to induce a specific indoor/outdoor pressure difference. Building airtightness is characterized by the airflow rate at a reference pressure, normalized by the building volume or surface area. Under proper test conditions, results of a pressurization test are independent of weather conditions. Instrumentation requirements for pressurization testing include air-moving equipment, a device to measure airflow, and a differential pressure gage.

Commercial building envelope leakage can also be measured using building pressurization tests. Bahnfleth et al. (1999) describe a protocol for testing envelope leakage of tall buildings using the building's air-handling equipment.

Outdoor airflow can be measured directly using the flow rate measurement techniques described in this chapter. Take care in selecting the instrument most suitable for the operating conditions, range of airflows, and temperatures expected. The outdoor airflow rate is normally measured during testing and balancing, during commissioning, or for continuous ventilation flow rate control using permanently mounted flow sensors.

An additional factor that may be of interest is the building's air exchange rate, which compares airflow into the building with the building's volume. Typically, this includes both mechanical ventilation and infiltration. Building air exchange rates can be measured by injecting a tracer gas (ideally, a chemically stable, nontoxic gas not normally present in buildings) into a building and monitoring and analyzing the tracer gas concentration response. Equipment required for tracer testing includes (1) a means of injecting the tracer gas and (2) a tracer gas monitor. Various tracer gas techniques are used, distinguished by their injection strategy and analysis approach. These techniques include constant concentration (equilibrium tracer), decay or growth (ASTM *Standard* E741), and constant injection. Decay is the simplest of these techniques, but the other methods may be satisfactory if care is taken. A common problem in tracer gas testing is poor mixing of the tracer gas with the airstreams being measured.

Carbon Dioxide

Carbon dioxide is often used as a tracer gas because CO_2 gas monitors are relatively inexpensive and easy to use, and occupant-generated CO_2 can be used for most tracer gas techniques. Bottled CO_2 or CO_2 fire extinguishers are also readily available for tracer gas injection. Carbon dioxide may be used as a tracer gas to measure ventilation rates under the conditions and methods described in ASTM *Standard* D6245-98, for diagnostic purposes and point-in-time snapshots of the system's ventilation capabilities. CO_2 sensors are also used in building controls strategies to optimize ventilation by approximating the level of occupancy in a space; this is one method of demand-controlled ventilation. The concentration output may be used in a mathematical formula that allows the system to modulate ventilation rates when spaces with high density have highly variable or intermittent occupancy (e.g., churches, theaters, gymnasiums). This method of control is less effective in lower-density occupancies and spaces with more stable populations (Persily and Emmerich 2001). Carbon dioxide may also be used together with outdoor air intake rate data to estimate the current population of a space.

Because the steady-state concentration balance formula in Appendix C of ANSI/ASHRAE *Standard* 62.1-2007 depends totally on the validity of the assumed variables in the formula, CO_2 sensing for direct ventilation control should be used with caution, and possibly supplemented with other control measurements to establish the base and maximum design ventilation boundaries not to be exceeded. Also, ensure that intake air rates never fall below those required for building pressurization, which could affect energy use, comfort, health, and indoor air quality.

CO_2 input for ventilation control does not address contaminants generated by the building itself, and therefore cannot be used without providing a base level of ventilation for non-occupant-generated contaminants that have been shown to total a significant fraction if not a majority of those found in the space.

CARBON DIOXIDE MEASUREMENT

Carbon dioxide has become an important measurement parameter for HVAC&R engineers, particularly in indoor air quality (IAQ) applications. Although CO_2 is generally not of concern as a specific toxin in indoor air, it is used as a surrogate indicator of odor related to human occupancy. ANSI/ASHRAE *Standard* 62.1 recommends specific minimum outdoor air ventilation rates to ensure adequate indoor air quality.

NONDISPERSIVE INFRARED CO_2 DETECTORS

The most widespread technology for IAQ applications is the nondispersive infrared (NDIR) sensor (Figure 12). This device makes use of the strong absorption band that CO_2 produces at 4.2 μm when excited by an infrared light source. IAQ-specific NDIR instruments, calibrated between 0 and 5000 ppm, are typically accurate within 150 ppm, but the accuracy of some sensors can be improved to within 50 ppm if the instrument is calibrated for a narrower range. Portable NDIR meters are available with direct-reading digital displays; however, response time varies significantly among different instruments. Most NDIR cell designs facilitate very rapid CO_2 sample diffusion, although some instruments now in widespread use respond more slowly, resulting in stabilization times greater than 5 min (up to 15 min), which may complicate walk-through inspections.

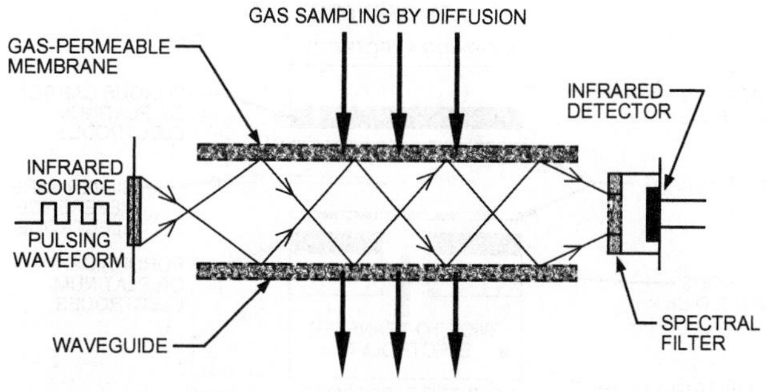

Fig. 12 Nondispersive Infrared Carbon Dioxide Sensor

Calibration

In a clean, stable environment, NDIR sensors can hold calibration for months, but condensation, dust, dirt, and mechanical shock may offset calibration. As with all other CO_2 sensor technologies, NDIR sensor readings are proportional to pressure, because the density of gas molecules changes when the sample pressure changes. This leads to errors in CO_2 readings when the barometric pressure changes from the calibration pressure. Weather-induced errors will be small, but all CO_2 instruments should be recalibrated if used at an altitude that is significantly different from the calibration altitude. Some NDIR sensors are sensitive to cooling effects when placed in an airstream. This is an important consideration when locating a fixed sensor or when using a portable system to evaluate air-handling system performance, because airflow in supply and return ducts may significantly shift readings.

Applications

Nondispersive infrared sensors are well suited for equilibrium tracer and tracer decay ventilation studies, and faster-response models are ideal for a quick, basic evaluation of human-generated pollution and ventilation adequacy. When properly located, these sensors are also appropriate for continuous monitoring and for control strategies using equilibrium tracer and air fraction tracer calculations.

AMPEROMETRIC ELECTROCHEMICAL CO_2 DETECTORS

Amperometric electrochemical CO_2 sensors (Figure 13) use a measured current driven between two electrodes by the reduction of CO_2 that diffuses across a porous membrane. Unlike NDIR sensors, which normally last the lifetime of the instrument, electrochemical CO_2 sensors may change in electrolyte chemistry over time (typically 12 to 18 months) and should be replaced periodically. These sensors typically hold their calibration for several weeks, but they may drift more if exposed to low humidity; this drift makes them less suitable for continuous monitoring applications. At low humidity (below 30% rh), the sensors must be kept moist to maintain specified accuracy.

Amperometric electrochemical sensors require less power than NDIR sensors, usually operating continuously for weeks where NDIR instruments typically operate for 6 h (older models) to 150 h (newer models). The longer battery life can be advantageous for spot checks and walk-throughs, and for measuring CO_2 distribution throughout a building and within a zone. Unlike most NDIR sensors, amperometric electrochemical sensors are not affected by high humidity,

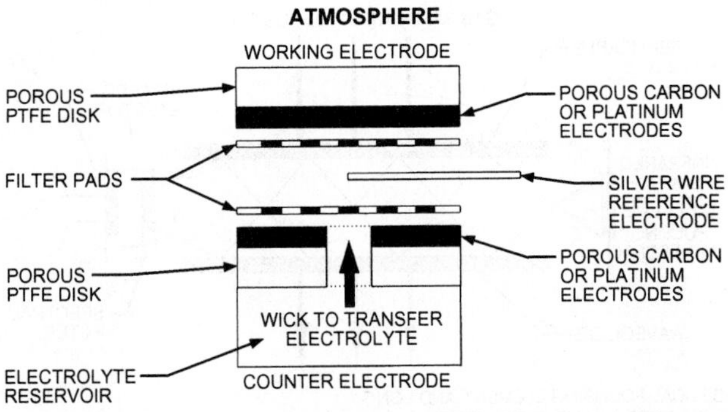

Fig. 13 Amperometric Carbon Dioxide Sensor

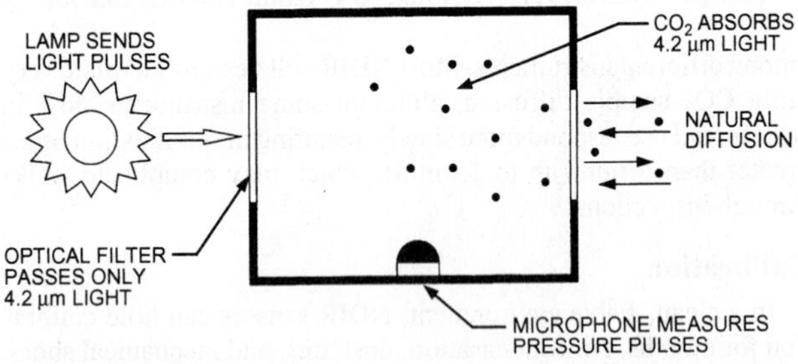

Fig. 14 Open-Cell Photoacoustic Carbon Dioxide Sensor

although readings may be affected if condensate is allowed to form on the sensor.

PHOTOACOUSTIC CO_2 DETECTORS

Open-Cell Sensors

Open-cell photoacoustic CO_2 sensors (Figure 14) operate as air diffuses through a permeable membrane into a chamber that is pulsed with filtered light at the characteristic CO_2 absorption frequency of 4.2 μm. The light energy absorbed by the CO_2 heats the sample chamber, causing a pressure pulse, which is sensed by a piezoresistor. Open-cell photoacoustic CO_2 sensors are presently unavailable in portable instruments, in part because any vibration during transportation would affect calibration and might affect the signal obtained for a given concentration of CO_2. Ambient acoustical noise may also influence readings. For continuous monitoring, vibration is a concern, as are temperature and airflow cooling effects. However, if a sensor is located properly and the optical filter is kept relatively clean, photoacoustic CO_2 sensors may be very stable. Commercially available open-cell photoacoustic transmitters do not allow recalibration to adjust for pressure differences, so an offset should be incorporated in any control system using these sensors at an altitude or duct pressure other than calibration conditions.

Closed-Cell Sensors

Closed-cell photoacoustic sensors (Figure 15) operate under the same principle as the open-cell version, except that samples are pumped into a sample chamber that is sealed and environmentally stabilized. Two acoustic sensors are sometimes used in the chamber to minimize vibration effects. Closed-cell units, available as portable or fixed monitors, come with particle filters that are easily replaced (typically at 3- to 6-month intervals) if dirt or dust accumulates on them. Closed-cell photoacoustic monitors allow recalibration to correct for drift, pressure effects, or other environmental factors that might influence accuracy.

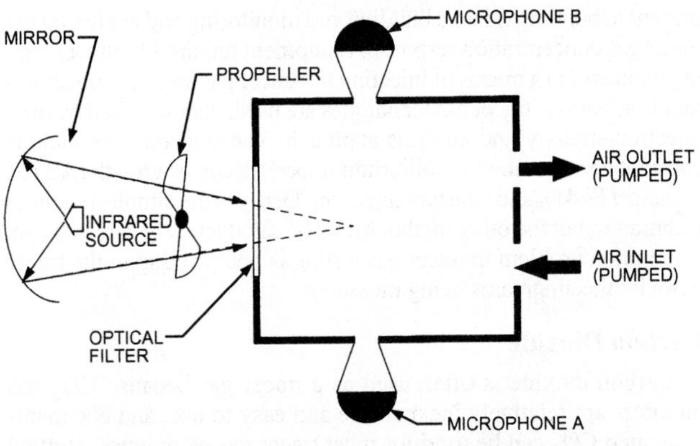

Fig. 15 Closed-Cell Photoacoustic Carbon Dioxide Sensor

POTENTIOMETRIC ELECTROCHEMICAL CO_2 DETECTORS

Potentiometric electrochemical CO_2 sensors use a porous fluorocarbon membrane that is permeable to CO_2, which diffuses into a carbonic acid electrolyte, changing the electrolyte's pH. This change is monitored by a pH electrode inside the cell. The pH electrode isopotential drift prohibits long-term monitoring to the accuracy and resolution required for continuous measurement or control or for detailed IAQ evaluations, although accuracy within 100 ppm, achievable short-term over the 2000 ppm range, may be adequate for basic ventilation and odor evaluations. In addition, this type of sensor has a slow response, which increases the operator time necessary for field applications or for performing a walk-through of a building.

COLORIMETRIC DETECTOR TUBES

Colorimetric detector tubes contain a chemical compound that discolors in the presence of CO_2 gas, with the amount of discoloration related to the CO_2 concentration. These detector tubes are often used to spot-check CO_2 levels; when used properly, they are accurate to within 25%. If numerous samples are taken (i.e., six or more), uncertainty may be reduced. However, CO_2 detector tubes are generally not appropriate for specific ventilation assessment because of their inaccuracy and inability to record concentration changes over time.

LABORATORY MEASUREMENTS

Laboratory techniques for measuring CO_2 concentration include mass spectroscopy, thermal conductivity, infrared spectroscopy, and gas chromatography. These techniques typically require taking on-site **grab samples** for laboratory analysis. Capital costs for each piece of equipment are high, and significant training is required. A considerable drawback to grab sampling is that CO_2 levels change significantly during the day and over the course of a week, making it sensible to place sensors on site with an instrument capable of recording or data logging measurements continuously over the course of a workweek. An automated grab sampling system capturing many samples of data would be quite cumbersome and expensive if designed to provide CO_2 trend information over time. However, an advantage to laboratory techniques is that they can be highly accurate. A mass spectrometer, for example, can measure CO_2 concentration to within 5 ppm from 0 to 2000 ppm. All laboratory measurement techniques are subject to errors resulting from interfering agents. A gas chromatograph is typically used in conjunction with the mass spectrometer to eliminate interference from nitrous oxide (N_2O), which has an equivalent mass, if samples are collected in a hospital or in another location where N_2O might be present.

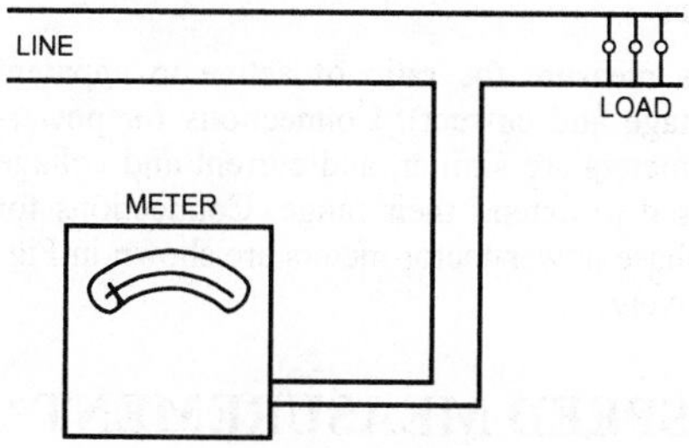

Fig. 16 Ammeter Connected in Power Circuit

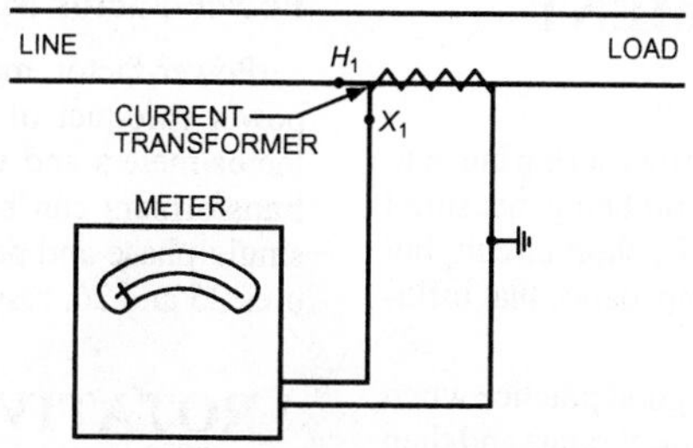

Fig. 17 Ammeter with Current Transformer

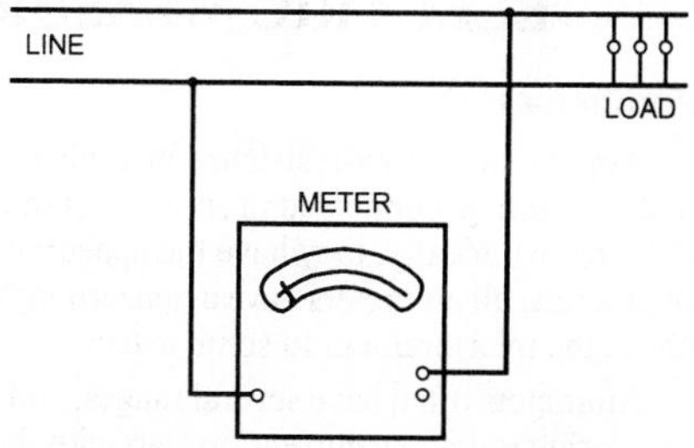

Fig. 18 Voltmeter Connected Across Load

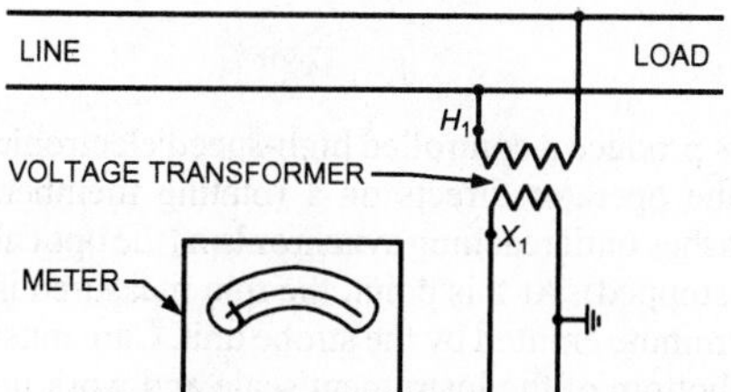

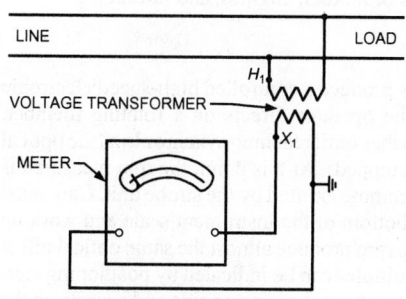

Fig. 19 Voltmeter with Potential Transformer

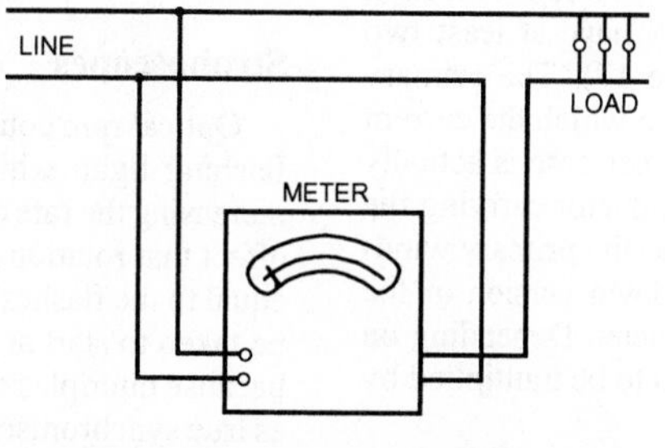

Fig. 20 Wattmeter in Single-Phase Circuit Measuring Power Load plus Loss in Current-Coil Circuit

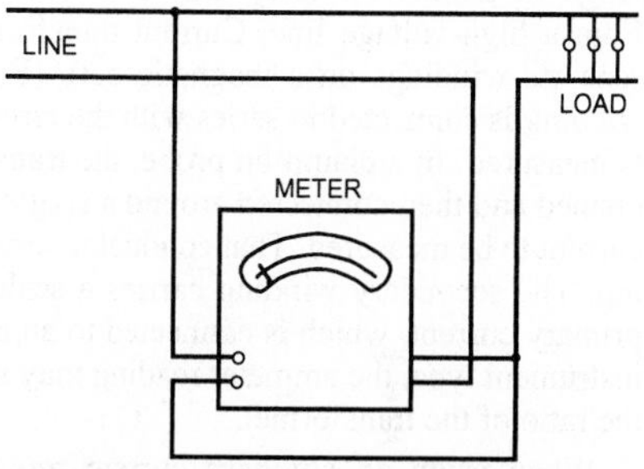

Fig. 21 Wattmeter in Single-Phase Circuit Measuring Power Load plus Loss in Potential-Coil Circuit

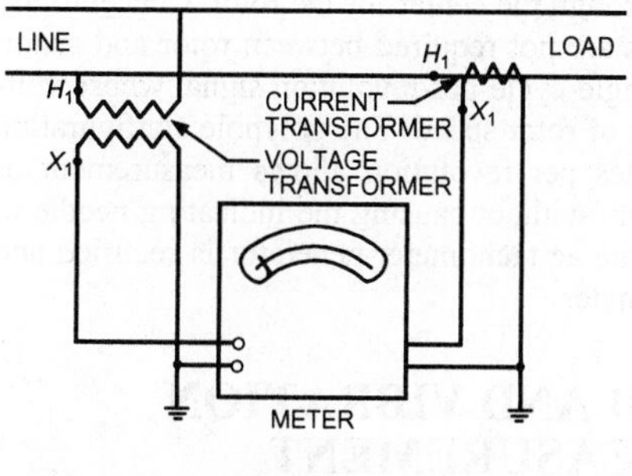

Fig. 22 Wattmeter with Current and Potential Transformer

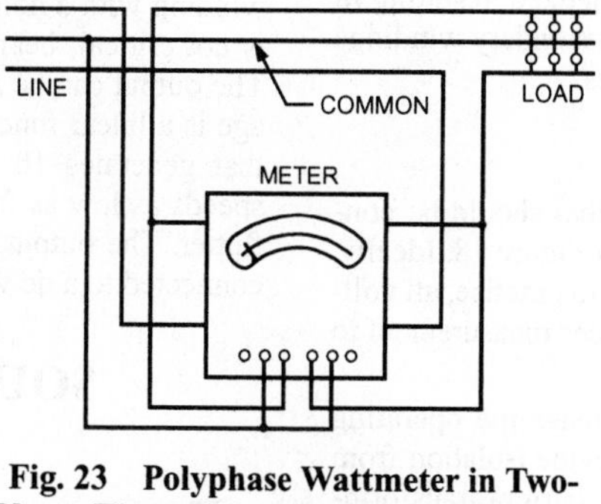

Fig. 23 Polyphase Wattmeter in Two-Phase, Three-Wire Circuit with Balanced or Unbalanced Voltage or Load

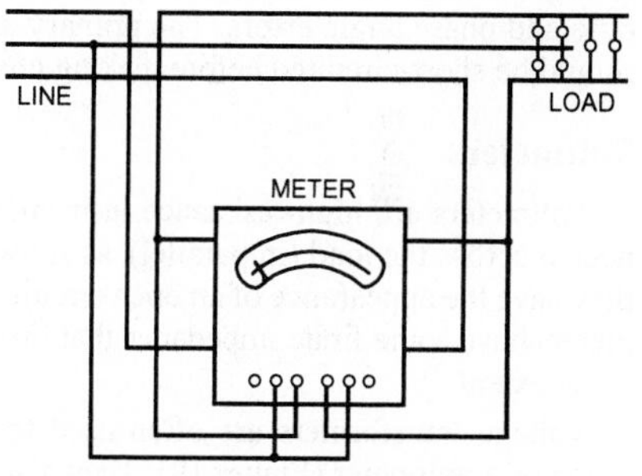

Fig. 24 Polyphase Wattmeter in Three-Phase, Three-Wire Circuit

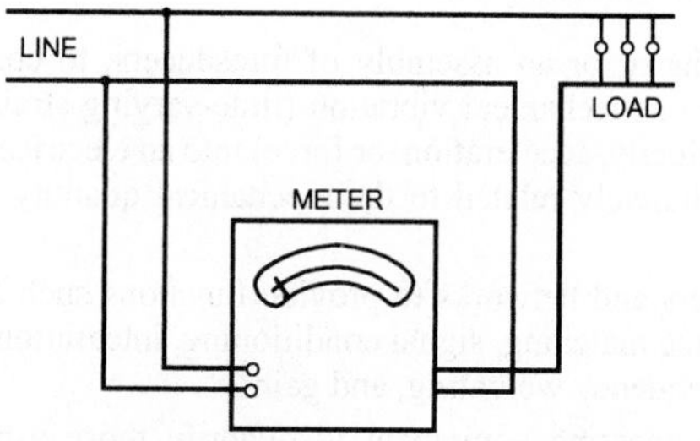

Fig. 25 Single-Phase Power-Factor Meter

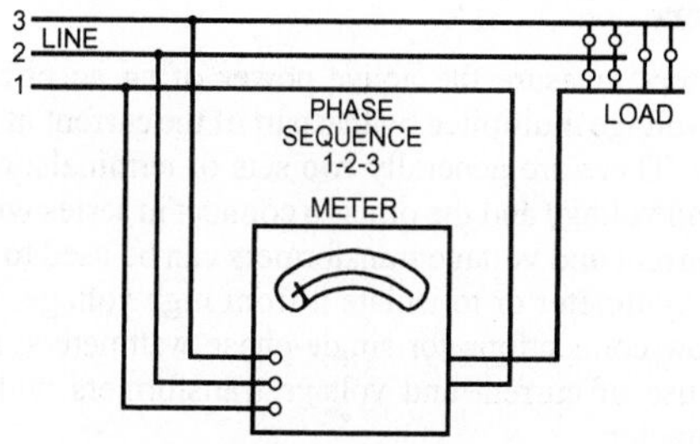

Fig. 26 Three-Wire, Three-Phase Power-Factor Meter

ELECTRIC MEASUREMENT

Ammeters

Ammeters are low-resistance instruments for measuring current. They should be connected in series with the circuit being measured (Figure 16). Ideally, they have the appearance of a short circuit, but in practice, all ammeters have a nonzero input impedance that influences the measurement to some extent.

Ammeters often have several ranges, and it is good practice when measuring unknown currents to start with the highest range and then reduce the range to the appropriate value to obtain the most sensitive reading. Ammeters with range switches maintain circuit continuity during switching. On some older instruments, it may be necessary to short-circuit the ammeter terminals when changing the range.

Current transformers are often used to increase the operating range of ammeters. They may also provide isolation/protection from a high-voltage line. Current transformers have at least two separate windings on a magnetic core (Figure 17). The primary winding is connected in series with the circuit in which the current is measured. In a clamp-on probe, the transformer core is actually opened and then connected around a single conductor carrying the current to be measured. That conductor serves as the primary winding. The secondary winding carries a scaled-down version of the primary current, which is connected to an ammeter. Depending on instrument type, the ammeter reading may need to be multiplied by the ratio of the transformer.

When using an auxiliary current transformer, the secondary circuit must not be open when current is flowing in the primary winding; dangerously high voltage may exist across the secondary terminals. A short-circuiting blade between the secondary terminals should be closed before the secondary circuit is opened at any point.

Transformer accuracy can be impaired by residual magnetism in the core when the primary circuit is opened at an instant when flux is large. The transformer core may be left magnetized, resulting in ratio and phase angle errors. The primary and secondary windings should be short-circuited before making changes.

Voltmeters

Voltmeters are high-resistance instruments that should be connected across the load (in parallel), as shown in Figure 18. Ideally, they have the appearance of an open circuit, but in practice, all voltmeters have some finite impedance that influences measurement to some extent.

Voltage transformers are often used to increase the operating range of a voltmeter (Figure 19). They also provide isolation from high voltages and prevent operator injury. Like current transformers, voltage transformers consist of two or more windings on a magnetic core. The primary winding is generally connected across the high voltage to be measured, and the secondary winding is connected to the voltmeter. It is important not to short-circuit the secondary winding of a voltage transformer.

Wattmeters

Wattmeters measure the active power of an ac circuit, which equals the voltage multiplied by that part of the current in phase with the voltage. There are generally two sets of terminals: one to connect the load voltage and the other to connect in series with the load current. Current and voltage transformers can be used to extend the range of a wattmeter or to isolate it from high voltage. Figures 20 and 21 show connections for single-phase wattmeters, and Figure 22 shows use of current and voltage transformers with a single-phase wattmeter.

Wattmeters with multiple current and voltage elements are available to measure polyphase power. Polyphase wattmeter connections are shown in Figures 23 and 24.

Power-Factor Meters

Power-factor meters measure the ratio of active to apparent power (product of voltage and current). Connections for power-factor meters and wattmeters are similar, and current and voltage transformers can be used to extend their range. Connections for single-phase and polyphase power-factor meters are shown in Figures 25 and 26, respectively.

ROTATIVE SPEED MEASUREMENT

Tachometers

Tachometers, or direct-measuring rpm counters, vary from hand-held mechanical or electric meters to shaft-driven and electronic pulse counters. They are used in general laboratory and shop work to check rotative speeds of motors, engines, and turbines.

Stroboscopes

Optical rpm counters produce a controlled high-speed electronic flashing light, which the operator directs on a rotating member, increasing the rate of flashes until reaching synchronism (the optical effect that rotation has stopped). At this point, the rpm measured is equal to the flashes per minute emitted by the strobe unit. Care must be taken to start at the bottom of the instrument scale and work up because multiples of the rpm produce almost the same optical effect as true synchronism. Multiples can be indicated by positioning suitable marks on the shaft, such as a bar on one side and a circle on the opposite side. If, for example, the two are seen superimposed, then the strobe light is flashing at an even multiple of the true rpm.

AC Tachometer-Generators

A tachometer-generator consists of a rotor and a stator. The rotor is a permanent magnet driven by the equipment. The stator is a winding with a hole through the center for the rotor. Concentricity is not critical; bearings are not required between rotor and stator. The output can be a single-cycle-per-revolution signal whose voltage is a linear function of rotor speed. The polypole configuration that generates 10 cycles per revolution allows measurement of speeds as low as 20 rpm without causing the indicating needle to flutter. The output of the ac tachometer-generator is rectified and connected to a dc voltmeter.

SOUND AND VIBRATION MEASUREMENT

Measurement systems for determining sound pressure level, intensity level, and mechanical vibration generally use transducers to convert mechanical signals into electrical signals, which are then processed electronically or digitally to characterize the measured mechanical signals. These measurement systems contain one or more of the following elements, which may or may not be contained in a single instrument:

- A transducer, or an assembly of transducers, to convert sound pressure or mechanical vibration (time-varying strain, displacement, velocity, acceleration, or force) into an electrical signal that is quantitatively related to the mechanical quantity being measured
- Amplifiers and networks to provide functions such as electrical impedance matching, signal conditioning, integration, differentiation, frequency weighting, and gain
- Signal-processing equipment to quantify those aspects of the signal that are being measured (peak value, rms value, time-weighted average level, power spectral density, or magnitude or phase of a complex linear spectrum or transfer function)

- A device such as a meter, oscilloscope, digital display, or level recorder to display the signal or the aspects of it that are being quantified
- An interface that allows cable, wireless, or memory card output

The relevant range of sound and vibration signals can vary over more than 12 orders of magnitude in amplitude and more than 8 orders of magnitude in frequency, depending on the application. References on instrumentation, measurement procedures, and signal analysis are given in the Bibliography. Product and application notes, technical reviews, and books published by instrumentation manufacturers are an excellent source of additional reference material. See Chapter 47 of the 2007 *ASHRAE Handbook—HVAC Applications* and Chapter 8 of this volume for further information on sound and vibration.

SOUND MEASUREMENT

Microphones

A microphone is a transducer that transforms an acoustical signal into an electrical signal. The two predominant transduction principles used in sound measurement (as opposed to broadcasting or recording) are the electrostatic and the piezoelectric. **Electrostatic (capacitor) microphones** are available either as electret microphones, which do not require an external polarizing voltage, or as condenser microphones, which do require an external polarizing voltage, typically in the range of 28 to 200 V (dc). **Piezoelectric microphones** may be manufactured using either natural piezoelectric crystals or poled ferroelectric crystals. The types of response characteristics of measuring microphones are pressure, free field, and random incidence (diffuse field).

The sensitivity and the frequency range over which the microphone has uniform sensitivity (flat frequency response) vary with sensing element diameter (surface area) and microphone type. Other critical factors that may affect microphone/preamplifier performance or response are atmospheric pressure, temperature, relative humidity, external magnetic and electrostatic fields, mechanical vibration, and radiation. Microphone selection is based on long- and short-term stability; the match between performance characteristics (e.g., sensitivity, frequency response, amplitude linearity, self-noise) and the expected amplitude of sound pressure, frequency, range of analysis, and expected environmental conditions of measurement; and any other pertinent considerations, such as size and directional characteristics.

Sound Measurement Systems

Microphone preamplifiers, amplifiers, weighting networks, filters, analyzers, and displays are available either separately or integrated into a measuring instrument such as a sound level meter, personal noise exposure meter, measuring amplifier, or real-time fractional octave or Fourier [e.g., fast Fourier transform (FFT)] signal analyzer. Instruments included in a sound measurement system depend on the purpose of the measurement and the frequency range and resolution of signal analysis. For community and industrial noise measurements for regulatory purposes, the instrument, signal processing, and quantity to be measured are usually dictated by the pertinent regulation. The optimal instrument set generally varies for measurement of different characteristics such as sound power in HVAC ducts, sound power emitted by machinery, noise criteria (NC) numbers, sound absorption coefficients, sound transmission loss of building partitions, and reverberation times (T_{60}).

Frequency Analysis

Measurement criteria often dictate using filters to analyze the signal, to indicate the spectrum of the sound being measured. Filters of different bandwidths for different purposes include fractional octave band (one, one-third, one-twelfth, etc.), constant-percentage bandwidth, and constant (typically narrow) bandwidth. The filters may be analog or digital and, if digital, may or may not be capable of real-time data acquisition during measurement, depending on the bandwidth of frequency analysis. FFT signal analyzers are generally used in situations that require very narrow-resolution signal analysis when the amplitudes of the sound spectra vary significantly with respect to frequency. This may occur in regions of resonance or when it is necessary to identify narrow-band or discrete sine-wave signal components of a spectrum in the presence of other such components or of broadband noise. However, when the frequency varies (e.g., because of nonconstant rpm of a motor), results from FFT analyzers can be difficult to interpret because the change in rpm provides what looks like a broadband signal.

Sound Chambers

Special rooms and procedures are required to characterize and calibrate sound sources and receivers. The rooms are generally classified into three types: anechoic, hemianechoic, and reverberant. The ideal **anechoic** room has all boundary surfaces that completely absorb sound energy at all frequencies. The ideal **hemianechoic** room would be identical to the ideal anechoic room, except that one surface would totally reflect sound energy at all frequencies. The ideal **reverberant** room would have boundary surfaces that totally reflect sound energy at all frequencies.

Anechoic chambers are used to perform measurements under conditions approximating those of a free sound field. They can be used in calibrating and characterizing individual microphones, microphone arrays, acoustic intensity probes, reference sound power sources, loudspeakers, sirens, and other individual or complex sources of sound.

Hemianechoic chambers have a hard reflecting floor to accommodate heavy machinery or to simulate large factory floor or outdoor conditions. They can be used in calibrating and characterizing reference sound power sources, obtaining sound power levels of noise sources, and characterizing sound output of emergency vehicle sirens when mounted on an emergency motor vehicle.

Reverberation chambers are used to perform measurements under conditions approximating those of a diffuse sound field. They can be used in calibrating and characterizing random-incidence microphones and reference sound power sources, obtaining sound power ratings of equipment and sound power levels of noise sources, measuring sound absorption coefficients of building materials and panels, and measuring transmission loss through building partitions and components such as doors and windows.

The choice of which room type to use often depends on the test method required for the subject units, testing costs, or room availability.

Calibration

A measurement system should be calibrated as a system from microphone or probe to indicating device before it is used to perform absolute measurements of sound. Acoustic calibrators and pistonphones of fixed or variable frequency and amplitude are available for this purpose. These calibrators should be used at a frequency low enough that the pressure, free-field, and random-incidence response characteristics of the measuring microphone(s) are, for practical purposes, equivalent, or at least related in a known quantitative manner for that specific measurement system. In general, the sound pressure produced by these calibrators may vary, depending on microphone type, whether the microphone has a protective grid, atmospheric pressure, temperature, and relative humidity. Correction factors and coefficients are required when conditions of use differ from those existing during the calibration of the acoustic calibrator or pistonphone. For demanding applications, precision sound sources and measuring microphones should periodically be sent to the manufacturer, a private testing laboratory, or a national standards laboratory for calibration.

VIBRATION MEASUREMENT

Except for seismic instruments that record or indicate vibration directly with a mechanical or optomechanical device connected to the test surface, vibration measurements use an electromechanical or interferometric vibration transducer. Here, the term *vibration transducer* refers to a generic electromechanical vibration transducer. Electromechanical and interferometric vibration transducers belong to a large and varied group of transducers that detect mechanical motion and furnish an electrical signal that is quantitatively related to a particular physical characteristic of the motion. Depending on design, the electrical signal may be related to mechanical strain, displacement, velocity, acceleration, or force. The operating principles of vibration transducers may involve optical interference; electrodynamic coupling; piezoelectric (including poled ferroelectric) or piezoresistive crystals; or variable capacitance, inductance, reluctance, or resistance. A considerable variety of vibration transducers with a wide range of sensitivities and bandwidths is commercially available. Vibration transducers may be contacting (e.g., seismic transducers) or noncontacting (e.g., interferometric, optical, or capacitive).

Transducers

Seismic transducers use a spring-mass resonator within the transducer. At frequencies much greater than the fundamental natural frequency of the mechanical resonator, the relative displacement between the base and the seismic mass of the transducer is nearly proportional to the displacement of the transducer base. At frequencies much lower than the fundamental resonant frequency, the relative displacement between the base and the seismic mass of the transducer is nearly proportional to the acceleration of the transducer base. Therefore, seismic displacement transducers and seismic electrodynamic velocity transducers tend to have a relatively compliant suspension with a low resonant frequency; piezoelectric accelerometers and force transducers have a relatively stiff suspension with a high resonant frequency.

Strain transducers include the metallic resistance gage and piezoresistive strain gage. For dynamic strain measurements, these are usually bonded directly to the test surface. The accuracy with which a bonded strain gage replicates strain occurring in the test structure is largely a function of how well the strain gage was oriented and bonded to the test surface.

Displacement transducers include the capacitance gage, fringe-counting interferometer, seismic displacement transducer, optical approaches, and the linear variable differential transformer (LVDT). Velocity transducers include the reluctance (magnetic) gage, laser Doppler interferometer, and seismic electrodynamic velocity transducer. Accelerometers and force transducers include the piezoelectric, piezoresistive, and force-balance servo.

Vibration Measurement Systems

Sensitivity, frequency limitations, bandwidth, and amplitude linearity of vibration transducers vary greatly with the transduction mechanism and the manner in which the transducer is applied in a given measurement apparatus. Contacting transducers' performance can be significantly affected by the mechanical mounting methods and points of attachment of the transducer and connecting cable and by the mechanical impedance of the structure loading the transducer. Amplitude linearity varies significantly over the operating range of the transducer, with some transducer types or configurations being inherently more linear than others. Other factors that may critically affect performance or response are temperature; relative humidity; external acoustic, magnetic, and electrostatic fields; transverse vibration; base strain; chemicals; and radiation. A vibration transducer should be selected based on its long- and short-term stability; the match between its performance characteristics (e.g., sensitivity, frequency response, amplitude linearity, self-noise) and the expected amplitude of vibration, frequency range of analysis, and expected environmental conditions of measurement; and any other pertinent considerations (e.g., size, mass, and resonant frequency).

Vibration exciters, or **shakers**, are used in structural analysis, vibration analysis of machinery, fatigue testing, mechanical impedance measurements, and vibration calibration systems. Vibration exciters have a table or moving element with a drive mechanism that may be mechanical, electrodynamic, piezoelectric, or hydraulic. They range from relatively small, low-power units for calibrating transducers (e.g., accelerometers) to relatively large, high-power units for structural and fatigue testing.

Conditioning amplifiers, power supplies, preamplifiers, charge amplifiers, voltage amplifiers, power amplifiers, filters, controllers, and displays are available either separately or integrated into a measuring instrument or system, such as a structural analysis system, vibration analyzer, vibration monitoring system, vibration meter, measuring amplifier, multichannel data-acquisition and modal analysis system, or real-time fractional-octave or FFT signal analyzer. The choice of instruments to include in a vibration measurement system depends on the mechanical quantity to be determined, purpose of the measurement, and frequency range and resolution of signal analysis. For vibration measurements, the signal analysis is relatively narrow in bandwidth and may be relatively low in frequency, to accurately characterize structural resonances. Accelerometers with internal integrated circuitry are available to provide impedance matching or servo control for measuring very-low-frequency acceleration (servo accelerometers). Analog integration and differentiation of vibration signals is available through integrating and differentiating networks and amplifiers, and digital is available through FFT analyzers. Vibration measurements made for different purposes (e.g., machinery diagnostics and health monitoring, balancing rotating machinery, analysis of torsional vibration, analysis of machine-tool vibration, modal analysis, analysis of vibration isolation, stress monitoring, industrial control) generally have different mechanical measurement requirements and a different optimal set of instrumentation.

Calibration

Because of their inherent long- and short-term stability, amplitude linearity, wide bandwidth, wide dynamic range, low noise, and wide range of sensitivities, seismic accelerometers have traditionally been used as a reference standard for dynamic mechanical measurements. A measurement system should be calibrated as a system from transducer to indicating device before it is used to perform absolute dynamic measurements of mechanical quantities. Calibrated reference vibration exciters, standard reference accelerometers, precision conditioning amplifiers, and precision calibration exciters are available for this purpose. These exciters and standard reference accelerometers can be used to transfer a calibration to another transducer. For demanding applications, a calibrated exciter or standard reference accelerometer with connecting cable and conditioning amplifier should periodically be sent to the manufacturer, a private testing laboratory, or a national standards laboratory for calibration.

LIGHTING MEASUREMENT

Light level, or **illuminance**, is usually measured with a photocell made from a semiconductor such as silicon or selenium. Photocells produce an output current proportional to incident luminous flux when linked with a microammeter, color- and cosine-corrected filters, and multirange switches; they are used in inexpensive handheld light meters and more precise instruments. Different cell heads allow multirange use in precision meters.

Cadmium sulfide photocells, in which resistance varies with illumination, are also used in light meters. Both gas-filled and vacuum photoelectric cells are in use.

Small survey-type meters are not as accurate as laboratory meters; their readings should be considered approximate, although consistent, for a given condition. Their range is usually from 50 to 50 000 lux. Precision low-level meters have cell heads with ranges down to 0 to 20 lux.

A photometer installed in a revolving head is called a **goniophotometer** and is used to measure the distribution of light sources or luminaires. To measure total luminous flux, the luminaire is placed in the center of a sphere painted inside with a high-reflectance white with a near-perfect diffusing matte surface. Total light output is measured through a small baffled window in the sphere wall.

To measure irradiation from germicidal lamps, a filter of fused quartz with fluorescent phosphor is placed over the light meter cell.

If meters are used to measure the number of lumens per unit area diffusely leaving a surface, luminance (cd/m^2) instead of illumination (lux) is read. Light meters can be used to measure luminance, or electronic lux meters containing a phototube, an amplifier, and a microammeter can read luminance directly.

Chapter 2 of the IESNA (2000) *Lighting Handbook* gives detailed information on measurement of light.

THERMAL COMFORT MEASUREMENT

Thermal comfort depends on the combined influence of clothing, activity, air temperature, air velocity, mean radiant temperature, and air humidity. Thermal comfort is influenced by heating or cooling of particular body parts through radiant temperature asymmetry (plane radiant temperature), draft (air temperature, air velocity, turbulence), vertical air temperature differences, and floor temperature (surface temperature).

A general description of thermal comfort is given in Chapter 9, and guidelines for an acceptable thermal environment are given in ASHRAE *Standard* 55 and ISO *Standard* 7730. ASHRAE *Standard* 55 also includes required measuring accuracy. In addition to specified accuracy, ISO *Standard* 7726 includes recommended measuring locations and a detailed description of instruments and methods.

Clothing and Activity Level

These values are estimated from tables (Chapter 9; ISO *Standards* 8996, 9920). Thermal insulation of clothing [(m^2·K)/W] can be measured on a thermal mannequin (McCullough et al. 1985; Olesen 1985). Activity (W/m^2) can be estimated from measuring CO_2 and O_2 in a person's expired air.

Air Temperature

Various types of thermometers may be used to measure air temperature. Placed in a room, the sensor registers a temperature between air temperature and mean radiant temperature. One way of reducing the radiant error is to make the sensor as small as possible, because the convective heat transfer coefficient increases as size decreases, whereas the radiant heat transfer coefficient is constant. A smaller sensor also provides a favorably low time constant. Radiant error can also be reduced by using a shield (an open, polished aluminum cylinder) around the sensor, using a sensor with a low-emittance surface, or artificially increasing air velocity around the sensor (aspirating air through a tube in which the sensor is placed).

Air Velocity

In occupied zones, air velocities are usually small (0 to 0.5 m/s), but do affect thermal sensation. Because velocity fluctuates, the mean value should be measured over a suitable period, typically 3 min. Velocity fluctuations with frequencies up to 1 Hz significantly increase human discomfort caused by draft, which is a function of air temperature, mean air velocity, and turbulence (see Chapter 9). Fluctuations can be given as the standard deviation of air velocity over the measuring period (3 min) or as the turbulence intensity (standard deviation divided by mean air velocity). Velocity direction may change and is difficult to identify at low air velocities. An omnidirectional sensor with a short response time should be used. A thermal anemometer is suitable. If a hot-wire anemometer is used, the direction of measured flow must be perpendicular to the hot wire. Smoke puffs can be used to identify the direction.

Plane Radiant Temperature

This refers to the uniform temperature of an enclosure in which the radiant flux on one side of a small plane element is the same as in the actual nonuniform environment. It describes the radiation in one direction. Plane radiant temperature can be calculated from surface temperatures of the environment (half-room) and angle factors between the surfaces and a plane element (ASHRAE *Standard* 55). It may also be measured by a net-radiometer or a radiometer with a sensor consisting of a reflective disk (polished) and an absorbent disk (painted black) (Olesen et al. 1989).

Mean Radiant Temperature

This is the uniform temperature of an imaginary black enclosure in which an occupant would exchange the same amount of radiant heat as in the actual nonuniform enclosure. Mean radiant temperature can be calculated from measured surface temperatures and the corresponding angle factors between the person and surfaces. It can also be determined from the plane radiant temperature in six opposite directions, weighted according to the projected area factors for a person. For more information, see Chapter 9.

Because of its simplicity, the instrument most commonly used to determine the mean radiant temperature is a **black globe thermometer** (Bedford and Warmer 1935; Vernon 1932). This thermometer consists of a hollow sphere usually 150 mm in diameter, coated in flat black paint with a thermocouple or thermometer bulb at its center. The temperature assumed by the globe at equilibrium results from a balance between heat gained and lost by radiation and convection.

Mean radiant temperatures are calculated from

$$\bar{t}_r = \left[(t_g + 273)^4 + \frac{1.10 \times 10^8 V_a^{0.6}}{\varepsilon D^{0.4}}(t_g - t_a)\right]^{1/4} - 273 \quad (11)$$

where

$\bar{t}_r$ = mean radiant temperature, °C
t_g = globe temperature, °C
V_a = air velocity, m/s
t_a = air temperature, °C
D = globe diameter, m
ε = emissivity (0.95 for black globe)

According to Equation (11), air temperature and velocity around the globe must also be determined. The globe thermometer is spherical, but mean radiant temperature is defined in relation to the human body. For sedentary people, the globe represents a good approximation. For people who are standing, the globe, in a radiant nonuniform environment, overestimates the radiation from floor or ceiling; an ellipsoidal sensor gives a closer approximation. A black globe also overestimates the influence of short-wave radiation (e.g., sunshine). A flat gray color better represents the radiant characteristic of normal clothing (Olesen et al. 1989). The hollow sphere is usually made of copper, which results in an undesirably high time constant. This can be overcome by using lighter materials (e.g., a thin plastic bubble).

Air Humidity

The water vapor pressure (absolute humidity) is usually uniform in the occupied zone of a space; therefore, it is sufficient to measure

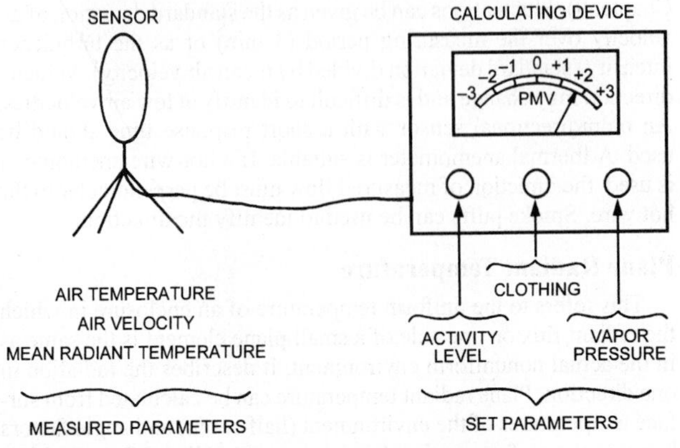

Fig. 27 Madsen's Comfort Meter
(Madsen 1976)

absolute humidity at one location. Many of the instruments listed in Table 3 are applicable. At ambient temperatures that provide comfort or slight discomfort, the thermal effect of humidity is only moderate, and highly accurate humidity measurements are unnecessary.

CALCULATING THERMAL COMFORT

When the thermal parameters have been measured, their combined effect can be calculated by the thermal indices in Chapter 9. For example, the effective temperature (Gagge et al. 1971) can be determined from air temperature and humidity. Based on the four environmental parameters and an estimation of clothing and activity, the **predicted mean vote** (PMV) can be determined with the aid of tables (Chapter 9; Fanger 1982; ISO *Standard* 7730). The PMV is an index predicting the average thermal sensation that a group of occupants may experience in a given space.

For certain types of normal activity and clothing, measured environmental parameters can be compared directly with those in ASHRAE *Standard* 55 or ISO *Standard* 7730.

INTEGRATING INSTRUMENTS

Several instruments have been developed to evaluate the combined effect of two or more thermal parameters on human comfort. Madsen (1976) developed an instrument that gives information on the occupants' expected thermal sensation by directly measuring the PMV value. The comfort meter has a heated elliptical sensor that simulates the body (Figure 27). The estimated clothing (insulation value), activity in the actual space, and humidity are set on the instrument. The sensor then integrates the thermal effect of air temperature, mean radiant temperature, and air velocity in approximately the same way the body does. The electronic instrument gives the measured operative and equivalent temperature, calculated PMV, and predicted percentage of dissatisfied (PPD).

MOISTURE CONTENT AND TRANSFER MEASUREMENT

Little off-the-shelf instrumentation exists to measure the moisture content of porous materials or moisture transfer through those materials. However, many measurements can be set up with a small investment of time and money. Three moisture properties are most commonly sought: (1) the sorption isotherm, the amount of water vapor a hygroscopic material adsorbs from humid air; (2) vapor permeability, the rate at which water vapor passes through a given material; and (3) liquid diffusivity, the rate at which liquid water passes through a porous material.

Sorption Isotherm

A sorption isotherm relates the **equilibrium moisture content (EMC)** of a hygroscopic material to the ambient relative humidity under constant temperature. Moisture content is the ratio of a sample's total mass of water to dry mass. Determining a sorption isotherm involves exposing a sample of material to a known relative humidity at a known temperature and then measuring the sample's moisture content after sufficient time has elapsed for the sample to reach equilibrium with its surroundings. Hysteresis in the sorption behavior of most hygroscopic materials requires that measurements be made for both increasing (adsorption isotherm) and decreasing relative humidity (desorption isotherm).

Ambient relative humidity can be controlled using saturated salt solutions or mechanical refrigeration equipment (Carotenuto et al. 1991; Cunningham and Sprott 1984; Tveit 1966). Precise measurements of the relative humidity produced by various salt solutions were reported by Greenspan (1977). ASTM *Standard* E104 describes the use of saturated salt solutions. A sample's EMC is usually determined gravimetrically using a precision balance. The sample's dry mass, necessary to calculate moisture content, can be found by oven drying or desiccant drying. Oven dry mass may be lower than desiccant dry mass because of the loss of volatiles other than water in the oven (Richards et al. 1992).

A major difficulty in measuring sorption isotherms of engineering materials is the long time required for many materials to reach equilibrium (often as long as weeks or months). The rate-limiting mechanism for these measurements is usually the slow process of vapor diffusion into the pores of the material. Using smaller samples can reduce diffusion time. Note that, although EMC isotherms are traditionally plotted as a function of relative humidity, the actual transport to or from materials is determined by vapor pressure differences. Thus, significant moisture content changes can occur because of changes in either the material vapor pressure or the surrounding air long before equilibrium is reached.

Vapor Permeability

Diffusive transfer of water vapor through porous materials is often described by a modified form of Fick's law:

$$w''_v = -\mu \frac{dp}{dx} \quad (12)$$

where

w''_v = mass of vapor diffusing through unit area per unit time, mg/(s·m²)
dp/dx = vapor pressure gradient, kPa/m
μ = vapor permeability, mg/(s·m·kPa)

In engineering practice, permeance may be used instead of permeability. **Permeance** is simply permeability divided by the material thickness in the direction of vapor flow; thus, permeability is a material property, whereas permeance depends on thickness.

Permeability is measured with wet-cup, dry-cup, or modified cup tests. Specific test methods for measuring water vapor permeability are given in ASTM *Standard* E96.

For many engineering materials, vapor permeability is a strong function of mean relative humidity. Wet and dry cups cannot adequately characterize this dependence on relative humidity. Instead, a modified cup method can be used, in which pure water or desiccant in a cup is replaced with a saturated salt solution (Burch et al. 1992; McLean et al. 1990). A second saturated salt solution is used to condition the environment outside the cup. Relative humidities on both sides of the sample material can be varied from 0 to 100%. Several cups with a range of mean relative humidities are used to map out the dependence of vapor permeability on relative humidity.

In measuring materials of high permeability, the finite rate of vapor diffusion through air in the cup may become a factor. Air-film resistance could then be a significant fraction of the sample's resistance to vapor flow. Accurate measurement of high-permeability materials may require an accounting of diffusive rates across all air gaps (Fanney et al. 1991).

Liquid Diffusivity

Transfer of liquid water through porous materials may be characterized as a diffusion-like process:

$$w_l'' = -\rho D_l \frac{d\gamma}{dx} \quad (13)$$

where

w_l'' = mass of liquid transferred through unit area per unit time, kg/(s·m^2)
ρ = liquid density, kg/m^3
D_l = liquid diffusivity, m^2/s
$d\gamma/dx$ = moisture content gradient, m^{-1}

D_l typically depends strongly on moisture content.

Transient measurement methods deduce the functional form of $D_l\gamma$ by observing the evolution of a one-dimensional moisture content profile over time. An initially dry specimen is brought into contact with liquid water. Free water migrates into the specimen, drawn in by surface tension. The resulting moisture content profile, which changes with time, must be differentiated to find the material's liquid diffusivity (Bruce and Klute 1956).

Determining the transient moisture content profile typically involves a noninvasive and nondestructive method of measuring local moisture content. Methods include gamma ray absorption (Freitas et al. 1991; Kumaran and Bomberg 1985; Quenard and Sallee 1989), x-ray radiography (Ambrose et al. 1990), neutron radiography (Prazak et al. 1990), and nuclear magnetic resonance (NMR) (Gummerson et al. 1979).

Uncertainty in liquid diffusivity measurement is often large because of the need to differentiate noisy experimental data.

HEAT TRANSFER THROUGH BUILDING MATERIALS

Thermal Conductivity

The thermal conductivity of a heat insulator, as defined in Chapter 25, is a unit heat transfer factor. Two methods of determining the thermal conductivity of flat insulation are the **guarded hot plate** and the **heat flow meter apparatus**, according to ASTM *Standards* C177 and C518, respectively. Both methods use parallel isothermal plates to induce a steady temperature gradient across the thickness of the specimen(s). The guarded hot plate is considered an absolute method for determining thermal conductivity. The heat flow meter apparatus requires calibration with a specimen of known thermal conductivity, usually determined in the guarded hot plate. The heat flow meter apparatus is calibrated by determining the voltage output of its heat flux transducer(s) as a function of the heat flux through the transducer(s).

Basic guarded hot plate design consists of an electrically heated plate and two liquid-cooled plates. Two similar specimens of a material are required for a test; one is mounted on each side of the hot plate. A cold plate is then pressed against the outside of each specimen by a clamp screw. The heated plate consists of two sections separated by a small gap. During tests, the central (metering) and outer (guard) sections are maintained at the same temperature to minimize errors caused by edge effects. The electric energy required to heat the metering section is measured carefully and converted to heat flow. Thermal conductivity of the material can be calculated under steady-state conditions using this heat flow quantity, area of the metering section, temperature gradient, and specimen thickness. Thermal conductivity of cylindrical or pipe insulation (Chapter 25) is determined similarly, but an equivalent thickness must be calculated to account for the cylindrical shape (ASTM *Standard* C335). Transient methods have been developed by D'Eustachio and Schreiner (1952), Hooper and Chang (1953), and Hooper and Lepper (1950) using a line heat source within a slender probe. These instruments are available commercially and have the advantages of rapidity and a small test specimen requirement. The probe is a useful research and development tool, but it has not been as accepted as the guarded hot plate, heat flow meter apparatus, or pipe insulation apparatus.

Thermal Conductance and Resistance

Thermal conductances (C-factors) and resistances (R-values) of many building assemblies can be calculated from the conductivities and dimensions of their components, as described in Chapter 27. Test values can also be determined experimentally by testing large, representative specimens in the hot box apparatus described in ASTM *Standards* C976 and C1363. This laboratory apparatus measures heat transfer through a specimen under controlled air temperature, air velocity, and radiation conditions. It is especially suited for large, nonhomogeneous specimens.

For in situ measurements, heat flux and temperature transducers are useful in measuring the dynamic or steady-state behavior of opaque building components (ASTM *Standard* C1046). A heat flux transducer is simply a differential thermopile within a core or substrate material. Two types of construction are used: (1) multiple thermocouple junctions wrapped around a core material, or (2) printed circuits with a uniform array of thermocouple junctions. The transducer is calibrated by determining its voltage output as a function of the heat flux through the transducer. For in situ measurements, the transducer is installed in either the wall or roof, or mounted on an exterior surface with tape or adhesive. Data obtained can be used to compute the thermal conductance or resistance of the building component (ASTM *Standard* C1155).

AIR CONTAMINANT MEASUREMENT

Three measures of particulate air contamination include the number, projected area, and mass of particles per unit volume of air (ASTM 2004). Each requires an appropriate sampling technique.

Particles are counted by capturing them in impingers, impactors, membrane filters, or thermal or electrostatic precipitators. Counting may be done by microscope, using stage counts if the sample covers a broad range of sizes (Nagda and Rector 2001).

Electronic particle counters can give rapid data on particle size distribution and concentration. **Inertial particle counters** use acceleration to separate sampled particles into different sizes. Real-time **aerodynamic particle sizers (APS)** use inertial effects to separate particles by size, but instead of capturing the particles, they are sized optically (Cox and Miro 1997), and can provide continuous sampling; however, they tend to be very expensive. Other, less costly types of **optical particle counters (OPCs)** are also available, but they typically require careful calibration using the type of particle that is being measured for accurate results (Baron and Willeke 2001). Their accuracy also depends heavily on appropriate maintenance and proper application. Correction for particle losses (dropout in the sampling lines) during sampling can be particularly important for accurate concentration measurements. Concentration uncertainty (random measurement uncertainty) also depends on the number of particles sampled in a given sampling interval.

Particle counters have been used in indoor office environments as well as in cleanrooms, and in aircraft cabin air quality testing (Cox and Miro 1997).

Projected area determinations are usually made by sampling onto a filter paper and comparing the light transmitted or scattered by this filter to a standard filter. The staining ability of dusts depends on the projected area and refractive index per unit volume. For sampling, filters must collect the minimum-sized particle of interest, so membrane or glass fiber filters are recommended.

To determine particle mass, a measured quantity of air is drawn through filters, preferably of membrane or glass fiber, and the filter mass is compared to the mass before sampling. Electrostatic or thermal precipitators and various impactors have also been used. For further information, see ACGIH (1983), Lodge (1989), and Lundgren et al. (1979).

Chapter 45 of the 2007 *ASHRAE Handbook—HVAC Applications* presents information on measuring and monitoring gaseous contaminants. Relatively costly analytical equipment, which must be calibrated and operated carefully by experienced personnel, is needed. Numerous methods of sampling the contaminants, as well as the laboratory analysis techniques used after sampling, are specified. Some of the analytical methods are specific to a single pollutant; others can present a concentration spectrum for many compounds simultaneously.

COMBUSTION ANALYSIS

Two approaches are used to measure the thermal output or capacity of a boiler, furnace, or other fuel-burning device. The direct or **calorimetric test** measures change in enthalpy or heat content of the fluid, air, or water heated by the device, and multiplies this by the flow rate to arrive at the unit's capacity. The indirect test or **flue gas analysis** method determines heat losses in flue gases and the jacket and deducts them from the heat content (higher heating value) of measured fuel input to the appliance. A **heat balance** simultaneously applies both tests to the same device. The indirect test usually indicates the greater capacity, and the difference is credited to radiation from the casing or jacket and unaccounted-for losses.

With small equipment, the expense of the direct test is usually not justified, and the indirect test is used with an arbitrary radiation and unaccounted-for loss factor.

FLUE GAS ANALYSIS

Flue gases from burning fossil fuels generally contain carbon dioxide (CO_2) and water, with some small amounts of hydrogen (H_2), carbon monoxide (CO), nitrogen oxides (NO_x), sulfur oxides (SO_x), and unburned hydrocarbons. However, generally only concentrations of CO_2 (or O_2) and CO are measured to determine completeness of combustion and efficiency.

Nondispersive infrared (NDIR) analyzers are the most common laboratory instruments for measuring CO and CO_2. Their advantages include the following: (1) they are not very sensitive to flow rate, (2) no wet chemicals are required, (3) they have a relatively fast response, (4) measurements can be made over a wide range of concentrations, and (5) they are not sensitive to the presence of contaminants in ambient air.

In the laboratory, oxygen is generally measured with an instrument that uses O_2's paramagnetic properties. Paramagnetic instruments are generally used because of their excellent accuracy and because they can be made specific to the measurement of oxygen.

For field testing and burner adjustment, portable combustion testing equipment is available. These instruments generally measure O_2 and CO with electrochemical cells. The CO_2 is then calculated by an on-board microprocessor and, together with temperature, is used to calculate thermal efficiency. A less expensive approach is to measure CO_2, O_2, and CO with a portable Orsat apparatus.

DATA ACQUISITION AND RECORDING

Almost every type of transducer and sensor is available with the necessary interface system to make it computer-compatible. The transducer itself begins to lose its identity when integrated into a system with features such as linearization, offset correction, self-calibration, and so forth. This has eliminated concern about the details of signal conditioning and amplification of basic transducer outputs, although engineering judgment is still required to review all data for validity, accuracy, and acceptability before making decisions based on the results. The personal computer is integrated into every aspect of data recording, including sophisticated graphics, acquisition and control, and analysis. Internet or intranet connections allow easy access to remote personal-computer-based data-recording systems from virtually any locale.

Direct output devices can be either multipurpose or specifically designed for a given sensor. Traditional chart recorders still provide a visual indication and a hard copy record of the data, but their output is now rarely used to process data. These older mechanical stylus-type devices use ink, hot wire, pressure, or electrically sensitive paper to provide a continuous trace. They are useful up to a few hundred hertz. Thermal and ink recorders are confined to chart speeds of several centimetres per second for recording relatively slow processes. Simple indicators and readouts are used mostly to monitor the output of a sensor visually, and have now usually been replaced by modern digital indicators. Industrial environments commonly use signal transmitters for control or computer data-handling systems to convert the signal output of the primary sensor into a compatible common signal span (e.g., the standard 4-20 mA current loop). All signal conditioning (ranging, zero suppression, reference-junction compensation) is provided at the transmitter. Thus, all recorders and controllers in the system can have an identical electrical span, with variations only in charts and scales offering the advantages of interchangeability and economy in equipment cost. Long signal transmission lines can be used, and receiving devices can be added to the loop without degrading performance. Newer instruments may be digitally bus-based, which removes the degradation that may occur with analog signals. These digital instruments are usually immune to noise, based on the communications scheme that is used. They also may allow for self-configuration of the sensor in the field to the final data acquisition device.

The vast selection of available hardware, often confusing terminology, and the challenge of optimizing the performance/cost ratio for a specific application make configuring a data acquisition system difficult. A system specifically configured to meet a particular measurement need can quickly become obsolete if it has inadequate flexibility. Memory size, recording speed, and signal processing capability are major considerations in determining the correct recording system. Thermal, mechanical, electromagnetic interference, portability, and meteorological factors also influence the selection.

Digital Recording

A digital data acquisition system must contain an interface, which is a system involving one or several analog-to-digital converters, and, in the case of multichannel inputs, circuitry for multiplexing. The interface may also provide excitation for transducers, calibration, and conversion of units. The digital data are arranged into one or several standard digital bus formats. Many data acquisition systems are designed to acquire data rapidly and store large records of data for later recording and analysis. Once the input signals have been digitized, the digital data are essentially immune to noise and can be transmitted over great distances.

Information is transferred to a computer/recorder from the interface as a pulse train, which can be transmitted as 4-, 8-, 12-, 16-, or 32-bit words. An 8-bit word is a byte; many communications methods are rated according to their bytes per second transfer rate. Digital data are transferred in either serial or parallel mode. Serial transmission means that the data are sent as a series of pulses, one bit at a time. Although slower than parallel systems, serial interfaces require only two wires, which lowers their cabling cost. The speed of serial transmissions is rated according to the symbols per second rate, or baud rate. In parallel transmission, the entire data word is transmitted at one time. To do this, each bit of a data word has to have its own transmission line; other lines are needed for clocking and control. Parallel mode is used for short distances or when high data transmission rates are required. Serial mode must be used for long-distance communications where wiring costs are prohibitive.

The two most popular interface bus standards currently used for data transmission are the IEEE 488, or general-purpose interface bus (GPIB), and the RS232 serial interface. The **IEEE 488 bus** system feeds data down eight parallel wires, one data byte at a time. This parallel operation allows it to transfer data rapidly at up to 1 million characters per second. However, the IEEE 488 bus is limited to a cable length of 20 m and requires an interface connection on every meter for proper termination. The **RS232** system feeds data serially down two wires, one bit at a time. An RS232 line may be over 300 m long. For longer distances, it may feed a modem to send data over standard telephone lines. Newer digital bus protocols are now available to digitally transmit data using proprietary or standardized methods and TCP/IP or USB connections between the data acquisition unit and a personal computer. These newer buses can provide faster throughput than the older IEEE 488 and RS232 methods, have no length constraints, and may also be available with wireless connections. A local area network (LAN) may be available in a facility for transmitting information. With appropriate interfacing, transducer data are available to any computer connected to the network.

Bus measurements can greatly simplify three basic applications: data gathering, automated limit testing, and computer-controlled processes. Data gathering collects readings over time. The most common applications include aging tests in quality control, temperature tests in quality assurance, and testing for intermittents in service. A controller can monitor any output indefinitely and then display the data directly on screen or record it on magnetic tape or disks for future use.

In automated limit testing, the computer compares each measurement with programmed limits. The controller converts readings to a good/bad readout. Automatic limit testing is highly cost-effective when working with large number of parameters of a particular unit under test.

In computer-controlled processes, the IEEE 488 bus system becomes a permanent part of a larger, completely automated system. For example, a large industrial process may require many electrical sensors that feed a central computer controlling many parts of the manufacturing process. An IEEE 488 bus controller collects readings from several sensors and saves the data until asked to dump an entire batch of readings to a larger central computer at one time. Used in this manner, the IEEE 488 bus controller serves as a slave of the central computer.

Dynamic range and accuracy must be considered in a digital recording system. **Dynamic range** refers to the ratio of the maximum input signal for which the system is useful to the noise floor of the system. The **accuracy** figure for a system is affected by the signal noise level, nonlinearity, temperature, time, crosstalk, and so forth. In selecting an 8-, 12-, or 16-bit analog-to-digital converter, the designer cannot assume that system accuracy is necessarily determined by the resolution of the encoders (i.e., 0.4%, 0.025%, and 0.0016%, respectively). If the sensor preceding the converter is limited to 1% full-scale accuracy, for example, no significant benefits are gained by using a 12-bit system over an 8-bit system and suppressing the least significant bit. However, a greater number of bits may be required to cover a larger dynamic range.

Data-Logging Devices

Data loggers digitally store electrical signals (analog or digital) to an internal memory storage component. The signal from connected sensors is typically stored to memory at timed intervals ranging from MHz to hourly sampling. Some data loggers store data based on an event (e.g., button push, contact closure). Many data loggers can perform linearization, scaling, or other signal conditioning and allow logged readings to be either instantaneous or averaged values. Most data loggers have built-in clocks that record the time and date together with transducer signal information. Data loggers range from single-channel input to 256 or more channels. Some are general-purpose devices that accept a multitude of analog and/or digital inputs, whereas others are more specialized to a specific measurement (e.g., a portable anemometer with built-in data-logging capability) or application (e.g., a temperature, relative humidity, CO_2, and CO monitor with data logging for IAQ applications). Stored data are generally downloaded using a serial interface with a temporary direct connection to a personal computer. Remote data loggers may also download by modem through land-based or wireless telephone lines. Some data loggers are designed to allow downloading directly to a printer, or to an external hard drive or tape drive that can later be connected to a PC.

With the reduction in size of personal computers (laptops, notebooks, hand-held PCs, and palmtops), the computer itself is now being used as the data logger. These mobile computers may be left in the field, storing measurements from sensors directly interfaced into the computer. Depending on the particular application and number of sensors to be read, a computer card mounted directly into the PC may eliminate the external data acquisition device completely.

STANDARDS

ASA. 2006. Reference quantities for acoustical levels. ANSI *Standard* S1.8-1989 (R2006). Acoustical Society of America, New York.

ASA. 2005. Measurement of sound pressure levels in air. ANSI *Standard* S1.13-2005. Acoustical Society of America, New York.

ASA. 2006. Specification for acoustical calibrators. ANSI *Standard* S1.40-2006. Acoustical Society of America, New York.

ASA. 2004. Techniques of machinery vibration measurement. ANSI *Standard* S2.17-1980 (R2004). Acoustical Society of America, New York.

ASA. 2005. Guide to the mechanical mounting of accelerometers. ANSI *Standard* S2.61-1989 (R2005). Acoustical Society of America, New York.

ASA. 2006. Statistical methods for determining and verifying stated noise emission values of machinery and equipment. ANSI *Standard* S12.3-1985 (R2006). Acoustical Society of America, New York.

ASA. 2008. Methods for determining the insertion loss of outdoor noise barriers. ANSI *Standard* S12.8-1998 (R2008). Acoustical Society of America, New York.

ASA. 2006. Method for the designation of sound power emitted by machinery and equipment. ANSI *Standard* S12.23-1989 (R2006). Acoustical Society of America, New York.

ASHRAE. 2006. Standard method for temperature measurement. ANSI/ASHRAE *Standard* 41.1-1986 (RA 2006).

ASHRAE. 1992. Standard methods for laboratory air flow measurement. ANSI/ASHRAE *Standard* 41.2-1987 (RA 1992).

ASHRAE. 1989. Standard method for pressure measurement. ANSI/ASHRAE *Standard* 41.3-1989.

ASHRAE. 2006. Standard method for measurement of proportion of lubricant in liquid refrigerant. ANSI/ASHRAE *Standard* 41.4-1996 (RA 2006).

ASHRAE. 2006. Standard method for measurement of moist air properties. ANSI/ASHRAE *Standard* 41.6-1994 (RA 2006).

ASHRAE. 2006. Method of test for measurement of flow of gas. ANSI/ASHRAE *Standard* 41.7-1984 (RA 2006).

ASHRAE. 1989. Standard methods of measurement of flow of liquids in pipes using orifice flowmeters. ANSI/ASHRAE *Standard* 41.8-1989.

ASHRAE. 2006. Calorimeter test methods for mass flow measurements of volatile refrigerants. ANSI/ASHRAE *Standard* 41.9-2000 (RA 2006).

ASHRAE. 2007. Laboratory methods of testing fans for aerodynamic performance rating. ANSI/ASHRAE *Standard* 51-07, also ANSI/AMCA *Standard* 210-07.

ASHRAE. 2004. Thermal environmental conditions for human occupancy. ANSI/ASHRAE *Standard* 55-2004.

ASHRAE. 2007. Ventilation for acceptable indoor air quality. ANSI/ASHRAE *Standard* 62.1-2007.

ASHRAE. 1997. Laboratory method of testing to determine the sound power in a duct. ANSI/ASHRAE *Standard* 68-1997, also ANSI/AMCA *Standard* 330-97.

ASHRAE. 2008. Measurement, testing, adjusting, and balancing of building HVAC systems. ANSI/ASHRAE *Standard* 111-2008.

ASHRAE. 2005. Engineering analysis of experimental data. *Guideline* 2-2005.

ASME. 2005. Pressure gauges and gauge attachments. ANSI/ASME *Standard* B40.100-2005. American Society of Mechanical Engineers, New York.

ASME. 2003. Glossary of terms used in the measurement of fluid flow in pipes. ANSI/ASME *Standard* MFC-1M-2003. American Society of Mechanical Engineers, New York.

ASME. 1983. Measurement uncertainty for fluid flow in closed conduits. ANSI/ASME *Standard* MFC-2M-1983 (R2001). American Society of Mechanical Engineers, New York.

ASME. 2004. Measurement of fluid flow in pipes using orifice, nozzle, and venturi. *Standard* MFC-3M-2004. American Society of Mechanical Engineers, New York.

ASME. 1988. Measurement of liquid flow in closed conduits by weighing methods. ANSI/ASME *Standard* MFC-9M-1988 (R2001). American Society of Mechanical Engineers, New York.

ASME. 2000. Method for establishing installation effects on flowmeters. ANSI/ASME *Standard* MFC-10M-2000. American Society of Mechanical Engineers, New York.

ASME. 2005. Test uncertainty. ANSI/ASME *Standard* PTC 19.1-2005. American Society of Mechanical Engineers, New York.

ASME. 1974. Temperature measurement. ANSI/ASME *Standard* PTC 19.3-1974 (R1998). American Society of Mechanical Engineers, New York.

ASME. 2004. Flow measurement. ANSI/ASME *Standard* PTC 19.5-2004. American Society of Mechanical Engineers, New York.

ASTM. 2004. Standard test method for steady-state heat flux measurements and thermal transmission properties by means of the guarded-hot-plate apparatus. *Standard* C177-04. American Society for Testing and Materials, West Conshohocken, PA.

ASTM. 2005. Standard test method for steady-state heat transfer properties of pipe insulation. *Standard* C335-05. American Society for Testing and Materials, West Conshohocken, PA.

ASTM. 2004. Standard test method for steady-state thermal transmission properties by means of the heat flow meter apparatus. *Standard* C518-04. American Society for Testing and Materials, West Conshohocken, PA.

ASTM. 2000. Standard test method for thermal performance of building assemblies by means of a calibrated hot box. *Standard* C976-00. American Society for Testing and Materials, West Conshohocken, PA.

ASTM. 2007. Standard practice for in-situ measurement of heat flux and temperature on building envelope components. *Standard* C1046-95 (2007). American Society for Testing and Materials, West Conshohocken, PA.

ASTM. 2003. Standard practice for thermographic inspection of insulation installations in envelope cavities of frame buildings. *Standard* C1060-90 (2003). American Society for Testing and Materials, West Conshohocken, PA.

ASTM. 2007. Standard practice for determining thermal resistance of building envelope components from the in-situ data. *Standard* C1155-95 (2007). American Society for Testing and Materials, West Conshohocken, PA.

ASTM. 2005. Standard test method for thermal performance of building materials and envelope assemblies by means of a hot box apparatus. *Standard* C1363-05. American Society for Testing and Materials, West Conshohocken, PA.

ASTM. 2007. Standard guide for using indoor carbon dioxide concentrations to evaluate indoor air quality and ventilation. *Standard* D6245-07. American Society for Testing and Materials, West Conshohocken, PA.

ASTM. 2005. Standard test methods for water vapor transmission of materials. *Standard* E96/E96M-05. American Society for Testing and Materials, West Conshohocken, PA.

ASTM. 2007. Standard practice for maintaining constant relative humidity by means of aqueous solutions. *Standard* E104-02 (2007). American Society for Testing and Materials, West Conshohocken, PA.

ASTM. 2003. Standard specification and temperature-electromotive force (emf) tables for standardized thermocouples. *Standard* E230-03. American Society for Testing and Materials, West Conshohocken, PA.

ASTM. 2006. Standard test method for determining air change in a single zone by means of a tracer gas dilution. *Standard* E741-00 (2006). American Society for Testing and Materials, West Conshohocken, PA.

ASTM. 2004. *Atmospheric analysis; occupational health and safety; protective clothing*, vol. 11.03. (182 standards.) American Society for Testing and Materials, West Conshohocken, PA.

ISO. 1998. Ergonomics of the thermal environment—Instruments for measuring physical quantities. *Standard* 7726:1998. International Organization for Standardization, Geneva.

ISO. 2005. Ergonomics of the thermal environment—Analytical determination and interpretation of thermal comfort using calculation of the PMV and PPD indices and local thermal comfort criteria. *Standard* 7730:2005. International Organization for Standardization, Geneva.

ISO. 2004. Ergonomics of the thermal environment—Determination of metabolic rate. *Standard* 8996:2004. International Organization for Standardization, Geneva.

ISO. 2007. Ergonomics of the thermal environment—Estimation of thermal insulation and water vapour resistance of a clothing ensemble. *Standard* 9920:2007. International Organization for Standardization, Geneva.

SYMBOLS

A = flow area, m^2
a = thermocouple constant
C = correction factor
c_p = specific heat at constant pressure, kJ/(kg·K)
D = distance; diameter
d = throat diameter
D_l = liquid diffusivity, m^2/s
$d\gamma/dx$ = moisture content gradient, m^{-1}
dp/dx = vapor pressure gradient, kPa/m
E = voltage
F_a = thermal expansion correction factor
H = height
J = mechanical equivalent of heat = 100 (N·m)/kJ
K = sensitivity (Figure 1); differential expansion coefficient for liquid in glass; constant (function of geometry and Reynolds number)
n = number of degrees that liquid column emerged from bath
p = absolute pressure, Pa
p_w = velocity pressure (pitot-tube manometer reading), Pa
P_{wet} = wetted perimeter
Q = discharge flow rate, m^3/s
R = resistance, Ω
r = (see Figure 9)
S = spot size
t = temperature, °C; wall thickness
$\bar{t}_r$ = mean radiant temperature, °C
V = velocity, m/s; volume
W = width
w = mass flow rate, kg/s
w''_l = mass of liquid transferred through unit area per unit time, kg/(s·m^2)
w''_v = mass of vapor diffusing through unit area per unit time, mg/(s·m^2)
X = variable; velocity of stream, m/s

Greek

β = systematic (bias) error; ratio of diameters D_2/D_1 for venturi and sharp-edge orifice and d/D for flow nozzle
δ = deviation
ε = random error; emissivity (0.95 for black globe)
μ = mean; vapor permeability, mg/(s·m·kPa)
ρ = density, kg/m^3

Subscripts

1 = entering conditions; state 1
2 = throat conditions; state 2
a = air
b = bath
c = cross-sectional
e = equivalent of stream velocity
eff = effective
g = globe
h = hydraulic
i = pertaining to variable X
k = reading number

s = average of emergent liquid column of n degrees
true = true

REFERENCES

Abernethy, R.B., R.B. Benedict, and R.B. Dowdell. 1985. ASME measurement uncertainty. *Transactions of ASME* 107:161-164.

ACGIH. 1983. *Air sampling instruments for evaluation of atmospheric contaminants*, 6th ed. American Conference of Governmental Industrial Hygienists, Cincinnati, OH.

Ambrose, J.H., L.C. Chow, and J.E. Beam. 1990. Capillary flow properties of mesh wicks. *AIAA Journal of Thermophysics* 4:318-324.

Amdur, E.J. 1965. Two-pressure relative humidity standards. In *Humidity and moisture*, vol. 3, p. 445. Reinhold, New York.

ASTM. 1993. Manual on the use of thermocouples in temperature measurement. *Manual* 12. American Society for Testing and Materials, West Conshohocken, PA.

Bahnfleth, W.P., G.K. Yuill, and B.W. Lee. 1999. Protocol for field testing of tall buildings to determine envelope air leakage rates. *ASHRAE Transactions* 105(2):27-38.

Baron, P.A. and K. Willeke. 2001. *Aerosol measurement.* Wiley, New York.

Bedford, T. and C.G. Warmer. 1935. The globe thermometer in studies of heating and ventilating. *Journal of the Institution of Heating and Ventilating Engineers* 2:544.

Benedict, R.P. 1984. *Fundamentals of temperature, pressure and flow measurements*, 3rd ed. John Wiley & Sons, New York.

Bentz, D.P. and J.W. Martin. 1987. Using the computer to analyze coating defects. *Journal of Protective Coatings and Linings* 4(5).

Brown, K.K., H.W. Coleman, and W.G. Steele. 1998. A methodology for determining experimental uncertainties in regressions. *ASME Journal of Fluids Engineering, Transactions of ASME* 120:445-456.

Bruce, R.R. and A. Klute. 1956. The measurement of soil moisture diffusivity. *Proceedings of the Soil Science Society of America* 20:458-462.

Burch, D.M. 1980. Infrared audits of roof heat loss. *ASHRAE Transactions* 86(2).

Burch, D.M. and C.M. Hunt. 1978. Retrofitting an existing residence for energy conservation—An experimental study. *Building Science Series* 105. National Institute of Standards and Technology, Gaithersburg, MD.

Burch, D.M., W.C. Thomas, and A.H. Fanney. 1992. Water vapor permeability measurements of common building materials. *ASHRAE Transactions* 98(2):486-494.

Burns, G.W., M.G. Scroger, G.F. Strouse, M.C. Croarkin, and W.F. Guthrie. 1992. Temperature-electromotive force reference functions and tables for the letter-designated thermocouple types based on the ITS-90. NIST *Monograph* 175. U.S. Government Printing Office, Washington, D.C.

Carotenuto, A., F. Fucci, and G. LaFianzi. 1991. Adsorption phenomena in porous media in the presence of moist air. *International Journal of Heat and Mass Transfer* 18:71-81.

Coleman, H.W. and W.G. Steele. 1989. *Experimentation and uncertainty analysis for engineers*. John Wiley & Sons, New York.

Coleman, H.W. and W.G. Steele. 1995. Engineering application of experimental uncertainty analysis. *AIAA Journal* 33(10):1888-1896.

Considine, D.M. 1985. *Process instruments and controls handbook*, 3rd ed. McGraw-Hill, New York.

Cox, J.E. and C.R. Miro. 1997. Aircraft cabin air quality. *ASHRAE Journal* 22.

Cunningham, M.J. and T.J. Sprott. 1984. Sorption properties of New Zealand building materials. Building Research Association of New Zealand *Research Report* 45, Judgeford.

DeCarlo, J.P. 1984. *Fundamentals of flow measurement.* Instrumentation Society of America, Research Triangle Park, NC.

D'Eustachio, D. and R.E. Schreiner. 1952. A study of transient heat method for measuring thermal conductivity. *ASHVE Transactions* 58:331.

DeWitt, D.P. and G.D. Nutter. 1988. *Theory and practice of radiation thermometry.* John Wiley & Sons, New York.

Fanger, P.O. 1982. *Thermal comfort.* Robert E. Krieger, Malabar, FL.

Fanney, A.H., W.C. Thomas, D.M. Burch, and L.R. Mathena. 1991. Measurements of moisture diffusion in building materials. *ASHRAE Transactions* 97:99-113.

Freitas, V., P. Crausse, and V. Abrantes. 1991. Moisture diffusion in thermal insulating materials. In *Insulation materials: Testing and applications*, vol. 2. ASTM *Special Technical Publication* STP 1116. American Society for Testing and Materials, West Conshohocken, PA.

Gagge, A.P., J.A.J. Stolwijk, and Y. Nishi. 1971. An effective temperature scale based on a simple model of human physiological regulatory response. *ASHRAE Transactions* 77(1).

Goldstein, R.J. 1978. Application of aerial infrared thermography. *ASHRAE Transactions* 84(1).

Greenspan, L. 1977. Humidity fixed points of binary saturated aqueous solutions. *Journal of Research of the National Bureau of Standards* 81A: 89-95.

Greenspan, L. and A. Wexler. 1968. An adiabatic saturation psychrometer. *Journal of Research of the National Bureau of Standards* 72C(1):33.

Gummerson, R.J., C. Hall, W.D. Hoff, R. Hawkes, G.N. Holland, and W.S. Moore. 1979. Unsaturated water flow within porous materials observed by NMR imaging. *Nature* 281:56-57.

Hasegawa, S. 1976. The NBS two-pressure humidity generator, mark 2. *Journal of Research of the National Bureau of Standards* 81A:81.

Holman, J.P. 2001. *Experimental methods for engineers*, 7th ed., pp. 383-389. McGraw-Hill, New York.

Hooper, F.C. and S.C. Chang. 1953. Development of thermal conductivity probe. *ASHVE Transactions* 59:463.

Hooper, F.C. and F.C. Lepper. 1950. Transient heat flow apparatus for the determination of thermal conductivity. *ASHVE Transactions* 56:309.

Hudson, R.D., Jr. 1969. *Infrared system engineering.* John Wiley & Sons, New York.

IESNA. 2000. *Lighting handbook*, 9th ed. Illuminating Engineering Society of North America, New York.

Kumaran, M.K. and M. Bomberg. 1985. A gamma-spectrometer for determination of density distribution and moisture distribution in building materials. *Proceedings of the International Symposium on Moisture and Humidity*, Washington, D.C., pp. 485-490.

Kusuda, T. 1965. Calculation of the temperature of a flat-plate wet surface under adiabatic conditions with respect to the Lewis relation. In *Humidity and moisture*, vol. 1, p. 16. Reinhold, New York.

Liptak, B.G., ed. 1972. *Instrument engineers handbook*, vol. 1. Chilton, Philadelphia, PA.

Lodge, J.P., ed. 1989. *Methods of air sampling and analysis*, 3rd ed. Lewis Publishers, MI.

Lundgren, D.A., M. Lippmann, F.S. Harris, Jr., W.H. Marlow, W.E. Clark, and M.D. Durham, eds. 1979. *Aerosol measurement.* University Presses of Florida, Gainesville.

Mack, R.T. 1986. Energy loss profiles: Foundation for future profit in thermal imager sales and service. *Proceedings of the 5th Infrared Information Exchange*, Book 1, AGEMA Infrared Systems, Secaucus, NJ.

Madding, R. 1989. *Infrared thermography.* McGraw-Hill, New York.

Madsen, T.L. 1976. Thermal comfort measurements. *ASHRAE Transactions* 82(1).

Mattingly, G.E. 1984. Workshop on fundamental research issues in orifice metering. GRI *Report* 84/0190. Gas Research Institute, Chicago.

Mattingly, G.E. 1992. The characterization of a piston displacement-type flowmeter calibration facility and the calibration and use of pulsed output type flowmeters. *Journal of Research of the National Institute of Standards and Technology* 97(5):509.

McCullough, E.A., B.W. Jones, and J. Huck. 1985. A comprehensive data base for estimating clothing insulation. *ASHRAE Transactions* 92:29-47.

McLean, R.C., G.H. Galbraith, and C.H. Sanders. 1990. Moisture transmission testing of building materials and the presentation of vapour permeability values. *Building Research and Practice* 18(2):82-103.

Mease, N.E., W.G. Cleveland, Jr., G.E. Mattingly, J.M. Hall. 1992. Air speed calibrations at the National Institute of Standards and Technology. *Proceedings of the 1992 Measurement Science Conference*, Anaheim, CA.

Miller, R.W. 1983. *Measurement engineering handbook.* McGraw-Hill, New York.

Nagda, N.L. and H.E. Rector. 2001. Instruments and methods for measuring indoor air quality. In *Indoor air quality handbook*, pp. 51.1-51.37. J.D. Spengler, J.M. Samet, and J.F. McCarthy, eds. McGraw-Hill.

NIST. 1976. Liquid-in-glass thermometry. NIST *Monograph* 150. National Institute of Standards and Technology, Gaithersburg, MD.

NIST. 1986. Thermometer calibrations. NIST *Monograph* 174. National Institute of Standards and Technology, Gaithersburg, MD.

Nottage, H.B., J.G. Slaby, and W.P. Gojsza. 1952. A smoke-filament technique for experimental research in room air distribution. *ASHVE Transactions* 58:399.

Olesen, B.W. 1985. A new and simpler method for estimating the thermal insulation of a clothing ensemble. *ASHRAE Transactions* 92:478-492.

Olesen, B.W., J. Rosendahl, L.N. Kalisperis, L.H. Summers, and M. Steinman. 1989. Methods for measuring and evaluating the thermal radiation in a room. *ASHRAE Transactions* 95(1).

Paljak, I. and B. Pettersson. 1972. *Thermography of buildings.* National Swedish Institute for Materials Testing, Stockholm.

Parmelee, G.V. and R.G. Huebscher. 1946. The shielding of thermocouples from the effects of radiation. *ASHVE Transactions* 52:183.

Persily, A. and S.J. Emmerich. 2001. *State-of-the-art review of CO_2 demand control ventilation and application.* NIST IR6729. National Institute of Standards and Technology, Gaithersburg, MD.

Prazak, J., J. Tywoniak, F. Peterka, and T. Slonc. 1990. Description of transport of liquid in porous media—A study based on neutron radiography data. *International Journal of Heat and Mass Transfer* 33:1105-1120.

Quenard, D. and H. Sallee. 1989. A gamma-ray spectrometer for measurement of the water diffusivity of cementitious materials. *Proceedings of the Materials Research Society Symposium*, vol. 137.

Quinn, T.J. 1990. *Temperature*, 2nd ed. Academic Press, New York.

Raffel, M., C. Willert, and J. Kompenhans. 1998. *Particle image velocimetry: A practical guide*. Springer.

Richards, R.F., D.M. Burch, W.C. Thomas. 1992. Water vapor sorption measurements of common building materials. *ASHRAE Transactions* 98(1).

Richardson, L. 1965. A thermocouple recording psychrometer for measurement of relative humidity in hot, arid atmosphere. In *Humidity and moisture*, vol. 1, p. 101. Reinhold, New York.

Schooley, J.F. 1986. *Thermometry.* CRC, Boca Raton, FL.

Schooley, J.F., ed. 1992. *Temperature: Its measurement and control in science and in industry*, vol. 6. American Institute of Physics, New York.

Seely, R.E. 1955. A circuit for measuring the resistance of energized A-C windings. *AIEE Transactions*, p. 214.

Shafer, M.R. 1961. Performance characteristics of turbine flowmeters. *Proceedings of the Winter Annual Meeting*, Paper 61-WA-25. American Society of Mechanical Engineers, New York.

Till, C.E. and G.E. Handegord. 1960. Proposed humidity standard. *ASHRAE Transactions* 66:288.

Tobiasson, W. and C. Korhonen. 1985. Roofing moisture surveys: Yesterday, today, and tomorrow. *Proceedings of the Second International Symposium on Roofing Technology*, Gaithersburg, MD.

Tveit, A. 1966. Measurement of moisture sorption and moisture permeability of porous materials. *Report* 45. Norwegian Building Research Institute, Oslo.

Vernon, H.M. 1932. The globe thermometer. *Proceedings of the Institution of Heating and Ventilating Engineers*, vol. 39, p. 100.

Wentzel, J.D. 1961. An instrument for measurement of the humidity of air. *ASHRAE Journal* 11:67.

Wile, D.D. 1947. Air flow measurement in the laboratory. *Refrigerating Engineering* 6:515.

Woodring, E.D. 1969. Magnetic turbine flowmeters. *Instruments and Control Systems* 6:133.

Worrall, R.W. 1965. Psychrometric determination of relative humidities in air with dry-bulb temperatures exceeding 212°F. In *Humidity and Moisture*, vol. 1, p. 105. Reinhold, New York.

BIBLIOGRAPHY

Beranek, L.L. 1988. *Acoustical measurements.* Published for the Acoustical Society of America by the American Institute of Physics, New York.

Beranek, L.L. 1989. *Noise and vibration control.* Institute of Noise Control Engineering, Poughkeepsie, NY.

Cohen, E.R. 1990. The expression of uncertainty in physical measurements. *1990 Measurement Science Conference Proceedings*, Anaheim, CA.

EPA. 1991. *Introduction to indoor air quality: A self-paced learning module.* EPA/400/3-91/002, U.S. Environmental Protection Agency, Washington, D.C.

Harris, C.M. 1987. *Shock and vibration handbook*, 3rd ed. McGraw-Hill, New York.

IEEE. 1987. Standard digital interface for programmable instrumentation. ANSI/IEEE *Standard* 488.1-87 (R 1994). Institute of Electrical and Electronics Engineers, Piscataway, NJ.

Lord, H.W., W.S. Gatley, and H.A. Evensen. 1987. *Noise control for engineers.* Krieger, Melbourne, FL.

Morrison, R. 1986. *Grounding and shielding techniques in instrumentation*, 3rd ed. John Wiley & Sons, New York.

Spitzer, D.W., ed. 1991. *Flow measurement.* Instrumentation Society of America, Research Triangle Park, NC.

Steele, W.G., R.A. Ferguson, R.P. Taylor, and H.W. Coleman. 1994. Comparison of ANSI/ASME and ISO models for calculation of uncertainty. *ISA Transactions* 33:339-352.

Tilford, C.R. 1992. Pressure and vacuum measurements. In *Physical methods of chemistry*, 2nd ed., vol. 6, pp. 106-173. John Wiley & Sons, New York.

CHAPTER 37

ABBREVIATIONS AND SYMBOLS

THIS chapter contains information about abbreviations and symbols for heating, ventilating, air-conditioning, and refrigerating (HVAC&R) engineers.

Abbreviations are shortened forms of names and expressions used in text, drawings, and computer programs. This chapter discusses conventional English-language abbreviations that may be different in other languages. A **letter symbol** represents a quantity or a unit, not its name, and is independent of language. Because of this, use of a letter symbol is preferred over abbreviations for unit or quantity terms. Letter symbols necessary for individual chapters are defined in the chapters where they occur.

Abbreviations are never used for mathematical signs, such as the equality sign (=) or division sign (/), except in computer programming, where the abbreviation functions as a letter symbol. Mathematical operations are performed only with symbols. Abbreviations should be used only where necessary to save time and space; avoid their usage in documents circulated in foreign countries.

Graphical symbols in this chapter of piping, ductwork, fittings, and in-line accessories can be used on scale drawings and diagrams.

Identifying piping by legend and color promotes greater safety and lessens the chance of error in emergencies. Piping identification is now required throughout the United States by the Occupational Safety and Health Administration (OSHA) for some industries and by many federal, state, and local codes.

ABBREVIATIONS FOR TEXT, DRAWINGS, AND COMPUTER PROGRAMS

Table 1 gives some abbreviations, as well as others commonly found on mechanical drawings and abbreviations (symbols) used in computer programming. Abbreviations specific to a single subject are defined in the chapters in which they appear. Additional abbreviations used on drawings can be found in the section on Graphical Symbols for Drawings.

Computer Programs

The abbreviations (symbols) used for computer programming for the HVAC&R industries have been developed by ASHRAE Technical Committee 1.5, Computer Applications. These symbols identify computer variables, subprograms, subroutines, and functions commonly applied in the industry. Using these symbols enhances comprehension of the program listings and provides a clearly defined nomenclature in applicable computer programs.

Certain programming languages differentiate between real numbers (numbers with decimals) and integers (numbers without decimals) by reserving certain initial letters of a variable for integer numbers. Many of the symbols listed in this chapter begin with these letters and, in order to make them real numbers, must be prefixed with a noninteger letter.

Some symbols have two or more options listed. The longest abbreviation is preferred and should be used if possible. However, it is sometimes necessary to shorten the symbol to further identify the variable. For instance, the area of a wall cannot be defined as WALLAREA because some computer languages restrict the number of letters in a variable name. Therefore, a shorter variable symbol is applied, and WALLAREA becomes WALLA or WAREA.

Many advanced computer programming languages such as Basic, C, and C^{++} do not have the limitations of older computer language compilers. It is good programming practice to include the complete name of each variable and to define any abbreviations in the comments section at the beginning of each module of code. Abbreviations should be used to help clarify the variables in an equation and not to obscure the readability of the code.

In Table 1, the same symbol is sometimes used for different terms. This liberty is taken because it is unlikely that the two terms would be used in the same program. If such were the case, one of the terms would require a suffix or prefix to differentiate it from the other.

LETTER SYMBOLS

Letter symbols include symbols for physical quantities (quantity symbols) and symbols for the units in which these quantities are measured (unit symbols). **Quantity symbols**, such as I for electric current, are listed in this chapter and are printed in italic type. A **unit symbol** is a letter or group of letters such as mm for millimetre or a special sign such as ° for degrees and is printed in Roman type. Subscripts and superscripts are governed by the same principles. Letter symbols are restricted mainly to the English and Greek alphabets.

Quantity symbols may be used in mathematical expressions in any way consistent with good mathematical usage. The product of two quantities, a and b, is indicated by ab. The quotient is a/b, or ab^{-1}. To avoid misinterpretation, parentheses must be used if more than one slash (/) is used in an algebraic term; for example, $(a/b)/c$ or $a/(b/c)$ is correct, but not $a/b/c$.

Subscripts and superscripts, or several of them separated by commas, may be attached to a single basic letter (kernel), but not to other subscripts or superscripts. A symbol that has been modified by a superscript should be enclosed in parentheses before an exponent is added $(X_a)^3$. Symbols can also have alphanumeric marks such as ′ (prime), + (plus), and * (asterisk).

More detailed information on the general principles of letter symbol standardization are in standards listed at the end of this chapter. The letter symbols, in general, follow these standards, which are out of print:

Y10.3M	Letter Symbols for Mechanics and Time-Related Phenomena
Y10.4-82	Letter Symbols for Heat and Thermodynamics

Other symbols chosen by an author for a physical magnitude not appearing in any standard list should be ones that do not already have different meanings in the field of the text.

The preparation of this chapter is assigned to TC 1.6, Terminology.

Table 1 Abbreviations for Text, Drawings, and Computer Programs

Term	Text	Drawings	Program
above finished floor	—	AFF	—
absolute	abs	ABS	ABS
accumulat(e, -or)	acc	ACCUM	ACCUM
air condition(-ing, -ed)	—	AIR COND	—
air-conditioning unit(s)	—	ACU	ACU
air-handling unit	—	AHU	AHU
air horsepower	ahp	AHP	AHP
alteration	altrn	ALTRN	—
alternating current	ac	AC	AC
altitude	alt	ALT	ALT
ambient	amb	AMB	AMB
American National Standards Institute[1]	ANSI	ANSI	—
American wire gage	AWG	AWG	—
ampere (amp, amps)	amp	AMP	AMP, AMPS
angle	—	—	ANG
angle of incidence	—	—	ANGI
apparatus dew point	adp	ADP	ADP
approximate	approx.	APPROX	—
area	—	—	A
atmosphere	atm	ATM	—
average	avg	AVG	AVG
azimuth	az	AZ	AZ
azimuth, solar	—	—	SAZ
azimuth, wall	—	—	WAZ
barometer(-tric)	baro	BARO	—
bill of material	b/m	BOM	—
boiling point	bp	BP	BP
Brown & Sharpe wire gage	B&S	B&S	—
Celsius	°C	°C	°C
center to center	c to c	C TO C	
circuit	ckt	CKT	CKT
clockwise	cw	CW	—
coefficient	coeff.	COEF	COEF
coefficient, valve flow	C_v	C_v	CV
coil	—	—	COIL
compressor	cprsr	CMPR	CMPR
condens(-er, -ing, -ation)	cond	COND	COND
conductance	—	—	C
conductivity	cndct	CNDCT	K
conductors, number of (3)	3/c	3/c	—
contact factor	—	—	CF
cooling load	clg load	CLG LOAD	CLOAD
counterclockwise	ccw	CCW	—
cubic centimetre	cm^3	CC	CC
cubic metre	m^3	CU M	CU M
decibel	dB	DB	DB
degree	deg. or °	DEG or °	DEG
density	dens	DENS	RHO
depth or deep	dp	DP	DPTH
dew-point temperature	dpt	DPT	DPT
diameter	dia.	DIA	DIA
diameter, inside	ID	ID	ID
diameter, outside	OD	OD	OD
difference or delta	diff., Δ	DIFF	D, DELTA
diffuse radiation	—		DFRAD
direct current	dc	DC	DC
direct radiation	dir radn	DIR RADN	DIRAD
dry	—		DRY
dry-bulb temperature	dbt	DBT	DB, DBT
effectiveness	—		EFT
effective temperature[2]	ET*	ET*	ET
efficiency	eff	EFF	EFF
efficiency, fin	—		FEFF
efficiency, surface	—		SEFF
electromotive force	emf	EMF	—
elevation	elev.	EL	ELEV
entering	entr	ENT	ENT
entering water temperature	EWT	EWT	EWT
entering air temperature	EAT	EAT	EAT
enthalpy	—	—	H
entropy	—	—	S
equivalent direct radiation	edr	EDR	—
evaporat(-e, -ing, -ed, -or)	evap	EVAP	EVAP
expansion	exp	EXP	XPAN
face area	fa	FA	FA
face to face	f to f	F to F	—
face velocity	fvel	FVEL	FV
factor, correction	—	—	CFAC, CFACT
factor, friction	—	—	FFACT, FF
fan	—	—	FAN
film coefficient,[3] inside	—	—	FI, HI
film coefficient,[3] outside	—	—	FO, HO
flow rate, air	—	—	QAR, QAIR
flow rate, fluid	—	—	QFL
flow rate, gas	—	—	QGA, QGAS
freezing point	fp	FP	FP
frequency	Hz	HZ	—
gage or gauge	ga	GA	GA, GAGE
gram	g	g	G
gravitational constant	*G*	G	G
greatest temp difference	GTD	GTD	GTD
heat	—	—	HT
heater	—	—	HTR
heat gain	HG	HG	HG, HEATG
heat gain, latent	LHG	LHG	HGL
heat gain, sensible	SHG	SHG	HGS
heat loss	—	—	HL, HEATL
heat transfer	—	—	Q
heat transfer coefficient	*U*	U	U
height	hgt	HGT	HGT, HT
high-pressure steam	hps	HPS	HPS
high-temperature hot water	hthw	HTHW	HTHW
hour(s)	h	HR	HR
humidity, relative	rh	RH	RH
humidity ratio	*W*	W	W
incident angle	—	—	INANG
indicated kilowatt	IkW	IkW	—
International Pipe Std	IPS	IPS	—
iron pipe size	ips	IPS	—
joule	J	J	J
kelvin	K	K	K
kilograms	kg	kg	KG
kilojoules	kJ	kJ	KJ
kilometres per hour	km/h	km/h	KPH
kilopascals	kPa	kPa	KPA
kilowatt	kW	kW	KW
kilowatt hour	kWh	KWH	KWH
latent heat	LH	LH	LH, LHEAT
least mean temp. difference[4]	LMTD	LMTD	LMTD
least temp. difference[4]	LTD	LTD	LTD
leaving air temperature	lat	LAT	LAT
leaving water temperature	lwt	LWT	LWT
length	lg	LG	LG, L
liquid	liq	LIQ	LIQ
load-sharing (hybrid) HVAC system	LSHVAC	LSHVAC	LSHVAC
litre	L	L	L
litres per second	L/s	L/s	LPS
logarithm (natural)	ln	LN	LN
logarithm to base 10	log	LOG	LOG

Term	Text	Drawings	Program
low-pressure steam	lps	LPS	LPS
low-temp. hot water	lthw	LTHW	LTHW
Mach number	Mach	MACH	—
mass flow rate	mfr	MFR	MFR
maximum	max.	MAX	MAX
mean effective temp.	MET	MET	MET
mean temp. difference	MTD	MTD	MTD
medium-pressure steam	mps	MPS	MPS
medium-temp. hot water	mthw	MTHW	MTHW
mercury	Hg	HG	HG
metre	m	m	M
metres per second	m/s	m/s	M/S
millilitres per second	mL/s	mL/s	MLPS
mL/s standard	mL/sS	mL/sS	MLPSS
minimum	min.	MIN	MIN
noise criteria	NC	NC	—
normally open	n o	N O	—
normally closed	n c	N C	—
not applicable	na	N/A	—
not in contract	n i c	N I C	—
not to scale	—	N T S	—
number	no.	NO	N, NO
number of circuits	—	—	NC
number of tubes	—	—	NT
outside air	oa	OA	OA
parts per million	ppm	PPM	PPM
pascal	Pa	Pa	PA
Pa (absolute)	Pa (abs)	Pa A	PAA
Pa (gage)	Pa (gage)	Pa G	PAG
percent	%	%	PCT
phase (electrical)	ph	PH	—
pipe	—	—	PIPE
pressure	—	PRESS	PRES, P
pressure, barometric	baro pr	BARO PR	BP
pressure, critical	—	—	CRIP
pressure, dynamic (velocity)	vp	VP	VP
pressure drop or difference	PD	PD	PD, DELTP
pressure, static	sp	SP	SP
pressure, vapor	vap pr	VAP PR	VAP
primary	pri	PRI	PRIM
radian	—	—	RAD
radiat(-e, -or)	—	RAD	—
radiant panel	RP	RP	RP
radiation	—	RADN	RAD
radius	—	—	R
receiver	rcvr	RCVR	REC
recirculate	recirc.	RECIRC	RCIR, RECIR
refrigerant (12, 22, etc.)	R-12, R-22	R12, R22	R12, R22
relative humidity	rh	RH	RH
resist(-ance, -ivity, -or)	res	RES	RES, OHMS
return air	ra	RA	RA
revolutions	rev	REV	REV
revolutions per minute	rpm	RPM	RPM
revolutions per second	rps	RPS	RPS
roughness	rgh	RGH	RGH, E
safety factor	sf	SF	SF
saturation	sat.	SAT	SAT
Saybolt seconds Furol	ssf	SSF	SSF
Saybolt seconds Universal	ssu	SSU	SSU
sea level	sl	SL	SE
second	s	s	SEC
sensible heat	SH	SH	SH
sensible heat gain	SHG	SHG	SHG
sensible heat ratio	SHR	SHR	SHR

Term	Text	Drawings	Program
shading coefficient	—	—	SC
solar	—	—	SOL
specification	spec	SPEC	—
specific heat	sp ht	SP HT	C
sp ht at constant pressure	c_p	c_p	CP
sp ht at constant volume	c_v	c_v	CV
specific volume	sp vol	SP VOL	V, CVOL
square	sq.	SQ	SQ
standard	std	STD	STD
standard time meridian	—	—	STM
static pressure	SP	SP	SP
suction	suct.	SUCT	SUCT, SUC
summ(-er, -ary, -ation)	—	—	SUM
supply	sply	SPLY	SUP, SPLY
supply air	sa	SA	SA
surface	—	—	SUR, S
surface, dry	—	—	SURD
surface, wet	—	—	SURW
system	—	—	SYS
tabulat(-e, -ion)	tab	TAB	TAB
tee	—	—	TEE
temperature	temp.	TEMP	T, TEMP
temperature difference	TD, Δt	TD	TD, TDIF
temperature entering	TE	TE	TE, TENT
temperature leaving	TL	TL	TL, TLEA
thermal conductivity	*k*	K	K
thermal expansion coeff.	—	—	TXPC
thermal resistance	*R*	R	RES, R
thermocouple	tc	TC	TC, TCPL
thermostat	T STAT	T STAT	T STAT
thick(-ness)	thkns	THKNS	THK
total	—	—	TOT
total heat	tot ht	TOT HT	—
transmissivity	—	—	TAU
U-factor	—	—	U
unit	—	—	UNIT
vacuum	vac	VAC	VAC
valve	v	V	VLV
vapor proof	vap prf	VAP PRF	—
variable	var	VAR	VAR
variable air volume	VAV	VAV	VAV
velocity	vel.	VEL	VEL, V
velocity, wind	w vel.	W VEL	W VEL
ventilation, vent	vent	VENT	VENT
vertical	vert.	VERT	VERT
viscosity	visc	VISC	MU, VISC
volt	V	V	E, VOLTS
volt ampere	VA	VA	VA
volume	vol.	VOL	VOL
volumetric flow rate	—	—	VFR
wall	—	—	W, WAL
water	—	—	WTR
watt	W	W	WAT, W
wet bulb	wb	WB	WB
wet-bulb temperature	wbt	WBT	WBT
width	—	—	WI
wind	—	—	WD
wind direction	wdir	WDIR	WDIR
wind pressure	wpr	WPR	WP, WPRES
year	yr	YR	YR
zone	z	Z	Z, ZN

[1]Abbreviations of most proper names use capital letters in both text and drawings.
[2]The asterisk (*) is used with ET*, effective temperature, as in Chapter 9 of this volume.
[3]These are surface heat transfer coefficients.
[4]Letter L also used for *Logarithm of* these temperature differences in computer programming.

LETTER SYMBOLS

Symbol	Description of Item	Typical Units
a	acoustic velocity	m/s
A	area	m^2
b	breadth or width	m
B	barometric pressure	kPa
c	concentration	kg/m^3
c	specific heat	kJ/(kg·K)
c_p	specific heat at constant pressure	kJ/(kg·K)
c_v	specific heat at constant volume	kJ/(kg·K)
C	coefficient	—
C	fluid capacity rate	W/K
C	thermal conductance	$W/(m^2·K)$
C_L	loss coefficient	—
C_P	coefficient of performance	—
d	prefix meaning differential	—
d or D	diameter	m
D_e or D_h	equivalent or hydraulic diameter	m
D_v	mass diffusivity	mm^2/s
e	base of natural logarithms	—
E	energy	kJ
E	electrical potential	V
f	film conductance (alternate for h)	$W/(m^2·K)$
f	frequency	Hz
f_D	friction factor, Darcy-Weisbach formulation	—
f_F	friction factor, Fanning formulation	—
F	force	N
F_{ij}	angle factor (radiation)	—
g	gravitational acceleration	m/s^2
G	mass velocity	$kg/(s·m^2)$
h	heat transfer coefficient	$W/(m^2·K)$
h	hydraulic head	m
h	specific enthalpy	kJ/kg
h_a	enthalpy of dry air	kJ/kg
h_D	mass transfer coefficient	m/s
h_s	enthalpy of moist air at saturation	kJ/kg
H	total enthalpy	kJ
I	electric current	A
k	thermal conductivity	W/(m·K)
k (or γ)	ratio of specific heats, c_p/c_v	—
K	proportionality constant	—
K_D	mass transfer coefficient	$kg/(h·m^2)$
l or L	length	m
L_p	sound pressure	dB
L_w	sound power	dB
m or M	mass	kg
M	molecular weight	kg/kg mol
n or N	number in general	—
N	rate of rotation	kPa
p or P	pressure	kPa
p_a	partial pressure of dry air	kPa
p_s	partial pressure of water vapor in moist air	kPa
p_w	vapor pressure of water in saturated moist air	kPa
P	power	kW
q	time rate of heat transfer	W
Q	total heat transfer	kJ
Q	volumetric flow rate	L/s
r	radius	m
r or R	thermal resistance	$m^2·K/W$
R	gas constant	J/(kg·K)
s	specific entropy	kJ/(kg·K)
S	total entropy	kJ/K
t	temperature	°C
Δt_m or ΔT_m	mean temperature difference	K
T	absolute temperature	K
u	specific internal energy	kJ/kg
U	total internal energy	kJ
U	overall heat transfer coefficient	$W/(m^2·K)$
v	specific volume	m^3/kg
V	total volume	m^3
V	linear velocity	
w	mass rate of flow	
W	weight	
W	humidity ratio of moist air (dry air basis)	g/kg
W	work	
W_s	humidity ratio of moist air at saturation (dry air basis)	g/kg
x	mole fraction	—
x	quality, mass fraction of vapor	—
x,y,z	lengths along principal coordinate axes	m
Z	figure of merit	—
α	absolute Seebeck coefficient	V/K
α	absorptivity, absorptance radiation	—
α	linear coefficient of thermal expansion	1/K
α	thermal diffusivity	
β	volume coefficient of thermal expansion	1/K
γ (or k)	ratio of specific heats, c_p/c_v	—
γ	specific weight	N/m^3
Δ	difference between values	—
ε	emissivity, emittance (radiation)	—
θ	time	s, h
η	efficiency or effectiveness	—
λ	wavelength	nm
μ	degree of saturation	—
μ	dynamic viscosity	mPa·s
ν	kinematic viscosity	m^2/s
ρ	density	kg/m^3
ρ	reflectivity, reflectance (radiation)	—
ρ	volume resistivity	Ω·m
σ	Stefan-Boltzmann constant	$W/(m^2·K^4)$
σ	surface tension	N/m
τ	stress	N/m^2
τ	time	s
τ	transmissivity, transmittance (radiation)	—
ϕ	relative humidity	—

DIMENSIONLESS NUMBERS

Fo	Fourier number	$\alpha\tau/L^2$
Gr	Grashof number	$L^3\rho^2\beta g(\Delta t)/\mu^2$
Gz	Graetz number	wc_p/kL
j_D	Colburn mass transfer	$Sh/ReSc^{1/3}$
j_H	Colburn heat transfer	$Nu/RePr^{1/3}$
Le	Lewis number	α/D_v
M	Mach number	V/a
Nu	Nusselt number	hD/k
Pe	Peclet number	GDc_p/k
Pr	Prandtl number	$c_p\mu/k$
Re	Reynolds number	$\rho VD/\mu$
Sc	Schmidt number	$\mu/\rho D_v$
Sh	Sherwood number	$h_D L/D_v$
St	Stanton number	h/Gc_p
Str	Strouhal number	fd/V

MATHEMATICAL SYMBOLS

equal to	$=$
not equal to	$\neq$
approximately equal to	$\approx$
greater than	$>$
less than	$<$
greater than or equal to	$\geq$
less than or equal to	$\leq$
plus	$+$
minus	$-$
plus or minus	$\pm$
a multiplied by b	ab, $a \cdot b$, $a \times b$
a divided by b	$\frac{a}{b}$, a/b, ab^{-1}

ratio of circumference of a circle to its diameter	π
a raised to the power n	a^n
square root of a	$\sqrt{a}$, $a^{0.5}$
infinity	∞
percent	%
summation of	Σ
natural log	ln
logarithm to base 10	log

SUBSCRIPTS

These are to be affixed to the appropriate symbols. Several subscripts may be used together to denote combinations of various states, points, or paths. Often the subscript indicates that a particular property is to be kept constant in a process.

a,b,...	referring to different phases, states or physical conditions of a substance, or to different substances
a	air
a	ambient
b	barometric (pressure)
c	referring to critical state or critical value
c	convection
db	dry bulb
dp	dew point
e	base of natural logarithms
f	referring to saturated liquid
f	film
fg	referring to evaporation or condensation
F	friction
g	referring to saturated vapor
h	referring to change of phase in evaporation
H	water vapor
i	referring to saturated solid
i	internal
if	referring to change of phase in melting
ig	referring to change of phase in sublimation
k	kinetic
L	latent
m	mean value
M	molar basis
p	referring to constant pressure conditions or processes
p	potential
r	refrigerant
r	radiant or radiation
s	referring to moist air at saturation
s	sensible
s	referring to isentropic conditions or processes
s	static (pressure)
s	surface
t	total (pressure)
T	referring to isothermal conditions or processes
v	referring to constant volume conditions or processes
v	vapor
v	velocity (pressure)
w	wall
w	water
wb	wet bulb
0	referring to initial or standard states or conditions
1,2,...	different points in a process, or different instants of time

GRAPHICAL SYMBOLS FOR DRAWINGS

Graphical symbols have been extracted from ANSI/ASHRAE *Standard* 134-2005. Additional symbols are from current practice and extracted from ASME *Standards* Y32.2.3 and Y32.2.4.

Piping

Heating

High-pressure steam	——HPS——
Medium-pressure steam	——MPS——
Low-pressure steam	——LPS——
High-pressure steam condensate	——HPC——
Medium-pressure steam condensate	——MPC——
Low-pressure steam condensate	——LPC——
Boiler blowdown	——BBD——
Pumped condensate	——PC——
Vacuum pump discharge	——VPD——
Makeup water	——MU——
Atmospheric vent	——ATV——
Fuel oil	—FO(NAME)—
Low-temperature hot water supply	——HWS——
Medium-temperature hot water supply	——MTWS——
High-temperature hot water supply	——HTWS——
Low-temperature hot water return	——HWR——
Medium-temperature hot water return	——MTWR——
High-temperature hot water return	——HTWR——
Compressed air	—A(NAME)—
Vacuum (air)	——VAC——
Existing piping	—(NAME)E—
Pipe to be removed	-XX- (NAME) -XX-

Air Conditioning and Refrigeration

Refrigerant discharge	——RD——
Refrigerant suction	——RS——
Brine supply	——B——
Brine return	——BR——
Condenser water supply	——CWS——
Condenser water return	——CWR——
Chilled water supply	——CHWS——
Chilled water return	——CHWR——
Fill line	——FILL——
Humidification line	——H——
Drain	——D——
Hot/chilled water supply	——H/C S——
Hot/chilled water return	——H/C R——
Refrigerant liquid	——RL——
Heat pump water supply	——HPWS——
Heat pump water return	——HPWR——

Plumbing

Sanitary drain above floor or grade	——SAN——
Sanitary drain below floor or grade	- - - - SAN - - - -
Storm drain above floor or grade	——ST——
Storm drain below floor or grade	- - - - ST - - - -
Condensate drain above floor or grade	——CD——
Condensate drain below floor or grade	- - - - CD - - - -
Vent	- - - - - - - - - - -
Cold water	-·-·-·-·-·-·-·-
Hot water	-··-··-··-··-··-
Hot water return	-···-···-···-···-
Gas	— G —— G —
Acid waste	——AW——
Drinking water supply	——DCW——
Chemical supply pipes[a]	——(NAME)——
Floor drain	
Funnel drain, open	Y

Fire Safety Devices[b]

Signal Initiating Detectors

Heat (thermal)		Gas	
Smoke		Flame	

Radiant Panels

Hydronic heating element ○

Electric heating element ●

RAD.1 – h / h / c
- c: *Cooling* (*c*)
- h: *Heating* (*h*)
- h: *Hydronic* (*h*) / *Electric* (*e*)

[a]See section on Piping Identification in this chapter.
[b]Refer to *Standard for Fire Safety Symbols*, 1999 edition (NFPA *Standard* 170).

Radiant Ceiling Panels

Embedded

Above ceiling

Surface mounted

Suspended

Radiant Floor Panels

Slab on grade

Above subfloor

Below subfloor

Slab above subfloor

Radiant Wall Panels

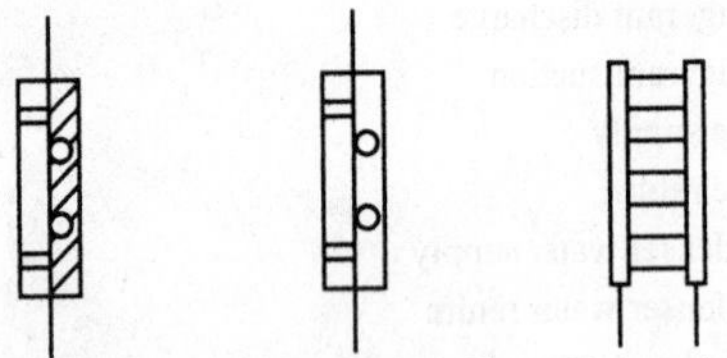

Embedded Surface mounted Decorative

Coils

Cooling coil

Heating coil

Electrical coil

Humidifier

Valves

Valves for Selective Actuators

Air line

Ball

Butterfly

Diaphragm

Gate

Gate, angle

Globe

Globe, angle

Plug valve

Three way

Valves Actuators

Manual

- Non-rising sun
- Outside stem & yoke
- Lever
- Gear

Electric

- Motor
- Solenoid

Pneumatic

- Motor
- Diaphragm

Valves, Special Duty

Check, swing gate

Check, spring

Control, electric-pneumatic

Control, pneumatic-electric

Hose end drain

Lock shield

Needle

Pressure-reducing regulator

Quick-opening

Quick-closing

Safety or relief

Solenoid

Square-head cock

Unclassified (number and specify)

Fittings

The following fittings are shown without connection notations. This reflects current practice. The symbol for the body of a fitting is the same for all types of connections, unless otherwise specified. The types of connections are often specified for a range of pipe sizes, but are shown with the fitting symbol where required. For example, an elbow would be:

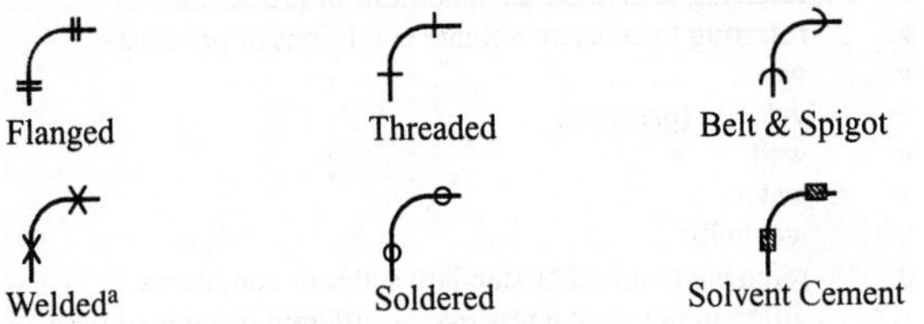

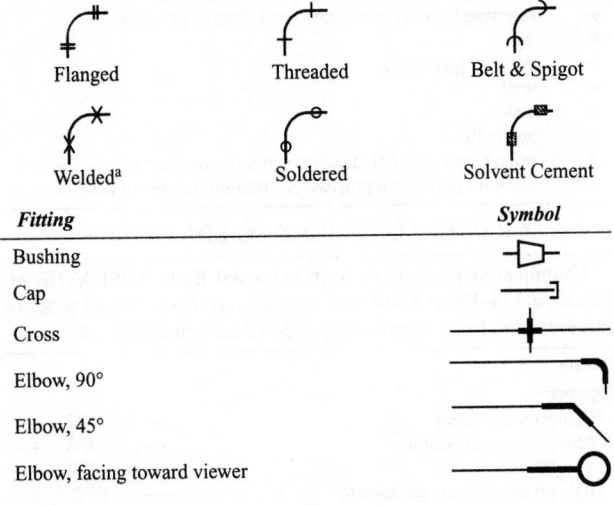

Flanged Threaded Belt & Spigot

Welded[a] Soldered Solvent Cement

Fitting	*Symbol*
Bushing	
Cap	
Cross	
Elbow, 90°	
Elbow, 45°	
Elbow, facing toward viewer	

[a] Includes fusion; specify type.

Elbow, facing away from viewer
Elbow, base-supported
Lateral
Reducer, concentric
Reducer, eccentric, flat on bottom
Reducer, eccentric, flat on top
Tee
Tee, facing toward viewer
Tee, facing away from viewer
Union, screwed
Union, flanged

Piping Specialties

Air vent, automatic
Air vent, manual
Air separator
Pipe guide
Anchor, intermediate
Anchor, main
Ball joint
Expansion joint
Expansion loop
Flexible connector
Flowmeter, orifice plate with flanges
Flowmeter, venturi
Flow switch
Hanger rod
Hanger spring
Heat exchanger, liquid
Heat transfer surface (indicate type)
Pitch of pipe, rise (R) drop (D)
Pressure gage and cock
Pressure switch
Pump (indicate use)
Pump suction diffuser
Spool piece, flanged
Strainer
Strainer, blow off
Strainer, duplex
Tank (indicate use)

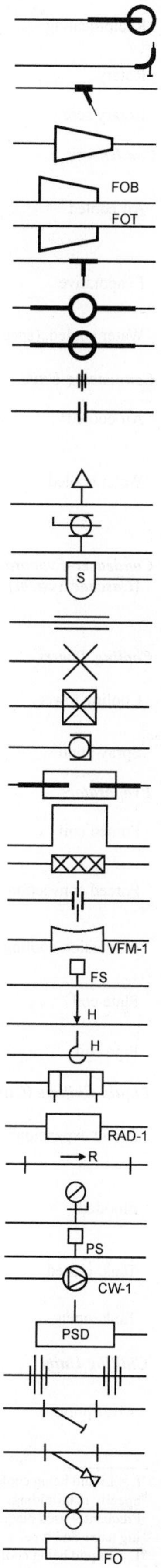

Thermometer
Thermometer well, only
Thermostat
Traps, steam (indicate type)
Unit heater (indicate type)

Air-Moving Devices and Components

***Fans* (indicate use)**

Centrifugal
Propeller
Roof ventilator, intake
Roof ventilator, exhaust
Roof ventilator, louvered
Vaneaxial

***Ductwork*[a,b]**

Direction of flow
Duct size, where first dimension is visible duct
Duct section, supply
Duct section, return
Duct section, exhaust
Change of elevation rise (R) drop (D)
Access doors, vertical or horizontal
Cowl, (gooseneck) and flashing
Duct lining
Flexible connection
Flexible duct
Sound attenuator
Terminal unit, mixing
Terminal unit, variable volume

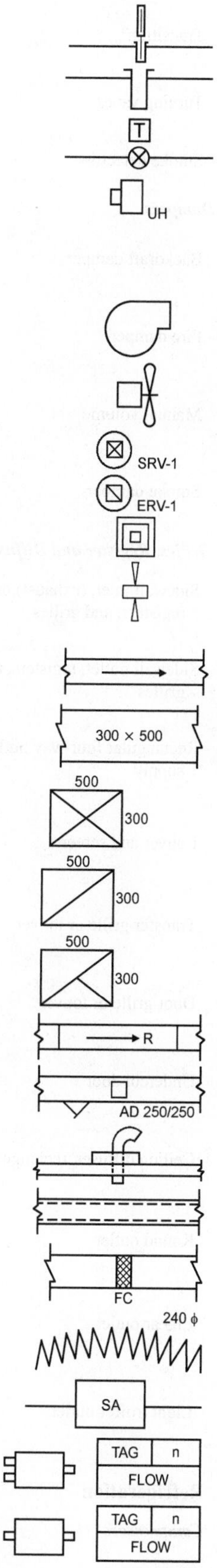

[a] Units of measurement are not shown here, but should be shown on drawings. The first dimension is visible duct dimension for duct size, top dimension for grilles, and horizontal dimension for registers.
[b] Show volumetric flow rate at each device.

Transition[a]

Turning vanes

Smoke detectors

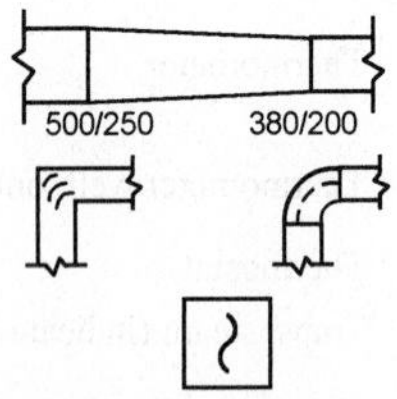

Dampers

Backdraft damper

Fire damper

Manual volume

Smoke damper

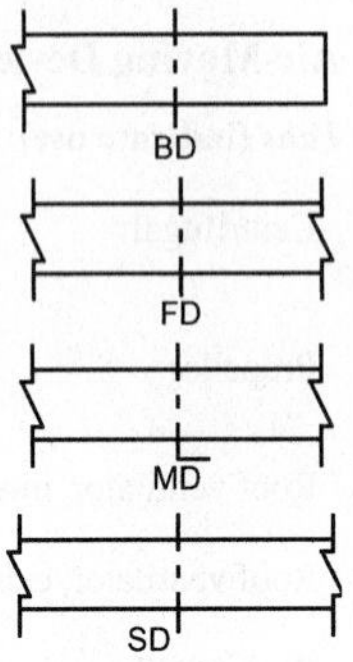

Grilles, Register and Diffusers[b]

Sidewall inlet, (exhaust) outlet, registers, and grilles

Sidewall outlet, registers, and grilles

Rectangular four-way outlet, supply

Louver and screen

Transfer grille or louver

Door grille or louver

Undercut door

Ceiling diffuser, rectangular

Round outlet

Linear outlet

Light troffer outlet

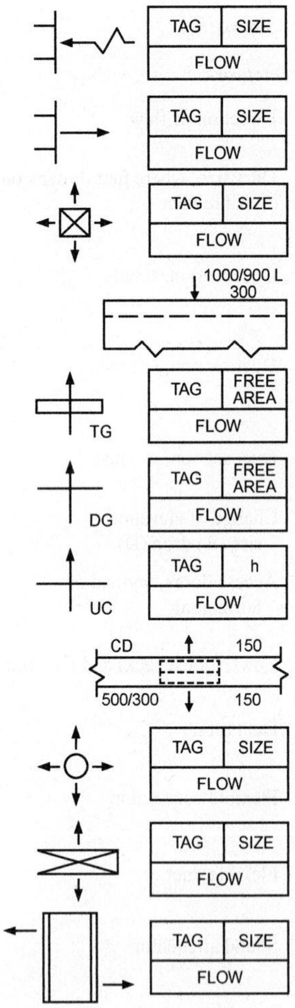

Refrigeration

Compressors

Centrifugal

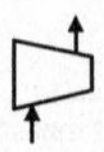

Reciprocating

Rotary

Rotary screw

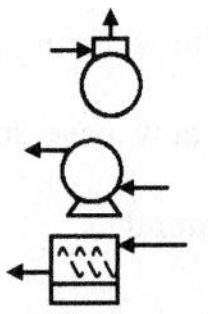

Condensers

Air cooled

Evaporative

Water cooled, (specify type)

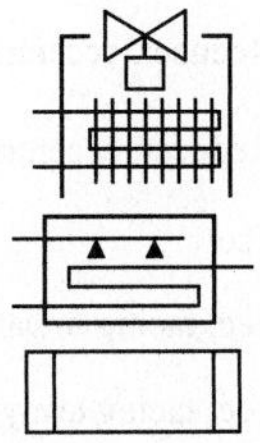

Condensing Units

Air cooled[a]

Water cooled[a]

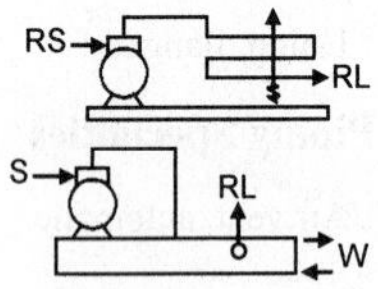

Condenser-Evaporator (Cascade System)

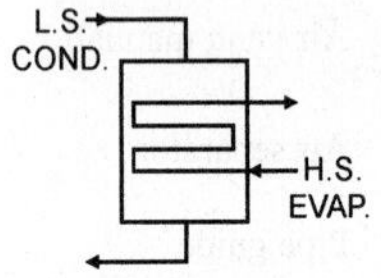

Cooling Towers

Cooling tower

Spray pond

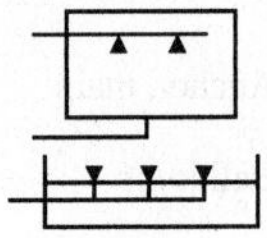

Evaporators[b]

Finned coil

Forced convection

Immersion cooling unit

Plate coil

Pipe coil[c]

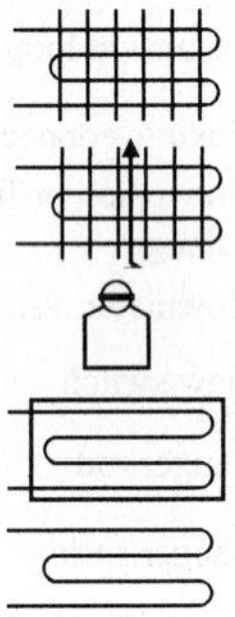

Liquid Chillers **(Chillers only)**

Direct expansion[d]

Flooded[d]

Tank, closed

Tank, open

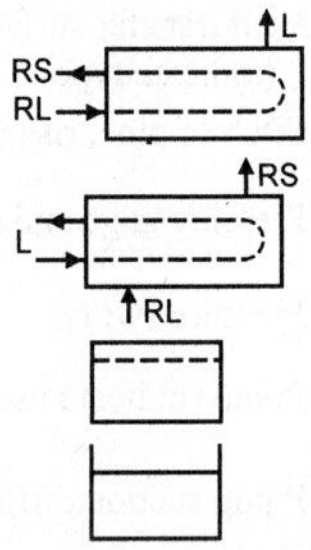

Chilling Units

Absorption

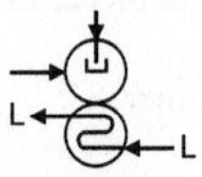

[a]Indicate flat on bottom or top (FOB or FOT), if applicable.
[b]Show volumetric flow rate at each device.

[a]L = Liquid being cooled, RL = Refrigerant liquid, RS = Refrigerant suction.
[b]Specify manifolding.
[c]Frequently used diagrammatically as evaporator and/or condenser with label indicating name and type.
[d]L = Liquid being cooled, RL = Refrigerant liquid, RS = Refrigerant suction.

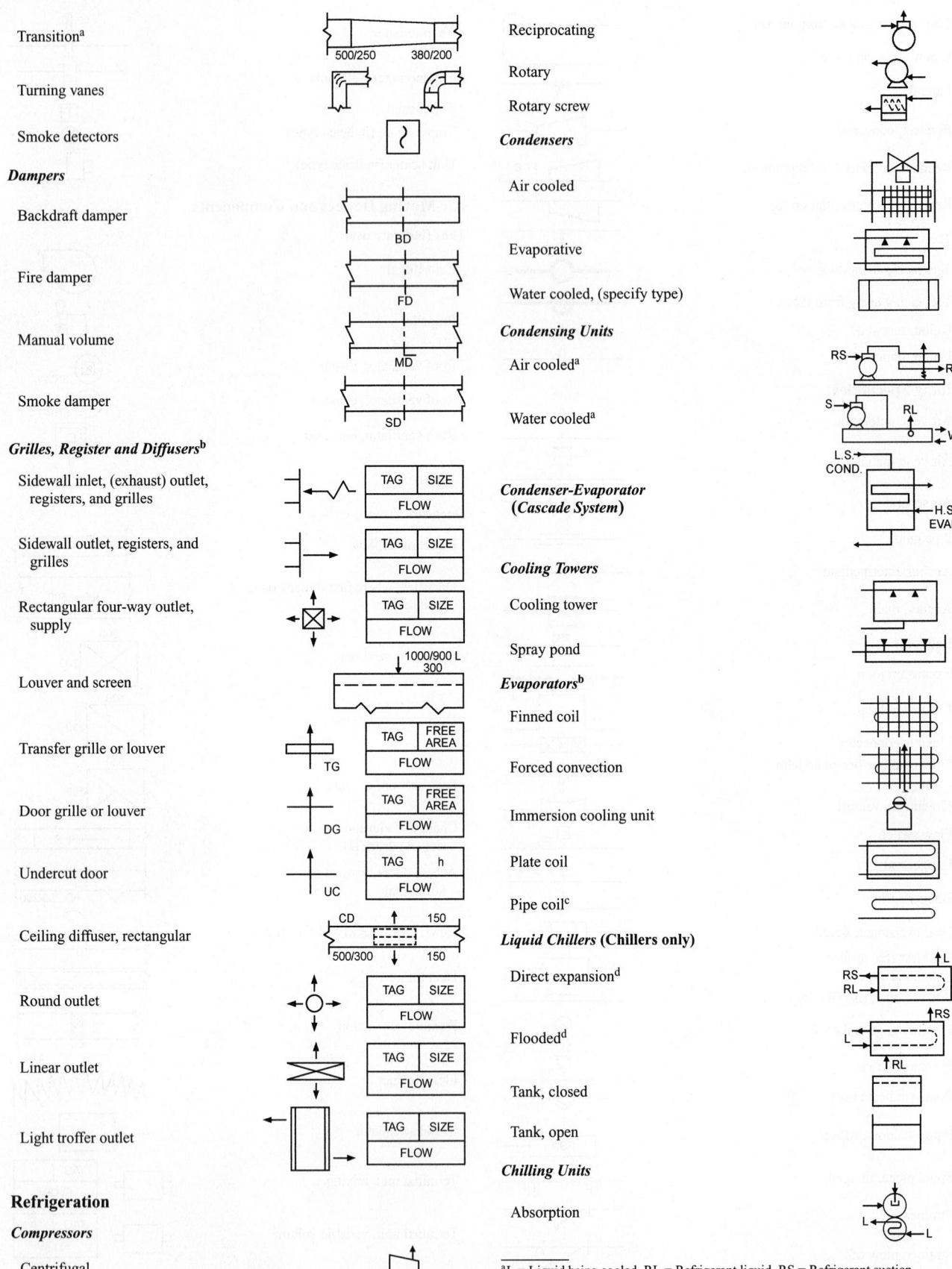

Centrifugal

Reciprocating

Rotary screw

Controls

Refrigerant Controls

Capillary tube

Expansion valve, hand

Expansion valve, automatic

Expansion valve, thermostatic

Float valve, high side, or liquid drain valve

Float valve, low side

Thermal bulb

Solenoid valve

Constant pressure valve, suction

Evaporator pressure regulating valve, thermostatic, throttling

Evaporator pressure regulating valve, thermostatic, snap-action

Evaporator pressure regulating valve, throttling-type, evaporator side

Compressor suction valve, pressure-limiting, throttling-type, compressor side

Thermosuction valve

Snap-action valve

Refrigerant reversing valve

Temperature or Temperature-Actuated Electrical or Flow Controls

Thermostat, self-contained

Thermostat, remote bulb

Sensor, temperature

Pressure-reducing regulator

Pressure regulator

Valve, condenser water regulating

Auxiliary Equipment

Refrigerant

Filter

Strainer

Filter and drier

Scale trap

Drier

Vibration absorber

Heat exchanger

Oil separator

Sight glass

Fusible plug

Rupture disk

Receiver, high-pressure, horizontal

Receiver, high-pressure, vertical

Receiver, low-pressure

Intercooler

Intercooler/desuperheater

Energy Recovery Equipment

Condenser, double bundle

Air to Air Energy Recovery

Rotary heat wheel

Coil loop

Heat pipe

Fixed plate

Plate fin, crossflow

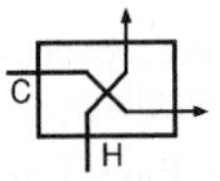

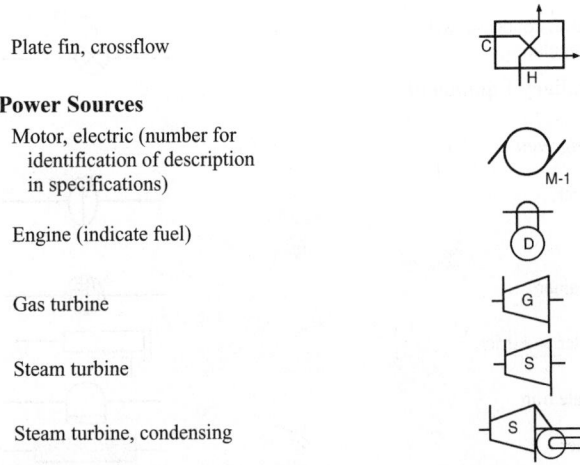

Power Sources

Motor, electric (number for identification of description in specifications)

Engine (indicate fuel)

Gas turbine

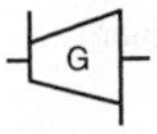

Steam turbine

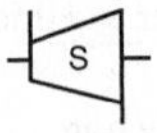

Steam turbine, condensing

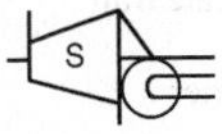

Electrical Equipment[a]

Symbols for electrical equipment shown on mechanical drawings are usually geometric figures with an appropriate name or abbreviation, with details described in the specifications. The following are some common examples.[b]

Motor control

Disconnect switch, unfused

Disconnect switch, fused

Time clock

Automatic filter panel

Lighting panel

Power panel

[a] See ARI *Standard* 130 for preferred symbols of common electrical parts.
[b] Number each symbol if more than one; see ASME *Standard* Y32.4.

PIPING SYSTEM IDENTIFICATION

The material in piping systems is identified to promote greater safety and lessen the chances of error, confusion, or inaction in times of emergency. Primary identification should be by means of a lettered legend naming the material conveyed by the piping. In addition to, but not instead of lettered identification, color can be used to identify the hazards or use of the material.

The data in this section have been extracted from ASME *Standard* A13.1.

Definitions

Piping Systems. Piping systems include pipes of any kind, fittings, valves, and pipe coverings. Supports, brackets, and other accessories are not included. Pipes are defined as conduits for the transport of gases, liquids, semiliquids, or fine particulate dust.

Materials Inherently Hazardous to Life and Property. There are four categories of hazardous materials:

- Flammable or explosive materials that are easily ignited, including materials known as fire producers or explosives
- Chemically active or toxic materials that are corrosive or are in themselves toxic or productive of poisonous gases
- Materials at extreme temperatures or pressures that, when released from the piping, cause a sudden outburst with the potential for inflicting injury or property damage by burns, impingement, or flashing to vapor state
- Radioactive materials that emit ionizing radiation

Materials of Inherently Low Hazard. All materials that are not hazardous by nature, and are near enough to ambient pressure and temperature that people working on systems carrying these materials run little risk through their release.

Table 2 Examples of Legends

HOT WATER
AIR 700 kPA
H.P. RETURN
STEAM 700 kPA

Table 3 Classification of Hazardous Materials and Designation of Colors[a]

Classification	Color Field	Colors of Letters for Legend
Materials Inherently Hazardous		
Flammable or explosive	Yellow	Black
Chemically active or toxic	Yellow	Black
Extreme temperatures or pressures	Yellow	Black
Radioactive[b]	Purple	Yellow
Materials of Inherently Low Hazard		
Liquid or liquid admixture[c]	Green	Black
Gas or gaseous admixture	Blue	White
Fire Quenching Materials		
Water, foam, CO_2, Halon, etc.	Red	White

[a] When preceding color scheme is used, colors should be as recommended in latest revision of NEMA *Standard* Z535.1.
[b] Previously specified radioactive markers using yellow or purple are acceptable if already installed and/or until existing supplies are depleted, subject to applicable federal regulations.
[c] Markers with black letters on green field are acceptable if already installed and/or until existing supplies are depleted.

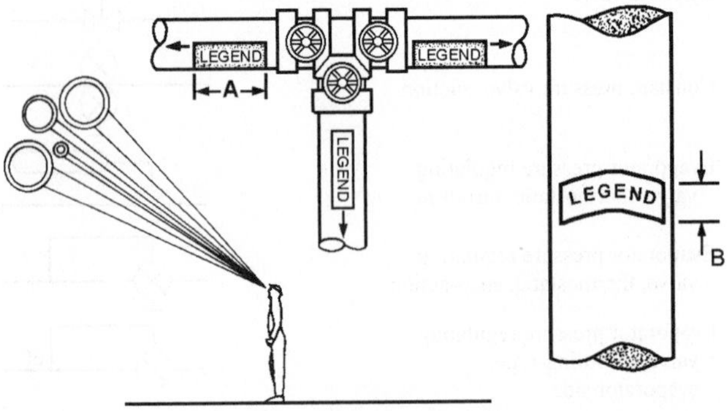

Fig. 1 Visibility of Pipe Markings

Fire Quenching Materials. This classification includes sprinkler systems and other piped fire fighting or fire protection equipment. This includes water (for fire fighting), chemical foam, CO_2, Halon, and so forth.

Method of Identification

Legend. The legend is the primary and explicit identification of content. Positive identification of the content of the piping system is by lettered legend giving the name of the contents, in full or abbreviated form, as shown in Table 2. Arrows should be used to indicate the direction of flow. Use the legend to identify contents exactly and to provide temperature, pressure, and other details necessary to identify the hazard.

The legend shall be brief, informative, pointed, and simple. Legends should be applied close to valves and adjacent to changes in direction, branches, and where pipes pass through walls or floors, and as frequently as needed along straight runs to provide clear and positive identification. Identification may be applied by stenciling, tape, or markers (see Figure 1). The number and location of identification markers on a particular piping system is based on judgment.

Color. Colors listed in Table 3 are used to identify the characteristic properties of the contents. Color can be shown on or contiguous

Table 4 Size of Legend Letters

Outside Diameter of Pipe or Covering, mm	Length of Color Field A, mm	Size of Letters B, mm
20 to 32	200	13
40 to 50	200	20
65 to 150	300	32
200 to 250	600	65
over 250	800	90

to the piping by any physical means, but it should be used in combination with a legend. Color can be used in continuous total length coverage or in intermittent displays.

Visibility. Pipe markings should be highly visible. If pipe lines are above the normal line of vision, the lettering is placed below the horizontal centerline of the pipe (Figure 1).

Type and Size of Letters. Provide the maximum contrast between color field and legend (Table 3). Table 4 shows the size of letters recommended. Use of standard size letters of 13 mm or larger is recommended. For identifying materials in pipes of less than 20 mm in diameter and for valve and fitting identification, use a permanently legible tag.

Unusual or Extreme Situations. When the piping layout occurs in or creates an area of limited accessibility or is extremely complex, other identification techniques may be required. While a certain amount of imagination may be needed, the designer should always clearly identify the hazard and use the recommended color and legend guidelines.

CODES AND STANDARDS

ARI. 1988. Graphic electrical/electronic symbols for air-conditioning and refrigeration equipment. *Standard* 130-88.

ASHRAE. 2005. Graphic symbols for heating, ventilating, air-conditioning, and refrigeration systems. ANSI/ASHRAE *Standard* 134-2005.

ASME. 2007. Standard markers for pipe identification. ANSI/ASME *Standard* A13.1-2007. American Society of Mechanical Engineers, New York.

ASME. 1988. Letter symbols: Glossary of terms concerning letter symbols. *Standard* Y10.1-1972 (R1988). American Society of Mechanical Engineers, New York.

ASME. 1984. Letter symbols and abbreviations for quantities used in acoustics. *Standard* Y10.11-1984. American Society of Mechanical Engineers, New York.

ASME. 1987. Illuminating engineering. *Standard* Y10.18-1967 (R1977). American Society of Mechanical Engineers, New York.

ASME. 1999. Graphical symbols for pipe fittings, valves, and piping. *Standard* Y32.2.3. American Society of Mechanical Engineers, New York.

ASME. 1998. Graphical symbols for heating, ventilating, and air conditioning. *Standard* Y32.2.4. American Society of Mechanical Engineers, New York.

IEEE. 2004. Standard letter symbols for units of measurement. *Standard* 260.1-2004. Institute of Electrical and Electronics Engineers, Piscataway, NJ.

IEEE. 1996. Letter symbols and abbreviations used in acoustics. *Standard* 260.4-1996. Institute of Electrical and Electronics Engineers, Piscataway, NJ.

NEMA. 2002. Safety color code. *Standard* Z535-2002. National Electrical Manufacturers Association, Rosslyn, VA.

NFPA. 2006. Standard for fire safety and emergency symbols, 2006 edition. *Standard* 170. National Fire Protection Association, Quincy, MA.

CHAPTER 38

UNITS AND CONVERSIONS

Table 1 Conversions to I-P and SI Units

(Multiply I-P values by conversion factors to obtain SI; divide SI values by conversion factors to obtain I-P)

Multiply I-P	By	To Obtain SI
acre (43 560 ft^2)	0.4047	ha
	4046.873	m^2
atmosphere (standard)	*101.325	kPa
bar	*100	kPa
barrel (42 U.S. gal, petroleum)	159.0	L
	0.1580987	m^3
Btu (International Table)	1055.056	J
Btu (thermochemical)	1054.350	J
Btu/ft^2 (International Table)	11,356.53	J/m^2
Btu/ft^3 (International Table)	37,258.951	J/m^3
Btu/gal	278,717.1765	J/m^3
Btu·ft/h·ft^2·°F	1.730735	W/(m·K)
Btu·in/h·ft^2·°F (thermal conductivity k)	0.1442279	W/(m·K)
Btu/h	0.2930711	W
Btu/h·ft^2	3.154591	W/m^2
Btu/h·ft^2·°F (overall heat transfer coefficient U)	5.678263	W/(m^2·K)
Btu/lb	*2.326	kJ/kg
Btu/lb·°F (specific heat c_p)	*4.1868	kJ/(kg·K)
bushel (dry, U.S.)	0.0352394	m^3
calorie (thermochemical)	*4.184	J
centipoise (dynamic viscosity μ)	*1.00	mPa·s
centistokes (kinematic viscosity ν)	*1.00	mm^2/s
clo	0.155	(m^2·K)/W
dyne	1.0×10^{-5}	N
dyne/cm^2	*0.100	Pa
EDR hot water (150 Btu/h)	43.9606	W
EDR steam (240 Btu/h)	70.33706	W
EER	0.293	COP
ft	*0.3048	m
	*304.8	mm
ft/min, fpm	*0.00508	m/s
ft/s, fps	*0.3048	m/s
ft of water	2989	Pa
ft of water per 100 ft pipe	98.1	Pa/m
ft^2	0.092903	m^2
ft^2·h·°F/Btu (thermal resistance R)	0.176110	(m^2·K)/W
ft^2/s (kinematic viscosity ν)	92,900	mm^2/s
ft^3	28.316846	L
	0.02832	m^3
ft^3/min, cfm	0.471947	L/s
ft^3/s, cfs	28.316845	L/s
ft·lb_f (torque or moment)	1.355818	N·m
ft·lb_f (work)	1.356	J
ft·lb_f/lb (specific energy)	2.99	J/kg
ft·lb_f/min (power)	0.0226	W
footcandle	10.76391	lx
gallon (U.S., *231 in^3)	3.785412	L
gph	1.05	mL/s
gpm	0.0631	L/s
gpm/ft^2	0.6791	L/(s·m^2)
gpm/ton refrigeration	0.0179	mL/J
grain (1/7000 lb)	0.0648	g
gr/gal	17.1	g/m^3
gr/lb	0.143	g/kg
horsepower (boiler) (33 470 Btu/h)	9.81	kW
horsepower (550 ft·lb_f/s)	0.7457	kW
inch	*25.4	mm
in. of mercury (60°F)	3.37	kPa
in. of water (60°F)	249	Pa
in/100 ft, thermal expansion	0.833	mm/m
To Obtain I-P	**By**	**Divide SI**

Multiply I-P	By	To Obtain SI
in·lb_f (torque or moment)	113	mN·m
in^2	645.16	mm^2
in^3 (volume)	16.3874	mL
in^3/min (SCIM)	0.273117	mL/s
in^3 (section modulus)	16387	mm^3
in^4 (section moment)	416 231	mm^4
kWh	*3.60	MJ
kW/1000 cfm	2.118880	kJ/m^3
kilopond (kg force)	9.81	N
kip (1000 lb_f)	4.45	kN
kip/in^2 (ksi)	6.895	MPa
litre	*0.001	m^3
met	58.15	W/m^2
micron (μm) of mercury (60°F)	133	mPa
mile	1.609	km
mile, nautical	*1.852	km
mile per hour (mph)	1.609344	km/h
	0.447	m/s
millibar	*0.100	kPa
mm of mercury (60°F)	0.133	kPa
mm of water (60°F)	9.80	Pa
ounce (mass, avoirdupois)	28.35	g
ounce (force or thrust)	0.278	N
ounce (liquid, U.S.)	29.6	mL
ounce inch (torque, moment)	7.06	mN·m
ounce (avoirdupois) per gallon	7.489152	kg/m^3
perm (permeance at 32°F)	5.72135×10^{-11}	kg/(Pa·s·m^2)
perm inch (permeability at 32°F)	1.45362×10^{-12}	kg/(Pa·s·m)
pint (liquid, U.S.)	4.73176×10^{-4}	m^3
pound		
lb (avoirdupois, mass)	0.453592	kg
	453.592	g
lb_f (force or thrust)	4.448222	N
lb_f/ft (uniform load)	14.59390	N/m
lb/ft·h (dynamic viscosity μ)	0.4134	mPa·s
lb/ft·s (dynamic viscosity μ)	1490	mPa·s
lb_f·s/ft^2 (dynamic viscosity μ)	47.88026	Pa·s
lb/h	0.000126	kg/s
lb/min	0.007559	kg/s
lb/h [steam at 212°F (100°C)]	0.2843	kW
lb_f/ft^2	47.9	Pa
lb/ft^2	4.88	kg/m^2
lb/ft^3 (density, ρ)	16.0	kg/m^3
lb/gallon	120	kg/m^3
ppm (by mass)	*1.00	mg/kg
psi	6.895	kPa
quad (10^{15} Btu)	1.055	EJ
quart (liquid, U.S.)	0.9463	L
square (100 ft^2)	9.29	m^2
tablespoon (approximately)	15	mL
teaspoon (approximately)	5	mL
therm (U.S.)	105.5	MJ
ton, long (2240 lb)	1.016	Mg
ton, short (2000 lb)	0.907	Mg; t (tonne)
ton, refrigeration (12 000 Btu/h)	3.517	kW
torr (1 mm Hg at 0°C)	133	Pa
watt per square foot	10.76	W/m^2
yd	*0.9144	m
yd^2	0.8361	m^2
yd^3	0.7646	m^3
To Obtain I-P	**By**	**Divide SI**

*Conversion factor is exact.

Notes: 1. Units are U.S. values unless noted otherwise.

2. Litre is a special name for the cubic decimetre. 1 L = 1 dm^3 and 1 mL = 1 cm^3.

The preparation of this chapter is assigned to TC 1.6, Terminology.

Table 2 Conversion Factors

Pressure psi	in. of water (60°F)	in. Hg (32°F)	atmosphere	mm Hg (32°F)	bar	kgf/cm²	pascal
1	= 27.708	= 2.0360	= 0.068046	= 51.715	= 0.068948	= 0.07030696	= 6894.8
0.036091	1	0.073483	2.4559×10^{-3}	1.8665	2.4884×10^{-3}	2.537×10^{-3}	248.84
0.491154	13.609	1	0.033421	25.400	0.033864	0.034532	3386.4
14.6960	407.19	29.921	1	760.0	1.01325*	1.03323	1.01325×10^{5}*
0.0193368	0.53578	0.03937	1.31579×10^{-3}	1	1.3332×10^{-3}	1.3595×10^{-3}	133.32
14.5038	401.86	29.530	0.98692	750.062	1	1.01972*	10^{5}*
14.223	394.1	28.959	0.96784	735.559	0.980665*	1	9.80665×10^{4}*
1.45038×10^{-4}	4.0186×10^{-3}	2.953×10^{-4}	9.8692×10^{-6}	7.50×10^{-3}	10^{-5}*	1.01972×10^{-5}*	1

Mass	lb (avoir.)	grain	ounce (avoir.)	kg
	1	= 7000*	= 16*	= 0.45359
	1.4286×10^{-4}	1	2.2857×10^{-3}	6.4800×10^{-5}
	0.06250	437.5*	1	0.028350
	2.20462	1.5432×10^{4}	35.274	1

Volume	cubic inch	cubic foot	gallon	litre	cubic metre (m³)
	1	= 5.787×10^{-4}	= 4.329×10^{-3}	= 0.0163871	= 1.63871×10^{-5}
	1728*	1	7.48052	28.317	0.028317
	231.0*	0.13368	1	3.7854	0.0037854
	61.02374	0.035315	0.264173	1	0.001*
	6.102374×10^{4}	35.315	264.173	1000*	1

Energy	Btu	ft·lb$_f$	calorie (cal)	joule (J) = watt-second (W·s)	watt-hour (W·h)
Note: MBtu, which is 1000 Btu, is confusing and is not used in the Handbook.	1	= 778.17	= 251.9958	= 1055.056	= 0.293071
	1.2851×10^{-3}	1	0.32383	1.355818	3.76616×10^{-4}
	3.9683×10^{-3}	3.08803	1	4.1868*	1.163×10^{-3}*
	9.4782×10^{-4}	0.73756	0.23885	1	2.7778×10^{-4}
	3.41214	2655.22	859.85	3600*	1

Density	lb/ft³	lb/gal	g/cm³	kg/m³
	1	= 0.133680	= 0.016018	= 16.018463
	7.48055	1	0.119827	119.827
	62.4280	8.34538	1	1000*
	0.0624280	0.008345	0.001*	1

Specific Volume	ft³/lb	gal/lb	cm³/g	m³/kg
	1	= 7.48055	= 62.4280	= 0.0624280
	0.133680	1	8.34538	0.008345
	0.016018	0.119827	1	0.001*
	16.018463	119.827	1000*	1

Viscosity (absolute) 1 poise = 1 dyne-sec/cm² = 0.1 Pa·s = 1 g/(cm·s)

	poise	lb$_f$·s/ft²	lb$_f$·h/ft²	kg/(m·s) = N·s/m²	lb$_m$/ft·s
	1	= 2.0885×10^{-3}	= 5.8014×10^{-7}	= 0.1*	= 0.0671955
	478.8026	1	2.7778×10^{-4}	47.88026	32.17405
	1.72369×10^{6}	3600*	1	1.72369×10^{5}	1.15827×10^{5}
	10*	0.020885	5.8014×10^{-6}	1	0.0671955
	14.8819	0.031081	8.6336×10^{-6}	1.4882	1

Temperature Scale		Temperature K	°C	°R	°F		Temperature Interval K	°C	°R	°F
Kelvin	xK =	x	x – 273.15	1.8x	1.8x – 459.67	1 K =	1	1	9/5 = 1.8	9/5 = 1.8
Celsius	x°C =	x + 273.15	x	1.8x + 491.67	1.8x + 32	1°C =	1	1	9/5 = 1.8	9/5 = 1.8
Rankine	x°R =	x/1.8	(x – 491.67)/1.8	x	x – 459.67	1°R =	5/9	5/9	1	1
Fahrenheit	x°F =	(x + 459.67)/1.8	(x – 32)/1.8	x + 459.67	x	1°F =	5/9	5/9	1	1

Notes: Conversions with * are exact.
The Btu and calorie are based on the International Table.
All temperature conversions and factors are exact.
The term centigrade is obsolete and should not be used.

When making conversions, remember that a converted value is no more precise than the original value. For many applications, rounding off the converted value to the same number of significant figures as those in the original value provides sufficient accuracy.

See ANSI *Standard* SI-10-1997 (available from ASTM or IEEE) for additional conversions.

CHAPTER 39

CODES AND STANDARDS

THE Codes and Standards listed here represent practices, methods, or standards published by the organizations indicated. They are useful guides for the practicing engineer in determining test methods, ratings, performance requirements, and limits of HVAC&R equipment. Copies of the standards can be obtained from most of the organizations listed in the Publisher column, from Global Engineering Documents at **global.ihs.com**, or from CSSINFO at **cssinfo.com**. Addresses of the organizations are given at the end of the chapter. A comprehensive database with over 250,000 industry, government, and international standards is at **www.nssn.org**.

Selected Codes and Standards Published by Various Societies and Associations

Subject	Title	Publisher	Reference
Air Conditioners	Commercial Application, Systems, and Equipment, 1st ed.	ACCA	ACCA Manual CS
	Residential Equipment Selection, 2nd ed.	ACCA	ANSI/ACCA Manual S
	Methods of Testing Air Terminal Units	ASHRAE	ANSI/ASHRAE 130-2008
	Non-Ducted Air Conditioners and Heat Pumps—Testing and Rating for Performance	ISO	ISO 5151:1994
	Ducted Air-Conditioners and Air-to-Air Heat Pumps—Testing and Rating for Performance	ISO	ISO 13253:1995
	Guidelines for Roof Mounted Outdoor Air-Conditioner Installations	SMACNA	SMACNA 1998
	Heating and Cooling Equipment (2005)	UL/CSA	ANSI/UL 1995/C22.2 No. 236-05
Central	Performance Standard for Single Package Central Air-Conditioners and Heat Pumps	CSA	CAN/CSA-C656-05
	Performance Standard for Rating Large and Single Packaged Air Conditioners and Heat Pumps	CSA	CAN/CSA-C746-06
	Performance Standard for Split-System and Single-Package Central Air Conditioners and Heat Pumps	CSA	CAN/CSA-C656-05
	Heating and Cooling Equipment (2005)	UL/CSA	ANSI/UL 1995/C22.2 No. 236-05
Gas-Fired	Gas-Fired, Heat Activated Air Conditioning and Heat Pump Appliances	CSA	ANSI Z21.40.1-1996 (R2002)/CGA 2.91-M96
	Gas-Fired Work Activated Air Conditioning and Heat Pump Appliances (Internal Combustion)	CSA	ANSI Z21.40.2-1996 (R2002)/CGA 2.92-M96
	Performance Testing and Rating of Gas-Fired Air Conditioning and Heat Pump Appliances	CSA	ANSI Z21.40.4-1996 (R2002)/CGA 2.94-M96
Packaged Terminal	Packaged Terminal Air-Conditioners and Heat Pumps	AHRI/CSA	AHRI 310/380-04/CSA C744-04
Room	Room Air Conditioners	AHAM	ANSI/AHAM RAC-1-2008
	Method of Testing for Rating Room Air Conditioners and Packaged Terminal Air Conditioners	ASHRAE	ANSI/ASHRAE 16-1983 (RA99)
	Method of Testing for Rating Room Air Conditioner and Packaged Terminal Air Conditioner Heating Capacity	ASHRAE	ANSI/ASHRAE 58-1986 (RA99)
	Method of Testing for Rating Fan-Coil Conditioners	ASHRAE	ANSI/ASHRAE 79-2002 (RA06)
	Performance Standard for Room Air Conditioners	CSA	CAN/CSA-C368.1-M90 (R2007)
	Room Air Conditioners	CSA	C22.2 No. 117-1970 (R2007)
	Room Air Conditioners (2007)	UL	ANSI/UL 484
Unitary	Unitary Air-Conditioning and Air-Source Heat Pump Equipment	AHRI	ANSI/AHRI 210/240-2006
	Sound Rating of Outdoor Unitary Equipment	AHRI	AHRI 270-95
	Application of Sound Rating Levels of Outdoor Unitary Equipment	AHRI	AHRI 275-97
	Commercial and Industrial Unitary Air-Conditioning and Heat Pump Equipment	AHRI	AHRI 340/360-2007
	Methods of Testing for Rating Electrically Driven Unitary Air-Conditioning and Heat Pump Equipment	ASHRAE	ANSI/ASHRAE 37-2005
	Methods of Testing for Rating Heat-Operated Unitary Air-Conditioning and Heat Pump Equipment	ASHRAE	ANSI/ASHRAE 40-2002 (RA06)
	Methods of Testing for Rating Seasonal Efficiency of Unitary Air Conditioners and Heat Pumps	ASHRAE	ANSI/ASHRAE 116-1995 (RA05)
	Method of Testing for Rating Computer and Data Processing Room Unitary Air Conditioners	ASHRAE	ANSI/ASHRAE 127-2007
	Method of Rating Unitary Spot Air Conditioners	ASHRAE	ANSI/ASHRAE 128-2001
Ships	Specification for Mechanically Refrigerated Shipboard Air Conditioner	ASTM	ASTM F1433-97 (2004)
Accessories	Flashing and Stand Combination for Air Conditioning Units (Unit Curb)	IAPMO	IAPMO PS 120-2004
Air Conditioning	Commercial Application, Systems, and Equipment, 1st ed.	ACCA	ACCA Manual CS
	Heat Pump Systems: Principles and Applications, 2nd ed.	ACCA	ACCA Manual H
	Residential Load Calculation, 8th ed.	ACCA	ANSI/ACCA Manual J
	Commercial Load Calculation, 4th ed.	ACCA	ACCA Manual N
	Comfort, Air Quality, and Efficiency by Design	ACCA	ACCA Manual RS
	Environmental Systems Technology, 2nd ed. (1999)	NEBB	NEBB

Selected Codes and Standards Published by Various Societies and Associations (*Continued*)

Subject	Title	Publisher	Reference
	Installation of Air Conditioning and Ventilating Systems	NFPA	NFPA 90A-02
	Standard of Purity for Use in Mobile Air-Conditioning Systems	SAE	SAE J1991-1999
	HVAC Systems—Applications, 1st ed.	SMACNA	SMACNA 1987
	HVAC Systems—Duct Design, 4th ed.	SMACNA	SMACNA 2006
	Heating and Cooling Equipment (2005)	UL/CSA	ANSI/UL 1995/C22.2 No. 236-05
Aircraft	Air Conditioning of Aircraft Cargo	SAE	SAE AIR806B-1997
	Aircraft Fuel Weight Penalty Due to Air Conditioning	SAE	SAE AIR1168/8-1989
	Air Conditioning Systems for Subsonic Airplanes	SAE	SAE ARP85E-1991
	Environmental Control Systems Terminology	SAE	SAE ARP147E-2001
	Testing of Airplane Installed Environmental Control Systems (ECS)	SAE	SAE ARP217D-1999
	Guide for Qualification Testing of Aircraft Air Valves	SAE	SAE ARP986C-1997
	Control of Excess Humidity in Avionics Cooling	SAE	SAE ARP987A-1997
	Engine Bleed Air Systems for Aircraft	SAE	SAE ARP1796-2007
	Aircraft Ground Air Conditioning Service Connection	SAE	SAE AS4262A-1997
	Air Cycle Air Conditioning Systems for Military Air Vehicles	SAE	SAE AS4073-2000
Automotive	Refrigerant 12 Automotive Air-Conditioning Hose	SAE	SAE J51-2004
	Design Guidelines for Air Conditioning Systems for Off-Road Operator Enclosures	SAE	SAE J169-1985
	Test Method for Measuring Power Consumption of Air Conditioning and Brake Compressors for Trucks and Buses	SAE	SAE J1340-2003
	Information Relating to Duty Cycles and Average Power Requirements of Truck and Bus Engine Accessories	SAE	SAE J1343-2000
	Rating Air-Conditioner Evaporator Air Delivery and Cooling Capacities	SAE	SAE J1487-2004
	Recovery and Recycle Equipment for Mobile Automotive Air-Conditioning Systems	SAE	SAE J1990-1999
	R134a Refrigerant Automotive Air-Conditioning Hose	SAE	SAE J2064-2005
	Service Hose for Automotive Air Conditioning	SAE	SAE J2196-1997
Ships	Mechanical Refrigeration and Air-Conditioning Installations Aboard Ship	ASHRAE	ANSI/ASHRAE 26-1996 (RA06)
	Practice for Mechanical Symbols, Shipboard Heating, Ventilation, and Air Conditioning (HVAC)	ASTM	ASTM F856-97 (2004)
Air Curtains	Laboratory Methods of Testing Air Curtains for Aerodynamic Performance	AMCA	AMCA 220-05
	Air Terminals	AHRI	AHRI 880-98
	Standard Methods for Laboratory Airflow Measurement	ASHRAE	ANSI/ASHRAE 41.2-1987 (RA92)
	Method of Testing the Performance of Air Outlets and Inlets	ASHRAE	ANSI/ASHRAE 70-2006
	Rating the Performance of Residential Mechanical Ventilating Equipment	CSA	CAN/CSA C260-M90 (R2007)
	Air Curtains for Entranceways in Food and Food Service Establishments	NSF	NSF/ANSI 37-2007
Air Diffusion	Air Distribution Basics for Residential and Small Commercial Buildings, 1st ed.	ACCA	ACCA Manual T
	Test Code for Grilles, Registers and Diffusers	ADC	ADC 1062:GRD-84
	Method of Testing the Performance of Air Outlets and Inlets	ASHRAE	ANSI/ASHRAE 70-2006
	Method of Testing for Room Air Diffusion	ASHRAE	ANSI/ASHRAE 113-2005
Air Filters	Comfort, Air Quality, and Efficiency by Design	ACCA	ACCA Manual RS
	Industrial Ventilation: A Manual of Recommended Practice, 26th ed. (2007)	ACGIH	ACGIH
	Air Cleaners	AHAM	ANSI/AHAM AC-1-2006
	Residential Air Filter Equipment	AHRI	AHRI 680-2004
	Commercial and Industrial Air Filter Equipment	AHRI	AHRI 850-2004
	Agricultural Cabs—Engineering Control of Environmental Air Quality—Part 1: Definitions, Test Methods, and Safety Procedures	ASABE	ANSI/ASAE S525-1.2-2003
	Part 2: Pesticide Vapor Filters—Test Procedure and Performance Criteria	ASABE	ANSI/ASAE S525-2-2003
	Method of Testing General Ventilation Air-Cleaning Devices for Removal Efficiency by Particle Size	ASHRAE	ANSI/ASHRAE 52.2-2007
	Code on Nuclear Air and Gas Treatment	ASME	ASME AG-1-2003
	Nuclear Power Plant Air-Cleaning Units and Components	ASME	ASME N509-2002
	Testing of Nuclear Air-Treatment Systems	ASME	ASME N510-2007
	Specification for Filter Units, Air Conditioning: Viscous-Impingement and Dry Types, Replaceable	ASTM	ASTM F1040-87 (2007)
	Test Method for Air Cleaning Performance of a High-Efficiency Particulate Air Filter System	ASTM	ASTM F1471-93 (2001)
	Specification for Filters Used in Air or Nitrogen Systems	ASTM	ASTM F1791-00 (2006)
	Method for Sodium Flame Test for Air Filters	BSI	BS 3928:1969
	Particulate Air Filters for General Ventilation: Determination of Filtration Performance	BSI	BS EN 779:2002
	Electrostatic Air Cleaners (2000)	UL	ANSI/UL 867
	High-Efficiency, Particulate, Air Filter Units (1996)	UL	ANSI/UL 586
	Air Filter Units (2004)	UL	ANSI/UL 900
	Exhaust Hoods for Commercial Cooking Equipment (1995)	UL	UL 710
	Grease Filters for Exhaust Ducts (2000)	UL	UL 1046

Selected Codes and Standards Published by Various Societies and Associations (*Continued*)

Subject	Title	Publisher	Reference
Air-Handling Units	Commercial Application, Systems, and Equipment, 1st ed.	ACCA	ACCA Manual CS
	Central Station Air-Handling Units	AHRI	ANSI/AHRI 430-99
	Non-Recirculating Direct Gas-Fired Industrial Air Heaters	CSA	ANSI Z83.4-2003/CSA 3.7-2003
Air Leakage	Residential Duct Diagnostics and Repair (2003)	ACCA	ACCA
	Air Leakage Performance for Detached Single-Family Residential Buildings	ASHRAE	ANSI/ASHRAE 119-1988 (RA04)
	Method of Determining Air Change Rates in Detached Dwellings	ASHRAE	ANSI/ASHRAE 136-1993 (RA06)
	Test Method for Determining Air Change in a Single Zone by Means of a Tracer Gas Dilution	ASTM	ASTM E741-00 (2006)
	Test Method for Determining Air Leakage Rate by Fan Pressurization	ASTM	ASTM E779-03
	Test Method for Field Measurement of Air Leakage Through Installed Exterior Window and Doors	ASTM	ASTM E783-02
	Practices for Air Leakage Site Detection in Building Envelopes and Air Retarder Systems	ASTM	ASTM E1186-03
	Test Method for Determining the Rate of Air Leakage Through Exterior Windows, Curtain Walls, and Doors Under Specified Pressure and Temperature Differences Across the Specimen	ASTM	ASTM E1424-91 (2000)
	Test Methods for Determining Airtightness of Buildings Using an Orifice Blower Door	ASTM	ASTM E1827-96 (2007)
	Practice for Determining the Effects of Temperature Cycling on Fenestration Products	ASTM	ASTM E2264-05
	Test Method for Determining Air Flow Through the Face and Sides of Exterior Windows, Curtain Walls, and Doors Under Specified Pressure Differences Across the Specimen	ASTM	ASTM E2319-04
	Test Method for Determining Air Leakage of Air Barrier Assemblies	ASTM	ASTM E2357-05
Boilers	Packaged Boiler Engineering Manual (1999)	ABMA	ABMA 100
	Selected Codes and Standards of the Boiler Industry (2001)	ABMA	ABMA 103
	Operation and Maintenance Safety Manual (1995)	ABMA	ABMA 106
	Fluidized Bed Combustion Guidelines (1995)	ABMA	ABMA 200
	Guide to Clean and Efficient Operation of Coal Stoker-Fired Boilers (2002)	ABMA	ABMA 203
	Guideline for Performance Evaluation of Heat Recovery Steam Generating Equipment (1995)	ABMA	ABMA 300
	Guidelines for Industrial Boiler Performance Improvement (1999)	ABMA	ABMA 302
	Measurement of Sound from Steam Generators (1995)	ABMA	ABMA 304
	Guideline for Gas and Oil Emission Factors for Industrial, Commercial, and Institutional Boilers (1997)	ABMA	ABMA 305
	Combustion Control Guidelines for Single Burner Firetube and Watertube Industrial/Commercial/Institutional Boilers (1999)	ABMA	ABMA 307
	Combustion Control Guidelines for Multiple-Burner Boilers (2001)	ABMA	ABMA 308
	Boiler Water Quality Requirements and Associated Steam Quality for Industrial/ Commercial and Institutional Boilers (2005)	ABMA	ABMA 402
	Commercial Application, Systems, and Equipment, 1st ed.	ACCA	ACCA Manual CS
	Method of Testing for Annual Fuel Utilization Efficiency of Residential Central Furnaces and Boilers	ASHRAE	ANSI/ASHRAE 103-2007
	Boiler and Pressure Vessel Code—Section I: Power Boilers; Section IV: Heating Boilers	ASME	BPVC-2007
	Fired Steam Generators	ASME	ASME PTC 4-1998
	Boiler, Pressure Vessel, and Pressure Piping Code	CSA	CSA B51-2003 (R2007)
	Testing Standard for Commercial Boilers, 2nd ed. (2007)	HYDI	HYDI BTS-2007
	Rating Procedure for Heating Boilers, 6th ed. (2005)	HYDI	IBR
	Prevention of Furnace Explosions/Implosions in Multiple Burner Boilers	NFPA	ANSI /NFPA 8502-99
	Heating, Water Supply, and Power Boilers—Electric (2004)	UL	ANSI/UL 834
	Boiler and Combustion Systems Hazards Code	NFPA	NFPA 85-07
Gas or Oil	Gas-Fired Low-Pressure Steam and Hot Water Boilers	CSA	ANSI Z21.13-2004/CSA 4.9-2004
	Controls and Safety Devices for Automatically Fired Boilers	ASME	ASME CSD-1-2006
	Industrial and Commercial Gas-Fired Package Boilers	CSA	CAN 1-3.1-77 (R2006)
	Oil-Burning Equipment: Steam and Hot-Water Boilers	CSA	B140.7-2005
	Single Burner Boiler Operations	NFPA	ANSI/NFPA 8501-01
	Prevention of Furnace Explosions/Implosions in Multiple Burner Boilers	NFPA	ANSI/NFPA 8502-99
	Oil-Fired Boiler Assemblies (1995)	UL	UL 726
	Commercial-Industrial Gas Heating Equipment (2006)	UL	UL 795
	Standards and Typical Specifications for Tray Type Deaerators, 7th ed. (2003)	HEI	HEI 2954
Terminology	Ultimate Boiler Industry Lexicon: Handbook of Power Utility and Boiler Terms and Phrases, 6th ed. (2001)	ABMA	ABMA 101
Building Codes	ASTM Standards Used in Building Codes	ASTM	ASTM
	Practice for Conducting Visual Assessments for Lead Hazards in Buildings	ASTM	ASTM E2255-04
	Standard Practice for Periodic Inspection of Building Facades for Unsafe Conditions	ASTM	ASTM E2270-05
	Structural Welding Code—Steel	AWS	AWS D1.1M/D1.1:2008
	BOCA National Building Code, 14th ed. (1999)	BOCA	BNBC
	Uniform Building Code, vol. 1, 2, and 3 (1997)	ICBO	UBC V1, V2, V3

Selected Codes and Standards Published by Various Societies and Associations (*Continued*)

Subject	Title	Publisher	Reference
	International Building Code (2006)	ICC	IBC
	International Code Council Performance Code (2006)	ICC	ICC PC
	International Existing Building Code (2006)	ICC	IEBC
	International Energy Conservation Code (2006)	ICC	IECC
	International Property Maintenance Code (2006)	ICC	IPMC
	International Residential Code (2006)	ICC	IRC
	Directory of Building Codes and Regulations, State and City Volumes (annual)	NCSBCS	NCSBCS (electronic only)
	Building Construction and Safety Code	NFPA	ANSI/NFPA 5000-2006
	National Building Code of Canada (2005)	NRCC	NRCC
	Standard Building Code (1999)	SBCCI	SBC
Mechanical	Safety Code for Elevators and Escalators	ASME	ASME A17.1-2004
	Natural Gas and Propane Installation Code	CSA	CAN/CSA-B149.1-05
	Propane Storage and Handling Code	CSA	CAN/CSA-B149.2-05
	Uniform Mechanical Code (2006)	IAPMO	IAPMO
	International Mechanical Code (2006)	ICC	IMC
	International Fuel Gas Code (2006)	ICC	IFGC
	Standard Gas Code (1999)	SBCCI	SBC
Burners	Guidelines for Burner Adjustments of Commercial Oil-Fired Boilers (1996)	ABMA	ABMA 303
	Domestic Gas Conversion Burners	CSA	ANSI Z21.17-1998 (R2004)/ CSA 2.7-M98
	Installation of Domestic Gas Conversion Burners	CSA	ANSI Z21.8-1994 (R2002)
	Installation Code for Oil Burning Equipment	CSA	CAN/CSA-B139-06
	Oil-Burning Equipment: General Requirements	CSA	CAN/CSA-B140.0-03
	Vapourizing-Type Oil Burners	CSA	B140.1-1966 (R2006)
	Oil Burners: Atomizing-Type	CSA	CAN/CSA-B140.2.1-M90 (R2005)
	Pressure Atomizing Oil Burner Nozzles	CSA	B140.2.2-1971 (R2006)
	Oil Burners (2003)	UL	ANSI/UL 296
	Waste Oil-Burning Air-Heating Appliances (1995)	UL	ANSI/UL 296A
	Commercial-Industrial Gas Heating Equipment (2006)	UL	UL 795
	Commercial/Industrial Gas and/or Oil-Burning Assemblies with Emission Reduction Equipment (2006)	UL	UL 2096
Chillers	Commercial Application, Systems, and Equipment, 1st ed.	ACCA	ACCA Manual CS
	Absorption Water Chilling and Water Heating Packages	AHRI	AHRI 560-2000
	Water Chilling Packages Using the Vapor Compression Cycle	AHRI	AHRI 550/590-2003
	Method of Testing Liquid-Chilling Packages	ASHRAE	ANSI/ASHRAE 30-1995
	Performance Standard for Rating Packaged Water Chillers	CSA	CAN/CSA C743-02 (R2007)
Chimneys	Specification for Clay Flue Liners	ASTM	ASTM C315-07
	Specification for Industrial Chimney Lining Brick	ASTM	ASTM C980-88 (2007)
	Practice for Installing Clay Flue Lining	ASTM	ASTM C1283-07a
	Guide for Design and Construction of Brick Liners for Industrial Chimneys	ASTM	ASTM C1298-95 (2007)
	Guide for Design, Fabrication, and Erection of Fiberglass Reinforced Plastic Chimney Liners with Coal-Fired Units	ASTM	ASTM D5364-93 (2002)
	Chimneys, Fireplaces, Vents, and Solid Fuel-Burning Appliances	NFPA	ANSI/NFPA 211-06
	Medium Heat Appliance Factory-Built Chimneys (2001)	UL	ANSI/UL 959
	Factory-Built Chimneys for Residential Type and Building Heating Appliance (2001)	UL	ANSI/UL 103
Cleanrooms	Practice for Cleaning and Maintaining Controlled Areas and Clean Rooms	ASTM	ASTM E2042-04
	Practice for Design and Construction of Aerospace Cleanrooms and Contamination Controlled Areas	ASTM	ASTM E2217-02 (2007)
	Practice for Tests of Cleanroom Materials	ASTM	ASTM E2312-04
	Practice for Aerospace Cleanrooms and Associated Controlled Environments—Cleanroom Operations	ASTM	ASTM E2352-04
	Test Method for Sizing and Counting Airborne Particulate Contamination in Clean Rooms and Other Dust-Controlled Areas Designed for Electronic and Similar Applications	ASTM	ASTM F25-04
	Practice for Continuous Sizing and Counting of Airborne Particles in Dust-Controlled Areas and Clean Rooms Using Instruments Capable of Detecting Single Sub-Micrometre and Larger Particles	ASTM	ASTM F50-07
	Procedural Standards for Certified Testing of Cleanrooms, 2nd ed. (1996)	NEBB	NEBB
Coils	Forced-Circulation Air-Cooling and Air-Heating Coils	AHRI	AHRI 410-2001
	Methods of Testing Forced Circulation Air Cooling and Air Heating Coils	ASHRAE	ANSI/ASHRAE 33-2000
Comfort Conditions	Threshold Limit Values for Physical Agents (updated annually)	ACGIH	ACGIH
	Good HVAC Practices for Residential and Commercial Buildings (2003)	ACCA	ACCA
	Comfort, Air Quality, and Efficiency by Design (1997)	ACCA	ACCA Manual RS
	Thermal Environmental Conditions for Human Occupancy	ASHRAE	ANSI/ASHRAE 55-2004

Selected Codes and Standards Published by Various Societies and Associations (*Continued*)

Subject	Title	Publisher	Reference
	Classification for Serviceability of an Office Facility for Thermal Environment and Indoor Air Conditions	ASTM	ASTM E2320-04
	Hot Environments—Estimation of the Heat Stress on Working Man, Based on the WBGT Index (Wet Bulb Globe Temperature)	ISO	ISO 7243:1989
	Ergonomics of the Thermal Environment—Analytical Determination and Interpretation of Thermal Comfort Using Calculation of the PMV and PPD Indices and Local Thermal Comfort Criteria	ISO	ISO 7730:2005
	Ergonomics of the Thermal Environment—Determination of Metabolic Rate	ISO	ISO 8996:2004
	Ergonomics of the Thermal Environment—Estimation of the Thermal Insulation and Water Vapour Resistance of a Clothing Ensemble	ISO	ISO 9920:2007
Compressors	Displacement Compressors, Vacuum Pumps and Blowers	ASME	ASME PTC 9-1970 (RA97)
	Performance Test Code on Compressors and Exhausters	ASME	ASME PTC 10-1997 (RA03)
	Compressed Air and Gas Handbook, 6th ed. (2003)	CAGI	CAGI
Refrigerant	Positive Displacement Condensing Units	AHRI	AHRI 520-2004
	Positive Displacement Refrigerant Compressors and Compressor Units	AHRI	AHRI 540-2004
	Safety Standard for Refrigeration Systems	ASHRAE	ANSI/ASHRAE 15-2004
	Methods of Testing for Rating Positive Displacement Refrigerant Compressors and Condensing Units	ASHRAE	ANSI/ASHRAE 23-2005
	Testing of Refrigerant Compressors	ISO	ISO 917:1989
	Refrigerant Compressors—Presentation of Performance Data	ISO	ISO 9309:1989
	Hermetic Refrigerant Motor-Compressors (1996)	UL/CSA	UL 984/C22.2 No.140.2-96 (R2001)
Computers	Method of Testing for Rating Computer and Data Processing Room Unitary Air Conditioners	ASHRAE	ANSI/ASHRAE 127-2007
	Method of Test for the Evaluation of Building Energy Analysis Computer Programs	ASHRAE	ANSI/ASHRAE 140-2007
	Protection of Electronic Computer/Data Processing Equipment	NFPA	NFPA 75-03
Condensers	Commercial Application, Systems, and Equipment, 1st ed.	ACCA	ACCA Manual CS
	Water-Cooled Refrigerant Condensers, Remote Type	AHRI	AHRI 450-2007
	Remote Mechanical-Draft Air-Cooled Refrigerant Condensers	AHRI	AHRI 460-2005
	Remote Mechanical Draft Evaporative Refrigerant Condensers	AHRI	AHRI 490-2003
	Safety Standard for Refrigeration Systems	ASHRAE	ANSI/ASHRAE 15-2007
	Method of Testing for Rating Remote Mechanical-Draft Air-Cooled Refrigerant Condensers	ASHRAE	ANSI/ASHRAE 20-1997 (RA06)
	Methods of Testing for Rating Water-Cooled Refrigerant Condensers	ASHRAE	ANSI/ASHRAE 22-2007
	Methods of Laboratory Testing Remote Mechanical-Draft Evaporative Refrigerant Condensers	ASHRAE	ANSI/ASHRAE 64-2005
	Steam Surface Condensers	ASME	ASME PTC 12.2-1998
	Standards for Steam Surface Condensers, 10th ed.	HEI	HEI 2629
	Standards for Direct Contact Barometric and Low Level Condensers, 7th ed. (1995)	HEI	HEI 2634
	Refrigerant-Containing Components and Accessories, Nonelectrical (2001)	UL	ANSI/UL 207
Condensing Units	Commercial Application, Systems, and Equipment, 1st ed.	ACCA	ACCA Manual CS
	Commercial and Industrial Unitary Air-Conditioning Condensing Units	AHRI	AHRI 365-2002
	Methods of Testing for Rating Positive Displacement Refrigerant Compressors and Condensing Units	ASHRAE	ANSI/ASHRAE 23-2005
	Heating and Cooling Equipment (2005)	UL/CSA	ANSI/UL 1995/C22.2 No. 236-95
Containers	Series 1 Freight Containers—Classifications, Dimensions, and Ratings	ISO	ISO 668:1995
	Series 1 Freight Containers—Specifications and Testing; Part 2: Thermal Containers	ISO	ISO 1496-2:1996
	Animal Environment in Cargo Compartments	SAE	SAE AIR1600A-1997
Controls	Temperature Control Systems (2002)	AABC	National Standards, Ch. 12
	BACnet®—A Data Communication Protocol for Building Automation and Control Networks	ASHRAE	ANSI/ASHRAE 135-2008
	Method of Test for Conformance to BACnet®	ASHRAE	ANSI/ASHRAE 135.1-2007
	Temperature-Indicating and Regulating Equipment	CSA	C22.2 No. 24-93 (R2003)
	Performance Requirements for Electric Heating Line-Voltage Wall Thermostats	CSA	C273.4-M1978 (R2003)
	Performance Requirements for Thermostats Used with Individual Room Electric Space Heating Devices	CSA	CAN/CSA C828-06
	Solid-State Controls for Appliances (2003)	UL	UL 244A
	Limit Controls (1994)	UL	ANSI/UL 353
	Primary Safety Controls for Gas- and Oil-Fired Appliances (1994)	UL	ANSI/UL 372
	Temperature-Indicating and -Regulating Equipment (2007)	UL	UL 873
	Tests for Safety-Related Controls Employing Solid-State Devices (2004)	UL	UL 991
	Control Centers for Changing Message Type Electric Signals (2003)	UL	UL 1433
	Automatic Electrical Controls for Household and Similar Use; Part 1: General Requirements (2002)	UL	UL 60730-1A
	Process Control Equipment (2002)	UL	UL 61010C-1

Selected Codes and Standards Published by Various Societies and Associations (*Continued*)

Subject	Title	Publisher	Reference
Commercial and Industrial	Guidelines for Boiler Control Systems (Gas/Oil Fired Boilers) (1998)	ABMA	ABMA 301
	Guideline for the Integration of Boilers and Automated Control Systems in Heating Applications (1998)	ABMA	ABMA 306
	Industrial Control and Systems: General Requirements	NEMA	NEMA ICS 1-2000 (R2005)
	Preventive Maintenance of Industrial Control and Systems Equipment	NEMA	NEMA ICS 1.3-1986 (R2001)
	Industrial Control and Systems, Controllers, Contactors, and Overload Relays Rated Not More than 2000 Volts AC or 750 Volts DC	NEMA	NEMA ICS 2-2000 (R2004)
	Industrial Control and Systems: Instructions for the Handling, Installation, Operation and Maintenance of Motor Control Centers Rated Not More than 600 Volts	NEMA	NEMA ICS 2.3-1995 (R2002)
	Industrial Control Equipment (1999)	UL	ANSI/UL 508
Residential	Manually Operated Gas Valves for Appliances, Appliance Connector Valves and Hose End Valves	CSA	ANSI Z21.15-1997 (R03)/CGA 9.1-1997
	Gas Appliance Pressure Regulators	CSA	ANSI Z21.18-2007/CSA 6.3-2007
	Automatic Gas Ignition Systems and Components	CSA	ANSI Z21.20-2007/C22.2 No. 199-2007
	Gas Appliance Thermostats	CSA	ANSI Z21.23-2000 (R2005)
	Manually-Operated Piezo-Electric Spark Gas Ignition Systems and Components	CSA	ANSI Z21.77-2005/CGA 6.23-2005
	Manually Operated Electric Gas Ignition Systems and Components	CSA	ANSI Z21.92-2005/CSA 6.29-2005 (R2007)
	Residential Controls—Electrical Wall-Mounted Room Thermostats	NEMA	NEMA DC 3-2003
	Residential Controls—Surface Type Controls for Electric Storage Water Heaters	NEMA	NEMA DC 5-2002
	Residential Controls—Temperature Limit Controls for Electric Baseboard Heaters	NEMA	NEMA DC 10-1983 (R2003)
	Hot-Water Immersion Controls	NEMA	NEMA DC 12-1985 (R2002))
	Line-Voltage Integrally Mounted Thermostats for Electric Heaters	NEMA	NEMA DC 13-1979 (R2002)
	Residential Controls—Class 2 Transformers	NEMA	NEMA DC 20-1992 (R2003)
	Safety Guidelines for the Application, Installation, and Maintenance of Solid State Controls	NEMA	NEMA ICS 1.1-1984 (R2003)
	Electrical Quick-Connect Terminals (2003)	UL	ANSI/UL 310
Coolers	Refrigeration Equipment	CSA	CAN/CSA-C22.2 No. 120-M91 (R2004)
	Unit Coolers for Refrigeration	AHRI	AHRI 420-2000
	Refrigeration Unit Coolers (2004)	UL	ANSI/UL 412
Air	Methods of Testing Forced Convection and Natural Convection Air Coolers for Refrigeration	ASHRAE	ANSI/ASHRAE 25-2001 (RA06)
Drinking Water	Methods of Testing for Rating Drinking-Water Coolers with Self-Contained Mechanical Refrigeration	ASHRAE	ANSI/ASHRAE 18-2008
	Drinking-Water Coolers (1993)	UL	ANSI/UL 399
	Drinking Water System Components—Health Effects	NSF	NSF/ANSI 61-2007a
Evaporative	Method of Testing Direct Evaporative Air Coolers	ASHRAE	ANSI/ASHRAE 133-2008
	Method of Test for Rating Indirect Evaporative Coolers	ASHRAE	ANSI/ASHRAE 143-2007
Food and Beverage	Terminology for Milking Machines, Milk Cooling, and Bulk Milk Handling Equipment	ASABE	ASAE S300.3-2003
	Methods of Testing for Rating Vending Machines for Bottled, Canned, and Other Sealed Beverages	ASHRAE	ANSI/ASHRAE 32.1-2004
	Methods of Testing for Rating Pre-Mix and Post-Mix Beverage Dispensing Equipment	ASHRAE	ANSI/ASHRAE 32.2-2003 (RA07)
	Manual Food and Beverage Dispensing Equipment	NSF	NSF/ANSI 18-2005
	Commercial Bulk Milk Dispensing Equipment	NSF	NSF/ANSI 20-2007
	Refrigerated Vending Machines (1995)	UL	ANSI/UL 541
Liquid	Refrigerant-Cooled Liquid Coolers, Remote Type	AHRI	AHRI 480-2007
	Methods of Testing for Rating Liquid Coolers	ASHRAE	ANSI/ASHRAE 24-2000 (RA05)
	Liquid Cooling Systems	SAE	SAE AIR1811A-1997
Cooling Towers	Cooling Tower Testing (2002)	AABC	National Standards, Ch 13
	Commercial Application, Systems, and Equipment, 1st ed.	ACCA	ACCA Manual CS
	Bioaerosols: Assessment and Control (1999)	ACGIH	ACGIH
	Atmospheric Water Cooling Equipment	ASME	ASME PTC 23-2003
	Water-Cooling Towers	NFPA	NFPA 214-05
	Acceptance Test Code for Water Cooling Towers	CTI	CTI ATC-105 (00)
	Code for Measurement of Sound from Water Cooling Towers (2005)	CTI	CTI ATC-128 (05)
	Acceptance Test Code for Spray Cooling Systems (1985)	CTI	CTI ATC-133 (85)
	Nomenclature for Industrial Water Cooling Towers (1997)	CTI	CTI NCL-109 (97)
	Recommended Practice for Airflow Testing of Cooling Towers (1994)	CTI	CTI PFM-143 (94)
	Fiberglass-Reinforced Plastic Panels (2002)	CTI	CTI STD-131 (02)
	Certification of Water Cooling Tower Thermal Performance (R2004)	CTI	CTI STD-201 (04)
Crop Drying	Density, Specific Gravity, and Mass-Moisture Relationships of Grain for Storage	ASABE	ANSI/ASAE D241.4-2003
	Dielectric Properties of Grain and Seed	ASABE	ASAE D293.2-1989 (R2005)
	Thermal Properties of Grain and Grain Products	ASABE	ASAE D243.4-2003
	Moisture Relationships of Plant-Based Agricultural Products	ASABE	ASAE D245.5-19995 (R2001)
	Construction and Rating of Equipment for Drying Farm Crops	ASABE	ASAE S248.3-1976 (R2005)

Selected Codes and Standards Published by Various Societies and Associations (*Continued*)

Subject	Title	Publisher	Reference
	Cubes, Pellets, and Crumbles—Definitions and Methods for Determining Density, Durability, and Moisture Content	ASABE	ASAE S269.4-1991
	Resistance to Airflow of Grains, Seeds, Other Agricultural Products, and Perforated Metal Sheets	ASABE	ASAE D272.3-1996
	Shelled Corn Storage Time for 0.5% Dry Matter Loss	ASABE	ASAE D535-2005
	Moisture Measurement—Unground Grain and Seeds	ASABE	ASAE S352.2-2003
	Moisture Measurement—Meat and Meat Products	ASABE	ASAE S353-2003
	Moisture Measurement—Forages	ASABE	ASAE S358.2-2003
	Moisture Measurement—Peanuts	ASABE	ASAE S410.1-2003
	Energy Efficiency Test Procedure for Tobacco Curing Structures	ASABE	ASAE S416-2003
	Thin-Layer Drying of Agricultural Crops	ASABE	ANSI/ASAE S448.1-2001 (R2006)
	Moisture Measurement—Tobacco	ASABE	ASAE S487-2003
	Thin-Layer Drying of Agricultural Crops	ASABE	ASAE S488-1990 (R2005)
	Temperature Sensor Locations for Seed-Cotton Drying Systems	ASABE	ASAE 530.1-2007
Dehumidifiers	Commercial Application, Systems, and Equipment, 1st ed.	ACCA	ACCA Manual CS
	Bioaerosols: Assessment and Control (1999)	ACGIH	ACGIH
	Dehumidifiers	AHAM	ANSI/AHAM DH-1-2008
	Method of Testing for Rating Desiccant Dehumidifiers Utilizing Heat for the Regeneration Process	ASHRAE	ANSI/ASHRAE 139-2007
	Moisture Separator Reheaters	ASME	PTC 12.4-1992 (RA04)
	Dehumidifiers	CSA	C22.2 No. 92-1971 (R2004)
	Performance of Dehumidifiers	CSA	CAN/CSA C749-07
	Dehumidifiers (2004)	UL	ANSI/UL 474
Desiccants	Method of Testing Desiccants for Refrigerant Drying	ASHRAE	ANSI/ASHRAE 35-1992
Documentation	Preparation of Operating and Maintenance Documentation for Building Systems	ASHRAE	ASHRAE *Guideline* 4-1993
Driers	Liquid-Line Driers	AHRI	ANSI/AHRI 710-2004
	Method of Testing Liquid Line Refrigerant Driers	ASHRAE	ANSI/ASHRAE 63.1-1995 (RA01)
	Refrigerant-Containing Components and Accessories, Nonelectrical (2001)	UL	ANSI/UL 207
Ducts and Fittings	Hose, Air Duct, Flexible Nonmetallic, Aircraft	SAE	SAE AS1501C-1994
	Ducted Electric Heat Guide for Air Handling Systems, 2nd ed.	SMACNA	SMACNA 1994
	Factory-Made Air Ducts and Air Connectors (2005)	UL	ANSI/UL 181
Construction	Industrial Ventilation: A Manual of Recommended Practice, 26th ed. (2007)	ACGIH	ACGIH
	Preferred Metric Sizes for Flat, Round, Square, Rectangular, and Hexagonal Metal Products	ASME	ASME B32.100-2005
	Sheet Metal Welding Code	AWS	AWS D9.1M/D9.1:2006
	Fibrous Glass Duct Construction Standards, 5th ed.	NAIMA	NAIMA AH116
	Residential Fibrous Glass Duct Construction Standards, 3rd ed.	NAIMA	NAIMA AH119
	Thermoplastic Duct (PVC) Construction Manual, 2nd ed.	SMACNA	SMACNA 1995
	Accepted Industry Practices for Sheet Metal Lagging, 1st ed.	SMACNA	SMACNA 2002
	Fibrous Glass Duct Construction Standards, 7th ed.	SMACNA	SMACNA 2003
	HVAC Duct Construction Standards, Metal and Flexible, 3rd ed.	SMACNA	SMACNA 2005
	Rectangular Industrial Duct Construction Standards, 2nd ed.	SMACNA	SMACNA 2004
Industrial	Round Industrial Duct Construction Standards, 2nd ed.	SMACNA	SMACNA 1999
	Rectangular Industrial Duct Construction Standards, 2nd ed.	SMACNA	SMACNA 2004
Installation	Flexible Duct Performance and Installation Standards, 4th ed.	ADC	ADC-91
	Installation of Air Conditioning and Ventilating Systems	NFPA	NFPA 90A-06
	Installation of Warm Air Heating and Air-Conditioning Systems	NFPA	NFPA 90B-06
Material Specifications	Specification for General Requirements for Flat-Rolled Stainless and Heat-Resisting Steel Plate, Sheet and Strip	ASTM	ASTM A480/A480M-06b
	Specification for General Requirements for Steel, Sheet, Carbon, and High-Strength, Low-Alloy, Hot-Rolled and Cold-Rolled	ASTM	ASTM A568/A568M-07a
	Specification for Steel Sheet, Zinc-Coated (Galvanized) or Zinc-Iron Alloy-Coated (Galvannealed) by the Hot-Dipped Process	ASTM	ASTM A653/A653M-07
	Specification for General Requirements for Steel Sheet, Metallic-Coated by the Hot-Dip Process	ASTM	ASTM A924/A924M-07
	Specification for Steel, Sheet and Strip, Cold-Rolled, Carbon, Structural, High-Strength Low-Alloy and High-Strength Low-Alloy with Improved Formability	ASTM	ASTM A1008/A1008M-07a
	Specification for Steel, Sheet and Strip, Hot-Rolled, Carbon, Structural, High-Strength Low-Alloy and High-Strength Low-Alloy with Improved Formability	ASTM	ASTM A1011/A1011M-07
	Practice for Measuring Flatness Characteristics of Coated Sheet Products	ASTM	ASTM A1030/A1030M-05
System Design	Installation Techniques for Perimeter Heating and Cooling, 11th ed.	ACCA	ACCA Manual 4
	Residential Duct Systems	ACCA	ANSI/ACCA Manual D
	Commercial Low Pressure, Low Velocity Duct System Design, 1st ed.	ACCA	ACCA Manual Q
	Air Distribution Basics for Residential and Small Commercial Buildings, 1st ed.	ACCA	ACCA Manual T
	Method of Test for Determining the Design and Seasonal Efficiencies of Residential Thermal Distribution Systems	ASHRAE	ANSI/ASHRAE 152-2004

Selected Codes and Standards Published by Various Societies and Associations (*Continued*)

Subject	Title	Publisher	Reference
	Closure Systems for Use with Rigid Air Ducts (2005)	UL	ANSI/UL 181A
	Closure Systems for Use with Flexible Air Ducts and Air Connectors (2005)	UL	ANSI/UL 181B
Testing	Duct Leakage Testing (2002)	AABC	National Standards, Ch 5
	Residential Duct Diagnostics and Repair (2003)	ACCA	ACCA
	Flexible Air Duct Test Code	ADC	ADC FD-72 (R1979)
	Test Method for Measuring Acoustical and Airflow Performance of Duct Liner Materials and Prefabricated Silencers	ASTM	ASTM E477-06a
	Method of Testing to Determine Flow Resistance of HVAC Ducts and Fittings	ASHRAE	ANSI/ASHRAE 120-2008
	Method of Testing HVAC Air Ducts and Fittings	ASHRAE	ANSI/ASHRAE/SMACNA 126-2008
	HVAC Air Duct Leakage Test Manual, 1st ed.	SMACNA	SMACNA 1985
	HVAC Duct Systems Inspection Guide, 3rd ed.	SMACNA	SMACNA 2005
Electrical	Electrical Power Systems and Equipment—Voltage Ratings	ANSI	ANSI C84.1-2006
	Test Method for Bond Strength of Electrical Insulating Varnishes by the Helical Coil Test	ASTM	ASTM D2519-07
	Standard Specification for Shelter, Electrical Equipment, Lightweight	ASTM	ASTM E2377-04
	Canadian Electrical Code, Part I (20th ed.)	CSA	C22.1-06
	Part II—General Requirements	CSA	CAN/CSA-C22.2 No. 0-M91 (R2006)
	ICC Electrical Code, Administrative Provisions (2006)	ICC	ICCEC
	Enclosures for Electrical Equipment (1000 Volts Maximum)	NEMA	ANSI/NEMA 250-2003
	Low Voltage Cartridge Fuses	NEMA	NEMA FU 1-2002 (R2007)
	Industrial Control and Systems: Terminal Blocks	NEMA	NEMA ICS 4-2005
	Industrial Control and Systems: Enclosures	NEMA	ANSI/NEMA ICS 6-1993 (R2006)
	Application Guide for Ground Fault Protective Devices for Equipment	NEMA	ANSI/NEMA PB 2.2-2004
	General Color Requirements for Wiring Devices	NEMA	NEMA WD 1-1999 (R2005)
	Wiring Devices—Dimensional Requirements	NEMA	ANSI/NEMA WD 6-2002
	National Electrical Code	NFPA	NFPA 70-08
	National Fire Alarm Code	NFPA	NFPA 72-07
	Compatibility of Electrical Connectors and Wiring	SAE	SAE AIR1329A-1988
	Molded-Case Circuit Breakers, Molded-Case Switches, and Circuit-Breaker Enclosures	UL	ANSI/UL489
Energy	Air-Conditioning and Refrigerating Equipment Nameplate Voltages	AHRI	AHRI 110-2002
	Comfort, Air Quality, and Efficiency by Design	ACCA	ACCA Manual RS
	Energy Standard for Buildings Except Low-Rise Residential Buildings	ASHRAE	ANSI/ASHRAE/IESNA 90.1-2007
	Energy-Efficient Design of Low-Rise Residential Buildings	ASHRAE	ANSI/ASHRAE/IESNA 90.2-2007
	Energy Conservation in Existing Buildings	ASHRAE	ANSI/ASHRAE/IESNA 100-2006
	Methods of Measuring, Expressing, and Comparing Building Energy Performance	ASHRAE	ANSI/ASHRAE 105-2007
	Method of Test for the Evaluation of Building Energy Analysis Computer Programs	ASHRAE	ANSI/ASHRAE 140-2007
	Method of Test for Determining the Design and Seasonal Efficiencies of Residential Thermal Distribution Systems	ASHRAE	ANSI/ASHRAE 152-2004
	Fuel Cell Power Systems Performance	ASME	PTC 50-2002
	International Energy Conservation Code (2006)	ICC	IECC
	Uniform Solar Energy Code (2000)	IAPMO	IAPMO
	Energy Management Guide for Selection and Use of Fixed Frequency Medium AC Squirrel-Cage Polyphase Induction Motors	NEMA	NEMA MG 10-2001 (R2007)
	Energy Management Guide for Selection and Use of Single-Phase Motors	NEMA	NEMA MG 11-1977 (R2007)
	HVAC Systems—Commissioning Manual, 1st ed.	SMACNA	SMACNA 1994
	Building Systems Analysis and Retrofit Manual, 1st ed.	SMACNA	SMACNA 1995
	Energy Systems Analysis and Management, 1st ed.	SMACNA	SMACNA 1997
	Energy Management Equipment (2007)	UL	UL 916
Exhaust Systems	Fan Systems: Supply/Return/Relief/Exhaust (2002)	AABC	National Standards, Ch 10
	Commercial Application, Systems, and Equipment, 1st ed.	ACCA	ACCA Manual CS
	Industrial Ventilation: A Manual of Recommended Practice, 26th ed. (2007)	ACGIH	ACGIH
	Fundamentals Governing the Design and Operation of Local Exhaust Ventilation Systems	AIHA	ANSI/AIHA Z9.2-2006
	Safety Code for Design, Construction, and Ventilation of Spray Finishing Operations	AIHA	ANSI/AIHA Z9.3-2007
	Laboratory Ventilation	AIHA	ANSI/AIHA Z9.5-2003
	Recirculation of Air from Industrial Process Exhaust Systems	AIHA	ANSI/AIHA Z9.7-2007
	Method of Testing Performance of Laboratory Fume Hoods	ASHRAE	ANSI/ASHRAE 110-1995
	Ventilation for Commercial Cooking Operations	ASHRAE	ANSI/ASHRAE 154-2003
	Performance Test Code on Compressors and Exhausters	ASME	PTC 10-1997 (RA03)
	Flue and Exhaust Gas Analyses	ASME	PTC 19.10-1981
	Mechanical Flue-Gas Exhausters	CSA	CAN B255-M81 (R2005)
	Exhaust Systems for Air Conveying of Vapors, Gases, Mists, and Noncombustible Particulate Solids	NFPA	ANSI/NFPA 91-04
	Draft Equipment (2006)	UL	UL 378

Selected Codes and Standards Published by Various Societies and Associations (*Continued*)

Subject	Title	Publisher	Reference
Expansion Valves	Thermostatic Refrigerant Expansion Valves	AHRI	ANSI/AHRI 750-2007
	Method of Testing Capacity of Thermostatic Refrigerant Expansion Valves	ASHRAE	ANSI/ASHRAE 17-2008
Fan-Coil Units	Industrial Ventilation: A Manual of Recommended Practice, 26th ed. (2007)	ACGIH	ACGIH
	Room Fan-Coils	AHRI	AHRI 440-2005
	Methods of Testing for Rating Fan-Coil Conditioners	ASHRAE	ANSI/ASHRAE 79-2002 (RA06)
	Heating and Cooling Equipment (2005)	UL/CSA	ANSI/UL 1995/C22.2 No. 236-95
Fans	Residential Duct Systems	ACCA	ANSI/ACCA Manual D
	Commercial Low Pressure, Low Velocity Duct System Design, 1st ed.	ACCA	ACCA Manual Q
	Industrial Ventilation: A Manual of Recommended Practice, 26th ed. (2007)	ACGIH	ACGIH
	Standards Handbook	AMCA	AMCA 99-03
	Drive Arrangements for Centrifugal Fans	AMCA	ANSIAMCA 99-2404-03
	Inlet Box Positions for Centrifugal Fans	AMCA	ANSI/AMCA 99-2405-03
	Designation for Rotation and Discharge of Centrifugal Fans	AMCA	ANSI/AMCA 99-2406-03
	Motor Positions for Belt or Chain Drive Centrifugal Fans	AMCA	ANSI/AMCA 99-2407-03
	Operating Limits for Centrifugal Fans	AMCA	AMCA 99-2408-69
	Drive Arrangements for Tubular Centrifugal Fans	AMCA	ANSI/AMCA 99-2410-03
	Impeller Diameters and Outlet Areas for Centrifugal Fans	AMCA	ANSI/AMCA 99-2412-03
	Impeller Diameters and Outlet Areas for Industrial Centrifugal Fans	AMCA	ANSI/AMCA 99-2413-03
	Impeller Diameters and Outlet Areas for Tubular Centrifugal Fans	AMCA	ANSI/AMCA 99-2414-03
	Dimensions for Axial Fans	AMCA	ANSI/AMCA 99-3001-03
	Drive Arrangements for Axial Fans	AMCA	ANSI/AMCA 99-3404-03
	Air Systems	AMCA	AMCA 200-95 (R2007)
	Fans and Systems	AMCA	AMCA 201-02 (R2007)
	Troubleshooting	AMCA	AMCA 202-98 (R2007)
	Field Performance Measurement of Fan Systems	AMCA	AMCA 203-90 (R2007)
	Balance Quality and Vibration Levels for Fans	AMCA	ANSI/AMCA 204-05
	Laboratory Methods of Testing Air Circulator Fans for Rating	AMCA	ANSI/AMCA 230-07
	Laboratory Method of Testing Positive Pressure Ventilators for Rating	AMCA	ANSI/AMCA 240-06
	Reverberant Room Method for Sound Testing of Fans	AMCA	AMCA 300-05
	Methods for Calculating Fan Sound Ratings from Laboratory Test Data	AMCA	AMCA 301-06
	Application of Sone Ratings for Non-Ducted Air Moving Devices	AMCA	AMCA 302-73 (R2008)
	Application of Sound Power Level Ratings for Fans	AMCA	AMCA 303-79 (R2008)
	Recommended Safety Practices for Users and Installers of Industrial and Commercial Fans	AMCA	AMCA 410-96
	Industrial Process/Power Generation Fans: Site Performance Test Standard	AMCA	AMCA 803-02
	Mechanical Balance of Fans and Blowers	AHRI	AHRI *Guideline* G-2002
	Acoustics—Measurement of Noise and Vibration of Small Air-Moving Devices—Part 1: Airborne Noise Emission	ASA	ANSI S12.11-2003/Part 1/ISO 10302:1996 (MOD)
	Part 2: Structure-Borne Vibration	ASA	ANSI S12.11-2003/Part 2
	Laboratory Methods of Testing Fans for Certified Aerodynamic Performance Rating	ASHRAE/ AMCA	ANSI/ASHRAE 51-2007 ANSI/AMCA 210-07
	Laboratory Method of Testing to Determine the Sound Power in a Duct	ASHRAE/ AMCA	ANSI/ASHRAE 68-1997 ANSI/AMCA 330-97
	Methods of Testing Fan Vibration—Blade Vibrations and Critical Speeds	ASHRAE	ANSI/ASHRAE 87.1-1992
	Laboratory Methods of Testing Fans Used to Exhaust Smoke in Smoke Management Systems	ASHRAE	ANSI/ASHRAE 149-2000 (RA09)
	Ventilation for Commercial Cooking Operations	ASHRAE	ANSI/ASHRAE 154-2003
	Fans	ASME	ANSI/ASME PTC 11-1984 (RA03)
	Fans and Ventilators	CSA	C22.2 No. 113-M1984 (R2004)
	Rating the Performance of Residential Mechanical Ventilating Equipment	CSA	CAN/CSA C260-M90 (R2007)
	Energy Performance of Ceiling Fans	CSA	CAN/CSA C814-96 (R2007)
	Electric Fans (1999)	UL	ANSI/UL 507
	Power Ventilators (2004)	UL	ANSI/UL 705
Fenestration	Test Method for Accelerated Weathering of Sealed Insulating Glass Units	ASTM	ASTM E773-01
	Practice for Calculation of Photometric Transmittance and Reflectance of Materials to Solar Radiation	ASTM	ASTM E971-88 (2003)
	Test Method for Solar Photometric Transmittance of Sheet Materials Using Sunlight	ASTM	ASTM E972-96 (2007)
	Test Method for Solar Transmittance (Terrestrial) of Sheet Materials Using Sunlight	ASTM	ASTM E1084-86 (2003)
	Practice for Determining the Load Resistance of Glass in Buildings	ASTM	ASTM E1300-07e1
	Practice for Installation of Exterior Windows, Doors and Skylights	ASTM	ASTM E2112-07
	Test Method for Insulating Glass Unit Performance	ASTM	ASTM E2188-02
	Test Method for Testing Resistance to Fogging Insulating Glass Units	ASTM	ASTM E2189-02
	Specification for Insulating Glass Unit Performance and Evaluation	ASTM	ASTM E2190-02
	Guide for Assessing the Durability of Absorptive Electrochemical Coatings within Sealed Insulating Glass Units	ASTM	ASTM E2354-04

Selected Codes and Standards Published by Various Societies and Associations (*Continued*)

Subject	Title	Publisher	Reference
	Tables for Reference Solar Spectral Irradiance: Direct Normal and Hemispherical on 37° Tilted Surface	ASTM	ASTM G173-03e1
	Windows	CSA	A440-08
	Energy Performance of Windows and Other Fenestration Systems	CSA	A440.3-04
	Window, Door, and Skylight Installation	CSA	A440.4-98
	Energy Performance Evaluation of Swinging Doors	CSA	A453-95 (R2000)
Filter-Driers	Flow-Capacity Rating of Suction-Line Filters and Suction-Line Filter-Driers	AHRI	AHRI 730-2005
	Method of Testing Liquid Line Filter-Drier Filtration Capability	ASHRAE	ANSI/ASHRAE 63.2-1996 (RA06)
	Method of Testing Flow Capacity of Suction Line Filters and Filter-Driers	ASHRAE	ANSI/ASHRAE 78-1985 (RA07)
Fireplaces	Factory-Built Fireplaces (1996)	UL	ANSI/UL 127
	Fireplace Stoves (2007)	UL	ANSI/UL 737
Fire Protection	Test Method for Surface Burning Characteristics of Building Materials	ASTM/NFPA	ASTM E84-08
	Test Methods for Fire Test of Building Construction and Materials	ASTM	ASTM E119-08
	Test Method for Room Fire Test of Wall and Ceiling Materials and Assemblies	ASTM	ASTM E2257-03
	Test Method for Determining Fire Resistance of Perimeter Fire Barriers Using Intermediate-Scale Multi-Story Test Apparatus	ASTM	ASTM E2307-04e1
	Guide for Laboratory Monitors	ASTM	ASTM E2335-04
	Test Method for Fire Resistance Grease Duct Enclosure Systems	ASTM	ASTM E2336-04
	Practice for Specimen Preparation and Mounting of Paper or Vinyl Wall Coverings to Assess Surface Burning Characteristics	ASTM	ASTM E2404-07a
	BOCA National Fire Prevention Code, 11th ed. (1999)	BOCA	BNFPC
	Uniform Fire Code	IFCI	UPC 1997
	International Fire Code (2006)	ICC	IFC
	International Mechanical Code (2006)	ICC	IMC
	International Urban-Wildland Interface Code (2006)	ICC	IUWIC
	Fire-Resistance Tests—Elements of Building Construction; Part 1: Gen. Requirements	ISO	ISO 834-1:1999
	Fire-Resistance Tests—Door and Shutter Assemblies	ISO	ISO 3008:2007
	Reaction to Fire Tests—Ignitability of Building Products Using a Radiant Heat Source	ISO	ISO 5657:1997
	Fire-Resistance Tests—Ventilating Ducts	ISO	ISO 6944:1985
	Fire Service Annunciator and Interface	NEMA	NEMA SB 30-2005
	Fire Protection Handbook (2008)	NFPA	NFPA
	National Fire Codes (issued annually)	NFPA	NFPA
	Fire Protection Guide to Hazardous Materials	NFPA	NFPA HAZ-01
	Uniform Fire Code	NFPA	NFPA 1-06
	Installation of Sprinkler Systems	NFPA	NFPA 13-2007
	Flammable and Combustible Liquids Code	NFPA	NFPA 30-08
	Fire Protection for Laboratories Using Chemicals	NFPA	NFPA 45-04
	National Fire Alarm Code	NFPA	NFPA 72-07
	Fire Doors and Fire Windows	NFPA	NFPA 80-07
	Health Care Facilities	NFPA	NFPA 99-05
	Life Safety Code	NFPA	NFPA 101-06
	Methods of Fire Tests of Door Assemblies	NFPA	NFPA 252-08
	Standard Fire Code (1999)	SBCCI	SFPC
	Fire, Smoke and Radiation Damper Installation Guide for HVAC Systems, 5th ed.	SMACNA	SMACNA 2002
	Fire Tests of Door Assemblies (2008)	UL	ANSI/UL 10B
	Heat Responsive Links for Fire-Protection Service (2003)	UL	ANSI/UL 33
	Fire Tests of Building Construction and Materials (2003)	UL	ANSI/UL 263
	Fire Dampers (2006)	UL	ANSI/UL 555
	Fire Tests of Through-Penetration Firestops (2003)	UL	ANSI/UL 1479
Smoke Management	Commissioning Smoke Management Systems	ASHRAE	ASHRAE *Guideline* 5-1994 (RA01)
	Laboratory Methods of Testing Fans Used to Exhaust Smoke in Smoke Management Systems	ASHRAE	ANSI/ASHRAE 149-2000 (RA09)
	Recommended Practice for Smoke-Control Systems	NFPA	NFPA 92A-06
	Smoke Management Systems in Malls, Atria, and Large Areas	NFPA	NFPA 92B-05
	Ceiling Dampers (2006)	UL	ANSI/UL 555C
	Smoke Dampers (1999)	UL	ANSI/UL 555S
Freezers	Energy Performance and Capacity of Household Refrigerators, Refrigerator-Freezers, and Freezers	CSA	C300-00 (R2005)
	Energy Performance Standard for Food Service Refrigerators and Freezers	CSA	C827-98 (R2003)
	Refrigeration Equipment	CSA	CAN/CSA-C22.2 No. 120-M91 (R2004)
Commercial	Dispensing Freezers	NSF	NSF/ANSI 6-2007
	Commercial Refrigerators and Freezers	NSF	NSF/ANSI 7-2007
	Commercial Refrigerators and Freezers (2006)	UL	ANSI/UL 471
	Ice Makers (1995)	UL	ANSI/UL 563

Selected Codes and Standards Published by Various Societies and Associations (*Continued*)

Subject	Title	Publisher	Reference
	Ice Cream Makers (2005)	UL	ANSI/UL 621
Household	Household Refrigerators, Refrigerator-Freezers and Freezers	AHAM	ANSI/AHAM HRF-1-2007
	Household Refrigerators and Freezers (1993)	UL/CSA	ANSI/UL 250/C22.2 No. 63-93 (R1999)
Fuels	Threshold Limit Values for Chemical Substances (updated annually)	ACGIH	ACGIH
	International Gas Fuel Code (2006)	AGA/NFPA	ANSI Z223.1/NPFA 54-2006
	Reporting of Fuel Properties when Testing Diesel Engines with Alternative Fuels Derived from Biological Materials	ASABE	ASAE EP552-1996
	Coal Pulverizers	ASME	PTC 4.2 1969 (RA03)
	Classification of Coals by Rank	ASTM	ASTM D388-05
	Specification for Fuel Oils	ASTM	ASTM D396-08
	Test Method for Determination of Homogeneity and Miscibility in Automotive Engine Oils	ASTM	ASTM D922-00a (2006)
	Specification for Diesel Fuel Oils	ASTM	ASTM D975-07b
	Specification for Gas Turbine Fuel Oils	ASTM	ASTM D2880-03
	Specification for Kerosene	ASTM	ASTM D3699-07
	Practice for Receipt, Storage and Handling of Fuels	ASTM	ASTM D4418-00 (2006)
	Test Method for Determination of Yield Stress and Apparent Viscosity of Used Engine Oils at Low Temperature	ASTM	ASTM D6896-03 (2007)
	Test Method for Total Sulfur in Naphthas, Distillates, Reformulated Gasolines, Diesels, Biodiesels, and Motor Fuels by Oxidative Combustion and Electrochemical Detection	ASTM	ASTM D6920-07
	Test Method for Measurement of Hindered Phenolic and Aromatic Amine Antioxidant Content in Non-Zinc Turbine Oils by Linear Sweep Voltammetry	ASTM	ASTM D6971-04
	Practice for Enumeration of Viable Bacteria and Fungi in Liquid Fuels—Filtration and Culture Procedures	ASTM	ASTM D6974-04a
	Test Method for Evaluation of Aeration Resistance of Engine Oils in Direct-Injected Turbocharged Automotive Diesel Engine	ASTM	ASTM D6984-07a
	Specification for Middle Distillate Fuel Oil-Military Marine Applications	ASTM	ASTM D6985-04a
	Test Method for Determination of Ignition Delay and Derived Cetane Number DCN of Diesel Fuel Oils by Combustion in a Constant Volume Chamber	ASTM	ASTM D6890-07b
	Test Method for Determination of Total Sulfur in Light Hydrocarbon, Motor Fuels, and Oils by Online Gas Chromatography with Flame Photometric Detection	ASTM	ASTM D7041-04
	Test Method for Sulfur in Gasoline and Diesel Fuel by Monochromatic Wavelength Dispersive X-Ray Fluorescence Spectrometry	ASTM	ASTM D7044-04a
	New Draft Standard Test Method for Flash Point by Modified Continuously Closed Cup Flash Point Tester	ASTM	ASTM D7094-04
	Test Method for Determining the Viscosity-Temperature Relationship of Used and Soot-Containing Engine Oils at Low Temperatures	ASTM	ASTM D7110-05a
	Test Method for Determination of Trace Elements in Middle Distillate Fuels by Inductively Coupled Plasma Atomic Emission Spectrometry (ICPAES)	ASTM	ASTM D7111-05
	Test Method for Determining Stability and Compatibility of Heavy Fuel Oils and Crude Oils by Heavy Fuel Oil Stability Analyzer (Optical Detection)	ASTM	ASTM D7112-05a
	Test Method for Determination of Intrinsic Stability of Asphaltene-Containing Residues, Heavy Fuel Oils, and Crude Oils	ASTM	ASTM D7157-05
	Test Method for Hydrogen Content of Middle Distillate Petroleum Products by Low-Resolution Pulsed Nuclear Magnetic Resonance Spectroscopy	ASTM	ASTM D7171-05
	Gas-Fired Central Furnaces	CSA	ANSI Z21.47-2006/CSA 2.3-2006
	Gas Unit Heaters and Gas-Fired Duct Furnaces	CSA	ANSI Z83.8-2006/CSA-2.6-2006
	Industrial and Commercial Gas-Fired Package Furnaces	CSA	CGA 3.2-1976 (R2003)
	Uniform Mechanical Code (2006)	IAPMO	Chapter 13
	Uniform Plumbing Code (2006)	IAPMO	Chapter 12
	International Fuel Gas Code (2006)	ICC	IFGC
	Standard Gas Code (1999)	SBCCI	SGC
	Commercial-Industrial Gas Heating Equipment (2006)	UL	UL 795
Furnaces	Commercial Application, Systems, and Equipment, 1st ed.	ACCA	ACCA Manual CS
	Residential Equipment Selection, 2nd ed.	ACCA	ANSI/ACCA Manual S
	Method of Testing for Annual Fuel Utilization Efficiency of Residential Central Furnaces and Boilers	ASHRAE	ANSI/ASHRAE 103-2007
	Prevention of Furnace Explosions/Implosions in Multiple Burner Boilers	NFPA	NFPA 8502-99
	Residential Gas Detectors (2000)	UL	ANSI/UL 1484
	Heating and Cooling Equipment (2005)	UL/CSA	ANSI/UL 1995/C22.2 No. 236-95
	Single and Multiple Station Carbon Monoxide Alarms (2008)	UL	ANSI/UL 2034
Gas	International Gas Fuel Code (2006)	AGA/NFPA	ANSI Z223.1/NFPA 54-2006
	Gas-Fired Central Furnaces	CSA	ANSI Z21.47-2006/CSA 2.3-2006
	Gas Unit Heaters and Gas-Fired Duct Furnaces	CSA	ANSI Z83.8-2006/CSA-2.6-2006
	Industrial and Commercial Gas-Fired Package Furnaces	CSA	CGA 3.2-1976 (R2003)

Selected Codes and Standards Published by Various Societies and Associations (*Continued*)

Subject	Title	Publisher	Reference
	International Fuel Gas Code (2006)	ICC	IFGC
	Standard Gas Code (1999)	SBCCI	SGC
	Commercial-Industrial Gas Heating Equipment (2006)	UL	UL 795
Oil	Specification for Fuel Oils	ASTM	ASTM D396-08
	Specification for Diesel Fuel Oils	ASTM	ASTM D975-07b
	Test Method for Smoke Density in Flue Gases from Burning Distillate Fuels	ASTM	ASTM D2156-94 (2003)
	Standard Test Method for Vapor Pressure of Liquefied Petroleum Gases (LPG) (Expansion Method)	ASTM	ASTM D6897-2003a
	Oil Burning Stoves and Water Heaters	CSA	B140.3-1962 (R2006)
	Oil-Fired Warm Air Furnaces	CSA	B140.4-04
	Installation of Oil-Burning Equipment	NFPA	NFPA 31-06
	Oil-Fired Central Furnaces (2006)	UL	UL 727
	Oil-Fired Floor Furnaces (2003)	UL	ANSI/UL 729
	Oil-Fired Wall Furnaces (2003)	UL	ANSI/UL 730
Solid Fuel	Installation Code for Solid-Fuel-Burning Appliances and Equipment	CSA	B365-01 (R2006)
	Solid-Fuel-Fired Central Heating Appliances	CSA	CAN/CSA-B366.1-M91 (R2007)
	Solid-Fuel and Combination-Fuel Central and Supplementary Furnaces (2006)	UL	ANSI/UL 391
Heaters	Gas-Fired High-Intensity Infrared Heaters	CSA	ANSI Z83.19-2001/CSA 2.35-2001 (R2005)
	Gas-Fired Low-Intensity Infrared Heaters	CSA	ANSI Z83.20-2008/CSA 2.34-2008
	Threshold Limit Values for Chemical Substances (updated annually)	ACGIH	ACGIH
	Industrial Ventilation: A Manual of Recommended Practice, 26th ed. (2007)	ACGIH	ACGIH
	Thermal Performance Testing of Solar Ambient Air Heaters	ASABE	ANSI/ASAE S423-1991
	Air Heaters	ASME	ASME PTC 4.3-1968 (RA91)
	Guide for Construction of Solid Fuel Burning Masonry Heaters	ASTM	ASTM E1602-03
	Non-Recirculating Direct Gas-Fired Industrial Air Heaters	CSA	ANSI Z83.4-2003/CSA 3.7-2003
	Electric Duct Heaters	CSA	C22.2 No. 155-M1986 (R2004)
	Portable Kerosene-Fired Heaters	CSA	CAN3-B140.9.3 M86 (R2006)
	Standards for Closed Feedwater Heaters, 7th ed. (2004)	HEI	HEI 2622
	Electric Heating Appliances (2005)	UL	ANSI/UL 499
	Electric Oil Heaters (2003)	UL	ANSI/UL 574
	Oil-Fired Air Heaters and Direct-Fired Heaters (1993)	UL	UL 733
	Electric Dry Bath Heaters (2004)	UL	ANSI/UL 875
	Oil-Burning Stoves (1993)	UL	ANSI/UL 896
Engine	Electric Engine Preheaters and Battery Warmers for Diesel Engines	SAE	SAE J1310-1993
	Selection and Application Guidelines for Diesel, Gasoline, and Propane Fired Liquid Cooled Engine Pre-Heaters	SAE	SAE J1350-1988
	Fuel Warmer—Diesel Engines	SAE	SAE J1422-1996
Nonresidential	Installation of Electric Infrared Brooding Equipment	ASABE	ASAE EP258.3-2004
	Gas-Fired Construction Heaters	CSA	ANSI Z83.7-00 (R2005)/CSA 2.14-00 (R2006)
	Recirculating Direct Gas-Fired Industrial Air Heaters	CSA	ANSI Z83.18-2004
	Portable Industrial Oil-Fired Heaters	CSA	B140.8-1967 (R2006)
	Fuel-Fired Heaters—Air Heating—for Construction and Industrial Machinery	SAE	SAE J1024-1989
	Commercial-Industrial Gas Heating Equipment (2006)	UL	UL 795
	Electric Heaters for Use in Hazardous (Classified) Locations (2006)	UL	ANSI/UL 823
Pool	Methods of Testing and Rating Pool Heaters	ASHRAE	ANSI/ASHRAE 146-2006
	Gas-Fired Pool Heaters	CSA	ANSI Z21.56-2006/CSA 4.7-2006
	Oil-Fired Service Water Heaters and Swimming Pool Heaters	CSA	B140.12-03
Room	Specification for Room Heaters, Pellet Fuel Burning Type	ASTM	ASTM E1509-04
	Gas-Fired Room Heaters, Vol. II, Unvented Room Heaters	CSA	ANSI Z21.11.2-2007
	Gas-Fired Unvented Catalytic Room Heaters for Use with Liquefied Petroleum (LP) Gases	CSA	ANSI Z21.76-1994 (R2006)
	Vented Gas-Fired Space Heating Appliances	CSA	ANSI Z21.86-2004/CSA 2.32-2004
	Vented Gas Fireplace Heaters	CSA	ANSI Z21.88-2005/CSA 2.33-2005
	Unvented Kerosene-Fired Room Heaters and Portable Heaters (1993)	UL	UL 647
	Movable and Wall- or Ceiling-Hung Electric Room Heaters (2000)	UL	UL 1278
	Fixed and Location-Dedicated Electric Room Heaters (1997)	UL	UL 2021
	Solid Fuel-Type Room Heaters (1996)	UL	ANSI/UL 1482
Transport	Heater, Airplane, Engine Exhaust Gas to Air Heat Exchanger Type	SAE	SAE ARP86-1996
	Installation, Heaters, Airplane, Internal Combustion Heater Exchange Type	SAE	SAE ARP266-2001
	Heater, Aircraft, Internal Combustion Heat Exchanger Type	SAE	SAE AS8040-1996
	Motor Vehicle Heater Test Procedure	SAE	SAE J638-1998
	Heater, Aircraft, Internal Combustion Heat Exchanger Type	SAE	SAE AS8040-1996
Unit	Gas Unit Heaters and Gas-Fired Duct Furnaces	CSA	ANSI Z83.8-2006/CSA-2.6-2006

Selected Codes and Standards Published by Various Societies and Associations (*Continued*)

Subject	Title	Publisher	Reference
	Oil-Fired Unit Heaters (1995)	UL	ANSI/UL 731
Heat Exchangers	Remote Mechanical-Draft Evaporative Refrigerant Condensers	AHRI	AHRI 490-2003
	Method of Testing Air-to-Air Heat/Energy Exchangers	ASHRAE	ANSI/ASHRAE 84-2008
	Boiler and Pressure Vessel Code—Section VIII, Division 1: Pressure Vessels	ASME	ASME BPVC-2007
	Single Phase Heat Exchangers	ASME	ASME PTC 12.5-2000 (RA05)
	Air Cooled Heat Exchangers	ASME	ASME PTC 30-1991 (RA05)
	Standard Methods of Test for Rating the Performance of Heat-Recovery Ventilators	CSA	C439-00 (R2005)
	Standards for Power Plant Heat Exchangers, 4th ed. (2004)	HEI	HEI 2623
	Standards of Tubular Exchanger Manufacturers Association, 9th ed. (2007)	TEMA	TEMA
	Refrigerant-Containing Components and Accessories, Nonelectrical (2001)	UL	ANSI/UL 207
Heating	Commercial Application, Systems, and Equipment, 1st ed.	ACCA	ACCA Manual CS
	Comfort, Air Quality, and Efficiency by Design	ACCA	ACCA Manual RS
	Residential Equipment Selection, 2nd ed.	ACCA	ANSI/ACCA Manual S
	Heating, Ventilating and Cooling Greenhouses	ASABE	ANSI/ASAE EP406.4-2003
	Heater Elements	CSA	C22.2 No. 72-M1984 (R2004)
	Determining the Required Capacity of Residential Space Heating and Cooling Appliances	CSA	CAN/CSA-F280-M90 (R2004)
	Heat Loss Calculation Guide (2001)	HYDI	HYDI H-22
	Residential Hydronic Heating Installation Design Guide	HYDI	IBR Guide
	Radiant Floor Heating (1995)	HYDI	HYDI 004
	Advanced Installation Guide (Commercial) for Hot Water Heating Systems (2001)	HYDI	HYDI 250
	Environmental Systems Technology, 2nd ed. (1999)	NEBB	NEBB
	Pulverized Fuel Systems	NFPA	NFPA 8503-97
	Aircraft Electrical Heating Systems	SAE	SAE AIR860-2000
	Heating Value of Fuels	SAE	SAE J1498-2005
	Performance Test for Air-Conditioned, Heated, and Ventilated Off-Road Self-Propelled Work Machines	SAE	SAE J1503-2004
	HVAC Systems—Applications, 1st ed.	SMACNA	SMACNA 1987
	Electric Baseboard Heating Equipment (1994)	UL	ANSI/UL 1042
	Electric Duct Heaters (2004)	UL	ANSI/UL 1996
	Heating and Cooling Equipment (2005)	UL/CSA	ANSI/UL 1995/C22.2 No. 236-95
Heat Pumps	Commercial Application, Systems, and Equipment, 1st ed.	ACCA	ACCA Manual CS
	Geothermal Heat Pump Training Certification Program	ACCA	ACCA Training Manual
	Heat Pumps Systems, Principles and Applications, 2nd ed.	ACCA	ACCA Manual H
	Residential Equipment Selection, 2nd ed.	ACCA	ANSI/ACCA Manual S
	Industrial Ventilation: A Manual of Recommended Practice, 26th ed. (2007)	ACGIH	ACGIH
	Water-Source Heat Pumps	AHRI	AHRI 320-98
	Ground Water-Source Heat Pumps	AHRI	AHRI 325-98
	Ground Source Closed-Loop Heat Pumps	AHRI	AHRI 330-98
	Commercial and Industrial Unitary Air-Conditioning and Heat Pump Equipment	AHRI	AHRI 340/360-2007
	Methods of Testing for Rating Electrically Driven Unitary Air-Conditioning and Heat Pump Equipment	ASHRAE	ANSI/ASHRAE 37-2005
	Methods of Testing for Rating Seasonal Efficiency of Unitary Air-Conditioners and Heat Pumps	ASHRAE	ANSI/ASHRAE 116-1995 (RA05)
	Performance Standard for Split-System and Single-Package Central Air Conditioners and Heat Pumps	CSA	CAN/CSA-C656-05
	Installation Requirements for Air-to-Air Heat Pumps	CSA	C273.5-1980 (R2002)
	Performance of Direct-Expansion (DX) Ground-Source Heat Pumps	CSA	C748-94 (R2005)
	Water-Source Heat Pumps—Testing and Rating for Performance, Part 1: Water-to-Air and Brine-to-Air Heat Pumps	CSA	CAN/CSA C13256-1-01
	Part 2: Water-to-Water and Brine-to-Water Heat Pumps	CSA	CAN/CSA C13256-2-01 (R2005)
	Heating and Cooling Equipment (2005)	UL/CSA	ANSI/UL 1995/C22.2 No. 236-95
Gas-Fired	Gas-Fired, Heat Activated Air Conditioning and Heat Pump Appliances	CSA	ANSI Z21.40.1-1996 (R2002)/CGA 2.91-M96
	Gas-Fired, Work Activated Air Conditioning and Heat Pump Appliances (Internal Combustion)	CSA	ANSI Z21.40.2-1996 (R2002)/CGA 2.92-M96
	Performance Testing and Rating of Gas-Fired Air Conditioning and Heat Pump Appliances	CSA	ANSI Z21.40.4-1996 (R2002)/CGA 2.94-M96
Heat Recovery	Gas Turbine Heat Recovery Steam Generators	ASME	ANSI/ASME PTC 4.4-1981 (RA03)
	Water Heaters, Hot Water Supply Boilers, and Heat Recovery Equipment	NSF	NSF/ANSI 5-2007
Humidifiers	Commercial Application, Systems, and Equipment, 1st ed.	ACCA	ACCA Manual CS
	Comfort, Air Quality, and Efficiency by Design	ACCA	ACCA Manual RS
	Bioaerosols: Assessment and Control (1999)	ACGIH	ACGIH
	Humidifiers	AHAM	ANSI/AHAM HU-1-2006

Selected Codes and Standards Published by Various Societies and Associations (*Continued*)

Subject	Title	Publisher	Reference
	Central System Humidifiers for Residential Applications	AHRI	AHRI 610-2004
	Self-Contained Humidifiers for Residential Applications	AHRI	AHRI 620-2004
	Commercial and Industrial Humidifiers	AHRI	ANSI/AHRI 640-2005
	Humidifiers (2001)	UL/CSA	ANSI/UL 998/C22.2 No. 104-93
Ice Makers	Performance Rating of Automatic Commercial Ice Makers	AHRI	AHRI 810-2007
	Ice Storage Bins	AHRI	AHRI 820-2000
	Methods of Testing Automatic Ice Makers	ASHRAE	ANSI/ASHRAE 29-2009
	Refrigeration Equipment	CSA	CAN/CSA-C22.2 No. 120-M91 (R2004)
	Performance of Automatic Ice-Makers and Ice Storage Bins	CSA	C742-98 (R2003)
	Automatic Ice Making Equipment	NSF	NSF/ANSI 12-2007
	Ice Makers (1995)	UL	ANSI/UL 563
Incinerators	Incinerators and Waste and Linen Handling Systems and Equipment	NFPA	NFPA 82-04
	Residential Incinerators (2006)	UL	UL 791
Indoor Air Quality	Good HVAC Practices for Residential and Commercial Buildings (2003)	ACCA	ACCA
	Comfort, Air Quality, and Efficiency by Design (Residential) (1997)	ACCA	ACCA Manual RS
	Bioaerosols: Assessment and Control (1999)	ACGIH	ACGIH
	Ventilation for Acceptable Indoor Air Quality	ASHRAE	ANSI/ASHRAE 62.1-2007
	Ventilation and Acceptable Indoor Air Quality in Low-Rise Residential Buildings	ASHRAE	ANSI/ASHRAE 62.2-2007
	Test Method for Determination of Volatile Organic Chemicals in Atmospheres (Canister Sampling Methodology)	ASTM	ASTM D5466-01 (2007)
	Guide for Using Probability Sampling Methods in Studies of Indoor Air Quality in Buildings	ASTM	ASTM D5791-95 (2006)
	Guide for Using Indoor Carbon Dioxide Concentrations to Evaluate Indoor Air Quality and Ventilation	ASTM	ASTM D6245-07
	Guide for Placement and Use of Diffusion Controlled Passive Monitors for Gaseous Pollutants in Indoor Air	ASTM	ASTM D6306-98 (2003)
	Test Method for Determination of Metals and Metalloids Airborne Particulate Matter by Inductively Coupled Plasma Atomic Emissions Spectrometry (ICP-AES)	ASTM	ASTM D7035-04
	Test Method for Metal Removal Fluid Aerosol in Workplace Atmospheres	ASTM	ASTM D7049-04
	Practice for Emission Cells for the Determination of Volatile Organic Emissions from Materials/Products	ASTM	ASTM D7143-05
	Practice for Collection of Surface Dust by Micro-Vacuum Sampling for Subsequent Metals Determination	ASTM	ASTM D7144-05a
	Test Method for Determination of Beryllium in the Workplace Using Field-Based Extraction and Fluorescence Detection	ASTM	ASTM D7202-06
	Practice for Referencing Suprathreshold Odor Intensity	ASTM	ASTM E544-99 (2004)
	Guide for Specifying and Evaluating Performance of a Single Family Attached and Detached Dwelling—Indoor Air Quality	ASTM	ASTM E2267-04
	Classification for Serviceability of an Office Facility for Thermal Environment and Indoor Air Conditions	ASTM	ASTM E2320-04
	Practice for Continuous Sizing and Counting of Airborne Particles in Dust-Controlled Areas and Clean Rooms Using Instruments Capable of Detecting Single Sub-Micrometre and Larger Particles	ASTM	ASTM F50-07
	Ambient Air—Determination of Mass Concentration of Nitrogen Dioxide—Modified Griess-Saltzman Method	ISO	ISO 6768:1998
	Air Quality—Exchange of Data	ISO	ISO 7168:1999
	Environmental Tobacco Smoke—Estimation of Its Contribution to Respirable Suspended Particles—Determination of Particulate Matter by Ultraviolet Absorptance and by Fluorescence	ISO	ISO 15593:2001
	Indoor Air—Part 3: Determination of Formaldehyde and Other Carbonyl Compounds—Active Sampling Method	ISO	ISO 16000-3:2001
	Workplace Air Quality—Sampling and Analysis of Volatile Organic Compounds by Solvent Desorption/Gas Chromatography—Part 1: Pumped Sampling Method	ISO	ISO 16200-1:2001
	Part 2: Diffusive Sampling Method	ISO	ISO 16200-2:2000
	Workplace Air Quality—Determination of Total Organic Isocyanate Groups in Air Using 1-(2-Methoxyphenyl) Piperazine and Liquid Chromatography	ISO	ISO 16702:2007
	Installation of Household Carbon Monoxide (CO) Warning Equipment	NFPA	NFPA 720-2005
	Indoor Air Quality—A Systems Approach, 3rd ed.	SMACNA	SMACNA 1998
	IAQ Guidelines for Occupied Buildings Under Construction, 1st ed.	SMACNA	SMACNA 1995
	Single and Multiple Station Carbon Monoxide Alarms (1996)	UL	ANSI/UL 2034
Aircraft	Guide for Selecting Instruments and Methods for Measuring Air Quality in Aircraft Cabins	ASTM	ASTM D6399-04
	Guide for Deriving Acceptable Levels of Airborne Chemical Contaminants in Aircraft Cabins Based on Health and Comfort Considerations	ASTM	ASTM D7034-05
Insulation	Guidelines for Use of Thermal Insulation in Agricultural Buildings	ASABE	ANSI/ASAE S401.2-2003
	Terminology Relating to Thermal Insulating Materials	ASTM	ASTM C168-05a

Selected Codes and Standards Published by Various Societies and Associations (*Continued*)

Subject	Title	Publisher	Reference
	Test Method for Steady-State Heat Flux Measurements and Thermal Transmission Properties by Means of the Guarded-Hot-Plate Apparatus	ASTM	ASTM C177-04
	Test Method for Steady-State Heat Transfer Properties of Horizontal Pipe Insulations	ASTM	ASTM C335-05ae1
	Practice for Prefabrication and Field Fabrication of Thermal Insulating Fitting Covers for NPS Piping, Vessel Lagging, and Dished Head Segments	ASTM	ASTM C450-02
	Test Method for Steady-State and Thermal Transmission Properties by Means of the Heat Flow Meter Apparatus	ASTM	ASTM C518-04
	Specification for Preformed Flexible Elastometric Cellular Thermal Insulation in Sheet and Tubular Form	ASTM	ASTM C534-07a
	Specification for Cellular Glass Thermal Insulation	ASTM	ASTM C552-07
	Specification for Rigid, Cellular Polystyrene Thermal Insulation	ASTM	ASTM C578-07
	Practice for Inner and Outer Diameters of Rigid Thermal Insulation for Nominal Sizes of Pipe and Tubing (NPS System)	ASTM	ASTM C585-90 (2004)
	Specification for Unfaced Preformed Rigid Cellular Polyisocyanurate Thermal Insulation	ASTM	ASTM C591-07
	Practice for Determination of Heat Gain or Loss and the Surface Temperature of Insulated Pipe and Equipment Systems by the Use of a Computer Program	ASTM	ASTM C680-04e4
	Specification for Adhesives for Duct Thermal Insulation	ASTM	ASTM C916-85 (2007)
	Classification of Potential Health and Safety Concerns Associated with Thermal Insulation Materials and Accessories	ASTM	ASTM C930-05
	Practice for Thermographic Inspection of Insulation Installations in Envelope Cavities of Frame Buildings	ASTM	ASTM C1060-90 (2003)
	Specification for Fibrous Glass Duct Lining Insulation (Thermal and Sound Absorbing Material)	ASTM	ASTM C1071-05
	Specification for Faced or Unfaced Rigid Cellular Phenolic Thermal Insulation	ASTM	ASTM C1126-04
	Practice for Installation and Use of Radiant Barrier Systems (RBS) in Building Construction	ASTM	ASTM C1158-05
	Test Method for Steady-State and Thermal Performance of Building Assemblies by Means of a Hot Box Apparatus	ASTM	ASTM C1363-05
	Specification for Perpendicularly Oriented Mineral Fiber Roll and Sheet Thermal Insulation for Pipes and Tanks	ASTM	ASTM C1393-00a (2006)
	Guide for Measuring and Estimating Quantities of Insulated Piping and Components	ASTM	ASTM C1409-98 (2003)
	Specification for Cellular Melamine Thermal and Sound Absorbing Insulation	ASTM	ASTM C1410-05a
	Guide for Selecting Jacketing Materials for Thermal Insulation	ASTM	ASTM C1423-98 (2003)
	Specification for Preformed Flexible Cellular Polyolefin Thermal Insulation in Sheet and Tubular Form	ASTM	ASTM C1427-07
	Specification for Polyimide Flexible Cellular Thermal and Sound Absorbing Insulation	ASTM	ASTM C1482-04
	Specification for Cellulosic Fiber Stabilized Thermal Insulation	ASTM	ASTM C1497-04
	Test Method for Characterizing the Effect of Exposure to Environmental Cycling on Thermal Performance of Insulation Products	ASTM	ASTM C1512-07
	Specification for Flexible Polymeric Foam Sheet Insulation Used as a Thermal and Sound Absorbing Liner for Duct Systems	ASTM	ASTM C1534-07
	Standard Guide for Development of Standard Data Records for Computerization of Thermal Transmission Test Data for Thermal Insulation	ASTM	ASTM C1558-03 (2007)
	Guide for Determining Blown Density of Pneumatically Applied Loose Fill Mineral Fiber Thermal Insulation	ASTM	ASTM C1574-04
	Test Method for Determining the Moisture Content of Inorganic Insulation Materials by Weight	ASTM	ASTM C1616-07e1
	Specification for Cellular Polypropylene Thermal Insulation	ASTM	ASTM C1631-05
	Classification for Rating Sound Insulation	ASTM	ASTM E413-04
	Test Method for Determining the Drainage Efficiency of Exterior Insulation and Finish Systems (EIFS) Clad Wall Assemblies	ASTM	ASTM E2273-03
	Practice for Use of Test Methods E96 for Determining the Water Vapor Transmission (WVT) of Exterior Insulation and Finish Systems	ASTM	ASTM E2321-03
	Thermal Insulation—Vocabulary	ISO	ISO 9229:2007
	National Commercial and Industrial Insulation Standards, 6th ed.	MICA	MICA
	Accepted Industry Practices for Sheet Metal Lagging, 1st ed.	SMACNA	SMACNA 2002
Louvers	Laboratory Methods of Testing Dampers for Rating	AMCA	AMCA 500-D-07
	Laboratory Methods of Testing Louvers for Rating	AMCA	AMCA 500-L-07
Lubricants	Methods of Testing the Floc Point of Refrigeration Grade Oils	ASHRAE	ANSI/ASHRAE 86-1994 (RA06)
	Test Method for Pour Point of Petroleum Products	ASTM	ASTM D97-07
	Classification of Industrial Fluid Lubricants by Viscosity System	ASTM	ASTM D2422-97 (2007)
	Test Method for Relative Molecular Weight (Relative Molecular Mass) of Hydrocarbons by Thermoelectric Measurement of Vapor Pressure	ASTM	ASTM D2503-92 (2007)
	Test Method for Determination of Moderately High Temperature Piston Deposits by Thermo-Oxidation Engine Oil Simulation Test	ASTM	ASTM D7097-06a
	Petroleum Products—Corrosiveness to Copper—Copper Strip Test	ISO	ISO 2160:1998

Selected Codes and Standards Published by Various Societies and Associations (*Continued*)

Subject	Title	Publisher	Reference
Measurement	Industrial Ventilation: A Manual of Recommended Practice, 26th ed. (2007)	ACGIH	ACGIH
	Engineering Analysis of Experimental Data	ASHRAE	ASHRAE *Guideline* 2-2005
	Standard Method for Measurement of Proportion of Lubricant in Liquid Refrigerant	ASHRAE	ANSI/ASHRAE 41.4-1996 (RA06)
	Standard Method for Measurement of Moist Air Properties	ASHRAE	ANSI/ASHRAE 41.6-1994 (RA06)
	Method of Measuring Solar-Optical Properties of Materials	ASHRAE	ANSI/ASHRAE 74-1988
	Methods of Measuring, Expressing, and Comparing Building Energy Performance	ASHRAE	ANSI/ASHRAE 105-2007
	Method for Establishing Installation Effects on Flowmeters	ASME	ASME MFC-10M-2000
	Test Uncertainty	ASME	ASME PTC 19.1-2005
	Measurement of Industrial Sound	ASME	ANSI/ASME PTC 36-2004
	Test Methods for Water Vapor Transmission of Materials	ASTM	ASTM E96/E96M-05
	Specification for Temperature-Electromotive Force (EMF) Tables for Standardized Thermocouples	ASTM	ASTM E230-03
	Practice for Continuous Sizing and Counting of Airborne Particles in Dust-Controlled Areas and Clean Rooms Using Instruments Capable of Detecting Single Sub-Micrometre and Larger Particles	ASTM	ASTM F50-07
	Use of the International System of Units (SI): The Modern Metric System	IEEE/ASTM	IEEE/ASTM-SI10-2002
	Ergonomics of the Thermal Environment—Instruments for Measuring Physical Quantities	ISO	ISO 7726:1998
	Ergonomics of the Thermal Environment—Determination of Metabolic Rate	ISO	ISO 8996:2004
	Ergonomics of the Thermal Environment—Estimation of the Thermal Insulation and Water Vapour Resistance of a Clothing Ensemble	ISO	ISO 9920:2007
Fluid Flow	Standard Methods of Measurement of Flow of Liquids in Pipes Using Orifice Flowmeters	ASHRAE	ANSI/ASHRAE 41.8-1989
	Calorimeter Test Methods for Mass Flow Measurements of Volatile Refrigerants	ASHRAE	ANSI/ASHRAE 41.9-2000 (RA06)
	Flow Measurement	ASME	ASME PTC 19.5-2004
	Glossary of Terms Used in the Measurement of Fluid Flow in Pipes	ASME	ASME MFC-1M-2003
	Measurement Uncertainty for Fluid Flow in Closed Conduits	ASME	ANSI/ASME MFC-2M-1983 (RA01)
	Measurement of Fluid Flow in Pipes Using Orifice, Nozzle, and Venturi	ASME	ASME MFC-3M-2004
	Measurement of Liquid Flow in Closed Conduits Using Transit-Time Ultrasonic Flowmeters	ASME	ASME MFC-5M-1985 (RA01)
	Measurement of Fluid Flow in Pipes Using Vortex Flowmeters	ASME	ASME MFC-6M-1998 (RA05)
	Fluid Flow in Closed Conduits: Connections for Pressure Signal Transmissions Between Primary and Secondary Devices	ASME	ASME MFC-8M-2001
	Measurement of Liquid Flow in Closed Conduits by Weighing Method	ASME	ASME MFC-9M-1988 (RA01)
	Measurement of Fluid Flow by Means of Coriolis Mass Flowmeters	ASME	ASME MFC-11M-2006
	Measurement of Fluid Flow Using Small Bore Precision Orifice Meters	ASME	ASME MFC-14M-2003
	Measurement of Fluid Flow in Closed Conduits by Means of Electromagnetic Flowmeters	ASME	ASME MFC-16M-1995 (R01)
	Measurement of Fluid Flow Using Variable Area Meters	ASME	ASME MFC-18M-2001
	Test Method for Determining the Moisture Content of Inorganic Insulation Materials by Weight	ASTM	ASTM C1616-07e1
	Test Method for Indicating Wear Characteristics of Petroleum Hydraulic Fluids in a High Pressure Constant Volume Vane Pump	ASTM	ASTM D6973-05
	Test Method for Dynamic Viscosity and Density of Liquids by Stabinger Viscometer and the Calculation of Kinematic Viscosity	ASTM	ASTM D7042-04
	Test Method for Indicating Wear Characteristics of Petroleum and Non-Petroleum Hydraulic Fluids in a Constant Volume Vane Pump	ASTM	ASTM D7043-04a
	Practice for Calculating Viscosity of a Blend of Petroleum Products	ASTM	ASTM D7152-05e1
	Test Method for Same-Different Test	ASTM	ASTM E2139-05
	Practice for Field Use of Pyranometers, Pyrheliometers, and UV Radiometers	ASTM	ASTM G183-05
Gas Flow	Standard Methods for Laboratory Airflow Measurement	ASHRAE	ANSI/ASHRAE 41.2-1987 (RA92)
	Method of Test for Measurement of Flow of Gas	ASHRAE	ANSI/ASHRAE 41.7-1984 (RA06)
	Measurement of Gas Flow by Turbine Meters	ASME	ANSI/ASME MFC-4M-1986 (RA03)
	Measurement of Gas Flow by Means of Critical Flow Venturi Nozzles	ASME	ANSI/ASME MFC-7M-1987 (RA01)
Pressure	Standard Method for Pressure Measurement	ASHRAE	ANSI/ASHRAE 41.3-1989
	Pressure Gauges and Gauge Attachments	ASME	ASME B40.100-2005
	Pressure Measurement	ASME	ANSI/ASME PTC 19.2-1987 (RA04)
Temperature	Standard Method for Temperature Measurement	ASHRAE	ANSI/ASHRAE 41.1-1986 (RA06)
	Thermometers, Direct Reading and Remote Reading	ASME	ASME B40.200-2001
	Temperature Measurement	ASME	ASME PTC 19.3-1974 (RA04)
	Total Temperature Measuring Instruments (Turbine Powered Subsonic Aircraft)	SAE	SAE AS793-2001
Thermal	Method of Testing Thermal Energy Meters for Liquid Streams in HVAC Systems	ASHRAE	ANSI/ASHRAE 125-1992 (RA06)
	Test Method for Steady-State Heat Flux Measurements and Thermal Transmission Properties by Means of the Guarded-Hot-Plate Apparatus	ASTM	ASTM C177-04
	Test Method for Steady-State Heat Flux Measurements and Thermal Transmission Properties by Means of the Heat Flow Meter Apparatus	ASTM	ASTM C518-04

Selected Codes and Standards Published by Various Societies and Associations (*Continued*)

Subject	Title	Publisher	Reference
	Practice for In-Situ Measurement of Heat Flux and Temperature on Building Envelope Components	ASTM	ASTM C1046-95 (2007)
	Practice for Determining Thermal Resistance of Building Envelope Components from In-Situ Data	ASTM	ASTM C1155-95 (2007)
	Test Method for Thermal Performance of Building Materials and Envelope Assemblies by Means of a Hot Box Apparatus	ASTM	ASTM C1363-05
Mobile Homes and Recreational Vehicles	Residential Load Calculation, 8th ed.	ACCA	ANSI/ACCA Manual J
	Recreational Vehicle Cooking Gas Appliances	CSA	ANSI Z21.57-2007
	Oil-Fired Warm Air Heating Appliances for Mobile Housing and Recreational Vehicles	CSA	B140.10-06
	Mobile Homes	CSA	CAN/CSA-Z240 MH Series-92 (R2005)
	Recreational Vehicles	CSA	CAN/CSA-Z240 RV Series-08
	Gas Supply Connectors for Manufactured Homes	IAPMO	IAPMO TS 9-2003
	Fuel Supply: Manufactured/Mobile Home Parks & Recreational Vehicle Parks	IAPMO	Chapter 13, Part II
	Manufactured Housing Construction and Safety Standards	ICC/ANSI	ICC/ANSI 2.0-1998
	Manufactured Housing	NFPA	NFPA 501-05
	Recreational Vehicles	NFPA	NFPA 1192-08
	Plumbing System Components for Recreational Vehicles	NSF	NSF/ANSI 24-2006
	Low Voltage Lighting Fixtures for Use in Recreational Vehicles (2005)	UL	ANSI/UL 234
	Liquid Fuel-Burning Heating Appliances for Manufactured Homes and Recreational Vehicles (1995)	UL	ANSI/UL 307A
	Gas-Burning Heating Appliances for Manufactured Homes and Recreational Vehicles (2006)	UL	UL 307B
	Gas-Fired Cooking Appliances for Recreational Vehicles (2006)	UL	UL 1075
Motors and Generators	Installation and Maintenance of Farm Standby Electric Power	ASABE	ANSI/ASAE EP364.3-2006
	Nuclear Power Plant Air-Cleaning Units and Components	ASME	ASME N509-2002
	Testing of Nuclear Air Treatment Systems	ASME	ASME N510-2007
	Fired Steam Generators	ASME	ASME PTC 4-1998
	Gas Turbine Heat Recovery Steam Generators	ASME	ASME PTC 4.4-1981 (RA03)
	Test Methods for Film-Insulated Magnet Wire	ASTM	ASTM D1676-03
	Test Method for Evaluation of Engine Oils in a High Speed, Single-Cylinder Diesel Engine—Caterpillar 1R Test Procedure	ASTM	ASTM D6923-05
	Test Method for Evaluation of Diesel Engine Oils in the T-11 Exhaust Gas Recirculation Diesel Engine	ASTM	ASTM D7156-07a
	Energy Efficiency Test Methods for Three-Phase Induction Motors	CSA	C390-98 (R2005)
	Motors and Generators	CSA	C22.2 No. 100-04
	Emergency Electrical Power Supply for Buildings	CSA	CSA C282-05
	Energy Efficiency Test Methods for Single- and Three-Phase Small Motors	CSA	CAN/CSA C747-94 (R2005)
	Standard Test Procedure for Polyphase Induction Motors and Generators	IEEE	IEEE 112-1996
	Motors and Generators	NEMA	NEMA MG 1-2006
	Energy Management Guide for Selection and Use of Fixed Frequency Medium AC Squirrel-Cage Polyphase Industrial Motors	NEMA	NEMA MG 10-2001 (R2007)
	Energy Management Guide for Selection and Use of Single-Phase Motors	NEMA	NEMA MG 11-1977 (R2007)
	Magnet Wire	NEMA	NEMA MW 1000-2003
	Motion/Position Control Motors, Controls, and Feedback Devices	NEMA	NEMA ICS 16-2001
	Electric Motors (1994)	UL	UL 1004
	Electric Motors and Generators for Use in Division 1 Hazardous (Classified) Locations (2003)	UL	ANSI/UL 674
	Overheating Protection for Motors (1997)	UL	ANSI/UL 2111
Pipe, Tubing, and Fittings	Scheme for the Identification of Piping Systems	ASME	ASME A13.1-2007
	Pipe Threads, General Purpose (Inch)	ASME	ANSI/ASME B1.20.1-1983 (RA01)
	Wrought Copper and Copper Alloy Braze-Joint Pressure Fittings	ASME	ASME B16.50-2001
	Power Piping	ASME	ASME B31.1-2007
	Fuel Gas Piping	ASME	ASME B31.2-1968
	Process Piping	ASME	ASME B31.3-2006
	Refrigeration Piping and Heat Transfer Components	ASME	ASME B31.5-2006
	Building Services Piping	ASME	ASME B31.9-2004
	Practice for Obtaining Hydrostatic or Pressure Design Basis for "Fiberglass" (Glass-Fiber-Reinforced Thermosetting-Resin) Pipe and Fittings	ASTM	ASTM D2992-06
	Specification for Welding of Austenitic Stainless Steel Tube and Piping Systems in Sanitary Applications	AWS	AWS D18.1:1999
	Standards of the Expansion Joint Manufacturers Association, 8th ed. (2003)	EJMA	EJMA
	Pipe Hangers and Supports—Materials, Design and Manufacture	MSS	MSS SP-58-2002
	Pipe Hangers and Supports—Selection and Application	MSS	ANSI/MSS SP-69-2003
	General Welding Guidelines (2002)	NCPWB	NCPWB

Selected Codes and Standards Published by Various Societies and Associations (*Continued*)

Subject	Title	Publisher	Reference
	International Fuel Gas Code	AGA/NFPA	ANSI Z223.1/NFPA 54-2006
	Refrigeration Tube Fittings—General Specifications	SAE	SAE J513-1999
	Seismic Restraint Manual—Guidelines for Mechanical Systems, 2nd ed.	SMACNA	ANSI/SMACNA 001-2000 (1998)
	Tube Fittings for Flammable and Combustible Fluids, Refrigeration Service, and Marine Use (1997)	UL	ANSI/UL 109
Plastic	Specification for Acrylonitrile-Butadiene-Styrene (ABS) Plastic Pipe, Schedules 40 and 80	ASTM	ASTM D1527-99 (2005)
	Specification for Poly (Vinyl Chloride) (PVC) Plastic Pipe, Schedules 40, 80, and 120	ASTM	ASTM D1785-06
	Specification for Polyethylene (PE) Plastic Pipe, Schedule 40	ASTM	ASTM D2104-03
	Test Method for Obtaining Hydrostatic or Pressure Design Basis for Thermoplastic Pipe Products	ASTM	ASTM D2837-04e1
	Specification for Polybutylene (PB) Plastic Hot- and Cold-Water Distribution Systems	ASTM	ASTM D3309-96a (2002)
	Specification for Perfluoroalkoxy (PFA)-Fluoropolymer Tubing	ASTM	ASTM D6867-03
	Specification for Polyethylene Stay in Place Form System for End Walls for Drainage Pipe	ASTM	ASTM D7082-04
	Specification for Chlorinated Poly (Vinyl Chloride) (CPVC) Plastic Pipe, Schedules 40 and 80	ASTM	ASTM F441/F441M-02
	Specification for Crosslinked Polyethylene/Aluminum/Crosslinked Polyethylene Tubing OD Controlled SDR9	ASTM	ASTM F2262-05
	Test Method for Evaluating the Oxidative Resistance of Polyethylene (PE) Pipe to Chlorinated Water	ASTM	ASTM F2263-07e1
	Specification for 12 to 60 in. Annular Corrugated Profile-Wall Polyethylene (PE) Pipe and Fittings for Gravity-Flow Storm Sewer and Subsurface Drainage Applications	ASTM	ASTM F2306/F2306M-07
	Specification for Series 10 Poly (Vinyl Chloride) (PVC) Closed Profile Gravity Pipe and Fittings Based on Controlled Inside Diameter	ASTM	ASTM F2307-03
	Standard Test Method for Evaluating the Oxidative Resistance of Multilayer Polyolefin Tubing to Hot Chlorinated Water	ASTM	ASTM F2330-04
	Test Method for Determining Chemical Compatibility of Thread Sealants with Thermoplastic Threaded Pipe and Fittings Materials	ASTM	ASTM F2331-04e1
	Test Method for Determining Thermoplastic Pipe Wall Stiffness	ASTM	ASTM F2433-05
	Specification for Steel Reinforced Polyethylene (PE) Corrugated Pipe	ASTM	ASTM F2435-07
	Electrical Polyvinyl Chloride (PVC) Tubing and Conduit	NEMA	NEMA TC 2-2003
	PVC Plastic Utilities Duct for Underground Installation	NEMA	NEMA TC 6 and 8-2003
	Smooth Wall Coilable Polyethylene Electrical Plastic Duct	NEMA	NEMA TC 7-2005
	Fittings for PVC Plastic Utilities Duct for Underground Installation	NEMA	NEMA TC 9-2004
	Electrical Nonmetallic Tubing (ENT)	NEMA	NEMA TC 13-2005
	Plastics Piping System Components and Related Materials	NSF	NSF/ANSI 14-2007
	Rubber Gasketed Fittings for Fire-Protection Service (2004)	UL	ANSI/UL 213
Metal	Welded and Seamless Wrought Steel Pipe	ASME	ASME B36.10M-2004
	Stainless Steel Pipe	ASME	ASME B36.19M-2004
	Specification for Pipe, Steel, Black and Hot-Dipped, Zinc-Coated, Welded and Seamless	ASTM	ASTM A53/53M-07
	Specification for Seamless Carbon Steel Pipe for High-Temperature Service	ASTM	ASTM A106/A106M-06a
	Specification for Pipe, Steel, Electric-Fusion Arc-Welded Sizes NPS 16 and Over	ASTM	ASTM A1034-05b
	Specification for Steel Line Pipe, Black, Furnace-Butt-Welded	ASTM	ASTM A1037/A1037M-05
	Specification for Composite Corrugated Steel Pipe for Sewers and Drains	ASTM	ASTM A1042/A1042M-04
	Specification for Seamless Copper Pipe, Standard Sizes	ASTM	ASTM B42-02e1
	Specification for Seamless Copper Tube	ASTM	ASTM B75-02
	Specification for Seamless Copper Water Tube	ASTM	ASTM B88-03
	Specification for Seamless Copper Tube for Air Conditioning and Refrigeration Field Service	ASTM	ASTM B280-03
	Specification for Hand-Drawn Copper Capillary Tube for Restrictor Applications	ASTM	ASTM B360-01
	Specification for Welded Copper Tube for Air Conditioning and Refrigeration Service	ASTM	ASTM B640-07
	Specification for Copper-Beryllium Seamless Tube UNS Nos. C17500 and C17510	ASTM	ASTM B937-04
	Test Method for Rapid Determination of Corrosiveness to Copper from Petroleum Products Using a Disposable Copper Foil Strip	ASTM	ASTM D7095-04
	Thickness Design of Ductile-Iron Pipe	AWWA	ANSI/AWWA C150/A21.50-02
	Fittings, Cast Metal Boxes, and Conduit Bodies for Conduit and Cable Assemblies	NEMA	NEMA FB 1-2007
	Polyvinyl-Chloride (PVC) Externally Coated Galvanized Rigid Steel Conduit and Intermediate Metal Conduit	NEMA	NEMA RN 1-2005
Plumbing	Backwater Valves	ASME	ASME A112.14.1-2003
	Plumbing Supply Fittings	ASME	ASME A112.18.1-2005
	Plumbing Waste Fittings	ASME	ASME A112.18.2-2005
	Performance Requirements for Backflow Protection Devices and Systems in Plumbing Fixture Fittings	ASME	ASME A112.18.3-2002
	Uniform Plumbing Code (2006) (with IAPMO Installation Standards)	IAPMO	IAPMO
	International Plumbing Code (2006)	ICC	IPC

Selected Codes and Standards Published by Various Societies and Associations (*Continued*)

Subject	Title	Publisher	Reference
	International Private Sewage Disposal Code (2006)	ICC	IPSDC
	2006 National Standard Plumbing Code (NSPC)	PHCC	NSPC 2003
	2006 National Standard Plumbing Code—Illustrated	PHCC	PHCC 2003
	Standard Plumbing Code (1997)	SBCCI	SPC
Pumps	Centrifugal Pumps	ASME	ASME PTC 8.2-1990
	Specification for Horizontal End Suction Centrifugal Pumps for Chemical Process	ASME	ASME B73.1-2001
	Specification for Vertical-in-Line Centrifugal Pumps for Chemical Process	ASME	ASME B73.2-2003
	Specification for Sealless Horizontal End Suction Metallic Centrifugal Pumps for Chemical Process	ASME	ASME B73.3-2003
	Specification for Thermoplastic and Thermoset Polymer Material Horizontal End Suction Centrifugal Pumps for Chemical Process	ASME	ASME B73.5M-1995 (RA01)
	Liquid Pumps	CSA	CAN/CSA-C22.2 No. 108-01
	Energy Efficiency Test Methods for Small Pumps	CSA	CAN/CSA C820-02 (R2007)
	Performance Standard for Liquid Ring Vacuum Pumps, 3rd ed. (2005)	HEI	HEI 2854
	Centrifugal Pumps for Nomenclature and Definitions	HI	ANSI/HI 1.1-1.2 (2000)
	Centrifugal Pumps for Design and Applications	HI	ANSI/HI 1.3 (2000)
	Centrifugal Pumps for Installation, Operation, and Maintenance	HI	ANSI/HI 1.4 (2000)
	Vertical Pumps for Nomenclature and Definitions	HI	ANSI/HI 2.1-2.2 (2000)
	Vertical Pumps for Design and Application	HI	ANSI/HI 2.3 (2000)
	Vertical Pumps for Installation, Operation, and Maintenance	HI	ANSI/HI 2.4 (2000)
	Rotary Pumps for Nomenclature, Definitions, Application, and Operation	HI	ANSI/HI 3.1-3.5 (2000)
	Sealless Rotary Pumps for Nomenclature, Definitions, Application, Operation, and Test	HI	ANSI/HI 4.1-4.6 (2000)
	Sealless Centrifugal Pumps for Nomenclature, Definitions, Application, Operation, and Test	HI	ANSI/HI 5.1-5.6 (2000)
	Reciprocating Pumps for Nomenclature, Definitions, Application, and Operation	HI	ANSI/HI 6.1-6.5 (2000)
	Direct Acting (Steam) Pumps for Nomenclature, Definitions, Application, and Operation	HI	ANSI/HI 8.1-8.5 (2000)
	Pumps—General Guidelines for Types, Definitions, Application, Sound Measurement and Decontamination	HI	ANSI/HI 9.1-9.5 (2000)
	Centrifugal and Vertical Pumps for Allowable Nozzle Loads	HI	ANSI/HI 9.6.2 (2001)
	Centrifugal and Vertical Pumps for Allowable Operating Region	HI	ANSI/HI 9.6.3 (1997)
	Centrifugal and Vertical Pumps for Vibration Measurements and Allowable Values	HI	ANSI/HI 9.6.4 (2001)
	Centrifugal and Vertical Pumps for Condition Monitoring	HI	ANSI/HI 9.6.5 (2000)
	Pump Intake Design	HI	ANSI/HI 9.8 (1998)
	Engineering Data Book, 2nd ed.	HI	HI (1990)
	Circulation System Components and Related Materials for Swimming Pools, Spas/Hot Tubs	NSF	NSF/ANSI 50-2007
	Pumps for Oil-Burning Appliances (1997)	UL	UL 343
	Motor-Operated Water Pumps (2002)	UL	ANSI/UL 778
	Swimming Pool Pumps, Filters, and Chlorinators (2008)	UL	ANSI/UL 1081
Radiators	Testing and Rating Standard for Baseboard Radiation, 8th ed. (2005)	HYDI	IBR
	Testing and Rating Standard for Finned Tube (Commercial) Radiation, 6th ed. (2005)	HYDI	IBR
Receivers	Refrigerant Liquid Receivers	AHRI	AHRI 495-2005
	Refrigerant-Containing Components and Accessories, Nonelectrical (2001)	UL	ANSI/UL 207
Refrigerants	Threshold Limit Values for Chemical Substances (updated annually)	ACGIH	ACGIH
	Specifications for Fluorocarbon Refrigerants	AHRI	AHRI 700-2006
	Refrigerant Recovery/Recycling Equipment	AHRI	AHRI 740-98
	Refrigerant Information Recommended for Product Development and Standards	ASHRAE	ASHRAE *Guideline* 6-2008
	Method of Testing Flow Capacity of Refrigerant Capillary Tubes	ASHRAE	ANSI/ASHRAE 28-1996 (RA06)
	Designation and Safety Classification of Refrigerants	ASHRAE	ANSI/ASHRAE 34-2007
	Sealed Glass Tube Method to Test the Chemical Stability of Materials for Use Within Refrigerant Systems	ASHRAE	ANSI/ASHRAE 97-2007
	Refrigeration Oil Description	ASHRAE	ANSI/ASHRAE 99-2006
	Reducing the Release of Halogenated Refrigerants from Refrigerating and Air-Conditioning Equipment and Systems	ASHRAE	ANSI/ASHRAE 147-2002
	Test Method for Acid Number of Petroleum Products by Potentiometric Titration	ASTM	ASTM D664-07
	Test Method for Concentration Limits of Flammability of Chemical (Vapors and Gases)	ASTM	ASTM E681-04
	Refrigerant-Containing Components for Use in Electrical Equipment	CSA	C22.2 No. 140.3-M1987 (R2004)
	Refrigerants—Designation System	ISO	ISO 817:2005
	Procedure Retrofitting CFC-12 (R-12) Mobile Air-Conditioning Systems to HFC-134a (R-134a)	SAE	SAE J1661-1998
	Recommended Service Procedure for the Containment of CFC-12 (R-12)	SAE	SAE J1989-1998
	Standard of Purity for Recycled HFC-134a for Use in Mobile Air-Conditioning Systems	SAE	SAE J2099-1999
	HFC-134a (R-134a) Service Hose Fittings for Automotive Air-Conditioning Service Equipment	SAE	SAE J2197-1997
	Recommended Service Procedure for the Containment of HFC-134a	SAE	SAE J2211-1998
	HFC-134a (R-134a) Recovery/Recycling Equipment for Mobile Air-Conditioning Systems	SAE	SAE J2210-1999

Selected Codes and Standards Published by Various Societies and Associations (*Continued*)

Subject	Title	Publisher	Reference
	CFC-12 (R-12) Refrigerant Recovery Equipment for Mobile Automotive Air-Conditioning Systems	SAE	SAE J2209-1999
	Refrigerant-Containing Components and Accessories, Nonelectrical (2001)	UL	ANSI/UL 207
	Refrigerant Recovery/Recycling Equipment (2005)	UL	ANSI/UL 1963
	Field Conversion/Retrofit of Products to Change to an Alternative Refrigerant—Construction and Operation (1993)	UL	ANSI/UL 2170
	Field Conversion/Retrofit of Products to Change to an Alternative Refrigerant—Insulating Material and Refrigerant Compatibility (1993)	UL	ANSI/UL 2171
	Field Conversion/Retrofit of Products to Change to an Alternative Refrigerant—Procedures and Methods (1993)	UL	ANSI/UL 2172
	Refrigerants (2006)	UL	ANSI/UL 2182
Refrigeration	Safety Standard for Refrigeration Systems	ASHRAE	ANSI/ASHRAE 15-2007
	Mechanical Refrigeration Code	CSA	B52-05
	Refrigeration Equipment	CSA	CAN/CSA-C22.2 No. 120-M91 (R2004)
	Equipment, Design and Installation of Ammonia Mechanical Refrigerating Systems	IIAR	ANSI/IIAR 2-1999
	Refrigerated Medical Equipment (1993)	UL	ANSI/UL 416
Refrigeration Systems	Ejectors	ASME	ASME PTC 24-1976 (RA82)
	Reducing the Release of Halogenated Refrigerants from Refrigerating and Air-Conditioning Equipment and Systems	ASHRAE	ANSI/ASHRAE 147-2002
	Testing of Refrigerating Systems	ISO	ISO 916-1968
	Standards for Steam Jet Vacuum Systems, 6th ed.	HEI	HEI 2866-1
Transport	Mechanical Transport Refrigeration Units	AHRI	AHRI 1110-2006
	Mechanical Refrigeration and Air-Conditioning Installations Aboard Ship	ASHRAE	ANSI/ASHRAE 26-1996 (RA06)
	General Requirements for Application of Vapor Cycle Refrigeration Systems for Aircraft	SAE	SAE ARP731-2003
	Safety Standard for Motor Vehicle Refrigerant Vapor Compression Systems	SAE	SAE J639-2005
Refrigerators	Method of Testing Commercial Refrigerators and Freezers	ASHRAE	ANSI/ASHRAE 72-2005
Commercial	Energy Performance Standard for Commercial Refrigerated Display Cabinets and Merchandise	CSA	C657-04
	Energy Performance Standard for Food Service Refrigerators and Freezers	CSA	C827-98 (R2003)
	Gas Food Service Equipment	CSA	ANSI Z83.11-2006/CSA 1.8A-2006
	Mobile Food Carts	NSF	NSF/ANSI 59-2002e
	Food Equipment	NSF	NSF/ANSI 2-2007
	Commercial Refrigerators and Freezers	NSF	NSF/ANSI 7-2007
	Refrigeration Unit Coolers (2004)	UL	ANSI/UL 412
	Refrigerating Units (2006)	UL	ANSI/UL 427
	Commercial Refrigerators and Freezers (2006)	UL	ANSI/UL 471
Household	Household Refrigerators, Refrigerator-Freezers and Freezers	AHAM	ANSI/AHAM HRF-1-2007
	Refrigerators Using Gas Fuel	CSA	ANSI Z21.19-2002/CSA1.4-2002
	Energy Performance and Capacity of Household Refrigerators, Refrigerator-Freezers, and Freezers	CSA	CAN/CSA C300-00 (R2005)
	Household Refrigerators and Freezers (1993)	UL/CSA	ANSI/UL 250-1997/C22.2 No. 63-93
Retrofitting			
Building	Residential Duct Diagnostics and Repair (2003)	ACCA	ACCA
	Good HVAC Practices for Residential and Commercial Buildings (2003)	ACCA	ACCA
	Building Systems Analysis and Retrofit Manual, 1st ed.	SMACNA	SMACNA 1995
Refrigerant	Procedure for Retrofitting CFC-12 (R-12) Mobile Air Conditioning Systems to HFC-134a (R-134a)	SAE	SAE J1661-1998
	Field Conversion/Retrofit of Products to Change to an Alternative Refrigerant—Construction and Operation (1993)	UL	ANSI/UL 2170
	Field Conversion/Retrofit of Products to Change to an Alternative Refrigerant—Insulating Material and Refrigerant Compatibility (1993)	UL	ANSI/UL 2171
	Field Conversion/Retrofit of Products to Change to an Alternative Refrigerant—Procedures and Methods (1993)	UL	ANSI/UL 2172
Roof Ventilators	Commercial Low Pressure, Low Velocity Duct System Design, 1st ed.	ACCA	ACCA Manual Q
	Power Ventilators (2004)	UL	ANSI/UL 705
Solar Equipment	Thermal Performance Testing of Solar Ambient Air Heaters	ASABE	ANSI/ASAE S423-1991
	Testing and Reporting Solar Cooker Performance	ASABE	ASAE S580-2003
	Method of Measuring Solar-Optical Properties of Materials	ASHRAE	ASHRAE 74-1988
	Methods of Testing to Determine the Thermal Performance of Solar Collectors	ASHRAE	ANSI/ASHRAE 93-2003
	Methods of Testing to Determine the Thermal Performance of Solar Domestic Water Heating Systems	ASHRAE	ANSI/ASHRAE 95-1987
	Methods of Testing to Determine the Thermal Performance of Unglazed Flat-Plate Liquid-Type Solar Collectors	ASHRAE	ANSI/ASHRAE 96-1980 (RA89)

Selected Codes and Standards Published by Various Societies and Associations (*Continued*)

Subject	Title	Publisher	Reference
	Methods of Testing to Determine the Thermal Performance of Flat-Plate Solar Collectors Containing a Boiling Liquid	ASHRAE	ANSI/ASHRAE 109-1986 (RA03)
	Practice for Installation and Service of Solar Space Heating Systems for One and Two Family Dwellings	ASTM	ASTM E683-91 (2007)
	Practice for Evaluating Thermal Insulation Materials for Use in Solar Collectors	ASTM	ASTM E861-94 (2007)
	Practice for Installation and Service of Solar Domestic Water Heating Systems for One and Two Family Dwellings	ASTM	ASTM E1056-85 (2007)
	Reference Solar Spectral Irradiance at the Ground at Different Receiving Conditions—Part 1: Direct Normal and Hemispherical Solar Irradiance for Air Mass 1.5	ISO	ISO 9845-1:1992
	Solar Collectors	CSA	CAN/CSA F378-87 (R2004)
	Solar Domestic Hot Water Systems (Liquid to Liquid Heat Transfer)	CSA	CAN/CSA F379.1-88 (R2006)
	Seasonal Use Solar Domestic Hot Water Systems	CSA	CAN/CSA F379.2-M89 (R2006)
	Installation Code for Solar Domestic Hot Water Systems	CSA	CAN/CSA F383-87 (R2005)
	Solar Heating—Domestic Water Heating Systems—Part 2: Outdoor Test Methods for System Performance Characterization and Yearly Performance Prediction of Solar-Only Systems	ISO	ISO 9459-2:1995
	Test Methods for Solar Collectors—Part 1: Thermal Performance of Glazed Liquid Heating Collectors Including Pressure Drop	ISO	ISO 9806-1:1994
	Part 2: Qualification Test Procedures	ISO	ISO 9806-2:1995
	Part 3: Thermal Performance of Unglazed Liquid Heating Collectors (Sensible Heat Transfer Only) Including Pressure Drop	ISO	ISO 9806-3:1995
	Solar Water Heaters—Elastomeric Materials for Absorbers, Connecting Pipes and Fittings—Method of Assessment	ISO	ISO 9808:1990
	Solar Energy—Calibration of a Pyranometer Using a Pyrheliometer	ISO	ISO 9846:1993
Solenoid Valves	Solenoid Valves for Use with Volatile Refrigerants	AHRI	AHRI 760-2007
	Methods of Testing Capacity of Refrigerant Solenoid Valves	ASHRAE	ANSI/ASHRAE 158.1-2004
	Electrically Operated Valves (1999)	UL	UL 429
Sound Measurement	Threshold Limit Values for Physical Agents (updated annually)	ACGIH	ACGIH
	Specification for Sound Level Meters	ASA	ANSI S1.4-1983 (R2006)
	Specification for Octave-Band and Fractional-Octave-Band Analog and Digital Filters	ASA	ANSI S1.11-2004
	Microphones, Part 1: Specifications for Laboratory Standard Microphones	ASA	ANSI S1.15-1997/Part 1 (R2006)
	Part 2: Primary Method for Pressure Calibration of Laboratory Standard Microphones by the Reciprocity Technique	ASA	ANSI S1.15-2005/Part 2
	Specification for Acoustical Calibrators	ASA	ANSI S1.40-2006
	Measurement of Industrial Sound	ASME	ASME PTC 36-2004
	Test Method for Measuring Acoustical and Airflow Performance of Duct Liner Materials and Prefabricated Silencers	ASTM	ASTM E477-06a
	Test Method for Determination of Decay Rates for Use in Sound Insulation Test Methods	ASTM	ASTM E2235-04e1
	Sound and Vibration Design and Analysis (1994)	NEBB	NEBB
Fans	Reverberant Room Method for Sound Testing of Fans	AMCA	AMCA 300-05
	Methods for Calculating Fan Sound Ratings from Laboratory Test Data	AMCA	AMCA 301-06
	Application of Sone Ratings for Non-Ducted Air Moving Devices	AMCA	AMCA 302-73 (R2008)
	Application of Sound Power Level Ratings for Fans	AMCA	AMCA 303-79 (R2008)
	Acoustics—Measurement of Noise and Vibration of Small Air-Moving Devices—Part 1: Airborne Noise Emission	ASA	ANSI S12.11/1-2003/ISO 10302:1996 (MOD-2003)
	Part 2: Structure-Borne Vibration	ASA	ANSI S12.11/2-2003
	Laboratory Method of Testing to Determine the Sound Power in a Duct	ASHRAE/ AMCA	ANSI/ASHRAE 68-1997/ AMCA 330-97
Other Equipment	Sound Rating of Outdoor Unitary Equipment	AHRI	AHRI 270-95
	Application of Sound Rating Levels of Outdoor Unitary Equipment	AHRI	AHRI 275-97
	Sound Rating and Sound Transmission Loss of Packaged Terminal Equipment	AHRI	AHRI 300-2000
	Sound Rating of Non-Ducted Indoor Air-Conditioning Equipment	AHRI	AHRI 350-2000
	Sound Rating of Large Outdoor Refrigerating and Air-Conditioning Equipment	AHRI	AHRI 370-2001
	Method of Rating Sound and Vibration of Refrigerant Compressors	AHRI	AHRI 530-2005
	Method of Measuring Machinery Sound Within an Equipment Space	AHRI	AHRI 575-94
	Statistical Methods for Determining and Verifying Stated Noise Emission Values of Machinery and Equipment	ASA	ANSI S12.3-1985 (R2006)
	Sound Level Prediction for Installed Rotating Electrical Machines	NEMA	NEMA MG 3-1974 (R2006)
Techniques	Preferred Frequencies, Frequency Levels, and Band Numbers for Acoustical Measurements	ASA	ANSI S1.6-1984 (R2006)
	Reference Quantities for Acoustical Levels	ASA	ANSI S1.8-1989 (R2006)
	Measurement of Sound Pressure Levels in Air	ASA	ANSI S1.13-2005
	Procedure for the Computation of Loudness of Steady Sound	ASA	ANSI S3.4-2007
	Criteria for Evaluating Room Noise	ASA	ANSI S12.2-1995 (R1999)
	Methods for Determining the Insertion Loss of Outdoor Noise Barriers	ASA	ANSI S12.8-1998 (R2003)

Selected Codes and Standards Published by Various Societies and Associations (*Continued*)

Subject	Title	Publisher	Reference
	Engineering Method for the Determination of Sound Power Levels of Noise Sources Using Sound Intensity	ASA	ANSI S12.12-1992 (R2007)
	Procedures for Outdoor Measurement of Sound Pressure Level	ASA	ANSI S12.18-1994 (R2004)
	Methods for Measurement of Sound Emitted by Machinery and Equipment at Workstations and Other Specified Positions	ASA	ANSI S12.43-1997 (R2007)
	Methods for Calculation of Sound Emitted by Machinery and Equipment at Workstations and Other Specified Positions from Sound Power Level	ASA	ANSI S12.44-1997 (R2007)
	Acoustics—Determination of Sound Power Levels of Noise Sources Using Sound Pressure—Precision Method for Reverberation Rooms	ASA	ANSI S12.51-2002 (R2007)/ISO 3741:1999
	Acoustics—Determination of Sound Power Levels of Noise Sources—Engineering Methods for Small, Movable Sources in Reverberant Fields—Part 1: Comparison Method for Hard-Walled Test Rooms	ASA	ANSI S12.53/Part 1-1999 (R2004)/ISO 3743-1:1994
	Part 2: Methods for Special Reverberation Test Rooms	ASA	ANSI S12.53/Part 2-1999 (R2004)/ISO 3743-2:1994
	Acoustics—Determination of Sound Power Levels of Noise Sources Using Sound Pressure—Engineering Method in an Essentially Free Field over a Reflecting Plane	ASA	ANSI S12.54-1999 (R2004)/ISO 3744:1994
	Acoustics—Determination of Sound Power Levels of Noise Sources Using Sound Pressure—Survey Method Using an Enveloping Measurement Surface over a Reflecting Plane	ASA	ANSI S12.56-1999 (R2004)/ISO 3746:1995
	Test Method for Impedance and Absorption of Acoustical Materials by the Impedance Tube Method	ASTM	ASTM C384-04
	Test Method for Sound Absorption and Sound Absorption Coefficients by the Reverberation Room Method	ASTM	ASTM C423-07a
	Test Method for Measurement of Airborne Sound Insulation in Buildings	ASTM	ASTM E336-07
	Test Method for Impedance and Absorption of Acoustical Materials Using a Tube, Two Microphones and a Digital Frequency Analysis System	ASTM	ASTM E1050-08
	Test Method for Evaluating Masking Sound in Open Offices Using A-Weighted and One-Third Octave Band Sound Pressure Levels	ASTM	ASTM E1573-02
	Test Method for Measurement of Sound in Residential Spaces	ASTM	ASTM E1574-98 (2006)
	Acoustics–Measurement of Sound Insulation in Buildings and of Building Elements; Part 1: Requirements for Laboratory Test Facilities with Suppressed Flanking Transmission	ISO	ISO 140-1:1997
	Part 4: Field Measurements of Airborne Sound Insulation Between Rooms	ISO	ISO 140-4:1998
	Part 5: Field Measurements of Airborne Sound Insulation of Facade Elements and Facades	ISO	ISO 140-5:1998
	Part 6: Laboratory Measurements of Impact Sound Insulation of Floors	ISO	ISO 140-6:1998
	Part 7: Field Measurements of Impact Sound Insulation of Floors	ISO	ISO 140-7:1998
	Part 8: Laboratory Measurements of the Reduction of Transmitted Impact Noise by Floor Coverings on a Heavyweight Standard Floor	ISO	ISO 140-8:1997
	Acoustics—Method for Calculating Loudness Level	ISO	ISO 532:1975
	Acoustics—Determination of Sound Power Levels of Noise Sources Using Sound Intensity; Part 1: Measurement at Discrete Points	ISO	ISO 9614-1:1993
	Part 2: Measurement by Scanning	ISO	ISO 9614-2:1996
	Procedural Standards for Measurement and Assessment of Sound and Vibration, 2nd ed. (2006)	NEBB	NEBB
Terminology	Acoustical Terminology	ASA	ANSI S1.1-1994 (R2004)
	Terminology Relating to Environmental Acoustics	ASTM	ASTM C634-02e1
Space Heaters	Methods of Testing for Rating Combination Space-Heating and Water-Heating Appliances	ASHRAE	ANSI/ASHRAE 124-2007
	Gas-Fired Room Heaters, Vol. II, Unvented Room Heaters	CSA	ANSI Z21.11.2-2007
	Vented Gas-Fired Space Heating Appliances	CSA	ANSI Z21.86-2004/CSA 2.32-2004
	Movable and Wall- or Ceiling-Hung Electric Room Heaters (2000)	UL	UL 1278
	Fixed and Location-Dedicated Electric Room Heaters (1997)	UL	UL 2021
Symbols	Graphic Electrical/Electronic Symbols for Air-Conditioning and Refrigerating Equipment	AHRI	AHRI 130-88
	Graphic Symbols for Heating, Ventilating, Air-Conditioning, and Refrigerating Systems	ASHRAE	ANSI/ASHRAE 134-2005
	Graphical Symbols for Plumbing Fixtures for Diagrams Used in Architecture and Building Construction	ASME	ANSI/ASME Y32.4-1977 (RA04)
	Symbols for Mechanical and Acoustical Elements as Used in Schematic Diagrams	ASME	ANSI/ASME Y32.18-1972 (RA03)
	Practice for Mechanical Symbols, Shipboard Heating, Ventilation, and Air Conditioning (HVAC)	ASTM	ASTM F856-97 (2004)
	Standard Symbols for Welding, Brazing, and Nondestructive Examination	AWS	AWS A2.4:2007
	Standard Letter Symbols for Quantities Used in Electrical Science and Electrical Engineering	IEEE	IEEE 280-1982 (R2003)
	Graphic Symbols for Electrical and Electronics Diagrams	IEEE	ANSI 315-1975 (R1986)/IEEE 315A-1986
	Standard for Logic Circuit Diagrams	IEEE	IEEE 991-1986 (R1994)
	Use of the International System of Units (SI): The Modern Metric System	IEEE/ASTM	IEEE/ASTM-SI10-2002

Selected Codes and Standards Published by Various Societies and Associations (*Continued*)

Subject	Title	Publisher	Reference
	Abbreviations and Acronyms	ASME	ASME Y14.38-1999
	Engineering Drawing Practices	ASME	ASME Y14.100-2004
	Safety Color Code	NEMA	ANSI/NEMA Z535-2002
Terminals, Wiring	Electrical Quick-Connect Terminals (2003)	UL	ANSI/UL 310
	Wire Connectors (2003)	UL	ANSI/UL 486A-486B
	Splicing Wire Connectors (2004)	UL	ANSI/UL 486C
	Equipment Wiring Terminals for Use with Aluminum and/or Copper Conductors (1994)	UL	ANSI/UL 486E
Testing and Balancing	AABC National Standards for Total System Balance (2002)	AABC	AABC
	Industrial Process/Power Generation Fans: Site Performance Test Standard	AMCA	AMCA 803-02
	Guidelines for Measuring and Reporting Environmental Parameters for Plant Experiments in Growth Chambers	ASABE	ANSI/ASAE EP411.4-2002
	HVAC&R Technical Requirements for the Commissioning Process	ASHRAE	ASHRAE *Guideline* 1-2007
	Measurement, Testing, Adjusting, and Balancing of Building HVAC Systems	ASHRAE	ANSI/ASHRAE 111-2008
	Practices for Measuring, Testing, Adjusting, and Balancing Shipboard HVAR&R Systems	ASHRAE	ANSI/ASHRAE 151-2002
	Centrifugal Pump Tests	HI	ANSI/HI 1.6 (M104) (2000)
	Vertical Pump Tests	HI	ANSI/HI 2.6 (M108) (2000)
	Rotary Pump Tests	HI	ANSI/HI 3.6 (M110) (2000)
	Reciprocating Pump Tests	HI	ANSI/HI 6.6 (M114) (2000)
	Pumps—General Guidelines for Types, Definitions, Application, Sound Measurement and Decontamination	HI	HI 9.1-9.5 (M117) (2000)
	Submersible Pump Tests	HI	ANSI/HI 11.6 (M126) (2001)
	Procedural Standards for Certified Testing of Cleanrooms, 2nd ed. (1996)	NEBB	NEBB
	Procedural Standards for Testing, Adjusting, Balancing of Environmental Systems, 7th ed. (2005)	NEBB	NEBB
	HVAC Systems Testing, Adjusting and Balancing, 3rd ed.	SMACNA	SMACNA 2002
Thermal Storage	Thermal Energy Storage: A Guide for Commercial HVAC Contractors	ACCA	ACCA
	Method of Testing Active Latent-Heat Storage Devices Based on Thermal Performance	ASHRAE	ANSI/ASHRAE 94.1-2002 (RA06)
	Method of Testing Thermal Storage Devices with Electrical Input and Thermal Output Based on Thermal Performance	ASHRAE	ANSI/ASHRAE 94.2-1981 (RA06)
	Method of Testing Active Sensible Thermal Energy Devices Based on Thermal Performance	ASHRAE	ANSI/ASHRAE 94.3-1986 (RA06)
	Measurement, Testing, Adjusting, and Balancing of Building HVAC Systems	ASHRAE	ANSI/ASHRAE 111-2008
	Method of Testing the Performance of Cool Storage Systems	ASHRAE	ANSI/ASHRAE 150-2000 (RA04)
Transformers	Minimum Efficiency Values for Liquid-Filled Distribution Transformers	CSA	CAN/CSA C802.1-00 (R2005)
	Minimum Efficiency Values for Dry-Type Transformers	CSA	CAN/CSA C802.2-06
	Maximum Losses For Power Transformers	CSA	CAN/CSA C802.3-01 (R2007)
	Guide for Determining Energy Efficiency of Distribution Transformers	NEMA	NEMA TP-1-2002
Turbines	Steam Turbines	ASME	ASME PTC 6-2004
	Steam Turbines for Combined Cycle	ASME	ASME PTC 6.2-2004
	Hydraulic Turbines and Pump-Turbines	ASME	ASME PTC 18-2002
	Gas Turbines	ASME	ASME PTC 22-2005
	Wind Turbines	ASME	ASME PTC 42-1988 (RA04)
	Specification for Stainless Steel Bars for Compressor and Turbine Airfoils	ASTM	ASTM A1028-03
	Specification for Gas Turbine Fuel Oils	ASTM	ASTM D2880-03
	Land Based Steam Turbine Generator Sets, 0 to 33 000 kW	NEMA	NEMA SM 24-1991 (R2002)
	Steam Turbines for Mechanical Drive Service	NEMA	NEMA SM 23-1991 (R2002)
Valves	Face-to-Face and End-to-End Dimensions of Valves	ASME	ASME B16.10-2000 (R03)
	Valves—Flanged, Threaded, and Welding End	ASME	ASME B16.34-2004
	Manually Operated Metallic Gas Valves for Use in Aboveground Piping Systems up to 5 psi	ASME	ASME B16.44-2002
	Pressure Relief Devices	ASME	ASME PTC 25-2001
	Methods of Testing Capacity of Refrigerant Solenoid Valves	ASHRAE	ANSI/ASHRAE 158.1-2004
	Relief Valves for Hot Water Supply	CSA	ANSI Z21.22-1999 (R2003)/ CSA 4.4-M99 (R2004)
	Control Valve Capacity Test Procedures	ISA	ANSI/ISA-S75.02-1996
	Flow Equations for Sizing Control Valves	ISA	ANSI/ISA-S75.01.01-2002
	Industrial Valves—Part-Turn Actuator Attachments	ISO	ISO 5211-1:2001
	Metal Valves for Use in Flanged Pipe Systems—Face-to-Face and Centre-to-Face Dimensions	ISO	ISO 5752:1982
	Safety Valves for Protection Against Excessive Pressure, Part 1: Safety Valves	ISO	ISO 4126-1:2004
	Oxygen System Fill/Check Valve	SAE	SAE AS1225A-1997
	Valves for Anhydrous Ammonia and LP-Gas (Other Than Safety Relief) (2007)	UL	ANSI/UL 125
	Safety Relief Valves for Anhydrous Ammonia and LP-Gas (2007)	UL	ANSI/UL 132

Selected Codes and Standards Published by Various Societies and Associations (*Continued*)

Subject	Title	Publisher	Reference
	LP-Gas Regulators (1999)	UL	ANSI/UL 144
	Electrically Operated Valves (1999)	UL	UL 429
	Valves for Flammable Fluids (2007)	UL	ANSI/UL 842
Gas	Manually Operated Metallic Gas Valves for Use in Gas Piping Systems up to 125 psig (Sizes NPS 1/2 through 2)	ASME	ASME B16.33-2002
	Large Metallic Valves for Gas Distribution (Manually Operated, NPS-2 1/2 to 12, 125 psig Maximum)	ASME	ANSI/ASME B16.38-2007
	Manually Operated Thermoplastic Gas Shutoffs and Valves in Gas Distribution Systems	ASME	ASME B16.40-2002
	Manually Operated Gas Valves for Appliances, Appliance Connection Valves, and Hose End Valves	CSA	ANSI Z21.15-1997 (R2003)/CGA 9.1-M97
	Automatic Valves for Gas Appliances	CSA	ANSI Z21.21-2005/CGA 6.5-2005
	Combination Gas Controls for Gas Appliances	CSA	ANSI Z21.78-2005/CGA 6.20-2005
	Convenience Gas Outlets and Optional Enclosures	CSA	ANSI Z21.90-2001/CSA 6.24-2001 (R2005)
Refrigerant	Thermostatic Refrigerant Expansion Valves	AHRI	AHRI 750-2007
	Solenoid Valves for Use with Volatile Refrigerants	AHRI	AHRI 760-2007
	Refrigerant Pressure Regulating Valves	AHRI	AHRI 770-2001
Vapor Retarders	Practice for Selection of Vapor Retarders for Thermal Insulation	ASTM	ASTM C755-03
	Practice for Determining the Properties of Jacketing Materials for Thermal Insulation	ASTM	ASTM C921-03a
	Specification for Flexible, Low Permeance Vapor Retarders for Thermal Insulation	ASTM	ASTM C1136-06
	Test Method for Water Vapor Transmission Rate of Flexible Barrier Materials Using an Infrared Detection Technique	ASTM	ASTM F372-99 (2003)
Vending Machines	Methods of Testing for Rating Vending Machines for Bottled, Canned, and Other Sealed Beverages	ASHRAE	ANSI/ASHRAE 32.1-2004
	Methods of Testing for Rating Pre-Mix and Post-Mix Beverage Dispensing Equipment	ASHRAE	ANSI/ASHRAE 32.2-2003 (RA07)
	Vending Machines	CSA	C22.2 No. 128-95 (R2004)
	Energy Performance of Vending Machines	CSA	CAN/CSA C804-96 (R2007)
	Vending Machines for Food and Beverages	NSF	NSF/ANSI 25-2007
	Refrigerated Vending Machines (1995)	UL	ANSI/UL 541
	Vending Machines (1995)	UL	ANSI/UL 751
Vent Dampers	Automatic Vent Damper Devices for Use with Gas-Fired Appliances	CSA	ANSI Z21.66-1996 (R2001)/CSA 6.14-M96
	Vent or Chimney Connector Dampers for Oil-Fired Appliances (1994)	UL	ANSI/UL 17
Ventilation	Commercial Application, Systems, and Equipment, 1st ed.	ACCA	ACCA Manual CS
	Commercial Low Pressure, Low Velocity Duct System Design, 1st ed.	ACCA	ACCA Manual Q
	Comfort, Air Quality, and Efficiency by Design	ACCA	ACCA Manual RS
	Guide for Testing Ventilation Systems (1991)	ACGIH	ACGIH
	Industrial Ventilation: A Manual of Recommended Practice, 26th ed. (2007)	ACGIH	ACGIH
	Design of Ventilation Systems for Poultry and Livestock Shelters	ASABE	ASAE EP270.5-2003
	Design Values for Emergency Ventilation and Care of Livestock and Poultry	ASABE	ANSI/ASAE EP282.2-2004
	Heating, Ventilating and Cooling Greenhouses	ASABE	ANSI/ASAE EP406.4-2003
	Guidelines for Selection of Energy Efficient Agricultural Ventilation Fans	ASABE	ASAE EP566-1997
	Uniform Terminology for Livestock Production Facilities	ASABE	ASAE S501-1990
	Agricultural Ventilation Constant Speed Fan Test Standard	ASABE	ASABE S565-2005
	Ventilation for Acceptable Indoor Air Quality	ASHRAE	ANSI/ASHRAE 62.1-2007
	Ventilation and Acceptable Indoor Air Quality in Low-Rise Residential Buildings	ASHRAE	ANSI/ASHRAE 62.2-2007
	Method of Testing for Room Air Diffusion	ASHRAE	ANSI/ASHRAE 113-2005
	Measuring Air Change Effectiveness	ASHRAE	ANSI/ASHRAE 129-1997 (RA02)
	Method of Determining Air Change Rates in Detached Dwellings	ASHRAE	ANSI/ASHRAE 136-1993 (RA06)
	Ventilation for Commercial Cooking Operations	ASHRAE	ANSI/ASHRAE 154-2003
	Residential Mechanical Ventilation Systems	CSA	CAN/CSA F326-M91 (R2005)
	Parking Structures	NFPA	NFPA 88A-07
	Installation of Air Conditioning and Ventilating Systems	NFPA	NFPA 90A-02
	Ventilation Control and Fire Protection of Commercial Cooking Operations	NFPA	NFPA 96-08
	Food Equipment	NSF	NSF/ANSI 2-2007
	Class II (Laminar Flow) Biosafety Cabinetry	NSF	NSF/ANSI 49-2007
	Aerothermodynamic Systems Engineering and Design	SAE	SAE AIR1168/3-1989
	Heater, Airplane, Engine Exhaust Gas to Air Heat Exchanger Type	SAE	SAE ARP86-1996
	Test Procedure for Battery Flame Retardant Venting Systems	SAE	SAE J1495-2005
Venting	Commercial Application, Systems, and Equipment, 1st ed.	ACCA	ACCA Manual CS
	Draft Hoods	CSA	ANSI Z21.12-1990 (R2000)
	National Fuel Gas Code	AGA/NFPA	ANSI Z223.1/NFPA 54-2006
	Explosion Prevention Systems	NFPA	NFPA 69-08

Selected Codes and Standards Published by Various Societies and Associations (*Continued*)

Subject	Title	Publisher	Reference
	Smoke and Heat Venting	NFPA	NFPA 204-07
	Chimneys, Fireplaces, Vents and Solid Fuel-Burning Appliances	NFPA	NFPA 211-06
	Guide for Steel Stack Construction, 2nd ed.	SMACNA	SMACNA 1996
	Draft Equipment (2006)	UL	UL 378
	Gas Vents (1996)	UL	ANSI/UL 441
	Type L Low-Temperature Venting Systems (1995)	UL	ANSI/UL 641
Vibration	Balance Quality and Vibration Levels for Fans	AMCA	ANSI/AMCA 204-05
	Techniques of Machinery Vibration Measurement	ASA	ANSI S2.17-1980 (R2004)
	Mechanical Vibration and Shock—Resilient Mounting Systems—Part 1: Technical Information to Be Exchanged for the Application of Isolation Systems	ASA	ISO 2017-1:2005
	Evaluation of Human Exposure to Whole-Body Vibration—Part 2: Vibration in Buildings (1 Hz to 80 Hz)	ISO	ISO 2631-2:2003
	Guidelines for the Evaluation of the Response of Occupants of Fixed Structures, Especially Buildings and Off-Shore Structures, to Low-Frequency Horizontal Motion (0.063 to 1 Hz)	ISO	ISO 6897:1984
	Procedural Standards for Measurement and Assessment of Sound and Vibration, 2nd ed. (2006)	NEBB	NEBB
	Sound and Vibration Design and Analysis (1994)	NEBB	NEBB
Water Heaters	Desuperheater/Water Heaters	AHRI	AHRI 470-2006
	Safety for Electrically Heated Livestock Waterers	ASABE	ASAE EP342.2-1995 (R2005)
	Methods of Testing to Determine the Thermal Performance of Solar Domestic Water Heating Systems	ASHRAE	ANSI/ASHRAE 95-1987
	Method of Testing for Rating Commercial Gas, Electric, and Oil Service Water Heating Equipment	ASHRAE	ANSI/ASHRAE 118.1-2008
	Method of Testing for Rating Residential Water Heaters	ASHRAE	ANSI/ASHRAE 118.2-2006
	Methods of Testing for Rating Combination Space-Heating and Water-Heating Appliances	ASHRAE	ANSI/ASHRAE 124-2007
	Methods of Testing for Efficiency of Space-Conditioning/Water-Heating Appliances That Include a Desuperheater Water Heater	ASHRAE	ANSI/ASHRAE 137-2009
	Boiler and Pressure Vessel Code—Section IV: Heating Boilers	ASME	BPVC-2007
	Section VI: Recommended Rules for the Care and Operation of Heating Boilers	ASME	BPVC-2007
	Gas Water Heaters—Vol. I: Storage Water Heaters with Input Ratings of 75,000 Btu per Hour or Less	CSA	ANSI Z21.10.1-2004/CSA 4.1-2004
	Vol. III: Storage, with Input Ratings Above 75,000 Btu per Hour, Circulating and Instantaneous Water Heaters	CSA	ANSI Z21.10.3-2004/CSA 4.3-2004
	Oil Burning Stoves and Water Heaters	CSA	B140.3-1962 (R2006)
	Oil-Fired Service Water Heaters and Swimming Pool Heaters	CSA	B140.12-03
	Construction and Test of Electric Storage-Tank Water Heaters	CSA	CAN/CSA-C22.2 No. 110-94 (R2004)
	Performance of Electric Storage Tank Water Heaters for Household Service	CSA	C191-04
	Energy Efficiency of Electric Storage Tank Water Heaters and Heat Pump Water Heaters	CSA	CSA C745-03
	One Time Use Water Heater Emergency Shut-Off	IAPMO	IGC 175-2003
	Water Heaters, Hot Water Supply Boilers, and Heat Recovery Equipment	NSF	NSF/ANSI 5-2007
	Household Electric Storage Tank Water Heaters (2004)	UL	ANSI/UL 174
	Oil-Fired Storage Tank Water Heaters (1995)	UL	ANSI/UL 732
	Commercial-Industrial Gas Heating Equipment (2006)	UL	UL 795
	Electric Booster and Commercial Storage Tank Water Heaters (2004)	UL	ANSI/UL 1453
Welding and Brazing	Boiler and Pressure Vessel Code—Section IX: Welding and Brazing Qualifications	ASME	BPVC-2007
	Structural Welding Code—Steel	AWS	AWS D1.1M/D1.1:2008
	Specification for Welding of Austenitic Stainless Steel Tube and Piping Systems in Sanitary Applications	AWS	AWS D18.1:1999
Wood-Burning Appliances	Threshold Limit Values for Chemical Substances (updated annually)	ACGIH	ACGIH
	Specification for Room Heaters, Pellet Fuel Burning Type	ASTM	ASTM E1509-04
	Guide for Construction of Solid Fuel Burning Masonry Heaters	ASTM	ASTM E1602-03
	Installation Code for Solid-Fuel-Burning Appliances and Equipment	CSA	CAN/CSA-B365-01 (R2006)
	Solid-Fuel-Fired Central Heating Appliances	CSA	CAN/CSA-B366.1-M91 (R2007)
	Chimneys, Fireplaces, Vents, and Solid Fuel-Burning Appliances	NFPA	ANSI/NFPA 211-06
	Commercial Cooking, Rethermalization and Powered Hot Food Holding and Transport Equipment	NSF	NSF/ANSI 4-2007e

ORGANIZATIONS

Abbrev.	Organization	Address	Telephone	http://www.
AABC	Associated Air Balance Council	1518 K Street NW, Suite 503 Washington, D.C. 20005	(202) 737-0202	aabchq.com
ABMA	American Boiler Manufacturers Association	8221 Old Courthouse Road, Suite 207 Vienna, VA 22182	(703) 356-7171	abma.com
ACCA	Air Conditioning Contractors of America	2800 Shirlington Road, Suite 300 Arlington, VA 22206	(703) 575-4477	acca.org
ACGIH	American Conference of Governmental Industrial Hygienists	1330 Kemper Meadow Drive Cincinnati, OH 45240	(513) 742-2020	acgih.org
ADC	Air Diffusion Council	1901 North Roselle Road, Suite 800 Schaumburg, IL 60195	(847) 706-6750	flexibleduct.org
AGA	American Gas Association	400 N. Capitol Street NW, Suite 400 Washington, D.C. 20001	(202) 824-7000	aga.org
AHAM	Association of Home Appliance Manufacturers	1111 19th Street NW, Suite 402 Washington, D.C. 20036	(202) 872-5955	aham.org
AIHA	American Industrial Hygiene Association	2700 Prosperity Avenue, Suite 250 Fairfax, VA 22031	(703) 849-8888	aiha.org
AMCA	Air Movement and Control Association International	30 West University Drive Arlington Heights, IL 60004-1893	(847) 394-0150	amca.org
ANSI	American National Standards Institute	1819 L Street NW, 6th Floor Washington, D.C. 20036	(202) 293-8020	ansi.org
AHRI	Air-Conditioning, Heating, and Refrigeration Institute	4100 North Fairfax Drive, Suite 200 Arlington, VA 22203	(703) 524-8800	ari.org
ASA	Acoustical Society of America	2 Huntington Quadrangle, Suite 1NO1 Melville, NY 14747-4502	(516) 576-2360	asa.aip.org
ASABE	American Society of Agricultural and Biological Engineers	2950 Niles Road St. Joseph, MI 49085-9659	(269) 429-0300	asabe.org
ASHRAE	American Society of Heating, Refrigerating and Air-Conditioning Engineers	1791 Tullie Circle, NE Atlanta, GA 30329	(404) 636-8400	ashrae.org
ASME	ASME	3 Park Avenue New York, NY 10016-5990	(973) 882-1167	asme.org
ASTM	ASTM International	100 Barr Harbor Drive, P.O. Box C700 West Conshohocken, PA 19428-2959	(610) 832-9500	astm.org
AWS	American Welding Society	550 N.W. LeJeune Road Miami, FL 33126	(305) 443-9353	aws.org
AWWA	American Water Works Association	6666 W. Quincy Avenue Denver, CO 80235	(303) 794-7711	awwa.org
BOCA	Building Officials and Code Administrators International	(*see* ICC)		
BSI	British Standards Institution	389 Chiswick High Road London W4 4AL, UK	44(0)20-8996-9001	bsi-global.com
CAGI	Compressed Air and Gas Institute	1300 Sumner Avenue Cleveland, OH 44115-2851	(216) 241-7333	cagi.org
CSA	Canadian Standards Association International	5060 Spectrum Way Mississauga, ON L4W 5N6, Canada	(416) 747-4000	csa.ca
	Also available from CSA America	8501 East Pleasant Valley Road Cleveland, OH 44131-5575	(216) 524-4990	csa-america.org
CTI	Cooling Technology Institute	P.O. Box 73383 Houston, TX 77273-3383	(281) 583-4087	cti.org
EJMA	Expansion Joint Manufacturers Association	25 North Broadway Tarrytown, NY 10591	(914) 332-0040	ejma.org
HEI	Heat Exchange Institute	1300 Sumner Avenue Cleveland, OH 44115-2815	(216) 241-7333	heatexchange.org
HI	Hydraulic Institute	9 Sylvan Way Parsippany, NJ 07054-3802	(973) 267-9700	pumps.org
HYDI	Hydronics Institute Division of GAMA	2107 Wilson Boulevard, Suite 600 Arlington, VA 22201	(703) 525-7060	gamanet.org
IAPMO	International Association of Plumbing and Mechanical Officials	5001 E. Philadelphia Street Ontario, CA 91761-2816	(909) 472-4100	iapmo.org

ORGANIZATIONS (*Continued*)

Abbrev.	Organization	Address	Telephone	http://www.
ICBO	International Conference of Building Officials	(*see* ICC)		
ICC	International Code Council	500 New Jersey Ave NW, 6th Floor Washington, D.C. 20001	(888) 422-7233	iccsafe.org
IEEE	Institute of Electrical and Electronics Engineers	45 Hoes Lane Piscataway, NJ 08854-4141	(732) 981-0060	ieee.org
IESNA	Illuminating Engineering Society of North America	120 Wall Street, Floor 17 New York, NY 10005-4001	(212) 248-5000	iesna.org
IFCI	International Fire Code Institute	(*see* ICC)		
IIAR	International Institute of Ammonia Refrigeration	1110 North Glebe Road, Suite 250 Arlington, VA 22201	(703) 312-4200	iiar.org
ISA	The Instrumentation, Systems, and Automation Society	67 Alexander Drive, P.O. Box 12777 Research Triangle Park, NC 27709	(919) 549-8411	isa.org
ISO	International Organization for Standardization	1, ch. de la Voie-Creuse, Case postale 56 CH-1211 Geneva 20, Switzerland	41-22-749-01 11	iso.org
MCAA	Mechanical Contractors Association of America	1385 Piccard Drive Rockville, MD 20850	(301) 869-5800	mcaa.org
MICA	Midwest Insulation Contractors Association	16712 Elm Circle Omaha, NE 68130	(800) 747-6422	micainsulation.org
MSS	Manufacturers Standardization Society of the Valve and Fittings Industry	127 Park Street NE Vienna, VA 22180-4602	(703) 281-6613	mss-hq.com
NAIMA	North American Insulation Manufacturers Association	44 Canal Center Plaza, Suite 310 Alexandria, VA 22314	(703) 684-0084	naima.org
NCPWB	National Certified Pipe Welding Bureau	1385 Piccard Drive Rockville, MD 20850-4340	(301) 869-5800	mcaa.org/ncpwb
NCSBCS	National Conference of States on Building Codes and Standards	505 Huntmar Park Drive, Suite 210 Herndon, VA 20170	(703) 437-0100	ncsbcs.org
NEBB	National Environmental Balancing Bureau	8575 Grovemont Circle Gaithersburg, MD 20877	(301) 977-3698	nebb.org
NEMA	Association of Electrical and Medical Imaging Equipment Manufacturers	1300 North 17th Street, Suite 1752 Rosslyn, VA 22209	(703) 841-3200	nema.org
NFPA	National Fire Protection Association	1 Batterymarch Park Quincy, MA 02169-7471	(617) 770-3000	nfpa.org
NRCC	National Research Council of Canada, Institute for Research in Construction	1200 Montreal Road, Bldg M-58 Ottawa, ON K1A 0R6, Canada	(877) 672-2672	nrc-cnrc.ca
NSF	NSF International	P.O. Box 130140, 789 N. Dixboro Road Ann Arbor, MI 48113-0140	(734) 769-8010	nsf.org
PHCC	Plumbing-Heating-Cooling Contractors Association	180 S. Washington Street, P.O. Box 6808 Falls Church, VA 22046	(703) 237-8100	phccweb.org
SAE	Society of Automotive Engineers International	400 Commonwealth Drive Warrendale, PA 15096-0001	(724) 776-4841	sae.org
SBCCI	Southern Building Code Congress International	(*see* ICC)		
SMACNA	Sheet Metal and Air Conditioning Contractors' National Association	4201 Lafayette Center Drive Chantilly, VA 20151-1209	(703) 803-2980	smacna.org
TEMA	Tubular Exchanger Manufacturers Association	25 North Broadway Tarrytown, NY 10591	(914) 332-0040	tema.org
UL	Underwriters Laboratories	333 Pfingsten Road Northbrook, IL 60062-2096	(847) 272-8800	ul.com

ASHRAE HANDBOOK

Additions and Corrections

This report includes additional information, and technical errors found between June 15, 2005, and April 7, 2009, in the SI editions of the 2006, 2007, and 2008 *ASHRAE Handbook* volumes. Occasional typographical errors and nonstandard symbol labels will be corrected in future volumes. The most current list of Handbook additions and corrections is on the ASHRAE Web site (www.ashrae.org).

The authors and editor encourage you to notify them if you find other technical errors. Please send corrections to: Handbook Editor, ASHRAE, 1791 Tullie Circle NE, Atlanta, GA 30329, or e-mail mowen@ashrae.org.

2006 Refrigeration

p. 45.4, Testing for Leaks, 2nd paragraph. Change the first sentence to read, "ASHRAE *Standard* 147 established. . . ."

p. 45.7, References. Add the following source:

ASHRAE. 2002. Reducing the release of halogenated refrigerants from refrigerating and air-conditioning equipment and systems. ANSI/ ASHRAE *Standard* 147-2002.

2007 HVAC Applications

Contributors List. Wayne Lawton of X-nth should be listed as contributor for Chapters 29 and 30.

p. 13.30, Example 2, step 4. Replace the equation and bulleted item with the following:

$$C_{occ} = 10^{-3}(116 \text{ mg/m}^3)(22.5 - (0.773Q - 2.09P - 0.109X) - 0.346Z + 0.0159QZ + 0.236PX + 0.0407PZ + 0.00190XZ - 0.00499PXZ = 1.13 \text{ mg/m}^3$$

- Iterate between steps 5 and 4. With 5 ach, C_{occ} = 1.13 mg/m^3. This is greater than the desired limit of 0.94 mg/m^3. If the fan flow rate is increased to provide 10.5 ach, C_{occ} decreases to 0.94 mg/m^3. This meets the design criterion.

Ch. 14, Laboratories. Revisions were inadvertently omitted from the 2007 volume; please go to http://www.ashrae.org/publications/page/158 to download the revised chapter.

p. 16.13, Table 3. In the column headings, the first ceiling height should be 12.2 m.

p. 17.2, Fig. 1B. The title should read "Allowable Data Center Class 1, Class 2, and NEBS Operating Conditions."

p. 17.16, References. Please update the following two URLs:

For LBNL 2003,
http://hightech.lbl.gov/dc-benchmarking-results.html.

For NIOSH 1986,
http://www.cdc.gov/niosh/86-113.html.

p. 21.13, Table 3. Class AA control should be defined as "Precision control, no seasonal rh adjustment, very limited seasonal temperature adjustment possible."

p. 31.14, 1st col., 5th line. The outside air requirement for cafeterias and fast food should be based on 100 persons per 100 m^2.

p. 32.14, 2nd col., 1st paragraph. The reference to Table 5 should be to Table 4.

p. 32.15, Table 6. The column heads for 150 mm diameter bores should be 0.86, 1.73, and 2.60; please delete the extraneous "0.86" at the far right.

p. 32.15, 1st col., 1st paragraph, and definitions for Eq. (4). Change "outside pipe" to "borehole." In the definitions for Eq. (4), units should be m^2/day for α_g, days for τ, and m for d, which is defined as borehole diameter.

p. 32.21, Table 11. The units for the table multiplier values should be W/(m·K), not W(m·K).

p. 32.24, Table 14, 1st row, 3rd col. The minimum casing size for 100 mm diameter pump bowls should be 125 mm.

p. 35.13, Table 6. For fuel oil, household usage values should be 153.8 GJ (for "yes") and 97.0 GJ (for "no").

p. 41.21, 1st col, 10th line. In the numbered list, first item, the chiller should be 19.3 MW.

p. 41.22, Example 3. The reference to Table 6 should be to Table 5.

p. 41.25, Eq. (26). The second term on the left side of the equation should be $\dot{Q}_{blr,i}$.

p. 41.30, Eq. (33). Change D to Δ.

p. 47.26, Eq. (26). The final number subtracted should be 11, not 0.5.

p. 47.37, Eq. (29). The final term should be $10^{L_{w2}/10}$.

p. 47.38, Vibration Criteria, 1st paragraph. ANSI *Standard* 3.29 is the former designation; update this to ANSI *Standard* S2.71-1983 (R2006).

p. 47.39, Fig. 37. The corrected figure is shown on p. A.2, left.

p. 47.39, Table 46. In the next to the last row, change 0.0054 to 0.0064 mm/s.

p. 47.40, Table 48, Packaged AH, AC, H and V Units. In the Shaft Power kW and Other column, change all ≤ to ≥ (i.e., should be ≥11, ≥1 kPa SP).

p. 49.5, Table 1. In the leftmost column, change "1/2" to "13" and "3/4" (in two places) to "19."

p. 49.21, Eq. (19). The equation should read $F = 1000NPV_f/T$.

p. 49.26, Example 11. In the first equation, "DT_{lm}" should be "ΔT_{lm}."

p. 49.24, Figs. 25 and 26. Figure 26's caption should refer to Figure 25, not Figure 22.

p. 52.7, Figs. 8 and 9. Reverse the order: the current Figure 8 should be Figure 9, and the current Figure 9 should be Figure 8.

p. 52.10, Example 7, 3rd paragraph. The equation for A_{bo} should be 560(0.17 × 10^{-3}) = 0.095 m^2. Consequently, Δp_{sbt} (third line from bottom of example) should be 82.6 Pa.

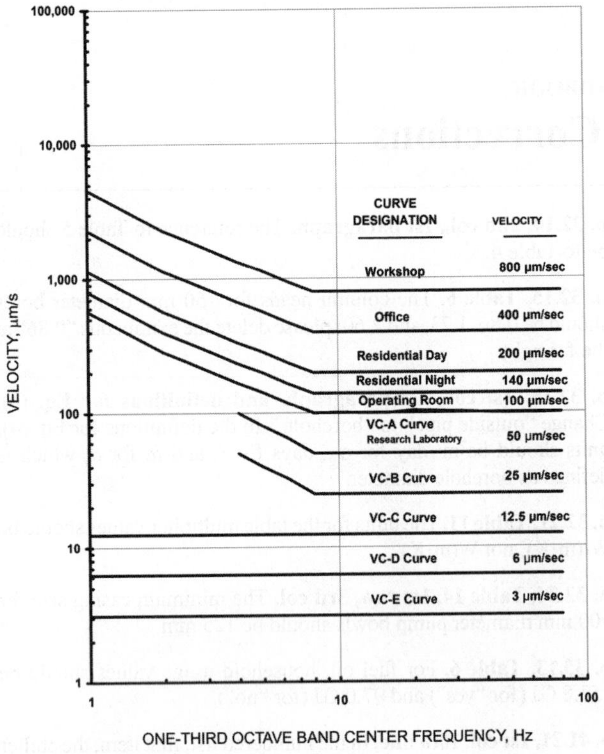

Fig. 37 Building Vibration Criteria for Vibration Measured on Building Structure
(2007 HVAC Applications, Chapter 47, p. 39)

p. 52.18, Symbols. The variable for floor-to-ceiling height should be *H*, and the variable for number of floors should be *N*.

p. 54.3, 2nd col., definition for R_p. The reference to Table 4 should be to Table 3.

p. 54.15, Example 1. For calculations using Eqs. (2) and (3), S_{DS} should be 0.623, not 0.85. The result using Eq. (2) should be 6728 N, and the result using Eq. (3) should be 1262 N.

p. 54.17, Example 2. For calculations using Eqs. (2) and (3), S_{DS} should be 0.623, not 0.85. The result using Eq. (2) should be 6728 N, and the result using Eq. (3) should be 1262 N.

p. 54.18, Example 3. For calculations using Eqs. (2) and (3), S_{DS} should be 0.623, not 0.85. The result using Eq. (2) should be 16 447 N, and the result using Eq. (3) should be 3084 N.

p. 54.19, Example 4. For calculations using Eqs. (2) and (3), S_{DS} should be 0.623, not 0.85. The result using Eq. (2) should be 3289 N, and the result using Eq. (3) should be 617 N.

2008 HVAC Systems and Equipment

p. 6.4, 1st col. After Eq. (9b), the multiplier for large spaces should be $(4.91/D_e)^{0.25}$.

p. 10.7, Fig. 9. The title should read "Trapping Temperature-Regulated Coils." Also, the bottom of the figure was cut off; please see the entire figure, presented above right.

p. 12.20, 2nd col., after Eq. (18). The reference to Equation (21) should be to Equation (18).

p. 12.24, Effect on Piping Pressure Loss. The reference to Equation (235) should be to Equation (18).

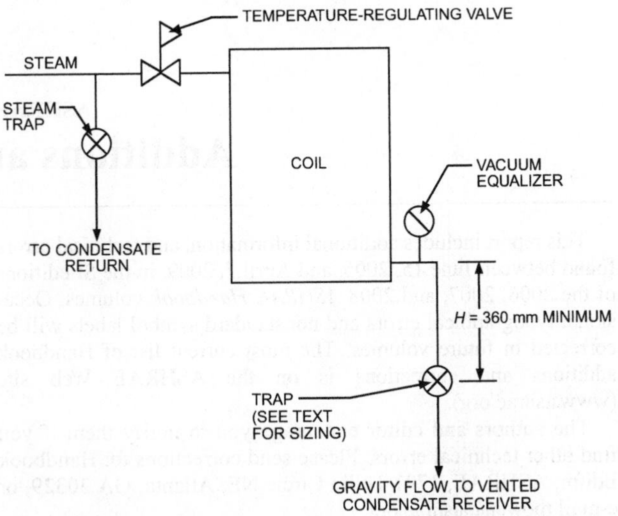

Fig. 9 Trapping Temperature-Regulated Coils
(2008 HVAC Systems and Equipment, Chapter 10, p. 7)

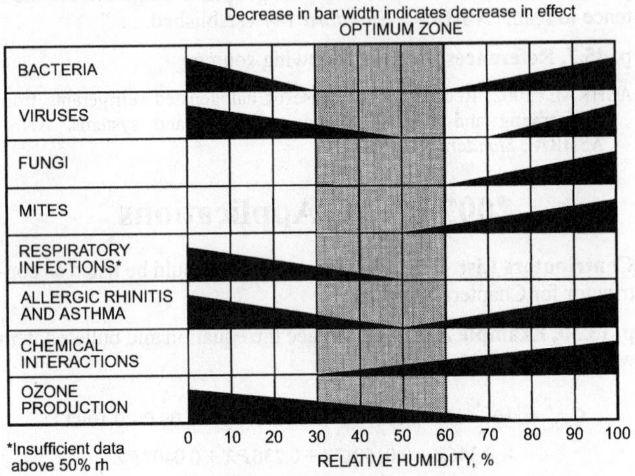

Fig. 1 Optimum Humidity Range for Human Comfort and Health
(Adapted from Sterling et al. 1985)
(2008 HVAC Systems and Equipment, Chapter 21, p. 1)

p. 21.1, Fig. 1. Please replace the figure with the one shown above.

p. 22.1, Fig. 1. Please replace the figure with the one provided on p. A.3, 1st column..

p. 23.4, Fig. 7. Replace the figure with the one provided on p. A.3, 2nd column.

p. 23.10, Dry Air-Conditioning Systems, 4th paragraph. After the second sentence, please add, "Dehumidified ventilation air that positively pressurizes the building may help counter moist air infiltration."

p. 30.10, 2nd col. Midway down the column, change "31.00 MJ/m³" to "31.21 MJ/m³."

p. 31.7, 2nd col., 4th line. Change "sue" to "use."

p. 43.6, Eq. (3). Change "Dp" to "Δp."

p. 49.3, 1st col., 3rd line. The Energy Policy and Conservation Act of 2005 should be Public Law 109-58.

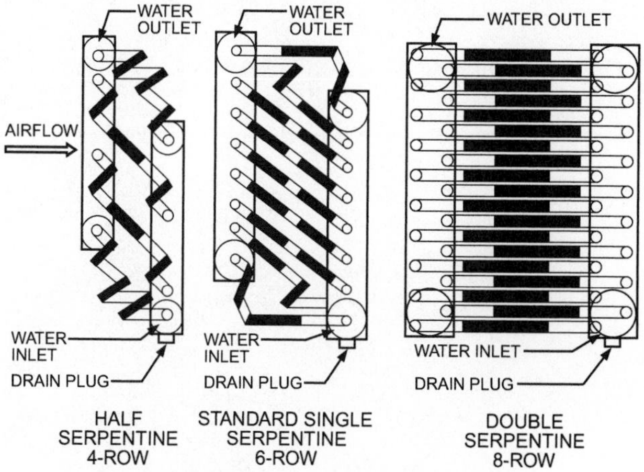

Fig. 1 Typical Water Circuit Arrangements
(2008 HVAC Systems and Equipment, Chapter 22, p. 1)

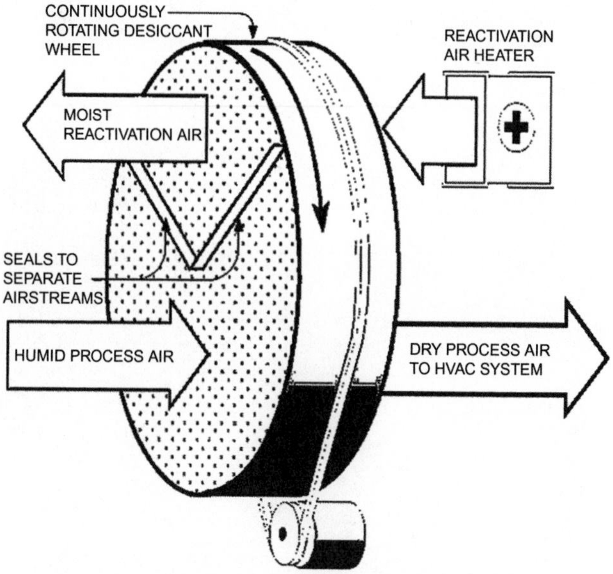

Fig. 7 Typical Rotary Dehumidification Wheel
(2008 HVAC Systems and Equipment, Chapter 23, p. 4)

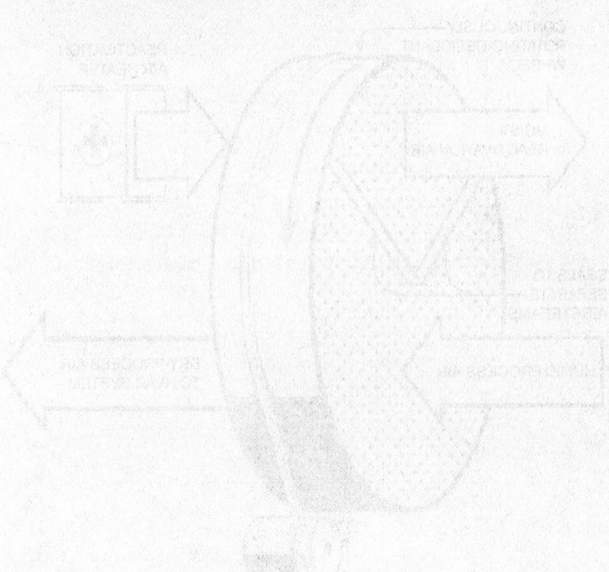

COMPOSITE INDEX
ASHRAE HANDBOOK SERIES

This index covers the current Handbook series published by ASHRAE. The four volumes in the series are identified as follows:

R = 2006 Refrigeration

A = 2007 HVAC Applications

S = 2008 HVAC Systems and Equipment

F = 2009 Fundamentals

Alphabetization of the index is letter by letter; for example, **Heaters** precedes **Heat exchangers**, and **Floors** precedes **Floor slabs**.

The page reference for an index entry includes the book letter and the chapter number, which may be followed by a decimal point and the beginning page in the chapter. For example, the page number S31.4 means the information may be found in the 2008 HVAC Systems and Equipment volume, Chapter 31, beginning on page 4.

Each Handbook volume is revised and updated on a four-year cycle. Because technology and the interests of ASHRAE members change, some topics are not included in the current Handbook series but may be found in the earlier Handbook editions cited in the index.

Comment Page

ASHRAE publications strive to present the most current and useful information possible. If you would like to comment on chapters in this or any volume of the *ASHRAE Handbook*, please use one of the following methods:

- Fill out the comment form on the ASHRAE Web site (www.ashrae.org)
- E-mail the editor at mowen@ashrae.org
- Cut out this page and fax it to the editor at 678-539-2187, or mail it to

Handbook Editor
ASHRAE
1791 Tullie Circle
Atlanta, GA 30329 USA

Please provide your contact information if you would like a response. (Personal identification information will not be used for any purpose beyond responding to your comments.)

Name: ____________________ **Phone:** ____________________

E-mail: ____________________ **Fax:** ____________________

Address: ____________________ **Preferred Contact Method(s):** ____________________

Comment Page

ASHRAE publications strive to present the most current and useful information possible. If you would like to comment on chapters in this or any volume of the *ASHRAE Handbook*, please use one of the following methods:

- Fill out the comment form on the ASHRAE Web site (www.ashrae.org)
- E-mail the editor at mowen@ashrae.org
- Cut out this page and fax it to the editor at 678-539-2187, or mail it to

  Handbook Editor
  ASHRAE
  1791 Tullie Circle
  Atlanta, GA 30329 USA

Please provide your contact information if you would like a response. (Personal identification information will not be used for any purpose beyond responding to your comments.)

Name: __________ **Phone:** __________

E-mail: __________ **Fax:** __________

Address: __________ **Preferred Contact Method(s):** __________

Comment Page

ASHRAE publications strive to present the most current and useful information possible. If you would like to comment on chapters in this or any volume of the *ASHRAE Handbook*, please use one of the following methods:

- Fill out the comment form on the ASHRAE Web site (www.ashrae.org)
- E-mail the editor at mowen@ashrae.org
- Cut out this page and fax it to the editor at 678-539-2187, or mail it to

Handbook Editor
ASHRAE
1791 Tullie Circle
Atlanta, GA 30329 USA

Please provide your contact information if you would like a response. (Personal identification information will not be used for any purpose beyond responding to your comments.)

Name: ____________________

E-mail: ____________________

Address: ____________________

____

Phone: ____________________

Fax: ____________________

Preferred Contact Method(s): ____________________

____

Comment Page

ASHRAE publications strive to present the most current and useful information possible. If you would like to comment on chapters in this or any volume of the *ASHRAE Handbook*, please use one of the following methods:

- Fill out the comment form on the ASHRAE Web site (www.ashrae.org)
- E-mail the editor at mowen@ashrae.org
- Cut out this page and fax it to the editor at 678-539-2187, or mail it to

Handbook Editor
ASHRAE
1791 Tullie Circle
Atlanta, GA 30329 USA

Please provide your contact information if you would like a response. (Personal identification information will not be used for any purpose beyond responding to your comments.)

Name: ____________________ **Phone:** ____________________

E-mail: ____________________ **Fax:** ____________________

Address: ____________________ **Preferred Contact Method(s):** ____________________

Comment Page

ASHRAE publications strive to present the most current and useful information possible. If you would like to comment on chapters in this or any volume of the *ASHRAE Handbook*, please use one of the following methods:

- Fill out the comment form on the ASHRAE Web site (www.ashrae.org)
- E-mail the editor at mowen@ashrae.org
- Cut out this page and fax it to the editor at 678-539-2187, or mail it to

Handbook Editor
ASHRAE
1791 Tullie Circle
Atlanta, GA 30329 USA

Please provide your contact information if you would like a response. (Personal identification information will not be used for any purpose beyond responding to your comments.)

Name:

E-mail:

Address:

Phone:

Fax:

Preferred Contact Method(s):